**SERVICE & REPAIR**

*SUPPLEMENT 2 of 2*

# ENGINE PERFORMANCE

*IMPORTED CARS, LIGHT TRUCKS & VANS*

## 1988 SUPPLEMENT

Mitchell

The Standard in Professional Estimating and Repair Information.

Mitchell International, Inc.

ACKNOWLEDGEMENT

Mitchell International, Inc. thanks the domestic and import automobile and light truck manufacturers, distributors, and dealers for their generous cooperation and assistance which make this manual possible.



Published By

MITCHELL INTERNATIONAL, INC.
9889 Willow Creek Road
P.O. Box 26260
San Diego, California 92126-0260

For Subscription Information:
CALL TOLL FREE 800-854-7030. In California CALL TOLL FREE 800-421-0159.
Or WRITE: P.O. Box 26260, San Diego, CA 92126-0260

ISBN 0-8470-0131-8

# INTRODUCTION

The 1988 Engine Performance Service and Repair manual covers dozens of imported cars and light trucks. More than 250 detailed articles written by our staff of automotive experts provide you with information you need to service and repair 1988 imported cars, light trucks and vans.

Clear, step-by-step testing procedures, maintenance recommendations and repair information enable you to do your job quicker and more profitably. Illustrations and diagrams make locating connections and components easier.

# SECTION DESCRIPTIONS

**GENERAL INFORMATION**

These pages include Maintenance Reminder Light reset procedures, Engine Identification Charts and English-Metric Conversion Charts. A detailed list of Abbreviations used by Mitchell is also located in this section of Volume I.

**TUNE-UP PROCEDURES**

Tune-up specification charts are your quick reference to important tune-up settings. The Tune-Up Procedure articles provide steps for setting vehicles to manufacturer's specifications and emission levels to maintain efficient engine performance.

**COMPUTERIZED ENGINE CONTROLS**

This section is arranged by manufacturer and includes full information on computerized engine control systems.

**FUEL SYSTEMS**

All carburetors and fuel injection systems are described fully within this section. Full description, operation, testing, and all specifications are included within each individual article. This section is arranged alphabetically by system manufacturer.

**EXHAUST EMISSION SYSTEMS**

The beginning of this section includes emission control system applications. Each manufacturer, model and engine application requires a different combination of systems to meet Clean Air Standards. This section explains major emission systems and their components, testing, trouble shooting and adjustment procedures.

**DISTRIBUTORS & IGNITION SYSTEMS**

This section covers ignition system testing and diagnosis procedures. Exploded views and specifications help make repairs easier and more accurate.

**LATEST CHANGES**

This is a very important section for keeping you up to date on important emission control tune-up information direct from the factory. Any revised procedure, modification or specification change which we received just before publication time is included in this section. DO NOT overlook these important articles.

## SECTION I

# GENERAL INDEX

## CONTENTS

### VEHICLE COMPONENTS Page

# 1988 GENERAL INDEX

## C

### COMPUTERIZED ENGINE CONTROLS

## SECTION 1a

# COMPUTERIZED ENGINE CONTROLS

## CONTENTS



**NOTE: ALSO SEE GENERAL INDEX.**

## CONTENTS (Cont.)



**NOTE: ALSO SEE GENERAL INDEX.**

# 1988 COMPUTERIZED ENGINE CONTROLS
## Emission Standards & Tune-Up

## MANUFACTURING STANDARDS

Federal and state governments have established air quality standards during the past 20 years. Automobile manufacturers design their vehicles to conform to standards where the vehicle will be sold and operated. These standards cover carbon monoxide (CO), hydrocarbons (HC) and oxides of nitrogen (NOx).

Federal and California standards which must be met by manufacturers are specified in units easily measured in a testing laboratory. Since 1970, these standards have been in "grams per mile". This means no vehicle, whether 2-cylinder or V8, may emit more than a set weight (in grams) of pollutants for each mile travelled. Since large engines burn more fuel per mile than do smaller engines, they must be "cleaner" per gallon burned if they are to meet these standards.

When manufacturers certify vehicle models prior to sale, the vehicles are placed on a dynamometer and the exhaust gases are collected in a bag. After the vehicle runs for a specified time, the gases are analyzed and weighed. Engines and emission systems are designed so the weight of emissions will be less than the specified grams per mile standard.

Infra-red exhaust analyzers are commonly used in vehicle test stations. The analyzer uses a test probe placed in the exhaust stream to sample the exhaust gases, and measure the percentage of CO and the parts per million of HC. These are not the same units used by the manufacturer when the vehicle is certified. The NOx emissions cannot be measured by an infra-red exhaust analyzer. Laboratory equipment must be used to determine NOx emissions.

## TUNE-UP STANDARDS

The technician must use the proper specifications when adjusting the vehicle during a tune-up. The first few years of emission-regulated vehicles were adjusted using an exhaust gas analyzer which measured CO and HC.

In the past few years, manufacturers have produced much cleaner running vehicles. The CO (percentage) and HC (ppm) have become very low, especially when measured downstream of catalytic converter. It has become difficult to measure the effect of fuel and ignition adjustments.

One solution to this problem for vehicles using carburetors requires the use of artifically-enriched propane adjustments. The added propane increases or decreases engine RPM for evaluation of carburetor rich/lean setting. This allows the technician to check carburetor setting quickly and accurately.

As computer-controlled systems were developed, it became possible for the vehicles to adjust the air/fuel ratio, ignition timing and emission control device operation throughout the entire driving range. These computer control systems use a variety of sensors that provide the electronic control unit with information on vehicle speed, altitude of vehicle operation and transmission gear position, along with engine operating conditions.

Fuel delivery to achieve a lean air/fuel ratio is controlled by the computer. The computer controls the on/off (duty cycle) time of the fuel injector(s) or carburetor mixture control solenoid to achieve leanest possible air/fuel ratio while maintaining good driveability.

Although most repair shops have exhaust gas analyzers, computer-controlled vehicles normally do not have a CO and HC specification for tuning. An abnormal exhaust gas reading on an exhaust analyzer may be helpful in diagnosing a problem, but should not be used as a basis for adjustments.

This manual provides procedures and specifications supplied by the manufacturer and may not list CO or HC specifications.

## STATE TEST STANDARDS

Some states have established standards for allowable pollutants for used vehicles. These standards are normally given in CO (percentage) and HC (ppm). Vehicle tail-pipe emissions can be checked against the standard using an exhaust gas analyzer. Typical standards for newer vehicles would be 0.5 percent CO and 200 ppm HC. If vehicle emissions are below this standard, vehicle would pass emissions test. These standards are used to determine if the vehicle is running properly, not to be used for tuning or adjusting the engine. If the vehicle will not pass emission test or is running poorly, use the manufacturer's diagnostic procedures and specifications for repair.

Test standards may change each year and vary from state to state, and even by county within each state. It is not possible to provide an accurate and up-to-date list of emissions standards in this manual. Emission standards can be obtained for your area by contacting your local county or state office. Remember, the emission standards are only for test purposes. The manufacturer's adjustment procedures and specifications must be followed when repairing vehicles.

# 1988 COMPUTERIZED ENGINE CONTROLS
# Acura & Sterling Electronic Control System

**Acura: Integra, Legend**
**Sterling: 825**

## DESCRIPTION & OPERATION

The ECU is the main controlling device of the electronic control system. The Electronic Control Unit (ECU) receives signals from various sensors. ECU then uses these signals to determine output signals to various control devices. On all models except Legend Coupe, ECU is mounted below passenger seat. On Legend Coupe, ECU is mounted under carpet, below passenger side of dash.

The ECU contains memories for the basic injector durations at various engine RPM and Manifold Absolute Pressures (MAP). The basic injector duration is read from calibration tables built into ECU internal memory. The ECU modifies the basic injector duration according to input signals from various sensors to obtain the final injector duration. The ECU on Acura models also controls ignition timing advance curve based upon sensor input signals. Timing on Sterling 825 is controlled by a centrifugal advance unit and a dual-diaphragm advance unit which is regulated by ECU controlled solenoids.

The ECU also controls cold start system, electric fuel pump (in fuel tank on Legend and Sterling 825) and fuel cut-off systems. The ECU contains a fail-safe system which monitors input signals, substituting pre-calibrated values in the event it detects any abnormalities. This provides safe driving (limp-home mode) even if one or more of the sensors are faulty, or the ECU malfunctions.

There are several input devices which provide operating information to the ECU. These include the throttle position sensor, crank angle sensor(s), vehicle speed sensor (in dash), Manifold Absolute Pressure (MAP) sensor, Atmospheric Pressure (PA) sensor, Coolant Temperature (TW) sensor, Intake Air Temperature (TA) sensor, oxygen sensor (2 used on Legend and Sterling 825), Idle Mixture Adjuster (IMA) sensor, starter crank signal and battery voltage signal (electronic load detector on Integra).

***NOTE: Crank angle sensor input signals vary depending on vehicle application.***

The ECU has a self-diagnostic capability to help diagnose problems. This system uses a dash mounted PGM-FI or Check Engine warning light and one or 2 ECU mounted self-diagnostic lights. All models use a Red LED on ECU for display of system failure codes. Legend and Sterling 825 also use a Yellow LED for idle speed adjustment. As a bulb check, the PGM-FI or Check Engine (Integra) warning light on instrument panel will glow for 2-8 seconds when ignition switch is turned to the "ON" position.

## INPUT SIGNALS

**Atmospheric Pressure (PA) Sensor** - The PA sensor converts atmospheric pressure into voltage signals and sends the signals to ECU.

**Battery Voltage Signal** - ECU uses the battery voltage signal to compensate for low voltage conditions which result in injector lag. ECU compensates by increasing injector opening time.

**Crank Angle Sensors** - On Legend and Sterling 825 models, the crank angle sensor consists of a combination CRK/CYL sensor mounted on the end of the camshaft. This sensor furnishes 2 separate input signals to the ECU. The ECU uses the CRK signal to help determine fuel injector timing, ignition timing and engine speed (RPM). The ECU uses the CYL signal to detect TDC position of No. 1 cylinder when engine is running. This signal is used to trigger the proper fuel injectors. *See Fig. 1.*

In conjunction with the CRK/CYL sensor, Legend uses a TDC sensor located in distributor housing. This sensor consists of a TDC pick-up coil and six-lobed TDC trigger wheel assembly. This signal is used by the ECU for initializing the triggering of the spark plugs upon start-up (cranking) and when crank angle signal from CRK/CYL sensor is abnormal. *See Fig. 2.*

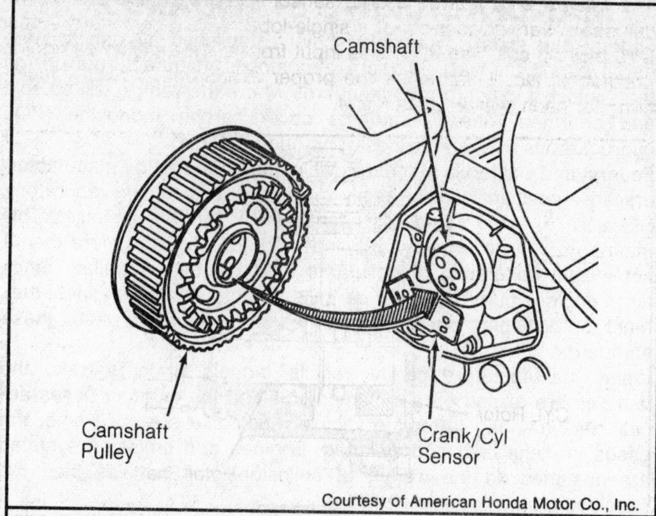
Camshaft
Camshaft Pulley
Crank/Cyl Sensor
Courtesy of American Honda Motor Co., Inc.

***Fig. 1: Legend & Sterling 825 CRK/CYL Sensor***

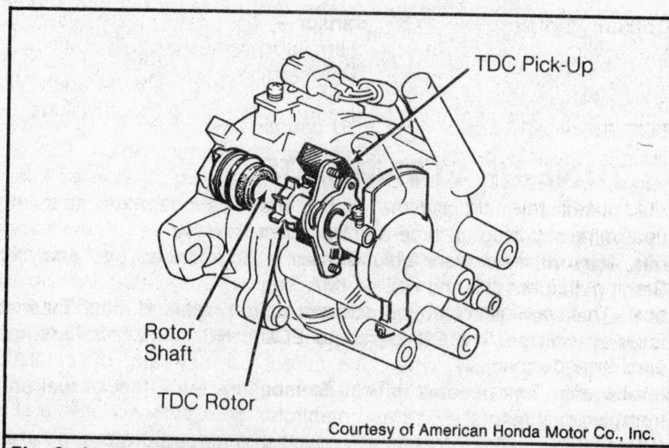
TDC Pick-Up
Rotor Shaft
TDC Rotor
Courtesy of American Honda Motor Co., Inc.

***Fig. 2: Legend TDC Sensor***

On Integra models, the crank angle sensor consists of a combination TDC/Crank sensor mounted in the distributor housing. The ECU uses input from the crank pick-up coil portion of this sensor to help determine ignition and fuel injector timing for each cylinder. This sensor also furnishes an engine speed (RPM) signal to the ECU. The ECU uses the TDC pick-up coil portion of this sensor to initialize ignition timing upon start-up (cranking) and when crank angle signal is abnormal. *See Fig. 3.*

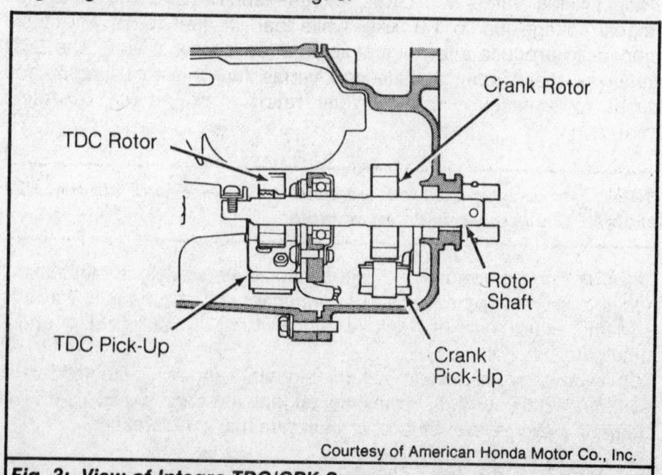
Crank Rotor
TDC Rotor
Rotor Shaft
TDC Pick-Up
Crank Pick-Up
Courtesy of American Honda Motor Co., Inc.

***Fig. 3: View of Integra TDC/CRK Sensor***

# Acura & Sterling Electronic Control System (Cont.)

The Integra also utilizes a CYL sensor located on the end of the camshaft. Sensor consists of a single-lobed CYL trigger rotor and a CYL pick-up coil. The ECU uses input from this sensor to determine position of No. 1 piston for the proper synchronization of injector firing for each cylinder. *See Fig. 4.*

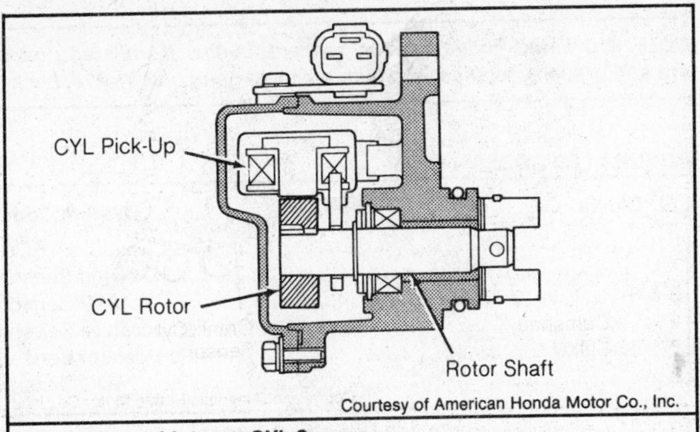
CYL Pick-Up
CYL Rotor
Rotor Shaft
Courtesy of American Honda Motor Co., Inc.

***Fig. 4: View of Integra CYL Sensor***

**Coolant Temperature (TW) Sensor** – The TW sensor uses a temperature sensitive resistor (thermistor) to measure differences in coolant temperature. Resistance of thermistor decreases with a rise in coolant temperature.

**EGR Position Sensor** – The ECU contains ideal EGR lift specifications for varying operating conditions in its internal memory. EGR lift sensor senses EGR valve position and relays information to ECU. ECU uses this information, along with other sensor input, to determine regulation of EGR control solenoid valve.

**Idle Mixture Adjuster (IMA) Sensor** – This sensor is used on Sterling 825 models only. The IMA sensor is mounted in control box. This sensor maintains correct air/fuel ratio at idle. Turning adjuster changes voltage signal to ECU, which in turn alters fuel discharge duration.

**Intake Air Temperature (TA) Sensor** – The TA sensor is a thermistor located in intake manifold. It reacts to intake air temperature changes much like coolant temperature sensor but with a reduced thermal capacity for quicker response.

**Manifold Air Pressure (MAP) Sensor** – The MAP sensor converts manifold air pressure readings into electrical voltage signals and sends the signals to ECU.

**Oxygen Sensor** – The oxygen sensor is mounted in the exhaust manifold where it is exposed to exhaust gases as they exit the combustion chamber. Sensor detects oxygen content of exhaust gas and produces a voltage signal proportional to that content for use by the ECU.

Rich air fuel ratios will cause oxygen sensor to produce a high signal voltage (up to 1.0 volt), while lean air/fuel ratios will cause sensor to produce a low signal voltage (as low as .1 volt). The ECU receives these input signals and varies fuel injector duration (on time) to maintain proper air/fuel ratios during most operating modes.

***NOTE: Two oxygen sensors are used on Legend and Sterling 825 models, one in each exhaust manifold.***

**Throttle Position Sensor** – This sensor is essentially a mechanical variable resistor (potentiometer) connected to throttle shaft. Throttle position sensor varies voltage signal to ECU as throttle angle changes.

Other input signals may include signals from A/C clutch, brake switch, clutch switch, cranking signal (starter switch), power steering pressure switch and/or gear position switch(es).

## CONTROL DEVICES

**By-Pass Control System (Legend)** – Two air intake paths are provided in the intake manifold. This allows the ECU to select path length most favorable (power/performance) for a given engine speed. High torque at low RPM is achieved by using the long intake path. High power at high RPM is achieved by using the short intake path. These air paths are selected by the ECU based upon sensor input signals. ECU controls by-pass valves in intake manifold through the use of 2 by-pass control solenoids and a by-pass valve control diaphragm.

**EGR Control Solenoid** – ECU controls ground circuit to EGR solenoid to regulate flow of recirculated exhaust gases into the intake system. EGR is not used on Integra models.

**Electronic Air Control Valve (EACV)** – The ECU controls electrical current to EACV to maintain correct idle speed. The EACV is activated (idle speed increased) when the engine is cold and/or under engine load conditions, such as when A/C is on, transmission is in gear (A/T only), power steering oil pressure is high, or sensed voltage is low.

**Fast Idle Valve** – On Legend and Sterling 825 models, to prevent erratic running during engine warm-up, a higher idle speed is needed. This is accomplished through use of a thermowax fast idle valve. When engine temperature is less than 86°F (30°C) this valve is open to by-pass additional air into intake manifold. This operation is dependent solely upon coolant temperature.

**Fuel Injector** – Injector receives power when ignition switch is in "ON" position. ECU controls injector ground circuit to energize injector. Sensor input signals are used to determine injector duration (on time).

During certain deceleration modes (throttle valve closed and engine speed greater than 1000 RPM) and acceleration modes (engine speed greater than 6600 RPM on Legend, 7500 RPM on Integra) ECU will activate its fuel cut-off control function by de-energizing injectors. This improves fuel economy and prevents engine from over-revving.

**Fuel Pump** – When ignition is first turned on, ECU supplies a ground circuit for the main relay for about 2 seconds. When relay is energized, power is transmitted to fuel pump (in tank on Legend and Sterling 825). When an RPM signal is received by the ECU (cranking or running), ECU provides a constant ground circuit for main relay.

**Idle Up Control** – At extremely low ambient temperatures, Integra models use an ECU controlled solenoid in conjunction with a diaphragm-type fast idle valve to by-pass additional air into intake manifold. Coolant temperature of less than 14°F (-10°C) and engine speed (less than 1800) inputs are used to determine control of idle-up solenoid.

**Ignition Control Solenoid Valves** – Solenoid valves are used by ECU to control vacuum advance at distributor when engine temperature is less than 140°F (60°C).

**Ignition Timing Adjuster (ITA)** – The Ignition Timing Adjuster (ITA) is used on Legend models. It is electrically connected to TA, TW and PA sensors, EGR valve lift sensor, throttle position sensor and ECU. The ITA allows electronic ignition advance to be set to 15 degrees BTDC at idle.

**Lock-Up Solenoid Valve** – On Integra and Sterling 825 models, lock-up solenoid valve allows a direct fluidic coupling between engine and transmission, causing a reduced slippage and increased fuel mileage. On Legend models, this function is controlled by a separate automatic transmission control unit.

**Main Relay** – One half of the main relay is used by the ECU to power the electric fuel pump. ECU provides a ground for this part of relay when ignition is first turned on (for 2 seconds) or when an RPM signal is received by the ECU (cranking or running). The second half of the main relay provides power from the ignition for the ECU, injectors (through a resistor) and power for the fuel pump part of the relay.

**Pressure Regulator Cut-Off Valve** – When coolant temperature on Legend and Sterling 825 models is greater than 221°F (105°C) or intake air temperature is greater than 76°F (80°C), the pressure regulator cut-off solenoid valve is energized, cutting manifold vacuum to the fuel pressure regulator to ensure high pressure to injector to prevent vapor lock.

**Warning Light** – Red PGM-FI or Check Engine warning light is used by ECU to indicate a fault has occured in the computer control system. When warning light is illuminated, a trouble code should be stored in ECU memory. As a bulb check, light will illuminate for 2-8 seconds when ignition is first turned on.

**Red ECU LED** – When the Red PGM-FI or Check Engine warning light is on, the red LED located on the ECU should indicate codes stored in ECU memory.

## TROUBLE SHOOTING

***NOTE: Observe PGM-FI or Check Engine light. If light is on and no codes are flashed by the Red LED on the ECU, this indicates that back-up system is in operation. See RED LED DOES NOT FLASH under CODE 0, NO CODES in this article.***

### ENGINE WON'T START

Check spark, fuel supply and EACV.

### DIFFICULT COLD START

Check coolant temperature sensor, TDC sensor and all other idle controls.

### FAST IDLE OUT OF SPECIFICATIONS

Check idle controls, coolant temperature sensor, throttle position sensor, TDC sensor, intake air temperature sensor and atmospheric pressure sensor.

### ROUGH IDLE WHEN WARM

Check EACV, MAP sensor, oxygen sensor, crank angle sensor, throttle position sensor, intake air temperature sensor, atmospheric pressure sensor and EGR and other emission control systems.

### IDLE RPM HIGH WHEN WARM

Check EACV and other idle controls. Check MAP sensor, atmospheric pressure sensor, air intake system and emission systems.

### IDLE RPM LOW WHEN WARM

Check EACV, air intake system, MAP sensor and other idle controls.

### STALLING DURING WARM UP

Check EACV, air intake system, MAP sensor, crank angle sensor, coolant temperature sensor, throttle position sensor, other idle controls, fuel supply and EGR control system.

### STALLING AFTER WARM UP

Check EGR control system, EACV, MAP sensor, throttle position sensor, crank angle sensor, vehicle speed sensor (if equipped), air intake and fuel supply.

### MISFIRE OR ROUGH OPERATION

Using a stethescope, check each injector for clicking at idle. Check fuel supply, MAP sensor, oxygen sensor, crank angle sensor, throttle position sensor, ignition output signal, EGR system and vehicle speed sensor.

### EMISSION TEST FAILURE

Check MAP sensor, oxygen sensor, all emission control systems, crank angle sensor and coolant temperature sensor.

### LACK OF POWER

Check for brakes binding. Check fuel supply, emission controls, MAP sensor, crank angle sensor, coolant temperature sensor, atmospheric pressure sensor, vehicle speed sensor, air intake system and EGR control system.

## TESTING

***NOTE: Before starting testing or trouble shooting, ensure engine is in good mechanical condition and adjusted to specifications.***

### SELF-DIAGNOSTIC CODES

On all models, a Red LED is located on ECU for self-diagnosis codes. Some models aalso have a Yellow LED which is for idle adjustment and is not related to Red LED trouble shooting codes. The Red LED is for codes set due to component failure. See appropriate LED CODES table in this article. To obtain ECU codes, turn ignition switch to the "ON" position and count flashes of Red LED on top of ECU.

***NOTE: If unlisted codes appear, recheck codes. If unlisted codes are still present, replace ECU with a known good unit and recheck.***

*INTEGRA LED CODES*

| LED Blinks | System Code |
|---|---|
| 0 | ECU |
| 1 | Oxygen Sensor |
| 3 & 5 | MAP Sensor |
| 6 | Coolant Temperature Sensor |
| 7 | Throttle Position Sensor |
| 8 | TDC Sensor |
| 9 | No. 1 Cylinder Position Sensor |
| 10 | Intake Air Temperature Sensor |
| 13 | Atmospheric Pressure Sensor |
| 14 | Electronic Air Control Valve |
| 15 | Ignition Output Signal |
| 16 | Fuel Injector |
| 17 | Vehicle Speed Sensor |
| 19 | Lock-Up Solenoid Valve (Auto.Trans.) |
| 20 | Electric Load |

*LEGEND LED CODES*

| LED Blinks | System Code |
|---|---|
| 0 | ECU |
| 1 | Front Oxygen Sensor |
| 2 | Rear Oxygen Sensor |
| 3 | MAP Sensor |
| 4 | Crank Angle Sensor |
| 5 | MAP Sensor |
| 6 | Coolant Temperature Sensor |
| 7 | Throttle Position Sensor |
| 8 | TDC Sensor |
| 9 | No 1 Cylinder Position |
| 10 | Intake Air Temperature Sensor |
| 12 | EGR System |
| 13 | Atmospheric Pressure Sensor |
| 14 | Electronic Air Control Valve |
| 15 | Ignition Output Signal |
| 17 | Vehicle Speed Sensor (Pulser) |
| 18 | Ignition Timing Adjustment |

*STERLING 825 LED CODES*

| LED Blinks | System Code |
|---|---|
| 0 | ECU |
| 1 | Front Oxygen Sensor |
| 2 | Rear Oxygen Sensor |
| 3 | MAP Sensor |
| 5 | MAP Sensor |
| 6 | Coolant Temperature Sensor |
| 7 | Throttle Position Sensor |
| 8 | TDC Sensor |
| 9 | CYL Crank Angle Sensor |
| 10 | Intake Air Temperature Sensor |
| 11 | Idle Mixture Adjustment (IMA) Sensor |
| 12 | EGR System |
| 13 | Atmospheric Pressure Sensor |
| 14 | Electronic Air Control Valve |

# 1988 COMPUTERIZED ENGINE CONTROLS
## Acura & Sterling Electronic Control System (Cont.)

On all Acura models a System Checker Harness (07999-PD60000A) is needed to test components. On Legend, an Inspection Adaptor (07GMJ-ML80100) is needed for testing specific sensors. Both of these devices function as breakout boxes to access pin voltage signals while component is either in or out of circuit. A special Fast Check Tester is necessary for component testing on Sterling 825. Limited information on component testing is available from manufacturer.

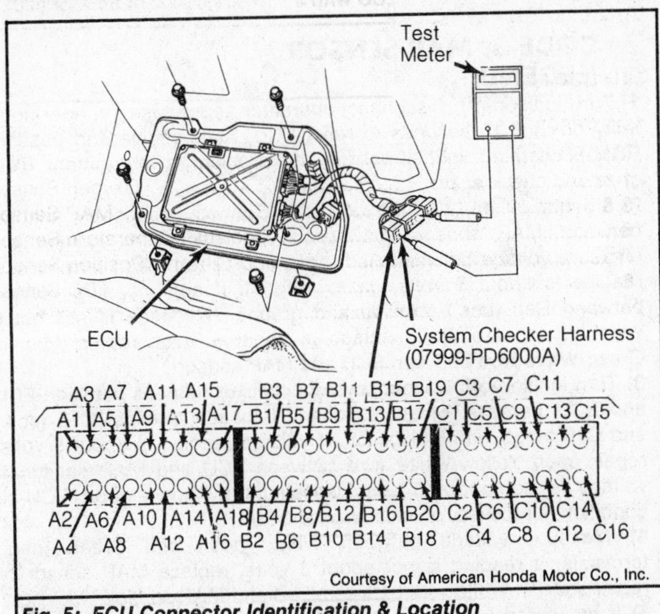

Test Meter
ECU
System Checker Harness (07999-PD6000A)
A3 A7 A11 A15
B3 B7 B11 B15 B19 C3 C7 C11
A1 A5 A9 A13 A17 B1 B5 B9 B13 B17 C1 C5 C9 C13 C15
A2 A6 A10 A14 A18 B4 B8 B12 B16 B20 C2 C6 C10 C14
A4 A8 A12 A16 B2 B6 B10 B14 B18 C4 C8 C12 C16

Courtesy of American Honda Motor Co., Inc.

*Fig. 5: ECU Connector Identification & Location*

To reset ECU, on Integra models, remove hazard fuse at battery terminal for 10 seconds. On Legend models, remove alternator sense fuse in the under-hood relay box for 10 seconds. Sterling 825 reset procedure not available from manufacturer.

***NOTE: The following test procedures apply to Acura models only. Sterling information was not available from manufacturer at time of publicaiton.***

### CODE 0, NO CODES (INTEGRA)

**No Check Engine Warning Light – 1)** Turn ignition on. If oil pressure light is on, go to step **2)**. If light is off, inspect No. 3 fuse. If No. 3 fuse is okay, repair open circuit in Yellow wire between fuse and combination meter.

**2)** Turn ignition off. Connect system checker harness between ECU and ECU connector. Jumper terminal B6 to ground. Turn ignition on. If warning light is now on, go to step **3)**. If light is off, replace warning light bulb or repair open in Green/Orange wire between ECU terminal B6 and combination meter.

**3)** Individually, connect terminal A2 and then terminal A4 to terminal B6. If warning light fails to illuminate, repair open in Black A2 and/or A4 wires between ECU and ground.

**4)** If warning light illuminated in step **3)**, substitute a known good ECU and retest. If condition is rectified, replace ECU.

**Check Engine light On, Red LED Does Not Flash – 1)** Connect system checker harness between ECU and ECU connectors. Disconnect "B" connector from ECU only, not from wire harness. Turn ignition on. If Check Engine light remains on, repair short to ground in Green/Orange wire between ECU terminal B6 and combination meter.

**2)** If Check Engine light goes out with ECU "B" connector unplugged, reconnect "B" connector. Individually, jumper terminal A2 to terminal A16 and then to terminal A18. If Check Engine light illuminates, go to step **3)**. If Check Engine light does not illuminate, repair open in Black/Red wire between ECU terminal A18 and ground or repair open in Brown/Black wire between ECU terminal A16 and ground.

**3)** Measure voltage between terminal A18 (neg.) and terminals A13 (pos.) and A15 (pos.). If battery voltage is present, go to step **4)**. If battery voltage is not present, repair open in Yellow/Black wires between ECU terminal A13 and/or A15 and main relay. Check main relay and wiring connectors at main relay.

**4)** Turn ignition off. Disconnect the 3-wire connector at MAP sensor. Start engine. If LED does not indicate the code for the disconnected sensor, replace sensor. Reconnect 3-wire connector. Repeat procedure with, throttle angle sensor, and then PA sensor. If all sensor codes are displayed, turn ignition off. With system checker harness installed between ECU and ECU connector, disconnect "C" connector from ECU only, not from main harness.

**5)** Check for continuity between ground and terminal C13. Check for continuity between ground and terminal C15. If continuity exists, repair short to ground in Red wire between ECU terminal C15 and MAP sensor or repair short to ground in Yellow/Red wire between ECU terminal C13 and altitude sensor or throttle angle sensor.

**6)** If continuity did not exist in step **5)**, substitute a known good ECU. If condition is rectified, replace original ECU.

### CODE 0, NO CODES (LEGEND)

**No PGM-FI Warning Light – 1)** Turn ignition on. If oil pressure light is on, go to step **2)**. If light is off, inspect fuse No 5. If fuse No. 5 is okay, repair open circuit in Yellow wire between fuse and combination meter.

**2)** Turn ignition off. Connect system checker harness between ECU and connector. Connect terminal B6 to ground. Turn ignition on. If warning light is now on, go to step **3)**. If light is off, replace warning light bulb or repair open in Blue wire between ECU and combination meter.

**3)** Individually, connect terminal A2 and then terminal A4 to terminal B6. If warning light fails to illuminate repair open in Black A2 or A4 wires between ECU and ground.

**4)** If warning light illuminated in step **3)**, individually connect terminals A16 and A18 to terminal B6. If light does not illuminate, repair Brown/Black A18 or Brown/White A16 wire between ECU and ground.

**5)** If warning light illuminated in step **4**, no problems were found. Substitute a known good ECU and retest. If condition is rectified, replace ECU.

**PGM-FI Warning Light On, Red LED Does Not Flash – 1)** Turn ignition on. One at a time, disconnect the 3-wire connectors at MAP sensor, throttle angle sensor and EGR position sensor. If LED remains lit, go to step **2)**. If LED goes out, replace the sensor which caused LED to go out when unplugged.

**2)** Reconnect all connectors. Disconnect the 3-wire connector at ignition timing adjuster and then atmospheric PA sensor. If LED flashes code 13 (and/or 18 on Legend coupe) when sensor is disconnected, replace faulty sensor. If code for disconnected sensor was not flashed, go to the next step.

**3)** Turn ignition off. Reconnect connector(s). Connect system checker harness between ECU and ECU harness. Disconnect "C" connector from ECU, not main harness. Check for continuity between ground and terminals C13 and C15. If continuity does not exist, go to step **4)**. If continuity exists, repair short to ground in Yellow/White wire from terminal C15 to MAP sensor or in Yellow/White wire from terminal C13 to PA sensor, ignition timing adjuster and EGR position sensor.

**4)** Reconnect "C" connector. Disconnect "B" connector from ECU only, not main harness. Turn ignition on. If LED is lit, repair short to ground in Blue wire between ECU and combination meter. If LED is not lit, one at a time, connect terminal B6 to terminal A16 and then to terminal A18. If LED illuminates, go to step **5)**. If not, repair open in Brown/Black A18 wire and/or Brown/White A16 wire between ECU and ground.

**5)** Measure voltage between terminal A15 (pos.) and A18 (neg.). If battery voltage is not present, repair open Yellow/Black A15 wire between ECU and main relay or repair main relay or relay wiring. If Battery voltage is present, substitute a known good ECU. If condition is rectified, replace original ECU.

## CODE 1 &/OR CODE 2 OXYGEN SENSOR (ALL MODELS)

**1)** Turn off ignition and reset ECU. On Integra models, remove hazard fuse at battery terminal for 10 seconds. On Legend models, remove alternator sense fuse in the under-hood relay box for 10 seconds. Start engine. Check fuel pressure at fuel filter. See appropriate FUEL INJECTION article. Repair fuel system if not within specifications. If fuel pressure is within specifications, proceed to next step.

**2)** Bring engine to operating temperature (cooling fan on). Hold engine at 1500 RPM for 15 minutes, without closing throttle completely during this time. Check if PGM-FI or Check Engine warning light is on. If not on, problem is intermittent. Test drive and check light again.

**3)** If light is on, disconnect indicated oxygen sensor connector. Attach voltmeter to vehicle ground and connector. With engine at normal operating temperature, momentarily open throttle wide open, then close throttle.

**4)** Voltage at wide open throttle should be greater than .6 volt, and less than .4 volt at full closed throttle. If not within specifications, replace oxygen sensor. If voltage is within specifications, proceed to next step.

**5)** Turn engine off and attach system checker harness between ECU and ECU connector. Using a voltmeter, connect negative terminal to connector terminal A18.

**6)** On Integra models, attach positive voltmeter lead to connector terminal C16. On Legend models, for front oxygen sensor, attach positive voltmeter lead to connector terminal C12 and attach to connector terminal C10 for rear oxygen sensor. *See Fig. 4*.

**7)** Start engine and warm to operating temperature. Momentarily open throttle wide open, then close throttle. Voltage at wide open throttle should be greater than .6 volt and less than .4 volt at full closed throttle. If not within specification, repair wire between ECU and oxygen sensor. If within specification, substitute a known good ECU. If condition is rectified, replace original ECU.

## CODE 3, MAP SENSOR (INTEGRA)

**1)** Turn ignition switch off and remove hazard fuse at battery positive terminal for 10 seconds to reset ECU. Start engine and observe Check Engine light. If light is off, problem is intermittent. Test drive and check again.

**2)** If light is on, turn ignition off. Disconnect 3-wire MAP sensor connector. Turn ignition on. Measure voltage between Red (pos.) and Brown/White (neg.) terminals. Go to step **4)** if reading is about 5 volts. If not, measure voltage between Red (pos.) terminal and ground. If voltage is still not 5 volts, go to step **3)**. If voltage is about 5 volts, repair open in Brown/White wire between ECU terminal C14 and MAP sensor.

**3)** Turn ignition off. Connect system checker harness between ECU and ECU connector. Measure voltage between terminal C15 (pos.) and C14 (neg.) with ignition on. If voltage reading is about 5 volts, repair open Red wire between ECU terminal C15 and MAP sensor. If voltage is not about 5 volts, substitute a known good ECU. If condition is rectified, replace original ECU.

**4)** Measure voltage between White (pos.) and Brown/White (neg.) terminals. If reading is not about 5 volts, go to step **6)**. If measured voltage is about 5 volts, turn ignition off. Connect system checker harness between ECU and ECU connector. Reconnect 3-wire MAP connector. Turn ignition on. Measure voltage between terminal C11 (pos.) and C14 (neg.). If there is not about 5 volts present, replace MAP sensor.

**5)** If there is about 5 volts present between C11 and C14, substitute a known good ECU. If condition is rectified, replace original ECU.

**6)** If voltage measured between White (pos.) and Brown/White (neg.) terminals in step **4)** was not about 5 volts, turn ignition off. Connect system checker harness between ECU and ECU connector. Turn ignition on. Measure voltage between terminals C11 (pos.) and C14 (neg.). If reading is not about 5 volts, repair short in White wire between ECU terminal C11 and MAP sensor. If voltage is about 5 volts, repair open in White wire between ECU terminal C11 and MAP sensor.

## CODE 3, MAP SENSOR (LEGEND)

**1)** Turn ignition off. Disconnect alternator sense fuse in under-hood relay box for 10 seconds to reset ECU. Start engine and observe PGM-FI warning light. If light is off, problem is intermittent. Test drive and check again.

**2)** If light is on, turn ignition off. Connect inspection adaptor between MAP sensor and sensor harness. Turn ignition on. Measure voltage between Red (pos.) and Green (neg.) terminals. If reading is about 5 volts, go to step **4)**. If not, measure voltage between Red (pos.) terminal and ground. If voltage is still not 5 volts, go to step **3)**. If voltage is about 5 volts, repair open in Green/White wire between ECU and MAP sensor.

**3)** Turn ignition off. Connect system checker harness between ECU and ECU harness. Measure voltage between terminal C15 (pos.) and C16 (neg.) with ignition on. If voltage reading is about 5 volts, repair open Yellow/White wire between ECU and MAP sensor. If voltage is not about 5 volts, substitute a known good ECU. If condition is rectified, replace original ECU.

**4)** Measure voltage between White (pos.) and Green (neg.) terminals. If reading is not about 3 volts, replace MAP sensor or repair short in White wire between ECU and MAP sensor.

**5)** If measured voltage is about 3 volts, turn ignition off. Connect system checker harness between ECU and ECU connectors. Turn ignition on. Measure voltage between terminal C11 (pos.) and C16 (neg.). If there is not about 3 volts present, repair open White wire between ECU and MAP sensor.

**6)** If there is about 3 volts present, substitute a known good ECU. If condition is rectified, replace original ECU.

## CODE 4, TDC/CRANK SENSOR (INTEGRA)

**1)** Turn ignition off and remove hazard fuse at battery positive terminal for 10 seconds to reset ECU. Start engine and observe Check Engine light. If light is off, problem is intermittent. Test drive and check again.

**2)** If light is on, turn ignition off. Disconnect 6-wire TDC/Crank sensor connector at distributor. Measure resistance between terminals D and E. *See Fig. 6*. If resistance is not 350-550 ohms, replace distributor assembly. If resistance is within specification, check for continuity between ground and terminals D and E. If continuity exists, sensor is shorted to ground. Replace distributor assembly.

**3)** If continuity to ground did not exist in step **2)**, reconnect 6-wire connector. Connect system checker harness to ECU main harness only, not to ECU. Measure resistance between terminals B10 and B12. If resistance is not 350-550 ohms, repair Orange and/or White wires.

**4)** If resistance is within specification, substitute a known good ECU. If condition is rectified, replace original ECU.

## CODE 4, CRK/CYL SENSOR (LEGEND)

**1)** Turn ignition off and disconnect alternator sense fuse in under-hood relay box for 10 seconds to reset ECU. Start engine and observe PGM-FI warning light. If light is off, problem is intermittent. Test drive and check again.

**2)** If light is on, turn engine off. Disconnect CRK/CYL sensor connector nearest the sensor. Measure resistance across Blue/Yel-

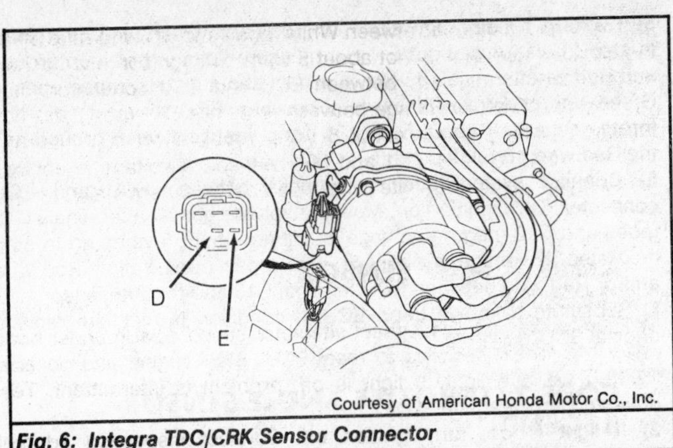
D
E
Courtesy of American Honda Motor Co., Inc.

*Fig. 6: Integra TDC/CRK Sensor Connector*

low and Blue/Green terminals at sensor. If reading is not 500-1000 ohms, replace sensor. If reading is within specification, proceed to next step.

**3)** Check continuity between ground and sensor Blue/Yellow wire terminal. Check continuity between ground and sensor Blue/Green terminal. If continuity exists, sensor is shorted to ground. Replace sensor. If no continuity exists, proceed to next step.

**4)** Reconnect sensor connector. Attach system checker harness to right side wire harness only, not to ECU. Check resistance between connector terminal B19 and B20. Resistance should be 500-1000 ohms.

**5)** If resistance is not within specification, repair open in Blue/Yellow and/or Blue/Green wire. If resistance is within specification, substitute a known good ECU. If condition is rectified, replace original ECU.

## CODE 5, MAP SENSOR (INTEGRA)

**1)** Turn ignition off and remove hazard fuse at battery positive terminal for 10 seconds to reset ECU. Start engine and observe Check Engine light. If light is off, problem is intermittent. Check all electrical connections and vacuum hoses. Test drive and check again.

**2)** If light is on, turn ignition off. Connect hand-held vacuum pump/gauge to MAP hose at throttle body. Apply vacuum. If vacuum holds, go to step **3)**. If vacuum does not hold, attach vacuum pump/gauge directly to MAP sensor. Apply vacuum. If vacuum does not hold, replace MAP sensor. If vacuum holds, check MAP sensor vacuum hose for cracks. splits or looseness. Repair as necessary.

**3)** Check vacuum supply to MAP sensor with engine running. If vacuum is not present, remove restriction from throttle body. If vacuum supply is okay, turn ignition off. Connect system checker harness between ECU and ECU connector. Measure voltage between terminals C11 (pos.) and C14 (neg.). If voltage reading is about 5 volts, go to next step. If voltage is not about 5 volts, check for open in White wire between MAP sensor and ECU. If wire is okay, replace MAP sensor.

**4)** Substitute a known good ECU. If condition is rectified, replace original ECU.

## CODE 5, MAP SENSOR (LEGEND)

**1)** Turn ignition off and disconnect alternator sense fuse in underhood relay box for 10 seconds to reset ECU. Start engine and observe PGM-FI warning light. If light is off, problem is intermittent. Test drive and check again.

**2)** If light is on, turn ignition off. Using a "T" fitting, connect a hand-held vacuum pump/gauge in the No. 4 vacuum hose from vacuum manifold. Start engine. If vacuum is not present, repair as necessary. If vacuum is present and holds, turn ignition off.

**3)** Connect inspection adaptor between MAP sensor and harness. Turn ignition on. Measure voltage between White (pos.) terminal and Green (neg.) terminal. If reading is not about 3 volts, replace MAP sensor. If voltage reading is about 3 volts, substitute a known good ECU. If condition is rectified, replace original ECU.

## CODE 6, COOLANT (TW) SENSOR (INTEGRA)

**1)** Turn ignition off and remove hazard fuse at battery positive terminal for 10 seconds to reset ECU. Start engine and observe Check Engine light. If light is off, problem is intermittent. Test drive and check again.

**2)** If light is on, warm engine to normal operating temperature (cooling fan on). Disconnect C76 and C1 connectors beside battery. *See Fig. 7.* Measure resistance between Red/White wire terminal and Green wire terminal of C1 connector, on sensor side of harness. If resistance value is not 200-400 ohms, inspect for short or open in Red/White or Green wire between C1 connector and coolant sensor. If wires are okay, replace coolant sensor.

**3)** If resistance values are within specification, reconnect C76 and C1 connectors. Disconnect 2-wire connector directly from coolant sensor. Measure voltage between ground and Red/White wire on sensor harness. If voltage is not about 5 volts, go to step **5)**. If voltage reads about 5 volts, measure voltage between Red/White (pos.) and Green (neg.) wires. If about 5 volts is not present, repair open in Green and/or Brown/Black wire between ECU terminal C12 and sensor.

**4)** If voltage reading from Green wire to Red/White wire of coolant sensor harness was about 5 volts, substitute a known good ECU. If about 5 volts is now read, replace original ECU.

**5)** If voltage reading from ground to Red/White wire of coolant sensor harness was not about 5 volts in step **3)**, turn ignition off. Connect system checker harness between ECU and ECU connector. Turn ignition on. Measure voltage between terminals C6 (pos.) and C12 (neg.). If about 5 volts is present, repair open in Red/White wire between ECU terminal C6 and coolant sensor.

**6)** If voltage reading is not about 5 volts, disconnect "C" connector from main wiring harness, not at ECU. Measure voltage between terminals C6 (pos.) and C12 (neg.). If about 5 volts is now indicated, repair short in Red/White wire between ECU terminal C6 and sensor.

**7)** If about 5 volts is not indicated, substitute a known good ECU. If condition is rectified, replace original ECU.

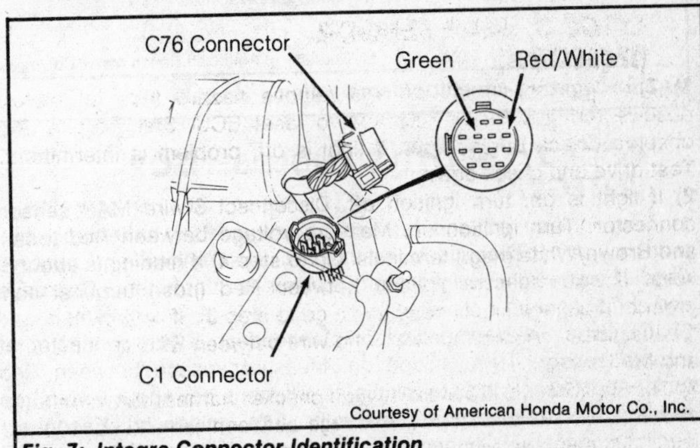
C76 Connector
Green
Red/White
C1 Connector
Courtesy of American Honda Motor Co., Inc.

*Fig. 7: Integra Connector Identification*

## CODE 6, COOLANT (TW) SENSOR (LEGEND)

**1)** Turn ignition off and disconnect alternator sense fuse in underhood relay box for 10 seconds to reset ECU. Start engine and observe PGM-FI warning light. If light is off, problem is intermittent. Test drive and check again.

**2)** If light is on, warm engine to normal operating temperature (cooling fan on). Disconnect C102, C103, C303 and C305 connectors. *See Fig. 8.* Measure resistance from Red/White wire of C103 connector to Green/White wire of C102 connector.

# Acura & Sterling Electronic Control System (Cont.)

**3)** If resistance is 200-400 ohms, go to next step. If resistance is not to specification, check Red/White or Green/White wire between coolant sensor and connectors C102 and C103 for open or short. If wires are okay, replace sensor.

**4)** Measure voltage between ground and Red/White wire of C303 connector. If reading is not about 5 volts, go to step **6)**. If reading is about 5 volts, measure voltage between Red/White (pos.) wire of C303 connector and Green/White (neg.) wire of C305 connector.

**5)** If voltage is not about 5 volts, repair open Green/White (neg.) wire between ECU terminal C14 and C305 connector. If voltage reading is correct, substitute a known good ECU. If condition is rectified, replace original ECU.

**6)** If voltage reading in step **4)**, between ground and Red/White wire of C303 connector, was not about 5 volts, turn ignition off. Connect system checker harness between ECU and ECU connector. Turn ignition on. Measure voltage between terminal C6 (pos.) and C14 (neg.) If voltage reading is about 5 volts, repair open Red/White wire between ECU terminal C6 and C303 connector.

**7)** If reading is not about 5 volts, disconnect "C" connector from right side wire harness only, not the ECU. Measure voltage between terminals C6 (pos.) and C14 (neg.). If reading is now about 5 volts, repair short in Red/White wire between ECU terminal C6 and C303 connector.

**8)** If voltage reading is still not about 5 volts, substitute a known good ECU. If condition is rectified, replace original ECU.

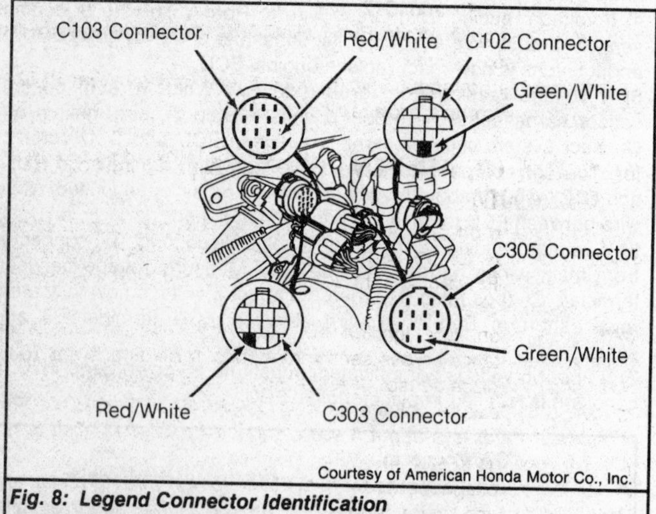
C103 Connector
Red/White
C102 Connector
Green/White
C305 Connector
Green/White
Red/White
C303 Connector
Courtesy of American Honda Motor Co., Inc.

***Fig. 8: Legend Connector Identification***

## CODE 7, THROTTLE ANGLE SENSOR (INTEGRA)

**1)** Turn ignition off and remove hazard fuse at battery positive terminal for 10 seconds to reset ECU. Start engine and observe Check Engine light. If light is off, problem is intermittent. Test drive and check again.

**2)** If light is on, turn ignition off. Disconnect 3-wire connector at throttle sensor. Turn ignition on. Measure voltage between Red (pos.) and Green (neg.) terminals. If voltage is not about 5 volts, go to step **5)**. If voltage is about 5 volts, turn ignition off. Reconnect sensor connector. Connect system checker harness between ECU and ECU connector.

**3)** Turn ignition on. measure voltage between terminals C7 (pos.) and C12 (neg.). Voltage should read .5 volts at closed throttle, and about 4.5 volts at wide open throttle, with a smooth transition between the lower and upper voltage specification as the throttle is depressed.

**4)** If sensor does not respond as indicated in step **3)**, replace throttle sensor or repair open or short in Red/Blue wire between ECU terminal C7 and throttle sensor. If throttle sensor responds as indicated, substitute a known good ECU. If condition is rectified, replace original ECU.

**5)** If voltage reading between Red (pos.) and Green (neg.) terminals in step **2)** was not about 5 volts, measure voltage between ground and Red wire terminal. If voltage is now about 5 volts, repair open in Green and/or Brown/Black wire between ECU terminal C12 and throttle sensor. If about 5 volts is not present between ground and the Red wire, turn ignition off.

**6)** Connect system checker harness between ECU and ECU connector. Turn ignition on. Measure voltage between terminals C13 (pos.) and C12 (neg.). If voltage is still not about 5 volts, go to step next step. If voltage is about 5 volts, repair open Yellow/Red wire and/or Red wire between ECU terminal C13 and throttle sensor.

**7)** Substitute a known good ECU. If condition is rectified, replace original ECU.

## CODE 7, THROTTLE ANGLE SENSOR (LEGEND)

**1)** Turn ignition off and disconnect alternator sense fuse in under-hood relay box for 10 seconds to reset ECU. Start engine and observe PGM-FI warning light. If light is off, problem is intermittent. Test drive and check again.

**2)** If light is on, turn ignition off. Connect inspection adaptor between throttle angle sensor and harness. Turn ignition on. Measure voltage between Red (pos.) and Green (neg.) terminals. If voltage is not about 5 volts, go to step **5)**.

**3)** If reading is about 5 volts, measure voltage between White (pos.) and Green (neg.) terminals at wide open throttle. If reading is about 4 volts, go to the next step. If reading is not about 4 volts, replace throttle angle sensor or repair short in Red/Yellow wire between ECU terminal C7 and sensor.

**4)** Turn ignition off. Connect system checker harness between ECU and connector. Turn ignition on. Measure voltage between terminals C7 (pos.) and C14 (neg.) at wide open throttle. If reading is not about 4 volts, repair open in Red/Yellow wire between ECU and throttle angle sensor. If reading is about 4 volts, substitute a known good ECU. If condition is rectified, replace original ECU.

**5)** If voltage reading in step **2)** was not about 5 volts, measure voltage between ground and Red terminal. If reading is not about 5 volts, go to the next step. If reading is about 5 volts, repair open in Green/White wire between ECU terminal C14 and throttle angle sensor.

**6)** Turn ignition off. Connect system checker harness between ECU and connector. Turn ignition on. Measure voltage between terminals C13 (pos.) and C14 (neg.). If voltage is about 5 volts, repair open Yellow/White wire between ECU terminal C13 and throttle angle sensor.

**7)** If voltage is not about 5 volts, substitute a known good ECU. If condition is rectified, replace original ECU.

## CODE 8, TDC/CRANK SENSOR (INTEGRA)

**1)** Turn ignition off and remove hazard fuse at battery positive terminal for 10 seconds to reset ECU. Start engine and observe Check Engine light. If light is off, problem is intermittent. Test drive and check again.

**2)** If light is on, turn ignition off. Disconnect sensor connector at distributor. *See Fig. 3.* Measure resistance between terminals "B" and "C". If resistance is not 350-550 ohms, replace distributor assembly. If resistance value is within specification, individually check for continuity between ground and terminal "B" and then terminal "C". If continuity exists, sensor is shorted to ground. Replace distributor assembly.

**3)** Reconnect sensor connector. Connect system checker harness to main wiring harness only, not to ECU. Measure resistance between terminals C3 and C4. If resistance is not 350-550 ohms, repair open or short in Orange/Blue and/or White/Blue wire. If resistance value is within specification, substitute a known good ECU. If condition is rectified, replace original ECU.

# 1988 COMPUTERIZED ENGINE CONTROLS
## Acura & Sterling Electronic Control System (Cont.)

### CODE 8, TDC SENSOR (LEGEND)

**1)** Turn ignition off and disconnect alternator sense fuse in underhood relay box for 10 seconds to reset ECU. Start engine and observe PGM-FI warning light. If light is off, problem is intermittent. Test drive and check again.
**2)** If light is on, turn engine off. Disconnect sensor connector at distributor. Measure resistance between Orange/Blue and White/Blue terminals. If reading is not 500-1000 ohms, replace sensor. If reading is within specification, proceed to next step.
**3)** Check continuity between ground and Orange/Blue wire terminal. Check continuity between ground and White/Blue wire terminal. If continuity exists, sensor is shorted to ground. Replace sensor. If no continuity exists, proceed to next step.
**4)** Reconnect sensor connector. Attach system checker harness to right side wire harness only, not to ECU. Using an ohmmeter, check resistance between connector C3 and C4 terminals. Resistance should be 500-1000 ohms.
**5)** If resistance is not within specifications, repair open in Orange/Blue and/or White/Blue wire. If resistance is within specifications, substitute a known good ECU. If condition is rectified, replace original ECU.

### CODE 9, CYL SENSOR (INTEGRA)

**1)** Turn ignition off and remove hazard fuse at battery positive terminal for 10 seconds to reset ECU. Start engine and observe PGM-FI warning light. If light is off, problem is intermittent. Test drive and check again.
**2)** If light is on, turn engine off. Disconnect sensor connector nearest the sensor. Connect ohmmeter leads to sensor connector. If reading is not 700-1000 ohms, replace sensor. If reading is within specifications, proceed to next step.
**3)** Check continuity between ground and each sensor terminal. If continuity exists, replace sensor. If no continuity exists, proceed to next step.
**4)** Reconnect sensor connector. Attach system checker harness to main wire harness only, not to ECU. Using an ohmmeter, check resistance between connector terminals C1 and C2. Resistance should be 700-1000 ohms.
**5)** If resistance is not within specifications, repair open in Orange and/or White wires. If resistance is within specification, substitute a known good ECU. If condition is rectified, replace original ECU.

### CODE 9, CRK/CYL SENSOR (LEGEND)

**1)** Turn ignition off and disconnect alternator sense fuse in underhood relay box for 10 seconds to reset ECU. Start engine and observe PGM-FI warning light. If light is off, problem is intermittent. Test drive and check again.
**2)** If light is on, turn engine off. Disconnect sensor connector near CRK/CYL sensor. Measure resistance between White and Orange wire terminals at sensor. If reading is not 500-1000 ohms, replace sensor. If reading is within specification, proceed to next step.
**3)** Check continuity between ground and White wire terminal. Check continuity between ground and Orange wire terminal. If continuity exists, sensor is shorted to ground. Replace sensor. If no continuity exists, proceed to next step.
**4)** Reconnect sensor connector. Attach system checker harness to right side wire harness only, not to ECU. Check resistance between connector terminals C1 and C2. Resistance should be 500-1000 ohms.
**5)** If resistance not within specification, repair open in Orange and/or White wire. If resistance is within specification, substitute a known good ECU. If condition is rectified, replace original ECU.

### CODE 10, AIR TEMPERATURE (TA) SENSOR (INTEGRA)

**1)** Turn ignition off and remove hazard fuse at battery positive terminal for 10 seconds to reset ECU. Start engine and observe Check Engine light. If light is off, problem is intermittent. Test drive and check again.
**2)** If light is on, turn ignition off, disconnect sensor connector. Measure resistance across sensor terminals. If reading is not 1000-4000 ohms, replace sensor. If resistance is within specification, measure voltage between ground and White/Black wire terminal. If reading is about 5 volts, go to step **3)**. If reading is not about 5 volts, go to step **4)**.
**3)** Measure voltage between White/Black (pos.) wire terminal and Green (neg.) wire terminal. If voltage is not about 5 volts, repair open in Green and Brown/Black wire between ECU terminal C12 and sensor. If reading is about 5 volts, substitute a known good ECU. If condition is rectified, replace original ECU.
**4)** If voltage in step **2)** was not about 5 volts, turn ignition off. Connect system checker harness between ECU and ECU connector. Turn ignition on. Measure voltage between terminals C5 (pos.) and C12 (neg.). If voltage reading is about 5 volts, repair open in White/Black and/or Red/Yellow wire between ECU terminal C5 and sensor.
**5)** If reading was not about 5 volts, disconnect "C" connector from the main wire harness only, not the ECU. Measure voltage between terminals C5 (pos.) and C12 (neg.). If voltage reading is about 5 volts, repair short in White Black and/or Red/Yellow wire between ECU and sensor.
**6)** If voltage is not about 5 volts, substitute a known good ECU. If voltage is now correct, replace original ECU.

### CODE 10, AIR TEMPERATURE (TA) SENSOR (LEGEND)

**1)** Turn ignition off and disconnect alternator sense fuse in underhood relay box for 10 seconds to reset ECU. Start engine and observe PGM-FI warning light. If light is off, problem is intermittent. Test drive and check again.
**2)** If light is on, turn ignition off. Disconnect sensor connector. Measure resistance across sensor terminals. If reading is not 1000-4000 ohms, replace sensor. If resistance is within specification, turn ignition on. Measure voltage between ground and Red/Black wire terminal. If reading is about 5 volts, go to step **3)**. If reading is not about 5 volts, go to step **4)**.
**3)** Measure voltage between Red/Black (pos.) wire terminal and Green/White (neg.) wire terminal. If voltage is not about 5 volts, repair open in Green/White wire between ECU terminal C14 and sensor. If reading is about 5 volts, substitute a known good ECU. If condition is rectified, replace original ECU.
**4)** If voltage in step **2)** was not about 5 volts, turn ignition off. Connect system checker harness between ECU and ECU connector. Turn ignition on. Measure voltage between terminals C5 (pos.) and C14 (neg.). If voltage reading is about 5 volts, repair open in Red/Black wire between ECU and sensor.
**5)** If reading was not about 5 volts, disconnect "C" connector from the right side wire harness only, not the ECU. Measure voltage between terminals C5 (pos.) and C14 (neg.). If voltage reading is about 5 volts, repair short in Red/Black wire between ECU and sensor.
**6)** If voltage is not about 5 volts, substitute a known good ECU. If voltage is now correct replace original ECU.

### CODE 12, EGR SYSTEM (LEGEND)

**1)** Check harness and connections between EGR valve and ECU. Verify vacuum supply to EGR control solenoid. Check vacuum hoses for cracks, splits or looseness. Repair as necessary. Warm engine to normal operating temperature (cooling fan on). Disconnect vacuum hose from EGR valve. Using a hand-held vacuum pump, apply vacuum to EGR valve. If vacuum does not hold, and engine does not stall, replace faulty EGR valve or clean blocked EGR passages.

**2)** If vacuum held and engine stalled in step **1)**, turn ignition off. Disconnect 6-wire connector on right side of firewall. *See Fig. 9*. Disconnect vacuum hoses from EGR solenoid. Apply vacuum to one side of EGR solenoid. Vacuum should hold. On solenoid side of sensor harness, jumper battery voltage to Yellow/Black wire and battery ground to White wire. Solenoid should energize and vacuum should bleed off. If solenoid does not respond as described, replace faulty solenoid.

**3)** If solenoid is okay, reconnect vacuum hoses. Turn ignition on. Check voltage between ground and Black/Yellow wire terminal on harness side of connector. If battery voltage is not present, repair open in wire between harness connector and No. 9 fuse. If battery voltage is present, turn ignition off.

**4)** Connect inspection adaptor between EGR valve lift sensor connector and harness connector. Turn ignition on. Measure voltage between Red (pos.) and Green (neg.) terminals. If reading is not about 5 volts, go to step **7)**. If voltage is about 5 volts, measure voltage between White (pos.) terminal and Green (neg.) terminal. If voltage is not about one volt, turn ignition off. Connect system checker harness between ECU and ECU connector.

**5)** Turn ignition on. Measure voltage between terminals C8 (pos.) and C14 (neg.). If reading is not about one volt, repair open in White/Green wire between ECU terminal C8 and EGR sensor. If reading was about one volt, disconnect "A" connector from the ECU only, not the right side wire harness.

**6)** Measure voltage between terminals A10 (pos.) and A18 (neg.). If battery voltage is not present, repair open White wire between ECU terminal A10 and EGR control solenoid. If battery voltage is present, substitute a known good ECU. If condition is rectified, replace original ECU.

**7)** If voltage reading between Red (pos.) and Green (neg.) terminals in step **2)** was not about 5 volts, measure voltage between ground and Red terminal. If reading is about 5 volts, repair open Green/White wire between ECU terminal C14 and sensor. If voltage is still not about 5 volts, turn ignition off. Connect system checker harness between ECU and ECU connector. Turn ignition on. Measure voltage between terminals C13 (pos.) and C14 (neg.).

**8)** If reading is about 5 volts, repair open Yellow/White wire between ECU terminal C13 and sensor. If reading is not about 5 volts, substitute a known good ECU. If condition is rectified, replace original ECU.

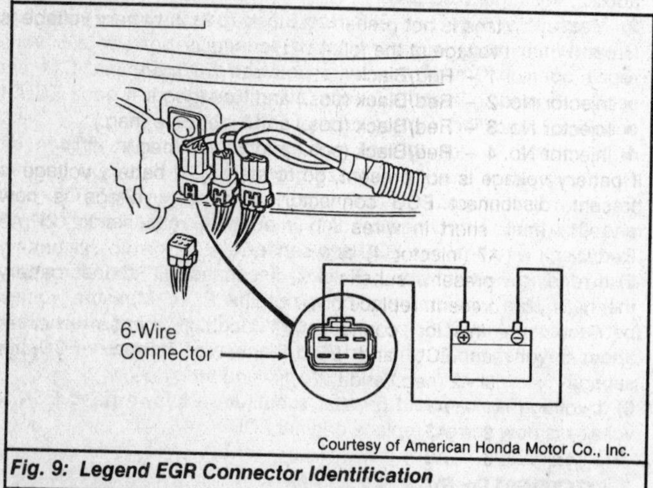
6-Wire
Connector
Courtesy of American Honda Motor Co., Inc.

*Fig. 9: Legend EGR Connector Identification*

## CODE 13 ATMOSPHERIC (PA) SENSOR (INTEGRA)

**1)** Turn ignition off and remove hazard fuse at battery positive terminal for 10 seconds to reset ECU. Start engine and observe Check Engine light. If light is off, problem is intermittent. Test drive and check again.

**2)** If light is on, turn ignition off. Connect system checker harness between ECU and ECU connector. Turn ignition on. Measure voltage between terminals C13 (pos.) and C12 (neg.). If about 5 volts is read, go to step **3)**. If not, substitute a known good ECU. If condition is rectified, replace original ECU.

**3)** Measure voltage between terminals C9 (pos.) and C12 (neg.). If about 3 volts is not present, go to step **4)**. If about 3 volts is present, substitute a known good ECU. If condition is rectified, replace original ECU.

**4)** Disconnect connector from atmospheric pressure sensor. Measure voltage between terminals C9 (pos.) and C12 (neg.) on harness side. If about 5 volts is read, go to step **5)**. If about 5 volts is not indicated, repair short in Red wire between ECU terminal C9 and sensor.

**5)** Measure voltage between Yellow/Red (pos.) and Brown/Black (neg.) wires. If reading is not about 5 volts, go to step **6)**. If about 5 volts is present, measure voltage between Red (pos.) and Brown/B-lack (neg.) terminals. If about 5 volts is not read, repair open Red wire between ECU terminal C9 and sensor. If about 5 volts is read, replace sensor.

**6)** Measure voltage between ground and Yellow/Red wire of harness. If about 5 volts is not present, repair open in Yellow/Red wire between ECU terminal C13 and sensor. If about 5 volts is present, repair open Brown/Black wire between ECU terminal C12 and sensor.

## CODE 13 ATMOSPHERIC (PA) SENSOR (LEGEND)

**1)** Turn ignition off and disconnect alternator sense fuse in under-hood relay box for 10 seconds to reset ECU. Start engine and observe PGM-FI warning light. If light is off, problem is intermittent. Test drive and check again.

**2)** If light is on, turn ignition off. Connect system checker harness between ECU and ECU connector. Turn ignition on. Measure voltage between Terminals C13 (pos.) and C14 (neg.). If about 5 volts is indicated, go to step **3)**. If not, substitute a known good ECU. If condition is rectified, replace original ECU.

**3)** Measure voltage between terminals C9 (pos.) and C14 (neg.). If about 3 volts is not read, go to step **4)**. If about 3 volts is read, substitute a known good ECU. If condition is rectified, replace original ECU.

**4)** Disconnect connector from atmospheric pressure sensor. Measure voltage between terminals C9 (pos.) and C14 (neg.) on harness side. If about 5 volts is indicated, go to step **5)**. If about 5 volts is not indicated, repair short in Red wire between ECU terminal C9 and sensor.

**5)** Measure voltage between Yellow/White (pos.) and Green/White (neg.) wires. If reading is not about 5 volts, go to step **6)**. If about 5 volts is present, measure voltage between Red (pos.) and Green/W-hite (neg.) terminals. If about 5 volts is not read, repair open Red wire between ECU terminal C9 and sensor. If about 5 volts is read, replace sensor.

**6)** Measure voltage between ground and Yellow/White wire of harness. If about 5 volts is not present, repair open in Yellow/White wire between ECU terminal C13 and sensor. If about 5 volts is present, repair open in Green/White wire between ECU terminal C14 and sensor.

## CODE 14, IDLE CONTROL SYSTEM EACV (ALL MODELS)

**1)** Turn igniton off. On Integra models, remove hazard fuse at battery positive terminal for 10 seconds to reset ECU. On Legend models, remove alternator sense fuse in under-hood relay box for 10 seconds to reset ECU.

**2)** Start engine and observe Check Engine or PGM-FI warning light. If light is off, problem is intermittent. Test drive and recheck. If light is on, stop engine. Disconnect Electronic Air Control Valve (EACV) connector. Check resistance between the 2 connector terminals on valve.

**3)** Resistance should be 8-15 ohms. If not within specification, replace Electronic Air Control Valve (EACV). If resistance is within specification, proceed to next step.
**4)** Check for continuity to ground on each EACV connector terminal. If continuity exists, replace EACV. If no continuity exists, turn ignition on. On Integra models, connect a voltmeter between Black/Yellow (pos.) and Blue/Yellow (neg.) terminals. On Legend models, connect voltmeter between Yellow/Black (pos.) and Blue/Red (neg.) terminals.
**5)** Check for battery voltage. If no battery voltage exists, proceed to step **6)**. If battery voltage exists, disconnect connector from ECU and again check for battery voltage. If battery voltage still does not exist, proceed to step **10)**. If battery voltage now exists, repair short in Blue/Red (Legend) or Blue/Yellow and Green/Red (Integra) wire between ECU and EACV.
**6)** If no battery voltage existed in step **4)**, measure voltage between Black/Yellow (Integra) or Yellow/Black (Legend) terminal and body ground. If battery voltage now exists, proceed to step **7)**. If battery voltage still does not exist, on Integra models, check No. 4 fuse and/or repair open Black/Yellow wire between fuse and EACV. On Legend models, repair open Yellow/Black wire between EACV and main relay.
**7)** If battery voltage exists, turn ignition off. Reconnect EACV connector. On Integra models, connect system checker harness "A" connector to main wire harness only, not ECU. On Legend models, connect system checker harness "A" to right side wire harness only, not ECU.
**8)** Turn ignition on. Using a voltmeter, measure voltage between connector terminals A11 (pos.) and A18 (neg.) on Legend or terminals A11 (pos.) and A2 (neg.) on Integra. If battery voltage does not exist, repair open in wire between ECU terminal A11 and EACV. If battery voltage exists, connect and disconnect terminal A11 to A18 on Legend or terminal A11 to A2 on Integra. If EACV does not click when connector is connected and disconnected, replace EACV. If EAVC clicks, go to step **10)** for Integra.
**9)** On Legend, substitute a known good EACV and recheck for code. If condition is rectified, replace original EACV. If code still persists, go to next step.
**10)** Substitute a known good ECU. If condition is rectified, replace original ECU.

## CODE 15, IGNITION OUTPUT SIGNAL (INTEGRA)

**1)** Turn ignition off and remove hazard fuse at battery positive terminal for 10 seconds to reset ECU. Start engine and observe Check Engine light. If light is off, problem is intermittent. Test drive and check again.
**2)** If light is on, turn ignition off. Disconnect 2-wire connector at distributor. Turn ignition on. Measure voltage between ground and Black/Yellow wire terminal on ignition side of harness. If battery voltage is not present, repair open Black/Yellow wire between connector and ignition switch.
**3)** If battery voltage is present, turn ignition off. Reconnect 2-wire connector. Connect system checker harness between ECU and ECU connector. Turn ignition on. Individually, measure voltage between terminal A18 (neg.) and terminals B15 and B17. If battery voltage is present, go to next step. If battery voltage is not present, repair open in wires between distributor and ECU terminals B15 or B17 or replace faulty ignitor unit.
**4)** Substitute a known good ECU. If condition is rectified, replace original ECU.

## CODE 15, IGNITION OUTPUT SIGNAL (LEGEND)

**1)** Turn ignition off and disconnect alternator sense fuse in underhood relay box for 10 seconds to reset ECU. Start engine and observe PGM-FI warning light. If light is off, problem is intermittent. Test drive and check again.
**2)** If light is on, turn ignition off. Disconnect 4-wire connector on ignitor unit. Turn ignition on. Using a voltmeter, measure voltage between Red/Blue (pos.) terminal and Black (neg.) terminal.
**3)** If battery voltage exists, proceed to step **4)**. If no battery voltage exists, measure voltage between Red/Blue terminal and body ground. If battery voltage still does not exist, repair open in Red/Blue wire. If battery voltage does exist, repair open in Black wire between ignitor unit and ground.
**4)** If battery voltage is present, measure voltage between Black/Yellow (pos.) Black (neg.) terminals of ignitor unit connector. If battery voltage exists, proceed to step **5)**. If no battery voltage exists, repair Black/Yellow wire between ignitor unit and ignition switch.
**5)** If battery voltage exists, turn ignition off. Connect system checker harness between ECU and ECU connector. Reconnect ignitor 4-wire connector. Turn ignition on. Measure voltage individually between terminal A18 (neg.) and terminals B15 and B16.
**6)** If battery voltage exists, substitute a known good ECU. If condition is rectified, replace original ECU. If no battery voltage exists, disconnect connector from ignitor unit and system checker harness from ECU. Check for continuity of Red/Blue wire between ECU and ignitor unit.
**7)** If no continuity exists, repair open in Red/Blue wire. If continuity exists, check for continuity to body ground and Red/Blue wire on ignitor unit connector.
**8)** If no continuity exists, replace ignitor unit. If continuity exists, repair short in Red/Blue wire and/or replace ignitor unit as unit may be broken internally.

## CODE 16, FUEL INJECTOR CIRCUIT (INTEGRA)

**1)** Turn ignition off and remove hazard fuse at battery positive terminal for 10 seconds to reset ECU. Attempt to start engine. If engine does not start, go to step **3)**. If engine starts, observe Check Engine light.
**2)** If light is off, problem is intermittent. Test drive and check again. If light is on, using a stethescope, check for clicking sound at each injector while engine is idling. If all injectors click, substitute a known good ECU. If condition is rectified, replace original ECU.
**3)** Turn ignition off. If engine does not start, check resistance of all injectors. If engine does start, check resistance of injectors which did not click. If resistance value is not 1.5-2.5 ohms, replace injector(s). If resistance values are within specification, turn ignition on. Measure voltage between ground and Red/Black wire at injector.
**4)** If battery voltage is not present, go to step **7)**. If battery voltage is present, check voltage at the following terminals.

- Injector No. 1 – Red/Black (pos.) and Brown (neg.).
- Injector No. 2 – Red/Black (pos.) and Red (neg.).
- Injector No. 3 – Red/Black (pos.) and Light Blue (neg.).
- Injector No. 4 – Red/Black (pos.) and Yellow (neg.).

If battery voltage is not present, go to step **5)**. If battery voltage is present, disconnect ECU connector. If battery voltage is now present, repair short in wires A1 (injector 1), A3 (injector 2), A5 (injector 3) or A7 (injector 4) between ECU and injector. If battery voltage is not present, substitute a known good ECU. If battery voltage is now present, replace original ECU.
**5)** Reconnect injector connector(s). Connect system checker harness between ECU and ECU connector. Measure voltage between terminal A2 (neg.) and the following terminals.

- Injector No. 1 – A1
- Injector No. 2 – A3
- Injector No. 3 – A5
- Injector No. 4 – A7

**6)** If battery voltage is not present, repair open in wire A1 (injector 1), A3 (injector 2), A5 (injector 3) or A7 (injector 4) between ECU and injector. If battery voltage is present, substitute a known good ECU. If condition is rectified, replace original ECU.
**7)** Turn ignition off. Disconnect injector resistor connector. Turn ignition on. Measure voltage between ground and Yellow/Black wire terminal. If battery voltage is present, replace injector resistor. If

battery voltage is not present, repair open in Yellow/Black wire between injector resistor and main relay.

## CODE 17, VEHICLE SPEED SENSOR (INTEGRA)

**1)** Block drive wheels and set parking brake. Raise front of vehicle and support with safety stands. With ignition off, connect system checker harness between ECU and ECU connector. Turn ignition on.

**2)** Slowly rotate left front wheel while measuring voltage between terminals B16 (pos.) and A18 (neg.). If voltmeter pulses between zero and 5 volts, substitute a known good ECU. If condition is rectified, replace original ECU.

**3)** If voltmeter does not pulse between zero and 5 volts, repair open or short in Yellow/Red wire between ECU terminal B16 and speed sensor. If wire is okay, replace faulty speed sensor.

## CODE 17, VEHICLE SPEED PULSER (LEGEND)

**1)** Operate cruise control. If cruise control does not function properly, repair cruise control prior to proceeding with test. If cruise control functions properly, proceed to next step.

**2)** Connect system checker harness between ECU and connector. Disconnect "B" connector from right side wire harness. Turn ignition on. Check voltage between terminals B11 (pos.) and A18 (neg.). Voltage should be approximately 5 volts.

**3)** If within specifications, proceed to step **4)**. If not within specifications, substitute a known good ECU. If condition is rectified, replace original ECU.

**4)** If voltage exists, turn ignition off. Reconnect "B" connector to right side wire harness. Block rear wheels and set parking brake. Raise front of vehicle and support with stands. Turn ignition on. Slowly rotate left front wheel and measure voltage between terminals B11 (pos.) and A18 (neg.).

**5)** If voltage pulses from 0-5 volts, proceed to step **7)**. If no voltage pulse exists, check if voltage holds at zero volt and at 5 volts. If voltage holds at 5 volts, repair open in Yellow/Red wire between ECU terminal B11 and speed pulser or replace speed pulser.

**6)** If voltage holds at zero volt, disconnect connectors from right side wire harness only, not ECU. Measure voltage between terminals B11 (pos.) and A18 (neg.). If reading is about 5 volts, repair short in Yellow/Red wire between ECU terminal B11 and speed pulser or replace speed pulser.

**7)** Substitute a known good ECU. If condition is rectified, replace original ECU.

## CODE 18, IGNITION TIMING ADJUSTER (LEGEND)

**1)** Turn ignition off and disconnect alternator sense fuse in under-hood relay box for 10 seconds to reset ECU. Start engine and observe PGM-FI warning light. If light is off, problem is intermittent. Test drive and check again.

**2)** If light is on, turn ignition off. Disconnect 4-terminal connector on right side of firewall which has only 3 wires. *See Fig. 10.* Measure resistance between Yellow/White wire terminal and Green/White wire terminal on ignition timing adjuster side of harness. If resistance is not 3000-6000 ohms, replace ignition timing adjuster.

**3)** If resistance is within specification, measure and record resistance between Brown wire terminal and Yellow/White wire terminal on timing adjuster side of harness. Measure and record resistance between Brown wire terminal and Green/White wire terminal on same side of connector. Add the 2 resistance values together. If the total of the resistance values is not 3500-6500 ohms, replace ignition timing adjuster.

**4)** If resistance values fall within 3500-6500 ohms, turn ignition on. Measure voltage between Yellow/White (pos.) wire terminal and Green/White (neg.) wire terminal on harness side of connector. If voltage is about 5 volts, go to step **6)**. If voltage reading is not about 5 volts, measure voltage between ground and Yellow/White wire terminal on harness side of connector. If voltage reading is about 5 volts, repair open in Green/White wire between ECU terminal C14 and ignition timing adjuster connector.

**5)** If reading is not about 5 volts, turn ignition off. Connect system checker harness between ECU and ECU connector. Turn ignition on. Measure voltage between terminals C13 (pos.) and C14 (neg.). If reading is about 5 volts, repair open in Yellow/White wire between ECU terminal C13 and ignition timing adjuster connector. If voltage is not 5 volts, substitute a known good ECU. If voltage is not about 5 volts, replace original ECU.

**6)** If voltage reading between Yellow/White wire terminal and Green/White (neg.) wire terminal in step **4)** was about 5 volts, turn ignition off. Connect system checker harness between ECU and ECU connector. Turn ignition on. Measure voltage between terminals B18 (pos.) and C14 (neg.). If voltage is not between .5 and 4.5 volts, repair open or short in Brown wire between ECU terminal B18 and ignition timing adjuster.

**7)** If voltage reads between .4 and 4.5 volts, substitute a known good ECU. If condition is rectified, replace original ECU.

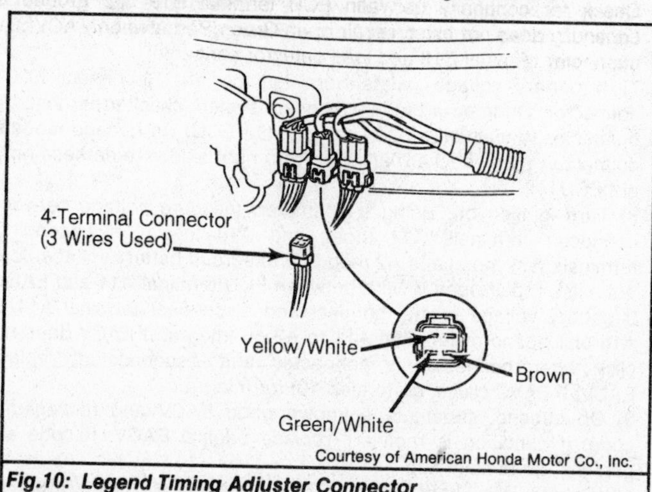
4-Terminal Connector
(3 Wires Used)
Yellow/White
Brown
Green/White
Courtesy of American Honda Motor Co., Inc.

*Fig.10: Legend Timing Adjuster Connector*

## CODE 19, LOCK-UP CONTROL SOLENOID AUTO TRANSMISSION (INTEGRA)

**1)** Turn ignition off and remove hazard fuse at battery positive terminal for 10 seconds to reset ECU. Drive vehicle and observe Check Engine light. If light is off, problem is intermittent. Test drive and check again.

**2)** If light is on, turn ignition off. Connect system checker harness between ECU and ECU connector. Disconnect "A" connector from ECU only, not from main harness. Turn ignition on. Measure voltage between terminals A17 (pos.) and A18 (neg.). If battery voltage is present, go to step **4)**.

**3)** If battery voltage is not present, inspect No. 4 fuse. If fuse is okay, repair open in Black/Yellow wire between ECU terminal A17 and No. 4 fuse.

**4)** Turn ignition off. Disconnect connector from lock-up control solenoid valve. Check terminal A8 at ECU harness for continuity to ground. If continuity exists, repair short in wire between ECU and solenoid valve.

**5)** If continuity does not exist, reconnect solenoid connector. Measure resistance between terminal A8 and A18. If resistance is 14-25 ohms, substitute a known good ECU. If condition is rectified, replace original ECU.

**6)** If resistance is not to specification, unplug solenoid connector. Check for continuity in Yellow wire between ECU and solenoid connector. If continuity does not exist, repair open in Yellow wire. If continuity does exist, replace faulty lock-up solenoid valve.

## CODE 20, ELECTRICAL LOAD DETECTOR (INTEGRA)

**1)** Turn ignition off and remove hazard at battery positive terminal for 10 seconds to reset ECU. Start engine and observe Check Engine light. If light is off, problem is intermittent. Test drive and check again.

**2)** If light is on, turn ignition off. Open lid of main fuse panel in engine compartment. Disconnect 3-wire electrical load detector. Turn ignition on. Measure voltage between Black/Yellow (pos.) and Black (neg.) wire terminals of harness. If battery voltage is present, go to step **4)**.

**3)** Measure voltage between Black/Yellow wire and ground. If battery voltage is now present, repair open in Black wire between connector and ground. If battery voltage is not present, repair open Black/Yellow wire between No. 4 fuse and connector.

**4)** Turn ignition off. Connect system checker harness between ECU and ECU connector. Disconnect "B" connector from ECU only, not main harness. Connect Green/Red terminal of connector to ground. Check for continuity between ECU terminal B19 and ground. If continuity does not exist, repair open Green/Red wire between ECU connector terminal B19 and load detector connector.

**5)** Reconnect "B" connector to ECU. Turn ignition on. Measure voltage between Green/Red (pos.) and Black (neg.) terminals of load detector harness. If 4.5-5 volts is present, go to step **7)**. If 4.5-5 volts is not present, disconnect "B" connector from main wiring harness, not ECU. Measure voltage between terminals B19 (pos.) and A18 (neg.)

**6)** If voltage is now 4.5-5 volts, repair short in Green/Red wire between ECU terminal B19 and load detector connector. If voltage is not 4.5-5 volts, substitute a known good ECU. If correct voltage is now available, replace original ECU.

**7)** Reconnect load detector connector. Measure voltage between terminals B19 (pos.) and A18 (neg.) under the following conditions.

- Headlight switch in first position – Voltage should be 2.5-3.5 volts.
- Headlight switch in second position – Voltage should be 1.5-2.5 volts.

**8)** If voltage is not as noted replace faulty electrical load detector. If voltage responds as indicated, substitute a known good ECU. If condition is rectified, replace original ECU.

***NOTE: Wiring schematics for 1988 Sterling 825 were not available from manufacturer at time of publication.***

# 1988 COMPUTERIZED ENGINE CONTROLS
## Acura & Sterling Electronic Control System (Cont.)

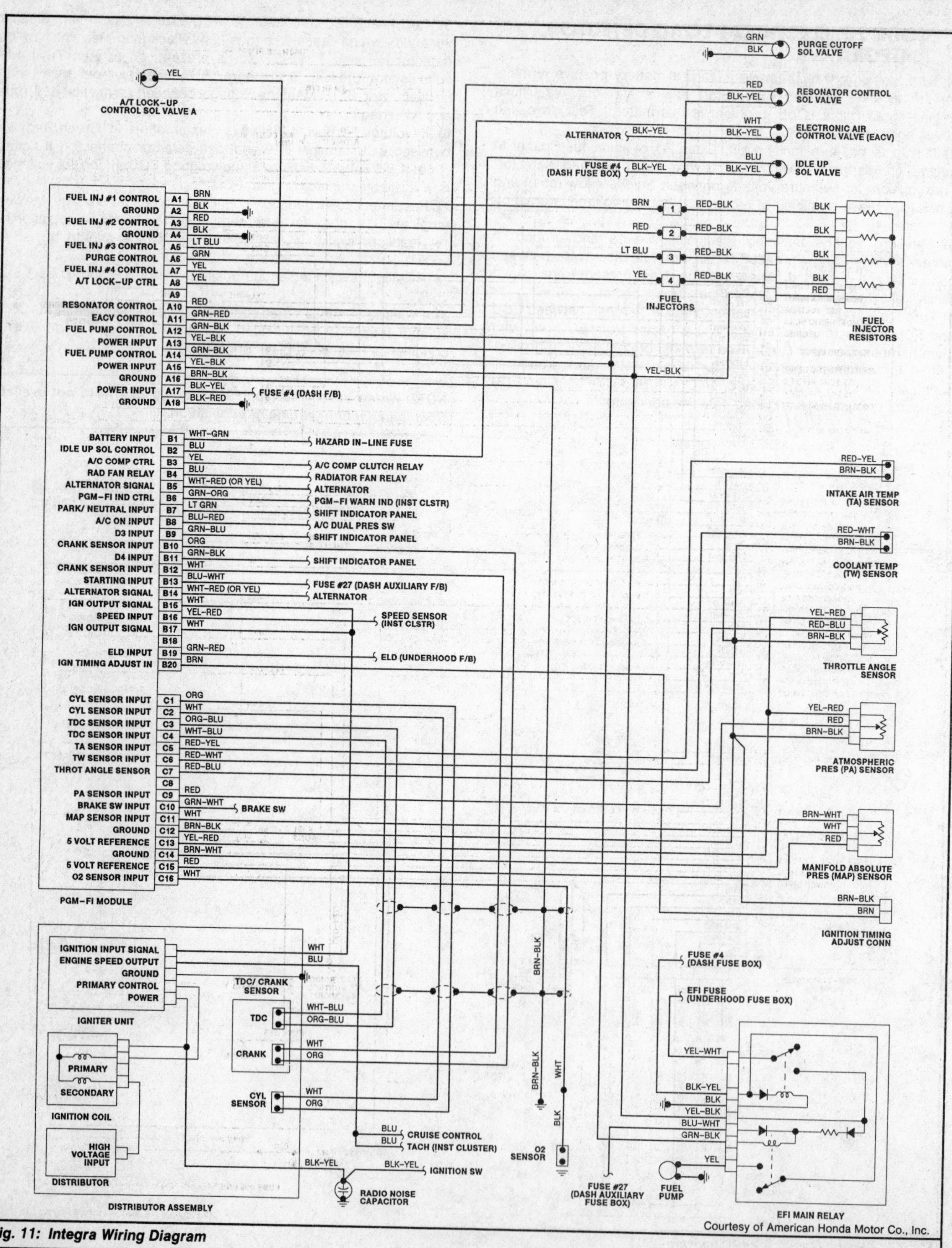

PURGE CUTOFF SOL VALVE
RESONATOR CONTROL SOL VALVE
ELECTRONIC AIR CONTROL VALVE (EACV)
IDLE UP SOL VALVE
A/T LOCK-UP CONTROL SOL VALVE A
ALTERNATOR
FUSE #4 (DASH FUSE BOX)
FUEL INJ #1 CONTROL A1
GROUND A2
FUEL INJ #2 CONTROL A3
GROUND A4
FUEL INJ #3 CONTROL A5
PURGE CONTROL A6
FUEL INJ #4 CONTROL A7
A/T LOCK-UP CTRL A8
A9
RESONATOR CONTROL A10
EACV CONTROL A11
FUEL PUMP CONTROL A12
POWER INPUT A13
FUEL PUMP CONTROL A14
POWER INPUT A15
GROUND A16
POWER INPUT A17
GROUND A18
FUSE #4 (DASH F/B)
FUEL INJECTORS
FUEL INJECTOR RESISTORS
BATTERY INPUT B1
IDLE UP SOL CONTROL B2
A/C COMP CTRL B3
RAD FAN RELAY B4
ALTERNATOR SIGNAL B5
PGM-FI IND CTRL B6
PARK/ NEUTRAL INPUT B7
A/C ON INPUT B8
D3 INPUT B9
CRANK SENSOR INPUT B10
D4 INPUT B11
CRANK SENSOR INPUT B12
STARTING INPUT B13
ALTERNATOR SIGNAL B14
IGN OUTPUT SIGNAL B15
SPEED INPUT B16
IGN OUTPUT SIGNAL B17
B18
ELD INPUT B19
IGN TIMING ADJUST IN B20
HAZARD IN-LINE FUSE
A/C COMP CLUTCH RELAY
RADIATOR FAN RELAY
ALTERNATOR
PGM-FI WARN IND (INST CLSTR)
SHIFT INDICATOR PANEL
A/C DUAL PRES SW
SHIFT INDICATOR PANEL
SHIFT INDICATOR PANEL
FUSE #27 (DASH AUXILIARY F/B)
ALTERNATOR
SPEED SENSOR (INST CLSTR)
ELD (UNDERHOOD F/B)
INTAKE AIR TEMP (TA) SENSOR
COOLANT TEMP (TW) SENSOR
THROTTLE ANGLE SENSOR
CYL SENSOR INPUT C1
CYL SENSOR INPUT C2
TDC SENSOR INPUT C3
TDC SENSOR INPUT C4
TA SENSOR INPUT C5
TW SENSOR INPUT C6
THROT ANGLE SENSOR C7
C8
PA SENSOR INPUT C9
BRAKE SW INPUT C10
MAP SENSOR INPUT C11
GROUND C12
5 VOLT REFERENCE C13
GROUND C14
5 VOLT REFERENCE C15
O2 SENSOR INPUT C16
BRAKE SW
PGM-FI MODULE
ATMOSPHERIC PRES (PA) SENSOR
MANIFOLD ABSOLUTE PRES (MAP) SENSOR
IGNITION TIMING ADJUST CONN
IGNITION INPUT SIGNAL
ENGINE SPEED OUTPUT
GROUND
PRIMARY CONTROL
POWER
IGNITER UNIT
TDC/ CRANK SENSOR
TDC
CRANK
CYL SENSOR
PRIMARY
SECONDARY
IGNITION COIL
HIGH VOLTAGE INPUT
DISTRIBUTOR
DISTRIBUTOR ASSEMBLY
CRUISE CONTROL
TACH (INST CLUSTER)
IGNITION SW
RADIO NOISE CAPACITOR
O2 SENSOR
FUSE #27 (DASH AUXILIARY FUSE BOX)
FUEL PUMP
FUSE #4 (DASH FUSE BOX)
EFI FUSE (UNDERHOOD FUSE BOX)
EFI MAIN RELAY


Courtesy of American Honda Motor Co., Inc.

*Fig. 11: Integra Wiring Diagram*

# 1988 COMPUTERIZED ENGINE CONTROLS
## Acura & Sterling Electronic Control System (Cont.)

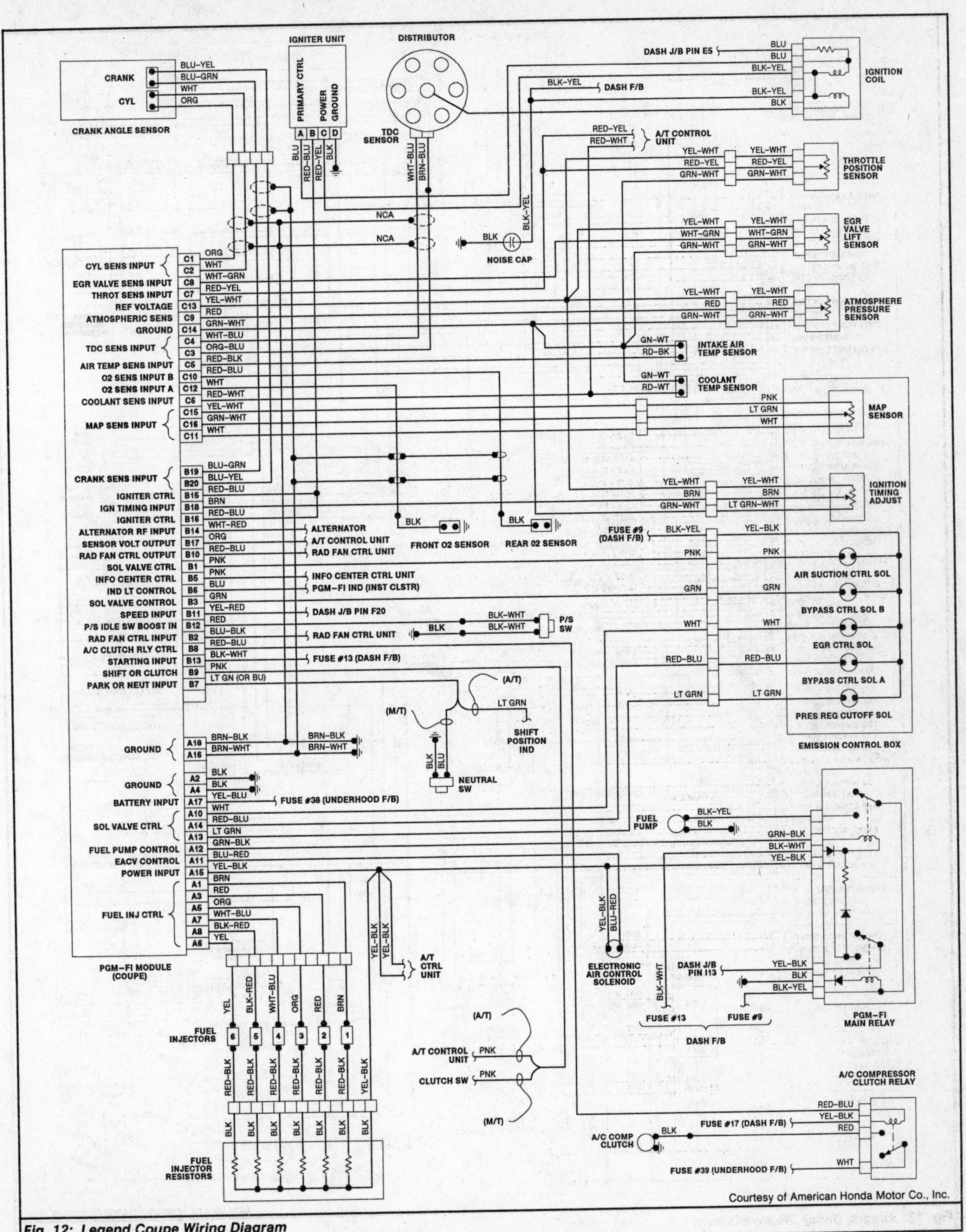
IGNITER UNIT
DISTRIBUTOR
CRANK
CYL
CRANK ANGLE SENSOR
BLU-YEL
BLU-GRN
WHT
ORG
PRIMARY CTRL
POWER GROUND
A B C D
BLU
RED-BLU
RED-YEL
BLK
TDC SENSOR
WHT-BLU
BRN-BLU
DASH J/B PIN E5
BLK-YEL
DASH F/B
BLK
IGNITION COIL
RED-YEL
RED-WHT
A/T CONTROL UNIT
YEL-WHT
GRN-WHT
THROTTLE POSITION SENSOR
WHT-GRN
EGR VALVE LIFT SENSOR
RED
ATMOSPHERE PRESSURE SENSOR
NCA
NOISE CAP
CYL SENS INPUT
EGR VALVE SENS INPUT
THROT SENS INPUT
REF VOLTAGE
ATMOSPHERIC SENS
GROUND
TDC SENS INPUT
AIR TEMP SENS INPUT
O2 SENS INPUT B
O2 SENS INPUT A
COOLANT SENS INPUT
MAP SENS INPUT
CRANK SENS INPUT
IGNITER CTRL
IGN TIMING INPUT
IGNITER CTRL
ALTERNATOR RF INPUT
SENSOR VOLT OUTPUT
RAD FAN CTRL OUTPUT
SOL VALVE CTRL
INFO CENTER CTRL
IND LT CONTROL
SOL VALVE CONTROL
SPEED INPUT
P/S IDLE SW BOOST IN
RAD FAN CTRL INPUT
A/C CLUTCH RLY CTRL
STARTING INPUT
SHIFT OR CLUTCH
PARK OR NEUT INPUT
C1 C2 C8 C7 C13 C9 C14 C4 C3 C5 C10 C12 C6 C15 C16 C11
B19 B20 B15 B18 B16 B14 B17 B10 B1 B5 B6 B3 B11 B12 B2 B8 B13 B9 B7
WHT-BLU
ORG-BLU
RED-BLK
RED-BLU
RED-WHT
GN-WT
RD-BK
INTAKE AIR TEMP SENSOR
RD-WT
COOLANT TEMP SENSOR
PNK
LT GRN
MAP SENSOR
BRN
LT GRN-WHT
IGNITION TIMING ADJUST
WHT-RED
ALTERNATOR
A/T CONTROL UNIT
RAD FAN CTRL UNIT
FRONT O2 SENSOR
REAR O2 SENSOR
FUSE #9 (DASH F/B)
BLK-YEL
YEL-BLK
AIR SUCTION CTRL SOL
GRN
BYPASS CTRL SOL B
EGR CTRL SOL
BYPASS CTRL SOL A
PRES REG CUTOFF SOL
EMISSION CONTROL BOX
INFO CENTER CTRL UNIT
PGM-FI IND (INST CLSTR)
YEL-RED
DASH J/B PIN F20
BLU-BLK
BLK-WHT
P/S SW
RAD FAN CTRL UNIT
FUSE #13 (DASH F/B)
LT GN (OR BU)
(A/T)
(M/T)
SHIFT POSITION IND
NEUTRAL SW
GROUND
A18 A16
BRN-BLK
BRN-WHT
A2 A4
BATTERY INPUT
A17
FUSE #38 (UNDERHOOD F/B)
SOL VALVE CTRL
A10 A14 A13
FUEL PUMP CONTROL
A12
EACV CONTROL
A11
POWER INPUT
A15
GRN-BLK
BLU-RED
FUEL PUMP
FUEL INJ CTRL
A1 A3 A5 A7 A8 A6
BLK-RED
YEL
PGM-FI MODULE (COUPE)
A/T CTRL UNIT
FUEL INJECTORS
6 5 4 3 2 1
FUEL INJECTOR RESISTORS
ELECTRONIC AIR CONTROL SOLENOID
DASH J/B PIN I13
FUSE #13
FUSE #9
DASH F/B
PGM-FI MAIN RELAY
A/T CONTROL UNIT
CLUTCH SW
A/C COMPRESSOR CLUTCH RELAY
FUSE #17 (DASH F/B)
A/C COMP CLUTCH
FUSE #39 (UNDERHOOD F/B)

Courtesy of American Honda Motor Co., Inc.

*Fig. 12: Legend Coupe Wiring Diagram*

# Acura & Sterling Electronic Control System (Cont.)

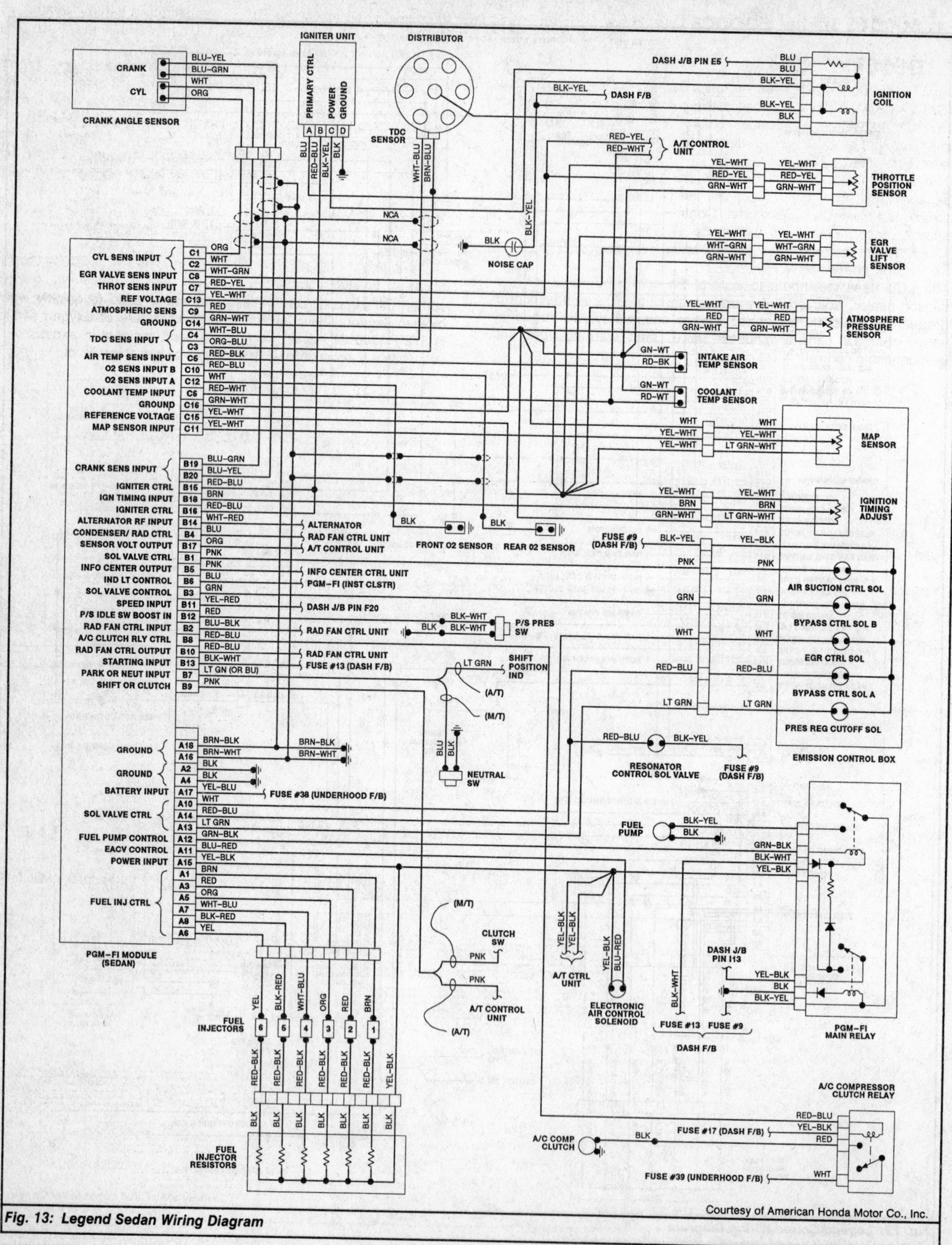

IGNITER UNIT
DISTRIBUTOR
CRANK
CYL
CRANK ANGLE SENSOR
PRIMARY CTRL
POWER GROUND
TDC SENSOR
DASH J/B PIN E5
DASH F/B
IGNITION COIL
A/T CONTROL UNIT
THROTTLE POSITION SENSOR
EGR VALVE LIFT SENSOR
ATMOSPHERE PRESSURE SENSOR
INTAKE AIR TEMP SENSOR
COOLANT TEMP SENSOR
MAP SENSOR
IGNITION TIMING ADJUST
NOISE CAP
CYL SENS INPUT
EGR VALVE SENS INPUT
THROT SENS INPUT
REF VOLTAGE
ATMOSPHERIC SENS
GROUND
TDC SENS INPUT
AIR TEMP SENS INPUT
O2 SENS INPUT B
O2 SENS INPUT A
COOLANT TEMP INPUT
REFERENCE VOLTAGE
MAP SENSOR INPUT
CRANK SENS INPUT
IGNITER CTRL
IGN TIMING INPUT
ALTERNATOR RF INPUT
CONDENSER/ RAD CTRL
SENSOR VOLT OUTPUT
SOL VALVE CTRL
INFO CENTER OUTPUT
IND LT CONTROL
SOL VALVE CONTROL
SPEED INPUT
P/S IDLE SW BOOST IN
RAD FAN CTRL INPUT
A/C CLUTCH RLY CTRL
RAD FAN CTRL OUTPUT
STARTING INPUT
PARK OR NEUT INPUT
SHIFT OR CLUTCH
ALTERNATOR
RAD FAN CTRL UNIT
A/T CONTROL UNIT
INFO CENTER CTRL UNIT
PGM-FI (INST CLSTR)
DASH J/B PIN F20
FUSE #13 (DASH F/B)
FRONT O2 SENSOR
REAR O2 SENSOR
FUSE #9 (DASH F/B)
P/S PRES SW
SHIFT POSITION IND
AIR SUCTION CTRL SOL
BYPASS CTRL SOL B
EGR CTRL SOL
BYPASS CTRL SOL A
PRES REG CUTOFF SOL
EMISSION CONTROL BOX
RESONATOR CONTROL SOL VALVE
NEUTRAL SW
BATTERY INPUT
FUSE #38 (UNDERHOOD F/B)
FUEL PUMP CONTROL
EACV CONTROL
POWER INPUT
FUEL INJ CTRL
PGM-FI MODULE (SEDAN)
FUEL PUMP
CLUTCH SW
A/T CTRL UNIT
ELECTRONIC AIR CONTROL SOLENOID
DASH J/B PIN I13
PGM-FI MAIN RELAY
DASH F/B
FUEL INJECTORS
FUEL INJECTOR RESISTORS
A/C COMPRESSOR CLUTCH RELAY
A/C COMP CLUTCH
FUSE #17 (DASH F/B)
FUSE #39 (UNDERHOOD F/B)


Courtesy of American Honda Motor Co., Inc.

*Fig. 13: Legend Sedan Wiring Diagram*

# 1988 COMPUTERIZED ENGINE CONTROLS
# Audi Digital Control System

### 5000CS Turbo, 5000CS Quattro

## DESCRIPTION

Audi Digital Control (DC) system uses Continuous Injection System (CIS LAMBDA) system for fuel delivery and electronic controls for mixture adjustment, emission control and ignition timing. An indicator light on the dash will illuminate if detonation continues or a fault is detected in the circuits.

The electronic controls consist of an intake manifold pressure sensor (built into the ECU), air temperature sensor, coolant temperature sensor, Electronic Control Unit (ECU), crankshaft speed sensor, crankshaft reference sensor, Hall Effect switch, knock sensor, throttle valve switch, brake switch, engine overheat sensor and oxygen sensor.

The ECU uses the inputs to control the cold start valve, oxygen sensor heater, cold engine warm-up enrichment, Lambda control (frequency) valve, transistorized ignition coil, wastegate frequency valve, charcoal canister shut-off valve, fault warning light and ignition timing control.

## OPERATION

### FUEL CONTROL

**Fuel Pump & Relay** – The fuel pump assembly, located in fuel tank, is equipped with a pressure damper at the suction end. Fuel pump is activated during start-up and when engine is running. Fuel pump relay switches off fuel pump in absence of signal from ECU and provides voltage for cold start valve.

**Mixture Control Unit (MCU)** – Fuel is metered and delivered to individual cylinders dependent on air intake quantity which is metered by airflow sensor. For more information of the MCU, airflow sensor plate, fuel distributor, frequency valve, see DESCRIPTION & OPERATION in the CIS (LAMBDA) SYSTEM article.

**Electronic Control Unit (ECU)** – The ECU is located behind cover in front passenger footwell. Ambient temperature around ECU must not exceed 180°F (85°C).

With ignition switched on, ECU is connected to battery voltage. An intake manifold pressure sensor is located within the ECU. This provides the ECU with engine load information.

The ECU controls the boost pressure, fuel mixture and ignition timing based on intake manifold pressure, coolant temperature and intake air temperature. The ECU also uses signals from the throttle switch to richen the mixture during wide open throttle operation.

**Cranking Enrichment** – During engine cranking, a signal from the starter relay is sent to the ECU to enrich the fuel mixture. The amount of enrichment or activation of the cold start valve is controlled by the ECU based on the coolant temperature sensor.

**Warm-Up Enrichment** – When coolant temperature sensor indicates a cold engine, ECU adjusts the duty cycle of frequency valve to about 80%.

**Oxygen Sensor** – Oxygen sensor is mounted in exhaust pipe in front of catalytic converter. Oxygen sensor measures oxygen content in exhaust gas. Heating element is used to quickly warm oxygen sensor. Minimum operating temperature of oxygen sensor is 572°F (300°C). A rich mixture will send a signal in excess of .5 volt while a lean mixture will give signal of less than .5 volt.

## IGNITION CONTROL

An ignition advance timing map is programmed into the ECU. The ECU will trigger the coil for base idle timing and timing advance. The actual timing advance depends on signals from the intake manifold pressure and input from ignition timing reference sensor, engine RPM speed sensor and coolant sensor.

**Engine RPM Speed Sensor** – An engine RPM speed sensor, located in the upper part of bell housing, detects movement of ring gear teeth on the flywheel. This signal is used to determine engine RPM and ignition timing point.

**Ignition Timing Reference Sensor** – This sensor is located next to the engine RPM speed sensor. It detects the rotation of a pin located 60 degrees BTDC. This sensor sends a signal to the ECU when TDC occurs for number one and number 4 cylinder. The Hall Effect switch, located in the distributor, produces only one signal for each revolution of the distributor. This signal occurs just before TDC

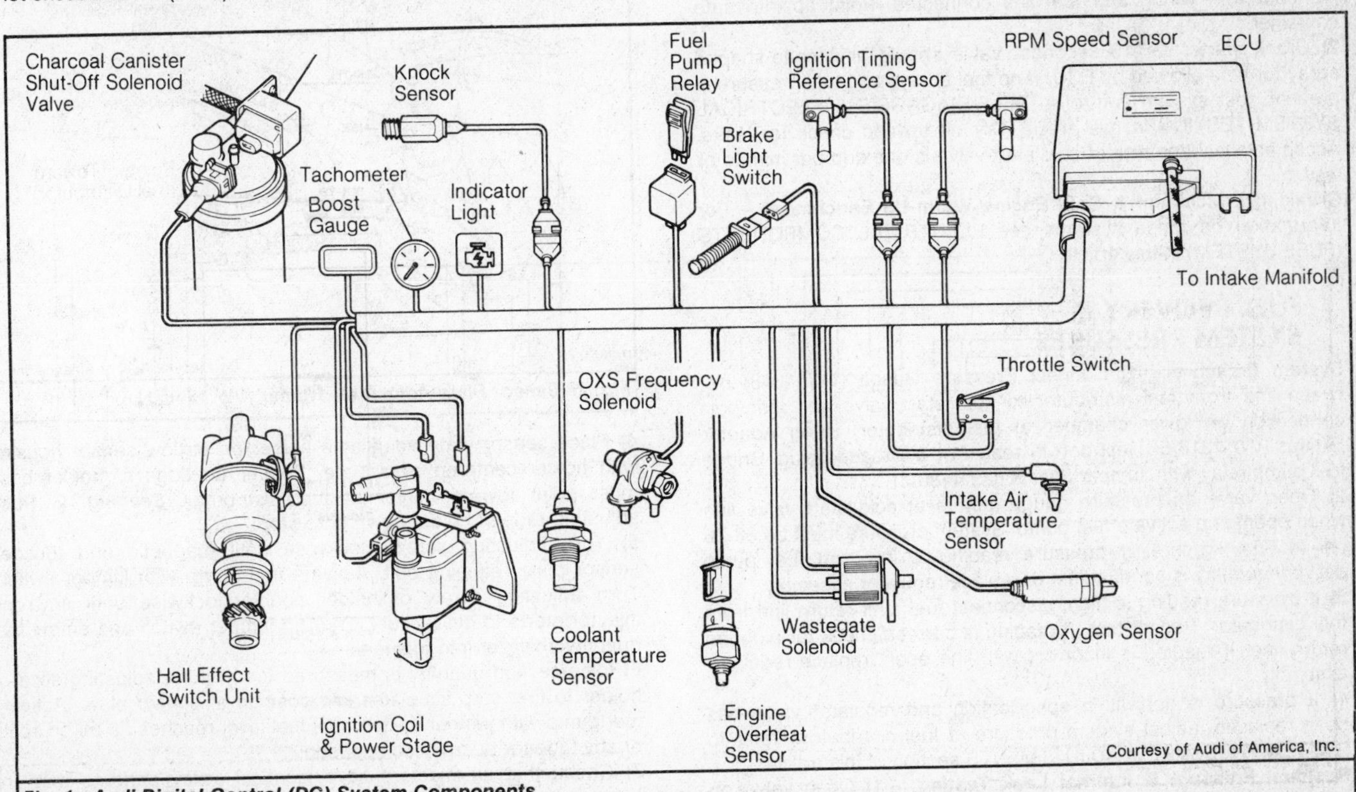
Charcoal Canister Shut-Off Solenoid Valve
Knock Sensor
Fuel Pump Relay
Ignition Timing Reference Sensor
RPM Speed Sensor
ECU
Brake Light Switch
Tachometer
Boost Gauge
Indicator Light
To Intake Manifold
Throttle Switch
OXS Frequency Solenoid
Intake Air Temperature Sensor
Hall Effect Switch Unit
Ignition Coil & Power Stage
Coolant Temperature Sensor
Wastegate Solenoid
Oxygen Sensor
Engine Overheat Sensor
Courtesy of Audi of America, Inc.

*Fig. 1: Audi Digital Control (DC) System Components*

of number one cylinder. This signal is used to determine which signal from the ignition timing reference sensor is the actual TDC signal for number one cylinder. Do not rotate distributor to set base timing.

**Knock Sensor** – The knock sensor is mounted at the center on the left side of cylinder block. A 3-wire connector (Red) transmits signals to the ECU. The knock sensors signal will retard ignition timing in 3 steps of 2.6 degrees, up to a total of 7.8 degrees retard. When knocking stops, the ECU will advance timing in steps of 1.3 degrees, up to the point knocking started.

### IDLE CONTROL

**Idle Speed Control** – Idle speed stabilizer is separate from digital control unit. The throttle switch is used to initiate idle speed control. Air control valve, located in throttle valve by-pass hose, receives signals from idle speed stabilizer.

With ignition on and engine off, air control valve is activated. This provides a valve opening which is determined by coolant temperature. After engine is started, idle stabilizer adjusts idle speed based on idle stabilizer thermo switch, throttle position, and engine RPM. A/C operation will also send a signal to the ECU which will modify the signal to the air control valve. Engine speed is controlled by temperature from 1000 RPM at 0°F (-20°C) to low of 720 RPM at 68°F (20°C).

### OTHER CONTROLS

No description of deceleration control, wastegate control or charcoal canister shut-off control is available from manufacturer.

## DIAGNOSIS & TESTING

### COLD START ENRICHMENT

**Cold Start Valve** – **1)** Check cold start valve with engine coolant temperature below 86°F (30°C). Disconnect and ground high tension lead at distributor cap end. Remove cold start valve from intake manifold with wiring and fuel line connected. Point tip into safe container.

**2)** Crank starter for 10 seconds. Valve should emit cone-shaped spray for time allowed by ECU. If no fuel sprays and fuel pressure is present, test system control in SELF-DIAGNOSIS & ELECTRICAL SYSTEM TESTING in this article. Dry off tip and check for leaks. Acceptable leakage rate of cold start valve is one drip per minute or less.

**Cranking Enrichment & Cold Engine Warm-Up Enrichment** – For information on these systems see ELECTRICAL COMPONENTS (FUEL SYSTEM) in this article.

### FUEL DELIVERY & SYSTEM PRESSURES

**System Pressure** – **1)** Connect Pressure Gauge (VW 1318) between line from fuel distributor to cold start valve and test port connection on lower chamber of fuel distributor, using Adapter Fittings (VW 1318/5). Test port is sealed by a threaded plug. Bridge fuel pump relay with Jumper Switch (US 4480/3).

**2)** Open valve on pressure gauge (points at cold start valve line when open) and activate fuel pump. System pressure must be 68-78 psi (4.7-5.4 kg/cm²). If pressure reading is low and fuel pump delivery quantity is good, adjust or replace regulator assembly.

**3)** If pressure reading is high, disconnect fuel tank return line from fuel distributor. Repeat test. If reading is correct, check for plugged return line. If reading is incorrect with line open, replace regulator assembly.

**4)** If pressure is not within specification and regulator valve has been replaced, adjust system pressure at fuel distributor. Refer to SYSTEM PRESSURE in ADJUSTMENTS section of this article.

**Residual Pressure & Internal Leak Testing** – **1)** Open valve on pressure gauge. Operate fuel pump for 30 seconds. Pressure can drop to a minimum of 38 psi (2.7 kg/cm²) after 10 minutes. If pressure drops below specification, inspect fuel pump check valve and all fuel fittings for leakage.

---

***NOTE: Pressure and leak testing does not include checking cold start valve.***

---

**2)** If there are no leaks, check sensor plate clearance. If plate clearance is correct, replace regulator assembly and repeat leak test. If pressure drop is not within specification, replace fuel distributor "O" rings.

**Main Pump Delivery Volume** – **1)** Check transfer pump (if equipped) and fuel filter. Disconnect fuel return line and place open end in measuring container. Switch on fuel pump with jumper switch. Check fuel pump delivery volume for 30 second period.

**2)** Minimum delivery volume is .71 qts. (.68L) for 30 seconds with reading of 11.4 volts at fuel pump. Voltage is measured with engine off and fuel pump activated by jumper switch.

**Injector Quantity Comparison** – **1)** Remove fuel pump relay, from relay panel, and install Jumper Switch (US 4480/3). Attach Fuel Quantity Analyzer (US 4480) to bumper and secure in place. Remove injectors from cylinder head with fuel lines attached. Check and replace fuel injector "O" rings as necessary.

**2)** Check tightness of injector insert (2-piece inserts). If inserts are loose, remove and clean threads. Use sealing compound when installing upper insert. Replace sealing washer that goes against cylinder head below lower portion of insert. Lubricate injector "O" rings with gasoline and install injectors, with fuel lines connected, into fuel quantity analyzer tubes.

**3)** Ensure lines are not kinked or bent. Loosen fittings to align fuel lines and retighten. Remove rubber boot from airflow sensor housing above sensor plate. Turn and lift setting screw and adjusting slide of Sensor Plate Adjustable Holder (VW 1348/1) into upper position. This simulates full throttle operation. *See Fig. 2.*

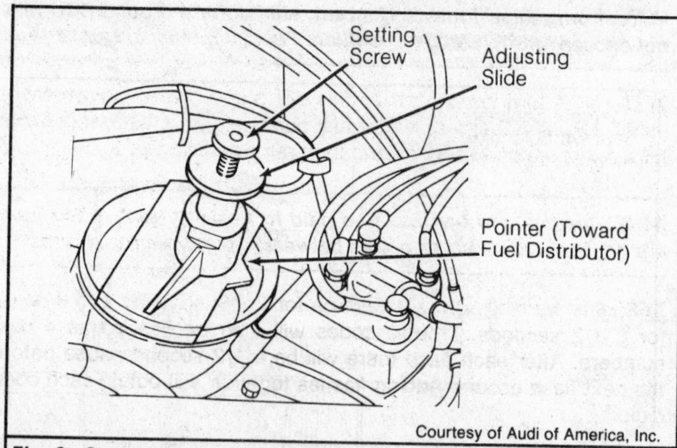
Setting
Screw
Adjusting
Slide
Pointer (Toward
Fuel Distributor)
Courtesy of Audi of America, Inc.

***Fig. 2: Sensor Plate Adjustable Holder (VW 1348/1)***

**4)** Place sensor plate adjustable holder on airflow sensor housing with holder centered over plate. Pointer on edge of holder base must point toward center of fuel distributor. *See Fig. 2.* Push adjusting slide of holder down onto stop.

**5)** Turn adjusting screw clockwise until magnetic end touches sensor plate retaining bolt. Activate fuel pump with jumper switch. Turn adjusting screw of holder counterclockwise until any one injector starts to deliver fuel. Turn off jumper switch and empty fuel quantity analyzer into fuel tank.

**6)** Idle injection quantity is measured first. Lifting adjusting slide of holder to first stop simulates idle position of sensor plate. Activate fuel pump with jumper switch until fuel level reaches 20 ml on scale of any tube for quantity comparison.

**7)** Check that all injectors have identical spray patterns that are even and cone-shaped. If not, raise sensor plate up quickly to full lift

# 1988 COMPUTERIZED ENGINE CONTROLS
# Audi Digital Control System (Cont.)

position and release. Repeat idle quantity test. Maximum difference in delivery quantity between injectors is 3.0 ml of fuel.

**8)** If fuel delivery quantity differs between high and low levels by more than 3.0 ml, interchange injectors and repeat test. If difference of delivery quantity changes with injectors, replace injectors. If difference of delivery quantity does not change with movement of injectors, either fuel lines are pinched or fuel distributor is defective.

**9)** Measure full throttle injection quantity. Empty analyzer into fuel tank and reinstall injectors in analyzer. Lift adjusting slide of holder to last stop to simulate full throttle position of sensor plate. Activate fuel pump with jumper switch until fuel level reaches 80 ml on scale of any tube of analyzer.

**10)** Check that all injectors have identical spray patterns that are even and cone-shaped. Maximum difference in delivery quantity between injectors is 8.0 ml of fuel.

**11)** If fuel delivery quantity differs between high and low levels by more than 8.0 ml, interchange injectors and repeat test. If difference of delivery quantity changes with injectors, replace injectors. If difference of delivery quantity does not change with movement of injectors, either fuel lines are pinched or fuel distributor is defective.

**12)** Check fuel injectors for leakage immediately after delivery quantity test is complete. Set sensor plate in rest position. Activate fuel pump with jumper switch for 2 minutes. Injectors should not drip. Replace injectors that do drip.

## SELF-DIAGNOSIS & ELECTRICAL SYSTEM TESTING

**Input Codes – 1)** Turn ignition on. Engine warning light (on instrument panel) should come on. Start engine. Engine warning light should go off. Drive vehicle for at least 5 minutes to store necessary information in control unit memory. During test drive, accelerate engine above 3000 RPM and briefly accelerate using full throttle.

***NOTE: If engine will not start, crank starter for at least 5 seconds. Return ignition key to "ON" position. Fault codes may now be read.***

**2)** DO NOT turn ignition off as this will erase control unit memory. Install a fuse in test terminal of fuel pump relay (in fuse/relay panel) for a minimum of 4 seconds and then remove. *See Fig. 3.*

***NOTE: Careful attention must be paid to flashing light, since there are no discernable break points between 4-digit number groups.***

**3)** Engine warning light will flash on for 2 1/2 seconds and then off for 2 1/2 seconds. Trouble codes will then be flashed as 4 digit numbers. After each flash there will be a 1/2 second pause before the next flash occurs. Adding flashes together will obtain each code digit.

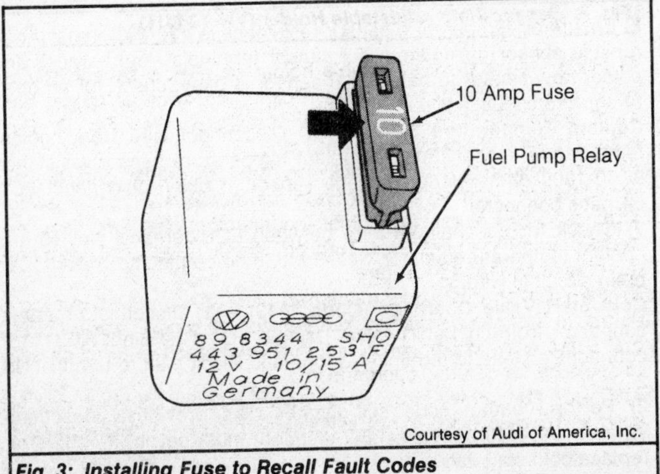
10 Amp Fuse
Fuel Pump Relay
10
89 8344 SHO
443 951 253 F
12V 10/15 A
Made in
Germany

Courtesy of Audi of America, Inc.

***Fig. 3: Installing Fuse to Recall Fault Codes***

**4)** After each digit code is flashed, there will be a 2 1/2 second pause. After fourth digit of number is flashed, a 2 1/2 second pause will follow before the fault code is repeated.

**5)** The fault code will be repeated until the ignition is turned off. Record fault code. Check the list of input codes and possible problems. *See Fig. 5.*

**6)** Check and repair circuits and/or sensors as indicated, see appropriate test in the ELECTRICAL COMPONENTS testing procedures in this article. After the fault is corrected, repeat step **1)** and check for additional codes.

**Output Codes – 1)** Control unit circuitry allows checking of certain components by generating specific output signals. During output diagnosis, components can be checked by listening for their operation. Diagnostic output code will flash during testing, indicating which step control unit is in.

**2)** Turn ignition switch off to erase fault memory. Turn ignition on. DO NOT crank or start engine. If this is done, system will automatically switch to input testing when diagnostic procedure has been activated.

**3)** To activate diagnostic procedure, insert spare fuse into fuel pump relay (in fuse/relay panel) for 4 seconds and then remove. *See Fig. 3.* This will activate the first of 5 output steps. To proceed to the next step, reinstall fuse in fuel pump relay for 4 seconds and then remove.

**4)** First step **(Code 4433)** will activate fuel pump. Pump will continute to activate throughout all 5 steps and until diagnostic procedure is ended by turning off ignition.

**5)** Second step **(Code 4441)** will operate OXS frequency valve at 50% duty cycle until next step is activated.

**6)** Third step **(Code 4442)** will cause wastegate frequency valve to switch on and off until next step is activated.

**7)** Fourth step **(Code 4443)** will cause cold start valve to switch on and off for about 10 seconds.

**8)** Fifth step **(Code 4343)** causes carbon canister shut-off valve to switch on and off until step is terminated by turning ignition switch off. If necessary, output tests may be continued by repeating steps **3)** through **8)** or cancelled by removing fuse.

**9)** If any device does not operate as indicated during output tests, see appropriate test in the following ELECTRICAL COMPONENTS testing procedures.

## ELECTRICAL COMPONENTS (FUEL SYSTEM)

**ECU Voltage Supply – 1)** Unplug ECU harness connector. Connect voltmeter positive test lead to pin No. 35. *See Fig. 6.* With ignition switch on, voltmeter should indicate 12 volts with negative test lead touching either No. 18 and No. 9. If not, repair ignition circuit 15 or battery to ignition switch.

**2)** Turn ignition switch off. Connect positive voltmeter lead to terminal No. 32 and negative lead to No. 9. With ignition switch on, ensure 12 volts are present when brake pedal is depressed. If not,

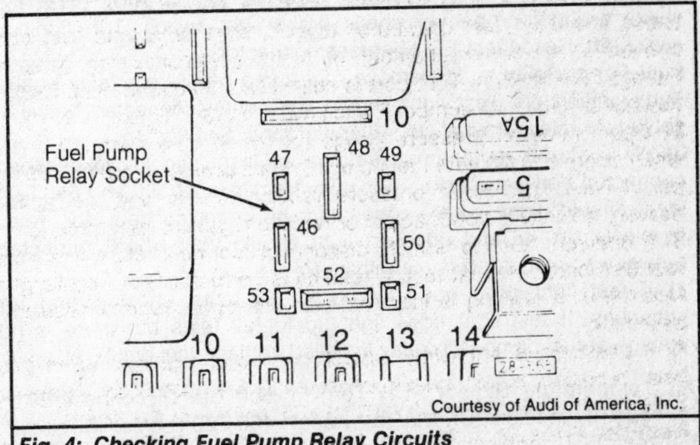
10
15A
Fuel Pump
Relay Socket
47
48
49
5
46
50
52
53
51
10
11
12
13
14

Courtesy of Audi of America, Inc.

***Fig. 4: Checking Fuel Pump Relay Circuits***

# Audi Digital Control System (Cont.)

| Code | Location of fault | Problem |
|---|---|---|
| 1111 | Control unit | Defective memory circuits in control unit |
| 2111 | Speed sensor | Control unit not receiving signal |
| 2112 | Reference sensor | Control unit not receiving signal or distributor is misadjusted |
| 2113 | Hall sender in distributor | Control unit not receiving signal or signal is out of phase (distributor misadjusted) |
| 2221 | Vacuum hose to pressure sensor in control unit | Vaccum hose disconnected, leaking, or plugged |
| 2222 | Pressure in control unit | Defective pressure sensor in control unit |
| 2141 | Knock regulation | Engine or ignition knock is causing timing to be retarded the maximum amount (7.8°) |
| 2142 | Knock sensor | Defective sensor or sensor wiring |
| 2123 | Full throttle switch | Faulty switch or problem in wiring to switch |
| 2121 | Idle switch | Faulty switch or problem in wiring to switch |
| 2312 | Engine coolant temperature sensor | Sensor or sensor wiring defective |
| 2322 | Intake air temperature senscr | Sensor or sensor wiring defective |
| 2342 | Oxygen sensor | Sensor or sensor wiring defective |
| 4444 | No faults have been recorded | |
| 0000 | End of diagnosis | This code is indicated by the warning light staying off for approximately 15 seconds after the start signal (t1) |

***Fig. 5: Input Fault Codes & Possible Diagnostic Problems***

Courtesy of Audi of America, Inc.

check wiring for open or check brake light switch. Turn ignition switch off. Reconnect ECU harness connector.

**Fuel Pump Relay – 1)** Remove fuel pump relay from relay board. Turn ignition on. Test light should light when connected between socket for relay terminal No. 46 and ground. *See Fig. 4.*

**2)** While starter motor is operating, test light should flicker when connected between sockets for relay terminals No. 50 and 51. Test light should light when connected between sockets for relay terminals No. 46 and 50. Test light should light when connected between sockets for relay terminals No. 46 and 52.

**3)** If test light does not light up for all tests, check wiring for continuity. If test light does light up for all tests but there is no voltage at fuel pump with relay installed, replace fuel pump relay.

**Air Temperature Sensor – 1)** Turn ignition off. Disconnect ECU harness connector. Check for about 400-700 ohms in circuit between ECU terminals No. 23 and 24. *See Fig. 6.* If ohms are not as specified, peel back air temperature connector boot.

**2)** Ensure air temperature sensor resistance is 400-700 ohms. If not, replace sensor. If required, cut sensor terminals from harness and solder new sensor to harness. If sensor is okay, check for an open or shorted circuit in wires.

**Coolant Temperature Sensor – 1)** Disconnect wire from coolant temperature sensor. Ensure coolant temperature sensor resistance is 60-1000 ohms. If not, replace sensor. If okay, disconnect ECU harness connector.

**2)** Check for continuity in wire between ECU terminal No. 10 and coolant temperature sensor. *See Fig. 6.* If no continuity, check for an open circuit in wire.

**Cold Start Valve Operation (Code 4443) – 1)** Disconnect harness connector from cold start valve. Using a LED Test Light (US 1115), connect Red lead to terminal No. one and Black lead to terminal No. 2.

**2)** Perform output code self-diagnosis as previously described. When code 4443 appears, LED test light must be on. If light is on, replace cold start valve.

**3)** If light did not come on, ensure 12 volts are present between cold start valve terminal No. 1 and ground. If necessary, repair wiring or circuits.
**4)** If 12 volts are present, turn ignition off. Disconnect ECU harness connector. Check for about .2 ohms in wire between ECU terminal No. one and cold start valve terminal No. 2. *See Fig. 6.* If ohms are not as specified, check for an open circuit in wire. If circuit is not open, replace ECU.

**Cold Crank Enrichment – 1)** Connect Dwell Meter (VW 1367) to vehicle. Using Adapter Cable (US 1112) connect Green test lead to OXS system test connector (Blue/Black wire). Set "%" button on duty meter.
**2)** Ensure engine is below 68°F (20°C). Unplug and ground high tension spark lead at coil. Crank engine and check that duty cycle is a constant 80%. If not, check coolant sensor. If sensor is okay replace ECU.
**3)** If duty cycle reading is okay, but cold start problems are present, check cold start valve and idle stabilization system.
**Cold Engine Warm-Up Enrichment – 1)** Connect Dwell Meter (VW 1367) to vehicle. Using Adapter Cable (US 1112) connect Green test lead to OXS system test connector, located near fuel filter, (Blue/Black wire). Set "%" button on duty meter.
**2)** Ensure engine is below 68°F (20°C). Start engine. Duty cycle should be at least 80%. After 30-60 seconds, duty cycle should gradually drop. If not, check coolant sensor and wiring circuits to coolant sensor. If okay replace ECU.
**Full Throttle Enrichment – 1)** Connect Dwell Meter (VW 1367) to vehicle. Using Adapter Cable (US 1112) connect Green test lead to OXS system test connector (Blue/Black wire). Set "%" button on duty meter.
**2)** Disconnect vacuum hose going to ECU. Remove throttle switch. Start and allow engine to idle. Bridge throttle switch terminals No. 2 and 3. Ensure that duty meter indicates a constant 60% duty cycle. If not, check continuity of throttle switch wiring back to ECU.
**Deceleration Fuel Shut-Off Check (Man. Trans. Only) – 1)** Engine oil temperature must be at minimum of 120°F (50°C). Reconnect wiring to temperature sensor. Start engine and run it at 2000 RPM briefly. Release throttle.
**2)** If intake boot does not visibly contract, disconnect harness plug from deceleration fuel shut-off valve. Attach a voltmeter to harness terminals. Start engine and run it at 2000 RPM briefly. Release throttle.
**3)** If 12 volts are present, ensure vacuum hose is okay and replace deceleration fuel shut-off valve. If 12 volts were not present, check operation and adjustment of throttle switch at idle. If okay, check throttle switch to ECU wiring for open.
**4)** If deceleration fuel shut-off valve still does not operate, connect Dwell Meter (VW 1367) to vehicle. Using Adapter Cable (US 1112) connect Green test lead to OXS system test connector. Set "%" button on duty meter. Disconnect harness connector from deceleration fuel shut-off valve. Using a jumper wire, connect terminal No. 2 to ground.
**5)** If duty meter does not indicate 40%, turn ignition off. Disconnect ECU harness connector. Check for 0.2 ohms in wire between ECU terminal No. 4 and deceleration fuel shut-off valve terminal No. 2. *See Fig. 6.* If ohms are not as specified, check for an open circuit in wire. If circuit is not open, replace ECU.

**Oxygen Sensor Heating Element – 1)** With engine cold, disconnect oxygen sensor heater connection. Connect ohmmeter between male terminals of sensor connector. Start and idle engine. Resistance should be 2-4 ohms. If resistance is incorrect replace oxygen sensor.
**2)** Connect voltmeter between terminals of oxygen sensor female connector. Battery voltage should be present. If not, check continuity of wiring back to fuel pump relay.
**OXS Frequency Valve (Code 4441) – 1)** Disconnect harness connector from OXS frequency valve. Using a LED Test Light (US 1115), connect Red lead to terminal No. one and Black lead to terminal No. 2.
**2)** Perform output code self-diagnosis as previously described. When code 4441 appears, LED test light must be off. If light is off, replace OXS frequency valve.
**3)** If light came on, ensure 12 volts are present between oxygen sensor terminal No. 1 and ground. If necessary, repair wiring or circuits.
**4)** If 12 volts are present, turn ignition off. Disconnect ECU harness connector. Check for about 10 ohms in wire between ECU terminal No. 8 and oxygen sensor terminal No. 2. *See Fig. 6.* If ohms are not as specified, check for an open circuit in wire. If circuit is not open, replace ECU.

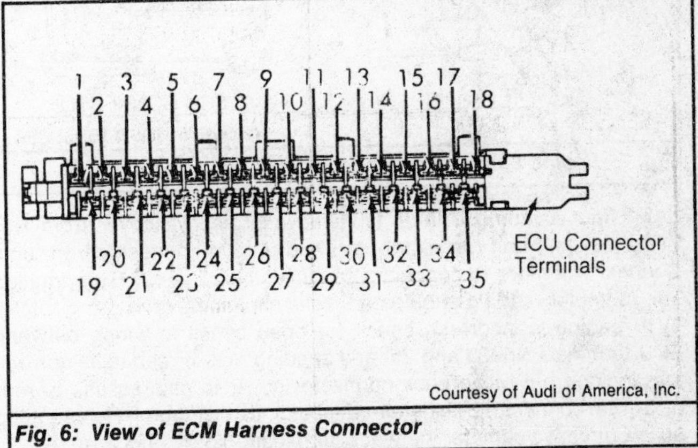
1 3 5 7 9 11 13 15 17
2 4 6 8 10 12 14 16 18
20 22 24 26 28 30 32 34
19 21 23 25 27 29 31 33 35
ECU Connector Terminals
Courtesy of Audi of America, Inc.
*Fig. 6: View of ECM Harness Connector*

## COMPONENT TESTING (IGNITION SYSTEM)

**ECU Voltage Supply – 1)** Remove control unit panel located on passenger side footwell. Unplug ECU connector. Turn ignition on. Using a voltmeter, check voltage between terminals No. 35 and 18, and between terminals No. 35 and 9. *See Fig. 6.* Voltmeter reading should be close to 12 volts.
**2)** Turn ignition off. Connect voltmeter between terminals No. 32 and 9. Turn ignition on and apply brake pedal. Voltmeter reading should be close to 12 volts. Turn ignition off. If readings are incorrect, check for open circuit in brake light wiring. If wiring is okay, replace brake light switch.
**Tachometer Signal Output – 1)** Peel back ECU connector boot. Attach a voltmeter positive lead to ECU terminal No. 7. Attach negative lead to any good ground. Start engine and check for a steady voltage increase as RPM is increased.
**2)** If engine does not run, check engine speed sensors. If engine runs, but voltage does not increase, replace ECU. If voltage increased, but vehicle tachometer did not respond, check wiring between ECU terminal No. 7 and tachometer. If okay, repair or replace tachometer.
**Engine Speed Sensors – 1)** Remove Gray (engine RPM) and Black (ignition timing reference) connectors from bracket near ignition coil. Connect ohmmeter to each sensor connector terminals No. 1 and 2. *See Fig. 7.* Ohmmeter reading should be 1000 ohms.
**2)** If not, replace sensor(s). If reading is correct, check continuity between each sensor connector terminals No. 1 and 3, and 2 and 3. If ohmmeter reading is not infinity (∞), replace sensor(s).

***ENGINE SPEED SENSOR CIRCUITS***

| Sensor Terminal | Connector Terminal |
|---|---|
| Engine RPM (Gray) | |
| 1 | 29 |
| 2 | 11 |
| 3 | 28 |
| Ignition Timing Reference (Black) | |
| 1 | 13 |
| 2 | 12 |
| 3 | 28 |

**3)** Unplug connector from ECU. Check wiring between harness side of each sensor connector and ECU. *See Fig. 6 and 7.* Ensure each wire between ECU and sensor connectors has zero ohms of resistance. See ENGINE SPEED SENSOR CIRCUITS chart.
**4)** Ensure clearance between ignition timing reference sensor and flywheel pin is .43" (1.10 mm) If engine speed sensors and wiring circuits are okay, replace control unit.

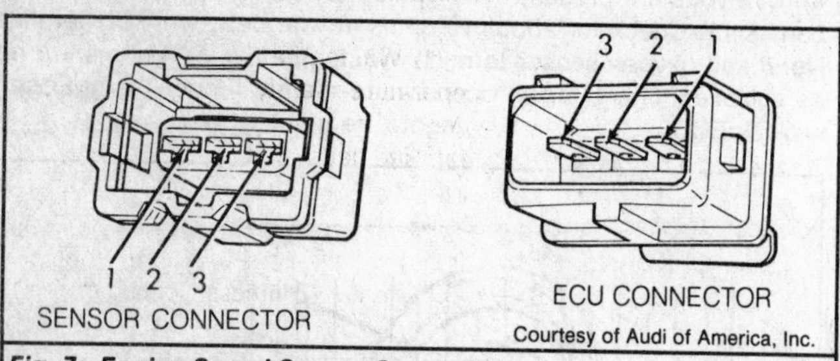
3 2 1
1 2 3
SENSOR CONNECTOR
ECU CONNECTOR
Courtesy of Audi of America, Inc.

***Fig. 7: Engine Speed Sensor Connectors***

**Hall Effect Sending Unit – 1)** Remove protective cover from Hall Effect sending unit (on distributor) and unplug connector from unit. Connect voltmeter to connector terminals No. 1 and 3. Turn ignition on. Voltmeter reading should be 9 volts minimum.
**2)** If reading is incorrect, check for open circuit in wiring between ECU terminals No. 23 and 25, and sending unit. If reading is correct, turn ignition off. Move back connector cover to gain access to rear of 3-wire connector. Reinstall connector to distributor Hall sending unit. Connect voltmeter between terminals No. 1 and 2 at rear of connector.
**3)** Remove distributor cap, rotor, and dust cover. Turn crankshaft by hand until rotor window clears sending unit. Turn ignition on. Voltmeter should indicate 4 volts minimum.
**4)** Turn crankshaft until rotor window fully aligns with sending unit. Voltmeter should indicate 0-.5 volts. Turn ignition off. If readings are incorrect, replace Hall sending unit. If readings are correct, check wiring between Hall Effect sending unit and ECU for shorts or opens in wires.
**5)** Repair wires if necessary. If circuits are okay, replace ECU.

**Knock Sensor** – If engine knocking is present, knock sensor will produce a small voltage of about 50-70 milivolts. If engine knocking continues, check fuel quality, compression pressure, knock sensor and wiring circuits. No other tests are available from the manufacturer.

**Coil Resistance Check** – Using ohmmeter, check ignition coil primary and secondary resistance. Disconnect coil primary and secondary ignition leads. Connect ohmmeter leads across primary terminals No. 1 and 15 at coil. *See Fig. 9.* Resistance value should be .5-1.5 ohms. Connect ohmmeter leads between positive terminal (No. 1) and coil high voltage tower. *See Fig. 8.* Secondary resistance value should be 5000-9000 ohms. If resistance values are not to specification, replace ignition coil.

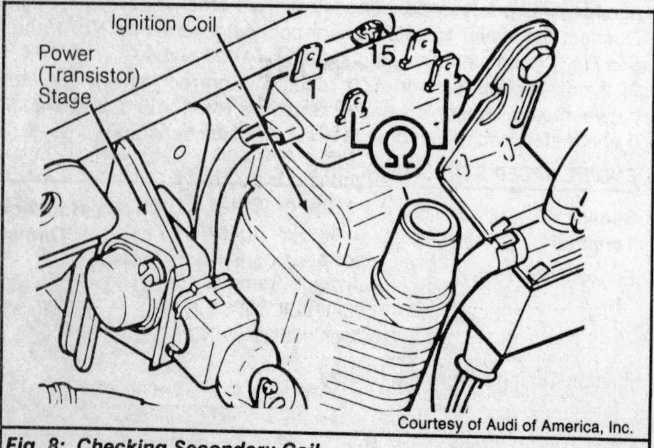
Ignition Coil
Power
(Transistor)
Stage
15
1
Ω
Courtesy of Audi of America, Inc.

***Fig. 8: Checking Secondary Coil***

**Ignition Coil Power (Transistor) Stage – 1)** Check Blue wire from terminal No. 1 of ignition coil to power transistor for any damage. Repair if necessary. Remove secondary ignition wire from coil tower. Using a jumper wire, connect coil tower wire to ground.
**2)** Disconnect power transistor connector (next to ignition coil). Connect voltmeter between terminal No. 1 (Green/White wire) and ground. *See Fig. 9.* Install a jumper wire between terminal No. 2 (Brown/White) and ground.

***NOTE: Ensure test lead connections are correct. If reversed, ECU will be damaged.***

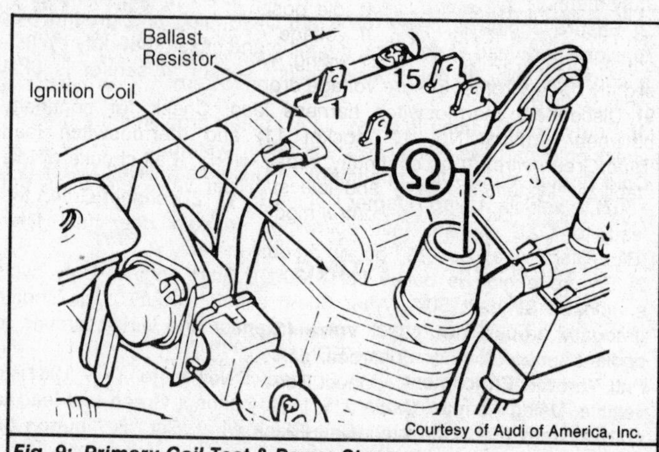
Ballast
Resistor
Ignition Coil
15
1
Ω
Courtesy of Audi of America, Inc.

***Fig. 9: Primary Coil Test & Power Stage***

**3)** Crank engine. Ensure voltmeter reading is .20 volts minimum. If reading is incorrect, check wiring between switching module and control unit connector as follows.
**4)** Unplug ECU connector. Using an ohmmeter, check continuity between terminal No. 2 of ECU connector and terminal No. 2 of power transistor connector.
**5)** Also check continuity between ECU connector terminal No. 22 and terminal No. 1 of power transistor connector. *See Fig. 6.* Ohmmeter reading should be close to zero ohms for both tests. If not, check for open circuit between ignition control unit and switching module. If wiring is okay, replace ECU.

**Spark Plug Wires & Rotor – 1)** Check coil wire resistance. If radio supression wires are used, reading should be 1200-2800 ohms. If not, reading should be zero ohms.
**2)** Check resistance of spark plug wires. If radio supression wires are used, reading should be 4600-7400 ohms. If not, reading should be 600-1400 ohms. Check spark plug connectors. If radio suppression connectors are used, reading should be 4000-6000 ohms. If not, reading should be 600-1400 ohms.
**3)** Check rotor and spark plug wire distributor cap connectors. Resistance should be 600-1400 ohms. Ensure rotor is marked "R1".

**Throttle Valve Switch** – See ADJUSTMENTS in this article for checking and adjusting procedure for idle and full throttle valve switches.

## COMPONENT TESTING (IDLE STABILIZATION)

**Idle Speed Stabilization System – 1)** Ensure engine temperature is below 68°F (20°C). Disconnect harness connector at the thermoswitch. Check for continuity to ground.
**2)** If no continuity, replace thermoswitch. If continuity is present, warm thermoswitch to at least 104°F (40°C). Thermoswitch should now show an open circuit. If not, replace thermoswitch.
**3)** Warm engine to 176°F (80°C) minimum. Disconnect electrical harness for idle stabilizer valve. Connect a voltmeter across both terminals. Turn ignition on. Battery voltage should be present.

**4)** If battery voltage is present, reconnect idle stabilizer valve. Touch idle stabilizer valve and check for vibrations. If not felt, replace idle stabilizer valve.
**5)** If no voltage present in step **3)**, remove idle stabilizer control unit (located in relay panel). Turn ignition on and check for 12 volts between terminals No. 14 (socket 11) and 5 (socket 12).
**6)** If no voltage present, repair wiring. Turn A/C on, and check for 12 volts between terminal No. 2 (socket 12) and 5 (socket 12). If no voltage, check wiring from A/C relay pin No. 87M.
**7)** Check resistance between terminals No. 4 (socket 12) and 11 (socket 11). Ohmmeter should indicate 20-40 ohms. If not, check continuity of wiring between idle stabilizer valve and relay board.
**8)** Ensure throttle switch is at idle position. Check for 12 volts at terminal No. 8 (Gray wire). If voltage is not present, check and adjust throttle switch or repair wiring. With voltage present at idle, slightly open throttle. Ensure voltage drops to zero.
**9)** Disconnect thermoswitch harness lead. Check for continuity between terminal No. 13 (socket 11) and thermoswitch lead (Blue/Green wire). If no continuity, repair wiring. If all circuits of idle stabilizer system are okay and idle stabilizer valve still does not work, replace idle stabilizer control module.

## COMPONENT TESTING (OTHER DEVICES)

**Charcoal Canister Shut-Off Valve (Code 4442) - 1)** Disconnect harness connector from charcoal canister shut-off valve. Using a LED Test Light (US 1115), connect Red lead to terminal No. one and Black lead to terminal No. 2.
**2)** Perform output code self-diagnosis as previously described. When code 4343 appears, LED test light must be on. If light is on, replace charcoal canister shut-off valve.
**3)** If light did not come on, ensure 12 volts are present between charcoal canister shut-off valve terminal No. 1 and ground. If necessary, repair wiring or circuits.
**4)** If 12 volts are present, turn ignition off. Disconnect ECU harness connector. Check for 0.2 ohms in wire between ECU terminal No. 3 and charcoal canister shut-off valve terminal No. 2. If ohms are not as specified, check for an open circuit in wire. If circuit is not open, replace ECU.
**Wastegate Frequency Valve (Code 4442) - 1)** If wastegate frequency valve did not click during self-diagnosis, go to step **3)**. If it did click, disconnect harness connector from wastegate frequency valve. Using a LED Test Light (US 1115), connect Red lead to Blue/Black wire and Black lead to Yellow wire.
**2)** Start and idle engine. Unplug throttle switch. Using a jumper wire, briefly short across throttle switch terminals No. 2 and 3. *See Fig. 10.* LED test light must be on for about 2 seconds or flicker. Remove jumper wire from throttle switch.
**3)** Disconnect harness connector from wastegate frequency valve. Using a LED Test Light (US 1115), connect Red lead to Blue/Black wire and Black lead to Yellow wire.
**4)** Perform output code self-diagnosis as previously described. When code 4442 appears, LED test light must be on or flicker. If light is on, replace wastegate frequency valve.

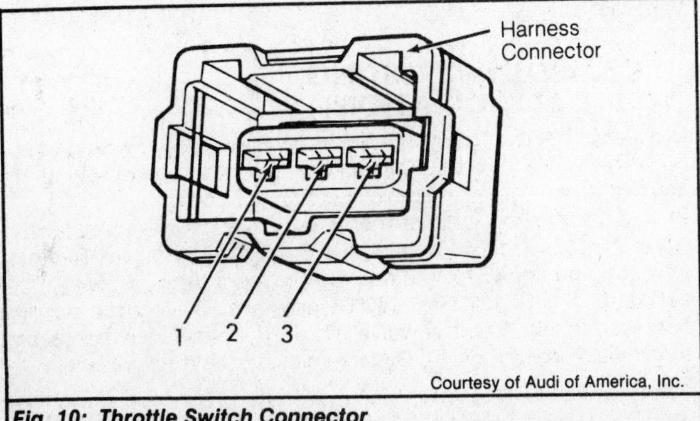
Harness Connector
1
2
3
Courtesy of Audi of America, Inc.

*Fig. 10: Throttle Switch Connector*

**5)** If light did not come on, ensure 12 volts are present between wastegate frequency valve Blue/Black wire and ground. If necessary, repair wiring or circuits.
**6)** If 12 volts are present, turn ignition off. Disconnect ECU harness connector. Check for 0.2 ohms in wire between ECU terminal No. 19 and wastegate frequency valve Yellow wire. See Fig. 6. If ohms are not as specified, check for an open circuit in wire. If circuit is not open, replace ECU.
**Temperature Safety Switch - 1)** Wastegate frequency valve must be okay before testing temperature safety switch. Disconnect harness connector from wastegate frequency valve. Using a LED Test Light (US 1115), connect Red lead to Blue/Black wire and Black lead to Green/Yellow wire.

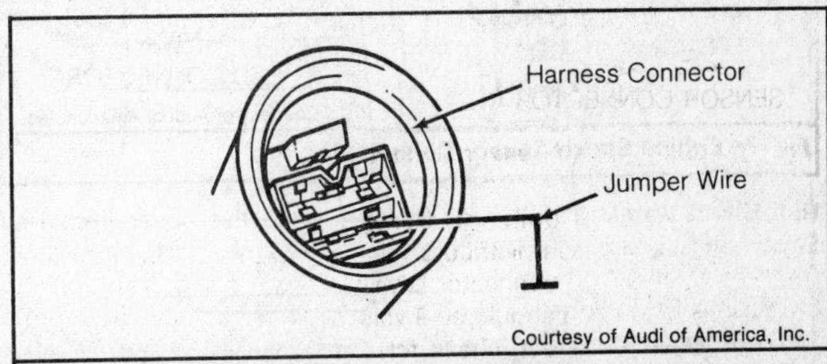
Harness Connector
Jumper Wire
Courtesy of Audi of America, Inc.

*Fig. 11: Temperature Safety Switch Connector*

**2)** Start and idle engine. Unplug throttle switch. Using a jumper wire, briefly short across throttle switch terminals No. 2 and 3. *See Fig. 10.* LED test light must be on for about 2 seconds. Remove jumper wire from throttle switch. If LED test light did not come on, replace temperature safety switch.
**3)** If LED test light came on, disconnect plug from temperature safety switch. Using a jumper wire, connect terminal R to ground. *See Fig. 11.* Using a jumper wire, briefly short across throttle switch terminals No. 2 and 3. *See Fig. 10.* LED test light must NOT be on or flash.
**4)** If not as specified, check circuits between temperature safety switch and ECU.
**Boost Pressure Indicator - 1)** Start and idle engine. Using a voltmeter, probe back side of ECU connector terminal No. 17. *See Fig. 6.* If voltage is not .25-2.5 volts, replace ECU.
**2)** If okay, check boost pressure gauge. If it does not indicate correct pressure, check wiring between ECU and instrument panel. If wiring okay, replace boost pressure gauge.

***NOTE: CIS (LAMBDA) fuel injection maintains constant fuel pressure throughout system. Relieve pressure before opening system. DO NOT allow fuel to leak on engine or electrical parts. DO NOT allow any open flame near fuel system being serviced.***

## ADJUSTMENTS

### AIRFLOW SENSOR PLATE

**Centering Sensor Plate & Lever - 1)** Check sensor plate for centered position in airflow sensor housing . If plate binds on housing or is off-center, remove 6 mm bolt holding plate to lever. Coat bolt with locking compound and install finger tight.
**2)** Use Centering Gauge (US 1109) or .004" (.10 mm) feeler gauges to set plate equidistant from sensor housing. If plate cannot be centered, remove airflow sensor housing to center sensor lever.
**3)** Turn housing upside-down and remove bolt clamping counterweight to sensor lever. Coat bolt with locking compound and install finger tight. Center sensor plate lever in housing and tighten clamping bolt. Complete centering of plate.
**Sensor Plate Rest Position -** Upper edge of sensor plate must be below lower edge of sensor cone .070-.080" (1.80-2.10 mm). If rest position is incorrect, raise sensor plate. Open or close wire clip to change position of sensor plate. DO NOT bend leaf spring.

# 1988 COMPUTERIZED ENGINE CONTROLS
# Audi Digital Control System (Cont.)

## THROTTLE VALVE HOUSING

***NOTE:** Stop screw is set by manufacturer and should not be moved.*

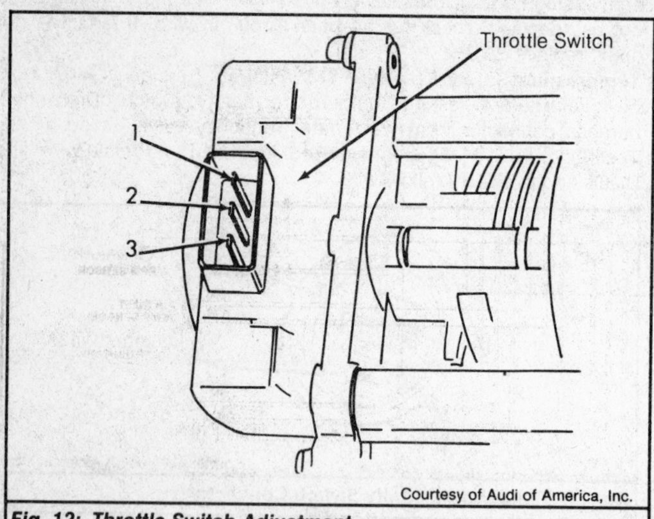
Throttle Switch
1
2
3
Courtesy of Audi of America, Inc.

*Fig. 12: Throttle Switch Adjustment*

**Throttle Switch – 1)** Disconnect throttle switch harness. Attach ohmmeter to switch terminals No. one and 2. *See Fig. 12.*
**2)** Ensure throttle is set at a idle position. Ohmmeter must read zero ohms. If not, loosen mounting screws and adjust switch.

## SYSTEM PRESSURE

**Fuel Pressure – 1)** Check and note existing pressure. Remove pressure regulating valve from fuel distributor.
**2)** Adjust pressure by changing shims in shim stack. Add shims to raise system pressure. Remove shims to lower system pressure.
**3)** A shim change of .020" (.5 mm) will change system pressure approximately 4.2 psi (.3 kg/cm²). Ensure any replacement shims are identical in diameter to existing shims.

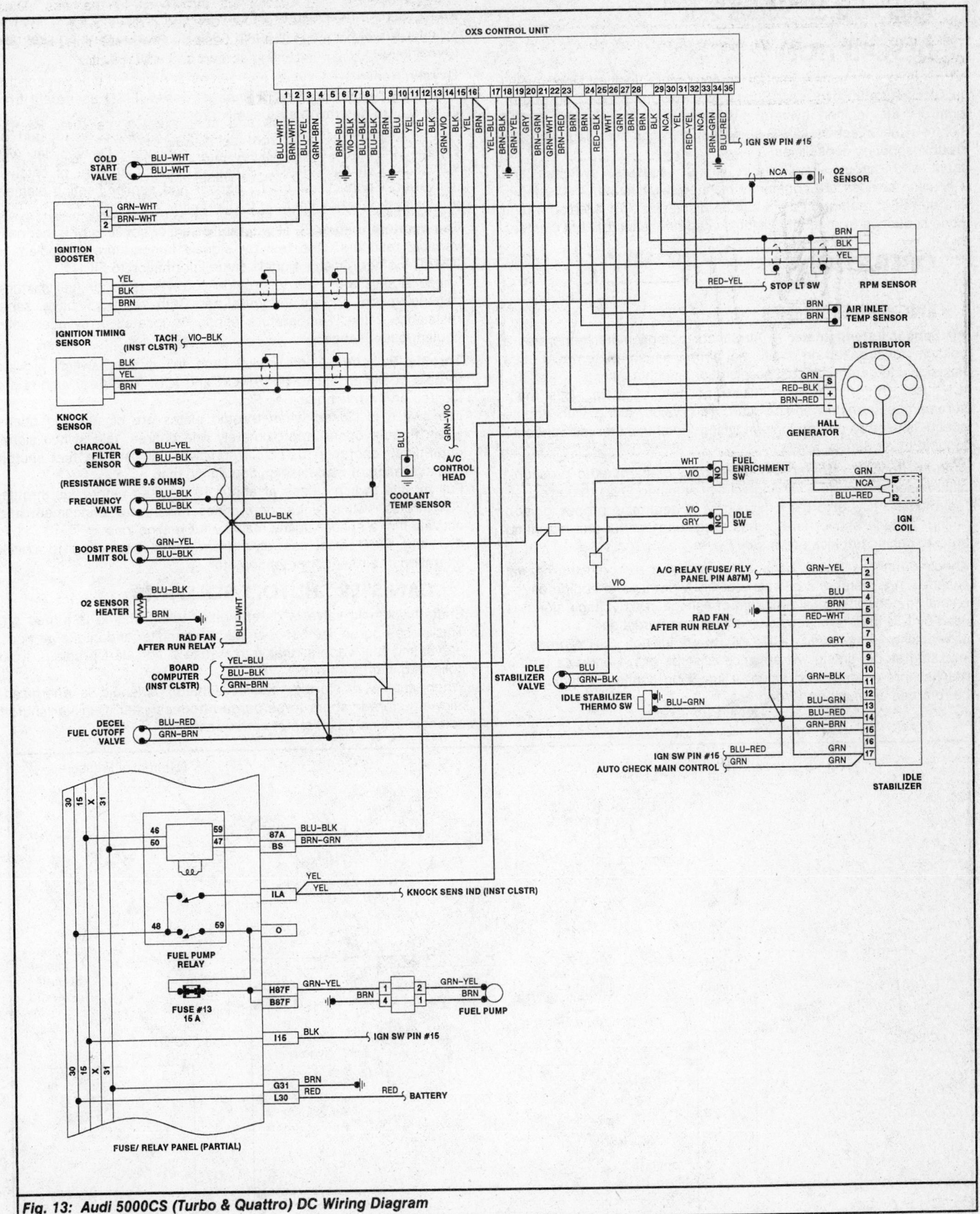
OXS CONTROL UNIT
COLD START VALVE
IGNITION BOOSTER
IGNITION TIMING SENSOR
TACH (INST CLSTR)
KNOCK SENSOR
CHARCOAL FILTER SENSOR
(RESISTANCE WIRE 9.6 OHMS)
FREQUENCY VALVE
BOOST PRES LIMIT SOL
O2 SENSOR HEATER
RAD FAN AFTER RUN RELAY
BOARD COMPUTER (INST CLSTR)
DECEL FUEL CUTOFF VALVE
COOLANT TEMP SENSOR
A/C CONTROL HEAD
IGN SW PIN #15
O2 SENSOR
RPM SENSOR
STOP LT SW
AIR INLET TEMP SENSOR
DISTRIBUTOR
HALL GENERATOR
FUEL ENRICHMENT SW
IGN COIL
IDLE SW
A/C RELAY (FUSE/ RLY PANEL PIN A87M)
RAD FAN AFTER RUN RELAY
IDLE STABILIZER VALVE
IDLE STABILIZER THERMO SW
IGN SW PIN #15
AUTO CHECK MAIN CONTROL
IDLE STABILIZER
FUEL PUMP RELAY
KNOCK SENS IND (INST CLSTR)
FUSE #13 15 A
FUEL PUMP
IGN SW PIN #15
BATTERY
FUSE/ RELAY PANEL (PARTIAL)

*Fig. 13: Audi 5000CS (Turbo & Quattro) DC Wiring Diagram*

## Audi 90 2.3L, 5000S 2.3L

## DESCRIPTION

CIS-E III system uses 2 interfacing computers. Ignition Control Unit (ICU) on Audi 90 or Knock Sensor Control Unit (KSCU) on 5000S, controls the ignition system. Fuel Injection Control Unit (FICU) controls fuel injection. CIS-E III system also has self diagnosis and trouble shooting capabilities.

Input and output signals from various sensors, switches and signalling devices are constantly monitored for faults. These faults are stored in memory. Faults can be displayed by a flashing 4-digit code sequence from an LED light located on the instrument cluster.

## OPERATION

### ENGINE SENSORS

**Air Sensor Potentiometer** – Air sensor potentiometer generates a voltage signal based on position of airflow sensor plate. FICU uses this signal to determine cold acceleration enrichment.

ICU uses information to measure position of plate. This measurement determines engine load. This value, along with engine speed, is used to control ignition timing. Potentiometer is connected to plate by air sensor lever.

**Altitude Sensor** – Depending on altitude or barometric pressure, altitude sensor sends a varying voltage signal to FICU to correct air fuel mixture. ICU also uses this signal to determine proper ignition timing. Altitude sensor is attached to ignition control unit mounting bracket behind left kick panel. *See Fig. 4.*

**Knock Sensor** – Knock sensor consists of a piezoelectric crystal encased in a metal and plastic housing. Vibrations in engine cause crystal to generate small amounts of voltage. This voltage signal is used by ICU to determine necessary timing retardation.

If knocking is detected, ICU will retard ignition 3.4 degrees. If knocking stops, timing will advance in steps of .54 degrees until it reaches pre-programmed value. If knocking continues, timing can be retarded as much as 12 degrees.

Knock sensor is located on left side of cylinder block, next to cylinder No. 3. Knock sensor connector is located on a bracket next to distributor.

**Oxygen Sensor** – Oxygen ($O_2$) sensor is a heated type sensor that measures oxygen content of exhaust gases. FICU uses data from $O_2$ sensor to determine air fuel mixture.

On vehicles with manual transmission, $O_2$ sensor is located on exhaust pipe just ahead of catalytic converter. On vehicles with automatic transmission, $O_2$ sensor is located at front of catalytic converter. Connections for $O_2$ sensor and sensor heating element are located on a bracket next to distributor.

**Temperature Sensor** – Temperature sensor consists of 2 thermally variable resistors. One resistor signals temperature of coolant to ICU. The other resistor signals same information to FICU.

These signals are used to provide corrections to air fuel mixture, depending on coolant temperature. Both resistors have same resistance value. Temperature sensor is located in cylinder head coolant outlet flange.

**Throttle Switches** – Idle switch and full throttle switch provide throttle position data to both FICU and ICU. Throttle switches are located on throttle body. *See Fig. 2.*

Idle switch is closed when throttle plates are closed and opens when throttle opens approximately one degree. Idle switch signal determines operation of stabilizer valve, deceleration fuel shutoff and activation of a special ignition timing map.

Full throttle switch closes at about 10 degrees before full throttle. Full throttle switch signal determines full throttle enrichment and activation of a special timing map for full engine load.

ICU and FICU also use data from throttle switches to check operation of air sensor potentiometer.

### CANISTER SHUTOFF SOLENOID

Shutoff solenoid valve is de-energized when engine is turned off. This closes purge line between carbon canister and intake air boot, preventing fuel vapors, that may cause a hot start problem, from collecting in intake tract.

When engine is started, canister shutoff solenoid is energized, allowing stored vapors to be purged from canister. Canister shutoff solenoid is located on top of carbon canister.

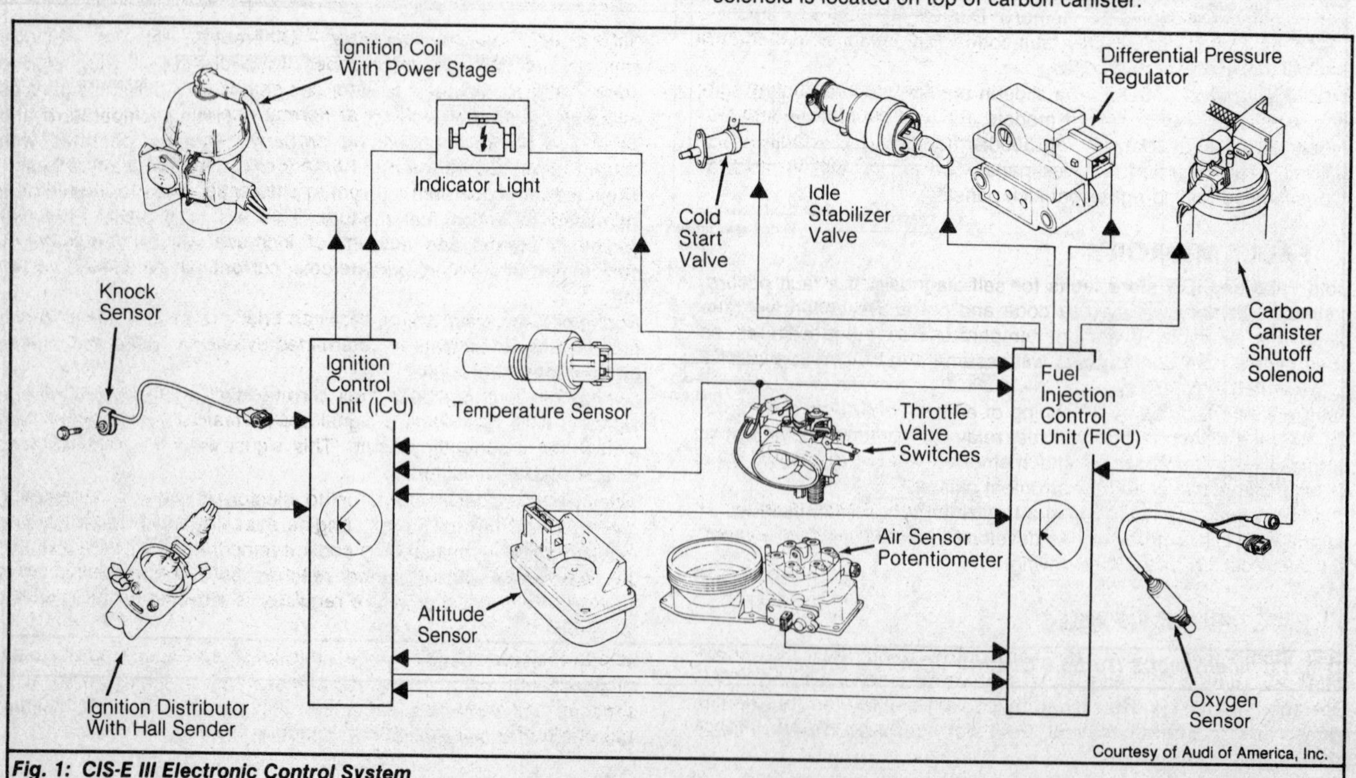
Ignition Coil
With Power Stage
Indicator Light
Differential Pressure
Regulator
Cold
Start
Valve
Idle
Stabilizer
Valve
Knock
Sensor
Carbon
Canister
Shutoff
Solenoid
Ignition
Control
Unit (ICU)
Temperature Sensor
Fuel
Injection
Control
Unit (FICU)
Throttle
Valve
Switches
Air Sensor
Potentiometer
Altitude
Sensor
Ignition Distributor
With Hall Sender
Oxygen
Sensor
Courtesy of Audi of America, Inc.

*Fig. 1: CIS-E III Electronic Control System*

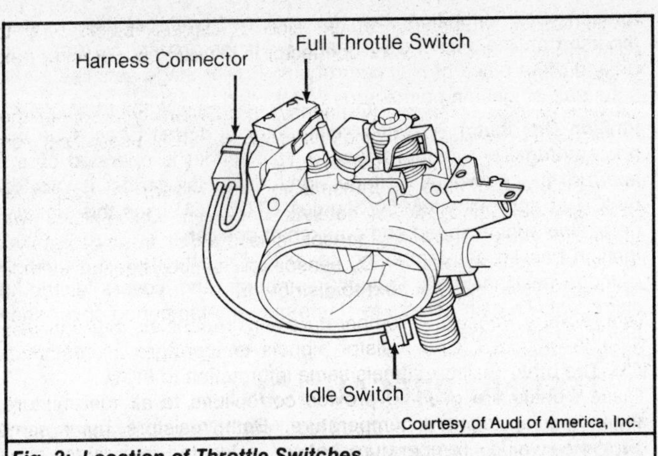
Harness Connector
Full Throttle Switch
Idle Switch
Courtesy of Audi of America, Inc.
*Fig. 2: Location of Throttle Switches*

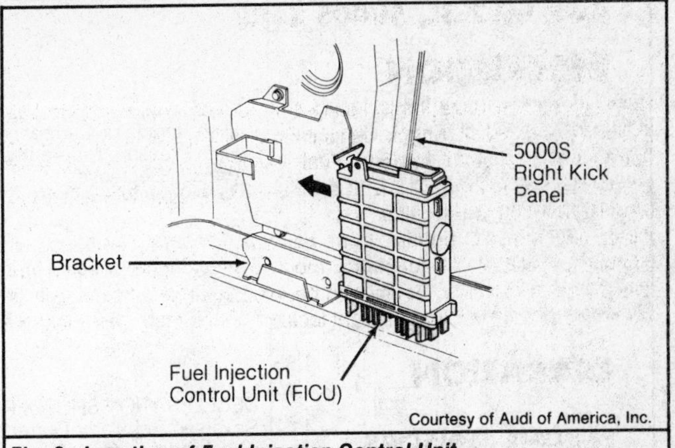
5000S
Right Kick
Panel
Bracket
Fuel Injection
Control Unit (FICU)
Courtesy of Audi of America, Inc.
*Fig. 3: Location of Fuel Injection Control Unit*

## CONTROL UNITS

Ignition Control Unit (ICU) collects signals from altitude sensor, ignition distributor, knock sensor, temperature sensor, throttle valve switches and fuel injection control unit. Using collected data, ICU continuously updates required degree of ignition advance/retard.

There are 2 separate ignition timing maps programmed into ICU. One is programmed for regular fuel. The other is programmed for premium fuel.

When coolant temperature reaches 149°F (65°C), ICU automatically switches to premium fuel map. Premium fuel map is programmed to have timing with a slightly advanced curve in some of lower RPM ranges.

If ignition knock occurs repeatedly, ICU will automatically switch to regular fuel map. ICU will switch back to premium fuel map after a fixed amount of time or whenever engine is restarted.

Fuel Injection Control Unit (FICU) receives signals from air sensor potentiometer, altitude sensor, oxygen sensor, temperature sensor, throttle valve switches and ignition control unit. Using this data, it varies air fuel mixture as necessary.

Both control units constantly interface with each other. Each control unit contains it's own fault memory. During self-diagnosis ignition control unit will always display fault codes first. Fuel injection control unit will then display fault codes.

On 5000S models, FICU is in a slide-in bracket located behind right kick panel. *See Fig. 3*. On 90 models, FICU is located behind A/C evaporator in right footwell. On 5000S models, ICU is bolted to a bracket located behind left kick panel. *See Fig. 4*. On 90 models, ICU is located behind right front kick panel.

## FAULT MEMORY

Both FICU and ICU store faults for self-diagnosis. If a fault occurs, computer memory will store a code and corrective action will take place. For example, if coolant temperature sensor developes an open circuit, both control units will assume a calculation value of a fully warmed engine.

Fault will be displayed by a flashing of engine control indicator light. By inserting a fuse into top of fuel relay for 4 seconds, diagnostic terminals will be grounded and memories will be displayed by a flashing sequential code on instrument cluster.

If ignition system is operating in a fully retarded position because of engine knock or a problem has developed in knock sensor system, indicator light will flash while driving.

## ENGINE CONTROLS

**Cold Start Valve** – Cold start valve injects extra fuel into intake manifold during cold starts. Cold start valve is controlled by FICU. Operation of valve is determined by coolant temperature to prevent excess fuel from being injected. Cold start valve is located on back of intake manifold.

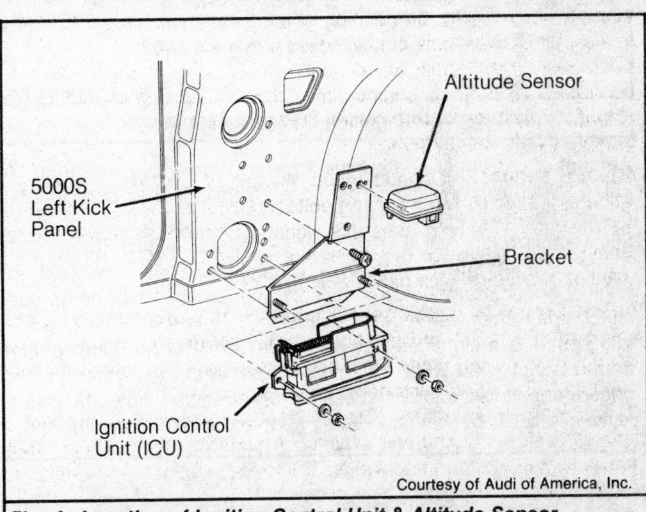
Altitude Sensor
5000S
Left Kick
Panel
Bracket
Ignition Control
Unit (ICU)
Courtesy of Audi of America, Inc.
*Fig. 4: Location of Ignition Control Unit & Altitude Sensor*

**Differential Pressure Regulator** – Differential pressure regulator controls fuel flow in lower chamber of fuel distributor. This helps to determine fuel mixture. Regulator designates zero Milliamps (mA) as reference point. With vehicle at normal operating temperature and all engine controls functioning properly, regulator operates with current from FICU between +10 mA (rich) to -10 mA (lean) ranges.

When starter is operated, current to differential pressure regulator is increased to enrich fuel mixture. This will take place whenever engine is started and amount of increase will be regulated by coolant temperature. In extreme cold, current can be as high as 140 mA.

During cold acceleration, current can briefly raise to 6 mA to enrich fuel mixture. Enrichment is determined by engine speed and signals from temperature sensor.

During full load operation, full throttle switch closes, sending a signal to ICU. ICU sends a signal approximately 3 mA greater than signal that is currently present. This signal will vary, depending on engine speed and altitude.

When vehicle is decelerated, fuel to injectors is shut off by reversing current to -50 mA to -60 mA. Engine speed at which this reversing will take place is regulated by coolant temperature. Current will also be reversed if engine speed reaches 6600 RPM, acting as a governor. Differential pressure regulator is attached to fuel distributor. *See Fig. 5*.

**Idle Stabilization Valve** – Idle stabilization valve consists of a small single-wound motor, rotary valve and a return spring attached to armature. Valve controls idle speed. Varying amounts of DC voltage cause motor to pull against return spring.

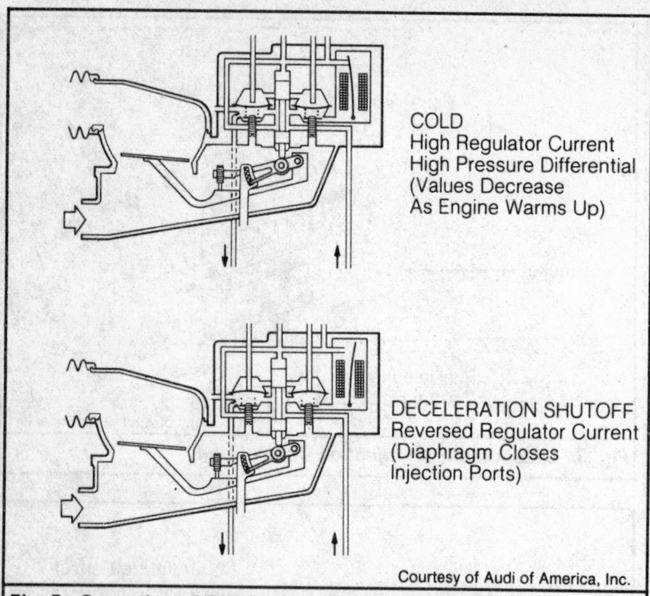
COLD
High Regulator Current
High Pressure Differential
(Values Decrease
As Engine Warms Up)
DECELERATION SHUTOFF
Reversed Regulator Current
(Diaphragm Closes
Injection Ports)
Courtesy of Audi of America, Inc.

*Fig. 5: Operation of Differential Pressure Regulator*

Amount of current will determine how far rotary valve is rotated. *See Fig. 6.* When rotary valve is rotated, air from intake air boot to intake manifold by-pass varies.

Idle stabilization valve receives a voltage signal from FICU. Variables that effect amount of voltage recieved from FICU are engine speed, temperature sensor, idle switch, A/C compressor clutch and transmission gear position.

Idle speed is maintained between 650-790 RPM on warm engines and at about 1000 RPM for cold engines. With this system, no idle speed adjustments are necessary or possible. Idle stabilization valve is located between intake air boot and intake manifold.

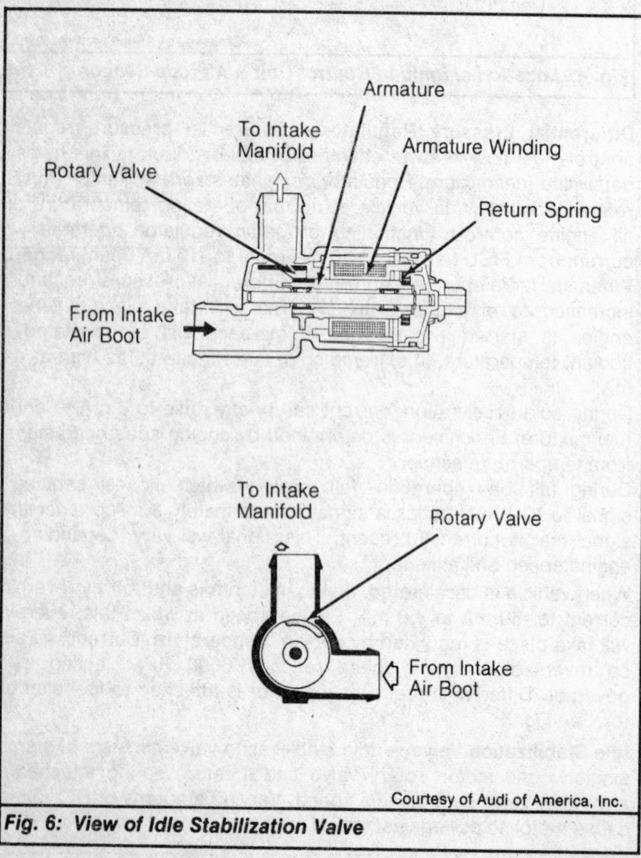
Armature
To Intake
Manifold
Armature Winding
Rotary Valve
Return Spring
From Intake
Air Boot
To Intake
Manifold
Rotary Valve
From Intake
Air Boot
Courtesy of Audi of America, Inc.

*Fig. 6: View of Idle Stabilization Valve*

**Ignition Coil** – Ignition coil is equipped with a power stage mounted on the side. Power stage switches primary current in coil on and off in place of Hall control unit. Power stage acts like a solid state pair of ignition points and is controlled by signals from ICU.

**Ignition Distributor** – Ignition distributor is a Hall Effect type with no centrifugal or vacuum advance. Hall sender is operated by a 5-aperture trigger wheel. Voltage signal from Hall sender is received by ICU at approximately 60 degrees BTDC. ICU uses this signal to determine engine speed and crankshaft position.

Ignition has an anti-tampering cover that is attached to a boss on cylinder head next to ignition distributor and covers distributor clamp nut. To gain access to clamp nut, anti-tampering cover shear bolt must be removed.

## TESTING PRECAUTIONS

When testing CIS-E III system, observe following precautions to avoid injury or damage to the system.

**1)** DO NOT touch or disconnect ignition wires with engine running. Disconnect or connect engine wiring and test leads ONLY with engine off. DO NOT connect test light to terminal No. 1 of ignition coil.

**2)** If engine must be turned over but not started, remove coil wire from ground. Using a jumper wire, ground coil wire. A fast charger can be used as a starting aid for no more than 15 seconds at a time with a one minute break between attempts and a maximum of 16.5 volts.

**3)** DO NOT use a standard ignition coil. Disconnect battery during any welding operations. When heating to more than 176°F (80°C), such as painting or steam cleaning, DO NOT start engine immediately.

**4)** Wash engine with engine not running and ignition off. DO NOT disconnect battery with engine running. DO NOT apply voltage to control units. DO NOT start engine with injectors removed.

## TESTING

### DIFFERENTIAL PRESSURE REGULATOR

**1)** Using Adapter (VW 1315 A/1), connect multimeter to differential pressure regulator. Set multimeter to 200 mA DC scale. Insert fuse in top of fuel pump relay. Turn ignition on. Remove fuse after 4 seconds.

**2)** Indicator light should display Code 4341. Multimeter should read 100 mA. Close full throttle switch. Multimeter reading should change to 10 mA. If no reading is shown, disconnect harness connector from differential pressure regulator.

**3)** Connect multimeter between terminal No. 2 of harness connector and engine ground. *See Fig. 7.* Turn ignition on. Multimeter should read 4.5-5.0 volts.

**4)** Connect multimeter between terminal No. 1 and terminal No. 2 of harness connector. Multimeter should read 4.5-5.0 volts. If specification is obtained, replace differential pressure regulator.

**5)** If specification is not obtained, remove FICU access cover and disconnect harness connector. Using multimeter, check for continuity between FICU connector terminal No. 4 and differential pressure regulator connector terminal No. 1.

**6)** Check for continuity between FICU connector terminal No. 5 and differential pressure regulator connector terminal No. 2. Resistance reading should be .2 ohm for both tests.

**7)** If specification is not obtained, repair break in wiring. If specification is obtained, replace FICU.

### CARBON CANISTER SHUTOFF SOLENOID

**1)** Turn ignition off. Insert fuse into fuel pump relay. Turn ignition on. Remove fuse after 4 seconds. Reinstall fuse for 4 seconds, then remove fuse. Indicator light should display Code 4343.

**2)** Close full throttle switch. Shutoff solenoid valve should energize, making a clicking sound when full throttle switch is closed. If no clicking sound is heard, disconnect carbon canister shutoff solenoid harness connector.

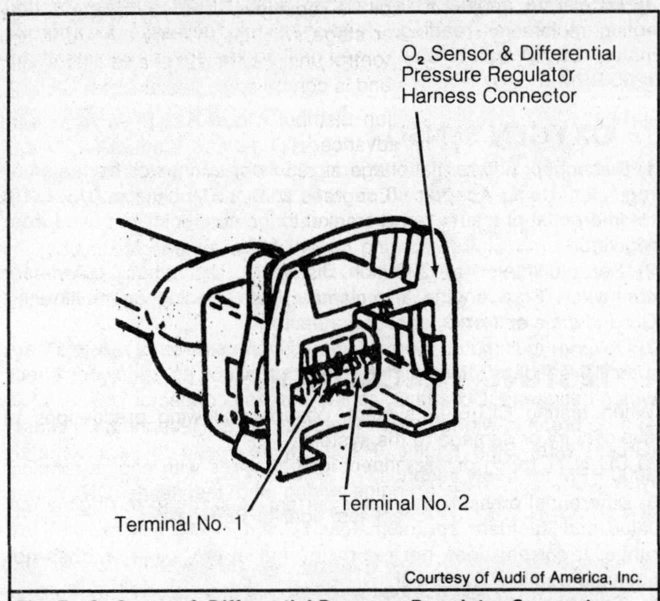
$O_2$ Sensor & Differential Pressure Regulator Harness Connector
Terminal No. 2
Terminal No. 1
Courtesy of Audi of America, Inc.

*Fig. 7: $O_2$ Sensor & Differential Pressure Regulator Connector*

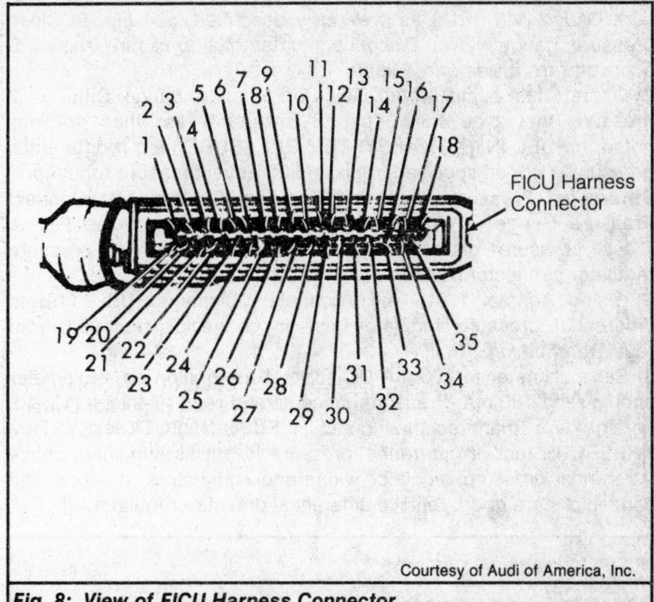
FICU Harness Connector
1 2 3 4 5 6 7 8 9 10 11 12 13 14 15 16 17 18
19 20 21 22 23 24 25 26 27 28 29 30 31 32 33 34 35
Courtesy of Audi of America, Inc.

*Fig. 8: View of FICU Harness Connector*

**3)** Connect LED Tester (US 1115) to connector terminals No. 1 and No. 2 using a jumper wire. LED tester must light (blink). If specification is obtained, replace carbon canister shutoff solenoid.
**4)** If specification is not obtained, connect multimeter between terminal No. 1 of connector and ground. Multimeter should read 12 volts. If 12 volts are not present, remove FICU access cover and disconnect connector.
**5)** Using multimeter, check resistance between terminal No. 2 and terminal No. 15 of FICU connector. Resistance reading should be .2 ohm. If specification is not obtained, repair break in wiring. If specification is obtained, replace FICU.

## COLD START VALVE

**1)** Turn ignition off. Insert fuse into fuel pump relay. Turn ignition on. Remove fuse for 4 seconds. Reinstall fuse for 4 seconds, then remove fuse. Indicator light should display Code 4443.
**2)** Close full throttle switch. Cold start valve should click on and off for 10 seconds maximum. If no click sound is heard, disconnect cold start valve connector.
**3)** Connect LED Tester (US 1115) between terminals No. 1 and No. 2 using jumper wire. LED tester should light up. If tester does light up, replace cold start valve. If tester does not light up, connect multimeter between connector terminal No. 1 and ground.
**4)** Multimeter should read 12 volts. If 12 volts are not present, repair break in wiring. If 12 volts are present, remove FICU access cover and disconnect connector.
**5)** Connect multimeter between terminal No. 2 of cold start valve and terminal No. 16 of FICU connector. Multimeter should read .2 ohm. If reading is not to specification, repair break in wiring. If reading is to specification, replace FICU.

## IDLE STABILIZER VALVE

**1)** Turn ignition off. Insert fuse into fuel pump relay. Turn ignition on. Remove fuse for 4 seconds. Reinstall fuse for 4 seconds, then remove fuse. Indicator light should display Code 4443.
**2)** Close full throttle switch. Idle stabilizer valve should cycle (click sound) when switch is closed. If no click sound is heard, disconnect idle stabilizer valve connector.
**3)** Connect LED Tester (US 1115) between terminals No. 1 and No. 2 using jumper wire. LED tester should light up. If tester does light up, replace idle stabilizer valve. If tester does not light up, connect multimeter between connector terminal No. 2 and ground.
**4)** Multimeter should read 12 volts. If 12 volts are not present, repair break in wiring. If 12 volts are present, turn ignition off. Remove FICU access cover and disconnect connector.
**5)** Connect multimeter between terminal No. 1 of idle stabilizer valve and terminal No. 17 of FICU connector and check for continuity. Multimeter should read .2 ohm. If reading is not to specification, repair break in wiring. If reading is to specification, replace FICU.

## FUEL INJECTION SYSTEM

**System Pressure – 1)** Remove fuel line from cold start valve. *See Fig. 9.* Remove test plug from distributor lower chamber. Connect Pressure Gauge (VW 1318) between fuel line from cold start valve and lower chamber. *See Fig. 9.*
**2)** Disconnect differential pressure regulator connector from side of regulator. Remove fuel pump relay. Jumper fuel pump relay socket. Open valve on pressure gauge.
**3)** Energize fuel pump. Note pressure reading on pressure gauge. Pressure should be 88-94 psi (6.2-6.6 kg/cm²). System pressure is not adjustable.

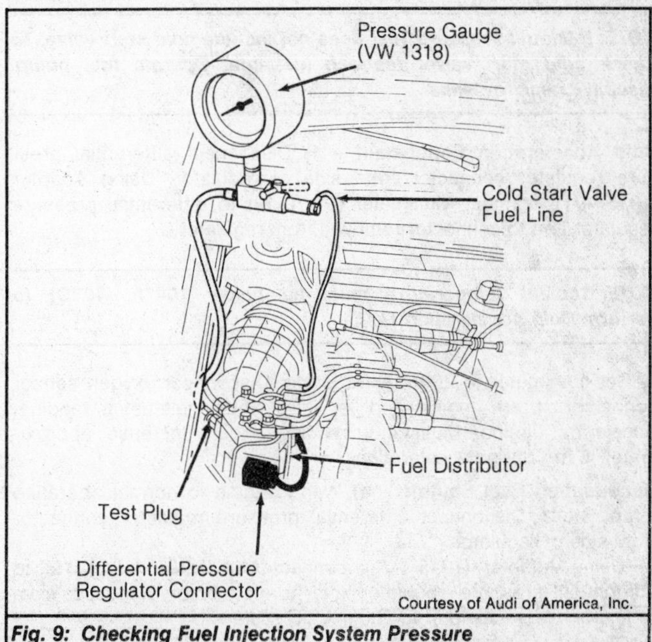
Pressure Gauge (VW 1318)
Cold Start Valve Fuel Line
Fuel Distributor
Test Plug
Differential Pressure Regulator Connector
Courtesy of Audi of America, Inc.

*Fig. 9: Checking Fuel Injection System Pressure*

# Bosch CIS-E III (Electronic Control) System (Cont.)

**Differential Pressure Regulator Fuel Pressure – 1)** Connect Pressure Gauge (VW 1318) as previously described. *See Fig. 9.* Close pressure gauge valve. Disconnect differential pressure regulator connector from side of regulator.

**2)** Operate fuel pump. Note reading on pressure gauge. Differential pressure should be 4.5-7.3 psi (.3-.5 kg/cm²) less than readings noted in FUEL INJECTION SYSTEM PRESSURE test. If differential pressure is not as specified, replace differential pressure regulator.

**Differential Pressure Regulator Electrical System – 1)** Connect Pressure Gauge (VW 1318) as previously described. *See Fig. 9.* Close pressure gauge valve. Disconnect differential pressure regulator connector from side of regulator.

**2)** Using Adapter (1315 A/1), connect Multimeter (US 1119) to differential pressure regulator and to connector removed from regulator. *See Fig. 10.*

**3)** Set multimeter to 200 mA DC scale. Turn ignition on. Multimeter should read 100 mA. Pressure gauge should read 17-22 psi (1.2-1.5 kg/cm²) less than readings noted in FUEL INJECTION SYSTEM PRESSURE test. If differential pressure is not as specified, check differential pressure regulator wiring and connectors. If wiring and connectors are good, replace differential pressure regulator.

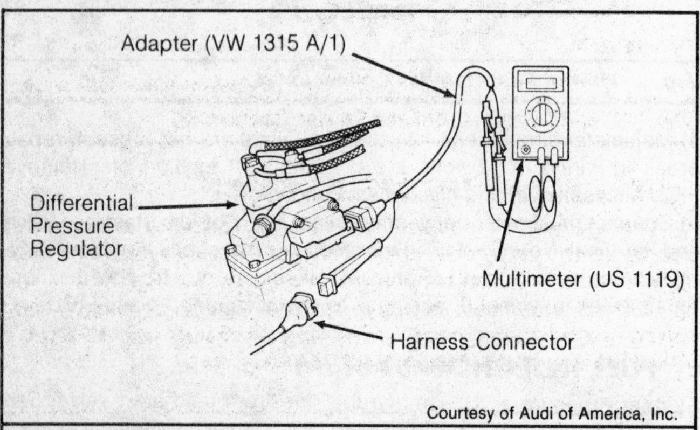
Adapter (VW 1315 A/1)
Differential Pressure Regulator
Multimeter (US 1119)
Harness Connector
Courtesy of Audi of America, Inc.

***Fig. 10: Attaching Multimeter to Differential Pressure Regulator***

**Residual Pressure – 1)** Connect Pressure Gauge (VW 1318) as previously described. *See Fig. 9.* Open pressure gauge valve. Operate fuel pump for at least 30 seconds.

**2)** Shut off fuel pump. Note system pressure. Pressure should be 51 psi (3.6 kg/cm²) after 10 minutes and 49 psi (3.4 kg/cm²) after 20 minutes.

***NOTE: Residual Pressure Test does not include cold start valve. To check cold start valve, reattach fuel line. Operate fuel pump. Visually check for leaks.***

**Cold Acceleration Enrichment – 1)** Disconnect differential pressure regulator connector from side of regulator. Using Adapter (1315 A/1), connect Multimeter (US 1119) to differential pressure regulator and to connector removed from regulator.

***NOTE: Coolant temperature must be below 104°F (40°C) to perform Cold Acceleration Test.***

**2)** Set multimeter to 200 mA DC scale. Disconnect oxygen sensor connector. Start engine and let idle. Note multimeter reading. Accelerate engine. Multimeter reading should increase approximately 6 mA during acceleration.

**Deceleration Fuel Shutoff – 1)** Warm engine to normal operating temperature. Disconnect differential pressure regulator connector from side of regulator.

**2)** Using Adapter (1315 A/1), connect Multimeter (US 1119) to differential pressure regulator and to connector removed from regulator. Set multimeter to 200 mA DC scale.

**3)** Accelerate engine to more than 3000 RPM. Release throttle, noting multimeter reading. Reading should decrease to approximately -50 mA with throttle closed until engine speed reaches about 1200 RPM.

## OXYGEN SENSOR

**1)** Disconnect differential pressure regulator connector from side of regulator. Using Adapter (1315 A/1), connect Multimeter (US 1119) to differential pressure regulator and to the connector removed from regulator.

**2)** Set multimeter to 200 mA DC scale. Disconnect $O_2$ sensor connector. Start engine and let idle. Note reading on multimeter. Ground male end of $O_2$ sensor connector.

**3)** Observe multimeter. Current should increase from 9 mA to 11 mA after 15 seconds. If multimeter reading is not as specified, check wiring between FICU and $O_2$ sensor harness connector.

**4)** If no break in wiring is found, replace FICU. Reconnect $O_2$ sensor (Green) wire. Start engine. Raise engine speed to approximately 3000 RPM for a few seconds.

**5)** Differential pressure regulator current must return to original mA value and fluctuate approximately 1-3 mA in -10 mA to +10 mA range. If current does not return to original mA value or does not fluctuate, replace $O_2$ sensor.

**6)** To check $O_2$ sensor heating element, disconnect $O_2$ sensor heating element connector from harness connector. Connect multimeter between connector terminal No. 1 and No. 2. *See Fig. 7.*

**7)** Turn ignition on. Multimeter should read 12 volts. If multimeter does not read as specified, repair break in wiring. Connect multimeter between terminals No. 1 and No. 2 of $O_2$ sensor heating element connector. *See Fig. 11.*

**8)** Multimeter should read 3-15 ohms. If multimeter does not read as specified, replace $O_2$ sensor.

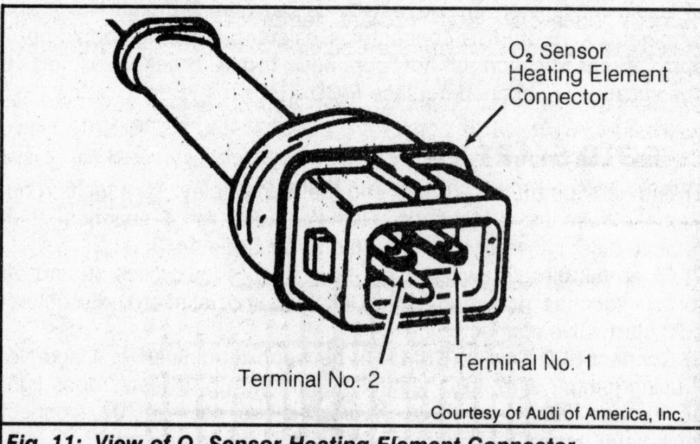
O₂ Sensor Heating Element Connector
Terminal No. 1
Terminal No. 2
Courtesy of Audi of America, Inc.

***Fig. 11: View of $O_2$ Sensor Heating Element Connector***

## FUEL PUMP RELAY CONTROL

**1)** With ignition off. Remove fuel pump relay from relay panel. Connect multimeter between terminals No. 48 and No. 50 of relay socket. *See Fig. 12.*

**2)** Multimeter should read 12 volts. Connect multimeter between terminals No. 46 and No. 50 of relay socket. Turn ignition on. Multimeter should read 12 volts.

**3)** If multimeter does not read as specified, repair break in wiring. Connect multimeter between terminals No. 46 and No. 47 of relay socket. Momentarily engage starter. Multimeter should read 7 volts.

**4)** If multimeter does not read 7 volts, partially remove ICU and disconnect harness connector. Using a multimeter, check continuity between ICU and relay socket.

**5)** Connect terminal No. 3 of ICU connector to terminal No. 49 of relay socket. Connect terminal No. 14 of ICU and terminal No. 47 of relay socket. Multimeter should read .2 ohm.

**6)** If reading is not as specified, repair break in wiring. If reading is as specified, replace knock sensor.

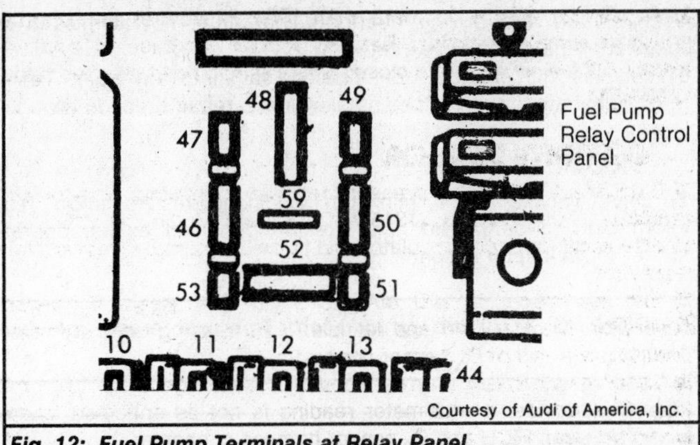
48
49
47
59
46
50
52
53
51
10
11
12
13
44
Fuel Pump
Relay Control
Panel
Courtesy of Audi of America, Inc.

*Fig. 12: Fuel Pump Terminals at Relay Panel*

## A/C COMPRESSOR CLUTCH (ON/OFF SIGNAL)

**1)** With ignition off, disconnect FICU harness connector. Connect multimeter between terminals No. 33 and No. 35 (ground). *See Fig. 8*. With A/C on "OFF" position, turn ignition on.

**2)** Multimeter should read zero volt. If reading is not as specified, repair break in wiring. With A/C in "AUTO" or "BI-LEVEL" position, turn ignition on.

**3)** A/C compressor clutch must cycle on and have 12 volts present at compressor clutch connector. If compressor does not cycle on or have 12 volts present at connector, repair break in wiring.

## COOLANT TEMPERATURE SENSOR

**1)** Ensure engine temperature is greater than 176°F (20°C). Remove harness connector from coolant temperature sensor. Connect multimeter between temperature sensor terminal No. 1 and engine ground.

**2)** Connect between terminal No. 2 and engine ground. For multimeter reading, see COOLANT TEMPERATURE SENSOR chart. Connect multimeter between harness connector terminal No. 1 and ground, then between terminal No. 2 and ground.

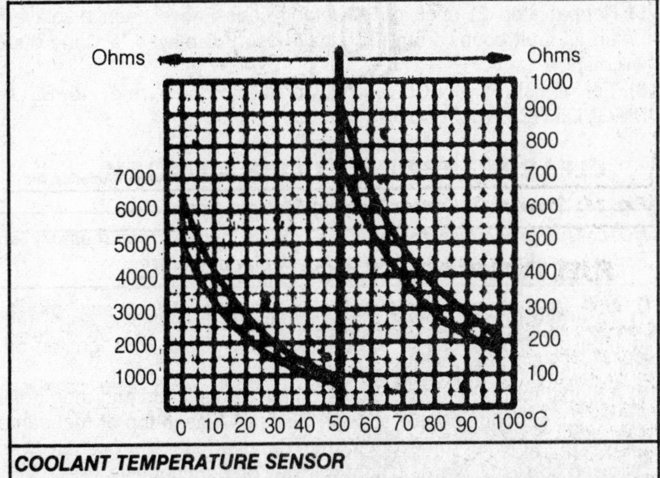
Ohms
Ohms
1000
900
800
7000
700
6000
600
5000
500
4000
400
3000
300
2000
200
1000
100
0 10 20 30 40 50 60 70 80 90 100°C

*COOLANT TEMPERATURE SENSOR*

**3)** Turn ignition on. Multimeter should read 4.5-5.5 volts. If no voltage is present, repair break in wiring. If no voltage is present and no break in wiring is found, replace respective control unit that controls that temperature sensor.

## ALTITUDE SENSOR (VOLTAGE SUPPLY)

**1)** With ignition off, remove altitude sensor harness connector. Connect multimeter between harness connector terminal No. 1 and engine ground. *See Fig. 13*.

**2)** Turn ignition on. Multimeter should read 5 volts. If 5 volts is not present, repair break in wiring between terminal No. 1 of altitude sensor connector and terminal No. 25 of FICU harness control.

**3)** With ignition off, connect multimeter between terminals No. 1 and No. 3 of altitude sensor. Connect multimeter between terminals No. 2 and No. 3. Turn ignition on. Multimeter should read 4.5-5.0 volts.

**4)** If no voltage is present, repair break in wiring or replace FICU. Check wiring between ICU and altitude sensor. If voltage is present and all wiring is good, replace altitude sensor.

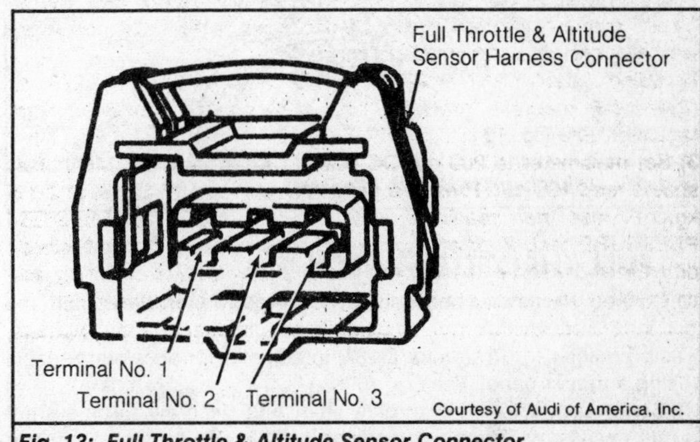
Full Throttle & Altitude
Sensor Harness Connector
Terminal No. 1
Terminal No. 2
Terminal No. 3
Courtesy of Audi of America, Inc.

*Fig. 13: Full Throttle & Altitude Sensor Connector*

## IDLE & FULL THROTTLE SWITCH

**1)** With ignition off, remove harness connector to idle and full throttle switch on throttle body. Connect Test Adapter (VW 1501) between throttle switch and harness connector. *See Fig. 14*.

**2)** Connect multimeter between terminal No. 2 of adapter and engine ground. Turn ignition on. Multimeter should read 12 volts. If 12 volts is not present, repair break in wiring.

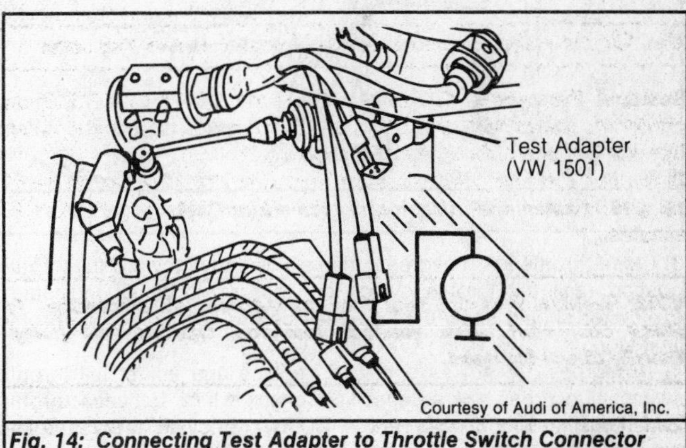
Test Adapter
(VW 1501)
Courtesy of Audi of America, Inc.

*Fig. 14: Connecting Test Adapter to Throttle Switch Connector*

## IDLE SWITCH

**1)** Connect multimeter between terminal No. 1 of Test Adapter (VW 1501) and ground. Multimeter should read battery voltage. Turn ignition off. Switch multimeter to ohms range.

**2)** Move throttle valve .20-.28" (.5-.7 mm). Measurement is made with feeler gauge between throttle valve stop and adjustment screw. Resistance should change from zero ohm (with throttle closed) to infinity as throttle gap increases beyond .020" (.5 mm).

**3)** If resistance is not as specified, adjust idle gap to .006-.020" (.15-.5 mm). *See Fig. 15*. If resistance is as specified, check full throttle switch.

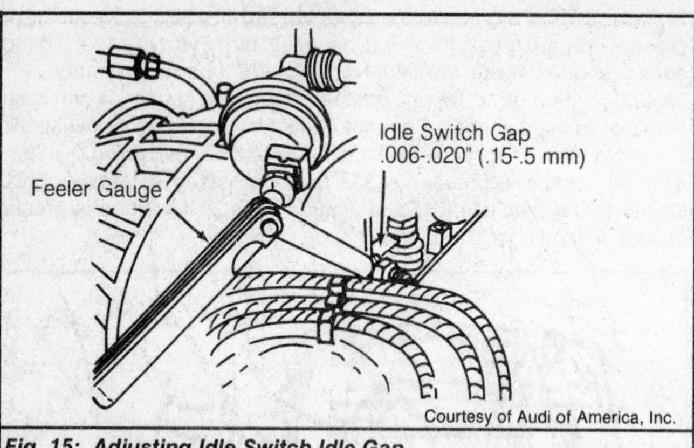
Idle Switch Gap
.006-.020" (.15-.5 mm)
Feeler Gauge
Courtesy of Audi of America, Inc.

*Fig. 15: Adjusting Idle Switch Idle Gap*

## FULL THROTTLE SWITCH

**1)** Connect multimeter between terminal No. 3 of throttle switch and ground. Turn ignition on. Multimeter should read battery voltage. Fasten pointer for Protractor (3084) to adjuster for accelerator cable (using a rubber band). *See Fig. 16*.

**2)** Screw protractor onto throttle shaft and unscrew throttle shaft nut (if necessary). Push throttle lever to full open (at stop limit) and zero pointer plus disc.

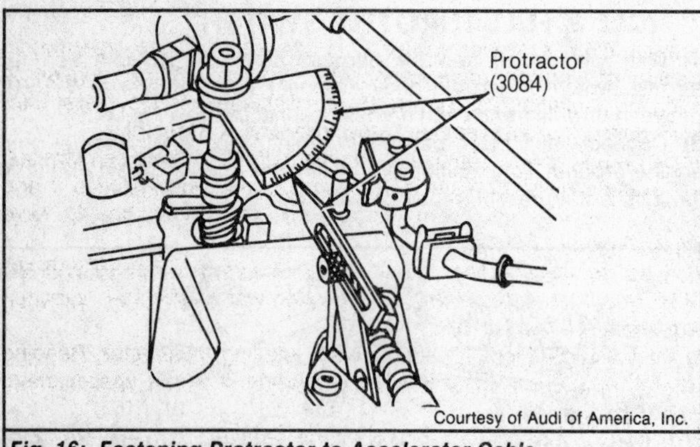
Protractor
(3084)
Courtesy of Audi of America, Inc.

*Fig. 16: Fastening Protractor to Accelerator Cable*

**3)** Close throttle to 30 degrees, then slowly move toward full throttle postion until full throttle switch engages (zero ohms indicated). Protractor should show 6-14 degrees before contacting full throttle limit stop.

**4)** If degrees are not as specified, replace and adjust full throttle switch. If degrees are as specified, check wiring between throttle switch harness connector and FICU by removing FICU harness connector.

**5)** Turn ignition off. Using multimeter, check continuity between throttle switch connector terminal No. 1 and ICU connector terminal No. 7. *See Fig. 13*. Then check continuity between throttle switch connector terminal No. 3 and ICU connector terminal No. 9. Multimeter should read .2 ohm.

**6)** Connect multimeter and check continuity between throttle switch connector terminal No. 1 and FICU connector terminal No. 28. Then check continuity between throttle switch connector terminal No. 3 and FICU connector terminal No. 31. Multimeter should read .2 ohm. If .2 ohm is not present, repair break in wiring.

## IDLE STABILIZATION (SHIFT MODE SIGNAL)

**1)** Turn ignition off. Disconnect FICU harness connector. Connect LED Tester (US 1115) between terminals No. 14 and No. 34 of FICU connector. Turn ignition on.

**2)** Vehicles with automatic transmission, engage selector lever in "N" and then "P". Tester must illuminate. Tester should not illuminate when shifted into driving gears. If light does not illuminate as specified, repair break in wiring.

**3)** Vehicles with manual transmission, shift into any gear. Tester must illuminate. If tester does not illuminate, repair break in wiring.

## TROUBLE CODES

**1)** Drive vehicle for a minimum of 5 minutes to allow fault information to be stored. If a no-start condition exists, operate starter for at least 6 seconds.

***CAUTION: DO NOT turn ignition off. This will erase the fault memory.***

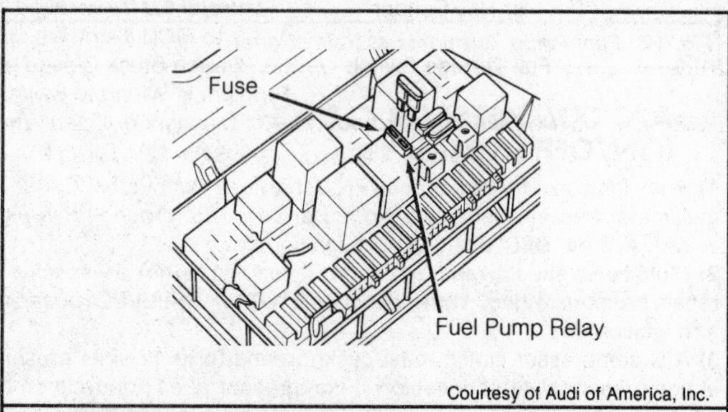
Fuse
Fuel Pump Relay
Courtesy of Audi of America, Inc.

*Fig. 17: Location of Fuel Pump Relay*

**2)** Insert fuse into fuel pump relay for at least 4 seconds. *See Fig. 17*. Indicator light on instrument cluster should display a 4-digit fault code from ICU.

**3)** If indicator light displays a Code 4444, no faults have been recorded. Record all fault codes by repeating step **2)** until a Code 0000 is displayed. This indicates that all fault codes from ICU have been displayed.

**4)** Repeat step **2)** after Code 0000 is displayed. This time, however, faults that are displayed will be from FICU. Engine speed may increase. Record all codes.

**5)** Repeat step **2)** until all FICU fault codes have been displayed. When all fault codes from FICU have been displayed, a Code 0000 will display.

**6)** For a list of all ICU and FICU fault codes, refer to SELF-DIAGNOSTIC FAULT CODES table.

## CLEARING TROUBLE CODE MEMORY

***NOTE: The procedure for erasing trouble codes from memory on Federal vehicles was not available from manufacturer.***

**1)** To erase trouble codes from memory (Calif. vehicles only), turn ignition off. Insert fuse in top of fuel pump relay. Turn ignition on. Wait at least 4 seconds then remove fuse.

**2)** A signal that repeatedly comes on for 2.5 seconds and then goes off for 2.5 seconds should appear. Reinstall fuse in top of fuel pump relay. Wait at least 10 seconds, then remove fuse. If procedure was followed correctly, warning light will stay on continuously.

## TROUBLE SHOOTING TROUBLE CODE MEMORY

**1)** If trouble code light does not illuminate with ignition on, check wiring between ICU connector terminal No. 3 and FICU connector terminal No. 13. If wiring checks good, connect LED Tester (US 1115) between FICU connector terminals No. 13 and No. 14 using a jumper wire.

**2)** Each time ignition is turned on, tester must blink 3 times. If tester does not blink 3 times, replace ICU.

***NOTE:** If ICU is replaced, check ignition timing. If trouble code warning light blinks while driving, knock regulation is at maximum control limit.*

***SELF-DIAGNOSTIC FAULT CODES***

| Code | Location of Fault | Problem |
|---|---|---|
| 1111 | ICU or FICU | Defective Memory Circuits In Control Unit |
| 2121 | Idle Switch | Switch Stuck Closed or Problem in Wiring to Switch |
| 2122 | Engine Speed Signal or Hall Sender | No Engine Speed Signal from ICU Term. No. 17 to FICU Term. No. 30 |
| 2123 | Full Throttle Switch | Switch Stuck Closed or Problem in Wiring to Switch |
| 2132 [1] | No Data Transmitted from FICU to ICU | Disconn. or Open Wire between ICU Term. No. 5 & FICU Term. No. 1 or ICU Term. No. 3 & FICU Term. No. 13 or Defective Control Units |
| 2141 | Knock Regulation | Engine or Ignition Knock is Causing Timing to be Retarded (Max. Limit) |
| 2142 | Knock Sensor | Defective Sensor or Sensor Wiring |
| 2223 | Altitude Sensor | No Signal from Sensor |
| 2232 | Air Sensor | No Signal from Sensor to FICU or Break in Wire between FICU Term. No. 21 & ICU Term. No. 8 |
| 2233 | Reference Voltage for Air Sensor & Altitude Sensor | No Reference Voltage from ICU Term. No. 21 & FICU Term. No. 26 |
| 2312 | Cool. Temp. Sensor | No Signal from Sensor |
| 2341 | $O_2$ Sensor Control | $O_2$ Sensor Control Operating at Rich or Lean limit |
| 2342 | $O_2$ Sensor | No Signal from Sensor |
| 4431 | Idle Stab. Valve | Problem in Wiring to Idle Stab. Valve |
| 4444 | No Faults Stored | |
| 0000 | End of Diagnosis | |

[1] – Calif. only.

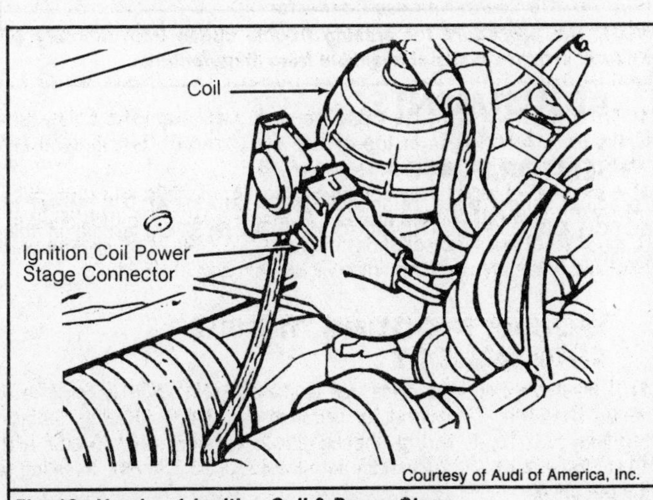
Coil
Ignition Coil Power Stage Connector
Courtesy of Audi of America, Inc.

***Fig. 18:** Version 1 Ignition Coil & Power Stage*

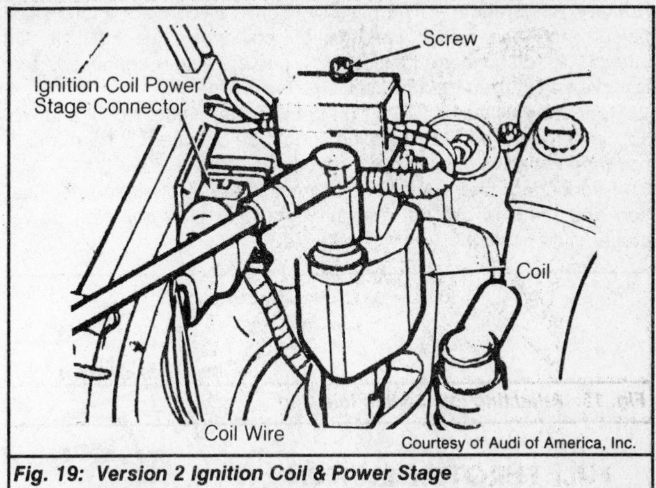
Screw
Ignition Coil Power Stage Connector
Coil
Coil Wire
Courtesy of Audi of America, Inc.

***Fig. 19:** Version 2 Ignition Coil & Power Stage*

## IGNITION COIL ASSEMBLY

***NOTE:** CIS-E III system uses 2 versions of coils. Both versions use a power stage. DO NOT separately test function of power stage. Refer to Figures 18 and 19 to determine which version you are testing.*

**Ignition Coil & Power Stage – 1)** On version one, disconnect ignition coil power stage connector. *See Fig. 18.* On version 2, disconnect ignition coil power stage connector. Remove coil wire from ignition coil and remove screw from top of assembly.

**2)** On both versions, connect Multimeter (US 1119) between terminal No. 1 and ground. Connect multimeter between terminals No. 1 and No. 3. *See Fig. 20.* Turn ignition on. Multimeter should read approximately 12 volts.

**3)** If not to specification, repair break in wiring. Refer to WIRING DIAGRAMS at end of this article. Connect multimeter between terminal No. 2 and No. 3.

**4)** Turn engine over with starter while reading multimeter. Reading should be approximately 2 volts. If reading is within specification, check ignition coil.

**5)** If not to specification, check wiring between terminal No. 2 of connector and terminal No. 16 of ICU. If wiring checks satisfactory, replace ICU.

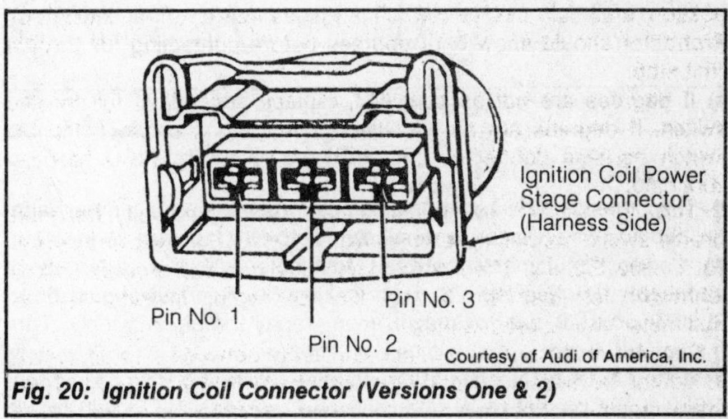
Ignition Coil Power Stage Connector (Harness Side)
Pin No. 1
Pin No. 2
Pin No. 3
Courtesy of Audi of America, Inc.

***Fig. 20:** Ignition Coil Connector (Versions One & 2)*

**Secondary Resistance – 1)** Check wiring between power stage and ignition coil and power stage ground wire for corrosion and damage. On version one, disconnect ignition coil power stage connector and ignition coil wire. *See Fig. 18.*

**2)** On version 2, disconnect ignition coil power stage connector and remove screw from top of assembly. *See Fig. 19.* On both versions, connect Multimeter (US 1119) between terminal No. 1 and coil wire socket.

**3)** Resistance should be between 5000-6000 ohms. If not to specification, replace ignition coil.

**Primary Resistance – 1)** On version one, disconnect ignition coil power stage connector and ignition coil wire. *See Fig. 18.* On version 2, disconnect ignition coil power stage connector and remove screw from top of assembly. *See Fig. 19.*

**2)** Connect Multimeter (US 1119) between terminals No. 1 and No. 15. *See Figs. 21 and 22.* Reading should be between .5-1.5 ohms. If not within specification, replace ignition coil.

**3)** If secondary and primary resistance values are within specification and there is still no ignition, replace ignition coil with power stage as an assembly.

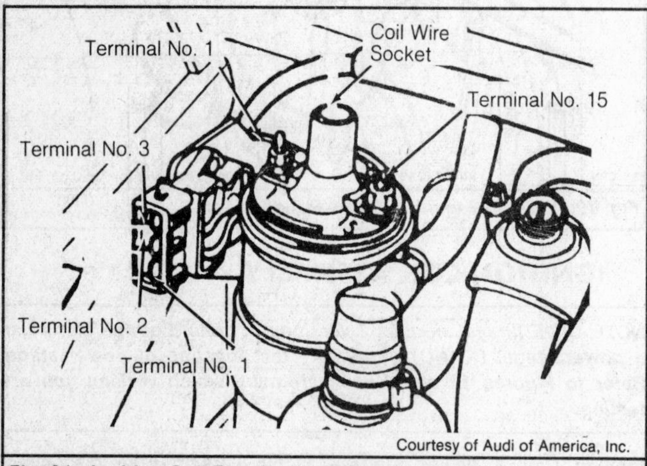
Terminal No. 1
Coil Wire Socket
Terminal No. 15
Terminal No. 3
Terminal No. 2
Terminal No. 1
Courtesy of Audi of America, Inc.

*Fig. 21: Ignition Coil Terminal Location (Version One)*

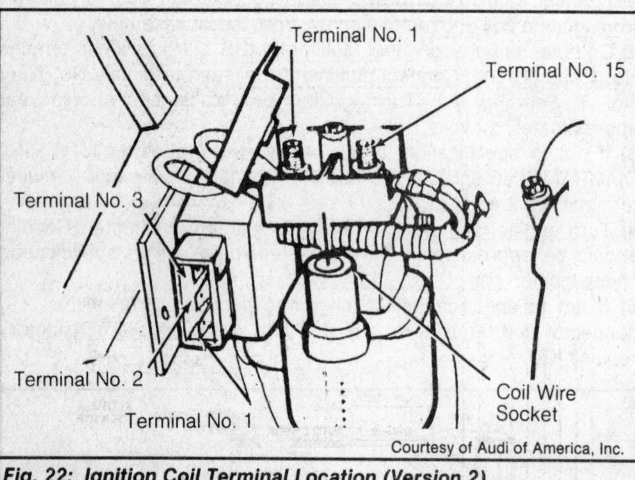
Terminal No. 1
Terminal No. 15
Terminal No. 3
Terminal No. 2
Terminal No. 1
Coil Wire Socket
Courtesy of Audi of America, Inc.

*Fig. 22: Ignition Coil Terminal Location (Version 2)*

## HALL SENDER

**1)** Disconnect coil wire from distributor cap. Using a jumper wire, ground coil wire. Disconnect hall sender-to-ICU harness connector.

**2)** Connect multimeter between terminals No. 1 and No. 3 of connector "D". *See Fig. 23.* Turn ignition on. Reading should be at least 9 volts. If not to specification, repair break in wiring. Turn ignition off.

**3)** If step **2)** tests satisfactory, push back rubber boot on hall sender connector. Connect multimeter between terminals No. 1 and No. 2. Reconnect hall sender-to-ICU harness connector.

**4)** Turn ignition on. Remove ignition distributor cap, rotor and dust cap. DO NOT allow spring clips to fall inward toward trigger wheel.

**5)** Using Wrench (2079), turn crankshaft until trigger wheel is clear of hall sender. Multimeter should read a minimum of 4 volts. Turn crankshaft until trigger window is aligned with hall sender.

**6)** Reading should be between .0-.5 volts. Turn ignition off. If reading was not to specification, replace hall sender. If reading was correct, check wiring between hall sender connector and ICU.

**7)** Remove ICU cover from left side kick panel. Disconnect harness connector from ICU and Connector "D" from distributor. Check for continuity between distributor connector pins and appropriate 25-pin ICU connector pins. For correct pin-to-pin reference, see figures 16 and 17 and the wiring diagram at end of this article.

**8)** If hall sender and wiring between connector "D" and ICU connector tested satisfactory, replace ICU.

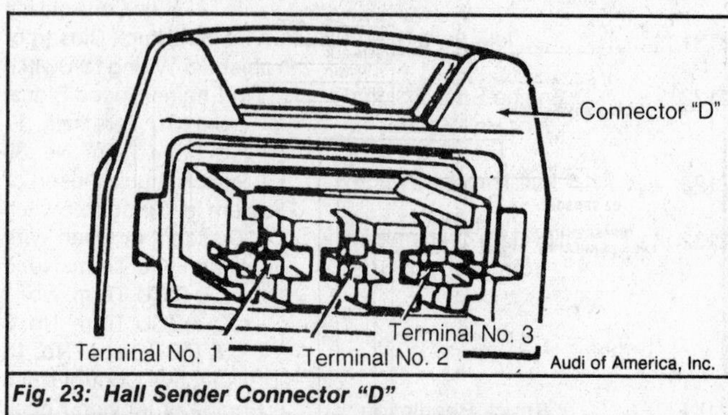
Connector "D"
Terminal No. 3
Terminal No. 1
Terminal No. 2
Audi of America, Inc.

*Fig. 23: Hall Sender Connector "D"*

## REMOVAL & INSTALLATION

***NOTE: Removal and installation procedures pertain to 5000S. Procedures for 90 model are similar.***

No procedures are available for removal and installation of CIS-E III related components. CIS-E III components are similar to those used in CIS-E system. Refer to appropriate article in REMOVAL & INSTALLATION section of BOSCH CIS-E (ELECTRONIC CONTROL) SYSTEM article in this section.

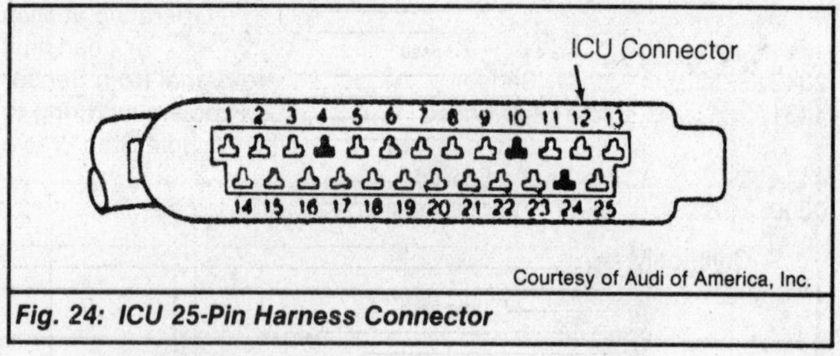
ICU Connector
1 2 3 4 5 6 7 8 9 10 11 12 13
14 15 16 17 18 19 20 21 22 23 24 25
Courtesy of Audi of America, Inc.

*Fig. 24: ICU 25-Pin Harness Connector*

## ADJUSTMENTS

### SENSOR PLATE

To adjust sensor plate, refer to SENSOR PLATE ADJUSTMENT in BOSCH CIS-E (ELECTRONIC CONTROL) SYSTEM article in this section.

# Bosch CIS-E III (Electronic Control) System (Cont.)

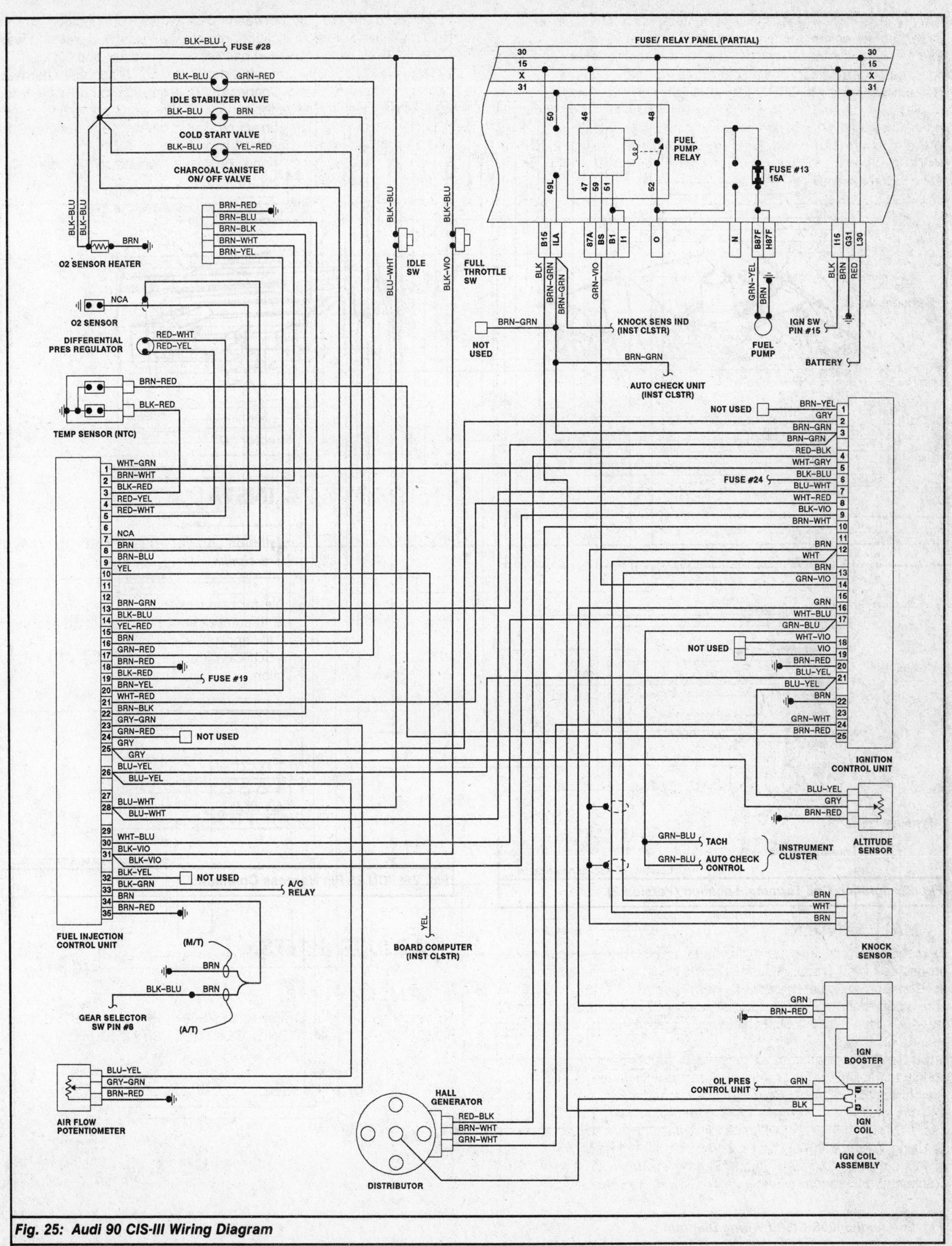

FUSE #28
IDLE STABILIZER VALVE
COLD START VALVE
CHARCOAL CANISTER ON/ OFF VALVE
O2 SENSOR HEATER
O2 SENSOR
DIFFERENTIAL PRES REGULATOR
TEMP SENSOR (NTC)
FUSE/ RELAY PANEL (PARTIAL)
FUEL PUMP RELAY
FUSE #13 15A
IDLE SW
FULL THROTTLE SW
NOT USED
KNOCK SENS IND (INST CLSTR)
AUTO CHECK UNIT (INST CLSTR)
FUEL PUMP
IGN SW PIN #15
BATTERY
FUSE #24
FUSE #19
A/C RELAY
FUEL INJECTION CONTROL UNIT
GEAR SELECTOR SW PIN #8
BOARD COMPUTER (INST CLSTR)
IGNITION CONTROL UNIT
ALTITUDE SENSOR
TACH
AUTO CHECK CONTROL
INSTRUMENT CLUSTER
KNOCK SENSOR
IGN BOOSTER
OIL PRES CONTROL UNIT
IGN COIL
IGN COIL ASSEMBLY
HALL GENERATOR
DISTRIBUTOR
AIR FLOW POTENTIOMETER


Fig. 25: Audi 90 CIS-III Wiring Diagram

# 1988 COMPUTERIZED ENGINE CONTROLS
## Bosch CIS-E III (Electronic Control) System (Cont.)

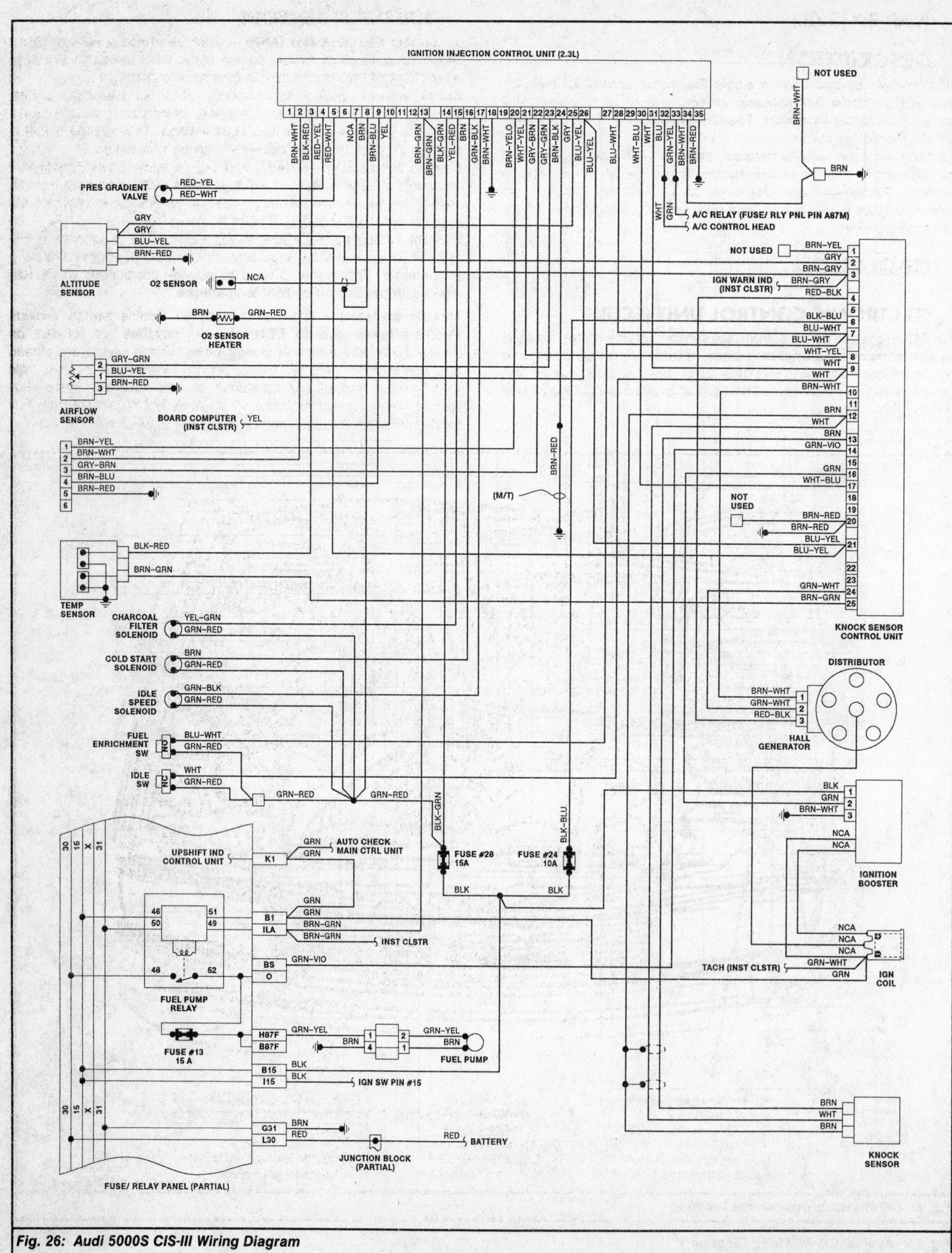

IGNITION INJECTION CONTROL UNIT (2.3L)
NOT USED
BRN-WHT
BRN
PRES GRADIENT VALVE
RED-YEL
RED-WHT
GRY
GRY
BLU-YEL
BRN-RED
ALTITUDE SENSOR
O2 SENSOR
NCA
BRN
GRN-RED
O2 SENSOR HEATER
GRY-GRN
BLU-YEL
BRN-RED
AIRFLOW SENSOR
BOARD COMPUTER (INST CLSTR)
YEL
BRN-YEL
BRN-WHT
GRY-BRN
BRN-BLU
BRN-RED
BLK-RED
BRN-GRN
TEMP SENSOR
CHARCOAL FILTER SOLENOID
YEL-GRN
GRN-RED
COLD START SOLENOID
IDLE SPEED SOLENOID
GRN-BLK
FUEL ENRICHMENT SW
BLU-WHT
IDLE SW
WHT
NO
NC
GRN-RED
(M/T)
BRN-RED
A/C RELAY (FUSE/ RLY PNL PIN A87M)
A/C CONTROL HEAD
NOT USED
BRN-YEL
BRN-GRY
IGN WARN IND (INST CLSTR)
RED-BLK
BLK-BLU
BLU-WHT
WHT-YEL
BRN-WHT
GRN-VIO
WHT-BLU
BLU-YEL
GRN-WHT
BRN-GRN
KNOCK SENSOR CONTROL UNIT
DISTRIBUTOR
BRN-WHT
GRN-WHT
RED-BLK
HALL GENERATOR
BLK
GRN
BRN-WHT
NCA
IGNITION BOOSTER
NCA
TACH (INST CLSTR)
GRN-WHT
GRN
IGN COIL
UPSHIFT IND CONTROL UNIT
K1
AUTO CHECK MAIN CTRL UNIT
BLK-GRN
BLK-BLU
FUSE #28 15A
FUSE #24 10A
BLK
B1
ILA
BRN-GRN
INST CLSTR
BS
O
GRN-VIO
FUEL PUMP RELAY
FUSE #13 15 A
H87F
B87F
GRN-YEL
BRN
FUEL PUMP
B15
I15
IGN SW PIN #15
G31
L30
RED
BATTERY
JUNCTION BLOCK (PARTIAL)
FUSE/ RELAY PANEL (PARTIAL)
30
15
X
31
KNOCK SENSOR


*Fig. 26: Audi 5000S CIS-III Wiring Diagram*

# Bosch CIS Motronic (Electronic Control) System

**Audi 80 (2.0L)**

## DESCRIPTION

CIS Motronic system uses a single Electronic Control Unit (ECU). This ECU controls fuel delivery, ignition system and operation of emission control components. The CIS MOTRONIC system also has self-diagnostic capabilities.

Input signals from various sensors, switches and signaling devices are constantly monitored for faults. These faults are stored in memory. Faults can be displayed by a flashing 4-digit code sequence from a "FAULT INDICATOR LIGHT" (FIL) located in the instrument cluster.

## OPERATION

### ELECTRONIC CONTROL UNIT (ECU)

The ECU receives signals from air sensor potentiometer, oxygen sensor, coolant temperature sensor, throttle valve switches and ignition control unit. Using this data, ECU varies air fuel mixture and ignition timing as necessary. The ECU is located behind glove box next to heater plenum.

### ECU INPUT SENSORS

**Air Sensor Potentiometer (ASP)** – ASP generates a voltage signal based on position of airflow sensor plate. ECU uses this signal to enrich air/fuel ratio during cold engine acceleration.

**Knock Sensor (KS)** – KS consists of a piezoelectric crystal encased in a metal and plastic housing. Vibrations in engine cause crystal to generate small amounts of voltage. This voltage signal is used by ECU to determine necessary timing retardation.

**Oxygen Sensor ($O_2$)** – The $O_2$ sensor is a heated type sensor that measures oxygen content of exhaust gases. ECU uses data from $O_2$ sensor to adjust fuel delivery. The $O_2$ sensor is located in the exhaust system just ahead of catalytic converter.

**Coolant Temperature Sensor (CTS)** – The CTS is located in the cylinder head coolant passage and informs ECU of engine operating temperature. This signal is used to provide corrections to air fuel mixture, depending on coolant temperature.

**Throttle Switches** – Idle switch and full throttle switch provide throttle position data to ECU. Throttle switches are located on throttle body. Idle switch is closed when throttle plates are closed and opens when throttle opens approximately one degree. Idle switch signal determines operation of idle stabilizer valve. Full throttle switch closes at about 10 degrees before full throttle. Full throttle switch signal determines full throttle enrichment.

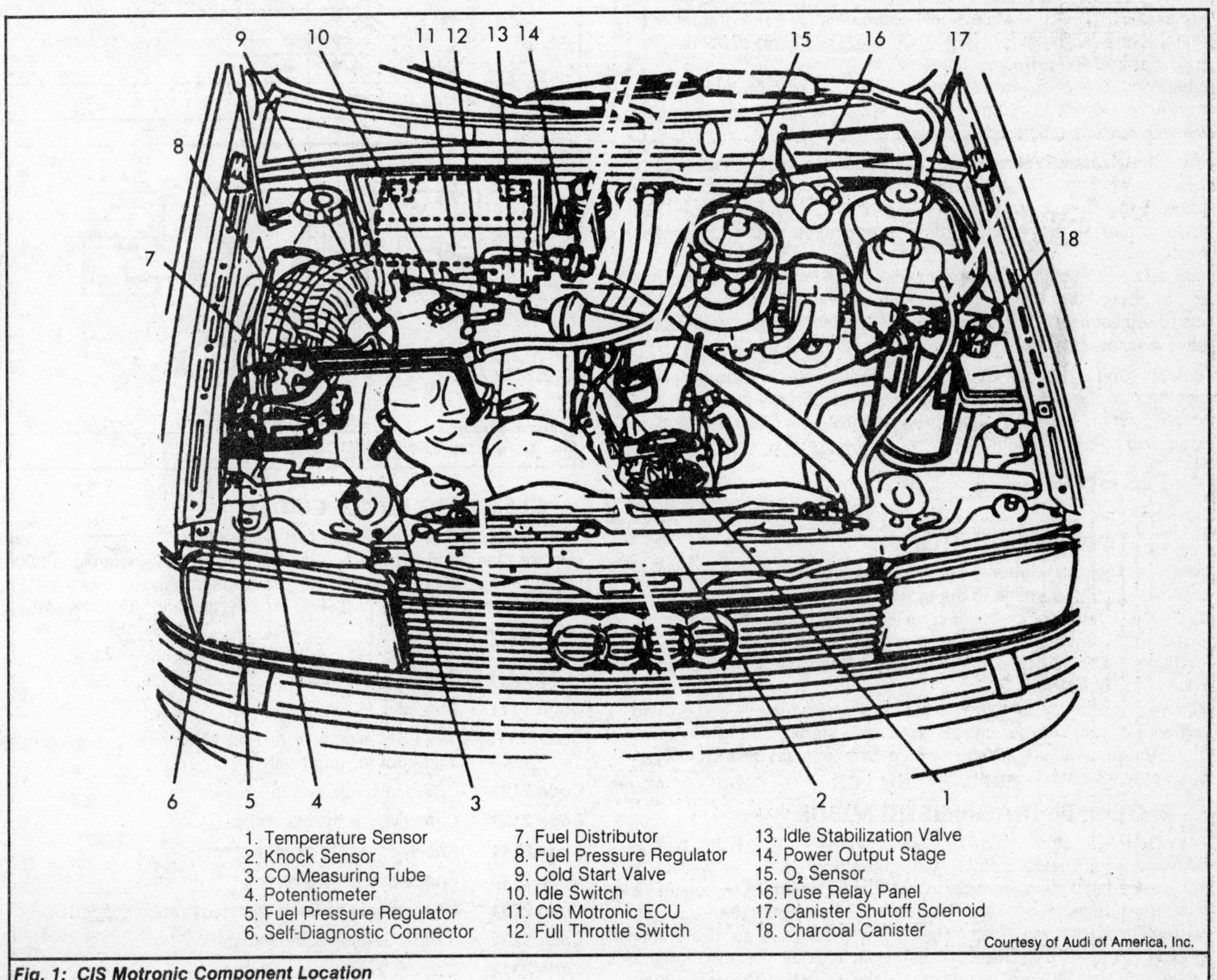
9
10
11 12
13 14
15
16
17
8
18
7
6
5
4
3
2
1

1. Temperature Sensor
2. Knock Sensor
3. CO Measuring Tube
4. Potentiometer
5. Fuel Pressure Regulator
6. Self-Diagnostic Connector
7. Fuel Distributor
8. Fuel Pressure Regulator
9. Cold Start Valve
10. Idle Switch
11. CIS Motronic ECU
12. Full Throttle Switch
13. Idle Stabilization Valve
14. Power Output Stage
15. $O_2$ Sensor
16. Fuse Relay Panel
17. Canister Shutoff Solenoid
18. Charcoal Canister

Courtesy of Audi of America, Inc.

*Fig. 1: CIS Motronic Component Location*

# Bosch CIS Motronic (Electronic Control) System (Cont.)

**Ignition Distributor** – Ignition distributor is a Hall Effect type with no centrifugal or vacuum advance. Voltage signal from Hall sender is received by ECU for engine RPM input and crankshaft position for ECU control of ignition timing.

## ECU CONTROLLED COMPONENTS

**Canister Shutoff Solenoid** – Shutoff solenoid valve is de-energized when engine is turned off. This closes purge line between carbon canister and intake, preventing fuel vapors from collecting in intake system.

When engine is started, canister shutoff solenoid is energized, allowing stored vapors to be purged from canister. Canister shutoff solenoid is located on top of carbon canister.

**Cold Start Valve** – Cold start valve injects extra fuel into intake manifold during cold starts. Cold start valve is controlled by FICU. Operation of valve is determined by coolant temperature to prevent excess fuel from being injected. Cold start valve is located on back of intake manifold.

**Differential Pressure Regulator** – Differential pressure regulator is attached to fuel distributor and controls fuel flow in lower chamber of fuel distributor. This helps to control fuel mixture. With vehicle at normal operating temperature and all engine controls functioning properly, regulator operates with current from ECU.

During full load operation, full throttle switch closes, sending a signal to ECU. ECU sends a signal approximately 3 mA greater than signal that is currently present. This signal will vary, depending on engine speed and altitude.

When vehicle is decelerated, fuel to injectors is shut off by reversing current to -50 mA to -60 mA. Engine speed at which this reversing will take place is regulated by coolant temperature.

**Idle Stabilization Valve** – Idle stabilization valve consists of a rotary valve and a return spring attached to an armature. Valve controls idle speed. Varying amounts of DC voltage sent by ECU cause motor to pull against return spring allowing air to by-pass throttle plate.

Idle speed is maintained between 650-790 RPM on warm engines and at about 1000 RPM for cold engines. With this system, no idle speed adjustments are necessary or possible. Idle stabilization valve is located between intake air boot and intake manifold.

**Ignition Coil** – Ignition coil is equipped with a power stage mounted on the side. Power stage switches primary current in coil on and off in place of Hall Effect control unit. Power stage is controlled by signals from ECU.

# TESTING

## TESTING PRECAUTIONS

When testing CIS Motronic system, observe following precautions to avoid injury or damage to the system.

**1)** DO NOT touch or disconnect ignition wires with engine running. Disconnect or connect engine wiring and test leads ONLY with ignition off. DO NOT disconnect battery with engine running or apply voltage to control units.

**2)** If engine must be turned over but not started, remove and ground coil wire. A fast charger can be used as a starting aid for no more than 15 seconds at a time with a one minute break between attempts and a maximum of 16.5 volts.

## ENTERING DIAGNOSTIC MODE

The ECU will store faults for self-diagnosis. The ECM has a permanent fault code memory (50 states and Calif.), as well as a temporary fault code memory (Calif. only). When ECU detects a temporary fault, the "FAULT INDICATOR LIGHT" (FIL) on the instrument panel will flash. The FIL will continue to flash until ignition is turned off. The ECU may clear the fault on next engine start, and the FIL will not flash unless fault is detected again. Vehicle will have to be test driven for at least 5 minutes to reset fault. When ECU detects a permanent fault, FIL will flash but fault will remain in ECU memory until physically erased.

Fault will be displayed by a flashing FIL. Access fault codes by inserting a fuse into top of fuel pump relay for 4 seconds, then remove fuse. Diagnostic terminals will be grounded and ECU memory will display any fault code via a flashing sequential code on instrument cluster. *See Figs. 2 and 3.*

Only one fault will be displayed and that fault code will be repeated until fuse is reinserted in fuel pump relay for 4 seconds and removed. Now the next stored fault code will be displayed. Continue with fuse insert/remove procedure until a Code 0000 is displayed indicating all fault codes have been displayed. Code 0000 is read when FIL is on for 2.5 seconds, then off 2.5 seconds, and continues this display with no pause in flashing.

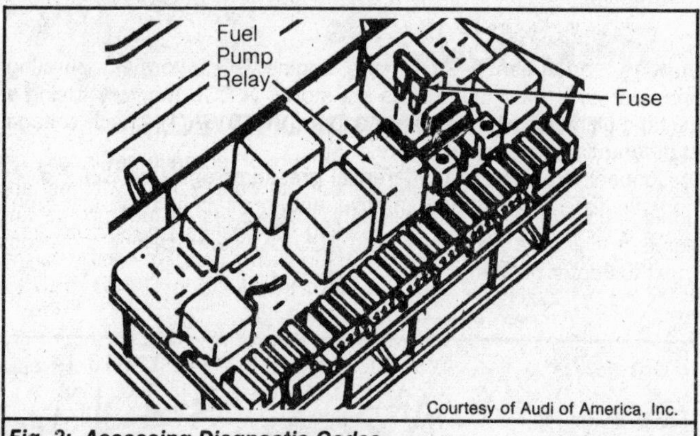
Fuel
Pump
Relay
Fuse
Courtesy of Audi of America, Inc.

***Fig. 2: Accessing Diagnostic Codes***

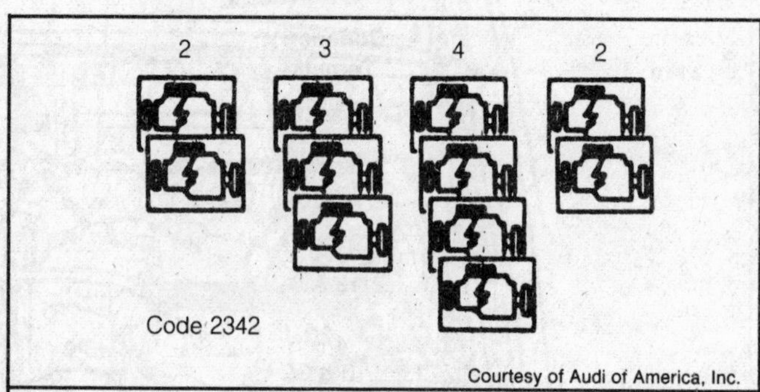
2
3
4
2
Code 2342
Courtesy of Audi of America, Inc.

***Fig. 3: Reading Diagnostic Codes***

## CLEARING FAULT CODES

Turn ignition off. Insert fuse in fuel pump relay. Turn ignition on and remove fuse after 4 seconds. FIL should start flashing a Code 0000. Insert fuse in fuel pump relay for 5 seconds, then remove fuse. FIL should not be flashing. If FIL is still flashing a code, repeat procedure.

## FAULT CODES

**Code 1111** – Defective ECU.

**Code 2113** – No RPM signal from Hall sensor or airflow sensor plate not moving freely.

**Code 2121** * – Defective idle switch.

**Code 2123** – Defective full throttle switch.

**Code 2141** – Knock control is at control limit.

**Code 2142** – Knock Sensor signal.

**Code 2231** * – Adjustment limits of idle stabilization exceeded.

**Code 2232** – Airflow Sensor potentiometer.

**Code 2312** – Coolant Temperature Sensor.

**Code 2341** – $O_2$ sensor control at control limit.

**Code 2342** – $O_2$ sensor control.

**Code 2343** * – Adjustment limits of fuel mixture exceeded (too lean).

**Code 2344** * – Adjustment limits of fuel mixture exceeded (too rich).

**Code 4431** * – Idle Stabilizer Valve.

**Code 4444** * – No faults recognized.

**Code 0000** – End of fault output display.

***NOTE: Codes marked with an asterisk (*) are set in temporary fault memory only.***

## COMPONENT TESTING

**Starting Enrichment** – **1)** Ensure engine is at normal operating temperature and no fault codes are stored in ECU memory. Using a digital multimeter and Harness Adapter (VW1315A/1), check voltage at differential pressure regulator.

**2)** Connect multimeter to differential pressure regulator. *See Fig. 4.* Remove fuse No. 13 and remove and ground ignition coil wire. Crank engine and observe volt reading. Control voltage should drop to 35-45 mA, during engine cranking, and remain there for a maximum of 3 seconds. After 3 seconds, voltage should drop to zero.

**3)** With multimeter still connected and ignition off, disconnect $O_2$ sensor and CTS harness connectors. Connect Adjustable Resistance Box (VW1630) leads to CTS harness connectors. Set resistance to 2500 ohms. Install ignition coil wire and start engine.

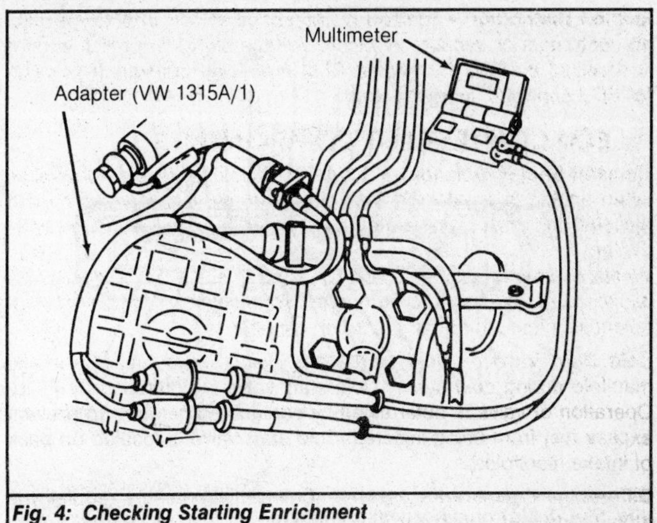
Multimeter
Adapter (VW 1315A/1)

***Fig. 4: Checking Starting Enrichment***

Control voltage should read 15-23mA in about 6-9 seconds, then slowly drop to 9-11 mA.

**4)** Move throttle quickly to full throttle and release throttle. Control voltage must increase briefly to 6 mA. If system fails test, perform electrical tests. See CIS-MOTRONIC VOLTAGE & RESISTANCE TESTS chart. *See Fig. 5.* If system electrical tests are okay, replace ECU. Clear fault codes.

***CIS-MOTRONIC VOLTAGE & RESISTANCE TESTS***

| Test Step | Connection Terminals | Test Conditions (Addition Steps) | Test Values |
|---|---|---|---|
| No. 1 | 14 & 35 | Ignition "ON" | About Battery Voltage |
| No. 2 | 17 & 35 | Ignition "ON" | About Battery Voltage |
| No. 3 | 32 & 35 | Ignition & A/C "ON" | About Battery Voltage |
| No. 4 | 33 & 35 | Ignition & A/C "ON" | About One Volt Below Battery Voltage |
| No. 5 | 19 & 35 | Ignition "ON" | About Battery Voltage |
| No. 6 [1] | 13 & 35 | Insert Fuel Relay Fuse | FIL Must Light |
| | | Ignition "ON" | FIL Must Light |
| No. 7 | 4 & 5 | Ignition "OFF" | 15-25 Ohms |
| No. 8 | 3 & 35 | Ignition "OFF" | 2500 Ohms @ 68°F (20°C) |
| | | | 200 Ohms @ 212°F (100°C) |
| No. 9 | 31 & 35 | Throttle Closed | Open (No Continuity) |
| | | Throttle Wide Open | Continuity |
| No. 10 | 28 & 35 | Throttle Closed & Open | Continuity |
| No. 11 [2] | 18 & 35 | .... | Continuity |
| No. 12 | 13 & 35 | Insert Fuel Relay Fuse | Continuity |
| | 13 & 35 | Ground Test Connector | Continuity |
| No. 13 | 14 & 16 | .... | About 10 Ohms |
| No. 14 | 14 & 15 | .... | 30-60 Ohms |
| No. 15 | .... | Unplug Hall Effect Sensor Connector | .... |
| | 30 & 35 | Terminals 1 & 2 To Hall Effect Sensor | Continuity |
| | 30 & 21 | Terminals 2 & 3 To Hall Effect Sensor | Continuity |
| No. 16 | 11 & 35 | Remove Terminal From Power Output Stage Of Coil. Ground Center Contact | Continuity |
| No. 17 | .... | Disconnect KS Harness Connector | Open (No Continuity) |
| | 6 & 8 | Connect Terminals 1 & 2 | Continuity |
| | | Connect Terminals 1 & 3 | Continuity |
| No. 18 | 7 & 35 | Disconnect $O_2$ Connector & Ground | Continuity |
| No. 19 | 23 & 26 | Sensor Plate In Rest Position | About 5000 ohms |
| No. 20 | 26 & 35 | Sensor Plate In Rest Position | About 4000 Ohms |
| No. 21 | 34 & 35 | Standard Transmission | Continuity |
| | | Automatic Transmission In "P" Or "N" | Open (No Continuity) |
| No. 22 | 12 & 35 | Remove Fuel Pump Relay And Ground Terminal No. 47 Of Fuse Panel Relay | Continuity |

[1] – Calif. only.
[2] – Non-Calif. only.

# Bosch CIS Motronic (Electronic Control) System (Cont.)

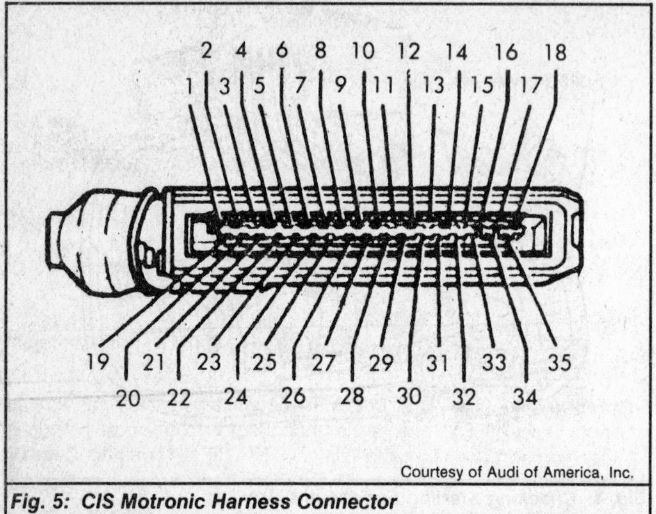

2 4 6 8 10 12 14 16 18
1 3 5 7 9 11 13 15 17
19 21 23 25 27 29 31 33 35
20 22 24 26 28 30 32 34
Courtesy of Audi of America, Inc.


*Fig. 5: CIS Motronic Harness Connector*

**Deceleration Fuel Shutoff – 1)** Ensure engine is at normal operating temperature and no fault codes are stored in ECU memory. Using a digital multimeter and Harness Adapter (VW1315A/1), check voltage at differential pressure regulator.

**2)** Connect multimeter to differential pressure regulator. *See Fig. 4.* Turn ignition on. Control voltage must read positive (+). If voltage reads negative (-), reverse test leads.

**3)** Start engine. Raise RPM to 3000 and release throttle. Control voltage must momentarily switch to negative (-). If system fails test, perform electrical tests. See CIS-MOTRONIC VOLTAGE & RESISTANCE TESTS chart. *See Fig. 5.* If system electrical tests are okay, replace ECU. Clear fault codes.

**Cold Start Valve – 1)** Disconnect and ground ignition coil wire. Disconnect CTS harness connector and insert 15,000 ohm side of Bridge Adapter (VW1490) into CTS harness connector. *See Fig. 6.*

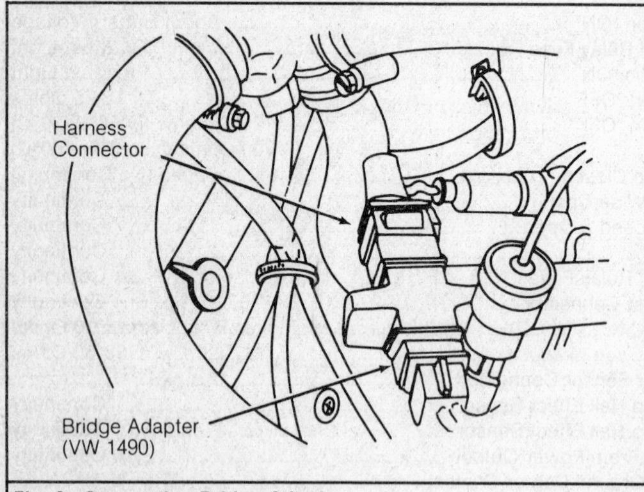

Harness Connector
Bridge Adapter (VW 1490)


*Fig. 6: Connecting Bridge Adapter*

**2)** Remove cold start valve and place in container to catch fuel spray. Crank engine. Cold start valve must spray fuel in a uniform cone pattern for 7 seconds.

**3)** Dry off tip of cold start valve. Inspect valve after one minute to ensure valve is dry and not leaking. Disconnect cold start valve connector and measure resistance across terminals of valve. Resistance should be about 10 ohms.

**4)** If resistance reading is wrong, replace cold start valve. If resistance value is okay, use multimeter connected to cold start valve harness connector and crank engine. Multimeter should show voltage for 7 seconds. If cold start valve resistance and harness check okay, replace ECU.

**Sensor Plate Lever/Control Plunger – 1)** Remove ignition coil wire and ground. Crank engine for 10 seconds.

**2)** Using pliers or a magnet, lift sensor plate through entire range. Even resistance should be felt through range of movement. Move sensor plate quickly from raised position to rest position. No resistance should be felt. If resistance is felt, replace airflow sensor.

**3)** If sensor plate is hard to move in one direction, and easy in opposite direction, control plunger is sticking and fuel distributor must be replaced.

**Airflow Sensor Plate – 1)** With engine off, upper edge of airflow sensor plate must be .118-.875" (1.9-3.0 mm) below edge of air cone. *See Fig. 7.*

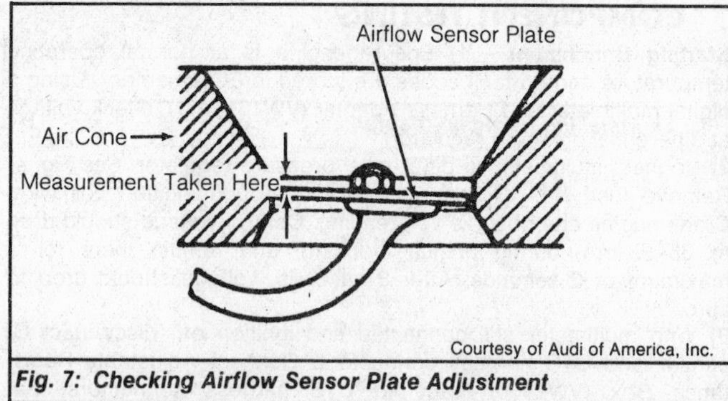

Airflow Sensor Plate
Air Cone
Measurement Taken Here
Courtesy of Audi of America, Inc.


*Fig. 7: Checking Airflow Sensor Plate Adjustment*

**2)** If sensor plate position is incorrect, adjust by bending wire clip located under sensor plate. Try to achieve the smaller setting of .118" (1.9 mm).

***CAUTION: Do not scratch venturi of airflow sensor or bend leaf spring.***

**3)** Airflow sensor plate free play is measured on the fuel distributor side of air plate. *See Fig. 8.* With ignition coil wire disconnected and grounded, crank engine for 10 seconds. Slightly lift airflow sensor plate until resistance is felt. Clearance should be .039-.118" (1.0-3.0 mm).

**4)** If airflow sensor plate clearance is incorrect, adjust by turning control plunger stop screw. Loosen stop screw lock nut and turn screw. Turning stop screw clockwise increases clearance about .05" (1.3 mm) for each 1/4 turn. Recheck free play and idle speed.

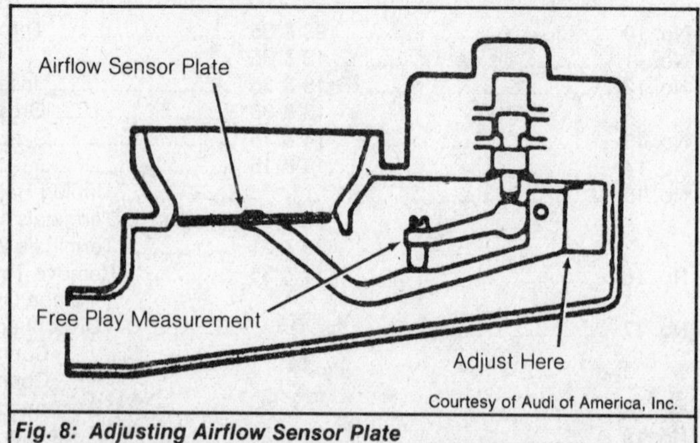

Airflow Sensor Plate
Free Play Measurement
Adjust Here
Courtesy of Audi of America, Inc.


*Fig. 8: Adjusting Airflow Sensor Plate*

**Potentiometer – 1)** Ensure engine is at normal operating temperature. Connect Test Adapter (VW1501) between potentiometer and harness. *See Fig. 9.* Connect multimeter to test adapter connectors 1 and 3. Switch multimeter to DC volts scale and turn on ignition. Reading should be 4.35-5.35 volts.

# Bosch CIS Motronic (Electronic Control) System (Cont.)

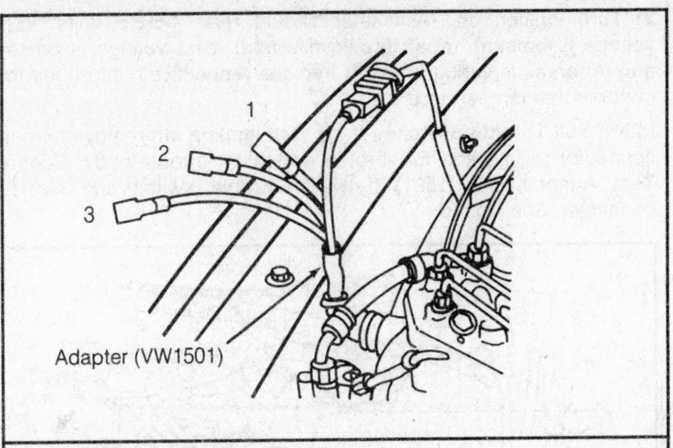
1
2
3
Adapter (VW1501)

*Fig. 9: Installing Harness Adapter*

**2)** Switch multimeter leads to test connectors 2 and 3. Start engine and let idle. Engine cooling fan must not come on during this test. Reading should be .4-.9 volt. If reading is slightly outside tolerance, correct by adjusting the potentiometer trim screw. If correction is not possible, replace potentiometer.

**3)** When replacing potentiometer, do not touch resistance strip or contact whiskers inside potentiometer. Loosely install potentiometer. Connect multimeter to test adapter connectors 2 and 3. Turn on ignition and measure voltage. Reading should be 10-100 mV. Adjust potentiometer to read correctly by turning trim screw.

**4)** Pull adjusting slide on Sensor Plate Gauge (VW1348/1) up to upper stop. Place gauge centrally on edge of airflow sensor with edge No. 3 pointing toward fuel distributor. *See Fig. 10.* Push adjusting slide down to stop. Rotate setting screw until base of magnet contacts sensor plate mounting screw.

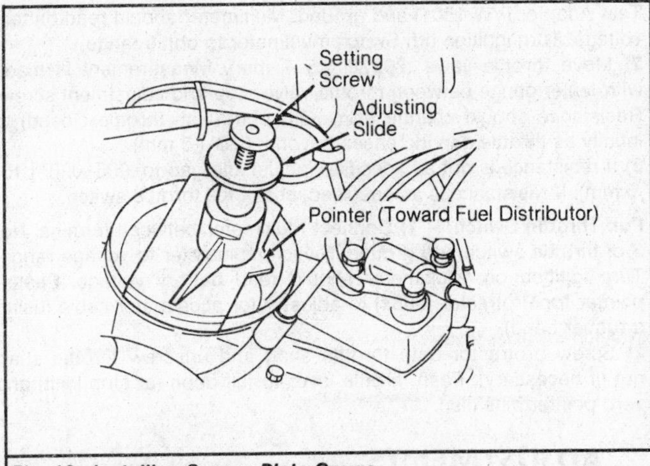
Setting Screw
Adjusting Slide
Pointer (Toward Fuel Distributor)

*Fig. 10: Installing Sensor Plate Gauge*

**5)** Pull adjusting slide up to first stop (idle position). Adjust potentiometer set screw to obtain .5-.8 volt.

**6)** Remove sensor plate gauge and install intake air boot. Start and run engine until cooling fan has cycled at least once. DO NOT take voltage readings while engine is running.

**7)** Stop engine and turn on ignition. Potentiometer voltage should be .4-.9 volt. If voltage reading is out of range, refer to step **2)** for procedure. If you have performed all of these procedures and still cannot obtain correct voltage readings, replace airflow sensor.

**Idle Stabilization Valve – 1)** Close full throttle switch. Idle stabilizer valve should cycle (click sound) when switch is closed. If no click sound is heard, disconnect idle stabilizer valve connector.

**2)** Connect LED Tester (US 1115) between terminals No. 1 and No. 2 using jumper wire. LED tester should light up. If tester does light up, replace idle stabilizer valve. If tester does not light up, connect multimeter between connector terminal No. 2 and ground.

**3)** Multimeter should read 12 volts. If 12 volts are not present, repair break in wiring. If wiring is okay, replace ECU.

**Oxygen Sensor – 1)** Ensure engine is at operating temperature. Idle speed adjustment, voltage to $O_2$ sensor heater and coolant temperature sensor must all be correct.

**2)** Connect multimeter to differential pressure regulator using Adapter (1315A/1). *See Fig. 4.* Start engine and idle for 2 minutes. Note control voltage at differential pressure regulator.

**3)** Remove a manifold vacuum hose to induce a lean mixture. Control voltage must increase. If control voltage did not change, disconnect $O_2$ sensor wire connector and ground harness end for 20 seconds. If control voltage changes, replace $O_2$ sensor.

**4)** If control voltage still does not change, perform wire harness checks for opens or shorts to ground or power. If harness checks okay, replace ECU.

**Ignition Signal – 1)** This check is necessary only if no ignition spark is present. Remove harness connector from output stage of ignition coil and connect LED Tester (US1115) to terminals 2 and 3. *See Fig. 11.*

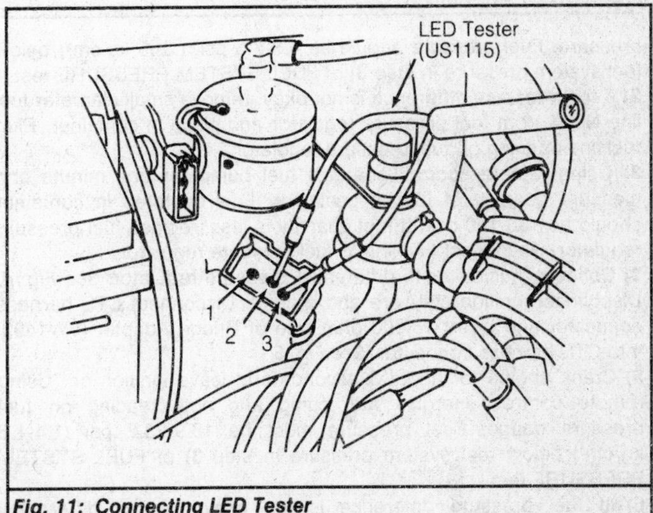
LED Tester (US1115)
1
2
3

*Fig. 11: Connecting LED Tester*

**2)** Crank engine and observe LED light on tester. If LED flickers, Hall Effect sensor is okay.

**3)** If LED does not flicker, remove harness connector from Hall Effect sensor on distributor. Connect multimeter to outer connections of harness connector. Turn on ignition. Voltage to Hall Effect sensor from ECU should be 9 volts minimum. If voltage is low, check battery, battery cables, all wiring and ECU.

***CAUTION: Fuel system is under high pressure. Use extreme care when removing fuel lines.***

**Fuel System Pressure – 1)** Ensure engine is at normal operating temperature. Connect Fuel Pressure Tester (VW1318) to measuring location No. 1 on fuel distributor using Adapter (VW1318/4). Close fuel pressure valve. *See Fig. 12.*

**2)** Remove fuel pump relay from fuse panel and connect Remote Control (US4480/3) in fuse panel fuel pump relay cavity. Ensure fuse No. 13 on fuse panel is good.

**3)** Open valve on pressure tester and energize fuel pump with remote control. Fuel pressure should be 89-94 psi. (6.3-6.6 kg/cm²). If fuel pressure is too high, carefully remove fuel return line from fuel pressure regulator and place in container.

**4)** Repeat test in step **2)**. If fuel pressure is still too high, replace fuel pressure regulator. If pressure is okay, check return line for obstruction or kinks. Repair or replace as necessary.

**Differential Pressure Regulator – 1)** Close valve on fuel pressure tester and relieve pressure. Disconnect harness connector at differential pressure regulator. Energize fuel pump and note fuel

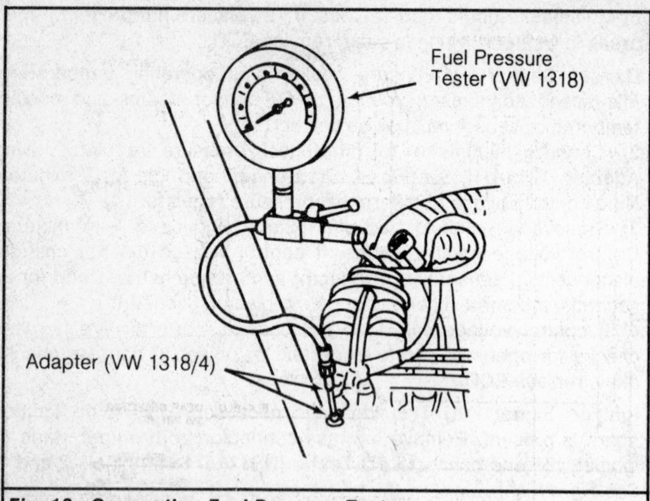
Fuel Pressure
Tester (VW 1318)
Adapter (VW 1318/4)

*Fig. 12: Connecting Fuel Pressure Tester*

pressure. Fuel pressure should be 4.3-7.3 psi. (.3-.5 kg.cm²) below fuel system pressure in step **3)** of FUEL SYSTEM PRESSURE test.

**2)** If fuel pressure difference is not okay, remove small diameter fuel line No. 1 from fuel pressure regulator and place in container. Plug fuel line opening on fuel pressure regulator.

**3)** Using remote control, energize fuel pump for one minute and measure quantity of fuel in container. Fuel captured in container should be 130-150 ccs. If fuel quantity is less, replace fuel pressure regulator. Reconnect fuel line to fuel pressure regulator.

**4)** Connect multimeter to differential pressure regulator. *See Fig. 4.* Disconnect ignition coil wire and ground. Disconnect CTS harness connector and insert 15,000 ohm side of Bridge Adapter (VW1490) into CTS harness connector. *See Fig. 6.*

**5)** Crank engine for about 5 seconds and leave ignition on. Using remote control, energize fuel pump and note reading on fuel pressure gauge. Fuel pressure must be 18.9-23.2 psi (1.4-1.6 kg/cm²) below fuel system pressure in step **3)** of FUEL SYSTEM PRESSURE test.

**6)** If fuel pressure difference is not okay, replace differential pressure regulator. If fuel pressure difference is okay, check wiring harness and ECU.

**Residual Pressure – 1)** This procedure is only required for hot start problems. Turn valve open on fuel pressure tester. Energize fuel pump for 5 seconds using remote control. Note fuel pressure drop over time. Fuel pressure should not drop more than 2 psi in 10 minutes.

**2)** If fuel pressure drop is greater than 2 psi in 10 minutes, check fuel pump check valve, airflow sensor plate free play and sealing rings on fuel distributor and fuel lines.

**Coolant Temperature Sensor – 1)** Ensure engine temperature is greater than 176°F (80°C). Remove harness connector from coolant temperature sensor. Connect multimeter between temperature sensor terminal No. 1 and engine ground.

**2)** Turn ignition on. Multimeter should read 4.5-5.5 volts. If no voltage is present, repair break in wiring. If no voltage is present and no break in wiring is found, replace respective control unit that controls that temperature sensor.

**Idle & Full Throttle Switches – 1)** With ignition off, remove harness connector to idle and full throttle switch on throttle body. Connect Test Adapter (VW 1501) between throttle switch and harness connector. *See Fig. 13.*

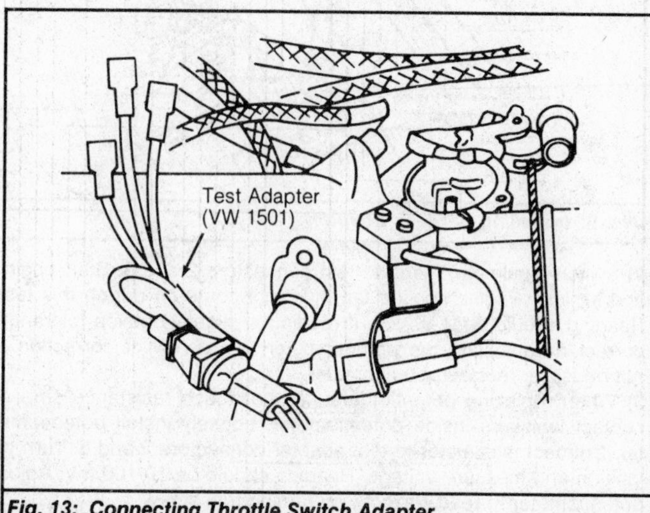
Test Adapter
(VW 1501)

*Fig. 13: Connecting Throttle Switch Adapter*

**2)** Connect multimeter between terminal No. 2 of adapter and engine ground. Turn ignition on. Multimeter should read 12 volts. If 12 volts is not present, repair break in wiring.

**Idle Switch – 1)** Connect multimeter between terminal No. 1 of Test Adapter (VW 1501) and ground. Multimeter should read battery voltage. Turn ignition off. Switch multimeter to ohms range.

**2)** Move throttle valve .20-.28" (.5-.7 mm). Measurement is made with feeler gauge between throttle valve stop and adjustment screw. Resistance should change from zero ohm (with throttle closed) to infinity as throttle gap increases beyond .020" (.5 mm).

**3)** If resistance is not as specified, adjust idle gap to .006-.020" (.15-.5 mm). If resistance is as specified, check full throttle switch.

**Full Throttle Switch – 1)** Connect multimeter between terminal No. 3 of throttle switch and ground. Switch multimeter to voltage range. Turn ignition on. Multimeter should read battery voltage. Fasten pointer for Protractor (3084) to adjuster for accelerator cable (using a rubber band).

**2)** Screw protractor onto throttle shaft and unscrew throttle shaft nut (if necessary). Push throttle lever to full open (at stop limit) and zero pointer plus disc.

## ADJUSTMENTS

See appropriate article in TUNE-UP PROCEDURES section.

## Bosch CIS Motronic (Electronic Control) System (Cont.)

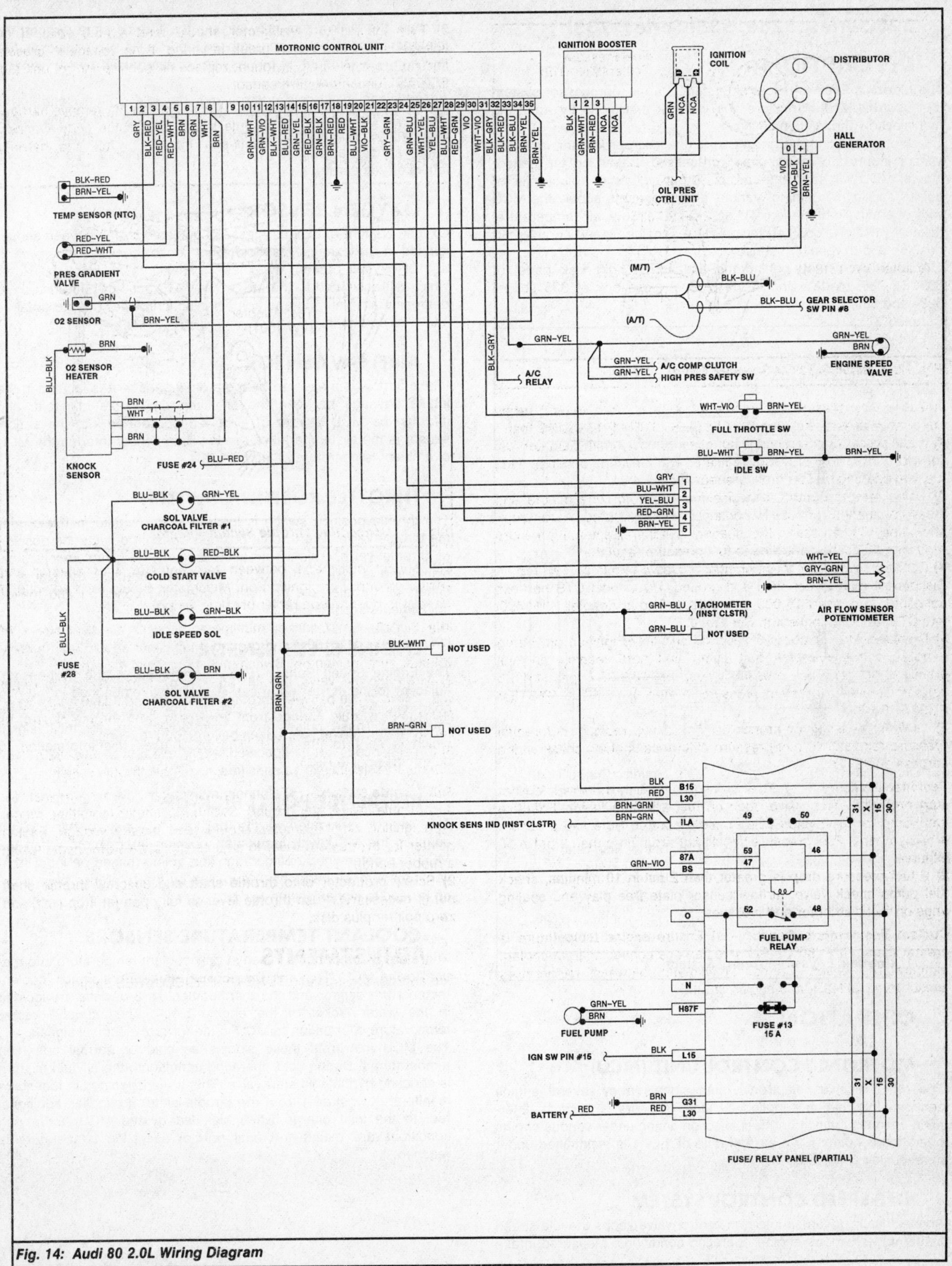
MOTRONIC CONTROL UNIT
IGNITION BOOSTER
IGNITION COIL
DISTRIBUTOR
HALL GENERATOR
OIL PRES CTRL UNIT
TEMP SENSOR (NTC)
PRES GRADIENT VALVE
O2 SENSOR
O2 SENSOR HEATER
KNOCK SENSOR
FUSE #24
SOL VALVE CHARCOAL FILTER #1
COLD START VALVE
IDLE SPEED SOL
FUSE #28
SOL VALVE CHARCOAL FILTER #2
(M/T)
(A/T)
GEAR SELECTOR SW PIN #8
A/C COMP CLUTCH
HIGH PRES SAFETY SW
A/C RELAY
ENGINE SPEED VALVE
FULL THROTTLE SW
IDLE SW
AIR FLOW SENSOR POTENTIOMETER
TACHOMETER (INST CLSTR)
NOT USED
NOT USED
NOT USED
NOT USED
KNOCK SENS IND (INST CLSTR)
FUEL PUMP RELAY
FUEL PUMP
FUSE #13 15 A
IGN SW PIN #15
BATTERY
FUSE/ RELAY PANEL (PARTIAL)

*Fig. 14: Audi 80 2.0L Wiring Diagram*

# 1988 COMPUTERIZED ENGINE CONTROLS
# BMW Motronic Emission Control System

## 325 Series, 528e, 535i Series, 735i

## DESCRIPTION

The Motronic Emission Control System is a microprocessor system that controls air/fuel mixture and exhaust emissions by adjusting fuel injection and ignition timing.

The Motronic Control Unit (MCU) is the microprocessor in which sensor inputs are received and processed. Based on the sensor inputs, MCU will send the correct output signals to adjust injector pulses and ignition timing. Various engine sensors supply the MCU with operating information. These include: airflow, air temperature, throttle position, coolant temperature, engine speed, crankshaft position and oxygen ($O_2$) sensor.

The MCU is located behind the speaker in right kick panel of 635CSi, 735i models and inside (above) glove box of 325 series, 528e and 535i series.

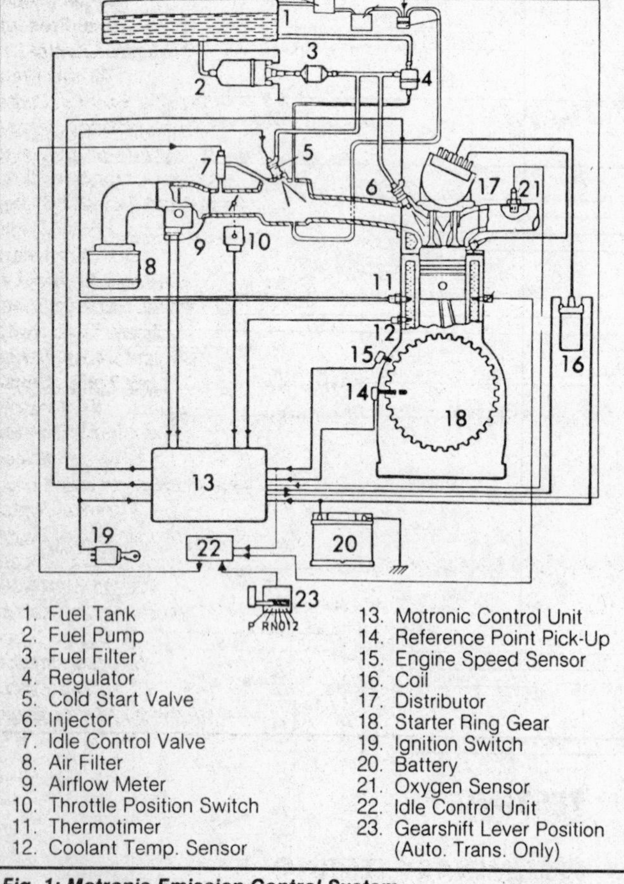
1
2
3
4
5
6
7
8
9
10
11
12
13
14
15
16
17
18
19
20
21
22
23
1. Fuel Tank
2. Fuel Pump
3. Fuel Filter
4. Regulator
5. Cold Start Valve
6. Injector
7. Idle Control Valve
8. Air Filter
9. Airflow Meter
10. Throttle Position Switch
11. Thermotimer
12. Coolant Temp. Sensor
13. Motronic Control Unit
14. Reference Point Pick-Up
15. Engine Speed Sensor
16. Coil
17. Distributor
18. Starter Ring Gear
19. Ignition Switch
20. Battery
21. Oxygen Sensor
22. Idle Control Unit
23. Gearshift Lever Position (Auto. Trans. Only)

*Fig. 1: Motronic Emission Control System*

## OPERATION

### MOTRONIC CONTROL UNIT (MCU)

The MCU receives electronic input signals from several engine sensors. Information supplied by these sensors is used to determine optimum ignition and fuel injection timing under various engine operating conditions. An air/fuel ratio of 14.7:1 is maintained under most driving conditions.

### IDLE SPEED CONTROL SYSTEM

An electrically governed idle rpm control valve keeps the idle speed stable under various engine operating conditions. Measured intake air from the airflow meter by-passes the throttle plate through the idle rpm control valve and subsequently calls for additional fuel injection. The amount of by-pass air is determined by the variable orifice of the control valve.

An additional electronic control unit, the Idle Speed Control Unit (ICU), controls the orifice opening according to the engine speed and engine operating conditions as related to engine coolant temperature, transmission position, air conditioner operation and intake air temperature.

### OXYGEN SENSOR

Oxygen content of exhaust gases is detected by the oxygen sensor located in the exhaust manifold. This sensor converts the percentage of oxygen present in exhaust gases into an electrical signal which is transmitted to the MCU. The MCU uses this information to determine air/fuel ratio and adjusts injection pulse width to obtain a 14.7:1 air/fuel ratio.

### AIRFLOW SENSOR

Intake airflow is measured by the airflow sensor. It is located in the intake passage between the air filter and intake manifold, and informs the MCU of rate of airflow. Incorporated into the airflow sensor is the air temperature sensor. This sensor informs the MCU of ambient temperature of incoming air.

### THROTTLE POSITION SWITCH

The throttle position switch is located on the intake manifold near the throttle valve. The throttle position switch it detects the position of throttle valve. This information is converted into an electrical signal and is sent to the MCU. The MCU interprets the signal as either full throttle, idle or normal operating condition and makes adjustments accordingly.

### ENGINE SPEED SENSOR

The Engine Speed Sensor (ESS) is mounted on the bellhousing, adjacent to the starter ring gear. A steel ball, embedded in the ring gear, causes an electronic pulse in the ESS with each engine revolution. These pulses are converted into an electrical signal which is sent to the MCU. The MCU uses this information to determine engine RPM.

### REFERENCE POINT PICK-UP

This sensor is located in the bellhousing, next to the ESS. It supplies the MCU with crankshaft position information. When the MCU has determined optimum ignition timing (based on input from various sources), information supplied by the reference point pick-up is used to signal ignition firing.

### COOLANT TEMPERATURE SENSORS

There are 3 components which supply coolant temperature information to the MCU. They are the coolant temperature switch, coolant temperature sensor and the thermotimer. All 3 devices are located in the water jacket of the engine block. They supply coolant temperature information to MCU in the form of electrical signals.

The MCU interprets these signals as cold or normal operating temperatures. During cold operating conditions, the air/fuel mixture is enriched by the cold start valve. This valve is located in the intake manifold, downstream from the throttle plate. It supplies additional fuel to the inlet charge when signaled by the MCU. Extra rich conditions are maintained until normal operating temperature is reached.

## TROUBLE SHOOTING

### MOTRONIC SYSTEM

The MOTRONIC TROUBLE SHOOTING CHART can be helpful in diagnosing problems related to the Motronic engine control system. This chart should be used before proceeding to the TESTING section.

***MOTRONIC SYSTEM TROUBLE SHOOTING***

| CONDITION | POSSIBLE CAUSE |
|---|---|
| Cold Engine Will Not Start | Fuel Pressure |
| | Fuel Injector |
| | Cold Start Valve |
| | Motronic Control Unit |
| | Speed Transmitter |
| | Reference Mark Transmitter |
| | Airflow Sensor |
| | Wire Connections and Plugs |
| | Ignition Coil |
| Cold Engine Starts, But Stalls | Fuel Injector |
| | Motronic Control Unit |
| | Wire Connections |
| Cold Engine Hard to Start | Fuel Pressure |
| | Thermo Time Switch |
| | Motronic Control Unit |
| | Cold Start Valve |
| | High Voltage Distributor |
| | Spark Plugs |
| Warm Engine Will Not Start | Fuel Pressure |
| | Fuel Injector-Motronic Control Unit |
| | Speed Transmitter |
| | Reference Mark Transmitter |
| | Wire Connections and Plugs |
| | Ignition Coil |
| | Secondary Air of Engine |
| Erratic Idle/Warm-Up Phase | Throttle Position Switch |
| | Coolant Temp. Sensor |
| | Idle Valve |
| | Motronic Control Unit |
| | Idle Control Unit |
| | Air Temp. Sensor |
| | Temp. Switch |
| | Wire Connections |
| | High Voltage Distributor |
| | Spark Plugs |
| | Ignition Circuit |
| | Intake System |
| | Coolant |
| Engine Backfiring | Fuel Injector |
| | Motronic Control Unit |
| | High Voltage Distributor |
| | Spark Plugs |
| | Ignition Circuit |
| | Exhaust System |
| Idle Speed Incorrect | Fuel Injector |
| | Cold Start Valve |
| | Motronic Control Unit |
| | Intake System |
| | Throttle Position Switch |
| | Thermo Time Switch |
| | Coolant Temp. Switch |
| | High Voltage Distributor |
| Acceleration Hesitation | Fuel Injector |
| | Motronic Control Unit |
| | Wire Connections |
| | High Voltage Distributor |
| | Spark Plugs |
| | Ignition Circuit |

***MOTRONIC SYSTEM TROUBLE SHOOTING (Cont.)***

| CONDITION | POSSIBLE CAUSE |
|---|---|
| Acceleration Knock | Motronic Control Unit |
| | Wire Connections |
| | Spark Plugs |
| | Ignition Circuit |
| Coasting Hesitation | Fuel Injector |
| | Motronic Control Unit |
| | Wire Connections |
| Engine Misfiring All Conditions | Fuel Injector |
| | Motronic Control Unit |
| | Wire Connections |
| | Ignition Circuit |
| | Intake System |
| | Exhaust System |
| | Secondary Air of Engine |
| | Insufficient Engine Power |
| | Fuel Injector |
| | Fuel Pressure |
| | Motronic Control Unit |
| | Airflow Meter |
| | Throttle Position Switch |
| | Coolant Temp. Sensor |
| | Air Temp. Sensor |
| | Ignition Circuit |
| | Intake and Exhaust System |
| High Fuel Consumption | Fuel Injector |
| | Cold Start Valve |
| | Motronic Control Unit. |
| | Throttle Position Switch |
| | Thero Time Switch |
| | Coolant Temp. Sensor |
| | Air Temp. Sensor |
| CO Level Incorrect | Fuel Injector |
| | Cold Start Valve |
| | Oxygen Sensor |
| | Wire Connections and Plugs |
| | Intake System |
| | Secondary Air of Engine |
| HC and NOx Excessive | Fuel Injector |
| | Cold Start Valve |
| | Motronic Control Unit |
| | Oxygen Sensor |
| | Wire Connections |
| | Intake System |
| | Secondary Air of Engine |

## TESTING

### PRELIMINARY TESTING

***NOTE: See MOTRONIC SYSTEM TROUBLE SHOOTING CHART before testing of components.***

Before starting test procedures, engine should be at operating temperature with oil temperature at 140°F (60°C). The Motronic system may be suspected when problems arise which are related to driveability, fuel economy or excess emissions. However, before beginning diagnosis ensure that all other systems are operating properly. Check all basic engine components and functions before beginning Motronic system diagnosis and testing.

When all other engine systems have been checked, Motronic diagnosis should be performed. Determine which component or area is the most probable source of engine operation problem and begin testing. Many component failures may be traced to faults in the wiring circuit. Therefore, before beginning other diagnostic procedures, check the appropriate circuit for opens or shorts and ensure that all electrical connections are clean and tight.

## TEST EQUIPMENT

In addition to a standard volt/ohmmeter, jumper wires and connectors, some special test procedures and BMW testing equipment must be used for proper diagnosis of the Motronic system. The "BMW Service Test" kit, Bosch L-Jetronic Fuel Injection testing procedures, and BMW Test Meters (12 6 400, 13 1 092, 13 1 094 and 22 13 100) are required to properly test Motronic systems. See appropriate article in FUEL SYSTEMS section. This equipment will be referred to throughout the following test procedures and must be used as indicated. Failure to do so may result in unnecessary replacement of good component parts.

## TEST 1: FUEL PRESSURE

**No Fuel Pressure – 1)** Check fuel supply to fuel pump(s). Repair if necessary. If fuel supply is okay, check fuel pump(s) fuse and replace if defective. If fuse is okay, unplug electrical connector from fuel pump.

**2)** Connect volt/ohmmeter between 2 wires in connector and start engine. Volt/ohmmeter should read battery voltage. If voltage is correct, replace fuel pump(s). If voltage reading is incorrect, check pump(s) power and ground circuits. Repair circuits as necessary.

**Fuel Pressure Too High – 1)** Check vacuum connection on fuel pressure regulator and vacuum hoses for leaks or kinks. Repair or replace as needed.

**2)** Check for defective pressure regulator and replace if faulty. Check fuel return line for bends, pinches or clogs. Repair or replace as needed.

**Fuel Pressure Too Low –** Check for fuel feed restriction. Check for kinked, bent or clogged fuel line. Repair or re-route as needed. Check fuel filter for excessive restriction and replace if dirty. Clean filter screen in fuel intake. Check pressure regulator operation and replace if defective.

## TEST 2: FUEL INJECTORS

**1)** Check for fuel delivery at injectors. If one or more injectors are not operating correctly, place finger on injector and feel for injector pulses (vibration).

**2)** If no pulses are detected, check circuits to injectors. Repair circuits as necessary. If circuits are okay, use BMW service test unit to check injector resistance. Replace defective fuel injectors as necessary.

## TEST 3: MOTRONIC CONTROL UNIT (MCU)

**1)** Check circuits to MCU. Repair any open or shorted circuits. If circuits are okay, connect BMW service test unit and perform appropriate L-Jetronic tests in FUEL SYSTEMS section.

**2)** In order to ensure that source of defect is only in control unit, it is recommended to replace unit for comparsion.

## TEST 4: COLD START VALVE

**Valve Does Not Open – 1)** Remove valve, leaving fuel lines connected. Energize fuel pump. Supply battery voltage to cold start valve with jumper wire and ensure valve is properly grounded. Cold start valve should deliver fuel. If not, replace valve.

**2)** If valve functions, check spray pattern and flow rate. Pull plug off valve and connect volt/ohmmeter between wires of plug. Start engine. Meter should read battery voltage while cranking engine. If not, trace circuit and repair wiring. See appropriate WIRING DIAGRAM at end of this article. Check thermotimer as described in TEST 12 and replace if necessary.

**Valve Leaks –** Check valve operation. If valve operates properly (fuel is delivered), remove jumper wire from battery voltage and check that fuel delivery stops. If fuel delivery continues, leaks, or seeps out, clean or replace valve as necessary.

## TEST 5: IDLE CONTROL VALVE

**1)** Valve should be open when vehicle is at rest (no voltage to valve). When voltage is applied to valve (engine on), valve should close. Remove 2 valve hoses and observe valve operation. If valve does not operate as described, replace valve.

**2)** If valve operates properly, pull off connector plug and connect volt/ohmmeter between 2 wires in plug. Start engine and turn A/C on. Voltmeter should read battery voltage. If it does not, check idle control unit. See TEST 6.

## TEST 6: IDLE CONTROL UNIT (ICU)

**1)** Check power supply to ICU. Pull connector plug off of ICU and connect volt/ohmmeter between terminal No. 2 of plug and ground. Start engine. Voltmeter should read battery voltage. If not, repair circuit.

**2)** If voltage is correct, check ground connection of ICU. Connect volt/ohmmeter between terminal No. 4 of plug and ground. Ohmmeter should read infinity. If not, trace circuit and repair wiring.

**3)** If resistance is correct, check speed signal to ICU at terminal No. 3 of ICU plug using BMW Test Meter (22 13 100). If signal is not correct, trace circuit and repair wiring.

**4)** If signal is correct, check for ground at terminal No. 6 of ICU. Connect volt/ohmmeter between terminal No. 6 of ICU plug and ground. With coolant temperature below 106°F (41°C), resistance should be zero. With coolant temperature above 117°F (47°C), resistance should be infinite. If values are incorrect, check coolant temperature sensor. See TEST 10. If sensor is good, trace idle control unit circuit and repair wiring. If resistance values are correct, go to next step.

**5)** On vehicles equipped with automatic transmission, check for battery voltage at terminal No. 7 of plug with ignition on and transmission shift lever in "N" position. If no voltage is present, trace circuit and repair wiring. If voltage is present at terminal No. 7, check for battery voltage at terminal No. 8 with shift lever in "P" position. If no voltage is present, trace circuit and repair wiring. If reading is correct, go to next step.

**6)** On vehicles with air conditioning, check for battery voltage at terminal No. 9 of A/C plug with air conditioner on. Trace circuit and repair wiring if voltage is incorrect. If reading is correct, go to next step.

**7)** On all models, check for battery voltage at terminal No. 10 of ICU plug with ignition on. Voltage should be present with air temperature below 41°F (5°C), and no voltage at higher temperatures. If values are incorrect, check air temperature sensor. See TEST 13. Replace if faulty. If sensor is okay, repair wiring.

**8)** If voltage readings are correct, check for ground at terminal No. 12 of ICU. Connect volt/ohmmeter between terminal No. 12 of plug and ground. Resistance should be zero with throttle closed, and infinite with throttle open. If values are incorrect, check throttle switch. See TEST 9. Replace or adjust as needed. If switch is good, repair wiring.

**9)** If resistance values are correct, check ground connection at terminal No. 11 of ICU plug. Connect volt/ohmmeter between terminal No. 11 and ground. Resistance value should be zero. If not, check coolant temperature sensor. See TEST 10. Replace sensor if faulty. If sensor is good, repair wiring.

**10)** If resistance values are correct, and idle control valve is good (Test 5), replace idle control unit.

## TEST 7: ENGINE SPEED SENSOR & REFERENCE POINT PICK-UP

**1)** Check sensor and pick-up general condition. Ensure that they are installed in proper position and firmly seated. Electrical contacts must be clean and tight. Check that sensor plugs are not reversed. Plugs are color coded for identification.

**2)** Install BMW Test Meter (22 13 100). Connect terminals and check for engine speed input signal to MCU. Connect check for reference signal to MCU. If signals are not correct, remove terminal connections and recheck signals. If either signal is absent, check wiring for open. If wiring is okay, replace sensor and/or pick-up as needed. See SPEED SENSOR RESISTANCE table.

***SPEED SENSOR RESISTANCE***

| Application | Ohms |
|---|---|
| All Except 735i | 864-1056 |
| 735i | 486-594 |

## TEST 8: AIRFLOW METER

Check electrical connections on airflow meter. Use BMW service test equipment and test equipment testing procedures to test airflow meter operation.

## TEST 9: THROTTLE POSITION SWITCH (TPS)

Check that switch is properly installed and firmly seated. To determine throttle sensor resistance values, use volt/ohmmeter connected across switch terminals. Check resistance at part throttle opening and full throttle opening. See THROTTLE POSITION SWITCH RESISTANCE table. If values are incorrect, adjust or replace sensor as needed.

***THROTTLE POSITION SWITCH RESISTANCE***

| Throttle Position | Ohms |
|---|---|
| Partially Open | 1000,000 |
| Fully Open | 3 |

## TEST 10: COOLANT TEMPERATURE SENSOR

Check that sensor is properly installed and firmly seated. Check that cooling system is full. Bleed system. Check resistance between switch connections. If resistance is incorrect, replace sensor. If resistance is correct, trace sensor circuit and repair wiring.

***COOLANT TEMPERATURE SENSOR RESISTANCE***

| Application<br>Coolant Temperature | Ohms |
|---|---|
| 2.5L & 2.7L | |
| 12°F (-10° C) | 7000-11,600 |
| 70°F (20°) | 2100-2900 |
| 175°F (80°) | 270-400 |
| 3.5L | |
| 12°F (-10°) | 8200-10,500 |
| 70°F (20°) | 2200-2700 |
| 175°F (80°) | 300-360 |

## TEST 11: COOLANT TEMPERATURE SWITCH

Switch must be tightly installed. Check that cooling system is full. Bleed system. Check resistance between switch contacts. Resistance below 106°F (41°C) should be zero. At higher temperatures, resistance should be infinite. If values are correct, trace circuit and repair wiring. If values are incorrect, replace switch.

## TEST 12: THERMOTIMER

**1)** Check that timer is properly installed and firmly seated. Check radiator for correct coolant level. Bleed cooling system.

**2)** Disconnect timer and check resistance values between plug terminals "G" and "W", "G" and ground, and "W" and ground. If values are correct, trace timer circuit and repair wiring. If values are incorrect, replace timer. See THERMOTIMER RESISTANCE table.

***THERMOTIMER RESISTANCE***

| Circuit Tested | Resistance |
|---|---|
| "G" to Ground | 40-70 Ohms |
| "G" to "W" & "W" to Ground | |
| Above 60°F (15°C) | Infinite |
| Below 60°F (15°C) | Zero |

## TEST 13: AIR TEMPERATURE SENSOR

Check electrical connections on airflow meter. Using volt/ohmmeter, check resistance between airflow meter terminals that connect to Gray/Violet and Gray/Blue wires. Compare with table. See AIR TEMPERATURE SENSOR RESISTANCE. If values are incorrect, replace airflow meter.

***AIR TEMPERATURE SENSOR RESISTANCE***

| Air Temperature<br>°F (°C) | Ohms |
|---|---|
| 14 (-10) | 8260-10,560 |
| 66-70 (19-21) | 2280-2720 |
| 120-124 (49-51) | 760-910 |

## TEST 14: OXYGEN SENSOR

**1)** After 50,000 miles of vehicle operation, a warning light in the dash will come on, indicating that oxygen sensor service is required. Trace wire from oxygen sensor to connector plug and disconnect. On 528e, pull off protective metal plate.

**2)** On all models, remove oxygen sensor. Using a light coat of copper paste (anti seize) applied to threads, install new sensor.

***NOTE: On all BMW models, if service light is on, always reset service light.***

**3)** Using Service Indicator Resetter (SIR 62 1 100), reset interval switch by turning ignition switch to "RUN" (DO NOT start engine). Turn off all electrical equipment. Plug SIR (62 1 100) into diagnosis socket. Push in and hold recessed Red INSPECTION button then Green light comes on. After approximately 3 seconds Red light comes on and after approximately 12 seconds Red light goes off. Release INSPECTION button, Green light should go out. Be careful to reset service indicator system properly

**4)** Check function of oxygen sensor. Disconnect plug of oxygen sensor and turn CO control screw in direction of rich mixture. Connect plug of oxygen sensor. If CO level at idle speed reads at specified value, oxygen sensor is okay.

**5)** If oxygen sensor light is on, lift out check control box and remove light for "OXYGEN SENSOR" display.

# 1988 COMPUTERIZED ENGINE CONTROLS
## BMW Motronic Emission Control System (Cont.)

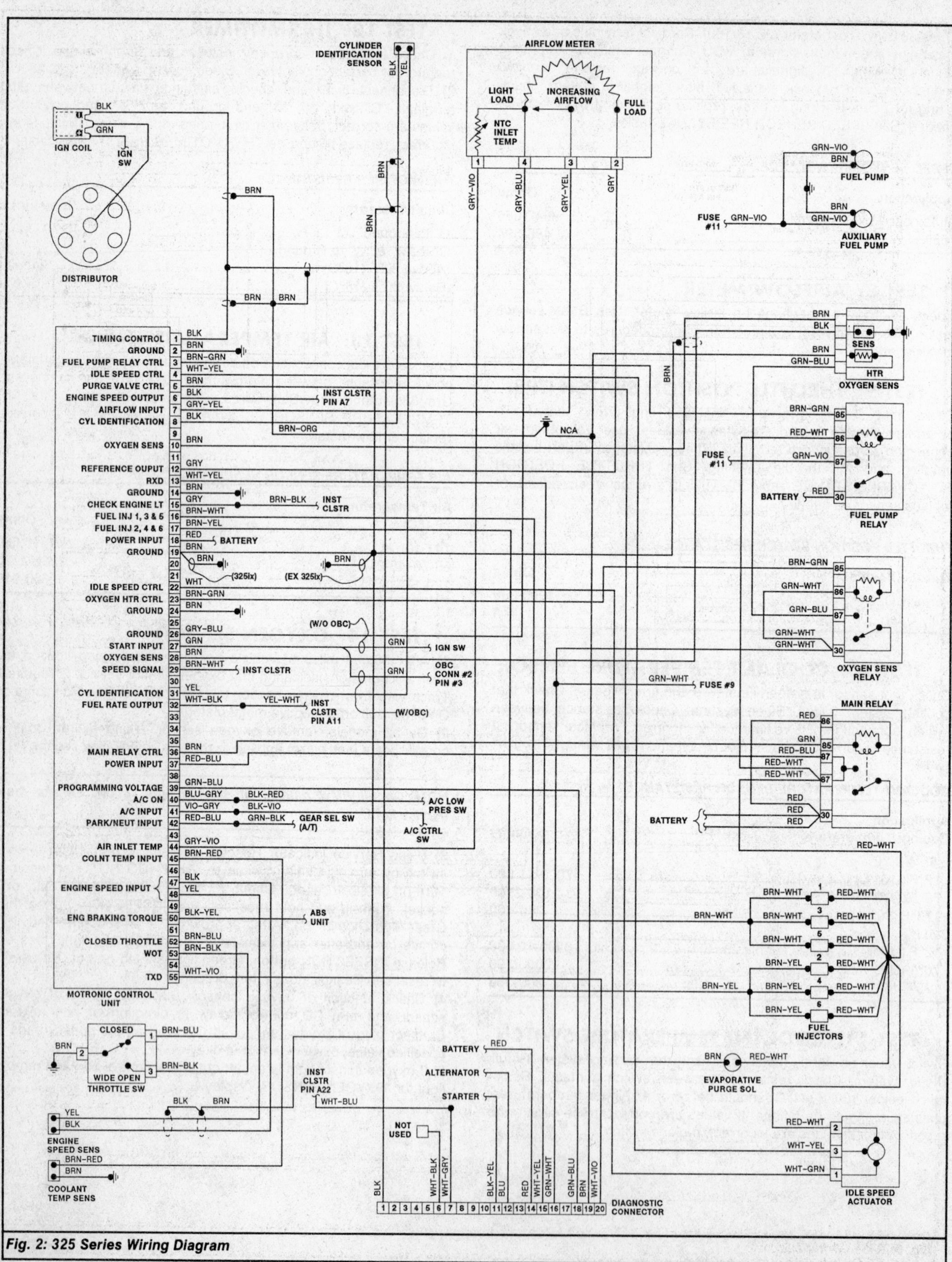
CYLINDER IDENTIFICATION SENSOR
AIRFLOW METER
LIGHT LOAD
INCREASING AIRFLOW
FULL LOAD
NTC INLET TEMP
IGN COIL
IGN SW
DISTRIBUTOR
FUEL PUMP
AUXILIARY FUEL PUMP
FUSE #11
OXYGEN SENS
SENS
HTR
TIMING CONTROL
GROUND
FUEL PUMP RELAY CTRL
IDLE SPEED CTRL
PURGE VALVE CTRL
ENGINE SPEED OUTPUT
AIRFLOW INPUT
CYL IDENTIFICATION
OXYGEN SENS
REFERENCE OUPUT
RXD
GROUND
CHECK ENGINE LT
FUEL INJ 1, 3 & 5
FUEL INJ 2, 4 & 6
POWER INPUT
GROUND
IDLE SPEED CTRL
OXYGEN HTR CTRL
GROUND
GROUND
START INPUT
OXYGEN SENS
SPEED SIGNAL
CYL IDENTIFICATION
FUEL RATE OUTPUT
MAIN RELAY CTRL
POWER INPUT
PROGRAMMING VOLTAGE
A/C ON
A/C INPUT
PARK/NEUT INPUT
AIR INLET TEMP
COLNT TEMP INPUT
ENGINE SPEED INPUT
ENG BRAKING TORQUE
CLOSED THROTTLE
WOT
TXD
MOTRONIC CONTROL UNIT
INST CLSTR PIN A7
NCA
INST CLSTR
BATTERY
(325ix)
(EX 325ix)
(W/O OBC)
IGN SW
OBC CONN #2 PIN #3
INST CLSTR
INST CLSTR PIN A11
(W/OBC)
A/C LOW PRES SW
GEAR SEL SW (A/T)
A/C CTRL SW
ABS UNIT
FUEL PUMP RELAY
BATTERY
OXYGEN SENS RELAY
FUSE #9
MAIN RELAY
BATTERY
FUEL INJECTORS
EVAPORATIVE PURGE SOL
IDLE SPEED ACTUATOR
CLOSED
WIDE OPEN
THROTTLE SW
ENGINE SPEED SENS
COOLANT TEMP SENS
INST CLSTR PIN A22
BATTERY
ALTERNATOR
STARTER
NOT USED
DIAGNOSTIC CONNECTOR

Fig. 2: 325 Series Wiring Diagram

# BMW Motronic Emission Control System (Cont.)

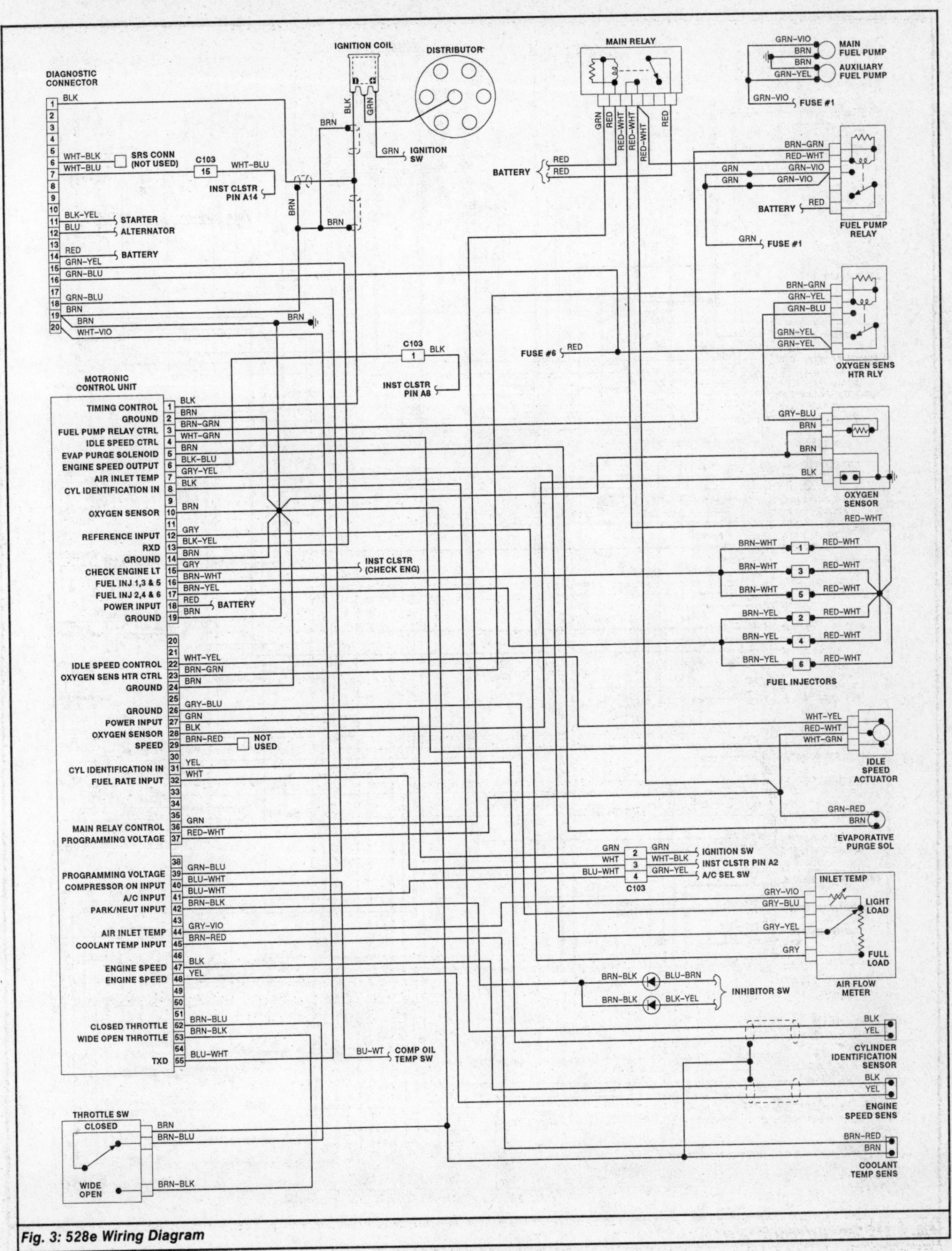
DIAGNOSTIC CONNECTOR
IGNITION COIL
DISTRIBUTOR
MAIN RELAY
MAIN FUEL PUMP
AUXILIARY FUEL PUMP
FUSE #1
SRS CONN (NOT USED)
C103
INST CLSTR PIN A14
IGNITION SW
BATTERY
STARTER
ALTERNATOR
FUEL PUMP RELAY
FUSE #6
OXYGEN SENS HTR RLY
C103
INST CLSTR PIN A8
MOTRONIC CONTROL UNIT
TIMING CONTROL
GROUND
FUEL PUMP RELAY CTRL
IDLE SPEED CTRL
EVAP PURGE SOLENOID
ENGINE SPEED OUTPUT
AIR INLET TEMP
CYL IDENTIFICATION IN
OXYGEN SENSOR
REFERENCE INPUT
RXD
GROUND
CHECK ENGINE LT
FUEL INJ 1,3 & 5
FUEL INJ 2,4 & 6
POWER INPUT
GROUND
INST CLSTR (CHECK ENG)
OXYGEN SENSOR
FUEL INJECTORS
IDLE SPEED CONTROL
OXYGEN SENS HTR CTRL
GROUND
GROUND
POWER INPUT
OXYGEN SENSOR
SPEED
NOT USED
CYL IDENTIFICATION IN
FUEL RATE INPUT
MAIN RELAY CONTROL
PROGRAMMING VOLTAGE
IDLE SPEED ACTUATOR
EVAPORATIVE PURGE SOL
IGNITION SW
INST CLSTR PIN A2
A/C SEL SW
PROGRAMMING VOLTAGE
COMPRESSOR ON INPUT
A/C INPUT
PARK/NEUT INPUT
AIR INLET TEMP
COOLANT TEMP INPUT
INLET TEMP
LIGHT LOAD
FULL LOAD
AIR FLOW METER
ENGINE SPEED
ENGINE SPEED
INHIBITOR SW
CLOSED THROTTLE
WIDE OPEN THROTTLE
TXD
COMP OIL TEMP SW
CYLINDER IDENTIFICATION SENSOR
ENGINE SPEED SENS
THROTTLE SW
CLOSED
WIDE OPEN
COOLANT TEMP SENS

*Fig. 3: 528e Wiring Diagram*

# 1988 COMPUTERIZED ENGINE CONTROLS
## BMW Motronic Emission Control System (Cont.)

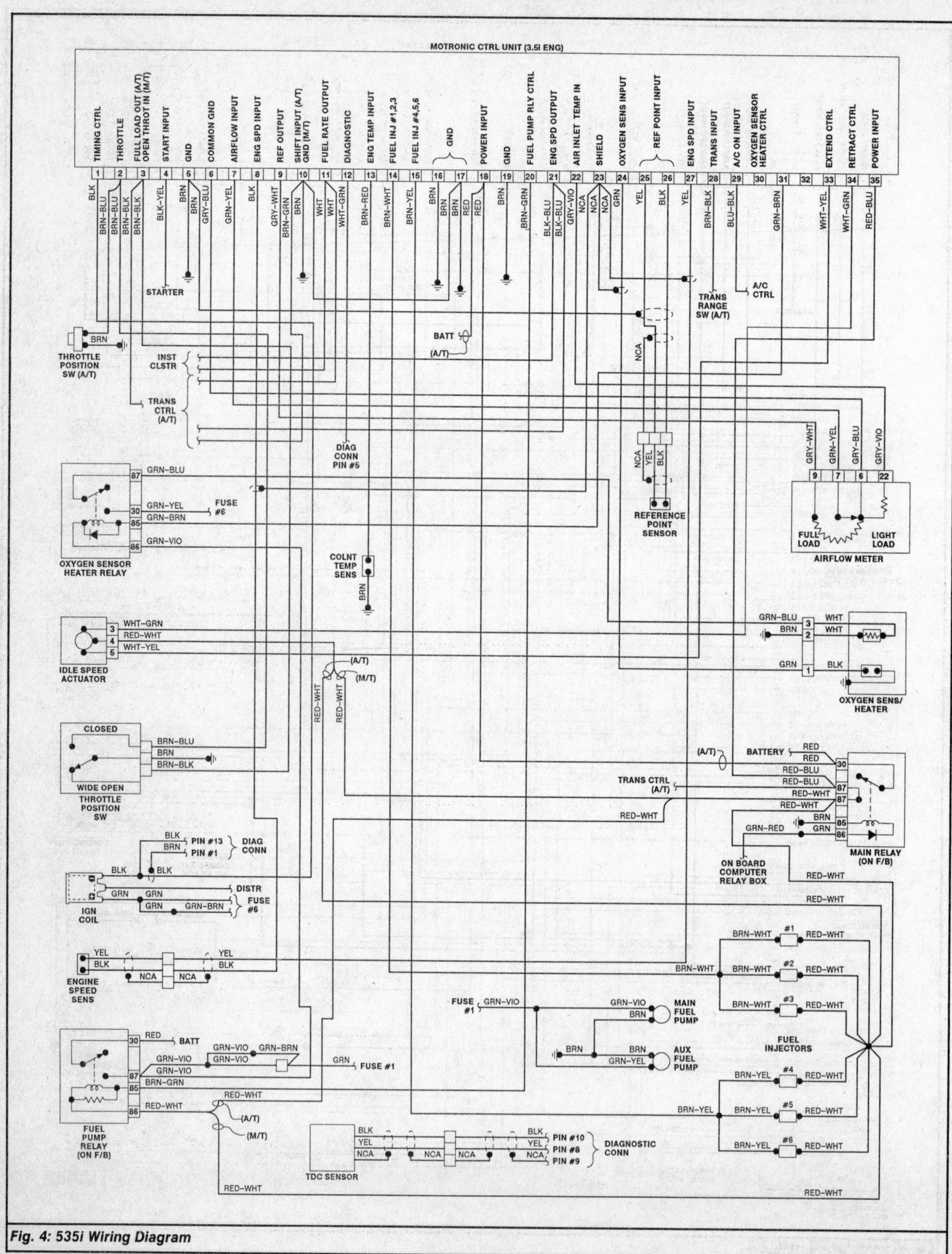

MOTRONIC CTRL UNIT (3.5i ENG)
TIMING CTRL
THROTTLE
FULL LOAD OUT (A/T) OPEN THROT IN (M/T)
START INPUT
GND
COMMON GND
AIRFLOW INPUT
ENG SPD INPUT
REF OUTPUT
SHIFT INPUT (A/T) GND (M/T)
FUEL RATE OUTPUT
DIAGNOSTIC
ENG TEMP INPUT
FUEL INJ #1,2,3
FUEL INJ #4,5,6
GND
POWER INPUT
GND
FUEL PUMP RLY CTRL
ENG SPD OUTPUT
AIR INLET TEMP IN
SHIELD
OXYGEN SENS INPUT
REF POINT INPUT
ENG SPD INPUT
TRANS INPUT
A/C ON INPUT
OXYGEN SENSOR HEATER CTRL
EXTEND CTRL
RETRACT CTRL
POWER INPUT
STARTER
THROTTLE POSITION SW (A/T)
INST CLSTR
TRANS CTRL (A/T)
BATT
DIAG CONN PIN #5
TRANS RANGE SW (A/T)
A/C CTRL
REFERENCE POINT SENSOR
FULL LOAD
LIGHT LOAD
AIRFLOW METER
OXYGEN SENSOR HEATER RELAY
FUSE #6
COLNT TEMP SENS
IDLE SPEED ACTUATOR
OXYGEN SENS/ HEATER
CLOSED
WIDE OPEN
THROTTLE POSITION SW
BATTERY
TRANS CTRL (A/T)
MAIN RELAY (ON F/B)
ON BOARD COMPUTER RELAY BOX
PIN #13
PIN #1
DIAG CONN
IGN COIL
DISTR
FUSE #6
ENGINE SPEED SENS
FUSE #1
MAIN FUEL PUMP
AUX FUEL PUMP
FUEL INJECTORS
BATT
FUSE #1
FUEL PUMP RELAY (ON F/B)
TDC SENSOR
PIN #10
PIN #8
PIN #9
DIAGNOSTIC CONN


*Fig. 4: 535i Wiring Diagram*

# 1988 COMPUTERIZED ENGINE CONTROLS
## BMW Motronic Emission Control System (Cont.)

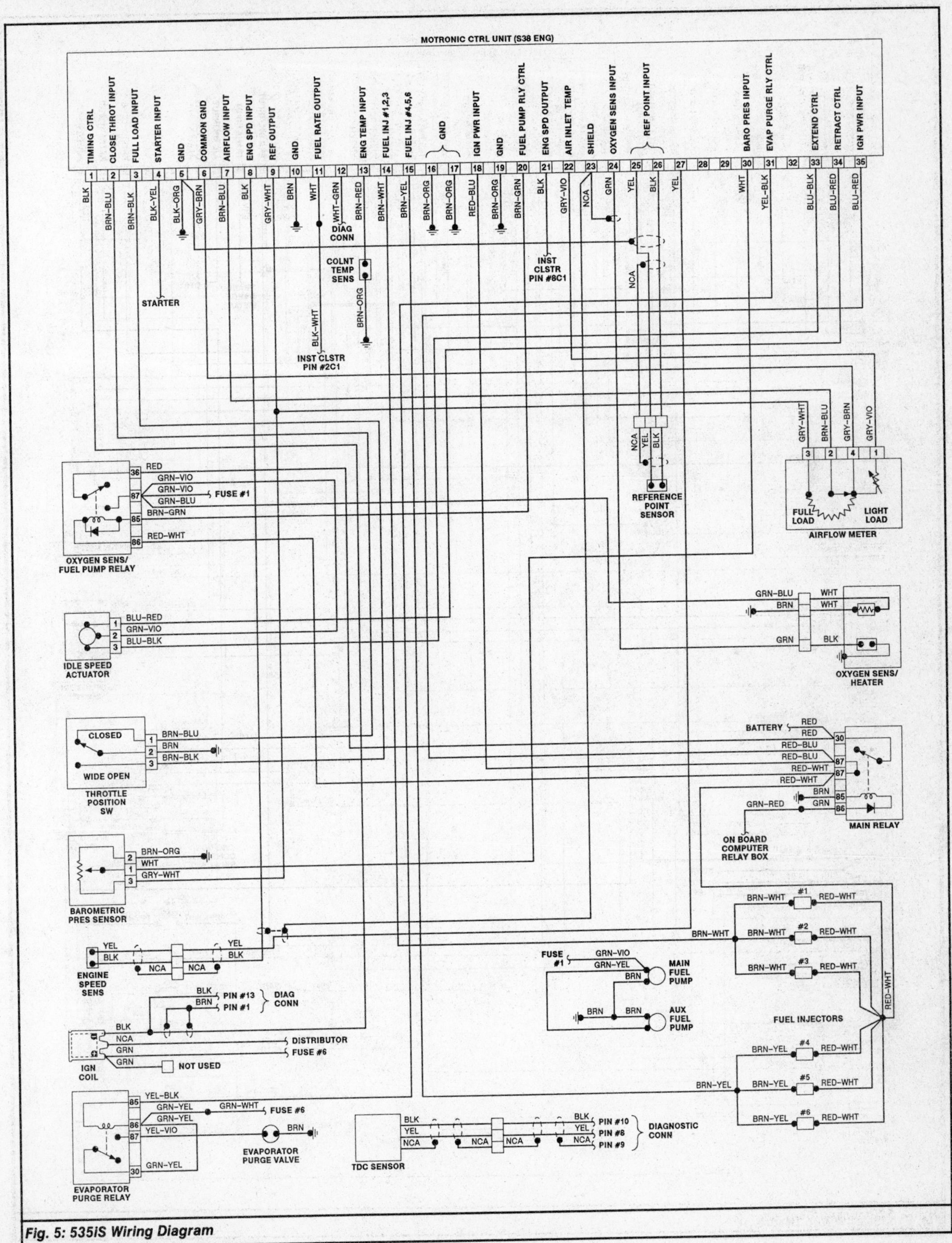

MOTRONIC CTRL UNIT (S38 ENG)
TIMING CTRL
CLOSE THROT INPUT
FULL LOAD INPUT
STARTER INPUT
GND
COMMON GND
AIRFLOW INPUT
ENG SPD INPUT
REF OUTPUT
GND
FUEL RATE OUTPUT
ENG TEMP INPUT
FUEL INJ #1,2,3
FUEL INJ #4,5,6
GND
IGN PWR INPUT
GND
FUEL PUMP RLY CTRL
ENG SPD OUTPUT
AIR INLET TEMP
SHIELD
OXYGEN SENS INPUT
REF POINT INPUT
BARO PRES INPUT
EVAP PURGE RLY CTRL
EXTEND CTRL
RETRACT CTRL
IGN PWR INPUT
DIAG CONN
COLNT TEMP SENS
INST CLSTR PIN #8C1
STARTER
INST CLSTR PIN #2C1
REFERENCE POINT SENSOR
FULL LOAD
LIGHT LOAD
AIRFLOW METER
FUSE #1
OXYGEN SENS/ FUEL PUMP RELAY
IDLE SPEED ACTUATOR
OXYGEN SENS/ HEATER
CLOSED
WIDE OPEN
THROTTLE POSITION SW
BATTERY
MAIN RELAY
ON BOARD COMPUTER RELAY BOX
BAROMETRIC PRES SENSOR
ENGINE SPEED SENS
MAIN FUEL PUMP
AUX FUEL PUMP
FUEL INJECTORS
PIN #13
PIN #1
DIAG CONN
DISTRIBUTOR
FUSE #6
NOT USED
IGN COIL
EVAPORATOR PURGE VALVE
EVAPORATOR PURGE RELAY
TDC SENSOR
PIN #10
PIN #8
PIN #9
DIAGNOSTIC CONN


*Fig. 5: 535IS Wiring Diagram*

# BMW Motronic Emission Control System (Cont.)

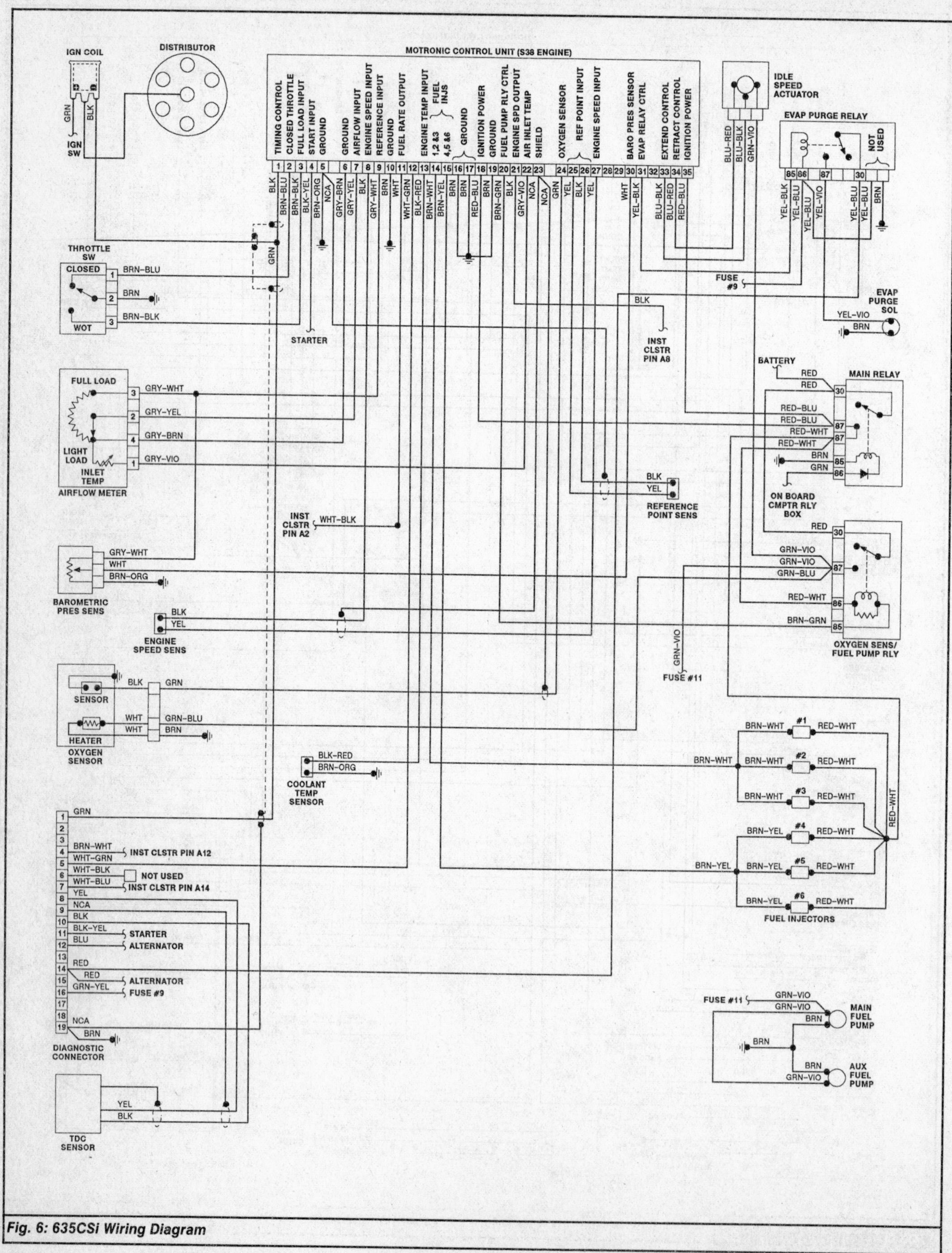

Fig. 6: 635CSi Wiring Diagram

# 1988 COMPUTERIZED ENGINE CONTROLS
## BMW Motronic Emission Control System (Cont.)

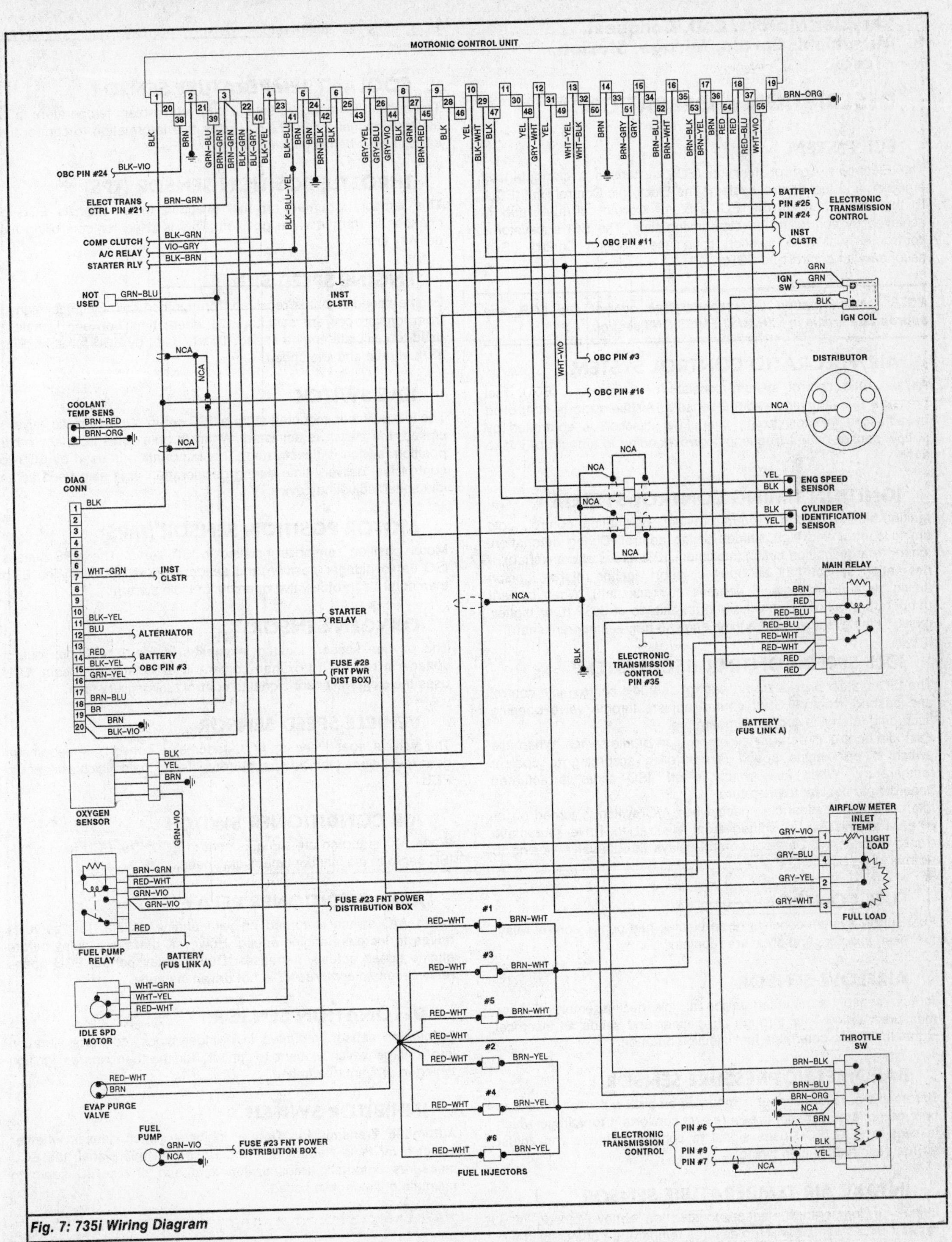
MOTRONIC CONTROL UNIT
OBC PIN #24
ELECT TRANS CTRL PIN #21
COMP CLUTCH
A/C RELAY
STARTER RLY
NOT USED
INST CLSTR
COOLANT TEMP SENS
DIAG CONN
ALTERNATOR
BATTERY
OBC PIN #3
STARTER RELAY
FUSE #28 (FNT PWR DIST BOX)
OXYGEN SENSOR
FUEL PUMP RELAY
BATTERY (FUS LINK A)
FUSE #23 FNT POWER DISTRIBUTION BOX
IDLE SPD MOTOR
EVAP PURGE VALVE
FUEL PUMP
FUEL INJECTORS
BATTERY
PIN #25
PIN #24
ELECTRONIC TRANSMISSION CONTROL
INST CLSTR
OBC PIN #11
IGN SW
IGN COIL
OBC PIN #3
OBC PIN #16
DISTRIBUTOR
ENG SPEED SENSOR
CYLINDER IDENTIFICATION SENSOR
MAIN RELAY
ELECTRONIC TRANSMISSION CONTROL PIN #35
BATTERY (FUS LINK A)
AIRFLOW METER
INLET TEMP
LIGHT LOAD
FULL LOAD
THROTTLE SW
ELECTRONIC TRANSMISSION CONTROL
PIN #6
PIN #9
PIN #7
NCA

*Fig. 7: 735i Wiring Diagram*

# 1988 COMPUTERIZED ENGINE CONTROLS
# Chrysler & Mitsubishi ECI System

**Chrysler Motors: Colt, Conquest**
**Mitsubishi: Cordia, Mirage, Starion, Tredia**

## DESCRIPTION & OPERATION

### ECI SYSTEM

The Electronic Control Injection (ECI) system is a computerized emission and fuel control system. The Electronic Control Unit (ECU) is the foundation of the ECI system. Correct air/fuel ratio is achieved by controlling injector driving time. The ECI subsystems control air/fuel ratio, ignition timing, Idle Speed Control (ISC), secondary air control and EGR.

***NOTE:** For information on secondary air control and EGR, see appropriate article in EXHAUST EMISSIONS section.*

### AIR/FUEL RATIO CONTROL SYSTEM

Air/fuel ratio control system consists of 2 injectors, ECU, fuel pressure regulator and various sensors. Air/fuel ratio is controlled by adjusting injector driving time. Fuel injection is controlled by airflow sensor output frequency corresponding to amount of intake air.

### IGNITION TIMING CONTROL SYSTEM

Ignition timing control system provides detonation control, cold timing control and high altitude timing control. During detonation, ignitor retards ignition timing (maximum 12 degrees at crankshaft). If detonation sensor has an open or short, ignitor retards ignition timing by a fixed angle (8 degrees at crankshaft). When coolant temperature is low or vehicle is at an altitude of 3937 ft. or higher, ignition timing is advanced a fixed angle (5 degrees at crankshaft).

### IDLE SPEED CONTROL (ISC) SYSTEM

The ISC system provides start control, fast idle control, idle control and dashpot control. Start control adjusts throttle valve opening according to engine coolant temperature.

Fast idle control is determined by position of idle switch. When idle switch is on, engine speed is controlled according to coolant temperature. When idle switch is off, ISC servo is actuated according to coolant temperature.

Idle control increases idle speed when A/C switch is turned on or when transmission is shifted from Neutral to Drive (automatic transmission only). Dashpot control delays throttle valve closing to normal idling position.

### FUEL CONTROL

Fuel supply system consists of an electric fuel pump, control relay, fuel filter, injectors and pressure regulator.

### AIRFLOW SENSOR

Airflow sensor is mounted inside air cleaner assembly. Sensor measures airflow rate through air cleaner and sends an electrical signal to ECU to determine fuel injection duration.

### BAROMETRIC PRESSURE SENSOR

Barometric pressure sensor is mounted on airflow sensor. It senses barometric (atmospheric) pressure and converts it to voltage which is sent to ECU. ECU uses signal to compute altitude and adjust air/fuel ratio and ignition timing.

### INTAKE AIR TEMPERATURE SENSOR

Intake air temperature sensor, located on airflow sensor, is a resistor-based sensor which measures temperature of incoming air. ECU uses air temperature sensor information to control fuel delivery.

### COOLANT TEMPERATURE SENSOR

The coolant temperature sensor converts coolant temperature to an electrical signal for ECU. ECU uses this information to control fuel enrichment when engine is cold.

### THROTTLE POSITION SENSOR (TPS)

This sensor, mounted on fuel injection mixer, signals ECU of changes in throttle valve position. This is used for controlling fuel delivery time.

### ENGINE SPEED SIGNAL

Engine speed signal is received from ignition coil. Electrical signals from ignition coil are sent to ECU where time between signals is used to calculate engine speed. This is used by ECU for controlling air/fuel ratio and idle speed.

### IDLE SWITCH

The idle switch is mounted at tip of ISC servo. When throttle valve is closed, the switch is activated. When throttle valve is at any other position, switch is deactivated. This information is used by ECU to control fuel delivery time during deceleration. It is also used as an idle speed adjusting device.

### MOTOR POSITION SENSOR (MPS)

Motor position sensor is installed in ISC servo. The MPS senses ISC servo plunger position and sends a signal to ECU. The ECU then controls throttle valve opening and idle speed.

### OXYGEN SENSOR

The oxygen sensor, located in exhaust system, produces output voltage in relation to oxygen content in exhaust gas stream. ECU uses the oxygen sensor signal to control fuel delivery time.

### VEHICLE SPEED SENSOR

The vehicle speed sensor in speedometer converts speedometer gear revolutions (vehicle speed) into pulse signals which are sent to ECU.

### AIR CONDITIONER SWITCH

When A/C is turned on, signal is sent to ECU. The ECU then drives ISC servo to maintain optimum idle speed.

### AIR CONDITIONER RELAY

When A/C switch is turned on with engine at idle, ISC servo is driven to increase engine speed. However, there is a delay before engine speed actually increases. During delay period, ECU opens relay circuit so compressor is not driven instantly.

### DETONATION SENSOR

Detonation sensor, mounted in cylinder block, converts vibration into voltage which is sent to ignitor. Ignitor then retards ignition timing to prevent detonation.

### INHIBITOR SWITCH

**Automatic Transmission Only** – Inhibitor switch senses whether select lever is in Neutral or Park. Based on this signal, the ECU measures automatic transmission load and drives ISC servo to maintain optimum idle speed.

# 1988 COMPUTERIZED ENGINE CONTROLS
# Chrysler & Mitsubishi ECI System (Cont.)

## COLD MIXTURE HEATER

**Colt & Mirage** – Cold mixture heater is a Positive Temperature Coefficient (PTC) heater installed on intake manifold. When engine coolant temperature is below 158°F (70°C), ECU energizes cold mixture heater relay to operate PTC heater. Fuel is heated and atomized before entering combustion chamber.

## TESTING & DIAGNOSIS

### PRETESTING INSPECTION

Before testing ECI components, perform diagnosis and basic engine checks (ignition system malfunctions, incorrect engine adjustments, etc.). Perform ECI diagnosis only after conventional components have been inspected.

### DIAGNOSIS

The diagnostic system, which monitors all input signals from each sensor, is an integral part of the ECU. If an abnormal input signal occurs, that item is memorized by the ECU. There are 6 diagnostic codes (7 for Cordia and Tredia) which can be confirmed using a voltmeter. See DIAGNOSTIC CODES table.

If 2 or more systems are non-functional, they are indicated in order of increasing code number. Indication is made by deflection of voltmeter pointer. A constant 12 volts indicates system is normal. If system is abnormal, voltmeter will alternate between 0-12 volts every .4 seconds to display codes. After indication of zero volts for 2 seconds, the higher code is indicated. *See Fig. 1.*

***NOTE: ECU abnormal diagnostic memory is kept by direct power from battery. Memory is not erased by turning ignition off, but will be erased if battery or ECU is disconnected.***

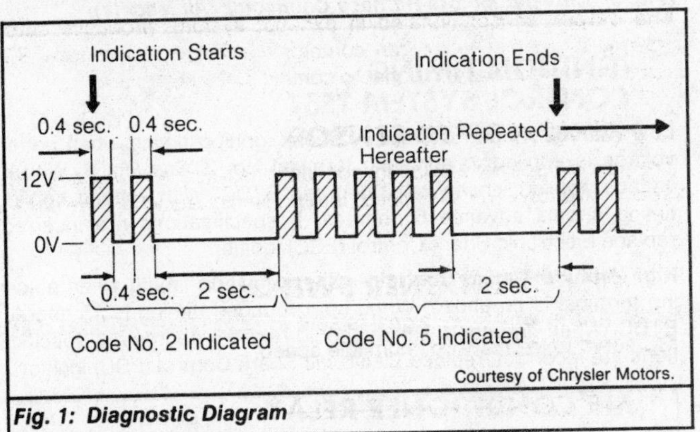

Indication Starts
Indication Ends
0.4 sec.
0.4 sec.
Indication Repeated
Hereafter
12V
0V
0.4 sec.
2 sec.
2 sec.
Code No. 2 Indicated
Code No. 5 Indicated
Courtesy of Chrysler Motors.


***Fig. 1: Diagnostic Diagram***

***DIAGNOSTIC CODES***

| Code Number | Diagnostic Item |
|---|---|
| 1 | Oxygen Sensor & Computer |
| 2 | Engine Speed Sensor |
| 3 | Airflow Sensor |
| 4 | [1] Pressure Sensor |
| 5 | Throttle Position Sensor |
| 6 | ISC Motor Position Sensor |
| 7 | Coolant Temperature Sensor |

[1] – Cordia/Tredia only.

## SELF-DIAGNOSTIC TEST

**1)** Turn ignition switch to "OFF" position. Connect voltmeter to self-diagnostic output harness connector located in glove box (Conquest and Starion) or engine compartment (all others). *See Fig. 2.*

**2)** Turn ignition switch to "ON" position and ECU will display code(s). Record any abnormal diagnostic codes and perform necessary component repairs. After checking and repair, turn ignition off and disconnect negative battery cable for 15 seconds or more to erase ECU memory.

***NOTE: Oxygen sensor memory is erased when ignition is turned off. To diagnose oxygen sensor, drive vehicle a good distance and keep engine running.***

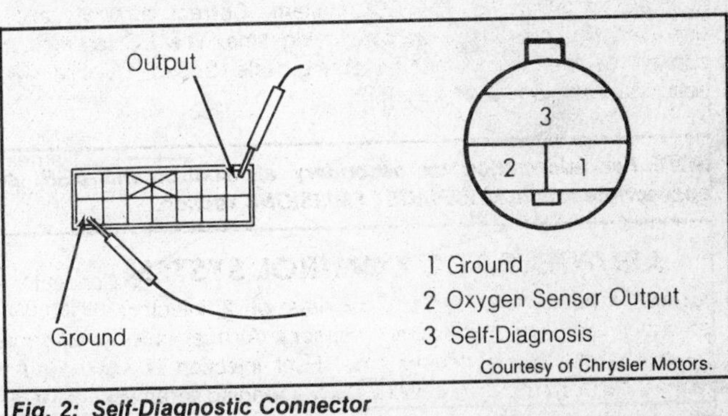

Output
Ground
3
2
1
1 Ground
2 Oxygen Sensor Output
3 Self-Diagnosis
Courtesy of Chrysler Motors.


***Fig. 2: Self-Diagnostic Connector***

**Diagnostic Code 1 (Oxygen Sensor)** – If oxygen sensor signal does not change for 20 seconds or more in feedback range, check wiring harness and connector, oxygen sensor and ECU.

**Diagnostic Code 2 (Engine Speed Sensor)** – While cranking engine, if input of ignition signal is not applied to computer for 3 seconds or more, check wiring harness and connector, ignitor and ECU.

**Diagnostic Code 3 (Airflow Sensor)** – On all models, if airflow sensor maximum output is 10 cycles per second while engine is idling, check wiring harness and connector, airflow sensor and ECU. On Cordia and Tredia models, if engine stalls and output rises to 100 cycles per second, check wiring harness and connector, airflow sensor and ECU.

**Diagnostic Code 4 (Pressure Sensor)** – If pressure sensor output is 4.5 volts or more, or .2 volt or less, check wiring harness and connector, pressure sensor and ECU.

**Diagnostic Code 5 (Throttle Position Sensor)** – If throttle position sensor output is .2 volt or less, or is 4 volts or higher for one second or more while engine is idling (idle switch on), check wiring harness and connector, TPS and ECU.

**Diagnostic Code 6 (ISC Motor Position Sensor)** – On Cordia and Tredia models, if throttle position sensor output is .4 volt with "L" switch off, check wiring harness and connector, ISC servo and ECU. On all others, if motor position sensor output is 4.8 volts or more, or .2 volt or less, check wiring harness and connector, MPS and ECU.

**Diagnostic Code 7 (Coolant Temperature Sensor)** – If coolant temperature sensor output is .1 volt or less, or 4.5 volts or more, check wiring harness and connector, coolant temperature sensor and ECU.

***NOTE: Perform ECI inspection test only after all steps of preceding Self-Diagnostic test are completed.***

## ECI INSPECTION TEST

***NOTE: Before disconnecting battery, ensure ignition is off. Disconnecting battery with ignition on or engine running could damage computer system.***

# 1988 COMPUTERIZED ENGINE CONTROLS
# Chrysler & Mitsubishi ECI System (Cont.)

**Cordia & Tredia – 1)** Turn ignition switch to "OFF" position and remove cover from ECU. Remove body side harness connectors "A" (17 pins) and "B" (13 pins) from ECU. On ECI Checker (MD998406), set check switch to "OFF" position and select switch to "A" position. Connect ECI checker connector by using ECI Harness Connector (MD998425) to ECU and body harness connectors. *See Fig. 3.* Place ECI checker on front passenger seat.

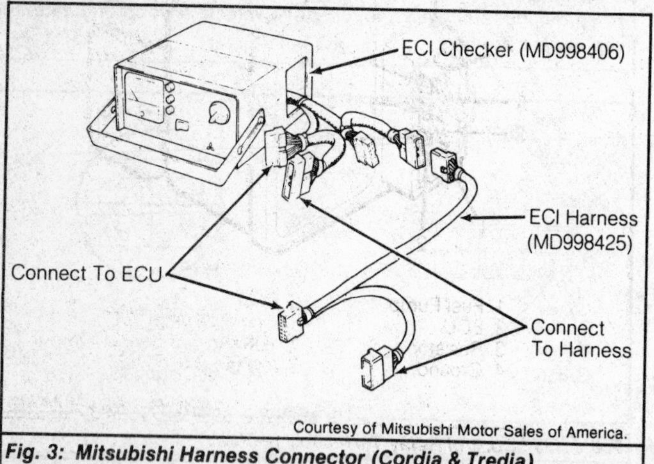
ECI Checker (MD998406)
ECI Harness
(MD998425)
Connect To ECU
Connect
To Harness

Courtesy of Mitsubishi Motor Sales of America.

***Fig. 3: Mitsubishi Harness Connector (Cordia & Tredia)***

**2)** Check output monitor operating condition (on or off) by switching ignition switch from "OFF" to "ON" position. Monitor operating condition should be: Airflow Sensor - ON, Injector Pulse - OFF, $O_2$ Sensor - OFF. Perform checks according to appropriate ECI SYSTEM OUTPUT SIGNAL CHARTS in this article.
**3)** If checker reading varies from specifications, check corresponding sensor and related wiring. After component repair or replacement, recheck to ensure system performance.
**4)** Airflow sensor and injector pulse may also be inspected by output monitors. Set select switch to "B". Normal operation is: Airflow Sensor and Injector are always flashing with check switch at "1" through "12". Oxygen sensor is flashing at closed loop zone. The flashes will be so quick that light will appear to be continuously on.
**5)** Set check switch of ECI checker to "OFF" position. Set ignition switch to "OFF" position. Carefully separate connectors of ECI checker from ECU and body side harness connectors. Connect body side harness connector to ECU. Install ECU cover.

**All Others (Output Signal Chart Step 1) – 1)** Turn ignition switch to "LOCK" position. Remove large and small harness connector from ECU. On ECI Checker (MD998406 for Mitsubishi models, MD998451 for Chrysler Motors models), set check switch to "OFF" position and select switch to "A" position.

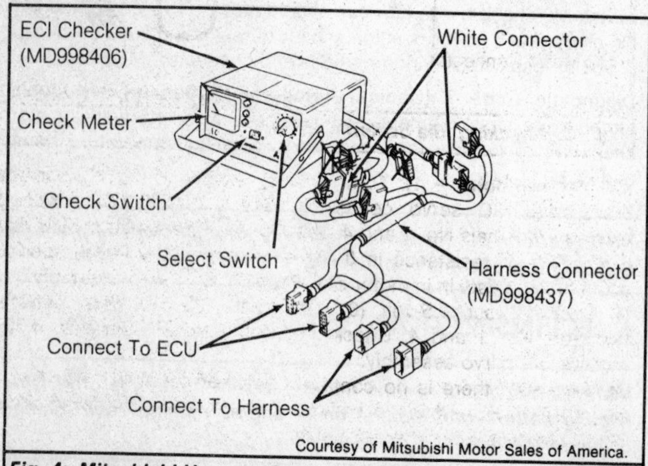
ECI Checker
(MD998406)
White Connector
Check Meter
Check Switch
Select Switch
Harness Connector
(MD998437)
Connect To ECU
Connect To Harness

Courtesy of Mitsubishi Motor Sales of America.

***Fig. 4: Mitsubishi Harness Connector (Except Cordia & Tredia)***

**2)** Connect White connectors (labeled "CHECKER") of Harness Connector (MD998437 for Mitsubishi models, MD998452 for Chrysler Motors models) to ECI checker. Connect harness connector to ECU and body side harness connectors. *See Figs. 4 and 5.* Perform checks according to appropriate ECI SYSTEM OUTPUT SIGNAL CHART-STEP 1.

**All Others (Output Signal Chart Step 2) – 1)** Turn ignition switch to "LOCK" position. On ECI checker, set check switch to "OFF" position. Disconnect White connectors (labeled "CHECKER") of harness connector from ECI checker. Connect Green connectors to ECI checker. Perform checks according to appropriate ECI SYSTEM OUTPUT SIGNAL CHART – STEP 2 at end of article.
**2)** If checker reading varies from specification, check corresponding sensor and related electrical wiring. After component repair or replacement, recheck to confirm system performance.
**3)** Set check switch of ECI checker to "OFF" position. Set ignition switch to "LOCK" position. Carefully separate connectors of ECI checker from ECU and body side harness connectors. Connect body side harness connector to ECU.

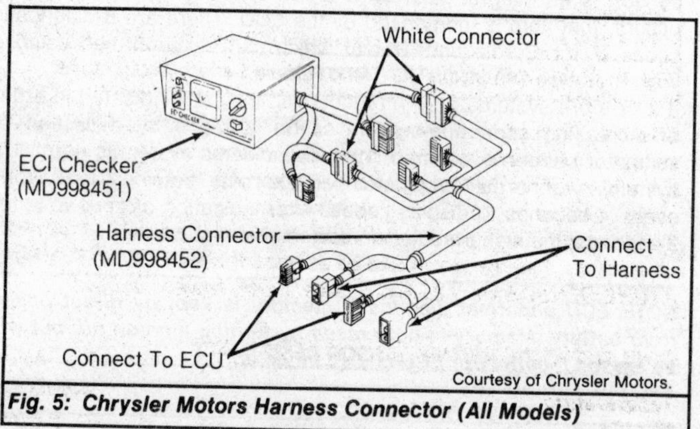
White Connector
ECI Checker
(MD998451)
Harness Connector
(MD998452)
Connect
To Harness
Connect To ECU

Courtesy of Chrysler Motors.

***Fig. 5: Chrysler Motors Harness Connector (All Models)***

## IGNITION TIMING CONTROL SYSTEM TEST

**Low Altitude Timing Control –** Check ignition timing when battery voltage is applied to adjusting terminal No. 2. *See Fig. 6.* With no voltage applied, timing is 10 degrees BTDC. With voltage applied, timing should advance 5 degrees. If specifications are incorrect, replace Electronic Spark Control (ESC) ignitier.

**High Altitude Timing Control –** Check ignition timing when adjusting terminal is grounded. When not grounded, timing is 15 degrees BTDC. When grounded, timing should retard 5 degrees. If specifications are incorrect, replace Electronic Spark Control (ESC) ignitior.

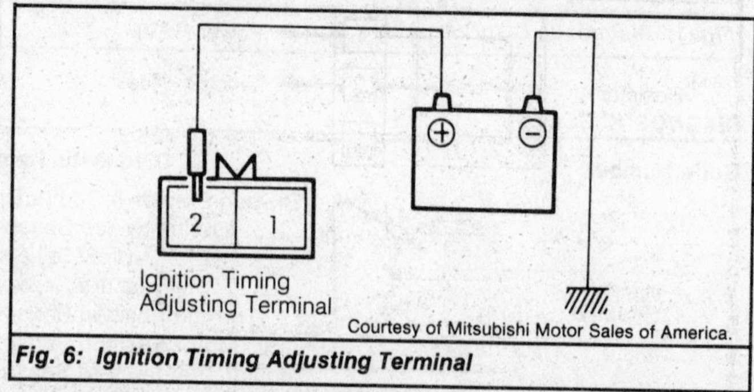
2
1
Ignition Timing
Adjusting Terminal

Courtesy of Mitsubishi Motor Sales of America.

***Fig. 6: Ignition Timing Adjusting Terminal***

## COMPONENT TESTING & INSPECTION

**Intake Air Temperature Sensor –** Disconnect airflow sensor connector. Check intake air temperature sensor by measuring resistance at terminals 2 and 4. Replace airflow sensor assembly if readings are not to specification. *See Fig. 7.*

# 1988 COMPUTERIZED ENGINE CONTROLS
# Chrysler & Mitsubishi ECI System (Cont.)

**INTAKE AIR TEMPERATURE SENSOR RESISTANCE**

| Temperature °F (°C) | Resistance (Ohms) |
|---|---|
| 32 (0) | 6000 |
| 68 (20) | 2650-2700 |
| 176 (80) | 400 |

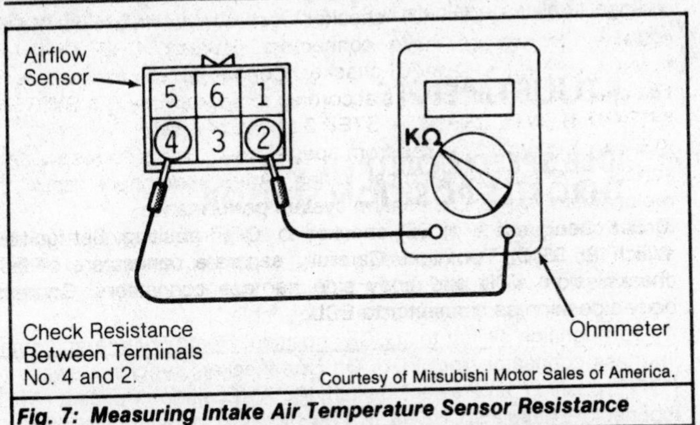
Airflow Sensor
5 6 1
4 3 2
KΩ
Check Resistance Between Terminals No. 4 and 2.
Ohmmeter
Courtesy of Mitsubishi Motor Sales of America.

*Fig. 7: Measuring Intake Air Temperature Sensor Resistance*

**Coolant Temperature Sensor – 1)** Remove coolant temperature sensor from intake manifold and place end of sensor in water. Do not allow sensor to touch container. Terminal connector portion of sensor should be .12" (3 mm) above water.

**2)** Gradually heat water and read resistance values at terminal connectors. Resistance should be as shown in COOLANT TEMPERATURE SENSOR RESISTANCE table. If not, replace sensor.

**COOLANT TEMPERATURE SENSOR RESISTANCE**

| Temperature °F (°C) | Resistance (Ohms) |
|---|---|
| 32 (0) | 5900 |
| 68 (20) | 2450 |
| 104 (40) | 1100 |
| 176 (80) | 300 |

**Resistor – 1)** Disconnect electrical connector from resistor. Connect Harness (MD998459) to resistor side of disconnected connector. Measure resistance across terminals No. 1 and 2, then 1 and 3. *See Fig. 8*. If resistance is between 5.5 and 6.5 ohms, resistor is good.

**2)** If resistance measures zero, or is abnormally large, resistor has short or open circuit. Replace resistor.

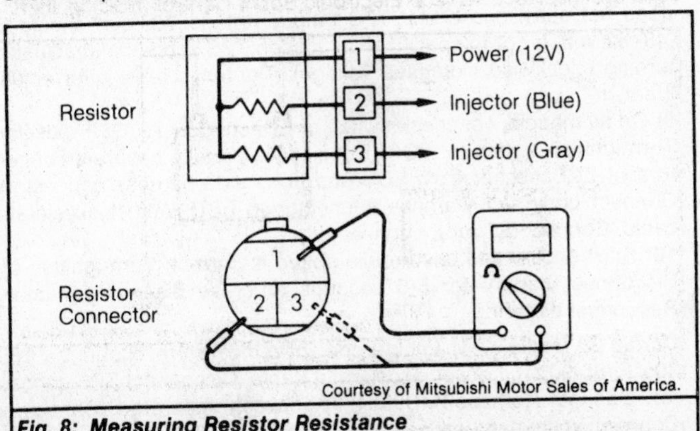
Resistor
1 Power (12V)
2 Injector (Blue)
3 Injector (Gray)
Resistor Connector
1
2 3
Ω
Courtesy of Mitsubishi Motor Sales of America.

*Fig. 8: Measuring Resistor Resistance*

**EFI Control Relay – 1)** Disconnect electrical harness and test continuity between terminals No. 1 and 7, then 3 and 7. *See Fig. 9*. If there is no continuity, relay is good. If continuity is measured, replace control relay.

**2)** Apply 12 volts across terminals No. 8 (positive) and 4 (negative) while testing continuity between terminals No. 3 and 7. If continuity exists, relay is good. If not, replace relay.

**3)** Apply 12 volts across terminals No. 6 (positive) and 4 (negative) while testing continuity between terminals No. 1 and 7. If continuity exists, relay is good. If not, replace relay.

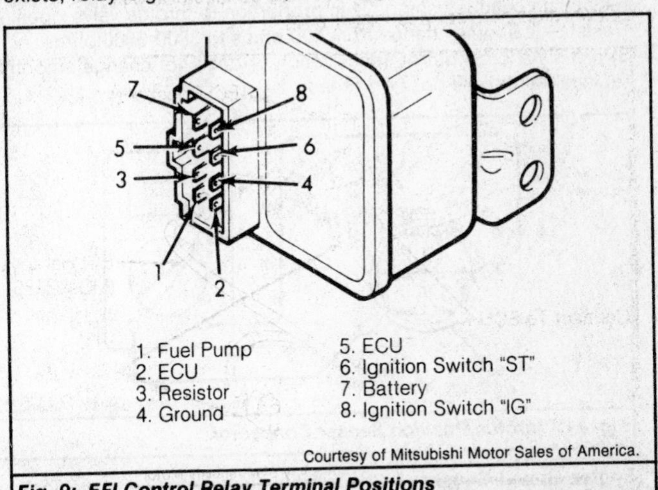
7
8
5
6
3
4
1
2
1. Fuel Pump
2. ECU
3. Resistor
4. Ground
5. ECU
6. Ignition Switch "ST"
7. Battery
8. Ignition Switch "IG"
Courtesy of Mitsubishi Motor Sales of America.

*Fig. 9: EFI Control Relay Terminal Positions*

**Injector Coil –** Turn ignition switch to "OFF" position. Disconnect connectors from injectors and check continuity. Resistance should be 2-3 ohms. If resistance measures zero, or is abnormally large, there is a short or open circuit in the coil. Replace injector.

**Idle Switch – 1)** Turn ignition switch to "OFF" position. Disconnect ISC servo connector. Check for continuity between terminal No. 2 and injection mixer body. *See Fig. 10*.

**2)** If continuity exists when throttle valve is placed in idle position and NO continuity exists when throttle valve is open (so that lever leaves idle switch), switch is good.

**3)** If continuity exists when throttle valve is in both positions, contacts are bound together. If no continuity exists when throttle valve is in both positions, grounding is defective. Replace ISC servo assembly.

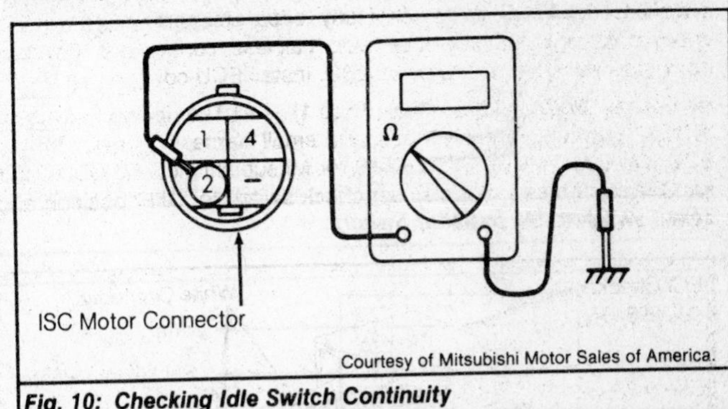
1 4
2 –
Ω
ISC Motor Connector
Courtesy of Mitsubishi Motor Sales of America.

*Fig. 10: Checking Idle Switch Continuity*

**ISC Servo Motor – 1)** Turn ignition switch to "OFF" position. Disconnect ISC servo connector. Check motor coil continuity between terminals No. 1 and 4. *See Fig. 10*. Resistance should read 5-11 ohms. If resistance is 0 ohms or abnormally large, open or short circuit exists in in motor coil. Replace ISC servo assembly.

**2)** Connect four 1.5-volt (6 volts total) DC dry cells between terminals No. 1 and 4. Check that servo motor operates. If not, replace ISC servo assembly.

**3)** Make sure there is no continuity between terminals No. 1 or 4 and injection mixer body. If continuity exists, there is a short circuit in coil. Replace ISC servo assembly.

**Throttle Position Sensor – 1)** Turn ignition switch to "OFF" position. Disconnect Throttle Position Sensor (TPS) connector. Check resistance across terminals No. 1 and 3. *See Fig. 11.* Resistance should be 3500-6500 ohms.
**2)** Check resistance across terminals No. 1 and 2. Operate throttle valve slowly from idle position to full open position. Check that resistance changes smoothly in proportion to throttle valve opening. Resistance should change from 500 ohms to 3500-6500 ohms.
**3)** If resistance is out of specification or does not change smoothly, replace the throttle position sensor.

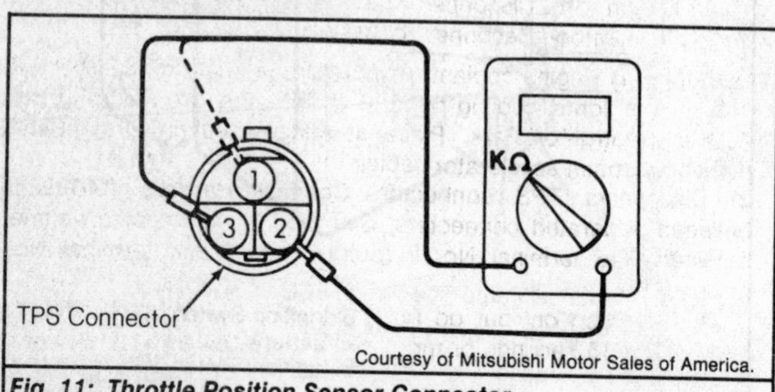
KΩ
1
3
2
TPS Connector
Courtesy of Mitsubishi Motor Sales of America.

***Fig. 11: Throttle Position Sensor Connector***

**Engine Speed Sensor** – Check for continuity between ignition coil terminal and appropriate ECU terminal. See appropriate OUTPUT SIGNAL CHART at end of article. If continuity exists, sensor is functioning.

**Oxygen Sensor** – Warm engine until coolant temperature is 185-205°F (85-95°C). Remove oxygen sensor connector and connect voltmeter. With engine above 1300 RPM, measure output voltage. Voltage should be approximately one volt. If not, replace oxygen sensor.

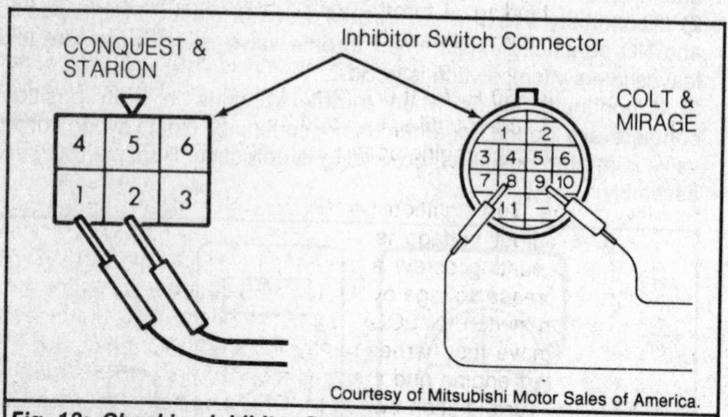
CONQUEST & STARION
Inhibitor Switch Connector
COLT & MIRAGE
4 5 6
1 2 3
1 2
3 4 5 6
7 8 9 10
11 –
Courtesy of Mitsubishi Motor Sales of America.

***Fig. 12: Checking Inhibitor Switch***

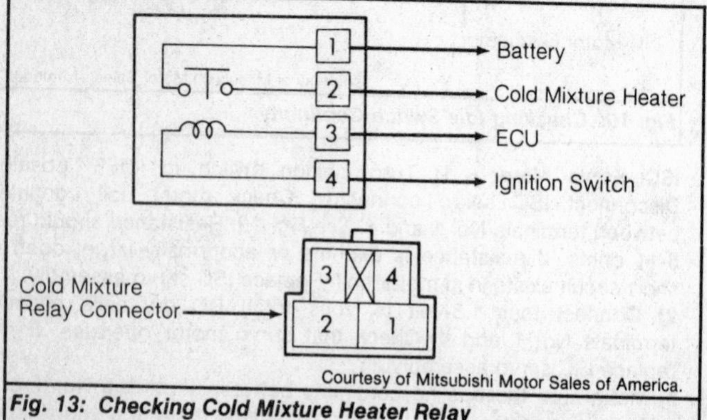
1 Battery
2 Cold Mixture Heater
3 ECU
4 Ignition Switch
Cold Mixture Relay Connector
3 4
2 1
Courtesy of Mitsubishi Motor Sales of America.

***Fig. 13: Checking Cold Mixture Heater Relay***

**Inhibitor Switch (Automatic Transmission Only)** – Disconnect inhibitor switch connector. Check for continuity between terminals No. 1 and 2 (Conquest and Starion) or No. 8 and 9 (Colt and Mirage) while operating select lever. *See Fig. 12.* Continuity should exist with lever in Park or Neutral. There should be no continuity when in other gears. If result is otherwise, adjust inhibitor switch.

**Cold Mixture Heater Relay** – Remove cold mixture heater relay. With battery voltage applied to terminals No. 3 and 4, there should be no continuity between terminals No. 1 and 2. With no battery voltage applied, terminals No. 1 and 2 should have continuity. *See Fig. 13.*

## ADJUSTMENTS

### IDLE SPEED CONTROL & THROTTLE POSITION SENSOR

**Colt & Conquest – 1)** Engine coolant temperature should be 185-205°F (85-95°C). Turn lights, cooling fan and accessories off. Place transmission in Neutral or Park. Place steering wheel in straight-ahead position and loosen accelerator cable.
**2)** Turn ignition switch to "LOCK" position. Remove large and small harness connector from ECU. On ECI checker, set check switch to "OFF" position and select switch to "A" position. Connect White connectors (labeled "CHECKER") of Harness Connector (MD998452) to ECI checker. Connect harness connector to ECU and body side harness connectors.
**3)** Connect voltmeter to terminals of ECI checker marked "EXTENSION". Set switch on ECI checker from "CHECK METER" to "EXTENSION" position. Set check switch to "6" position (Colt) or "7" position (Conquest) and select switch to "A" position.
**4)** Turn ignition on (do not start engine) and hold 15 seconds or more. This will set ISC motor at idle position. Turn ignition switch to "LOCK" position. Disconnect ISC servo motor connector. Put ISC motor in idle position.
**5)** Open throttle valve by hand 2-3 times and allow it to return with a snap each time. Loosen fixed servo adjusting screw. *See Fig. 14.* Start engine and run at idle. Check engine speed and motor position sensor output voltage. Engine speed should be 700 RPM (Colt) or 850 RPM (Conquest). Output voltage should be .9 volts. If not to specification, adjust using ISC adjusting screw. *See Fig. 14.*
**6)** Tighten fixed servo adjusting screw until RPM increases. Loosen screw until RPM ceases to drop, then tighten screw 1/2 turn (Colt) or one turn (Conquest).
**7)** Stop engine. On Colt models, turn ignition on (engine does not start) and check TPS output voltage. Voltage should be .48-.52 volt. If not to specification, loosen TPS screws and adjust by turning (clockwise increases voltage). Tighten screws after adjustment.
**8)** On Conquest models, set select switch of ECI checker to "A" position and check switch to "6" position. Turn ignition on (engine does not start) and check TPS output voltage. Voltage should be .48-.52 volt. If not to specification, loosen TPS screws and adjust by turning (clockwise increases voltage). Tighten screws after adjustment.
**9)** On all models, set check switch of ECI checker to "OFF" position. Turn ignition switch to "LOCK" position. Carefully separate connectors of ECI checker from ECU and body side harness connectors. Connect body side harness connector to ECU. Adjust accelerator cable. Connect ISC motor connector.
**10)** Start engine and ensure idle speed is correct. Turn ignition off. Disconnect battery for 5-6 seconds to erase diagnosis memory. Reconnect battery.

**Cordia & Tredia – 1)** Engine coolant temperature should be 185-205°F (85-90°C). Loosen accelerator cable. Disconnect TPS connector. Connect Harness (MD998459) between separated connectors. Connect voltmeter between terminals No. 2 (Blue: Output) and 1 (Black: Ground) of TPS connector.
**2)** Turn ignition on. Measure TPS output voltage. It should be between .2-.9 volt. If not, loosen mounting screws and turn TPS

until voltage is within specification. Tighten screws and turn ignition off.

**3)** Turn ignition on for more than 15 seconds, then turn ignition off. This will set ISC servo to specified position. Disconnect ISC servo harness connector. Start engine, check engine speed and adjust to 600 RPM with ISC adjusting screw. *See Fig. 14*.

**4)** Stop engine. Turn ignition on but do not start engine. Check TPS output voltage. It should be .45-.49 volt. If not, loosen mounting screws and turn TPS until voltage is within specification. Tighten screws after applying sealant.

**5)** Open throttle valve fully and return to original position. Check for proper TPS output voltage as readjust as necessary.

**6)** Turn ignition off. Remove harness and voltmeter. Reconnect ISC servo harness connector. Adjust accelerator cable. Ensure curb idle speed is normal. Disconnect battery for 5-6 seconds, then reconnect.

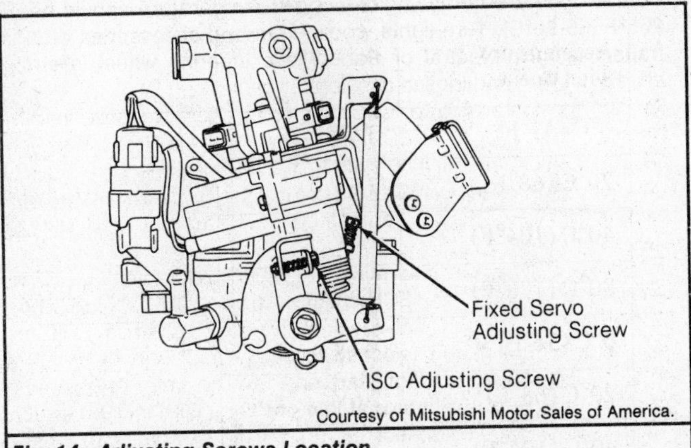
Fixed Servo
Adjusting Screw
ISC Adjusting Screw

Courtesy of Mitsubishi Motor Sales of America.

***Fig. 14: Adjusting Screws Location***

**Mirage – 1)** Engine coolant temperature should be 185-205°F (85-95°C). Turn lights, cooling fan and accessories off. Place transmission in Neutral or Park. Place steering wheel in straight-ahead position. Loosen accelerator cable.

**2)** Disconnect TPS connector. Connect Harness (MD998459) between separated connectors. *See Fig. 11*. Connect a voltmeter between Blue terminal No. 2 (output) and Black terminal No. 1 (ground).

**3)** Turn ignition on (do not start engine) and hold 15 seconds or more. This will set ISC motor at idle position. Turn ignition switch to "LOCK" position. Disconnect ISC servo motor connector. Put ISC motor in idle position.

**4)** Open throttle valve by hand 2-3 times and allow to return with a snap each time. Loosen fixed servo adjusting screw. *See Fig. 14*.

**5)** Start engine and run at idle. Check engine speed and motor position sensor output voltage. Engine speed should be 700 RPM and output voltage .9 volt. If not to specification, adjust using ISC adjusting screw. *See Fig. 14*.

**6)** Tighten fixed servo adjusting screw until RPM increases. Loosen screw until RPM ceases to drop, then loosen screw 1/2 turn.

**7)** Stop engine. Turn ignition on (engine does not start) and check TPS output voltage. Voltage should be .48-.52 volts. If not to specification, loosen TPS screws and adjust by turning (clockwise increases voltage). Tighten screws after adjustment.

**8)** Turn ignition off. Adjust accelerator cable. Connect ISC motor connector. Disconnect harness and voltmeter. Connect TPS connector.

**9)** Start engine and ensure idle speed is correct (700±100 RPM). Turn ignition off. Disconnect battery for 5-6 seconds to erase diagnosis memory. Reconnect battery.

**Starion – 1)** Engine coolant temperature should be 185-205°F (85-95°C). Turn lights, cooling fan and accessories off. Place transmission in Neutral or Park. Place steering wheel in straight-ahead position. Loosen accelerator cable.

**2)** Disconnect TPS connector. Connect Harness (MD998459) between separated connecters. *See Fig. 11*. Connect a voltmeter between Red terminal No. 2 (output) and Black terminal No. 1 (ground).

**3)** Turn ignition on, but do not start engine. Hold switch in "ON" position for 15 seconds or more and ensure ISC servo is set at idle position.

***NOTE: When ignition switch is turned to "ON" position, ISC servo extends to fast idle position opening. In 15 seconds, it retracts and stops at initial position.***

**4)** Turn ignition switch to "LOCK" position. Disconnect ISC servo connector to fix ISC servo at initial position. Connect Test Harness (MD998460) to ISC servo body side harness connector. Ground Red terminal of test harness. The ECU will now operate as if idle switch is on.

**5)** To prevent binding of throttle valve, open throttle valve by hand several times then release with a snap. Loosen fixed servo adjusting screw. *See Fig. 14*. Start engine and run at idle. Ensure engine speed is 850 RPM. If engine speed is incorrect, tighten fixed servo adjusting screw until speed begins to increase. Loosen servo adjusting screw until engine speed does not drop. Loosen screw an additional one turn.

**6)** Stop engine. Turn ignition switch to "ON" position (engine off). Ensure TPS output voltage is .48-.52 volt. If not to specification, loosen TPS mounting screw and increase voltage by turning TPS clockwise. Decrease voltage by turning TPS counterclockwise.

**7)** Turn ignition switch to "LOCK" position. Adjust accelerator cable slackness. Remove test harness and reconnect ISC servo and TPS connectors. Start engine and check idle speed. Idle RPM should be 750-950 RPM. Turn ignition switch to "OFF" position. To erase ECU memory, disconnect battery for 5-6 seconds.

# 1988 COMPUTERIZED ENGINE CONTROLS
## Chrysler & Mitsubishi ECI System (Cont.)

| Select switch | Check switch | Check item | Condition | | Check meter reading when normal | Terminal number of computer |
|---|---|---|---|---|---|---|
| A | 1 | Power supply | Ignition switch OFF → ON | | 11–13V | 51 |
| | 2 | Secondary air control solenoid valve | Ignition switch OFF → ST after warming up the engine | | After 15 seconds 0–0.5V ↓ 13–15V | 10 |
| | 3 | Throttle position switch | Ignition switch OFF → ON | Accelerator closed | 0.4–1.5V | 1 |
| | | | | Accelerator wide opened | 4.5–5.0V | |
| | 4 | Coolant temperature sensor | Ignition switch OFF → ON | 0°C (32°F) | 3.5V | 3 |
| | | | | 20°C (68°F) | 2.6V | |
| | | | | 40°C (104°F) | 1.8V | |
| | | | | 80°C (176°F) | 0.6V | |
| | 5 | Intake air temperature | Ignition switch OFF → ON | 0°C (32°F) | 3.5V | 4 |
| | | | | 20°C (68°F) | 2.6V | |
| | | | | 40°C (104°F) | 1.8V | |
| | | | | 80°C (176°F) | 0.6V | |
| | 6 | Idle position switch | Ignition switch OFF → ON | Accelerator closed | 0–0.4V | 5 |
| | | | | Accelerator wide opened | 11–13V | |
| | 7 | ISC motor position switch | Ignition switch OFF → ON | | 11–13V*[1] | 14 |
| | 8 | – | – | | – | – |
| | 9 | – | – | | – | – |
| | 10 | A/C (Air conditioner) relay | Ignition switch OFF → ON | A/C switch OFF | 0–0.5V | 62 |
| | | | | A/C switch ON | 11–13V | |
| | 11 | Lead switch for vehicle speed | Start engine, transaxle in first and operate vehicle slowly | | Flashing 0–0.5V ↕ Over 2V | 15 |
| | 12 | – | – | | – | – |
| B | 1 | Cranking signal | Ignition switch OFF → ST | | Over 8V | 13 |
| | 2 | Control relay | Idling | | 0 – 0.5V | 55 |
| | 3 | – | – | | – | – |

Courtesy of Mitsubishi Motor Sales of America.

***Output Signal Chart for Cordia & Tredia***

# 1988 COMPUTERIZED ENGINE CONTROLS
## Chrysler & Mitsubishi ECI System (Cont.)

| Select switch | Check switch | Check item | Condition | | Check meter reading when normal | Terminal location of computer |
|---|---|---|---|---|---|---|
| B | 4 | Ignition pulse | Idling | | 12 – 14V | 8 |
| | | | 3000 rpm | | 11 – 13V | |
| | 5 | Air flow sensor | Idling | | 2.2 – 3.2V | 7 |
| | | | 3000 rpm | | | |
| | 6 | Injector No. 1 | Idling | | 13 – 15V | 59 |
| | | | 3000 rpm | | 12 – 14V | |
| | 7 | Injector No. 2 | Idling | | 13 – 15V | 60 |
| | | | 3000 rpm | | 12 – 14V | |
| | 8 | Oxygen sensor | Keep 1300 rpm after warming up the engine | | Flashing 0.4–1V ↕ 2.7V | 6 |
| | 9 | EGR control solenoid valve | Keep idling after warming up the engine | | 13–15V | 54 |
| | | | Raise the engine 3500 rpm | | 0–0.5V | |
| | 10 | Pressure sensor | Ignition switch: OFF → ON | | 1.5–2.6V | 17 |
| | | | Idling | | 0.2–1.2V*[2] | |
| | 11 | ISC motor for extension | Idling | | 0–2V | 56 |
| | | | | A/C switch: OFF → ON | Momentarily Over 6V | |
| | 12 | ISC motor for retraction | Idling | | 0–2V | 61 |
| | | | | A/C switch: ON → OFF | Momentarily Over 6V | |

NOTE: *[1] : If ignition switch is turned to ON for 15 seconds or more, the reading drops below 5V momentarily.
*[2] : The reading rises to 1.5–2.6V every 2 minutes momentarily.

| | Check item | Condition | | | Check meter reading when normal | Terminal location of computer |
|---|---|---|---|---|---|---|
| Checking with voltmeter | Spark advance signal | Idling | Coolant temp. below 35°C (95°F) | | Over 5V | 12 |
| | | | Coolant temp. above 35°C (95°F) | Altitudes below 3,900 ft. | 0 – 0.5V | |
| | | | | Altitudes above 3,900 ft. | Over 5V | |
| | Inhibitor switch | Ignition switch OFF → ON | | Select lever in "P" or "N" | 0 – 0.5V | 11 |
| | | | | Select lever in "D" | 11 – 13V | 11 |

Courtesy of Mitsubishi Motor Sales of America.

*Output Signal Chart for Cordia & Tredia (Cont.)*

# 1988 COMPUTERIZED ENGINE CONTROLS
# Chrysler & Mitsubishi ECI System (Cont.)

| ECI Checker Operation | | Check Item | ECU Terminal # Checked | Condition | | Test Specification |
|---|---|---|---|---|---|---|
| Select Switch | Check Switch | | | | | |
| "A" | 1 | Power supply | 51 | Ignition switch "LOCK" → "ON" | | 11V – 13V |
| | 2 | Ignition pulse | 1 | Ignition switch "LOCK" → "START" | | 4V – 10V |
| | 3 | Intake air temperature sensor | 5 | Ignition switch "LOCK" → "ON" | 0°C (32°F) | 3.4V – 3.6V |
| | | | | | 20°C (68°F) | 2.5V – 2.7V |
| | | | | | 40°C (104°F) | 1.7V – 1.9V |
| | | | | | 80°C (176°F) | 0.6V – 0.8V |
| | 4 | Engine coolant temperature sensor | 6 | Ignition switch "LOCK" → "ON" | 0°C (32°F) | 3.4V – 3.6V |
| | | | | | 20°C (68°F) | 2.5V – 2.7V |
| | | | | | 40°C (104°F) | 1.5V – 1.7V |
| | | | | | 80°C (176°F) | 0.5V – 0.7V |
| | 5 | Power supply for sensor | 10 | Ignition switch "LOCK" → "ON" | | 4.5V – 5.5V |
| | 6 | Throttle position sensor | 15 | Ignition switch "LOCK" → "ON" (Warm engine) | Accelerator fully closed | 0.4V – 0.7V |
| | | | | | Accelerator fully opened | 4.5V – 5.5V |
| | 7 | Motor position sensor | 3 | Ignition switch "LOCK" → "ON" | After 15 seconds | 0.8V – 1.2V |
| | 8 | Idle position switch | 7 | Ignition switch "LOCK" → "ON" | Accelerator fully closed | 0V – 0.6V |
| | | | | | Accelerator fully opened | 8V – 13V |
| | 9 | Cranking signal | 55 | Ignition switch "LOCK" → "START" | | Over 8V |
| | 10 | Vehicle speed sensor reed switch | 19 | Start engine and operate vehicle slowly in 1st or DRIVE range | | 0V – 0.6V ↑ (pulsates) ↓ Over 2V |
| | 11 | Air conditioner switch | 56 | Ignition switch "LOCK" → "ON" | Air conditioner switch "OFF" | 0V – 0.6V |
| | | | | | Air conditioner switch "ON" *1 | 11V – 13V |
| | 12 | Inhibitor switch | 58 | Ignition switch "LOCK" → "ON" | At "P" or "N" range | 0V – 0.6V |
| | | | | | At "D" range | 11V – 13V |

NOTE
*1: ON means compressor clutch engaged.

Courtesy of Mitsubishi Motor Sales of America.

***Output Signal Chart for All Except Cordia & Tredia (Step 1)***

| ECI Checker Operation: Select Switch | ECI Checker Operation: Check Switch | Check Item | ECU Terminal # Checked | Condition | | Test Specification |
|---|---|---|---|---|---|---|
| | 1 | | | | | |
| | 2 | | | | | |
| | 3 | | | | | |
| | 4 | Spark advance signal | 13 | Idling | Engine coolant temperature less than 35°C (95°F) | Over 5V |
| | | | | | Engine coolant temperature 35°C (95°F) or higher, altitude up to approx. 1,200 m (3,900 ft.) | 0 – 0.6V |
| | | | | | Engine coolant temperature 35°C (95°F) or higher, altitude approx. 1,200 m (3,900 ft.) or above | Over 5V |
| "B" | 5 | Air flow sensor | 2 | Idling | | 2.2 – 3.2V |
| | | | | 3,000 rpm | | |
| | 6 | | | | | |
| | 7 | EGR control solenoid valve | 54 | Hold engine at a speed less than 2500 rpm after warming up | | 13V – 15V |
| | | | | Hold engine at a speed 2500 rpm or higher | | 0V – 0.6V |
| | 8 | Oxygen sensor | 11 | Hold engine at a constant speed above 1,300 rpm, after 30 seconds from start of warm engine | | 0V – 0.6V *2 ↑ (pulsates) ↓ 2V – 3V |
| | 9 | | | | | |
| | 10 | | | | | |
| | 11 | | | | | |
| | 12 | | | | | |

NOTE
*2: Failure of parts other than the oxygen sensor can also cause deviation from the specifications.

Courtesy of Mitsubishi Motor Sales of America.

**Output Signal Chart for All Except Cordia & Tredia (Step 1 Cont.)**

| ECI Checker Operation | | Check Item | ECU Terminal # Checked | Condition | Test Specification |
|---|---|---|---|---|---|
| Select Switch | Check Switch | | | | |
| "A" | 1 | | | | |
| | 2 | Secondary air control solenoid valve | 20 | Hold engine over 1,500 rpm, 15 seconds after start of warm engine | 0V – 0.6V then 13V – 15V |
| | 3 | | | | |
| | 4 | | | | |
| | 5 | Atmospheric pressure sensor | 16 | Ignition switch at sea level "LOCK" → "ON" | 3.8V – 4.2V |
| | | | | Idling | |
| | 6 | | | | |
| | 7 | Self-diagnosis | 21 | Ignition switch "LOCK" → "ON" | Refer to P.14-62 |
| | 8 | | | | |
| | 9 | | | | |
| | 10 | | | | |
| | 11 | | | | |
| | 12 | | | | |

Courtesy of Mitsubishi Motor Sales of America.

**Output Signal Chart for All Except Cordia & Tredia (Step 2)**

| ECI Checker Setting | | Check item | ECU Terminal # Checked | Condition | | Test Specification |
|---|---|---|---|---|---|---|
| Select switch | Check switch | | | | | |
| "B" | 1 | ISC motor for extension | 23 | Idling | Air conditioner switch OFF → ON *1 | Momentarily over 4V, then 0V – 2V *2 |
| | 2 | ISC motor for retraction | 12 | Idling | Air conditioner switch ON → OFF *1 | Momentarily over 4V, then 0V – 2V *2 |
| | 3 | Air conditioner cutoff relay | 24 | Idling | Air conditioner switch OFF → ON *1 | 12V – 15V, then 0V – 0.6V |
| | 4 | Control relay | 22 | Ignition switch "LOCK" → "ON" | | 11V – 13V |
| | | | | Idling | | 0V – 0.6V |
| | 5 | | | | | |
| | 6 | Boost meter | 59 | Idling | | 12V – 14V |
| | | | | Quick acceleration from idling to above 2,000 rpm in "N" or "P" position | | Slight drop |
| | 7 | Injector No. 1 pulse | 60 | Idling | | 12V – 14V |
| | | | | Quick acceleration from idling to above 2,000 rpm in "N" or "P" position | | Slight drop |
| | 8 | | | | | |
| | 9 | Detonation retard signal | 61 | Idling | | Over 5V |
| | | | | Quick acceleration from idling to above 2,000 rpm in "N" or "P" position | | 0V – 0.6V |
| | 10 | | | | | |
| | 11 | Injector No. 2 pulse | 62 | Idling | | 12V – 15V |
| | | | | Quick acceleration from idling to above 2,000 rpm in "N" or "P" position | | Slight drop |
| | 12 | | | | | |

NOTE
*1: ON means compressor clutch engaged.
*2: Pointer indicates over 6V momentarily. If it is hard to read indication, repeat OFF → ON or ON → OFF operation of air conditioner switch several times. If the pointer of voltmeter deflects, ISC motor is normal.

Courtesy of Mitsubishi Motor Sales of America.

***Output Signal Chart for All Except Cordia & Tredia (Step 2 Cont.)***

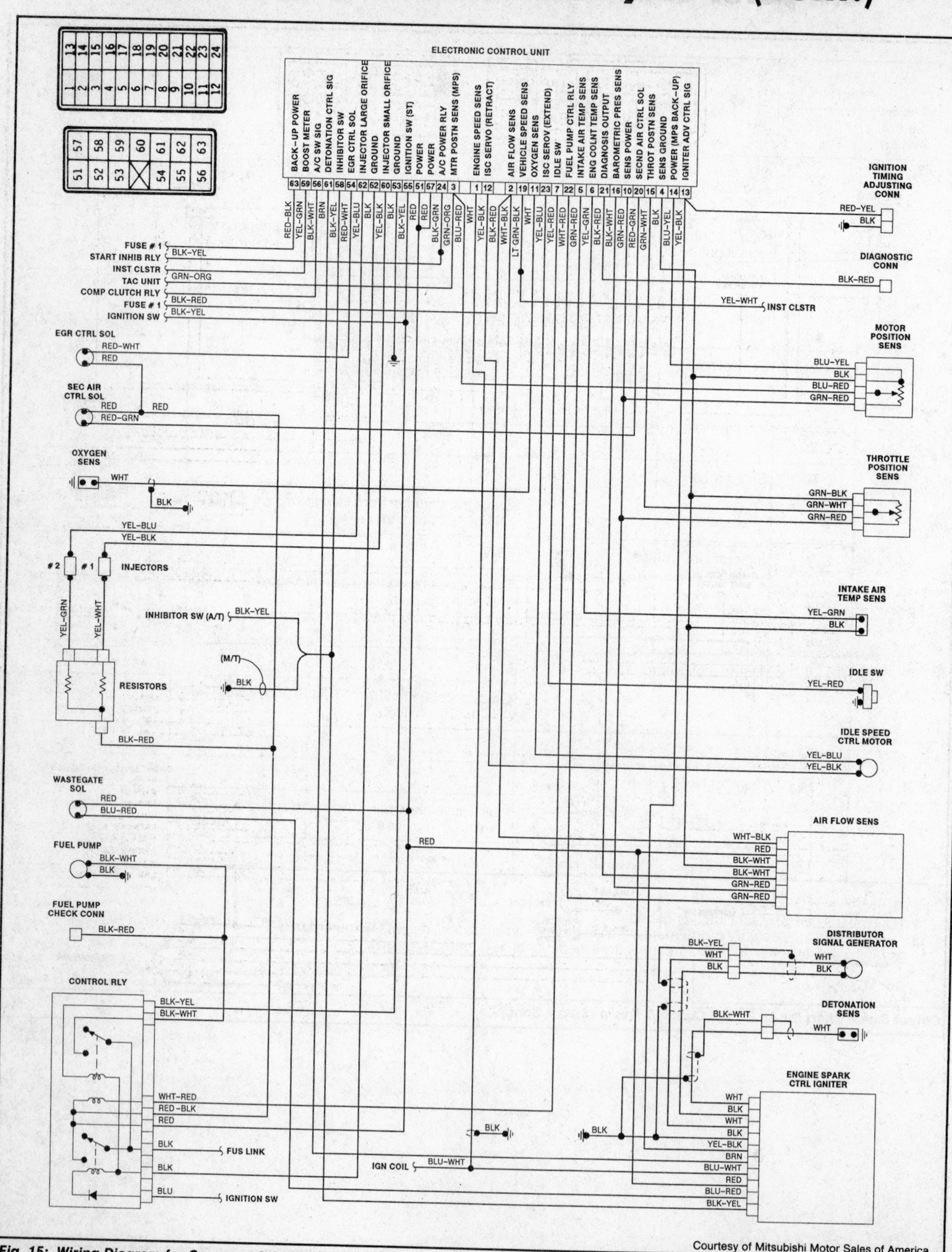
ELECTRONIC CONTROL UNIT
BACK-UP POWER
BOOST METER
A/C SW SIG
DETONATION CTRL SIG
INHIBITOR SW
EGR CTRL SOL
INJECTOR LARGE ORIFICE
GROUND
INJECTOR SMALL ORIFICE
GROUND
IGNITION SW (ST)
POWER
POWER
A/C POWER RLY
MTR POSTN SENS (MPS)
ENGINE SPEED SENS
ISC SERVO (RETRACT)
AIR FLOW SENS
VEHICLE SPEED SENS
OXYGEN SENS
ISC SEROV (EXTEND)
IDLE SW
FUEL PUMP CTRL RLY
INTAKE AIR TEMP SENS
ENG COLNT TEMP SENS
DIAGNOSIS OUTPUT
BAROMETRIC PRES SENS
SENS POWER
SECND AIR CTRL SOL
THROT POSTN SENS
SENS GROUND
POWER (MPS BACK-UP)
IGNITER ADV CTRL SIG
FUSE # 1
START INHIB RLY
INST CLSTR
TAC UNIT
COMP CLUTCH RLY
FUSE # 1
IGNITION SW
EGR CTRL SOL
SEC AIR CTRL SOL
OXYGEN SENS
INJECTORS
INHIBITOR SW (A/T)
(M/T)
RESISTORS
WASTEGATE SOL
FUEL PUMP
FUEL PUMP CHECK CONN
CONTROL RLY
FUS LINK
IGN COIL
IGNITION SW
IGNITION TIMING ADJUSTING CONN
DIAGNOSTIC CONN
INST CLSTR
MOTOR POSITION SENS
THROTTLE POSITION SENS
INTAKE AIR TEMP SENS
IDLE SW
IDLE SPEED CTRL MOTOR
AIR FLOW SENS
DISTRIBUTOR SIGNAL GENERATOR
DETONATION SENS
ENGINE SPARK CTRL IGNITER

Courtesy of Mitsubishi Motor Sales of America.

*Fig. 15: Wiring Diagram for Conquest & Starion*

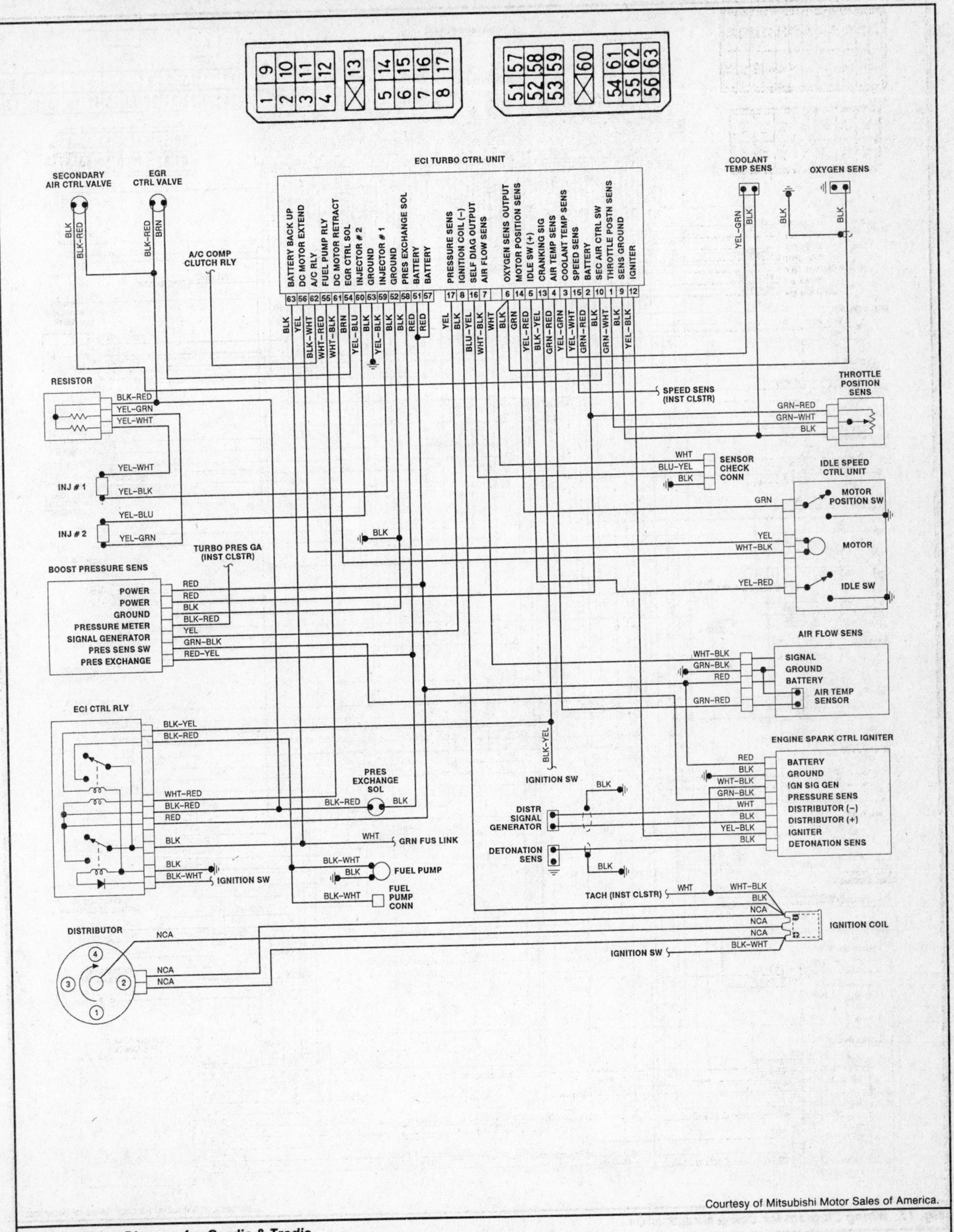
ECI TURBO CTRL UNIT
SECONDARY AIR CTRL VALVE
EGR CTRL VALVE
A/C COMP CLUTCH RLY
COOLANT TEMP SENS
OXYGEN SENS
RESISTOR
SPEED SENS (INST CLSTR)
THROTTLE POSITION SENS
SENSOR CHECK CONN
IDLE SPEED CTRL UNIT
MOTOR POSITION SW
MOTOR
IDLE SW
INJ # 1
INJ # 2
TURBO PRES GA (INST CLSTR)
BOOST PRESSURE SENS
AIR FLOW SENS
AIR TEMP SENSOR
ECI CTRL RLY
PRES EXCHANGE SOL
IGNITION SW
ENGINE SPARK CTRL IGNITER
DISTR SIGNAL GENERATOR
DETONATION SENS
GRN FUS LINK
FUEL PUMP
FUEL PUMP CONN
TACH (INST CLSTR)
IGNITION COIL
DISTRIBUTOR
Courtesy of Mitsubishi Motor Sales of America.

Fig. 16: Wiring Diagram for Cordia & Tredia

# 1988 COMPUTERIZED ENGINE CONTROLS
## Chrysler & Mitsubishi ECI System (Cont.)

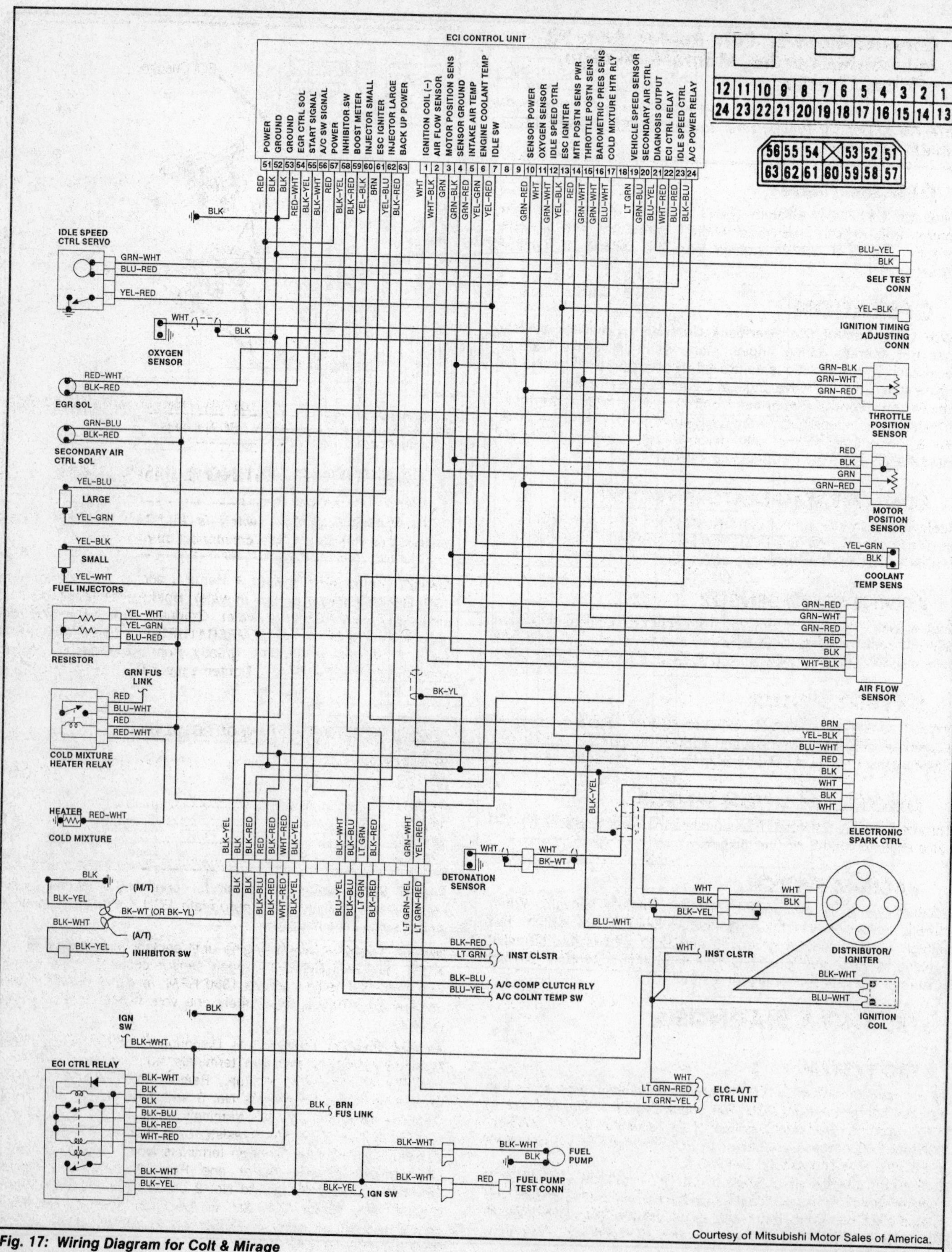
ECI CONTROL UNIT
POWER
GROUND
GROUND
EGR CTRL SOL
START SIGNAL
A/C SW SIGNAL
POWER
INHIBITOR SW
BOOST METER
INJECTOR SMALL
ESC IGNITER
INJECTOR LARGE
BACK UP POWER
IGNITION COIL (–)
AIR FLOW SENSOR
MOTOR POSITION SENS
SENSOR GROUND
INTAKE AIR TEMP
ENGINE COOLANT TEMP
IDLE SW
SENSOR POWER
OXYGEN SENSOR
IDLE SPEED CTRL
ESC IGNITER
MTR POSTN SENS PWR
THROTTLE POSTN SENS
BAROMETRIC PRES SENS
COLD MIXTURE HTR RLY
VEHICLE SPEED SENSOR
SECONDARY AIR CTRL
DIAGNOSIS OUTPUT
ECI CTRL RELAY
IDLE SPEED CTRL
A/C POWER RELAY
IDLE SPEED CTRL SERVO
OXYGEN SENSOR
EGR SOL
SECONDARY AIR CTRL SOL
LARGE
SMALL
FUEL INJECTORS
RESISTOR
GRN FUS LINK
COLD MIXTURE HEATER RELAY
HEATER
COLD MIXTURE
(M/T)
BK-WT (OR BK-YL)
(A/T)
INHIBITOR SW
IGN SW
ECI CTRL RELAY
SELF TEST CONN
IGNITION TIMING ADJUSTING CONN
THROTTLE POSITION SENSOR
MOTOR POSITION SENSOR
COOLANT TEMP SENS
AIR FLOW SENSOR
ELECTRONIC SPARK CTRL
DETONATION SENSOR
DISTRIBUTOR/ IGNITER
IGNITION COIL
INST CLSTR
A/C COMP CLUTCH RLY
A/C COLNT TEMP SW
ELC–A/T CTRL UNIT
BRN FUS LINK
FUEL PUMP
FUEL PUMP TEST CONN
IGN SW

**Fig. 17: Wiring Diagram for Colt & Mirage**

Courtesy of Mitsubishi Motor Sales of America.

# Chrysler & Mitsubishi FBC System

**Chrysler Motors: Colt, Raider, Ram-50**
**Mitsubishi: Cordia, Montero, Mirage, Pickup, Tredia**

***NOTE:** For Mitsubishi Precis, refer to appropriate Hyundai Excel article in this section.*

## DESCRIPTION

Feedback Carburetor System (FBC) consists of an Electronic Control Unit (ECU), 2-barrel downdraft carburetor and various sensors. The ECU utilizes signals from the sensors to control air/fuel ratio.

## OPERATION

**Open Loop Control (No Feedback Control)** – Feedback system does not operate during engine start, warm-up, heavy load or deceleration. Air/fuel ratio is controlled by predetermined values for engine speed, throttle valve angle and coolant temperature.

**Closed Loop Control (Feedback Control)** – After engine warm-up, air/fuel ratio is determined by the oxygen sensor signal to the ECU. The ECU controls air/fuel ratio through the Feedback Solenoid Valve (FBSV) and Slow-Cut Solenoid Valve (SCSV).

### COOLANT TEMPERATURE SENSOR

Coolant temperature sensor converts engine coolant temperature to an electrical signal for the ECU. The ECU uses this information to provide extra fuel when engine is cold.

### ENGINE SPEED SENSOR

Engine speed signals are received from negative terminal of ignition coil and sent to ECM. Time between signals is used to calculate engine speed. Engine speed is used by ECU to control air/fuel ratio.

### OXYGEN SENSOR

Oxygen sensor is located in exhaust system. Output voltage of oxygen sensor varies with oxygen content in engine exhaust. The oxygen sensor signal is used by ECU to control air/fuel ratio.

### THROTTLE POSITION SENSOR

Throttle Position Sensor (TPS) signals ECU of changes in throttle valve angle to control air/fuel mixture.

### VACUUM SWITCH

Vacuum switch is operated by intake manifold vacuum. When throttle valve closes, intake manifold vacuum closes switch. The voltage on ECU side is grounded and ECU senses throttle valve opening is near idle position. This information controls air/fuel mixture at idle with secondary air control.

## TESTING & DIAGNOSIS

### FBC SYSTEM

**1)** Turn ignition switch to "LOCK" position. Remove large and small harness connector from ECU. Set check switch of ECI checker to "OFF" position. Set select switch of ECI checker to "A" position. Connect FBC harness connector to ECI checker and then connect to ECU harness connectors. *See Fig. 1.*

**2)** Perform checks as outlined in OUTPUT SIGNAL CHARTS. If checker varies from specifications, check corresponding sensor and related electrical wiring, and repair as necessary. See COMPONENT TESTING & INSPECTION. Recheck with ECI checker to confirm repair has corrected problem.

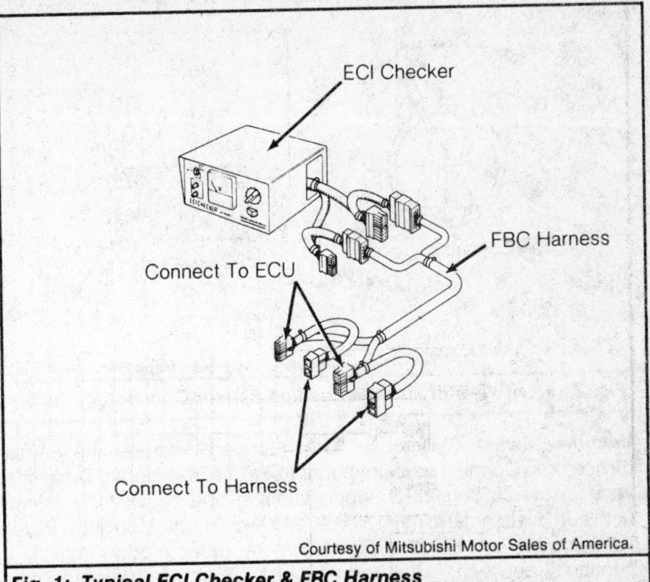
ECI Checker
FBC Harness
Connect To ECU
Connect To Harness

Courtesy of Mitsubishi Motor Sales of America.

*Fig. 1: Typical ECI Checker & FBC Harness*

## COMPONENT TESTING & INSPECTION

***CAUTION:** Ensure ignition switch is in "OFF" position. Before removing or installing a part, disconnect battery terminal.*

**Coolant Temperature Sensor** – Remove sensor from intake manifold. Immerse sensor portion in water. Hold sensor housing .12" (3 mm) away from surface of water. Gradually heat water and read resistance. See COOLANT TEMPERATURE SENSOR RESISTANCE table. If resistance deviates greatly from specification, replace coolant temperature sensor. Tighten sensor to 14-29 ft. lbs. (20-40 N.m).

***COOLANT TEMPERATURE SENSOR RESISTANCE***

| Temperature °F (°C) | Ohms |
|---|---|
| 32 (0) | 5900 |
| 68 (20) | 2500 |
| 104 (40) | 1100 |
| 176 (80) | 300 |

**Engine Speed Sensor** – Check for continuity between ignition negative coil terminal and appropriate ECU terminal. If continuity exists, sensor is functioning.

**Oxygen Sensor** – Warm engine until coolant temperature is 185-205°F (85-95°C). Remove oxygen sensor connector and connect voltmeter. With engine above 1300 RPM, measure output voltage. Voltage should be approximately one volt. If not, replace oxygen sensor.

**Throttle Position Sensor – 1)** Disconnect carburetor connector. Measure resistance between terminals No. 1 (power) and No. 8 (ground) on Montero, Pickup, Raider and Ram-50. Measure resistance between terminals No. 3 and 2 on Cordia and Tredia. Measure resistance between terminals No. 1 and No. 3 on all other models. *See Fig. 2.* Standard resistance is 3500-6500 ohms.

**2)** Connect ohmmeter between terminals No. 2 (output) and No. 8 on Montero, Pickup, Raider and Ram-50. Connect ohmmeter between terminals No. 3 and No. 2 on all other models. Operate throttle valve slowly from idle to full open position. Resistance should change smoothly in proportion to throttle valve opening, from 500 ohms to 3500-6500 ohms.

# Chrysler & Mitsubishi FBC System (Cont.)

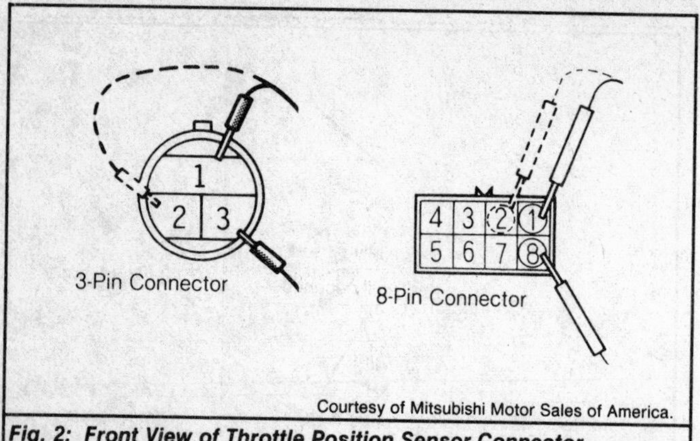
1
2 3
3-Pin Connector
4 3 2 1
5 6 7 8
8-Pin Connector
Courtesy of Mitsubishi Motor Sales of America.

***Fig. 2: Front View of Throttle Position Sensor Connector***

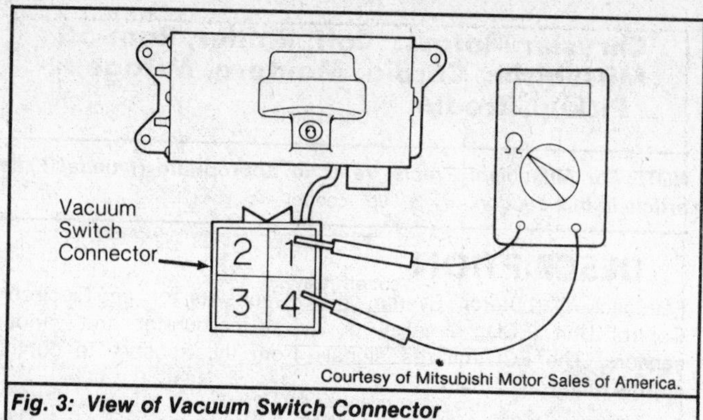
Vacuum
Switch
Connector
2 1
3 4
Ω
Courtesy of Mitsubishi Motor Sales of America.

***Fig. 3: View of Vacuum Switch Connector***

**Vacuum Switch** – Remove Green-striped vacuum hose from device box. Connect vacuum pump to device box nipple. Disconnect vacuum switch connector. Apply vacuum and check for continuity between switch terminals No. 1 and No. 4 on Montero, Pickup, Raider and Ram-50. *See Fig. 3.* On all other models, check for continuity between switch terminals. At 7.7 In. Hg, there should be no continuity. At 11.9 In. Hg, there should be continuity.

**Feedback Solenoid Valve (FBSV) & Slow-Cut Solenoid Valve (SCSV)** – Disconnect connectors at solenoid valves to test. Apply battery voltage to solenoid valve terminals. Solenoid valve should click. If no click is heard, replace solenoid valve. For solenoid valve terminal identification, see appropriate wiring diagram at end of this article.

| ECI Checker Operation: Select Switch | ECI Checker Operation: Check Switch | Check Item | ECU Terminal # Checked | Condition | | Test Specification |
|---|---|---|---|---|---|---|
| Set to "A" | 1 | Power supply | 7 | Ignition switch "LOCK→ON" | | 11V to 13V |
| | 2 | Ignition pulse | 10 | Ignition switch "LOCK→ON" | | 2V to 8V |
| | 3 | | | | | |
| | 4 | Coolant temperature sensor | 12 | Ignition switch "LOCK→ON" | 0 °C (32 °F) | 3.4V to 3.6V |
| | | | | | 20 °C (68 °F) | 2.4V to 2.7V |
| | | | | | 40 °C (104 °F) | 1.5V to 1.8V |
| | | | | | 80 °C (176 °F) | 0.5V to 0.7V |
| | 5 | Power supply for sensor | 3 | Ignition switch "LOCK→ON" | | 4.5V to 5.5V |
| | 6 | Throttle position sensor (TPS) [1] | 13 | Ignition switch "Lock→ON" (warm engine) | Acceleratror fully closed | 0.4V to 0.7V |
| | | | | | Accelerator fully opened | 4.5V to 5.5V |
| | 7 | Vacuum switch for idle position | 5 | Ignition switch "LOCK→ON" | | 9V to 13V |
| | | | | Idling (warm engine) | | 0V to 0.6V |
| | 8 | | | | | |
| | 9 | Feed back solenoid valve (FBS) | 59 | Ignition switch "LOCK→ON" | | 11V to 13V |
| | | | | Idling (warm engine) | | 2V to 12V |
| | 10 | Slow cut-off solenoid valve (SCS) | 53 | Idling | | 0V to 0.6V |
| | | | | Quick deceleration from above 4000 rpm to idling with "N" position | | Momentarily 13V to 15V |

[1] – On Raider and Ram-50, use check switch No. 3 to check TPS.

Courtesy of Mitsubishi Motor Sales of America.

***Output Signal Chart For Montero, Pickup, Raider & Ram-50 (Part 1 of 2)***

# 1988 COMPUTERIZED ENGINE CONTROLS
# Chrysler & Mitsubishi FBC System (Cont.)

| ECI Checker Operation: Select Switch | ECI Checker Operation: Check Switch | Check Item | ECU Terminal # Checked | Test Result | Condition | Test Specification |
|---|---|---|---|---|---|---|
| Set to "B" | 1 | Idle up control solenoid valve | 54 | Idling | A/C switch ON[1] | 0V to 0.6V |
| | | | | 2000 rpm | | 9V to 15V |
| | 2 | A/C cut-off relay | 57 | Ignition switch "LOCK→ON" and A/C switch "ON"*[1] | Accelerator fully closed | 0V to 0.6V |
| | | | | | Accelerator fully opened | 0V to 0.6V |
| | 3 | | | | | |
| | 4 | Secondary air control solenoid valve | 55 | Idling 70 seconds after start of warm engine | | 0V to 0.6V then 13V to 15V |
| | | | | Quick deceleration from above 2000 rpm to idling with "N" | | Momentarily drop |
| | 5 | | | | | |
| | 6 | Electric choke relay[3] | 56 | Ignition switch "LOCK→ON" | | 0V to 0.6V |
| | | | | Idling | | 13V to 15V |
| | 7 | | | | | |
| | 8 | Oxygen sensor | 1 | Hold rpm constant above 1300 rpm, after 70 seconds from start of warm engine | | 0V to 1V ↑ (pulsates) ↓ [2] 2V to 3V |
| | 9 | | | | | |
| | 10 | | | | | |
| | 11 | | | | | |
| | 12 | | | | | |

1 – ON means compressor clutch engaged.
2 – Failure of parts other than oxygen sensor can also cause deviation from the specifications.
3 – Used on Raider and Ram-50 only.

Courtesy of Mitsubishi Motor Sales of America.

***Output Signal Chart For Montero, Pickup, Raider & Ram-50 (Part 2 of 2)***

# 1988 COMPUTERIZED ENGINE CONTROLS
# Chrysler & Mitsubishi FBC System (Cont.)

| ECI Checker Setting: Select Switch | ECI Checker Setting: Check Switch | Check Item | ECU Terminal # Checked | Condition | | Test Specification |
|---|---|---|---|---|---|---|
| | 1 | Power supply | 2 | Ignition switch "LOCK" → "ON" | | 11V – 13V |
| | 2 | Spark advance control solenoid valve | 13 | Idling (warm engine) | | 0V – 0.6V |
| | | | | Start engine. Drive vehicle for some seconds at a speed higher than 8 km/h (5 mph), then hold 2,000 rpm (warm engine) | | 13V – 15V |
| | 3 | Throttle position sensor (TPS) | 59 | Ignition switch "LOCK" → "ON" (warm engine) | Accelerator fully closed | 0.4V – 0.7V |
| | | | | | Accelerator fully opened | 4.5V – 5.5V |
| | 4 | Engine coolant temperature sensor | 53 | Ignition switch "LOCK" → "ON" | 0°C (32°F) | 3.4V – 3.6V |
| | | | | | 20°C (68°F) | 2.4V – 2.7V |
| | | | | | 40°C (104°F) | 1.5V – 1.8V |
| | | | | | 80°C (176°C) | 0.5V – 0.7V |
| | 5 | – | – | – | | – |
| "A" | 6 | Vacuum switch for idle position | 6 | Ignition switch "LOCK" → "ON" | | 9V – 13V |
| | | | | Idling (warm engine) | | 0V – 0.6V |
| | 7 | Throttle opener control solenoid valve | 12 | Idling | Air conditioner switch ON *1 or lighting switch ON | 0V – 0.6V |
| | | | | 2,000 rpm | Air conditioner switch ON *1 or lighting switch ON | 9V – 15V |
| | 8 | Electric choke relay | 14 | Ignition switch "LOCK" → "ON" | | 0V – 0.6V |
| | | | | Idling | | 13V – 15V |
| | 9 | Air conditioner cut-off relay | 8 | Ignition switch "LOCK" → "ON" and air conditioner switch "ON" *1 | Accelerator fully closed | 0V – 0.6V |
| | | | | | Accelerator fully opened | M/T 0V–0.6V |
| | | | | | | A/T 13V–15V |
| | 10 | Power supply for sensor | 51 | Ignition switch "LOCK" → "ON" | | 4.5 V – 5.5V |
| | 11 | Vehicle speed sensor reed switch | 56 | Start engine, and drive vehicle slowly with transmission in first gear or drive range. | | 0V – 0.6V ↑ (pulsates) ↓ Over 2V |
| | 12 | Secondary air control solenoid valve | 9 | Idling, 70 seconds after start of warm engine | | 0V – 0.6V then 13V – 15V |
| | | | | Quick deceleration from above 2,000 rpm to idling with gear in "N" position | | Momentarily drop |

*1 ON means compressor clutch engaged.

Courtesy of Mitsubishi Motor Sales of America.

***Output Signal Chart For Colt & Mirage (Part 1 of 2)***

# 1988 COMPUTERIZED ENGINE CONTROLS
## Chrysler & Mitsubishi FBC System (Cont.)

| ECI Checker Setting: Select Switch | ECI Checker Setting: Check Switch | Check Item | ECU Terminal # Checked | Condition | | Test Specification |
|---|---|---|---|---|---|---|
| "B" | 1 | Shift select lever 4th or 5th switch | 17 | Ignition switch "LOCK" → "ON" | Transmission in 1st | 0V to 0.6V |
| | | | | | Transmission in 4th or 5th | 11V to 13V |
| | 2 | Feed back solenoid valve (FBS) | 11 | Ignition switch "LOCK" → "ON" | | 11V to 13V |
| | | | | Idling (warm engine) | | 2V to 12V |
| | 3 | Cold advance control solenoid valve [1] | 5 | Start engine. Drive vehicle for some seconds at a speed higher than 8 km/h (5MPH), then hold engine idling | Engine coolant temp. lower than 50°C (122°F) | 0V to 0.6V |
| | | | | | Engine coolant temp. 50°C (122°F) or higher | 13V to 15V |
| | 4 | Ignition pulse | 15 | Ignition switch "LOCK → START" | | 2V to 8V |
| | 5 | Cold mixture heater relay [1] | 57 | Idling | Engine coolant temp. lower than 60°C (140°F) | 0V to 0.6V |
| | | | | | Engine coolant temp. 60°C (140°F) or higher | 13V to 15V |
| | 6 | – | – | – | | – |
| | 7 | Slow cut solenoid valve (SCS) | 10 | Idling | | 0V to 0.6V |
| | | | | Quick deceleration from above 4,000 rpm to idling with gear at "N" position | | Momentarily 13V to 15V |
| | 8 | Oxygen sensor | 55 | Hold speed constant above 1,300 rpm, 70 seconds after start of warm engine | | 0V to 1V [2] ↑ (Pulsates) ↓ 2V to 3V |
| | 9 | – | – | – | | – |
| | 10 | – | – | – | | – |
| | 11 | – | – | – | | – |
| | 12 | Shift indicator lamp (SIL) [1] | 7 | Ignition switch "LOCK" → "ON" | After 5 seconds, voltage drops | 8V to 13V then 0V to 0.5V |

[1] – Used on Colt only.
[2] – Failure of parts other than oxygen sensor can also cause deviation from the specifications.

Courtesy of Mitsubishi Motor Sales of America.

***Output Signal Chart For Colt & Mirage (Part 2 of 2)***

# 1988 COMPUTERIZED ENGINE CONTROLS
## Chrysler & Mitsubishi FBC System (Cont.)

| ECI Checker Operation: Select Switch | ECI Checker Operation: Check Switch | Check Item | ECU Terminal # Checked | Condition | | Test Specification |
|---|---|---|---|---|---|---|
| Set to "A" | 1 | Power supply | 7 | Ignition switch "LOCK → ON" | | 11V to 13V |
| | 2 | Ignition pulse | 10 | Idling | | 4V to 10V |
| | 3 | – | – | – | | – |
| | 4 | Coolant temperature sensor | 12 | Ignition switch "LOCK → ON" | 0°C (32°F) | 3.4V to 3.6V |
| | | | | | 20°C (68°F) | 2.4V to 2.7V |
| | | | | | 40°C (104°F) | 1.5V to 1.8V |
| | | | | | 80°C (176°F) | 0.5V to 0.7V |
| | 5 | Power supply for sensor | 3 | Ignition switch "LOCK → ON" | | 4.5V to 5.5V |
| | 6 | Throttle position sensor (TPS) | 13 | Ignition switch "LOCK → ON" (warm engine) | Accelerator fully closed | 0.4V to 0.7V |
| | | | | | Accelerator fully opened | 4.5V to 5V |
| | 7 | Vacuum switch for idle position | 5 | Ignition switch "LOCK → ON" | | 9V to 13V |
| | | | | Idling (warm engine) | | 0V to 0.6V |
| | 8 | – | – | – | | – |
| | 9 | Feed back solenoid valve (FBS) | 59 | Ignition switch "LOCK → ON" | | 11V to 13V |
| | | | | Idling (warm engine) | | 2V to 12V |
| | 10 | Slow cut-off solenoid valve (SCS) | 53 | Idling | | 0V to 0.6V |
| | | | | Quick deceleration from above 4000 rpm to idling with "N" position | | Momentarily 13V to 15V |
| | 11 | Spark advance control solenoid valve | 58 | Idling (warm engine) | | 0V to 0.6V |
| | | | | 2000 rpm | | 13V to 15V |
| | 12 | – | – | – | | – |

Courtesy of Mitsubishi Motor Sales of America.

***Output Signal Chart For Cordia & Tredia With Manual Transmission (Part 1 of 2)***

| ECI Checker Operation | | Check Item | ECU Terminal # Checked | Condition | | Test Specification |
|---|---|---|---|---|---|---|
| Select Switch | Check Switch | | | | | |
| Set to "B" | 1 | Idle up control solenoid valve | 54 | Idling | Air conditioner switch ON *[1] or lighting switch ON | 0V to 0.6V |
| | | | | 2000 rpm | | 9V to 15V |
| | 2 | A/C cutoff relay | 57 | Ignition switch "LOCK → ON" and A/C switch "ON" *[1] | Accelerator fully closed | 0V to 0.6V |
| | | | | | Accelerator fully opened | 0V to 0.6V |
| | 3 | – | – | – | | – |
| | 4 | Second air control solenoid valve | 55 | Idling, after 70 seconds from start of warm engine | | 13V to 15V |
| | | | | Quick deceleration from above 2000 rpm to idling with "N" | | Momentarily drop |
| | 5 | – | – | – | | – |
| | 6 | – | – | – | | – |
| | 7 | – | – | – | | – |
| | 8 | Oxygen sensor *[2] | 1 | Hold rpm constant above 1300 rpm, after 70 seconds from start of warm engine | | 0V to 1V ↑ (pulsates) ↓ 2V to 3V |
| | 9 | – | – | – | | – |
| | 10 | – | – | – | | – |
| | 11 | – | – | – | | – |
| | 12 | – | – | – | | – |

*[1] ON means compressor clutch engaged.
*[2] Because there are sometimes malfunctions and differences from the specifications in parts other than oxygen sensor, take care to inspect the parts connecting the other air-fuel ratio controls.

Courtesy of Mitsubishi Motor Sales of America.

***Output Signal Chart For Cordia & Tredia With Manual Transmission (Part 2 of 2)***

# 1988 COMPUTERIZED ENGINE CONTROLS
## Chrysler & Mitsubishi FBC System (Cont.)

| ECI Checker Operation | | Check Item | ECU Terminal # Checked | Condition | | Test Specification |
|---|---|---|---|---|---|---|
| Select Switch | Check Switch | | | | | |
| Set to "A" | 1 | Power supply | 51 | Ignition switch "LOCK → ON" | | 11V to 13V |
| | 2 | Spark advance control solenoid valve | 13 | Idling (warm engine) | | 0V to 0.6V |
| | | | | 2000 rpm | | 13V to 15V |
| | 3 | Throttle position sensor (TPS) | 55 | Ignition switch "LOCK → ON" (warm engine) | Accelerator fully closed | 0.4V to 0.7V |
| | | | | | Accelerator fully opened | 4.5V to 5V |
| | 4 | ISC motor for retraction | 10 | Idling | Air conditioner switch ON → OFF *[1] | Momentarily over 6V, then 0V to 2V *[2] |
| | 5 | ISC motor for extension | 11 | Idling | Air conditioner switch ON → OFF *[1] | Momentarily over 6V, then 0V to 2V *[2] |
| | 6 | Idle position switch | 1 | Ignition switch "LOCK → ON" (warm engine) | Accelerator fully closed | 0V to 0.6V |
| | | | | | Accelerator fully opened | 9V to 13V |
| | 7 | ISC high motor position switch | 17 | Ignition switch "LOCK → ON" | After 15 seconds voltage drops | 8V to 13V then 0V to 0.6V |
| | 8 | Electric choke relay | 9 | Ignition switch "LOCK → ON" | | 0V to 0.6V |
| | | | | Idling | | 13V to 15V |
| | 9 | ISC low motor position switch | 3 | Ignition switch "LOCK → ON" | Voltage drops toward 0V after 15 seconds | 8V to 13V, then momentarily drop |
| | 10 | Power steering switch | 7 | Idling | | 9V to 13V |
| | | | | Turn steering wheel to stop | | 0V to 0.6V |
| | 11 | Air conditioner switch | 2 | Ignition switch "LOCK → ON" | Air conditioner switch OFF | 0V to 0.6V |
| | | | | | Air conditioner switch ON *[1] | 11V to 13V |
| | 12 | Secondary air control solenoid valve | 5 | Idling, 70 seconds after start of warm engine | | 13V to 15V |
| | | | | Quick deceleration from above 2000 rpm to idling with "N" or "P" position | | Momentarily drop |

*[1] ON means compressor clutch engaged.
*[2] Pointer indicates over 6V momentarily. If it is hard to read indication, repeat the OFF → ON or ON → OFF operation of air conditioner switch several times. If the pointer of voltmeter deflects, ISC motor is normal.

Courtesy of Mitsubishi Motor Sales of America.

***Output Signal Chart For Cordia & Tredia With Automatic Transmission (Part 1 of 2)***

| ECI Checker Operation | | Check Item | ECU Terminal # Checked | Condition | | Test Specification |
|---|---|---|---|---|---|---|
| Select Switch | Check Switch | | | | | |
| Set to "B" | 1 | Air conditioner cutoff relay | 14 | Idling | Air conditioner switch OFF → ON *1 | 12V to 15V, then 0V to 0.6V |
| | 2 | Feed back solenoid valve (FBS) | 8 | Ignition switch "LOCK → ON" | | 11V to 13V |
| | | | | Idling (warm engine) | | 2V to 12V |
| | 3 | – | – | – | | – |
| | 4 | Ignition pulse | 54 | Idling | | 4V to 10V |
| | 5 | Coolant temperature sensor | 60 | Ignition switch "LOCK → ON" | 0°C (32°F) | 3.4V to 3.6V |
| | | | | | 20°C (68°F) | 2.4V to 2.7V |
| | | | | | 40°C (104°F) | 1.5V to 1.8V |
| | | | | | 80°C (176°F) | 0.5V to 0.7V |
| | 6 | Select lever "N" switch | 6 | Ignition switch "LOCK → ON" | Transaxle in "P" or "N" | 0V to 0.6V |
| | | | | | Transaxle in "D" | 6V to 13V |
| | 7 | Slow cutoff solenoid valve (SCS) | 12 | Idling | | 0V to 0.6V |
| | | | | Quick deceleration from above 4000 rpm to idling with "D" position *2 | | Momentarily 11V to 15V |
| | 8 | Oxygen sensor *3 | 15 | Hold rpm constant above 1300, after 70 seconds from start of warm engine | | 0V to 1V ↑ (pulsates) ↓ 2V to 3V |
| | 9 | – | – | – | | – |
| | 10 | – | – | – | | – |
| | 11 | – | – | – | | – |
| | 12 | – | – | – | | – |

*1 ON means compressor clutch engaged.
*2 Speed sensor must show vehicle is moving.
*3 Because there are somtimes malfunctions and differences from the specifications in parts other than the oxygen sensor, take care to inspect the parts connecting the other air-fuel ratio controls.

Courtesy of Mitsubishi Motor Sales of America.

**Output Signal Chart For Cordia & Tredia With Automatic Transmission (Part 2 of 2)**

# 1988 COMPUTERIZED ENGINE CONTROLS
## Chrysler & Mitsubishi FBC System (Cont.)

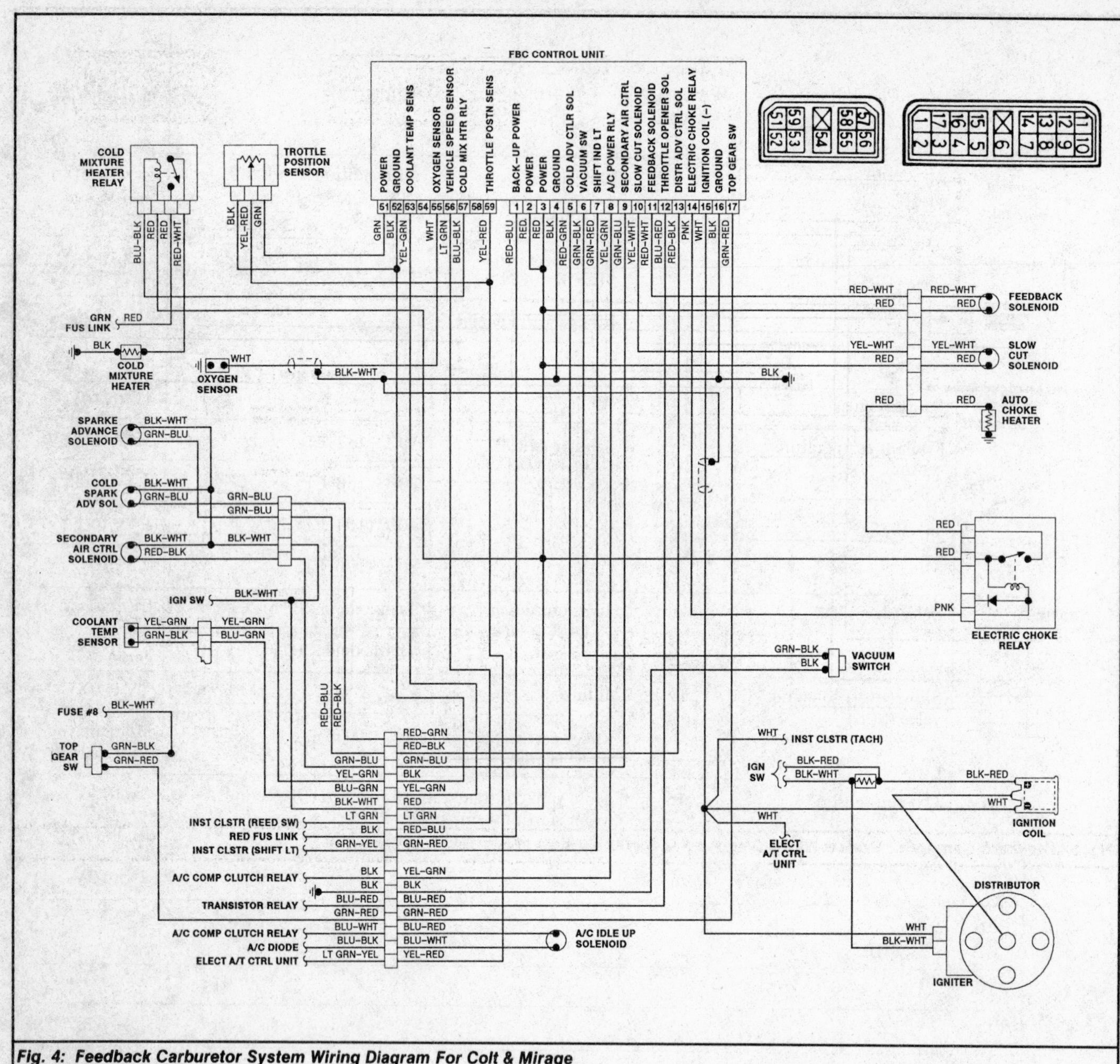
FBC CONTROL UNIT
POWER
GROUND
COOLANT TEMP SENS
OXYGEN SENSOR
VEHICLE SPEED SENSOR
COLD MIX HTR RLY
THROTTLE POSTN SENS
BACK-UP POWER
POWER
POWER
GROUND
COLD ADV CTLR SOL
VACUUM SW
SHIFT IND LT
A/C POWER RLY
SECONDARY AIR CTRL
SLOW CUT SOLENOID
FEEDBACK SOLENOID
THROTTLE OPENER SOL
DISTR ADV CTRL SOL
ELECTRIC CHOKE RELAY
IGNITION COIL (-)
GROUND
TOP GEAR SW
COLD MIXTURE HEATER RELAY
TROTTLE POSITION SENSOR
GRN FUS LINK
COLD MIXTURE HEATER
OXYGEN SENSOR
SPARKE ADVANCE SOLENOID
COLD SPARK ADV SOL
SECONDARY AIR CTRL SOLENOID
IGN SW
COOLANT TEMP SENSOR
FUSE #8
TOP GEAR SW
INST CLSTR (REED SW)
RED FUS LINK
INST CLSTR (SHIFT LT)
A/C COMP CLUTCH RELAY
TRANSISTOR RELAY
A/C COMP CLUTCH RELAY
A/C DIODE
ELECT A/T CTRL UNIT
A/C IDLE UP SOLENOID
FEEDBACK SOLENOID
SLOW CUT SOLENOID
AUTO CHOKE HEATER
ELECTRIC CHOKE RELAY
VACUUM SWITCH
INST CLSTR (TACH)
IGN SW
ELECT A/T CTRL UNIT
IGNITION COIL
DISTRIBUTOR
IGNITER

Fig. 4: Feedback Carburetor System Wiring Diagram For Colt & Mirage

# 1988 COMPUTERIZED ENGINE CONTROLS
## Chrysler & Mitsubishi FBC System (Cont.)

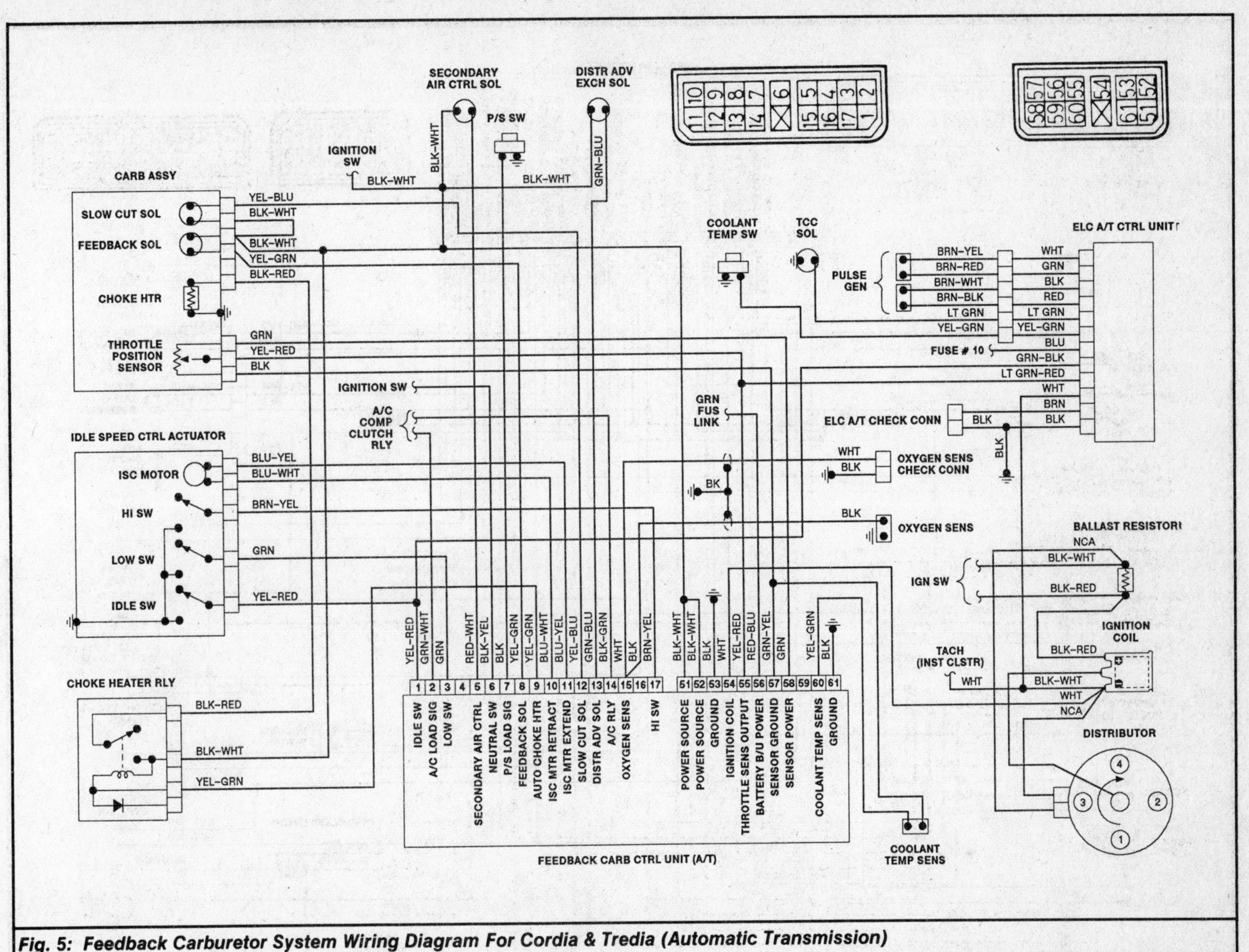

SECONDARY AIR CTRL SOL
DISTR ADV EXCH SOL
P/S SW
IGNITION SW
CARB ASSY
SLOW CUT SOL
FEEDBACK SOL
CHOKE HTR
THROTTLE POSITION SENSOR
IDLE SPEED CTRL ACTUATOR
ISC MOTOR
HI SW
LOW SW
IDLE SW
CHOKE HEATER RLY
A/C COMP CLUTCH RLY
COOLANT TEMP SW
TCC SOL
PULSE GEN
FUSE # 10
GRN FUS LINK
ELC A/T CHECK CONN
ELC A/T CTRL UNIT
OXYGEN SENS CHECK CONN
OXYGEN SENS
BALLAST RESISTOR
IGN SW
IGNITION COIL
TACH (INST CLSTR)
DISTRIBUTOR
COOLANT TEMP SENS
IDLE SW
A/C LOAD SIG
LOW SW
SECONDARY AIR CTRL
NEUTRAL SW
P/S LOAD SIG
FEEDBACK SOL
AUTO CHOKE HTR
ISC MTR RETRACT
ISC MTR EXTEND
SLOW CUT SOL
DISTR ADV SOL
A/C RLY
OXYGEN SENS
HI SW
POWER SOURCE
POWER SOURCE
GROUND
IGNITION COIL
THROTTLE SENS OUTPUT
BATTERY B/U POWER
SENSOR GROUND
SENSOR POWER
COOLANT TEMP SENS
GROUND
FEEDBACK CARB CTRL UNIT (A/T)


*Fig. 5: Feedback Carburetor System Wiring Diagram For Cordia & Tredia (Automatic Transmission)*

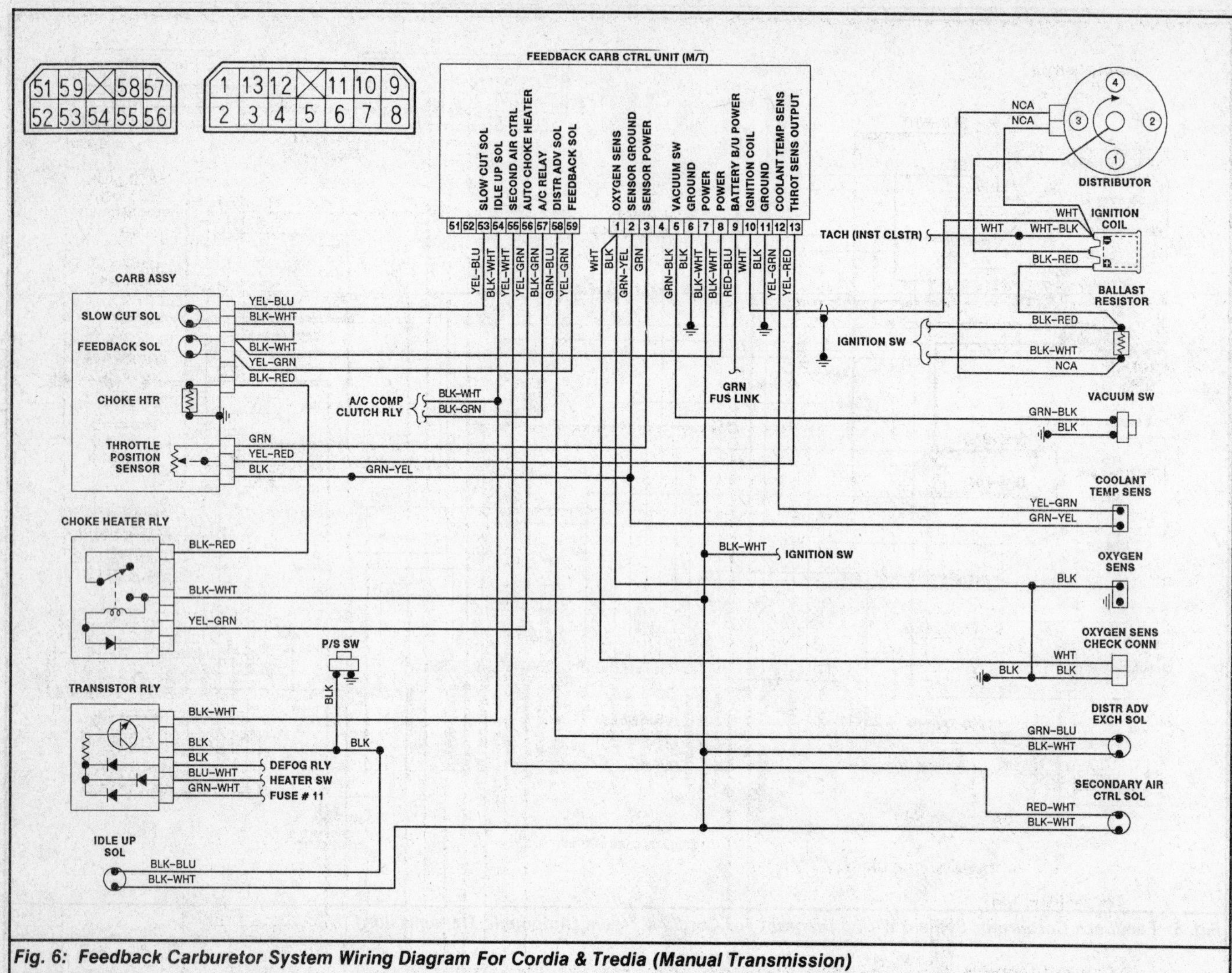
FEEDBACK CARB CTRL UNIT (M/T)
SLOW CUT SOL
IDLE UP SOL
SECOND AIR CTRL
AUTO CHOKE HEATER
A/C RELAY
DISTR ADV SOL
FEEDBACK SOL
OXYGEN SENS
SENSOR GROUND
SENSOR POWER
VACUUM SW
GROUND
POWER
POWER
BATTERY B/U POWER
IGNITION COIL
GROUND
COOLANT TEMP SENS
THROT SENS OUTPUT
CARB ASSY
SLOW CUT SOL
FEEDBACK SOL
CHOKE HTR
THROTTLE POSITION SENSOR
A/C COMP CLUTCH RLY
CHOKE HEATER RLY
P/S SW
TRANSISTOR RLY
DEFOG RLY
HEATER SW
FUSE # 11
IDLE UP SOL
DISTRIBUTOR
TACH (INST CLSTR)
IGNITION COIL
BALLAST RESISTOR
IGNITION SW
GRN FUS LINK
VACUUM SW
COOLANT TEMP SENS
IGNITION SW
OXYGEN SENS
OXYGEN SENS CHECK CONN
DISTR ADV EXCH SOL
SECONDARY AIR CTRL SOL

*Fig. 6: Feedback Carburetor System Wiring Diagram For Cordia & Tredia (Manual Transmission)*

# 1988 COMPUTERIZED ENGINE CONTROLS
## Chrysler & Mitsubishi FBC System (Cont.)

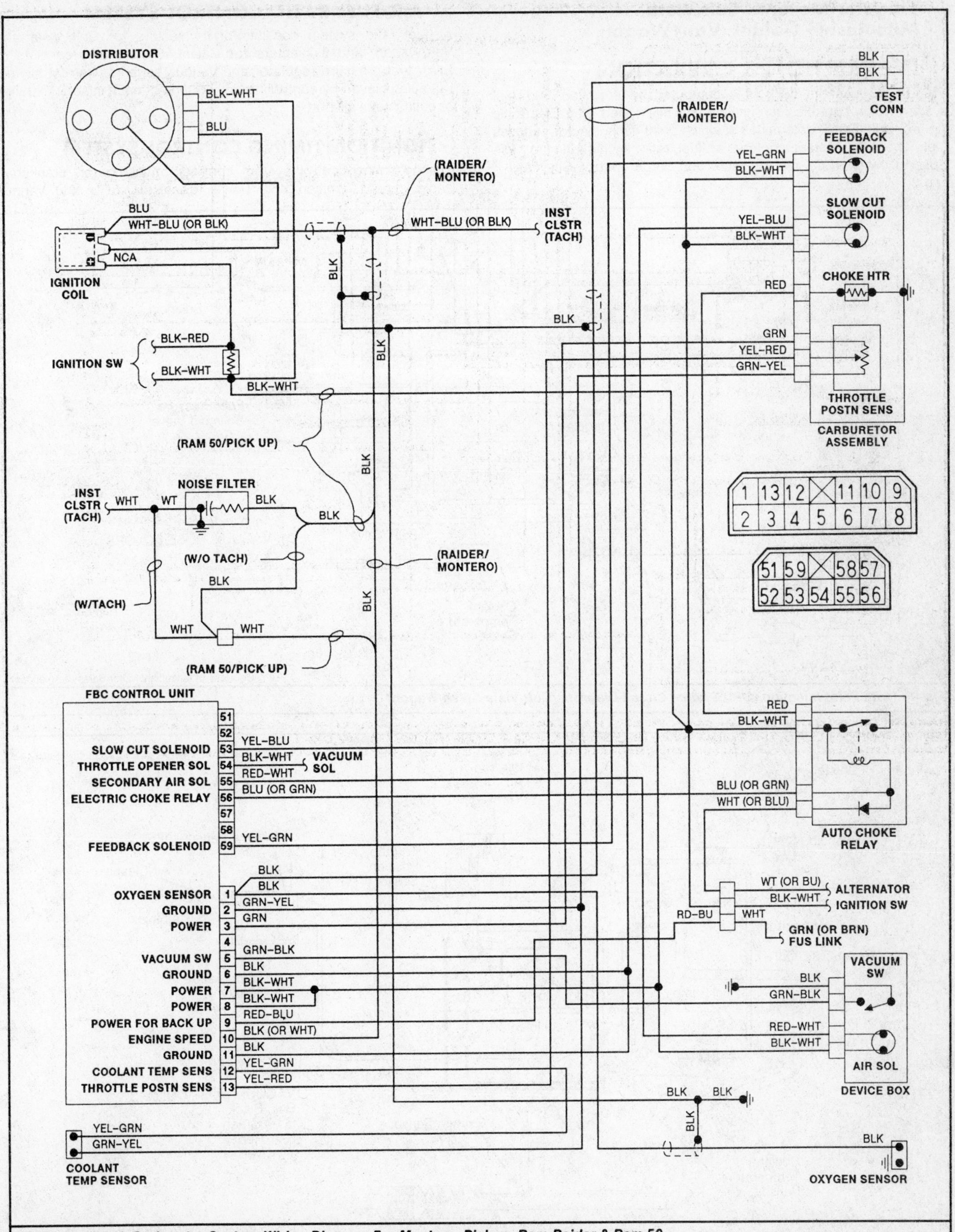

DISTRIBUTOR
BLK-WHT
BLU
BLU
WHT-BLU (OR BLK)
NCA
IGNITION COIL
(RAIDER/ MONTERO)
WHT-BLU (OR BLK)
INST CLSTR (TACH)
BLK
BLK
BLK-RED
IGNITION SW
BLK-WHT
BLK-WHT
(RAM 50/PICK UP)
BLK
INST CLSTR (TACH)
WHT
WT
NOISE FILTER
BLK
BLK
(W/O TACH)
(RAIDER/ MONTERO)
BLK
(W/TACH)
WHT
WHT
BLK
(RAM 50/PICK UP)
BLK
BLK
TEST CONN
(RAIDER/ MONTERO)
FEEDBACK SOLENOID
YEL-GRN
BLK-WHT
SLOW CUT SOLENOID
YEL-BLU
BLK-WHT
CHOKE HTR
RED
GRN
YEL-RED
GRN-YEL
THROTTLE POSTN SENS
CARBURETOR ASSEMBLY
1 13 12 11 10 9
2 3 4 5 6 7 8
51 59 58 57
52 53 54 55 56
FBC CONTROL UNIT
51
52
SLOW CUT SOLENOID 53 YEL-BLU
THROTTLE OPENER SOL 54 BLK-WHT
SECONDARY AIR SOL 55 RED-WHT
VACUUM SOL
ELECTRIC CHOKE RELAY 56 BLU (OR GRN)
57
58
FEEDBACK SOLENOID 59 YEL-GRN
BLK
OXYGEN SENSOR 1 BLK
GROUND 2 GRN-YEL
POWER 3 GRN
4
VACUUM SW 5 GRN-BLK
GROUND 6 BLK
POWER 7 BLK-WHT
POWER 8 BLK-WHT
POWER FOR BACK UP 9 RED-BLU
ENGINE SPEED 10 BLK (OR WHT)
GROUND 11 BLK
COOLANT TEMP SENS 12 YEL-GRN
THROTTLE POSTN SENS 13 YEL-RED
RED
BLK-WHT
BLU (OR GRN)
WHT (OR BLU)
AUTO CHOKE RELAY
WT (OR BU)
BLK-WHT
ALTERNATOR
IGNITION SW
RD-BU
WHT
GRN (OR BRN) FUS LINK
VACUUM SW
BLK
GRN-BLK
RED-WHT
BLK-WHT
AIR SOL
DEVICE BOX
BLK
BLK
BLK
YEL-GRN
GRN-YEL
COOLANT TEMP SENSOR
BLK
OXYGEN SENSOR


*Fig. 7: Feedback Carburetor System Wiring Diagram For Montero, Pickup, Ram Raider & Ram-50*

# 1988 COMPUTERIZED ENGINE CONTROLS
# Chrysler & Mitsubishi MPI System

**Chrysler Motors: Colt Vista**
**Mitsubishi: Galant, Van/Wagon**

## DESCRIPTION & OPERATION

Multi-Point Injection (MPI) is a computerized emission and fuel system which controls fuel, ignition and idle speed. The Electronic Control Unit (ECU), determines at which point each injector supplies fuel. The MPI system controls air/fuel ratio, ignition timing, Idle Speed Control (ISC), fuel pressure and purge control. *See Figs. 1 and 2.*

## AIR/FUEL RATIO CONTROL SYSTEM

Air/fuel ratio system consists of 4 injectors for Colt Vista and Van/Wagon, and 6 injectors for Galant. System also consists of ECU, fuel pressure regulator and various sensors. Correct air/fuel ratio is achieved by controlling driving time of each injector installed at each intake air port.

## IGNITION TIMING CONTROL SYSTEM

Ignition timing control system consists of distributor, crankshaft angle sensor, ignition coil, power transistor, ECU and various

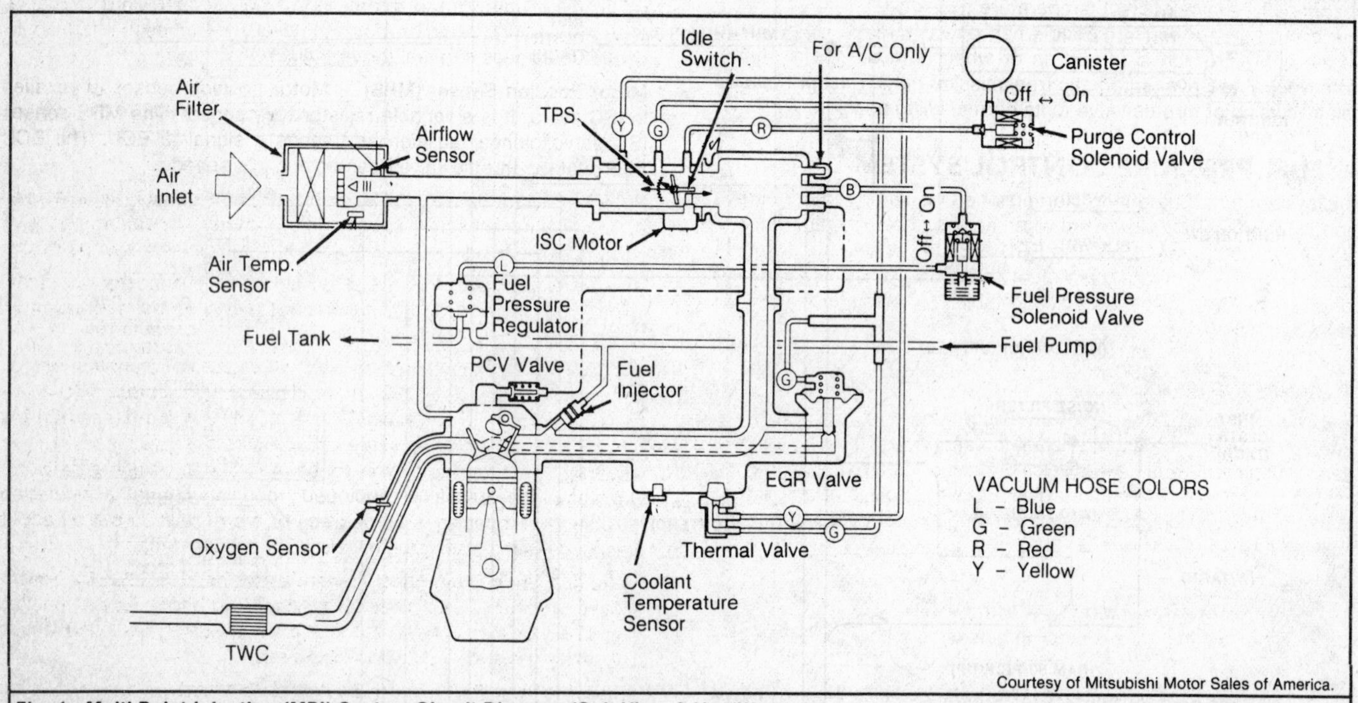
Idle Switch
For A/C Only
Canister
Off ↔ On
Air Filter
TPS
Airflow Sensor
Purge Control Solenoid Valve
Air Inlet
ISC Motor
Off ↔ On
Air Temp. Sensor
Fuel Pressure Regulator
Fuel Pressure Solenoid Valve
Fuel Tank
Fuel Pump
PCV Valve
Fuel Injector
EGR Valve
VACUUM HOSE COLORS
L - Blue
G - Green
R - Red
Y - Yellow
Oxygen Sensor
Thermal Valve
Coolant Temperature Sensor
TWC
Courtesy of Mitsubishi Motor Sales of America.

*Fig. 1: Multi-Point Injection (MPI) System Circuit Diagram (Colt Vista & Van/Wagon)*

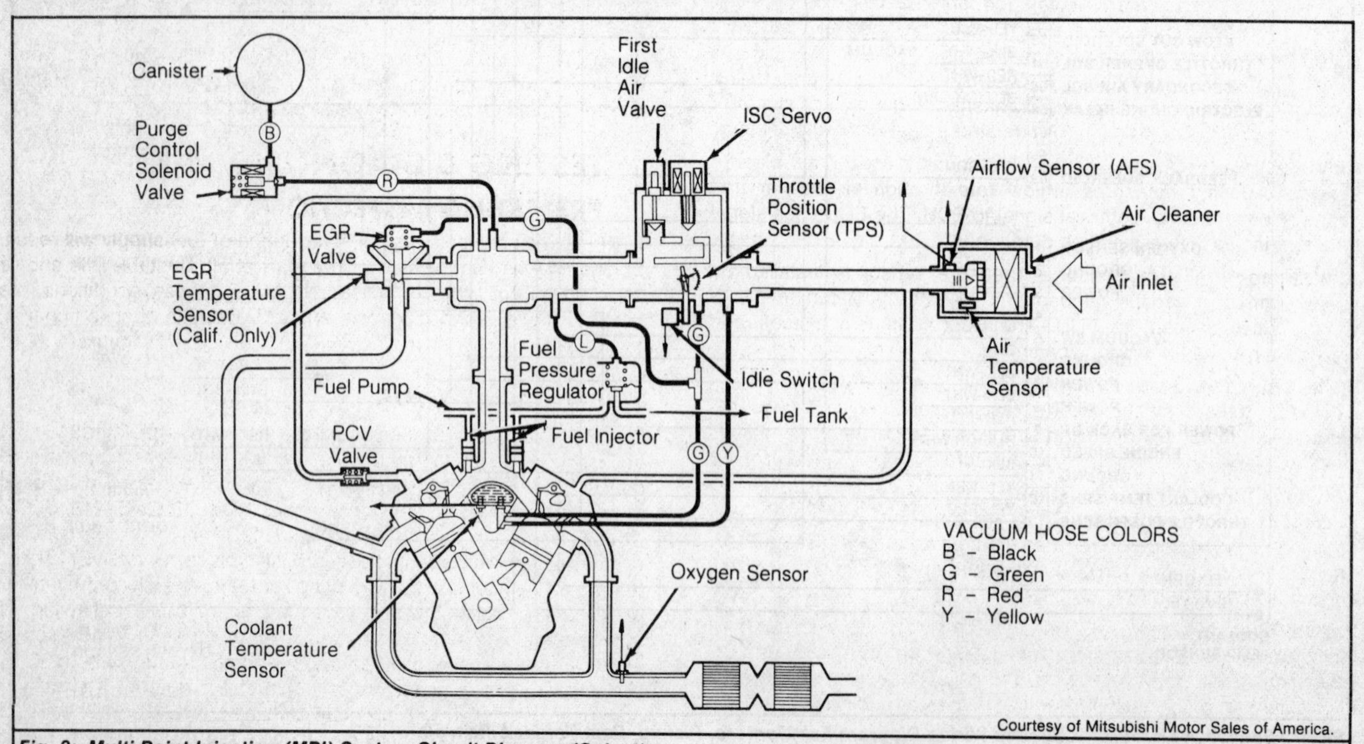
Canister
First Idle Air Valve
ISC Servo
Purge Control Solenoid Valve
Airflow Sensor (AFS)
Throttle Position Sensor (TPS)
Air Cleaner
EGR Valve
Air Inlet
EGR Temperature Sensor (Calif. Only)
Fuel Pressure Regulator
Air Temperature Sensor
Idle Switch
Fuel Pump
Fuel Tank
PCV Valve
Fuel Injector
VACUUM HOSE COLORS
B - Black
G - Green
R - Red
Y - Yellow
Oxygen Sensor
Coolant Temperature Sensor
Courtesy of Mitsubishi Motor Sales of America.

*Fig. 2: Multi-Point Injection (MPI) System Circuit Diagram (Galant)*

sensors. It controls ignition timing by making ignition coil primary current intermittent, by on-off control of power transistor.

## IDLE SPEED CONTROL (ISC) SYSTEM

ISC system provides start control, fast idle control, idle control and dashpot control. Start control adjusts throttle valve opening according to coolant temperature and atmospheric pressure.

Fast idle control is determined by idle switch position. When idle switch is on, engine speed is controlled according to coolant temperature. When idle switch is off, ISC servo is actuated according to engine coolant temperature.

Idle control increases idle speed when power steering oil pressure switch or A/C switch is turned on or when transmission is shifted from Neutral to Drive (automatic transmission only). Dashpot control delays closing of throttle valve to its normal idling position.

## FUEL PRESSURE CONTROL SYSTEM

This system functions during starting when intake air temperature is high, 122°F (50°C) or more, and when engine coolant temperature is high, 194°F (90°C) or more. The ECU turns on power transistor for approximately 2 minutes so fuel pressure solenoid valve is conductive. This maintains idling stability immediately after re-starting at high temperatures.

## FUEL CONTROL

Fuel control system consists of an electric fuel pump, control relay, fuel filter, injectors, pressure regulator and airflow sensor. Engine fuel is supplied through electronically pulsed (timed) injector valves located in the delivery pipe(s). The ECU controls amount of fuel metered through injectors based on engine demand information received from the sensors.

## DATA SENSORS

Each sensor furnishes electrical impulses to the ECU. From this input, the ECU computes fuel delivery and spark timing.

**No. 1 Cylinder TDC Sensor & Crankshaft Angle Sensor –** These sensors are a metal disc and unit assembly. Disc has 4 slits, 90 degrees apart (crankshaft angle) and one additional slit (No. 1 cylinder) located inside the 4 slits. Disc is attached to distributor shaft. When shaft rotates, slits in disc are optically read by unit assembly. The ECU uses No. 1 TDC sensor signal to determine fuel injection cylinder. The ECU uses crankshaft angle sensor signal to determine fuel injection timing for one stroke of engine revolution.

**Airflow Sensor –** Airflow sensor is mounted inside air cleaner assembly. Sensor measures airflow rate through air cleaner and sends a proportionate electrical signal to ECU. The ECU uses signal to determine basic fuel injection duration.

**Atmospheric Pressure Sensor –** Pressure sensor is installed on airflow sensor. It senses atmospheric pressure and converts it to voltage which is sent to ECU. The ECU computes altitude and corrects air/fuel ratio and ignition timing.

**Intake Air Temperature Sensor –** Air temperature sensor is located on the airflow sensor. The resistor-based sensor measures temperature of incoming air and supplies air density information to the ECU. The ECU uses air temperature sensor information for controlling fuel delivery.

**Coolant Temperature Sensor (CTS) –** Coolant temperature sensor converts coolant temperature to an electrical signal for use by ECU. The ECU uses coolant temperature information for controlling fuel enrichment when engine is cold.

**Engine Speed Sensor –** Engine speed signal is received from ignition coil. Electrical signals from ignition coil are sent to ECU where time between signals is used to calculate engine speed. This information is used by ECU for controlling air/fuel ratio and idle speed.

**Idle Switch –** Idle switch is mounted at tip of ISC servo. When throttle valve is closed, the switch is activated. When throttle valve is at any other position, switch is deactivated. This is used by ECU for controlling fuel delivery time during deceleration and also as an idle speed adjusting device.

**Oxygen Sensor –** Oxygen sensor is located in exhaust system. Output voltage of oxygen sensor varies with oxygen content in exhaust gas stream. Oxygen sensor signal is used to control fuel delivery time.

**Throttle Position Sensor –** Throttle Position Sensor (TPS) is a rotary meter attached to throttle body. The sensor signals ECU of changes in throttle valve position where information is used to control idle speed and fuel delivery time.

**Motor Position Sensor (MPS) –** Motor position sensor is installed in ISC servo. It is a variable resistor type sensor. The MPS senses ISC servo plunger position and sends a signal to ECU. The ECU then controls throttle valve opening and idle speed.

**Vehicle Speed Sensor –** The vehicle speed sensor uses a reed switch. Speed sensor in speedometer converts speedometer gear revolution (vehicle speed) into pulse signals which are sent to ECU.

**Air Conditioner Switch –** When air conditioner is turned on, signal is sent to ECU. The ECU then drives ISC servo to maintain optimum idle speed.

**Air Conditioner Relay –** When A/C switch is turned on with engine at idle, ISC servo is driven to increase engine speed. However, there is a delay before engine speed actually increases. During delay period, ECU opens relay circuit so compressor is not driven instantly. This prevents engine speed drop due to compressor load.

On automatic transaxle equipped models, during acceleration (throttle valve opening is 65 degrees or more) relay is cut off about 5 seconds to maintain good acceleration performance.

**Inhibitor Switch (Automatic Transmission Only) –** Inhibitor switch senses whether select lever is in Neutral or Park. Based on this signal, the ECU measures automatic transmission load and drives ISC servo to maintain optimum idle speed.

**Power Steering Oil Pressure Switch (Colt Vista) –** Power steering switch detects power steering oil pressure. When oil pressure rises, switch signals ECU to prevent engine speed drop due to power steering load.

**Power Transistor –** Power transistor is installed on intake manifold. It controls ignition timing by turning ignition coil primary current on and off by signals from the ECU.

# TESTING & DIAGNOSIS

## PRETESTING INSPECTION

If MPI system components fail, interruption of fuel supply will result. Engine may be hard to start or not start at all. Unstable idle and/or poor driveability will be noticed. If any of these conditions are present, first perform diagnosis and basic engine checks (ignition, engine adjustments, etc.).

## SELF-DIAGNOSIS

The Self-Diagnostic system monitors all input signals from each sensor. If an abnormal input signal occurs, that item is memorized by the ECU. For Colt Vista and Van/Wagon, there are 8 diagnostic codes. Galant has 12 diagnostic codes. See DIAGNOSTIC CODE TABLE. They can be confirmed by using a voltmeter. On Galant, codes can also be confirmed with a Multi-Use Tester (MB991194).

If 2 or more systems are non-functional, they are indicated by order of increasing code number. Indication is made by deflection of voltmeter pointer. A constant repetition of 12 volts at .5 second intervals with 1.5 seconds in between indicates system is normal.

If multi-use tester is used, "No Irregularity" is displayed. If system is abnormal, voltmeter will alternate between zero and 12 volts. If multi-use tester is used, trouble code is represented by a 2-digit number.

***NOTE: ECU diagnostic memory is kept by direct power supply from the battery. Memory is not erased by turning off ignition but is erased if battery or ECU is disconnected.***

*DIAGNOSTIC CODE TABLE*

| Code Number | Diagnostic Item |
|---|---|
| **Colt Vista & Van/Wagon** | |
| 1 | Oxygen Sensor |
| 2 | Crankshaft Angle Sensor |
| 3 | Airflow Sensor |
| 4 | Atmospheric Pressure Sensor |
| 5 | Throttle Position Sensor |
| 6 | Motor Position Sensor |
| 7 | Coolant Temperature Sensor |
| 8 | TDC Sensor (No. 1 Cylinder) |
| **Galant** | |
| 11 | Oxygen Sensor |
| 12 | Airflow Sensor |
| 13 | Intake Air Temperature Sensor |
| 14 | Throttle Position Sensor |
| 21 | Coolant Temperature Sensor |
| 22 | Crank Angle Sensor |
| 23 | TDC Sensor (No. 1 Cylinder) |
| 24 | Vehicle Speed Reed Switch |
| 25 | Atmospheric Pressure Sensor |
| 41 | Injector |
| 42 | Fuel Pump |
| 43 | EGR (California Only) |

## SELF-DIAGNOSTIC TEST (USING VOLTMETER)

***NOTE: Oxygen sensor memory is erased when ignition switch is turned off. To diagnose oxygen sensor, drive vehicle a good distance and keep engine running.***

**1)** Turn ignition switch to "OFF" position. Connect voltmeter between MPI self-diagnosis output and Ground of diagnosis connector. *See Fig. 3.* Turn ignition switch to "ON" position and disclosure of ECU memory will begin.

**2)** It is important that voltage signals are accurately timed. Signals will appear in .5, 1.5 or 3 second intervals. All codes begin with voltmeter registering 12 volts for 3 seconds. If more than one code is stored in memory, codes will be separated by a 3 second voltmeter indication.

**3)** All codes are revealed by a 12 volt pulse, 1.5 second duration. The time between pulses is .5 second. An example of code 5 is 12 volts for 3 seconds, zero voltage for .5 second and 12 volts 1.5 seconds. The indications of zero voltage for .5 second and 12 volts 1.5 seconds will be repeated 5 times. *See Fig. 4.*

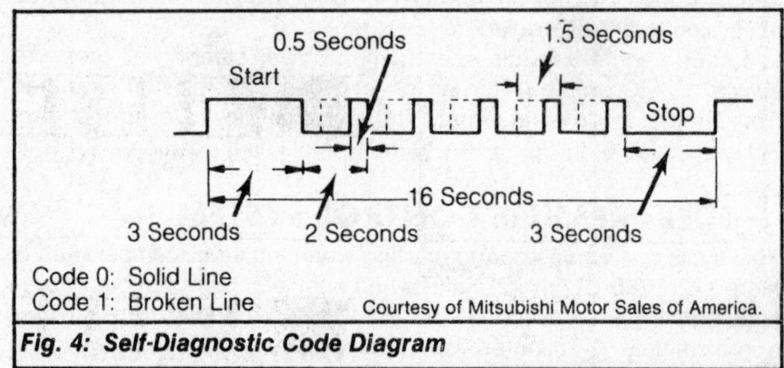
0.5 Seconds
1.5 Seconds
Start
Stop
16 Seconds
3 Seconds
2 Seconds
3 Seconds
Code 0: Solid Line
Code 1: Broken Line
Courtesy of Mitsubishi Motor Sales of America.

*Fig. 4: Self-Diagnostic Code Diagram*

**4)** If more than one code is stored, they will be separated by 12 volt pulses, 3 seconds in duration. After recording abnormal code, perform necessary repair as shown in appropriate SELF-DIAGNOSTIC CODE CHART. After repair, turn ignition off and disconnect negative battery cable for 15 seconds to erase ECU memory. Reconnect power supply and repeat self-diagnostics to confirm repair.

## SELF-DIAGNOSTIC TEST (USING MULTI-USE TESTER MB991194)

***NOTE: Multi-Use Tester (MB991194) is only used on Galant models.***

**Galant Only – 1)** Turn ignition off. Connect multi-use tester to diagnosis connector in glove compartment. Check inspection points and repair affected area as indicated in GALANT MULTI-USE TESTER CHECK CHARTS at end of this article.

**2)** After repair, recheck repaired area to ensure defect was corrected. Turn ignition off and remove tester. Disconnect battery for 15 seconds to erase memory.

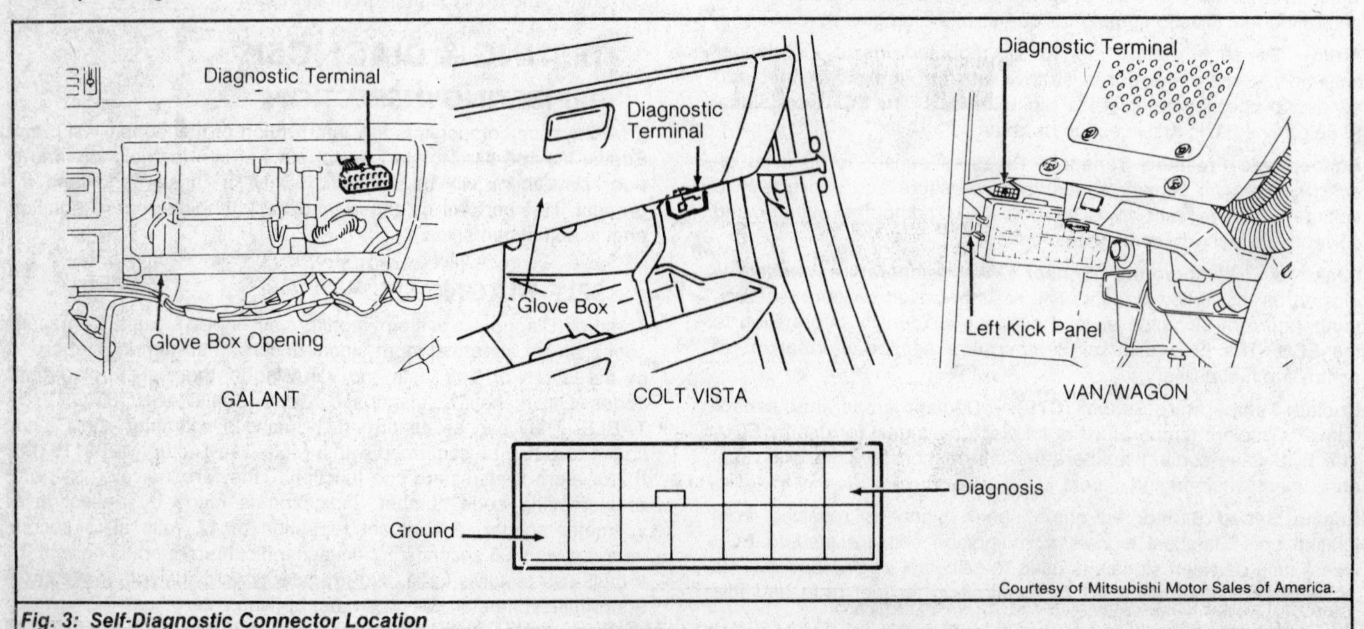
Diagnostic Terminal
Glove Box Opening
GALANT
Diagnostic Terminal
Glove Box
COLT VISTA
Diagnostic Terminal
Left Kick Panel
VAN/WAGON
Diagnosis
Ground
Courtesy of Mitsubishi Motor Sales of America.

*Fig. 3: Self-Diagnostic Connector Location*

**SELF-DIAGNOSTIC CODE CHART**

| Malfunction No. | Diagnosis item | Self-diagnosis output pattern and output code | Problem | Check item |
|---|---|---|---|---|
| 0 | Normal | 0 0 0 0 0 | None of malfunctions are present. | – |
| 1 | Oxygen sensor | 1 0 0 0 0 | (1) When engine stalls, and for 15 seconds after start<br>(2) Until output voltage reaches 0.6V or higher<br>(3) When oxygen sensor signal doesn't change for 20 seconds or longer during urban driving mode | • Harness and connector<br>• Oxygen sensor |
| 2 | Crank angle sensor | 0 1 0 0 0 | Ignition switch (ST) ON (continuous) and, moreover, there is no crank angle signal input for three seconds or longer | • Harness and connector<br>• Crank angle sensor |
| 3 | AFS | 1 1 0 0 0 | (1) AFS output of 10 Hz or less, with engine rpm 500 rpm or higher<br>(2) AFS output 100 Hz or more, at time of engine stall | • Harness and connector<br>• AFS |
| 4 | Atmospheric pressure sensor | 0 0 1 0 0 | (1) Atmospheric pressure sensor output voltage 4.5V (equivalent to 855 mmHg) or higher<br>(2) Atmospheric pressure sensor output voltage 0.2V or lower | • Harness and connector<br>• Atmospheric pressure sensor |
| 5 | TPS | 1 0 1 0 0 | (1) TPS output voltage 4V or higher continuously for one seconds or longer, with idling switch ON<br>(2) TPS output voltage 0.2V or lower | • Harness and connector<br>• TPS |
| 6 | MPS | 0 1 1 0 0 | (1) MPS output voltage 4.8V or higher<br>(2) MPS output voltage 0.2V or lower | • Harness and connector<br>• MPS |
| 7 | Coolant temperature sensor | 1 1 1 0 0 | (1) Coolant temperature sensor thermistor resistance value 45kΩ or higher<br>(2) Coolant temperature sensor thermistor resistance value 50Ω or lower | • Harness and connector<br>• Coolant temperature sensor |
| 8 | No. 1 cylinder TDC sensor | 0 0 0 1 0 | Absolutely no input of No. 1 cylinder TDC sensor signal during eight ignitions after ignition switch turned to ON or after input of No. 1 cylinder TDC signal | • Harness and connector<br>• No. 1 cylinder TDC sensor |

Courtesy of Mitsubishi Motor Sales of America.

*Self-Diagnostic Code Chart (Colt Vista & Van/Wagon)*

| Output preference order | Diagnosis item | Malfunction code | | | Check item (Remedy) |
|---|---|---|---|---|---|
| | | Output signal pattern | No. | Memory | |
| 1 | Computer | H / L | – | – | (Replace electronic control unit) |
| 2 | Oxygen sensor | H / L | 11 | Retained | • Harness and connector<br>• Oxygen sensor<br>• Fuel pressure<br>• Injectors (Replace if defective.)<br>• Intake air leaks |
| 3 | Air flow sensor | H / L | 12 | Retained | • Harness and connector (If harness and connector are normal, replace air flow sensor assembly.) |
| 4 | Intake air temperature sensor | H / L | 13 | Retained | • Harness and connector<br>• Intake air temperature sensor |
| 5 | Throttle position sensor | H / L | 14 | Retained | • Harness and connector<br>• Throttle position sensor<br>• Idle switch |
| 6 | Coolant temperature sensor | H / L | 21 | Retained | • Harness and connector<br>• Coolant temperature sensor |
| 7 | Crank angle sensor | H / L | 22 | Retained | • Harness and connector (If harness and connector are normal, replace distributor assembly.) |

Courtesy of Mitsubishi Motor Sales of America.

*Self-Diagnostic Code Chart (Galant 1 of 2)*

| Output preference order | Diagnosis item | Malfunction code | | | Check item (Remedy) |
|---|---|---|---|---|---|
| | | Output signal pattern | No. | Memory | |
| 8 | Top dead center sensor (No. 1 cylinder) |  | 23 | Retained | • Harness and connector (If harness and connector are normal, replace distributor assembly.) |
| 9 | Vehicle-speed sensor (reed switch) |  | 24 | Retained | • Harness and connector<br>• Vehicle-speed sensor (reed switch) |
| 10 | Barometric pressure sensor |  | 25 | Retained | • Harness and connector (If harness and connector are normal, replace air flow sensor assembly.) |
| 11 | Injector | | 41 | Retained | • Harness and connector<br>• Injector coil resistance |
| 12 | Fuel pump | | 42 | Retained | • Harness and connector<br>• Control relay |
| 13 | EGR* |  | 43 | Retained | • Harness and connector<br>• EGR thermo-sensor<br>• EGR valve<br>• Thermo-valve<br>• EGR valve control vacuum |
| 14 | Normal state |  | – | – | – |

Remarks
1. Replace the electronic control unit (ECU) is a malfunction code is output although the inspection reveals that there is no problem with the check items.
2. The diagnosis item marked * is applicable to vehicles for California only.

Courtesy of Mitsubishi Motor Sales of America.

***Self-Diagnostic Code Chart (Galant 2 of 2)***

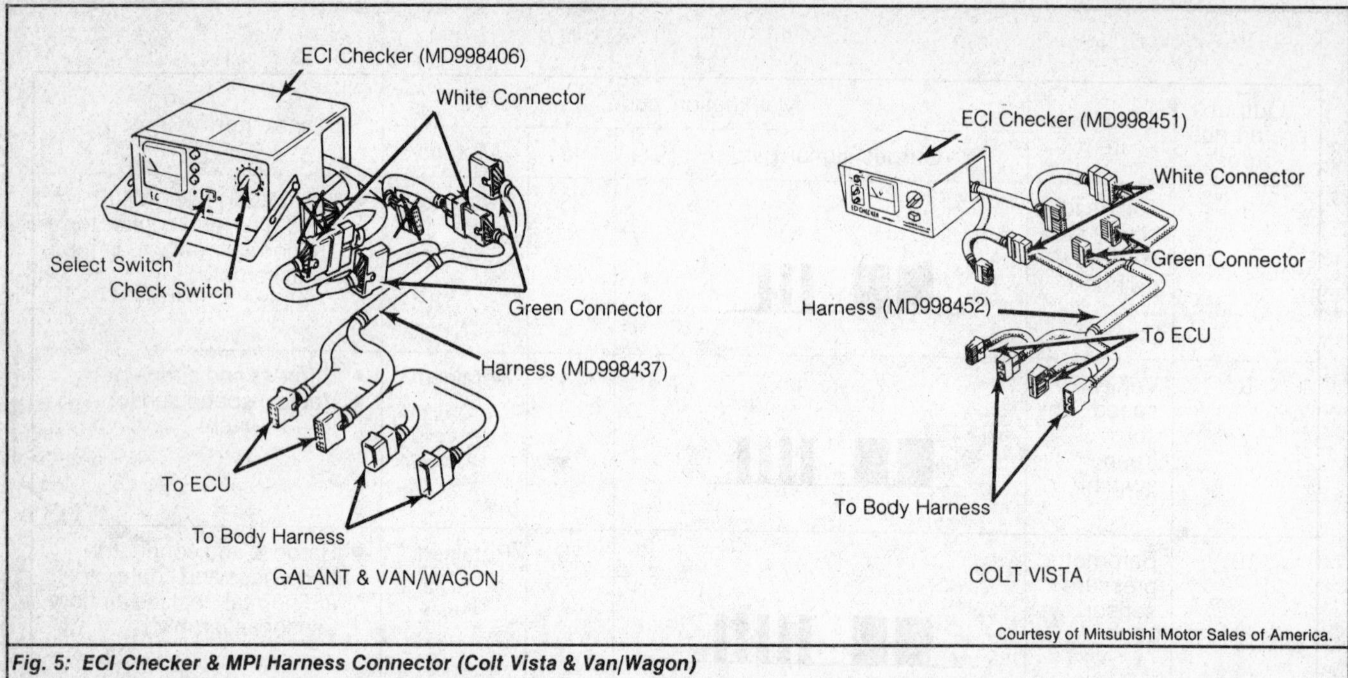
ECI Checker (MD998406)
White Connector
Select Switch
Check Switch
Green Connector
Harness (MD998437)
To ECU
To Body Harness
GALANT & VAN/WAGON
ECI Checker (MD998451)
White Connector
Green Connector
Harness (MD998452)
To ECU
To Body Harness
COLT VISTA
Courtesy of Mitsubishi Motor Sales of America.

*Fig. 5: ECI Checker & MPI Harness Connector (Colt Vista & Van/Wagon)*

***NOTE: On Colt Vista and Van/Wagon, perform MPI Inspection Test only after completing all steps of preceding Self-Diagnosis test.***

## MPI INSPECTION TEST (USING ECI CHECKER MD998451 OR MD998406)

***NOTE: ECI Checker (MD998451 or MD998406) is only used on Colt Vista and Van/Wagon models.***

**Output Signal Chart-Step 1 – 1)** Turn ignition off and disconnect negative battery cable. Remove large and small harness connectors from ECU. On Colt Vista, ECU is located under driver's seat. On Van/Wagon, ECU is located behind driver's side seat belt retractor.
**2)** Turn ignition switch to "LOCK" position. On ECI Checker (MD998451 for Colt Vista, MD998406 for Van/Wagon), set check switch to "OFF" position and select switch to "A" position.
**3)** Connect White connectors (labeled "CHECKER") of Harness Connector (MD998452 for Colt Vista, MD998437 for Van/Wagon) to ECI checker. Connect harness connector to ECU and harness connectors. *See Fig. 5*.
**4)** Perform checks according to appropriate MPI SYSTEM OUTPUT SIGNAL CHARTS-STEP 1 at end of this article. If checker shows any deviation from specification, check sensor and related electrical wiring. Repair or replace as necessary. After repair, recheck with ECI checker to ensure repair has corrected problem.

**Output Signal Chart-Step 2 – 1)** Turn ignition switch to "LOCK" position. Set check switch of ECI checker to "OFF" position. Disconnect White connectors from ECI checker. Connect Green connectors to ECI checker. *See Fig. 5*. Perform checks according to appropriate MPI SYSTEM OUTPUT SIGNAL CHARTS-STEP 2 at end of this article..
**2)** If checker shows any deviation from specification, check sensor and related wiring harness. Repair or replace as necessary. After repair, recheck with ECI checker to ensure repair has corrected problem.
**3)** Set ignition switch to "LOCK" position. Set check switch of ECI checker to "OFF" position. Remove connectors of ECI checker and harness connector from ECU and body side harness connectors.
**4)** Ensure power supply to ECU is disconnected for at least 15 seconds. This will erase memory from ECU. Connect body side harness connectors to ECU. Perform road test to ensure trouble has been eliminated.

## COMPONENT TESTING & INSPECTION

***NOTE: For components and models not shown, special multi-use tester or ECI tester must be used. See appropriate GALANT MULTI-USE TESTER CHECK CHARTS or COLT VISTA & VAN/WAGON MPI SYSTEM OUTPUT SIGNAL CHARTS at end of this article.***

**Airflow Sensor (Van/Wagon) – 1)** Disconnect airflow sensor connector. Install Harness (MD998463) between unattached connectors. *See Fig. 6*. Warm engine and bring to normal idle. Measure voltage between terminals No. 5 (Red) and No. 4 (Black).
**2)** With engine idling or at 3000 RPM, 2.2-3.2 volts should be present. If not, replace airflow sensor.

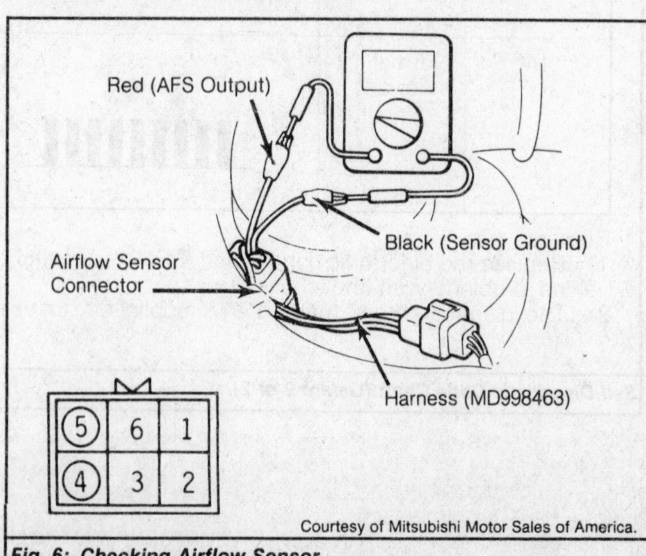
Red (AFS Output)
Black (Sensor Ground)
Airflow Sensor
Connector
Harness (MD998463)
5 6 1
4 3 2
Courtesy of Mitsubishi Motor Sales of America.

*Fig. 6: Checking Airflow Sensor*

**Atmospheric/Barometric Pressure Sensor (Van/Wagon) – 1)** Disconnect airflow sensor connector. Install Harness (MD998463) between unattached connectors. *See Fig. 6*. Warm engine and bring to normal idle.

**2)** Measure voltage between terminals No. 3 (Green) and No. 4 (Black). Slowly cover about half of air cleaner intake. Voltage should drop as air intake is covered. If not, replace airflow sensor assembly.

**Intake Air Temperature Sensor** – Disconnect airflow sensor connector. Check intake air temperature sensor by measuring resistance between terminals No. 2 and 4. *See Fig. 6*. Replace airflow sensor assembly if not to specification.

***INTAKE AIR TEMPERATURE SENSOR RESISTANCE***

| Temperature °F (°C) | Ohms |
|---|---|
| 32 (0) | 6000 |
| 68 (20) | 2700 |
| 176 (80) | 400 |

**Coolant Temperature Sensor – 1)** Remove coolant temperature sensor from intake manifold and place end of sensor in water. Do not allow sensor to touch container. Terminal connector portion of sensor should be .12" (3.0 mm) above water.

**2)** Gradually heat water and read resistance values at terminal connectors. See COOLANT TEMPERATURE SENSOR RESISTANCE table. If not within specifications, replace sensor.

***COOLANT TEMPERATURE SENSOR RESISTANCE***

| Temperature °F (°C) | Ohms |
|---|---|
| 32 (0) | 5900 |
| 68 (20) | 2500 |
| 104 (40) | 1100 |
| 176 (80) | 300 |

**Idle Switch (Galant)** – Disconnect TPS connector and connect Harness (MD998464) on idle switch side. Check continuity across TPS connector terminal No. 1 and ground. *See Fig. 7*. With accelerator pedal depressed, no continuity should be present. With accelerator pedal released, continuity should be present. Replace idle switch if not to specification.

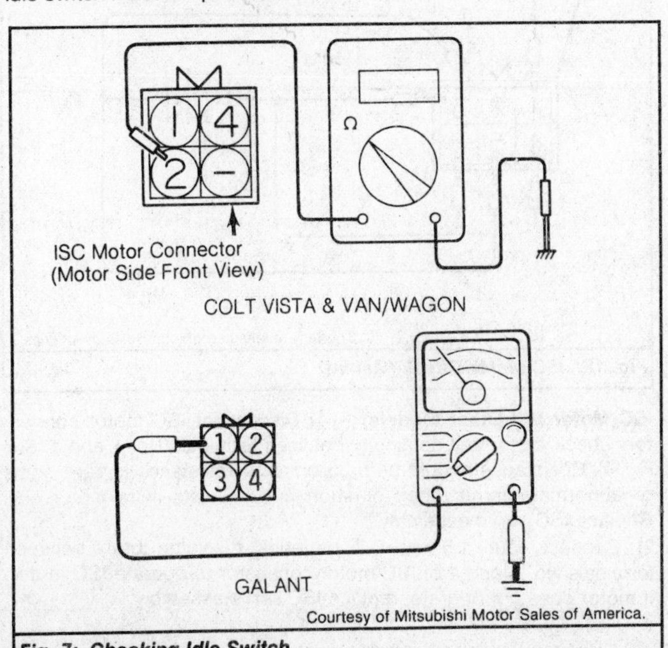
ISC Motor Connector
(Motor Side Front View)
COLT VISTA & VAN/WAGON
GALANT
Courtesy of Mitsubishi Motor Sales of America.

***Fig. 7: Checking Idle Switch***

**Idle Switch (All Other Models) – 1)** Disconnect ISC servo connector. Check for continuity between terminal No. 2 and ground. *See Fig. 7*.

**2)** With accelerator pedal depressed, continuity should be present. With accelerator depressed, no continuity should be present. If out of specification, replace ISC servo assembly.

**Throttle Position Sensor (Galant) – 1)** Disconnect TPS sensor connector. Connect Harness (MD998464) to disconnected sensor. Using an ohmmeter, measure resistance between terminals No. 2 (Red) and No. 3 (White). *See Fig. 8*. Resistance should be 3.5-6.5 ohms.

**2)** Check resistance between terminals No. 2 (Red) and No. 4 (Blue). Operate throttle valve from closed to wide open throttle. Ensure resistance changes smoothly throughout entire range. If not to specification, replace TPS.

**Throttle Position Sensor (All Other Models) – 1)** Disconnect throttle position sensor connector. Check resistance between terminals No. 1 and 3. *See Fig. 8*. Total resistance should be 3500-6500 ohms.

**2)** Attach ohmmeter between terminals No. 1 and 2. Operate throttle valve from closed to wide open throttle. Ensure resistance changes smoothly throughout entire range. If not to specification, replace TPS.

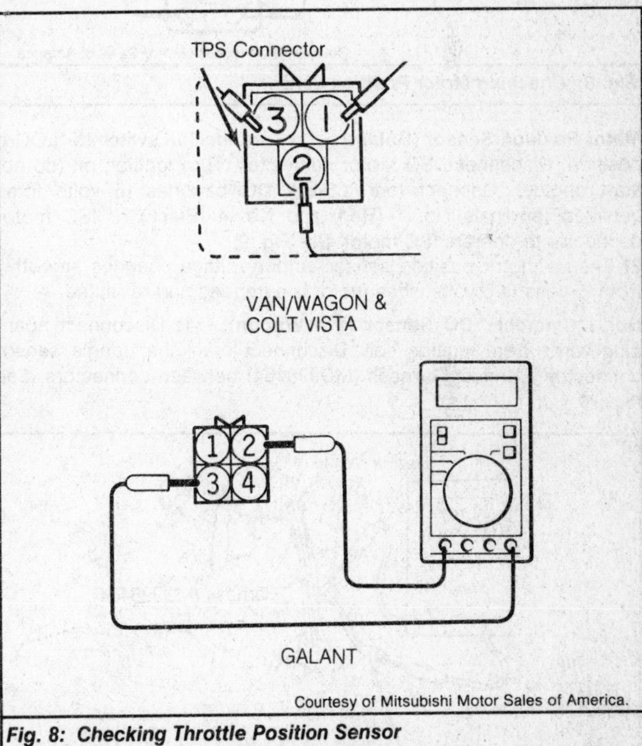
TPS Connector
VAN/WAGON &
COLT VISTA
GALANT
Courtesy of Mitsubishi Motor Sales of America.

***Fig. 8: Checking Throttle Position Sensor***

**Motor Position Sensor (Van/Wagon) – 1)** Disconnect motor position sensor connector and attach Harness (MD998464) to disconnected sensor connector. Disconnect ISC motor connector and connect Harness (MD998464) to disconnected ISC motor connector. DO NOT connect to ECU side connector. *See Fig. 9*.

**2)** Measure resistance between terminals No. 3 (White) and No. 4 (Black) of motor position sensor. Resistance should be 4000-6000 ohms.

**3)** Attach ohmmeter between terminals No. 1 (Red) and No. 4 (Black) of motor position sensor. Connect four 6-volt DC batteries between terminals No. 1 (Red) and No. 4 (Black) of ISC motor connector to operate ISC motor. *See Fig. 9*.

**4)** Ensure motor position sensor resistance changes smoothly when motor is extended or retracted. Resistance should change from 500 ohms to approximately 4000-6000 ohms. If not to specification, replace ISC servo assembly.

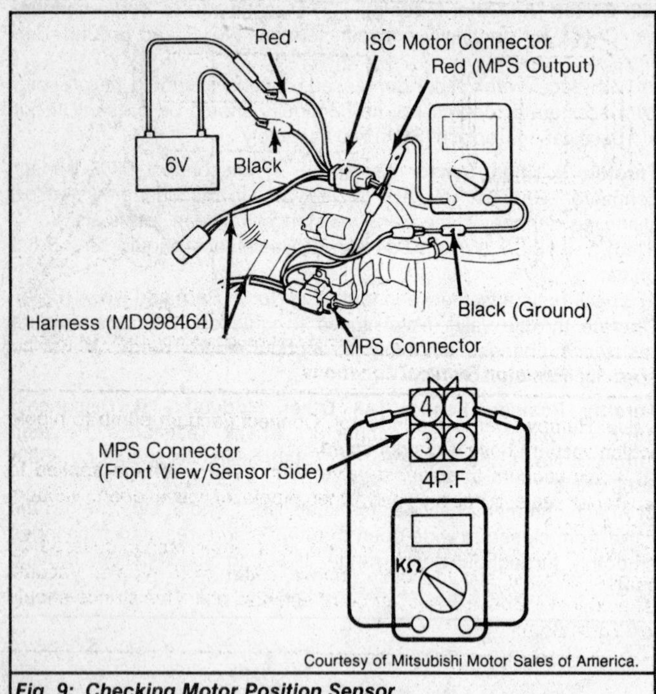
Red
ISC Motor Connector
Red (MPS Output)
6V
Black
Black (Ground)
Harness (MD998464)
MPS Connector
MPS Connector
(Front View/Sensor Side)
4P.F
KΩ
Courtesy of Mitsubishi Motor Sales of America.

*Fig. 9: Checking Motor Position Sensor*

**Motor Position Sensor (Galant) – 1)** Turn ignition switch to "LOCK" position. Disconnect ISC motor connector. Turn ignition on (do not start engine). Connect four 1.5-volt DC batteries (6 volts total) between terminals No. 1 (Red) and No. 4 (Black) of ISC motor connector to operate ISC motor. *See Fig. 9.*

**2)** Ensure motor position sensor output voltage changes smoothly from .5 volts to 5 volts when motor is extended and retracted.

**No. 1 Cylinder TDC Sensor (Van/Wagon) – 1)** Disconnect spark plug wires from ignition coil. Disconnect crankshaft angle sensor connector. Connect Harness (MD998464) between connectors. *See Fig. 10.*

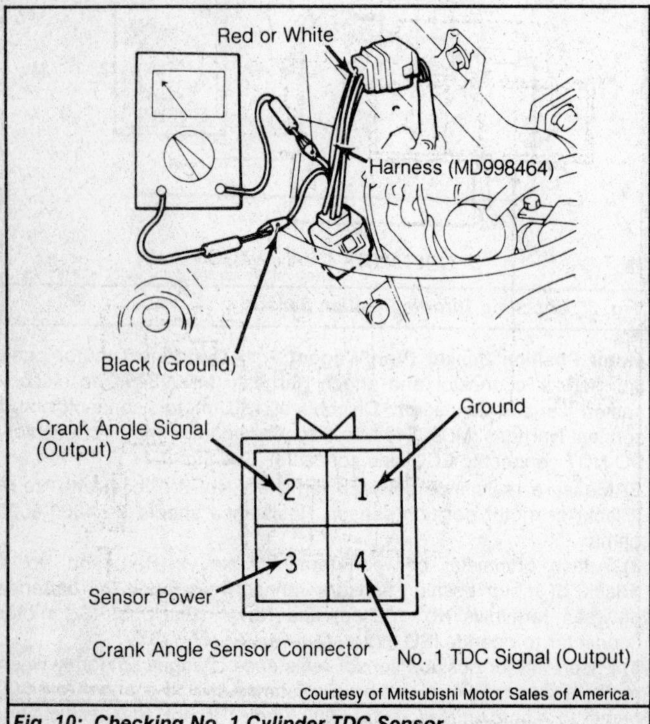
Red or White
Harness (MD998464)
Black (Ground)
Crank Angle Signal
(Output)
Ground
Sensor Power
Crank Angle Sensor Connector
No. 1 TDC Signal (Output)
Courtesy of Mitsubishi Motor Sales of America.

*Fig. 10: Checking No. 1 Cylinder TDC Sensor*

**2)** Measure output voltage between terminals No. 2 and 1 (crank angle signal) and No. 4 and 1 (No. 1 TDC signal) while cranking engine. Voltage between terminals No. 2 and 1 should be .5-1 volt (needle wavers). Voltage between terminals No. 4 and 1 should be 2-2.5 volts. If voltage is not to specification, check sensor power and ground circuit. If okay, check distributor.

**Oxygen Sensor** – Warm engine until coolant temperature is 185-205°F (85-95°C). Remove oxygen sensor connector and connect voltmeter. With engine above 1300 RPM, measure output voltage. Voltage should be approximately one volt. If not, replace oxygen sensor.

**Inhibitor Switch (Colt Vista Automatic Transmission Only)** – Disconnect inhibitor switch connector. Check for continuity between terminals No. 8 and 9 while operating select lever. *See Fig. 11.* Continuity should exist with lever in Park or Neutral. No continuity should be present when in other gears. If result is otherwise, adjust inhibitor switch.

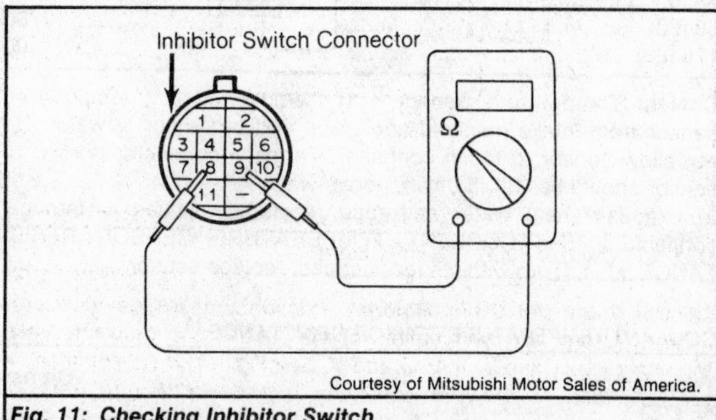
Inhibitor Switch Connector
Ω
Courtesy of Mitsubishi Motor Sales of America.

*Fig. 11: Checking Inhibitor Switch*

**ISC Motor (Galant)** – Disconnect ISC motor connector. Connect positive voltage of four 1.5 volt (6 volts total) DC batteries between terminals No. 2 and 5. Connect negative battery voltage, in turn, to terminals No. 3-6, 1-6, 1-4 and 3-4. *See Fig. 12.* Motor is okay if it vibrates during inspection.

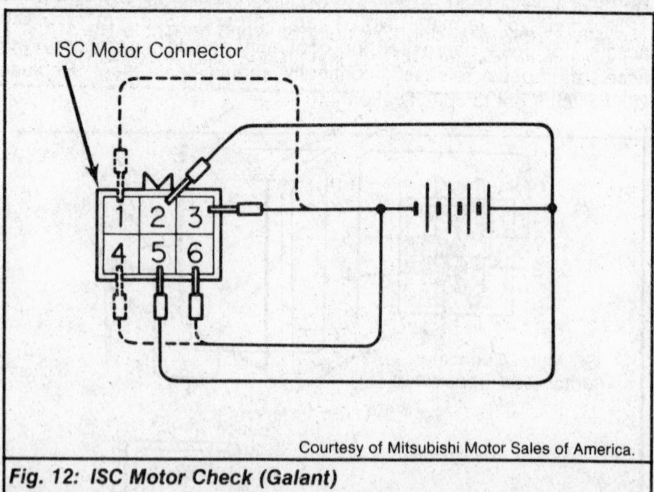
ISC Motor Connector
Courtesy of Mitsubishi Motor Sales of America.

*Fig. 12: ISC Motor Check (Galant)*

**ISC Motor (All Other Models) – 1)** Disconnect ISC motor connector. Check motor coil continuity between terminals No. 1 and 4. *See Fig. 7.* Resistance should be 5-35 ohms. If resistance is zero ohms or abnormally large, open or short circuit exists in in motor coil. Replace ISC servo assembly.

**2)** Connect four 1.5-volt DC batteries (6 volts total) between terminals No. 1 and 4 of ISC motor connector to operate ISC motor. If motor does not operate, replace ISC servo assembly.

**Control Relay (Galant) – 1)** Remove cover under glove box and remove glove box. Disconnect control relay and 10 pin connector. Apply positive battery voltage to terminal No. 10 and negative battery voltage to terminal No. 8. Using a voltmeter, ensure battery voltage is present between terminal No. 4 and ground and terminal No. 5 and ground. *See Fig. 13.*.

**2)** Apply negative battery voltage to terminal No. 6 and positive battery voltage to terminal No. 9. Using an ohmmeter, ensure continuity is present at terminals No. 3 and 2. With negative voltage disconnected, no continuity should be present.

**3)** Connect positive battery voltage to terminal No. 3 and negative battery voltage to terminal No. 7. Battery voltage should be present between terminal No. 2 and ground.

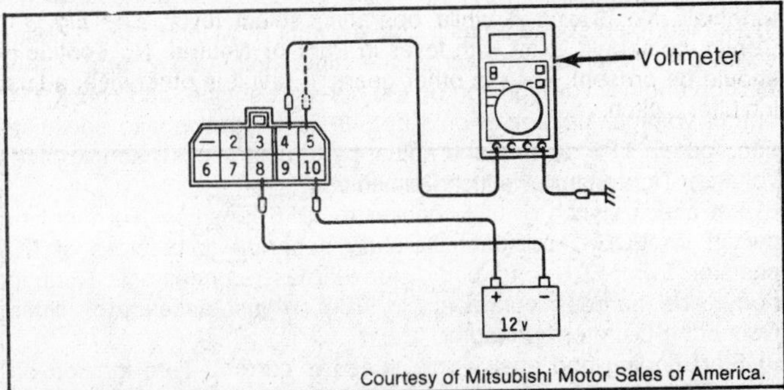
Voltmeter
2
3
4
5
6
7
8
9
10
12 v
Courtesy of Mitsubishi Motor Sales of America.

*Fig. 13: Control Relay Check (Galant)*

**Control Relay (All Other Models) – 1)** Disconnect electrical connector. Using an ohmmeter, check continuity between relay terminals No. 1 and 7, then 3 and 7. *See Fig. 14.* If no continuity is present, relay is okay. If continuity is present, control relay is defective.

**2)** Apply battery voltage across terminals No. 8 (positive) and No. 4 (negative) while checking continuity between terminals No. 3 and 7. If continuity is present, relay is okay. If not, replace relay.

**3)** Apply battery voltage across terminals No. 6 (positive) and No. 4 (negative) while checking continuity between terminals No. 1 and 7. If continuity is present, relay is okay. If not, replace relay.

**4)** Apply battery voltage across terminals No. 5 (positive) and No. 2 (negative) while checking continuity between terminals No. 1 and 7. If continuity is present, relay is okay. If not, relay is defective.

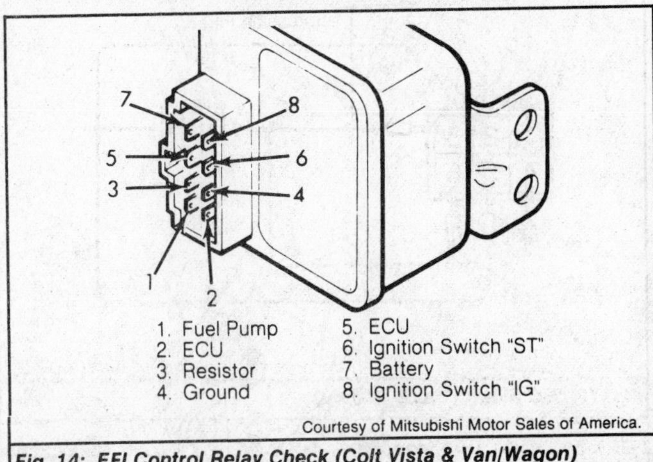
7
8
5
6
3
4
1
2
1. Fuel Pump
2. ECU
3. Resistor
4. Ground
5. ECU
6. Ignition Switch "ST"
7. Battery
8. Ignition Switch "IG"
Courtesy of Mitsubishi Motor Sales of America.

*Fig. 14: EFI Control Relay Check (Colt Vista & Van/Wagon)*

**Resistor (Colt Vista & Van/Wagon)** – Disconnect resistor harness connector and check resistance between resistor terminal No. 1 and other terminals one at a time. *See Fig. 15.* If resistance is 5.5-6.5 ohms, resistor is okay. If resistance is zero or abnormally large, resistor is defective.

**Fuel Pressure Solenoid Valve (Colt Vista & Van/Wagon) – 1)** Disconnect vacuum hose (Black with Blue stripe) from solenoid valve. Remove harness connector. Connect vacuum pump to nipple which vacuum hose was connected.

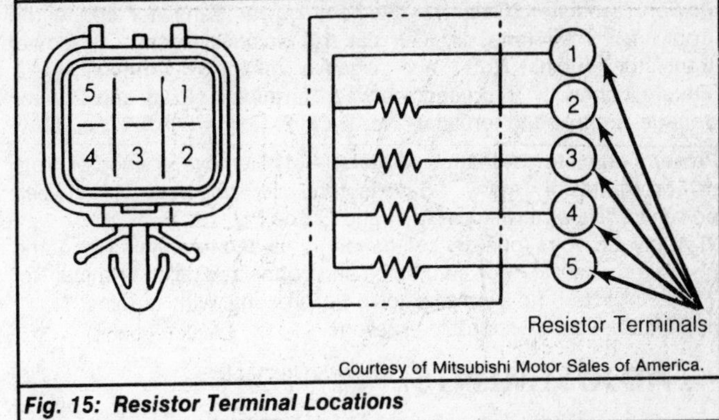
5
1
4
3
2
1
2
3
4
5
Resistor Terminals
Courtesy of Mitsubishi Motor Sales of America.

*Fig. 15: Resistor Terminal Locations*

**2)** Apply vacuum to solenoid valve. With battery voltage applied to solenoid valve terminals, and other nipple of valve open, vacuum should hold.

**3)** With no battery voltage applied, and other nipple covered by finger, vacuum should hold. Remove finger from nipple. Vacuum should leak. Measure resistance of solenoid coil. Resistance should be 28-34 ohms.

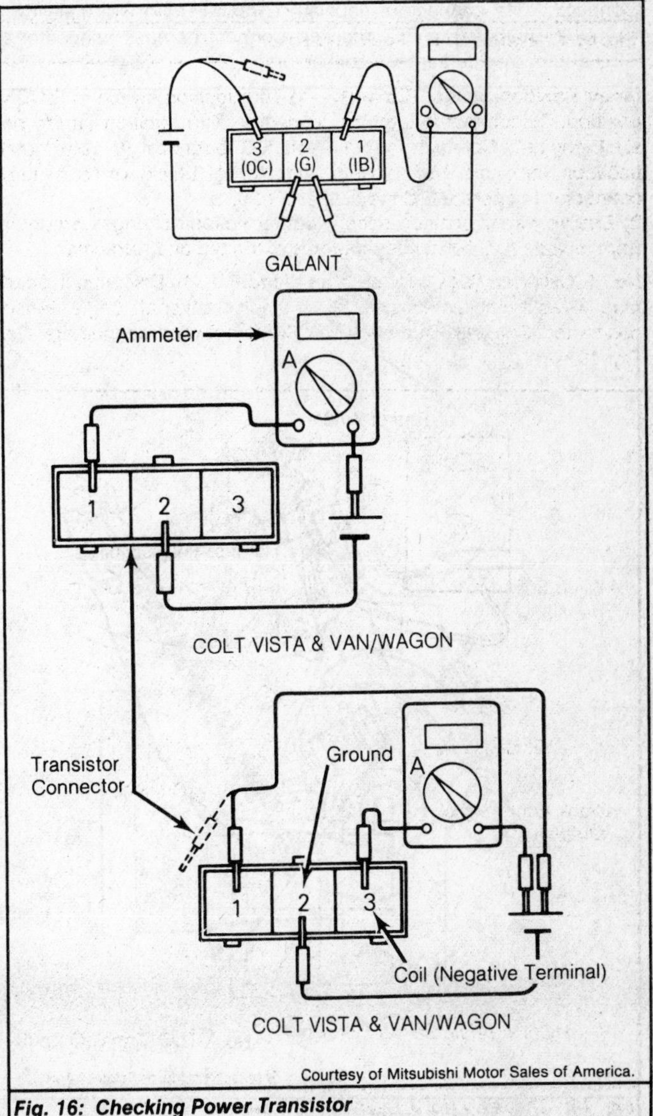
3 (0C)
2 (G)
1 (IB)
GALANT
Ammeter
A
1
2
3
COLT VISTA & VAN/WAGON
Transistor Connector
Ground
A
1
2
3
Coil (Negative Terminal)
COLT VISTA & VAN/WAGON
Courtesy of Mitsubishi Motor Sales of America.

*Fig. 16: Checking Power Transistor*

**Power Transistor (Galant)** - Remove power transistor connector. Apply 1.5 volts (one dry cell battery) positive voltage to power transistor terminal No. 1 and negative voltage to terminal No. 2. Ensure continuity is present between terminals No. 3 and 2 when voltage is applied to terminals No. 1 and 2.

**Power Transistor (All Other Models)** - **1)** Remove connector from power transistor. Apply 1.5 volts (one dry cell battery) between power transistor terminals No. 1 and 2. *See Fig. 16*.

**2)** Apply 1.5 volts (one dry cell battery) between terminals No. 3 and 2 with terminal No. 1 disconnected and connected. With terminal No. 1 disconnected, no voltage should be present. With terminal No. 1 connected, voltage should be present.

## ADJUSTMENTS

### IDLE SPEED CONTROL & THROTTLE POSITION SENSOR

**Colt Vista** - **1)** Engine coolant temperature should be 185-205°F (85-95°C). Turn lights, cooling fan and accessories off. Place transmission in Neutral or Park. Place steering wheel in straight-ahead position. Loosen accelerator cable. Connect a tachometer.

**2)** Turn ignition switch to "LOCK" position. Remove large and small harness connector from ECU. On ECI Checker (MD998451), set check switch to "OFF" position and select switch to "A" position. Connect White connectors (labeled "CHECKER") of Harness Connector (MD998452) to ECI checker. Connect harness connector to ECU and body side harness connectors.

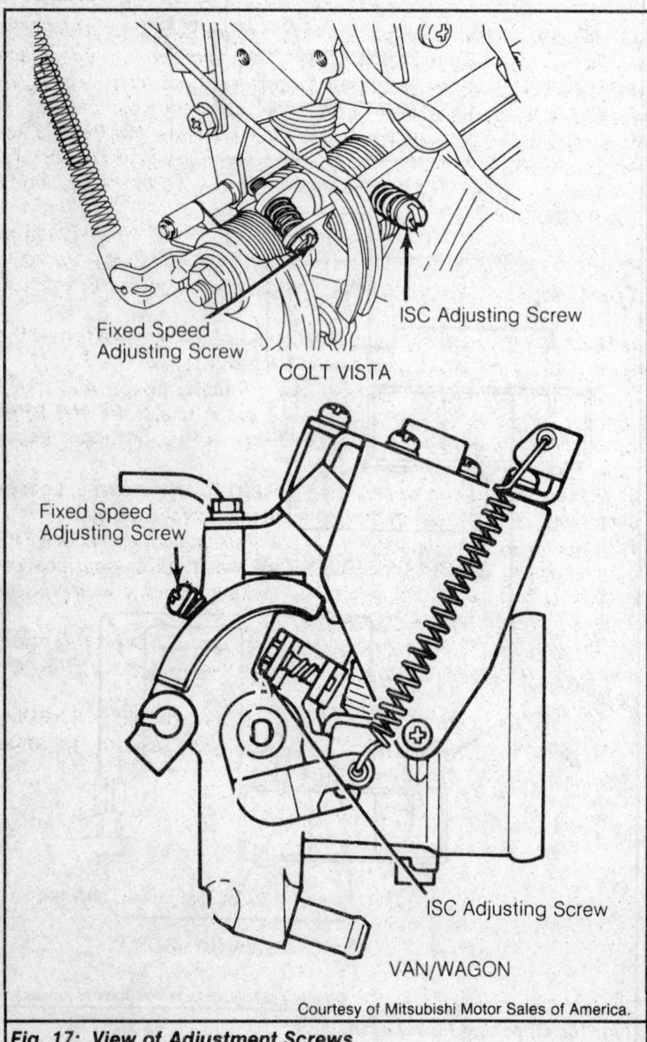
Fixed Speed Adjusting Screw
ISC Adjusting Screw
COLT VISTA
Fixed Speed Adjusting Screw
ISC Adjusting Screw
VAN/WAGON
Courtesy of Mitsubishi Motor Sales of America.

*Fig. 17: View of Adjustment Screws*

**3)** Connect voltmeter to "Extension" terminals of ECI checker. Set switch on ECI checker from "CHECK METER" to "EXTENSION" position. Set check switch to "6" position and select switch to "A" position.

**4)** Turn ignition on (do not start engine) and hold for 15 seconds or more. This will set ISC motor at idle position. Turn ignition switch to "LOCK" position. Disconnect ISC servo motor connector. Put ISC motor in idle position.

**5)** Open throttle valve by hand 2-3 times and allow to return with a snap each time. Loosen fixed speed adjusting screw. *See Fig. 17*. Start engine and run at idle. Check engine speed and motor position sensor output voltage. Engine speed should be 700 RPM. Output voltage should be .9 volts. If not to specification, adjust using ISC adjusting screw. *See Fig. 17*.

**6)** Tighten fixed speed adjusting screw until RPM increases. Loosen screw until RPM ceases to drop, then tighten screw 1/2 turn.

**7)** Stop engine. Turn ignition on (do not start engine) and check TPS output voltage. Voltage should be .48-.52 volts. If not to specification, loosen TPS screws and adjust by turning (clockwise increases voltage). Tighten screws after adjustment.

**8)** Set check switch of ECI checker to "OFF" position. Turn ignition switch to "LOCK" position. Carefully separate connectors of ECI checker from ECU and body side harness connectors. Connect body side harness connector to ECU. Adjust accelerator cable. Connect ISC motor connector.

**9)** Start engine and ensure idle speed is correct. Turn ignition off. Disconnect battery for 5-6 seconds to erase diagnosis memory. Reconnect battery.

**Galant** - **1)** Connect timing light. Start and warm engine to normal operating temperature. Ensure front wheels are in straight-ahead position, transaxle is in Neutral, and all accessories and cooling fan are off.

**2)** Insert paper clip into connector located between radio noise supression filter and primary side of ignition coil. *See Fig. 18*. Connect tachometer lead to paper clip.

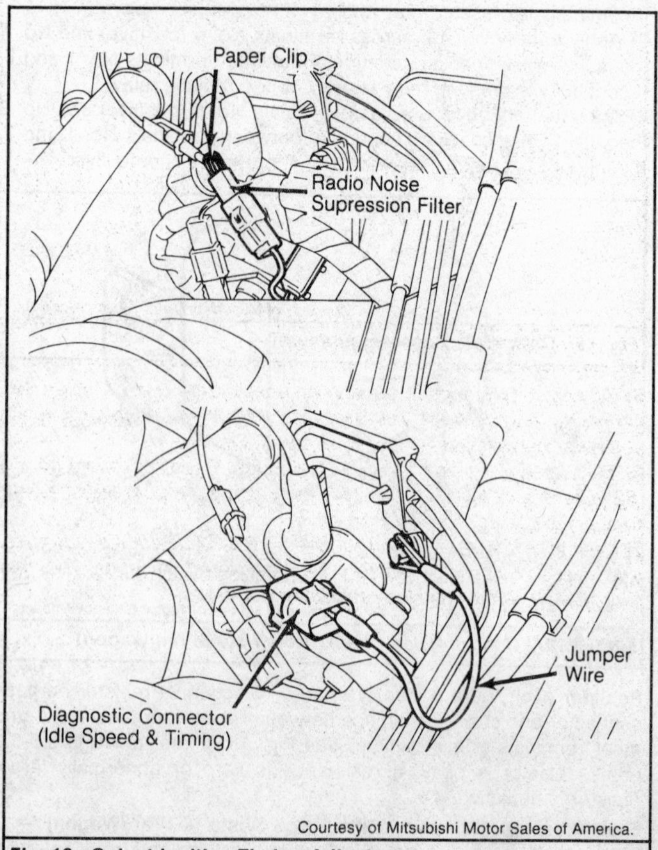
Paper Clip
Radio Noise Supression Filter
Jumper Wire
Diagnostic Connector (Idle Speed & Timing)
Courtesy of Mitsubishi Motor Sales of America.

*Fig. 18: Galant Ignition Timing Adjustment*

**3)** Connect jumper wire to diagnostic connector to fix idle speed and ignition timing. Using a jumper wire, ground test terminal of self-diagnostic connector. *See Fig. 19*. Start and run engine at 2000-3000 RPM for 5 seconds. Allow engine to idle for at least 2 minutes, then check curb idle speed. See IDLE SPEED SPECIFICATIONS table.

**4)** If incorrect, turn idle speed adjustment screw. Turn ignition off and remove jumper wire self-diagnostic connector. Start engine and check base idle speed. If base idle is incorrect, check Idle Speed Control (ISC) system.

***GALANT IDLE SPEED SPECIFICATIONS***

| Application | RPM |
|---|---|
| Curb Idle | 650-750 |
| Base Idle | 600-800 |

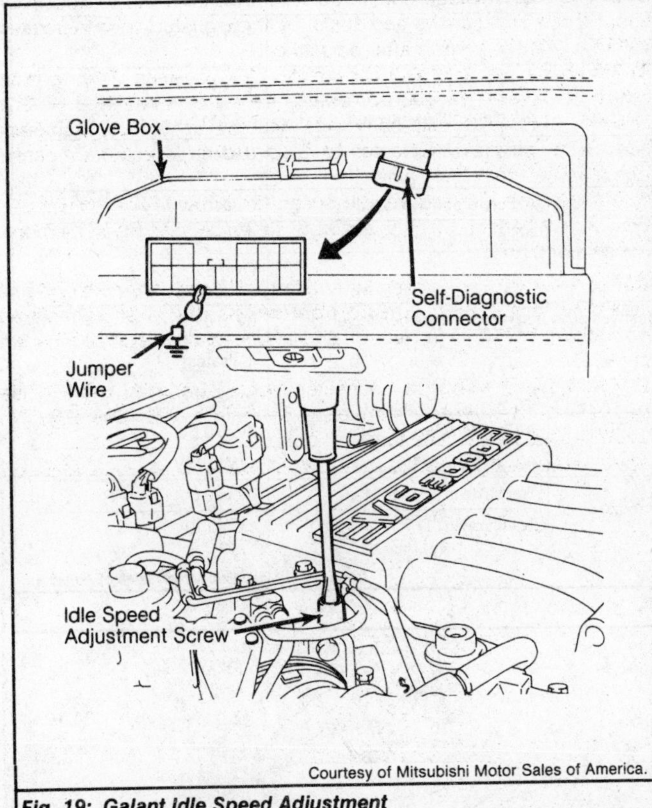
Glove Box
Self-Diagnostic Connector
Jumper Wire
Idle Speed Adjustment Screw
Courtesy of Mitsubishi Motor Sales of America.

***Fig. 19: Galant Idle Speed Adjustment***

**5)** To adjust TPS, loosen tension on accelerator cable. Unplug TPS connector and connect Test Harness (MD998464). Connect digital voltmeter between terminals No. 2 and 4. *See Fig. 20*.

**6)** Turn ignition on and check TPS voltage. Reading should be .48-.52 volts. If incorrect, loosen TPS mounting bolts and adjust sensor to specified value. Turn ignition off.

**7)** Unplug test harness and reconnect TPS. Start engine and check idle speed. Disconnect battery terminal for 5 seconds and then reconnect it. Adjust tension on accelerator cable.

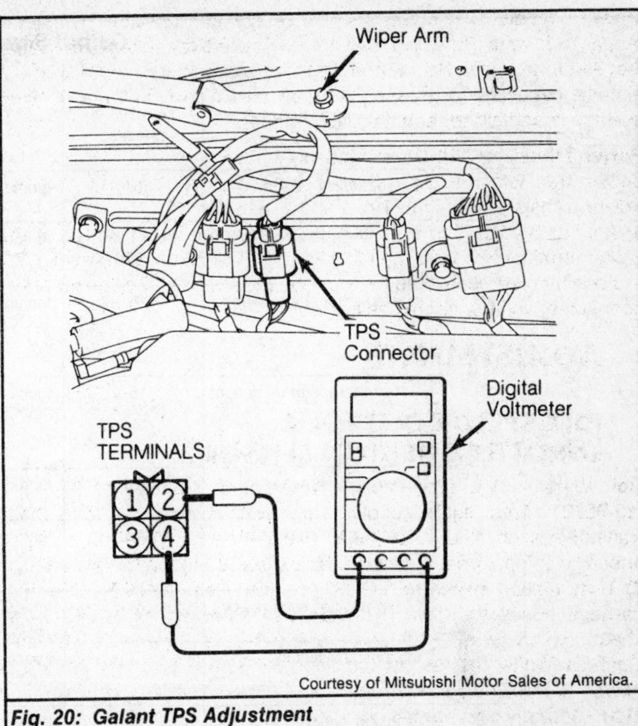
Wiper Arm
TPS Connector
Digital Voltmeter
TPS TERMINALS
1
2
3
4
Courtesy of Mitsubishi Motor Sales of America.

***Fig. 20: Galant TPS Adjustment***

**Van/Wagon – 1)** Engine coolant temperature should be 185-205°F (85-95°C). Turn lights, cooling fan and accessories off. Place transmission in Neutral or Park. Place steering wheel in straight-ahead position. Loosen accelerator cable. Connect a tachometer.

**2)** Disconnect TPS connector. Connect Harness (MD998459 for Galant, MD998478 for Van/Wagon) between separated connectors. Connect a voltmeter between harness Blue output terminal No. 2 and Black ground terminal No. 1.

**3)** Turn ignition on (do not start engine) and hold 15 seconds or more. This will set ISC motor at idle position. Turn ignition switch to "LOCK" position. Disconnect ISC servo motor connector. Put ISC motor in idle position.

**4)** Open throttle valve by hand 2-3 times and allow to return with a snap each time. Loosen fixed speed adjusting screw. *See Fig. 17*.

**5)** Start engine and run at idle. Check engine speed and motor position sensor output voltage. Engine speed should be 750 RPM. Output voltage should be .9 volts. If not to specification, adjust using ISC adjusting screw. *See Fig. 17*.

**6)** Tighten fixed speed adjusting screw until RPM increases. Loosen screw until RPM ceases to drop, then loosen screw 1/2 turn.

**7)** Stop engine. Turn ignition on (do not start engine) and check TPS output voltage. Voltage should be .48-.52 volt. If not to specification, loosen TPS screws and adjust by turning (clockwise increases voltage). Tighten screws after adjustment.

**8)** Turn ignition off and adjust accelerator cable. Connect ISC motor connector. Disconnect harness and voltmeter. Connect TPS connector.

**9)** Start engine and ensure idle speed is correct (750 ± 100 RPM). Turn ignition off. Disconnect battery for 5-6 seconds to erase diagnosis memory. Reconnect battery.

***Output Signal Chart (Step 1)***

| ECI Checker Operation | | Check Item | ECU Terminal # Checked | Condition | | Test Specification |
|---|---|---|---|---|---|---|
| Select Switch | Check Switch | | | | | |
| | 1 | Power supply | 51 | Ignition switch "LOCK → ON" | | 11V to 13V |
| | 2 | Crank angle sensor | 1 | Ignition switch "LOCK→START" | | 1.8V to 2.5V |
| | | | | 3000 rpm | | |
| | 3 | Intake air temperature sensor | 5 | Ignition switch "LOCK → ON" | 0°C (32°F)<br>20°C (68°F)<br>40°C (104°F)<br>80°C (176°F) | 3.4V to 3.6V<br>2.5V to 2.7V<br>1.7V to 1.9V<br>0.6V to 0.8V |
| | 4 | Coolant temperature sensor | 6 | Ignition switch "LOCK → ON" | 0°C (32°F)<br>20°C (68°F)<br>40°C (104°F)<br>80°C (176°F) | 3.4V to 3.6V<br>2.5V to 2.7V<br>1.5V to 1.7V<br>0.5V to 0.7V |
| | 5 | Power supply for sensor | 10 | Ignition switch "LOCK → ON" | | 4.5V to 5.5V |
| Set to "A" | 6 | Throttle position sensor | 15 | Ignition switch "LOCK → ON" (Warm engine) | Accelerator fully closed | 0.4V to 0.7V |
| | | | | | Accelerator fully opened | 4.5V to 5.5V |
| | 7 | Motor position sensor | 3 | Ignition switch "LOCK → ON" | After 15 seconds | 0.8V to 1.2V |
| | 8 | Idle position switch | 7 | Ignition switch "LOCK → ON" | Accelerator fully closed | 0V to 0.6V |
| | | | | | Accelerator fully opened | 8V to 13V |
| | 9 | Cranking signal | 55 | Ignition switch "LOCK → START" | 21 | Over 8V |
| | 10 | Reed switch for vehicle speed | 19 | Start engine, transmission in first or drive and operate vehicle slowly | | 0V to 0.6V ↑ (pulsates) ↓ Over 2V |
| | 11 | A/C switch | 56 | Ignition switch "LOCK → ON" | A/C switch OFF | 0V to 0.6V |
| | | | | | A/C switch ON*2 | 11V to 13V |
| | 12 | Inhibitor switch | 58 | Ignition switch "LOCK → ON" | Transaxle in "P" or "N" | 0V to 0.6V |
| | | | | | Transaxle in "D" | 11V to 13V |

NOTE *2 ON means compressor clutch engaged.

Courtesy of Mitsubishi Motor Sales of America.

***Output Signal Chart (Colt Vista & Van/Wagon, Step 1)***

# 1988 COMPUTERIZED ENGINE CONTROLS
# Chrysler & Mitsubishi MPI System (Cont.)

**Output Signal Chart (Step 1 Cont.)**

| ECI Checker Operation: Select Switch | ECI Checker Operation: Check Switch | Check Item | ECU Terminal # Checked | Condition | | Test Specification |
|---|---|---|---|---|---|---|
| Set to "B" | 1 | Fuel pressure exhange solenoid valve | 8 | Ignition switch "LOCK → START" | Coolant temp. less than 90°C (194°F) or air temp. less than 50° (122°F) | Over 8V |
| | | | | | Coolant temp. more than 90°C (194°F) or air temp. more than 50° (122°F) | 0V to 0.6V |
| | 2 | | | | | |
| | 3 | | | | | |
| | 4 | No. 1 cylinder sensor | 13 | Ignition switch "LOCK→ START" | | 0.2V to 1.5V (oscillatiing) |
| | | | | 3000 rpm | | 0.8V to 1.2V |
| | 5 | Air-flow sensor | 2 | Idling | | 2.2V to 3.2V |
| | | | | 3000 rpm | | |
| | 6 | | | | | |
| | 7 | Ignition control signal | 54 | Idling | | 0.3V to 0.8V |
| | | | | 3000 rpm | | 1.0V to 2V |
| | 8 | Oxygen Sensor *1 | 11 | Hold rpm constant above 1300, after 30 seconds from start of warm engine | | 0V to 0.6V ↑ (pulsates) ↓ 2V to 3V |
| | 9 | | | | | |
| | 10 | | | | | |
| | 11 | | | | | |
| | 12 | | | | | |

*1 There may also be differences from specifications if there is a malfunction of components other than the oxygen sensor

Courtesy of Mitsubishi Motor Sales of America.

**Output Signal Chart (Colt Vista & Van/Wagon, Step 1 Cont.)**

**Output Signal Chart (Step 2)**

| ECI Checker Operation: Select Switch | ECI Checker Operation: Check Switch | Check Item | ECU Terminal # Checked | Condition | | Test Specification |
|---|---|---|---|---|---|---|
| Set to "A" | 1 | | | | | |
| | 2 | Atmospheric pressure sensor | 20 | Ignition switch "LOCK → ON" | at sea level | 3.8V to 4.2V |
| | | | | Idling | | |
| | 3 | | | | | |
| | 4 | | | | | |
| | 5 | Power steering switch | 16 | Idling | | 12V to 15V |
| | | | | Turn steering wheel to stop | | 0V to 0.6V |
| | 6 | | | | | |
| | 7 | | | | | |
| | 8 | | | | | |
| | 9 | | | | | |
| | 10 | | | | | |
| | 11 | | | | | |
| | 12 | | | | | |

Courtesy of Mitsubishi Motor Sales of America.

**Output Signal Chart (Colt Vista & Van/Wagon, Step 2)**

### Output Signal Chart (Step 2 Cont.)

| ECI Checker Operation: Select Switch | ECI Checker Operation: Check Switch | Check Item | ECU Terminal # Checked | Condition | | Test Specification |
|---|---|---|---|---|---|---|
| Set to "B" | 1 | ISC motor for extension | 23 | Idling | A/C switch OFF → ON | Momentarily over 4V, then 0V to 2V |
| | 2 | ISC motor for retraction | 12 | Idling | A/C switch ON → OFF | Momentarily over 4V, then 0V to 2V |
| | 3 | A/C cutoff relay | 24 | Idling | A/C switch OFF → ON | Over 12V, then 0V to 0.6V |
| | 4 | Control relay | 22 | Ignition switch "LOCK → ON" | | 11V to 13V |
| | | | | Idling | | 0V to 0.6V |
| | 5 | | | | | |
| | 6 | Injector No. 1 pulse | 59 | Idling | | 12V to 14V |
| | | | | Quick acceleration from idling to above 2000 rpm with "N" or "P" position | | Slight drop |
| | 7 | Injector No. 2 pulse | 60 | Idling | | 12V to 14V |
| | | | | Quick acceleration from idling to above 2000 rpm with "N" or "P" position | | Slight drop |
| | 8 | | | | | |
| | 9 | Injector No. 3 pulse | 61 | Idling | | 12V to 14V |
| | | | | Quick acceleration from idling to above 2000 rpm with "N" or "P" position | | Slight drop |
| | 10 | | | | | |
| | 11 | Injector No. 4 pulse | 62 | Idling | | 12V to 14V |
| | | | | Quick acceleration from idling to above 2000 rpm with "N" or "P" position | | Slight drop |
| | 12 | Purge control solenoid valve | 17 | Idling (warm engine) | A/C switch OFF | 12V to 15V |
| | | | | | A/C switch ON | 0V to 0.6V |

Courtesy of Mitsubishi Motor Sales of America.

***Output Signal Chart (Colt Vista & Van/Wagon, Step 2 Cont.)***

| Check item (item No.) | Tester mode | Condition | | Test specification | Troubleshooting when outside the test specifications |
|---|---|---|---|---|---|
| Power supply (16) | Data transfer | Ignition switch: ON | | 11–13V | • Measure the battery voltage.<br>• Check the circuit that supplies the ECU power. |
| Throttle position sensor (14) | | Ignition switch: ON<br>Throttle valve: Idle position | | 400–600mV | • Check the throttle position sensor.<br>• Check the sensor circuit.<br>• Adjust the throttle position sensor. |
| Malfunction code read out | Self-diagnosis | Execute cranking for 4 seconds or more.<br>Ignition switch: ON | | Malfunction code is not output. | • Check the check items. (Refer to the self-diagnosis section.) |
| Fuel pump (07) | Actuator forced drive | Ignition switch: ON<br>Actuator drive | Squeeze the return hose. | Feel the fuel pulse with a finger. | • Check the fuel pump.<br>• Check the circuit that supplies power to the fuel pump. |
| | | | Listen near the fuel tank. | Pump driving sound is heard. | |
| TDC sensor (22) | Data transfer | Engine: Cranking<br>Tachometer: Connect | Cranking revolution speed [rpm] | Revolution speed [rpm] | • Check the power transistor and the ignition coil. (The tachometer reading is not proper.)<br>• Check the TDC sensor circuit. If the circuit is proper, replace the distributor assembly and recheck the system. |
| | | | Approx. 200 | Approx. 200 | |
| Ignition switch-ST (18) | | Ignition switch: ON | Engine stop | OFF | • Check the ignition switch-ST circuit.<br>• Check the ignition switch. |
| | | | Cranking | ON | |

Courtesy of Mitsubishi Motor Sales of America.

***Multi-Use Tester Check Chart (Galant Cranking Check)***

**Sensor inspection–Multi-use tester (MB991194) using**

| Check item (item No.) | Tester mode | Condition | | Test specification | Troubleshooting when outside the test specifications |
|---|---|---|---|---|---|
| Intake air temperature sensor (13) | Data transfer | Ignition switch: ON | Intake air temperature [°C (°F)] | Voltage [V] | • Check the air intake temperature sensor.<br>• Check the sensor circuit. |
| | | | 0 (32) | 3.4–3.6 | |
| | | | 20 (68) | 2.5–2.7 | |
| | | | 40 (104) | 1.7–1.9 | |
| | | | 80 (176) | 0.6–0.8 | |
| Coolant temperature sensor (21) | | Ignition switch: ON | Coolant temperature [°C (°F)] | Voltage [V] | • Check the engine coolant temperature sensor.<br>• Check the sensor circuit. |
| | | | 0 (32) | 3.4–3.6 | |
| | | | 20 (68) | 2.5–2.7 | |
| | | | 40 (104) | 1.5–1.7 | |
| | | | 80 (176) | 0.5–0.7 | |
| Barometric pressure sensor (25) | | Ignition switch: ON | Altitude [m (ft.)] | Pressure [mmHg] | • Check the barometric pressure sensing circuit. If the circuit is proper, replace the air flow sensor assembly and recheck the system. |
| | | | 0 (sea level) | 760 | |
| | | | 600 (1,970) | 710 | |
| | | | 1200 (3,940) | 660 | |
| | | | 1800 (5,910) | 610 | |
| Ignition switch-ST (18) | | Ignition switch: ON | | OFF | • Check the ignition switch-ST circuit.<br>• Check the ignition switch. |
| Throttle position sensor (14) | | Ignition switch: ON | Throttle valve | Voltage [mV] | • Check the throttle position sensor.<br>• Check the sensor circuit.<br>• Check for traces that the idle switch has moved. If traces are found, adjust the idle switch<br>• Adjust the throttle position sensor. |
| | | | Fully closed | 480–520 | |
| | | | Gradually open | The pressure increases according to the degree of opening of the valve. | |
| | | | Fully opened | 4,500–5,500 | |
| Idle switch (26) | Data transfer | Ignition switch: ON | Throttle valve: Idle position | ON | • Check the idle switch.<br>• Check the idle switch circuit.<br>• Adjustment of the accelerator cable.<br>• Adjustment of the automatic speed-control cable. |
| | | | Slightly open the throttle valve. | OFF | |
| TDC sensor (22) | | Engine: After warming up, idle the engine.<br>Tachometer: Connect | Engine revolution speed [rpm] | Revolution speed [rpm] | • Check the TDC sensor circuit. If the circuit is proper, replace the distributor assembly and recheck the system. |
| | | | 700 | 700 | |
| Power steering oil pressure switch (27) | | Engine: After warming up, idle the engine. | Steering wheel in neutral (foward direction) | OFF | • Check the power steering oil pressure switch.<br>• Check the oil pressure switch circuit. |
| | | | The steering wheel is turned a half turn. | ON | |
| Air conditioner switch (28) | | Engine: After warming up, idle the engine. | Air conditioner switch "OFF" | OFF | • Check the air conditioner system. |
| | | | Air conditioner switch "ON" | ON | |
| Inhibitor switch (29) | | Ignition switch: ON<br>NOTE: Automatic transaxle only | Shift lever "P" or "N" | N | • Check the inhibitor switch.<br>• Check the inhibitor circuit.<br>• Adjustment of the control cable between the shift lever and the inhibitor switch. |
| | | | Shift lever "D", "2", "L" or "R" | D | |

Courtesy of Mitsubishi Motor Sales of America.

***Multi-Use Tester Check Chart (Galant Sensor Inspection)***

**Engine control system inspection–Multi-use tester (MB991194) using**

| Check item (item No.) | Tester mode | Condition | | | Test specification | Troubleshooting when outside the test specifications |
|---|---|---|---|---|---|---|
| Stepper motor (45) | Data transfer | Engine: After warming up, idle the engine.<br>NOTE<br>The compressor clutch operates when the air conditioner switch is turned on. | Air conditioner switch | Engine revolution speed [rpm] | Step | • When the step is large during idling<br>(1) Deposite sticks to the throttle valve area.<br>(2) Engine resistance may increase.<br>(3) EGR valve may leak.<br>• When the step is small during idling, check the intake air for leakage.<br>• Adjust the speed adjusting screw.<br>• If engine revolution speed does not increase when the air conditioner switch is turned on, check the stepper motor and the circuit. |
| | | | OFF | 700 (Idling) | 4–14 | |
| | | | ON | 900 | 45–55 | |
| Power transistor (44) | | Engine: Warming up<br>Timing light: set<br>NOTE<br>1. Even though the ignition timing varies during idling, no problem occurs.<br>2. At high altitude, the farther advancing angle value (approximately 5 degrees) is indicated. | Engine revolution speed [rpm] | | Ignition timing [BTDC] | • Adjust the ignition timing. |
| | | | 700 (Idling) | | 13–20 | |
| | | | 2,000 | | 27–31 | |
| Air-flow sensor (12) | | Engine: Warming up | Engine revolution speed [rpm] | | Frequency [Hz] | • If both frequency and drive time are large,<br>(1) Engine resistance may increase.<br>(2) EGR valve may leak.<br>(3) Compression pressure may leak. |
| | | | 700 (Idling) | | 30–45 | |
| | | | 2,000 | | 95–115 | |
| Injector (41) | | Engine: Warming up | Engine revolution speed [rpm] | | Drive time [ms] | |
| | | | 700 (Idling) | | 2.7–3.2 | |
| | | | 2,000 | | 2.4–2.9 | |

Courtesy of Mitsubishi Motor Sales of America.

***Multi-Use Tester Check Chart (Galant Engine Control System, Step 1)***

| Check item (item No.) | Tester mode | Condition | | Test specification | Troubleshooting when outside the test specifications |
|---|---|---|---|---|---|
| Injector (1-6) | Actuator forced drive | Engine: After warming up, idle the engine. | Injector No. | Engine | • If there is a cylinder in which the idling state does not vary, check the injector and the spark plug of the cylinder. |
| | | | 1 | Idling state varies unstably. | |
| | | | 2 | | |
| | | | 3 | | |
| | | | 4 | | |
| | | | 5 | | |
| | | | 6 | | |
| Oxygen sensor (11) | Data transfer | Engine: Warming up | Engine condition | Voltage [mV] | • When low voltage continues during idling, check the intake air for leakage.<br>• When the voltage is higher than 1000 mV, check the oxygen sensor circuit.<br>• When the voltage is low during racing, check the oxygen sensor and the oxygen sensor circuit. |
| | | | Idling | 400 or less ↕ (pulsates) | |
| | | | 2,000 rpm | 600–1,000 | |
| | | | Rapid deceleration from 4,000 rpm | 200 or less | |
| | | | Rapid racing is repeated. | 600–1,000 | |
| EGR temperature sensor (43) | | Engine: Warming up<br>NOTE<br>Engine is maintained in a constant state for 2 minutes or more. | Engine revolution speed | Voltage [V] | • Check the EGR temperature sensor.<br>• Check the EGR control system.<br>• Check the EGR valve.<br>• Check the thermo valve.<br>• Check the EGR valve control negative pressure. |
| | | | 700 (idling) | 2.5 or more | |
| | | | 3,000 | 1.5 or more | |
| Purge control solenoid valve (8) | Actuator forced drive | Ignition switch: ON (Engine stop)<br>Disconnect the purge hose (red striped) from the throttle body, and connect the hand vacuum pump to the hose end. | Actuator is not driven. | Negative pressure is maintained. | • Check the purge control solenoid valve.<br>• Check the purge hose for leakage.<br>• Check the purge control solenoid valve drive circuit. |
| | | | Actuator forced drive | Negative pressure leaks. | |

Courtesy of Mitsubishi Motor Sales of America.

***Multi-Use Tester Check Chart (Galant Engine Control System, Step 2)***

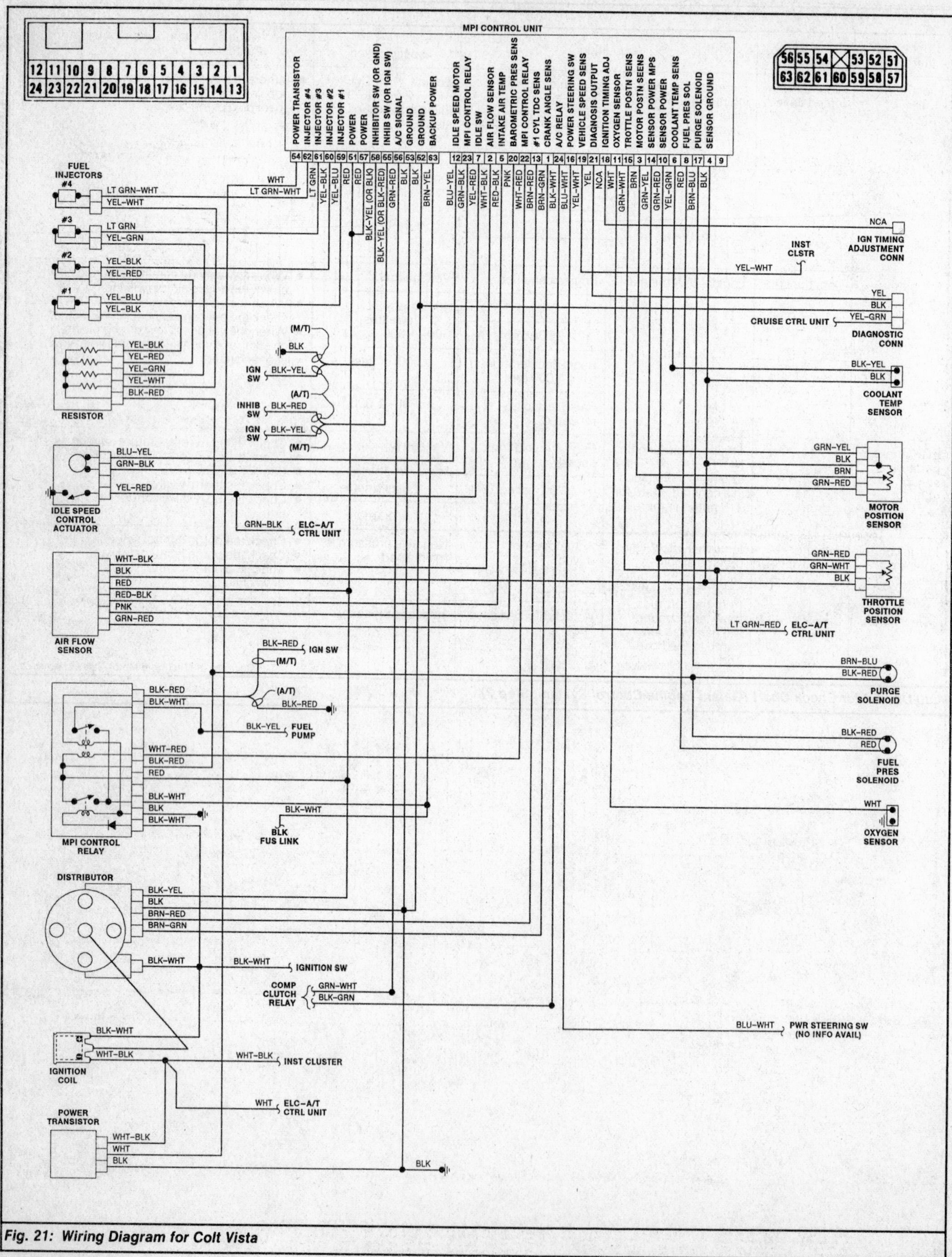
MPI CONTROL UNIT
POWER TRANSISTOR
INJECTOR #4
INJECTOR #3
INJECTOR #2
INJECTOR #1
POWER
POWER
INHIBITOR SW (OR GND)
INHIB SW (OR IGN SW)
A/C SIGNAL
GROUND
GROUND
BACKUP POWER
IDLE SPEED MOTOR
MPI CONTROL RELAY
IDLE SW
AIR FLOW SENSOR
INTAKE AIR TEMP
BAROMETRIC PRES SENS
MPI CONTROL RELAY
#1 CYL TDC SENS
CRANK ANGLE SENS
A/C RELAY
POWER STEERING SW
VEHICLE SPEED SENS
DIAGNOSIS OUTPUT
IGNITION TIMING ADJ
OXYGEN SENSOR
TROTTLE POSTN SENS
MOTOR POSTN SENS
SENSOR POWER MPS
SENSOR POWER
COOLANT TEMP SENS
FUEL PRES SOL
PURGE SOLENOID
SENSOR GROUND
FUEL INJECTORS
RESISTOR
IDLE SPEED CONTROL ACTUATOR
AIR FLOW SENSOR
MPI CONTROL RELAY
DISTRIBUTOR
IGNITION COIL
POWER TRANSISTOR
IGN SW
INHIB SW
ELC-A/T CTRL UNIT
FUEL PUMP
BLK FUS LINK
IGNITION SW
COMP CLUTCH RELAY
INST CLUSTER
IGN TIMING ADJUSTMENT CONN
INST CLSTR
CRUISE CTRL UNIT
DIAGNOSTIC CONN
COOLANT TEMP SENSOR
MOTOR POSITION SENSOR
THROTTLE POSITION SENSOR
PURGE SOLENOID
FUEL PRES SOLENOID
OXYGEN SENSOR
PWR STEERING SW (NO INFO AVAIL)

*Fig. 21: Wiring Diagram for Colt Vista*

# Chrysler & Mitsubishi MPI System (Cont.)

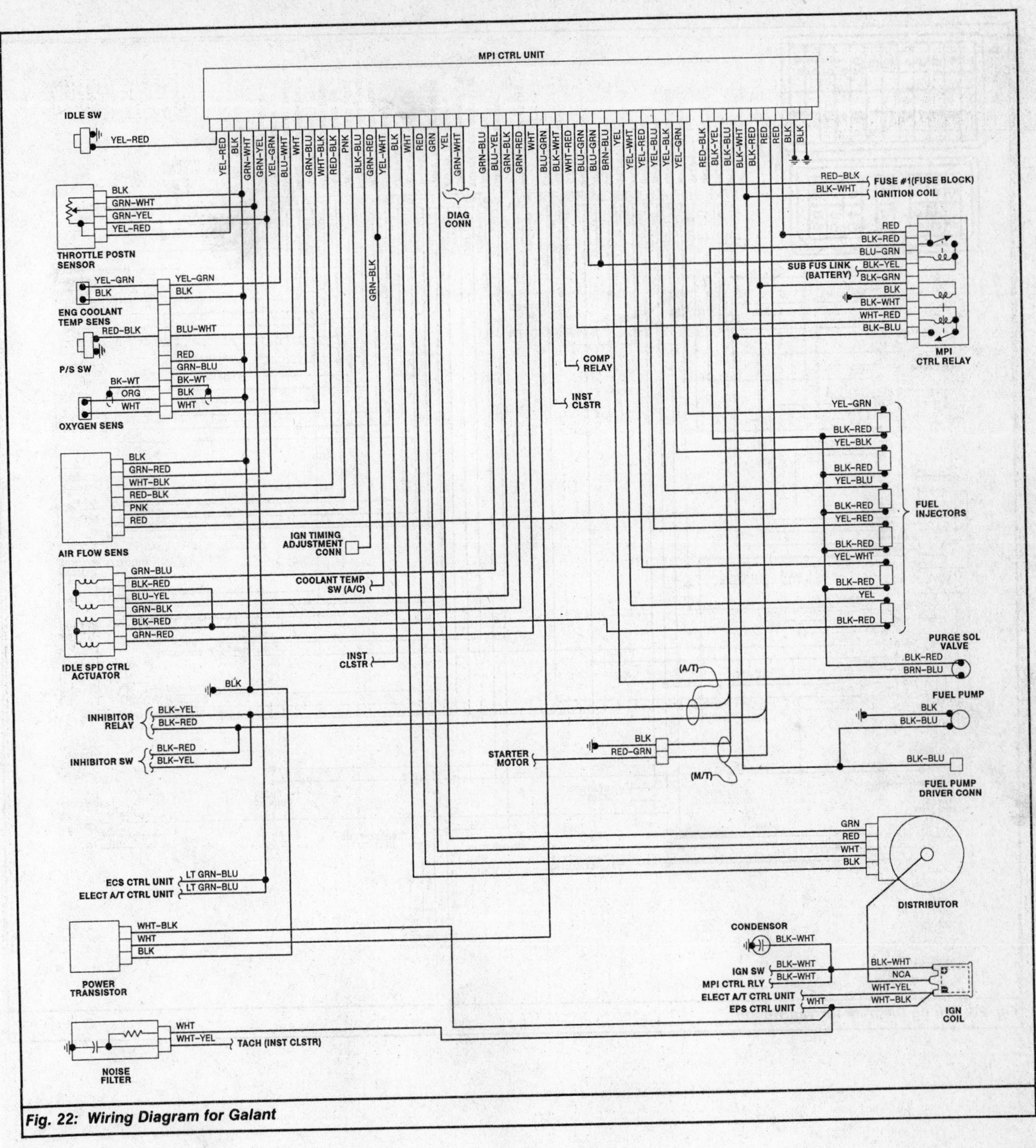
MPI CTRL UNIT
IDLE SW
YEL-RED
THROTTLE POSTN SENSOR
ENG COOLANT TEMP SENS
P/S SW
OXYGEN SENS
AIR FLOW SENS
IGN TIMING ADJUSTMENT CONN
COOLANT TEMP SW (A/C)
IDLE SPD CTRL ACTUATOR
INST CLSTR
INHIBITOR RELAY
INHIBITOR SW
ECS CTRL UNIT
ELECT A/T CTRL UNIT
POWER TRANSISTOR
NOISE FILTER
TACH (INST CLSTR)
DIAG CONN
COMP RELAY
STARTER MOTOR
FUSE #1(FUSE BLOCK)
IGNITION COIL
SUB FUS LINK (BATTERY)
MPI CTRL RELAY
FUEL INJECTORS
PURGE SOL VALVE
FUEL PUMP
FUEL PUMP DRIVER CONN
DISTRIBUTOR
CONDENSOR
IGN SW
MPI CTRL RLY
EPS CTRL UNIT
IGN COIL
(A/T)
(M/T)

*Fig. 22: Wiring Diagram for Galant*

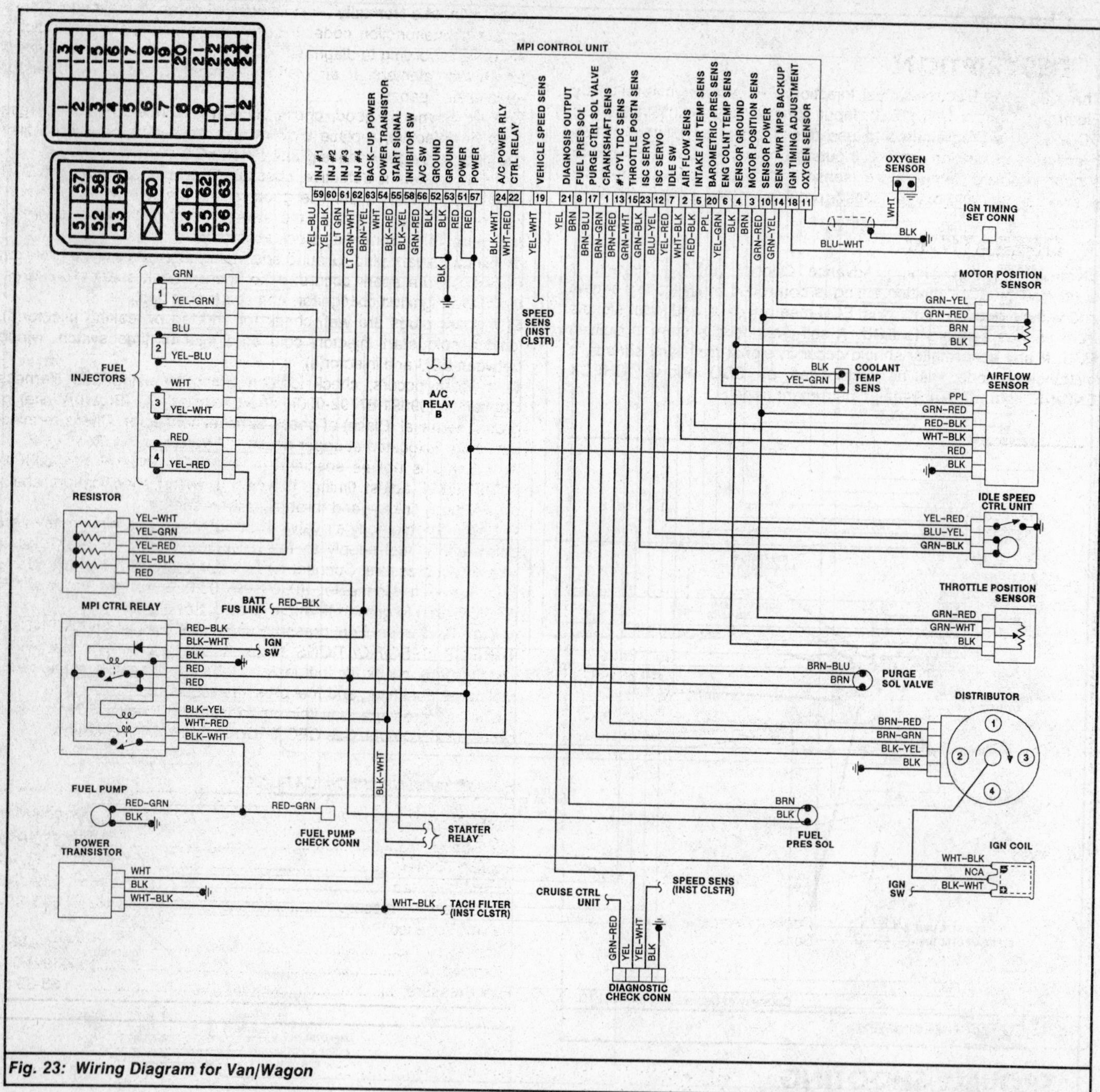
MPI CONTROL UNIT
INJ #1
INJ #2
INJ #3
INJ #4
BACK-UP POWER
POWER TRANSISTOR
START SIGNAL
INHIBITOR SW
A/C SW
GROUND
GROUND
POWER
POWER
A/C POWER RLY
CTRL RELAY
VEHICLE SPEED SENS
DIAGNOSIS OUTPUT
FUEL PRES SOL
PURGE CTRL SOL VALVE
CRANKSHAFT SENS
#1 CYL TDC SENS
THROTTLE POSTN SENS
ISC SERVO
ISC SERVO
IDLE SW
AIR FLOW SENS
INTAKE AIR TEMP SENS
BAROMETRIC PRES SENS
ENG COLNT TEMP SENS
SENSOR GROUND
MOTOR POSITION SENS
SENSOR POWER
SENS PWR MPS BACKUP
IGN TIMING ADJUSTMENT
OXYGEN SENSOR
OXYGEN SENSOR
IGN TIMING SET CONN
MOTOR POSITION SENSOR
COOLANT TEMP SENS
AIRFLOW SENSOR
IDLE SPEED CTRL UNIT
THROTTLE POSITION SENSOR
PURGE SOL VALVE
DISTRIBUTOR
FUEL PRES SOL
IGN COIL
IGN SW
FUEL INJECTORS
RESISTOR
MPI CTRL RELAY
BATT FUS LINK
IGN SW
FUEL PUMP
FUEL PUMP CHECK CONN
STARTER RELAY
POWER TRANSISTOR
TACH FILTER (INST CLSTR)
SPEED SENS (INST CLSTR)
A/C RELAY B
CRUISE CTRL UNIT
SPEED SENS (INST CLSTR)
DIAGNOSTIC CHECK CONN

*Fig. 23: Wiring Diagram for Van/Wagon*

# 1988 COMPUTERIZED ENGINE CONTROLS
## Daihatsu

### Charade

## DESCRIPTION

The 1.0L uses Electronic Fuel Injection (EFI) system controlled by Electronic Control Unit (ECU). Input sensors supply information to ECU. ECU is programmed to use this information to control fuel injection and ignition timing. Inputs from intake air temperature sensor, coolant temperature sensor, pressure sensor, throttle position sensor and oxygen sensor provide input to ECU.

## OPERATION

Electronic Ignition Timing Advance Control (EITAC) system is controlled by ECU. Ignition timing is controlled by detecting engine and vehicle running conditions, ECU memory data, and input signals from various sensors to ECU. A self-diagnostic system is built in ECU. If any abnormality should occur in signal from any sensor, a malfunction code will be memorized by ECU and a "CHECK ENGINE" light will illuminate at instrument panel.

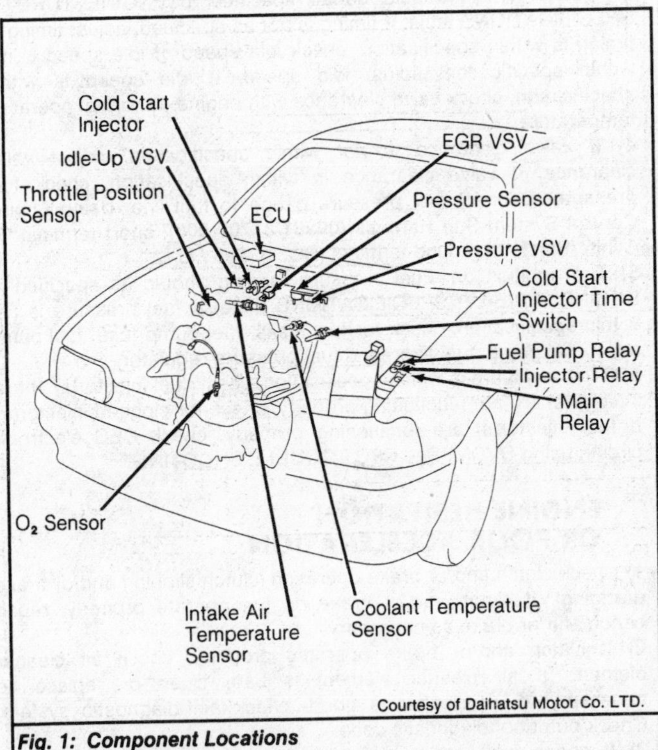
Cold Start Injector
Idle-Up VSV
Throttle Position Sensor
ECU
EGR VSV
Pressure Sensor
Pressure VSV
Cold Start Injector Time Switch
Fuel Pump Relay
Injector Relay
Main Relay
$O_2$ Sensor
Intake Air Temperature Sensor
Coolant Temperature Sensor
Courtesy of Daihatsu Motor Co. LTD.

*Fig. 1: Component Locations*

## TROUBLE SHOOTING

***NOTE:*** ***Before performing any testing, ensure that all systems are in normal operating condition (ignition and fuel components). Before starting CEC trouble shooting, check power supply, body ground, fuel supply, ignition system, air induction system, idle speed, idle-up VSV operation, and EGR valve operation. When checking CEC system, check for bad connectors and/or wiring. A Digital Volt/Ohmmeter (DVOM) with an internal resistance greater than 10K ohms should be used for trouble shooting CEC system. If a DVOM with an internal resistance less than 10K ohms is used, ECU may be damaged.***

### HARD STARTING OR NO START

**Engine Will Not Crank or Cranks Slowly** – Check vehicle battery, starting, and charging systems.

**Engine Cranks Normally** – **1)** Check self-diagnostic system. Check output of malfunction code. If codes are present, perform trouble shooting according to diagnostic codes. If codes are normal, inspect air cleaner element. If air cleaner element is defective, clean or replace air cleaner.

**2)** If air cleaner is good, check blow-by gas hose. If blow-by gas hose is defective, replace blow-by gas hose and inspect oil filler cap. If blow-by gas hose is good, check EGR system.

**3)** If EGR system is defective, check EGR valve, EGR VSV, and EGR modulator. If EGR system is good, check ignition system. Disconnecting cold start injector time switch. Remove injector relay and fuel pump relay from relay block assembly.

**4)** Remove spark plug. Ground spark plug to engine. While cranking engine, ensure spark occurs. If no spark, check spark plug wires, distributor, ignition coil/ignitor, and spark plug gap.

**5)** If spark plugs are wet, check for shorted or leaking injector(s), leaking cold start injector, cold start injector time switch, wiring between ECU and injector(s).

**6)** If spark occurs, check ignition timing by using Sub Harness Connector (09991-87702-000). Short terminal "T" (Brown/White) to ground terminal (Black) of check terminal connector. Check terminal connector is located at upper section of transmission. *See Fig. 2.*

**7)** If timing is not as specified in ENGINE TUNE-UP SPECIFICATIONS table, adjust timing. If timing is within specification, check throttle body linkage and throttle position sensor.

**8)** Check throttle body air valve. If throttle body and components are good, check fuel supply to fuel injectors. Check for fuel in tank. Check fuel pressure. Connect fuel pressure gauge to fuel line. Using Sub Harness Connector (09991-87702-000), short terminal "F" (White/Black) to ground terminal (Black). *See Fig. 2.*

**9)** Turn ignition on. Fuel pressure should be as specified in ENGINE TUNE-UP SPECIFICATIONS table. If fuel pressure is not within specification, check for fuel leaks, fuel pump fuse, fuel pump relay, fuel pump, fuel filter, and fuel pressure regulator.

**10)** If fuel pressure is within specification, Check CEC electronic circuit, using DVOM. See CEC TROUBLE SHOOTING charts.

***ENGINE TUNE-UP SPECIFICATIONS***

| Application | Specification |
|---|---|
| Idle Speed | 750-850 RPM |
| Ignition Timing | 5° BTDC @ Idle |
| Spark Plug Gap | .039-.043" |
| Compression Pressure | 142 psi @ 350 RPM |
| Valve Clearance | |
| Intake | .0059-.0098" |
| Exhaust | .0059-.0098" |
| Fuel Pressure | 33-39 psi |

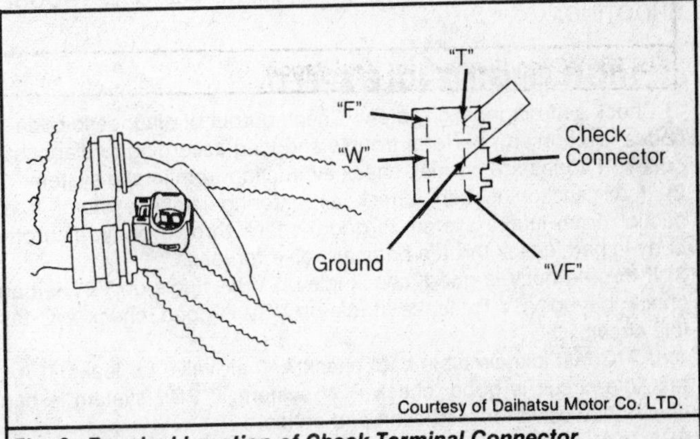
"T"
"F"
"W"
Check Connector
Ground
"VF"
Courtesy of Daihatsu Motor Co. LTD.

*Fig. 2: Terminal Location of Check Terminal Connector*

## ENGINE STALLS, ROUGH IDLE OR MISSING

**1)** Check self-diagnostic system. Check output of diagnostic code. If codes are present, perform trouble shooting according to diagnostic codes. If codes are normal, inspect air cleaner element. If air cleaner element is defective, replace air cleaner.
**2)** If air cleaner is good, check idle speed. See ENGINE TUNE-UP SPECIFICATIONS table. If idle speed is not within specification, adjust idle speed. If idle speed is within specification, check ignition system.
**3)** If no spark occurs, check distributor, spark plug wires, ignition coil, and ignitor. If spark occurs, check spark plug gap, compression pressure and valve clearance with engine normal operating temperature.
**4)** If spark plugs, compression pressure and valve clearance are good, check timing by using Engine Control System Sub Harness (09991-87702-000), short terminal "T" (Brown/White) to ground terminal (Black) of check terminal connector. Check terminal connector is located at upper section of transmission. *See Fig. 2.*
**5)** Ignition timing should be as specified in ENGINE TUNE-UP SPECIFICATIONS table. If timing is not as specified, adjust timing. If timing is within specification, check PCV system. If PCV system is bad, check orifice for restriction. If PCV system is good, check idle-up VSV system.
**6)** If idle-up VSV system is bad, check idle-up VSV and idle-up VSV signal circuit. If idle-up VSV system is good, check throttle body. If throttle body is bad, check throttle body air valve and idle switch.
**7)** If throttle body is good, check EGR system. If EGR system is bad, check EGR valve, EGR modulator, Electric Vacuum Switching Valve (EVSV), EVSV signal circuit (wiring and ECU). See EGR SYSTEM article in EXHAUST EMISSION SYSTEMS section.
**8)** If EGR system is good, check fuel pressure. Connect fuel pressure gauge to fuel line. Using Sub Harness Connector (09991-87702-000), short terminal "F" (White/Black) to ground terminal (Black). *See Fig. 2.*
**9)** Turn ignition on. Fuel pressure reading should be as specified in ENGINE TUNE-UP SPECIFICATIONS table. If fuel pressure is not within specification, check for fuel leaks, fuel pump fuse, fuel pump relay, fuel pump, fuel filter, and fuel pressure regulator.
**10)** If fuel pressure is within specification, check fuel flow. Fuel flow rate should be 14.2 ounces (.42L) in 15 seconds at 12.5-13.0 volts. If fuel flow is not within specification, check fuel pump and fuel filter.
**11)** If fuel flow is within specification, check fuel injectors. If fuel injectors are not operating properly, check injector condition or leaks. If fuel injectors are operating properly, check cold start injector. See COLD START INJECTOR article in FUEL SYSTEMS section.
**12)** If cold start injector is not operating properly, check cold start injector condition or leaks. If cold start injector is operating properly, Check CEC electronic circuit, using DVOM. See CEC TROUBLE SHOOTING.

## HIGH ENGINE IDLE SPEED

**1)** Check self-diagnostic system. Check output of diagnostic code. If codes are present, perform trouble shooting according to diagnostic codes. If codes are normal, check air suction from intake system.
**2)** If air suction is bad, check air entering intake system. If air suction from intake system is good, check throttle body. If throttle body is bad, check throttle body air valve for leaks.
**3)** If throttle body is good, check idle-up VSV. If idle-up VSV is bad, check idle-up VSV for leaks. If idle-up VSV is good, check A/C fast idle circuit.
**4)** If A/C fast idle circuit is bad, check A/C air valve for leaks. If A/C fast idle circuit is good, check PCV system. If PCV system is bad, check PCV valve for restriction and orifice.
**5)** If PCV system is good, check throttle position sensor. If throttle position sensor is bad, check throttle body. If throttle position sensor is good, check fuel pressure. Connect fuel pressure gauge to fuel line. Using Engine Control System Sub Harness (09991-87702-000), short terminal "F" (White/Black) to ground terminal (Black). *See Fig. 2.*
**6)** Turn ignition on. Fuel pressure reading should be as specified in ENGINE TUNE-UP SPECIFICATIONS table. If fuel pressure is not within specification, check for fuel leaks, fuel pump fuse, fuel pump relay, fuel pump, fuel restriction, and fuel pressure regulator.
**7)** If fuel pressure is within specification, check CEC electronic circuit, using DVOM. See CEC TROUBLE SHOOTING.

## ENGINE BACKFIRES OR DIESELS

**1)** Check self-diagnostic system. Check output of malfunction code. If codes are present, perform trouble shooting according to diagnostic codes. If codes are normal, inspect air cleaner element. If air cleaner element is defective, replace air cleaner.
**2)** If air cleaner is good, check ignition timing by using Engine Control System Sub Harness (09991-87702-000), short terminal "T" (Brown/White) to ground terminal (Black) of check terminal connector. Check terminal connector is located at upper section of transmission. *See Fig. 2.*
**3)** Ignition timing should be as specified in ENGINE TUNE-UP SPECIFICATIONS table. If timing is not as specified, adjust timing. If timing is within specification, check idle speed. If idle speed is not within specification, adjust idle speed. If idle speed is within specification, check valve clearance with engine at normal operating temperature.
**4)** If valve clearance is not within specification, adjust valve clearance. If valve clearance is within specification, check fuel pressure. Connect fuel pressure gauge to fuel line. Using Engine Control System Sub Harness (09991-87702-000), short terminal "F" (White/Black) to ground terminal (Black). *See Fig. 2.*
**5)** Turn ignition on. Fuel pressure reading should as specified in ENGINE TUNE-UP SPECIFICATIONS table. If fuel pressure is not within specification, check for fuel leaks, fuel pump fuse, fuel pump relay, fuel pump, fuel filter, and fuel pressure regulator.
**6)** If fuel pressure is within specification, check fuel injector(s). If fuel injector(s) are not functioning properly, check for clogged injector(s). If fuel injector(s) are functioning properly, check CEC electronic circuit, using DVOM. See CEC TROUBLE SHOOTING.

## ENGINE HESITATION OR POOR ACCELERATION

**1)** Check clutch and/or brake operation (clutch slipping and/or brake dragging). If clutch and/or brake do not operate properly, repair clutch and/or brake as necessary.
**2)** If clutch and/or brake operates properly, check air cleaner element. If air cleaner element is bad, clean or replace as necessary. If air cleaner is good, check self-diagnostic system. Check output of diagnostic code.
**3)** If codes are present, perform trouble shooting according to diagnostic codes. If codes are normal, check ignition timing by using Engine Control System Sub Harness (09991-87702-000), short terminal "T" (Brown/White) to ground terminal (Black) of check terminal connector. Check terminal connector is located at upper section of transmission. *See Fig. 2.*
**4)** Ignition timing should be as specified in ENGINE TUNE-UP SPECIFICATIONS table. If timing is not as specified, adjust timing. If timing is within specification, check spark plugs and plug gap.
**5)** Replace spark plugs (if necessary). If spark plugs are good, check compression pressure. If compression pressure is not within specification, engine overhaul may be necessary.
**6)** If compression pressure is within specification, check ignition system. Disconnect cold start injector time switch. Remove injector relay and fuel pump relay from relay block assembly.
**7)** Remove spark plug. Ground spark plug to engine. While cranking engine, ensure spark occurs. If no spark, check spark plug wires, distributor, ignition coil/ignitor.
**8)** If spark is present, check idle-up VSV system. If idle-up VSV is not functioning properly, check idle-up VSV and idle-up circuit. If

idle-up VSV is functioning properly, check atmospheric pressure VSV. If atmospheric pressure VSV is bad, check atmospheric pressure VSV and circuit.

**9)** If atmospheric pressure VSV is operating properly, check fuel pressure. Connect fuel pressure gauge to fuel line. Using Engine Control System Sub Harness (09991-87702-000), short terminal "F" (White/Black) to ground terminal (Black). *See Fig. 2.*

**10)** Turn ignition on. Fuel pressure reading should be as specified in ENGINE TUNE-UP SPECIFICATIONS table. If fuel pressure is not within specification, check for fuel leaks, fuel pump fuse, fuel pump relay, fuel pump, fuel filter, and fuel pressure regulator.

**11)** If fuel pressure is within specification, check cold start injector. Check cold start injector for leaks. If cold start injector is functioning properly, check fuel flow rate.

**12)** Fuel flow rate should be 14.2 ounces (.42L) in 15 seconds at 12.5-13.0 volts. If fuel flow is not within specification, check fuel pump and fuel filter.

**13)** If fuel flow is within specification, check fuel injector(s). If fuel injector(s) are not functioning properly, check fuel injector(s) for leaks. If fuel injector(s) are functioning properly, check CEC electronic circuit, using DVOM. See CEC TROUBLE SHOOTING.

# TESTING

## CEC SYSTEM DIAGNOSTICS

**Testing "CHECK ENGINE" Warning Light** – With ignition on, "Check Engine" light should illuminate. When engine is started, "Check Engine" light should go off. If "Check Engine" light remains illuminated, this indicates that the self-diagnostic system has detected a system malfunction.

**Output of Diagnostic Codes** – **1)** Battery voltage must be 11 volts or more, throttle valve fully closed, and all accessories must be off. Using Engine Control System Sub Harness (09991-87702-000), short terminal "T" (Brown/White) to ground terminal (Black) of check terminal connector. Check terminal connector is located at upper section of transmission. *See Fig. 2.*

## DIAGNOSTIC CODE CHART

| Code No. | Number of glowing of check engine lamp | Diagnosis item | Diagnosis contents | Trouble area |
|---|---|---|---|---|
| 1 | | Normal | — | — |
| 2 | | Pressure sensor | When the signal from pressure sensor becomes open or shorted | 1. Pressure sensor circuit<br>2. Pressure sensor<br>3. ECU |
| 3 | | Ignition signal | • No ignition confirmation signal (IGf) is inputted. | 1. Ignition circuit (+B, IGF)<br>2. Ignitor<br>3. ECU |
| 4 | | Water temperature sensor | • When the signal from the water temperature sensor circuit becomes open or shorted: | 1. Water temperature sensor circuit<br>2. Water temperature sensor<br>3. ECU |
| 5 | | Oxygen sensor signal | • When the oxygen sensor signal circuit becomes open or shorted: | 1. Oxygen sensor circuit<br>2. Oxygen sensor<br>3. ECU |
| 6 | | Revolution signal | • When Ne and/or G signal is not inputted within a few seconds after starting of engine cranking:<br>• When the Ne signal of a few decade milliseconds is not inputted when the engine speed is 1000 rpm or more: | 1. Distributor circuit<br>2. Distributor<br>3. ECU |
| 7 | | Throttle position sensor signal | • When the throttle position sensor signal circuit becomes open or shorted: | 1. Throttle position sensor circuit<br>2. Throttle position sensor<br>3. ECU |
| 8 | | Intake air temperature sensor signal | • When the intake air temperature signal circuit becomes open or shorted: | 1. Air temperature sensor circuit<br>2. Air temperature sensor<br>3. ECU |
| 9 | | Vehicle speed sensor signal | • When the vehicle speed sensor signal circuit becomes open or shorted: | 1. Vehicle speed sensor circuit<br>2. Vehicle speed sensor<br>3. ECU |
| 10 | | Starter signal | When the starter signal becomes open or shorted:However, it should be noted that this code may be memorized when the vehicle is started by being pushed. | 1. Starter signal circuit<br>2. ECU |
| 11 | | Switch signal | When the air conditioner is turned ON or the idle switch is turned OFF with the terminal T shorted: However, no memorizing will take place. | 1. Air conditioner switch circuit<br>2. Idle switch circuit<br>3. Air conditioner switch<br>4. Throttle position sensor<br>5. ECU |
| 12 | | EGR control system | When the EGR system is not operating normally: | 1. EGR valve<br>2. Modulator<br>3. EVSV<br>4. Water temperature sensor<br>5. ECU |

**2)** Turn ignition on. DO NOT start engine at this time. Read diagnostic code by observing flashing number sequence of "Check Engine" light. If a code No. 1 is memorized by ECU, "Check Engine" light will flash for .48 second, pause for 4.5 seconds, then flash for .48 second again. This pattern will be repeated.

**3)** If more than one code has been memorized by ECU, there will be a 2.5 second lapse between each code. ECU will flash smaller number code first and proceed to larger number code. After codes have been read, remove Engine Control System Sub Harness (09991-87702-000) from check terminal. Install cap on check terminal.

**Clearing Diagnostic Code** – To clear diagnostic code from ECU memory after malfunction has been repaired, disconnect negative battery cable or remove back-up fuse from relay block assembly located in engine compartment for at least 10 seconds with ignition off and ambient temperature below 68° F (20° C).

***NOTE: When disconnecting fuse, be sure to use a fuse puller. The fuse puller is located at upper section of inside fuse block.***

**Testing With DVOM – 1)** Disconnect negative battery cable. Remove glove compartment box. Install ECU Check Sub Harness (09842-87704-000) between ECU and engine harness. Reconnect negative battery cable.

***CAUTION: After inspection of ECU, before ECU Check Sub Harness (09842-87704-000) is removed, ensure negative battery cable is disconnected. After ECU and engine wiring have been connected, reconnected negative battery cable. Before ECU Check Sub Harness is connected, ensure that there is no open circuit or short between terminals.***

**2)** CEC circuit can be checked by measuring resistance and voltages at ECU Check Sub Harness terminals. *See Fig. 3.* Voltage check should be conducted under a condition where all connectors are connected. Ensure battery voltage is 11 volts or more when ignition is turned on.

**3)** Using DVOM, check each ECU Check Sub Harness (09842-87704-000) terminal voltage readings according to ECU WIRING CONNECTORS (DIAGNOSTIC CODES) and ECU CONNECTORS charts. If voltage reading are to specifications shown in chart, check each individual component. If each individual component checks out good according to test procedure, install a known good ECU and retest.

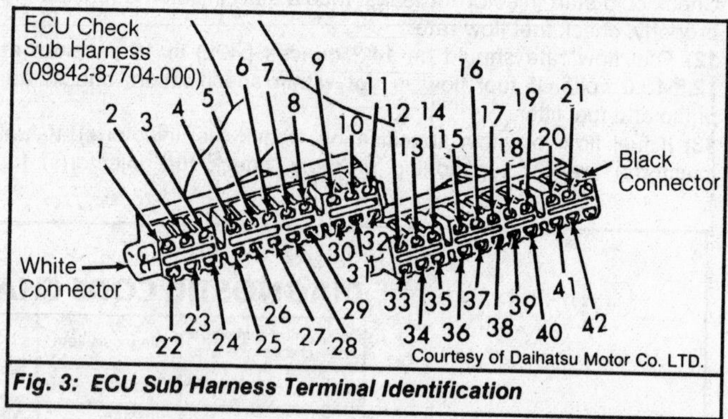
ECU Check
Sub Harness
(09842-87704-000)
1 2 3 4 5 6 7 8 9 10 11 12 13 14 15 16 17 18 19 20 21
Black
Connector
White
Connector
22 23 24 25 26 27 28 29 30 31 32 33 34 35 36 37 38 39 40 41 42
Courtesy of Daihatsu Motor Co. LTD.

***Fig. 3: ECU Sub Harness Terminal Identification***

## COMPONENT TESTING

**Coolant Temperature Sensor – 1)** Disconnect coolant temperature sensor connector. Using a DVOM, measure temperature resistance of coolant temperature sensor body. Measure resistance between

## ECU CONNECTORS CHART

| Code | | Contents of connection |
|---|---|---|
| 1 | +B1 | Main relay (power supply) |
| 2 | BATT | Battery (back-up power supply) |
| 3 | | |
| 4 | FC | Fuel pump relay |
| 5 | | |
| 6 | | |
| 7 | | |
| 8 | THW | Water temperature sensor |
| 9 | PIM | Intake manifold pressure sensor |
| 10 | THA | Intake air temperature sensor |
| 11 | T | Check terminal |
| 12 | IGF | Ignition moniter |
| 13 | GI | Crank angle sensor |
| 14 | G– | Crank angle sensor ground |
| 15 | OX | O2 sensor |
| 16 | | |
| 17 | DSW | Electrical load signal |
| 18 | EVSV | VSV for EGR |
| 19 | STA | Starter switch |
| 20 | #10 | Injector |
| 21 | E01 | Power system ground (engine block) |

| Code | | Contents of connection |
|---|---|---|
| 22 | +B | Main relay (power supply) |
| 23 | W | Diagnosis lamp |
| 24 | | |
| 25 | A/C | Air conditioner amplifier |
| 26 | SPD | Vehicle speed sensor |
| 27 | | |
| 28 | | |
| 29 | E2 | Sensor system ground |
| 30 | VTH | Linear throttle sensor |
| 31 | VCC | Sensor power supply output (4.5-5.5) |
| 32 | IDL | Throttle sensor full closing signal |
| 33 | B/K | Brake signal |
| 34 | NE | Crank angle sensor revolution speed |
| 35 | E21 | Pressure sensor ground |
| 36 | VF | O2 sensor checker |
| 37 | VSV | Idle-up VSV |
| 38 | PVSV | VSV for introducing atmospheric pressure |
| 39 | EI | Operation system ground (engine block) |
| 40 | IGT | Ignitor control output |
| 41 | | |
| 42 | | |

| | | | | | | | | | | | | | | | | | | | | |
|---|---|---|---|---|---|---|---|---|---|---|---|---|---|---|---|---|---|---|---|---|
| EO1 | #10 | STA | EVSV | DSW | | OX | G- | GI | IGF | T | THA | PIM | THW | | | | FC | | BATT | +B1 |
| | | IGT | EI | PVSV | VSV | VF | E21 | NE | B/K | IDL | VCC | YTH | E2 | | | SPD | A/C | | W | +B |

## VOLTAGE AT ECU WIRING CONNECTORS CHART

| Terminals | STD voltage | Condition | |
|---|---|---|---|
| +B1−E1 | 10 - 15.5 | Ignition switch ON | |
| BATT−E1 | 10 - 15.5 | At all time | |
| FC−E1 | 10 - 15.5 | Ignition switch ON | When engine is stopped: |
| | 0.1 - 1.5 | Ignition switch ON | When engine is running: |
| THW−E2 | 0.1 - 0.7 | Ignition switch ON | Coolant temperature 176 °F (80 °C) |
| PIM−E2 | 2.1 - 2.7 | Ignition switch ON | When atmospheric pressure is 760 mmHg: |
| THA−E2 | About 0.9 - 3.0 | Ignition switch ON | Temperature of air in surge tank 68 °F (20 °C) |
| T−E1 | 4.5 - 5.5 | Ignition switch ON | T terminal OFF |
| IGF−E1 | 0.5 - 1.5 | Ignition switch ON | |
| GI−E1 | About 0.6 | Ignition switch ON | |
| GΘ−E1 | About 0.6 | | |
| OX−E1 | Change in output voltage | When engine speed is held at 3000 rpm for two minutes after engine has been fully warmed up: | |
| DSW−E1 | 10 - 15.5 | Ignition switch ON | When defogger and/or headlamp switch is turned ON: |
| EVSV−E1 | 10 - 15.5 | Ignition switch ON | Coolant temperature is below 104 °F (40 °C) |
| | 1.0 - 3.5 | | Coolant temperature is above 104 °F (40 °C) |
| STA−E1 | 0 | At all time | |
| | 6 - 15.5 | When ignition switch is set to ST position: | |
| #10−E1 | 10 - 15.5 | Ignition switch ON | |
| +B−E1 | 10 - 15.5 | Ignition switch ON | |
| W−E1 | 1.0 - 3.5 | Ignition switch ON | |
| | 10 - 15.5 | When engine is running with ignition switch turned ON and diagnosis code is normal during diagnosis code check: | |
| AC−E1 | 10 - 15.5 | When air conditioner switch is turned ON while engine is running: | |
| SPD−E1 | Change in voltage between 0 to 4.5–5.5 | Ignition switch ON | When vehicle is moved: |
| VTH−E2 | About 0.55 | Ignition switch ON | Throttle valve fully closed: |
| | About 3.91 | | Throttle valve fully opened: |
| VCC−E2 or E21 | 4.5 - 5.5 | Ignition switch ON | |
| IDL−E2 | 0 | Ignition switch ON | Throttle valve fully closed: |
| | 4.5 - 5.5 | | Throttle valve fully opened: |
| B/K−E1 | 10 - 15.5 | Brake pedal is depressed: | |
| NE−E1 | About 0.6 | Ignition switch ON | |
| VSV−E1 | 1.0 - 3.5 | Ignition switch ON | |
| | 10 - 15.5 | After a lapse of at least 60 seconds after engine starting. | |
| PVSV−E1 | 10 - 15.5 | Ignition switch ON | |
| IGT−E1 | 0 | Ignition switch ON | |
| | AC 0.3 - 0.9 | When engine is running: | |
| VF−E1 | 1.5 - 3.5 | Ignition switch ON | |
| | 0 - 0.5 | Ignition switch ON | When diagnosis code is memorized while throttle valve is closed fully, SST (09991-87702-000) is installed on check terminal, and terminal T is shorted with ground terminal: |
| | 4.5 - 5.5 | | When no diagnosis code is memorized while throttle valve is closed fully, SST (09991-87702-000) is installed on check terminal, and terminal T is shorted with ground terminal: |
| | Change in voltage occurs eight times or more for 10 seconds between 0 - 5. | | When engine speed is held at 3000 rpm for two minutes after engine has been fully warmed up, SST (09991-87702-000) is installed on check terminal, and terminal T is shorted with ground terminal: |

coolant temperature sensor terminals. *See Fig. 4*. If resistance is not as shown, replace coolant temperature sensor.

***NOTE:** Before coolant temperature sensor is removed, drain cooling system and refill cooling system if sensor is replaced.*

**2)** Check to ensure there is no continuity between each terminal of coolant temperature sensor and sensor body. If continuity is present, replace coolant temperature sensor.

**Intake Air Temperature Sensor – 1)** Disconnect intake air temperature sensor connector. Using a DVOM, measure temperature resistance of air inside surge tank. Disconnect air hose from throttle body.

***NOTE:** Ensure that DVOM test lead does not make contact with surge tank or throttle body during measurement.*

**2)** Measure temperature of air inside surge tank by opening throttle valve. Measure resistance between terminals of intake air temperature sensor. *See Fig. 4*.
**3)** If resistance is not as shown, replace intake air temperature sensor. Check to ensure there is no continuity between each terminal of intake air temperature sensor and sensor body. If continuity is present, replace intake air temperature sensor.

**Throttle Position Sensor – 1)** Disconnect throttle position sensor connector. Using a DVOM, measure resistance between terminals "VCC" and "E2". *See Fig. 5*. Resistance should be 4250-8250 ohms. If resistance is not within specification, replace throttle body.
**2)** Measure resistance between terminals "VCC" and "VTH". *See Fig. 5*. With throttle valve fully closed, resistance should be 3500-10,300

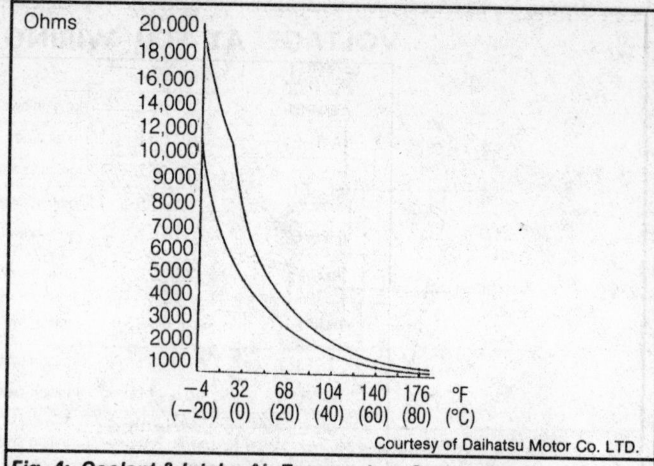
Ohms
20,000
18,000
16,000
14,000
12,000
10,000
9000
8000
7000
6000
5000
4000
3000
2000
1000
−4 (−20)
32 (0)
68 (20)
104 (40)
140 (60)
176 (80)
°F (°C)
Courtesy of Daihatsu Motor Co. LTD.

*Fig. 4: Coolant & Intake Air Temperature Sensor Graph*

ohms. With throttle valve fully opened, resistance should be 300-6300 ohms. Resistance value should change smoothly from full closing to full opening of throttle valve.
**3)** If resistance is not within specification, replace throttle body. Measure resistance between terminals "IDL" and "E2". *See Fig. 5*. With throttle valve fully closed, resistance should be 15-35 ohms. With throttle valve opened more than 1.5 degrees, resistance should be 100,000 ohms. If resistance is not within specification, replace throttle body.

**Pressure Sensor – 1)** Disconnect negative battery cable. Remove glove compartment subassembly. Connect ECU Check Sub Harness (09842-87704-000) between ECU and engine wiring.

## VOLTAGE AT ECU WIRING CONNECTORS (DIAGNOSTIC CODES) CHART

| No. | Terminal code (SST terminal) | STD voltage. | Conditions | |
|---|---|---|---|---|
| 1 | BATT–E1 | 10 - 15.5 | At all time | |
| | +B1 / +B –E1 | | Ignition switch ON | |
| 2 | VCC–E21 | 4.5 - 5.5 | Ignition switch ON | |
| | PIM–E21 | 2.1 - 2.7 | Ignition switch ON | When atmospheric pressure is 29.9 inchHg (760 mmHg): |
| 3 | IGF-E1 | 0.5 - 1.5 | Ignition switch ON | |
| 4 | THW–E2 | 0.1 - 0.7 V | Ignition switch ON | Coolant temperature 176 °F (80 °C) |
| 5 | OX–E1 | Voltage chenges more than 8 time with in 10 seconds | Ignition switch ON | When engine speed is held at 3000 rpm for two minutes after engine has been fully warmed up: |
| 6 | NE–E1 | 0.5 - 1.5 | Ignition switch ON | |
| | GI–E1 | 0.5 - 1.5 | Ignition switch ON | |
| 7 | VCC–E2 | 4.5 - 5.5 | Ignition switch ON | |
| | VTH–E2 | About 0.55 | Ignition switch ON | Throttle valve fully closed |
| | | About 3.91 | | Throttle valve fully opened |
| 8 | THA–E2 | About 0.9 - 3.0 | Ignition switch ON | Intake air temperature 68 °F (20 °C) |
| 9 | SPD–E1 | 0 - 4.5 to 5.5 | Ignition switch ON | When vehicle is moved 1.5 meters, a cycle of 0 - 4.5 to 5.5 Volt is repeated four times. |
| 10 | STA–E1 | 6 - 15.5 | When ignition switch is set to ST position: | |
| 11 | A/C–E1 | 10 - 15.5 | When engine is idling | Air conditioner switch ON |
| | IDL–E2 | 0 - 0.6 | Ignition switch ON | Throttle valve fully closed |
| | | 4.5 - 5.5 | | Throttle valve opened |
| 12 | EVSV–E1 | 10 - 15.5 | When engine is idling. | Coolant temperature bellow 104 °F (40 °C) |
| | | 1.0 - 3.5 | | Coolant temperature above 104 °F (40 °C) |

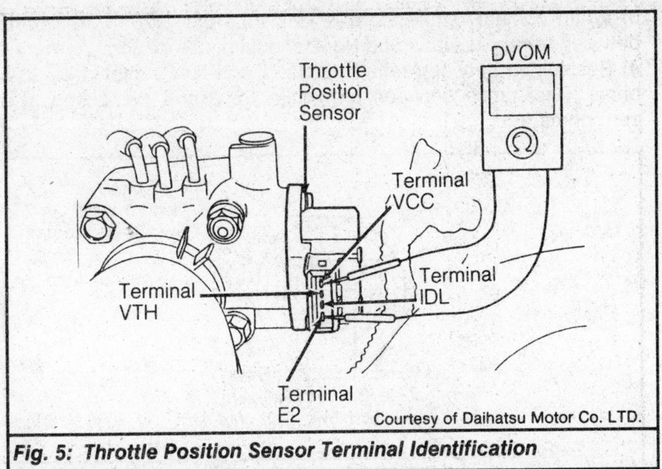
DVOM
Throttle
Position
Sensor
Terminal
VCC
Terminal
IDL
Terminal
VTH
Terminal
E2
Courtesy of Daihatsu Motor Co. LTD.

***Fig. 5: Throttle Position Sensor Terminal Identification***

***NOTE: Before ECU Check Sub Harness (09842-87704-000) is installed, be sure to perform continuity and short tests between ECU Check Sub Harness terminals.***

**2)** Check output of pressure sensor. Using a DVOM, measure voltage between ECU Check Sub Harness terminals "PIM" (9) and "E2" (39) with ignition turned on. See PRESSURE SENSOR SPECIFIED VALUE chart.

***PRESSURE SENSOR SPECIFIED VALUE***

| Altitude Ft. (mm) | Atmos. Pressure In. Hg | Voltage |
|---|---|---|
| 0 (0) | 29.92 | 2.1-2.7 |
| 1640 (500) | 28.19 | 1.9-2.5 |
| 3280 (1000) | 26.54 | 1.8-2.4 |

**3)** If voltage is not as specified in chart, measure voltage between ECU Check Sub Harness terminals "VCC" (31) and "E2" (39). If measured voltage is within 4.5-5.5 volts, replace pressure sensor.
**4)** When pressure sensor is replaced, replace gas and air filter also. If voltage is not within 4.5-5.5 volts, check wiring between ECU and pressure sensor.
**5)** Disconnect rubber hose connected to pressure sensor. Using a vacuum pump, apply 7.87 in. Hg to disconnected hose. Check that measured voltage between ECU Check Sub Harness terminals "PIM" (9) and "E2" (39) drops .55-.7 volt. If voltage fails to drop as specified, replace pressure sensor.

**Pressure VSV - 1)** Disconnect negative battery cable. Remove glove compartment subassembly. Connect ECU Check Sub Harness between ECU and engine wiring.
**2)** Reconnect negative battery cable. Start engine and warm to normal operating temperature. Measure voltage between ECU Check Sub Harness terminals "PVSV" (38) and "E2" (39) while depressing accelerator pedal and increase engine speed to 4000 RPM.
**3)** Depress brake pedal and release accelerator pedal. Ensure voltage drops momentarily. If voltage fails to drop, check wiring between stoplight switch and ECU.
**4)** Repeat step **2)** test. If voltage fails to drop, go to step **5)**. If voltage drops as specified, check ECU. If no voltage is present between ECU Check Sub Harness terminals "PVSV" (38) and "E01" (21), check wiring between main relay and ECU terminal "PVSV" (38).
**5)** Check pressure VSV operation. Disconnect negative battery cable. Remove glove compartment subassembly. Connect ECU Check Sub Harness between ECU and engine wiring.
**6)** Reconnect negative battery cable. Disconnect rubber hose connected to pressure VSV. Using a vacuum pump, apply 3.94 in. Hg to check for air leaks.
**7)** If any air leaks are present, replace pressure VSV. Turn ignition on. Short ECU Check Sub Harness terminal "PVSV" (38) to terminal "E01" (21). Ensure vacuum applied in step **6)** now reads zero.
**8)** Turn ignition off. Connect vacuum pump to pressure side port of pressure VSV. Ensure that no vacuum is present. If vacuum is present at side port, replace VSV.

**EGR VSV - 1)** Disconnect negative battery cable. Remove glove compartment subassembly. Connect ECU Check Sub Harness (09842-87704-000) between ECU and engine wiring.
**2)** Reconnect negative battery cable. Disconnect rubber hose connected to EGR VSV. Connect vacuum pump to modulator side port of EGR VSV and apply vacuum. Ensure that no vacuum is applied.
**3)** If vacuum is applied, replace EGR VSV. Connect a vacuum pump to surge tank side port of EGR VSV and apply 3.94 in. Hg.
**4)** If no vacuum is applied, replace EGR VSV. Ensure that vacuum applied in step **3)** becomes zero with ignition on. If vacuum fails to become zero, check if any voltage is present between ECU Check Sub Harness terminal "EVSV" (18) and "E01" (21).
**5)** If voltage is present, check ECU. If no voltage is present, check EGR VSV for power supply. Measure resistance of EGR VSV and check wiring for open wire. Resistance should be 30-55 ohms.
**6)** If no problems are found, replace EGR VSV. If problem is found, repair and/or replace (as necessary). Start engine. With coolant temperature less than 104°F (40°C), connect a vacuum pump to port at EGR VSV surge tank side.
**7)** Ensure vacuum is present. If vacuum is not present, check coolant pressure sensor. With coolant temperature greater than 104°F (40°C), connect a vacuum pump to port at EGR VSV surge tank side.
**8)** Engine should run rough or stall when a vacuum is applied. If engine does not run rough or stall when vacuum is applied, check coolant temperature sensor or EGR system.
**9)** Reconnect rubber hoses that were disconnected during inspection. With coolant temperature less than 104°F (40°C), start engine. While engine is warming up, measure voltage between ECU Check Sub Harness terminal "EVSV" (18) and "E01" (21).
**10)** Ensure that measured voltage drops before cooling fan motor comes on. If no drop in voltage occurs, check and/or repair coolant temperature sensor system. If coolant temperature is operating properly, check ECU.

**Idle-Up VSV - 1)** Disconnect negative battery cable. Remove glove compartment subassembly. Connect ECU Check Sub Harness (09842-87704-000) between ECU and engine wire.
**2)** Reconnect negative battery cable. Disconnect rubber hose connected to idle-up VSV. Connect a vacuum pump to idle-up VSV and apply 3.94 in. Hg. If no vacuum is present, replace idle-up VSV.
**3)** Turn all accessories off. Turn ignition on. Ensure that vacuum applied in step **2)** becomes zero. If vacuum fails to become zero, check that voltage is present between ECU Check Sub Harness terminals "VSV" (37) and "E01" (21).
**4)** If no voltage is present, check that resistance between VSV terminals is within 30-50 ohms range. If resistance is not to specification, replace idle-up VSV. If resistance between VSV terminals is within specification, check wiring between ECU and main relay and repair wiring (as necessary).
**5)** Start engine. After one minute, connect a vacuum pump to idle-up VSV and apply 3.94 in. Hg. If no vacuum is present, check and/or repair wiring between VSV and ECU.
**6)** If wiring is good, check that there is voltage between ECU Check Sub Harness terminals "DSW" (17) and "E01" (21). If voltage is present, check wiring between headlight switch and/or defogger switch and ECU.
**7)** Turn headlight and/or defogger switch on. Ensure that vacuum applied in step **5)** becomes zero. If vacuum fails to become zero, check that there is voltage between ECU Check Sub Harness terminals "DSW" (17) and "E01" (21).

**8)** If no voltage is present, check wiring between headlight and/or defogger switch and ECU. Repair wiring (as necessary). Turn headlight and/or defogger switch off. Apply 3.94 in. Hg to idle-up VSV.

**9)** Turn blower fan switch on. Check that vacuum applied in step **8)** becomes zero. If vacuum fails to become zero, check wiring between idle-up VSV and blower fan switch. Repair wiring (as necessary).

**$O_2$ Sensor – 1)** Install Engine Control System Sub Harness (09991-87702-000) to check terminal. Start and warm engine to normal operating temperature and hold idle speed to 3000 RPM for 2 minutes.

**2)** Short Engine Control System Sub Harness terminal "T" (Brown) with ground terminal (Black). Connect DVOM between Engine Control System Sub Harness terminal "VF" (Green) and engine ground.

**3)** Hold engine speed to 1500 RPM. Ensure DVOM reading changes 8 times or more for 10 seconds. If change in voltage occurs 8 times or more, $O_2$ sensor is functioning properly.

**4)** If voltage reading does not change, proceed to step **7)**. If voltage reading occurs less than 8 times, disconnect short between Engine Control System Sub Harness terminal "T" (Brown) and ground (Black) terminal. Hold engine speed to 3000 RPM.

**5)** Reduce and hold engine speed to 2500 RPM. Short Engine Control System Sub Harness terminal "T" (Brown) and ground (Black) terminal. Ensure DVOM reading changes 8 times or more.

**6)** If change in voltage reading occurs 8 times or more, $O_2$ sensor is functioning properly. If change in voltage reading occurs less than 8 times, replace $O_2$ sensor.

**7)** If voltage reading does not change, perform diagnostic check and read diagnostic code(s). If code(s) other than normal code(s) are indicated, perform trouble shooting according to diagnostic code(s).

**8)** If normal codes are indicated, start engine and warm to normal operating temperature. Hold engine speed for 2 minutes at 3000 RPM, then reduce engine speed to 1500 RPM.

**9)** Short Engine Control System Sub Harness terminal "T" (Brown) and ground (Black) terminal. Measure voltage between Engine Control System Sub Harness terminal "VF" (Green) and engine ground.

**10)** If measured voltage is 5 volts, air/fuel ratio of fuel mixture is too rich. Repair for too rich fuel mixture. If measured voltage is zero volt and engine is idling normally, replace $O_2$ sensor. If measured voltage is zero volt and engine is not idling normally, repair too lean fuel mixture.

**Start Injector Time Switch – 1)** Disconnect start injector time switch connector. Measure resistance between terminals. *See Fig. 6.* When coolant temperature is greater than 75°F (24°C), resistance between terminals No. 1 and No. 2 should be 67-79 ohms.

**2)** Resistance between terminals No. 1 and No. 3 should be 67-79 ohms. Resistance between terminals No. 2 and No. 3 should be 140-155 ohms.

**3)** When coolant temperature is less than 68°F (20°C), resistance between terminals No. 1 and No. 2 should be 33-41 ohms.

**4)** Resistance between terminals No. 1 and No. 3 should be 33-41 ohms. Resistance between terminals No. 2 and No. 3 should be zero ohms.

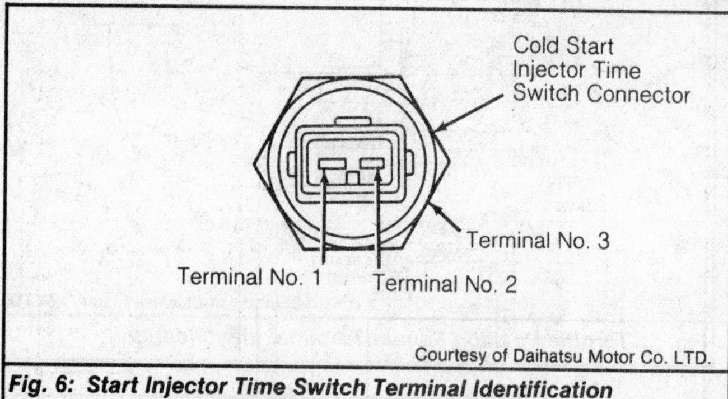
Cold Start
Injector Time
Switch Connector
Terminal No. 3
Terminal No. 1
Terminal No. 2
Courtesy of Daihatsu Motor Co. LTD.

***Fig. 6: Start Injector Time Switch Terminal Identification***

**Electronic Control Unit (ECU)** – Disconnect negative battery cable. Remove glove compartment subassembly. Connect ECU Check Sub Harness (09842-87704-000) between ECU and engine wiring. Reconnect negative battery cable. Connect DVOM to ECU and check for voltage and resistance readings, see VOLTAGE AT ECU WIRING CONNECTORS and RESISTANCE AT ECU TERMINALS charts. If voltage and resistance readings are within specifications and engine still malfunctions, replace ECU.

***NOTE: Wiring circuit of EFI can be checked by measuring voltage and resistance at ECU terminals. Measurement of voltage should be conducted while all connectors are connected. Ensure battery voltage is 11 volts or more when ignition is turned "ON". Be sure to conduct resistance measurement at ECU Check Sub Harness.***

***RESISTANCE AT ECU TERMINALS***

| Terminals | Conditions | Ohms |
|---|---|---|
| THW-E2 | Cool. Temp. 176°F | 320 |
| THA-E2 | Surge Tank Air Temp. 68°F | 2450 |
| VCC-VTH | Throttle Valve (Fully Closed) | 3500-10,300 |
| VCC-VTH | Throttle Valve (Fully Open) | 300-6300 |
| IDL-E2 | Throttle Valve (Fully Closed) | 17 |
| IDL-E2 | Throttle Valve (Fully Open) | 100,000 or more |
| NE-G | | 140-180 |
| G1-G | | 140-180 |

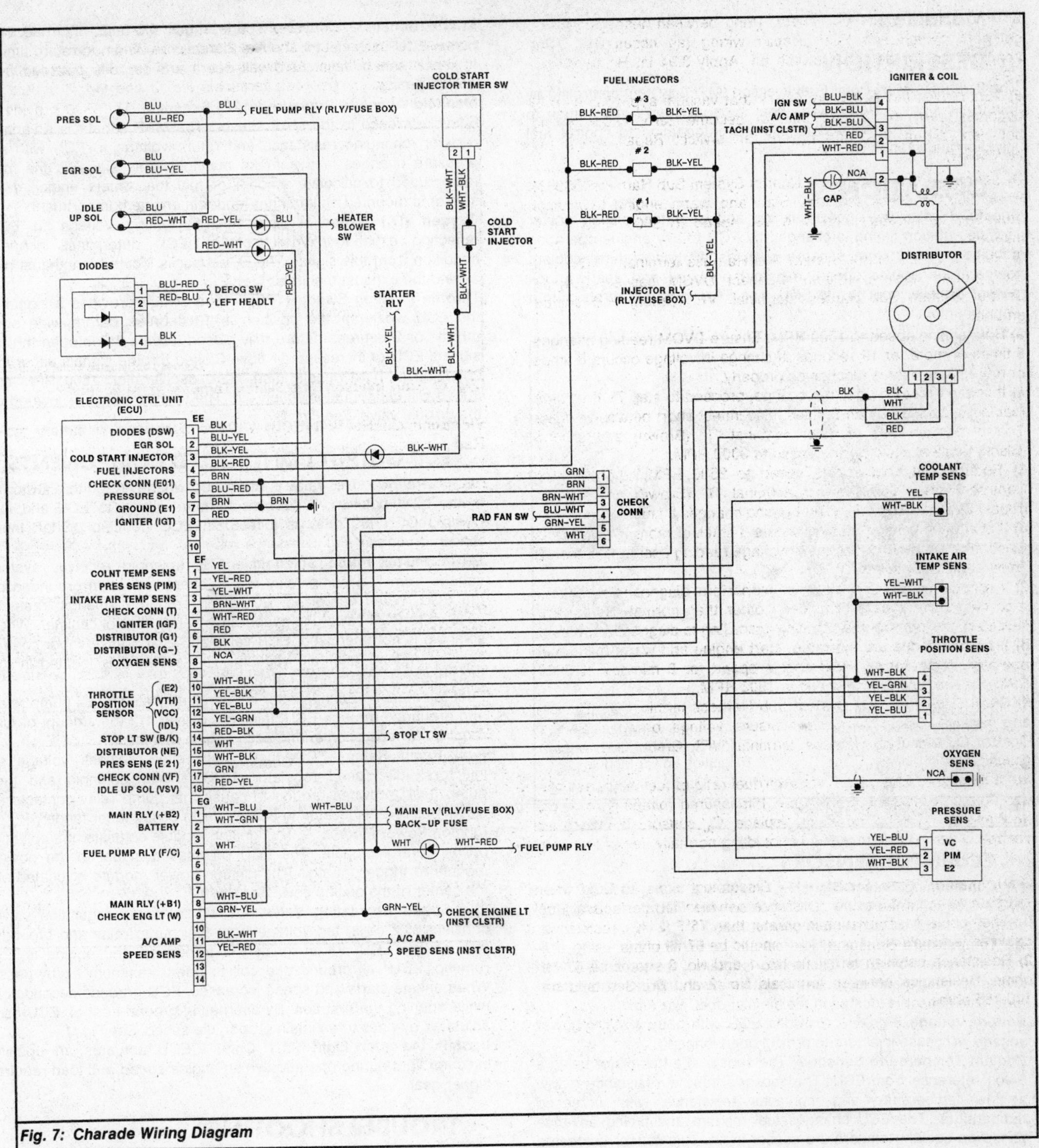
PRES SOL
EGR SOL
IDLE UP SOL
DIODES
ELECTRONIC CTRL UNIT (ECU)
FUEL PUMP RLY (RLY/FUSE BOX)
HEATER BLOWER SW
DEFOG SW
LEFT HEADLT
COLD START INJECTOR TIMER SW
COLD START INJECTOR
STARTER RLY
FUEL INJECTORS
INJECTOR RLY (RLY/FUSE BOX)
IGNITER & COIL
IGN SW
A/C AMP
TACH (INST CLSTR)
CAP
DISTRIBUTOR
CHECK CONN
RAD FAN SW
COOLANT TEMP SENS
INTAKE AIR TEMP SENS
THROTTLE POSITION SENS
OXYGEN SENS
PRESSURE SENS
STOP LT SW
MAIN RLY (RLY/FUSE BOX)
BACK-UP FUSE
FUEL PUMP RLY
CHECK ENGINE LT (INST CLSTR)
A/C AMP
SPEED SENS (INST CLSTR)

*Fig. 7: Charade Wiring Diagram*

## Medallion

# DESCRIPTION

The 2.2L uses Multi-Point Fuel Injection (MPFI) system controlled by Electronic Control Unit (ECU). Input sensors supply information to ECU. ECU is programmed to use this information to control fuel injection and ignition timing.

# OPERATION

The ECU calculates ignition timing and operates ignition power module. Ignition timing is changed by ECU to any engine operating condition. Inputs from sensors such as air temperature, coolant temperature, engine speed, manifold pressure and spark knock sensor provide input to the ECU. The ECU in turn controls output components.

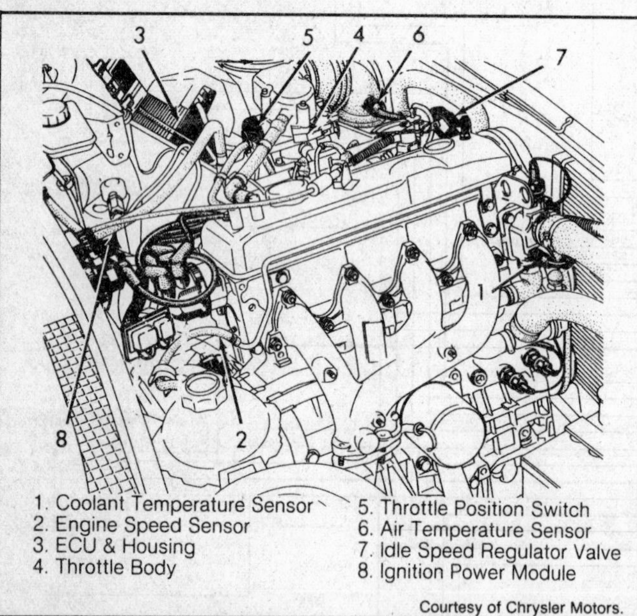
3
5
4
6
7
1
8
2
1. Coolant Temperature Sensor
2. Engine Speed Sensor
3. ECU & Housing
4. Throttle Body
5. Throttle Position Switch
6. Air Temperature Sensor
7. Idle Speed Regulator Valve
8. Ignition Power Module
Courtesy of Chrysler Motors.

*Fig. 1: Component Locations*

## ECU INPUT SENSORS

**Air Conditioning Select Signal** – Provides a signal to ECU when A/C switch is turned to the "ON" position. The ECU corrects air/fuel charge as required to maintain engine speed.

**Air Temperature Sensor** – The sensor is a thermistor using a 5-volt reference from ECU. The sensor's internal resistance is low at low temperature and increases resistance with increased temperature. This sensor is located in the air inlet duct. *See Fig. 1.*

**Battery Voltage Signal** – Provides ECU with battery state. Lower voltage will cause injectors to remain open longer.

**Coolant Temperature Sensor** – The sensor is a thermistor using a 5-volt reference from ECU. The sensor's internal resistance is low at low temperature and increases resistance with increased temperature. The ECU changes fuel mixture and timing advance based on coolant temperature sensor input. This sensor is located in the upper outlet hose housing. *See Fig. 1.*

**Engine Crank Signal (A/T Only)** – Provides a signal from starter relay to ECU when starter is engaged.

**Engine Speed Sensor** – Engine speed sensor is located on side of transmission converter housing. The sensor detects magnetized teeth as they pass during engine operation and sends an electrical signal to the ECU, which calculates engine speed and crankshaft angle. This signal is used to determine proper fuel injection and ignition timing. *See Fig. 1.*

**Gear Indicator Signal (A/T Only)** – Provides electrical signal to ECU when transmission is in gear. ECU will then compensate air/fuel charge to maintain correct engine speed.

**Knock Sensor** – Converts spark knock vibration into electrical pulse. ECU uses electrical pulse to determine when to retard timing. If knock sensor fails, ECU will operate 3 degrees retarded from normal timing.

**Manifold Absolute Pressure (MAP) Sensor** – The ECU provides a 5-volt reference to the MAP sensor. The MAP sensor is a variable resistor, changing resistance and return voltage to ECU with any pressure changes in the intake manifold. This signal is the main factor used to calculate amount of fuel that enters engine. MAP sensor is mounted on left inner fender in engine compartment.

**Oxygen ($O_2$) Sensor** – Generates fluctuating voltage to ECU, reflecting exhaust oxygen content. ECU determines rich/lean condition from this signal. The $O_2$ sensor is located in exhaust pipe behind the exhaust manifold.

**Throttle Position Switch (TPS)** – The switch provides a signal to the ECU when throttle position is 10 degrees before wide open throttle or 2 degrees before fully closed throttle. Wide open throttle signals ECU of increased air flow. Closed throttle signals either idle condition or hard deceleration. Hard deceleration 1500 RPM and above will cause fuel injection cut. The throttle switch is located on the throttle valve. *See Fig. 1.*

## ECU OUTPUT CONTROLLED COMPONENTS

**"B +" Relay** – This relay is energized whenever ignition switch is in the "ON" position. It supplies battery voltage to ECU and fuel pump relay. This relay is located in ECU housing on left inner fender.

**EGR/Canister Purge Solenoid** – This solenoid receives system voltage from fuel pump relay and is energized when grounded by the ECU. When energized, EGR/canister purge solenoid restricts vacuum to EGR valve and evaporative vapor control canister. When solenoid is not energized, EGR valve and evaporative vapor control canister receive manifold vacuum. This solenoid is located in the ECU housing on left inner fender.

**Fuel Injectors** – Each injector is energized through fuel pump relay and grounded through ECU. Injectors deliver 1/2 the amount of fuel required for operation during each engine revolution.

**Fuel Pump Relay** – The fuel pump relay provides voltage to injectors, idle speed regulator, EGR/canister solenoid and fuel pump. ECU provides ground to cause fuel pump relay contacts to close.This relay is located in ECU housing on left inner fender.

**Ignition Power Module** – The ignition module consists of a coil and power control module. The ECU provides a signal to the power module to trigger the coil. The ignition power module is located on the center of the engine cowl. *See Fig. 1.*

**Idle Speed Regulating Valve** – The idle speed regulating valve consists of 2 coils, fed voltage from fuel pump relay and grounds through the ECU. When ignition is turned on and engine is not running, ECU will ground one coil to open maximum air by-pass. When engine starts and speed increases, ECU grounds second coil while opening the first coil. By alternating ground control, ECU can adjust air by-pass to maintain proper idle speed. *See Fig. 1.*

**Upshift Indicator Light (M/T Only)** – ECU actuates an upshift indicator light during operation when engine speed and load require higher gear.

# TROUBLE SHOOTING

***NOTE: Before performing any testing, ensure that all systems are in normal operating condition (ignition and fuel components).***

## ENGINE STARTING

**Engine No Start or Hard Start** – Vacuum leak. Defective injectors. Low or no fuel pressure. Inoperative idle speed regulator. MAP sensor, speed sensor, ignition power module, "B +" relay or ECU defective. Wiring harness or connections faulty.

**Engine Starts & Stalls** – MAP sensor, air sensor, "B +" relay or ECU defective. Wiring harness or connections faulty.

### INCORRECT IDLE SPEED

**Idle Speed Too High** – Throttle Position Switch (TPS) faulty. Vacuum leak. Inoperative idle speed regulator. ECU defective. Wiring harness or connections faulty.

**Idle Speed Too Low** – Inoperative idle speed regulator. ECU defective. Wiring harness or connection faulty.

**Rough Idle** – TPS faulty. Vacuum leak. Defective injectors. Low or no fuel pressure. Throttle not closing. ECU defective. Wiring harness or connections faulty.

### POOR ENGINE PERFORMANCE

**Excessive Fuel Consumption** – Defective injectors. Fuel pressure too high. Wiring harness or connection faulty.

**Loss of Power** – TPS faulty. Defective injectors. Low or no fuel pressure. Air sensor defective. Throttle not opening fully. Wiring harness or connections faulty.

**Misfiring at All Speeds** – ECU defective. Wiring harness or connections faulty.

**Poor Acceleration** – TPS faulty. Vacuum leak. ECU defective. Wiring harness or connections faulty.

**Spark Knock** – Wiring harness or connections faulty.

## COMPONENT TESTING

### AIR TEMPERATURE SENSOR

Measure resistance across temperature sensor. Compare readings with specifications in AIR TEMPERATURE SENSOR RESISTANCE table. Replace sensor if not within specification.

*AIR TEMPERATURE SENSOR RESISTANCE*

| Temperature F° (C°) | Resistance Ohms |
|---|---|
| 31-33 (0) | 254-266 |
| 67-69 (20) | 283-297 |
| 103-105 (40) | 315-329 |

### COOLANT TEMPERATURE SENSOR

Measure resistance across temperature sensor. Compare readings with specifications in COOLANT TEMPERATURE SENSOR RESISTANCE table. Replace sensor if not within specification.

*COOLANT TEMPERATURE SENSOR RESISTANCE*

| Temperature F° (C°) | Resistance Ohms |
|---|---|
| 67-69 (20) | 283-297 |
| 175-179 (80) | 383-397 |
| 193-195 (90) | 403-417 |

### ENGINE SPEED SENSOR

Disconnect speed sensor connector from ignition control module. Measure resistance between terminal "A" and "B" (marked on connector). Resistance should be 125-275 ohms with engine hot. Replace sensor if not within specification.

### FUEL PUMP

**Fuel Pump Pressure – 1)** Disconnect hose from fuel pressure regulator to fuel rail. Connect fuel pressure guage to fuel rail. Disconnect vacuum hose from pressure regulator and connect vacuum pump.

**2)** Start engine. Check and record pressure reading. Pressure should be 33-39 psi (2.3-2.7 kg/cm$_2$).

**3)** Apply 15 in. Hg of vacuum to pressure regulator. Fuel pressure should drop to 26-31 psi (1.8-2.2 kg/cm$_2$).

**Fuel Pump Volume – 1)** Disconnect fuel return hose at pressure regulator. Place hose in a 4 quart graduated beaker. Disconnect ECU.

**2)** Start fuel pump by placing jumper wire between terminals 3 and 5 (large wires) on fuel pump relay connector. Minimum delivery should be 2 qts. (1.8 liters) in one minute. *See Fig. 2.*

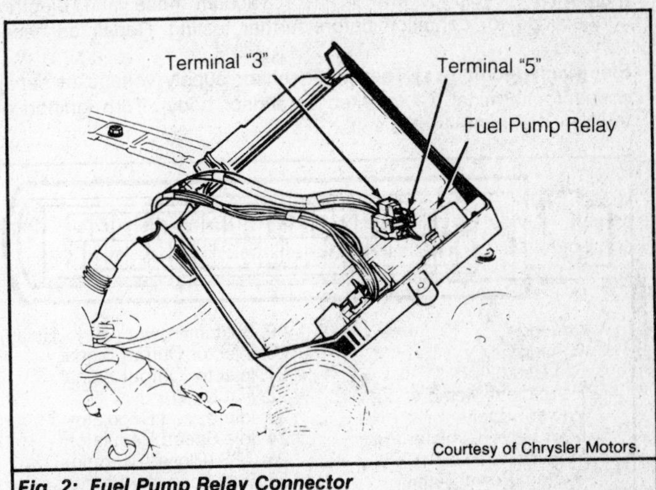
Terminal "3"
Terminal "5"
Fuel Pump Relay
Courtesy of Chrysler Motors.

***Fig. 2: Fuel Pump Relay Connector***

### FUEL INJECTORS

**Injector Test with Engine Stopped – 1)** Disconnect injector connectors. Remove fuel rail and injectors as an assembly. Use Injector Clamp (KM.01) to hold injectors in fuel rail during test. *See Fig. 3.*

**2)** Place assembly so each injector can be placed in a container. Energize fuel pump and inspect injectors tips for leaks.

**3)** Slight dampness at tip of injector is acceptable. Replace any leaking injectors as necessary.

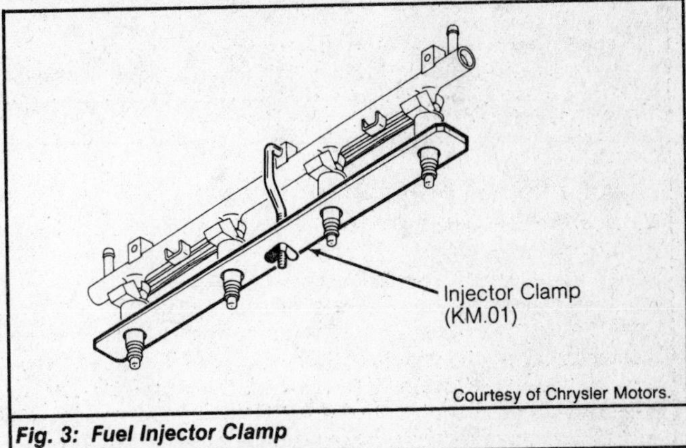
Injector Clamp
(KM.01)
Courtesy of Chrysler Motors.

***Fig. 3: Fuel Injector Clamp***

**Injector Test with Engine Running – 1)** Start engine and bring to operating temperature. Disconnect injector wire, one at a time.

**2)** Engine RPM should drop, each time an injector is disconnected. If any cylinder does not change RPM, switch wire connectors between operational injector.

**3)** If injector that did not operate does, wire harness is defective. If injector that did not operate does not, injector is defective.

### IDLE SPEED REGULATOR

**Electrical Testing – 1)** Disconnect connector at idle speed regulator. Supply battery voltage to terminal "4" (marked on regulator) of idle speed regulator.

**2)** Start engine. Briefly ground terminal "5" (marked on regulator) of idle speed regulator. Valve should close and engine speed should drop.

**3)** Briefly ground terminal "3" (marked on regulator) of idle speed regulator. Valve should open and engine speed should increase to above 2000 RPM.

## MAP SENSOR

**Inspection** – Inspect MAP sensor vacuum hose and electrical connections for condition before further testing. Repair as necessary.

**Electrical Circuit** – **1)** Test MAP sensor supply voltage at sensor connector terminal "C" (marked on sensor body). Turn ignition on. Voltage should be 4.5-5.5 volts.

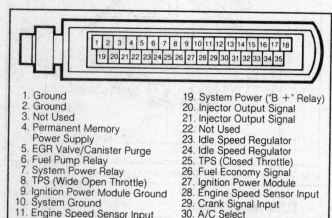

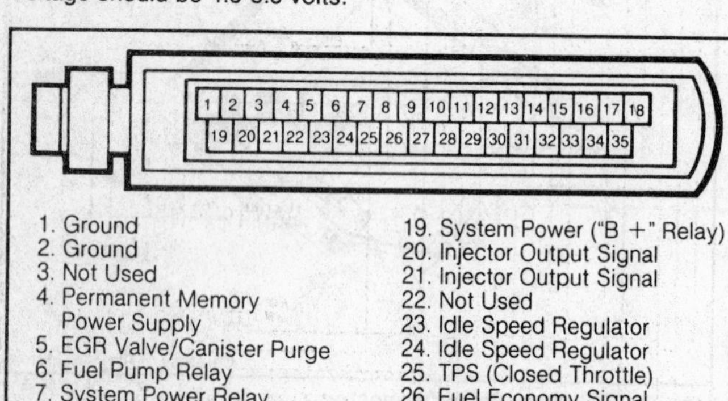
1 2 3 4 5 6 7 8 9 10 11 12 13 14 15 16 17 18
19 20 21 22 23 24 25 26 27 28 29 30 31 32 33 34 35

1. Ground
2. Ground
3. Not Used
4. Permanent Memory Power Supply
5. EGR Valve/Canister Purge
6. Fuel Pump Relay
7. System Power Relay
8. TPS (Wide Open Throttle)
9. Ignition Power Module Ground
10. System Ground
11. Engine Speed Sensor Input
12. "P-N" Switch (A/T only)
13. Knock Sensor Ground
14. Air Temperature Sensor
15. Coolant Temperature Sensor
16. MAP Sensor (Ref. Volt)
17. MAP & $O_2$ Gound
18. Shift Light (M/T only)
19. System Power ("B +" Relay)
20. Injector Output Signal
21. Injector Output Signal
22. Not Used
23. Idle Speed Regulator
24. Idle Speed Regulator
25. TPS (Closed Throttle)
26. Fuel Economy Signal
27. Ignition Power Module
28. Engine Speed Sensor Input
29. Crank Signal Input
30. A/C Select
31. Knock Sensor Input
32. Temperature Sensor Ground
33. MAP Sensor Output
34. A/C Thermostat
35. $O_2$ Sensor Input

Courtesy of Chrysler Motors.

***Fig. 4: ECU Connector Terminal Identification.***

**2)** Measure voltage at ECU connector terminal "16". With ignition on, voltage should be the same. If voltage is not present, repair or replace wiring harness as necessary. *See Fig. 4.*

**3)** Test MAP sensor output voltage at sensor connector terminal "B" (marked on sensor body). Turn ignition on with engine off. Voltage should be 4-5 volts.

**4)** Measure voltage at ECU connector terminal "33". With ignition on and engine off, voltage should be 4-5 volts. If voltage is not present, repair or replace wiring harness as necessary.

**5)** Start and warm engine. With engine idling, voltage at MAP sensor connector terminal "B" (marked on sensor body) and ECU connector terminal "33" should be .5-1.5 volts.

**6)** Using an ohmmeter, test MAP sensor ground circuit. Check for continuity between MAP sensor connector terminal "A" (marked on sensor body) and ECU connector terminal "17". Repair or replace wiring harness if no continuity exists.

**7)** Check for continuity between ECU connector terminal "17" and "2". Check continuity between ECU connector terminal "2" and ground connection at right side of engine block.

## THROTTLE POSITION SWITCH (TPS)

Disconnect TPS connector and check continuity using THROTTLE POSITION SWITCH CONTINUITY table. If continuity is not as specified, adjust switch by loosening attaching screws and rotating switch. If continuity is still not within specifications, replace TPS.

***THROTTLE POSITION SWITCH CONTINUITY***

| Throttle Position | [1] "B" & "C" | [1] "A" & "B" |
|---|---|---|
| Closed | Continuity | No Continuity |
| Partial | No Continuity | No Continuity |
| Full | No Continuity | Continuity |

[1] – Markings are on connector.

# Eagle (Cont.)

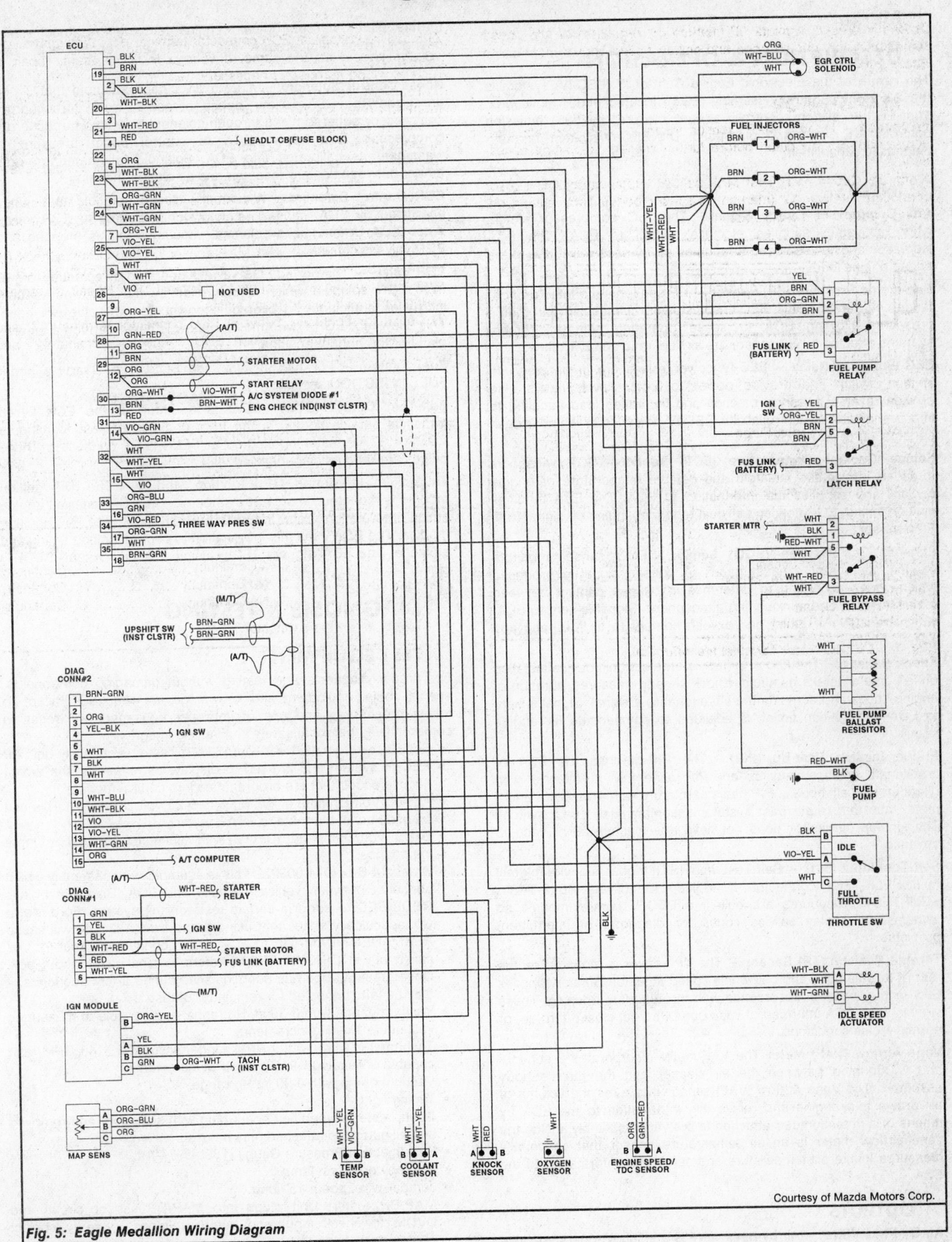
ECU
BLK
BRN
BLK
BLK
WHT-BLK
WHT-RED
RED
HEADLT CB(FUSE BLOCK)
ORG
WHT-BLK
WHT-BLK
ORG-GRN
WHT-GRN
WHT-GRN
ORG-YEL
VIO-YEL
VIO-YEL
WHT
WHT
VIO
NOT USED
ORG-YEL
GRN-RED
(A/T)
ORG
BRN
STARTER MOTOR
ORG
ORG
START RELAY
ORG-WHT
VIO-WHT
A/C SYSTEM DIODE #1
BRN
BRN-WHT
ENG CHECK IND(INST CLSTR)
RED
VIO-GRN
VIO-GRN
WHT
WHT-YEL
WHT
VIO
ORG-BLU
GRN
VIO-RED
ORG-GRN
THREE WAY PRES SW
WHT
BRN-GRN
(M/T)
UPSHIFT SW (INST CLSTR)
BRN-GRN
BRN-GRN
(A/T)
DIAG CONN#2
BRN-GRN
ORG
YEL-BLK
IGN SW
WHT
BLK
WHT
WHT-BLU
WHT-BLK
VIO
VIO-YEL
WHT-GRN
ORG
A/T COMPUTER
(A/T)
WHT-RED
STARTER RELAY
DIAG CONN#1
GRN
YEL
IGN SW
BLK
WHT-RED
WHT-RED
STARTER MOTOR
RED
FUS LINK (BATTERY)
WHT-YEL
(M/T)
IGN MODULE
ORG-YEL
YEL
BLK
GRN
ORG-WHT
TACH (INST CLSTR)
ORG-GRN
ORG-BLU
ORG
MAP SENS
WHT-YEL
VIO-GRN
TEMP SENSOR
WHT
WHT-YEL
COOLANT SENSOR
WHT
RED
KNOCK SENSOR
WHT
OXYGEN SENSOR
ORG
GRN-RED
ENGINE SPEED/ TDC SENSOR
ORG
WHT-BLU
WHT
EGR CTRL SOLENOID
FUEL INJECTORS
BRN
ORG-WHT
WHT-YEL
WHT-RED
WHT
YEL
BRN
ORG-GRN
BRN
FUS LINK (BATTERY)
RED
FUEL PUMP RELAY
IGN SW
YEL
ORG-YEL
BRN
BRN
FUS LINK (BATTERY)
RED
LATCH RELAY
STARTER MTR
WHT
BLK
RED-WHT
WHT
WHT-RED
WHT
FUEL BYPASS RELAY
WHT
WHT
FUEL PUMP BALLAST RESISITOR
RED-WHT
BLK
FUEL PUMP
BLK
IDLE
VIO-YEL
WHT
FULL THROTTLE
THROTTLE SW
BLK
WHT-BLK
WHT
WHT-GRN
IDLE SPEED ACTUATOR

Courtesy of Mazda Motors Corp.

*Fig. 5: Eagle Medallion Wiring Diagram*

# Merkur

## DESCRIPTION & OPERATION

The center of the Electronic Engine Control IV (EEC-IV) system is the Electronic Control Assembly (ECA), located under glove box. The EEC-IV system controls air/fuel mixture, ignition, emission controls, A/C clutch and idle speed. The EEC-IV system has self-diagnostic capabilities.

### INPUTS

**A/C Compressor Clutch Signal** – The A/C compressor clutch, when activated, supplies electrical signal to ECA. The ECA increases engine idle speed through an air by-pass valve, due to the added engine load.

**Barometric Pressure (BP) Sensor** – BP sensor is mounted on right fender by starter relay. BP sensor senses changes in barometric pressure, allowing ECA to sense operating altitude. Primary systems affected by BP sensor are air/fuel ratio and EGR flow.

**EEC-IV Power Relay** – EEC-IV power relays are in parallel with ignition switch and provide power to ECA. Power relays also provide reverse battery protection and increased load handling to improve ignition switch reliability. EEC-IV power relay is under dash panel to left of glove box.

**Engine Coolant Temperature (ECT) Sensor** – ECT sensor is threaded into intake manifold and detects temperature of engine coolant and supplies the information to ECA. The ECA modifies ignition timing, EGR flow and air/fuel ratio, depending on signal from ECT sensor.

**Exhaust Gas Oxygen (EGO) Sensor** – EGO sensor monitors oxygen content of exhaust gases. A voltage signal is produced which varies according to difference in oxygen content between exhaust gases and surrounding atmosphere. Signal is sent to ECA, which translates exhaust gas oxygen content to air/fuel ratio and adjusts mixture accordingly.

**Knock Sensor** – The knock sensor is an electronic device installed on left side of intake manifold. Knock sensor measures vibration of engine knock and converts the vibration into a signal. Signal is sent to ECA and ignition timing is adjusted to compensate for engine knock.

**Profile Ignition Pick-Up (PIP)** – The PIP informs the ECA of crankshaft position and speed. PIP assembly is integral with distributor on all models. PIP has an armature with 4 windows and 4 metal tabs that rotate past a stator assembly (Hall Effect switch). The ignition distributor does not have any mechanical or vacuum advance.

**Self-Test Input (STI)** – Self-Test Input (STI) trigger is a wire (pigtail) near SELF-TEST connector. It is used to activate SELF-TEST. SELF-TEST procedures are built into EEC-IV control module so system can display service codes for diagnosis of intermittent problems.

**Throttle Position (TP) Sensor** – The TP sensor is mounted on the rear of throttle body and below idle speed actuator. Sensor supplies ECA with a signal in accordance with throttle plate opening. These signals keep ECA informed of wide open throttle, closed throttle, or normal cruise conditions.

**Vane Airflow (VAF) Meter** The VAF meter incorporates 2 sensors and is mounted between the air cleaner and the throttle body assembly. The Vane Airflow (VAF) sensor measures the volume of air drawn into engine and relays this information to the ECA by means of a potentiometer attached to the vane assembly. Inside the vane airflow meter is an air temperature sensor that continually measures intake air temperature and sends this information to the ECA.

### OUTPUTS

**Air By-Pass Valve** – Air by-pass valve is a solenoid-operated valve controlled by the ECA. The valve allows air to by-pass around throttle plates to control cold engine fast idle, no touch start, dashpot, over temperature idle boost, and engine idle load correction.

**Boost Control Solenoid** – A normally closed solenoid that, when energized by ECA, allow boost pressure from turbocharger compressor outlet to bleed through solenoid back into turbocharger compressor. This allows ECA to control boost pressure to wastegate as calibrated into ECA. Solenoid is located on right fender between coolant reservoir and air cleaner housing.

**EGR Control Solenoid** – A normally closed solenoid that, when energized by ECA, causes vacuum signal to flow to EGR valve. When ECA de-energizes solenoid, vacuum signal is stopped and EGR valve is closed.

**EGR Valve** – The ported EGR valve is operated by a vacuum signal from EGR solenoid which is controlled by the ECA. As vacuum increases sufficiently to overcome power spring, valve will open. This allows for EGR flow. Amount of flow is dependent on a tapered pintle or the poppet position.

**Fuel System** – For fuel system, see BOSCH AFC article under FUEL INJECTION section.

**Self-Test Output (STO)** – STO is a circuit in the ECA which transmits service codes, in the form of timed pulses, to either a VOM or STAR tester hooked-up at SELF-TEST connector. These pulses are read as diagnostic codes.

**Thick Film Integrated (TFI) Ignition Module** – The TFI ignition module is mounted on side of distributor. The ECA receives engine timing information from the distributor through the TFI ignition module. The ECA uses this information to control ignition timing and advance. The ECA triggers TFI by using a Spark Output (SPOUT) signal.

## DIAGNOSIS & TESTING

### TEST EQUIPMENT

For proper diagnosis and testing without damaging components, special tools, equipment and knowledge are required. Failure to follow procedures and use of improper equipment will result in compromising personal safety and vehicle integrity.

- Self-Test Automatic Read-Out (STAR) Tester is specially built for EEC-IV system and is used to display, as numerals, the 2-digit service codes that are programmed into control module.
- Analog Volt/Ohmmeter (VOM) with 0-20 volt DC range. This can be used as an alternate to STAR tester.
- Digital Volt/Ohmmeter (DVOM) with minimum 10-megaohm input impedance.
- Breakout Box (014-00322). This is a jumper wire assembly which connects between vehicle harness and ECA. Breakout box is REQUIRED to perform certain tests on the system. Ford Motor Co. specifically states that using probe from a DVOM will cause PERMANENT DAMAGE to ECA 60-pin connector. "Test Pin" as called out in CIRCUIT TESTS refers to pins on breakout box. Once breakout box has been installed during a test sequence, it may be left connected for remainder of test.
- Vacuum gauge with 0-30 in. Hg range, and capable of measuring vacuum in 1 in. Hg increments.
- Tachometer with 0-6000 RPM range, accuracy ± 40 RPM, and capable of reading RPM in 20 RPM increments.
- Vacuum pump with 0-30 in. Hg range.
- Timing light.
- Spark tester. A modified spark plug with side electrode removed and alligator clip attached may be used.
- Fuel Injection Pressure Gauge (T80L-9974-A).
- Non-powered test lamp.
- Jumper wire, about 15" long.
- MAP/BP tester. Unit plugs into MAP/BP sensor circuit and DVOM to check input and output voltages to verify correct sensor operation.

# 1988 COMPUTERIZED ENGINE CONTROLS
# Ford Motor Co. Merkur EEC-IV (Cont.)

## READING SELF-TEST CODES

Service codes are transmitted to Pin No. 4 (Self-Test Output) of SELF-TEST connector in the form of timed pulses. All service codes are 2 digit numbers which are generated one digit at a time. Codes are shown as voltage pulses (needle sweeps) on an analog volt/ohmmeter (VOM).

If a VOM is being used, careful attention to length of pauses is necessary in order to read codes correctly. There will be a 2 second pause between each DIGIT in a code. There will be a 4 second pause between each CODE. Continuous memory codes are separated from functional test service codes by a 6-second delay, a single 1/2 second sweep, and another 6-second delay.

If a Self-Test Automatic Read-Out (STAR) tester is used, it will count pulses and display them as a digital code. The STAR tester will add a zero (0) to single digit codes.

**Separator Pulse** – A single 1/2 second separator pulse is issued 6-9 seconds after last functional KEY ON/ENGINE OFF SELF-TEST code. Then 6-9 seconds after the single 1/2 second separator pulse, the continuous memory codes will be displayed.

**Continuous Memory Codes** – These codes are issued as a result of information stored during CONTINUOUS MONITOR (WIGGLE) TEST. These codes are displayed only during KOEO SELF-TEST and after separator code. These codes should be used to diagnose ONLY when KOEO and KEY ON ENGINE RUNNING (KOER) SELF-TESTS result in Code 11 and all QUICK TEST steps have been successfully completed.

## SELF-TEST CONNECTOR LOCATIONS

The SELF-TEST connector should be found behind right front shock tower, near battery.

## DIAGNOSTIC PROCEDURE

The diagnostic procedure is used to test and service the EEC-IV system. It is divided into 2 test formats: QUICK TEST, a functional system test, and PIN POINT TESTS, a number of specific component tests. To test and service EEC-IV system, perform QUICK TEST first.

QUICK TEST consists of 3 phases, KEY ON/ENGINE OFF, ENGINE RUNNING, and CONTINUOUS TESTING. Perform QUICK TEST before running any pin point tests. If QUICK TEST fails, perform only those pin point tests specified by the failed step. After all tests and services have been completed, repeat entire QUICK TEST.

---

***NOTE:* *Failure to follow steps in sequence or to perform each step completely can cause misdiagnosis and/or component failure or unnecssary replacement of non-faulty components.***

---

**Preparation** – Correct test results for system are dependent on correct operation of several related non-EEC-IV components and systems. All non-EEC-IV problems should be corrected before attempting to diagnose EEC-IV system.

Before hooking up any equipment to diagnose EEC-IV system, make following checks:

- Verify condition of air cleaner and air ducting.
- Check all vacuum hoses for leaks, restrictions, and proper routing.
- Check the EEC-IV system wiring harness and electrical connections for corrosion, loose or detached connectors, loose wires, terminals and proper routing.
- Check the ECA, sensors and actuators for physical damage.
- Perform all necessary safety precautions to prevent personal injury or vehicle damage.
- Set parking brake and place shift lever in "P" for automatic transmission and Neutral for manual transmission. Do not move shift lever during testing unless specifically directed to do so.
- Turn off all lights and accessories. Ensure that vehicle doors are closed when making readings.
- Check and correct coolant level.
- Start engine and idle until upper radiator hose is hot, pressurized and throttle is off fast idle. Check for leaks around exhaust manifold, exhaust gas oxygen sensor and vacuum hose connections.
- If equipped, place octane switch in premium position.
- Turn ignition switch to "OFF" position. Service items as required, then go to EQUIPMENT HOOK-UP.

If engine will not start, starts but stalls, idles rough or runs rough, see KEY ON/ENGINE OFF SELF-TEST in this article. If any of the above conditions are still present after a code 11 in KEY ON/ENGINE OFF SELF-TEST, see CIRCUIT TEST A in this article. If engine stalls or runs rough, see DIAGNOSIS BY SYMPTOM TEST in this article.

## EQUIPMENT HOOK-UP

**Analog VOM** – **1)** Turn ignition switch to "OFF" position. Connect jumper wire from Self-Test Input (STI) pigtail to pin No. 2 (Signal Return) on SELF-TEST connector. Set VOM at 0-15 volt DC range and connect positive lead of VOM to positive battery terminal.

**2)** Connect negative VOM lead to pin No. 4 (STO) on SELF-TEST connector. *See Fig. 1.* Connect timing light, then go to KEY ON/ENGINE OFF SELF-TEST.

**STAR Tester** – Turn ignition switch to "OFF" position. Connect color coded adapter cable leads to STAR tester. *See Fig. 1.* Connect adapter cable's service connectors to vehicle's SELF-TEST connectors. Connect timing light and proceed to KEY ON/ENGINE OFF SELF-TEST in this article.

## QUICK TEST

The QUICK TEST diagnostic procedure is a functional test of EEC-IV system, consisting of basic test steps. These basic steps must be carefully followed in sequence, otherwise a misdiagnosis, or replacement of non-faulty components may result.

- VISUAL CHECK AND PREPARATION is checking for obvious faults and defects and preparing vehicle for testing.
- EQUIPMENT HOOK–UP ensures proper equipment is used and is properly operating prior to testing.
- KEY ON/ENGINE OFF SELF-TEST is a static check of EEC-IV system inputs and outputs.
- TIMING CHECK verifies ability of the system to compute and maintain a fixed spark timing during SELF-TEST.
- ENGINE RUNNING SELF-TEST is a dynamic system check with engine under actual operating conditions and at normal operating temperature.
- CONTINUOUS SELF-TEST checks sensor inputs for opens and shorts while vehicle is in operation.
- KEY ON/ENGINE OFF and ENGINE RUNNING SELF-TESTS are intended to detect faults present at time of testing, not intermittent faults. Intermittent faults are detected by CONTINUOUS SELF-TEST.

## KEY ON/ENGINE OFF SELF-TEST

---

***NOTE:* *Continuous memory codes recorded in this step will be used for diagnosis in CONTINUOUS SELF-TEST.***

---

**Code Output** – Correct test results for system are dependent on correct operation of several related non-EEC-IV components and systems. It may be necessary to correct faults in these areas before EEC-IV will pass QUICK TEST.

Verify that vehicle has been properly prepared. See PREPARATION and EQUIPMENT HOOK-UP under DIAGNOSTIC PROCEDURE. To start SELF-TEST, turn ignition on. DO NOT depress throttle during test. Observe and record all service codes.

**1)** If engine does not start, go to CIRCUIT TEST A, step **2)**. If KEY ON/ENGINE OFF code and continuous memory indicate code 11 (pass), go to TIMING CHECK.

**2)** If any KEY ON/ENGINE OFF code is displayed with continuous memory code 11, KEY ON/ENGINE OFF SELF-TEST indicates a fault. Record codes and see TEST RESULTS & ACTION TO TAKE in this article.

**3)** If any KEY ON/ENGINE OFF codes or any continuous memory codes are displayed indicates a fault. Record codes, but DO NOT repair continuous memory codes at this time. KEY ON/ENGINE OFF and ENGINE RUNNING SELF-TEST codes MUST be repaired first. See TEST RESULTS & ACTION TO TAKE in this article.

**4)** If KEY ON/ENGINE OFF code 11 (pass), is displayed with ANY continuous memory code (except code 15), continuous memory indicates a fault. Record codes, but DO NOT repair continuous memory codes at this time. KEY ON/ENGINE OFF and ENGINE RUNNING SELF-TEST codes MUST be repaired first. Go to TIMING CHECK.

**5)** If KEY ON/ENGINE OFF code 11 (pass), is displayed and continuous memory code 15 is displayed, go to CIRCUIT TEST NN, step **11)**. If NO CODES are displayed, repeat SELF-TEST and verify that no service codes are present. If no service codes present, go to CIRCUIT TEST NN, step **1)**.

**Test Results & Action To Take – 1)** Perform test indicated as in KEY ON/ENGINE OFF SELF-TEST table in this article. Start with first code displayed. If the test refers you to other checks, perform them as instructed.

**2)** When more than one code is displayed, repair problems in order codes are displayed. Whenever a repair is made, repeat QUICK TEST. If no codes appear, repeat SELF-TEST. If no service codes are present, go to CIRCUIT TEST NN, step **1)** in this article.

***KEY ON/ENGINE OFF SELF-TEST***

| Service Codes | Test |
|---|---|
| 15 | Circuit Test NN, Step **13)** |
| 21 | Circuit Test G |
| 22 | Circuit Test H |
| 23 | Circuit Test J |
| 24 | Circuit Test D |
| 26 | Circuit Test K |
| 51 | Circuit Test G, Step **4)** |
| 53 | Circuit Test J, Step **3)** |
| 54 | Circuit Test D, Step **4)** |
| 56 | Circuit Test K, Step **3)** |
| 61 | Circuit Test G, Step **6)** |
| 63 | Circuit Test J, Step **6)** |
| 64 | Circuit Test D, Step **6)** |
| 66 | Circuit Test K, Step **6)** |
| 67 | Circuit Test M |

## TIMING CHECK

***NOTE:** If engine will not start, go to CIRCUIT TEST A. If engine starts but stalls while testing, go to DIAGNOSIS BY SYMPTOM TEST.*

**1)** Turn ignition switch to "OFF" position, and then wait 10 seconds. Verify that SELF-TEST has been activated. Restart engine and check timing while in SELF-TEST mode. You are allowed 2 minutes to check timing from time last code is displayed.

**2)** Correct SELF-TEST timing equals base ignition timing (10 degrees BTDC on all engines) plus 17-23 degrees BTDC. If timing is not 27-33 degrees BTDC, go to CIRCUIT TEST MM. If timing is 27-33 degrees BTDC, go to ENGINE RUNNING SELF-TEST.

## ENGINE RUNNING SELF-TEST

***NOTE:** If engine will not start, go to CIRCUIT TEST A. If engine starts but stalls while testing, go to DIAGNOSIS BY SYMPTOM TEST.*

**Code Output – 1)** Deactivate SELF-TEST (disconnect jumper wire). Start engine and run it at 2000 RPM for 2 minutes to warm up EGO sensor. Turn engine off and wait 10 seconds. Insert jumper to activate SELF-TEST. DO NOT depress throttle during test unless a Dynamic Response code occurs.

**2)** Start engine. The engine ID code will be displayed. Run test. If Dynamic Response code one (10 with STAR tester) occurs, briefly accelerate engine to wide open throttle. The ENGINE RUNNING SELF-TEST service codes will then be displayed. Observe and record all codes.

**Test Results & Action To Take – 1)** If no codes appear, repeat SELF-TEST and verify that no service codes are present, and then go to CIRCUIT TEST NN. If code 98 and any other code appears, perform KEY ON/ENGINE OFF SELF-TEST and obtain a Code 11 for KEY ON/ENGINE OFF portion of QUICK TEST.

**2)** If engine ID code is 2, 3 or 4 (20, 30 or 40 with STAR tester), and code 11 is displayed, ENGINE RUNNING SELF-TEST portion is okay. If symptom was of an intermittent nature, go to CONTINUOUS SELF-TEST. If symptom is present, go to DIAGNOSIS BY SYMPTOM TEST. Otherwise QUICK TEST is complete, and EEC-IV system is okay.

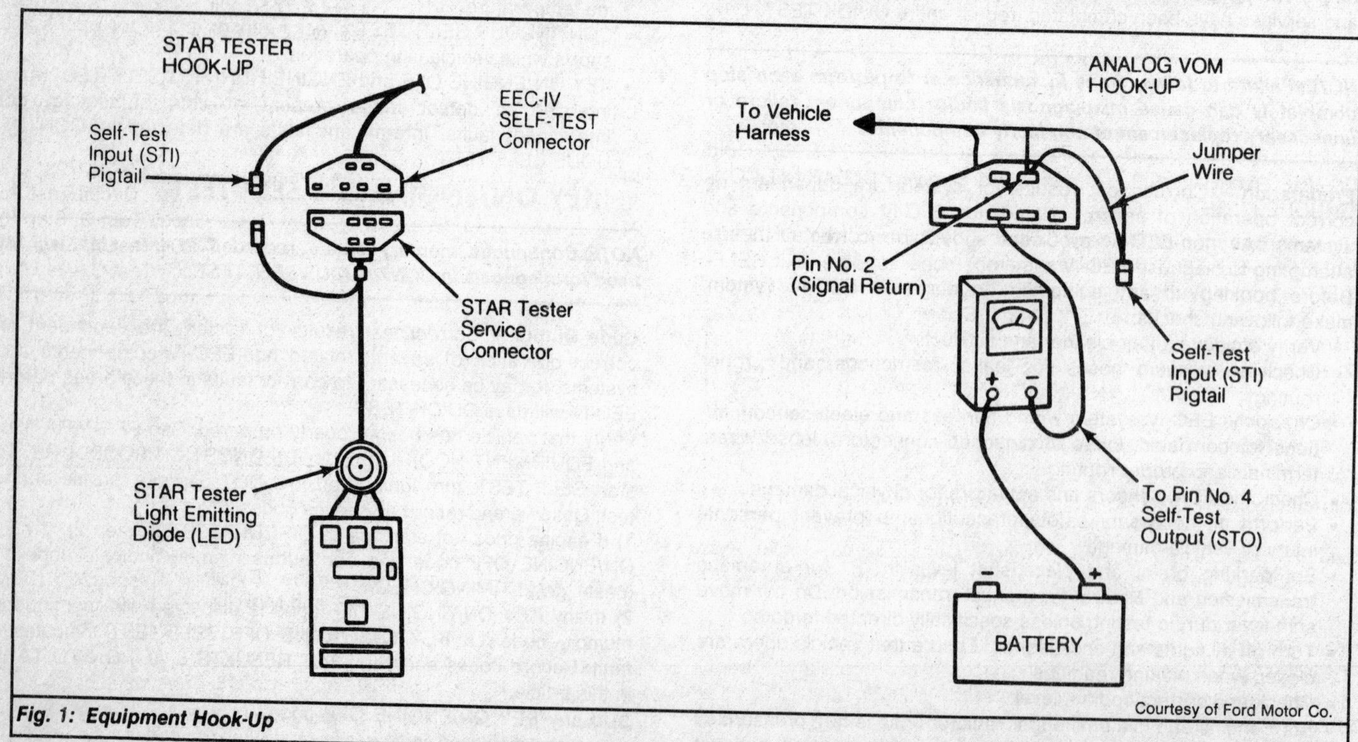
STAR TESTER
HOOK-UP
EEC-IV
SELF-TEST
Connector
Self-Test
Input (STI)
Pigtail
STAR Tester
Service
Connector
STAR Tester
Light Emitting
Diode (LED)
ANALOG VOM
HOOK-UP
To Vehicle
Harness
Jumper
Wire
Pin No. 2
(Signal Return)
Self-Test
Input (STI)
Pigtail
To Pin No. 4
Self-Test
Output (STO)
BATTERY
Courtesy of Ford Motor Co.

***Fig. 1: Equipment Hook-Up***

# 1988 COMPUTERIZED ENGINE CONTROLS
# Ford Motor Co. Merkur EEC-IV (Cont.)

**3)** If engine ID code is 2, 3 or 4 (20, 30 or 40 with STAR tester), and any code other than 11 appears, ENGINE RUNNING SELF-TEST portion is at fault. Perform test indicated in ENGINE RUNNING SELF-TEST table for that specific engine.
**4)** Start with first code displayed. If tests refer you to other checks, perform them as instructed. When more than one code is displayed, repair problems in the order that codes are displayed. Whenever a repair is made, repeat QUICK TEST.

*ENGINE RUNNING SELF-TEST*

| Service Codes | Test |
|---|---|
| 12 | Circuit Test Z |
| 13 | Circuit Test Z, Step **10)** |
| 21 | Circuit Test G |
| 22 | Circuit Test H |
| 23 | Circuit Test J |
| 24 | Circuit Test D |
| 25 | Circuit Test I |
| 26 | Circuit Test K |
| 34 | Circuit Test W |
| 41 | Circuit Test Q, Step **11)** |
| 42 | Circuit Test Q, Step **8)** |
| 73 | Circuit Test J, Step **10)** |
| 76 | Circuit Test K, Step **10)** |
| 77 | Circuit Test KK |
| 99 | [1] |

[1] – Idle Speed Control (ISC) has not "learned" yet. Repeat QUICK TEST.

## CONTINUOUS SELF-TEST

***NOTE:*** *CONTINUOUS SELF-TEST has 4 steps: CONTINUOUS MEMORY CODES, CLEARING CONTINUOUS MEMORY CODES, CONTINUOUS MEMORY CODES TO BE TESTED, and TEST RESULTS & ACTION TO TAKE. Perform steps in sequence.*

**Continuous Memory Codes – 1)** To ensure proper diagnosis of continuous memory codes, PREPARATION, EQUIPMENT HOOK-UP, KEY ON/ENGINE OFF SELF-TEST, TIMING CHECK, and ENGINE RUNNING SELF-TEST must be successfully completed. If both KEY ON/ENGINE OFF and ENGINE RUNNING SELF-TEST display code 11 (Pass), go to CLEARING CONTINUOUS MEMORY CODES.
**2)** If code 11 is not present, return to PREPARATION step and make necessary repairs indicated in KEY ON/ENGINE OFF and ENGINE RUNNING SELF-TEST before going to CLEARING CONTINUOUS MEMORY CODES.

**Clearing Continuous Memory Codes – 1)** Perform KEY ON/ENGINE OFF SELF-TEST. When first service code appears, exit SELF-TEST program by disconnecting STAR tester or by removing jumper wire from Self-Test Input (STI) pigtail. Exiting QUICK TEST in this manner will clear all codes stored in continuous memory.
**2)** Repeat KEY ON/ENGINE OFF SELF-TEST. If code output is 11-10-11, go to CONTINUOUS MEMORY CODES TO BE TESTED. If code output is not correct, check Self-Test Input (STI) circuit for short to ground. Repair short and repeat CLEARING CONTINUOUS MEMORY CODES step.

**Continuous Memory Codes To Be Tested** – Check list of continuous memory codes that were recorded in KEY ON/ENGINE OFF and ENGINE RUNNING SELF-TESTS. Disregard any codes that have already been repaired. To confirm remaining codes, go to TEST RESULTS & ACTION TO TAKE.

**Test Results & Action To Take – 1)** Ensure that all previous QUICK TEST steps have been successfully completed. Verify proper test equipment hook-up. See EQUIPMENT HOOK-UP in this article. Make sure that SELF-TEST is deactivated. DO NOT activate SELF-TEST unless specifically instructed to do so.
**2)** Using service codes obtained in CONTINUOUS MEMORY CODES TO BE TESTED, perform test(s) indicated in CONTINUOUS SELF-TEST table for that specific engine. While performing CIRCUIT TESTS, one or both of CONTINUOUS MONITOR (WIGGLE) TESTS may have to be used to find intermittent fault.

## CONTINUOUS MONITOR (WIGGLE) TEST

The Self-Test Output (STO) will be activated each time a fault is detected. If STO is activated long enough during wiggle tests a service code will be stored. A fault is indicated by a deflection of 10.5 volts or greater on VOM. STAR tester LED turns off.

- **KEY ON/ENGINE OFF Test**: With SELF-TEST deactivated, turn ignition on to enter into wiggle mode.
- **ENGINE RUNNING Test**: Activate SELF-TEST and perform ENGINE RUNNING SELF-TEST. After service code output has finished, do not turn engine off or deactivate SELF-TEST. About 2 minutes after code 11 has been displayed, wiggle mode will start. The system will remain in wiggle mode until SELF-TEST is deactivated or engine is turned off.

***NOTE:*** *An alternate method of entering CONTINUOUS MONITOR (WIGGLE) TEST with engine running is to start ENGINE RUNNING SELF-TEST, exit and re-enter ENGINE RUNNING SELF-TEST without turning engine off.*

**1)** Observe VOM while moving, wiggling, and tapping system harness (in short sections), connectors and sensors. If an intermittent condition is created, monitor will indicate this by storing a service code. Carefully inspect harness and associated connectors of affected circuits.
**2)** If an intermittent condition is not created, carefully disconnect suspected sensor from harness. Remove terminals from connector and visually inspect terminals at both ends for corrosion, bad crimps, improperly seated terminals, etc.
**3)** Reconnect harness after inspection. Disconnect processor from harness as carefully as possible. Remove and inspect terminals associated with sensor being checked.
**4)** If an intermittent condition cannot be created, reconnect connector and erase CONTINUOUS SELF-TEST service codes. To erase service codes, activate KEY ON/ENGINE OFF SELF-TEST.
**5)** Remove jumper from Self-Test Input terminal as soon as first service code appears. Repeat SELF-TEST with jumper to verify that service codes have been erased. QUICK TEST is complete.

*CONTINUOUS SELF-TEST*

| Continuous Memory | Test |
|---|---|
| 14 | Circuit Test OO |
| 18 | Circuit Test LL |
| 21 | Circuit Test G, Step **9)** |
| 22 | Circuit Test H, Step **14)** |
| 51 | Circuit Test G, Step **10)** |
| 53 | Circuit Test J, Step **11)** |
| 54 | Circuit Test D, Step **9)** |
| 56 | Circuit Test K, Step **11)** |
| 61 | Circuit Test G, Step **10)** |
| 63 | Circuit Test J, Step **15)** |
| 64 | Circuit Test D, Step **9)** |
| 66 | Circuit Test K, Step **11)** |

## QUICK TEST DIAGNOSTIC AIDS

**Dynamic Response Check** – The Dynamic Response Check verifies movement of TPS, VAF, and MAP sensors during wide open throttle (WOT) as part of ENGINE RUNNING SELF-TEST. The signal to perform WOT is a single pulse when using a VOM, or code 10 on STAR tester. Briefly accelerate engine to WOT for one second.

**Output State Check** – The Output State Check is used as an aid in servicing output actuators associated with EEC-IV system. It allows you to energize and de-energize most of system output actuators on and off, on command.

This mode is entered after all codes have been received from KEY ON/ENGINE OFF and CONTINUOUS SELF-TEST. At this time, leave SELF-TEST activated and depress throttle. Each time throttle is depressed, output actuators will change state (go from on to off, or off to on).

## DIAGNOSIS BY SYMPTOM TEST

Use this test procedure only when directed to do so by results of QUICK TEST or steps in CIRCUIT TESTS. Follow test procedures carefully.

**1)** When engine stalls in operation or during SELF-TEST, runs rough or misses, has an "always rich" or "always lean" condition, perform following checks:

- Perform SYSTEM CHECK, ISC Check. Use CIRCUIT TEST SS, step **1)**.
- Check BP sensor, using CIRCUIT TEST H, step **11)**.
- Check Idle Speed Control (ISC), using CIRCUIT TEST Z, step **1)**.
- Check for, and repair, any bad ground or power connections.
- Check ignition components (cap, rotor, wires, coil and plugs).
- Check for short to ground, using CIRCUIT TEST V, step **9)**.
- Check basic engine components (valves, cam timing, compression, etc.).

**2)** When detonation (spark knock) occurs, go to CIRCUIT TEST I, step **1)**.

**3)** If on restarts, high idle speeds and 3-5 minutes of detonation occur, go to CIRCUIT TEST I, step **1)**.

**4)** If no fast idle occurs when A/C is turned on, go to CIRCUIT TEST M, step **1)**.

**5)** If gasoline fumes accumulate in engine compartment, go to CIRCUIT TEST Y, step **1)**.

**6)** If shift indicator light is always on or off, go to CIRCUIT TEST FF, step **1)**.

**7)** If A/C does not cut-off under wide open throttle (WOT) conditions, go to CIRCUIT TEST GG, step **1)**.

**8)** If vehicle is sluggish or if performance is poor, boost control is not working correctly. Go to CIRCUIT TEST HH, step **1)**. Also perform this test if detonation (engine knock) occurs.

## CIRCUIT TESTS

### HOW TO USE CIRCUIT TESTS

**1)** DO NOT perform any CIRCUIT TEST unless specified by QUICK TEST. Ensure all non-EEC-IV related faults are corrected. Do not replace any part unless directed to do so. When more than one service code is received, start with first code displayed.

**2)** Do not measure voltage or resistance at ECA or connect any test lamp to ECA unless specified. All measurements are made by probing REAR of the connector. Isolate both ends of a circuit and turn key off whenever checking for shorts or continuity, unless specified.

**3)** Disconnect solenoids and switches from harness before measuring continuity, resistance, or applying 12 volts. Follow each test step in order until fault is found. After each repair, check all component connections and repeat CIRCUIT TEST(S).

**4)** An "open" is defined as any resistance reading higher than 5 ohms, unless otherwise specified. A "short" is defined as any resistance reading less than 10,000 ohms to ground, unless otherwise specified.

**5)** On CIRCUIT TEST Q, to prevent replacement of good components, be aware that non-EEC-IV related areas may also be at fault.

***NOTE: Fuel contaminated engine oil will affect some service codes. If this is suspected, remove PCV valve from valve cover and repeat QUICK TEST. If problem is corrected, change engine oil and filter.***

# 1988 COMPUTERIZED ENGINE CONTROLS
# Ford Motor Co. Merkur EEC-IV (Cont.)

## CIRCUIT TEST A

### NO START

To prevent replacement of good components, be aware that the following non-EEC related areas may be at fault: fuel quantity and quality, ignition system damage, cracks, moisture, etc., engine mechanical conditions such as valves, timing belt, etc. Also included are starter and battery circuit problems.

**1)** Try to start engine. If engine does not crank, check vehicle starting and charging systems. If engine cranks, but does not start or else stalls after starting, go to next step.

**2)** Turn key off and wait 10 seconds. Set DVOM on 20-volt scale and disconnect Throttle Position Sensor (TPS). Turn key on, leaving engine off. Measure voltage at TPS harness connector between voltage reference (VREF) and signal return. If reading is less than 4.0 volts or higher than 6.0 volts, go to CIRCUIT TEST C. If reading is between 4.0 and 6.0 volts, reconnect TPS and go to next step.

**3)** Disconnect any spark plug wire and connect spark tester between plug wire and engine ground. Crank engine and check for spark. If spark exists, connect spark plug wire and go to step **13)**. If no spark, connect spark plug wire and go to next step.

**4)** Remove high tension coil wire from distributor and install spark tester. Check for spark while cranking engine. If there is no spark, connect coil wire and go to next step. If spark exists (with no start condition), connect coil wire and check ignition cap rotor and wires. Repair as needed. If ignition cap rotor and wires are okay, test TFI ignition module using Module Tester (1105-00002) and replace as needed. If TFI ignition module checks out okay, try known good ignition coil.

**5)** Turn key off and wait 10 seconds. Install breakout box, leaving ECA disconnected. Set DVOM on 200 ohm scale and disconnect TFI. Measure resistance between test pin No. 16 and TFI harness connector ignition ground. If reading is more than 5 ohms, repair harness and repeat QUICK TEST. If reading is less than 5 ohms, go to next step.

**6)** With breakout box installed and box timing switch on "Distributor" position, connect TFI and ECA. Try to start vehicle. If vehicle starts, go to step **10)**. If vehicle does not start, go to next step.

**7)** Move breakout box timing switch to "Computed" position. Set DVOM on 20-volt scale and measure voltage between test pin No. 36 and chassis ground while cranking engine. If voltage is between 3.0 and 6.0 volts, EEC system is NOT at fault. TFI ignition system should be diagnosed. If voltage is less than 3.0 volts or more than 6.0 volts, go to next step.

**8)** Turn key off and wait 10 seconds. With breakout box installed, disconnect ECA and TFI. Set DVOM on 200,000 ohm scale and measure resistance between test pin No. 36 and test pins No. 16, 20, 26, 40, and 60 for short to ground. Measure resistance between test pin No. 36 and test pins No. 37 and 57 for short to power. Measure resistance between test pins No. 36 and 56 for short to PIP. If any reading is less than 10,000 ohms, repair short in harness and repeat QUICK TEST. If engine still does not start, go to next step. If all readings are 10,000 ohms or higher, go to next step.

**9)** Turn key off and wait 10 seconds. With breakout box installed, connect ECA, but leave TFI disconnected. Set DVOM on 200 ohm scale. Measure resistance between test pin No. 36 and test pins No. 37 and 57 for short to power. Measure resistance between test pin No. 36 and test pins No. 40 and 60 for short to ground. If any reading is less than 5 ohms, replace ECA and repeat QUICK TEST. If all readings are 5 ohms or higher, connect TFI and go to next step.

**10)** With breakout box installed and DVOM on 20-volt scale, measure voltage between test pins No. 56 and 16, while cranking engine. If reading is between 3.0 and 6.0 volts, remove breakout box. Replace ECA and repeat QUICK TEST. If reading is less than 3.0 volts or higher than 6.0 volts, go to next step.

**11)** Install breakout box, turn key off and wait 10 seconds. Set DVOM on 200 ohm scale. Disconnect TFI and ECA. Measure resistance between test pin No. 56 and TFI connector PIP circuit. If reading is 5 ohms or more, repair open PIP circuit and repeat QUICK TEST. If readings is less than 5 ohms, go to next step.

**12)** With breakout box installed and ECA disconnected, turn key off. Disconnect TFI connector and set DVOM on 200,000 ohm scale. Measure resistance between test pin No. 56 and test pins No. 16, 20, 26, 40, and 60 for short to ground. Measure resistance between test pin No. 56 and test pins No. 37 and 57 for short to power. Measure resistance between test pin No. 56 and test pin No. 36 for short to Spark Output (SPOUT). If any reading is less than 10,000 ohms, repair PIP circuit and repeat QUICK TEST. If all readings are higher than 10,000 ohms, diagnose TFI ignition system.

## CIRCUIT TEST A (Cont.)

**13)** Turn key off and wait 10 seconds. Disconnect ECA 60-pin connector and inspect for damaged, loose, or corroded pins or wires. Repair wiring as necessary. Install breakout box and connect ECA. Make sure that box timing switch is in "Computed" position. Set DVOM on 20-volt scale and measure voltage between test pin No. 36 and chassis ground while cranking engine. If reading is between 3.0 and 6.0 volts, go to next step. If reading is less than 3.0 volts or higher than 6.0 volts, go to step **10)**.

**14)** Disconnect all electrical connections at injectors. Connect pressure gauge to fuel diagnostic valve (if equipped) on fuel rail. Note initial pressure reading, then pressurize fuel system by turning key on for one second, turning key off, and then waiting 10 seconds. Repeat on, off, and wait sequence 5 times. Turn key off and wait 10 seconds. Connect all injectors. If pressure increased, go to CIRCUIT TEST SS, step **1)**. If pressure did not increase, go to next step.

**15)** With key off and fuel pressure gauge installed, locate fuel pump inertia switch and push button on switch to reset it to on. If switch will not reset to on, replace inertia switch and repeat step **14)**. If switch button was already on, go to CIRCUIT TEST V, step **1)**. Observe pressure gauge as system is pressurized as in step **14)**. If pressure reading increases, repeat QUICK TEST. If pressure reading does not increase, go to CIRCUIT TEST V, step **1)**.

***TFI Module Circuits***

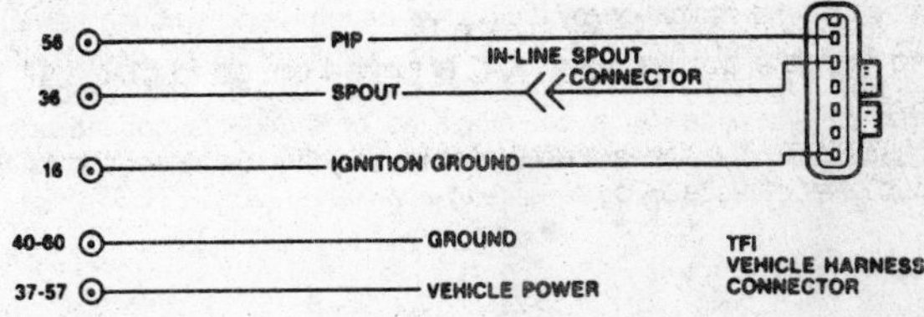
Breakout Box
Test Pins
56
36
16
40-60
37-57
PIP
SPOUT
IGNITION GROUND
GROUND
VEHICLE POWER
IN-LINE SPOUT CONNECTOR
TFI VEHICLE HARNESS CONNECTOR

## CIRCUIT TEST B

### VEHICLE BATTERY

To prevent replacement of good components, be aware that the following non-EEC related areas may be at fault: battery cables and ground straps, voltage regulator and alternator, and ignition switch.

**1)** Turn key on, leaving engine off. Set DVOM on 20-volt scale and measure voltage across battery terminals. If reading is less than 10.5 volts, service or replace discharged battery. If reading is 10.5 volts or higher, go to next step.

**2)** Turn key on, leaving engine off. With ECA connected, set DVOM on 20-volt scale and measure voltage between battery negative post and signal return circuit in SELF-TEST connector. If reading is less than 0.5 volts, go to step **6)**. If reading is 0.5 volts or higher, go to next step.

**3)** With breakout box installed and ECA connected, turn key on, leaving engine off. Set DVOM on 20-volt scale. Measure voltage between battery negative post and test pins No. 40 and 60. If either reading is 0.5 volts or higher, repair ground circuit having a resistance higher than 0.5 volts and repeat QUICK TEST. If both readings are less than 0.5 volts, go to next step.

**4)** With breakout box installed and ECA connected, turn key off and wait 10 seconds. Set DVOM on 200 ohm scale. Measure resistance between test pin No. 46 and test pins No. 40 and 60. If either reading is 5 ohms or higher, disconnect ECA connector and inspect for corrosion or damage. Repair wiring and recheck resistance. If reading is still too high, replace ECA and repeat QUICK TEST. If both readings are less than 5 ohms, go to next step.

**5)** With breakout box installed and ECA connected, turn key off and wait 10 seconds. Set DVOM on 200-ohm scale. Measure resistance between test pin No. 46 and signal return circuit at SELF-TEST

## CIRCUIT TEST B (Cont.)

connector. If reading is less than 5 ohms, system is okay, repeat QUICK TEST. If reading is 5 ohms or higher, repair cause of excessive resistance in signal return circuit, then repeat QUICK TEST.

**6)** Turn key on, leaving engine off. With ECA connected, set DVOM on 20-volt scale. Measure voltage between battery negative post and Keep Alive Power (KAPWR) circuit at EEC power relay. If reading is less than 10.5 volts, check KAPWR and Vehicle Power (V Power) circuits for shorts to ground. Also check KAPWR circuit from EEC power relay to battery positive post for open circuit. If reading is 10.5 volts or higher, go to next step.

**7)** Turn key on, leaving engine off. With ECA connected, set DVOM on 20-volt scale. Measure voltage between battery negative post and ignition circuit at EEC power relay. If readings is less than 10.5 volts, check for open ignition switch circuits. Repair wiring and repeat QUICK TEST. If reading is 10.5 volts or higher, go to next step.

**8)** Turn key on, leaving engine off. With ECA connected, set DVOM on 20-volt scale. Measure voltage between battery negative post and ground circuit at EEC power relay. If reading is 0.5 volts or higher, repair open circuit or short to ground in ground circuit and repeat QUICK TEST. If you entered this test for a code 78 and if reading is less than 0.5 volts, go to step **10)**. If you entered this test for any other code and if reading is less than 0.5 volts, go to next step.

**9)** Turn key on, leaving engine off. With ECA connected, set DVOM on 20-volt scale. Measure voltage between battery negative post and vehicle power circuit at EEC power relay. If reading is less than 10.5 volts, replace EEC power relay and repeat QUICK TEST. If reading is 10.5 volts or higher, repair short to ground or open in vehicle power circuit from EEC power relay to test pins No. 37 and 57. Repeat QUICK TEST.

**10)** Turn key on, leaving engine off. Connect VOM or STAR tester to SELF-TEST connector. With SELF-TEST deactivated, enter into CONTINUOUS MONITOR (WIGGLE) TEST. Observe VOM or STAR tester LED for indication of fault while bending and twisting harness from EEC power relay to ECA. If code 78 is displayed or if fault is indicated, isolate fault in vehicle power circuit, and repair as necessary. If code 78 is not displayed or if fault is not indicated, inspect EEC power relay and connectors for damaged pins, corrosion, etc. If okay, replace EEC power relay and repeat QUICK TEST.

***Battery Test Circuits***

Breakout Box
Test Pins

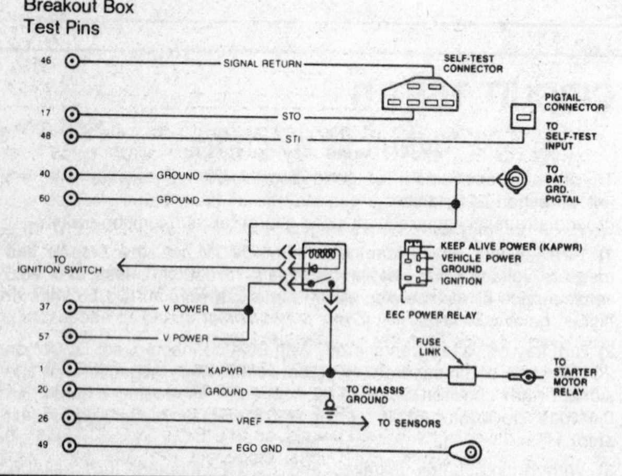
46 SIGNAL RETURN
SELF-TEST CONNECTOR
PIGTAIL CONNECTOR
17 STO
48 STI
TO SELF-TEST INPUT
40 GROUND
60 GROUND
TO BAT. GRD. PIGTAIL
TO IGNITION SWITCH
KEEP ALIVE POWER (KAPWR)
VEHICLE POWER
GROUND
IGNITION
EEC POWER RELAY
37 V POWER
57 V POWER
FUSE LINK
TO STARTER MOTOR RELAY
1 KAPWR
20 GROUND
TO CHASSIS GROUND
26 VREF
TO SENSORS
49 EGO GND

## CIRCUIT TEST C

### REFERENCE VOLTAGE

**1)** Install breakout box, leaving ECA connected. Turn key on, leaving engine off. Set DVOM on 20-volt scale and measure voltage between test pin No. 37 and signal return in SELF-TEST connector. If reading is less than 10.5 volts, go to CIRCUIT TEST B, step **1)**. If reading is 10.5 volts or higher, go to next step.

**2)** With breakout box installed and ECA connected, turn key on, leaving engine off. Set DVOM on 20-volt scale and measure voltage between test pins No. 26 and 46. If reading is 6.0 volts or higher, go to

## CIRCUIT TEST C (Cont.)

step **4)**. If reading is 4.0 volts or lower, go to step **5)**. If reading is between 4.0 and 6.0 volts, go to next step.

**3)** With breakout box installed and ECA disconnected, turn key off. Set DVOM on 200-ohm scale. Measure resistance from test pins No. 26 and 46 to suspect VREF sensor harness connector. If all readings are less than 5 ohms, connect sensors. VREF circuit is okay, repeat QUICK TEST. If any reading is 5 ohms or higher, repair open circuit in VREF or signal return and then repeat QUICK TEST.

**4)** Turn key off and wait 10 seconds. With breakout box installed and ECA disconnected, turn key on, leaving engine off. Set DVOM on 20-volt scale and measure voltage between test pin No. 26 and battery ground. If reading is less than 0.5 volts, replace ECA and repeat QUICK TEST. If reading is 0.5 volts or higher, repair short to battery power in EEC harness. Repeat QUICK TEST. Replace ECA if fault still occurs.

**5) Shorted TPS Sensor.** Turn key off and wait for 10 seconds. With breakout box installed and ECA connected, disconnect Throttle Position Sensor (TPS) from vehicle harness. Turn key on, leaving engine off. Set DVOM on 20-volt scale and measure voltage between test pin No. 26 and 46. If reading is 4.0 volts or higher, replace TPS and repeat QUICK TEST. If less than 4.0 volts on models without EGR Valve Position (EVP) sensor, go to step **7)**. If reading is less than 4.0 volts on models with EVP sensor, go to next step.

**6) Shorted EVP Sensor.** Turn key off and wait 10 seconds. With breakout box installed and ECA connected, disconnect EVP sensor. Turn key on, leaving engine off. Set DVOM on 20-volt scale. Measure voltage between test pins No. 26 and 46. If reading is 4.0 volts or higher, replace EVP sensor and repeat QUICK TEST. If reading is less than 4.0 volts, go to next step.

**7) Shorted MAP/BP Sensor.** Turn key off and wait 10 seconds. With breakout box installed and ECA connected, disconnect MAP/BP sensor. Turn key on, leaving engine off. Set DVOM on 20-volt scale. Measure voltage between test pins No. 26 and 46. If reading is 4.0 volts or higher, replace MAP/BP sensor and repeat QUICK TEST. If reading is less than 4.0 volts on models without Vane Airflow (VAF) sensor, go to step **9)**. If reading is less than 4.0 volts on models with VAF sensor, go to next step.

**8) Shorted VAF Sensor.** Turn key off and wait 10 seconds. With breakout box installed and ECA connected, disconnect VAF sensor. Turn key on, leaving engine off. Set DVOM on 20-volt scale. Measure voltage between test pins No. 26 and 46. If reading is 4.0 volts or higher, replace VAF sensor and repeat QUICK TEST. If reading is less than 4.0 volts, go to next step.

**9)** With breakout box installed and ECA disconnected, turn key off and wait 10 seconds. Disconnect TPS, MAP/BP, EVP, and VAF sensor (if equipped). Set DVOM on 200-ohm scale. Measure resistance between test pin No. 26 and test pins No. 20, 40, 46, and 60. If reading is less than 5 ohms, repair short to ground, connect all sensors and repeat QUICK TEST. If original problem still occurs, replace ECA and repeat QUICK TEST. If reading is 5 ohms or higher, connect sensors, replace ECA and repeat QUICK TEST.

***Reference Voltage Circuits***

Breakout Box
Test Pins

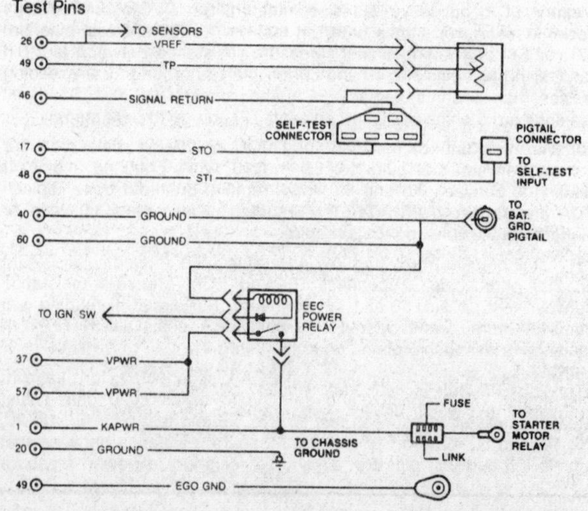
TO SENSORS
26 VREF
49 TP
46 SIGNAL RETURN
SELF-TEST CONNECTOR
PIGTAIL CONNECTOR
TO SELF-TEST INPUT
17 STO
48 STI
40 GROUND
60 GROUND
TO BAT. GRD. PIGTAIL
TO IGN SW
EEC POWER RELAY
37 VPWR
57 VPWR
FUSE
TO STARTER MOTOR RELAY
1 KAPWR
20 GROUND
TO CHASSIS GROUND
LINK
49 EGO GND

# 1988 COMPUTERIZED ENGINE CONTROLS
# Ford Motor Co. Merkur EEC-IV (Cont.)

## CIRCUIT TEST D

### VANE AIR TEMPERATURE (VAT) SENSOR

Ambient air temperature must be at least 50°F (10°C) for test results to be valid. Avoid performing test in unusually hot or cold conditions.

*Typical Vane Air Temp. (VAT) Sensor Resistance*

| Ambient Temperature F° (C°) | Ohms Between Test Pins No. 25 & 46 |
|---|---|
| 32 (0) | 5800 |
| 65 (18) | 2700 |
| 185 (85) | 300 |
| 220 (104) | 180 |
| 240 (116) | 125 |

**1) Code 24 Displayed.** Make sure ambient air temperature is at least 50°F (10°C). If not, repeat QUICK TEST. If temperature is high enough, go to next step.

**2)** Turn key off and wait 10 seconds. Set DVOM on 20-volt scale. Disconnect Throttle Position Sensor (TPS). Turn key on, leaving engine off. Measure voltage at TPS connector between voltage reference (VREF) and signal return. If reading is less than 4.0 volts or higher than 6.0 volts, go to CIRCUIT TEST C, step **1)**. If reading is between 4.0 and 6.0 volts, connect TPS and go to next step.

**3)** Turn key off and wait 10 seconds. Disconnect harness from airflow meter. Set DVOM on 200,000 ohm scale. Measure resistance at VAT sensor between VAT signal and signal return. If reading is from 125 ohms at 240°F (116°C) to 3700 ohms at 50°F (10°C), replace ECA. Connect airflow meter and repeat QUICK TEST. If reading is out of range, replace airflow meter and repeat QUICK TEST.

**4) Code 54 Displayed.** Turn key off and wait 10 seconds. Disconnect harness from airflow meter. Inspect for and repair any damaged wiring. Install a jumper wire between VAT signal and signal return at airflow meter connector. Perform KEY ON/ENGINE OFF SELF-TEST. If code 64 is displayed, replace airflow meter. Remove jumper wire, connect airflow meter, and repeat QUICK TEST. If code 64 is not displayed, remove jumper wire and go to next step.

**5)** Turn key off and wait 10 seconds. With jumper wire removed, leave airflow meter disconnected. Disconnect ECA 60-pin connector. Inspect for and repair any damaged wiring. Install breakout box, leaving ECA disconnected. Set DVOM on 200 ohm scale. Measure resistance between test pin No. 25 and VAT signal at connector. Also measure resistance between test pin No. 46 and signal return at connector. If both readings are less than 5 ohms, replace ECA. Remove breakout box and connect wiring to ECA and airflow meter. Repeat QUICK TEST. If either reading is 5 ohms or higher, repair open circuit. Remove breakout box, connect wiring to ECA and airflow meter, then repeat QUICK TEST.

**6) Code 64 Displayed.** Turn key off and wait 10 seconds. Disconnect harness from airflow meter. Inspect for and repair any damaged wiring. Perform KEY ON/ENGINE OFF SELF-TEST. If code 54 is displayed, replace airflow meter and connect harness. Repeat QUICK TEST. If code 54 is not displayed, go to next step.

**7)** Turn key off and wait 10 seconds. Set DVOM on 20-volt scale. Disconnect TPS. Turn key on, leaving engine off. Measure voltage between VREF and signal return at connector. If reading is less than 4.0 volts or higher than 6.0 volts, go to CIRCUIT TEST C, step **1)**. If reading is between 4.0 and 6.0 volts, connect TPS and go to next step.

**8)** Turn key off and wait 10 seconds. Leave airflow meter disconnected. Disconnect ECA 60-pin connector. Inspect for and repair any damaged wiring. Install breakout box, leaving ECA disconnected. Set DVOM on 200,000 ohm scale. Measure resistance between test pin No. 25 and test pins No. 40, 46, and 60. If any reading is less than 10,000 ohms, repair shorts. Remove breakout box, connect ECA and airflow meter, then repeat QUICK TEST. If all readings are 10,000 ohms or higher, replace ECA. Remove breakout box and connect ECA. Repeat QUICK TEST.

**9) Continuous Code 54 or 64 Displayed.** Using CONTINUOUS MONITOR (WIGGLE) TEST, observe VOM or STAR tester LED for indication of fault while tapping VAT sensor lightly and wiggling connector. If fault is indicated, inspect connector and terminals. If connector and terminals are good, replace VAT sensor and repeat QUICK TEST. If no fault is indicated, go to next step.

## CIRCUIT TEST D (Cont.)

**10)** While in CONTINUOUS MONITOR (WIGGLE) TEST, wiggle and bend EEC-IV harness from VAT sensor to firewall, a small section at a time. Also check harness from firewall to ECA. If fault is indicated, isolate fault and repair as necessary. Repeat QUICK TEST. If no fault is found, go to next step.

**11)** Turn key off and wait 10 seconds. Disconnect ECA 60-pin connector. Inspect both connector and connector terminals for obvious damage. If connectors and terminals are not okay, repair as necessary and repeat QUICK TEST. If connectors and terminals are okay, and you are unable to duplicate fault at this time, continuous code 54 or 64 testing is complete.

*VAT Sensor Circuit*

Breakout Box
Test Pins

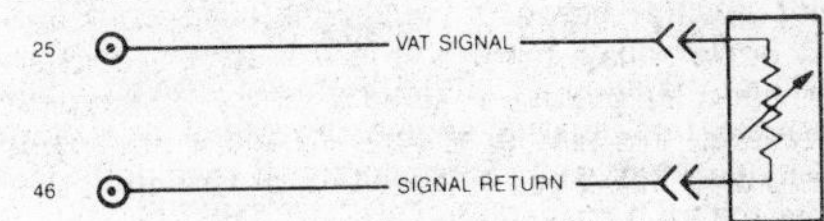
25
VAT SIGNAL
46
SIGNAL RETURN

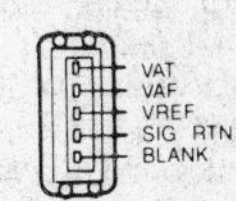
VAT
VAF
VREF
SIG RTN
BLANK

## CIRCUIT TEST G

### ENGINE COOLANT TEMPERATURE (ECT) SENSOR

**NOTE: For purposes of this test, a "warmed up" engine has a coolant temperature of 50-240°F (10-116°C) for KEY ON/ENGINE OFF SELF-TEST and 180-240°F (82-116°C) for ENGINE RUNNING SELF-TEST. The test procedure will be invalid outside these ranges.**

*Typical Engine Coolant Temperature (ECT) Sensor Resistance*

| Ambient Temperature F° (C°) | Ohms Between TEST Pins No. 7 & 46 |
|---|---|
| 50 (10) | 58,750 |
| 65 (18) | 40,500 |
| 180 (82) | 3600 |
| 220 (104) | 1840 |

To prevent replacement of good components, be aware that the following non-EEC related areas may be at fault: Coolant or oil level. Blocked or obstructed air flow. Engine not at normal operating temperature. Cooling fan.

**1) Code 21 Displayed.** Start engine and run it at 2000 RPM for 2 minutes. Check that upper radiator hose is hot and pressurized. Repeat QUICK TEST before continuing. If vehicle stalls, DO NOT service code 21 at this time, go directly to DIAGNOSIS BY SYMPTOM TEST. If code 21 is not displayed, service other codes as necessary (if displayed). If code 21 appears, go to next step.

**2)** Turn key off and wait 10 seconds. Disconnect TPS. Set DVOM on 20-volt scale. Turn key on, leaving engine off. Measure voltage at TPS harness connector between VREF and signal return. If voltage is less than 4.0 volts or higher than 6.0 volts, go to CIRCUIT TEST C, step **1)**. If voltage is between 4 and 6 volts, reconnect TPS and go to next step.

**3)** Make sure engine is fully warmed up for this step. Turn key off and wait 10 seconds. Disconnect wiring harness at ECT sensor. Set DVOM on 200,000-ohm scale and measure resistance of ECT sensor. If reading is 1300-7700 ohms at engine coolant temperature of 240-140°F (116-60°C) with engine off and 1550-4550 ohms at 230-180°F (110-82°C) with engine running, replace ECA, connect ECT sensor, then repeat QUICK TEST. If readings are not correct for coolant temperature, replace ECT sensor, connect harness, and repeat QUICK TEST.

**4) Code 51 Displayed.** Turn key off and wait 10 seconds. Disconnect ECT sensor at wiring harness and inspect wiring for damage or corrosion. Connect a jumper wire between ECT signal and signal return terminals in sensor harness connector. Repeat KEY ON/ENGINE OFF SELF-TEST. If code 61 is displayed, replace ECT sensor and

## CIRCUIT TEST G (Cont.)

remove jumper wire. Reconnect harness to ECT sensor and repeat QUICK TEST. If code 61 is not displayed, go to next step.

**5)** Turn key off and wait 10 seconds. With harness disconnected at ECT sensor and jumper removed from harness connector, disconnect ECA 60-pin connector. Inspect for and repair any damaged wiring. Install breakout box, leaving ECA disconnected. Set DVOM on 200-ohm scale. Measure resistance between ECT signal at ECT connector and test pin No. 7. Measure resistance between signal return at ECT connector and test pin No. 46. If both readings are less than 5 ohms, replace ECA. Remove breakout box and connect ECA and ECT sensor. Repeat QUICK TEST. If either reading is 5 ohms or higher, repair open circuits. Remove breakout box, connect ECA and ECT sensor. Repeat QUICK TEST.

**6) Code 61 Displayed.** Turn key off and wait 10 seconds. Disconnect ECT sensor and inspect connector for damage or corrosion. Repair wiring and repeat KEY ON/ENGINE OFF SELF-TEST. If code 51 is displayed, replace ECT sensor, connect sensor, then repeat QUICK TEST. If code 51 is not displayed, go to next step.

**7)** Turn key off and wait 10 seconds. Set DVOM on 20-volt scale. Disconnect TPS. Turn key on, leaving engine off. Measure voltage between VREF and signal return at TPS connector. If reading is less than 4.0 volts or higher than 6.0 volts, go to CIRCUIT TEST C, step **1)**. If voltage is between 4.0 and 6.0 volts, connect TPS and go to next step.

**8)** Turn key off and wait 10 seconds. Disconnect harness from ECT sensor. Disconnect ECA 60-pin connector. Inspect for and repair any damaged wiring. Install breakout box, leaving ECA disconnected. Set DVOM on 200,000-ohm scale. Measure resistance between test pin No. 7 and test pins No. 40, 46, and 60. If any reading is less than 10,000 ohms, repair short circuits. Remove breakout box, connect ECA and ECT sensor, then repeat QUICK TEST. If all readings are 10,000 ohms or higher, replace ECA. Remove breakout box, connect ECA and ECT sensor. Repeat QUICK TEST.

**9) Continuous Code 21 Displayed.** Turn key off and wait 10 seconds. Disconnect all SELF-TEST equipment and prepare vehicle for test drive. While driving vehicle, attempt to copy driving style in which complaint was noticed. If problem occurs, try to maintain condition for one or more minutes. After road test, repeat KEY ON/ENGINE OFF SELF-TEST. If code 21 is present in CONTINUOUS SELF-TEST, make sure that thermostat is working properly. If thermostat functions properly, replace ECT sensor and repeat QUICK TEST. If code 21 is not displayed, fault cannot be duplicated at this time. Continuous code 21 testing is complete.

**10) Continuous Code 51 or 61 Displayed.** Using CONTINUOUS MONITOR (WIGGLE) TEST, observe VOM or STAR tester LED while tapping ECT sensor and wiggling ECT connector. If fault is indicated, disconnect and inspect ECT connector and terminals. If connector and terminals are okay, replace ECT sensor and repeat QUICK TEST. If no fault is indicated, go to next step.

**11)** While in CONTINUOUS MONITOR (WIGGLE) TEST, observe VOM or STAR tester LED for fault as you bend, shake or wiggle EEC-IV harness. Start at sensor connector and work toward firewall. Also test harness from firewall to ECA in same manner. If fault is indicated, isolate fault in wiring and repair as necessary. Repeat QUICK TEST. If fault is not indicated, go to next step.

**12)** Turn key off and wait 10 seconds. Disconnect ECA 60-pin connector. Inspect both connectors and terminals for obvious damage. If connectors and terminals are damaged, repair as necessary and repeat QUICK TEST. If connectors and terminals are okay, fault cannot be duplicated at this time. Continuous code 51 or 61 testing is complete.

***Engine Coolant Temperature (ECT) Sensor Circuit***

Breakout Box
Test Pins

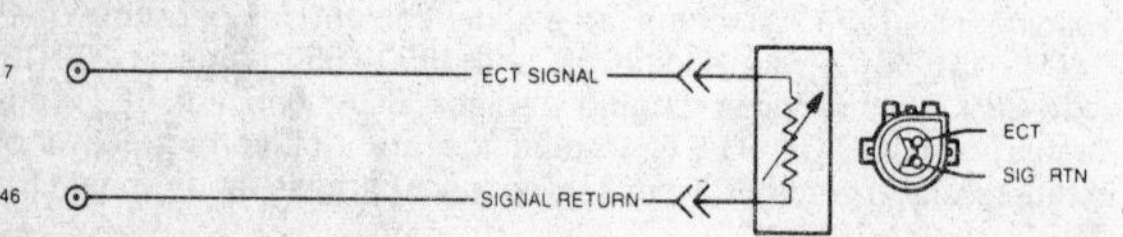
7
ECT SIGNAL
46
SIGNAL RETURN
ECT
SIG RTN

## CIRCUIT TEST H

### MANIFOLD ABSOLUTE PRESSURE (MAP)/ BAROMETRIC PRESSURE (BP) SENSOR

**NOTE: Barometric pressure sensor output is digital and must be measured with MAP/BP tester.**

To prevent replacement of good components, be aware that the following non-EEC related areas may be at fault: Unusually high/low atmospheric barometer reading. Kinked or blocked vacuum lines. Engine condition (valves, vacuum leaks, valve timing, EGR valve, etc.).

**1) Code 22 Displayed, Engine Off.** Turn key off. Disconnect MAP/BP sensor from harness. Connect MAP/BP tester between wiring harness and MAP/BP sensor. Connect banana plugs of tester into DVOM and set DVOM on 20-volt scale. Go to next step.

***Fig. 1: Correct Hookup For MAP/BP Tester***

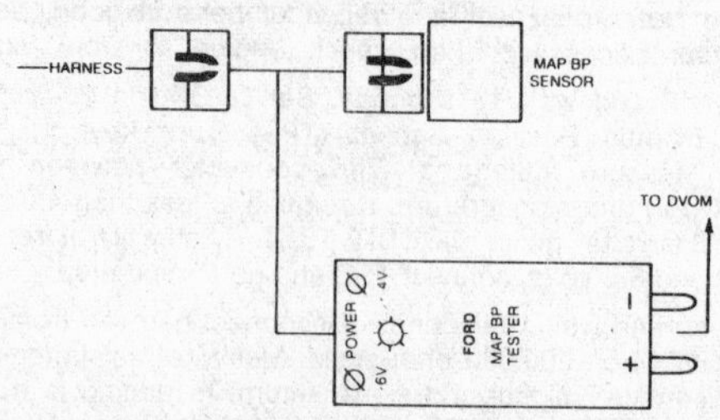
HARNESS
MAP BP SENSOR
TO DVOM
POWER
4V
6V
FORD MAP BP TESTER
-
+

**2)** With MAP/BP tester connected, turn key on. If only Green light on tester is lit, VREF is correct. Go to step **4)**. If "less than 4 volts" Red light or no lights come on, VREF is too low. If "more than 6 volts" Red light comes on, VREF is too high. If VREF is too high or too low, go to next step.

**3)** With MAP/BP tester connected, turn key on. Disconnect MAP/BP sensor and repeat step **2)**. If only Green light comes on, VREF is correct. Replace MAP/BP sensor and repeat QUICK TEST. If "less than 4 volts" Red light or no lights come on, VREF is too low. If "more than 6 volts" Red light comes on, VREF is too high. If VREF is too high or too low, remove MAP/BP tester, connect sensor, then go to CIRCUIT TEST C, step **1)**.

**4)** With MAP/BP tester connected and key on, measure sensor output voltage. If voltage output is in correct range for altitude of vehicle being tested, go to next step. If output reading is outside range, go to step **6)**.

**NOTE: Measure several known good MAP/BP sensors on available vehicles. Mean voltage reading will be typical for your location on date of testing.**

***MAP VOLTAGE OUTPUT***

| Elevation (Ft.) | Voltage Output (Volts) |
|---|---|
| 0 | 1.55-1.63 |
| 1000 | 1.52-1.60 |
| 2000 | 1.49-1.57 |
| 3000 | 1.46-1.54 |
| 4000 | 1.43-1.51 |
| 5000 | 1.40-1.48 |
| 6000 | 1.37-1.45 |
| 7000 | 1.35-1.43 |

**5)** Turn key off and wait 10 seconds. Disconnect MAP/BP sensor from harness. Disconnect ECA 60-pin connector. Inspect for and repair any damaged wiring. Install breakout box, leaving ECA disconnected. Set DVOM on 200-ohm scale. Measure resistance between MAP/BP signal at sensor connector and test pin No. 45. If reading is less than 5 ohms, replace ECA. Connect ECA and MAP/BP sensor and repeat QUICK TEST. If reading is 5 ohms or higher, repair opens in wiring. Remove breakout box, connect ECA and MAP/BP sensor. Repeat QUICK TEST.

**6)** Turn key off and wait 10 seconds. Disconnect ECA 60-pin connector. Inspect for and repair any damaged wiring. Install breakout box, leaving ECA disconnected. Disconnect harness at MAP/BP sensor. Set DVOM on 200,000-ohm scale. Measure resistance between test pin No. 45 and test pins No. 26, 46, 40, and 60. If any reading is less than 10,000 ohms, repair shorts in wiring. Remove breakout box and connect ECA and MAP/BP sensor. Repeat QUICK

### CIRCUIT TEST H (Cont.)

TEST. If all readings are 10,000 ohms or higher, replace MAP/BP sensor. Remove breakout box and connect all wiring. Repeat QUICK TEST.

**7) Code 22 Displayed, Engine Running.** Turn key off and wait 10 seconds. Disconnect vacuum line from MAP sensor. Hook vacuum pump to MAP sensor and apply 18 in. Hg vacuum to sensor. If sensor does not hold vacuum, replace sensor, connect vacuum line and repeat QUICK TEST. If MAP sensor does hold vacuum, go to next step.

**8)** Turn key off and wait 10 seconds. Plug vacuum supply hose to MAP sensor. Start engine and hold in 1400-1600 RPM range. Slowly apply 15 in. Hg vacuum to MAP sensor. Perform ENGINE RUNNING SELF-TEST while holding RPM range. Ignore all other codes at this time. If code 22 is still displayed, replace MAP sensor. Connect vacuum hose and repeat QUICK TEST. If code 22 is not displayed, check vacuum hose to sensor and repair. If hose is good, service other codes as necessary, then check engine for low vacuum condition.

**NOTE: Use DYNAMIC RESPONSE CHECK as specified in step 9). For additional information see QUICK TEST DIAGNOSTIC AIDS, DYNAMIC RESPONSE CHECK in front of this article.**

**9) Code 72 Displayed.** Turn key off and wait 10 seconds. Install vacuum gauge with "T" in manifold vacuum line at MAP sensor. Perform ENGINE RUNNING SELF-TEST and observe vacuum reading before and during DYNAMIC RESPONSE CHECK portion of test. Record service codes. If vacuum decreased 10 in. Hg or more and code 72 is not displayed, disconnect vacuum gauge and service other codes as necessary. If vacuum decreased 10 in. Hg and code 72 is displayed, replace MAP sensor and repeat QUICK TEST. If vacuum decreased less than 10 in. Hg, go to next step.

**10)** Check vacuum lines for correct routing, using vehicle emissions decal as a guide. Also check MAP sensor vacuum lines for kinks or blockage. If lines are good, EEC-IV system is okay. Check engine for cause of low vacuum. If vacuum lines are bad, repair as necessary and repeat step **9)**.

**11)** Turn key off. Disconnect MAP/BP sensor from harness. Connect MAP/BP tester between wiring harness and MAP/BP sensor. Connect plugs of tester into DVOM and set DVOM on 20-volt scale. Go to next step.

**12)** Turn key on and measure sensor output. Compare values to MAP VOLTAGE OUTPUT table. If reading is within range, go to DIAGNOSIS BY SYMPTOM TEST. If reading is within range, go to next step. If reading is out of range, replace MAP/BP sensor. Repeat QUICK TEST.

**13)** Check map sensor vacuum lines for leaks, bad connections, kinks or blockage. If vacuum lines are okay, go to DIAGNOSIS BY SYMPTOM TEST. If vacuum lines are bad, repair as necessary and repeat QUICK TEST.

**14) Continuous Code 22 Displayed.** Using CONTINUOUS MONITOR (WIGGLE) TEST, observe VOM or STAR tester LED for indication of fault while doing the following: connect vacuum pump to MAP sensor and slowly apply 25 in. Hg. Bleed vacuum slowly, tap MAP sensor lightly, and wiggle MAP connector. If fault is indicated, disconnect sensor. Inspect connector and terminals for damage. If connector and terminals are okay, replace MAP sensor and repeat QUICK TEST. If no fault is indicated, go to next step.

**15)** Stay in CONTINUOUS MONITOR (WIGGLE) TEST. Observe VOM or STAR tester LED for indication of fault while shaking, bending or wiggling small sections of harness from sensor connector to firewall. Check harness from firewall to ECA in same manner. If fault is indicated, isolate fault in harness and repair as necessary. Repeat QUICK TEST. If no fault is indicated, go to next step.

**16)** Turn key off and wait 10 seconds. Disconnect ECA 60-pin connector. Inspect both connectors and terminals for obvious damage. If connectors and terminals are not okay, repair as necessary. Repeat QUICK TEST. If connectors and terminals are okay, fault cannot be duplicated at this time. Continuous code 22 testing is complete.

### CIRCUIT TEST H (Cont.)

***MAP/BP Sensor Circuit***


Breakout Box
Test Pins
46
SIG RTN
45
MAP BP SIG
26
VREF
SIG RTN
MAP BP SIG
VREF

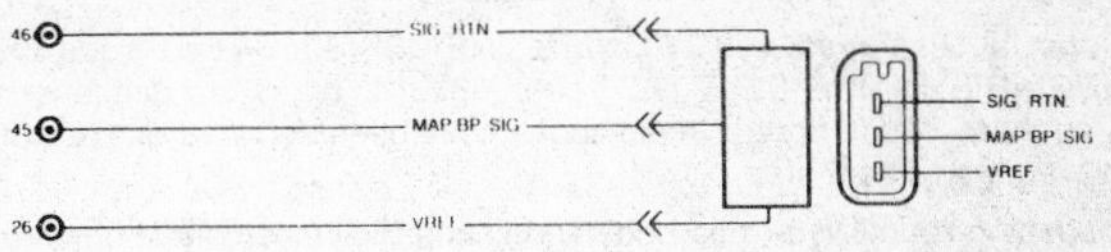

### CIRCUIT TEST I

#### KNOCK (DETONATION) SENSOR

**NOTE: Use DYNAMIC RESPONSE CHECK as specified in steps 1) and 6). There is no need to perform WOT during this test. For additional information see QUICK TEST DIAGNOSTIC AIDS, DYNAMIC RESPONSE CHECK in front of this article.**

To prevent replacement of good components, be aware that the following non-EEC related areas may be at fault: fuel quality, engine condition (valves, vacuum leaks, valve timing, EGR valve, etc.) and spark timing.

**1) Code 25 Displayed.** Perform ENGINE RUNNING SELF-TEST. When DYNAMIC RESPONSE CHECK signal appears, lightly tap above knock sensor with 4 oz. hammer. After 15 seconds, check for code 25. Ignore all other codes at this time. If code 25 is displayed, go to next step. If code 25 is not displayed, knock system is okay. Repeat ENGINE RUNNING SELF-TEST and service other codes.

**2)** Turn key off and wait 10 seconds. Disconnect knock sensor. Inspect for and repair any damaged wiring. Set DVOM on 20-volt scale. Turn key on, leaving engine off. Measure voltage at knock sensor connector between KS signal and signal return. If reading is higher than 4 volts, go to step **5)**. If voltage is between 1 and 4 volts, go to step **6)**. If reading is less than 1 volt, go to next step.

**3)** Turn key off and wait 10 seconds. Disconnect ECA 60-pin connector. Inspect for and repair any damaged wiring. Install breakout box, leaving ECA and knock sensor disconnected. With DVOM on 200-ohm scale, measure resistance between knock sensor connector signal return and test pin No. 46, and between knock sensor connector KS signal and test pin No. 23. If either reading is 5 ohms or more, service open circuit and repeat QUICK TEST. If both readings are less than 5 ohms, go to next step.

**4)** Turn key off and wait 10 seconds. With breakout box installed, ECA and knock sensor disconnected, set DVOM on 200,000-ohm scale. Measure resistance between knock sensor connector KS signal and test pins No. 40, 46 and 60. If all readings are 10,000 ohms or higher, go to step **6)**. If any reading is less than 10,000 ohms, repair shorts in harness and repeat QUICK TEST.

**5)** Turn key off and wait 10 seconds. With breakout box installed, ECA and knock sensor disconnected, set DVOM on 20-volt scale. Turn key on, leaving engine off. Measure voltage between test pins No. 23 and 40. If reading is 0.5 volt or more, repair knock sensor harness short to power, and then repeat QUICK TEST. If reading is less than 0.5 volt, go to next step.

**6)** Turn key off and wait 10 seconds. Remove breakout box and connect ECA. Connect substitute knock sensor (same part No.) into harness but do not install in engine. Perform ENGINE RUNNING SELF-TEST. When DYNAMIC RESPONSE CHECK signal appears, lightly tap above knock sensor with 4 oz. hammer. If code 25 appears 15 seconds later, replace ECA. Remove substitute knock sensor and repeat QUICK TEST with original sensor. If code 25 does not appear 15 seconds later, install new knock sensor and repeat QUICK TEST.

***Knock (Detonation) Sensor Circuit***


Breakout Box
Test Pins
23
KS
46
SIGNAL RETURN
KNOCK SENSOR
KS
SIGNAL RETURN

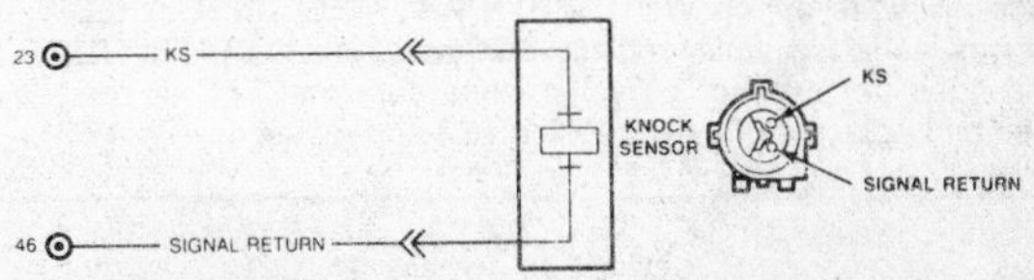

## CIRCUIT TEST J

### THROTTLE POSITION SENSOR (TPS)

To prevent replacement of good components, be aware that the following non-EEC related areas may be at fault: idle speed/throttle stop adjustment, binding throttle shaft/linkage or cruise control linkage, or choke/high cam system, if equipped.

**1) Code 23 Displayed**. If KEY ON/ENGINE OFF SELF-TEST code 68 or ENGINE RUNNING SELF-TEST codes 31, 41, or 58 are displayed, service these codes first. If these codes have been serviced or are not displayed, go to next step.

**2)** Inspect carburetor/throttle body and linkage for mechanical binding or sticking. Make sure linkage is set with throttle in closed position. If throttle plate or linkage is binding, check for binding throttle or cruise control linkage, vacuum line or harness interference, etc. Repair problem(s) and repeat QUICK TEST. If no mechanical problem is found, go to next step.

**3)** Turn key off and wait 10 seconds. Disconnect TPS from harness at throttle body. Inspect for and repair any damaged wiring. Perform KEY ON/ENGINE OFF SELF-TEST. Check for code 63. Ignore all other codes at this time. If code 63 is not displayed, go to step **5)**. If code 63 is displayed, go to next step.

**4)** Turn key off and wait 10 seconds. Set DVOM on 20-volt scale and disconnect TPS from harness. Inspect for and repair any damaged wiring. Turn key on, leaving engine off. Measure voltage at TPS connector between VREF and signal return. If reading is less than 4 volts or higher than 6 volts, go to CIRCUIT TEST C, step **1)**. If reading is between 4 and 6 volts, replace TPS and repeat QUICK TEST.

**5)** Turn key off and wait 10 seconds. Disconnect TPS from harness. Set DVOM on 200,000-ohm scale. Disconnect ECA 60-pin connector. Inspect for and repair any damaged wiring. Install breakout box, leaving ECA disconnected. Measure resistance between test pin No. 47 and test pins No. 26 and 57. If either reading is less than 10,000 ohms, repair short in harness and repeat QUICK TEST. If both readings are 10,000 ohms or higher, replace ECA and repeat QUICK TEST.

**6) Code 63 Displayed.** Turn key off and wait 10 seconds. Disconnect TPS from harness. Install a jumper wire between VREF and TPS signal at connector. Perform KEY ON/ENGINE OFF SELF-TEST. Check for codes 53 or 23, ignore all other codes at this time. If no codes are displayed, immediately remove jumper wire, and go to step **9)**. If either code 53 or 23 are displayed, replace TPS and repeat QUICK TEST. If neither code 53 or 23 are displayed, go to next step.

**7)** Turn key off and wait 10 seconds. Disconnect TPS from harness. Inspect for and repair any damaged wiring. Set DVOM on 20-volt scale. Turn key on, leaving engine off. Measure voltage between VREF and signal return at TPS connector. If reading is less than 4 volts or more than 6 volts, go to CIRCUIT TEST C, step **1)**. If reading is between 4 and 6 volts, go to next step.

**8)** Turn key off and wait 10 seconds. Leave TPS disconnected. Set DVOM on 200-ohm scale and disconnect ECA 60-pin connector. Inspect for and repair any damaged wiring. Install breakout box and connect ECA. Measure resistance between TPS signal at connector and test pin No. 47. If reading is 5 ohms or more, repair faulty circuit. Remove breakout box, connect ECA and TPS, and then repeat QUICK TEST. If reading is less than 5 ohms, go to next step.

**9)** Turn key off and wait 10 seconds. Leave TPS disconnected. Disconnect ECA 60-pin connector. Inspect for and repair any damaged wiring. Install breakout box and set DVOM on 200,000-ohm scale. Measure resistance at connector between TPS signal and ground, and between TPS signal and test pin No. 46. If either reading is less than 10,000 ohms, repair short circuit and repeat QUICK TEST. If both readings are 10,000 ohms or more, replace ECA. Remove breakout box, connect TPS, and then repeat QUICK TEST.

**NOTE: Code 73 in step 10) indicates that TPS did not exceed 25% of its rotation during DYNAMIC RESPONSE CHECK. For additional information see QUICK TEST DIAGNOSTIC AIDS, DYNAMIC RESPONSE CHECK in front of this article.**

**10) Code 73 Displayed.** Turn key off. Install breakout box and set DVOM on 20-volt scale. Connect DVOM to test pins No. 46 and 47. Perform ENGINE RUNNING SELF-TEST. Verify that DVOM reading exceeds 3.5 volts during WOT of DYNAMIC RESPONSE CHECK. If reading exceeds 3.5 volts, replace ECA and repeat QUICK TEST. If reading does not exceed 3.5 volts, make sure that TPS is correctly installed and adjusted. If okay, replace TPS and repeat QUICK TEST.

## CIRCUIT TEST J (Cont.)

**11) Continuous Code 53 Displayed.** Using CONTINUOUS MONITOR (WIGGLE) TEST, observe VOM or STAR tester LED for indication of fault while slowly opening throttle to WOT. Slowly bring throttle to closed position and lightly tap TPS and wiggle connector. If no fault is indicated, go to step **13)**. If fault is indicated, go to next step.

**12)** Turn key off and wait 10 seconds. Disconnect ECA 60-pin connector. Inspect for and repair any damaged wiring. Install breakout box, leaving ECA connected. Stay in CONTINUOUS MONITOR (WIGGLE) TEST and connect DVOM between test pins No. 47 and 46. Set DVOM on 20-volt scale. Turn key on, leaving engine off. Observe DVOM and repeat step **11)**. If fault occurs below 4.25 volts, inspect TPS connectors and terminals. If okay, replace TPS and repeat QUICK TEST. If fault does not occur below 4.25 volts, TPS over-travel may have caused continuous code 53. TPS is good, go to next step to check harness.

**13)** While in CONTINUOUS MONITOR (WIGGLE) TEST, shake, bend and wiggle small sections of EEC-IV harness from TPS sensor to firewall, and from firewall to ECA. If fault is indicated, isolate fault in wiring and repair as necessary. Repeat QUICK TEST. If no fault is indicated, go to next step.

**14)** Turn key off and wait 10 seconds. Disconnect ECA 60-pin connector. Inspect both connectors and terminals for obvious damage. If connectors and teminals are damaged, repair as necessary. Repeat QUICK TEST. If connectors and terminals are okay, fault cannot be duplicated at this time. Continuous code 53 testing is complete.

**15) Continuous Code 63 Displayed.** Using CONTINUOUS MONITOR (WIGGLE) TEST, observe VOM or STAR tester LED for indication of fault while slowly opening throttle to WOT. Slowly bring throttle to closed position and lightly tap TPS and wiggle connector. If fault is indicated, disconnect TPS. Inspect connectors and terminals. If connectors and terminals are okay, replace TPS and repeat QUICK TEST. If no fault is indicated, go to next step.

**16)** While in CONTINUOUS MONITOR (WIGGLE) TEST, shake, bend and wiggle small sections of EEC-IV harness from TPS sensor to firewall, and from firewall to ECA. If fault is indicated, isolate fault in wiring and repair as necessary. Repeat QUICK TEST. If no fault is indicated, go to next step.

**17)** Turn key off and wait 10 seconds. Disconnect ECA 60-pin connector. Inspect both connectors and terminals for obvious damage. If connectors and teminals are damaged, repair as necessary. Repeat QUICK TEST. If connectors and terminals are okay, fault cannot be duplicated at this time. Continuous code 63 testing is complete.

***Throttle Position Sensor (TPS) Circuit***

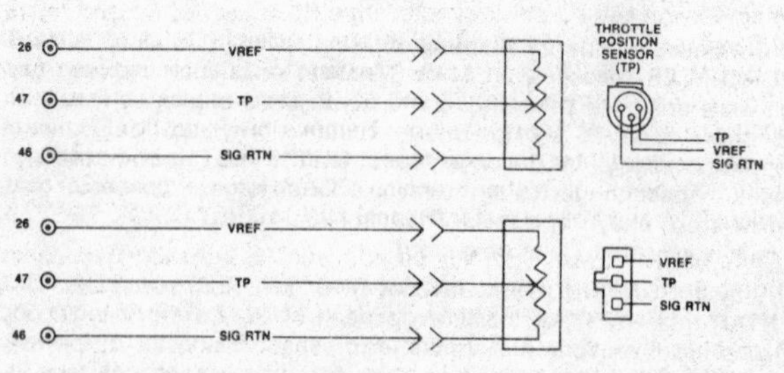
Breakout Box
Test Pins
26
VREF
47
TP
46
SIG RTN
THROTTLE POSITION SENSOR (TP)
TP
VREF
SIG RTN
26
VREF
47
TP
46
SIG RTN
VREF
TP
SIG RTN

## CIRCUIT TEST K

### VANE AIRFLOW (VAF) SENSOR

To prevent replacement of good components, be aware that the following non-EEC related areas may be at fault: Check for air leaks between vane airflow meter and throttle body. Check for vacuum leaks. Check engine sealing at PCV, CANP, valve cover(s), and at dipstick seal.

## CIRCUIT TEST K (Cont.)

**1) Code 26 Displayed.** Code 26 indicates VAF sensor input to ECA is out of closed (engine not running) or idle limits (engine off 0.15 to 0.50 volts; engine idling 1.5 to 2.7 volts). There have been no shorts or opens in VAF circuit; either code 56 (signal always high) or code 66 (signal always low) would have been displayed. Turn key off and wait 10 seconds. Remove air filter and check for contamination (oil or foreign matter). If code 26 appears in KEY ON/ENGINE OFF SELF-TEST, replace airflow meter. Install air cleaner and repeat QUICK TEST. If code 26 is not displayed, go to next step.

**2)** With key off and air filter installed, check for air leaks allowing unmetered air into system between airflow meter and throttle body. Disconnect ECA 60-pin connector. Inspect for and repair any damaged wiring. Install breakout box and connect ECA to box. Set DVOM on 20-volt scale. Turn key on, leaving engine off. Place new, unsharpened wooden pencil through air inlet opening of airflow meter. Measure voltage between test pins No. 43 and 46. If reading is between 2.8 and 3.7 volts, airflow meter is okay. Code 26 has been caused by incorrect engine speed or vacuum leak. Repair problem, remove breakout box, then repeat QUICK TEST. If reading is not between 2.8 and 3.7 volts, replace ECA, remove breakout box, and then repeat QUICK TEST.

***Fig. 1: VAF Sensor Check***

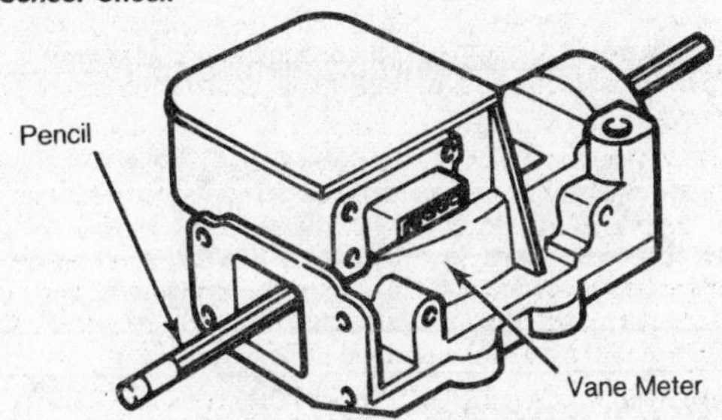
Pencil
Vane Meter

**3) Code 56 Displayed.** Turn key off and wait 10 seconds. Disconnect harness from airflow meter. Inspect for and repair any damaged wiring. Perform KEY ON/ENGINE OFF SELF-TEST. If code 66 is not displayed, go to step **5)**. If code 66 is displayed, go to next step. Disconnecting airflow meter also disconnects VAT sensor, code 54 should be displayed. Ignore all codes except VAF codes at this time.

**4)** Turn key off and wait 10 seconds. Leave harness disconnected from airflow meter. Turn key on, leaving engine off. Set DVOM on 20-volt scale. Measure voltage at harness connector between VREF and signal return. If reading is between 4.0 and 6.0 volts, replace airflow meter. Connect harness and repeat QUICK TEST. If reading is less than 4.0 or more than 6.0 volts, go to CIRCUIT TEST C, step **1)**.

**5)** Turn key off and wait 10 seconds. Leave airflow meter disconnected. Disconnect 60-pin connector from ECA. Inspect for and repair any damaged wiring. Install breakout box, leaving ECA disconnected. Set DVOM on 200,000-ohm scale. Measure resistance between test pin No. 43 and test pins No. 26 and 57. If either reading is less than 10,000 ohms, repair short in wiring. Remove breakout box. Connect ECA and airflow meter and then repeat QUICK TEST. If both readings are 10,000 ohms or higher, replace ECA. Remove breakout box. Connect ECA and airflow meter. Repeat QUICK TEST.

**6) Code 66 Displayed.** Turn key off and wait 10 seconds. Disconnect harness from airflow meter. Install jumper wire between VREF and VAF signal at connector. Perform KEY ON/ENGINE OFF SELF-TEST. Ignore all codes except VAF codes at this time. If no codes are displayed, immediately remove jumper wire and go directly to step **9)**. If code 56 is displayed, replace airflow meter. Remove jumper wire, connect airflow meter, and then repeat QUICK TEST. If code 56 is not displayed, remove jumper wire and go to next step.

**7)** Turn key off and wait 10 seconds. Leave airflow meter disconnected. Turn key on, leaving engine off. Set DVOM on 20-volt scale. Measure voltage between VREF and signal return at airflow meter harness connector. If reading is less than 4.0 volts or more than 6.0 volts, go to CIRCUIT TEST C, step **1)**. If reading is between 4.0 and 6.0 volts, go to next step.

**8)** With key off and airflow meter disconnected, disconnect ECA 60-pin connector. Inspect for and repair any damaged wiring. Install breakout box, leaving ECA disconnected. Set DVOM on 200-ohm scale. Measure resistance between VAF signal at airflow connector and test pin No. 43. If reading is 5 ohms or more, repair open circuit. Remove breakout box, connect ECA and airflow meter. Repeat QUICK TEST. If reading is less than 5 ohms, go to next step.

**9)** Turn key off and wait 10 seconds. Leave ECA and airflow meter disconnected. Set DVOM on 200,000-ohm scale. Measure resistance between VAF signal and signal return at harness connector. Also measure resistance between VAF signal and negative battery terminal. If either reading is less than 10,000 ohms, repair shorts. Connect airflow meter and repeat QUICK TEST. If both readings are 10,000 ohms or more, replace ECA. Remove breakout box, and connect ECA and airflow meter. Repeat QUICK TEST.

**NOTE: A sharp snap of the throttle may not be sufficient to pass step 10). Be sure to move throttle to WOT. Use DYNAMIC RESPONSE CHECK as specified. For additional information see QUICK TEST DIAGNOSTIC AIDS, DYNAMIC RESPONSE CHECK in front of this article.**

**10) Code 76 Displayed.** Turn key off and wait 10 seconds. Disconnect ECA 60-pin connector. Inspect for and repair any damaged wiring. Install breakout box and connect ECA to box. Set DVOM on 20-volt scale and connect to test pins No. 43 and 46. Perform ENGINE RUNNING SELF-TEST while observing DVOM. As soon as DYNAMIC RESPONSE CHECK signal is displayed, perform WOT. Reading on DVOM should increase by more than 2.0 volts from reading before WOT. Observe service codes at end of test. If reading increased by more than 2.0 volts and code 76 is still displayed, replace ECA. Remove breakout box and repeat QUICK TEST. If reading did not increase more than 2.0 volts, check air cleaner duct for blockage. If duct is clear, replace airflow meter. If reading increased by more than 2.0 volts and code 76 is not displayed, airflow meter is okay. Service other codes as necessary.

**11) Continuous Code 56 or 66 Displayed.** Using CONTINUOUS MONITOR (WIGGLE) TEST, observe VOM or STAR tester LED for indication of fault while lightly tapping VAF sensor and wiggling connector. If a fault is indicated, disconnect connector. Inspect connector and terminals for damage. If connector and terminals are okay, replace VAF sensor and repeat QUICK TEST. If no fault is indicated, go to next step.

**12)** While in CONTINUOUS MONITOR (WIGGLE) TEST, shake, bend and wiggle small sections of EEC-IV harness from VAF sensor connector to firewall and from firewall to ECA. If fault is indicated, isolate and repair damaged wiring. Repeat QUICK TEST. If no fault is indicated, go to next step.

**13)** Turn key off and wait 10 seconds. Disconnect ECA 60-pin connector. Inspect both connectors and terminals for obvious damage. If connectors and terminals are damaged, repair as necessary and repeat QUICK TEST. If connectors and terminals are okay, fault cannot be duplicated at this time. Continuous code 56 or 66 testing is complete.

***VAF Sensor Circuits***

Breakout Box
Test Pins

26 VREF
43 VAF SIG
46 SIG RTN

VAT
VAF
VREF
SIG. RTN.
BLANK

## CIRCUIT TEST M

### NEUTRAL DRIVE SWITCH-A/C INPUT

**1) Code 67 Displayed.** When this code is displayed, determine which engine and system is being tested.

- For 2.3L EFI/Turbo models with man. trans. go to step **7)**.
- For 2.3L EFI/Turbo models with Octane Switch, go to step **8)**.
- For all other models, go to next step.

## CIRCUIT TEST M (Cont.)

**2)** Turn key off and wait 10 seconds. Make sure heater control is in "OFF" position and that transaxle is in Neutral or Park. Disconnect ECA 60-pin connector. Inspect for and repair any damaged wiring. Install breakout box and connect ECA. Turn key on, leaving engine off. Set DVOM on 20-volt scale and measure voltage between test pin No. 30 and chassis ground. If reading is less than 1.0 volt, go to step **4)**. If reading is 1.0 volt or higher, go to next step.

**3)** Turn key off and wait 10 seconds. Leave breakout box installed and ECA connected. Locate neutral drive switch and disconnect harness at switch. Set DVOM on 200-ohm scale and measure resistance across switch. If reading is less than 5 ohms, repair open in neutral drive circuit. Repeat QUICK TEST. If reading is 5 ohms or more, replace neutral drive switch and repeat QUICK TEST.

**4)** Install breakout box and connect ECA. Turn key on, leaving engine off. Set DVOM on 20-volt scale, and turn A/C control switch off. Measure voltage between test pin No. 10 and chassis ground. Models with Automatic Transmission, check for continuous code 18. On all others, if reading is 1.0 volt or more, repair short to power in A/C clutch circuit. Repeat QUICK TEST. If reading is less than 1.0 volt, replace ECA and repeat QUICK TEST.

**5)** Turn key off and wait 10 seconds. Make sure that A/C is off, if equipped. Ensure that transaxle/transmission is in Neutral and that clutch is released. Disconnect ECA 60-pin connector. Inspect for and repair any damaged wiring. Install breakout box and connect ECA. With DVOM on 200-ohm scale, measure resistance between test pins No. 30 and 46. If reading is less than 5 ohms, go to step **4)**. If reading is 5 ohms or more, go to next step.

**6)** Turn key off. With breakout box and ECA connected, set DVOM on 200-ohm scale. Locate neutral switch (on transaxle) and clutch switch (under dash). Disconnect wiring harness from both switches. Measure resistance across each switch. If reading at both switches is less than 5 ohms, go to step **4)**. If reading at either or both switches is 5 ohms or more, replace defective switch(es). Connect harness and repeat QUICK TEST.

**7)** Turn key off and wait 10 seconds. Make sure A/C is off, if equipped. Disconnect ECA 60-pin connector. Inspect for and repair any damaged wiring. Install breakout box, leaving ECA disconnected. With DVOM on 200-ohm scale, measure resistance between test pins No. 30 and 46. If reading is less than 5 ohms, go to step **4)**. If reading is 5 ohms or more, repair open neutral input or signal return circuit. Repeat QUICK TEST.

**8)** Turn key off and wait 10 seconds. Disconnect ECA 60-pin connector. Inspect for and repair any damaged wiring. Install breakout box and connect ECA. Set DVOM on 20-volt scale. Connect positive lead to test pin No. 30 and negative lead to test pin 46. Turn key on, leaving engine off. Cycle octane switch several times while reading DVOM. If voltage changes from zero volts to 5 volts, replace ECA and repeat QUICK TEST. If voltage does not change, EEC-IV system is okay. Check turbocharging system.

***Neutral Drive-A/C Input Circuit for Models with Auto. Trans.***

Breakout Box
Test Pins

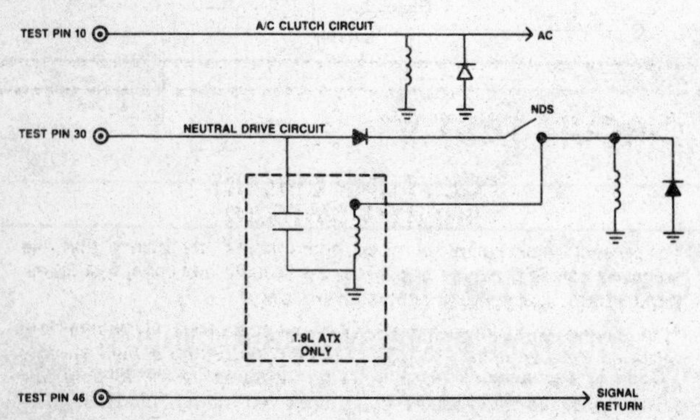
TEST PIN 10
A/C CLUTCH CIRCUIT
AC
TEST PIN 30
NEUTRAL DRIVE CIRCUIT
NDS
1.9L ATX ONLY
TEST PIN 46
SIGNAL RETURN

## CIRCUIT TEST M (Cont.)

***Neutral Drive Input Circuit for Models with Man. Trans.***

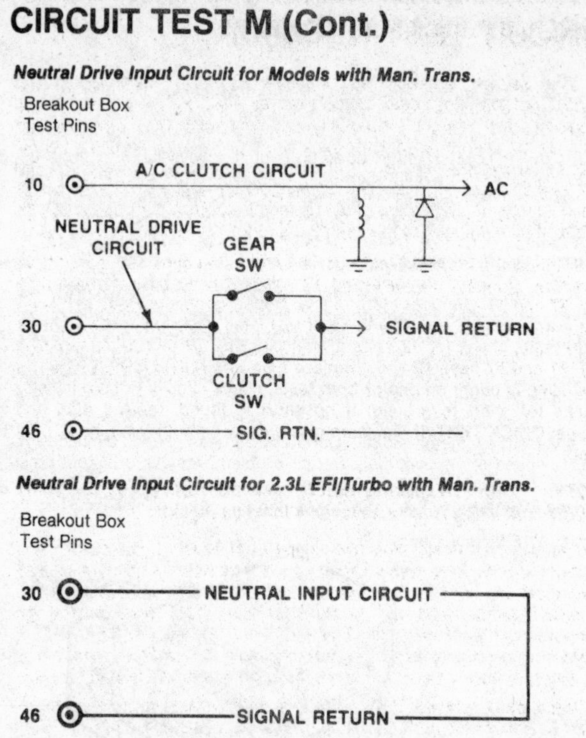
Breakout Box
Test Pins
10
A/C CLUTCH CIRCUIT
AC
NEUTRAL DRIVE CIRCUIT
GEAR SW
30
SIGNAL RETURN
CLUTCH SW
46
SIG. RTN.

***Neutral Drive Input Circuit for 2.3L EFI/Turbo with Man. Trans.***

Breakout Box
Test Pins

30 NEUTRAL INPUT CIRCUIT

46 SIGNAL RETURN

## CIRCUIT TEST Q

### FUEL CONTROL

**NOTE: See HOW TO USE CIRCUIT TESTS before performing this test. Fuel contaminated engine oil may affect service codes 41 and 42. If this is suspected, remove PCV valve from valve cover and repeat QUICK TEST. If problem is corrected, change engine oil and filter.**

**1)** Turn key off and wait 10 seconds. Install fuel pressure gauge. Start and run engine. Fuel pressure must be 35-45 psi (2.5-3.2 kg/cm²). If engine will not run, cycle key from off to on several times to build up fuel pressure. If fuel pressure is outside range, check electric fuel pump and fuel pressure regulator. If fuel pressure is correct, go to next step.

**2)** With pressure gauge installed, cycle key from off to on several times to pressurize system. Pressure must remain at 35-45 psi (2.5-3.2 kg/cm²) for 60 seconds after key is turned off. If pressure is not maintained, go to step **7)**. If pressure is maintained, go to next step.

**3)** With pressure gauge installed, cycle key from off to on several times to pressurize system. Disconnect fuel pump relay. Crank engine for 5 seconds and take pressure reading immediately after cranking. If pressure reading is 10-20 psi (0.7-1.4 kg/cm²) after cranking, EEC-IV system is not at fault for no start. If problem is rough running, missing, fuel code, or if pressure is incorrect after cranking, go to next step.

**NOTE: Make sure that fuel is of good quality and not contaminated by air or water, as pressure readings may be incorrect with bad or contaminated fuel. Also, pressure drop will be greater when engine is cold than when engine is warm. If coolant is 200°F (93°C) pressure should drop approximately 10 psi (0.7 kg/cm²) in 5 seconds while a pressure drop of 20 psi (1.4 kg/cm²) should occur in 5 seconds with engine coolant at 60°F (15.6°C).**

**4)** Turn key off and wait 10 seconds. Disconnect ECA 60-pin connector. Inspect for and repair any damaged wiring. Install breakout box, leaving ECA disconnected. Set DVOM on 200-ohm scale. Measure resistance between test pins No. 37 and 58 for injector bank No. 1. Measure resistance between test pins No. 37 and 59 for injector bank 2. If both readings are between 1.2 and 1.8 ohms, go to step **6)**. If both readings are not between 1.2 and 1.8 ohms, go to next step.

# 1988 COMPUTERIZED ENGINE CONTROLS
# Ford Motor Co. Merkur EEC-IV (Cont.)

## CIRCUIT TEST Q (Cont.)

**5)** With key off, breakout box installed and ECA disconnected, set DVOM on 200-ohm scale. Disconnect all injectors on suspect bank. Connect each injector individually and test resistance between test pins No. 37 and 58 for injector bank No. 1 or between test pins No. 37 and 59 for injector bank No. 2. If all readings are not between 2.0 and 2.7 ohms, check harness and connectors on injector for shorted or open circuits. If circuits are okay, replace injector(s) and repeat QUICK TEST. If all readings are between 2.0 and 2.7 ohms, go to next step.

**6)** With key off, breakout box installed and ECA connected, connect all injectors. Connect non-powered 12-volt test lamp between test pins No. 37 and 58. Crank or start engine. Repeat procedure with test lamp between test pins No. 37 and 59. If test lamp does not light on one or both tests, check for 12 volts at test pins No. 37 and 57. If test pins No. 37 and 57 have 12 volts, replace ECA and repeat QUICK TEST. If test lamp is bright on one or both tests, check circuits to both injector banks for short to ground. If no short is found, replace ECA and repeat QUICK TEST. If test lamp glows dimly on both tests, go to next step.

**NOTE: After completing step 7), reset curb idle speed and verify ISC hookup using vehicle emissions label as a guide.**

**7)** Connect tachometer and run engine at 2000 RPM. Disconnect ISC and use throttle stop screw to set speed if necessary. Disconnect and reconnect one injector at a time and note RPM drop for each injector. If each injector does not produce at least 150 RPM drop when disconnected, replace faulty injector(s) and repeat QUICK TEST. If RPM drop is correct for all injectors, problem is in an area common to all cylinders such as vacuum leaks, fuel contamination, EGR, etc.

**8) Code 42 Displayed.** This code indicates an always rich condition. Turn key off and wait 10 seconds. Disconnect vehicle harness at EGO sensor. Using a jumper wire, ground EGO circuit at EGO sensor to engine block. Repeat ENGINE RUNNING SELF-TEST. If service code 41 is displayed, go to step **10)**. If service code 41 is not displayed, go to next step.

**9)** Turn key off and wait 10 seconds. Install breakout box. Measure resistance of EGO sensor ground circuit between test pins No. 49 and EGO ground at engine block. Measure resistance of EGO sensor circuit between test pin No. 29 and EGO sensor harness connector. If both circuits have less than 5 ohms resistance, disconnect ECA connector and inspect for damage or corrosion. If connector is okay, replace ECA and repeat QUICK TEST. If both circuits have more than 5 ohms resistance, repair circuit having a resistance greater than 5 ohms and repeat QUICK TEST.

**10)** Set DVOM on 20-volt scale. Disconnect EGO sensor from harness and connect DVOM between EGO sensor and engine ground. Start and run engine at 2000 RPM for one minute. Observe DVOM while disconnecting intake manifold vacuum hose. If reading is 0.4 volts or higher, replace EGO sensor and repeat QUICK TEST. If reading is less than 0.4 volts, go to step **1)**.

***Fig. 1: Intake Manifold Hose Removal For Test***

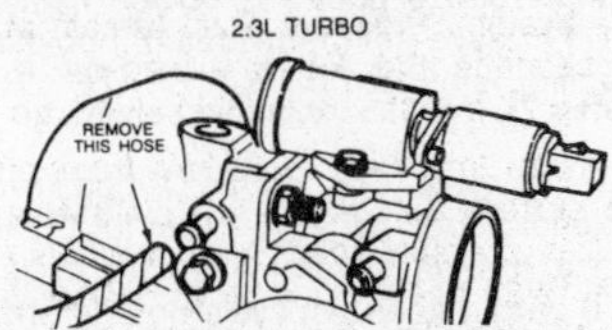
2.3L TURBO
REMOVE THIS HOSE

**11) Code 41 Displayed.** This code indicates an always lean condition. With key off and DVOM set on 20-volt scale, disconnect EGO sensor from harness. Connect DVOM between EGO sensor and engine ground. Remove air cleaner in order to reach airflow meter inlet. Use wood pencil to prop air meter door in partially open position. Start and run engine at 2000 RPM for 2 minutes. If reading is not greater than 0.5 volts after one minute, replace EGO sensor and repeat QUICK TEST. If reading is greater than 0.5 volts after one minute, go to next step.

**12)** Turn key off. Install breakout box, leaving ECA disconnected. Measure resistance of EGO circuit between test pin No. 49 and engine block ground. Measure resistance of EGO circuit between test pin No. 29 and EGO sensor connector. If both readings are 5 ohms or higher, repair circuit with high resistance and repeat QUICK TEST. If both readings are less than 5 ohms, go to next step.

## CIRCUIT TEST Q (Cont.)

**13)** With key off, breakout box installed and ECA disconnected, set DVOM on 200,000-ohm scale. Measure resistance between test pins No. 29 and 40. If reading is less than 10,000 ohms, correct cause of resistance to ground and repeat QUICK TEST. If resistance is 10,000 ohms or higher, go to next step.

**14)** With key off, connect EGO sensor. Remove air cleaner and prop airflow meter door partially open with wood pencil. Start and run engine at 2000 RPM for 2 minutes. Perform ENGINE RUNNING SELF-TEST. If code 41 is displayed, check for corrosion or damaged pins at ECA connector. If connector is okay, replace ECA and repeat QUICK TEST. If code 41 is not displayed, EGO sensor input circuit is okay, go to step **1)**.

**15) Continuous Codes 41 & 42 Displayed.** If code 41 appears it indicates that the fuel system was lean for more than 15 seconds. If code 42 appears, it indicates that the fuel system was rich for more than 15 seconds. Before attempting to correct a code 41 or 42, first diagnose all other complaints such as rough idle, missing, etc. Areas to check to isolate fuel control problems are as follows:

- Unmetered Air. Vacuum or intake air leaks in canister purge system, PCV, engine sealing or air leaks between airflow meter and throttle body.
- EGO Sensor Fuel Fouled. If fuel fouled spark plugs are observed, make complete check of ignition system. If EGO sensor is fuel fouled (low output and/or slow response), run vehicle at high (but legal) sustained speeds. Follow speed run with a few hard accelerations to burn off contamination and restore EGO sensor to correct operation.
- Fuel Pressure. Perform step **1)**.
- Ignition System. If always in default spark (10 degrees), perform TIMING CHECK.
- Improper Fueling. Lead fouled EGO sensor.
- TPS. If not moving, check for mechanical damage. Connect DVOM on test pins No. 47 and 46. Turn key on, leaving engine off. Observe DVOM while moving throttle. Reading must increase with throttle opening. If not, replace TPS as necessary. If, at this point, drive problem is still present, perform steps **3)** through **6)** only.

***EFI Fuel Control Circuits***

Breakout Box
Test Pins

RUN CIRCUIT
29 (HEGO) FUSE LINK
29 (EGO) EGO
49 (EGO GND.) EGO GROUND
58 (INJ. BANK 1)
59 (INJ. BANK 2)
37 (PWR)
57 (PWR)
INJ. BANK 1
INJ. BANK 2
TO IGNITION SWITCH
EEC POWER RELAY
BATTERY

## CIRCUIT TEST V

### FUEL PUMP CIRCUIT (INERTIA SWITCH)

To prevent replacement of good components, be aware that the following non-EEC related areas may be at fault: fuel lines, fuel filters, throttle body, fuel pump or contaminated fuel.

**1)** Install fuel pressure gauge. Check if fuel pump runs. Cycle key from off to on several times. DO NOT crank engine. Pump should operate each time key is on. If pump runs as indicated, check electric fuel pump system for problems. If pump does not run as indicated, go to next step.

**2)** Turn key off and wait 10 seconds. Disconnect ECA 60-pin connector. Inspect for and repair any damaged wiring. Install breakout box and connect ECA. Turn key on, leaving engine off. Set DVOM on

## CIRCUIT TEST V (Cont.)

20-volt scale. Measure voltage between test pins No. 37 and 40, and between test pins No. 57 and 60. If either reading is less than 10.5 volts, go to CIRCUIT TEST B, step **1)**. If both readings are 10.5 volts or more, go to next step.

**3)** Turn key off and wait 10 seconds. Leave breakout box installed and ECA connected. Locate and disconnect fuel pump inertia switch. Set DVOM on 200-ohm scale and measure switch resistance. If reading is 5 ohms or more, replace inertia switch and repeat QUICK TEST. If reading is less than 5 ohms, go to next step.

**4)** Turn key on, leaving engine off. Leave breakout box installed and ECA connected. Locate fuel pump relay. Set DVOM on 20-volt scale. Measure voltage between chassis ground and power-to-pump(s) circuit at fuel pump relay while cranking engine. If reading is less than 8 volts, go to step **6)**. If reading is 8 volts or more, go to next step.

**5)** Turn key on, leaving engine off. Leave breakout box installed and ECA connected. Locate fuel pump(s). Set DVOM on 20-volt scale. Measure voltage between chassis ground and power-to-pump(s) circuit at fuel pump(s) while cranking. If reading is 8 volts or more, service electric fuel pump(s). If reading is less than 8 volts, repair open in power-to-pump(s) circuit and repeat QUICK TEST.

**6)** Turn key on, leaving engine off. Leave breakout box installed and ECA connected. Locate fuel pump relay. Set DVOM on 20-volt scale. Measure voltage between chassis ground and V BATT circuit at fuel pump relay. If reading is less than 10.5 volts, repair open in V BATT circuit between fuel pump relay and battery positive post. Repeat QUICK TEST. If reading is 10.5 volts or more, go to next step.

**7)** Turn key on, leaving engine off. Leave breakout box installed and ECA connected. Locate fuel pump relay. Set DVOM on 20-volt scale. Measure voltage between chassis ground and V POWER circuit at fuel pump relay. If reading is less than 10.5 volts, repair open in V POWER circuit between fuel pump relay and ECA. Repeat QUICK TEST. If reading is 10.5 volts or more, go to next step.

**8)** Turn key off and wait 10 seconds. Leave breakout box installed and ECA connected. With DVOM on 200-ohm scale, measure resistance between fuel pump circuit at pump relay and test pin No. 22. If reading is 5 ohms or more, repair open in fuel pump circuit. Repeat QUICK TEST. If reading is less than 5 ohms, go to next step.

**9)** Turn key off. Leave breakout box installed and disconnect ECA. Disconnect fuel pump relay. With DVOM on 200,000-ohm scale, measure resistance between test pin No. 22 and test pins No. 40 and 60. If reading is less than 10,000 ohms, repair short in fuel pump circuit. Repeat QUICK TEST. If reading is 10,000 ohms or more, go to next step.

**10)** Turn key off and wait 10 seconds. Leave breakout box installed. Leave fuel pump relay and ECA disconnected. With DVOM on 200,000-ohm scale, measure resistance between test pin No. 22 and test pins No. 37 and 57. If reading is less than 10,000 ohms, repair short to power in fuel pump circuit. Connect ECA and attempt to start engine. If engine does not start, replace ECA. Repeat QUICK TEST. If reading is 10,000 ohms or more, connect fuel pump relay and go to next step.

**11)** Leave breakout box installed and ECA disconnected. Install a jumper wire between test pin No. 22 and either test pin No. 40 or No. 60. Set DVOM on 20-volt scale. Turn key on, leaving engine off. Measure voltage between chassis ground and power-to-pump(s) circuit at fuel pump relay. If reading is 10.5 volts or more, replace ECA and repeat QUICK TEST. If reading is less than 10.5 volts, replace fuel pump relay. Connect ECA and repeat QUICK TEST.

**12)** Turn key off. Remove fuel pump relay. If fuel pump turns off, replace fuel pump relay. Repeat QUICK TEST. If fuel pump does not turn off, repair short to power-to-pump(s) circuit.

## CIRCUIT TEST V (Cont.)

***Fuel Pump (Inertia Switch) Circuits***

Breakout Box
Test Pins

**Type I:**

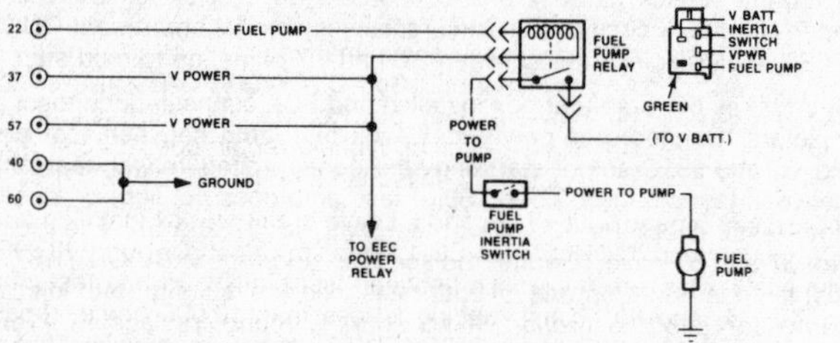

**Type II:**

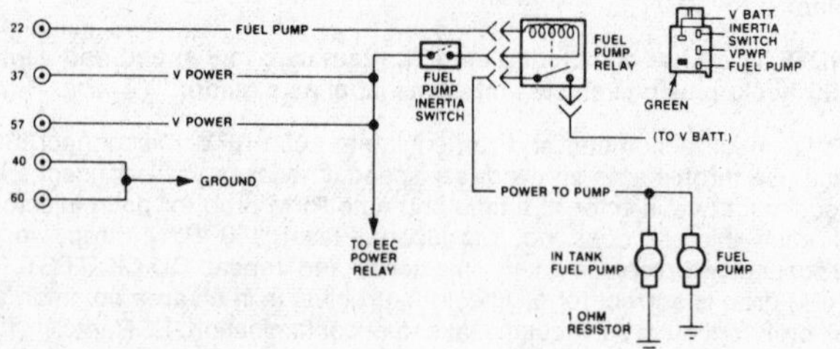

## CIRCUIT TEST W

### EGR ON/OFF CHECK

**NOTE: Code 34 may be result of high volume exhaust vent system reducing backpressure. If this is suspected, perform test in well-ventilated area without exhaust vent connected.**

To prevent replacement of good components, be aware that the following non-EEC related areas may be at fault: air or vacuum leaks, EGR flow restrictions or EGR value.

**1) Code 34 Displayed.** Use only VOM/DVOM, not STAR tester, for this step. Turn key off and wait 10 seconds. Set DVOM on 20-volt scale. Connect negative DVOM lead to STO and positive lead to positive battery terminal. Insert jumper wire between STI and signal return circuit at SELF-TEST connector. Perform KEY ON/ENGINE OFF SELF-TEST until end of CONTINUOUS SELF-TEST code display (DVOM will read zero volts). Depress and release throttle and observe DVOM reading. If DVOM did not show high voltage, depress throttle to WOT and release. If output voltage does not go too high, go to CIRCUIT TEST NN, step **17)**. Leave test equipment hooked up. If DVOM registered high reading, stay in OUTPUT STATE CHECK and go to next step.

**2)** Set DVOM on 20-volt scale. Connect DVOM positive lead to VPWR circuit at EGR solenoid and negative lead to EGR output circuit. Depress and release throttle several times to cycle EGR solenoid output on and off. If output does not cycle on and off, remove jumper wire and go to step **5)**. If output cycles on and off, go to next step.

**3)** Connect vacuum pump to solenoid vacuum supply port and vacuum gauge to output port of solenoid. Apply minimum vacuum of 6 in. Hg. Depress and release throttle several times to cycle EGR solenoid output while maintaining vacuum at supply port. Note gauge reading. If vacuum output does not cycle, replace EGR solenoid and repeat QUICK TEST. If vacuum output cycles, go to next step.

**4)** With vacuum lines disconnected at EGR solenoid, start engine. If vacuum is present, EEC-IV system is not cause of problem. Check exhaust gas recirculation system. If vacuum is not present, correct vacuum source blockage or leak and repeat QUICK TEST.

**5)** Turn key off and wait 10 seconds. Disconnect EGR solenoid. Set DVOM on 200-ohm scale and measure solenoid resistance. If reading is less than 65 ohms or more than 110 ohms, replace solenoid and repeat QUICK TEST. If resistance is between 65 and 110 ohms, connect solenoid and go to next step.

## CIRCUIT TEST W (Cont.)

**6)** Turn key on, leaving engine off. Set DVOM on 20-volt scale. Measure voltage at EGR solenoid connector between VPWR circuit and ground. If reading is less than 10.5 volts, repair open in harness and repeat QUICK TEST. If reading is 10.5 volts or higher, go to next step.

**7)** Turn key off and wait 10 seconds. Disconnect ECA 60-pin connector. Inspect for and repair any damaged wiring. Install breakout box, leaving ECA disconnected. Set DVOM on 200-ohm scale. Measure resistance between test pin No. 35 and EGR circuit at connector. If reading is 5 ohms or higher, repair open circuit and repeat QUICK TEST. If reading is less than 5 ohms, go to next step.

**8)** Turn key off and wait 10 seconds. Leave breakout box installed and ECA disconnected. Disconnect EGR solenoid. Set DVOM on 200,000-ohm scale. Measure resistance between test pin No. 35 and test pins No. 40, 46, and 60. If any reading is less than 10,000 ohms, repair short to ground and repeat QUICK TEST. If any reading is 10,000 ohms or more, go to next step.

**9)** Turn key off and wait 10 seconds. Leave breakout box installed with ECA and EGR solenoid disconnected. With DVOM on 200,000-ohm scale, measure resistance between test pin No. 35 and test pins No. 37 and 57. If any reading is less than 10,000 ohms, repair short to power and repeat QUICK TEST. If code is still repeated, replace ECA. If any reading is 10,000 ohms or more, replace ECA and repeat QUICK TEST.

***EGR ON/OFF Circuit***

Breakout Box
Test Pins

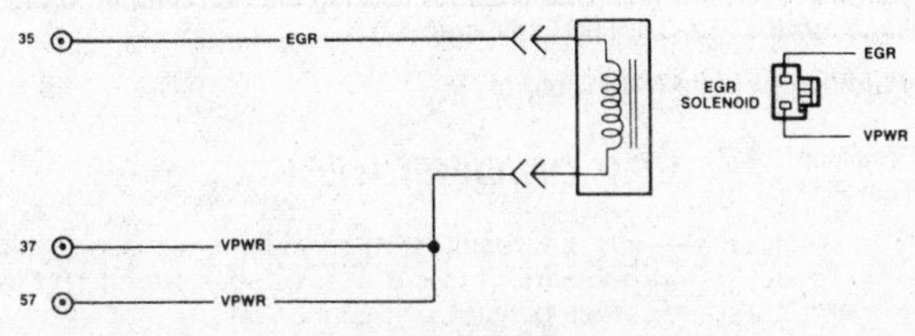
35
EGR
EGR
SOLENOID
EGR
VPWR
37
VPWR
57
VPWR

## CIRCUIT TEST Y

### CANISTER PURGE (CANP) CHECK

**1)** Use only VOM/DVOM, not STAR tester, for this step. Turn key off and wait 10 seconds. Set DVOM on 20-volt scale. Connect DVOM negative test lead to STO and positive test lead to positive battery terminal. Using a jumper wire, connect STI circuit to signal return at SELF-TEST connector. Perform KEY ON/ENGINE OFF SELF-TEST until end of CONTINUOUS SELF-TEST codes (DVOM reads zero volts). Depress and release throttle. DVOM reading should change to a high voltage reading. If reading did not change, depress throttle to WOT and release. If STO voltage does not go high, go to CIRCUIT TEST NN, step **17)**. Leave test equipment hooked up. If reading changed, remain in OUTPUT STATE CHECK and go to next step.

**2)** Set DVOM on 20-volt scale. Connect DVOM positive test lead to VPWR on CANP solenoid and negative test lead to CANP output circuit on solenoid. Depress and release throttle several times to cycle solenoid on and off. If CANP solenoid does not cycle, remove jumper wire and go to step **4)**. If CANP solenoid does cycle, go to next step.

**3)** Turn key off and wait 10 seconds. Remove jumper wire from STI to signal return. Disconnect vacuum hose from CANP solenoid on PCV side. Apply 16 in. Hg vacuum to solenoid. If CANP solenoid does not hold vacuum, replace it and repeat QUICK TEST. If code 42 is still displayed, service fuel evaporation system. If CANP holds vacuum, EEC-IV is okay. Check fuel system.

**4)** Turn key off and wait 10 seconds. Set DVOM on 200-ohm scale. Disconnect CANP solenoid connector. Measure solenoid resistance. If reading is less than 40 ohms or more than 90 ohms, replace CANP solenoid and repeat QUICK TEST. If reading is between 40 and 90 ohms, connect solenoid and go to next step.

## CIRCUIT TEST Y (Cont.)

**5)** Turn key on, leaving engine off. Set DVOM on 20-volt scale. Measure voltage between VPWR at CANP harness connector and ground. If reading is less than 10.5 volts, repair open circuit and repeat QUICK TEST. If reading is 10.5 volts or more, go to next step.

**6)** Turn key off and wait 10 seconds. Disconnect ECA 60-pin connector. Inspect for and repair any damaged wiring. Install breakout box, leaving ECA disconnected. Set DVOM on 200-ohm scale. Measure resistance between CANP signal at connector and test pin No. 35. If reading is 5 ohms or more, repair open circuit and repeat QUICK TEST. If reading is less than 5 ohms, go to next step.

**7)** Turn key off and wait 10 seconds. Leave breakout box installed and ECA disconnected. Disconnect CANP solenoid. Set DVOM on 200,000-ohm scale. Measure resistance between test pins No. 40, 46, 60 and test pin No. 35. If any reading is less than 10,000 ohms, repair short to power and repeat QUICK TEST. If any reading is 10,000 ohms or more, go to next step.

**8)** Turn key off and wait 10 seconds. Leave CANP solenoid disconnected. Leave breakout box installed and ECA disconnected. Measure resistance between test pins No. 37, 57 and test pin No. 35. If any reading is less than 10,000 ohms, repair short to ground and repeat QUICK TEST. If code is repeated, replace ECA and repeat QUICK TEST. If any reading is 10,000 ohms or more, remove breakout box. Replace ECA and repeat QUICK TEST.

***Canister Purge (CANP) Circuit***

Breakout Box
Test Pins

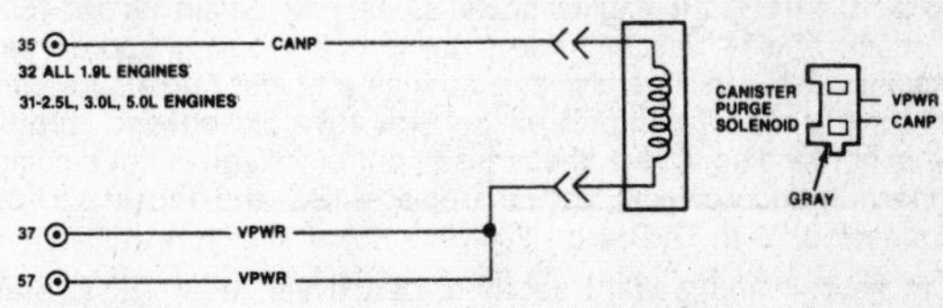
35
CANP
32 ALL 1.9L ENGINES
31-2.5L, 3.0L, 5.0L ENGINES
CANISTER
PURGE
SOLENOID
VPWR
CANP
GRAY
37
VPWR
57
VPWR

## CIRCUIT TEST Z

### IDLE SPEED CONTROL (BY-PASS AIR)

**NOTE: If engine is running rough or has rough idle, correct before running test. Causes may be in ignition system, fuel system or EGR system. If fuel system problems are encountered, go to CIRCUIT TEST Q, step 1) through 7).**

To prevent replacement of good components, be aware that the following non-EEC related areas may be at fault: engine temperature not up to operating temperature, engine over operating temperature, improper idle speed/throttle stop adjustment or cruise control linkage.

**1)** Turn key off. Connect engine tachometer and start engine. Disconnect Idle Speed Control (ISC) harness. If RPM drops or if engine stalls, go to next step. If not, go to step **3)**.

**2)** If EGR service codes 31, 32, 33 or 34 are displayed, go to ENGINE RUNNING SELF-TEST table and perform appropriate test. If not, service next code. If codes 12 or 23 are displayed, go to next step.

**3)** Turn key off. Disconnect ISC harness. With DVOM on 200-ohm scale, measure resistance of ISC solenoid. If resistance is between 7 and 13 ohms, go to next step. If resistance is less than 7 ohms or more than 13 ohms, replace ISC solenoid and repeat QUICK TEST.

**4)** With key off and ISC harness disconnected, set DVOM on 200,000-ohm scale. Measure resistance from either ISC pin to ISC solenoid housing. If reading is 10,000 ohms or greater, go to step **5)**. If reading is less than 10,000 ohms, replace ISC solenoid. Repeat QUICK TEST.

**5)** Leave ISC harness disconnected. Turn key on, leaving engine off. Measure voltage between VPWR circuit at ISC harness and battery ground terminal. If reading is less than 10.5 volts, repair open in circuit and repeat QUICK TEST. If reading is 10.5 volts or more, go to next step.

# 1988 COMPUTERIZED ENGINE CONTROLS
# Ford Motor Co. Merkur EEC-IV (Cont.)

## CIRCUIT TEST Z (Cont.)

**6)** Turn key off and wait 10 seconds. Leave ISC harness disconnected. Disconnect ECA 60-pin connector. Inspect for and repair any damaged wiring. Install breakout box, leaving ECA disconnected. With DVOM on 200-ohm scale, measure resistance between test pin No. 21 and ISC circuit at ISC harness connector. If reading is 5 ohms or more, repair open circuit and repeat QUICK TEST. If reading is less than 5 ohms, go to next step.

**7)** Turn key off and wait 10 seconds. Leave ISC harness disconnected. Install breakout box, leaving ECA disconnected. Set DVOM on 200,000-ohm scale. Measure resistance between test pin No. 21 and test pins No. 40, 46, and 60. If all readings are less than 10,000 ohms, repair short to ground and repeat QUICK TEST. If any reading is 10,000 ohms or more, go to next step.

**8)** Turn key off and wait 10 seconds. Leave breakout box installed. Leave ECA and ISC solenoid disconnected. With DVOM on 200,000-ohm scale, measure resistance between test pins No. 21 and 37. If reading is less than 10,000 ohms, repair short to power and repeat QUICK TEST. If reading is 10,000 ohms or more, go to next step.

**9)** With key off, connect ECA and ISC. Leave breakout box installed. With vehicle prepared for QUICK TEST, set DVOM on 20-volt scale. Connect DVOM between test pins No. 21 and 40. Start engine and observe DVOM. If meter reading varies during QUICK TEST, replace ISC and repeat QUICK TEST. If meter reading does not vary during QUICK TEST, go to next step.

**10) Code 13 Displayed.** Disconnect ISC harness. Connect tachometer and repeat ENGINE RUNNING SELF-TEST. Record service codes. If engine speed remains below 1500 RPM during test, replace ECA and repeat QUICK TEST. If engine speed does not remain below 1500 RPM, check engine vacuum hoses for proper routing and/or bad connections. Use vehicle emissions label as a guide. Make sure curb idle is correct. Ensure throttle plates are fully closed and throttle linkage is not binding. Check that cruise control linkage is not binding. If no mechanical problems appear, replace ISC and repeat QUICK TEST.

**11)** Turn key off and wait 10 seconds. Deactivate SELF-TEST. Start and run engine at 2000 RPM for 2 minutes, until inlet radiator hose is hot and pressurized. Turn key and wait 10 seconds. Perform ENGINE RUNNING SELF-TEST. If code 17 is still displayed, inspect throttle body and air inlet for contamination. Service as necessary. If okay, adjust curb idle speed and repeat QUICK TEST. If code 17 is not displayed, service other codes as necessary.

***Idle Speed Control (By-Pass Air) Circuit***

Breakout Box
Test Pins

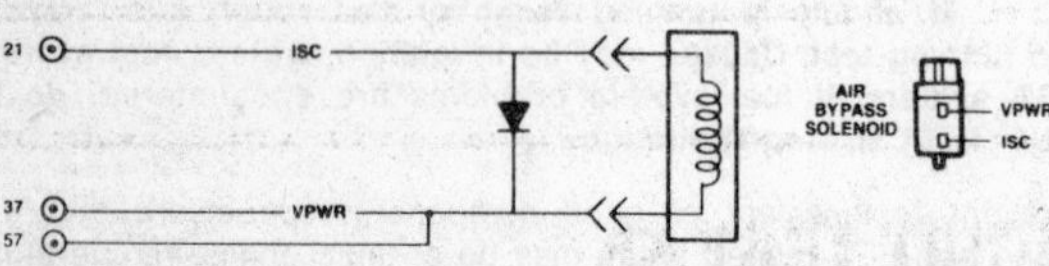
21
ISC
37
VPWR
57
AIR BYPASS SOLENOID
VPWR
ISC

## CIRCUIT TEST FF

### SHIFT INDICATOR LIGHT (SIL)

**1)** Use only VOM/DVOM, not STAR tester, for this step. Turn key off and wait 10 seconds. Put transmission in Neutral. Set DVOM on 20-volt scale. Connect DVOM negative test lead to STO at SELF-TEST connector and positive test lead to positive battery terminal. Install a jumper wire between STI and signal return at SELF-TEST connector. Perform KEY ON/ENGINE OFF SELF-TEST until end of CONTINUOUS SELF-TEST codes (DVOM reads zero volts). Depress and release throttle while watching DVOM reading. If reading did not change to a high voltage, depress throttle to WOT position and release. If STO voltage does not go to high reading, go to step **7)**. Leave test equipment hooked up. If reading changes to high voltage, remain in OUTPUT STATE CHECK and go to next step.

**2)** Set DVOM on 20-volt scale. Connect DVOM positive test lead to battery positive terminal and negative test lead to pin No. 1 on dimmer relay. Depress and release throttle several times to cycle relay on and off. If relay does not cycle, go to step **5)**. If relay cycles, go to next step.

## CIRCUIT TEST FF (Cont.)

**3)** Set DVOM on 20-volt scale. Connect DVOM positive test lead to battery positive terminal and negative test lead to pin No. 2 on dimmer relay. Depress and release throttle several times to cycle relay on and off. If relay does not cycle, remove jumper wire and replace dimmer relay. If relay does cycle, remove jumper wire and go to next step.

**4)** Turn key off and wait 10 seconds. With DVOM set to 200-ohm scale, measure resistance between pin No. 2 of dimmer relay and SIL bulb. If reading is less than 5 ohms, replace SIL bulb. If reading is 5 ohms or more, repair open circuit in harness. Repeat QUICK TEST.

**5)** Set DVOM on 20-volt scale. Connect DVOM positive test lead to battery positive terminal and negative test lead to SIL circuit of top gear switch. Depress and release throttle several times to cycle SIL circuit on and off. If SIL circuit cycles, repair open circuit in harness and repeat QUICK TEST. If SIL circuit does not cycle, go to next step.

**6)** Set DVOM on 20-volt scale. Connect DVOM positive test lead to positive battery terminal and negative test lead to STO circuit of top gear switch. Depress and release throttle several times to cycle STO circuit on and off. If STO circuit cycles, replace top gear switch. If STO does not cycle, repair open circuit in harness and repeat QUICK TEST.

**7)** Use only VOM/DVOM, not STAR tester, for this step. Turn key off and wait 10 seconds. Put transmission in top gear. Set DVOM on 20-volt scale. Connect DVOM negative test lead to STO at SELF-TEST connector and positive test lead to positive battery terminal. Install a jumper wire between STI and signal return at SELF-TEST connector. Perform KEY ON/ENGINE OFF SELF-TEST until end of CONTINUOUS SELF-TEST codes (DVOM reads zero volts). Depress and release throttle while watching DVOM reading. If reading changed to high voltage, check SIL bulb and fuse No. 15. If bulb and fuse are good, repair short to ground in SIL circuit. If reading did not change to high voltage, go to CIRCUIT TEST NN, step **17)**.

***Shift Indicator Light (SIL) Circuits***

Breakout Box
Test Pins

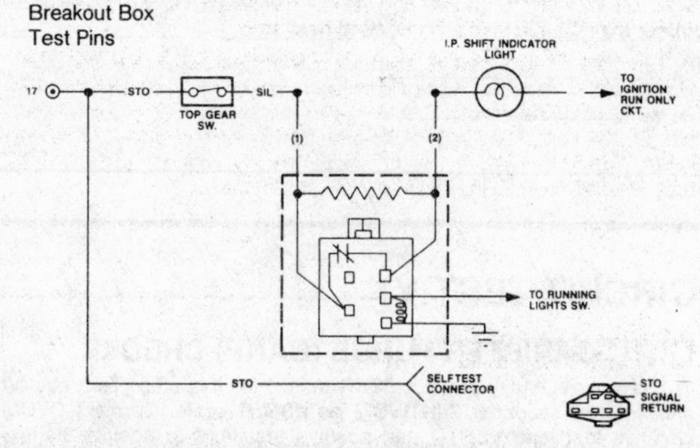
17
STO
TOP GEAR SW.
SIL
(1)
(2)
I.P. SHIFT INDICATOR LIGHT
TO IGNITION RUN ONLY CKT.
TO RUNNING LIGHTS SW.
STO
SELFTEST CONNECTOR
STO
SIGNAL RETURN

## CIRCUIT TEST GG

### WOT A/C CUTOFF (WAC)

**1)** Use only VOM/DVOM, not STAR tester for this step. Turn key off and wait 10 seconds. Set DVOM on 20-volt scale. Connect DVOM negative test lead to STO at SELF-TEST connector and positive test lead to positive battery terminal. Install a jumper wire between STI and signal return at SELF-TEST connector.

**2)** Perform KEY ON/ENGINE OFF SELF-TEST until end of CONTINUOUS SELF-TEST codes (DVOM reads zero volts). Depress and release throttle while watching DVOM reading. If reading did not change to a high voltage, depress throttle to WOT position and release.

**3)** If STO voltage does not go to high reading, go to CIRCUIT TEST NN, step **17)**. Leave test equipment connected. If reading changes to high voltage, remain in OUTPUT STATE CHECK and go to next step.

**4)** Turn key on and leave engine off. Disconnect ECA 60-pin connector and inspect for damage, corrosion or loose wires. Repair as necessary. Connect breakout box to harness and reconnect ECA. Place A/C switch to the A/C position. Set DVOM to 20-volt scale.

## CIRCUIT TEST GG (Cont.)

**5)** Connect DVOM positive lead to test pin No. 37 and negative lead to test pin No. 54 at the breakout box. While monitoring DVOM, depress and release throttle several times to cycle output on and off.

**6)** If A/C clutch output cycle goes on and off, EEC-IV system checks okay and A/C system needs to be checked. If on and off does not occur, remove jumper wire and proceed to next step.

**7)** Turn key off and wait 10 seconds. Leave breakout box installed and ECA disconnected. Set DVOM to 200,000 ohm scale. Measure resistance between test pin No. 54 and test pins No. 40, 46 and 60, at breakout box.

**8)** If resistance reading is 10,000 or greater, replace ECA and repeat QUICK TEST. If resistance reading is less than specification, proceed to next step.

**9)** Turn key off and wait 10 seconds. Set DVOM to 200 ohm scale. Disconnect WAC relay connector and measure relay resistance. If resistance is not between 50 and 70 ohms, replace WAC relay and repeat QUICK TEST. If resistance is between 50 and 70 ohms, connect WAC solenoid and proceed to next step.

**10)** Turn key off and wait 10 seconds. Disconnect ECA 60-pin connector and inspect for damage, corrosion or loose wires. Repair as necessary. Connect breakout box to harness and leave ECA disconnected.

**11)** Set DVOM to 200 ohm scale. Measure resistance between test pin No. 54 at breakout box and WAC circuit at harness connector. If resistance is 5 ohms or greater, repair open circuit in harness and repeat QUICK TEST. If resistance is not 5 ohms or greater, proceed to next step.

**12)** Turn key off and wait 10 seconds. Leave breakout box connected and ECA disconnected. Set DVOM to 200,000 ohm scale. Measure resistance between test pin No. 54 and test pins No. 40, 46 and 60, at breakout box. If resistance readings are not greater than 10,000 ohms, repair short to ground and repeat QUICK TEST. If resistance is greater than 10,000 ohms, proceed to next step.

**13)** Turn key off and wait 10 seconds. Disconnect ECA. Set DVOM to 20-volt scale. Measure voltage between test pin No. 10 and test pin No. 40 at breakout box. If output cycles low to high (high being 10.5 volts or greater), when A/C switch is cycled, replace ECA and repeat QUICK TEST. If cycle not within specifications, repair open in A/C input to test pin No. 10 and repeat QUICK TEST.

## CIRCUIT TEST HH

### TURBO BOOST

**1)** Use only VOM/DVOM, not STAR tester for this step. Turn key off and wait 10 seconds. Set DVOM on 20-volt scale. Connect DVOM negative test lead to STO at SELF-TEST connector and positive test lead to positive battery terminal. Install a jumper wire between STI and signal return at SELF-TEST connector. Perform KEY ON/ENGINE OFF SELF-TEST until end of CONTINUOUS SELF-TEST codes (DVOM reads zero volts). Depress and release throttle while watching DVOM reading. If reading did not change to a high voltage, depress throttle to WOT position and release. If STO voltage does not go to high reading, go to CIRCUIT TEST NN, step **17)**. Leave test equipment hooked up. If reading changes to high voltage, remain in OUTPUT STATE CHECK and go to next step.

**2)** Turn key on, leave engine off. Set DVOM on 20-volt scale. Connect DVOM positive test lead to VPWR circuit at boost solenoid connector and negative test lead to boost output on boost solenoid connector. Depress and release throttle several times while reading DVOM. If boost solenoid does not cycle, remove jumper wire and go to step **4)**. If boost solenoid cycles, go to next step.

**3)** Remain in OUTPUT STATE CHECK. Disconnect plain Black (not Black/Yellow) solenoid vacuum hose from turbocharger end. Attach vacuum pump to hose. Depress throttle once to cycle solenoid to closed position. Apply vacuum to solenoid, then depress throttle to cycle solenoid to open position and release vacuum. If solenoid does not hold and release vacuum properly, replace solenoid and repeat QUICK TEST. If solenoid works correctly, EEC-IV is okay. Check turbocharger boost system.

## CIRCUIT TEST HH (Cont.)

**4)** Turn key off and wait 10 seconds. Disconnect boost solenoid connector. With DVOM on 200-ohm scale, measure resistance of boost solenoid. If reading is less than 65 ohms or more than 110 ohms, replace boost solenoid and repeat QUICK TEST. If reading is between 65 and 110 ohms, connect boost solenoid and go to next step.

**5)** Turn key on, leaving engine off. Set DVOM on 20-volt scale. Measure voltage between VPWR circuit at solenoid connector and battery ground. If reading is less than 10.5 volts, repair open in harness and repeat QUICK TEST. If reading is 10.5 volts or more, go to next step.

**6)** Turn key off and wait 10 seconds. Disconnect ECA 60-pin connector. Inspect for and repair any damaged wiring. Install breakout box, leaving ECA disconnected. Set DVOM on 200-ohm scale. Measure resistance between test pin No. 32 and boost circuit at harness connector. If reading is 5 ohms or more, repair open and repeat QUICK TEST. If reading is less than 5 ohms, go to next step.

**7)** Turn key off and wait 10 seconds. Leave breakout box installed and ECA disconnected. Disconnect boost solenoid and set DVOM on 200,000-ohm scale. Measure resistance between test pin No. 32 and test pins No. 40, 46, and 60. If any reading is less than 10,000 ohms, repair short to ground and repeat QUICK TEST. If all readings are 10,000 ohms or more, go to next step.

**8)** Turn key off and wait 10 seconds. Leave breakout box installed, ECA disconnected, and DVOM on 200,000-ohm scale. With boost solenoid disconnected, measure resistance between test pin No. 32 and test pins No. 37 and 57. If any reading is less than 10,000 ohms, repair short to power and repeat QUICK TEST. If symptom is still present, replace ECA. If all readings are 10,000 ohms or more, replace ECA and repeat QUICK TEST.

***Turbo Boost Circuit***

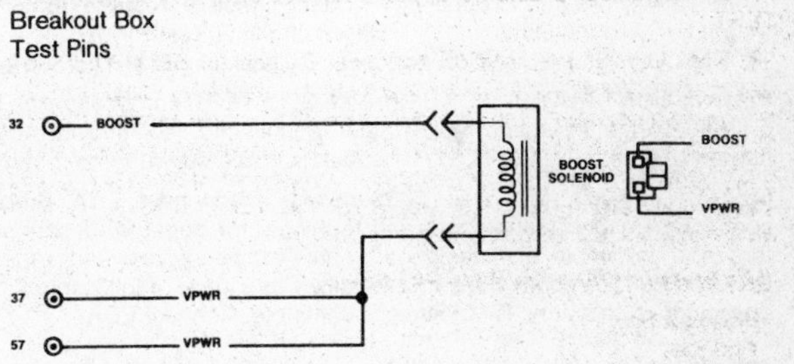

Breakout Box
Test Pins

32 BOOST
BOOST SOLENOID
BOOST
VPWR
37 VPWR
57 VPWR

## CIRCUIT TEST KK

### DYNAMIC RESPONSE TEST

To prevent replacement of good components, be aware that the following non-EEC related areas may be at fault: person testing EEC-IV system did not perform brief wide open throttle (WOT) after Dynamic Response code, mechanical engine problems, or engine did not go over 2000 RPM.

**Code 77 Displayed.** Repeat ENGINE RUNNING SELF-TEST. With SELF-TEST activated, restart engine. Code 2 (20 on STAR tester) indicates start of test. After Dynamic Response code 1 (10 on STAR tester) is displayed, perform brief WOT. Dynamic Response service codes will be displayed. If code 77 is still present, replace ECA and repeat QUICK TEST. If code 77 is not displayed, DYNAMIC RESPONSE TEST passed. Service other codes (if displayed) as required.

## CIRCUIT TEST LL

### IGNITION DIAGNOSTIC MONITOR (IDM)

To prevent replacement of good components, be aware that the following non-EEC related areas may be at fault: ignition module, ignition coil, spark plugs and/or high tension cables, distributor and PIP sensor.

**1)** Turn key off and wait 10 seconds. Disconnect E-Core ignition connector from coil. Disconnect ECA 60-pin connector. Inspect for and repair any damaged wiring. Install breakout box, leaving ECA disconnected. Set DVOM on 200,000-ohm scale. Measure resistance between test pin 4 and negative terminal on ignition coil. If reading is less than 20,000 ohms or higher than 24,000 ohms, repair open circuit and repeat QUICK TEST. If reading is between 20,000 and 24,000 ohms, go to next step.

**2)** Turn key off and wait 10 seconds. Leave breakout box installed and ECA disconnected. With DVOM on 200,000-ohm scale, measure resistance between test pin 4 and test pins 40, 46, and 60. If any reading is less than 10,000 ohms, repair short to ground and repeat QUICK TEST. If all readings are 10,000 ohms or more, go to next step.

**3)** Turn key off and wait 10 seconds. Deactivate SELF-TEST. Using CONTINUOUS MONITOR (WIGGLE) TEST, observe VOM or STAR tester LED for indication of fault while lightly tapping on TFI module and wiggling TFI harness connector. If fault is indicated, disconnect TFI harness. Inspect connector and terminals for damage. If connector and terminals are okay, check TFI ignition system. If no fault is indicated, go to next step.

**4)** While in CONTINUOUS MONITOR (WIGGLE) TEST, observe VOM or STAR tester LED for indication of fault while wiggling, shaking, or bending small sections of harness while working from TFI connector toward firewall. Repeat process from firewall to ECA. Perform this test to check for faults in the following circuits:

- PIP Open/Shorted to Ground — Check circuit at Test Pin 56.
- SPOUT Shorted to Ground — Check circuit at Test Pin 36.
- Ignition Ground Open — Check circuit at Test Pin 16.
- IDM Open/Shorted to Ground/Power — Check circuit at Test Pin 4.

Perform CONTINUOUS MONITOR (WIGGLE) TEST on circuits one at a time in order to isolate fault. If fault is indicated, isolate and repair harness. Repeat QUICK TEST. If no fault is indicated, go to next step.

**5)** Turn key off and wait 10 seconds. Disconnect ECA 60-pin connector. Inspect connectors and terminals for damage. If connectors and terminals are damaged, repair as necessary and repeat QUICK TEST. If connectors and terminals are okay, fault cannot be duplicated at this time. IDM testing is complete. Connect ECA.

***IDM Circuits***

Breakout Box
Test Pins

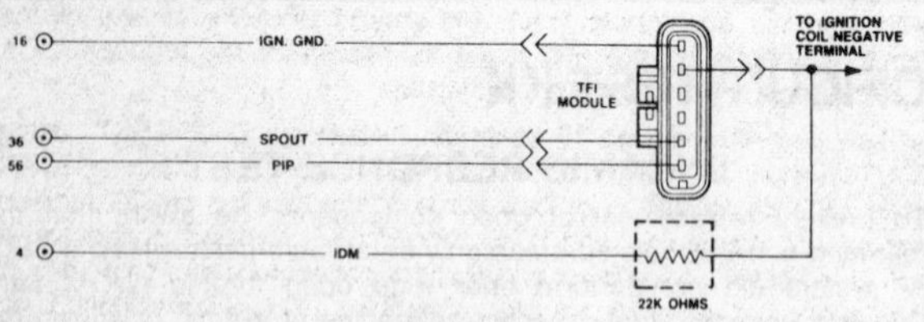
16
IGN. GND.
TO IGNITION COIL NEGATIVE TERMINAL
TFI MODULE
36
SPOUT
56
PIP
4
IDM
22K OHMS

## CIRCUIT TEST MM

### SPARK TIMING CHECK

To prevent replacement of good components, be aware that the following non-EEC related areas may be at fault: engine condition (valves, vacuum leaks, valve timing, EGR valve, etc.), PIP sensor, TFI ignition module.

**1)** Perform ENGINE RUNNING SELF-TEST and verify that SELF-TEST is activated. Check and record timing while in ENGINE RUNNING SELF-TEST. System locks timing then returns to normal 2 minutes after last service code is displayed. If timing is 27-33 degrees, spark timing is correct. Go to ENGINE RUNNING SELF-TEST. If timing is not 27-33 degrees, go to next step.

## CIRCUIT TEST MM (Cont.)

**2)** Locate Spark Output (SPOUT) connector and open the connection. Start engine and check for 10 degrees BTDC base timing ± 3 degrees. If base timing is correct, go to next step. If base timing is not correct, adjust base timing. After timing is adjusted, connect SPOUT and perform TIMING CHECK. See TIMING CHECK in QUICK TEST (ALL VEHICLES) section of this article.

**3)** Turn key off and wait 10 seconds. Disconnect ECA 60-pin connector. Inspect for and repair any damaged wiring. Install breakout box. Turn key on, leaving engine off. With DVOM on 20-volt scale, measure voltage between test pins No. 37 and 40, and between test pins No. 57 and 60. If either reading is less than 10.5 volts, go to CIRCUIT TEST B, step **1)**. If both readings are 10.5 volts or more, go to next step.

**4)** Turn key off and wait 10 seconds. Disconnect harness connector at TFI module. With DVOM on 200-ohm scale, measure resistance between test pin No. 36 and pin No. 2 (SPOUT circuit) at TFI harness connector. If reading is greater than 5 ohms, repair open circuit. Connect SPOUT connector and check timing as described in step **1)**. If reading is 5 ohms or less, go to next step.

**5)** Leave breakout box installed and TFI harness disconnected. Turn key off and set DVOM on 200-ohm scale. Measure resistance between test pin No. 16 and pin No. 6 (IGN GRND circuit) at TFI harness connector. If reading is less than 5 ohms, go to CIRCUIT TEST A, step **7)**. If reading is 5 ohms or more, repair harness as necessary and repeat QUICK TEST.

***Spark Advance Circuit***

Breakout Box
Test Pins

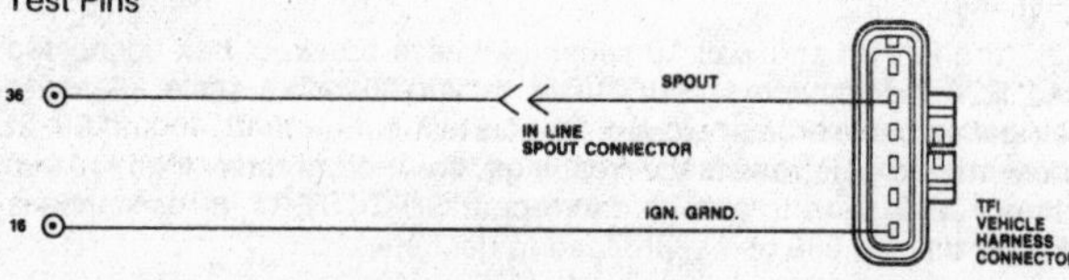
36
SPOUT
IN LINE SPOUT CONNECTOR
16
IGN. GRND.
TFI VEHICLE HARNESS CONNECTOR

## CIRCUIT TEST NN

### NO CODES/ CODES NOT LISTED

**1)** Turn key off and wait 10 seconds. Set DVOM on 20-volt scale. Disconnect Throttle Position Sensor (TPS). Turn key on, leaving engine off. Measure voltage between VREF circuit at TPS harness connector and signal return circuit in SELF-TEST connector. If reading is less than 4 volts or more than 6 volts, go to CIRCUIT TEST C, step **1)**. If reading is between 4 and 6 volts, connect TPS and go to next step.

**2)** Turn key off and wait 10 seconds. Disconnect ECA 60-pin connector. Inspect for and repair any damaged wiring. Install breakout box, leaving ECA disconnected. Set DVOM on 200-ohm scale. Measure resistance between test pin No. 48 and Self-Test Input (STI) at SELF-TEST connector pigtail. If reading is 5 ohms or more, repair open in circuit. If reading is less than 5 ohms, go to next step.

**3)** With breakout box installed and DVOM on 200 ohm scale, measure resistance between test pin No. 17 and Self-Test Output (STO) at SELF-TEST connector. If reading is 5 ohms or more, repair open in circuit. If reading is less than 5 ohms, go to next step.

**4)** Turn key off. With breakout box installed and DVOM on 200 ohm scale, measure resistance between test pin No. 29 and EGO sensor engine block ground. If reading is 5 ohms or more, repair EGO sensor ground wire or open circuit bad connection. If reading is less than 5 ohms, go to next step.

**5)** With breakout box installed and DVOM on 200 ohm scale, measure resistance between STO at SELF-TEST connector and engine block ground. If reading is more than 5 ohms, replace ECA and repeat QUICK TEST. If reading is less than 5 ohms, go to step **8)**.

**6)** Turn key off. Leave breakout box installed and ECA disconnected. Disconnect HEGO sensor and set DVOM on 200,000 ohm scale. Measure resistance between test pin No. 29 and test pins No. 37 and 57. If reading is less than 10,000 ohms, go to next step. If reading is not less than 10,000 ohms, repair harness short to power. Repeat QUICK TEST.

# 1988 COMPUTERIZED ENGINE CONTROLS
# Ford Motor Co. Merkur EEC-IV (Cont.)

## CIRCUIT TEST NN (Cont.)

**7)** Leave key off, DVOM on 200,000 ohm scale, and HEGO sensor disconnected. Measure resistance between RUN circuit and EGO circuit at HEGO connector. If reading is less than 10,000 ohms, replace HEGO and repeat QUICK TEST. If reading is not less than 10,000 ohms, go to next step.

**8)** Leave key off and breakout box installed. Set DVOM on 20-volt scale. Connect DVOM to test pin No. 30 and test pins No. 40 or 60. Perform ENGINE RUNNING SELF-TEST. If reading is greater than one volt, repair intermittent fault in NDS harness connector or switch. If okay, go to ENGINE RUNNING SELF-TEST for appropriate service codes. If reading is not greater than one volt, repair intermittent fault in NDS harness connector or switch. If okay, go to next step.

**9)** Leave key off and breakout box installed. Set DVOM on 20-volt scale. Connect DVOM to test pins No. 37 or 57 and test pins No. 40 or 60. Turn key on, then off. Wait 10 seconds. If reading does not changes from 10.5 volts (or higher) to zero volts, replace EEC power relay or Integral Relay Control Module (IRCM). Repeat QUICK TEST. If reading changes from 10.5 volts (or higher) to zero volts, go to next step.

**10)** If vehicle is not equipped with shift indicator light, repair Self-Test Output (STO) circuit for short to ground. Repeat QUICK TEST. If vehicle is equipped with shift indicator light, go to next step.

**11) Continuous Code 15 Displayed.** Clear continuous memory codes using procedure described in CONTINUOUS SELF-TEST. Repeat KEY ON/ENGINE OFF SELF-TEST through continuous memory code output. If continuous code 15 is not displayed, continuous code 15 testing is complete. If continuous code 15 is displayed, go to next step.

**NOTE: Continuous code 15 is displayed when power to Keep Alive Memory (KAM), test pin No. 1 at ECA is interrupted. Code 15 may also be displayed the first time SELF-TEST is performed and power is restored to ECA. Repeat SELF-TEST to ensure correct diagnosis.**

**12)** Ensure that EEC-IV components and wiring are not close to high tension secondary voltage wires or ignition components. If EEC-IV wiring is close to high tension wires, reroute EEC wiring and repeat QUICK TEST. If continuous code 15 is no longer displayed, continuous code 15 testing is complete. If continuous code 15 is still displayed, go to next step.

**13)** Turn key off and wait 10 seconds. Disconnect ECA 60-pin connector. Install breakout box, leaving ECA disconnected. Set DVOM on 20-volt scale. Connect DVOM positive test lead to test pin No. 1 and negative test lead to pins No. 40 or 60. Turn key on and observe voltage reading. If reading is less than 10 volts, repair open to KAM circuit. Repeat QUICK TEST. If reading is 10 volts or greater, replace ECA and repeat QUICK TEST.

**14)** Check or perform diagnosis of non-EEC related areas. Check all areas that may contribute to a particular condition in order of probability, ease of accomplishment, and accessibility. Use your technical knowledge and experience to determine which areas may be the source of problem before starting a more involved diagnosis. After correcting faults, go to next step.

**15)** Turn key off and wait 10 seconds. Install tachometer. Start engine and attempt to maintain engine at 2000 RPM for 2 minutes. If 2000 RPM can be maintained, go to CIRCUIT TEST A, step **13)**. If 2000 RPM cannot be maintained, go to next step.

**16)** With engine at operating temperature and tachometer installed, turn key off and wait 10 seconds. Perform ENGINE RUNNING SELF-TEST while maintaining engine at 2000 RPM. If code 11 (Pass) is displayed, go to ENGINE RUNNING SELF-TEST. If any other service code is displayed, go to ENGINE RUNNING SELF-TEST table and service code(s) as instructed. If no codes are displayed, go to step **1)**.

**17) Output State Check Not Functioning.** Turn key off and wait 10 seconds. Perform KEY ON/ENGINE OFF SELF-TEST and leave key on to enter OUTPUT STATE CHECK. If codes 23, 53, 63 or 68 are displayed, go to KEY ON/ENGINE OFF SELF-TEST table and service code(s) as instructed. If no codes are displayed, go to step **1)**. If code 11 (Pass) is displayed, go to next step.

**18)** Check throttle and linkage for sticking or binding. If throttle and linkage are okay, replace TPS and repeat QUICK TEST. If throttle and linkage are binding, repair as necessary and repeat QUICK TEST.

## CIRCUIT TEST NN (Cont.)

**19) Power To ECA Check.** Turn key off and wait 10 seconds. Disconnect ECA 60-pin connector. Inspect for and repair any damaged wiring. Install breakout box. Turn key on, leaving engine off. Set DVOM on 20-volt scale. Measure voltage between test pins No. 37 and 40, and between test pins No. 57 and 60. If either reading is less than 10.5 volts, go to CIRCUIT TEST UU, step **1)** for the 2.5L HSC/CFI and 3.0L EFI engine. If either reading is less than 10.5 volts, go to CIRCUIT TEST B, step **1)** for all others. If both readings are 10.5 volts or more, replace ECA and repeat QUICK TEST.

***No Codes/Codes Not Listed Circuits***

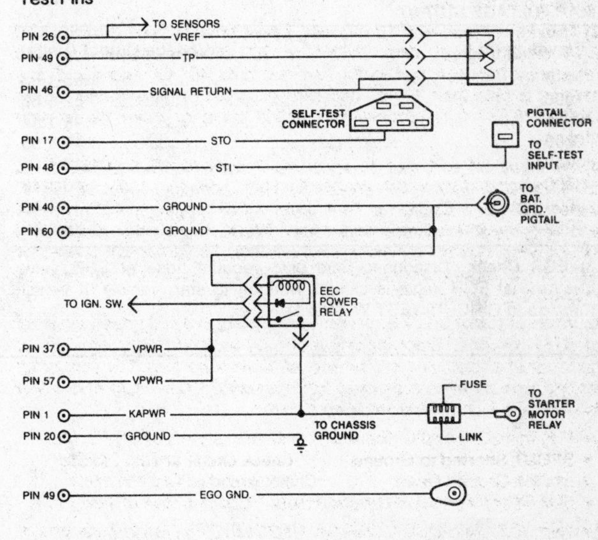
Breakout Box
Test Pins
TO SENSORS
PIN 26
VREF
PIN 49
TP
PIN 46
SIGNAL RETURN
SELF-TEST CONNECTOR
PIGTAIL CONNECTOR
PIN 17
STO
TO SELF-TEST INPUT
PIN 48
STI
PIN 40
GROUND
TO BAT. GRD. PIGTAIL
PIN 60
GROUND
TO IGN. SW.
EEC POWER RELAY
PIN 37
VPWR
PIN 57
VPWR
FUSE
TO STARTER MOTOR RELAY
PIN 1
KAPWR
PIN 20
GROUND
TO CHASSIS GROUND
LINK
PIN 49
EGO GND.

## CIRCUIT TEST OO

### ERRATIC IGNITION

**1) Code 14 Displayed.** This code indicates that 2 successive erratic Profile Ignition Pick-Up (PIP) pulses were sent to ECA, causing possible engine miss or stall. Check EEC-IV and TFI ignition system for loose wires and connections, arcing secondary ignition components (coil, cap, wires, etc.), or an on-board 2-way radio. Make sure radio antenna and power leads are routed properly. If any of the above conditions are present, repair as necessary and repeat QUICK TEST. If none are present, go to next step.

**2)** Turn key off and wait 10 seconds. Deactivate SELF-TEST. Using CONTINUOUS MONITOR (WIGGLE) TEST, observe VOM or STAR tester LED for indication of fault while lightly tapping on TFI ignition module and distributor, and while wiggling TFI harness connector. If fault is indicated, disconnect and inspect connectors and terminals. If connectors and terminals are okay, diagnose TFI ignition system. If no fault is indicated, go to next step.

**3)** While in CONTINUOUS MONITOR (WIGGLE) TEST, observe VOM or STAR tester LED for fault while wiggling, shaking, or bending small sections of harness from TFI module to firewall. Also check harness from firewall to ECA. Isolate PIP circuit, if required. If fault is indicated, isolate and repair problem and repeat QUICK TEST. If no fault indicated, go to next step.

**4)** Turn key off and wait 10 seconds. Disconnect ECA 60-pin connector. Inspect connectors and terminals for damage. If connectors and terminals are okay, fault cannot be duplicated at this time. Diagnose TFI ignition system. If connectors and terminals are damaged, repair as necessary and repeat QUICK TEST.

## CIRCUIT TEST SS

### SYSTEM CHECK

**1) ISC Check.** Attemp to start engine at part throttle. If engine runs only at part throttle, go to CIRCUIT TEST Z, step **3)**. If engine does not run, go to step **3)**.

**2) MAP Check.** Turn key off and disconnect MAP sensor. Connect MAP tester between harness and MAP sensor. Connect banana plugs of tester into DVOM and set DVOM on 20-volt scale. Turn key on and measure sensor output voltage while cranking engine. If DVOM reading does not decrease from specified range, go to CIRCUIT TEST H, step **13)**. If DVOM reading decreases from specified range, go to next step.

***MAP VOLTAGE OUTPUT***

| Elevation (Ft.) | Voltage Output (Volts) |
|---|---|
| 0 | 1.55-1.63 |
| 1000 | 1.52-1.60 |
| 2000 | 1.49-1.57 |
| 3000 | 1.46-1.54 |
| 4000 | 1.43-1.51 |
| 5000 | 1.40-1.48 |
| 6000 | 1.37-1.45 |
| 7000 | 1.35-1.43 |

**3) EGR Check.** Disconnect and plug vacuum hose at EGR valve. Ensure that EGR valve is closed. Attempt to start vehicle. If vehicle runs, go to CIRCUIT TEST W, step **1)**.

# 1988 COMPUTERIZED ENGINE CONTROLS
## Ford Motor Co. Merkur EEC-IV (Cont.)

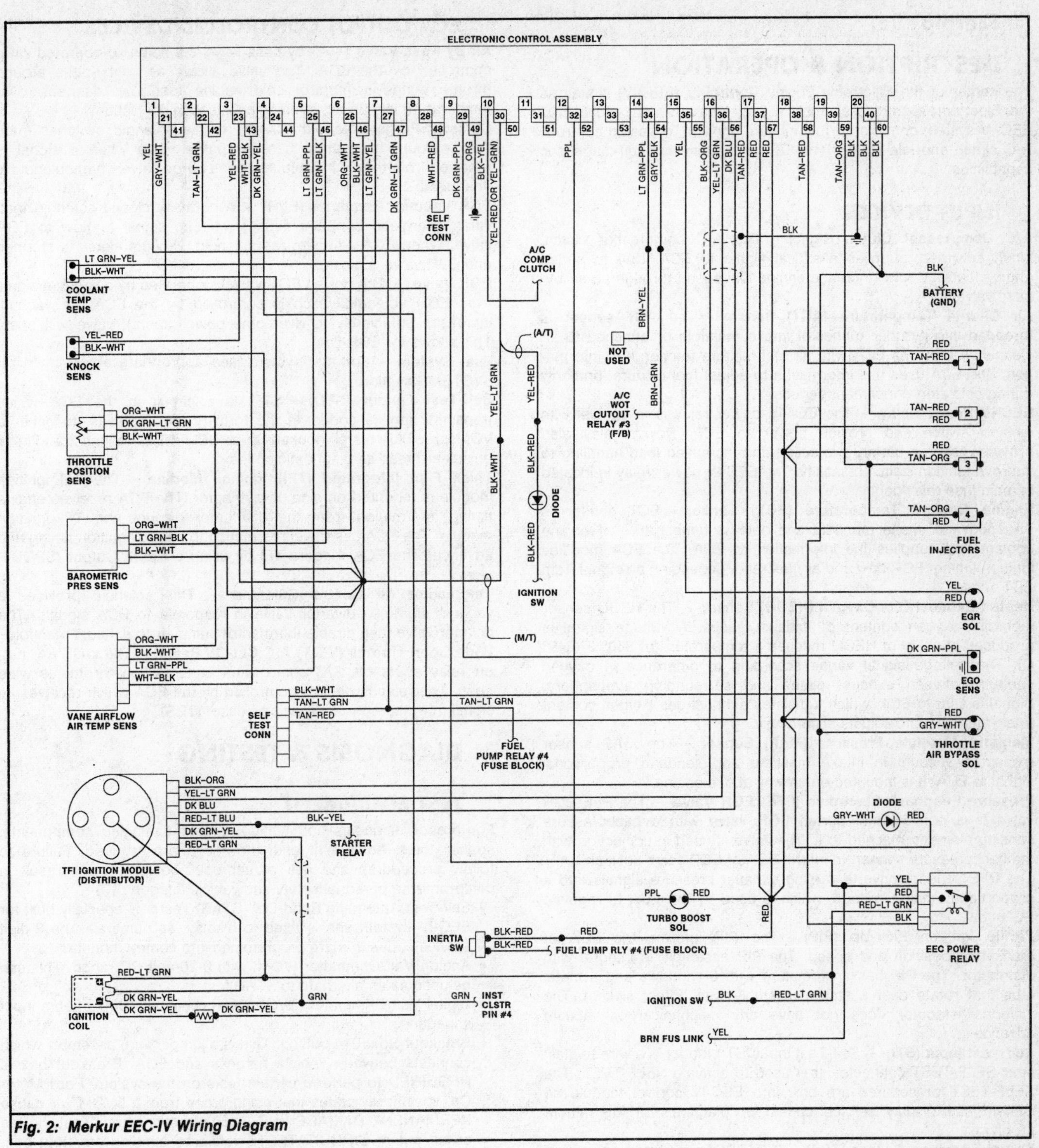

ELECTRONIC CONTROL ASSEMBLY
COOLANT TEMP SENS
KNOCK SENS
THROTTLE POSITION SENS
BAROMETRIC PRES SENS
VANE AIRFLOW AIR TEMP SENS
SELF TEST CONN
TFI IGNITION MODULE (DISTRIBUTOR)
IGNITION COIL
STARTER RELAY
INERTIA SW
FUEL PUMP RLY #4 (FUSE BLOCK)
INST CLSTR PIN #4
FUEL PUMP RELAY #4 (FUSE BLOCK)
A/C COMP CLUTCH
IGNITION SW
DIODE
NOT USED
A/C WOT CUTOUT RELAY #3 (F/B)
BATTERY (GND)
FUEL INJECTORS
EGR SOL
EGO SENS
THROTTLE AIR BYPASS SOL
TURBO BOOST SOL
EEC POWER RELAY
BRN FUS LINK


Fig. 2: Merkur EEC-IV Wiring Diagram

# 1988 COMPUTERIZED ENGINE CONTROLS
# Ford Motor Co. EEC-IV

### Scorpio

## DESCRIPTION & OPERATION

The center of the Electronic Engine Control-IV (EEC-IV) system is the Electronic Control Assembly (ECA), located under glove box. EEC-IV system controls air/fuel mixture, ignition, emission controls, A/C clutch and idle speed. The EEC-IV system has self-diagnostic capabilities.

### INPUT DEVICES

**A/C Compressor Clutch Signal** – The A/C compressor clutch, when activated, supplies electrical signal to ECA. Due to added engine load, ECA will increase engine idle speed through an air by-pass valve.

**Air Charge Temperature (ACT) Sensor** – The ACT sensor is threaded into cylinder runner of intake manifold or attached to air cleaner. It provides ECA with air/fuel mixture temperature information. The ECA uses this information to adjust fuel mixture, primarily during cold start enrichment periods.

**EEC-IV Power Relay** – The EEC-IV power relay is in parallel with ignition switch and provide power to ECA. Power relay also provides reverse battery protection and increased load handling to improve ignition switch reliability. The EEC-IV power relay is located in main fuse relay panel.

**Engine Coolant Temperature (ECT) Sensor** – ECT sensor is threaded into intake manifold and detects temperature of engine coolant and supplies the information to ECA. The ECA modifies ignition timing, EGR flow and air/fuel ratio, depending on signal from ECT sensor.

**Heated Exhaust Gas Oxygen (HEGO) Sensor** – The HEGO sensor monitors oxygen content of exhaust gases. A voltage signal is produced after tip of HEGO reaches a temperature of 660° F (349° C). The voltage signal varies according to difference in oxygen content between exhaust gases and surrounding atmosphere. Signal is sent to ECA, which translates exhaust gas oxygen content to air/fuel ratio and adjusts accordingly.

**Manifold Absolute Pressure (MAP) Sensor** – The MAP sensor measures vacuum in intake manifold and sends a proportional signal to ECA. It is mounted on firewall above engine.

**Pressure Feedback Electronic (PFE) EGR Valve** – The PFE EGR valve is a conventional ported EGR valve with a backpressure sensing element attached to it. The valve is used in conjuction with the backpressure sensor, to inform ECA of EGR valve position.
The PFE sensor converts varying exhaust pressure signals into a proportional analog voltage, which is used by the ECA to regulate EGR flow.

**Profile Ignition Pick-Up (PIP)** – The PIP informs the ECA of crankshaft position and speed. The PIP assembly is integral with distributor. The PIP has an armature with 6 windows and 6 metal tabs that rotate past a stator assembly (Hall Effect switch). The ignition distributor does not have any mechanical or vacuum advance.

**Self-Test Input (STI)** – Self-Test Input (STI) trigger is a wire (pigtail) near SELF-TEST connector. It is used to activate SELF-TEST. The SELF-TEST procedures are built into EEC-IV control module so system can display service codes for diagnosis of intermittent problems.

**Throttle Position Sensor (TPS)** – The TPS is mounted on rear of throttle body and below idle speed actuator. Sensor supplies ECA with a signal in accordance with throttle plate opening. These signals keep ECA informed of wide open throttle, closed throttle, or normal cruise conditions.

**Vehicle Speed Sensor (VSS)** – The VSS is a 12-volt Hall Effect sensor that provides ECA with a signal proportional to vehicle speed. The signal is used by ECA to enhance idle speed control and provide an input for lean cruise operation. The VSS also provides the fuel computer, speedometer, speed control module and transmission kickdown relay with a vehicle speed signal. The VSS is mounted on the transmission.

### ECA OUTPUT CONTROLLED DEVICES

**Air By-Pass Valve** – Air by-pass valve is a solenoid-operated valve controlled by the ECA. The valve allows air to by-pass around throttle plates to control cold engine fast idle, dashpot, over temperature idle boost, and engine idle load correction.

**Canister Purge Solenoid (CANP)** – This solenoid switches manifold vacuum to operate canister purge valve when a signal is received from the ECA. Vacuum opens purge valve when solenoid is energized.

**EGR Vacuum Regulator (EVR)** – A normally closed solenoid that, when energized by ECA, causes vacuum signal to flow to EGR valve. When ECA de-energizes solenoid, vacuum signal is stopped and EGR valve is closed.

**EGR Valve** – The ported EGR valve is operated by a vacuum signal from EGR solenoid which is controlled by the ECA. As vacuum increases sufficiently to overcome power spring, valve will open. This allows for EGR flow.

**Fuel System** – For fuel system, see appropriate article in FUEL SYSTEMS section.

**Self-Test Output (STO)** – STO is a circuit in the ECA which transmits service codes, in the form of timed pulses, to either a VOM or STAR tester hooked-up at SELF-TEST connector. These pulses are read as diagnostic codes.

**Thick Film Integrated (TFI) Ignition Module** – The TFI ignition module is mounted on side of distributor. The ECA receives engine timing information from the distributor through the TFI ignition module. The ECA uses this information to control ignition timing and advance. The ECA triggers TFI by using a Spark Output (SPOUT) signal.

**Thermactor Air Control Solenoid** – This solenoid provides a vacuum signal to diverter valve in response to ECA signals. The diverter valve then directs thermactor pump air to exhaust manifold.

**Wide Open Throttle (WOT) A/C Cut-Off Relay** – The WOT A/C cut-off relay shuts off A/C compressor clutch when throttle is wide open. The relay is directly controlled by the ECA which receives its signal from the Throttle Position Sensor (TPS).

## DIAGNOSIS & TESTING

### TEST EQUIPMENT

For proper diagnosis and testing without damaging components, special tools, equipment and knowledge are required. Failure to follow procedures and use of improper equipment will result in compromising personal safety and vehicle integrity.

- Self-Test Automatic Read-Out (STAR) Tester is specially built for EEC-IV system and is used to display, as numerals, the 2-digit service codes that are programmed into control module.
- Analog Volt/Ohmmeter (VOM) with 0-20 volt DC range. This can be used as an alternate to STAR tester.
- Digital Volt/Ohmmeter (DVOM) with minimum 10-megaohm input impedance.
- Breakout Box (014-00322). This is a jumper wire assembly which connects between vehicle harness and ECA. Breakout box is REQUIRED to perform certain tests on the system. Ford Motor Co. specifically states that using probe from a DVOM will cause PERMANENT DAMAGE to ECA 60-pin connector. "Test Pin" as called out in CIRCUIT TESTS refers to pins on breakout box. Once breakout box has been installed during a test sequence, it may be left connected for remainder of test.
- Vacuum gauge with 0-30 in. Hg range, and capable of measuring vacuum in 1 in. Hg increments.
- Tachometer with 0-6000 RPM range, accuracy ± 40 RPM, and capable of reading RPM in 20 RPM increments.
- Vacuum pump with 0-30 in. Hg range.
- Timing light.
- Spark tester. A modified spark plug with side electrode removed and alligator clip attached may be used.
- Fuel Injection Pressure Gauge (T80L-9974-A).

- Non-powered test lamp.
- Jumper wire, about 15" long.
- MAP/BP tester. Unit plugs into MAP/BP sensor circuit and DVOM to check input and output voltages to verify correct sensor operation.

## READING SELF-TEST CODES

Service codes are transmitted to Pin No. 4 (Self-Test Output) of SELF-TEST connector in the form of timed pulses. All service codes are 2 digit numbers which are generated one digit at a time. Codes are shown as voltage pulses (needle sweeps) on an analog volt/ohmmeter (VOM).

If a VOM is being used, careful attention to length of pauses is necessary in order to read codes correctly. There will be a 2 second pause between each DIGIT in a code. There will be a 4 second pause between each CODE. Continuous memory codes are separated from functional test service codes by a 6-second delay, a single 1/2 second sweep, and another 6-second delay.

If a Self-Test Automatic Read-Out (STAR) tester is used, it will count pulses and display them as a digital code. The STAR tester will add a zero (0) to single digit codes.

**Separator Pulse** – A single 1/2 second separator pulse is issued 6-9 seconds after last functional KEY ON ENGINE OFF (KOEO) SELF-TEST code. Then 6-9 seconds after the single 1/2 second separator pulse, the continuous memory codes will be displayed. The EEC-IV system must not have any stored codes other than "Pass (code 11)", in order to proceed to trouble shoot continuous memory codes.

**Continuous Memory Codes** – These codes are issued as a result of information stored during CONTINUOUS MONITOR (WIGGLE) TEST. These codes are displayed only during KOEO SELF-TEST and after separator code. These codes should be used to diagnose ONLY when KOEO and KEY ON ENGINE RUNNING (KOER) SELF-TESTS result in Code 11 and all QUICK TEST steps have been successfully completed.

## SELF-TEST CONNECTOR LOCATION

The SELF-TEST connector should be found near right front shock tower. *See Fig. 1.*

## DIAGNOSTIC PROCEDURE

The diagnostic procedure is used to test and service the EEC-IV system. It is divided into 2 test formats: QUICK TEST, a functional system test that produces fault codes, and PIN POINT TESTS, a number of tests in areas indicated by fault codes. To test and service EEC-IV system, perform QUICK TEST first.

QUICK TEST consists of 3 phases, KEY ON ENGINE OFF (KOEO), KEY ON ENGINE RUNNING (KOER), and CONTINUOUS TESTING. Perform QUICK TEST before running any pin point tests. If QUICK TEST fails, perform only those pin point tests specified by the failed step. After all tests and services have been completed, repeat entire QUICK TEST.

***NOTE: Failure to follow steps in sequence or to perform each step completely can cause misdiagnosis and/or component failure or unnecessary replacement of non-faulty components.***

**Preparation** – Correct test results for system are dependent on correct operation of several related non-EEC-IV components and systems. All non-EEC-IV problems should be corrected before attempting to diagnose EEC-IV system.

Before hooking up any equipment to diagnose EEC-IV system, make following checks:

- Verify condition of air cleaner and air ducting.
- Check all vacuum hoses for leaks, restrictions, and proper routing.
- Check the EEC-IV system wiring harness and electrical connections for corrosion, loose or detached connectors, loose wires, terminals and proper routing.
- Check the ECA, sensors and actuators for physical damage.
- Perform all necessary safety precautions to prevent personal injury or vehicle damage.
- Set parking brake and place shift lever in "P" for automatic transmission and Neutral for manual transmission. Do not move shift lever during testing unless specifically directed to do so.
- Turn off all lights and accessories. Ensure that vehicle doors are closed when making readings.
- Check and correct coolant level.

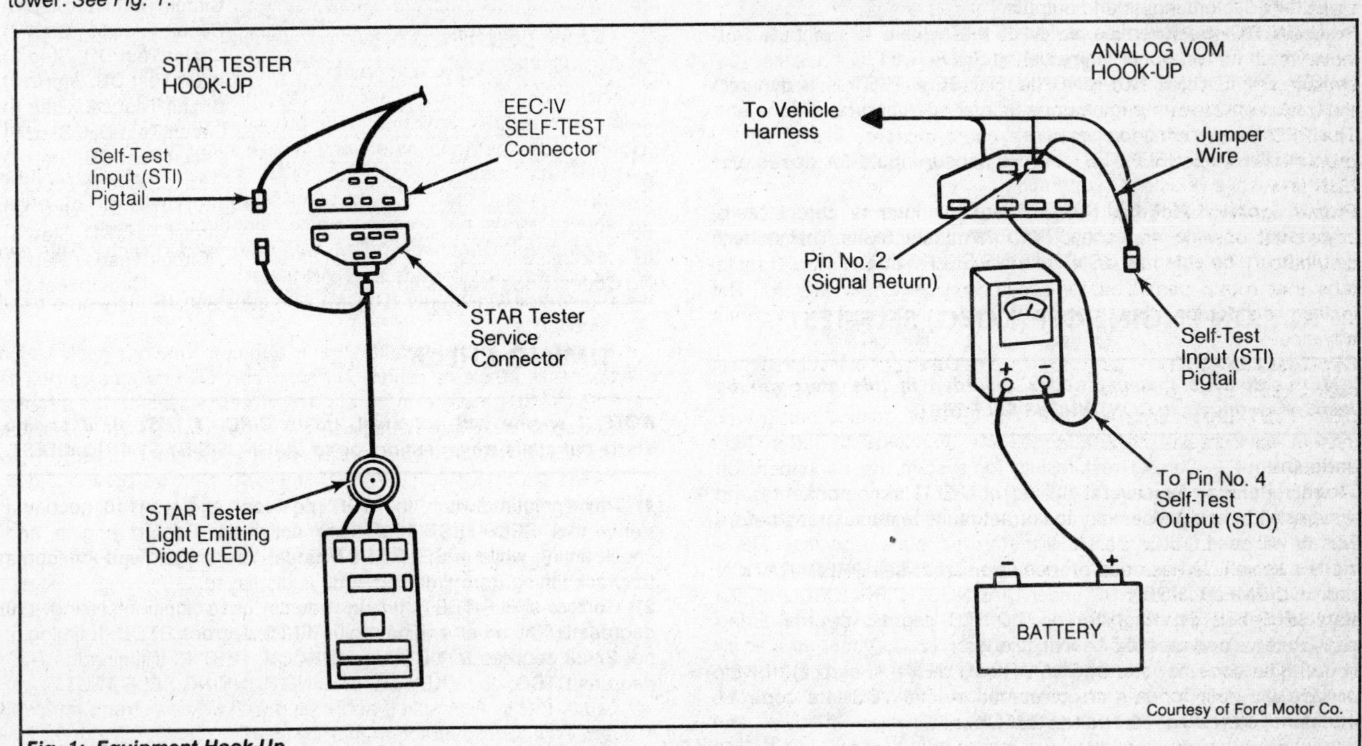
STAR TESTER
HOOK-UP
Self-Test
Input (STI)
Pigtail
EEC-IV
SELF-TEST
Connector
STAR Tester
Service
Connector
STAR Tester
Light Emitting
Diode (LED)
ANALOG VOM
HOOK-UP
To Vehicle
Harness
Jumper
Wire
Pin No. 2
(Signal Return)
Self-Test
Input (STI)
Pigtail
To Pin No. 4
Self-Test
Output (STO)
BATTERY
Courtesy of Ford Motor Co.

*Fig. 1: Equipment Hook-Up*

- Start engine and idle until upper radiator hose is hot, pressurized and throttle is off fast idle. Check for leaks around exhaust manifold, exhaust gas oxygen sensor and vacuum hose connections.
- If equipped, place octane switch in premium position.
- Turn ignition switch to "OFF" position. Service items as required, then go to EQUIPMENT HOOK-UP.

If engine will not start, starts but stalls, idles rough or runs rough, see KOEO SELF-TEST in this article. If any of the above conditions are still present after a code 11 in KOEO SELF-TEST, see CIRCUIT TEST A in this article. If engine stalls or runs rough, see DIAGNOSIS BY SYMPTOM TEST in this article.

### EQUIPMENT HOOK-UP

**Analog VOM – 1)** Turn ignition switch to "OFF" position. Connect jumper wire from Self-Test Input (STI) pigtail to pin No. 2 (Signal Return) on SELF-TEST connector. Set VOM at 0-15 volt DC range and connect positive lead of VOM to positive battery terminal.
**2)** Connect negative VOM lead to pin No. 4 (STO) on SELF-TEST connector. *See Fig. 1.* Connect timing light, then go to KOEO SELF-TEST.

**STAR Tester** – Turn ignition switch to "OFF" position. Connect color coded adapter cable leads to STAR tester. *See Fig. 1.* Connect adapter cable's service connectors to vehicle's SELF-TEST connectors. Connect timing light and proceed to KOEO SELF-TEST in this article.

## QUICK TEST

The QUICK TEST diagnostic procedure is a functional test of EEC-IV system, consisting of basic test steps. These basic steps must be carefully followed in sequence, otherwise a misdiagnosis, or replacement of non-faulty components may result.

- VISUAL CHECK AND PREPARATION is checking for obvious faults and defects and preparing vehicle for testing.
- EQUIPMENT HOOK-UP ensures proper equipment is used and is properly operating prior to testing.
- KEY ON ENGINE OFF (KOEO) SELF-TEST is a static check of EEC-IV system inputs and outputs.
- TIMING CHECK verifies ability of the system to compute and maintain a fixed spark timing during SELF-TEST.
- KEY ON ENGINE RUNNING (KOER) SELF-TEST is a dynamic system check with engine under actual operating conditions and at normal operating temperature.
- CONTINUOUS SELF-TEST checks sensor inputs for opens and shorts while vehicle is in operation.
- KOEO and KOER SELF-TESTS are intended to detect faults present at time of testing, not intermittent faults. Intermittent faults are detected by CONTINUOUS SELF-TEST.

### KEY ON ENGINE OFF (KOEO) SELF-TEST

***NOTE:** Continuous memory codes recorded in this step will be used for diagnosis in CONTINUOUS SELF-TEST.*

**Code Output** – Correct test results for system are dependent on correct operation of several related non-EEC-IV components and systems. It may be necessary to correct faults in these areas before EEC-IV will pass QUICK TEST.
Verify that vehicle has been properly prepared. See PREPARATION and EQUIPMENT HOOK-UP under DIAGNOSTIC PROCEDURE. To start SELF-TEST, turn ignition on. DO NOT depress throttle during test. Observe and record all service codes.
**1)** If engine does not start, go to CIRCUIT TEST A, step **2)**. If KEY ON ENGINE OFF code and continuous memory indicate code 11 (codes not stored), go to TIMING CHECK.
**2)** If any KOEO code is displayed with continuous memory code 11, KOEO SELF-TEST indicates a fault. Record codes and see TEST RESULTS & ACTION TO TAKE in this article.
**3)** If any KOEO codes or any continuous memory codes are displayed, this indicates a fault. Record codes, but DO NOT repair continuous memory codes at this time. KOEO and KOER SELF-TEST codes MUST be repaired first. See TEST RESULTS & ACTION TO TAKE in this article.
**4)** If KOEO code 11 (pass), is displayed with ANY continuous memory code (except code 15), continuous memory indicates a fault. Record codes, but DO NOT repair continuous memory codes at this time. The KOEO and KOER SELF-TEST codes MUST be repaired first. Go to TIMING CHECK.
**5)** If KOEO code 11 (pass), is displayed and continuous memory code 15 is displayed, go to CIRCUIT TEST Q2. If NO CODES are displayed, repeat SELF-TEST and verify that no service codes are present. If no service codes present, go to CIRCUIT TEST Q1.

**Test Results & Action To Take – 1)** Perform test indicated as in KOEO SELF-TEST table in this article. Start with first code displayed. If the test refers you to other checks, perform them as instructed.
**2)** When more than one code is displayed, repair problems in order codes are displayed. Whenever a repair is made, repeat QUICK TEST. If no codes appear, repeat SELF-TEST. If no service codes are present, go to CIRCUIT TEST Q1.

***KEY ON ENGINE OFF (KOEO) SELF-TEST***

| Service Codes | Test |
|---|---|
| 11 | Pass Code |
| 15 | Circuit Test Q2 |
| 19 | Circuit Test Q4 |
| 21 | Circuit Test DE |
| 22 | Circuit Test DF |
| 23 | Circuit Test DH |
| 24 | Circuit Test DB |
| 31 | Circuit Test DL |
| 34 | Circuit Test DL, Step **8)** |
| 35 | Circuit Test DL, Step **5)** |
| 51 | Circuit Test DE, Step **4)** |
| 53 | Circuit Test DH, Step **3)** |
| 54 | Circuit Test DB, Step **10)** |
| 61 | Circuit Test DE, Step **6)** |
| 63 | Circuit Test DH, Step **6)** |
| 64 | Circuit Test DB, Step **7)** |
| 67 | Circuit Test FA |
| 84 | Circuit Test DL, Step **11)** |
| 85 | Circuit Test KD, Step **4)** |
| 87 | Circuit Test J, Step **6)** |
| No Codes/Code Not Listed | Circuit Test Q1 |

### TIMING CHECK

***NOTE:** If engine will not start, go to CIRCUIT TEST A. If engine starts but stalls while testing, go to DIAGNOSIS BY SYMPTOM TEST.*

**1)** Turn ignition switch to "OFF" position, and wait 10 seconds. Verify that SELF-TEST has been activated. Restart engine and check timing while in SELF-TEST mode. You are allowed 2 minutes to check timing from time last code is displayed.
**2)** Correct SELF-TEST timing equals base ignition timing (10 degrees BTDC on all engines) plus 17-23 degrees BTDC. If timing is not 27-33 degrees BTDC, go to CIRCUIT TEST P. If timing is 27-33 degrees BTDC, go to KEY ON ENGINE RUNNING SELF-TEST.

## KEY ON ENGINE RUNNING (KOER) SELF-TEST

***NOTE: If engine will not start, go to CIRCUIT TEST A. If engine starts but stalls while testing, go to DIAGNOSIS BY SYMPTOM TEST.***

**Code Output – 1)** Deactivate SELF-TEST (disconnect jumper wire). Start engine and run it at 2000 RPM for 2 minutes to warm up EGO sensor. Turn engine off and wait 10 seconds. Insert jumper to activate SELF-TEST. DO NOT depress throttle during test unless a Dynamic Response code occurs.
**2)** Start engine. The engine ID code will be displayed. Run test. If Dynamic Response code one (10 with STAR tester) occurs, briefly accelerate engine to wide open throttle. The KOER SELF-TEST service codes will then be displayed. Observe and record all codes.
**Test Results & Action To Take – 1)** If no codes appear, repeat SELF-TEST and verify that no service codes are present, and then go to CIRCUIT TEST Q1.
**2)** If engine ID code is 3 ( 30 with STAR tester), and code 11 is displayed, KOER SELF-TEST portion is okay. If symptom was of an intermittent nature, go to CONTINUOUS SELF-TEST. If symptom is present, go to DIAGNOSIS BY SYMPTOM TEST. Otherwise QUICK TEST is complete, and EEC-IV system is okay.
**3)** If engine ID code is 3 ( 30 with STAR tester), and any code other than 11 appears, KOER SELF-TEST portion is at fault. Perform test indicated in KOER SELF-TEST table.
**4)** When more than one code is displayed, repair problems in the order that codes are displayed. Whenever a repair is made, repeat QUICK TEST.

*KEY ON ENGINE RUNNING (KOER) SELF-TEST*

| Service Codes | Test |
|---|---|
| 12 | Circuit Test KE |
| 13 | Circuit Test KE, Step **10)** |
| 16 | Circuit Test KE |
| 21 | Circuit Test DE |
| 22 | Circuit Test DF, Step **7)** |
| 23 | Circuit Test DH |
| 24 | Circuit Test DB |
| 31 | Circuit Test DL, Step **16)** |
| 32 | Circuit Test DL, Step **15)** |
| 33 | Circuit Test DL, Step **20)** |
| 34 | Circuit Test DL, Step **19)** |
| 35 | Circuit Test DL, Step **19)** |
| 41 | Circuit Test HG, Step **10)** |
| 42 | Circuit Test HG, Step **8)** |
| 72 | Circuit Test DF, Step **9)** |
| 73 | Circuit Test DH, Step **10)** |
| 77 | Circuit Test M |
| 99 | [1] |
| No Codes/Codes Not Listed | Circuit Test Q1 |

[1] – Idle Speed Control (ISC) has not "learned" yet. Repeat QUICK TEST.

## CONTINUOUS SELF-TEST

***NOTE: CONTINUOUS SELF-TEST has 4 steps: CONTINUOUS MEMORY CODES, CLEARING CONTINUOUS MEMORY CODES, CONTINUOUS MEMORY CODES TO BE TESTED, and TEST RESULTS & ACTION TO TAKE. Perform steps in sequence.***

**Continuous Memory Codes – 1)** To ensure proper diagnosis of continuous memory codes, PREPARATION, EQUIPMENT HOOK-UP, KOEO SELF-TEST, TIMING CHECK, and KOER SELF-TEST must be successfully completed. If both KOEO and KOER SELF-TEST display code 11 (Pass), go to CLEARING CONTINUOUS MEMORY CODES.
**2)** If code 11 is not present, return to PREPARATION step and make necessary repairs indicated in KOEO and KOER SELF-TEST before going to CLEARING CONTINUOUS MEMORY CODES.

**Clearing Continuous Memory Codes – 1)** Perform KOEO SELF-TEST. When first service code appears, exit SELF-TEST program by disconnecting STAR tester or by removing jumper wire from Self-Test Input (STI) pigtail. Exiting QUICK TEST in this manner will clear all codes stored in continuous memory.
**2)** Repeat KOEO SELF-TEST. If code output is 11-10-11, go to CONTINUOUS MEMORY CODES TO BE TESTED. If code output is not correct, check Self-Test Input (STI) circuit for short to ground. Repair short and repeat CLEARING CONTINUOUS MEMORY CODES step.

**Continuous Memory Codes To Be Tested –** Check list of continuous memory codes that were recorded in KOEO and KOER SELF-TESTS. Disregard any codes that have already been repaired. To confirm remaining codes, go to TEST RESULTS & ACTION TO TAKE.

**Test Results & Action To Take – 1)** Ensure that all previous QUICK TEST steps have been successfully completed. Verify proper test equipment hook-up. See EQUIPMENT HOOK-UP in this article. Make sure that SELF-TEST is deactivated. DO NOT activate SELF-TEST unless specifically instructed to do so.
**2)** Using service codes obtained in CONTINUOUS MEMORY CODES TO BE TESTED, perform test(s) indicated in CONTINUOUS SELF-TEST table. While performing CIRCUIT TESTS, one or both of CONTINUOUS MONITOR (WIGGLE) TESTS may have to be used to find intermittent fault.

## CONTINUOUS MONITOR (WIGGLE) TEST

The Self-Test Output (STO) will be activated each time a fault is detected. If STO is activated long enough during wiggle tests a service code will be stored. A fault is indicated by a deflection of 10.5 volts or greater on VOM. STAR tester LED turns off.

- **KEY ON ENGINE OFF (KOEO) Test (Automatic Transmissions Only)**: With SELF-TEST deactivated, turn ignition on to enter into wiggle mode.
- **KEY ON ENGINE RUNNING (KOER) Test**: Activate SELF-TEST and perform KOER SELF-TEST. After service code output has finished, do not turn engine off or deactivate SELF-TEST. About 2 minutes after code 11 has been displayed, wiggle mode will start. The system will remain in wiggle mode until SELF-TEST is deactivated or engine is turned off.

**1)** Observe VOM while moving, wiggling, and tapping system harness (in short sections), connectors and sensors. If an intermittent condition is created, monitor will indicate this by storing a service code. Carefully inspect harness and associated connectors of affected circuits.
**2)** If an intermittent condition is not created, carefully disconnect suspected sensor from harness. Remove terminals from connector and visually inspect terminals at both ends for corrosion, bad crimps, improperly seated terminals, etc.
**3)** Reconnect harness after inspection. Disconnect ECA from harness as carefully as possible. Remove and inspect terminals associated with sensor being checked.
**4)** If an intermittent condition cannot be created, reconnect connector and erase CONTINUOUS SELF-TEST service codes. To erase service codes, activate KOEO SELF-TEST.
**5)** Remove jumper from Self-Test Input terminal as soon as first service code appears. Repeat SELF-TEST with jumper to verify that service codes have been erased. QUICK TEST is complete.

*CONTINUOUS SELF-TEST*

| Continuous Memory | Test |
|---|---|
| 14 | Circuit Test Y |
| 15 | Circuit Test Q2 |
| 22 | Circuit Test DF, Step **14)** |
| 31 | Circuit Test DL, Step **24)** |
| 32 | Circuit Test DL, Step **28)** |
| 34 | Circuit Test DL, Step **27)** |
| 35 | Circuit Test DL, Step **24)** |
| 51 | Circuit Test DE, Step **10)** |
| 53 | Circuit Test DH, Step **11)** |
| 54 | Circuit Test DB, Step **10)** |
| 61 | Circuit Test DE, Step **6)** |
| 63 | Circuit Test DH, Step **15)** |
| 64 | Circuit Test DB, Step **10)** |
| No Codes/Codes Not Listed | Circuit Test Q1 |

## QUICK TEST DIAGNOSTIC AIDS

**Dynamic Response Check** – The Dynamic Response Check verifies movement of TPS and MAP sensors during Wide Open Throttle (WOT) as part of KOER SELF-TEST. The signal to perform WOT is a single pulse when using a VOM, or code 10 on STAR tester. Briefly accelerate engine to WOT for one second.

**Output State Check** – The Output State Check is used as an aid in servicing output actuators associated with EEC-IV system. It allows you to energize and de-energize Self Test Output, WOT Cutout Relay, Electronic Vacuum Regulator and Canister Purge Solenoid. This mode is entered after all codes have been received from KOEO and CONTINUOUS SELF-TEST. At this time, leave SELF-TEST activated and depress throttle. Each time throttle is depressed, output actuators will change state (go from on to off, or off to on).

## DIAGNOSIS BY SYMPTOM TEST

**1)** When engine stalls, runs rough or misses, perform following checks or tests:

- CIRCUIT TEST S.
- Check MAP sensor, using CIRCUIT TEST DF, step **11)**.
- Check EGR operation.
- Check fuel delivery.
- Check for, and repair, any bad ground or power connections.
- Check ignition components (cap, rotor, wires, coil and plugs).
- Check basic engine components (valves, cam timing, compression, etc.).

**2)** If gasoline fumes accumulate in engine compartment, go to CIRCUIT TEST KD.

**3)** If fuel pump always runs, go to CIRCUIT TEST J, step **11)**.

**4)** If engine stumbles after hot restart, go to CIRCUIT TEST HG, step **15)**.

**5)** If no A/C operation, go to CIRCUIT TEST X.

**6)** If no A/C cutout at WOT, go to CIRCUIT TEST X, step **3)**.

**7)** If no thermactor air management (manual only), go to CIRCUIT TEST Z.

**8)** If CHECK ENGINE light is glowing, preform QUICK TEST.

# CIRCUIT TESTS

## HOW TO USE CIRCUIT TESTS

**1)** DO NOT perform any CIRCUIT TEST unless specified by QUICK TEST. Ensure all non-EEC-IV related faults are corrected. Do not replace any part unless directed to do so. When more than one service code is received, start with first code displayed.

**2)** Do not measure voltage or resistance at ECA or connect any test lamp to ECA unless specified. All measurements are made by probing REAR of the connector. Isolate both ends of a circuit and turn key off whenever checking for shorts or continuity, unless specified.

**3)** Disconnect solenoids and switches from harness before measuring continuity, resistance, or applying 12 volts. Follow each test step in order until fault is found. After each repair, check all component connections and repeat CIRCUIT TEST(S).

**4)** An "open" is defined as any resistance reading higher than 5 ohms, unless otherwise specified. A "short" is defined as any resistance reading less than 10,000 ohms to ground, unless otherwise specified.

**5)** On CIRCUIT TEST Q, to prevent replacement of good components, be aware that non-EEC-IV related areas may also be at fault.

***NOTE: Fuel contaminated engine oil will affect some service codes. If this is suspected, remove PCV valve from valve cover and repeat QUICK TEST. If problem is corrected, change engine oil and filter.***

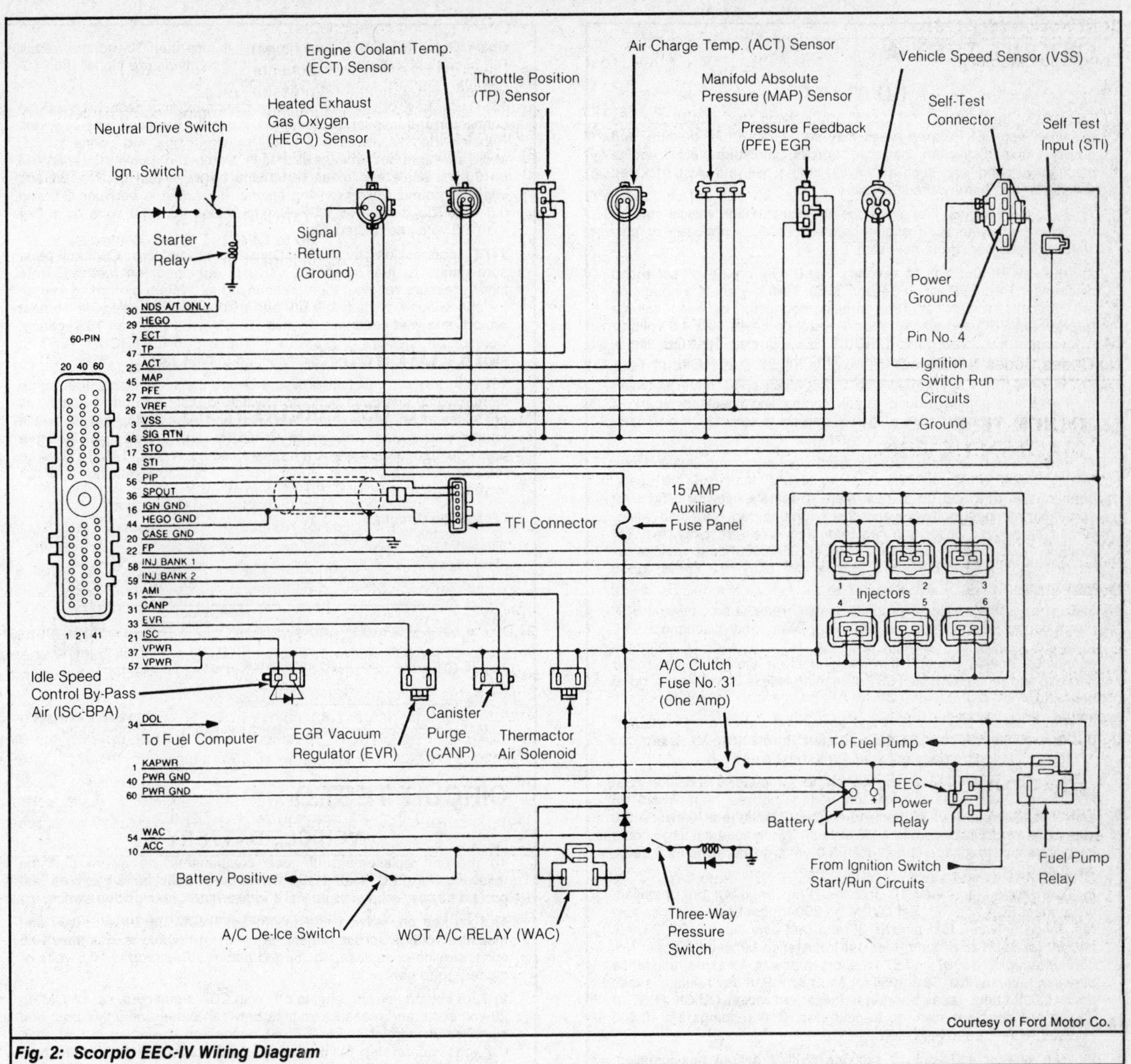
Engine Coolant Temp. (ECT) Sensor
Throttle Position (TP) Sensor
Heated Exhaust Gas Oxygen (HEGO) Sensor
Neutral Drive Switch
Ign. Switch
Starter Relay
Signal Return (Ground)
Air Charge Temp. (ACT) Sensor
Manifold Absolute Pressure (MAP) Sensor
Pressure Feedback (PFE) EGR
Vehicle Speed Sensor (VSS)
Self-Test Connector
Self Test Input (STI)
Power Ground
Pin No. 4
Ignition Switch Run Circuits
Ground
60-PIN
20 40 60
1 21 41
30 NDS A/T ONLY
29 HEGO
7 ECT
47 TP
25 ACT
45 MAP
27 PFE
26 VREF
3 VSS
46 SIG RTN
17 STO
48 STI
56 PIP
36 SPOUT
16 IGN GND
44 HEGO GND
20 CASE GND
22 FP
58 INJ BANK 1
59 INJ BANK 2
51 AMI
31 CANP
33 EVR
21 ISC
37 VPWR
57 VPWR
TFI Connector
15 AMP Auxiliary Fuse Panel
Injectors
1 2 3
4 5 6
Idle Speed Control By-Pass Air (ISC-BPA)
34 DOL
To Fuel Computer
EGR Vacuum Regulator (EVR)
Canister Purge (CANP)
Thermactor Air Solenoid
A/C Clutch Fuse No. 31 (One Amp)
To Fuel Pump
1 KAPWR
40 PWR GND
60 PWR GND
Battery
EEC Power Relay
54 WAC
10 ACC
Battery Positive
Fuel Pump Relay
From Ignition Switch Start/Run Circuits
A/C De-Ice Switch
WOT A/C RELAY (WAC)
Three-Way Pressure Switch
Courtesy of Ford Motor Co.

*Fig. 2: Scorpio EEC-IV Wiring Diagram*

## CIRCUIT TEST A

### NO START

To prevent replacement of good components, be aware that the following non-EEC related areas may be at fault: fuel quantity and quality, ignition system damage, cracks, moisture, etc., engine mechanical conditions such as valves, timing belt, etc. Also included are starter and battery circuit problems.

**1)** Try to start engine. If engine does not crank, check vehicle starting and charging systems. If engine cranks, but does not start or else stalls after starting, go to next step.

**2)** Turn key off and wait 10 seconds. Set DVOM on 20-volt scale and disconnect Throttle Position Sensor (TPS). Turn key on, leaving engine off. Measure voltage at TPS harness connector between voltage reference (VREF) and signal return. If reading is less than 4.0 volts or higher than 6.0 volts, go to CIRCUIT TEST C step **1)**. If reading is between 4.0 and 6.0 volts, reconnect TPS and go to next step.

**3)** Disconnect any spark plug wire and connect spark tester between plug wire and engine ground. Crank engine and check for spark. If spark exists, connect spark plug wire and go to step **13)**. If no spark, connect spark plug wire and go to next step.

**4)** Remove high tension coil wire from distributor and install spark tester. Check for spark while cranking engine. If there is no spark, connect coil wire and go to next step. If spark exists (with no start condition), connect coil wire and check ignition cap rotor and wires. Repair as needed. If ignition cap rotor and wires are okay, test TFI ignition module using Module Tester (1105-00002) and replace as needed. If TFI ignition module checks out okay, try known good ignition coil.

**5)** Turn key off and wait 10 seconds. Install breakout box, leaving ECA disconnected. Set DVOM on 200-ohm scale and disconnect TFI. Measure resistance between test pin No. 16 and TFI harness connector ignition ground. If reading is more than 5 ohms, repair harness and repeat QUICK TEST. If reading is less than 5 ohms, go to next step.

**6)** With breakout box installed and box timing switch on "Distributor" position, connect TFI and ECA. Try to start vehicle. If vehicle starts, go to step **10)**. If vehicle does not start, go to next step.

**7)** Move breakout box timing switch to "Computed" position. Set DVOM on 20-volt scale and measure voltage between test pin No. 36 and chassis ground while cranking engine. If voltage is between 3.0 and 6.0 volts, EEC system is NOT at fault. TFI ignition system should be diagnosed. If voltage is less than 3.0 volts or more than 6.0 volts, go to next step.

**8)** Turn key off and wait 10 seconds. With breakout box installed, disconnect ECA and TFI. Set DVOM on 200-k/ohm scale and measure resistance between test pin No. 36 and test pins No. 16, 20, 26, 40, and 60 for short to ground. Measure resistance between test pin No. 36 and test pins No. 37 and 57 for short to power. Measure resistance between test pins No. 36 and 56 for short to PIP. If any reading is less than 10,000 ohms, repair short in harness and repeat QUICK TEST. If engine still does not start, go to next step. If all readings are 10,000 ohms or higher, go to next step.

**9)** Turn key off and wait 10 seconds. With breakout box installed, connect ECA, but leave TFI disconnected. Set DVOM on 200 ohm scale. Measure resistance between test pin No. 36 and test pins No. 37 and 57 for short to power. Measure resistance between test pin No. 36 and test pins No. 40 and 60 for short to ground. If any reading is less than 5 ohms, replace ECA and repeat QUICK TEST. If all readings are 5 ohms or higher, connect TFI and go to next step.

**10)** With breakout box installed and DVOM on 20-volt scale, measure voltage between test pins No. 56 and 16, while cranking engine. If reading is between 3.0 and 6.0 volts, remove breakout box. Replace ECA and repeat QUICK TEST. If reading is less than 3.0 volts or higher than 6.0 volts, go to next step.

**11)** Install breakout box, turn key off and wait 10 seconds. Set DVOM on 200-ohm scale. Disconnect TFI and ECA. Measure resistance between test pin No. 56 and TFI connector PIP circuit. If reading is 5 ohms or more, repair open PIP circuit and repeat QUICK TEST. If readings is less than 5 ohms, go to next step.

**12)** With breakout box installed and ECA disconnected, turn key off. Disconnect TFI connector and set DVOM on 200-k/ohm scale. Measure resistance between test pin No. 56 and test pins No. 16, 20, 26, 40, and 60 for short to ground. Measure resistance between test pin No. 56 and test pins No. 37 and 57 for short to power. Measure resistance between test pin No. 56 and test pin No. 36 for short to Spark Output (SPOUT). If any reading is less than 10-k/ohms, repair PIP circuit and repeat QUICK TEST. If all readings are higher than 10-k/ohms, diagnose TFI ignition system.

**13)** Turn key off and wait 10 seconds. Disconnect ECA 60-pin connector and inspect for damaged, loose, or corroded pins or wires. Repair wiring as necessary. Install breakout box and connect ECA. Make sure that box timing switch is in "Computed" position. Set DVOM on 20-volt scale and measure voltage between test pin No. 36 and chassis ground while cranking engine. If reading is between 3.0 and 6.0 volts, go to next step. If reading is less than 3.0 volts or higher than 6.0 volts, go to step **10)**.

**14)** Disconnect all electrical connections at injectors. Connect pressure gauge to fuel diagnostic valve (if equipped) on fuel rail. Note initial pressure reading, then pressurize fuel system by turning key on for one second, turning key off, and then waiting 10 seconds. Repeat on, off, and wait sequence 5 times. Turn key off and wait 10 seconds. Connect all injectors. If pressure increased, go to CIRCUIT TEST S, step **2)**. If pressure did not increase, go to next step.

**15)** With key off and fuel pressure gauge installed, locate fuel pump inertia switch and push button on switch to reset it to on. If switch will not reset to on, replace inertia switch and repeat step **14)**. If switch button was already on, go to CIRCUIT TEST J, step **4)**. Observe pressure gauge as system is pressurized as in step **14)**. If pressure reading increases, repeat QUICK TEST. If pressure reading does not increase, go to CIRCUIT TEST J, step **4)**.

***TFI Module Circuits***

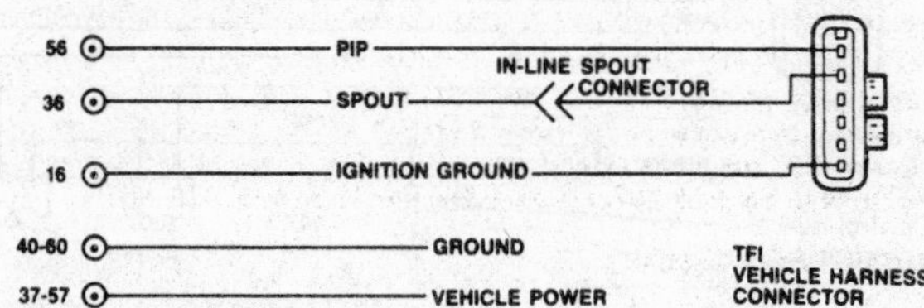
Breakout Box
Test Pins
56
PIP
IN-LINE SPOUT
CONNECTOR
36
SPOUT
16
IGNITION GROUND
40-60
GROUND
37-57
VEHICLE POWER
TFI
VEHICLE HARNESS
CONNECTOR

## CIRCUIT TEST B

### VEHICLE BATTERY

To prevent replacement of good components, be aware that the following non-EEC related areas may be at fault: battery cables and ground straps, voltage regulator and alternator, and ignition switch.

**1)** Turn key on, leaving engine off. Set DVOM on 20-volt scale and measure voltage across battery terminals. If reading is less than 10.5 volts, service or replace discharged battery. If reading is 10.5 volts or higher, go to next step.

**2)** Turn key on, leaving engine off. With ECA connected, set DVOM on 20-volt scale and measure voltage between battery negative post and signal return circuit in SELF-TEST connector. If reading is less than 0.5 volts, go to step **6)**. If reading is 0.5 volts or higher, go to next step.

**3)** With breakout box installed and ECA connected, turn key on, leaving engine off. Set DVOM on 20-volt scale. Measure voltage between battery negative post and test pins No. 40 and 60. If either reading is 0.5 volts or higher, repair ground circuit having a resistance higher than 0.5 volts and repeat QUICK TEST. If both readings are less than 0.5 volts, go to next step.

**4)** With breakout box installed and ECA connected, turn key off and wait 10 seconds. Set DVOM on 200-ohm scale. Measure resistance between test pin No. 46 and test pins No. 40 and 60. If either reading is 5 ohms or higher, disconnect ECA connector and inspect for corrosion or damage. Repair wiring and recheck resistance. If reading is still too high, replace ECA and repeat QUICK TEST. If both readings are less than 5 ohms, go to next step.

**5)** With breakout box installed and ECA connected, turn key off and wait 10 seconds. Set DVOM on 200-ohm scale. Measure resistance between test pin No. 46 and signal return circuit at SELF-TEST connector. If reading is less than 5 ohms, system is okay, repeat QUICK TEST. If reading is 5 ohms or higher, repair cause of excessive resistance in signal return circuit, then repeat QUICK TEST.

**6)** If reading in step **2)** was less than 0.5 volts, turn key on, leaving engine off. With ECA connected, set DVOM on 20-volt scale. Measure

### VEHICLE BATTERY (Cont.)

voltage between battery negative post and Keep Alive Power (KAPWR) circuit at EEC power relay. If reading is less than 10.5 volts, check KAPWR and Vehicle Power (V Power) circuits for shorts to ground. Also check KAPWR circuit from EEC power relay to battery positive post for open circuit. If reading is 10.5 volts or higher, go to next step.

**7)** Turn key on, leaving engine off. With ECA connected, set DVOM on 20-volt scale. Measure voltage between battery negative post and ignition circuit at EEC power relay. If readings is less than 10.5 volts, check for open ignition switch circuits. Repair wiring and repeat QUICK TEST. If reading is 10.5 volts or higher, go to next step.

**8)** Turn key on, leaving engine off. With ECA connected, set DVOM on 20-volt scale. Measure voltage between battery negative post and ground circuit at EEC power relay. If reading is 0.5 volts or higher, repair open circuit or short to ground in ground circuit and repeat QUICK TEST. If you entered this test for a code 78 and if reading is less than 0.5 volts, go to step **10)**. If you entered this test for any other code and if reading is less than 0.5 volts, go to next step.

**9)** Turn key on, leaving engine off. With ECA connected, set DVOM on 20-volt scale. Measure voltage between battery negative post and vehicle power circuit at EEC power relay. If reading is less than 10.5 volts, replace EEC power relay and repeat QUICK TEST. If reading is 10.5 volts or higher, repair short to ground or open in vehicle power circuit from EEC power relay to test pins No. 37 and 57. Repeat QUICK TEST.

**10)** Turn key on, leaving engine off. Connect VOM or STAR tester to SELF-TEST connector. With SELF-TEST deactivated, enter into CONTINUOUS MONITOR (WIGGLE) TEST. Observe VOM or STAR tester LED for indication of fault while bending and twisting harness from EEC power relay to ECA. If code 78 is displayed or if fault is indicated, isolate fault in vehicle power circuit, and repair as necessary. If code 78 is not displayed or if fault is not indicated, inspect EEC power relay and connectors for damaged pins, corrosion, etc. If okay, replace EEC power relay and repeat QUICK TEST.

***Battery Power Circuits***

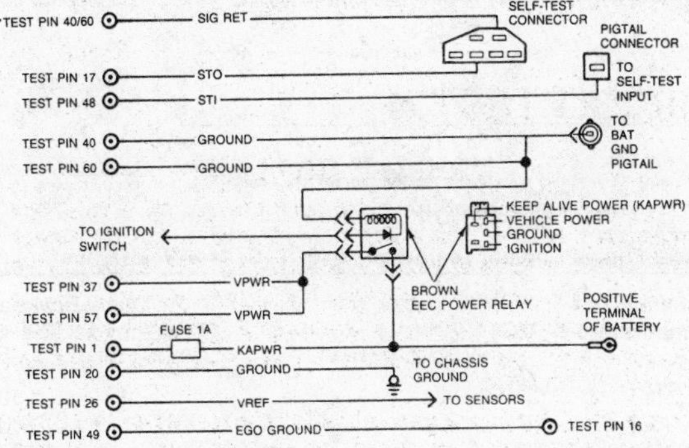

*TEST PIN 40/60
SIG RET
SELF-TEST CONNECTOR
PIGTAIL CONNECTOR
TEST PIN 17
STO
TEST PIN 48
STI
TO SELF-TEST INPUT
TEST PIN 40
GROUND
TO BAT GND PIGTAIL
TEST PIN 60
GROUND
KEEP ALIVE POWER (KAPWR)
VEHICLE POWER
GROUND
IGNITION
TO IGNITION SWITCH
TEST PIN 37
VPWR
TEST PIN 57
VPWR
BROWN EEC POWER RELAY
POSITIVE TERMINAL OF BATTERY
FUSE 1A
TEST PIN 1
KAPWR
TEST PIN 20
GROUND
TO CHASSIS GROUND
TEST PIN 26
VREF
TO SENSORS
TEST PIN 49
EGO GROUND
TEST PIN 16


## CIRCUIT TEST C

### REFERENCE VOLTAGE

**1)** Install breakout box, leaving ECA connected. Turn key on, leaving engine off. Set DVOM on 20-volt scale and measure voltage between test pin No. 37 and signal return in SELF-TEST connector. If reading is less than 10.5 volts, go to CIRCUIT TEST B, step **1)**. If reading is 10.5 volts or higher, go to next step.

**2)** With breakout box installed and ECA connected, turn key on, leaving engine off. Set DVOM on 20-volt scale and measure voltage between test pins No. 26 and 46. If reading is 6.0 volts or higher, go to step **4)**. If reading is 4.0 volts or lower, go to step **5)**. If reading is between 4.0 and 6.0 volts, go to next step.

**3)** With breakout box installed and ECA disconnected, turn key off. Set DVOM on 200-ohm scale. Measure resistance from test pins No. 26 and 46 to suspect VREF sensor harness connector. If all readings are less than 5 ohms, VREF circuit is okay. Connect sensors and repeat QUICK TEST. If any reading is 5 ohms or higher, repair open circuit in VREF or signal return and then repeat QUICK TEST.

**4)** Turn key off and wait 10 seconds. With breakout box installed and ECA disconnected, turn KOEO. Set DVOM on 20-volt scale and measure voltage between test pin No. 26 and battery ground. If reading is less than 0.5 volts, replace ECA and repeat QUICK TEST. If reading is 0.5 volts or higher, repair short to battery power in EEC harness. Repeat QUICK TEST. Replace ECA if fault still occurs.

**5) Shorted TPS.** Turn key off and wait for 10 seconds. With breakout box installed and ECA connected, disconnect Throttle Position Sensor (TPS) from vehicle harness. Turn key on, leaving engine off. Set DVOM on 20-volt scale and measure voltage between test pin No. 26 and 46. If reading is 4.0 volts or higher, replace TPS and repeat QUICK TEST. If less than 4.0 volts on models without EGR Valve Position (EVP) sensor, go to step **7)**. If reading is less than 4.0 volts on models with EVP sensor, go to next step.

**6) Shorted PFE Sensor.** Turn key off and wait 10 seconds. With breakout box installed and ECA connected, disconnect PFE sensor. Turn key on, leaving engine off. Set DVOM on 20-volt scale. Measure voltage between test pins No. 26 and 46. If reading is 4.0 volts or higher, replace PFE sensor and repeat QUICK TEST. If reading is less than 4.0 volts, go to next step.

**7) Shorted MAP Sensor.** Turn key off and wait 10 seconds. With breakout box installed and ECA connected, disconnect MAP sensor. Turn KOEO and set DVOM on 20-volt scale. Measure voltage between test pins No. 26 and 46. If reading is 4.0 volts or higher, replace MAP sensor and repeat QUICK TEST. If reading is less than 4.0 volts, go to next step.

**8)** With breakout box installed and ECA disconnected, turn key off and wait 10 seconds. Disconnect TPS, MAP, EVP, and PFE sensors. Set DVOM on 200-ohm scale. Measure resistance between test pin No. 26 and test pins No. 20, 40, 46, and 60. If reading is less than 5 ohms, repair short to ground, connect all sensors and repeat QUICK TEST. If original problem still occurs, replace ECA and repeat QUICK TEST. If reading is 5 ohms or higher, connect sensors, replace ECA and repeat QUICK TEST.

***Reference Voltage Circuits***

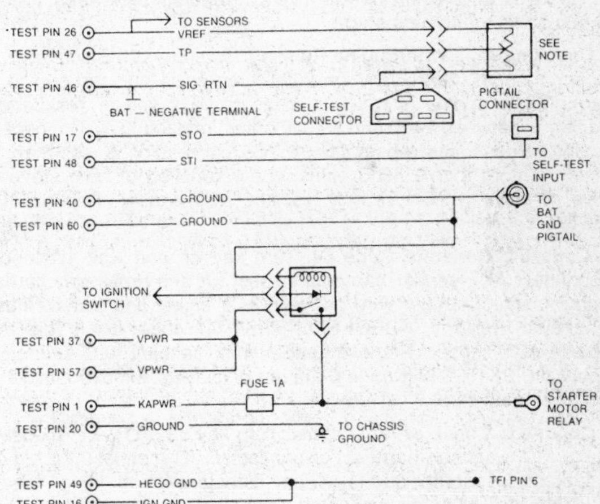

*TEST PIN 26
TO SENSORS
VREF
TEST PIN 47
TP
SEE NOTE
TEST PIN 46
SIG RTN
BAT — NEGATIVE TERMINAL
SELF-TEST CONNECTOR
PIGTAIL CONNECTOR
TEST PIN 17
STO
TEST PIN 48
STI
TO SELF-TEST INPUT
TEST PIN 40
GROUND
TEST PIN 60
GROUND
TO BAT GND PIGTAIL
TO IGNITION SWITCH
TEST PIN 37
VPWR
TEST PIN 57
VPWR
FUSE 1A
TEST PIN 1
KAPWR
TO STARTER MOTOR RELAY
TEST PIN 20
GROUND
TO CHASSIS GROUND
TEST PIN 49
HEGO GND
TFI PIN 6
TEST PIN 16
IGN GND


## CIRCUIT TEST DB

### AIR CHARGE TEMPERATURE (ACT) SENSOR

**NOTE: Perform this test when Service Code 24, 54, or 64 is displayed during QUICK TESTS or when directed here by other test procedures.**

***Typical Air Charge Temperature (ACT) Sensor Resistance***

| Ambient Temperature F° (C°) | Ohms Between Test Pin 25 & 46 |
|---|---|
| 50 (10) | 58,750 |
| 65 (18) | 40,500 |
| 180 (82) | 3600 |
| 220 (104) | 1840 |

## ACT SENSOR (Cont.)

To prevent replacement of good components, be aware that the following non-EEC related areas may be at fault: cooling system, improper engine oil level, or air cleaner duct problems. Ambient air temperature must be at least 50°F (10°C) for test results to be valid. Avoid performing test in unusually hot or cold conditions.

*Air Charge Temperature (ACT) Sensor Circuit*

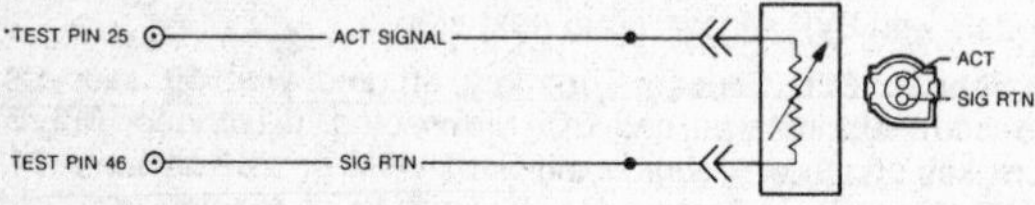
*TEST PIN 25
ACT SIGNAL
TEST PIN 46
SIG RTN
ACT
SIG RTN

**1) Code 24: Checking ACT Sensor.** For vehicles with ACT sensor mounted in intake manifold, go to next step. If sensor is properly mounted in air cleaner on all other models, go to next step. If sensor is not properly mounted, install ACT sensor properly and repeat QUICK TEST.

**2) Checking VREF at TPS.** Turn key off and wait 10 seconds. Set DVOM on 20-volt scale and disconnect Throttle Position Sensor (TPS). With Key On, Engine Off (KOEO), measure voltage between VREF and signal return at TPS connector. If reading is less than 4.0 volts or more than 6.0 volts, go to CIRCUIT TEST C, step **1)**. If reading is between 4.0 and 6.0 volts, connect TPS and go to next step.

**3) Checking ACT With Engine Off.** Start engine and ensure engine reaches normal operating temperature. Turn key off and wait 10 seconds. Disconnect ACT sensor, set DVOM on 200-k/ohms scale, and measure ACT sensor resistance. If reading is less than 1100 ohms or more than 58,000 ohms, check function of heat stove duct valve. If valve is operating correctly, replace ACT sensor. Connect ACT sensor, and repeat QUICK TEST. If reading is between 1100 and 58,000 ohms, go to next step.

**4) Checking ACT With Engine Running.** Turn key off. Disconnect ACT sensor harness. Set DVOM on 200-k/ohm scale and run engine until warm. While engine is running, measure ACT sensor resistance. If reading is between 2400 and 29,000 ohms, replace ECA. Connect ACT sensor harness, and repeat QUICK TEST. If reading is less than 2400 ohms or more than 29,000 ohms, check function of heat stove duct valve. If valve works properly, replace ACT sensor. Repeat QUICK TEST.

**5) Code 54: Generate Code 64.** Turn key off and wait 10 seconds. Disconnect ACT sensor harness. Inspect for and repair any damaged wiring. Install a jumper wire between ACT signal and signal return at connector. Perform KOEO SELF-TEST. If code 64 is displayed, replace ACT sensor. Remove jumper wire, connect ACT sensor, and repeat QUICK TEST. If code 64 is not displayed, remove jumper wire and go to next step.

**6) Continuity Check of ACT Signal.** Turn key off and wait 10 seconds. Leave ACT sensor harness disconnected. Disconnect ECA 60-pin connector. Inspect for and repair any damaged wiring. Install breakout box, leaving ECA disconnected. Set DVOM on 200-ohm scale. Measure resistance between test pin No. 25 and ACT signal at ACT connector, and between test pin No. 46 and signal return at ACT connector. If both readings are less than 5 ohms, replace ECA and remove breakout box. Connect ECA and ACT sensor, and then repeat QUICK TEST. If either reading is 5 ohms or more, repair opens in circuit. Remove breakout box. Connect ECA and ACT sensor. Repeat QUICK TEST.

**7) Code 64: Generate Code 54.** Turn key off and wait 10 seconds. Disconnect ACT sensor. Inspect for and repair any damaged wiring. Perform KOEO SELF-TEST. If code 54 is displayed, replace ACT sensor. Connect harness, and repeat QUICK TEST. If code 54 is not displayed, go to next step.

**8) Checking VREF at TPS.** Turn key off and wait 10 seconds. Set DVOM on 20-volt scale and disconnect TPS. Turn key on, leaving engine off. Measure voltage between VREF and signal return at TPS connector. If reading is less than 4.0 volts or more than 6.0 volts, go to CIRCUIT TEST C, step **1)**. If reading is between 4.0 and 6.0 volts, connect TPS and go to next step.

**9) Checking ACT Signal for Ground Short.** Turn key off and wait 10 seconds. Disconnect harness at ACT sensor. Disconnect ECA 60-pin connector. Inspect for and repair any damaged wiring. Install breakout box and set DVOM on 200-k/ohm scale. Measure resistance between test pin No. 25 and test pins No. 40, 46, and 60. If any reading is less than 10,000 ohms, repair shorts. Remove breakout box, and connect ECA and ACT sensor. Repeat QUICK TEST. If all readings are 10,000 ohms or more, replace ECA. Remove breakout box, and connect ECA and ACT sensor. Repeat QUICK TEST.

**10) Continuous Code 54 or 64 Displayed.** Using CONTINUOUS MONITOR (WIGGLE) TEST, observe VOM or diagnostic tester for indication of fault while tapping ACT sensor lightly and wiggling connector. If fault is indicated, inspect connector and terminals. If connector and terminals are good, replace ACT sensor and repeat QUICK TEST. If no fault is indicated, go to next step.

**11) Wiggle Testing ACT Sensor Harness.** While in CONTINUOUS MONITOR (WIGGLE) TEST, wiggle and bend small sections of harness from ACT sensor to firewall. Repeat action from firewall to ECA. If fault is indicated, isolate fault and repair as necessary. Repeat QUICK TEST. If no fault is indicated, go to next step.

**12) Inspecting Connectors and Terminals.** Turn key off and wait 10 seconds. Disconnect ECA 60-pin connector. Inspect both connector and connector terminals for obvious damage. If connectors and terminals are not okay, repair as necessary and repeat QUICK TEST. If connectors and terminals are okay, and you are unable to duplicate fault at this time, continuous code 54 or 64 testing is complete.

# CIRCUIT TEST DE

## ENGINE COOLANT TEMPERATURE (ECT) SENSOR

**NOTE: Perform this test when directed to by a Code 21, 51, or 61 during QUICK TEST procedure. For purposes of this test, a "warmed up" engine has a coolant temperature of 50-240°F (10-116°C) for KOEO SELF-TEST and 180-240°F (82-116°C) for KEY ON ENGINE RUNNING (KOER) SELF-TEST. The test procedure will be invalid outside these ranges.**

*Engine Coolant Temperature (ECT) Sensor Circuit*

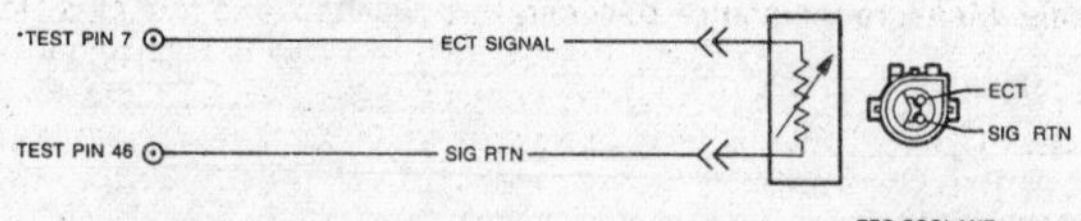
*TEST PIN 7
ECT SIGNAL
TEST PIN 46
SIG RTN
ECT
SIG RTN

NOTE: TO PASS THIS TEST, ENGINE COOLANT TEMPERATURE MUST BE:
KEY ON ENGINE OFF (50°F TO 240°F)
ENGINE RUNNING (180°F TO 240°F)

EEC COOLANT TEMPERATURE FRONT OF ENGINE

*Typical Engine Coolant Temperature (ECT) Sensor Resistance*

| Ambient Temperature F° (C°) | Ohms Between Test Pins No. 7 & 46 |
|---|---|
| 50 (10) | 58,750 |
| 65 (18) | 40,500 |
| 180 (82) | 3600 |
| 220 (104) | 1840 |

To prevent replacement of good components, be aware that the following non-EEC related areas may be at fault: coolant or oil level, blocked or obstructed airflow, engine not at normal operating temperature, or cooling fan.

**1) Code 21: Check Engine Temperature.** Start engine and run at 2000 RPM for 2 minutes. Check that upper radiator hose is hot and pressurized. Repeat QUICK TEST before continuing. If vehicle stalls, DO NOT service code 21 at this time, go directly to DIAGNOSIS BY SYMPTOM TEST. If code 21 is not displayed, service other codes as necessary (if displayed). If code 21 appears, go to next step.

**2) Checking for VREF at TPS.** Turn key off and wait 10 seconds. Disconnect TPS. Set DVOM on 20-volt scale. With KOEO measure voltage at TPS harness connector between VREF and signal return. If voltage is less than 4.0 volts or more than 6.0 volts, go to CIRCUIT TEST C, step **1)**. If voltage is between 4.0 and 6.0 volts, reconnect TPS and go to next step.

**3) ECT Sensor Resistance.** Ensure engine is fully warmed up for this step. Turn key off and wait 10 seconds. Disconnect wiring harness at ECT sensor. Set DVOM on 200-k/ohm scale and measure resistance of ECT sensor. If reading is 1300-7700 ohms at engine coolant temperature of 140-240°F (60-116°C) with engine off and 1550-4550 ohms at 180-230°F (82-110°C) with engine running, replace ECA, connect ECT sensor and repeat QUICK TEST. If readings are not

## ECT SENSOR (Cont.)

correct for coolant temperature, replace ECT sensor, connect harness, and repeat QUICK TEST.

**4) Code 51: Generate Code 61.** Turn key off and wait 10 seconds. Disconnect ECT sensor at wiring harness and inspect wiring for damage or corrosion. Connect a jumper wire between ECT signal and signal return terminals in sensor harness connector. Repeat KOEO SELF-TEST. If code 61 is displayed, replace ECT sensor and remove jumper wire. Reconnect harness to ECT sensor and repeat QUICK TEST. If code 61 is not displayed, go to next step.

**5) ECT Signal and Return Continuity Check.** Turn key off and wait 10 seconds. With harness disconnected at ECT sensor and jumper removed from harness connector, disconnect ECA 60-pin connector. Inspect for and repair any damaged wiring. Install breakout box, leaving ECA disconnected. Set DVOM on 200-ohm scale. Measure resistance between ECT signal at ECT connector and test pin No. 7. Measure resistance between signal return at ECT connector and test pin No. 46. If both readings are less than 5 ohms, replace ECA. Remove breakout box and connect ECA and ECT sensor. Repeat QUICK TEST. If either reading is 5 ohms or more, repair open circuits. Remove breakout box, and connect ECA and ECT sensor. Repeat QUICK TEST.

**6) Code 61: Generate Code 51.** Turn key off and wait 10 seconds. Disconnect ECT sensor and inspect connector for damage or corrosion. Repair wiring and repeat KOEO SELF-TEST. If code 51 is displayed, replace ECT sensor. Repeat QUICK TEST. If code 51 is not displayed, go to next step.

**7) Checking VREF at TPS.** Turn key off and wait 10 seconds. Set DVOM on 20-volt scale. Disconnect TPS. Turn key on, leaving engine off. Measure voltage between VREF and signal return at TPS connector. If reading is less than 4.0 volts or more than 6.0 volts, go to CIRCUIT TEST C, step **1)**. If voltage is between 4.0 and 6.0 volts, connect TPS and go to next step.

**8) Checking ECT Signal for Ground Short.** Turn key off and wait 10 seconds. Disconnect harness from ECT sensor. Disconnect ECA 60-pin connector. Inspect for and repair any damaged wiring. Install breakout box, leaving ECA disconnected. Set DVOM on 200-k/ohm scale. Measure resistance between test pin No. 7 and test pins No. 40, 46, and 60. If any reading is less than 10,000 ohms, repair short circuits. Remove breakout box, connect ECA and ECT sensor, and repeat QUICK TEST. If all readings are 10,000 ohms or more, replace ECA. Remove breakout box, connect ECA and ECT sensor. Repeat QUICK TEST.

**9) Continuous Code 21: Test Drive.** Turn key off and wait 10 seconds. Disconnect all SELF-TEST equipment and prepare vehicle for test drive. While driving vehicle, attempt to copy driving style in which complaint was noticed. If problem occurs, try to maintain condition for one or more minutes. After road test, repeat KOEO SELF-TEST. If code 21 is present in CONTINUOUS SELF-TEST, ensure that thermostat is working properly. If thermostat functions properly, replace ECT sensor and repeat QUICK TEST. If code 21 is not displayed, fault cannot be duplicated at this time. Continuous code 21 testing is complete.

**10) Continuous Code 51 or 61: Check ECT Sensor.** Using CONTINUOUS MONITOR (WIGGLE) TEST, observe VOM or diagnostic tester for indication of fault while tapping ECT sensor and wiggling ECT connector. If fault is indicated, disconnect and inspect ECT connector and terminals. If connector and terminals are okay, replace ECT sensor and repeat QUICK TEST. If no fault is indicated, go to next step.

**11) Checking Harness.** While in CONTINUOUS MONITOR (WIGGLE) TEST, observe VOM or diagnostic tester for indication of fault as you bend, shake or wiggle EEC-IV harness. Start at sensor connector and work toward firewall. Also test harness from firewall to ECA in same manner. If fault is indicated, isolate fault in wiring and repair as necessary. Repeat QUICK TEST. If fault is not indicated, go to next step.

**12) Checking ECA and Harness Connectors.** Turn key off and wait 10 seconds. Disconnect ECA 60-pin connector. Inspect both connectors and terminals for obvious damage. If connectors and terminals are damaged, repair as necessary and repeat QUICK TEST. If connectors and terminals are okay, fault cannot be duplicated at this time. Continuous code 51 or 61 testing is complete.

## CIRCUIT TEST DF

### MANIFOLD ABSOLUTE PRESSURE (MAP)/ BAROMETRIC PRESSURE (BP) SENSOR

**NOTE: This test should be performed when Service Code 22 or 72 is displayed in QUICK TEST procedures, or when directed here by another test. Barometric pressure sensor output is digital and must be measured with MAP/BP tester.**

To prevent replacement of good components, be aware the following non-EEC related areas may be at fault: unusually high/low atmospheric barometer reading, kinked or blocked vacuum lines, or engine condition (valves, vacuum leaks, valve timing, EGR valve, etc.).

**1) Code 22: Engine Off.** Turn key off. Disconnect MAP sensor from harness. Connect MAP/BP tester between wiring harness and MAP sensor. Connect banana plugs of tester into DVOM and set DVOM on 20-volt scale. See MAP/BP TESTER HOOK-UP. Go to next step.

***MAP/BP Tester Hook-Up***

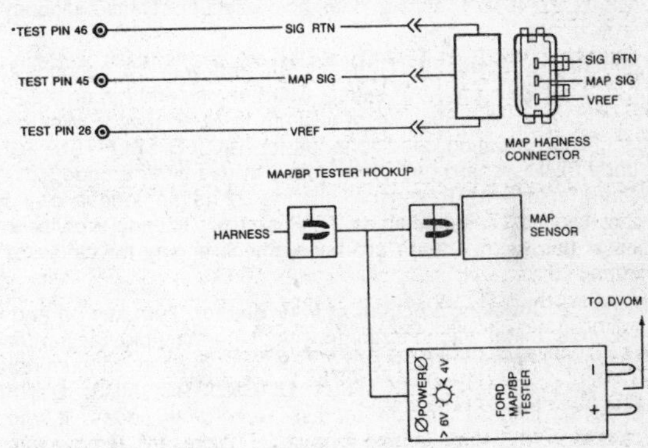
TEST PIN 46
SIG RTN
TEST PIN 45
MAP SIG
TEST PIN 26
VREF
SIG RTN
MAP SIG
VREF
MAP HARNESS CONNECTOR
MAP/BP TESTER HOOKUP
HARNESS
MAP SENSOR
TO DVOM
FORD MAP/BP TESTER

**2) Checking Power to Tester.** With MAP/BP tester connected, turn key on. If only Green light on tester is lit, VREF is correct. Go to step **4)**. If "LESS THAN 4.0 VOLTS" Red light or no lights come on, VREF is too low. If "MORE THAN 6.0 VOLTS" Red light comes on, VREF is too high. If VREF is too high or too low, go to next step.

**3) VREF Testing.** With MAP/BP tester connected, turn key on. Disconnect MAP sensor and repeat step **2)**. If only Green light comes on, VREF is correct. Replace MAP sensor and repeat QUICK TEST. If "LESS THAN 4.0 VOLTS" Red light or no lights come on, VREF is too low. If "MORE THAN 6.0 VOLTS" Red light comes on, VREF is too high. If VREF is too high or too low, remove MAP/BP tester, connect sensor, then go to CIRCUIT TEST C step **1)**.

**4) Tester Output Reading.** With MAP/BP tester connected and key on, measure sensor output voltage. If voltage output is in correct range for altitude of vehicle being tested, remove MAP/BP tester and go to next step. If output reading is outside range, remove MAP/BP tester and go to step **6)**.

**NOTE: Measure several known good MAP/BP sensors on available vehicles. Mean voltage reading will be typical for your location on date of testing.**

***MAP VOLTAGE OUTPUT***

| Elevation (Ft.) | Voltage Output (Volts) |
|---|---|
| 0 | 1.55-1.63 |
| 1000 | 1.52-1.60 |
| 2000 | 1.49-1.57 |
| 3000 | 1.46-1.54 |
| 4000 | 1.43-1.51 |
| 5000 | 1.40-1.48 |
| 6000 | 1.37-1.45 |
| 7000 | 1.35-1.43 |

**5) Checking Signal Continuity.** Turn key off and wait 10 seconds. Disconnect MAP sensor from harness. Disconnect ECA 60-pin connector. Inspect for and repair any damaged wiring. Install breakout box, leaving ECA disconnected. Set DVOM on 200-ohm scale.

## MAP/BP SENSOR (Cont.)

Measure resistance between MAP signal at sensor connector and test pin No. 45. If reading is less than 5 ohms, replace ECA. Connect ECA and MAP sensor and repeat QUICK TEST. If reading is 5 ohms or higher, repair opens in wiring. Remove breakout box, connect ECA and MAP sensor. Repeat QUICK TEST.

**6) Checking MAP/BP Signal For Shorts.** Turn key off and wait 10 seconds. Disconnect ECA 60-pin connector. Inspect for and repair any damaged wiring. Install breakout box, leaving ECA disconnected. Disconnect harness at MAP sensor. Set DVOM on 200-k/ohm scale. Measure resistance between test pin No. 45 and test pins No. 26, 46, 40, and 60. If any reading is less than 10-k/ohms, repair shorts in wiring. Remove breakout box and connect ECA and MAP sensor. Repeat QUICK TEST. If all readings are 10-k/ohms or more, replace MAP sensor. Remove breakout box and connect all wiring. Repeat QUICK TEST.

**7) Code 22: Checking MAP Sensor.** Turn key off and wait 10 seconds. Disconnect vacuum hose from MAP sensor. Connect vacuum pump to MAP sensor and apply 18 in. Hg of vacuum to sensor. If sensor does not hold vacuum, replace sensor, connect vacuum line and repeat QUICK TEST. If MAP sensor does hold vacuum, release vacuum and go to next step.

**8) Eliminating Code 22.** Turn key off and wait 10 seconds. Plug vacuum hose going to MAP sensor. Start engine and run at 1400-1600 RPM. Slowly apply 15 in. Hg of vacuum to MAP sensor. With engine under these operating conditions, perform KOER SELF-TEST. Check for code 22, disregard any other codes at this time. If code 22 is still present, replace MAP sensor. If code 22 is no longer displayed, inspect vacuum hose going to MAP sensor. If okay, service other codes at this time. If there are none, check engine for cause of low vacuum.

**9) Code 72: Checking Vacuum at MAP Sensor.** Turn key off and wait 10 seconds. Install vacuum gauge with "T" in manifold vacuum line at MAP sensor. Perform KOER SELF-TEST and observe vacuum reading before and during QUICK TEST DIAGNOSTIC AIDS, DYNAMIC RESPONSE CHECK portion of test. Record all codes. If vacuum decreased 10 in. Hg or more with a code 72 present, remove vacuum gauge. Reconnect all components, replace MAP sensor, and rerun QUICK TEST. If vacuum decreased 10 in. Hg or more without a code 72 present, disconnect vacuum equipment and service other codes as necessary. If vacuum decreased less than 10 in. Hg, go to next step.

**10) Vacuum Line Check.** Using vehicle emissions decal as a guide, check vacuum lines for correct routing. Also check MAP sensor vacuum lines for kinks or blockage. If lines are good, EEC-IV system is okay. Check engine for cause of low vacuum. If vacuum lines are bad, repair as necessary and repeat step **9)**.

**11) Connecting MAP/BP Tester.** Turn key off. Disconnect MAP sensor from harness. Connect MAP/BP tester between wiring harness and MAP sensor. Connect banana plugs of tester into DVOM and set DVOM on 20-volt scale. See MAP/BP TESTER HOOK-UP. Go to next step.

**12) Tester Output Reading.** Turn key on and measure sensor output. Compare values to MAP VOLTAGE OUTPUT table. If reading is within range, go to next step. If reading is out of range, replace MAP sensor. Repeat QUICK TEST.

**13) Vacuum Line Check.** Check map sensor vacuum lines for leaks, bad connections, kinks or blockage. If vacuum lines are okay, go to DIAGNOSIS BY SYMPTOM TEST. If vacuum lines are bad, repair as necessary and repeat QUICK TEST.

**14) Code 22 Displayed: Operate MAP Sensor.** Using CONTINUOUS MONITOR (WIGGLE) TEST, observe VOM or diagnostic tester for indication of fault while doing the following: connect vacuum pump to MAP sensor and slowly apply 25 in. Hg. Bleed vacuum slowly, tap MAP sensor lightly, and wiggle MAP connector. If fault is indicated, disconnect sensor. Inspect connector and terminals for damage. If connector and terminals are okay, replace MAP sensor and repeat QUICK TEST. If no fault is indicated, go to next step.

**15) Checking Harness.** Stay in CONTINUOUS MONITOR (WIGGLE) TEST. Observe VOM or diagnostic tester for indication of fault while shaking, bending or wiggling small sections of harness from sensor connector to firewall. Check harness from firewall to ECA in same manner. If fault is indicated, isolate fault in harness and repair as necessary. Repeat QUICK TEST. If no fault is indicated, go to next step.

**16) Checking ECA Connector and Harness.** Turn key off and wait 10 seconds. Disconnect ECA 60-pin connector. Inspect both connectors and terminals for obvious damage. If connectors and terminals are not okay, repair as necessary. Repeat QUICK TEST. If connectors and terminals are okay, fault cannot be duplicated at this time. Continuous code 22 testing is complete.

# CIRCUIT TEST DH

## THROTTLE POSITION SENSOR (TPS)

**NOTE: Perform this test when Service Code 23, 53, 63, or 73 is displayed during QUICK TEST.**

***Throttle Position Sensor (TPS) Circuit***

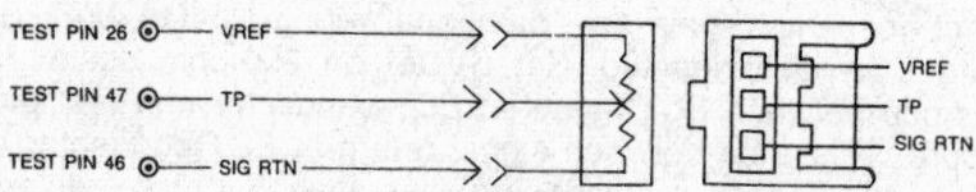
TEST PIN 26
VREF
TEST PIN 47
TP
TEST PIN 46
SIG RTN
VREF
TP
SIG RTN

To prevent replacement of good components, be aware that the following non-EEC related areas may be at fault: idle speed/throttle stop adjustment, binding throttle shaft/linkage or cruise control linkage.

**1) Code 23 Displayed.** If KOER SELF-TEST codes 31, or 41 are displayed, service these codes first. Disregard code 23 at this time. If codes 32 or 41 have been serviced or are not displayed, go to next step.

**2) Check Throttle Plate.** Inspect throttle body and linkage for mechanical binding or sticking. Make sure linkage is set with throttle in closed position. If throttle plate or linkage is binding, check for binding throttle or cruise control linkage, vacuum line or harness interference, etc. Repair problem(s) and repeat QUICK TEST. If no mechanical problem is found, go to next step.

**3) Code 53: Generate Code 63.** Turn key off and wait 10 seconds. Disconnect TPS from harness at throttle body. Inspect for and repair any damaged wiring. Perform KOEO SELF-TEST. Check for code 63. Ignore all other codes at this time. If code 63 is not displayed, go to step **5)**. If code 63 is displayed, go to next step.

**4) Check VREF to Signal Return.** Turn key off and wait 10 seconds. Set DVOM on 20-volt scale and disconnect TPS from harness. Inspect for and repair any damaged wiring. With KOEO, measure voltage at TPS connector between VREF and signal return. If reading is less than 4 volts or more than 6 volts, go to CIRCUIT TEST C, step **1)**. If reading is between 4 and 6 volts, replace TPS and repeat QUICK TEST.

**5) Checking TPS Signal For Shorts.** Turn key off and wait 10 seconds. Disconnect TPS from harness. Set DVOM on 200-k/ohm scale. Disconnect ECA 60-pin connector. Inspect for and repair any damaged wiring. Install breakout box, leaving ECA disconnected. Measure resistance between test pin No. 47 and test pins No. 26 and 57. If either reading is less than 10,000 ohms, repair short in harness and repeat QUICK TEST. If both readings are 10,000 ohms or more, replace ECA and repeat QUICK TEST.

**6) Code 63: Generate Code 53.** Turn key off and wait 10 seconds. Disconnect TPS from harness. Install a jumper wire between VREF and TPS signal at connector. Perform KOEO SELF-TEST. Check for code 53. Ignore all other codes at this time. If no codes are displayed, immediately remove jumper wire, and go to step **9)**. If code 53 is displayed, replace TPS and repeat QUICK TEST. If code 53 is not displayed, go to next step.

**7) Code 63: Check Voltage VREF to Signal Return.** Turn key off and wait 10 seconds. Disconnect TPS from harness. Inspect for and repair any damaged wiring. Set DVOM on 20-volt scale. Turn key on, leaving engine off. Measure voltage between VREF and signal return at TPS connector. If reading is less than 4 volts or more than 6 volts, go to CIRCUIT TEST C, step **1)**. If reading is between 4 and 6 volts, go to next step.

**8) Checking TPS Circuit Continuity.** Turn key off and wait 10 seconds. Leave TPS disconnected. Set DVOM on 200-ohm scale and disconnect ECA 60-pin connector. Inspect for and repair any damaged wiring. Install breakout box and connect ECA. Measure resistance between TPS signal at connector and test pin No. 47. If reading is 5 ohms or more, repair faulty circuit. Remove breakout box, connect ECA and TPS, and then repeat QUICK TEST. If reading is less than 5 ohms, go to next step.

**9) Checking Resistance of Ground/Signal Return.** Turn key off and wait 10 seconds. Leave TPS disconnected. Disconnect ECA 60-pin

### TPS (Cont.)

connector. Inspect for and repair any damaged wiring. Install breakout box and set DVOM on 200-k/ohm scale. Measure resistance at connector between TPS signal and ground, and between TPS signal and test pin No. 46. If either reading is less than 10,000 ohms, repair short circuit and repeat QUICK TEST. If both readings are 10,000 ohms or more, replace ECA. Remove breakout box, connect TPS, and then repeat QUICK TEST.

**NOTE: Code 73 in step 10) indicates that TPS did not exceed 25% of its rotation during DYNAMIC RESPONSE CHECK. See QUICK TEST DIAGNOSTIC AIDS, DYNAMIC RESPONSE CHECK in front of this article.**

**10) Code 73: TPS Movement.** Turn key off. Install breakout box and set DVOM on 20-volt scale. Connect DVOM to test pins No. 46 and 47. Perform KOER SELF-TEST. Verify that DVOM reading exceeds 3.5 volts during KOER SELF-TEST step **2)** WOT DYNAMIC RESPONSE CHECK. If reading exceeds 3.5 volts, replace ECA and repeat QUICK TEST. If reading does not exceed 3.5 volts, ensure TPS is correctly installed and adjusted. If okay, replace TPS and repeat QUICK TEST.

**11) Code 53: TPS Movement.** Using CONTINUOUS MONITOR (WIGGLE) TEST, observe VOM or diagnostic tester for indication of fault while slowly opening throttle to WOT. Slowly bring throttle to closed position, lightly tap TPS and wiggle connector. If no fault is indicated, go to step **13)**. If fault is indicated, go to next step.

**12) TPS Voltage Measurement.** Turn key off and wait 10 seconds. Disconnect ECA 60-pin connector. Inspect for and repair any damaged wiring. Install breakout box, leaving ECA connected. Stay in CONTINUOUS MONITOR (WIGGLE) TEST and connect DVOM between test pins No. 47 and 46. Set DVOM on 20-volt scale. Turn key on, leaving engine off. Observe DVOM and repeat step **11)**. If fault occurs at less than 4.55 volts, inspect TPS connectors and terminals. If okay, replace TPS and repeat QUICK TEST. If fault does not occur at less than 4.55 volts, TPS over-travel may have caused continuous code 53. TPS is good, go to next step to check harness.

**13) Checking Harness.** While in CONTINUOUS MONITOR (WIGGLE) TEST, shake, bend and wiggle small sections of EEC-IV harness from TPS sensor to firewall, and from firewall to ECA. If fault is indicated, isolate fault in wiring and repair as necessary. Repeat QUICK TEST. If no fault is indicated, go to next step.

**14) Checking Harness Connectors.** Turn key off and wait 10 seconds. Disconnect ECA 60-pin connector. Inspect both connectors and terminals for obvious damage. If connectors and terminals are damaged, repair as necessary. Repeat QUICK TEST. If connectors and terminals are okay, fault cannot be duplicated at this time. Continuous code 53 testing is complete.

**15) Continuous Code 63 Displayed.** Using CONTINUOUS MONITOR (WIGGLE) TEST, observe VOM or diagnostic tester for indication of fault while slowly opening throttle to WOT. Slowly bring throttle to closed position and lightly tap TPS and wiggle connector. If fault is indicated, disconnect TPS. Inspect connectors and terminals. If connectors and terminals are okay, replace TPS and repeat QUICK TEST. If no fault is indicated, go to next step.

**16) Harness Test.** While in CONTINUOUS MONITOR (WIGGLE) TEST, shake, bend and wiggle small sections of EEC-IV harness from TPS sensor to firewall, and from firewall to ECA. If fault is indicated, isolate fault in wiring and repair as necessary. Repeat QUICK TEST. If no fault is indicated, go to next step.

**17) ECA Connector Test.** Turn key off and wait 10 seconds. Disconnect ECA 60-pin connector. Inspect both connectors and terminals for obvious damage. If connectors and teminals are damaged, repair as necessary. Repeat QUICK TEST. If connectors and terminals are okay, fault cannot be duplicated at this time. Continuous code 63 testing is complete.

## CIRCUIT TEST DL

### PRESSURE FEEDBACK EGR (PFE) & EGR VALVE REGULATOR (EVR)

**NOTE: Perform this test when Service Code 31, 32, 33, 34, 35, or 84 is displayed during QUICK TESTS or when directed here by other test procedures.**

***Pressure Feedback EGR (PFE) & EGR Valve Regulator (EVR) Circuits***

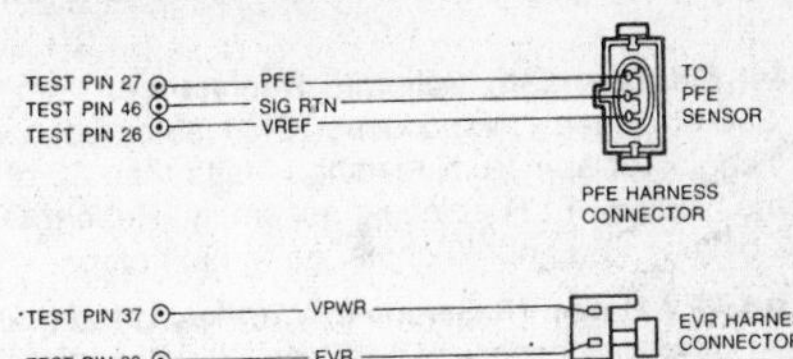
TEST PIN 27
TEST PIN 46
TEST PIN 26
PFE
SIG RTN
VREF
TO PFE SENSOR
PFE HARNESS CONNECTOR
TEST PIN 37
TEST PIN 33
VPWR
EVR
EVR HARNESS CONNECTOR

**1) Code 31: Generate Code 35.** Turn key off. Disconnect PFE harness at sensor. Install a jumper wire between VREF and PFE signal at sensor connector. Perform KOEO SELF-TEST. Check for code 35. Ignore all other codes at this time. If no codes are displayed, immediately remove jumper wire and go directly to step **4)**. If code 35 is displayed, remove jumper wire and replace PFE sensor. Repeat QUICK TEST. If code 35 is not displayed, remove jumper and go to next step.

**2) Measuring VREF Signal Return Voltage.** With key off and PFE harness disconnected, set DVOM on 20-volt scale. With KOEO, measure voltage at PFE connector between VREF and signal return. If reading is less than 4 volts or more than 6 volts, go to CIRCUIT TEST C, step **1)**. If reading is between 4 and 6 volts, go to next step.

**3) PFE Signal Continuity.** With key off and PFE harness disconnected, set DVOM on 200-ohm scale. Disconnect ECA 60-pin connector. Inspect for and repair any damaged wiring. Install breakout box, with ECA connected to breakout box. Measure resistance between PFE signal at connector and test pin No. 27. If reading is 5 ohms or more, repair faulty circuit. Connect PFE sensor and remove breakout box. Repeat QUICK TEST. If reading is less than 5 ohms, go to next step.

**4) PFE Signal Circuit Resistance.** With key off and PFE harness disconnected, install breakout box leaving ECA disconnected. Set DVOM on 200-k/ohm scale. Measure resistance between ground and PFE signal at connector. Measure resistance between PFE signal at connector and test pin No. 46. If either reading is less than 10,000 ohms, repair short circuit. Connect PFE and remove breakout box. Repeat QUICK TEST. If both readings are 10,000 ohms or more, replace ECA. Connect PFE and remove breakout box. Repeat QUICK TEST.

**5) Code 35: Generate Code 31.** Turn key off and disconnect PFE harness at sensor. Inspect for and repair any damaged wiring. Perform KOEO SELF-TEST. Check for code 31. Ignore all other codes at this time. If code 31 is not displayed, go to step **7)**. If code 31 is displayed, go to next step.

**6) Measuring VREF Signal Voltage.** With key off and PFE harness disconnected, set DVOM on 20-volt scale. Turn key on, leaving engine off. Measure voltage at PFE connector between VREF and signal return. If reading is between 4 and 6 volts, replace PFE sensor. Repeat QUICK TEST. If reading is less than 4 volts or more than 6 volts, go to CIRCUIT TEST C, step **1)**.

**7) Checking PFE Circuit For Shorts.** With key off and PFE harness disconnected, disconnect ECA 60-pin connector. Inspect for and repair any damaged wiring. Install breakout box, leaving ECA disconnected. Set DVOM on 200-k/ohm scale. Measure resistance between Test Pin No. 27 and Test Pins No. 26 and 57. If either reading is less than 10,000 ohms, repair short. Connect PFE and remove breakout box. Repeat QUICK TEST. If both readings are 10,000 ohms or more, replace ECA. Connect PFE and remove breakout box. Repeat QUICK TEST.

**8) Code 34: PFE Sensor Beyond Range.** The PFE system can detect lack of pressure in exhaust system. An efficient garage exhaust ventilation system, installed during KOEO SELF-TEST may cause PFE sensor to generate code 34. Remove garage exhaust ventilation system and retest. If code 34 is not displayed, service other codes displayed during KOEO SELF-TEST. If none are displayed, continue with QUICK TEST. If code 34 is displayed, go to next step.

**9) Inspecting Supply to PFE Sensor.** Remove pressure feed tube from PFE sensor. Inspect complete tube, including PFE inlet for blockage. If blockage is found, repair as necessary. Repeat QUICK TEST. If no blockage is found, go to next step.

**10) Measuring VREF Signal Return Voltage.** Turn key off and disconnect PFE sensor. Inspect for and repair any damaged wiring. Set DVOM on 20-volt scale. Turn key on, leaving engine off. Measure voltage at PFE connector between VREF and signal return. If reading is between 4 and 6 volts, replace PFE sensor. Repeat QUICK TEST. If

## PFE & EVR (Cont.)

reading is less than 4 volts or more than 6 volts, go to CIRCUIT TEST C, step **1**).

**11) Code 84: Measure EVR Solenoid Resistance.** Turn key off. Set DVOM on 200-ohm scale. Disconnect EVR solenoid connector and measure solenoid resistance. If reading is less than 30 ohms or more than 70 ohms, replace EVR solenoid assembly. Repeat QUICK TEST. If reading is between 30 and 70 ohms, go to next step.

**12) Checking VPWR at EVR Solenoid.** With key off and EVR solenoid disconnected from harness, set DVOM on 20-volt scale. Turn key on, leaving engine off. Measure voltage between negative battery terminal and VPWR circuit at EVR solenoid connector. If reading is less than 10.5 volts, repair VPWR open circuit. Repeat QUICK TEST. If reading is 10.5 volts or more, go to next step.

**13) Checking Continuity of EVR Circuit.** Turn key off and disconnect EVR solenoid from harness. Disconnect ECA 60-pin connector. Inspect for and repair any damaged wiring. Install breakout box, leaving ECA disconnected. Set DVOM on 200-ohm scale. Measure resistance between test pin No. 33 and EVR signal at EVR solenoid connector. If reading is 5 ohms or more, repair open circuit. Connect EVR solenoid and remove breakout box. Repeat QUICK TEST. If reading is less than 5 ohms, go to next step.

**14) Checking EVR Circuit For Ground Shorts.** Turn key off. Install breakout box, leaving ECA disconnected. Disconnect EVR solenoid. Set DVOM on 200-k/ohm scale. Measure resistance between test pin No. 33 and test pins No. 37, 57, 40, 46 and 60 at breakout box. If any reading is less than 10,000 ohms, repair short circuit. Remove breakout box. Connect ECA and EVR solenoid. Repeat QUICK TEST. If code is repeated, replace ECA. If all readings are 10,000 ohms or more, replace ECA. Remove breakout box. Connect ECA and EVR solenoid. Repeat QUICK TEST.

**15) Code 32: Verify Engine Running Codes.** The PFE system can detect a lack of pressure in exhaust system. An efficient garage exhaust ventilation system, installed during KOER SELF-TEST may cause PFE sensor to generate code 32. Temporarily remove garage exhaust ventilation system and retest. If code 32 is not displayed, service other codes displayed during KOER SELF-TEST. If no codes, continue with QUICK TEST. If code 32 is displayed, go to next step.

**16) Separating EVR From PFE.** Turn key off. Disconnect and plug EGR valve vacuum hose. Perform KOER SELF-TEST. If codes 31 or 32 are present, go to next step. If not, go to step **18**).

**17) Checking PFE Supply Tube.** With key off, check PFE sensor supply tube for blockage and/or leaks. If these faults are found, repair as necessary. Connect all lines and repeat QUICK TEST. If no faults are found, service EGR system.

**18) EVR Filter Inspection.** Turn key off. Remove and inspect EVR filter for contamination. A blocked filter will cause vacuum to be applied to EGR valve prematurely. If filter is contaminated, replace filter. Connect all lines and repeat QUICK TEST. If filter is not contaminated, replace EVR solenoid. Repeat QUICK TEST.

**19) Codes 34 or 35: Excessive Backpressure.** Service codes 34 and 35 in KOER SELF-TEST indicate excessive exhaust backpressure. There are 2 possible causes: the exhaust system is blocked, or PFE sensor has shifted into high. Turn key off. Susbtitute known good PFE sensor in place of original. Repeat KOER SELF-TEST. If code 34 or 35 is not displayed, replace PFE sensor. Repeat QUICK TEST. If code 34 or 35 is displayed, check exhaust system for restrictions.

**20) Code 33: Verify Vacuum Supply.** Turn key off. Using a vacuum "T", connect vacuum gauge at EGR valve. Perform KOER SELF-TEST while observing vacuum gauge. Disregard code output. If vacuum reading is greater than one in. Hg, service EGR system as necessary. If vacuum reading is one in. Hg or less, go to next step.

**21) Vacuum Hose Inspection.** With key off, check vacuum hose from EVR solenoid to EGR valve and from vacuum source to EVR solenoid for loose connections, obstructions, cracks, etc. If vacuum hoses are damaged, repair or replace as necessary. Repeat QUICK TEST. If hoses are okay, go to next step.

**22) Vacuum Supply Verification.** Start engine. Attach vacuum gauge to EVR solenoid hose coming from engine manifold (vacuum source). If vacuum is present, replace EVR solenoid. Repeat QUICK TEST. If no vacuum is present, replace vacuum hose to EVR solenoid and repeat QUICK TEST.

**23) Checking PFE Sensor Tube.** Turn key off. If control pressure input tube to PFE sensor is disconnected, blocked or cracked, repair or replace tube as necessary. Repeat QUICK TEST. If tube is okay, replace PFE sensor. Repeat QUICK TEST.

**24) Continuous Code 31 or 35: Testing PFE Sensor.** Using CONTINUOUS MONITOR (WIGGLE) TEST, observe VOM or diagnostic tester for indication of fault while performing the following steps: connect a vacuum pump to PFE sensor, slowly apply 5 in. Hg to sensor, and then slowly bleed vacuum off PFE sensor. Lightly tap on PFE sensor and wiggle PFE connector. If fault is indicated, disconnect harness and inspect connector. If connector and terminals are okay, replace PFE sensor. Repeat QUICK TEST. If no fault is indicated, go to next step.

**25) Checking Harness.** Observe VOM or diagnostic tester for fault indication while grasping harness close to sensor connector, then wiggling, shaking or bending small sections of harness while working your way to firewall. Also wiggle, shake or bend harness from firewall to ECA. If fault is indicated, isolate fault and repair as necessary. Repeat QUICK TEST. If fault is not indicated, go to next step.

**26) Checking ECA and Harness Connectors.** Turn key off and wait 10 seconds. Disconnect ECA 60-pin connector. Inspect both connector and terminals for damage. If connector and terminals are damaged, repair as necessary. Repeat QUICK TEST. If connector and terminals are okay, fault cannot be duplicated at this time. Continuous code 31 or 35 testing is complete.

**27) Continuous Code 34: PFE Supply Tube.** Turn key off. Remove PFE sensor and inspect sensor supply inlet for liquids and/or any type of blockage. Inspect PFE supply tube at EGR valve base for liquids and/or blockage. If supply tube is blocked, clean or service as necessary. Repeat QUICK TEST. If supply tube is not blocked, fault cannot be duplicated at this time. Continuous code 34 testing is complete.

**28) Continuous Code 32: EGR Valve Operation.** Turn key off. Connect vacuum pump to EGR valve and apply 10 in. Hg. While observing EGR valve, release vacuum, and repeat step if necessary. If EGR valve does not work smoothly, service EGR system. If EGR valve works smoothly, go to next step.

**29) Vacuum Line Inspection.** Inspect EGR valve vacuum supply line from EVR solenoid for kinks and/or obstructions. If vacuum supply line is blocked, repair as necessary. Repeat QUICK TEST. If vacuum supply line is okay, go to next step.

**30) EVR Filter Inspection.** Carefully check EVR filter for contamination and/or obstructions. If EVR filter is contaminated, replace filter and repeat QUICK TEST. If EVR filter is not contaminated, fault cannot be duplicated at this time. Continuous code 32 testing is complete.

**31) Continuous Code 33: EGR Valve Operation.** Turn key off. Connect a vacuum pump to EGR valve. While observing EGR valve, slowly apply 10 in. Hg. EGR valve should begin to open at about one in. Hg and be fully open at 4 in. Hg. If EGR valve does not move freely and smoothly, service exhaust gas recirculation system. If EGR valve moves freely and smoothly, go to next step.

**32) EVR Harness Test.** With key off, disconnect ECA 60-pin connector. Inspect for and repair any damaged wiring. Install breakout box, then connect ECA to box. Enter OUTPUT STATE CHECK. Set DVOM on 20-volt scale. Connect DVOM negative (–) test lead to test pin No. 40 and DVOM positive (+) test lead on test pin No. 33. Move throttle valve to indicate 10.5 volts or more and maintain position. While observing DVOM, grasp harness closest to EVR connector. Wiggle, shake or bend a small sections of harness while working your way to firewall. Lightly tap EVR solenoid to simulate road vibration. If DVOM reads 10.5 volts or less, isolate fault and repair as necessary. Repeat QUICK TEST. If DVOM reads 10.5 volts or more, fault cannot be duplicated at this time. Continuous code 33 testing is complete.

# CIRCUIT TEST FA

## NEUTRAL DRIVE SWITCH A/C INPUT

**1) Code 67 Displayed.** Turn key off and wait 10 seconds. Disconnect ECA 60 pin connector. Inspect for and repair any damaged wiring. With breakout box and ECA connected. With KOEO, set DVOM on 20-volt scale. Measure voltage between test pin No. 30 and chassis ground. If reading is less than 1.0 volt in Park or Neutral and less than 4.5-5.0 volts in Drive or Reverse, go to next step. If readings are over specifications go to step **3**).

**2) A/C Input Check.** With breakout box installed and KOER, set DVOM to 20-volt scale. While using ECON button on electronic Automatic Temperature Control (ATC) module, cycle A/C clutch on and off while measuring voltage between test pin No. 10 and chassis ground. If

## NEUTRAL DRIVE SWITCH A/C INPUT (Cont.)

reading of 12 volts is not present with compressor cycled on, replace ECA. If more than one volt is present with compressor cycled off, repair short to power in A/C clutch circuit. Repeat QUICK TEST.

*Neutral Drive Switch & A/C Input Circuits*

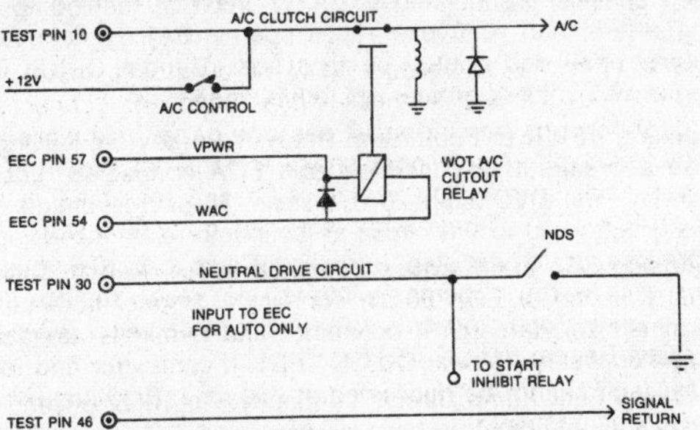
TEST PIN 10
A/C CLUTCH CIRCUIT
A/C
+12V
A/C CONTROL
EEC PIN 57
VPWR
WOT A/C CUTOUT RELAY
EEC PIN 54
WAC
NDS
TEST PIN 30
NEUTRAL DRIVE CIRCUIT
INPUT TO EEC FOR AUTO ONLY
TO START INHIBIT RELAY
SIGNAL RETURN
TEST PIN 46

**3) Neutral Drive Switch Check.** Turn key off and wait 10 seconds. With breakout box installed, set DVOM on 200-ohm scale. Disconnect harness from neutral drive switch. Measure resistance across switch. If less than 5 ohms is present repair open in neutral drive circuit. Repeat QUICK TEST. If 5 ohms or greater is present, replace neutral drive switch. Repeat QUICK TEST.

# CIRCUIT TEST HG

## FUEL CONTROL

**NOTE: See HOW TO USE CIRCUIT TESTS before performing this test. Fuel contaminated engine oil may affect service codes 41 and 42. If this is suspected, remove PCV valve from valve cover and repeat QUICK TEST. If problem is corrected, change engine oil and filter.**

*Fuel Control Circuit*

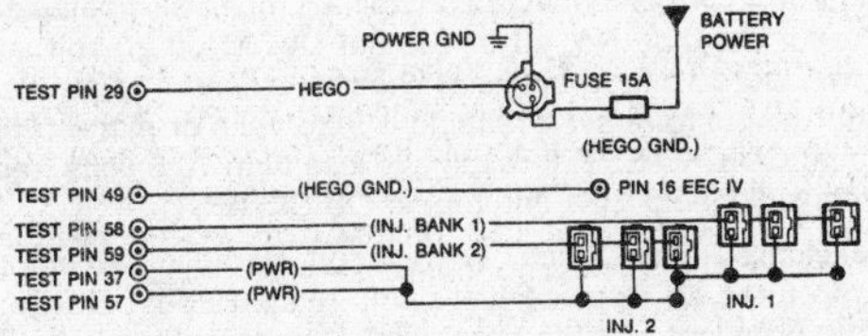
BATTERY POWER
POWER GND
TEST PIN 29
HEGO
FUSE 15A
(HEGO GND.)
TEST PIN 49
(HEGO GND.)
PIN 16 EEC IV
TEST PIN 58
TEST PIN 59
TEST PIN 37
TEST PIN 57
(INJ. BANK 1)
(INJ. BANK 2)
(PWR)
(PWR)
INJ. 2
INJ. 1

**1) Fuel Pressure Test.** Turn key off and wait 10 seconds. Install fuel pressure gauge. Start and run engine. Fuel pressure must be 35-45 psi (2.5-3.2 kg/cm²). If engine will not run, cycle key from off to on several times to build up fuel pressure. If fuel pressure is outside range, check electric fuel pump and fuel pressure regulator. If fuel pressure is correct, go to next step.

**2)** With pressure gauge installed, cycle key from off to on several times to pressurize system. Pressure must remain at 35-45 psi (2.5-3.2 kg/cm²) for 60 seconds after key is turned off. If pressure is not maintained, go to step **7)**. If pressure is maintained, go to next step.

**3) Fuel Delivery Test.** With pressure gauge installed, cycle key from off to on several times to pressurize system. Disconnect fuel pump relay. Crank engine for 5 seconds and take pressure reading immediately after cranking. If pressure reading is 10-20 psi (0.7-1.4 kg/cm²) after cranking, EEC-IV system is not at fault for no start. If problem is rough running, missing, fuel code, or if pressure is incorrect after cranking, go to next step.

**NOTE: Make sure that fuel is of good quality and not contaminated by air or water, as pressure readings may be incorrect with bad or contaminated fuel. Also, pressure drop will be greater when engine is cold than when engine is warm. If coolant is 200°F (93°C) pressure should drop approximately 10 psi (0.7 kg/cm²) in 5 seconds while a pressure drop of 20 psi (1.4 kg/cm²) should occur in 5 seconds with engine coolant at 60°F (15.6°C).**

**4) Injector Harness Resistance Test** Turn key off and wait 10 seconds. Disconnect ECA 60-pin connector. Inspect for and repair any damaged wiring. Install breakout box, leaving ECA disconnected. Set DVOM on 200-ohm scale. Measure resistance between test pins No. 37 and 58 for injector bank No. 1. Measure resistance between test pins No. 37 and 59 for injector bank No. 2. If both readings are between 5.0 and 6.5 ohms, go to step **6)**. If both readings are not between 5.0 and 6.5 ohms, go to next step.

**5) Isolate Faulty Injector Test** With key off, breakout box installed and ECA disconnected, set DVOM on 200-ohm scale. Disconnect all injectors on suspect bank. Connect each injector individually and test resistance between test pins No. 37 and 58 for injector bank No. 1 or between test pins No. 37 and 59 for injector bank No. 2. If all readings are not between 1.6 and 1.8 ohms, check harness and connectors on injector for shorted or open circuits. If circuits are okay, replace injector(s) and repeat QUICK TEST. If all readings are between 1.6 and 1.8 ohms, go to next step.

**6) Injector Drive Signal Test** With key off, breakout box installed and ECA connected, connect all injectors. Connect non-powered 12-volt test lamp between test pins No. 37 and 58. Crank or start engine. Repeat procedure with test lamp between test pins No. 37 and 59. If test lamp does not light on one or both tests, check for 12 volts at test pins No. 37 and 57. If test pins No. 37 and 57 have 12 volts, replace ECA and repeat QUICK TEST. If test lamp is bright on one or both tests, check circuits to both injector banks for short to ground. If no short is found, replace ECA and repeat QUICK TEST. If test lamp glows dimly on both tests, go to next step.

**7) Injector Balance Test** Connect tachometer and run engine at idle. Disconnect and reconnect one injector at a time and note RPM drop for each injector. If each injector does not produce at least 100 RPM drop when disconnected, replace faulty injector(s) and repeat QUICK TEST. If RPM drop is correct for all injectors, problem is in an area common to all cylinders such as vacuum leaks, fuel contamination, EGR, etc.

**8) Code 42 Displayed.** This code indicates an always rich condition. Check for non-EEC related problem such as fuel in engine oil, ignition misfire or canister purge problem. Repair non-EEC related problem(s) (if present), and repeat QUICK TEST. If non-EEC related problem is not present, turn key off and wait 10 seconds. Disconnect vehicle harness at HEGO sensor. Using a jumper wire, ground HEGO circuit at HEGO sensor to engine block. Repeat ENGINE RUNNING SELF-TEST. If service code 41 is displayed replace HEGO sensor, go to step **1)**. If service code 41 is not displayed, go to next step.

**9) EGO Harness Check.** Turn key off and wait 10 seconds. Install breakout box. Disconnect ECA. Disconnect HEGO sensor harness. Measure resistance between test pin No. 16 and HEGO case. Measure resistance between test pins No. 16 and 49. Measure resistance between test pin No. 29 and EGO sensor harness connector. If all circuits have less than 5 ohms resistance, disconnect ECA connector and inspect for damage or corrosion. If connector is okay, replace ECA and repeat QUICK TEST. If any circuit has more than 5 ohms resistance, repair as necessary and repeat QUICK TEST.

**10) Code 41 Verification.** Run vehicle at 2000 RPM for 2 minutes. Turn key off and wait 10 seconds. Preform ENGINE RUNNING QUICK TEST. If code 41 is not present, go to step **15)**. If Code 41 is not present go to next step.

**NOTE: Vacuum leaks in non-EEC areas could cause a code 41. Check for leaking A/C control motor, EGR, PCV, ect. Also check for lead contaminated HEGO sensor.**

**11)** Set DVOM on 20-volt scale. Disconnect HEGO sensor from harness and connect DVOM between HEGO sensor and engine ground. Disconnect vacuum line to fuel pressure regulator and plug end of vacuum line. Start engine and run for approximately 2000 RPM. If reading is less than 0.5 volts within one minute, replace HEGO sensor and repeat QUICK TEST. If reading is more than 0.5 volts in one minute, go to next step.

**12)** Turn key off and wait 10 seconds. Install breakout box, leaving ECA disconnected. Disconnect HEGO harness. Measure resistance of HEGO circuit between test pin No. 16 and HEGO case, test pins No. 16 and 49. Measure resistance of EGO circuit between test pin No. 29 and EGO harness connector. If all readings are 5 ohms or higher, repair circuit with high resistance and repeat QUICK TEST. If both readings are less than 5 ohms, go to next step.

**13)** With key off, breakout box installed and ECA disconnected, set DVOM on 200,000-ohm scale. Measure resistance between test pins No. 29 and 40. If reading is less than 10,000 ohms, correct cause of resistance to ground and repeat QUICK TEST. If resistance is 10,000 ohms or higher, go to next step.

## FUEL CONTROL (Cont.)

**14) Attempt to Eliminate Code 41** With key off, connect HEGO sensor. With pressure regulator vacuum line disconnected. Start and run engine at 2000 RPM for one minute. Allow engine to return to idle. Preform ENGINE RUNNING SELF-TEST. Disregard any other codes at this time. If code 41 is displayed, check for corrosion or damaged pins at ECA connector. If connector is okay, replace ECA and repeat QUICK TEST. If code 41 is not displayed, HEGO sensor input circuit is okay, go to step 1).

**15) Check Heater Element Resistance Of HEGO.** With KOEO, disconnect HEGO sensor. Set DVOM to 20-volt scale. Measure resistance of heater element at HEGO connector at room temperature. If resistance is less than 2.5 ohms or greater than 5.0 ohms, replace HEGO sensor. If resistance is between 2.5 and 5.0 ohms, go to next step.

**16) Check For Power at HEGO Harness Connector** With KOEO, set DVOM to 20-volt scale. Connect positive lead of DVOM to VPWR circuit and negative lead to ground at HEGO harness connector. If a reading of 10.5 volts or greater is obtained, HEGO sensor system is okay. Reconnect HEGO sensor. If reading is less than 10.5 volts go to next step.

**17) Check Continuity Of Ground To HEGO Connector** Turn key off and wait 10 seconds. Set DVOM to 200 ohm scale. Measure resistance of ground circuit from HEGO harness connector to battery ground. If reading is less than 5.0 ohms, repair open in VPWR circuit. If reading is 5.0 ohms or greater, repair open in ground circuit.

## CIRCUIT TEST J

### FUEL PUMP CIRCUIT (INERTIA SWITCH)

**NOTE: Perform this test when Service Code 87 is displayed during QUICK TESTS or when directed here by other test procedures.**

*Fuel Pump Schematic*

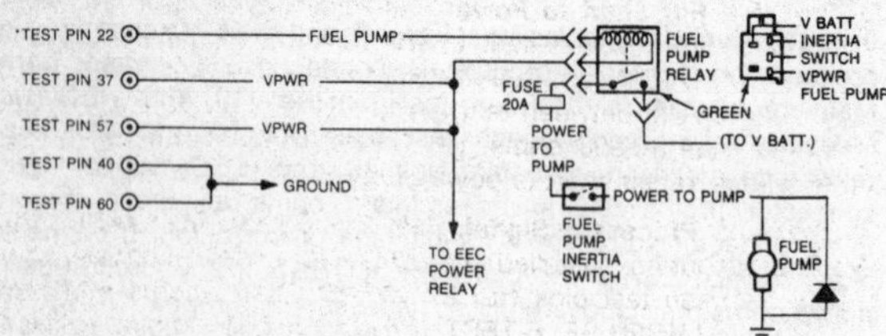
*TEST PIN 22
FUEL PUMP
TEST PIN 37
VPWR
TEST PIN 57
VPWR
TEST PIN 40
TEST PIN 60
GROUND
FUSE 20A
FUEL PUMP RELAY
V BATT
INERTIA SWITCH
VPWR
FUEL PUMP
GREEN
(TO V BATT.)
POWER TO PUMP
POWER TO PUMP
FUEL PUMP INERTIA SWITCH
TO EEC POWER RELAY
FUEL PUMP
*TEST PINS LOCATED ON BREAKOUT BOX.
ALL HARNESS CONNECTORS VIEWED INTO MATING SURFACE.

To prevent replacement of good components, be aware that the following non-EEC related areas may be at fault: fuel lines, fuel filters, throttle body, fuel pump or contaminated fuel.

**1) No Fuel Pressure: Electrical Check.** Install fuel pressure gauge. Cycle key from off to on several times to check if fuel pump runs. DO NOT crank engine. Pump should operate each time key is on. If pump runs as indicated, check fuel pump for problems. If pump does not run as indicated, go to next step.

**2) Checking For VPWR to ECA.** Turn key off and wait 10 seconds. Disconnect ECA 60-pin connector. Inspect connector for damaged pins, corrosion, or loose wires. Install breakout box and reconnect ECA. With KOEO, set DVOM on 20-volt scale and measure voltage between test pins No. 37 and 40, and between test pins No. 57 and 60. If either reading is less than 10.5 volts, go to CIRCUIT TEST A2, step 1). If both readings are 10.5 volts or more, go to next step.

**3) Checking Inertia Switch Resistance.** Turn key off and wait 10 seconds. Leave breakout box installed and ECA connected. Locate and disconnect fuel pump inertia switch. Set DVOM on 200-ohm scale and measure switch resistance. If reading is 5 ohms or more, reset or replace inertia switch. Repeat QUICK TEST. If reading is less than 5 ohms, reconnect inertia switch and go to next step.

**4) Check Voltage to Pump.** With KOEO, breakout box installed and ECA connected. Locate fuel pump relay. Set DVOM on 20-volt scale. Measure voltage between chassis ground and power-to-pump circuit at fuel pump relay while cranking engine. If reading is less than 8 volts, go to next step. If reading is 8 volts or more, check the following: Open in power-to-pump circuit, open in pump and open in ground circuit.

**5) Checking Battery Voltage to Fuel Pump Relay.** Turn key on, leaving engine off. Leave breakout box installed and ECA connected, locate fuel pump relay. Set DVOM on 20-volt scale. Measure voltage between chassis ground and V BATT circuit at fuel pump relay. If reading is less than 10.5 volts, repair open in BATT+ circuit between fuel pump relay and battery positive post. Repeat QUICK TEST. If reading is 10.5 volts or greater, go to next step.

**6) Checking VPWR to Fuel Pump Relay.** Turn key on, leaving engine off. Leave breakout box installed and ECA connected. Locate fuel pump relay. Set DVOM on 20-volt scale. Measure voltage between chassis ground and VPWR circuit at fuel pump relay. If reading is 10.5 volts or more, go to next step. If reading is less than 10.5 volts, ensure inertia switch is on. If inertia switch will not reset, replace switch. If switch is okay, repair open in VPWR circuit between ECA and fuel pump relay. Repeat QUICK TEST.

**7) Checking Fuel Pump Circuit Continuity.** Turn key off and wait 10 seconds. Leave breakout box installed and ECA connected. With DVOM on 200-ohm scale, measure resistance between fuel pump circuit at pump relay and test pin No. 22 at breakout box. If reading is 5 ohms or more, repair open in fuel pump circuit. Repeat QUICK TEST. If reading is less than 5 ohms, go to next step.

**8) Checking For Shorts to Ground.** Turn key off. Leave breakout box installed and disconnect ECA. Disconnect fuel pump relay. With DVOM on 200-k/ohm scale, measure resistance between test pin No. 22 and test pins No. 40 and 60. If reading is less than 10,000 ohms, repair short in fuel pump circuit. Repeat QUICK TEST. If reading is 10,000 ohms or more, go to next step.

**9) Checking For Short to Power.** Turn key off, wait 10 seconds. Disconnect ECA and fuel pump relay. With key on, and breakout box installed, set DVOM on 200-k/ohm scale. Measure resistance between test pin No. 22 and test pins No. 40 and 60. If resistance is 10,000 ohms or more, reconnect fuel pump relay and go to next step. If resistance is less than 10,000 ohms, service short to power in fuel pump circuit. Reconnect fuel pump relay and ECA. Attempt to start vehicle. If vehicle fails to start, replace ECA. Rerun QUICK TEST.

**10) Checking Voltage at Power-to-Pump Circuit.** Leave breakout box installed and ECA disconnected. Install a jumper wire between test pin No. 22 and test pins No. 40 or 60. Set DVOM on 20-volt scale. With KOEO, measure voltage between chassis ground and power-to-pump circuit at fuel pump relay. If reading is 10.5 volts or more, replace ECA and repeat QUICK TEST. If reading is less than 10.5 volts, replace fuel pump relay. Connect ECA and repeat QUICK TEST.

**11) Fuel Pump Relay Check.** Turn key off. Remove fuel pump relay. If fuel pump turns off, replace fuel pump relay. Repeat QUICK TEST. If fuel pump does not turn off, repair short to power-to-pump circuit.

## CIRCUIT TEST KD

### CANISTER PURGE (CANP) CHECK

**NOTE: Perform this test when Service Code 85 is displayed during QUICK TESTS or when directed here by other test procedures.**

*Canister Purge (CANP) Circuit*

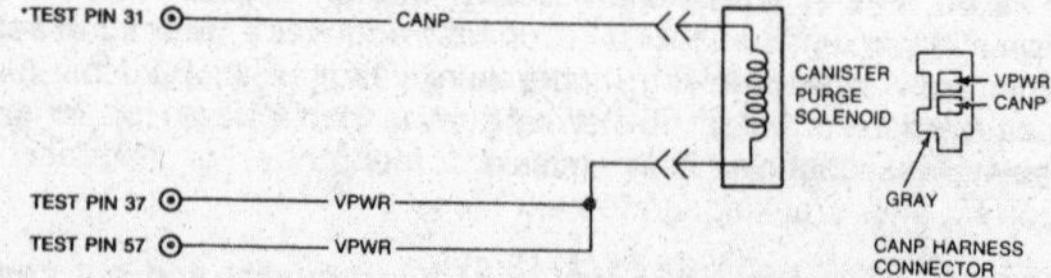
*TEST PIN 31
CANP
CANISTER PURGE SOLENOID
VPWR
CANP
TEST PIN 37
VPWR
TEST PIN 57
VPWR
GRAY
CANP HARNESS CONNECTOR

**1) Checking System Function.** Enter OUTPUT STATE CHECK, see OUTPUT STATE CHECK, under QUICK TEST DIAGNOSTIC AIDS. Use only DVOM, not diagnostic tester, for this step. Turn key off and wait 10 seconds. Set DVOM on 20-volt scale. Connect DVOM negative test lead to STO circuit and positive test lead to positive battery terminal. Using jumper wire, connect STI circuit to signal return at SELF-TEST connector. Perform KOEO SELF-TEST until end of CONTINUOUS SELF-TEST codes (DVOM reads zero volts). Depress

# 1988 COMPUTERIZED ENGINE CONTROLS
# Ford Motor Co. EEC-IV (Cont.)

## CANP CHECK (Cont.)

and release throttle. DVOM should change to a high voltage reading. If reading did not change, depress throttle to WOT and release. If STO voltage does not go high, go to CIRCUIT TEST Q3, step **1)**. Leave test equipment hooked up. If reading changed, remain in OUTPUT STATE CHECK and go to next step.

**2) Checking Solenoid Electrical Function.** With KOEO, set DVOM on 20-volt scale. Disconnect CANP solenoid. Connect DVOM positive test lead to VPWR circuit at CANP solenoid. Connect negative test lead to CANP output circuit on harness connector. While observing DVOM, depress and release throttle several times to cycle output on and off. If CANP circuit does not cycle on and off, remove jumper wire and go to step **4)**. If CANP circuit cycles, go to next step.

**3) Checking Solenoid For Vacuum Leaks.** Turn key off, wait 10 seconds. Remove jumper from STI to signal return. Leave CANP solenoid disconnected. Disconnect vacuum hose from canister purge solenoid on PCV side. Apply 16 in. Hg to CANP solenoid. If CANP solenoid does not hold vacuum for 20 seconds, replace it and repeat QUICK TEST. If CANP holds vacuum for 20 seconds, check fuel system for proper operation.

**4) Measuring Solenoid Resistance.** Turn key off and wait 10 seconds. Set DVOM on 200-ohm scale. Disconnect CANP solenoid connector and measure solenoid resistance. If reading is between 40-90 ohms, connect CANP solenoid and go to next step. If reading is incorrect, replace CANP solenoid and repeat QUICK TEST.

**5) Checking Voltage of VPWR Circuit.** With KOEO. Set DVOM on 20-volt scale. Measure voltage between VPWR circuit at CANP solenoid harness connector and battery negative terminal. If reading is 10.5 volts or greater, go to next step. If reading is less than 10.5 volts, repair open in circuit and repeat QUICK TEST.

**6) Checking Continuity of CANP Circuit.** Turn key off and wait 10 seconds. Disconnect ECA 60-pin connector. Inspect connector for damaged pins, corrosion, or loose wires. Repair if necessary. Connect breakout box, leaving ECA disconnected. Set DVOM on 200-ohm scale. Measure resistance between test pin No. 31 and CANP harness connector. If reading is less than 5 ohms, go to next step. If reading is 5 ohms or more, repair open circuit and repeat QUICK TEST.

**7) Checking For Short to Ground.** Turn key off and wait 10 seconds. Install breakout box, leaving ECA disconnected. Set DVOM on 200-k/ohm scale and disconnect CANP solenoid. Measure resistance between test pin No. 31 and test pins No. 40, 46, and 60. If all readings are 10,000 ohms or more, go to next step. If any reading is less than 10,000 ohms, repair short to ground and repeat QUICK TEST.

**8) Checking For Short to Power.** Turn key off and wait 10 seconds. Install breakout box, leaving ECA disconnected. Set DVOM on 200-k/ohm scale and disconnect CANP solenoid. Measure resistance between test pin No. 31 and test pins No. 37 and 57. If all reading are 10,000 ohms or more, remove breakout box. Replace ECA and repeat QUICK TEST. If any reading is less than 10,000 ohms, repair short to power and repeat QUICK TEST. If code is repeated, replace ECA and repeat QUICK TEST.

## CIRCUIT TEST KE

### IDLE SPEED CONTROL (AIR BY-PASS)

**NOTE: Perform this test when Service Code 12 or 13 is displayed during QUICK TESTS or when directed here by other test procedures. If engine is running rough or has rough idle, correct these conditions before performing test. Causes may be in ignition system, fuel system or EGR system.**

*Idle Speed Control (Air By-Pass) Circuit*

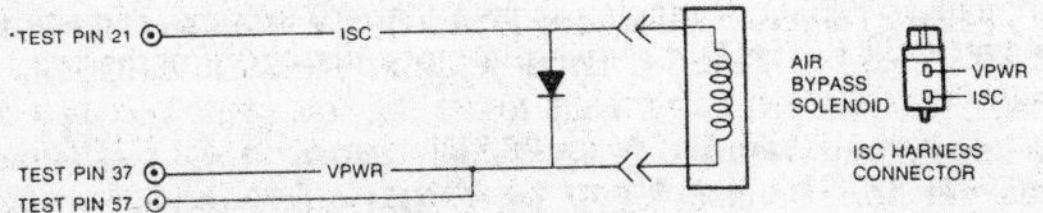
TEST PIN 21
ISC
AIR BYPASS SOLENOID
VPWR
ISC
ISC HARNESS CONNECTOR
TEST PIN 37
VPWR
TEST PIN 57

To prevent replacement of good components, be aware that the following non-EEC related areas may be at fault: engine temperature not up to operating temperature, engine over operating temperature, A/C input (electrical problem), improper idle speed/throttle stop adjustment or cruise control linkage.

**1) Check For RPM Drop.** Turn key off. Connect engine tachometer and start engine. Disconnect Idle Speed Control (ISC) harness. If RPM drops or if engine stalls, go to next step. If not, go to step **3)**.

**2) Checking For EGR Codes.** If EGR service codes 31, 32, 33 or 34 are displayed, go to ENGINE RUNNING SELF-TEST table and perform appropriate CIRCUIT TEST. If these codes are not displayed, or if code 12 or 13 are only displayed, go to next step.

**3) Measuring ISC Solenoid Resistance.** Turn key off. Disconnect ISC solenoid. Set DVOM on 200-ohm scale, and measure resistance of ISC solenoid. If resistance is between 7 and 13 ohms, go to next step. If resistance is less than 7 ohms or more than 13 ohms, replace ISC solenoid and repeat QUICK TEST.

**4) Checking For Internal Short.** With key off and ISC harness disconnected, set DVOM on 200-k/ohm scale. Measure resistance from either ISC pins to ISC solenoid housing. If reading is greater than 10,000 ohms, go to next step. If reading is 10,000 ohms or less, replace ISC solenoid. Repeat QUICK TEST.

**5) Checking VPWR Circuit.** Leave ISC harness disconnected. Turn key on, leaving engine off. Measure voltage between VPWR circuit at ISC harness connector and battery ground terminal. If reading is less than 10.5 volts, repair open in circuit and repeat QUICK TEST. If reading is 10.5 volts or more, go to next step.

**6) Checking Circuit Continuity.** Turn key off and wait 10 seconds. Leave ISC harness disconnected. Disconnect ECA 60-pin connector. Inspect connector for damaged pins, corrosion, or loose wires. Repair if necessary. Install breakout box, leaving ECA disconnected. With DVOM on 200-ohm scale, measure resistance between test pin No. 21 and ISC circuit at ISC harness connector. If reading is greater than 5 ohms, repair open circuit and repeat QUICK TEST. If reading is less than 5 ohms, go to next step.

**7) Checking For Circuit Short to Ground.** Turn key off and wait 10 seconds. Leave ISC harness disconnected. Install breakout box, leaving ECA disconnected. Set DVOM on 200-k/ohm scale. Measure resistance between test pin No. 21 and test pins No. 40, 46, and 60. If any reading is less than 10,000 ohms, repair short to ground and repeat QUICK TEST. If all readings are 10,000 ohms or more, go to next step.

**8) Checking For Short to Power.** Turn key off and wait 10 seconds. Leave breakout box installed. Leave ECA and ISC solenoid disconnected. Set DVOM on 200-k/ohm scale. Measure resistance by connecting DVOM between test pin No. 21 test pin No. 37. If reading is greater than 10,000 ohms, go to next step. If reading is 10,000 ohms or less, repair short to power and repeat QUICK TEST.

**9) Checking Processor Signal.** With key off, connect ECA and ISC. Leave breakout box installed and set DVOM on 20-volt scale. Connect DVOM between test pins No. 21 and 40. Start engine and observe DVOM during KOER SELF-TEST. If DVOM reading varies, replace ISC actuator. Repeat QUICK TEST. If DVOM reading does not vary during QUICK TEST, go to next step.

**10) Code 13 Displayed:** Disconnect ISC harness connector. Connect tachometer. Repeat ENGINE RUNNING SELF-TEST. At end of test, record sevice codes for future use. If RPM remains below 1500 RPM, replace ECA. Repeat QUICK TEST. If RPM remains above 1500 RPM, check engine vacuum hoses for proper routing. Use emission label as a guide. Ensure curb idle is correct. Make sure throttle plates are fully closed. Check throttle and/or cruise control linkage for binding. Repair if necessary. If these items are okay, replace ISC and repeat QUICK TEST.

**11)** Curb Idle Check Turn key off, wait 10 seconds. Deactivate SELF TEST. Run engine at 2000 RPM for 2 minutes. Turn key off, wait 10 seconds. Activate KOER SELF-TEST. If code 17 is present, inspect throttle body and air inlet for contamination. Service as necessary. If throttle body and air inlet are okay, adjust curb idle speed. Repeat QUICK TEST. If code 17 is not present, service other codes as necessary.

## CIRCUIT TEST M

### DYNAMIC RESPONSE TEST

To prevent replacement of good components, be aware that the following non-EEC related areas may be at fault: person testing EEC system did not perform brief Wide Open Throttle (WOT) after Dynamic Response code, mechanical engine problems, or engine did not go over 2000 RPM.

## DYNAMIC RESPONSE TEST (Cont.)

**NOTE: If throttle is snapped open briefly it may not pass the WOT test. Ensure that the throttle is depressed fully to WOT and that engine exceeds 2000 RPM.**

**Code 77 Displayed: System Failed to Recognize WOT Test.** Rerun KOER SELF TEST as follows:

- Activate KOER test and start engine.
- Observe ID code 2 (0 with STAR tester)
- Observe Dynamic Response Code 1 (0 with STAR tester)
- Perform WOT
- Testing complete, service code output begins.

If code 77 is still displayed, replace ECA and rerun QUICK TEST. If code 77 is no longer present, vehicle has passed Dynamic Response test, service other codes as necessary.

## CIRCUIT TEST P

### SPARK TIMING CHECK

**NOTE: Perform this test when directed here by other test procedures.**

*Spark Timing Check Circuit*

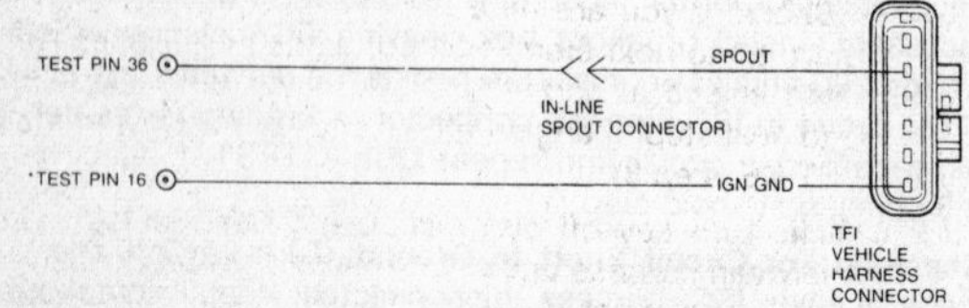
TEST PIN 36
SPOUT
IN-LINE SPOUT CONNECTOR
TEST PIN 16
IGN GND
TFI VEHICLE HARNESS CONNECTOR

To prevent replacement of good components, be aware that the following non-EEC related areas may be at fault: engine condition (valves, vacuum leaks, valve timing, EGR valve, etc.), PIP sensor, and TFI ignition module.

**1) Checking Spark Timing.** Perform ENGINE RUNNING SELF-TEST and verify that SELF-TEST is activated. Check and record timing while in ENGINE RUNNING SELF-TEST. System locks timing and then returns to normal 2 minutes after last service code is displayed. If timing is equal to base plus 15 degrees (±3 degrees), spark timing is correct. See Vehicle Emission Control Information (VECI) decal for base timing specification. Go to ENGINE RUNNING SELF-TEST. If timing is not to specification, go to next step.

**2) Checking Spark Output (SPOUT) Circuit of TFI Module.** Locate Spark Output (SPOUT) connector and open it's connection. Start engine and check for 10 degrees BTDC base timing ± 3 degrees. If base timing is correct, reconnect SPOUT connector and go to next step. If base timing is not correct, adjust base timing. After timing is adjusted, reconnect SPOUT and perform TIMING CHECK. See TIMING CHECK in QUICK TEST section of this article.

**3) Checking For Power to ECA.** Turn key off and wait 10 seconds. Disconnect ECA 60-pin connector. Inspect connector for damaged pins, corrosion, or loose wires. Repair if necessary. Install breakout box. With KOEO, and DVOM set on 20-volt scale, measure voltage between test pins No. 37 and 40. Measure between test pins No. 57 and 60. If either reading is less than 10.5 volts, go to CIRCUIT TEST B, step 1). If both readings are 10.5 volts or more, go to next step.

**4) Checking Continuity of Harness.** Turn key off and wait 10 seconds. Disconnect harness connector at TFI module and connect SPOUT connector. With DVOM on 200-ohm scale, measure resistance between test pin No. 36 at breakout box and pin No. 2 (SPOUT circuit) at TFI harness connector. If reading is greater than 5 ohms, repair open circuit. Connect TFI connector and check timing as described in step 1). If reading is 5 ohms or less, go to next step.

**5) Checking Harness For Ignition Ground.** Leave breakout box installed. With key off. Set DVOM on 200-ohm scale. Measure resistance between test pin No. 16 and TFI pin No. 6 (ignition ground) at TFI vehicle harness. If resistance is less than 5 ohms. Diagnose TFI ignition system. If resistance is 5 ohms or more, repair harness as necessary. Repeat QUICK TEST.

## CIRCUIT TEST Q1

### NO CODES/CODES NOT LISTED

**NOTE: Perform this CIRCUIT TEST when directed by other test procedures.**

*No Codes/Codes Not Listed Circuits*

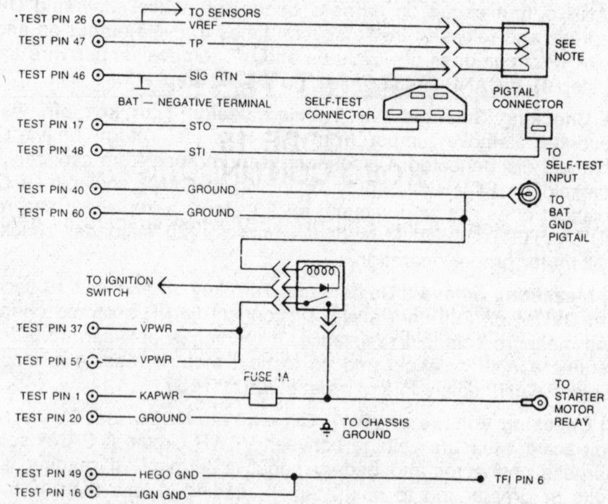
TEST PIN 26
TO SENSORS
VREF
TEST PIN 47
TP
SEE NOTE
TEST PIN 46
SIG RTN
BAT — NEGATIVE TERMINAL
SELF-TEST CONNECTOR
PIGTAIL CONNECTOR
TEST PIN 17
STO
TEST PIN 48
STI
TO SELF-TEST INPUT
TEST PIN 40
GROUND
TEST PIN 60
GROUND
TO BAT GND PIGTAIL
TO IGNITION SWITCH
TEST PIN 37
VPWR
TEST PIN 57
VPWR
FUSE 1A
TEST PIN 1
KAPWR
TO STARTER MOTOR RELAY
TEST PIN 20
GROUND
TO CHASSIS GROUND
TEST PIN 49
HEGO GND
TFI PIN 6
TEST PIN 16
IGN GND

**1) Checking For VREF.** Turn key off and wait 10 seconds. Set DVOM on 20-volt scale. Disconnect TP sensor. With KOEO, measure voltage between VREF at TP harness connector and signal return at SELF-TEST connnector. If reading is less than 4 volts or more than 6 volts, go to CIRCUIT TEST C, step 1). If reading is between 4 and 6 volts, go to next step.

**2) Checking SELF-TEST Input Continuity.** Turn key off and wait 10 seconds. Disconnect ECA 60-pin connector. Inspect connector for damaged pins, corrosion, or loose wires. Repair if necessary. Install breakout box. Disconnect ECA. Set DVOM on 200-ohm scale. Measure resistance between test pin No. 48 and Self-Test Input (STI) at SELF-TEST connector. If reading is 5 ohms or more, repair open in circuit. If reading is less than 5 ohms, go to next step.

**3) Checking SELF-TEST Output Circuit Continuity.** With breakout box installed and ECA disconnected. Set DVOM on 200-ohm scale. Measure resistance between test pin No. 17 and Self-Test Output (STO) at SELF-TEST connector. If reading is 5 ohms or more, repair open in circuit. If reading is less than 5 ohms, go to next step.

**4) Checking HEGO Sensor Ground Continuity.** Turn key off. With breakout box installed and ECA disconnected. Set DVOM on 200-ohm scale. Measure resistance between test pin No. 16 and HEGO sensor case. Measure resistance between test pins No. 16 and 49. If both readings are 5 ohms or more, repair open circuits. If both readings are less than 5 ohms, go to next step.

**5) Checking For STO Short to Ground.** Install breakout box. Set DVOM on 200-ohm scale. Measure resistance between STO at SELF-TEST connector and engine block ground. If reading is 5 ohms or less, go to next step. If reading is greater than 5 ohms, replace ECA and repeat QUICK TEST.

**6) Checking HEGO Harness Short to Power.** Turn key off. Install breakout box and leave ECA disconnected. Disconnect HEGO. Set DVOM on 200-k/ohm scale. Measure resistance between test pin No. 29 and test pins No. 37 and 57. If reading is over 10,000 ohms, repair harness short to power. Repeat QUICK TEST. If reading is less than 10,000 ohms, go to next step.

**7) Checking HEGO For Short to Power.** Turn key off. Disconnect HEGO. Measure resistance between power terminal and EGO circuit terminal on HEGO. If reading is less than 10 k/ohms, replace HEGO. Repeat QUICK TEST. If reading is more than 10 k/ohms, go to next step.

**8) Intermittent Neutral Drive Switch (NDS).** Turn key off. Install breakout box. Connect ECA. Set DVOM on 20-volt scale. Connect DVOM between test pin No. 30 and test pins No. 40 or 60. Perform KOER SELF-TEST. If reading is greater than one volt, repair intermittent fault in NDS harness connector or switch. If okay, go to KOER SELF-TEST for appropriate service codes. If reading is less

## NO CODES–CODES NOT LISTED (Cont.)

than one volt, check for intermittent in NDS circuit. If no intermittent is found, go to next step.

**9) Power Relay Always On.** Leave key off and breakout box installed. Set DVOM on 20-volt scale. Connect DVOM between test pins No. 37 or 57 and test pins No. 40 or 60. Turn key on and off. Wait 10 seconds. If reading does not change from 10.5 volts (or more) to zero volts, replace EEC power relay. Repeat QUICK TEST. If reading changes from 10.5 volts (or more) to zero volts, repair STO circuit for short to ground. Repeat QUICK TEST.

# CIRCUIT TEST Q2

## CODE 15
## KOEO CONTINUOUS

**NOTE: Perform this CIRCUIT TEST when directed by other test procedures.**

**1) Continuous Code 15 Displayed.** Clear continuous memory codes using procedure outlined in CONTINUOUS SELF-TEST. Repeat KOEO SELF-TEST through continuous memory code output. If continuous code 15 is not displayed, continuous code 15 testing is complete. If continuous code 15 is displayed, go to next step.

**NOTE: Continuous code 15 may be displayed when power to Keep Alive Memory (KAM) Test Pin No. 1 at ECA is interrupted. Code 15 may also be displayed the first time SELF-TEST is performed and power is restored to ECA. Repeat SELF-TEST to ensure correct diagnosis.**

**2) Engine Compartment Wire Routing.** Ensure that EEC components and wiring are not close to high tension secondary voltage wires or ignition components. If EEC wiring is close to high tension wires, reroute EEC wiring. Repeat QUICK TEST. If continuous code 15 is no longer displayed, continuous code 15 testing is complete. If continuous code 15 is still displayed, go to next step.

**3) Checking Power Circuit For Keep Alive Memory (KAM).** Turn key off and wait 10 seconds. Disconnect ECA 60-pin connector and inspect for damage. Install breakout box, leaving ECA disconnected. Set DVOM on 20-volt scale. Connect DVOM positive test lead to test pin No. 1 and negative test lead to pins No. 40 or 60. Turn key on and observe voltage reading. If reading is less than 10 volts, repair open to KAM circuit. Repeat QUICK TEST. If reading is 10 volts or more, replace ECA and repeat QUICK TEST.

# CIRCUIT TEST Q3

## OUTPUT STATE CHECK NOT FUNCTIONING

**NOTE: Perform this CIRCUIT TEST when directed by other test procedures.**

**1) Checking Service Codes.** Turn key off and wait 10 seconds. Perform KOEO SELF-TEST and leave key on to enter OUTPUT STATE CHECK. If codes 23, 53, 63 or 68 are displayed, go to KOEO SELF-TEST table and service code(s) as instructed. If no codes are displayed, go to CIRCUIT TEST Q1, step **1)**. If code 11 (Pass) is displayed, go to next step.

**2) Checking Throttle Linkage.** Check throttle and linkage for sticking or binding. If throttle and linkage are okay, replace TP and repeat QUICK TEST. If throttle and linkage are binding, repair as necessary and repeat QUICK TEST.

# CIRCUIT TEST Q4

## ECA POWER CHECK

**NOTE: Perform this CIRCUIT TEST when directed by other test procedures.**

**1)** Power to ECA Check. Turn key off and wait 10 seconds. Disconnect ECA 60-pin connector. Inspect connector for damaged pins, corrosion, or loose wires. Repair if necessary. Install breakout box and set DVOM on 20-volt scale. With KOEO, measure voltage between test pins No. 37 and 40, and between test pins No. 57 and 60.

**2)** If either reading is less than 10.5 volts, go to CIRCUIT TEST B, step **1)**. If both readings are 10.5 volts or more, replace ECA and repeat QUICK TEST.

# CIRCUIT TEST S

## SYSTEM CHECK

Perform this test ONLY after code 11 is displayed in KOEO SELF-TEST and you have been directed here from CIRCUIT TEST A step **14)** or by DIAGNOSIS BY SYMPTOM TEST.

**1) ISC-BPA Check.** If you are here for any reason other than engine stall or no start, go to next step. If engine stalls or if it does not start, attempt to start engine at part throttle. If engine runs rough or does not start, go to next step. If engine runs smoothly at part throttle, go to CIRCUIT TEST KE, step **3)**.

**2) MAP Check.** Turn key off and disconnect MAP sensor. Connect MAP tester between harness and MAP sensor. Connect banana plugs of tester into DVOM and set DVOM on 20-volt scale. Turn key on and measure sensor output voltage while cranking engine. See MAP VOLTAGE OUTPUT table. If DVOM reading decreases from specified range, go to next step. If MAP voltage does not reduce to appropriate RPM while cranking, go to CIRCUIT TEST DF, step **13)**.

***MAP VOLTAGE OUTPUT***

| Elevation (Ft.) | Voltage Output (Volts) |
|---|---|
| 0 | 1.59 |
| 1000 | 1.56 |
| 2000 | 1.53 |
| 3000 | 1.50 |
| 4000 | 1.47 |
| 5000 | 1.44 |
| 6000 | 1.41 |
| 7000 | 1.39 |

**3) EGR Vacuum Check.** Disconnect and plug vacuum hose at EGR valve. Apply 16 in. Hg to EGR valve and release, verify valve is working. Start or attempt to start engine. If symptom is gone, check EGR system. If symptom is still present, check fuel control system.

## CIRCUIT TEST X

### WIDE OPEN THROTTLE (WOT) A/C CUT-OUT (WAC) & A/C DEMAND SWITCH

*A/C Cut-Out & A/C Demand Circuits*

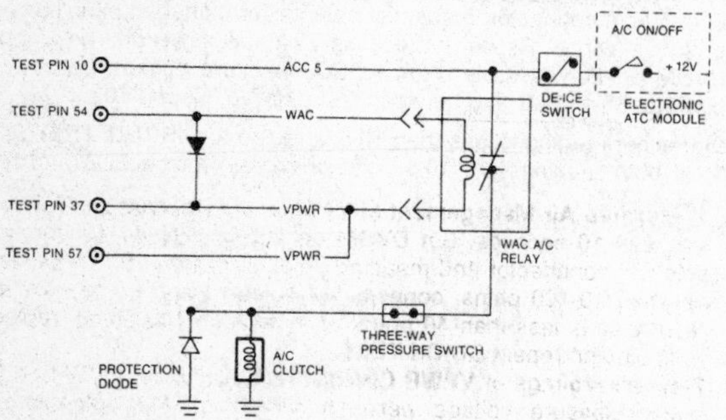
A/C ON/OFF
TEST PIN 10
ACC 5
+ 12V
TEST PIN 54
WAC
DE-ICE SWITCH
ELECTRONIC ATC MODULE
TEST PIN 37
VPWR
TEST PIN 57
VPWR
WAC A/C RELAY
THREE-WAY PRESSURE SWITCH
PROTECTION DIODE
A/C CLUTCH

**1) No A/C: Check For Voltage at A/C Clutch.** Use only DVOM, not diagnostic tester, for this step. With KOEO, set DVOM on 20-volt scale. Measure voltage between A/C clutch harness connector and negative battery terminal. If voltage is greater than 10.5 volts, EEC-IV system is okay, diagnose A/C system. If voltage is less than 10.5 volts, go to next step.

**2) Checking Continuity of Power-to-Clutch Circuit.** Turn key off and wait 10 seconds. Set DVOM on 200-ohm scale. Disconnect A/C clutch harness and harness from WAC relay. Measure resistance between power side of A/C clutch harness connector and power pin at WAC relay. If resistance is less than 5 ohms, reconnect WAC relay and go to next step. If resistance is more than 5 ohms, service open circuit and re-test system.

**3) Checking A/C Output at WOT.** Enter OUTPUT STATE CHECK, see OUTPUT STATE CHECK, under QUICK TEST DIAGNOSTIC AIDS. Use a VOM or DVOM meter for this test. Turn key off and wait 10 seconds. Set meter on 20-volt scale. Connect meter negative (-) lead to STO at Self-Test connector and positive lead to positive (+) battery terminal. Jumper STI to SIG RTN at Self-Test connector. Perform KOEO SELF-TEST until completion of Continuous Memory Code sequence. Meter will indicate less than one volt when test is complete. Depress and release throttle. If voltage increases to 10.5 volts or more, remain in OUTPUT STATE CHECK and go to next step. If voltage does not increase to 10.5 volts, leave test equipment connected and go to test Q3, step **1)**.

**4) Checking WAC System For Cycling.** With vehicle in OUTPUT STATE CHECK, disconnect ECA 60 pin connector and inspect for damaged connections. Service as necessary. Connect breakout box, with ECA connected. Perform KOEO SELF-TEST to receive codes. Set DVOM on 20-volt scale. Connect positive (+) test lead to test pin No. 37 and negative (-) test lead to test pin No. 54. Check DVOM while depressing and releasing throttle several times, to cycle system. If voltage cycles from high to low, go to next step. If voltage does not cycle, remove jumper and go to step **12)**.

**5) Check For Voltage at A/C Input to ECA.** Leave breakout box, ECA and WAC relay connected. With KOEO, turn on A/C. Set DVOM to 20-volt scale. Measure voltage between test pins No. 10 and 40. If voltage is 10.5 volts or greater, go to next step. If voltage is less than 10.5 volts, go to step **7)**.

**6) Checking Continuity of WAC Circuit.** Turn key off and wait 10 seconds. Disconnect ECA 60-pin connector. Inspect for and repair any damaged wiring. Install breakout box, leaving ECA and WAC relay disconnected. Set DVOM on 200-ohm scale. Measure resistance between test pin No. 10 and WAC circuit at WAC relay connector. If reading is 5 ohms or more, repair open in harness and repeat QUICK TEST. If reading is less than 5 ohms, replace WAC relay repeat QUICK TEST.

**7) Voltage Check at A/C Control Module Side of De-Ice.** With KOEO and A/C on. Set DVOM to 20-volt scale. Leave breakout box installed, with ECA and WAC relays connected. Measure voltage between climate control module side of de-icing switch harness connector and test pin No. 40. If voltage is 10.5 volts or greater, go to next step. If voltage is less than 10.5 volts, go to step **9)**.

**8) Checking ECA to De-Ice Switch Continuity.** Turn key off and wait 10 seconds. Disconnect ECA, WAC relay and de-ice switch. Set DVOM on 200-ohm scale. Measure resistance between test pin No. 10 and ECA side of de-ice switch connector. If resistance is 5 ohms or less, go to step **10)**. If resistance is more than 5 ohms, repair open circuit and repeat QUICK TEST.

**9) Checking De-Ice Switch to Climate Control Module Continuity.** Turn key off and wait 10 seconds. Disconnect de-ice switch. Set DVOM to 200-ohm scale. Measure circuit resistance between de-ice switch harness connector and climate control module harness connector. If resistance is more than 5 ohms, repair open. Repeat QUICK TEST. If resistance is less than 5 ohms, go to step **11)**.

**10) Check For Short to Ground.** Turn key off and wait 10 seconds. Disconnect ECA, WAC relay and de-ice switch. Set DVOM to 200-k/ohm scale. Measure resistance between test pin No. 10 and negative (-) battery terminal. Measure between test pins No. 10 and 40. Measure between test pins No. 10 and 60. If reading is 10,000 ohms or more, replace de-ice switch. Repeat QUICK TEST. If reading is less than 10,000 ohms, repair short to ground. Repeat QUICK TEST.

**11) Check For Short to Ground.** Turn key off and wait 10 seconds. Disconnect de-ice switch and Air Temperature Control (ATC) module. Set DVOM on 200-k/ohm scale. Measure resistance between de-ice switch pin No. 4 and negative (-) battery terminal. Measure between de-ice switch pin No. 4 and test pins No. 40 and No. 60. If any reading is 10,000 ohms or greater, replace ATC module. Repeat QUICK TEST. If reading is less than 10,000 ohms, repair short to ground. Repeat QUICK TEST.

**12) Measure WAC Relay Resistance.** Set DVOM on 200-ohm scale. Disconnect WAC relay connector and measure relay resistance. If resistance is between 70-120 ohms, go to next step. If resistance is less than 70 ohms or greater than 120 ohms, replace WAC relay. Repeat QUICK TEST.

**13) Check Continuity From WAC Relay to ECA.** Turn key off and wait 10 seconds. Disconnect ECA and check connector for bad connections. Repair as necessary. Connect breakout box leaving ECA disconnected. Set DVOM on 200-ohm scale. Measure circuit resistance between test pin No. 54 and WAC harness connector. If resistance is 5 ohms or less, go to next step. If resistance is more than 5 ohms, repair open in WAC circuit. Repeat QUICK TEST.

**14) Check WAC Circuit For Shorts to Ground.** Turn key off and wait 10 seconds. Leave breakout box installed and processor disconnected. Set DVOM on 200-k/ohm scale. Measure resistance between test pins No. 54 and No. 40. Measure resistance between test pins No. 46 and No 54. Also measure resistance between test pins No. 54 and negative (-) battery terminal. If all readings are 10,000 ohms or greater, go to next step. If any reading is less than 10,000 ohms, repair shorts to ground in WAC circuit. Repeat QUICK TEST.

**15) Check WAC Circuit For Shorts to Ground.** Turn key off and wait 10 seconds. Install breakout box. Disconnect ECA and WAC. Set DVOM to on 200-k/ohm scale. Measure resistance between test pin No. 54 and No. 37. Measure resistance between test pin No. 54 and positive (+) battery terminal. If all readings are 10-k/ohms or greater, go to next step. If any readings are less than 10,000 ohms, repair shorts to power in WAC circuit and go to next step.

**16) Check Continuity From WAC to VPWR** Turn key off and wait 10 seconds. Connect breakout box. Disconnect ECA and WAC. Set DVOM on 200-ohm scale. Measure circuit resistance between test pin No. 37 and WAC. If resistance is 50 ohms or less, go to next step. If reading is more than 50 ohms, repair open in power to WAC circuit. Repeat QUICK TEST.

**17) Check WAC Circuit For Shorts to Ground.** Turn key off and wait 10 seconds. Connect breakout box. Disconnect ECA and WAC. Using DVOM on 200-ohm scale, measure between test pin No. 37 and WAC harness connector. Measure between test pin No. 37 and No. 40. Measure between test pin No. 37 and No. 60. Measure between test pin No. 37 and battery ground. If all readings are are 10,000 ohms or greater, go to next step. If any reading less than 10,000 ohms, repair shorts to ground. Repeat QUICK TEST.

**18) Check For Voltage at A/C Clutch.** Turn key off and wait 10 seconds. Connect breakout box. Disconnect ECA and A/C clutch. Turn on A/C. With KOEO, set DVOM on 20-volt scale. Measure voltage between A/C demand input pin at WAC relay harness connector and ground. If voltage is 10.5 volts or greater, replace ECA. Repeat QUICK TEST. If voltage is less than 10.5 volts, replace WAC relay and repeat QUICK TEST.

## CIRCUIT TEST Y

### ERRATIC IGNITION

**NOTE: Perform this test ONLY when a code 14 is displayed in QUICK TEST.**

***TFI Ignition Circuit***

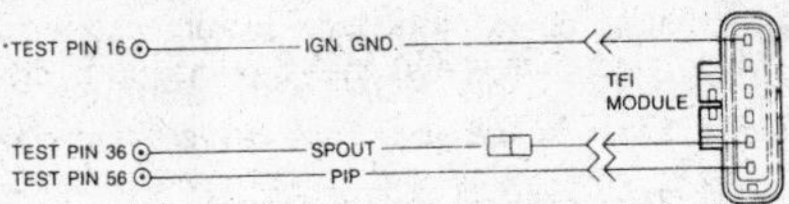
·TEST PIN 16
IGN. GND.
TFI MODULE
TEST PIN 36
SPOUT
TEST PIN 56
PIP

**1) Code 14 Displayed.** This code indicates that 2 successive erratic Profile Ignition Pick-Up (PIP) pulses were sent to ECA causing possible engine miss or stall. Check EEC and TFI ignition system for loose wires and connections, arcing secondary ignition components (coil, cap, wires, etc.), or an on-board 2-way radio. Ensure radio antenna and power leads are routed properly. If any of the above conditions are present, repair as necessary and repeat QUICK TEST. If none are present, go to next step.

**2) Distributor Check.** Turn key off and wait 10 seconds. Deactivate SELF-TEST. Using CONTINUOUS MONITOR (WIGGLE) TEST, observe VOM or diagnostic tester for indication of fault while lightly tapping on TFI ignition module and distributor, and while wiggling TFI harness connector. If fault is indicated, disconnect and inspect connectors and terminals. If connectors and terminals are okay, diagnose TFI ignition system. If no fault is indicated, go to next step.

**3) Checking EEC-IV Harness.** While in CONTINUOUS MONITOR (WIGGLE) TEST, observe VOM or diagnostic tester for indication of fault while wiggling, shaking, or bending small sections of harness from TFI module to firewall. Also check harness from firewall to ECA. Isolate PIP circuit, if possible. If fault is indicated, isolate and repair problem and repeat QUICK TEST. If no fault is indicated, go to next step.

**4) Checking ECA and Harness Connectors.** Turn key off and wait 10 seconds. Disconnect ECA 60-pin connector. Inspect connector for damaged pins, corrosion, or loose wires. If connectors and terminals are okay, fault cannot be duplicated at this time. Diagnose TFI ignition system. If connectors and terminals are damaged, repair as necessary and repeat QUICK TEST.

## CIRCUIT TEST Z

### THERMACTOR AIR MANAGEMENT

***Thermactor Air Managment Circuits***

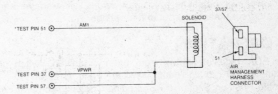

·TEST PIN 51
AM1
SOLENOID
37/57
51
AIR MANAGEMENT HARNESS CONNECTOR
TEST PIN 37
VPWR
TEST PIN 57

**1) Measure Air Management (AM) Solenoid Resistance.** Turn key off and wait 10 seconds. Set DVOM on 200-ohm scale. Disconnect AM solenoid connnector and measure solenoid resistance. If resistance is between 40-100 ohms, connect AM solenoid and go to next step. If resistance is less than 40 ohms or more than 100 ohms, replace AM solenoid and repeat QUICK TEST.

**2) Check Voltage of VPWR Circuit.** With KOEO, set DVOM on 20-volt scale. Measure voltage between VPWR at AM solenoid vehicle harness connector and battery ground. If reading is less than 10.5 volts repair open circuit, and repeat QUICK TEST. If voltage reading is 10.5 volts or greater, go to next step.

**3) Check Continuity of AM Circuit.** Turn key off and wait 10 seconds. Diconnect ECA. Inspect connectors for loose connections. Repair if necessary. Connect beakout box to harness, leaving ECA disconnected. Set DVOM on 200-ohm scale. Measure resistance between test pin No. 51 and AM vehicle harness connector. If resistance is 5 ohms or greater repair open circuit and repeat QUICK TEST. If resistance is less than 5 ohms go to next step.

**4) Check For Short to Ground** Turn key off and wait 10 seconds. Disconnect breakout box and ECA. Disconnect AM solenoid. Set DVOM on 200-k/ohm scale. Measure resistance between test pin No. 51 and test pins No. 40, 46, and 60. If all resistance readings are 10,000 ohms or more, go to next step. If any resistance is less than 10,000 ohms, repair short to ground. Repeat QUICK TEST.

**5) Check For Short to Power** Turn key off and wait 10 seconds. Set DVOM on 200-k/ohm scale. Leave breakout box installed and ECA disconnected. Disconnect AM solenoid. Measure resistance between test pins No. 51 and No. 37. Measure resistance between test pin No. 51 and No. 57. If all readings are less than 10,000 ohms, repair short to power. Repeat QUICK TEST. If code is still present, replace ECA. Repeat QUICK TEST. If any resistance reading is 10,000 ohms or greater. Remove breakout box. Replace ECA. Rerun QUICK TEST.

# 1988 COMPUTERIZED ENGINE CONTROLS
# Ford Motor Co. Tracer

## DESCRIPTION

The Electronic Control Assembly (ECA) is the center of the system. The ECA receives and processes information. The ECA controls various outputs based on information received. A "Check Engine" light (malfunction indicator light) is used to alert the driver of certain malfunctions in the engine control system. If such a fault occurs, the processor will substitute a value or values, allowing the engine to operate from these preprogrammed values.

## OPERATION

The ECA receives inputs from battery, ignition switch, ignition module (RPM signal), neutral switch, Vane Airflow (VAF) meter, Throttle Position Sensor (TPS), Engine Coolant Temperature (ECT) sensor, Barometric Pressure (BARO) sensor, clutch switch, Coolant Temperature Switch (CTS) and Exhaust Gas Oxygen (EGO) sensor. The ECA uses this information in controlling the following outputs: injectors, A/C cut relay, purge solenoids No. 1 and 2, Idle Speed Control (ISC) solenoid and ignition module.

The ECA detects engine operation, driving condition, and exhaust gas oxygen content, from various switches, sensors and components. ECA uses this information in controlling the amount of fuel injected into engine. The ECA also has some control over the evaporative emission, idle-up, ignition and deceleration systems.

## INPUTS

**Air Charge Temperature Sensor** – The ACT sensor is a thermistor. It is mounted in the VAF meter and senses intake air temperature.

**BARO Sensor** – The BARO sensor is mounted in the engine compartment and sends atmospheric pressure information to the ECA.

**Battery** – The battery supplies the ECA with keep alive power, allowing ECA to store information after vehicle is turned off.

**Coolant Temperature Switch** – The CTS is mounted in the radiator. The switch is closed below 63°F (17°C) and sends this information to the ECA.

**Clutch Switch** – The switch informs the ECA when the clutch is depressed. The switch is closed when the pedal is depressed and open when the pedal is released.

**Engine Coolant Temperature Sensor** – The ECT sensor is a thermistor that is mounted in the intake manifold coolant passage. It provides engine coolant temperature information to the ECA.

**EGO Sensor** – The EGO sensor is mounted in the exhaust manifold and provides the ECA with exhaust oxygen content information.

**Ignition Pulse** – The ignition pulse provides engine speed information to the ECA. The pulse is produced by the ignition module which is located in the distributor.

**Ignition Switch** – The ignition switch informs the ECA of ignition key position.

**Neutral Switch (Automatic Transaxle)** – The switch informs the ECA when the automatic transaxle is in Neutral.

**Neutral Switch (Manual Transaxle)** – The switch informs the ECA when the manual transaxle is in Neutral. The switch is closed in Neutral and open in all other positions.

**Throttle Position Sensor** – The TPS consists of a lever attached coaxially to the throttle valve, a guide cam driven by the lever, and movable idle and power contacts. It detects idle and high load conditions based on the opening of the throttle valve. The sensor sends a signal to ECA when throttle is in the following positions:

- Idle – Throttle valve opening 1.5 degrees or less (idle or deceleration).
- Heavy load (or PSW) – Throttle valve opening 70 degrees or more.

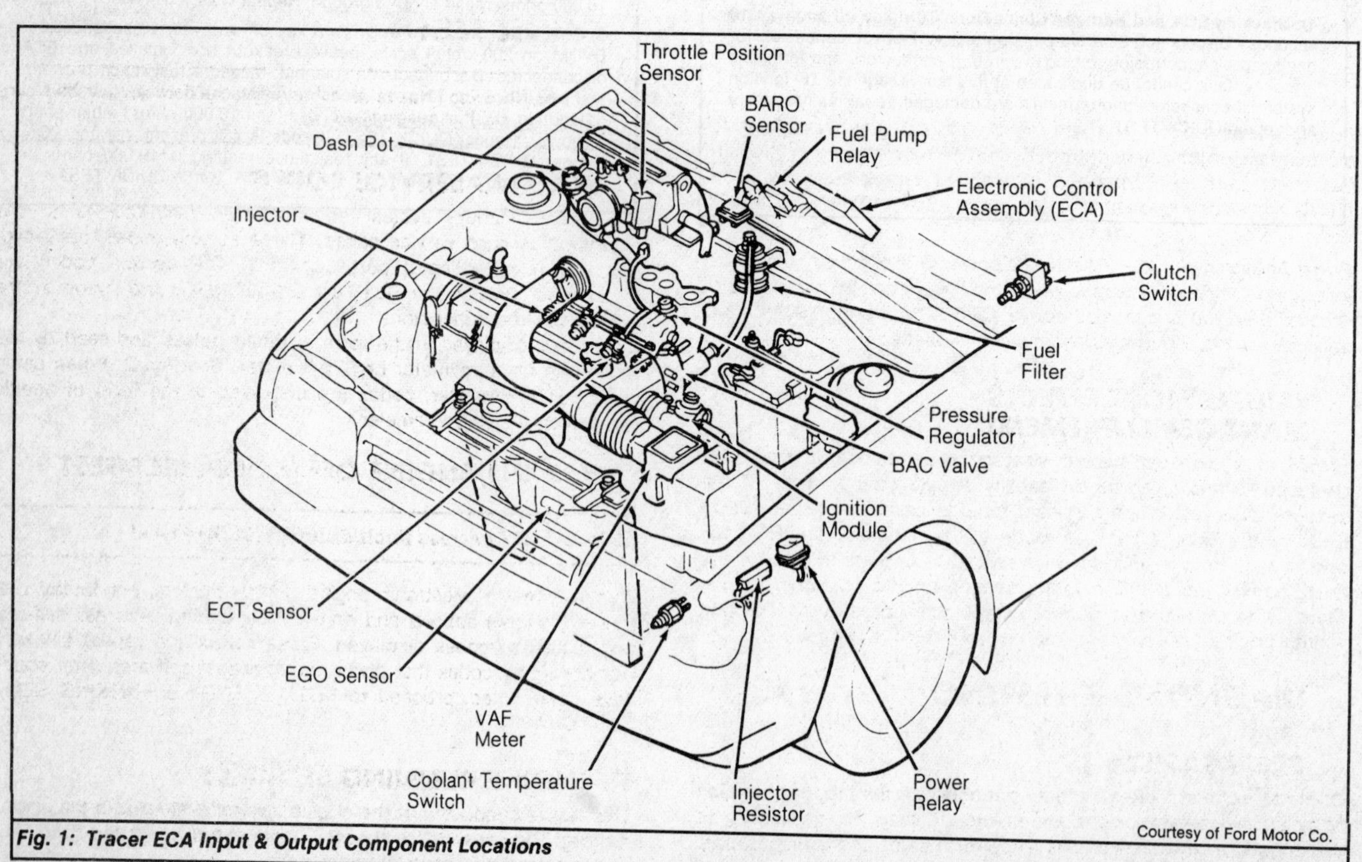
Throttle Position Sensor
BARO Sensor
Fuel Pump Relay
Dash Pot
Electronic Control Assembly (ECA)
Injector
Clutch Switch
Fuel Filter
Pressure Regulator
BAC Valve
Ignition Module
ECT Sensor
EGO Sensor
VAF Meter
Coolant Temperature Switch
Injector Resistor
Power Relay
Courtesy of Ford Motor Co.

*Fig. 1: Tracer ECA Input & Output Component Locations*

**Vane Airflow Meter** – The VAF meter, through the use of a potentiometer, converts intake air volume into a voltage signal that varies depending on airflow. This signal is sent to the ECA. The voltage increases as airflow increases, and decreases as airflow decreases. The VAF meter also incorporates a sensor to detect intake air temperature and fuel pump switch to control fuel pump operation.

### OUTPUTS

**A/C Cut Relay** – The ECA uses the A/C cut relay to disengage the air conditioning clutch during power steering operation and during rapid acceleration. When the power steering is operated and engine RPM drops below 500, the ECA will switch the A/C off.
During rapid acceleration or Wide Open Throttle (WOT), the ECA will switch off the A/C cut relay for a period of about 16 seconds. If the throttle is released before 16 seconds has elasped, the A/C will be switched on again after 3 seconds.

**Fuel Injectors** – The fuel injectors are electro-mechanical devices which supply metered and atomized fuel to the engine. The amount of fuel supplied to the engine is determined by how long the injection solenoid coil is energized.
The length of time that injector is energized is known as pulse width. The ECA controls pulse width according to the inputs received from the various engine sensors and switches. When the injectors are energized, the needle valve is pulled off its seat. Fuel is then injected around the back face of intake valve.

**Ignition Module** – The ECA modifies ignition timing when the vehicle is operated at high altitudes. Based on input from the BARO sensor, at altitudes of 3280 feet or higher, the ECA will signal the ignition module to advance ignition timing.

**ISC Solenoid** – The ISC solenoid is controlled by the ECA. On deceleration and during high altitude operation, the ECA uses the ISC solenoid to provide increased airflow to the intake plenum.

**Malfunction Indicator Light (MIL)** – The MIL is designed to warn the driver or technician of an emission related fault detected by the ECA. The ECA will illuminate the indicator light when the fault is recognized.

**Purge Solenoid No. 1** – The ECA uses No. 1 solenoid to control the evaporative emission control system in relation to temperature. When the vehicle is operated at ambient temperature of 122°F (50°C) and engine coolant temperature is above 122°F (50°C), ECA opens the No. 1 purge solenoid valve.

**Purge Solenoid No. 2** – The No. 2 solenoid is used to control the evaporative emission control system in relation to engine load. When the engine is operated above 1500 RPM, during WOT or low vacuum, the No. 2 purge solenoid valve is opened.

### FAILURE MODE EFFECTS MANAGEMENT (FMEM)

FMEM is a back-up system strategy programmed in the ECA, designed to allow vehicle driveability should one or more of the sensor inputs fail. When a sensor input is perceived to be out-of-limits by the ECA, a back-up mode will be initiated. The ECA will substitute a fixed in-limit sensor value and continue to monitor the faulty sensor input. If the faulty sensor returns to within normal limits, ECA will return to normal engine running strategy. The MIL "Check Engine" light will remain on when FMEM is in effect.

## DIAGNOSIS & TESTING

### PREPARATION

Correct results of the testing are dependent on the proper operation of related non-electronic components. It may be necessary to disconnect harness assemblies to perform some of the inspections. Pin locations should be noted before disassembly. If the engine will not start, starts but stalls, idles rough or runs rough, proceed to Key On Engine Off (KOEO) test.

***NOTE: On vehicles built AFTER 11/2/87, proceed to SWITCH MONITOR TEST (VEHICLES BUILT AFTER 11/2/87 ONLY) before servicing a code, on all others, proceed to EQUIPMENT HOOK-UP.***

**Visual Check** – Inspect air cleaner and inlet ducting. Check all engine vacuum hoses for damage, leaks, cracks, blockage, proper routing, etc.

**Vehicle Preparation** – Perform all safety steps required to start and run vehicle tests. Turn off all electrical loads. Start engine and run until operating temperature is reached. Turn engine off and proceed to EQUIPMENT HOOK-UP.

### EQUIPMENT HOOK-UP

**MIL Equipped Vehicles** – **1)** Turn ignition off and connect color coded adapter cable to STAR tester.
**2)** Connect adapter cable leads to the proper self-test connectors and latch center button. Slide switch in "MECS" position and turn ignition on. Ensure that "Fast-Slow" switch is in "Slow" position.

**Using Analog Volt/Ohm Meter (VOM)** – **1)** Turn ignition off and connect a jumper wire from the self-test input connector to ground. Set volt/ohmmeter on a DC voltage range to read from 0-20 volts.
**2)** Connect volt/ohmmeter between White/Green (Black/Green on vehicles built BEFORE 11/2/87) wire terminal on 6-pin self-test output connector and battery negative terminal.

**Non-MIL Equipped Vehicles Using Analog VOM** – **1)** Turn ignition off and set volt/ohmmeter on a DC voltage range to read from 0-20 volts.
**2)** Connect volt/ohmmeter between Green terminal and Black terminal on the 6-pin self-test connector, located under dash.

## QUICK TEST

***NOTE: The following charts used in this portion the article, are provided courtesy of Ford Motor Co.***

### READING SERVICE CODES

The engine control system communicates malfunctions to the technician through service codes. These service codes are 2 digit numbers representing a particular fault. The service codes are transmitted through the Self-Test Output (STO) line found in the vehicle self-test connector.
Codes are displayed in the form of timed pulses and read by the technician on a voltmeter or STAR tester. *See Fig. 2.* When using analog volt/ohmmeter, codes are displayed in the form of needle sweeps on the volt/ohmmeter.

### KEY ON/ENGINE OFF (KOEO) SELF-TEST

***NOTE: DO NOT depress throttle during KOEO self-test.***

This is a test of electronic engine control system, conducted with power (voltage) applied and engine not running. Activate self-test and record all codes displayed. Erase codes and repeat self-test. Diagnose only codes that occur during repeat self-test. After codes have been noted, proceed to KOEO & ENGINE RUNNING SELF-TEST CHART.

### ENGINE RUNNING SELF-TEST

This test is conducted of the engine control system with the engine running. The sensors are checked under actual operating conditions and at normal operating temperatures.

# 1988 COMPUTERIZED ENGINE CONTROLS
## Ford Motor Co. Tracer (Cont.)

**FAULT CODE CHART – VEHICLES BUILT AFTER 11/2/87**

| Code No. | Input devices | Malfunction | Code Pattern | Fail-safe function | Code in constant memory |
|---|---|---|---|---|---|
| 01 | Ignition pulse | Broken wire, short circuit | ON / OFF | — | Yes |
| 08 | Vane air flow meter | Broken wire, short circuit | ON / OFF | Basic fuel injection amount fixed as for 2 driving modes 1) Idle switch: ON 2) Idle switch: OFF | Yes |
| 09 | Engine coolant temp. | Broken wire, short circuit | ON / OFF | Coolant temp. input fixed at 80°C (176°F) | Yes |
| 10 | Vane air temp. sensor | Broken wire, short circuit | ON / OFF | Intake air temp. input fixed at 20°C (68°F) | Yes |
| 14 | Barometric pressure sensor | Broken wire, short circuit | ON / OFF | Atmospheric pressure input fixed at 760 mmHg (29.9 in Hg) | Yes |
| 15 | EGO sensor | Sensor output continues less than 0.55V 120 sec. after engine starts (1500 rpm) | ON / OFF | Feedback system operation cancelled | Yes |
| 17 | Feedback system | Oxygen sensor output not changed 20 sec. after engine exceeds 1500 rpm | ON / OFF | Feedback system operation cancelled | Yes |

| Code No. | Output devices | Pattern of output signals (Self-Diagnosis Checker or MIL) | Code in constant memory |
|---|---|---|---|
| 25 | Pressure regulator control solenoid valve | ON / OFF | No |
| 26 | Canister purge regulator solenoid valve | ON / OFF | No |
| 27 | Canister purge solenoid valve | ON / OFF | No |
| 34 | Idle speed control solenoid valve | ON / OFF | No |

# 1988 COMPUTERIZED ENGINE CONTROLS
# Ford Motor Co. Tracer (Cont.)

## FAULT CODE CHART – MIL EQUIPPED VEHICLES BUILT BEFORE 11/2/87

| Code No. | Location of Problem | MIL Indication | Service Code Pattern | FMEM Function |
|---|---|---|---|---|
| 01 | Ignition pulse | Yes | 1 Cycle; On; Off | — |
| 08 | Vane air flow meter | Yes | 1 Cycle; On; Off | Maintain a basic signal at a preset value |
| 09 | Engine coolant temperature sensor | Yes | 1 Cycle; On; Off | Maintain a constant 80°C (176°F) command |
| 10 | Vane air temperature sensor | Yes | 1 Cycle; On; Off | Maintains a constant 20°C (68°F) command |
| 14 | Barometric pressure sensor | Yes | 1 Cycle; On; Off | Maintains a constant command of the sea-level pressure |
| 15 | Exhaust gas oxygen sensor | Yes | 1 Cycle; On; Off | Stops feedback correction |
| 17 | Feedback system | No | 1 Cycle; On; Off | Stops feedback correction |
| 71 | Throttle position sensor | Yes | 1 Cycle; On; Off | — |

***NOTE:** If there is trouble in more than 2 places, the fault indication will be for the lowest code number first. If after a malfunction has occurred, and the ignition is turned off, the malfunction indicator will not be displayed. The ECA has a built-in, fail-safe mechanism. If a malfunction occurs during driving, the ECA will operate on its own initiative as shown in the above chart and driving performance will be affected. If the problem is corrected during indication, ECA memory must be erased by disconnecting negative battery cable for 5 or more seconds.*

## FAULT CODE CHART – NON-MIL EQUIPPED VEHICLES

| Code No. | Location of Problem | Code Pattern | FMEM Function |
|---|---|---|---|
| 1 | Ignition pulse | On / Off — 1 Cycle | ———— |
| 2 | Vane air flow meter | On / Off — 1 Cycle | Maintains the basic signal at a preset value |
| 3 | Engine temperature sensor | On / Off — 1 Cycle | Maintains a constant 80°C (176°F) command |
| 4 | Vane air temperature sensor | On / Off — 1 Cycle | Maintains a constant 20°C (68°F) command |
| 10 | Feedback system | On / Off — 1 Cycle | Stops feed back correction |
| 14 | Barometric pressure sensor | On / Off — 1 Cycle | Maintains a constant command of the sea-level pressure |

***NOTE:** If there is trouble in more than 2 places, the fault indication will be for the lowest code number first. Even if the problem is corrected during indication, 1 cycle will be indicated. If after a malfunction has occurred, and the ignition is turned off, the malfunction indicator will not be displayed. The ECA has a built-in, fail-safe mechanism. If a malfunction occurs during driving, the ECA will operate on its own initiative as shown in the above chart and driving performance will be affected.*

# 1988 COMPUTERIZED ENGINE CONTROLS
# Ford Motor Co. Tracer (Cont.)

## KOEO & ENGINE RUNNING SELF-TEST CHART

| | CIRCUIT TEST | CIRCUIT TEST | CIRCUIT TEST |
|---|---|---|---|
| KEY ON ENGINE OFF SERVICE CODE | 1.6L NON-MIL EQUIPPED | 1.6L BUILT BEFORE 11/2/87 | 1.6L BUILT AFTER 11/2/87 |
| 01 GO to ▶ | A1 | A1 | A1 |
| 02 GO to ▶ | DK1 | — | — |
| 03 GO to ▶ | DE1 | — | — |
| 04 GO to ▶ | DA1 | — | — |
| 08 GO to ▶ | — | DK1 | DK1 |
| 09 GO to ▶ | — | DE1 | DE1 |
| 10 GO to ▶ | HA1 | DA1 | DA1 |
| 14 GO to ▶ | DF1 | DF1 | DF1 |
| 15 GO to ▶ | — | HE1 | HE1 |
| 17 GO to ▶ | — | HA1 | HA1 |
| 25 GO to ▶ | — | — | KV1 |
| 26 GO to ▶ | — | — | KD1 |
| 27 GO to ▶ | — | — | KW1 |
| 34 GO to ▶ | — | — | KE1 |
| 71 GO to ▶ | — | DH1 | — |
| CODE 88 FLASHING | NB1 | NB1 | NB1 |
| CODES NOT LISTED | Q1 | Q1 | Q1 |
| NO CODES | GO TO ENGINE RUNNING SELF-TEST | | |

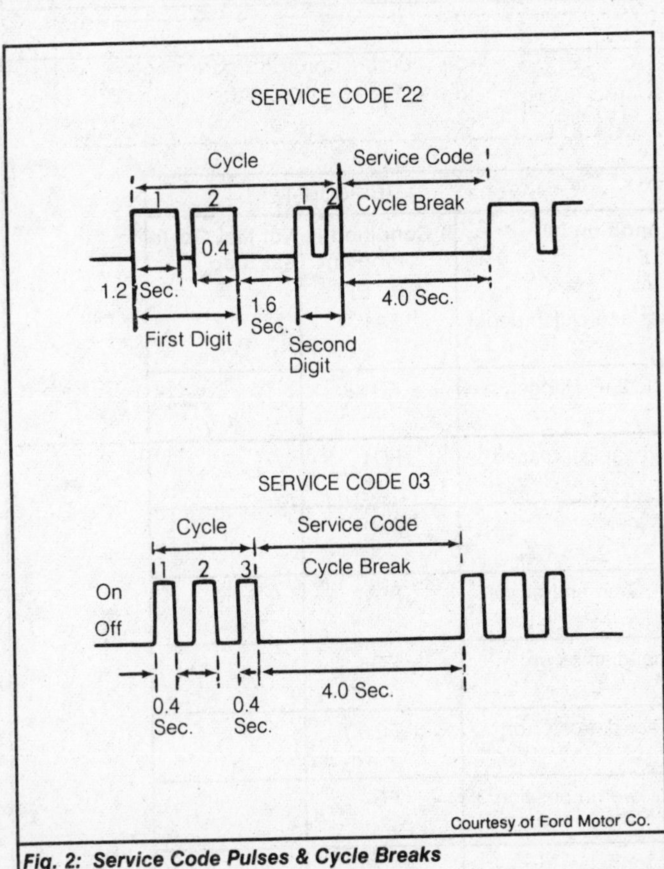
SERVICE CODE 22
Cycle
Service Code
1
2
1
2
Cycle Break
0.4
1.2
Sec.
1.6
Sec.
4.0 Sec.
First Digit
Second
Digit
SERVICE CODE 03
Cycle
Service Code
1
2
3
Cycle Break
On
Off
0.4
Sec.
0.4
Sec.
4.0 Sec.
Courtesy of Ford Motor Co.

*Fig. 2: Service Code Pulses & Cycle Breaks*

***NOTE:** It is necessary to clear codes in memory before continuing with this test. Also DO NOT depress throttle during test.*

**Performing Test – 1)** If the symptom is a no-start, proceed to CONTINUOUS SELF-TEST. Verify a pass Code 00 was received in the KOEO SELF-TEST before continuing.

**2)** Deactivate self-test. Start and run engine at 2000 RPM for 5 minutes to warm up EGO sensor. Turn engine off and wait 10 seconds.

**3)** Restart engine and activate self-test. Record all service codes displayed and proceed to KOEO & ENGINE RUNNING SELF-TEST CHART.

These codes are issued as a result of information stored during continuous self-test and are stored in permanent memory until they are erased. These codes are displayed only during KOEO testing. These codes should be used for diagnosis only when KOEO and ENGINE RUNNING SELF-TESTS result in Code 00 and all QUICK TEST steps have been successfully completed.

***NOTE:** Verify that a Pass Code 00 was received in both KOEO and ENGINE RUNNING SELF-TESTS before continuing with this test. Clear codes before continuing with test.*

**Clearing Continuous Memory Codes**

- Run KOEO SELF-TEST.
- When service codes are being displayed, deactivate self-test. On STAR tester, unlatching center button (switch in "UP" position) will deactivate self-test. On analog volt/ohmmeter, remove jumper wire from between self-test input (STI) connector and ground.
- Disconnect negative battery cable and depress brake pedal for 5-10 seconds.

# 1988 COMPUTERIZED ENGINE CONTROLS
# Ford Motor Co. Tracer (Cont.)

## CONTINUOUS MEMORY/MONITOR SELF-TEST CHART

| KEY ON ENGINE OFF SERVICE CODE | CIRCUIT TEST 1.6L NON-MIL EQUIPPED | CIRCUIT TEST 1.6L BUILT BEFORE 11/2/87 | CIRCUIT TEST 1.6L BUILT AFTER 11/2/87 |
|---|---|---|---|
| 01 GO to ▶ | A1 | A1 | A1 |
| 02 GO to ▶ | DK1 | — | — |
| 03 GO to ▶ | DE1 | — | — |
| 04 GO to ▶ | DA1 | — | — |
| 08 GO to ▶ | — | DK1 | DK1 |
| 09 GO to ▶ | — | DE1 | DE1 |
| 10 GO to ▶ | HA1 | DA1 | DA1 |
| 14 GO to ▶ | DF1 | DF1 | DF1 |
| 15 GO to ▶ | — | HE1 | HE1 |
| 17 GO to ▶ | — | HA1 | HA1 |
| 25 GO to ▶ | — | — | KV1 |
| 26 GO to ▶ | — | — | KD1 |
| 27 GO to ▶ | — | — | KW1 |
| 34 GO to ▶ | — | — | KE1 |
| 71 GO to ▶ | — | DH1 | — |
| CODE 88 FLASHING | NB1 | NB1 | NB1 |
| CODES NOT LISTED | Q1 | Q1 | Q1 |
| NO CODES | Q1 | Q1 | GO TO SWITCH MONITOR TEST |

## SWITCH MONITOR TEST CHART

| SWITCH MONITOR TEST | | CIRCUIT TEST | |
|---|---|---|---|
| Switch | Led or Analog VOM Condition | If Condition Is Not Met Go To Pinpoint Test Step 1.6L EFI | |
| Neutral Gear Switch and clutch engage switch (MTX) | LED "ON" or 12 V in gear and clutch pedal released (VOM) | FA1 | |
| Inhibitor Switch (ATX) | LED "ON" or 12 V in D, 1, 2, R Range (VOM) | FB1 | |
| Brake On-Off | LED "ON" or 12 V with Pedal Depressed (VOM) | FD1 | |
| Throttle Position Sensor | LED "ON" or 12 V with Accelerator Depressed (VOM) | DH1 | |
| A/C Switch | LED "ON" or 12 V with A/C on and blower in position 1 (VOM) | FF1 | |
| Headlamp Switch | LED "ON" or 12 V with headlamps on (VOM) | FG8 | |
| Rear Defroster | LED "ON" or 12 V with rear defroster on (VOM) | FG6 | |
| A/C-Heater Blower Control Switch | LED "ON" or 12 V with blower in position 3 or 4 (VOM) | FG4 | |
| Cooling Fan Temperature Switch | LED "ON" or 12 V with connector disconnected (VOM) | FG2 | |

## CONTINUOUS MEMORY/MONITOR SELF-TEST

**Determining Continuous Memory Codes To Be Tested** – The cause of some of the continuous memory codes may have been eliminated during either KOEO or ENGINE RUNNING SELF-TEST repairs. Diagnose only those continuous memory codes for which a similar code has not been previously serviced. Once this has been determined, go to KOEO & ENGINE RUNNING SELF-TEST procedures.

**KOEO – 1)** Connect STAR tester or volt/ohmmeter as described in EQUIPMENT HOOK-UP. Turn on STAR tester and latch center button or ground STI if using volt/ohmmeter.
**2)** Turn ignition key to the "ON" position to place system in "CONTINUOUS MONITOR" mode. Tap, move and wiggle the suspect sensor and/or harness.
**3)** If a fault is detected, a service code will be stored in memory and will be indicated. Proceed to CONTINUOUS MEMORY/MONITOR SELF-TEST CHART to continue with diagnosis.

**Engine Running – 1)** Connect STAR tester or volt/ohmmeter as described in EQUIPMENT HOOK-UP. Start engine and run until operating temperature is reached.
**2)** Activate self-test and wait 2 minutes. Deactivate and reactivate self-test. DO NOT turn off engine. System is now in Engine Running "CONTINUOUS MONITOR" Mode.
**3)** Tap, move and wiggle the suspect sensor and/or harness. If a fault is detected, a service code will be stored and indicated. Proceed to CONTINUOUS MEMORY/MONITOR SELF-TEST CHART to continue with diagnosis.

## SWITCH MONITOR TEST (VEHICLES BUILT AFTER 11/2/87 ONLY)

***NOTE: All switches must be tested individually. Allowing a switch to remain on while testing another will lead to false test results.***

This test checks input signals from the individual input switches to the ECA. Before activating this test, deactivate self-test and turn all accessories off. Place transmission selector in Neutral and proceed to Using STAR Tester or Using Analog Volt/Ohmmeter. If all switches are okay, proceed to CIRCUIT TEST Q1.

**Using STAR Tester** – Connect STAR tester adapter cable. Note output of LED on the adapter cable as each switch is actuated. Record all tests results and proceed to SWITCH MONITOR TEST CHART.

**Using Analog Volt/Ohmmeter – 1)** Ground STI connector. Connect volt/ohmmeter between Red/Blue (Pos.) and Yellow/Green (Neg.) wire terminals on 6-pin self-test output connector.
**2)** Note output of the analog volt/ohmmeter as each switch is actuated. Record all tests results and proceed to SWITCH MONITOR TEST CHART.

***NOTE: DO NOT depress throttle, clutch or engage transmission, unless directed.***

## CONTINUOUS MONITOR (WIGGLE) TEST

**Systematic Use – 1)** Visually inspect sensor, switch or solenoid affected. Enter CONTINUOUS SELF-TEST and lightly tap sensor, switch or solenoid.
**2)** Push/pull on sensor, switch or solenoid connector while not disconnecting. Test and wiggle (shake) harness vigorously, working from sensor, switch or solenoid toward dash panel and from the dash panel to ECA in small sections.
**3)** If volt/ohmmeter does not have a positive indication of an intermittent fault, carefully disconnect sensor, switch or solenoid from harness. Remove terminals from connector.
**4)** Inspect terminals at both ends for corrosion, bad crimps and improperly seated terminals. Reconnect after inspection and unplug processor from harness.
**5)** Inspect terminals for corrosion, bad crimps and improperly seated terminals. If volt/ohmmeter does not indicate an intermittent fault plug in connector and erase CONTINUOUS SELF-TEST codes. See CONTINUOUS SELF-TEST for clearing codes.

# CIRCUIT TESTS

## HOW TO USE CIRCUIT TESTS

**1)** DO NOT perform any CIRCUIT TEST unless specified by QUICK TEST. Ensure all non-EEC-IV related faults are corrected. Do not replace any part unless directed to do so. When more than one service code is received, start with first code displayed.
**2)** Do not measure voltage or resistance at ECA or connect any test light to ECA unless specified. All measurements are made by probing REAR of the connector. Isolate both ends of a circuit and turn key off whenever checking for shorts or continuity, unless specified.
**3)** Disconnect solenoids and switches from harness before measuring continuity, resistance, or applying 12 volts. Follow each test step in order until fault is found. After each repair, check all component connections and repeat CIRCUIT TEST(S).
**4)** An "open" is defined as any resistance reading greater than 5 ohms, unless otherwise specified. A "short" is defined as any resistance reading less than 10,000 ohms to ground, unless otherwise specified.
**5)** On CIRCUIT TEST Q, to prevent replacement of good components, be aware that non-EEC-IV related areas may also be at fault.

***NOTE: Fuel contaminated engine oil will affect some service codes. If this is suspected, remove PCV valve from valve cover and repeat QUICK TEST. If problem is corrected, change engine oil and filter.***

***NOTE: The following acronyms are used throughout the circuit test portion of this article, and can be described as Self-Test Output (STO), Self-Test Input (STI), Switch Monitor Lamp (SML), Reference Voltage (VREF), Signal Return (SIGRTN), Vehicle Power (VPRW) and Keep Alive Power (KAPWR).***

# 1988 COMPUTERIZED ENGINE CONTROLS
# Ford Motor Co. Tracer (Cont.)

## CIRCUIT TEST A

### NO START

To prevent replacement of good components, be aware that the following non-EEC related areas may be at fault: fuel quantity and quality, ignition system damage, cracks, moisture, etc., engine mechanical conditions such as valves, timing belt, etc. Also included are starter and battery circuit problems.

**1) Distributor Pulse Check.** With distributor plugged in, connect test light between distributor Black (Yellow/Blue on vehicles built after 11/2/87) wire and ground. Crank engine and check for test light illumination. If test light does not illuminate go to next step. If test light illuminates, proceed to step **5**).

**2) Voltage at Distributor.** Turn ignition key to "ON" position. Using DVOM, measure voltage between distributor Black/White wire and ground (also between Blue/Red wire and ground on vehicles built PRIOR to 11/2/87). Check for reading greater than 10 volts. If reading is greater than 10 volts, diagnose for mechanical problem. If reading is less than 10 volts on Black/White wire, proceed to next step. If reading is less than 10 volts on White/Black and Blue/Red wires, proceed to step **4**).

**3) Ignition Switch Power Check.** Place DVOM on 20-volt scale and turn ignition key to "ON" position. Measure voltage between ignition switch Black/White wire and ground. If reading is greater than 10 volts, repair Black/White wire from ignition switch to coil and/or distributor. Also, check fuses. If voltage is 10 volts or less, proceed to CIRCUIT TEST FC, step **1**).

**4) Voltage at ECA.** With breakout box installed and using DVOM on 20-volt scale, turn ignition key to "ON" position. Measure voltage between test pin No. 56 and pin No. 40 (ground) on vehicles built before 11/2/87. On vehicles built after 11/2/87, test pin No. 36 and pin No. 40 (ground). If reading is greater than 10 volts, check for open or short in White/Black wire from distributor to ECA on vehicles built after 11/2/87. On all others, check Blue/Red wire. If reading is 10 volts or less, proceed to CIRCUIT TEST FC step **1**).

**5) Coil-Pulse Check.** With coil connected, connect test light between tach pulse connector and ground. Crank engine and check for test light flash. If test light does not flash, repair Yellow/Blue wire from coil to ECA on vehicles built after 11/2/87 (Black wire on all other models). If test light flashes, proceed to next step.

**6) Voltage at Coil.** Place DVOM on 20-volt scale and turn ignition key to "ON" position. Measure voltage between ignition coil Black/White and ground. If reading is greater than 10 volts, proceed to next step. If reading is 10 volts or less, repeat step **3**).

**7) PIP Signal Check.** Install breakout box and connect test light between pin No. 47 and pin No. 40 (ground) on vehicles built before 11/2/87. On all other models, use pin No. 6 and pin No. 40 (ground). Crank engine and check for test light flashes. If test light does not flash, repair open in Yellow/Blue wire from distributor to ECA on vehicles built after 11/2/87. On all others, check Black wire. If test light flashes, proceed to next step.

**8) Spark at Plugs.** Connect spark tester between each plug wire and ground. Crank engine and check for good spark. If spark jumps tester gap, replace ECA. If spark does not jump tester air gap, diagnose for mechanical problem.

*Ignition Pulse Circuit*

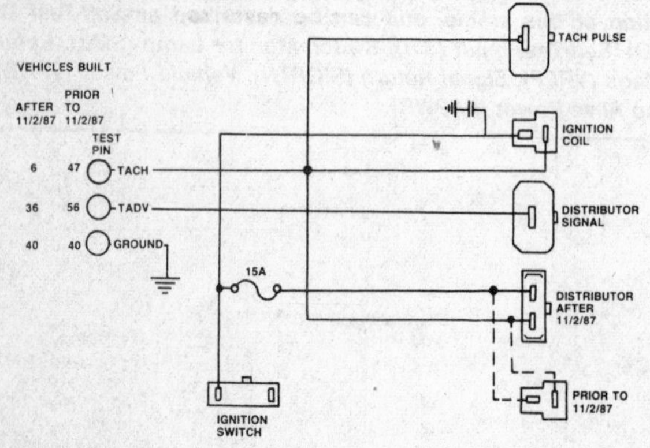

VEHICLES BUILT
AFTER 11/2/87
PRIOR TO 11/2/87
TEST PIN
6 47 TACH
36 56 TADV
40 40 GROUND
15A
TACH PULSE
IGNITION COIL
DISTRIBUTOR SIGNAL
DISTRIBUTOR AFTER 11/2/87
PRIOR TO 11/2/87
IGNITION SWITCH


## CIRCUIT TEST B

### VEHICLE BATTERY

To prevent replacement of good components, be aware that the following non-EEC related areas may be at fault: battery cables and ground straps, voltage regulator and alternator, and ignition switch.

**1) Power Check.** With ignition off, install breakout box. Using DVOM on 20-volt scale, measure voltage between pin No. 1, ignition switch (Black wire) and battery ground. Also measure voltage between power relay (Blue wire) and battery ground on vehicles built after 11/2/87. Measure voltage between power relay No. 1 (Blue/White wire), power relay No. 2 (Blue wire) and battery ground on vehicles built before 11/2/87. If reading is greater than 10 volts, proceed to step **3**). If reading is 10 volts or less, proceed to next step.

**2) Check for Opens.** Install breakout box and remove 30, 60 and 80 amp fuses. Disconnect battery. Using DVOM on 200-ohm scale, measure resistance between battery and 30, 60 and 80 amp fuses. Also between 60 and 15 amp fuses, and both relay (Blue wires) on vehicles built after 11/2/87. Measure resistance between 30 amp fuse and relay No. 1 (Blue/White wire), and 30 amp fuse and relay No. 2 (Blue wire) on vehicles built before 11/2/87. If resistance is greater than 5 ohms, repair open in wire(s) in question or replace main fuse block as required. If resistance is 5 ohms or less, proceed to next step.

**3) Relay Ground Check.** With ignition off and DVOM on 200-ohm scale, measure resistance between power relay (Black wire) and battery negative terminal on vehicles built after 11/2/87. On all others, measure resistance between power relay No. 1 and No. 2 (Black wires), and battery negative. If resistance is 5 ohms or more, repair open Black wire in question from power relay(s) to ground. If resistance is less than 5 ohms, proceed to next step.

**4) ECA Ground Check.** With ignition off and DVOM on 200-ohm scale, measure resistance between ECA case, pins No. 49, 46, 20 and 40, and battery negative terminal. If resistance is 5 ohms or more, repair open in wire(s) in question from power relay(s) to ground. If resistance is less than 5 ohms, proceed to next step.

**5) ECA Ground Fault Isolation.** With ignition off, install breakout box. Unplug harness from ECA. With DVOM on 200-ohm scale, measure resistance between pins No. 46 and 49, pins No. 46 and 20, and pins No. 46 and 40. If resistances are less than 5 ohms, ECA is okay. Repeat QUICK TEST. If resistance is 5 ohms or more, replace ECA.

*Vehicle Battery Circuit*

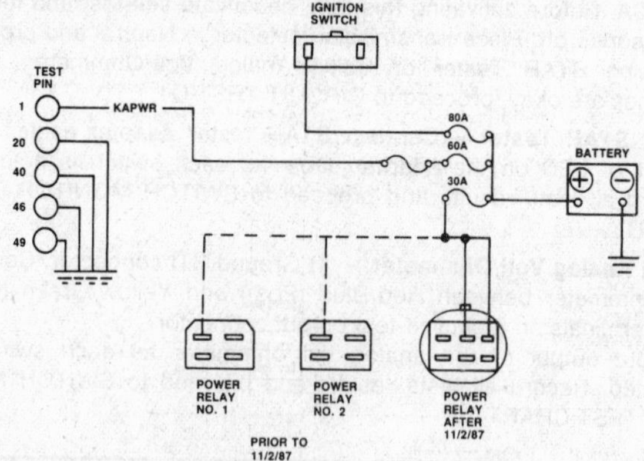

IGNITION SWITCH
TEST PIN
1 KAPWR
20
40
46
49
80A
60A
30A
BATTERY
POWER RELAY NO. 1
POWER RELAY NO. 2
PRIOR TO 11/2/87
POWER RELAY AFTER 11/2/87


## CIRCUIT TEST DA

### VANE AIR TEMPERATURE SENSOR

To prevent replacement of good components, ensure that the following conditions are met:

- Test not performed in unusually cold or hot ambient temperature conditions.
- Ambient temperature must be greater than 50°F (10°C) for this test.
- Inspect all wiring, harness, connectors and components for evidence of overheating, insulation damage, looseness, shorting or other damage. If none of the above mentioned is present, proceed to test step **1**).

# 1988 COMPUTERIZED ENGINE CONTROLS
# Ford Motor Co. Tracer (Cont.)

## CIRCUIT TEST DA (Cont.)

**1) VAT Resistance Check.** With ignition off, install breakout box and unplug ECA. Using DVOM on 10K scale, measure resistance between pins No. 25 and 40. If resistance is not within specification, proceed to step **5)**. If resistance is within specification, proceed to next step.

*TYPICAL VANE AIR TEMP. (VAT) SENSOR RESISTANCE*

| Ambient Temperature F° (C°) | Ohms Between Test Pins No. 25 & 46 |
|---|---|
| 32 (0) | 5800 |
| 65 (18) | 2700 |
| 185 (85) | 300 |
| 220 (104) | 180 |
| 240 (116) | 125 |

**2) VAT Voltage Check.** Install breakout box. Using DVOM on 10-volt scale, turn ignition on and measure voltage between pins No. 25 and 40. At 68°F (30°C), voltage reading should be 2.4 volts. Measure voltage between pins No. 46 and 44. At 68°F (30°C), voltage reading should be zero. If all readings are within specification, replace ECA. If all readings are not within specification, proceed to next step.

**3) Short Between VAT & ECA Check.** Turn ignition off and disconnect battery negative terminal. Install breakout box and unplug ECA. With DVOM on 200-ohm scale, measure resistance between the following pins:

- No. 25 and No. 1.
- No. 25 and No. 37.
- No. 25 and No. 40 (ground).
- No. 46 and No. 1.
- No. 46 and No. 37.

If any of the resistances are less than 10,000 ohms, repair wire(s) in question. If all resistances are 10,000 ohms or more, reconnect battery and proceed to next step.

**4) Signal Return Check.** With ignition off and ECA unplugged, install breakout box. Using DVOM on 200-ohm scale, measure resistance between pins No. 46 and 40 (ground), and pin No. 40 (ground) and chassis ground. If resistance is less than 5 ohms, replace ECA. If resistance is 5 ohms or greater, repair open wire(s) in question.

**5) Opens Between ECA & VAT.** With ignition off and ECA unplugged, install breakout box. Using DVOM on 200-ohm scale, measure resistance between pin No. 25 and pin No. 46 (VAF meter Brown/Yellow wire), and VAF meter Blue/Yellow wire. If resistance is 5 ohms or more, repair wire(s) in question. If resistance is less than 5 ohms, reconnect ECA and proceed to next step.

**6) VAF Sensor Resistance Check.** With ignition off, unplug VAF connector. Using DVOM on 10-k/ohm scale, measure resistance between VAF meter terminals (Brown/Yellow and Yellow/Green wires, and Brown/Yellow and Blue/Yellow wires). If resistance is 2000-2500 ohms, repair short in Brown/Yellow wire from VAF to ECA. If resistance is not within specification, replace VAF meter.

*VAT Sensor Circuit*

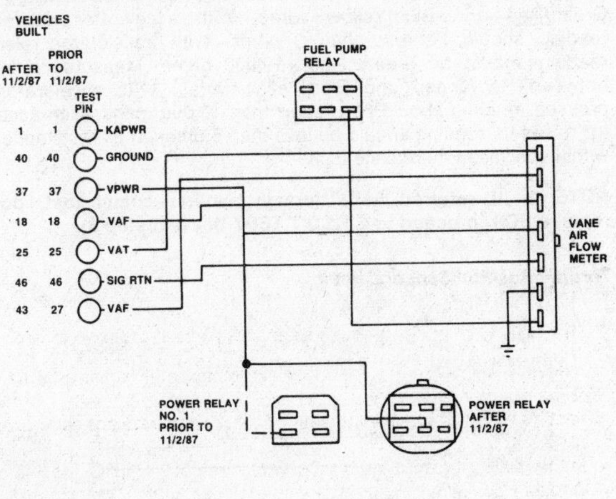

VEHICLES BUILT
AFTER 11/2/87
PRIOR TO 11/2/87
TEST PIN
FUEL PUMP RELAY
1 1 KAPWR
40 40 GROUND
37 37 VPWR
18 18 VAF
25 25 VAT
46 46 SIG RTN
43 27 VAF
VANE AIR FLOW METER
POWER RELAY NO. 1 PRIOR TO 11/2/87
POWER RELAY AFTER 11/2/87


## CIRCUIT TEST DE

### ENGINE COOLANT TEMPERATURE SENSOR

To help prevent replacement of good components, check coolant level, oil level, cooling fan operation, thermostat and other related components for proper condition and operation.

**1) Engine Coolant Temperature (ECT) Sensor Resistance Check.** Turn ignition off and install breakout box. Unplug ECA. Using DVOM on 200-k/ohm scale, measure resistance between Pins No. 7 and 46. Resistances should indicate as shown in ENGINE COOLANT TEMPERATURE SENSOR RESISTANCE table. If resistance is within specification, proceed to next step. If resistance is not within specification, proceed to step **5)**.

*ENGINE COOLANT TEMPERATURE SENSOR RESISTANCE*

| Ambient Temperature F° (C°) | Ohms Between TEST Pins No. 7 & 46 |
|---|---|
| 50 (10) | 58,750 |
| 65 (18) | 40,500 |
| 180 (82) | 3600 |
| 220 (104) | 1840 |

**2) ECT Sensor Voltage Check.** Install breakout box. Using DVOM on 20-volt scale and ignition on, measure voltage between Pins No. 7 and 46. Voltage reading should indicate 2.5 volts at 68°F (20°C). After warming up, voltage reading should indicate 0.3-0.6 volts. If voltage reading is within specification, replace ECA. If voltage reading is not within specification, proceed to next step.

**3) Short Between ECT & ECA Check.** Turn ignition off and disconnect battery negative terminal. Install breakout box and unplug ECA. Using DVOM on 200-k/ohm scale, measure resistance between the following pins:

- No. 7 and No. 1.
- No. 7 and No. 19 (vehicles built before 11/2/87).
- No. 7 and No. 26 (vehicles built after 11/2/87).
- No. 7 and No. 37.
- No. 7 and No. 40.
- No. 46 and No. 1.
- No. 46 and No. 19.
- No. 46 and No. 37.

If resistances are 10,000 ohms or more, proceed to next step. If resistances are less than 10,000 ohms, repair wire(s) in question.

**4) Signal Return Check.** Turn ignition off and install breakout box. Using DVOM on 200-ohm scale, measure resistance between pins No. 46 and 40, and pin No. 40 and chassis ground. If resistance is less than 5 ohms, replace ECA. If resistance is 5 ohms or more, repair ground wire.

**5) Open Between ECT Sensor & ECA Check.** Turn ignition off and install breakout box. Using DVOM on 200-ohm scale, measure resistance between ECT Blue/Red wire and pin No. 7, and ECT Blue/Yellow wire and pin No. 46. If resistance is 5 ohms or greater, repair wire(s) in question. If resistance is less than 5 ohms, proceed to next step.

**6) ECT Sensor Resistance Check.** Turn ignition off and unplug ECT sensor. Using DVOM on 200-ohm scale, measure resistance across ECT sensor. See ENGINE COOLANT TEMPERATURE SENSOR RESISTANCE table. If resistance is within specification, repair short in wire(s). If resistance is not within specification, replace ECT.

*ECT Sensor Circuit*

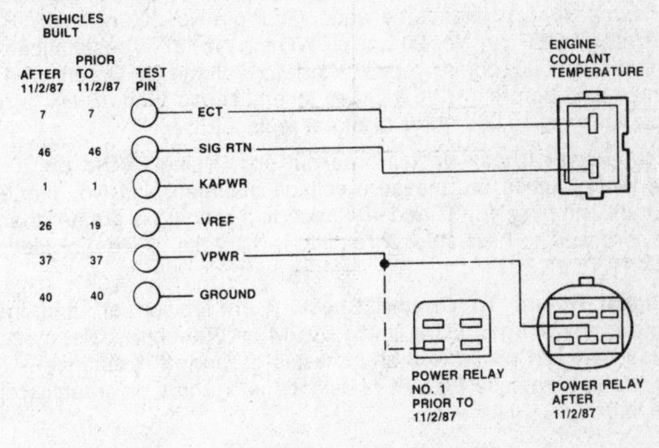

VEHICLES BUILT
AFTER 11/2/87
PRIOR TO 11/2/87
TEST PIN
ENGINE COOLANT TEMPERATURE
7 7 ECT
46 46 SIG RTN
1 1 KAPWR
26 19 VREF
37 37 VPWR
40 40 GROUND
POWER RELAY NO. 1 PRIOR TO 11/2/87
POWER RELAY AFTER 11/2/87

## CIRCUIT TEST DF

### BARO SENSOR

Inspect for obstructed vacuum lines, basic engine mechanical operation, wiring, wiring harness and insulation condition, before proceeding with test procedures.

**1) VREF & Signal Return Check.** Install breakout box and connect ECA. Using DVOM on 20-volt scale, turn ignition on and measure voltage between the following pins:

Vehicles built before 11/2/87.

- No. 19 and No. 46.
- No. 19 and No. 40.
- No. 46 and No. 40

Vehicles built after 11/2/87.

- No. 26 and No. 46.
- No. 26 and No. 40.
- No. 46 and No. 40.

Voltage reading should indicate 4-6 volts on all except those readings taken from pins No. 46 and 40. Voltage reading on pins No. 46 and 40 should indicate zero volts. If voltage readings are within specification, proceed to next step. If voltage reading is greater than specification, proceed to step **5**). If voltage reading is less than specification, proceed to step **6**).

**2) Check For BARO Sensor Voltage.** Connect vacuum pump to BARO sensor and install breakout box. Using DVOM on 20-volt scale, with ignition on, measure voltage between pins No. 45 and 46. With zero vacuum, reading should be 3.5-4.5 volts. At 30 in. Hg, reading should indicate zero volts. If reading is within specification, replace ECA. If reading is not within specification, proceed to next step.

**3) BARO Sensor Power Check.** Using DVOM on 20-volt scale and ignition turned on, measure voltage between wires indicated in BARO POWER CHECK table. If voltage is not within specification, repair appropriate wire(s) in question. If voltage is within specification, proceed to next step.

***BARO POWER CHECK (VEHICLES BUILT AFTER 11/2/87)***

| Between | Voltage |
|---|---|
| White/Black Wire & Ground | 4-6 |
| White/Black & Blue/Yellow Wires | Zero |
| Blue/Yellow Wire & Ground | Zero |

***BARO POWER CHECK (VEHICLES BUILT BEFORE 11/2/87)***

| Between | Voltage |
|---|---|
| Green Wire & Ground | 4-6 |
| Green Wire & Blue/Yellow Wires | 4-6 |
| Blue/Yellow Wire & Ground | Zero |

**4) BARO Sensor Voltage Check.** Connect vacuum pump to BARO sensor. Unplug BARO sensor connector. Using DVOM on 20-volt scale, turn ignition on and measure voltage between Light Green wire and ground. With zero vacuum, reading should be zero volts. At 30 in. Hg, reading should be 3.5-4.5 volts. If reading is within specification, repair open in Light Green wire from BARO sensor to ECA. If reading is not within specification, replace BARO sensor.

**5) VREF Short Check.** Turn ignition off and install breakout box. Unplug ECA and using DVOM on 200-k/ohm scale, measure resistance between VREF pin No. 19 and KAPWR pin No. 1, and VREF pin No. 19 and VPWR pin No. 37 on vehicles built before 11/2/87. On all others, measure resistance between VREF pin No. 26 and KAPWR pin No. 1, and VREF pin No. 26 and VPWR pin No. 37. If resistances are less than 10,000 ohms, repair short to voltage in Green wire on vehicles built before 11/2/87. On all others, repair White/Black wire. If resistances are 10,000 ohms or more, replace ECA.

**6) ECA Power Check.** Install breakout box. Using DVOM on 20-volt scale, with ignition on, measure voltage between pins No. 1 and 40 (ground), and pins No. 37 and 40 (ground). If reading is greater than 10 volts, proceed to next step. If reading is 10 volts or less, proceed to CIRCUIT TEST FC.

**7) Signal Return To Ground Check.** Turn ignition off and install breakout box. Plug in ECA. Using DVOM on 200-ohm scale, measure voltage between pin No. 40 and chassis ground. If resistance is less than 5 ohms, replace ECA. If resistance is 5 ohms or greater, repair open in ground (Black wire).

## CIRCUIT TEST DF (Cont.)

**8) ECA Ground Check.** Turn ignition off and install breakout box. Using DVOM on 200-ohm scale, measure resistance between pin No. 40 and chassis ground. If resistance is less than 5 ohms, replace ECA. If resistance is 5 ohms or greater, repair open in ground (Black wire).

***BARO Sensor Circuit***

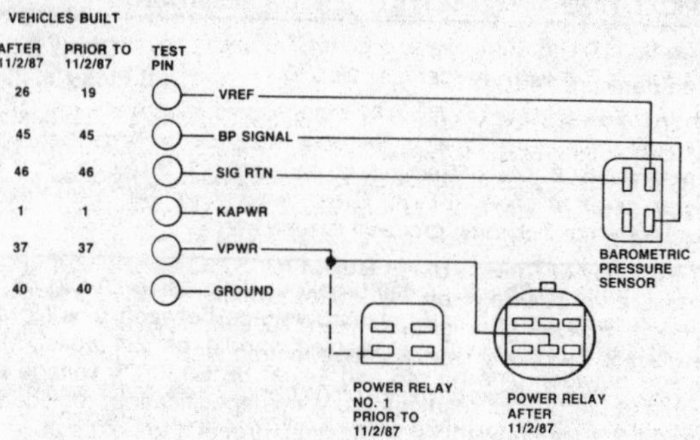
VEHICLES BUILT
AFTER 11/2/87
PRIOR TO 11/2/87
TEST PIN
26 19 VREF
45 45 BP SIGNAL
46 46 SIG RTN
1 1 KAPWR
37 37 VPWR
40 40 GROUND
BAROMETRIC PRESSURE SENSOR
POWER RELAY NO. 1 PRIOR TO 11/2/87
POWER RELAY AFTER 11/2/87

## CIRCUIT TEST DH

### THROTTLE POSITION SENSOR

To prevent replacement of good components, check throttle stop adjustment, speed control linkage, wiring, wiring harness, connectors and other mechanically related components.

**1) TPS Voltage Check.** Install breakout box and turn ignition key to "ON" position. Using DVOM on 20-volt scale, measure voltage between pins No. 28 and 40, and pins No. 47 and 40 on vehicles built after 11/2/87. On all others, measure resistance between pins No. 24 and 40. With accelerator depressed, reading should be greater than 10 volts on pin No. 28 and less than 1.5 volts on pins No. 47 and 24. With accelerator released, reading should be less than 1.5 volts on pin No. 28 and greater than 10 volts on pins No. 47 and 24.

**2) Signal Return Check.** Turn ignition off and install breakout box. Using DVOM on 200-ohm scale, measure resistance between pin No. 46 and TPS Blue/Yellow wire, and pin No. 46 and chassis ground. If resistance is 5 ohms or more, repair open in wire(s) in question. If resistance is less than 5 ohms, proceed to next step.

**3) TPS Operation Check.** With ignition off and using DVOM on 200-ohm scale, on vehicles built after 11/2/87, measure resistance between Green/Orange and Blue/Yellow wires. With accelerator depressed, reading should be less than 5 ohms. With accelerator released, reading should be greater than 10,000 ohms. Measure resistance between Orange and Blue/Yellow wires. With accelerator depressed, reading should be greater than 10,000 ohms. With accelerator released, reading should be less than 5 ohms.

**4)** On vehicles built before 11/2/87, measure resistance between Light Green/Red and Blue/Yellow wires. With accelerator depressed, reading should be less than 5 ohms. With accelerator released, reading should be greater than 10,000 ohms. Measure resistance between Red/Green and Blue/Yellow wires. With accelerator depressed, reading should be greater than 10,000 ohms. With accelerator released, reading should be less than 5 ohms. If all resistances are within specification, replace ECA.

**NOTE: If referred here through another circuit test, do not replace ECA, proceed to CIRCUIT TEST DK, test step 8).**

***Throttle Position Sensor Circuit***

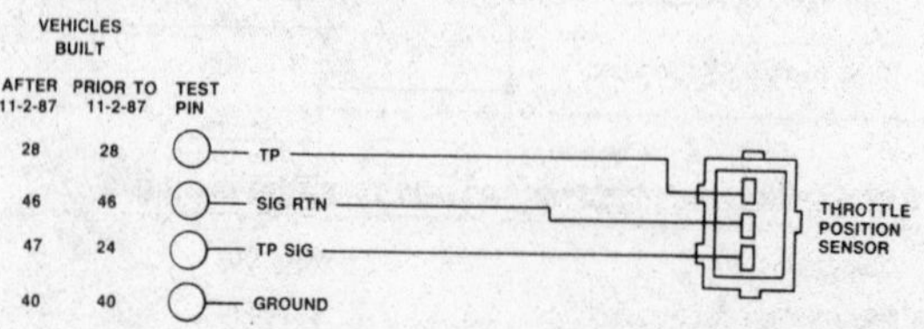
VEHICLES BUILT
AFTER 11-2-87
PRIOR TO 11-2-87
TEST PIN
28 28 TP
46 46 SIG RTN
47 24 TP SIG
40 40 GROUND
THROTTLE POSITION SENSOR

## CIRCUIT TEST DK

### VANE AIRFLOW (VAF) METER

Check for unmetered air leaks between VAF meter and throttle body. Check for vacuum leaks. Inspect wiring, wiring harness, connectors and other related components for visible damage.

**1) VAF Voltage Check.** Install breakout box and unplug ECA. Using DVOM on 20-volt scale, with ignition on, measure voltage between pins No. 18 and 40. If reading is not 7-9 volts, proceed to next step. If reading is 7-9 volts, proceed to step **5)**.

**2) VAF Power Check.** With VAF meter connected and using DVOM on 20-volt scale, turn ignition on and measure voltage between VAF meter terminal (Light Green wire) and ground. If reading is 7-9 volts, repair open or short in Light Green wire from VAF meter to ECA. If reading is not 7-9 volts, proceed to next step.

**3) VAF Power Check.** Using DVOM on 20-volt scale and ignition on, measure voltage between VAF meter terminal (Yellow/Green wire) and ground. If reading is greater than 10 volts, replace VAF meter. If reading is 10 volts or less, proceed to next step.

**4) Relay Power Check.** Using DVOM on 20-volt scale and ignition on, measure voltage between relay (Yellow/Green wire) and ground. If reading is greater than 10 volts, repair open or short in Yellow/Green wire from relay to VAF meter. If reading is 10 volts or less, proceed to CIRCUIT TEST FC.

**5) Signal Return Check.** Turn ignition off and install breakout box. Using DVOM on 200-ohm scale, measure resistance between pins No. 46 and 40, pin No. 46 and chassis ground. If resistance is less than 5 ohms, proceed to next step. If resistance is 5 ohms or more, replace ECA.

**6) VAF Signal Return Check.** Turn ignition off and install breakout box. Using DVOM on 200-ohm scale, measure resistance between VAF meter terminal (Blue/Yellow wire) and pin No. 46. If resistance is 5 ohms or more, repair Blue/Yellow wire from VAF meter to ECA. If resistance is less than 5 ohms, proceed to next step.

**7) VAF Voltage Check.** Install breakout box and using DVOM on 20-volt scale, measure voltage between pins shown in appropriate VAF VOLTAGE CHECK table. If reading is within specifications, replace ECA. If reading is not within specifications, proceed to next step.

***VAF VOLTAGE CHECK (VEHICLES BUILT AFTER 11/2/87)***

| Between Pins | Key On | Idle |
|---|---|---|
| No. 43 & 40 | 2 Volts | 4-6 Volts |
| No. 43 & 46 | 2 Volts | 4-6 Volts |
| No. 40 & 46 | Zero Volts | Zero Volts |

***VAF VOLTAGE CHECK (VEHICLES BUILT BEFORE 11/2/87)***

| Between Pins | Key On | Idle |
|---|---|---|
| No. 27 & 40 | 2 Volts | 4-6 Volts |
| No. 27 & 46 | 2 Volts | 4-6 Volts |
| No. 40 & 46 | Zero Volts | Zero Volts |

**8) VAF Signal Check.** Plug in VAF meter connector. Using DVOM on 20-volt scale and ignition turned on, measure voltage as indicated in appropriate VAF SIGNAL CHECK table. If readings are within specification, repair wire from VAF meter to ECA. If readings are not within specification, replace VAF meter.

***VAF SIGNAL CHECK (VEHICLES BUILT AFTER 11/2/87)***

| Between | Key On | Idle |
|---|---|---|
| Light Green & Ground | 2 Volts | 4-6 Volts |
| Light Green/Black & Blue/Yellow | 2 Volts | 4-6 Volts |
| Blue/Yellow & Ground | Zero Volts | Zero Volts |

***VAF SIGNAL CHECK (VEHICLES BUILT BEFORE 11/2/87)***

| Between | Key On | Idle |
|---|---|---|
| Blue/White & Ground | 2 Volts | 4-6 Volts |
| Blue/White & Blue/Yellow | 2 Volts | 4-6 Volts |
| Blue/Yellow & Ground | Zero Volts | Zero Volts |

## CIRCUIT TEST DK (Cont.)

***VAF Meter Circuit***

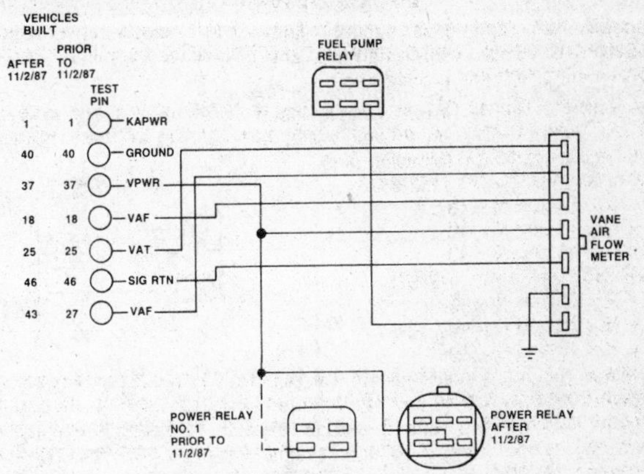

VEHICLES BUILT
AFTER 11/2/87
PRIOR TO 11/2/87
TEST PIN
1 1 KAPWR
40 40 GROUND
37 37 VPWR
18 18 VAF
25 25 VAT
46 46 SIG RTN
43 27 VAF
FUEL PUMP RELAY
VANE AIR FLOW METER
POWER RELAY NO. 1 PRIOR TO 11/2/87
POWER RELAY AFTER 11/2/87

## CIRCUIT TEST FA

### NEUTRAL GEAR SWITCH & CLUTCH ENGAGE SWITCH

To prevent replacement of good components, check clutch switch adjustment, pedal operation, transaxle operation and neutral switch installation. Also check wiring, wiring harness and other related components for visible damage.

**1) Check For Open Circuit.** Install breakout box and unplug ECA. Using DVOM on 200-ohm scale, measure resistance between pins No. 30 (No. 8 on vehicles built after 11/2/87) and No. 40 (ground). On vehicles built after 11/2/87, with clutch released, resistance should be zero to 5 ohms. With clutch depressed, resistance should be 10,000 ohms or more. On vehicles built before 11/2/87, with clutch released (transmission in gear), resistance should be 10,000 ohms or more. With clutch released and depressed (transmission in Neutral), resistance should be 0-5 ohms. With clutch depressed (transmission in gear), resistance should be 0-5 ohms. If readings are within specification, proceed to step **4)**. If readings are not within specification, proceed to next step.

**2) Clutch Engage Switch Operation Check.** Unplug clutch engage switch. Using DVOM on 200-ohm scale, measure resistance between terminals on clutch engage switch with pedal depressed and released. With pedal depressed, resistance should be greater than 10,000 ohms. With pedal released, resistance should be less than 5 ohms. If readings are within specification, proceed to next step. If readings are not within specification, adjust or replace clutch engage switch.

**3) Neutral Gear Switch Operation Check.** Unplug neutral gear switch. Using DVOM on 200-ohm scale, measure resistance between terminals on neutral gear switch connector. On vehicles built after 11/2/87, resistance should be less than 5 ohms in gear and greater than 10,000 ohms in neutral. On vehicles built before 11/2/87, resistance should be less than 5 ohms in neutral and greater than 10,000 ohms in gear. If readings are within specification, repair open in wire between ECA and clutch switch, or between clutch switch and neutral switch (or ground wire). If readings are not within specification, replace neutral gear switch.

**4) Check For Short To VPWR & KAPWR.** Install breakout box and unplug ECA. Unplug neutral gear and clutch engage switch. Turn ignition key to "ON" position. Using DVOM on 20-volt scale, measure voltage between pins No. 30 (No. 8 on vehicles built after 11/2/87) and No. 40 (ground). Also measure voltage between pins No. 30 (No. 8 on vehicles built after 11/2/87) and No. 20 (ground). If reading is greater than one volt, repair short in wiring harness to VPWR or KAPWR as required. If reading is one volt or less, proceed to next step.

**5) ECA Pin Voltage Check.** Install breakout box and plug in ECA. Place transaxle in gear. Turn ignition on. Using DVOM on 20-volt scale, measure voltage between pins No. 30 (No. 8 on vehicles built after 11/2/87) and No. 40. On vehicles built after 11/2/87, reading should be greater than 10 volts with clutch pedal depressed and less than 4 volts with clutch pedal released. On vehicles built before 11/2/87, reading should be greater than 10 volts with clutch pedal

## CIRCUIT TEST FA (Cont.)

released and less than 4 volts with clutch pedal depressed. If readings are within specification, replace ECA. If readings are not within specfication, repair short to ground in wiring harness between ECA terminal No. 1G and neutral switch Brown/Black wire terminal.

***Neutral Gear & Clutch Engage Switch Circuit***

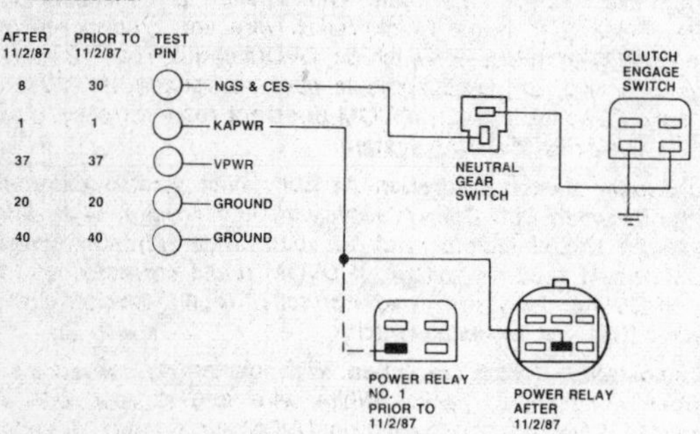
VEHICLES BUILT
AFTER 11/2/87
PRIOR TO 11/2/87
TEST PIN
8
30
NGS & CES
1
1
KAPWR
37
37
VPWR
20
20
GROUND
40
40
GROUND
CLUTCH ENGAGE SWITCH
NEUTRAL GEAR SWITCH
POWER RELAY NO. 1 PRIOR TO 11/2/87
POWER RELAY AFTER 11/2/87

## CIRCUIT TEST FB

### INHIBITOR SWITCH (AUTOMATIC TRANSAXLE)

To prevent possible replacement of good components, check transaxle operation and inhibitor switch installation. Also, visually inspect wiring, wiring harness and other related components for damage.

**1) Voltage At ECA From Inhibitor Switch.** Using DVOM on 20-volt scale, measure voltage between pins No. 2 and 40 (ground). With ignition on, reading should be less than 1.5 volts. With engine cranking, reading should be 7-9 volts. Also, measure voltage between pins No. 5 and 40 (ground). With transaxle in Park or Neutral and ignition on, reading should be less than 1.5 volts, and with engine cranking, reading should be 7-9 volts. If readings are within specification, replace ECA. If readings are not within specification, proceed to next step.

**2) Power At Inhibitor Switch.** Using DVOM on 20-volt scale, measure voltage between inhibitor switch (Black/Yellow wire) and ground. With ignition on, reading should be less than 1.5 volts. With engine cranking, reading should be 7-9 volts. If reading is within specification, proceed to next step. If reading is not within specification, proceed to step **4)**.

**3) Continuity Across Inhibitor Switch.** Turn ignition off and unplug switch. Using DVOM on 200-ohm scale, measure resistance between inhibitor switch Black terminals in transaxle gear ranges. With transaxle in Park and Neutral, reading should be greater than 5 ohms. With transaxle in all other ranges, reading should be less than 5 ohms. If resistances are within specification, repair open in Black/Yellow wire from ignition switch to inhibitor switch. If resistances are not within specification, replace inhibitor switch.

**4) Power At Ignition Switch.** Plug in inhibitor switch. Using DVOM on 20-volt scale, measure voltage between ignition switch (Black/Yellow wire) and ground. With ignition on, reading should be less than 1.5 volts. With engine cranking, reading should be 7-9 volts. If readings are okay, repair open in Black/Yellow wire from ignition switch to inhibitor switch. If readings are not okay, diagnose battery and charging system.

***Inhibitor Switch Circuit***

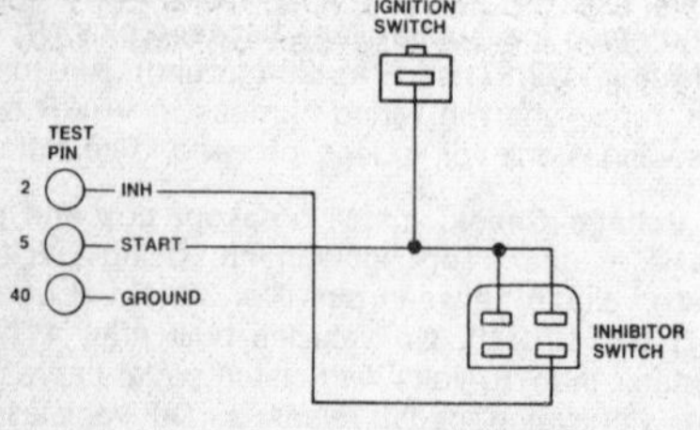
IGNITION SWITCH
TEST PIN
2
INH
5
START
40
GROUND
INHIBITOR SWITCH

## CIRCUIT TEST FC

### VEHICLE POWER

To prevent replacement of good components, check ignition switch, fuses, battery and charging system. Inspect wiring, wiring harness, connectors and other related components for visible damage.

**1) Check For VPWR To ECA.** Install breakout box. Unplug ECA and turn ignition on. Using DVOM on 20-volt scale, measure voltage between pins No. 37 and 40 (ground). If reading is 10 volts or less, proceed to step **4)**. If reading is greater than 10 volts, proceed to next step.

**2) Check For Cranking Power To ECA.** Install breakout box. Unplug ECA and turn ignition on. Using DVOM on 20-volt scale, measure voltage between pins No. 5 and 40 (ground) while cranking engine. If reading is greater than 10 volts, proceed to next step. If reading is 10 volts or less, repair open circuit between ECA terminal No. 3B and starter (Black/Red wire). If circuit is okay, diagnose battery and charging system.

**3) Check For ECA Grounds.** Install breakout box and unplug ECA. Using DVOM on 200-ohm scale, measure resistance between ground pins No. 20, 40, and 49, and chassis ground. If reading is greater than 5 ohms, repair open in wiring harness between ground terminal in question and chassis ground. If reading is 5 ohms or less, proceed to CIRCUIT TEST B.

**4) Check Power At Relay.** Turn ignition on. Using DVOM on 20-volt scale, measure voltage at power relay White/Green wire terminal on vehicles built after 11/2/87. Also measure voltage at power relay No. 1 (Yellow/Green wire) and power relay No. 2 (Black/White wire) on vehicles built before 11/2/87. If all readings are greater than 10 volts, proceed to next step. If all readings are 10 volts or less, check wire(s) for opens or shorts.

**5) Check Power To Relay.** Turn ignition on. Using DVOM on 20-volt scale, measure voltage at power relay Blue and Black wire terminals on vehicles built after 11/2/87. Also measure voltage at power relay No. 1 (Blue/White wire), power relay No. 2 (Blue wire) and power relays No. 1 and 2 (Black/White wire) on vehicles built before 11/2/87. If readings are greater than 10 volts, proceed to next step. If readings are 10 volts or less, check wire(s) for opens or shorts.

**6) Check Ground At Relay.** Unplug power relay. Using DVOM on 200-ohm scale, measure resistance between power relay(s) connector (Black terminal) and ground. If reading is less than 5 ohms, proceed to next step. If reading is 5 ohms or more, repair open in wiring harness between power relay(s) Black terminal and ground.

**7) Power Relay Operation Check.** Unplug power relay and ground Black terminal. Using DVOM on 200-ohm scale, measure the resistance between Blue and Black/White wire terminals, and Blue and White/Green wire terminals. On vehicles built after 11/2/87, jumper battery voltage to power relay Black/White wire terminal. Measure resistance between relay No. 1, Black/White and Yellow/Green wires, relay No. 2, Blue and Black/White wires, relay No. 1, Black/White and Black wires, and relay No. 2, Black/White and Black wires. On vehicles built before 11/2/87, jumper battery voltage to power relay(s) (Black/White wire). If reading is less than 5 ohms with voltage applied and greater than 10,000 ohms with voltage removed, proceed to CIRCUIT TEST B. If reading is 5 ohms or more with voltage applied and 10,000 ohms or less with voltage removed, replace power relay(s).

***Vehicle Power Circuit***

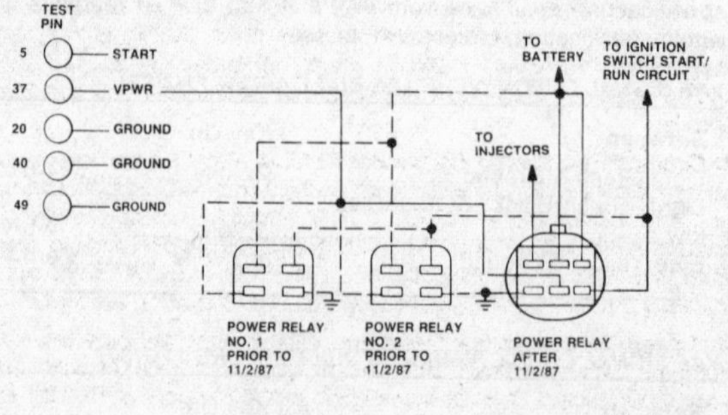
TEST PIN
5
START
37
VPWR
20
GROUND
40
GROUND
49
GROUND
TO BATTERY
TO IGNITION SWITCH START/ RUN CIRCUIT
TO INJECTORS
POWER RELAY NO. 1 PRIOR TO 11/2/87
POWER RELAY NO. 2 PRIOR TO 11/2/87
POWER RELAY AFTER 11/2/87

## CIRCUIT TEST FD

### BRAKE ON/OFF SWITCH

Perform a comprehensive visual inspection of wiring and harness connectors at ECA and brake switch assembly. Repair or replace defective wiring or components as necessary.

**1) Brake Switch Operation At ECA.** Install breakout box. Disconnect ECA connector. Turn ignition on. Using a DVOM, measure voltage between pins No. 3 and 40. Measure voltage between pins No. 3 and 20. Voltmeter should read less than 4 volts with brake pedal released and more than 10 volts with pedal depressed. If DVOM readings were correct, replace ECA assembly. If DVOM readings were incorrect, proceed to next step.

**2) Voltage From Brake Switch.** With key on, measure voltage between brake switch White/Green wire and ground. Voltmeter should read less than 4 volts with brake pedal released and more than 10 volts with pedal depressed. If DVOM readings were correct, repair open or short to power in wiring harness between ECA terminal No. 1J and brake switch. If DVOM reading is incorrect, proceed to next step.

**3) Power To Brake Switch.** With key on, measure voltage between brake switch Green/White wire and ground. If DVOM reads more than 10 volts, adjust or replace brake switch. If DVOM reads less than 10 volts, go to next step.

**4) Power At Battery.** With key on, measure voltage across vehicle battery terminals. If DVOM reading is more than 10 volts, replace bad fuse or repair open in Green/Yellow wire between vehicle battery and brake switch. If DVOM reads less than 10 volts, proceed to CIRCUIT TEST B1.

*Brake On/Off Switch Circuit*

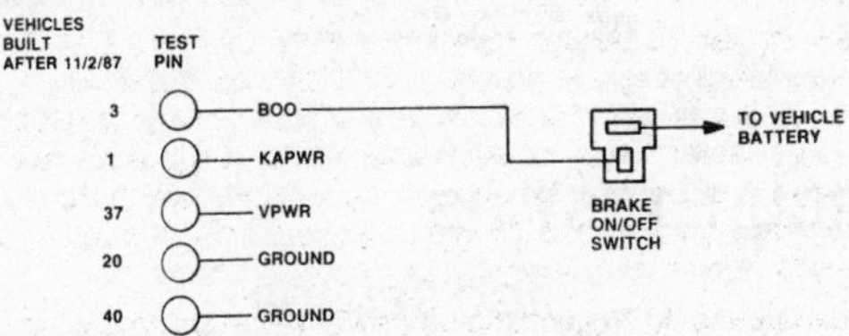
VEHICLES BUILT AFTER 11/2/87
TEST PIN
3
1
37
20
40
BOO
KAPWR
VPWR
GROUND
GROUND
TO VEHICLE BATTERY
BRAKE ON/OFF SWITCH

## CIRCUIT TEST FG

### ELECTRICAL LOAD UNIT (ELU)

**1) System Inspection** Perform a visual inspection of wiring and harness connectors. Ensure cooling fan motor, blower motor, lighting system, BAC valve, alternator condition, idle adjustment and general engine performance are not malfunctioning before proceeding with test. If a problem is found with wiring or harness connectors, repair or replace as necessary. If cooling fan is not operating properly, go to next step. If blower control is not functioning properly, go to step **4)**. If defroster is not functioning properly, go to step **6)**. If combination switch is not functioning properly, go to step **8)**.

**2) Coolant Fan Temperature Switch Operation.** Disconnect cooling fan switch. Turn ignition on. Using a DVOM, measure voltage between fan switch Yellow/Green wire and ground without piercing wire. With coolant temperature more than 206°F (97°C), DVOM should read no voltage. With coolant temperature less than 206°F (97°C), DVOM should read 10 volts. If DVOM reads correctly, go to next step. If DVOM does not read correctly, diagnose heating and air conditioning system.

**3) Coolant Fan Switch Operation At ELU.** With ignition on, measure voltage between ELU Yellow wire and ground. With coolant temperature more than 206°F (97°C), DVOM should read no voltage. With coolant temperature less than 206°F (97°C), DVOM should read 10 volts. If DVOM reads correctly, go to step **10)**. If DVOM does not read correctly, repair Yellow wire between ELU and cooling fan switch.

**4) Blower Control Switch Operation.** With ignition on, measure voltage between blower switch Blue/Green wire and ground with blower switch connected. With blower switch in "OFF" position, DVOM should read 10 volts. With blower switch in "LO", "ML", "MH", or "HI" position, DVOM should read no voltage. If DVOM reads correctly, go to next step. If DVOM does not read correctly, diagnose heating and air conditioning system.

## CIRCUIT TEST FG (Cont.)

**5) Blower Control Switch Operation At ELU.** With ignition on, measure voltage between ELU Blue/Green wire and ground. With blower switch in "OFF" position, DVOM should read 10 volts. With blower switch in "LO", "ML", "MH", or "HI" position, DVOM should read no voltage. If DVOM reads correctly, go to step **10)**. If DVOM does not read correctly, repair Blue/Green wire between blower control and ELU.

**6) Defroster Switch Operation.** With ignition on, measure voltage between defroster switch Black/Yellow wire and ground with switch connected. With defroster switch on, DVOM should read 10 volts. With defroster switch off, DVOM should read no voltage. If DVOM reads correctly, go to next step. If DVOM does not read correctly, diagnose heating and air conditioning system.

**7) Defroster Switch Operation At ELU.** With ignition on, measure voltage between ELU Black/Yellow wire and ground. With defroster switch on, DVOM should read 10 volts. With defroster switch off, DVOM should read no voltage. If DVOM reads correctly, go to step **10)**. If DVOM does not read correctly, repair Black/Yellow wire between ELU and defroster switch.

**8) Combination Switch Operation.** With ignition on, measure voltage between combination switch White wire and ground with switch connected. With headlight switch on, DVOM should read 10 volts. With headlight switch off, DVOM should read no voltage. If DVOM reads correctly, go to next step. If DVOM does not read correctly, diagnose lighting system.

**9) Combination Switch Operation At ELU.** With ignition on, measure voltage between ELU White wire and ground. With headlight switch on, DVOM should read 10 volts. With headlight switch off, DVOM should read no voltage. If DVOM reads correctly, go to next step. If DVOM does not read correctly, repair White wire between ELU and combination switch.

**10) ELU Operation At ECA.** Disconnect ECA connector. Install breakout box. Turn ignition on. Using a DVOM, measure voltage between pins No. 24 and 40. Operate one switch at a time leaving all other switches off. See SWITCH VOLTAGE SPECIFICATIONS table. If DVOM reads correctly, replace ECA assembly. If DVOM does not read correctly, go to next step.

***SWITCH VOLTAGE SPECIFICATIONS***

| Switch Position | Approximate Voltage |
|---|---|
| Blower Control "OFF" | 10 |
| Blower Control "ON" | 2.5 |
| Combination "OFF" | 10 |
| Combination "ON" | 2.5 |
| Cooling Fan "OFF" | 10 |
| Cooling Fan "ON" | 2.5 |
| Defroster "OFF" | 10 |
| Defroster "ON" | 2.5 |

**11) ELU Operation.** With ignition on, measure voltage between ELU Black wire and ground. Operate one switch at a time leaving all other switches off. See SWITCH VOLTAGE SPECIFICATIONS table. If DVOM reads correctly, repair Black wire between ELU and ECA. If DVOM does not read correctly, go to next step.

**12) Power At ELU.** With ignition on, measure voltage between ELU Yellow/Green wire and ground. If DVOM reads more than 10 volts, go to step **14)**. If DVOM reads less than 10 volts, go to next step.

**13) Power At Power Relay.** With ignition on, measure voltage between power relay Yellow/Green wire and ground with relay connected. If DVOM reads more than 10 volts, repair Yellow/Green wire between power relay and ELU. If DVOM reads less than 10 volts, go to CIRCUIT TEST FC.

**14) Ground At ELU.** With ignition off, measure resistance between ELU Black wire and ground. If DVOM reads more than 5 ohms, replace ELU. If DVOM reads less than 5 ohms, repair Black wire between ELU and ground.

## CIRCUIT TEST FG (Cont.)

*ELU Circuit*

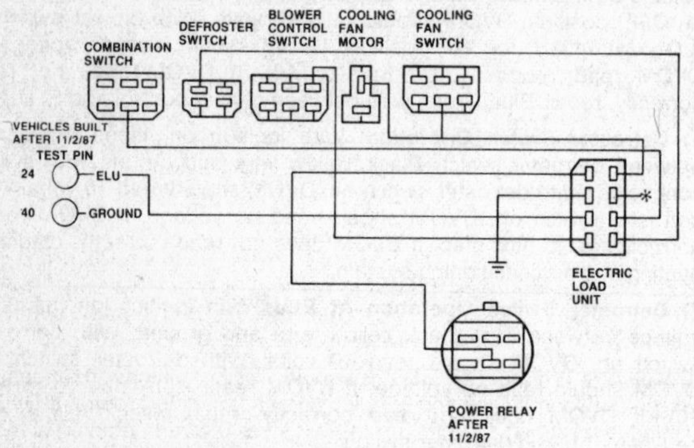
COMBINATION SWITCH
DEFROSTER SWITCH
BLOWER CONTROL SWITCH
COOLING FAN MOTOR
COOLING FAN SWITCH
VEHICLES BUILT AFTER 11/2/87
TEST PIN
24
ELU
40
GROUND
ELECTRIC LOAD UNIT
POWER RELAY AFTER 11/2/87

## CIRCUIT TEST HA

### FUEL CONTROL

To prevent replacement of good components, inspect all related wiring, wiring harness, connectors and components for evidence of overheating, looseness and other visible damage. Visually inspect intake air cleaner, duct, fuel delivery system for leaks or severe wear.

**1) EGO Sensor Sensitivity Test.** This test is for vehicles built after 11/2/87. On all others, proceed to next step. With STAR tester adapter connected to STO and ground (STI open), start engine and run until operating temperature is reached. Increase engine speed to 2500 RPM. If the monitor light flashes 8 times in 10 seconds, proceed to step **4)**. If monitor light does not flash 8 times in 10 seconds, proceed to next step.

**2) Check EGO Sensor Output.** Warm engine and allow to idle. Unplug EGO sensor. Using DVOM on 5-volt scale, measure voltage between EGO sensor connector (sensor side) and ground. Raise engine speed to 4000-4500 RPM until voltmeter indicates 0.7 volts. Decrease and increase engine RPM rapidly and note voltmeter reading. At 1000-2500 RPM, reading should be 0-0.4 volts. At 3000-4500 RPM, reading should be 0.5-1.0 volts. If readings are within specification, proceed to next step. If readings are not within specification, proceed to CIRCUIT TEST HE.

**3) Check EGO Switching Voltage.** With EGO sensor connected and breakout box installed, start engine and bring to operating temperature. Using DVOM on 5-volt scale, measure voltage between pins No. 29 and 40. Decrease and increase engine RPM rapidly and note voltmeter reading. At 1000-2500 RPM, reading should be 0-0.4 volts. At 3000-4500 RPM, reading should be 0.5-1.0 volts. If readings are within specification, proceed to next step. If readings are not within specification, proceed to CIRCUIT TEST HE.

**4) Injector Drive Signal Check.** Install breakout box and connect standard 12-volt non-power test light between pins No. 58 and 37. Crank or start engine and note test light. Repeat test between pins No. 37 and 59. If test light glows dim on both tests, proceed to step **7)**. If test light does not illuminate on one or both tests, proceed to next step. If test light illuminates brightly on one or both tests, proceed to step **6)**.

**5) ECA Power Test.** Install breakout box and unplug ECA. Turn ignition on. Using DVOM on 20-volt scale, measure voltage between pins No. 1 and 40, and between pins No. 37 and 40. If readings are greater than 10 volts, replace ECA. If readings are 10 volts or less, proceed to CIRCUIT TEST FC.

**6) Injector Circuit Check For Shorts.** Unplug ECA and disconnect battery. Install breakout box. Using DVOM on 200,000-ohm scale, measure resistance between pins No. 59 and 37, 20, 40, 1 and 49. Repeat test between pins No. 58 and 37, 20, 40, 1 and 49. If any of the readings are less than 10,000 ohms, check for shorts to ground or VPRW in related harness. If any of the readings are 10,000 ohms or more, replace ECA.

**7) Injector Balance Test.** Unplug ISC connector. Start and run engine at 2000 RPM. Unplug and plug in injectors one at a time while noting RPM drop for each injector. Plug in ISC. If each injector produced at

## CIRCUIT TEST HA (Cont.)

least 150 RPM drop, proceed to next step. If each injector did not produce at least 150 RPM drop, repair circuit of injector in question. On vehicles built before 11/2/87, confirm operation of solenoid resistor in fuel delivery system. If operation is okay, replace faulty injector.

**8) Deceleration Fuel Cut-Off Test.** Install breakout box and plug in ECA. Connect standard non-powered 12-volt test light between pins No. 58 and 37. Start engine and allow to idle. Increase and decrease engine speed between idle and 4000 RPM and note test light. During idle, test light should flash. During deceleration (2000-4000 RPM range), test light should not illuminate. Repeat test between pins No. 59 and 37. If test light responds as described, diagnose for mechnical problem. If test light does not respond as described, replace ECA.

*Fuel Control Circuit*

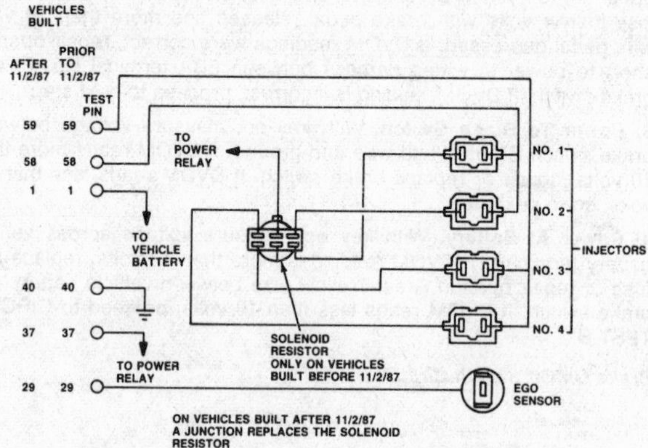
VEHICLES BUILT
AFTER 11/2/87
PRIOR TO 11/2/87
TEST PIN
59 59
58 58
1 1
40 40
37 37
29 29
TO POWER RELAY
TO VEHICLE BATTERY
TO POWER RELAY
NO. 1
NO. 2
NO. 3
NO. 4
INJECTORS
SOLENOID RESISTOR ONLY ON VEHICLES BUILT BEFORE 11/2/87
EGO SENSOR
ON VEHICLES BUILT AFTER 11/2/87 A JUNCTION REPLACES THE SOLENOID RESISTOR

## CIRCUIT TEST HE

### EGO SENSOR

To prevent replacement of good components, inspect wiring, wiring harness and connectors for visible damage.

**1) EGO Output Voltage Check.** Start and run engine to operating temperature. Unpug EGO sensor and allow engine to idle. Using DVOM on 5-volt scale, connect DVOM between EGO sensor and ground. Raise engine speed to 4000-4500 RPM until DVOM indicates about 0.7 volts. Increase and decrease engine RPM rapidly and note DVOM reading. Reading at 3000-4500 RPM should be 0.5-1.0 volts. Reading at 1000-2500 RPM should be 0-0.4 volts. If readings are correct, proceed to step **4)**. If readings are not correct, proceed to next step.

**2) Isolate EGO Sensor Open.** Unplug EGO sensor and turn ignition off. Inspect wire from EGO sensor connector for possible opens. If wire is okay, proceed to next step. If wire is not okay, repair wire or replace EGO sensor (if open is between sensor and connector).

**3) Isolate EGO Sensor Short.** Unplug EGO sensor and turn ignition off. Using DVOM on 20-k/ohm scale, measure resistance between EGO sensor connector (sensor side) and ground. If resistance is greater than 10,000 ohms, replace EGO sensor. If resistance is 10,000 ohms or less, repair short in EGO sensor wire or replace EGO sensor.

**4) EGO Sensor Sensitivity Test.** This test step is only for vehicles built after 11/2/87. With EGO sensor connected, start engine. Connect STAR tester adapter cable to STO connector and ground (STI connector open). Raise engine speed to 2500 RPM. If monitor light flashes 8 or more times in 10 seconds, proceed to step **7)**. If monitor light does not flash 8 or more times in 10 seconds, proceed to next step.

**5) Check EGO Sensor Circuit.** Turn ignition off and install breakout box. Unplug ECA and EGO sensor. Using DVOM on 200-ohm scale, measure resistance between EGO sensor connector (harness side) and pin No. 29 at breakout box. If resistance is greater than 10 ohms, repair open circuit and reconnect EGO sensor. If resistance is 10 ohms or less, proceed to next step.

**6) Check EGO Sensor Circuit.** Turn ignition off and install breakout box. Unplug ECA and EGO sensor. Using DVOM on 200-ohm scale, measure resistance between pins No. 29 and No. 1, 20, 37 and 40. If

## CIRCUIT TEST HE (Cont.)

any of the resistances are less than 10,000 ohms, repair short in EGO sensor circuit to VPWR, VREF, KAPWR or ground. If any of the resistances are 10,000 ohms or more, replace EGO sensor.

**7) ECA Input Voltage.** Start engine and bring to operating temperature. Install breakout box and unplug ECA. Using DVOM on 5-volt scale, measure voltage between pins No. 29 and 49 while increasing and decreasing engine speed between 1500 and 4000 RPM. If reading varies between 0.5-1.0 volts, inspect ECA and ECA connector for damage, looseness, corrosion or damaged pins. If reading does not vary between 0.5-1.0 volts, replace ECA.

*EGO Sensor Circuit*

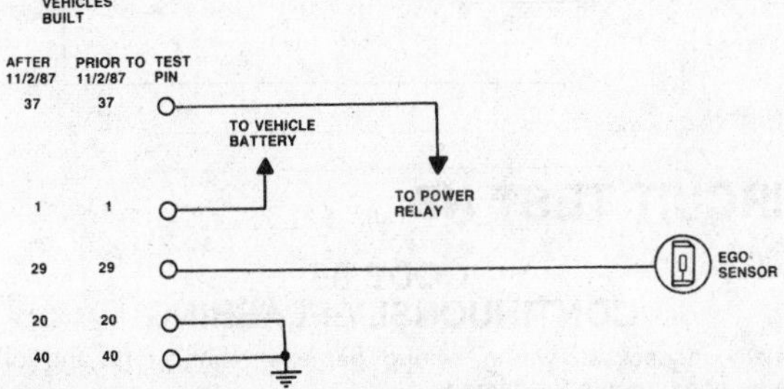
VEHICLES BUILT
AFTER 11/2/87
PRIOR TO 11/2/87
TEST PIN
37 37
TO VEHICLE BATTERY
TO POWER RELAY
1 1
29 29
EGO SENSOR
20 20
40 40

## CIRCUIT TEST KD

### CANISTER PURGE (CANP)

To prevent replacement of good components, inspect wiring, wiring harness, connectors and other related components for visible damage.

**1) Measure Voltage At ECA.** Install breakout box and unplug ECA. Turn ignition on. Using DVOM on 20-volt scale, measure voltage between pins No. 32 and 40 (ground). If reading is less than 10 volts, proceed to next step. If reading is 10 volts or more, repair wire between ECA and CANP solenoid.

**2) Measure Voltage From Canister Purge Solenoid.** Turn ignition on and unplug ECA. CANP should remain connected. Using DVOM on 20-volt scale, measure voltage between CANP solenoid Yellow (Brown on vehicles built before 11/2/87) wire and ground. If reading is less than 10 volts, proceed to next step. If reading is 10 volts or more, repair wire between ECA and CANP solenoid.

**3) Measure Voltage To Canister Purge Solenoid.** Turn ignition on and unplug ECA. Using DVOM on 20-volt scale, measure voltage between CANP solenoid Yellow/Green wire and ground. If reading is less than 10 volts, proceed to next step. If reading is 10 volts or more, replace CANP solenoid.

**4) Measure Voltage From Power Relay.** Turn ignition on. Power relay should remain connected. Using DVOM on 20-volt scale, measure voltage between power relay Yellow/Green wire and ground. If reading is less than 10 volts, proceed to CIRCUIT TEST FC. If reading is 10 volts or more, repair Yellow/Green wire between CANP solenoid and power relay.

**5) Check Canister Purge Circuit For Short To VPWR.** Install breakout box and unplug ECA. Unplug CANP solenoid connector. Turn ignition on. Using DVOM on 20-volt scale, measure voltage between pins No. 32 and 40 (ground). If reading is greater than zero volts, repair short to VPWR. If reading is zero volts, replace ECA.

*CANP Solenoid Circuit*

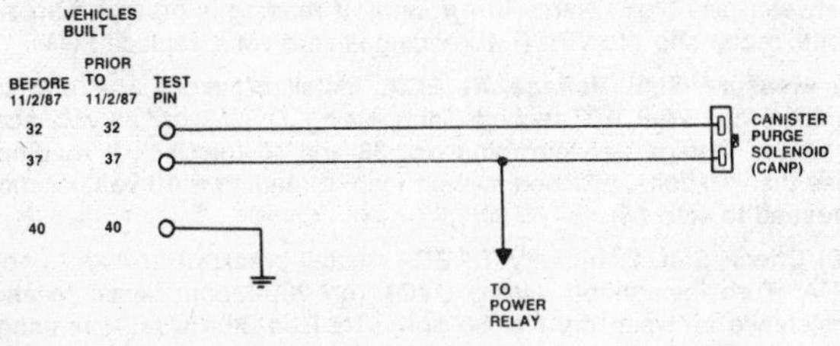
VEHICLES BUILT
BEFORE 11/2/87
PRIOR TO 11/2/87
TEST PIN
32 32
37 37
CANISTER PURGE SOLENOID (CANP)
40 40
TO POWER RELAY

## CIRCUIT TEST KE

### IDLE SPEED CONTROL

To prevent replacement of good components, ensure idle speed is properly adjusted and inspect vehicle for vacuum leaks. Perform a visual inspection of all wiring and wiring harness connectors.

**1) Measure Voltage At ECA.** Install breakout box. Disconnect ECA connector. Turn igniton on. Wait 2 minutes. Using a DVOM, measure voltage between pins No. 40 and 41. If DVOM reads less than 10 volts, go to next step. If DVOM reads more than 10 volts, go to step **5)**.

**2) Measure Voltage From ISC Solenoid.** With ignition on, wait 2 minutes. With ISC solenoid connected, measure voltage between ISC solenoid Green wire and ground without piercing wire. If DVOM reading is less than 10 volts, go to next step. If DVOM reading is more than 10 volts, repair Green wire between ECA and ISC solenoid.

**3) Measure Voltage To ISC Solenoid.** With ignition on, measure voltage between ISC solenoid Yellow/Green wire and ground. If DVOM reading is less than 10 volts, go to next step. If DVOM reading is more than 10 volts, replace ISC solenoid.

**4) Measure Voltage From Power Relay.** With ignition on and power relay connected, measure voltage between power relay Yellow/Green wire and ground. If DVOM reading is less than 10 volts, go to CIRCUIT TEST FC1. If DVOM reading is more than 10 volts, repair the Yellow/Green wire between ISC solenoid and power relay.

**5) Check ISC Circuit For Short To VPWR.** Disconnect ISC solenoid connector. With ignition on, measure voltage between breakout box pins No. 40 and 41. If DVOM indicates voltage (amount of voltage is not important), repair short to VPWR. If DVOM indicates no voltage, replace ECA.

*Idle Speed Control Circuit*

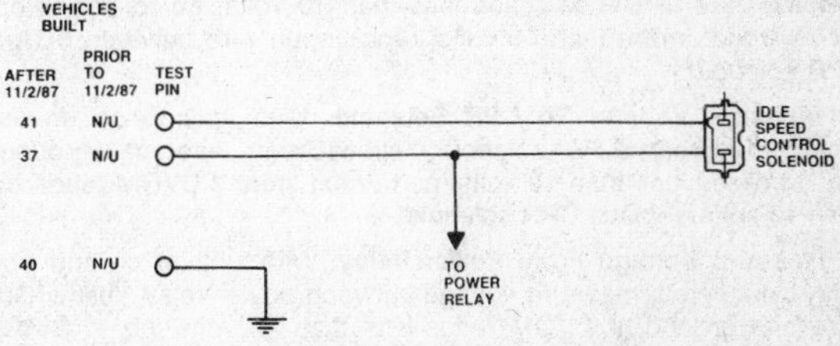
VEHICLES BUILT
AFTER 11/2/87
PRIOR TO 11/2/87
TEST PIN
41 N/U
37 N/U
IDLE SPEED CONTROL SOLENOID
40 N/U
TO POWER RELAY

## CIRCUIT TEST KV

### PRESSURE REGULATOR CONTROL (PRC)

To prevent replacement of good components, inspect vehicle for vacuum leaks and fuel pressure regulator for obvious defects. Perform a visual inspection of wiring and harness connectors.

**1) Measure Voltage ECA.** Install breakout box. Unplug ECA connector. Turn ignition on. Wait 2 minutes. Using a DVOM, measure voltage between pins No. 31 and 40. If DVOM reads less than 10 volts, to to next step. If DVOM reading is more than 10 volts, go to step **5)**.

**2) Measure Voltage From PRC Solenoid.** With ignition on and PRC solenoid connected, measure voltage between PRC solenoid Brown wire and ground. If DVOM reading is less than 10 volts, go to next step. If DVOM reading is more than 10 volts, repair Brown wire between ECA and PRC solenoid.

**3) Measure Voltage To PRC Solenoid.** With ignition on, measure voltage between PRC solenoid Yellow/Green wire and ground. If DVOM reads less than 10 volts, go to next step. If DVOM reads more than 10 volts, replace PRC solenoid.

**4) Measure Voltage From Power Relay.** With ignition on and power relay connected, measure voltage between power relay Yellow/Green wire and ground without piercing wire. If DVOM reads less than 10 volts, go to CIRCUIT TEST FC. If DVOM reads more than 10 volts, repair Yellow/Green wire between PRC solenoid and power relay.

**5) Check PRC Circuit For Short To VPWR.** With ignition on and PRC solenoid disconnected, measure voltage between pins No. 31 and 40. If DVOM indicates voltage (amount of voltage is not important), repair short to VPWR. If DVOM indicates no voltage, replace ECA.

## CIRCUIT TEST KV (Cont.)

*Pressure Regulator Control Circuit*

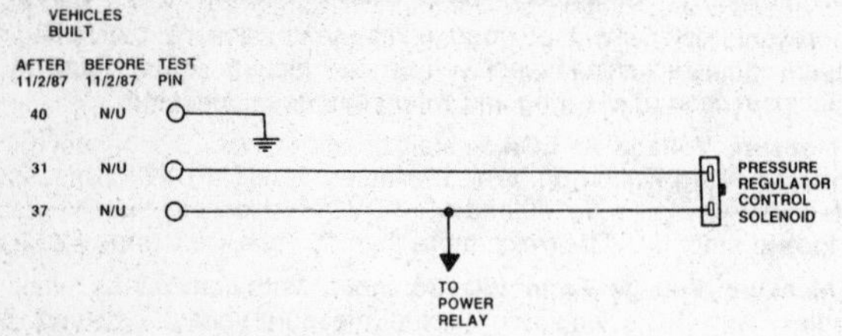
VEHICLES BUILT
AFTER 11/2/87
BEFORE 11/2/87
TEST PIN
40
N/U
31
N/U
37
N/U
PRESSURE REGULATOR CONTROL SOLENOID
TO POWER RELAY

## CIRCUIT TEST KW

### CANISTER PURGE REGULATOR (CPR)

To prevent replacement of good components, inspect vehicle for vacuum leaks and canister purge regulator for obvious defects. Visually inspect all wiring and harness connectors. Repair components as necessary.

**1) Measure Voltage At ECA.** Install breakout box. Disconnect ECA connector. Turn ignition on. Wait 2 minutes. If vehicle is manufactured after 11/2/87, measure voltage between pins No. 22 and 40. If vehicle is manufactured before 11/2/87, measure voltage between pins No. 31 and 40. If DVOM reads less than 10 volts, go to next step. If DVOM reads more than 10 volts, go to step **5)**.

**2) Measure Voltage From CPR Solenoid.** With ignition on and CPR solenoid connected, measure voltage between CPR solenoid Blue wire (Yellow wire on vehicles built before 11/2/87) and ground without piercing wire. If DVOM reads less than 10 volts, go to next step. If DVOM reads more than 10 volts, repair open wire between ECA and CPR solenoid.

**3) Measure Voltage To CPR Solenoid.** With ignition on, measure voltage between CPR solenoid Yellow/Green wire and ground. If DVOM reads less than 10 volts, go to next step. If DVOM reads more than 10 volts, replace CPR solenoid.

**4) Measure Voltage From Power Relay.** With ignition on and power relay connected, measure voltage between power relay Yellow/Green wire and ground. If DVOM reads less than 10 volts, go to CIRCUIT TEST FC. If DVOM reads more than 10 volts, repair Yellow/Green wire between CPR solenoid and power relay.

**5) Check CPR Circuit For Short To VPWR.** With ignition on and CPR solenoid disconnected, measure voltage between pins No. 22 and 40 (pins No. 31 and 40 on vehicles manufactured before 11/2/87). If DVOM indicates voltage (amount of voltage is not important), repair short to VPWR. If DVOM indicates no voltage, replace ECA.

*Canister Purge Regulator Circuit*

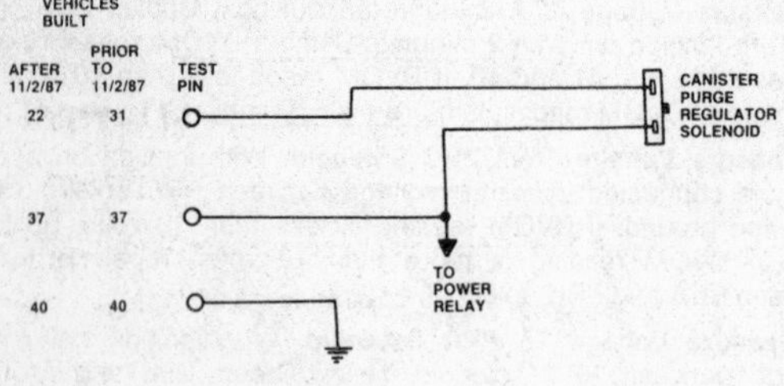
VEHICLES BUILT
AFTER 11/2/87
PRIOR TO 11/2/87
TEST PIN
22
31
37
37
40
40
CANISTER PURGE REGULATOR SOLENOID
TO POWER RELAY

## CIRCUIT TEST ML

### MALFUNCTION INDICATOR LAMP "CHECK ENGINE" LIGHT

To prevent replacement of good components, check fuse, bulb or socket. Inspect wiring, wiring harness and connectors for visible damage.

**1) Determine If ECA Is Providing Ground.** Install breakout box and unplug ECA. Turn ignition on. Using jumper wire, jumper pins No. 51 to 40 (ground). If MIL illuminates, proceed to CIRCUIT TEST FC. If MIL does not illuminate, proceed to next step.

## CIRCUIT TEST ML (Cont.)

**2) Check MIL Circuit For Power.** Turn ignition on and plug in MIL. Ground Light Green wire using a jumper at terminal C-01 connector at rear of instrument panel. If MIL illuminates, repair Light Green wire between MIL light and ECA. If MIL does not illuminate, problem is in instrument cluster.

*MIL Lamp Circuit*

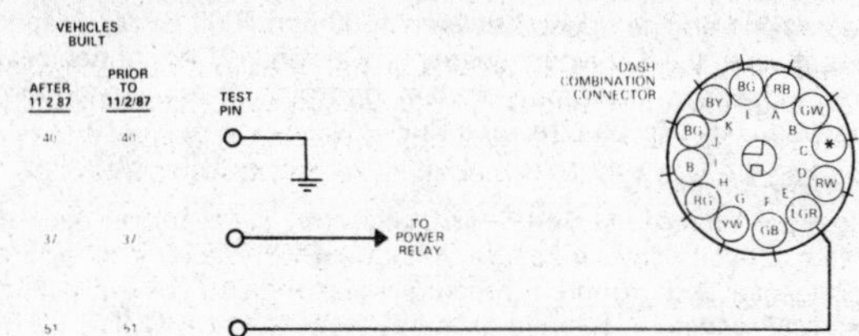
VEHICLES BUILT
AFTER 11/2/87
PRIOR TO 11/2/87
TEST PIN
TO POWER RELAY
DASH COMBINATION CONNECTOR

## CIRCUIT TEST NB

### CODE 88 CONTINUOUSLY FLASHING

Visually inspect all wiring, wiring harness, connectors and other related components for damage.

**1) Measure STI Voltage At ECA.** Install breakout box and turn ignition on. Using DVOM on 20-volt scale, measure voltage between pins No. 48 and 40 (ground). If reading is less than 10 volts, proceed to nest step. If reading is 10 volts or greater, proceed to step **5)**.

**2) Check STI Continuity To ECA.** Install breakout box and unplug ECA. Turn ignition off. Using DVOM on 200-ohm scale, measure resistance between pin No. 48 and STI Yellow wire connector. If reading is less than 5 ohms, proceed to next step. If reading is 5 ohms or more, repair Yellow wire between ECA and Self-Test Input (STI) connector.

**3) Check STI For Short To Ground.** Install breakout box and unplug ECA. Turn ignition off. Using DVOM on 200,000-ohm scale, measure resistance between pin No. 48 and ground pins No. 20, 40 and 49. If reading is greater than 10,000 ohms, proceed to next step. If reading is 10,000 ohms or less, repair short to ground.

**4) Check STI For Short To VPWR.** Install breakout box and unplug ECA. Turn ignition on. Using DVOM on 20-volt scale, measure voltage between pins No. 48 and 40 (ground). If reading is greater than zero volts, repair short to VPWR. If reading is zero volts, replace ECA.

**5) Measure STO Voltage At ECA.** Install breakout box. Jumper STI connector to ground. Turn ignition on and wait 10 seconds. Using DVOM on 20-volt scale, measure voltage between pins No. 17 and 40 (ground). If reading is less than 10 volts, proceed to next step. If reading is 10 volts or more, proceed to step **9)**.

**6) Check STO Continuity To ECA.** Install breakout box and unplug ECA. Turn ignition off. Using DVOM on 200-ohm scale, measure the resistance between pin No. 17 and Self-Test Output (STO) Green/Black wire connector. If reading is less than 5 ohms, proceed to next step. If reading is 5 ohms or more, repair Green/Black wire between ECA and STO connector.

**7) Check STO For Short To Ground.** Install breakout box and unplug ECA. Turn ignition off. Using DVOM on 200,000-ohm scale, measure resistance between pin No. 17 and ground pins No. 20, 40 and 49. If readings are greater than 10,000 ohms, proceed to next step. If readings are 10,000 ohms or less, repair short to ground.

**8) Check STO For Short To VPRW.** Install breakout box and unplug ECA. Turn ignition on. Using DVOM on 20-volt scale, measure voltage between pins No. 17 and 40 (ground). If reading is greater than zero volts, repair short to VPWR. If reading is zero volts, replace ECA.

**9) Measure SML Voltage At ECA.** Install breakout box and turn ignition on. Wait 10 seconds and Using DVOM on 20-volt scale, measure voltage between pins No. 38 and 40 (ground). If reading is less than 10 volts, proceed to next step. If reading is 10 volts or more, proceed to step **13)**.

**10) Check SML Continuity To ECA.** Install breakout box and unplug ECA. Turn ignition off. Using DVOM on 200-k/ohm scale, measure resistance between pin No. 38 and STO Red/Blue wire. If reading is

## CIRCUIT TEST NB (Cont.)

less than 5 ohms, proceed to next step. If reading is 5 ohms or greater, repair Red/Blue wire between ECA and STO connector.

**11) Check SML For Short To Ground.** Install breakout box and unplug ECA. Turn ignition off. Using DVOM on 200-k/ohm scale, measure resistance pin No. 38 and ground pins No. 20, 40 and 49. If reading is greater than 10,000 ohms, proceed to next step. If reading is 10,000 ohms or less, repair short to ground.

**12) Check SML For Short To VPWR.** Install breakout box and unplug ECA. Turn ignition on. Using DVOM on 20-volt scale, measure voltage between pins No. 38 and 40 (ground). If reading is greater than zero volts, repair short to VPWR. If reading is zero volts, replace ECA.

**13) Measure Voltage At Self-Test Connector.** Turn ignition on. Using DVOM on 20-volt scale, measure voltage between STO Yellow/Green wire connector and ground. If reading is less than 10 volts, proceed to next step. If reading is 10 volts or more, proceed to CIRCUIT TEST B.

**14) Measure Voltage From Power Relay.** Turn ignition on. Power relay should remain connected. Using DVOM on 20-volt scale, measure voltage between power relay Yellow/Green wire and ground. If reading is less than 10 volts, proceed to CIRCUIT TEST FC. If reading is 10 volts or more, repair Yellow/Green wire between STO connector and power relay.

*Self-Test Connector Circuit*

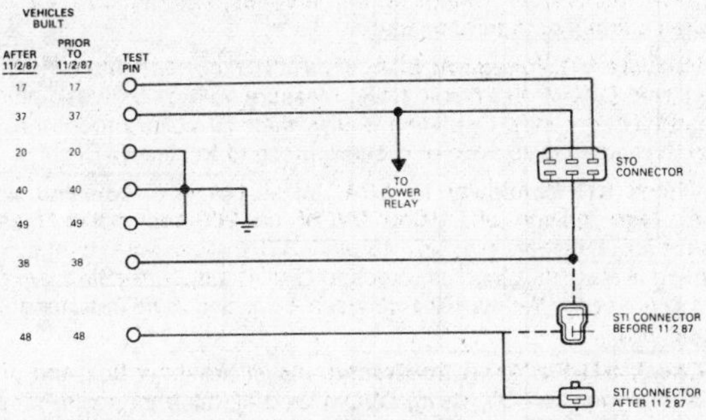
VEHICLES BUILT
AFTER 11/2/87
PRIOR TO 11/2/87
TEST PIN
17 17
37 37
20 20
40 40
49 49
38 38
48 48
TO POWER RELAY
STO CONNECTOR
STI CONNECTOR BEFORE 11 2 87
STI CONNECTOR AFTER 11 2 87

## CIRCUIT TEST Q

### NO CODES/CODES NOT LISTED

Perform visual inspection of wiring, harness connectors and components. Repair or replace components as necessary.

**1) Signal Return Check.** Ensure ignition is off. Install breakout box with ECA connected. Using a DVOM, measure resistance between signal return pin No. 46 and ground pin No. 40. Measure resistance between signal return pin No. 46 and chassis ground. If DVOM reads less than 5 ohms, go to next step. If DVOM reads more than 5 ohms, repair ground wires of ECA.

**2) Check Voltages At ECA.** With ignition on, measure voltage between pins on breakout box indicated in ECA VOLTAGE SPECIFICATIONS table. If DVOM readings are within specification, go to step **5)**. If DVOM readings are not within specification, go to next step.

*ECA VOLTAGE SPECIFICATIONS*

| Pins No. | Voltage |
|---|---|
| 17 & 40 | [1] More Than 10 |
| 38 & 40 | More Than 10 |
| 48 & 40 | More Than 10 |
| Manufactured After 11/2/87 | |
| 16 & 40 | [2] 7.3 |
| 19 & 40 | [3] More Than 10 |
| Manufactured Before 11/2/87 | |
| 23 & 40 | [1] Less Than 1.5 |

[1] – Self-Test Input connector grounded.
[2] – Radiator temperature must be below 63°F (17°C).
[3] – Front wheels straight.

## CIRCUIT TEST Q (Cont.)

**3) Check Circuits For Continuity.** With breakout box installed, ECA disconnected and ignition off, measure resistance between breakout box pin indicated and switch or connector in CIRCUIT CONTINUITY CHECK table. If DVOM readings are less than 5 ohms, go to next step. If DVOM readings are more than 5 ohms, repair circuit.

*CIRCUIT CONTINUITY CHECK*

| Pins No. | Wire Color |
|---|---|
| Self-Test Output Connector | |
| 17 | GRN/BLK |
| 38 | RED/BLU |
| 48 | YEL |
| Manufactured After 11/2/87 | |
| ECT Switch & 16 | BRN/WHT |
| Power Steering Switch & 19 | GRN/RED |
| Manfactured Before 11/2/87 | |
| ECT Switch & 23 | BRN/WHT |

**4) Check Circuits For Shorts To Ground.** With breakout box installed, ECA disconnected and ignition off, measure resistance between breakout box pins indicated in SHORTS TO GROUND CHECK table. If DVOM readings are less than 10,000 ohms, go to CIRCUIT TEST FC. If DVOM readings are less than 10,000 ohms, repair shorted circuit. Refer to CIRCUIT CONTINUITY CHECK table for circuit identification.

*SHORTS TO GROUND CHECK*

| Ground Pins No. | Pin No. |
|---|---|
| 20, 40, 46, 49 | [1] 23, [2] 16, 17, [2] 19, 38, 48 |

[1] – Vehicles manfactured before 11/2/87.
[2] – Vehicles manfactured after 11/2/87.

**5) Check Voltage At Self-Test Connector.** With ignition on, measure voltage between Self-Test output connector Yellow/Green wire and ground. If DVOM reads less than 10 volts, go to next step. If DVOM reads more than 10 volts, diagnose for mechanical problem.

**6) Check Voltage At Power Relay.** With ignition on and power relay connected, measure voltage between power relay Yellow/Green wire and ground without piercing wire. If DVOM reads less than 10 volts, go to CIRCUIT TEST FC. If DVOM reads more than 10 volts, repair Yellow/Green wire between STO connector and power relay.

*Self-Test Connector Circuit*

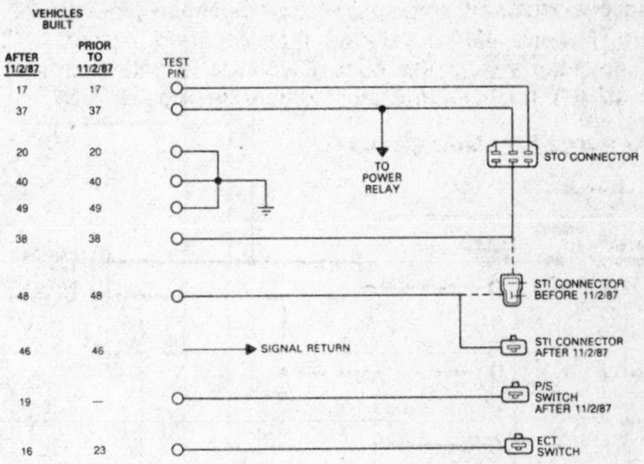
VEHICLES BUILT
AFTER 11/2/87
PRIOR TO 11/2/87
TEST PIN
17 17
37 37
20 20
40 40
49 49
38 38
48 48
46 46
19 —
16 23
TO POWER RELAY
STO CONNECTOR
STI CONNECTOR BEFORE 11/2/87
STI CONNECTOR AFTER 11/2/87
SIGNAL RETURN
P/S SWITCH AFTER 11/2/87
ECT SWITCH

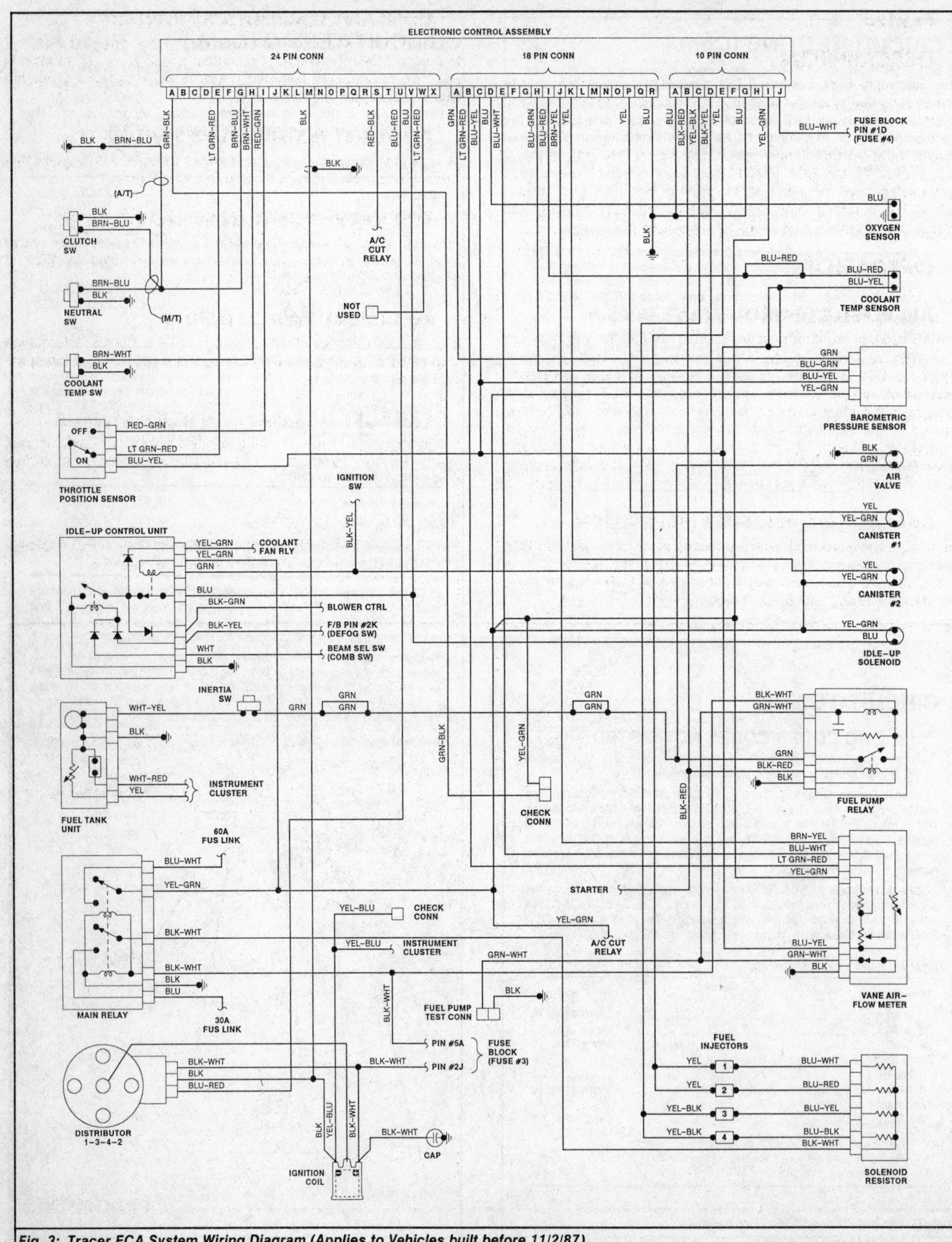

Fig. 3: Tracer ECA System Wiring Diagram (Applies to Vehicles built before 11/2/87)

## Festiva

# DESCRIPTION

The Electronic Fuel Control (EFC) system maintains the proper air/fuel ratio during engine operation to maximize fuel economy and minimize emissions. EFC system consists of 10 sensors, the Electronic Control Assembly (ECA) and a combination Air Bleed Control Valve (ABCV)/stepper motor. *See Fig. 1.* This stepper motor is controlled by the ECA based upon input signals from various sensors, primarily exhaust gas oxygen content. The ECA is also capable of detecting malfunctions within the EFC system, and storing and outputting fault codes for diagnostic purposes.

# OPERATION

## AIR BLEED CONTROL VALVE (ABCV)

The ABCV/stepper motor modifies air/fuel ratio at idle and cruise by controlling air bleeds to idle and primary main metering circuits. When the ECA determines a lean condition exists, or conditions exist which require a richer air/fuel ratio, the ECA responds by energizing the stepper motor windings. A magnetic field is then created in the windings which steps the ABCV plunger upward, counteracting internal spring pressure and restricting airflow. De-energizing the windings of the ABCV allows internal spring pressure to return the ABCV to its rest position, leaning the air/fuel ratio.

## BAROMETRIC PRESSURE (BP) SWITCH

Barometric Pressure (BP) switch provides electrical signals to ECA reflecting barometric pressure (altitude). Signal is used by ECA in air/fuel mixture computations and controlling of EGR vacuum valve, fuel shutoff solenoid and up-shift indicator light.

## COOLANT TEMPERATURE SENSOR

Mounted in the engine coolant passage, sensor provides electrical signals to ECA reflecting engine coolant temperature. Information is used by the ECA in controlling ABCV, EGR, pulse air, up-shift indicator light and EFE heater relay.

## COOLANT TEMPERATURE SWITCH

Mounted in radiator, this switch provides a simple "on" signal when coolant temperature in radiator is above 62.6°F (17°C).

## EGR VALVE POSITION SENSOR

Provides ECA with electrical signals which reflect EGR valve position (flow) at any given time. Signals are used by ECA in determining control of EGR vacuum valve.

## ELECTRICAL SWITCH INPUTS

ECA monitors various electrical switch voltage signals. Information is used by ECA for calculating idle speed adjustments to compensate for electrical loads.

## EXHAUST GAS OXYGEN (EGO) SENSOR

Sensor provides ECA with voltage signals reflective of exhaust gas oxygen content. Information is used by ECA for computing air/fuel mixture adjustments.

## A/C CLUTCH SWITCH

Switch provides ECA with an "on" signal when A/C clutch engages. Signal is used by ECA in idle speed control calculations.

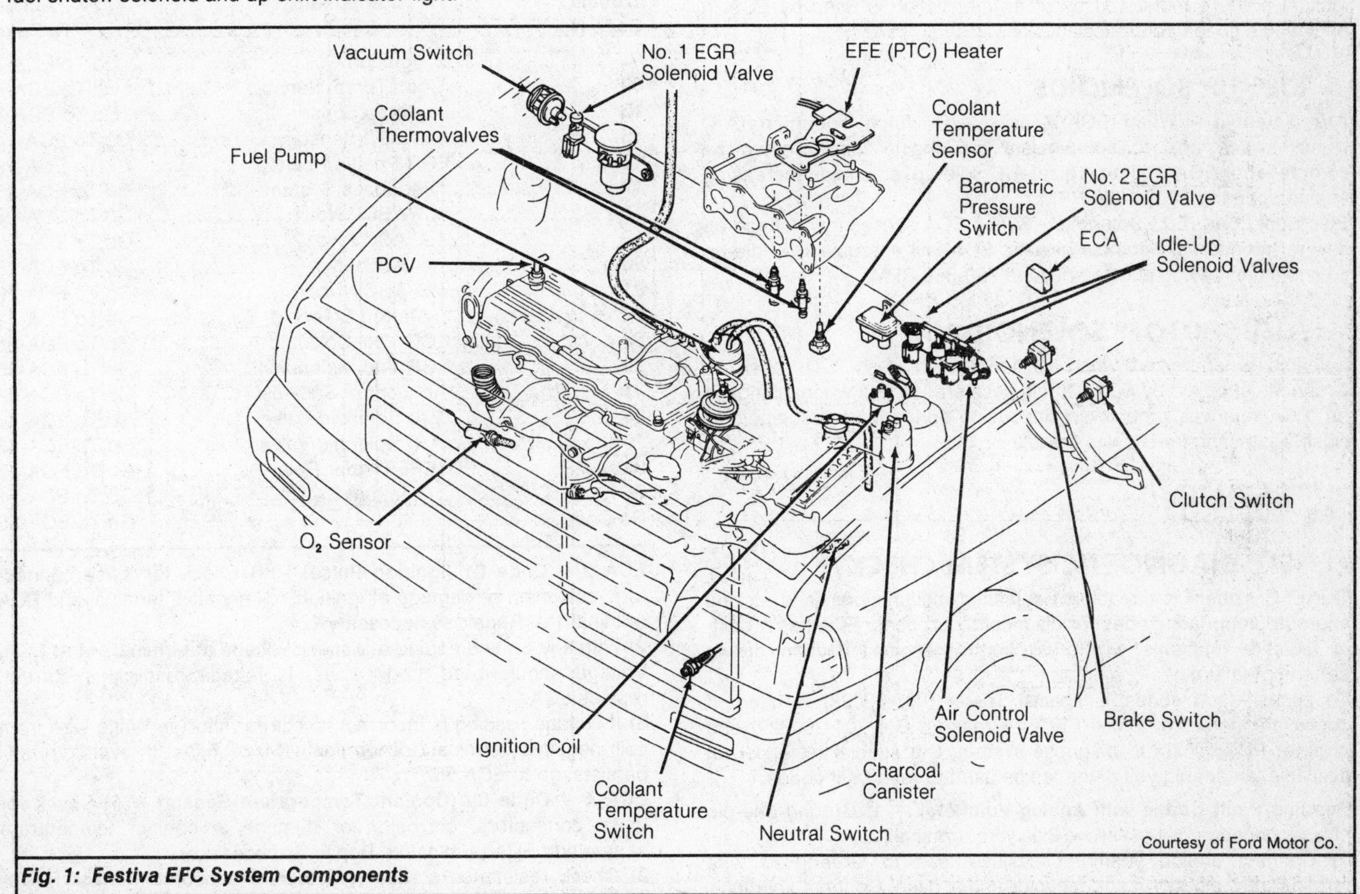
Vacuum Switch
No. 1 EGR Solenoid Valve
EFE (PTC) Heater
Coolant Thermovalves
Coolant Temperature Sensor
Fuel Pump
Barometric Pressure Switch
No. 2 EGR Solenoid Valve
ECA
Idle-Up Solenoid Valves
PCV
Clutch Switch
$O_2$ Sensor
Air Control Solenoid Valve
Brake Switch
Ignition Coil
Charcoal Canister
Coolant Temperature Switch
Neutral Switch
Courtesy of Ford Motor Co.

*Fig. 1: Festiva EFC System Components*

## GEAR POSITION SWITCHES

Switches are monitored by ECA for input signals used to determine control of engine idle speed, up-shift light, pulse air switching system, ABCV and fuel shutoff solenoid.

**Clutch Switch** - Switch closes, providing ECA with an "on" signal when clutch pedal is depressed. Switch opens when clutch pedal is released.

**Neutral Switch** - Switch closes, providing ECA with an "on" signal when transmission is shifted into Neutral. Switch is open in all other gears.

## IDLE SWITCH

Switch opens, providing ECA with an "off" signal when throttle is open (about 1200 RPM). Switch is closed when throttle is closed. Information is used by ECA to determine control of fuel shutoff solenoid and ABCV.

## MANIFOLD ABSOLUTE PRESSURE (MAP) SENSOR

Sensor is a variable resistor which modifies an ECA-monitored voltage signal based upon intake manifold pressure (vacuum) changes. Information is used by ECA to determine control of fuel shutoff solenoid, ABCV, EGR and pulse air system.

## VACUUM SWITCH

Switch closes, providing ECA with an "on" signal when vacuum is present. Signal is used by the ECA in air/fuel mixture computations.

## ENGINE SPEED SIGNAL

Although not a true sensor or switch signal, RPM signals from ignition coil are monitored by ECA. Information is used by ECA in engine idle speed control calculations.

## IDLE-UP SOLENOIDS

**A/C Solenoid** - When ECA senses A/C clutch operation (A/C clutch switch on), to compensate for engine load created by compressor, ECA will energize A/C idle-up solenoid, increasing engine speed to 1200-1300 RPM.

**Electrical Load (E/L) Solenoid** - When ECA senses low voltage on several monitored electrical circuits, ECA will energize E/L idle-up solenoid, increasing engine speed to 750-850 RPM.

## FUEL SHUTOFF SOLENOID VALVE

Solenoid is energized when ignition switch is in "ON" position. Ground is supplied by ECA. During deceleration and when ignition is off, ECA removes ground circuit causing spring loaded solenoid to close, restricting fuel flow in the idle circuit.

# TESTING

## SELF-DIAGNOSTIC SYSTEM CHECK

The EFC system is capable of detecting malfunctions, and storing and outputting fault codes for diagnostic purposes. ECA has a built-in fail-safe functions which will control engine function during periods of failure.

To access fault codes, a special Tester (007-00028) is used. If codes are detected, install EEC-IV Breakout Box (014-00322) and Adaptor (007-00027) to diagnose system. If a special tester is not available, an analog voltmeter can be used to read fault codes.

**Reading Fault Codes with Analog Voltmeter** - **1)** Ground one-pin check connector B-14 (Yellow/Blue wire terminal).

**2)** Connect analog voltmeter positive lead to Green/Red wire terminal of 6-pin self-test connector under dash. Connect voltmeter negative lead to ground.

**3)** Diagnostic codes may be read by observing voltmeter needle long and short pulses.

**4)** Codes are indicated by a 2-digit number. Long pulses indicate first digit. Short pulses indicate second digit. If zero is the first digit, no long pulses will be indicated and needle sweeps will begin with short pulses. A short pause will occur between codes. *See Fig. 2.*

## MALFUNCTION INDICATOR LIGHT (MIL)

**1)** Malfunction indicator light comes on whenever an emissions related fault occurs. The fault warning light should go out after repairing fault in vehicle.

**2)** A fault code will remain in ECA memory until erased. To erase memory, disconnect negative battery cable and depress brake pedal for at least 5 seconds. Reconnect battery cable and ensure malfunction indicator light is off.

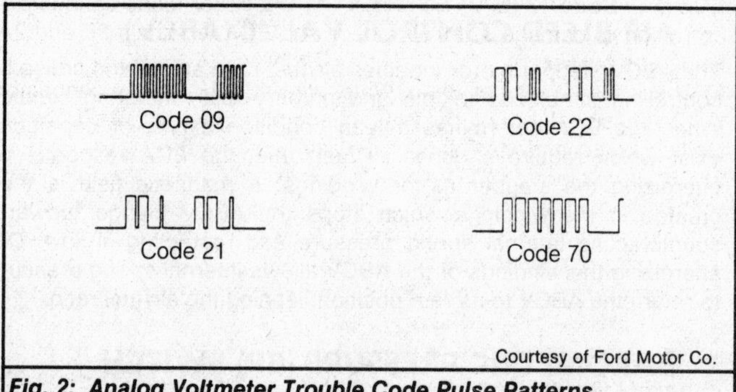
Code 09
Code 22
Code 21
Code 70
Courtesy of Ford Motor Co.

*Fig. 2: Analog Voltmeter Trouble Code Pulse Patterns*

***ECA FAULT CODES***

| Trouble Code No. | Component Circuit | Action To Take |
|---|---|---|
| 01 | Ignition Coil (-) | Go To ECA-2 |
| 09 | Cool. Temp. Sensor | Go To ECA-4 |
| 13 | Map Sensor | Go To ECA-8 |
| 15 | EGO Sensor | Go To ECA-14 |
| 16 | EGR Position Sensor | Go To ECA-19 |
| 17 | Feedback System | Go To ECA-23 |
| 18 | ABCV No. 1 | Go To ECA-28 |
| 19 | ABCV No. 2 | Go To ECA-28 |
| 20 | ABCV No. 3 | Go To ECA-28 |
| 21 | ABCV No. 4 | Go To ECA-28 |
| 22 | Shutoff Solenoid | Go To ECA-31 |
| 28 | EGR Vac. Solenoid 1 | Go To ECA-35 |
| 29 | EGR Vac. Solenoid 2 | Go To ECA-35 |
| 31 | Air Control Solenoid | Go To ECA-39 |
| 34 | E/L Solenoid Valve | Go To ECA-43 |
| 35 | A/C Solenoid Valve | Go To ECA-43 |
| 38 | EFE Heater Relay | Go To ECA-47 |
| 70 | Vacuum Switch | Go To ECA-51 |
| No Code | ..... | Go To ECA-55 |

**ECA 2 - Code 01 (Ignition Pulse)** - **1)** Check for loose connectors, corrosion or damage at ignition coil negative terminal and ECA terminal 1M. Repair as necessary.

**2)** With key on and engine off, check voltage at terminal 1M at ECA. Voltage should read 12-14 volts. If voltage reading is correct, replace ECA.

**3)** If voltage reading is incorrect, check for short in White wire from coil negative terminal to terminal 1M of ECA. If symptom still persists, go to ECA 55.

**ECA 4 - Code 09 (Coolant Temperature Sensor)** - **1)** Check for loose connectors, corrosion or damage at coolant temperature sensor and ECA terminal 2I. Repair as necessary.

**2)** Check resistance across temperature sensor terminals. Resistance should be as shown in COOLANT TEMPERATURE SENSOR RESISTANCE table. If resistance is incorrect, replace temperature sensor.

### COOLANT TEMPERATURE SENSOR RESISTANCE

| Coolant Temperature | Ohms |
|---|---|
| -4°F (-20°C) | 14,600-17,800 |
| 68°F (20°C) | 2210-2690 |
| 176°F (80°C) | 290-354 |

**3)** If resistance is within specification, turn ignition on and check for voltage at ECA terminal 2I. If voltage reading is 5 volts, check for open in wire between temperature sensor Brown/Red terminal and ECA terminal 2I. Repair as necessary.
**4)** If voltage reading is 0-2.5 volts, check for short in wire between temperature sensor Brown/Red terminal and ECA terminal 2I. Repair as necesssary.
**5)** If no short is indicated, go to ECA 8. If symptom persists, go to ECA 55.
**ECA 8 - Code 13 (MAP Sensor) - 1)** Check for loose connectors, corrosion or damage at MAP sensor and ECA terminals 2E and 2A. Repair as necessary.
**2)** Check for 12 volts at Black/White wire at MAP sensor connector. If 12-volt signal is not present, check for open in wire between ignition switch and MAP sensor. Repair as necessary.
**3)** Check voltage at MAP sensor Light Green wire terminal. Voltage reading should be about 5 volts. If 5-volt signal is not present, check for open or short in wire between MAP sensor and ECA terminal 2A. If no problem is found, replace ECA.
**4)** With engine warm and idling, check voltage at MAP sensor Brown/Black terminal. Voltage reading should be .8-1.5 volts. If voltage is not within specification, replace MAP sensor.
**5)** Check continuity of wiring from MAP sensor to ECA. Repair or replace as necessary. If symptom persists after repairs are made, go to ECA 55.
**6)** Check wiring for shorts from MAP sensor Black terminal to ECA terminal 2C and from MAP sensor Black/Brown terminal to ECA terminal 2E. Repair as necessary. If no problems are found, replace ECA.
**ECA 14 - Code 15 (EGO Sensor) - 1)** Run engine at 2500 RPM for one minute. Recheck code. If code is no longer in memory, problem is intermittent.
**2)** If code is still stored, check for air leaks. Repair as necessary.
**3)** Check for fouled spark plugs. Clean and replace as necessary.
**4)** Connect voltmeter between EGO sensor connector and ground. Run engine at 4000 RPM until .55 volt is indicated. Increase and decrease engine speed quickly. Note voltage.
**5)** Speeds greater than 4000 RPM should produce a .5-1.0-volt signal. Decreased speed should produce a voltage of 0-0.4 volt. If voltage signal is not within specification, replace EGO sensor.
**6)** Check voltage at ECA terminal 2D. With key on and engine off, reading should be zero volts. With engine at idle, reading should be .05 volt. With engine running above 2000 RPM, voltage should read .2-.7 volt.
**7)** If voltage is incorrect, check for open or short in wiring between EGO sensor and ECA terminal 2D. Repair as necessary. If symptom persists, go to ECA 55. If voltage is correct, replace ECA.
**ECA 19 - Code 16 (EGR Valve Position Sensor) - 1)** Check for loose connectors, corrosion or damage at EVP sensor and ECA terminals 2F and 2C. Repair as necessary.
**2)** Check resistance from Light Green wire terminal to Black wire terminal. Resistance should measure 4500-5500 ohms. Check resistance from Light Green wire terminal to Light Green/Black wire terminal. Resistance should measure 0-5500 ohms.
**3)** If resistance is not within specification, replace EVP sensor. If resistance is within specification, check EGR valve operation before continuing with diagnosis.
**4)** Check voltage at Light Green wire terminal to EVP sensor. If voltage reading is not about 5 volts, check for open or short in wiring between EVP sensor Light Green wire terminal and ECA terminal 2A. If no problem is found in wiring, replace ECA.
**5)** Check continuity between EVP sensor and ECA. Check continuity between Light Green/Black wire and ECA terminal 2F. Check continuity between Black EVP sensor wire and ECA terminal 2C. Check for shorts in same wires. If wiring is okay, replace ECA.
**6)** If continuity does not exist in wires, repair or replace as necessary. If symptom persists, go to ECA 55.
**ECA 23 - Code 17 (Feedback System) - 1)** Run engine at 2500 RPM for one minute and recheck code. If code is no longer in memory, problem is intermittent.
**2)** If code is still stored, check for intake air leaks. Repair as necessary.
**3)** Check for fouled spark plugs. Clean and replace as necessary.
**4)** Connect voltmeter between EGO sensor connector and ground. Run engine at 4000 RPM until .55 volt is indicated. Increase and decrease engine speed quickly. Note voltage.
**5)** Speeds greater than 4000 RPM should produce a .5-1.0-volt signal. Decreased speed should produce a voltage of 0-.4 volt. If voltage reading is not within specification, replace EGO sensor.
**6)** Check voltage at ECA terminal 2D. With key on and engine off, reading should be zero volts. With engine at idle, reading should be .5 volt. With engine running above 2000 RPM, voltage should read .2-.7 volt.
**7)** If voltage is incorrect, check for open or short in wiring between EGO sensor and ECA terminal 2D. Repair as necessary. If symptom persists, go to ECA 55. If voltage is correct, replace ECA.
**ECA 28 - Codes 18, 19, 20 & 21 (Air Bleed Control Valve) - 1)** Check for loose connectors, corrosion or damage at ABCV and ECA terminals 3C, 3E, 3F and 3H. Repair as necessary.
**2)** Check ABCV resistance. If resistance is not within specification, replace ABCV.

### ABCV RESISTANCE

| Code No. | ABCV Terminal | Ohms |
|---|---|---|
| 18 | F-A | 65-75 |
| 19 | E-B | 65-75 |
| 20 | F-C | 65-75 |
| 21 | E-D | 65-75 |

**3)** Check for continuity between ABCV terminals and ECA. If continuity does not exist, check for open in wiring between ECA and ABCV. Repair as necessary. If symptom still persists, go to ECA 55.
**4)** If continuity exists, check for shorts in wiring between ECA and ABCV. If no problem is found in wiring, replace ECA.

### ABCV-TO-ECA CONTINUITY CHECK

| ABCV Terminal | ECA Terminal | Continuity |
|---|---|---|
| A | 3C | Yes |
| B | 3E | Yes |
| C | 3F | Yes |
| D | 3H | Yes |

**ECA 31 - Code 22 (Fuel Shutoff Solenoid) - 1)** Check for loose connectors, corrosion or damage at fuel shutoff solenoid and ECA terminals. Repair as necessary.
**2)** Check for continuity across Black/White and Red/White wire terminals at fuel shutoff solenoid. If continuity does not exist, replace fuel shutoff solenoid.
**3)** Turn ignition on. Check for battery voltage at Black/White wire terminal of fuel shutoff solenoid valve. If voltage is not present, check for open or short in solenoid Black/White wire to ignition switch.
**4)** Check for continuity between solenoid Red/White wire and ECA terminal 2P. If continuity exists, check for short in wiring from solenoid to ECA. If short does not exist, replace ECA.
**5)** If continuity does not exist, check for open in wiring from solenoid to ECA. Repair as necessary. If symptom still persists, go to ECA 55.
**ECA 35 - Codes 28 & 29 (EGR Solenoid Valve) - 1)** Check for loose connectors, corrosion or damage at EGR solenoid valves and ECA terminals 2N and 2M. Repair as necessary.

**2)** Check continuity across EGR solenoid valve terminals. If continuity is not within specification, replace defective valve(s).

***EGR SOLENOID VALVE CONTINUITY CHECK***

| Code/Valve | EGR Terminal | Continuity |
|---|---|---|
| 28/1 | Blk/White-Brown | Yes |
| 29/2 | Blk/White-Brown/White | Yes |

**3)** Check for battery voltage at Black/White wire of each solenoid valve. If battery voltage is not present, check for open or short between EGR solenoid valve(s) and ignition switch. Repair as necessary.
**4)** Check continuity of wiring between EGR solenoid valves and ECA. If code 28 was stored in memory, check Brown wire from No. 1 solenoid valve to ECA terminal 2N. If code 29 was stored in memory, check No. 2 solenoid valve Brown/White wire to ECA terminal 2M.
**5)** If continuity exists between solenoid valves and ECA, check for short in wiring between ECA and solenoid valves. If no problem is found in wiring, replace ECA.
**6)** If continuity does not exist between EGR solenoid valves and ECA, check for open in wiring between EGR solenoid valve(s) and ECA. Repair or replace as necessary. If symptoms persist, go to ECA 55.
**ECA 39 - Code 31 (Air Control Valve) - 1)** Check for loose connectors, corrosion or damage at ACV and ECA terminal 2R. Repair as necessary.
**2)** Check continuity across terminals of ACV. If continuity does not exist, replace ACV.
**3)** Check for battery voltage at Black/White wire terminal of ACV. If voltage is not present, check for open or short in wiring between ACV and ignition switch. Repair as necessary.
**4)** Check continuity between ACV Yellow/Blue wire terminal and ECA terminal 2R. If continuity does not exist between ACV and ECA, check for open in wiring between ACV and ECA. Repair as necessary. If symptom persists, see ECA 55.
**5)** If continuity exists between ACV Yellow/Blue wire terminal and ECA terminal 2R, check for short in wiring between ACV and ECA. If no problem is found in wiring, replace ECA.
**ECA 43 - Codes 34 & 35 (Idle-Up System) - 1)** Check for loose connectors, corrosion or damage at idle-up solenoid valves and ECA terminals 1C and 2K. Repair as necessary.
**2)** Check for continuity across terminals of idle-up solenoid valves. If code 34 was set in memory, check continuity of Electrical Load (E/L) solenoid Black/White wire terminal to Light Green/Red wire terminal. If code 35 was set in memory, check continuity of A/C solenoid Black/White wire terminal to Blue/Yellow wire terminal. If continuity does not exist, replace defective solenoid(s).
**3)** Check for battery voltage on Black/White wire terminals of A/C and E/L solenoid. If voltage is not present, check for short or open in wiring between idle-up solenoid valves and ignition switch. Repair as necessary.
**4)** Check for continuity between idle-up solenoids and ECA. *See Fig. 3.* Check continuity between E/L solenoid Light Green/Red wire terminal and ECA terminal 1C. Check continuity between A/C solenoid Blue/Yellow wire terminal and ECA terminal 2K.
**5)** If continuity does not exist, check for open in wiring between idle-up solenoids and ECA. Repair as necessary. If symptom persists, go to ECA 55.
**6)** If continuity exists, check for shorts in wiring between idle-up solenoids and ECA. If no problem is found in wiring, replace ECA.

**ECA 47 - Code 38 (EFE Heater Relay) - 1)** Check for loose connectors, corrosion or damage at EFE heater relay and ECA terminal 2Q. Repair as necessary.
**2)** Check for continuity between EFE heater relay Black/White and Black/Red wire terminals. If continuity does not exist, replace EFE heater relay.

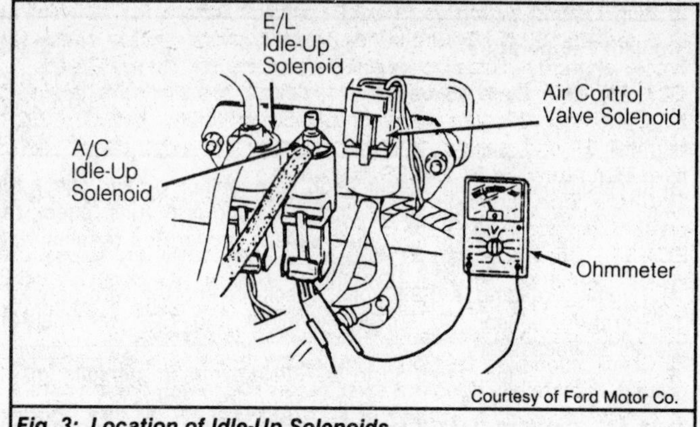
E/L
Idle-Up
Solenoid
Air Control
Valve Solenoid
A/C
Idle-Up
Solenoid
Ohmmeter
Courtesy of Ford Motor Co.

***Fig. 3: Location of Idle-Up Solenoids***

**3)** Check EFE heater relay Black/White lead for battery voltage. If battery voltage is not present, check for open or short in wiring between EFE heater relay and ignition switch.
**4)** Check for continuity between EFE heater relay Black/Red wire terminal and ECA terminal 2Q. If continuity does not exist, check for open in wiring between EFE heater relay and ECA. Repair as necessary. If symptom persists, go to ECA 55.
**5)** If continuity does exist, check for short in wiring between EFE heater relay and ECA. If no problem is found in wiring, replace ECA.
**ECA 51 - Code 70 (Vacuum Switch) - 1)** Check for loose connectors, corrosion or damage at vacuum switch and ECA terminal 2J. Repair as necessary.
**2)** Apply vacuum to vacuum switch and test for continuity across switch terminals. *See Fig. 4.* If continuity does not exist, replace vacuum switch. Continuity should exist with as little as 2.36 in. Hg applied.
**3)** Check for continuity between vacuum switch Black wire and ground. If continuity does not exist, repair ground circuit.
**4)** Check for continuity between vacuum switch Blue/Black wire terminal and ECA terminal 2J. If continuity does not exist, check for open in wiring between vacuum switch and ECA. Repair as required. If symptom persists, go to ECA 55.
**5)** If continuity does exist, check for short in wiring between vacuum switch and ECA. If no problem is found in wiring, replace ECA.

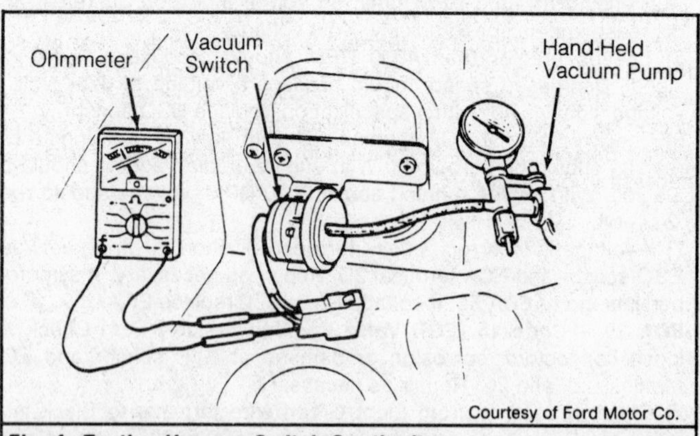
Ohmmeter
Vacuum
Switch
Hand-Held
Vacuum Pump
Courtesy of Ford Motor Co.

***Fig. 4: Testing Vacuum Switch Continuity***

**ECA 55 - No Code (Keep Alive Power) - 1)** With key off, check for 12 volts at ECA terminal 3J. If battery voltage is not present, check for open or short in wiring between battery positive terminal and ECA terminal 3J. Repair as necessary.
**2)** With key on, check for 12 volts at ECA terminal 3J. If 12 volts is not present, check ignition switch for proper operation. Repair or replace as necessary. Go to ECA 57.
**ECA 57 - No Code (Key On Power) - 1)** With key on, check for 12 volts at ECA terminal 3I. If voltage is not present, check for opens or shorts in wiring between ignition switch and ECA. Repair as necessary.

**2)** With ignition switch in "START" position, check for 12 volts at ECA terminal 3I. If 12 volts is not present, check ignition switch for proper operation. Repair or replace as necessary. Go to ECA 59.

**ECA 59 - No Code (Ground) - 1)** Check for continuity between ECA terminal 3G and ground. Check continuity between ECA terminal 3A and ground. If continuity does not exist, check wiring from ECA terminals 3A and 3G to ground.

**2)** Check ECA terminals 3A and 3G for zero volts. If voltage is present, replace ECA. Go to ECA 61.

**ECA 61 - No Code (Idle Switch) - 1)** Check continuity across idle switch terminals at idle. Continuity should not exist. Check continuity at 1160 RPM. Continuity should now exist. If continuity does not exist, adjust or replace idle switch as necessary.

**2)** Check continuity between idle switch Black wire terminal and ground. If continuity does not exist, repair idle switch ground circuit.

**3)** Check idle switch voltage at ECA terminal 1E. At idle, voltage should read 12-14 volts. At about 2000 RPM, voltage should read 0-2.5 volts. If voltage is not present, check for opens or shorts in wiring between idle switch and ECA. Repair as necessary. Go to ECA 64.

**ECA 64 - No Code (4th Gear Switch) - 1)** Check continuity across 4th gear switch terminals. Continuity should exist in 1st, 2nd and 3rd gear. Continuity should not exist in 4th gear. If continuity readings are not correct, replace 4th gear switch.

**2)** Check continuity between 4th gear switch Black wire terminal and ground. If continuity does not exist, repair 4th gear switch ground circuit.

**3)** Check for voltage at ECA terminal 1F. Voltage should read 0-2.5 volts when vehicle is in 1st, 2nd or 3rd gear. Voltage should read 12-13 volts when vehicle is in 4th gear. If voltage readings are not within specification, check for opens or shorts in wiring between 4th gear switch Light Green terminal and ECA terminal 1F. Repair as necessary. Go to ECA 67.

**ECA 67 - No Code (Clutch & Neutral Switches) - 1)** Check for continuity across clutch switch. Continuity should exist only when clutch is depressed.

**2)** Check for continuity across neutral switch. Continuity should exist only when vehicle is in Neutral. If continuity readings are not correct, replace defective switch.

**3)** Check continuity between Black wire terminal of clutch and ground. Repeat check with neutral switch. If continuity does not exist, repair ground circuit(s).

**4)** Check for voltage at ECA terminal 1G. Voltage should read 12-14 volts when clutch pedal is released or vehicle is in any gear except Neutral. When clutch is depressed or transmission is in Neutral, voltage should read 0-2.5 volts. If voltage readings are not correct, check for opens or shorts in wiring between clutch and neutral switch Blue/White wire terminals and ECA terminal 1G. Repair as necessary. Go to ECA 70.

**ECA 70 - No Code (Coolant Temperature Switch) - 1)** Check continuity across coolant temperature switch (mounted in radiator). With engine cold, continuity should exist. With radiator temperature above 62.6°F (17°C), switch should open (no continuity). If switch continuity is incorrect, replace switch.

**2)** Check continuity between switch Black wire terminal and ground. If continuity does not exist, repair switch ground circuit.

**3)** Check voltage at ECA terminal 1L. With engine cold, voltage should read 12-14 volts. With engine warm, voltage should read 0-2.5 volts. If voltage readings are incorrect, check for opens or shorts in wiring between Light Green wire terminal and ECA terminal 1L. Repair as necessary. Go to ECA 73.

**ECA 73 - No Code (Barometric Pressure Switch) - 1)** Check for loose connectors, corrosion or damage at BP switch and ECA terminal 2H. Repair as necessary.

**2)** Check continuity across BP switch. Continuity across switch should exist when 0-27.2 in. Hg is applied to switch. With 27.3-30 in. Hg applied to BP switch, there should be no continuity. If continuity readings are incorrect, replace switch.

**3)** With 27.3-30 in. Hg applied to BP switch, check voltage at ECA terminal 2H. Voltage should read 0-2.5 volts. Release vacuum and voltage should increase to 12-14 volts. If voltage readings are not to specification, check for opens or shorts in wiring between BP switch Blue/Orange wire terminal and ECA terminal 2H. Repair as necessary. Go to ECA 76.

**ECA 76 - No Code (Electrical Switch Inputs) -** Check switch input voltages at ECA. If voltage readings are incorrect, check for opens, shorts or bad connections in wiring between switches and ECA. Repair as necessary. If all harnesses are okay, replace ECA.

***ECA ELECTRICAL SWITCH VOLTAGE INPUTS***

| Terminal | Condition | Voltage |
|---|---|---|
| 1I | Headlight Switch On | 12-14 |
| 1I | Headlight Switch Off | 0-2.5 |
| 1J | Rear Defrost Switch On | 12-14 |
| 1J | Rear Defrost Switch Off | 0-2.5 |
| 1K | Cooling Fan On | 12-14 |
| 1K | Cooling Fan Off | 0-2.5 |
| 1H | Blower Switch High | 0-2.5 |
| 1H | Blower Switch Off | 12-14 |
| 2B | Brake Light Switch On | 12-14 |
| 2B | Brake Light Switch Off | 0-2.5 |
| 3B | A/C Switch & Blower On | 10-14 |
| 3B | A/C Switch & Blower Off | 0-2.5 |

# Ford Motor Co. Festiva EFC System (Cont.)

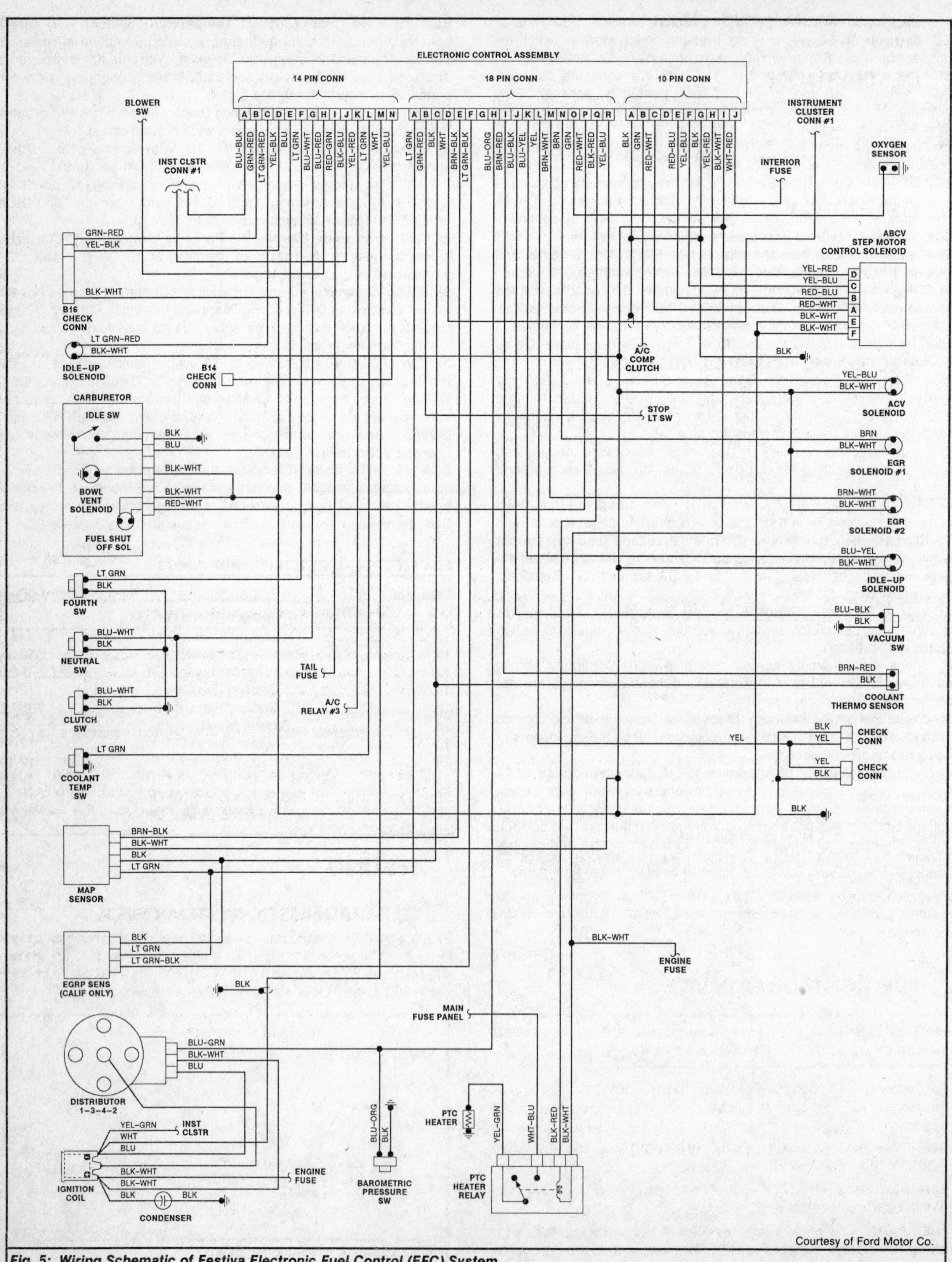
ELECTRONIC CONTROL ASSEMBLY
14 PIN CONN
18 PIN CONN
10 PIN CONN
BLOWER SW
INST CLSTR CONN #1
INSTRUMENT CLUSTER CONN #1
INTERIOR FUSE
OXYGEN SENSOR
ABCV STEP MOTOR CONTROL SOLENOID
A/C COMP CLUTCH
B16 CHECK CONN
IDLE-UP SOLENOID
B14 CHECK CONN
CARBURETOR
IDLE SW
BOWL VENT SOLENOID
FUEL SHUT OFF SOL
STOP LT SW
ACV SOLENOID
EGR SOLENOID #1
EGR SOLENOID #2
IDLE-UP SOLENOID
VACUUM SW
COOLANT THERMO SENSOR
CHECK CONN
CHECK CONN
FOURTH SW
NEUTRAL SW
CLUTCH SW
TAIL FUSE
A/C RELAY #3
COOLANT TEMP SW
MAP SENSOR
EGRP SENS (CALIF ONLY)
ENGINE FUSE
MAIN FUSE PANEL
DISTRIBUTOR 1-3-4-2
INST CLSTR
ENGINE FUSE
IGNITION COIL
CONDENSER
BAROMETRIC PRESSURE SW
PTC HEATER
PTC HEATER RELAY

Courtesy of Ford Motor Co.

*Fig. 5: Wiring Schematic of Festiva Electronic Fuel Control (EFC) System*

# 1988 COMPUTERIZED ENGINE CONTROLS
# General Motors & Isuzu 1.5L EFI Turbo

**General Motors: Spectrum**
**Isuzu: I-Mark**

## DESCRIPTION

This system uses an Electronic Control Module (ECM) to control fuel injectors, ignition timing and emission control devices. The ECM, through input from various sensors, constantly adjusts air/fuel ratio and ignition timing to provide low emissions with good driveability.

## OPERATION

The ECM is provided information on vehicle electrical load, exhaust gas oxygen concentration, engine coolant temperature, engine speed (RPM), engine load, throttle valve position, intake air temperature, vehicle speed and turbocharger boost. This information is used by ECM to calculate proper operation of fuel injectors, ignition timing, idle air control valve and emission control devices.

### ELECTRONIC CONTROL MODULE (ECM)

The ECM is located under the glove box. The ECM has self-diagnosis capability that allows for troubleshooting the system through a check engine light. The check engine light on the dash will illuminate to inform driver of a system malfunction. The ECM stores a maximum of 3 system malfunction, and will display problem(s) via a 2-digit code displayed by the check engine light.

### INPUT SENSORS

**Coolant Temperature Sensor (CTS)** – The CTS is threaded into the intake manifold coolant passage and informs ECM of engine coolant temperature.

**Detonation Sensor** – The detonation sensor is attached to side of engine block. If this sensor hears any detonation, it retards ignition timing through a controller incorporated in the ignition control module.

**Engine Speed Sensor** – This signal is taken from the ignition distributor and informs ECM of engine speed.

**Manifold Absolute Pressure Sensor (MAP)** – The MAP sensor monitors intake manifold vacuum and informs ECM of engine load.

**Manifold Air Temperature Sensor (MAT)** – The MAT is located in the lower part of intake manifold and informs ECM of intake air temperature.

**Vehicle Speed Sensor (VSS)** – The VSS is located in the speedometer and informs ECM of vehicle road speed.

**Oxygen ($O_2$) Sensor** – The $O_2$ sensor is threaded into the exhaust manifold and informs ECM of amount of oxygen in exhaust gases.

**Throttle Position Sensor (TPS)** – The TPS is mounted on the throttle body throttle shaft and informs ECM of changes in throttle position.

### ECM CONTROLLED DEVICES

***NOTE:** In addition to the devices listed below, ECM also controls ignition timing and air conditioner clutch operation.*

**Canister Purge Vacuum Solenoid Valve (CPVSV)** – ECM energizes CPVSV to control operation of fuel evaporative purge system.

**EGR Vacuum Solenoid Valve (EGRVSV)** – ECM energizes EGRVSV to control operation of EGR valve.

**Fuel Injectors** – The ECM controls the on/off time (duty cycle) of fuel injectors to regulate air/fuel ratio.

**Fuel Pump Control** – When ignition is turned on, the ECM energizes the fuel pump relay. The relay will operate the fuel pump

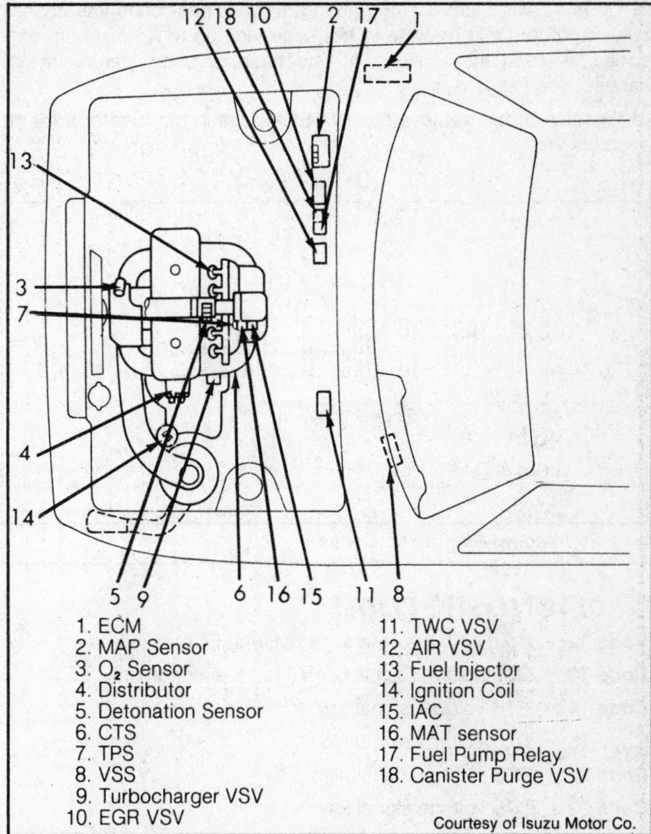
12 18 10 2 17 1
13
3
7
4
14
5 9 6 16 15 11 8
1. ECM
2. MAP Sensor
3. $O_2$ Sensor
4. Distributor
5. Detonation Sensor
6. CTS
7. TPS
8. VSS
9. Turbocharger VSV
10. EGR VSV
11. TWC VSV
12. AIR VSV
13. Fuel Injector
14. Ignition Coil
15. IAC
16. MAT sensor
17. Fuel Pump Relay
18. Canister Purge VSV
Courtesy of Isuzu Motor Co.

*Fig. 1: Spectrum & I-Mark Component Location*

for 4 seconds to pressurize fuel system. After engine start, the relay contacts are held closed by ECM. If engine-running signals to ECM are interrupted, ECM will de-energize relay.

**Idle Air Control Valve (IAC)** – The ECM controls idle speed through opening and closing the IAC to allow air to by-pass throttle body.

**Turbocharger Wastegate Control Vacuum Solenoid Valve (TCVSV)** – The TCVSV is energized or de-energized by the ECM to control turbocharger boost pressure by modulating the wastegate via a vacuum diaphragm.

## TESTING

### SELF-DIAGNOSTIC SYSTEM CHECK

**1)** Locate ALDL diagnostic connector near ECM. Using a jumper wire, jump between terminals "A" and "C". *See Fig. 2.* Turn ignition on, but do not start engine. CHECK ENGINE light will begin to flash diagnostic code 12 indicating the system is working.

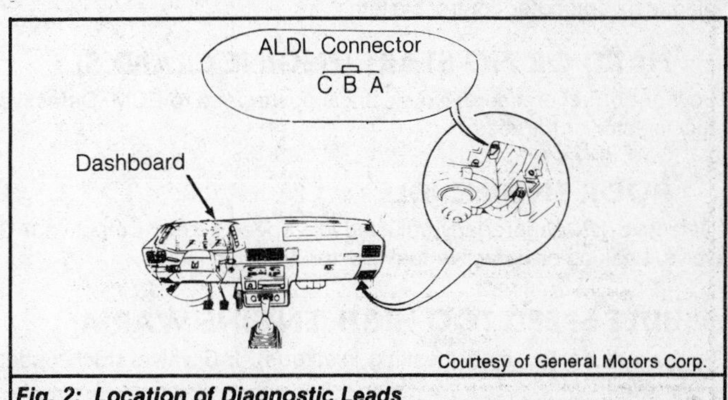
ALDL Connector
C B A
Dashboard
Courtesy of General Motors Corp.

*Fig. 2: Location of Diagnostic Leads*

**2)** Code 12 will flash 3 times, then any additional code will flash 3 times and continue to cycle in this sequence up to a maximum of 3 codes. A code 12 consists of one flash, a short pause and 2 flashes. *See Fig. 3.*

**3)** To clear codes, remove the 10A ECM fuse in the fuse box for 10 seconds.

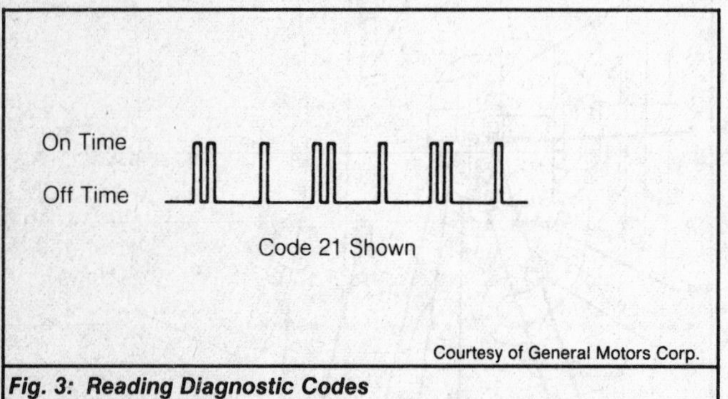
On Time
Off Time
Code 21 Shown
Courtesy of General Motors Corp.

***Fig. 3: Reading Diagnostic Codes***

## DIAGNOSTIC CODES

**Code 12** – No distributor reference pulse to ECM.
**Code 13** – $O_2$ sensor circuit is open (lean fuel condition).
**Code 14** – CTS voltage signal low.
**Code 15** – CTS voltage signal high.
**Code 21** – TPS voltage signal high.
**Code 22** – TPS voltage signal low.
**Code 23** – MAT sensor voltage signal high.
**Code 24** – VSS malfunction.
**Code 25** – MAT sensor voltage signal low.
**Code 31** – Turbocharger wastegate control malfunction.
**Code 32** – EGR system control malfunction.
**Code 33** – MAP sensor voltage signal high.
**Code 34** – MAP sensor voltage signal low.
**Code 42** – Electronic Spark Timing (EST) malfunction.
**Code 43** – Detonation sensor malfunction.
**Code 44** – Lean exhaust indication.
**Code 45** – Rich exhaust indication.
**Code 51** – MEM-CAL failure.

# TROUBLE SHOOTING

## PRELIMINARY CHECKS

Ensure all basic systems, engine mechanical, charging system, ignition system, etc. are functioning properly before attempting to diagnosis computer control system.

## HARD OR NO START (ENGINE CRANKS)

Low or no fuel pressure. No electrical power feed to ECM. Defective fuel injector or harness.

## POOR ENGINE IDLE

Defective TPS. Improperly adjusted idle speed screw. Defective IAC valve. Leaking or defective fuel injector. Vacuum leaks.

## IDLE SPEED TOO HIGH (ENGINE WARM)

Fuel pressure too high. Leaking injector(s). IAC valve stuck open. Defective ECM.

## POOR PERFORMANCE (NO POWER)

Fuel pressure too low. Defective injector(s). Defective turbocharger. Defective detonation sensor. Defective ECM.

## ENGINE KNOCKING

Defective detonation sensor, detonation sensor wiring or ECM.

## ENGINE RUNNING TOO RICH OR TOO LEAN

Defective injector(s). Fuel pressure too high or too low. Defective $O_2$ sensor signal. Defective ECM.

## COMPONENT TESTING BY TROUBLE CODE

**Code 13, 44 & 45 ($O_2$) – 1)** Jumper ALDL. With engine at normal operating temperature, above 158°F (70°C), run engine at 2000 RPM for 2 minutes. If check engine light is flashing closed loop (light flashes once per second), go to step **4)**.

**2)** If check engine light is flashing open loop (light flashes 25 times per second), turn engine off. Disconnect $O_2$ sensor harness and ground Yellow wire. Start engine and note check engine light. Light should flash open loop for about 2 minutes then go out. If light goes out in 2 minutes, replace $O_2$ sensor.

**3)** If light stays on, check continuity in $O_2$ sensor harness. Check that continuity exists between ECM harness connector B23 and Yellow connector wire at $O_2$ sensor, and between B22 and ground. If harness checks bad, repair or replace. If harness checks good, replace ECM.

**4)** If check engine light is flashing closed loop, remove ALDL jumper wire and clear code. Run engine above 2000 RPM for one minute. Note check engine light.

**5)** If check engine light is on, turn engine off. Jumper ALDL and turn ignition on. Note code and refer to applicable code diagnosis. If check engine light is off, problem may be intermittent.

**Code 14 & 15 (CTS) – 1)** Remove CTS connector and check voltage across harness terminals. Turn ignition on. If reading is below 4 volts, go to step **2)**. If reading is above 4 volts, connect an ohmmeter across CTS terminals. Read resistance on ohmmeter. See COOLANT TEMPERATURE SENSOR RESISTANCE VALUES table. If resistance is not equal to table reading, replace CTS.

***COOLANT TEMPERATURE SENSOR RESISTANCE VALUES***

| Temperature | Ohms |
|---|---|
| -22°F (-30°C) | 26,000 |
| -4°F (-20°C) | 15,000 |
| 32°F (0°C) | 5600 |
| 68°F (20°C) | 2500 |
| 104°F (40°C) | 1200 |
| 140°F (60°C) | 600 |
| 176°F (80°C) | 320 |
| 212°F (100°C) | 180 |

**2)** Disconnect B connector at ECM. Using an ohmmeter, check that continuity exists in CTS harness B10 and Green/Black wire at CTS, and B18 and Blue/Green (Red on I-Mark) wire at CTS.

**3)** Check that no continuity exists between B10 and B18, and between B10 and ground or B18 and ground.

**4)** Using a voltmeter, check voltage in CTS harness Green/Black wire and ground. Reading should be 4-6 volts. If harness checks bad, repair or replace. If harness checks good, replace ECM.

**Code 21 (TPS) – 1)** Clear code. Start engine and idle for one minute with A/C off. If check engine light is off, problem is intermittent.

**2)** If check engine light is on, jumper ALDL and note codes. If code 22 is present, go to appropriate test. If code 21 is present, turn engine off. Remove jumper from ALDL and clear codes.

# 1988 COMPUTERIZED ENGINE CONTROLS
## General Motors & Isuzu 1.5L EFI Turbo (Cont.)

**3)** Disconnect TPS sensor. Start engine and idle with A/C off for one minute or until check engine light comes on. Stop engine. Jumper ALDL and turn ignition on. Note code. If code 21 is present, check that continuity exists between TPS harness connector B13 to Red wire connector at TPS.
**4)** With ECM connector installed and ignition on, check that no voltage is present between Red wire at TPS connector and ground. If harness tests bad, repair or replace.
**5)** With ECM connector installed and ignition on, probe TPS Green wire connector with a test light to 12 volts. If light is on, TPS or harness connection is faulty. If test light is off, harness from Green wire connector to ECM connector A11 is faulty or bad ECM.

**Code 22 (TPS) – 1)** Clear codes. Start engine and idle for one minute or until check engine light comes on. If light will not come on, problem is intermittent.
**2)** If check engine light comes on, turn off engine. Jumper ALDL and turn ignition on. Note codes. If code 22 is present, turn off engine. Clear code and remove ALDL jumper.
**3)** Disconnect TPS connector and jumper between Red and Light Green/Red (Light Green/Yellow on I-Mark) wire connectors. Start engine and idle for one minute or until light comes on. Turn engine off. Jumper ALDL and turn ignition on. Note code.
**4)** If code 21 is present, remove jumper wire and connect harness. Adjust TPS to proper specification. If TPS cannot be adjusted, replace TPS.
**5)** If code 22 is present, remove jumper wire. Using a digital voltmeter, check voltage between Green and Light Green/Red (Light Green/Yellow on I-Mark) wire terminals at TPS connector. With ignition on, reading should be 4-6 volts.
**6)** If reading is above 6 volts, check TPS harness Red wire connector to ECM connector B13 for short or ground, faulty connection or bad ECM.
**7)** If reading is below 4 volts, repeat step **6)** for Light Green/Red (Light Green/Yellow on I-Mark) harness connector and B14.

**Code 23 & 25 (MAT) – 1)** Clear codes. Start engine and run for one minute or until light comes on. Turn engine off and turn ignition on. Note codes.
**2)** If code 23 is present, disconnect MAT sensor harness. Turn ignition on and check voltage between MAT sensor harness terminals. If voltage is below 4 volts, check voltage between MAT Black/Yellow (Green/Blue on I-Mark) harness connector and ground.
**3)** If voltage check is below 4 volts, check for open in harness, faulty connection or ECM. If voltage in Black/Yellow (Green/Blue on I-Mark) wire is over 4 volts, check for faulty circuit in Red/Black (Green on I-Mark) wire to ECM harness connector A11.
**4)** If reading across harness terminals in step **2)** was over 4 volts, check resistance across MAT sensor terminals. See MAT SENSOR RESISTANCE VALUES table. If resistance values are not approximately as indicated, replace MAT sensor.

***MAT SENSOR RESISTANCE VALUES***

| Temperature | Ohms |
|---|---|
| -4°F (-20°C) | 28,677 |
| 32°F (0°C) | 9423 |
| 68°F (20°C) | 3515 |
| 104°F (40°C) | 1459 |
| 140°F (60°C) | 667 |
| 176°F (80°C) | 332 |
| 212°F (100°C) | 177 |

**Code 24 (VSS) – 1)** Verify speedometer operation. Disconnect speedometer cable at transaxle. Turn ignition on and check voltage at ECM harness connector A10 and ground while turning speedometer cable slowly.
**2)** If voltage varies from 1-6 volts, problem is intermittent. If voltage is 8-12 volts and steady, check VSS harness for open or short. If harness is good, replace VSS.
**3)** If voltage is below one volt, disconnect harness at VSS and check voltage. With ignition on, if voltage is above 10 volts, replace VSS.
**4)** If voltage is below 10 volts, check VSS harness to ECM connector A10 for shorting to ground. If harness tests good, repair harness connector or replace ECM.

**Code 31 (Turbocharger Wastegate Control) – 1)** Clear codes. Disconnect hoses at turbocharger Vacuum Solenoid Valve (VSV) and air duct. Turn ignition on and blow air through VSV. If air passes through valve, check that VSV harness White wire and ECM harness connector B2 is not shorted to ground. If harness tests good, replace VSV.
**2)** If air will not pass through VSV, jumper ALDL and turn ignition on. Blow air through VSV. If air will not pass through VSV, check circuit B2 for open or faulty ECM.
**3)** If air will pass through VSV in step **2)**, check turbocharger wastegate valve diaphragm. If diaphragm is defective, replace turbocharger. If diaphragm tests good, check for clogged or defective hoses.

**Code 32 (EGR System Control) – 1)** With engine off and ignition on, jumper ALDL and check for additional codes. Repair other codes first. If only code 32 is present, continue with test.
**2)** With engine at normal operating temperature, raise RPM to 3000 and check for movement of EGR valve diaphragm. If EGR is operating, go to step **5)**.
**3)** If EGR is inoperative, shut off engine and disconnect vacuum hose from Back Pressure Transducer (BPT) to EGR valve. Connect vacuum gauge to BPT. Start engine and run at 3000 RPM. If vacuum is present, replace EGR valve.
**4)** If vacuum is not present in step **3)**, check VSV by applying battery voltage to Blue/Yellow wire terminal while grounding White/Green wire terminal of VSV. If VSV operates when voltage is applied, VSV is good. Start engine and check vacuum signal to VSV. Correct if
**5)** If EGR operation was proper in step **2)**, stop engine and remove EGR Gas Temperature Sensor (GTS) from EGR valve. Heat the sensing portion of the GTS and check resistance. See EGR GTS SENSOR RESISTANCE VALUES table. If GTS values are improper, replace GTS.
**6)** If GTS check good, check for clogged exhaust passage. If exhaust passage is clear, replace ECM.

***EGR GTS SENSOR RESISTANCE VALUES***

| Temperature | Ohms |
|---|---|
| 32°F (0°C) | 8,200,000 |
| 122°F (50°C) | 635,000 |
| 212°F (100°C) | 85,300 |
| 392°F (200°C) | 5000 |

**Code 33 (MAP) – 1)** Clear codes. Start engine and run for one minute or until check engine light comes on. Turn engine off. Jumper ALDL and turn ignition on.
**2)** If code 33 is present, clear code. Disconnect MAP sensor connector. Remove ALDL jumper. Start engine and run engine for one minute. If check engine light comes on, jumper ALDL and note code.
**3)** If code 33 is present, check for short circuit in Green wire MAP sensor connector and B11. Repair harness or replace ECM.
**4)** If code 34 is present in step **2)**, check for plugged or leaking vacuum hoses to MAP sensor. If vacuum hoses are good, check for open in circuit B18 to MAP sensor Red wire harness terminal. If harness good, replace ECM.

**Code 34 (MAP) – 1)** Clear codes. Disconnect MAP sensor connector and jumper connector terminal Green to Light Green/Yellow. With ALDL jumper removed, start engine and run for one minute. If check engine light comes on, stop engine. Jumper ALDL and turn ignition on.
**2)** If code 33 is present, replace MAT sensor. If code 34 is present, remove jumper wire from connector. With ignition on, check voltage between Red wire and Light Green/Yellow wire at connector.

**3)** If reading is 4-6 volts, check for open in Green wire at connector to B11 at ECM harness connector. If harness tests good, repair harness connector or replace ECM.
**4)** If reading in step **2)** was below 4 volts, check for open or short in Light Green/Yellow wire at connector and B14 at ECM harness connector. If harness tests good, repair harness connector or replace ECM.

**Code 42 (Electronic Spark Timing)** – **1)** Clear code. Turn ignition off. Disconnect ECM harness connectors. Turn ignition on. Using an ohmmeter, probe harness connector terminal B20 to ground. Reading should be less than 500 ohms.
**2)** If resistance test is not proper, check circuit B20 for open. If circuit B20 has continuity, check connectors for poor connections. If connections are good, replace ECM.
**3)** If resistance reading in step **1)** was proper, probe ECM harness connector terminal B21 with a test light connected to 12 volts. If test light comes on, go to step **6)**
**4)** If test light does not light, connect an ohmmeter between ECM harness connector B20 and ground. Probe harness connector B21 with test light connected to 12 volts. Ohmmeter reading should change from less than 500 ohms to over 5000 ohms when B21 is probed.
**5)** If resistance does not change, disconnect distributor 4-way connector. Ohmmeter should indicate an open circuit (high reading). If open circuit is not indicated, repair circuit B20. If open circuit is indicated, check circuit B21 for open, poor connection at distributor or bad ECM.

If open circuit is not indicated, repair circuit B20. If open circuit is indicated, check circuit B21 for open, poor connection at distributor or bad ECM.
**6)** If test light came on in step **3)**, disconnect distributor 4-way connector. If test light is still on, circuit B21 is shorted to ground.
**7)** If test light goes off in step **6)**, check for short to ground between 4-way connector and Green/White wire ignition module terminal. If no short is present, replace ignition module.

**Code 43 (EST Detonation Control)** – **1)** Check connection between detonation sensor and harness. If connection good, disconnect wire at sensor and turn ignition on. Check voltage between sensor harness connector and ground.
**2)** If reading is less than 4 volts or over 6 volts, check circuit A23 for shorting to ground or shorting to voltage.
**3)** If reading in step **1)** is 4-6 volts, check resistance across detonation sensor terminal to ground. Reading should be 2550-3450 ohms. If reading is bad, replace detonation sensor. If reading is good, check for weak connections at terminals.

**Code 51 (MEM-CAL Failure)** – Check that all pins are fully inserted into socket. If good, replace MEM-CAL. Clear code. If code 51 reappears, replace ECM.

## ADJUSTMENTS

See appropriate TUNE UP PROCEDURES article in this manual.

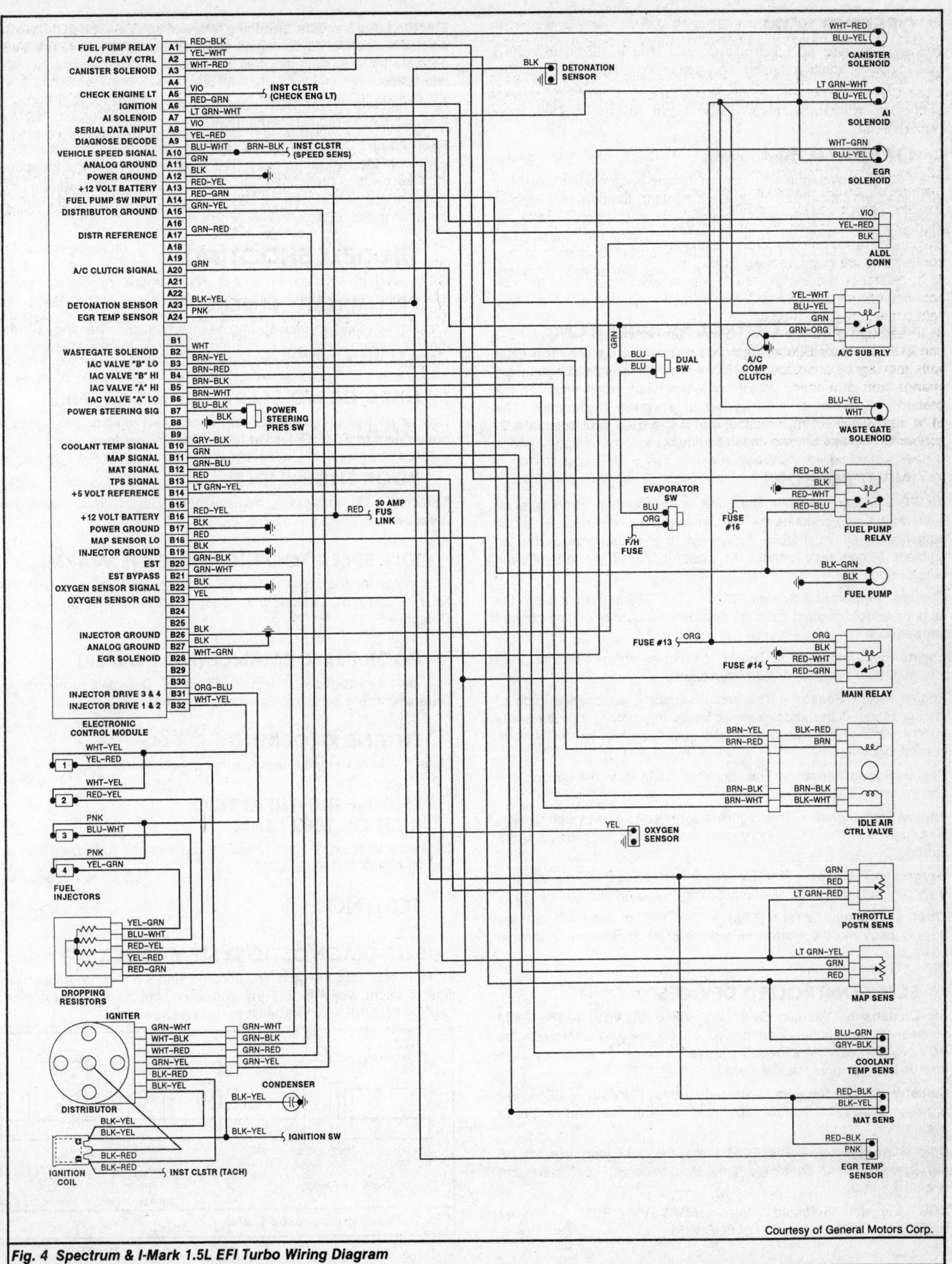
FUEL PUMP RELAY A1 RED-BLK
A/C RELAY CTRL A2 YEL-WHT
CANISTER SOLENOID A3 WHT-RED
A4
CHECK ENGINE LT A5 VIO
IGNITION A6 RED-GRN
AI SOLENOID A7 LT GRN-WHT
SERIAL DATA INPUT A8 VIO
DIAGNOSE DECODE A9 YEL-RED
VEHICLE SPEED SIGNAL A10 BLU-WHT
ANALOG GROUND A11 GRN
POWER GROUND A12 BLK
+12 VOLT BATTERY A13 RED-YEL
FUEL PUMP SW INPUT A14 RED-GRN
DISTRIBUTOR GROUND A15 GRN-YEL
A16
DISTR REFERENCE A17 GRN-RED
A18
A19
A/C CLUTCH SIGNAL A20 GRN
A21
A22
DETONATION SENSOR A23 BLK-YEL
EGR TEMP SENSOR A24 PNK
B1
WASTEGATE SOLENOID B2 WHT
IAC VALVE "B" LO B3 BRN-YEL
IAC VALVE "B" HI B4 BRN-RED
IAC VALVE "A" HI B5 BRN-BLK
IAC VALVE "A" LO B6 BRN-WHT
POWER STEERING SIG B7 BLU-BLK
B8 BLK
B9
COOLANT TEMP SIGNAL B10 GRY-BLK
MAP SIGNAL B11 GRN
MAT SIGNAL B12 GRN-BLU
TPS SIGNAL B13 RED
+5 VOLT REFERENCE B14 LT GRN-YEL
B15
+12 VOLT BATTERY B16 RED-YEL
POWER GROUND B17 BLK
MAP SENSOR LO B18 RED
INJECTOR GROUND B19 BLK
EST B20 GRN-BLK
EST BYPASS B21 GRN-WHT
OXYGEN SENSOR SIGNAL B22 BLK
OXYGEN SENSOR GND B23 YEL
B24
B25
INJECTOR GROUND B26 BLK
ANALOG GROUND B27 BLK
EGR SOLENOID B28 WHT-GRN
B29
B30
INJECTOR DRIVE 3 & 4 B31 ORG-BLU
INJECTOR DRIVE 1 & 2 B32 WHT-YEL
ELECTRONIC CONTROL MODULE
INST CLSTR (CHECK ENG LT)
BRN-BLK INST CLSTR (SPEED SENS)
BLK DETONATION SENSOR
POWER STEERING PRES SW
RED 30 AMP FUS LINK
WHT-RED BLU-YEL CANISTER SOLENOID
LT GRN-WHT BLU-YEL AI SOLENOID
WHT-GRN BLU-YEL EGR SOLENOID
VIO YEL-RED BLK ALDL CONN
YEL-WHT BLU-YEL GRN GRN-ORG A/C SUB RLY
A/C COMP CLUTCH
GRN BLU BLU DUAL SW
BLU-YEL WHT WASTE GATE SOLENOID
RED-BLK BLK RED-WHT RED-BLU FUEL PUMP RELAY
EVAPORATOR SW BLU ORG
F/H FUSE
FUSE #16
BLK-GRN BLK FUEL PUMP
FUSE #13 ORG
ORG BLK RED-WHT RED-GRN MAIN RELAY
FUSE #14
BRN-YEL BRN-RED BLK-RED BRN
BRN-BLK BRN-WHT BRN-BLK BLK-WHT
IDLE AIR CTRL VALVE
YEL OXYGEN SENSOR
GRN RED LT GRN-RED THROTTLE POSTN SENS
LT GRN-YEL GRN RED MAP SENS
BLU-GRN GRY-BLK COOLANT TEMP SENS
RED-BLK BLK-YEL MAT SENS
RED-BLK PNK EGR TEMP SENSOR
WHT-YEL YEL-RED 1
WHT-YEL RED-YEL 2
PNK BLU-WHT 3
PNK YEL-GRN 4
FUEL INJECTORS
YEL-GRN BLU-WHT RED-YEL YEL-RED RED-GRN
DROPPING RESISTORS
IGNITER
GRN-WHT WHT-BLK WHT-RED GRN-YEL BLK-RED BLK-YEL
GRN-WHT GRN-BLK GRN-RED GRN-YEL
CONDENSER
BLK-YEL
DISTRIBUTOR
BLK-YEL BLK-YEL
BLK-YEL IGNITION SW
BLK-RED BLK-RED
IGNITION COIL
INST CLSTR (TACH)
Courtesy of General Motors Corp.

Fig. 4 Spectrum & I-Mark 1.5L EFI Turbo Wiring Diagram

# General Motors Sprint EFI Turbo

## DESCRIPTION

This system uses an Electronic Control Module (ECM) to control fuel injectors, ignition timing and emission control devices. The ECM, through input from various sensors, constantly adjusts air/fuel ratio and ignition timing to provide low emissions with good driveability.

## OPERATION

The ECM is provided information on vehicle electrical load, exhaust gas oxygen concentration, engine coolant temperature, engine speed (RPM), engine load, throttle valve position, intake air temperature, intake air volume and turbocharger boost. This information is used by ECM to calculate proper operation of fuel injectors, ignition timing, idle control valves and emission control devices.

### ELECTRONIC CONTROL MODULE (ECM)

The ECM is located under dash left of steering column. The ECM has self-diagnosis capability which allows for trouble shooting the system through a check engine light. The check engine light on the dash will illuminate to inform driver of a system malfunction. The ECM stores system malfunction, and will display problem via a 2-digit code displayed by the check engine light.

### INPUT SENSORS

**Air Flow Meter (AFM)** – The AFM is mounted in the intake air system and also contains the inlet air temperature sensor. This unit contains an air vane plate connected to a potentiometer and an ambient temperature sensor to signal ECM of air volume and temperature.

**Coolant Temperature Sensor (CTS)** – The CTS is threaded into the intake manifold coolant passage and informs ECM of engine coolant temperature.

**Engine Electrical Load** – The ECM receives engine electrical load information to maintain proper idle speed.

**Engine Knock Sensor** – The knock sensor is attached to side of engine block. If the knock sensor hears any detonation, it retards ignition timing through a controller incorporated in the ignition control module.

**Engine Speed Sensor** – This signal is taken from the ignition coil and informs ECM of engine speed.

**Engine Start Signal** – This signal is supplied to ECM when ignition is turned on. The ECM increases fuel delivery to provide quick starting.

**Oxygen ($O_2$) Sensor** – The $O_2$ sensor is threaded into the exhaust manifold and informs ECM of amount of oxygen in exhaust gases.

**Throttle Position Sensor (TPS)** – The TPS is mounted on the throttle body throttle shaft and informs ECM of changes in throttle position.

### ECM CONTROLLED DEVICES

**Air Conditioner Vacuum Switching Valve (ACVSV)** – The ECM senses air conditioner load placed on engine and energizes the ACVSV. The ACVSV allows a metered amount of air to by-pass throttle body to increase idle speed.

**Canister Purge Vacuum Solenoid Valve (CPVSV)** – ECM energizes CPVSV to control operation of fuel evaporative purge system.

**Cold Start Injector** – The ECM turns the cold start injector on through a coolant controlled time switch during cold start and engine warm-up.

**EGR Vacuum Solenoid Valve (EGRVSV)** – ECM energizes EGRVSV to control operation of EGR valve.

**Electric Load Vacuum Switching Valve (EVSV)** – The ECM senses electrical load placed on engine and energizes the EVSV. The EVSV allows a metered amount of air to by-pass throttle body to increase idle speed.

**Fuel Injectors** – The ECM controls the on/off time (duty cycle) of fuel injectors to regulate air/fuel ratio.

**Fuel Pump Control** – When ignition is turned on, the ECM energizes the fuel pump relay. The relay will operate the fuel pump for 4 seconds to pressurize fuel system. After engine start, the relay contacts are held closed by ECM. If engine-running signals to ECM are interrupted, ECM will de-energize relay.

## TROUBLE SHOOTING

### PRELIMINARY CHECKS

Ensure all basic systems, engine mechanical, charging system, ignition system, etc. are functioning properly before attempting to diagnosis computer control system.

### HARD OR NO START (ENGINE CRANKS)

Low or no fuel pressure. Defective cold start injector. No electrical power feed to ECM. Defective fuel injector or harness.

### POOR ENGINE IDLE

Defective TPS. Improperly adjusted idle speed screw. Leaking or defective fuel injector. Vacuum leaks.

### IDLE SPEED TOO HIGH (ENGINE WARM)

Fuel pressure too high. Defective EVSV or ACVSV (see COMPONENT TESTING). Leaking injector(s). Cold start injector stays on. Defective ECM.

### POOR PERFORMANCE (NO POWER)

Fuel pressure too low. Defective injector(s). Defective turbocharger. Defective knock sensor or ignition control module.

### ENGINE KNOCKING

Defective knock sensor, knock sensor controller or wiring.

### ENGINE RUNNING TOO RICH OR TOO LEAN

Defective injector(s). Fuel pressure too high or low. Defective $O_2$ sensor signal. Defective ECM.

## TESTING

### SELF-DIAGNOSTIC SYSTEM CHECK

1) Turn diagnostic switch on, (located under steering column left side of dash). *See Fig. 2.* Turn ignition on, but do not start engine. CHECK ENGINE light will begin to flash a code 12.

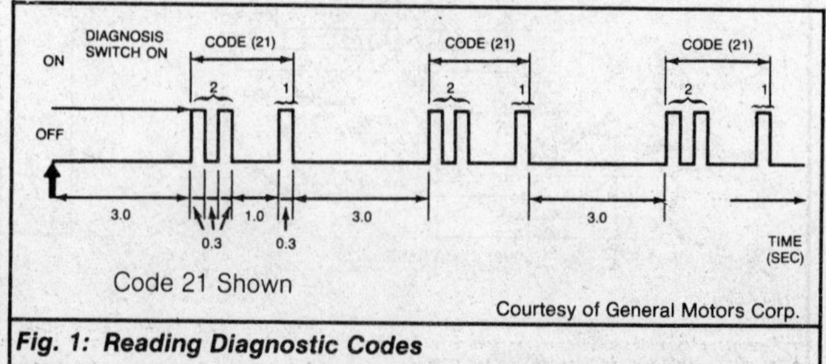
DIAGNOSIS SWITCH ON
ON
OFF
CODE (21)
CODE (21)
CODE (21)
2
1
2
1
2
1
3.0
0.3
1.0
0.3
3.0
3.0
TIME (SEC)
Code 21 Shown
Courtesy of General Motors Corp.

***Fig. 1: Reading Diagnostic Codes***

**2)** Code 12 will flash 3 times, then any diagnostic code stored in ECM memory will flash 3 times and continue to cycle in this sequence. A code 21 consists of 2 flashes, a short pause and one flash. *See Fig. 1.*

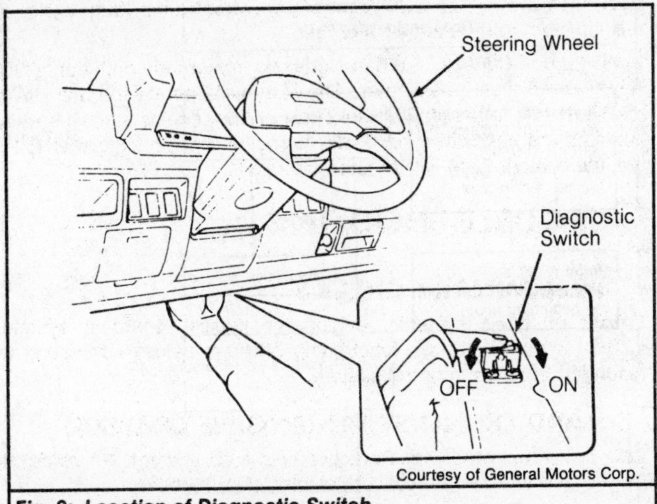
Steering Wheel
Diagnostic Switch
OFF
ON
Courtesy of General Motors Corp.

***Fig. 2: Location of Diagnostic Switch***

### DIAGNOSTIC CODES

**Code 12** – System check. No problem indicated.

**Code 13** – Oxygen ($O_2$) sensor circuit is open causing a lean fuel condition.

**Code 14** – Coolant temperature sensor (CTS) circuit is open.

**Code 15** – Coolant temperature sensor (CTS) circuit is shorted.

**Code 21** – Throttle position sensor (TPS) circuit is open.

**Code 22** – Throttle position sensor (TPS) circuit is shorted.

**Code 23** – Intake air temperature sensor circuit is open.

**Code 25** – Intake air temperature sensor circuit is shorted.

**Code 31** – Turbocharger boost pressure too high.

**Code 33** – Airflow meter circuit open or shorted.

**Code 41** – Ignition signal to ECM interrupted.

**Light "ON" Not Flashing** – ECM failure.

### COMPONENT TESTING

**Airflow Meter** – Disconnect airflow connector. Using an ohmmeter, check resistance at meter terminals. *See Fig. 3.* See AIRFLOW METER RESISTANCE VALUES table.

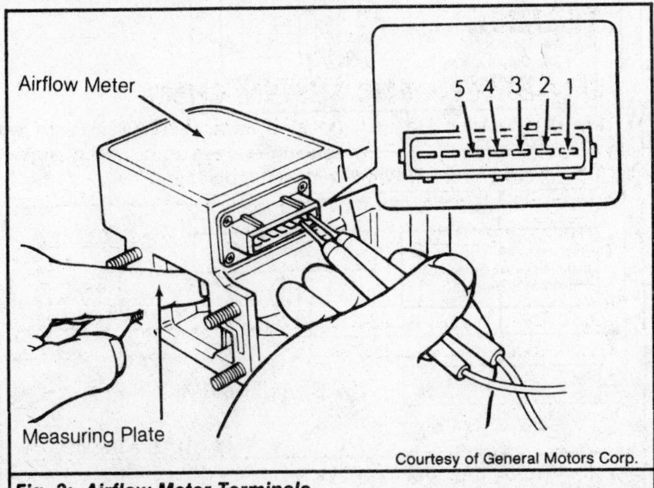
Airflow Meter
5 4 3 2 1
Measuring Plate
Courtesy of General Motors Corp.

***Fig. 3: Airflow Meter Terminals***

***AIRFLOW METER RESISTANCE VALUES***

| Terminals | Ohms |
|---|---|
| 5-3 | 100-300 |
| 5-4 | 200-400 |
| 5-1 | |
| @ -4°F (-20°C) | 10,000-20,000 |
| @ 32°F (0°C) | 4000-7000 |
| @ 68°F (20°C) | 2000-3000 |
| @ 104°F (40°C) | 900-1300 |
| 5-2 | |
| Measuring Plate Fully Closed | 20-400 |
| Measuring Plate Fully Opened | 20-1000 |

**Coolant Temperature Sensor (CTS)** – Remove CTS and warm sensor tip in water. Gradually raise water temperature and read resistance on ohmmeter. See COOLANT TEMPERATURE SENSOR RESISTANCE VALUES table. If resistance at each temperature is not equal to table reading, replace sensor.

***COOLANT TEMPERATURE SENSOR RESISTANCE VALUES***

| Temperature | Ohms |
|---|---|
| 32°F (0°C) | 6000 |
| 68°F (20°C) | 3000 |
| 104°F (40°C) | 1500 |
| 140°F (60°C) | 700 |
| 176°F (80°C) | 400 |
| 212°F (100°C) | 200 |

**Oxygen ($O_2$) Sensor** – **1)** Disconnect $O_2$ sensor connector. Connect a high impedence or digital voltmeter to $O_2$ sensor lead. With engine warm and running above 3000 RPM, $O_2$ sensor voltage should exceed .7 volt.

**2)** With engine at idle and a vacuum hose remove to allow a lean mixture, voltage of $O_2$ sensor should be zero volt.

**Starter Injector Time Switch** – Remove time switch. Connect an ohmmeter across time switch terminals and warm sensor tip in water. With sensor temperature below 66°F (19°C), resistance should be 34-39 ohms. With temperature raised above 77°F (25°C), resistance should be 68-78 ohms.

**Fuel Cut System** – Warm engine to operating temperature. Using a listening (sound) scope, raise engine RPM above 3000 and release throttle. Injectors should stop working until engine RPM falls below 1900.

**Electric Load Vacuum Switching Valve (EVSV)** – **1)** Disconnect air supply hoses from EVSV. *See Fig. 4.* With ignition off, blow air through either hose. Air should not pass through EVSV.

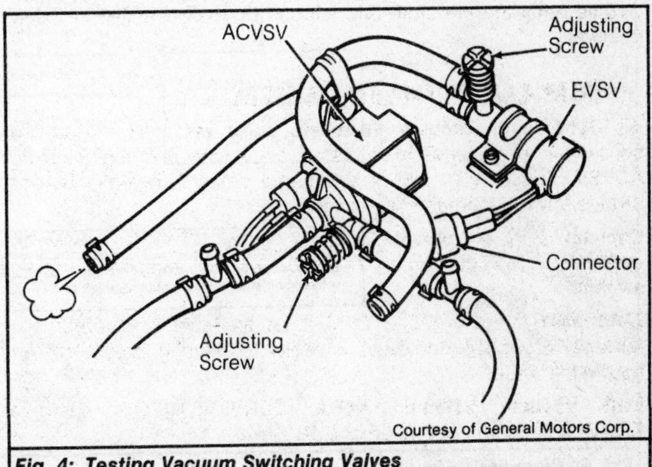
ACVSV
Adjusting Screw
EVSV
Connector
Adjusting Screw
Courtesy of General Motors Corp.

***Fig. 4: Testing Vacuum Switching Valves***

# General Motors Sprint EFI Turbo (Cont.)

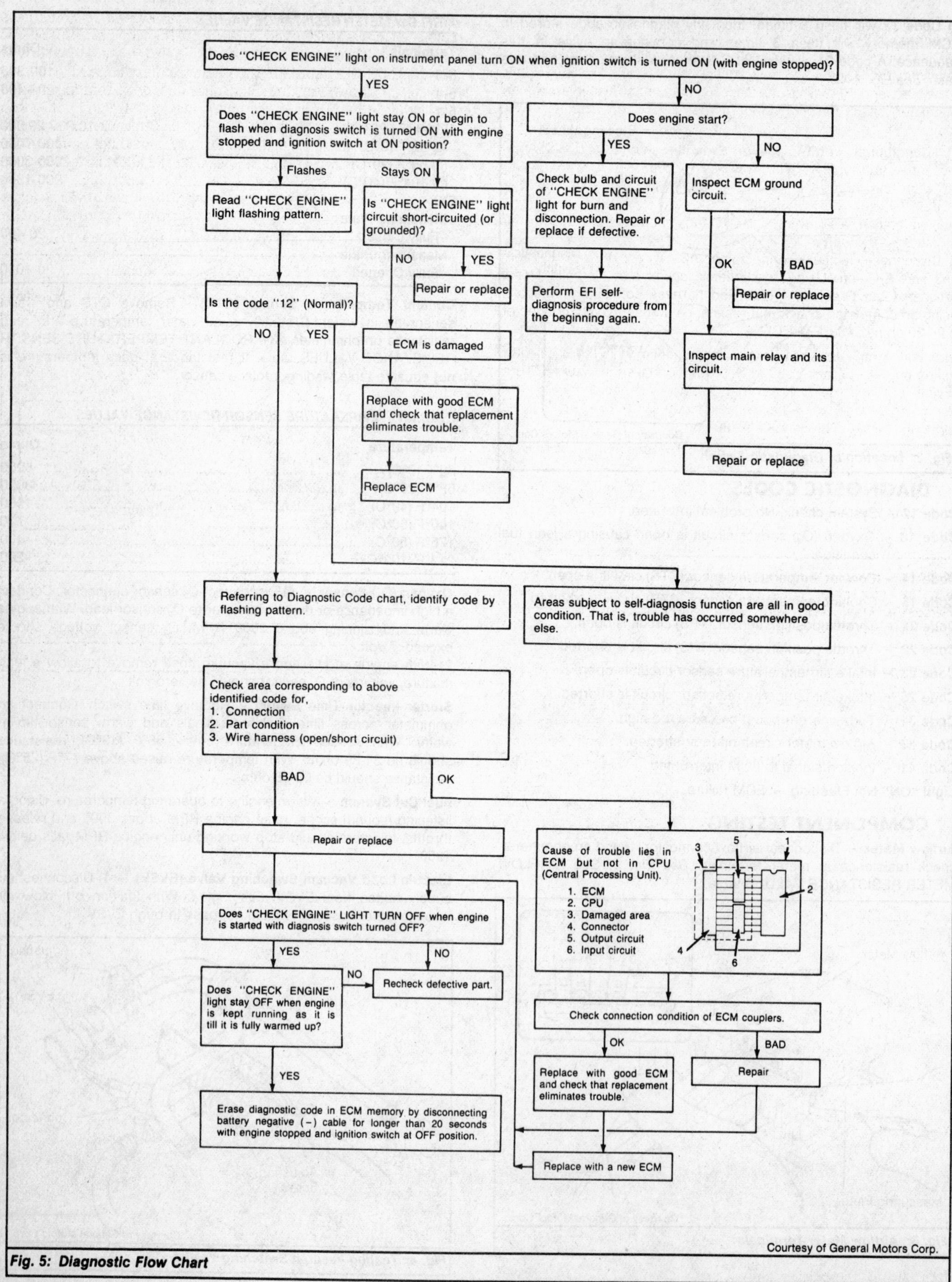

Does "CHECK ENGINE" light on instrument panel turn ON when ignition switch is turned ON (with engine stopped)?
YES
NO
Does "CHECK ENGINE" light stay ON or begin to flash when diagnosis switch is turned ON with engine stopped and ignition switch at ON position?
Flashes
Stays ON
Read "CHECK ENGINE" light flashing pattern.
Is "CHECK ENGINE" light circuit short-circuited (or grounded)?
NO
YES
Repair or replace
ECM is damaged
Replace with good ECM and check that replacement eliminates trouble.
Replace ECM
Is the code "12" (Normal)?
NO
YES
Does engine start?
YES
NO
Check bulb and circuit of "CHECK ENGINE" light for burn and disconnection. Repair or replace if defective.
Perform EFI self-diagnosis procedure from the beginning again.
Inspect ECM ground circuit.
OK
BAD
Repair or replace
Inspect main relay and its circuit.
Repair or replace
Referring to Diagnostic Code chart, identify code by flashing pattern.
Areas subject to self-diagnosis function are all in good condition. That is, trouble has occurred somewhere else.
Check area corresponding to above identified code for,
1. Connection
2. Part condition
3. Wire harness (open/short circuit)
BAD
OK
Repair or replace
Does "CHECK ENGINE" LIGHT TURN OFF when engine is started with diagnosis switch turned OFF?
YES
NO
Does "CHECK ENGINE" light stay OFF when engine is kept running as it is till it is fully warmed up?
NO
Recheck defective part.
YES
Erase diagnostic code in ECM memory by disconnecting battery negative (–) cable for longer than 20 seconds with engine stopped and ignition switch at OFF position.
Cause of trouble lies in ECM but not in CPU (Central Processing Unit).
1. ECM
2. CPU
3. Damaged area
4. Connector
5. Output circuit
6. Input circuit
Check connection condition of ECM couplers.
OK
BAD
Replace with good ECM and check that replacement eliminates trouble.
Repair
Replace with a new ECM
Courtesy of General Motors Corp.


**Fig. 5: Diagnostic Flow Chart**

**2)** Turn ignition and headlights on and repeat step **1)**. Air should pass through EVSV freely.
**3)** Disconnect electrical connector at EVSV and turn ignition and headlights on. Using a voltmeter, check that 12 volts exists between White/Red and Red/White harness connector terminals. Using an ohmmeter, check that resistance across EVSV connector is 51-57 ohms.

**Air Conditioner Load Vacuum Switching Valve (ACVSV) – 1)** Disconnect air supply hoses from ACVSV. *See Fig. 4.* With ignition off, blow air through either hose. Air should not pass through ACVSV.
**2)** Turn ignition, A/C switch and A/C fan on and repeat step **1)**. Air should pass through ACVSV freely.
**3)** Disconnect electrical connector at ACVSV and turn on ignition, A/C and A/C fan. Using a voltmeter, check that 12 volts exists between Light Green and Blue/Red harness connector terminals. Using an ohmmeter, check that resistance across ACVSV connector is 24-30 ohms at 68°F (20°C).

**Fuel Injectors –** Using a sound scope, check that each injector makes proper operating sound in proportion to engine speed. Turn engine off and disconnect fuel injector connector. Using an ohmmeter, check that resistance across injector terminals is approximately 13.8 ohms at 68°F (20°C).

**Cold Start Injector –** Remove electrical connector at cold start injector. Using an ohmmeter, check that resistance across injector terminal is 2-4 ohms.

**Fuel Pump Relay – 1)** If fuel pump will not run, remove fuel pump relay and main relay from bracket on right strut tower.

***NOTE: Fuel pump and main relay are identical. Identify fuel pump relay by wire color code of Pink, Pink/White, White/Blue and White/Blue. Main relay wire color code is Black, Black/White, White/Blue, and White/Green.***

**2)** Turn ignition and headlights on and repeat step **1)**. Air should pass through EVSV freely.
**3)** Disconnect electrical connector at EVSV and turn ignition and headlights on. Using a voltmeter, check that 12 volts exists between White/Red and Red/White harness connector terminals. Using an ohmmeter, check that resistance across EVSV connector is 51-57 ohms.

**Throttle Position Sensor (TPS) – 1)** Disconnect TPS harness connector and check continuity across TPS terminals. Check that continuity exists between terminals No. 3 and 4 when throttle is at idle. No continuity should exist at wide open throttle. *See Fig. 6.*
**2)** Ensure TPS switching from continuity to open is at proper throttle position. Insert a .016" (.40 mm) feeler gauge between throttle stop screw and throttle stop lever. *See Fig. 6.* Continuity should exist between terminals No. 3 and 4. Continuity should not exist when a .031" (.80 mm) feeler gauge is inserted. If switching is incorrect, adjust TPS.
**3)** Check resistance between terminals No. 1 and 4. Resistance should be 4.4-8.1 ohms. If any test values are incorrect, replace TPS.

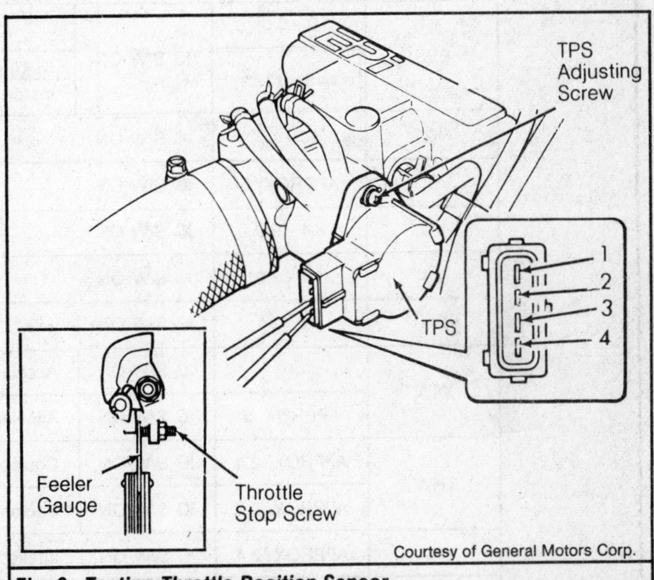
TPS
Adjusting
Screw
1
2
3
4
TPS
Feeler
Gauge
Throttle
Stop Screw
Courtesy of General Motors Corp.

***Fig. 6: Testing Throttle Position Sensor***

## ADJUSTMENTS

See appropriate article in TUNE UP PROCEDURES section.

# General Motors Sprint EFI Turbo (Cont.)

| TERMINAL | STANDARD VOLTAGE (V) | CONDITION | |
|---|---|---|---|
| DNL | 1 - 2 | IG S/W ON | |
| | 10 - 14 | Idling with engine fully warmed up | |
| FP | 0 - 1 | IG S/W ON | During about 4 seconds after IG S/W turned ON |
| | 10 - 14 | | After the about 4 seconds |
| IDL | 0 - 0.5 | IG S/W ON | Accelerator pedal released |
| EPS | 0 - 0.5 | IG S/W ON | |
| | 9 - 13 | | Head light, heater fan switch, rear defogger, stop light or cooling fan motor is turned ON |
| IG | 10 - 14 | IG S/W ON | |
| VCC | APPROX. 5 | IG S/W ON | |
| VC | 6.4 - 9.0 | IG S/W ON | |
| VS | 1.4 - 2.0 | IG S/W ON | |
| DN | 10 - 14 | IG S/W ON | |
| VTA | 0 - 1 | IG S/W ON | Accelerator pedal released |
| | APPROX. 5 | IG S/W ON | Accelerator pedal fully depressed |
| THW | APPROX. 2.4 | IG S/W ON | Coolant temperature 20°C (68°F) |
| | APPROX. 0.6 | IG S/W ON | Coolant temperature 80°C (176°F) |
| THA | APPROX. 2.4 | IG S/W ON | Intake air temperature 20°C (68°F) |
| IDU | 1 - 3 | IG S/W ON | |
| EGR | 10 - 14 | IG S/W ON | |
| PUG | 10 - 14 | IG S/W ON | |
| TSI | 10 - 14 | IG S/W ON | |
| TIL | 10 - 14 | IG S/W ON | |
| STA | 0 - 0.5 | IG S/W ON | |
| | 10 - 14 | Starter switch turned ON with clutch pedal fully depressed | |
| NO. 10 | 10 - 14 | IG S/W ON | |
| +B | 10 - 14 | IG S/W ON | |
| +BB | 10 - 14 | IG S/W ON and OFF | |

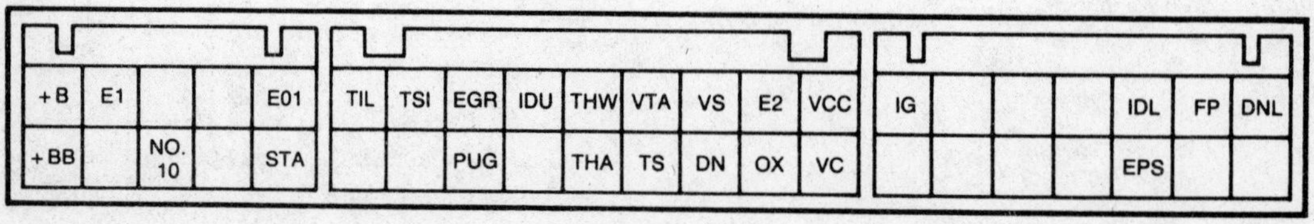

| | | | | | | | | | | | | | | | | | | | | |
|---|---|---|---|---|---|---|---|---|---|---|---|---|---|---|---|---|---|---|---|---|
| +B | E1 | | | E01 | TIL | TSI | EGR | IDU | THW | VTA | VS | E2 | VCC | IG | | | | IDL | FP | DNL |
| +BB | | NO. 10 | | STA | | | PUG | | THA | TS | DN | OX | VC | | | | | EPS | | |

Courtesy of General Motors Corp.

*Fig. 7: ECM Connector Identification & Test Values*

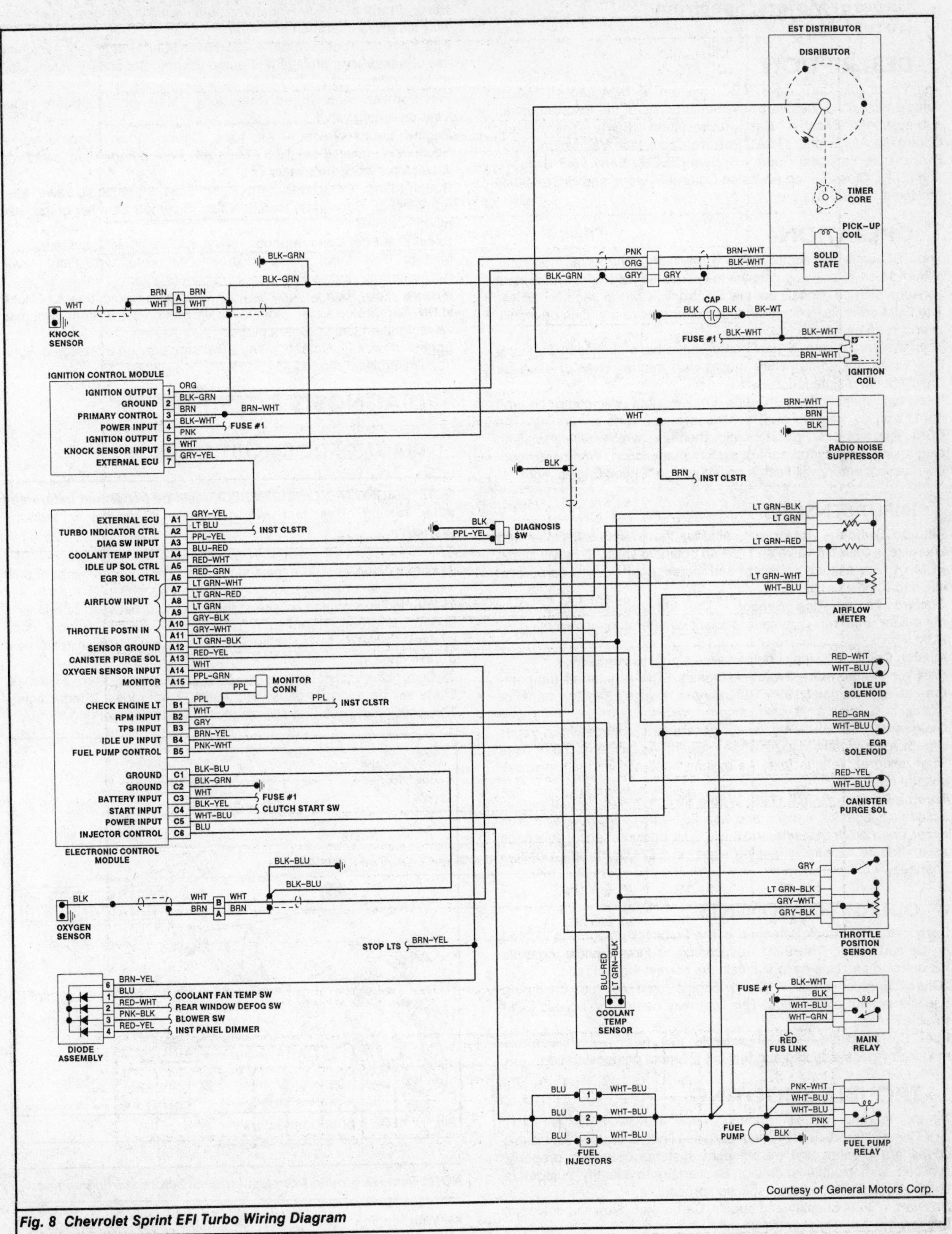
EST DISTRIBUTOR
DISRIBUTOR
TIMER CORE
PICK-UP COIL
SOLID STATE
BRN-WHT
BLK-WHT
PNK
ORG
GRY
BLK-GRN
CAP
BLK
BK-WT
FUSE #1
IGNITION COIL
KNOCK SENSOR
WHT
BRN
IGNITION CONTROL MODULE
IGNITION OUTPUT 1 ORG
GROUND 2 BLK-GRN
PRIMARY CONTROL 3 BRN
POWER INPUT 4 BLK-WHT
IGNITION OUTPUT 5 PNK
KNOCK SENSOR INPUT 6 WHT
EXTERNAL ECU 7 GRY-YEL
RADIO NOISE SUPPRESSOR
INST CLSTR
EXTERNAL ECU A1 GRY-YEL
TURBO INDICATOR CTRL A2 LT BLU
DIAG SW INPUT A3 PPL-YEL
COOLANT TEMP INPUT A4 BLU-RED
IDLE UP SOL CTRL A5 RED-WHT
EGR SOL CTRL A6 RED-GRN
AIRFLOW INPUT A7 LT GRN-WHT
A8 LT GRN-RED
A9 LT GRN
THROTTLE POSTN IN A10 GRY-BLK
A11 GRY-WHT
SENSOR GROUND A12 LT GRN-BLK
CANISTER PURGE SOL A13 RED-YEL
OXYGEN SENSOR INPUT A14 WHT
MONITOR A15 PPL-GRN
DIAGNOSIS SW
MONITOR CONN
CHECK ENGINE LT B1 PPL
RPM INPUT B2 WHT
TPS INPUT B3 GRY
IDLE UP INPUT B4 BRN-YEL
FUEL PUMP CONTROL B5 PNK-WHT
GROUND C1 BLK-BLU
GROUND C2 BLK-GRN
BATTERY INPUT C3 WHT
START INPUT C4 BLK-YEL
POWER INPUT C5 WHT-BLU
INJECTOR CONTROL C6 BLU
ELECTRONIC CONTROL MODULE
CLUTCH START SW
LT GRN-BLK
LT GRN-RED
LT GRN-WHT
WHT-BLU
AIRFLOW METER
IDLE UP SOLENOID
EGR SOLENOID
CANISTER PURGE SOL
OXYGEN SENSOR
BLK-BLU
STOP LTS
BRN-YEL
THROTTLE POSITION SENSOR
COOLANT TEMP SENSOR
BLU-RED
LT GRN-BLK
DIODE ASSEMBLY
6 BRN-YEL
5 BLU
1 RED-WHT COOLANT FAN TEMP SW
2 PNK-BLK REAR WINDOW DEFOG SW
3 RED-YEL BLOWER SW
4 INST PANEL DIMMER
MAIN RELAY
WHT-GRN
RED FUS LINK
FUEL PUMP RELAY
PNK-WHT
FUEL PUMP
FUEL INJECTORS
Courtesy of General Motors Corp.

*Fig. 8 Chevrolet Sprint EFI Turbo Wiring Diagram*

# 1988 COMPUTERIZED ENGINE CONTROLS
# General Motors & Isuzu FBC System

**General Motors: Spectrum**
**Isuzu: I-Mark**

## DESCRIPTION

The Feedback Carburetor (FBC) system is designed to reduce vehicle emission. The overall system consists of the following major sub-systems: Exhaust Gas Recirculation (EGR), Thermostatic Controlled Air Cleaner (TCA), Positive Crankcase Ventilation (PCV), Evaporative Emission Control System (EECS), Early Fuel Evaporation (EFE), Closed Loop Emission Control System, and High Altitude Emission Control System.

## OPERATION

The FBC emission control system precisely controls air/fuel ratio, allowing use of a 3-way catalyst to reduce emissions. Several input sensors provide signals to the Electronic Control Module (ECM). The ECM controls various output components to maintain driveability and keep emissions low.

This system utilizes a dashboard mounted malfunction indicator light which, for some failure modes, will inform driver of need for unscheduled maintenance.

If system malfunctions, "Check Engine" light will come on and remain on as long as fault continues and engine is running. The ECM incorporates a diagnostic memory which will assist in diagnosing closed loop control system malfunction. When activated, diagnostic memory will flash a code through "Check Engine" light.

### INPUT SENSORS

**Altitude Switch** – At a given altitude, the switch will close and energize a solenoid valve and idle-up solenoid valve. This will signal ECM of high altitude condition and increase air flow to carburetor idle and off idle circuits.

**Coolant Temperature Sensor** – The temperature sensor is a thermistor that relays engine coolant temperature information to ECM.

**Ignition Coil** – Provides engine speed signal to the ECM.

**Inlet Air Temperature Switch** – Signals ECM of inlet air temperature at approximately 32°F (0°C). As a switch, it only opens or closes.

**Oxygen ($O_2$) Sensor** – $O_2$ sensor generates a voltage which varies with oxygen content in exhaust gas stream. As oxygen content rises (lean mixture), voltage falls. As oxygen content falls (rich mixture), voltage rises.

**Throttle Position Switch (TPS) W/Idle Switch** – The TPS assembly includes a position sensor and an idle switch. The idle switch is either open or closed, idle or off idle. The position sensor functions as a variable resistor, changing signal to ECM as throttle position changes.

### OUTPUT COMPONENTS

**Carburetor Feedback Solenoid** – The feedback solenoid is located in the carburetor. The ECM, responding to input signals, controls it's opening and closing to maintain the correct air/fuel ratio.

**"Check Engine" Light** – "Check Engine" light will turn on during specific system malfunction. This light may be used to access ECM trouble codes.

**Fuel Cut-Off Relay** – ECM controls this relay, which controls mixture by-pass solenoid and fuel-cut solenoid on deceleration.

## TROUBLE SHOOTING

Before starting trouble shooting, see DIAGNOSTIC CIRCUIT CHECK in this article. If "Check Engine" light operates, no trouble codes are present and all standard systems operating properly, proceed with trouble shooting. Be certain to identify customers complaint and use correct inspection procedure.

**No Start** – Fuel quantity and supply. Carburetor. Slow-cut solenoid. Evaporative emission control circuit.

**Hard Starting** – Fuel quantity and supply. Choke operation. Throttle valve operation and wear.

**Flat Spot on Acceleration** – Idle speed. Carburetor vent switching valve. Accelerator linkage and pump volume. Secondary valve. Slow air bleed. Main jet.

**Flat Spot on High Speed Operation** – Main jet. Secondary valve. Vent switching valve.

**Engine Lacks Power** – Air filter. Choke valve. Throttle valve. Secondary valve. Fuel filter. Main jet. Fuel pump. Vent switching valve. Mixture control valve.

**Rough Idling** – Carburetor mounting. Slow-cut solenoid valve. Idle-up solenoid. Secondary throttle valve. Slow jet. Slow air bleed. Idle mixture screw.

**Excessive Fuel Consumption** – Fuel mixture. Ignition system.

**Mixture Too Lean** – Idle mixture. Carburetor jet. Float level. Carburetor mounting. Fuel supply. Slow-cut solenoid valve.

**Mixture Too Rich** – Air cleaner. Carburetor adjustment. Choke valve. Carburetor air jet. Float level. Ventilation valve. Vent switching valve. Ignition timing. Spark plugs.

**Engine Knock** – Octane rating. Transmission gear selected. Ignition timing. Heat range.

## DIAGNOSIS & TESTING

### DIAGNOSTIC CIRCUIT CHECK

***NOTE: DIAGNOSTIC CIRCUIT CHECK must be performed before any other testing. This test will determine if system is working properly.***

**1)** With ignition on and engine stopped, "Check Engine" light should be on. This is a bulb check.

**2)** With ignition on and engine stopped, jumper between terminals A and C or ground terminal A of ALDL to activate trouble code system. *See Fig. 1.* The "Check Engine" light will begin to flash a trouble code 12.

**3)** Code 12 consists of one flash, a short pause, then 2 flashes. There will be a longer pause and code 12 will repeat 2 more times. This check indicates that self-diagnostic system is working.

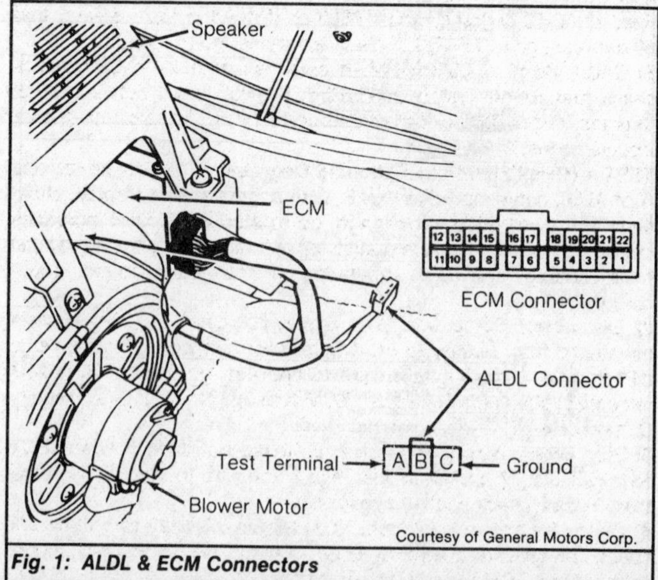
Speaker
ECM
12 13 14 15 16 17 18 19 20 21 22
11 10 9 8 7 6 5 4 3 2 1
ECM Connector
ALDL Connector
Test Terminal
A B C
Ground
Blower Motor
Courtesy of General Motors Corp.

***Fig. 1: ALDL & ECM Connectors***

***NOTE: Remove ground from test terminal before starting engine.***

**4)** With engine running, "Check Engine" light off. Ground test terminal A, check for trouble codes. If any codes exist, refer to TROUBLE CODE table.

### TROUBLE CODES

| Trouble Code | Application |
|---|---|
| 12 | No Distributor Reference |
| 13 | Oxygen Sensor Circuit |
| 14 | Shorted Coolant Sensor Circuit |
| 15 | Open Coolant Sensor Circuit |
| 21 | Idle Switch Circuit |
| 22 | Open Fuel Cut-Off Relay Circuit |
| 23 | Open or Grounded Feedback Solenoid Circuit |
| 25 | Vacuum Switching Valve Circuit |
| 42 | High Voltage from Fuel Cut Relay |
| 44 | Lean Oxygen Sensor Condition |
| 45 | Rich Oxygen Sensor Condition |
| 51 | Faulty Calibration Unit (PROM) |
| 53 | High Voltage from Vacuum Switching Valve |
| 54 | High Voltage from Feedback Solenoid |
| 55 | Faulty ECM or $O_2$ Sensor |

## CLEARING TROUBLE CODE MEMORY

After a fault has been corrected. Remove ECM fuse for 10 seconds to clear ECM stored memory codes.

## SYSTEM PERFORMANCE CHECK

**1)** Set parking brake. Place transmission in "P" (A/T) or "N" (M/T) and block wheels. Start engine. Disconnect and plug vacuum hose from charcoal canister and vent switch valve. Connect tachometer. Disconnect feedback solenoid at 3-pin carburetor connector. Ground feedback solenoid dwell terminal.

**2)** Run engine at 3000 RPM. Keep throttle constant and reconnect feedback solenoid. Note RPM. If RPM dropped more than 100 RPM, go to step **3)**. If RPM dropped less than 100 RPM or increased, check feedback solenoid connections or repair carburetor. Remove ground from feedback solenoid dwell terminal before returning to idle.

**3)** Disconnect idle set connector and connect dwell meter (6-cyl. scale) to feedback solenoid dwell terminal. Warm engine at part throttle until upper radiator hose is warm. Return engine to idle and note dwell.

**4)** If dwell is fixed less than 15 degrees, go to **TEST 1**. If dwell is fixed at 15-50 degrees, go to **TEST 2**. If dwell is fixed greater than 50 degrees, go to **TEST 3**. If dwell is varying, go to step **5)**.

**5)** Check dwell at 3000 RPM. If dwell is between 10-50 degrees, check fuel cut-off system in **TEST 7**. If dwell is not between 10-50 degrees, check TPS or repair carburetor. If no trouble found, clear trouble codes.

**TEST 1 (Dwell Fixed Less Than 15 Degrees) – 1)** Ground terminal A of ALDL connector. *See Fig. 2.* With engine at part throttle, choke engine. If dwell does not change, go to step **2)**. If dwell increases, check for vacuum leak, exhaust leaks before $O_2$ sensor, vacuum hose routing and EGR operation. If no leaks found, repair carburetor.

**2)** Disconnect $O_2$ sensor. With digital voltmeter on 20-volt scale, connected from battery to ECM $O_2$ sensor connector. Note dwell at part throttle. If dwell is less than 15 degrees, go to step **3)**. If dwell increases, check for open from ECM terminal No. 3. If okay, replace $O_2$ sensor.

**3)** Stop engine, turn ignition on and measure voltage between ECM terminals No. 17 and 22. If less than 3 volts, go to step **4)**. If greater than 3 volts, check coolant sensor circuit.

**4)** Check for open circuit from ECM terminal No. 20 to ground and check for grounded wire to ECM terminal No. 3. If okay, check voltage from ECM terminal No. 5 to ground.

**5)** If voltage is less than 2 volts, go to step **6)**. If voltage is greater than 2 volts, check for open from ECM terminals No. 22 to TPS terminal A. If okay, repair ECM connector or replace ECM.

**6)** Check voltage at ECM terminal No. 7. Voltage should be 5 volts, if not, replace ECM. If voltage is okay, check wiring between ECM terminal No. 5 and TPS terminal B and ECM terminal No.7 and TPS terminal C. If wiring is okay, adjust or replace TPS.

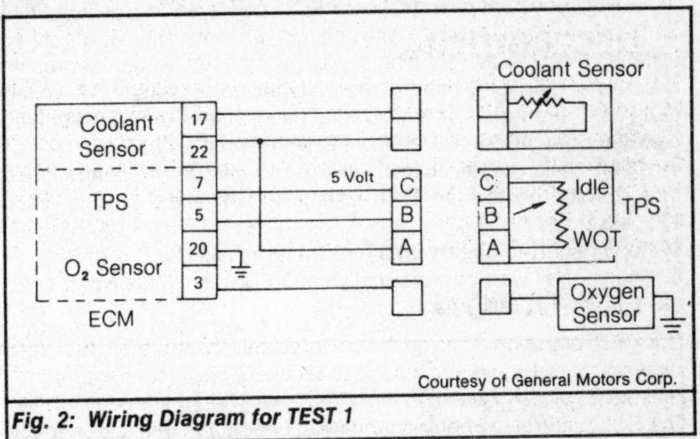
Coolant Sensor
Coolant Sensor
17
22
7
5
20
3
TPS
$O_2$ Sensor
ECM
5 Volt
C
B
A
Idle
TPS
WOT
Oxygen Sensor
Courtesy of General Motors Corp.

*Fig. 2: Wiring Diagram for TEST 1*

**TEST 2 (Dwell Fixed Between 15-50 Degrees) – 1)** Start engine and ground terminal A of ALDL. Run engine at part throttle for one minute. With engine at part throttle, note dwell. Disconnect coolant temperature sensor and jumper connector terminals. *See Fig. 3.* Note dwell.

**2)** If dwell does not change, go to step **4)**. If dwell changes more than 5 degrees, check resistance of coolant sensor. If resistance is less than 1000 ohms, go to step **3)**. If resistance is greater than 1000 ohms, replace coolant sensor.

**3)** Reconnect coolant sensor and note dwell at part throttle. If dwell is fixed, go to step **4)**. If dwell is varying, connection was poor at coolant sensor.

**4)** Reconnect coolant sensor, return engine to idle. Disconnect $O_2$ sensor and jumper ECM connector terminals. Note dwell change. If no dwell change, go to step **5)**. If dwell is less than 10 degrees, repair open in wires to $O_2$ sensor.

**5)** Jumper ECM terminals No. 17 and 22. Note dwell change. If no dwell change, go to step **6)**. If dwell changes more than 5 degrees, repair open in wires to coolant sensor. Reconnnect $O_2$ sensor.

**6)** Check connection to ECM terminals No. 3, 17, 22 and 20. Check TPS adjustment. If no trouble found, replace ECM.

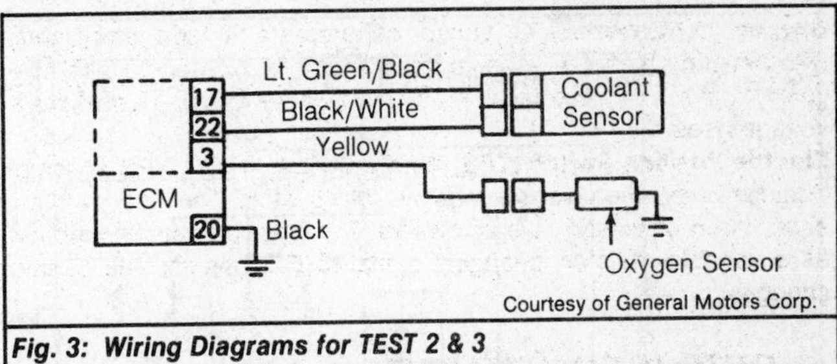
Lt. Green/Black
Black/White
Yellow
17
22
3
ECM
20
Black
Coolant Sensor
Oxygen Sensor
Courtesy of General Motors Corp.

*Fig. 3: Wiring Diagrams for TEST 2 & 3*

**TEST 3 (Dwell Fixed Greater Than 50 Degrees) – 1)** Run engine at fast idle, then idle. Remove large vacuum hose to cause an air leak. Do not stall engine. If dwell does not change, go to step **2)**. If dwell changes, check evaporative canister and related valves. If okay, repair carburetor.

**2)** Disconnect $O_2$ sensor and grond connector terminal to ECM. *See Fig. 3.* If dwell drops to less than 10 degrees, go to step **3)**. If dwell does not change, check ECM connetion or replace ECM.

**3)** Check voltage on $O_2$ sensor wire from $O_2$ sensor at ECM with digital voltmeter with $O_2$ sensor disconnected. If voltage is greater than .5 volts, go to step **4)**. If voltage is less than .5 volts, replace $O_2$ sensor.

**4)** Repeat voltage check with ECM disconnected. If voltage is less than .5 volts, replace ECM. If voltage is greater than .5 volts, check for short in $O_2$ wiring.

**TEST 4 (TPS Wide Open Throttle) – 1)** Ground terminal A on ALDL with engine idling. Connect dwell meter (6-cyl. scale). Warm engine until dwell starts to vary.

**2)** Connect jumper between ECM terminals No. 5 and 22 and note dwell. *See Fig. 4.* Dwell changes to less than 20 degrees, go to step **3)**. If dwell does not change, check ECM connector or replace ECM.
**3)** Remove jumper wire. With ignition on and engine off, check voltage from ECM terminals No. 5 to 22 while depressing accelerator pedal. If there is no voltage, go to step **4)**. If voltage decreased from greater than 3 volts (idle) to less than 3 volts (wide open throttle), preform SYSTEM PERFORMANCE CHECK.
**4)** If voltage is greater than 6 volts, go to step **5)**. If voltage is less than 2 volts, go to step **6)**. If voltage is between 2-6 volts, check TPS assembly.
**5)** Repair short to battery wire to ECM terminals No. 5, 7 or 22.
**6)** Check open wire or grounded wire to ECM terminals No. 5 or 7, if okay check TPS assembly.

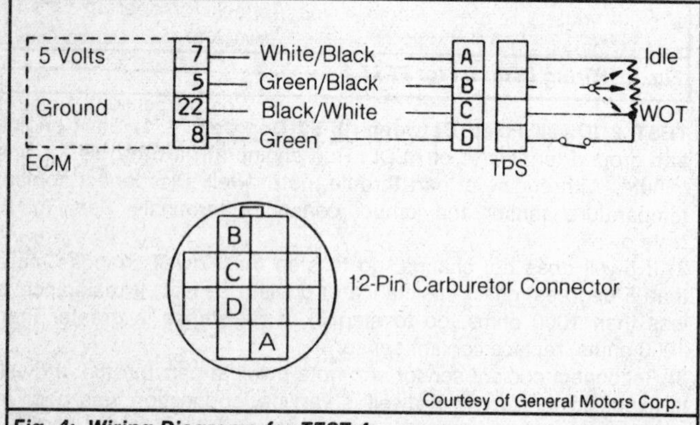
5 Volts
Ground
ECM
7
5
22
8
White/Black
Green/Black
Black/White
Green
A
B
C
D
TPS
Idle
WOT
B
C
D
A
12-Pin Carburetor Connector
Courtesy of General Motors Corp.

*Fig. 4: Wiring Diagrams for TEST 4*

**TEST 5 ("Check Engine" Light Inoperative) - 1)** With ignition on and engine stopped, ground terminal A of ALDL. *See Fig. 5.* If light comes on, go to step **2)**. If light is off, check for failed gauge fuse, open in wire from ALDL, failed bulb or connection.
**2)** Check voltage from remote lamp driver terminal C to ground. If voltage is less than 6 volts, go to step **3)**. If voltage is 6-11 volts, go to step **5)**. If voltage is greater than 11 volts, check for open from lamp driver terminal D to ground. If okay, replace lamp driver.

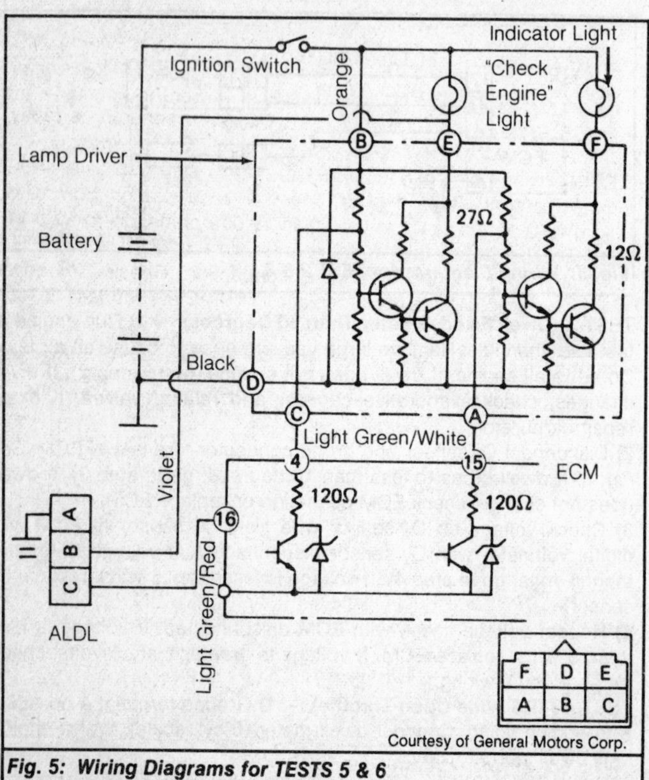
Indicator Light
Ignition Switch
Orange
"Check Engine" Light
Lamp Driver
B
E
F
Battery
27Ω
12Ω
Black
D
C
A
Light Green/White
4
15
ECM
120Ω
120Ω
Violet
16
C B A
ALDL
Light Green/Red
F D E
A B C
Courtesy of General Motors Corp.

*Fig. 5: Wiring Diagrams for TESTS 5 & 6*

**3)** Check voltage from driver terminal B to ground. If voltage is greater than 10 volts, go to step **4)**. If voltage is less than 10 volts, repair open in circuit to gauge fuse from terminal B.
**4)** Remove wire from driver connector terminal C and reconnect driver. If "Check Engine" light is on, repair ground wire from driver terminal C to ECM terminal No. 4. If "Check Engine" light is off, driver or connections are faulty.
**5)** Ground driver terminal E. If "Check Engine" light is on, driver or connections are faulty. If "Check engine" is off, repair open in wire to driver terminal E.

**TEST 6 (Will Not Flash Code 12) - 1)** Check fuse to ECM. Disconnect ground from A terminal of ALDL. With ignition on and engine stopped, check voltage from remote lamp driver terminal C to ground. *See Fig. 5.* If voltage is less than 11 volts, go to step **2)**. If voltage is greater than 11 volts, check for short from terminal C wire to battery. If not shorted, replace lamp driver and repeat DIAGNOSTIC CIRCUIT CHECK.
**2)** Ground lamp driver terminal C. If "Check Engine" light is off, go to step **5)**. If "Check Engine" light is on, disconnect driver.
**3)** If light is on, go to step **4)**. If light is off, driver connection at terminal C or driver is faulty. Repeat DIAGNOSTIC CIRCUIT CHECK.
**4)** Repair ground in wire from driver terminal E to "Check Engine" light. Repeat DIAGNOSTIC CIRCUIT CHECK.
**5)** Ground terminal No. 4 at ECM. If "Check Engine" light is off, go to step **6)**. If "Check Engine" light is on, repair open in wire from ECM terminal No. 4 to driver terminal C and repeat DIAGNOSTIC CIRCUIT CHECK.
**6)** Ground terminal No. 16 at ECM. If light is on, go to step **7)**. If light flashes, repair open in wire from ECM terminal No. 16 to ALDL and repeat DIAGNOSTIC CIRCUIT CHECK.
**7)** Disconnect ground from ECM terminal No. 16 and check voltage from ECM terminals No. 11 or 12 to ground. If voltage is greater than 9 volts, go to step **8)**. If voltage is less than 9 volts, repair poor connection or open in circuit to terminals No. 11 or 12 to ignition switch and repeat DIAGNOSTIC CIRCUIT CHECK.
**8)** Check voltage from ECM terminals No. 1 or 2 to ground. If voltage is less than one volt, go to step **9)**. If voltage is greater than one volt, repair open or poor connection from terminals No. 1, 2 or 22 to ground and repeat DIAGNOSTIC CIRCUIT CHECK.
**9)** Turn ignition off, remove PROM and turn ignition on. After 30 seconds, check for code 12 and 51. If code 12 and 51 appear, go to step **10)**. If no code 12 and 51 appear, ECM or connection is faulty. Repeat DIAGNOSTIC CIRCUIT CHECK.
**10)** Check for proper PROM installation. If okay, replace PROM and recheck. If code 12 does not flash, replace ECM and repeat DIAGNOSTIC CIRCUIT CHECK.
**TEST 7 (Fuel-Cut System Operational Check) - 1)** Warm engine until choke is fully open, A/C off and connect tachometer. Connect voltmeter between ground and terminal A (Black/Green wire) of fuel-cut relay *See Fig. 6.*

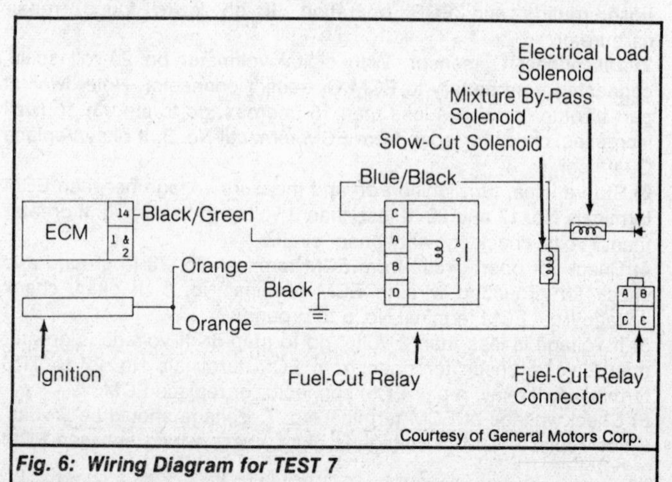
Electrical Load Solenoid
Mixture By-Pass Solenoid
Slow-Cut Solenoid
Blue/Black
ECM
14
1 & 2
Black/Green
Orange
Black
Orange
C
A
B
D
A B
C C
Ignition
Fuel-Cut Relay
Fuel-Cut Relay Connector
Courtesy of General Motors Corp.

*Fig. 6: Wiring Diagram for TEST 7*

**2)** Open throttle slightly and keep engine at 3500 RPM. Note voltage. If voltage is less than 6 volts, go to step **3)**. If voltage is greater than 6 volts, check for open between terminal A to ECM terminal No. 14. If wire is not open, adjust idle switch. If adjustment is okay, ECM or connection is faulty.

**3)** Return throttle to idle and check voltage. If voltage changes, go to step **4)**. If voltage does not change, check adjustment of idle switch and A/C fast idle diaphragm.

**4)** Voltage rises greater than 6 volts, then falls again to low level, when engine drops below 2000-2500 RPM. Fuel-cut circuit and idle switch adjustment are okay. If A/C equipped, repeat test with A/C on.

### TROUBLE CODES

**CODE 12 (No Distributor Reference Pulse to ECM) – 1)** Check connections at tachometer filter assembly. *See Fig. 7.* If okay, go to step **2)**.

**2)** With ignition on and engine stopped, check voltage from ECM side of tachometer filter to ground. If voltage is less than 4 volts, go to step **3)**. If voltage is greater than 4 volts, check for open in wire from filter to ECM terminal No. 19. If wire is okay, ECM or connection is faulty.

**3)** Disconnect wire from tachometer filter to ECM. Recheck voltage at filter side of connector. If voltage is less than 4 volts, go to next step. If voltage is greater than 4 volts, check for grounded wire from tachometer filter to ECM terminal No. 19. If okay, replace ECM.

**4)** Check voltage at tachometer lead from ignition coil with lead disconnected from tachometer filter. If voltage is less than 4 volts, go to step **5)**. If greater than 4 volts, replace tachometer filter.

**5)** Repair open in wire from filter to tachometer terminal of ignition coil.

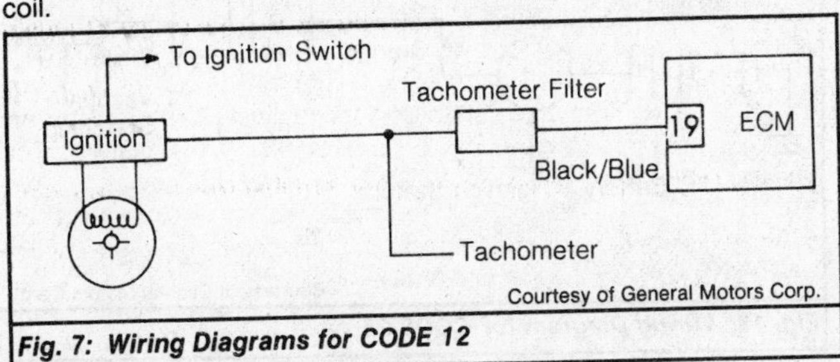
To Ignition Switch
Tachometer Filter
Ignition
19
ECM
Black/Blue
Tachometer
Courtesy of General Motors Corp.

*Fig. 7: Wiring Diagrams for CODE 12*

**CODE 13 (Open $O_2$ Sensor Circuit) – 1)** Ground test terminal at ALDL and connect dwell meter to feedback solenoid (6-cyl. scale). With engine idling, disconnect and ground $O_2$ sensor connector to ECM. *See Fig. 8.* If dwell is greater than 10 degrees after 30 seconds, go to step **2)**. If dwell is less than 10 degrees after 30 seconds, $O_2$ sensor or connection is faulty.

**2)** Connect jumper between ECM terminals No. 3 and 20. If dwell is greater than 10 degrees after 30 seconds, go to step **3)**. If dwell is less than 10 degrees after 30 seconds, repair open from $O_2$ sensor to ECM.

**3)** Check ground at ECM terminal No. 20. If okay, ECM or connection are faulty.

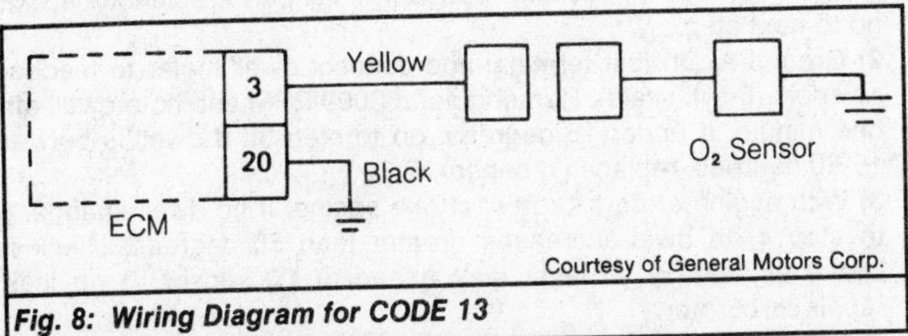
3
Yellow
20
Black
$O_2$ Sensor
ECM
Courtesy of General Motors Corp.

*Fig. 8: Wiring Diagram for CODE 13*

**CODE 14 (Shorted Coolant Sensor Circuit) – 1)** Ground ALDL test terminal and connect dwell meter to feedback solenoid (6-cyl. scale). Run engine at part throttle until dwell starts to vary.

**2)** Remove connector from coolant sensor. If dwell varies, go to step **3)**. If dwell is fixed, replace coolant sensor.

**3)** Remove wire terminal No. 17 from ECM connector. Connect test light from battery to wire terminal No. 17. DO NOT connect test light to ECM. If light is on, repair grounded wire. If light is not on, check for open or shorted wire. If okay, replace ECM.

**CODE 15 (Open Coolant Sensor Circuit) – 1)** Disconnect coolant sensor. *See Fig. 9.* With ignition on and engine stopped, check voltage between sensor connector terminals. Voltage should be greater than 4 volts. If voltage is less than 4 volts, go to step **3)**. If voltage is okay, check resistance of coolant sensor with engine warm.

**2)** If resistance is greater than 1000 ohms, replace sensor. If resistance is less than 1000 ohms, sensor connection is poor or coolant is low.

**3)** Check voltage from ECM terminals No. 17 to 22 with sensor disconnected. If voltage is less than 4 volts, ECM or connection is faulty. If voltage is greater than 4 volts, check for open in wire to ECM terminals No. 17 and 22.

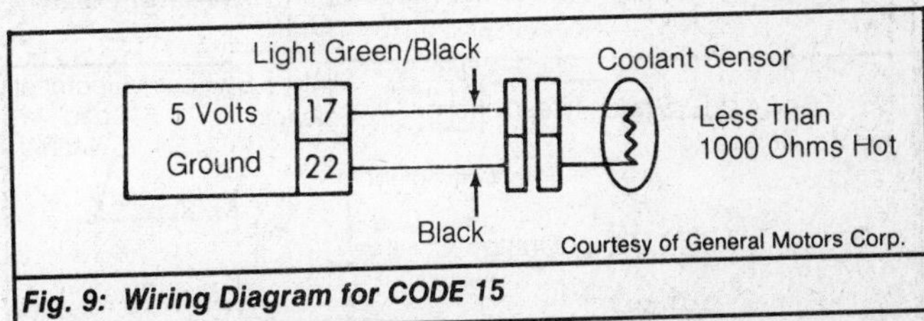
Light Green/Black
Coolant Sensor
5 Volts
17
Ground
22
Less Than
1000 Ohms Hot
Black
Courtesy of General Motors Corp.

*Fig. 9: Wiring Diagram for CODE 15*

**CODE 21 (TPS & Idle Switch Circuit) – 1)** Warm engine until dwell starts to vary. Ground ALDL test connector with ignition on and engine off. Check voltage from ECM connetor terminals No. 8 to 22. *See Fig. 10.* If voltage is less than 2 volts, go to step **4)**. If voltage is greater than 2 volts, adjust TPS and recheck voltage.

**2)** If voltage is greater than 2 volts, go to step **3)**. If voltage is less than 2 volts, recheck TPS and adjustment.

**3)** Check open wire from terminal No. 8 to D. If not open, disconnect 12-pin carburetor connector and check idle switch. If okay, replace ECM.

**4)** Open throttle lever to wide open throttle. Check voltage. If voltage is greater than 2 volts, go to step **5)**. If voltage is less than 2 volts, go to step **3)**.

**5)** Check idle switch operation. If okay, go to next step.

**6)** Disconnect 12-pin connector of carburetor. Check voltage from connector terminal A to B with digital voltmeter with ignition on and engine stopped. If voltage is greater than 2 volts, go to step **7)**. If voltage is less than 2 volts, check voltage from ECM terminals No. 7 to 22. If voltage is less than 2 volts, ECM or connector is faulty. If voltage is greater than 2 volts, repair open in TPS harness.

**7)** Check open or grounded wire from terminals No. 5 to B or ECM connector connection. If okay, check TPS resistance from a to b and c to d. If resistance is less than 10,000 ohms, go to step **8)**. If resistance is greater than 10,000 ohms, replace TPS.

**8)** Check TPS connector terminal connection. Check TPS adjustment. If unable to adjust, replace TPS. Clear codes. If code reappears, replace ECM.

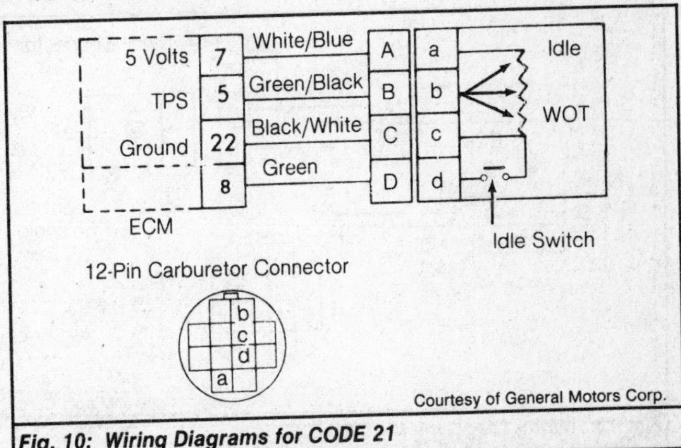
5 Volts
7
White/Blue
A
a
Idle
TPS
5
Green/Black
B
b
WOT
Black/White
C
c
Ground
22
Green
8
D
d
ECM
Idle Switch
12-Pin Carburetor Connector
b
c
d
a
Courtesy of General Motors Corp.

*Fig. 10: Wiring Diagrams for CODE 21*

**CODE 22 (Fuel-Cut Relay Circuit Open or Grounded) – 1)** Check connection at fuel-cut relay. *See Fig. 11.* If okay, clear code and recheck for codes. If no code 22, circuit is okay. If code 22 reappears, go to next step.

**2)** Disconnect ECM connector. With ignition on and engine stopped, check voltage at ECM connector terminal No. 14. If voltage is less than 10 volts, go to step **3)**. If voltage is greater than 10 volts, check fuel-cut relay resistance. If resistance is less than 15 ohms, replace relay. If resistance is greater than 15 ohms, ECM or connection is faulty.

**3)** Connect ECM connector and disconnect fuel-cut relay connector. Connect test light from relay connector battery terminal (Orange wire) to ground. If test light is on, go to step **4)**. If test light is off, check for open in battery circuit.

**4)** Connect test light between relay connector terminals A to B. If light is on, check for ground in wire from relay to ECM. If okay, relay or connector is faulty. If light is off, repair open in wire from relay to ECM.

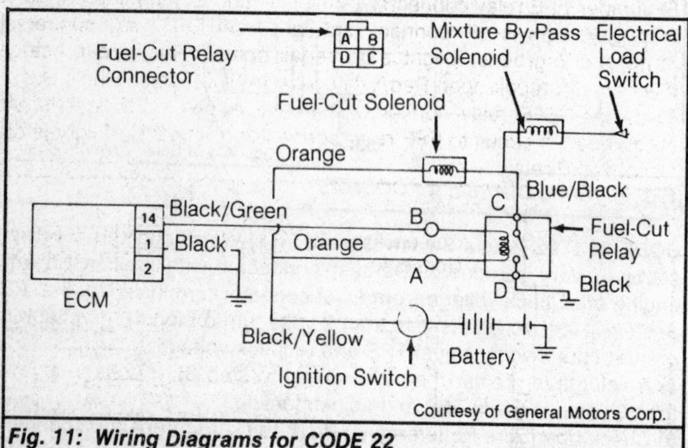
Fuel-Cut Relay Connector
A B
D C
Mixture By-Pass Solenoid
Electrical Load Switch
Fuel-Cut Solenoid
Orange
Blue/Black
14
1
2
Black/Green
Black
Orange
B
C
A
D
Fuel-Cut Relay
Black
ECM
Black/Yellow
Battery
Ignition Switch
Courtesy of General Motors Corp.

*Fig. 11: Wiring Diagrams for CODE 22*

**CODE 23 (Feedback Solenoid Circuit) – 1)** Check connections at feedback solenoid. *See Fig. 12.* If okay, clear codes and recheck. If no code 23 reappears, circuit is okay. If code 23 reappears, go to next step.

**2)** Do not ground ALDL test connector. With ignition on and engine stopped, check voltage at feedback solenoid dwell lead. If voltage is less than 10 volts, go to step **5)**. If voltage is greater than 10 volts, check voltage at ECM terminal No. 21.

**3)** If voltage is greater than 10 volts, go to step **4)**. If voltage is less than 10 volts, repair open in solenoid to ECM.

**4)** Check feedback solenoid resistance. If resistance is less than 10 ohms, replace ECM and solenoid. If resistance is greater than 10 ohms, ECM or connections are faulty.

**5)** Disconnect feedback solenoid and connect test light solenoid connector B and ground. If light is on, go to step **6)**. If light is off, check for open from solenoid to ignition switch.

**6)** Connect test light between solenoid harness connector terminals A to B. If light is on, go to step **7)**. If light is off, check for open wire from feedback solenoid to dwell connector. If not open, feedback solenoid or connection faulty.

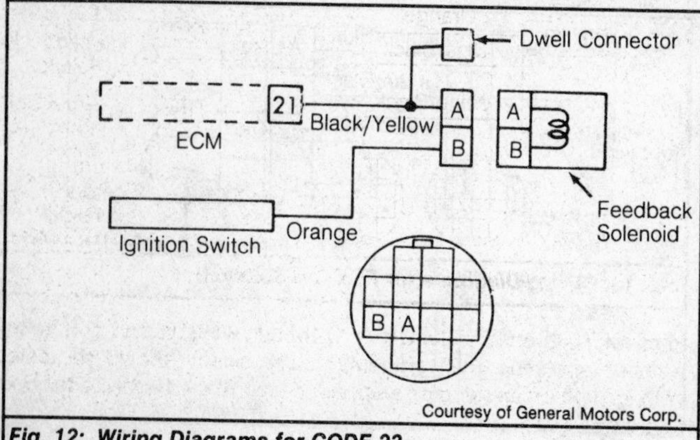
Dwell Connector
21
ECM
Black/Yellow
A
B
A
B
Feedback Solenoid
Ignition Switch
Orange
B A
Courtesy of General Motors Corp.

*Fig. 12: Wiring Diagrams for CODE 23*

**7)** Remove ECM connector terminal No. 21. If light is off, replace ECM. If light is on, repair ground in wire from solenoid to ECM terminal No. 21.

**CODE 25 (Vacuum Switching Valve Circuit) – 1)** Check connections at vacuum switching valve. *See Fig. 13.* If okay, clear codes and recheck. If no codes reappear circuit is okay. If code 25 reappears, go to next step.

**2)** Disconnect ECM connector terminal No. 13. With ignition on and engine stopped, check voltage at ECM connector terminal No. 13. If voltage is less than 10 volts, go to step **4)**. If voltage is greater than 10 volts, check vacuum switching valve resistance.

**3)** If resistance is less than 40 ohms, replace solenoid. If resistance is greater than 40 ohms, ECM or connection is faulty.

**4)** Connect ECM connector and disconnect vacuum switching valve connector. Connect test light from vacuum switching valve connector battery terminal (Orange wire) to ground. If light is on, go to next step. If light is off, check for open battery circuit to switching valve.

**5)** Connect test light between vacuum switching valve harness terminal A to B. If light is on, check for ground in wire from vacuum switching valve to ECM. If light is off, check for open in wire from vacuum switching valve to ECM.

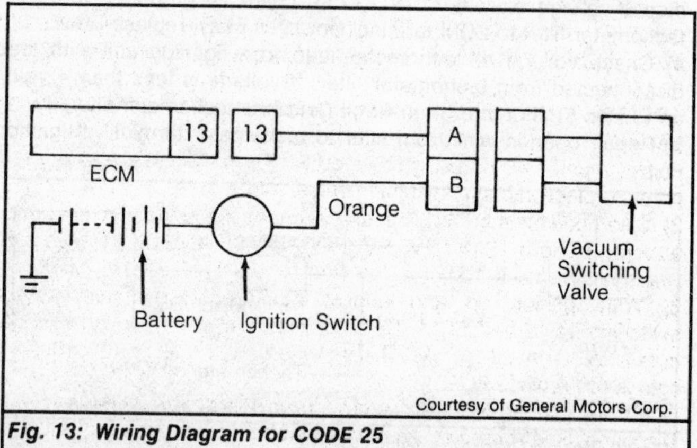
13
13
ECM
A
B
Orange
Vacuum Switching Valve
Battery
Ignition Switch
Courtesy of General Motors Corp.

*Fig. 13: Wiring Diagram for CODE 25*

**CODE 42 (Constant High Voltage from Fuel-Cut Relay) – 1)** Check fuel-cut relay resistance. If resistance is less than 15 ohms, replace fuel-cut relay and go to step **3)**. If resistance is greater than 15 ohms, go to step **2)**. *See Fig. 6.*

**2)** With ignition on and engine, disconnect fuel-cut relay connector and ECM connector terminal No. 14. Connect test light from ground to ECM harness terminal No. 14. If light is on, repair short and go to step **3)**. If light is off, replace ECM.

**3)** Clear code, start engine and recheck codes. If no code, perform SYSTEM PERFORMANCE CHECK. If code 42 remain, replace ECM.

**CODE 44 (Lean Exhaust Indication) – 1)** If feedback solenoid does not click with ignition on and ALDL test terminal grounded and no code 23, check for sticking feedback solenoid. If solenoid is okay, go to next step.

**2)** Ground ALDL test terminal and connect dwell meter to feedback solenoid (6-cyl. scale). Run engine at 3000 RPM and note dwell after one minute. If under 15 degrees, go to step **3)**. If dwell is between 15-50 degrees, replace $O_2$ sensor.

**3)** With engine at part throttle, choke engine. If no dwell change, go to step **4)**. If dwell increases greater than 50 degrees, check for intake air leak or exhaust leak ahead of $O_2$ sensor. If no leaks, repair carburetor.

**4)** Disconnect $O_2$ sensor and connect digital voltmeter (20-volt scale) to $O_2$ sensor harness to ECM. Note dwell. If dwell increases, check for open circuit from ECM connector terminal No. 20 to ground. If okay, $O_2$ sensor or connection is faulty. If dwell is under 10 degrees, check for grounded or open circuit to ECM connector terminal No. 3. If okay, ECM or connection is faulty.

**CODE 45 (Rich Exhaust Indication) – 1)** If feedback solenoid does not click with ignition on and ALDL test terminal grounded and no code 23, check for sticking solenoid. If solenoid is okay, go to next step.

**2)** Connect dwell meter to feedback solenoid (6-cyl. scale), run engine at 3000 RPM. Note dwell. If dwell is greater than 50 degrees, go to step **3)**. If dwell is less than 50 degrees, trouble is intermittent and system is okay at this time.

**3)** With engine idling, note dwell. Remove large vacuum hose to cause air leak. Do not let engine stall. If dwell does not change, go to step **4)**. If dwell decreased, check feedback solenoid connection and evaporative canister and valves for excess fuel. If okay, repair carburetor.

**4)** Disconnect $O_2$ sensor and ground $O_2$ connector terminal to ECM. If dwell drops to less than 10 degrees, go to step **6)**. If dwell does not change, ground ECM connector terminal No. 3.

**5)** If dwell still does not change, ECM is faulty. If dwell now drops to under 10 degrees, repair open or short in wire from $O_2$ sensor and ECM connector terminal No. 3.

**6)** With ignition on and engine stopped, remove ground from $O_2$ sensor connector terminal. Using a digital voltmeter, check voltage from $O_2$ sensor connector terminal to ground. If voltage is less than .55 volts, $O_2$ sensor is faulty. If voltage is greater than .55 volts, check wire from ECM connector terminal No. 3 for short to battery. If okay, ECM is faulty.

**CODE 51 (PROM Problem)** – Check that PROM is fully seated. If okay, replace PROM and recheck. If code 51 reappears, replace ECM.

**CODE 53 (Constant High Voltage Reading from Vacuum Switching Valve) – 1)** Check vacuum switching valve resistance. If resistance is greater than 40 ohms, go to step **3)**. If resistance is less than 40 ohms, replace vacuum switching valve.

**2)** Clear codes, start engine and recheck for codes. If no codes appear, perform SYSTEM PERFORMANCE CHECK. If code 53 reappears, replace ECM.

**3)** With ignition on and engine stopped, disconnect vacuum switching valve and ECM. Connect test light from ground to ECM connector terminal No. 13. If light is on, repair short to battery. If light is off, replace ECM.

**CODE 54 (Constant High Voltage from Feedback Solenoid) – 1)** Disconnect carburetor 12-pin connector and check feedback solenoid resistance from terminals A to B. If resistance is greater than 10 ohms, go to step **3)**. If resistance is less than 10 ohms, replace feedback solenoid.

**2)** Reconnect 12-pin connector, clear codes and start engine. Recheck for codes. If no codes appear, perform SYSTEM PERFORMANCE CHECK. If code reappears, retest circuit.

**3)** With ignition on, engine stopped and solenoid disconnected, connect test light from ground to dwell lead at solenoid. Disconnect ECM. If light is off, replace ECM. If light is on, repair short in wire to ECM connector terminal No. 21.

**CODE 55 (Faulty $O_2$ Sensor or ECM) – 1)** Check for corrosion at ECM connector. Disconnect ALDL test terminal and $O_2$ sensor, note "Check Engine" light with engine idling for less than one minute. If light is off, go to step **3)**. If light is on, stop engine and turn ignition on. Check voltage from ECM connector terminal No. 7 to 20.

**2)** If voltage is greater than 4 volts, go to step **3)**. If voltage is less than 4 volts, check for ground in ECM connector terminal No. 7 wiring, including TPS. If not grounded or shorted, replace ECM.

**3)** With ignition on and engine stopped, disconnect $O_2$ sensor. Check voltage from ECM connector terminal No. 3 to ground. If voltage is greater than 1 volt, go to step **4)**. If voltage is less than 1 volt, check for intermittent ground in ECM connector terminal No. 7 harness, including TPS. If circuit is okay, replace $O_2$ sensor.

**4)** Turn ignition off and disconnect ECM. With ignition on, check voltage from ECM connector terminal No. 3 to ground. If voltage is greater than 1 volt, check for short in ECM connector terminal No. 3 circuit. If voltage is less than 1 volt, check for open circuit from ECM connector terminal No. 20 to ground. If not open, replace ECM.

## COMPONENT TESTING

**Early Fuel Evaporation (EFE) – 1)** With ignition on and engine stopped, disconnect connector at EFE heater. *See Fig. 14.* Connect test light between Red wire at heater and ground. Disconnect auto choke relay and jump harness terminals F to I. Ground ALDL test terminal. If light is off, go to step **4)**. If light is on, remove ground from test terminal. If light is now on, go to step **3)**. If light is now off, go to step **2)**.

**2)** Check resistance of heater. If resistance is less than 2 ohms, heater is okay. If resistance is greater than 2 ohms, replace heater.

**3)** Disconnect wire from EFE relay connector terminal B at relay. If light is on, replace relay. If light is off, check for grounded wire from EFE connector terminal B to ECM connector terminal No. 10. If not grounded, replace ECM.

**4)** Ground EFE relay connector terminal B. If light is off, go to next step. If light is on, check for open wire from EFE connector terminal B to ECM connector terminal No. 10. If okay, ECM or connector is faulty.

**5)** Jumper EFE relay connector terminal A and E. If light is on, go to step **6)**. If light is off, connect test light from EFE relay connector terminal E to ground. If light is on, repair open in Red wire to heater. If light is off, repair open Red/White wire to ECM fuse.

**6)** Jumper EFE relay connector terminal A and C. If light is off, repair open in circuit to EFE relay connector terminal C. If light is on, replace EFE relay.

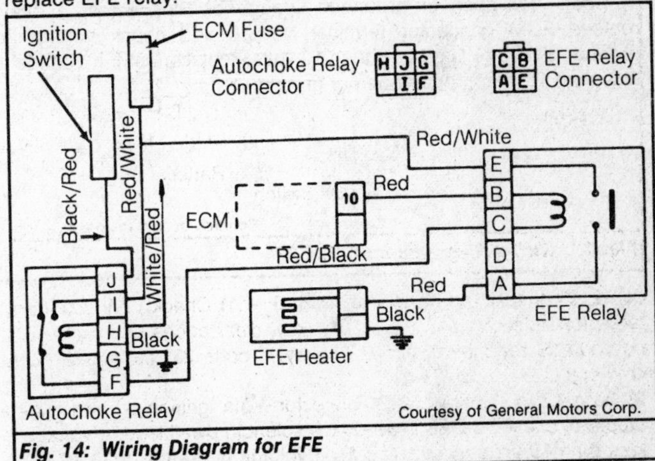
Ignition Switch
ECM Fuse
Autochoke Relay Connector
H J G
I F
C B
A E
EFE Relay Connector
Red/White
Black/Red
Red/White
White/Red
ECM
10
Red
Red/Black
E
B
C
D
A
J
I
H
G
F
Black
Red
Black
EFE Heater
EFE Relay
Autochoke Relay
Courtesy of General Motors Corp.

***Fig. 14: Wiring Diagram for EFE***

**Fuel-Cut Solenoid – 1)** With ignition on and engine stopped, disconnect 12-pin carburetor connector. *See Fig. 15.* Check voltage from harness connector terminal A to B. If voltage is greater than 8 volts, go to step **2)**. If voltage is less than 8 volts, check battery voltage. If okay, harness from ignition to terminal A is open or shorted.

**2)** Connect carburetor connector terminal a to battery and terminal b to ground. If solenoid does not click, check for open in carburetor harness or solenoid. If solenoid does click, solenoid and harness are okay.

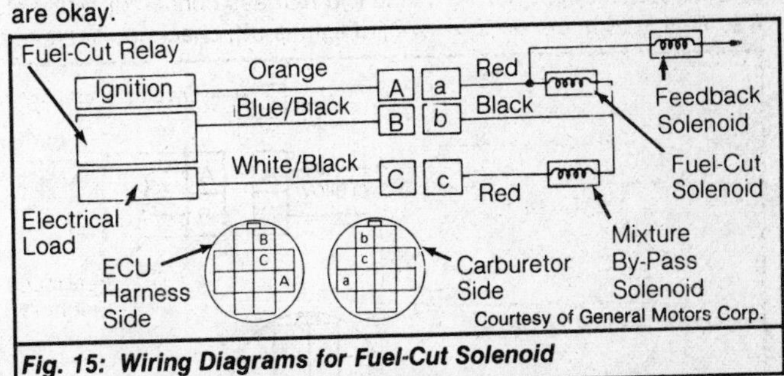
Fuel-Cut Relay
Ignition
Orange
Blue/Black
White/Black
A a
B b
C c
Red
Black
Red
Feedback Solenoid
Fuel-Cut Solenoid
Electrical Load
ECU Harness Side
Carburetor Side
Mixture By-Pass Solenoid
Courtesy of General Motors Corp.

***Fig. 15: Wiring Diagrams for Fuel-Cut Solenoid***

**Inlet Air Temperature Switch – 1)** If code 44 is stored during cold weather operation, inlet air temperature switch should be tested. With ignition on and engine stopped, check Black/Red wire for open or ground. *See Fig. 16.*

**2)** If Black/Red wire is okay, check Black wire ground connection. If okay, check switch for continuity. Switch should have no continuity above 32°F (0°C).´Switch should have continuity below 32°F (0°C).

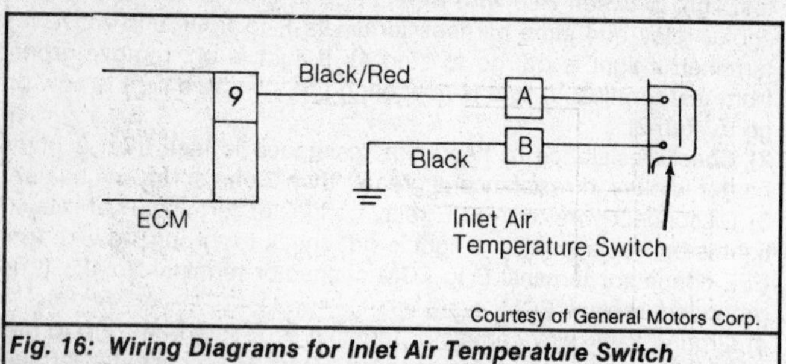
Black/Red
9
A
B
Black
ECM
Inlet Air
Temperature Switch
Courtesy of General Motors Corp.

*Fig. 16: Wiring Diagrams for Inlet Air Temperature Switch*

**High Altitude Operation** – **1)** With ignition on and engine stopped, disconnect high altitude switch connector terminals C and D. *See Fig. 17.* Check voltage at connector terminal C. If voltage is less than 10 volts, go to step **3)**. If voltage is greater than 10 volts, check Black wire ground. If okay, go to next step.

**2)** Connect jumper wire to connector terminal C, ground jumper wire repeatedly. High altitude solenoid should click. If solenoid clicks, solenoid is okay. If solenoid does not click, replace solenoid.

**3)** Check for open or grounded Orange or Blue wires. If okay, remove ECM connector terminal No. 18 and check voltage to ground. If voltage is greater than 10 volts, replace ECM. If voltage is less than 10 volts, repair open or ground.

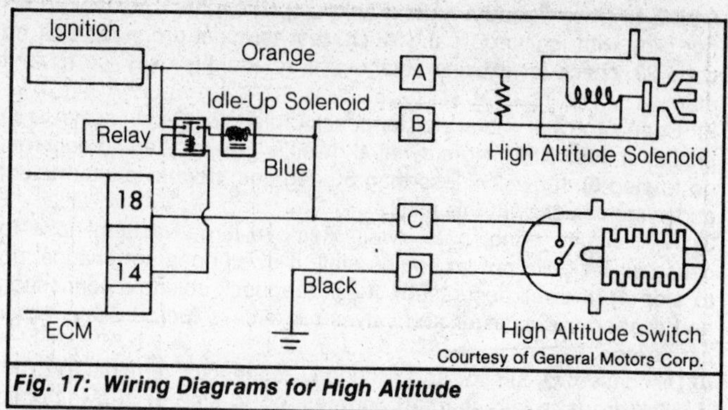
Ignition
Orange
Idle-Up Solenoid
Relay
A
B
High Altitude Solenoid
Blue
18
C
14
D
Black
ECM
High Altitude Switch
Courtesy of General Motors Corp.

*Fig. 17: Wiring Diagrams for High Altitude*

**Mixture By-Pass Solenoid** – **1)** With ignition on and engine stopped, apply electrical load (headlights, rear defogger, etc.). Disconnect 12-pin carburetor connector. Check voltage from carburetor harness connector terminal C to B. If voltage is greater than 8 volts, go to step **2)**. If voltage is less than 8 volts, check battery. If okay, check harness to terminal C.

**2)** Connect carburetor connector terminal c to battery and terminal b to ground. If solenoid does not click, check for open in carburetor harness or defective solenoid. If solenoid does click, solenoid and harness are okay.

# General Motors & Isuzu FBC System (Cont.)

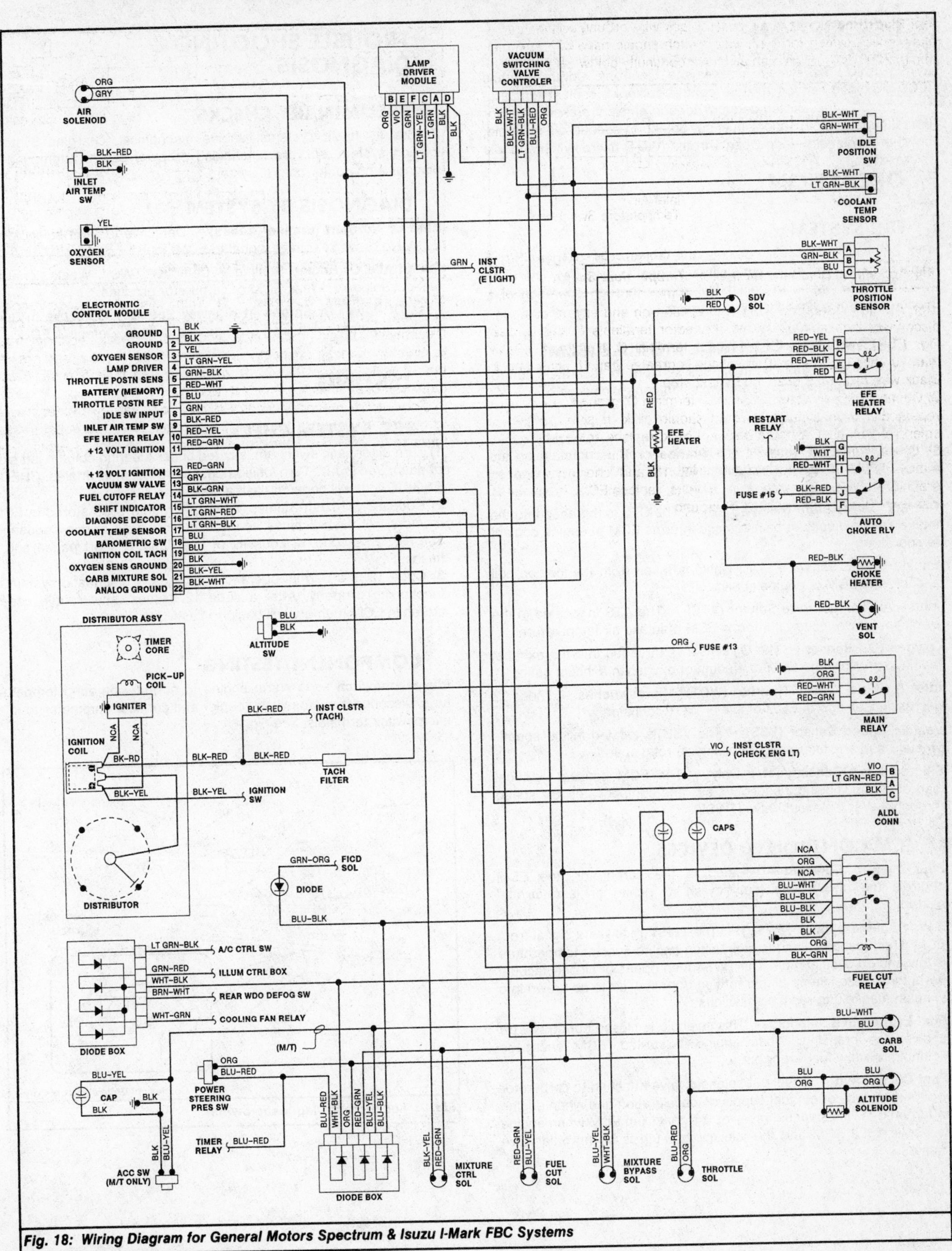

AIR SOLENOID
ORG
GRY
INLET AIR TEMP SW
BLK-RED
BLK
OXYGEN SENSOR
YEL
LAMP DRIVER MODULE
B E F C A D
VACUUM SWITCHING VALVE CONTROLER
IDLE POSITION SW
BLK-WHT
GRN-WHT
COOLANT TEMP SENSOR
LT GRN-BLK
THROTTLE POSITION SENSOR
GRN-BLK
BLU
INST CLSTR (E LIGHT)
SDV SOL
RED
ELECTRONIC CONTROL MODULE
GROUND 1 BLK
GROUND 2 BLK
OXYGEN SENSOR 3 YEL
LAMP DRIVER 4 LT GRN-YEL
THROTTLE POSTN SENS 5 GRN-BLK
BATTERY (MEMORY) 6 RED-WHT
THROTTLE POSTN REF 7 BLU
IDLE SW INPUT 8 GRN
INLET AIR TEMP SW 9 BLK-RED
EFE HEATER RELAY 10 RED-YEL
+12 VOLT IGNITION 11 RED-GRN
+12 VOLT IGNITION 12 RED-GRN
VACUUM SW VALVE 13 GRY
FUEL CUTOFF RELAY 14 BLK-GRN
SHIFT INDICATOR 15 LT GRN-WHT
DIAGNOSE DECODE 16 LT GRN-RED
COOLANT TEMP SENSOR 17 LT GRN-BLK
BAROMETRIC SW 18 BLU
IGNITION COIL TACH 19 BLU
OXYGEN SENS GROUND 20 BLK
CARB MIXTURE SOL 21 BLK-YEL
ANALOG GROUND 22 BLK-WHT
EFE HEATER RELAY
RED-YEL
RED-BLK
EFE HEATER
RESTART RELAY
AUTO CHOKE RLY
FUSE #15
CHOKE HEATER
VENT SOL
FUSE #13
MAIN RELAY
INST CLSTR (CHECK ENG LT)
VIO
ALDL CONN
CAPS
FUEL CUT RELAY
NCA
BLU-WHT
BLU-BLK
CARB SOL
ALTITUDE SOLENOID
DISTRIBUTOR ASSY
TIMER CORE
PICK-UP COIL
IGNITER
IGNITION COIL
BK-RD
BLK-YEL
DISTRIBUTOR
ALTITUDE SW
INST CLSTR (TACH)
TACH FILTER
IGNITION SW
FICD SOL
GRN-ORG
DIODE
DIODE BOX
A/C CTRL SW
ILLUM CTRL BOX
REAR WDO DEFOG SW
COOLING FAN RELAY
GRN-RED
WHT-BLK
BRN-WHT
WHT-GRN
(M/T)
POWER STEERING PRES SW
BLU-RED
BLU-YEL
CAP
TIMER RELAY
ACC SW (M/T ONLY)
DIODE BOX
MIXTURE CTRL SOL
FUEL CUT SOL
MIXTURE BYPASS SOL
THROTTLE SOL


*Fig. 18: Wiring Diagram for General Motors Spectrum & Isuzu I-Mark FBC Systems*

## DESCRIPTION

The Feedback Carburetor (FBC) system maintains a controlled air/fuel ratio. The system includes the Electronic Control Module (ECM), oxygen sensor, mixture control solenoid, coolant temperature sensor, intake air temperature sensor, ambient pressure sensor (for altitude compensation), fuel-cut solenoid, second air solenoid, bowl vent solenoid, Wide Open Throttle (WOT) microswitch and idle microswitch.

## OPERATION

### FBC SYSTEM

The oxygen sensor ($O_2$) detects the amount of oxygen in the exhaust gases and sends an electrical signal to the ECM. The ECM uses this information to adjust fuel supply through operation of a mixture control solenoid in the carburetor.

### ELECTRONIC CONTROL MODULE (ECM)

The ECM receives input from various sensors to accurately control air/fuel ratio, ignition timing, and emission control devices.

### INPUT SENSORS

**Clutch Switch (M/T Only)** – The clutch switch is mounted on the clutch pedal arm under the dash. It informs ECM if clutch released or applied.

**Coolant Temperature Sensor (CTS)** – The CTS is threaded into the intake manifold coolant passage and informs ECM of engine coolant temperature.

**Engine Speed Sensor** – This signal is taken from the ignition coil and informs ECM of engine speed.

**Intake Air Temperature Sensor (ATS)** – The ATS is located in the air cleaner lower cover. It informs ECM of intake air temperature.

**Oxygen ($O_2$) Sensor** – The $O_2$ sensor is threaded into the exhaust manifold and informs ECM of amount of oxygen in exhaust gases.

**Idle & Wide Open Throttle (WOT) Microswitches** – These 2 microswitches inform ECM of idle or WOT condition.

**Vehicle Speed Sensor (VSS)** – The VSS is located in the speedometer head and informs ECM of vehicle road speed.

**Electric Load Sensing (M/T Only)** – The ECM senses electrical load of airconditioning, headlights, etc. and compensates idle speed through 3-Way Solenoid Valve (TWSV).

### ECM CONTROLLED DEVICES

**Fuel Mixture Solenoid** – Located in the carburetor, the ECM controls the on/off time (duty cycle) to richen or lean air/fuel mixture.

**3-Way Solenoid Valve (TWSV)** – The TWSV receives a signal from ECM when electrical load is high, when engine coolant temperature is low and on deceleration. The TWSV then opens or closes vacuum ports to operate idle-up diaphragm and/or allow air to be drawn into exhaust manifold to reduce emissions.

**Fuel Evaporative Solenoid** – This solenoid is closed during key off and engine cranking. When engine is started, ECM energizes solenoid to allow fuel vapor purge.

**Fuel-Cut System** – A fuel-cut solenoid valve attached to carburetor works to reduce or cut fuel supply on deceleration and when engine is turned off. This solenoid receives a signal from ECM when engine is above 2500 RPM and the idle microswitch is on (throttle valve closed).

## TROUBLE SHOOTING & DIAGNOSIS

### PRELIMINARY CHECKS

Ensure all basic systems, engine mechanical, charging system, ignition system, etc. are functioning properly before attempting to diagnosis computer control system.

### DIAGNOSIS BY SYSTEM

**Hard Or No Start (Engine Cranks)** – Defective fuel-cut solenoid or ECM. No or weak voltage signal to ECM.

**Rough Idle Or Engine Stalling** – Defective TWSV. Weak signal to fuel-cut solenoid. Weak ECM or carburetor grounds.

**Loss Of Power Or Surges At Highway Speed** – Defective mixture control solenoid valve. Bad ECM ground circuits. Defective ECU.

## TESTING

### FBC SYSTEM CHECK

**1)** Turn diagnostic switch on, located under steering column left side of dash. *See Fig. 1.* Turn ignition on, but do not start engine. CHECK ENGINE light will begin to flash a code 12.
**2)** Code 12 will flash 3 times, then any trouble code stored in ECM memory will flash 3 times and continue to cycle in this sequence. *See Fig. 2.* A code 12 consists of one flash, a short pause and 2 flashes.
**3)** Code 12 is a normal operation and means diagnostic system is functioning properly. After a code 12 flashes, any trouble codes stored in ECM memory will begin to flash. *See Fig. 3.*

### COMPONENT TESTING

**Idle Microswitch** – **1)** Warm engine to normal operating temperature. Disconnect microswitch coupler and connect ohmmeter to idle microswitch terminals. *See Fig. 4.*

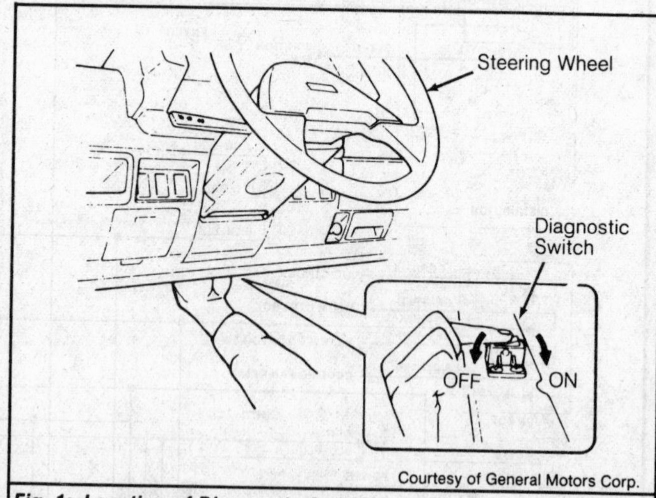
Steering Wheel
Diagnostic Switch
OFF
ON
Courtesy of General Motors Corp.

*Fig. 1: Location of Diagnostic Switch*

## General Motors Sprint FBC System (Cont.)

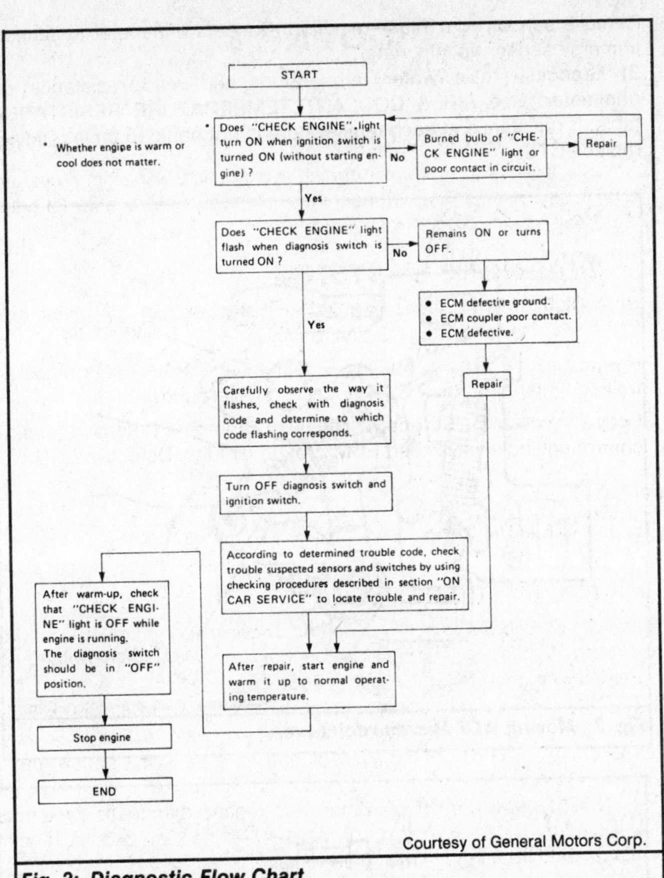

START
Does "CHECK ENGINE" light turn ON when ignition switch is turned ON (without starting engine)?
* Whether engine is warm or cool does not matter.
No
Burned bulb of "CHECK ENGINE" light or poor contact in circuit.
Repair
Yes
Does "CHECK ENGINE" light flash when diagnosis switch is turned ON?
No
Remains ON or turns OFF.
• ECM defective ground.
• ECM coupler poor contact.
• ECM defective.
Repair
Yes
Carefully observe the way it flashes, check with diagnosis code and determine to which code flashing corresponds.
Turn OFF diagnosis switch and ignition switch.
According to determined trouble code, check trouble suspected sensors and switches by using checking procedures described in section "ON CAR SERVICE" to locate trouble and repair.
After repair, start engine and warm it up to normal operating temperature.
After warm-up, check that "CHECK ENGINE" light is OFF while engine is running. The diagnosis switch should be in "OFF" position.
Stop engine
END
Courtesy of General Motors Corp.

Fig. 2: Diagnostic Flow Chart

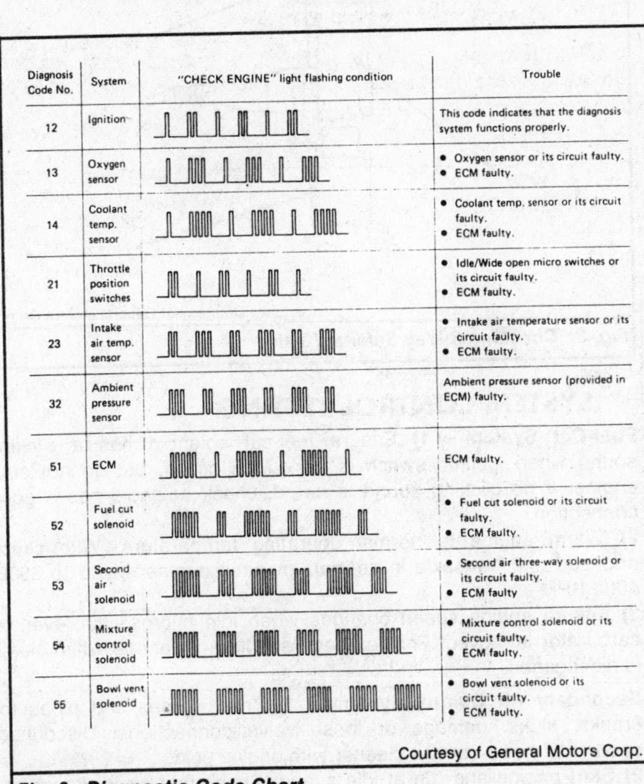

| Diagnosis Code No. | System | "CHECK ENGINE" light flashing condition | Trouble |
|---|---|---|---|
| 12 | Ignition | | This code indicates that the diagnosis system functions properly. |
| 13 | Oxygen sensor | | • Oxygen sensor or its circuit faulty. • ECM faulty. |
| 14 | Coolant temp. sensor | | • Coolant temp. sensor or its circuit faulty. • ECM faulty. |
| 21 | Throttle position switches | | • Idle/Wide open micro switches or its circuit faulty. • ECM faulty. |
| 23 | Intake air temp. sensor | | • Intake air temperature sensor or its circuit faulty. • ECM faulty. |
| 32 | Ambient pressure sensor | | Ambient pressure sensor (provided in ECM) faulty. |
| 51 | ECM | | ECM faulty. |
| 52 | Fuel cut solenoid | | • Fuel cut solenoid or its circuit faulty. • ECM faulty. |
| 53 | Second air solenoid | | • Second air three-way solenoid or its circuit faulty. • ECM faulty |
| 54 | Mixture control solenoid | | • Mixture control solenoid or its circuit faulty. • ECM faulty. |
| 55 | Bowl vent solenoid | | • Bowl vent solenoid or its circuit faulty. • ECM faulty. |

Courtesy of General Motors Corp.

Fig. 3: Diagnostic Code Chart

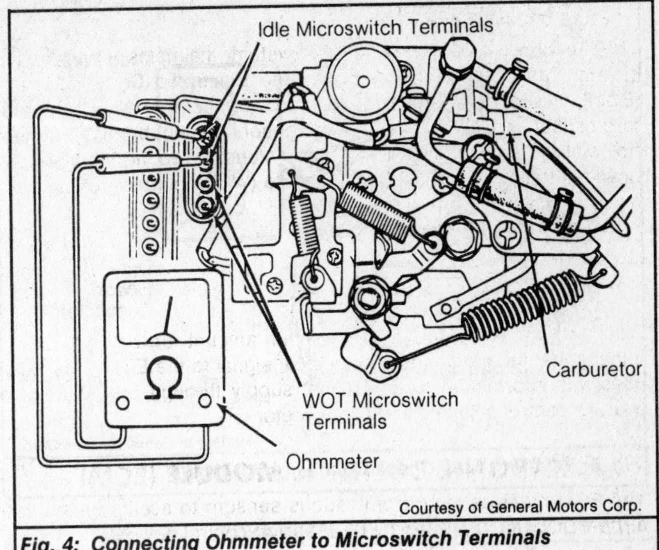

Idle Microswitch Terminals
Carburetor
WOT Microswitch Terminals
Ohmmeter
Courtesy of General Motors Corp.

**Fig. 4: Connecting Ohmmeter to Microswitch Terminals**

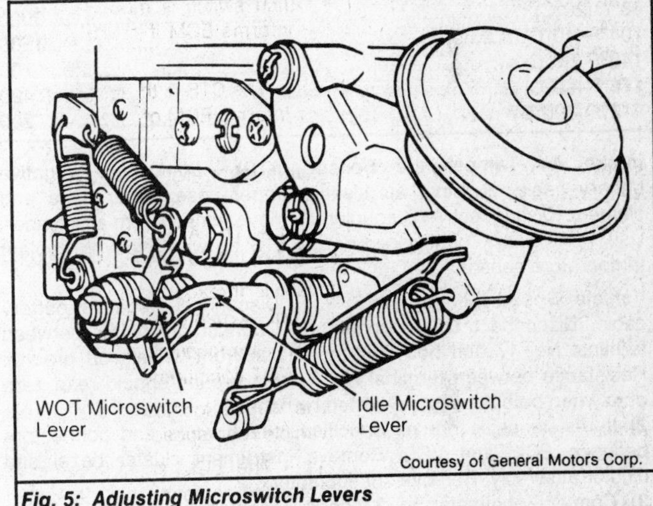

WOT Microswitch Lever
Idle Microswitch Lever
Courtesy of General Motors Corp.

**Fig. 5: Adjusting Microswitch Levers**

**2)** Run engine at idle and make sure ohmmeter indicator is at zero ohm. Connect tachometer to engine. Increase engine speed gradually, checking that ohmmeter indicates infinity when engine speed is 1500-2400 RPM.

**3)** If engine speed is not within specified range, adjust idle microswitch lever. *See Fig. 5.* Bend lever down if engine speed is below range, and bend up if engine speed is above range.

**Wide Open Throttle Microswitch – 1)** Remove air cleaner and carburetor. Connect ohmmeter to microswitch. *See Fig. 4.* Check that resistance between microswitch terminals is infinity.

**2)** Open throttle valve gradually until ohmmeter indicates zero ohm. Using a vernier caliper, measure clearance between throttle valve and primary carburetor bore.

**3)** Clearance should be .28-.33" (7.2-8.4 mm). If clearance is incorrect, bend WOT microswitch lever to adjust clearance to specification. *See Fig. 5.*

**Mixture Control Solenoid Valve (MCSV) – 1)** Remove duty check connector cap and short the terminals with a lead wire. *See Fig. 6.* Turn ignition on and off repeatedly without starting engine.

**2)** Using finger, touch carburetor body near MCSV and make sure solenoid pulses can be felt. Pulses from MCSV indicate proper operation. If there are no pulses, replace MCSV.

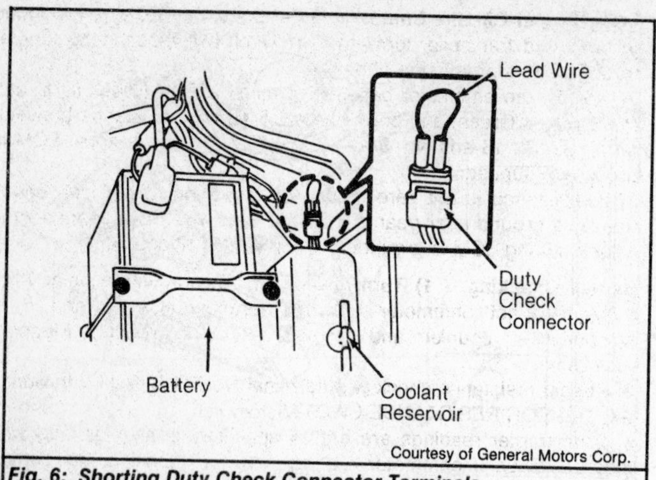
Lead Wire
Duty
Check
Connector
Battery
Coolant
Reservoir
Courtesy of General Motors Corp.
*Fig. 6: Shorting Duty Check Connector Terminals*

**AIR & COOLANT TEMPERATURE RESISTANCE**

| Temperature | Ohms |
|---|---|
| 32°F (0°C) | 6000 |
| 68°F (20°C) | 3000 |
| 104°F (40°C) | 1500 |
| 140°F (60°C) | 700 |
| 176°F (80°C) | 400 |
| 212°F (100°C) | 200 |

**Intake Air Temperature Sensor (ATS) –** Disconnect negative battery cable. Remove air cleaner upper case, lower case and element. Disconnect ATS coupler. Remove sensor from air cleaner. Use same check out procedure on ATS as was used on coolant temperature sensor.

**Vehicle Speed Sensor (VSS) – 1)** Disconnect negative battery cable. Disconnect ECM connectors. Connect ohmmeter between terminal No. 17 and body ground. Raise front wheels off ground. Resistance between terminal No. 17 and ground should read zero ohm when both wheels are turned by hand.

**2)** If resistance is not as specified, check wires and connectors between ECM and VSS. Remove instrument cluster bezel and cluster assembly. Remove speedometer.

**3)** Connect ohmmeter to 2 speed sensor terminals on back of speedometer. Ohmmeter should indicate open or closed circuit. Turn speedometer cable joint one full turn gradually clockwise.

**4)** Ohmmeter should indicate open or closed circuit 4 times opposite than step **3)**. If sensor does not operate as specified, replace speedometer.

**Oxygen ($O_2$) Sensor – 1)** Warm engine to normal operating temperature. Disconnect $O_2$ sensor connector.

**2)** Connect voltmeter between $O_2$ sensor harness terminal and ground. DO NOT apply voltage to $O_2$ sensor.

**3)** With engine at 1500-2000 RPM, turn WOT microswitch on by moving microswitch lever. *See Fig. 7.* Check that voltmeter reads about .8 volts.

**4)** With engine at 1000-1500 RPM, disconnect vacuum hose at intake manifold. Check that voltmeter reads near zero. Reconnect vacuum hose and $O_2$ sensor connector.

**3-Way Solenoid Valve (TWSV) – 1)** Disconnect 2 vacuum hoses from Blue TWSV. Blow air into nozzle one. Air should come out nozzle 3 only. *See Fig. 8.*

**2)** Disconnect TWSV connector and connect 12 volts to TWSV connector terminals. Blow air into nozzle one.

**3)** Air should come out of nozzle 2 only. If TWSV does not operate as specified, replace valve.

**Coolant Temperature Sensor (CTS) – 1)** Disconnect negative battery cable. Drain cooling system. Disconnect CTS coupler. Remove sensor from intake manifold. Connect ohmmeter to sensor. Immerse sensor tip into water.

**2)** Gradually raise water temperature and read resistance on ohmmeter. See AIR & COOLANT TEMPERATURE RESISTANCE table. If resistance at each temperature is not equal to table reading, replace CTS.

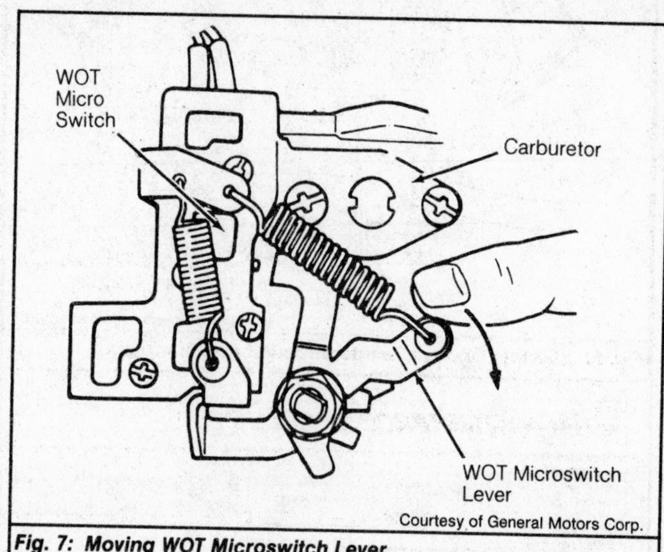
WOT
Micro
Switch
Carburetor
WOT Microswitch
Lever
Courtesy of General Motors Corp.
*Fig. 7: Moving WOT Microswitch Lever*

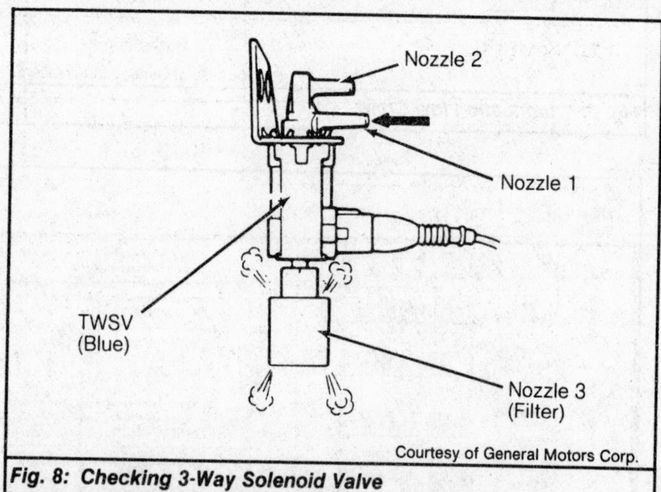
Nozzle 2
Nozzle 1
TWSV
(Blue)
Nozzle 3
(Filter)
Courtesy of General Motors Corp.
*Fig. 8: Checking 3-Way Solenoid Valve*

## SYSTEM CONTROL TESTING

**Fuel-Cut System – 1)** Ensure fuel-cut solenoid has a clicking sound when ignition switch is turned on or off, but do not start engine. If no clicking sound is heard, check solenoid has a good connection.

**2)** Warm engine to normal operating temperature. With clutch engaged and transaxle in neutral, increase engine speed to 3000-4000 RPM.

**3)** Ensure engine speed changes when idle microswitch lever on carburetor is moved. Engine speed should not change when clutch is disengaged.

**Secondary Air Control System – 1)** Check hoses and pipes for cracks, kinks, damage or loose valve connections. Disconnect second air hose from air cleaner with engine cold.

**2)** Start engine and run at idle speed. Check that air is drawn into hose (bubbling sound). Warm engine to normal operating temperature. Air should not be drawn into hose (no bubbling sound).

**3)** Increase engine speed to 3000 RPM and quickly release accelerator pedal. Air should be drawn into hose. Disconnect coolant temperature connector. Connect a 10,000 ohm resistance jumper wire. *See Fig. 9.* Air should be drawn into hose at engine idle speed.

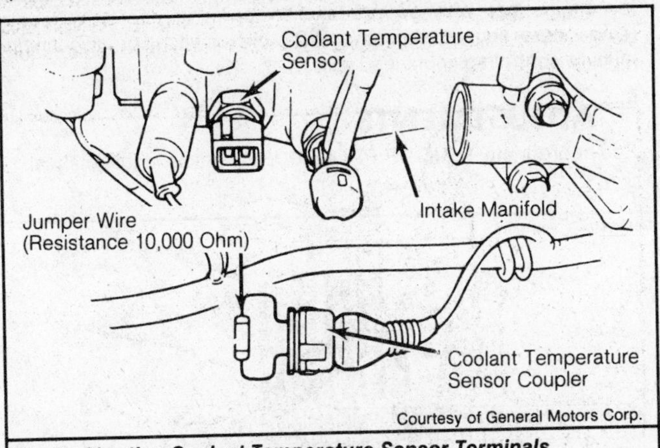
Coolant Temperature Sensor
Intake Manifold
Jumper Wire (Resistance 10,000 Ohm)
Coolant Temperature Sensor Coupler
Courtesy of General Motors Corp.

***Fig. 9: Shorting Coolant Temperature Sensor Terminals***

**ECM Ground Circuits Check – 1)** To check that ECM is grounded to body and transaxle, turn ignition switch off. Disconnect coupler from ECM (under left side of dash).

**2)** Connect an ohmmeter between terminal No. 18 (Black wire) and No. 9 (Black/Green) and body ground. Measure resistance between terminals No. 18 and No. 9 and body. If resistance is zero, ECM is properly grounded.

**3)** If resistance is not zero, check body ground at left kick panel, transaxle ground near gear shift guide case and ECM connections. After ensuring ECM is grounded, reconnect ECM coupler.

**Sensor Checking – 1)** Turn ignition off. Disconnect coupler from ECM. Connect ohmmeter between terminal Nos. 5 and 6 of disconnected coupler and terminal No. 9 (ground). Measure resistance.

**2)** Repeat resistance check with terminal Nos. 2, 3 and 11 (ground). See SENSOR RESISTANCE CHART.

**3)** If ohmmeter readings are not as specified, sensor or lead wire may be faulty. If ohmmeter readings are as specified, the sensor and lead wire circuit are in good condition. Reconnect coupler to ECM after sensor check is completed.

***SENSOR RESISTANCE CHART***

| Sensor | Terminal | Ohms | Condition |
|---|---|---|---|
| Coolant Temperature Sensor<br>Intake Air Temperature Sensor | Nos. 3 & 11<br>2 & 11 | 6000 @30° to<br>200 @212° | Sensor resistance changed.<br>Sensor resistance changed. |
| Idle Microswitch | Nos. 5 & 9 | 0<br>Infinity | Engine warm. Accelerator not depressed.<br>Accelerator slightly depressed. |
| WOT Microswitch | Nos. 6 & 9 | Infinity<br>0 | Accelerator not depressed.<br>Accelerator fully depressed. |

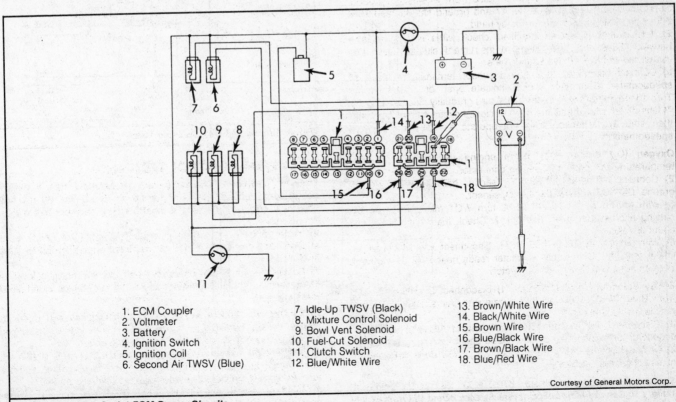

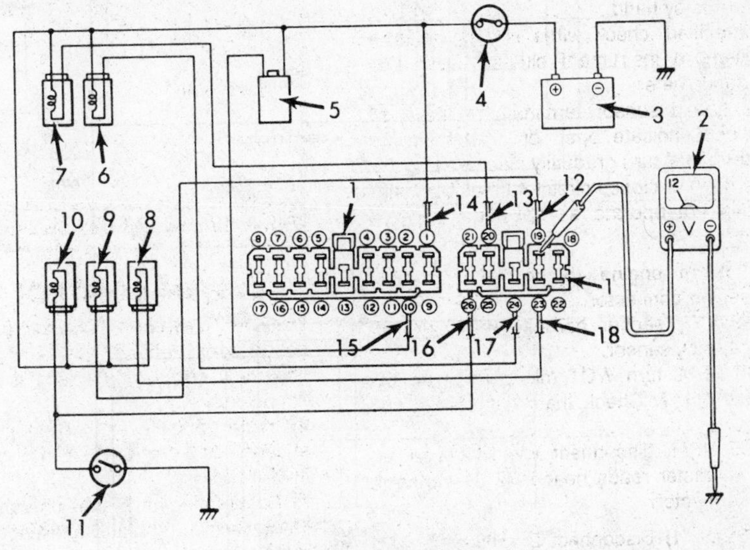

1. ECM Coupler
2. Voltmeter
3. Battery
4. Ignition Switch
5. Ignition Coil
6. Second Air TWSV (Blue)
7. Idle-Up TWSV (Black)
8. Mixture Control Solenoid
9. Bowl Vent Solenoid
10. Fuel-Cut Solenoid
11. Clutch Switch
12. Blue/White Wire
13. Brown/White Wire
14. Black/White Wire
15. Brown Wire
16. Blue/Black Wire
17. Brown/Black Wire
18. Blue/Red Wire

Courtesy of General Motors Corp.

***Fig. 10: Checking Sprint ECM Power Circuits***

**Oxygen ($O_2$) Sensor Signal Check – 1)** Remove ECM from instrument panel without disconnecting coupler. Connect coupler if disconnected. Warm engine to normal operating temperature and keep at idle.

**2)** Connect voltmeter between terminal Nos. 10 ($O_2$ sensor signal) and 9 (ground). If voltmeter indicator deflects between zero and .8 volts when engine speed varies from idle to 1500-2000 RPM, feedback system is operating properly.

**3)** If voltmeter indicator remains at zero, check for $O_2$ sensor lead wire disconnected, intake system leak, air/fuel ratio too lean, second air constantly sent to exhaust, voltmeter inner resistance too small, or faulty $O_2$ sensor.

**4)** If voltmeter does not deflect and indicates about .8 volts, check for engine not warmed up (choke operating), defective coolant temperature sensor, defective WOT microswitch, or disconnected mixture control solenoid lead wire.

## ADJUSTMENTS

See appropriate TUNE-UP PROCEDURES article in this manual.

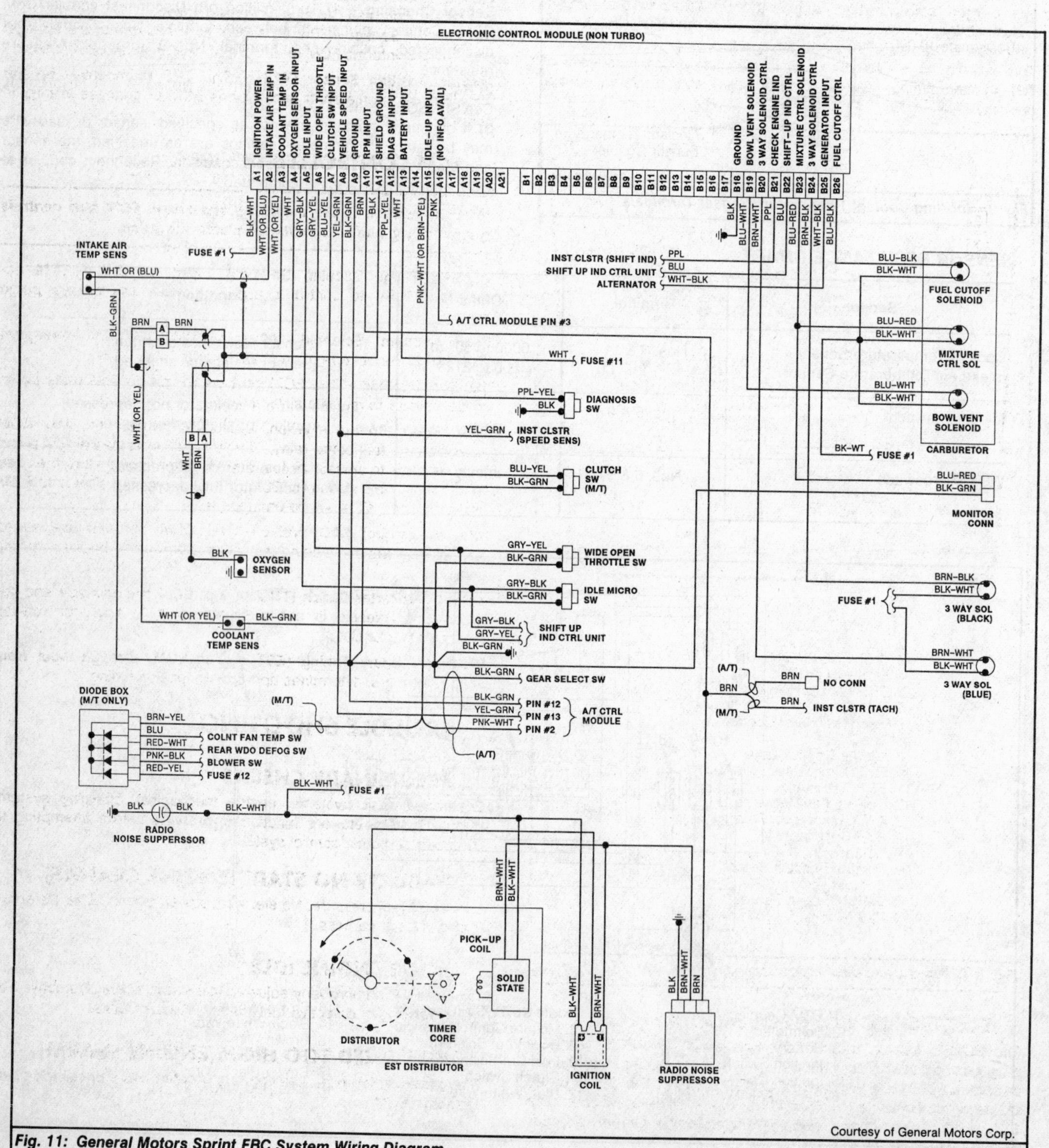
ELECTRONIC CONTROL MODULE (NON TURBO)
IGNITION POWER
INTAKE AIR TEMP IN
COOLANT TEMP IN
OXYGEN SENSOR INPUT
IDLE INPUT
WIDE OPEN THROTTLE
CLUTCH SW INPUT
VEHICLE SPEED INPUT
GROUND
RPM INPUT
SHIELD GROUND
DIAG SW INPUT
BATTERY INPUT
IDLE-UP INPUT
(NO INFO AVAIL)
GROUND
BOWL VENT SOLENOID
3 WAY SOLENOID CTRL
CHECK ENGINE IND
SHIFT-UP IND CTRL
MIXTURE CTRL SOLENOID
3 WAY SOLENOID CTRL
GENERATOR INPUT
FUEL CUTOFF CTRL
A1 A2 A3 A4 A5 A6 A7 A8 A9 A10 A11 A12 A13 A14 A15 A16 A17 A18 A19 A20 A21
B1 B2 B3 B4 B5 B6 B7 B8 B9 B10 B11 B12 B13 B14 B15 B16 B17 B18 B19 B20 B21 B22 B23 B24 B25 B26
INTAKE AIR TEMP SENS
FUSE #1
A/T CTRL MODULE PIN #3
FUSE #11
DIAGNOSIS SW
INST CLSTR (SPEED SENS)
CLUTCH SW (M/T)
OXYGEN SENSOR
WIDE OPEN THROTTLE SW
IDLE MICRO SW
SHIFT UP IND CTRL UNIT
COOLANT TEMP SENS
GEAR SELECT SW
PIN #12
PIN #13
PIN #2
A/T CTRL MODULE
DIODE BOX (M/T ONLY)
COLNT FAN TEMP SW
REAR WDO DEFOG SW
BLOWER SW
FUSE #12
RADIO NOISE SUPPERSSOR
INST CLSTR (SHIFT IND)
SHIFT UP IND CTRL UNIT
ALTERNATOR
FUEL CUTOFF SOLENOID
MIXTURE CTRL SOL
BOWL VENT SOLENOID
CARBURETOR
FUSE #1
MONITOR CONN
3 WAY SOL (BLACK)
3 WAY SOL (BLUE)
NO CONN
INST CLSTR (TACH)
PICK-UP COIL
SOLID STATE
DISTRIBUTOR
TIMER CORE
EST DISTRIBUTOR
IGNITION COIL
RADIO NOISE SUPPRESSOR

Courtesy of General Motors Corp.

*Fig. 11: General Motors Sprint FBC System Wiring Diagram*

# 1988 COMPUTERIZED ENGINE CONTROLS
# General Motors LeMans 1.6L TBI

## DESCRIPTION

This system uses an Electronic Control Module (ECM) to control Throttle Body Injection (TBI), ignition timing and emission control devices. The ECM uses input from various sensors, constantly adjusting air/fuel ratio and ignition timing to provide low emissions with good driveability.

## OPERATION

The ECM is provided information on vehicle electrical load, exhaust gas oxygen concentration, engine coolant temperature, engine speed (RPM), engine load, throttle valve position, intake air temperature, vehicle speed and air conditioner pressure switches. This information is used by ECM to calculate proper operation of TBI, ignition timing, idle air control valve and emission control devices.

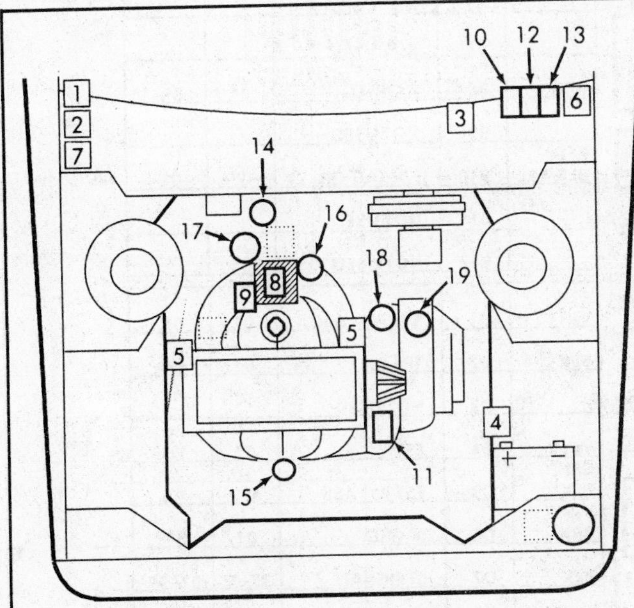

1. Electronic Control Module
2. ALDL Diagnostic Connector
3. "SERVICE ENGINE SOON" (SES) Light
4. ECM Power Feed
5. ECM Harness Ground
6. Fuse Panel
7. Fuel Pump Test Connector
8. Fuel Injector
9. Idle Air Control Valve
10. Fuel Pump Relay
11. EST Distributor
12. Cooling Fan Relays
13. A/C Compressor Relays
14. MAP Sensor
15. $O_2$ Sensor
16. Throttle Position Sensor
17. Coolant Temperature Sensor
18. Vehicle Speed Sensor
19. Park/Neutral Switch

Courtesy of General Motors Corp.

***Fig. 1: LeMans Component Location***

## ELECTRONIC CONTROL MODULE (ECM)

The ECM is located behind right kick panel. The ECM has self-diagnosis capability that allows for trouble shooting the system through a "SERVICE ENGINE SOON" (SES) light. The SES light on the dash will illuminate to inform driver of a system malfunction. The ECM stores malfunctions, and will display problem(s) via a 2-digit code displayed by the SES light.

## INPUT SENSORS

**Coolant Temperature Sensor (CTS)** - The CTS is threaded into the intake manifold coolant passage and informs ECM of engine coolant temperature.

**Engine Speed Sensor** - This signal is taken from the ignition distributor and informs ECM of engine speed.

**Manifold Absolute Pressure (MAP) Sensor** - The MAP sensor monitors intake manifold vacuum and informs ECM of engine load.

**Vehicle Speed Sensor (VSS)** - The VSS is located in the speedometer and informs ECM of vehicle road speed.

**Oxygen ($O_2$) Sensor** - The $O_2$ sensor is threaded into the exhaust manifold and informs ECM of amount of oxygen in exhaust gases.

**Throttle Position Sensor (TPS)** - The TPS is mounted on the throttle body throttle shaft and informs ECM of changes in throttle position.

## ECM CONTROLLED DEVICES

***NOTE: In addition to the devices listed below, ECM also controls ignition timing and air conditioner clutch operation.***

**Canister Purge Vacuum Solenoid Valve (CPVSV)** - ECM energizes CPVSV to control operation of fuel evaporative purge system.

**EGR Vacuum Solenoid Valve (EGRVSV)** - ECM energizes EGRVSV to control operation of EGR valve.

**TBI Fuel Injector** - The ECM controls the on-off time (duty cycle) of fuel injector to regulate air/fuel ratio.

**Fuel Pump Control** - When ignition is turned on, the ECM energizes the fuel pump relay. The relay will operate the fuel pump for 4 seconds to pressurize fuel system. After engine start, the relay contacts are held closed by ECM. If engine-running signals to ECM are interrupted, ECM will de-energize relay.

**Idle Air Control (IAC) Valve** - The ECM controls idle speed through opening and closing the IAC to allow air to by-pass throttle plate.

**Torque Converter Clutch (TCC)** - The ECM will energize and de-energize a solenoid in automatic transaxle to apply or release torque converter clutch.

**Electronic Spark Timing (EST)** - The ECM, through input from various sensors, determines appropriate ignition timing.

## TROUBLE SHOOTING

### PRELIMINARY CHECKS

Ensure all basic systems, engine mechanical, charging system, ignition system, etc. are functioning properly before attempting to diagnosis computer control system.

### HARD OR NO START (ENGINE CRANKS)

Low or no fuel pressure. No electrical power feed to ECM. Defective fuel injector or harness.

### POOR ENGINE IDLE

Defective TPS. Improperly adjusted idle speed screw. Defective IAC valve. Leaking or defective fuel injector. Vacuum leaks.

### IDLE SPEED TOO HIGH (ENGINE WARM)

Fuel pressure too high. Leaking fuel injector. IAC valve stuck open. Defective ECM.

# 1988 COMPUTERIZED ENGINE CONTROLS
## General Motors LeMans 1.6L TBI (Cont.)

This ECM voltage chart is for use with a digital voltmeter.

| | VOLTAGE KEY "ON" | VOLTAGE ENG. RUN | CIRCUIT | PIN | WIRE COLOR |
|---|---|---|---|---|---|
| 2 | 0* | B+ | FUEL PUMP RELAY | A1 | GRN/WHT |
| | 0* | 0* | TCC | | |
| | B+ | B+ | SHIFT LT. | A2 | BRN/BLK |
| | | | NOT USED | A3 | |
| | B+ | B+ | A/C CONTROL | A4 | BLU |
| | □ | B+ | SERV. ENG. SOON | A5 | GRY |
| | B+ | B+ | 12V IGN | A6 | RED/WHT/BLK |
| | | | NOT USED | A7 | |
| | 2-5 VARIES | 2-5 VARIES | SERIAL DATA | A8 | RED/YEL |
| | 5 | 5 | DIAGNOSTIC TEST | A9 | WHT/BLK |
| 1 | | | VSS | A10 | BRN |
| | 0* | 0* | COOLANT, MAP GROUND | A11 | BLK/WHT |
| | 0* | 0* | SYSTEM GROUND | A12 | BLK/WHT |
| | B+ | B+ | HIGH SPEED FAN RELAY CONTROL | C1 | GRN/WHT |
| | | | NOT USED | C2 | |
| | N.U. | N.U. | IAC "B" LO | C3 | GRN/BLK |
| | N.U. | N.U. | IAC "B" HI | C4 | GRN/WHT |
| | N.U. | N.U. | IAC "A" HI | C5 | BLU/WHT |
| | N.U. | N.U. | IAC "A" LO | C6 | BLU/BLK |
| | | | NOT USED | C7 | |
| | | | NOT USED | C8 | |
| | 0* | B+ | FAN REQUEST | C9 | YEL/BLK |
| 3 | 1.9 | 1.9 | COOLANT TEMP. SIGNAL | C10 | YEL |
| | 5.0 | 1.3 | MAP SIGNAL | C11 | WHT/GRN |
| | | | NOT USED | C12 | |
| | .6 | .6 | TPS SIGNAL | C13 | BLU |
| | 5.0 | 5.0 | 5 VOLT REF. | C14 | GRY |
| | | | NOT USED | C15 | |
| | B+ | B+ | BATTERY | C16 | RED/YEL |

BACK VIEW OF CONNECTOR

A1 B1

24 PIN A-B CONNECTOR

BACK VIEW OF CONNECTOR

C1 D1

32 PIN C-D CONNECTOR

| WIRE COLOR | PIN | CIRCUIT | VOLTAGE KEY "ON" | VOLTAGE ENG. RUN |
|---|---|---|---|---|
| RED/YEL | B1 | BATT. | B+ | B+ |
| | B2 | NOT USED | | |
| BLK/WHT | B3 | HEI GRD. | 0* | 0* |
| | B4 | NOT USED | | |
| PPL/WHT | B5 | HEI REF. | 0* | .9 |
| | B6 | NOT USED | | |
| | B7 | NOT USED | | |
| BRN | B8 | A/C REQ. | 0* | B+ |
| | B9 | NOT USED | | |
| RED/BLK/YEL | B10 | P/N (A/T ONLY) | 0* | 0* |
| | B11 | NOT USED | | |
| | B12 | NOT USED | | |
| BLK/WHT | D1 | SYSTEM GRD. | 0* | 0* |
| BLK | D2 | TPS GRD. | 0* | 0* |
| | D3 | NOT USED | | |
| WHT | D4 | EST | 0* | 1.3 |
| BRN/BLK | D5 | EST BYPASS | 0* | 4.6 |
| WHT/BRN | D6 | 0² GRD. | 0* | 0* |
| BLK | D7 | 0² SIGNAL | .35-.55 | .01-.99 |
| | D8 | NOT USED | | |
| GRN | D9 | JUMPER | 0* | 0* |
| GRN | D10 | JUMPER | 0* | 0* |
| | D11 | NOT USED | | |
| | D12 | NOT USED | | |
| | D13 | NOT USED | | |
| | D14 | NOT USED | | |
| | D15 | NOT USED | | |
| BLU | D16 | INJECTOR | B+ | VARIES B+ |

B+ – Battery Voltage
□ – Less Than One Volt
* – Less Than .5 Volt

1 – Varies from .6 to 12 Volts Depending On Position Of Wheel
2 – 12 Volts First 2 Seconds
3 – Varies With Temperature
4 – System Voltage In Reverse Or Drive

**NOTE:**
**This ECM voltage chart can be used with a digital voltmeter to help save time in diagnosis. Voltages on the car being tested may vary slightly from these due to battery or alternator charging level.**

The following conditions must be met before testing:
- Engine at operating temperature.
- Engine in "closed loop" operation.
- Engine idling ("Engine Run" column).
- ALDL "Test" terminal NOT grounded.
- "Scan" tester or ALDL jumper NOT installed.

Courtesy of General Motors Corp.

*Fig. 2: ECM Connector Identification*

# General Motors LeMans 1.6L TBI (Cont.)

## POOR PERFORMANCE (NO POWER)

Fuel pressure too low. Defective injector. Defective coolant temperature sensor. Defective ECM.

## ENGINE KNOCKING

Electronic spark timing malfunction. Defective or ECM.

## ENGINE RUNNING TOO RICH OR TOO LEAN

Defective injector. Fuel pressure too high or too low. Defective $O_2$ sensor signal. Defective ECM.

# TESTING

## SELF-DIAGNOSTIC SYSTEM CHECK

**1)** Locate ALDL diagnostic connector near ECM in right kick panel. Using a jumper wire, jump between terminals "A" and "B". *See Fig. 3.* Turn ignition on, but do not start engine. SES light will begin to flash diagnostic code 12 indicating the system is working.

**2)** Code 12 will flash 3 times, then any additional code will flash 3 times and continue to cycle in this sequence. A code 12 consists of one flash, a short pause and 2 flashes. *See Fig. 4.*

**3)** To clear codes, remove the battery cable for 30 seconds.

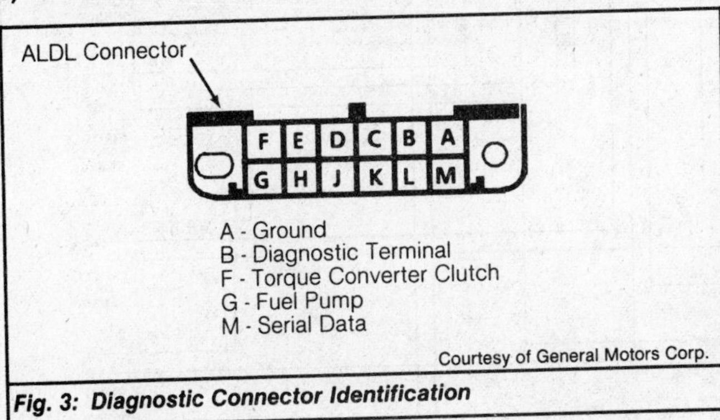
ALDL Connector
F E D C B A
G H J K L M
A - Ground
B - Diagnostic Terminal
F - Torque Converter Clutch
G - Fuel Pump
M - Serial Data
Courtesy of General Motors Corp.

***Fig. 3: Diagnostic Connector Identification***

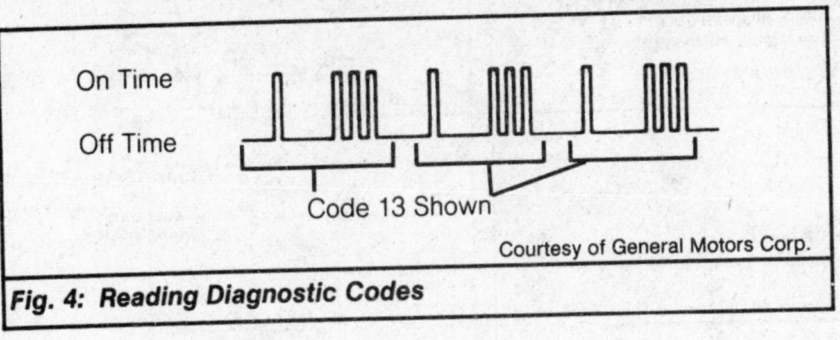
On Time
Off Time
Code 13 Shown
Courtesy of General Motors Corp.

***Fig. 4: Reading Diagnostic Codes***

## DIAGNOSTIC CODES

**Code 12** – No distributor reference pulse to ECM.

**Code 13** – Oxygen ($O_2$) sensor circuit is open causing lean fuel condition.

**Code 14** – Coolant Temperature Sensor (CTS) voltage signal low.

**Code 15** – Coolant Temperature Sensor (CTS) voltage signal high.

**Code 21** – Throttle Position Sensor (TPS) voltage signal high.

**Code 22** – Throttle Position Sensor (TPS) voltage signal low.

**Code 24** – Vehicle Speed Sensor (VSS) malfunction.

**Code 33** – Manifold Absolute Pressure (MAP) sensor voltage signal high.

**Code 34** – Manifold Absolute Pressure (MAP) sensor voltage signal low.

**Code 35** – Idle Speed Error.

**Code 42** – Electronic Spark Timing (EST) malfunction.

**Code 43** – Detonation sensor malfunction.

**Code 44** – Lean exhaust indication.

**Code 45** – Rich exhaust indication.

**Code 51** – MEM-CAL failure.

**Code 53** – Charging system rate too high.

# ADJUSTMENTS

See appropriate TUNE-UP PROCEDURES article in this manual.

***NOTE: All illustrations and diagnostic charts are supplied courtesy of General Motors Corp.***

## General Motors LeMans 1.6L TBI (Cont.)

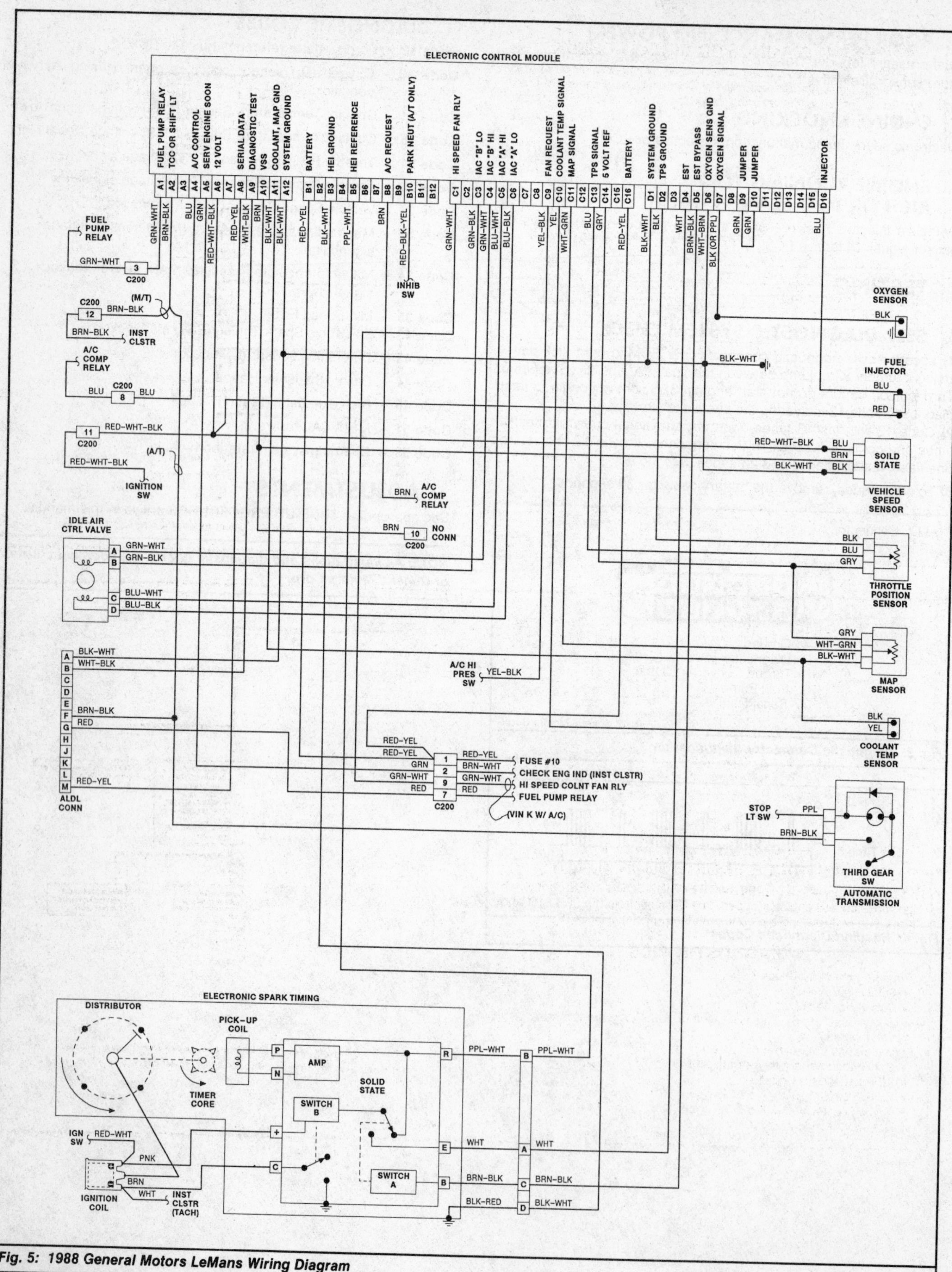

*Fig. 5: 1988 General Motors LeMans Wiring Diagram*

# General Motors LeMans 1.6L TBI (Cont.)

## "SCAN" DIAGNOSTIC CIRCUIT CHECK

The "Scan" Diagnostic Circuit Check is an organized approach to identifying a problem created by a Computerized Engine Controls system. It must be the starting point for any driveability complaint diagnosis.

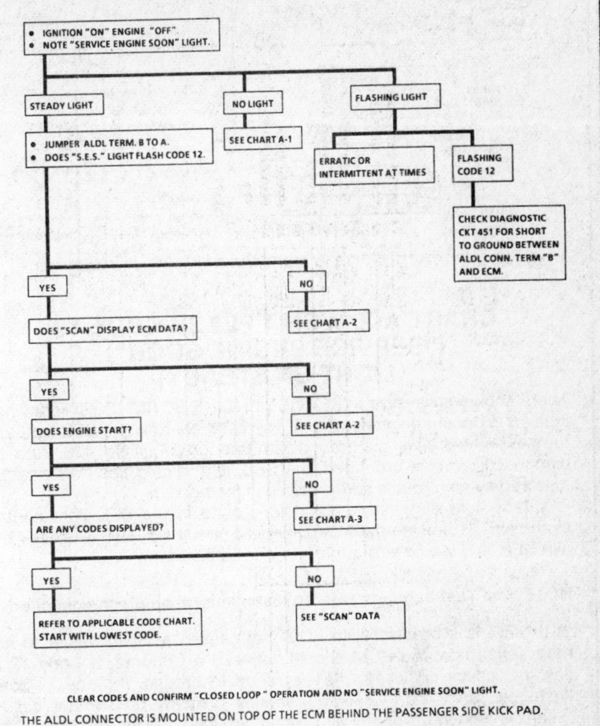

• IGNITION "ON" ENGINE "OFF".
• NOTE "SERVICE ENGINE SOON" LIGHT.
STEADY LIGHT
NO LIGHT
FLASHING LIGHT
• JUMPER ALDL TERM. B TO A.
• DOES "S.E.S." LIGHT FLASH CODE 12.
SEE CHART A-1
ERRATIC OR INTERMITTENT AT TIMES
FLASHING CODE 12
CHECK DIAGNOSTIC CKT 451 FOR SHORT TO GROUND BETWEEN ALDL CONN. TERM "B" AND ECM.
YES
NO
SEE CHART A-2
DOES "SCAN" DISPLAY ECM DATA?
YES
NO
DOES ENGINE START?
SEE CHART A-2
YES
NO
ARE ANY CODES DISPLAYED?
SEE CHART A-3
YES
NO
REFER TO APPLICABLE CODE CHART. START WITH LOWEST CODE.
SEE "SCAN" DATA
CLEAR CODES AND CONFIRM "CLOSED LOOP" OPERATION AND NO "SERVICE ENGINE SOON" LIGHT.
THE ALDL CONNECTOR IS MOUNTED ON TOP OF THE ECM BEHIND THE PASSENGER SIDE KICK PAD.


## "SCAN" DATA

Engine at idle/upper radiator hose hot/Closed Loop/Acc. off

| "SCAN" Position | Units Displayed | Typical Data Value |
|---|---|---|
| Desired RPM | RPM | ECM idle command (varies with temp.) |
| RPM | RPM | ± 150 RPM from desired RPM |
| Coolant Temp. | C° | 85° - 105° |
| MAP | Volts | 1.0 - 2.0 (depends on Vac. & Baro pressure) |
| BPW (base pulse width) | m/Sec | .8 - 3.0 |
| $O_2$ | Volts | .10 - 1.0 and varies |
| TPS | Volts | .4 - 1.25 |
| Throttle Angle | 0 - 100% | 0 |
| IAC | Counts (steps) | 1 - 30 |
| P/N Switch | P/N and RDL | Park/Neutral (P/N) |
| INT (Integrator) | Counts | 110 - 140 Normal |
| BLM (Block Learn) | Counts | 118 - 138 Normal |
| Open/Closed Loop | Open/Closed | Closed Loop (May go open with extended idle) |
| VSS | MPH | 0 |
| TCC | On/Off | Off/ (on with TCC commanded) |
| Spark Advance | # of Degrees | Varies |
| Battery | Volts | 13.5 - 14.5 |
| Fan | On/Off | Off (below 102°C) |
| Fan Request | Yes/No | No |
| A/C Request | Yes/No | No (yes, with A/C requested) |
| A/C Clutch | On/Off | Off (on, with A/C commanded on) |
| Shift Light (M/T) | On/Off | Off |

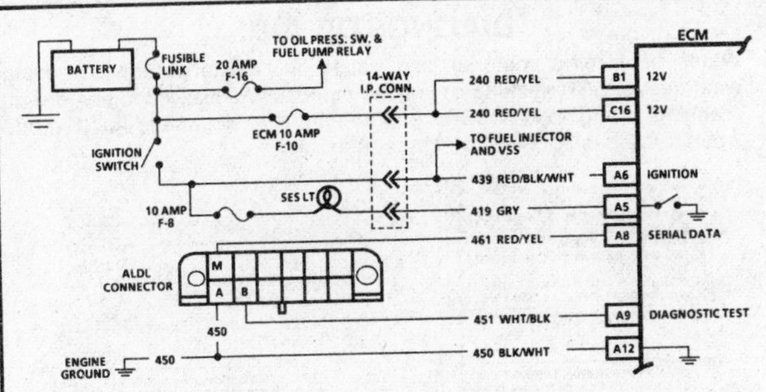

BATTERY
FUSIBLE LINK
20 AMP F-16
TO OIL PRESS. SW. & FUEL PUMP RELAY
14-WAY I.P. CONN.
ECM
240 RED/YEL
B1
12V
240 RED/YEL
C16
12V
ECM 10 AMP F-10
IGNITION SWITCH
TO FUEL INJECTOR AND VSS
439 RED/BLK/WHT
A6
IGNITION
SES LT
10 AMP F-8
419 GRY
A5
461 RED/YEL
A8
SERIAL DATA
ALDL CONNECTOR
M
A
B
450
451 WHT/BLK
A9
DIAGNOSTIC TEST
ENGINE GROUND
450
450 BLK/WHT
A12


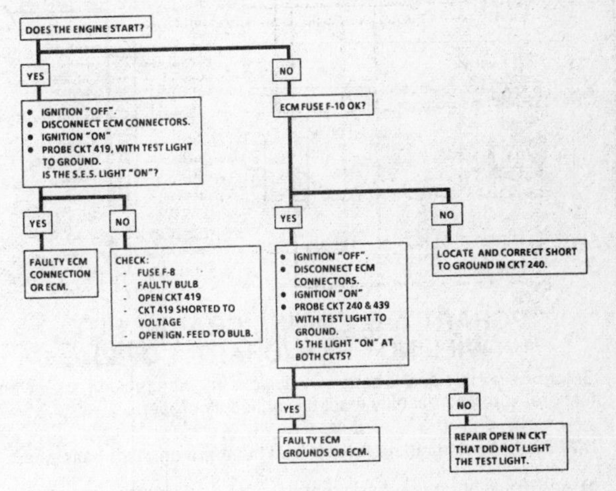

DOES THE ENGINE START?
YES
NO
• IGNITION "OFF".
• DISCONNECT ECM CONNECTORS.
• IGNITION "ON"
• PROBE CKT 419, WITH TEST LIGHT TO GROUND. IS THE S.E.S. LIGHT "ON"?
ECM FUSE F-10 OK?
YES
NO
YES
NO
FAULTY ECM CONNECTION OR ECM.
CHECK:
- FUSE F-8
- FAULTY BULB
- OPEN CKT 419
- CKT 419 SHORTED TO VOLTAGE
- OPEN IGN. FEED TO BULB.
• IGNITION "OFF".
• DISCONNECT ECM CONNECTORS.
• IGNITION "ON"
• PROBE CKT 240 & 439 WITH TEST LIGHT TO GROUND. IS THE LIGHT "ON" AT BOTH CKTS?
LOCATE AND CORRECT SHORT TO GROUND IN CKT 240.
YES
NO
FAULTY ECM GROUNDS OR ECM.
REPAIR OPEN IN CKT THAT DID NOT LIGHT THE TEST LIGHT.
CLEAR CODES AND CONFIRM "CLOSED LOOP" OPERATION AND NO "SERVICE ENGINE SOON" LIGHT.
THE ALDL CONNECTOR IS MOUNTED ON TOP OF THE ECM BEHIND THE PASSENGER SIDE KICK PAD.


## CHART A-1, NO "SERVICE ENGINE SOON" LIGHT

There should always be a "SERVICE ENGINE SOON" (SES) light when ignition is on and engine stopped. The ECM controls the SES light and turns it on by providing a ground path through circuit No. 419.

## DIAGNOSTIC AIDS

If engine runs okay, check:

- Faulty light bulb.
- Circuit No. 419 open.
- Gauge fuse blown. This will result in no oil or generator light, seat belt reminder, etc.

Engine cranks but will not run, check:

- Continuous battery fuse or fusible link.
- ECM ignition fuse open.
- Battery circuit No. 240 to ECM open.
- Ignition circuit No. 439 to ECM open.
- Poor connection at ECM.

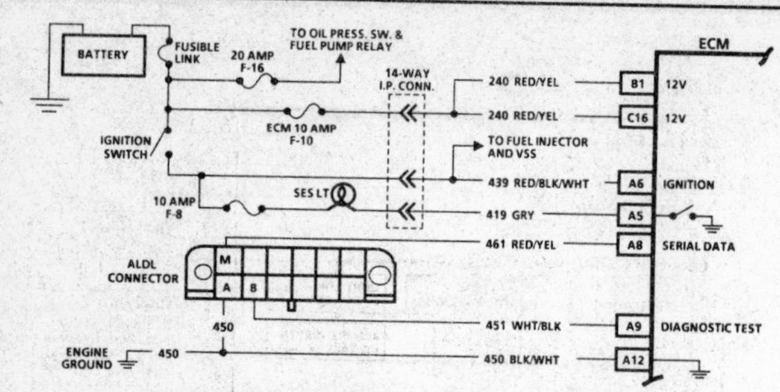
BATTERY
FUSIBLE LINK
20 AMP F-16
TO OIL PRESS. SW. & FUEL PUMP RELAY
14-WAY I.P. CONN.
ECM
240 RED/YEL
B1
12V
240 RED/YEL
C16
12V
IGNITION SWITCH
ECM 10 AMP F-10
TO FUEL INJECTOR AND VSS
439 RED/BLK/WHT
A6
IGNITION
10 AMP F-8
SES LT
419 GRY
A5
461 RED/YEL
A8
SERIAL DATA
ALDL CONNECTOR
M
A
B
450
451 WHT/BLK
A9
DIAGNOSTIC TEST
ENGINE GROUND
450
450 BLK/WHT
A12

## CHART A-2, WON'T FLASH CODE 12 ("SERVICE ENGINE SOON") LIGHT ON STEADY)

There should always be a "SERVICE ENGINE SOON" (SES) light when ignition is on and engine stopped. The ECM controls the SES light and turns it on by providing a ground path through circuit No. 419. With the diagnostic terminal grounded, the SES light should flash a Code 12, followed by any trouble codes stored in memory.

A steady light suggests a short to ground in the SES light control circuit No. 419, or an open in diagnostic circuit No. 451. A steady but dim SES light would indicate failure of a Quad-driver.

**NOTE: Test numbers refer to test numbers on diagnostic chart.**

**1)** If there is a problem with ECM that causes a "Scan" tester to not read serial data, the ECM should not read a Code 12. If Code 12 is flashing, check circuit No. 451 for short to ground. If Code 12 does flash, be sure "Scan" tester is working properly on another car. If "Scan" is working properly and circuit No. 461 is okay, the MEM-CAL or ECM may be at fault.

**2)** If SES light goes off when ECM connector is disconnected, circuit No. 419 is not shorted to ground.

**3)** This step will check for an open diagnostic circuit No. 451.

**4)** At this point the SES light wiring is okay. The problem is a faulty MEM-CAL or ECM. If Code 12 does not flash, the ECM should be replaced using the original MEM-CAL. Replace the MEM-CAL only after trying an ECM.

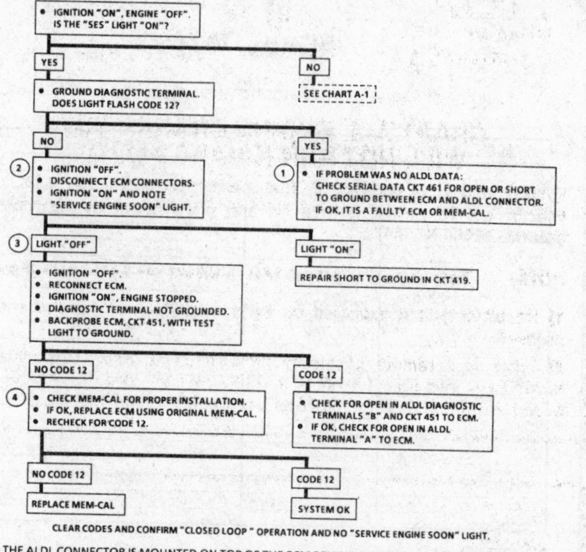
• IGNITION "ON", ENGINE "OFF". IS THE "SES" LIGHT "ON"?
YES
NO
SEE CHART A-1
• GROUND DIAGNOSTIC TERMINAL. DOES LIGHT FLASH CODE 12?
NO
YES
2
• IGNITION "OFF".
• DISCONNECT ECM CONNECTORS.
• IGNITION "ON" AND NOTE "SERVICE ENGINE SOON" LIGHT.
1
• IF PROBLEM WAS NO ALDL DATA: CHECK SERIAL DATA CKT 461 FOR OPEN OR SHORT TO GROUND BETWEEN ECM AND ALDL CONNECTOR. IF OK, IT IS A FAULTY ECM OR MEM-CAL.
3
LIGHT "OFF"
LIGHT "ON"
REPAIR SHORT TO GROUND IN CKT 419.
• IGNITION "OFF".
• RECONNECT ECM.
• IGNITION "ON", ENGINE STOPPED.
• DIAGNOSTIC TERMINAL NOT GROUNDED.
• BACKPROBE ECM, CKT 451, WITH TEST LIGHT TO GROUND.
NO CODE 12
CODE 12
4
• CHECK MEM-CAL FOR PROPER INSTALLATION.
• IF OK, REPLACE ECM USING ORIGINAL MEM-CAL.
• RECHECK FOR CODE 12.
• CHECK FOR OPEN IN ALDL DIAGNOSTIC TERMINALS "B" AND CKT 451 TO ECM.
• IF OK, CHECK FOR OPEN IN ALDL TERMINAL "A" TO ECM.
NO CODE 12
CODE 12
REPLACE MEM-CAL
SYSTEM OK
CLEAR CODES AND CONFIRM "CLOSED LOOP" OPERATION AND NO "SERVICE ENGINE SOON" LIGHT.
THE ALDL CONNECTOR IS MOUNTED ON TOP OF THE ECM BEHIND THE PASSENGER SIDE KICK PAD.

ECM
INJECTOR DRIVER
467 BLU D16
INJECTOR
450 BLK/WHT A12
439 RED
439 RED/WHT/BLK A6 IGNITION
RED/WHT TO IGNITION COIL
JUMPER D9 D10 INJECTOR DRIVER LOW
423 WHT D4 EST
430 PPL/WHT B5 REFERENCE
424 BRN/BLK D5 BYPASS
450 BLK/WHT B3 GROUND
I.P. CONNECTOR
439 RED/BLK/WHT
IGNITION SWITCH
REMOTE CONNECTOR LATE BUILD 1.6L ENGINES
REMOTE CONNECTOR (EARLY PRODUCTION 1.6L ENGINES)

## CHART A-3, ENGINE CRANKS BUT WILL NOT RUN (CHART 1 OF 2)

Before using this chart, battery condition, engine cranking speed and fuel pressure and quantity must be verified as proper.

**NOTE: Test numbers refer to test numbers on diagnostic chart.**

**1)** An SES light on is a basic test to verify a 12 volt supply to ignition and ECM. If TPS is over 2.5 volts, the ECM will be in a "clear flood" mode which will make starting difficult. The "Scan" tester should read an RPM reference pulse during cranking.

**2)** If RPM is indicated during cranking, the ignition module is receiving a crank signal. No spark at this test indicates the ignition module is not triggering the coil.

**3)** With fuel injector wiring disconnected, there should be no fuel spray when cranking engine. If fuel is present, replace injector.

**4)** Using Test Light (BT-8329), ensure the test light blinks indicating the ECM is controlling the injector okay.

**5)** Fuel spray from injector indicates fuel is available. However, the engine could be flooded. No fuel spray indicates a faulty fuel system or ECM.

**6)** This test will determine if ignition module is not generating a reference pulse, or if wiring or ECM are faulty. By touching and removing a test light to 12 volts on circuit No. 430, a reference pulse should be generated. If reference is generated, ECM and wiring are okay.

## DIAGNOSTIC AIDS

Water or foreign material can cause a no start during freezing weather. An EGR sticking or leaking can cause a lean condition during cranking. If engine is flooded, ensure engine enters "clear flood" mode when throttle is opened during crank.

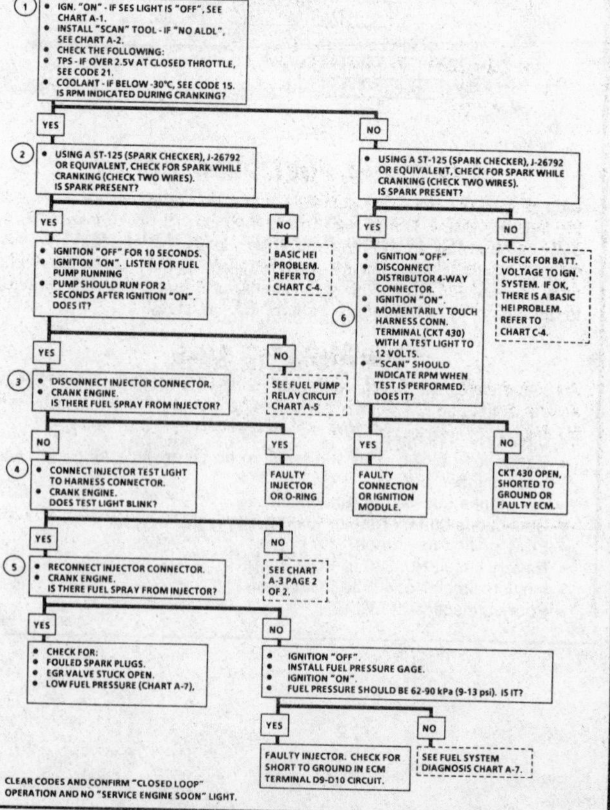
1
• IGN. "ON" - IF SES LIGHT IS "OFF", SEE CHART A-1.
• INSTALL "SCAN" TOOL - IF "NO ALDL", SEE CHART A-2.
• CHECK THE FOLLOWING:
• TPS - IF OVER 2.5V AT CLOSED THROTTLE, SEE CODE 21.
• COOLANT - IF BELOW -30°C, SEE CODE 15. IS RPM INDICATED DURING CRANKING?
YES
NO
2
• USING A ST-125 (SPARK CHECKER), J-26792 OR EQUIVALENT, CHECK FOR SPARK WHILE CRANKING (CHECK TWO WIRES). IS SPARK PRESENT?
• USING A ST-125 (SPARK CHECKER), J-26792 OR EQUIVALENT, CHECK FOR SPARK WHILE CRANKING (CHECK TWO WIRES). IS SPARK PRESENT?
YES
NO
YES
NO
• IGNITION "OFF" FOR 10 SECONDS.
• IGNITION "ON". LISTEN FOR FUEL PUMP RUNNING
• PUMP SHOULD RUN FOR 2 SECONDS AFTER IGNITION "ON". DOES IT?
BASIC HEI PROBLEM. REFER TO CHART C-4.
• IGNITION "OFF".
• DISCONNECT DISTRIBUTOR 4-WAY CONNECTOR.
• IGNITION "ON".
• MOMENTARILY TOUCH HARNESS CONN. TERMINAL (CKT 430) WITH A TEST LIGHT TO 12 VOLTS.
• "SCAN" SHOULD INDICATE RPM WHEN TEST IS PERFORMED. DOES IT?
6
CHECK FOR BATT. VOLTAGE TO IGN. SYSTEM. IF OK, THERE IS A BASIC HEI PROBLEM. REFER TO CHART C-4.
YES
NO
3
• DISCONNECT INJECTOR CONNECTOR.
• CRANK ENGINE. IS THERE FUEL SPRAY FROM INJECTOR?
SEE FUEL PUMP RELAY CIRCUIT CHART A-5
NO
YES
YES
NO
4
• CONNECT INJECTOR TEST LIGHT TO HARNESS CONNECTOR.
• CRANK ENGINE. DOES TEST LIGHT BLINK?
FAULTY INJECTOR OR O-RING
FAULTY CONNECTION OR IGNITION MODULE.
CKT 430 OPEN, SHORTED TO GROUND OR FAULTY ECM.
YES
NO
5
• RECONNECT INJECTOR CONNECTOR.
• CRANK ENGINE. IS THERE FUEL SPRAY FROM INJECTOR?
SEE CHART A-3 PAGE 2 OF 2.
YES
NO
• CHECK FOR:
• FOULED SPARK PLUGS.
• EGR VALVE STUCK OPEN.
• LOW FUEL PRESSURE (CHART A-7).
• IGNITION "OFF".
• INSTALL FUEL PRESSURE GAGE.
• IGNITION "ON".
• FUEL PRESSURE SHOULD BE 62-90 kPa (9-13 psi). IS IT?
YES
NO
FAULTY INJECTOR. CHECK FOR SHORT TO GROUND IN ECM TERMINAL D9-D10 CIRCUIT.
SEE FUEL SYSTEM DIAGNOSIS CHART A-7.
CLEAR CODES AND CONFIRM "CLOSED LOOP" OPERATION AND NO "SERVICE ENGINE SOON" LIGHT.

# 1988 COMPUTERIZED ENGINE CONTROLS
## General Motors LeMans 1.6L TBI (Cont.)

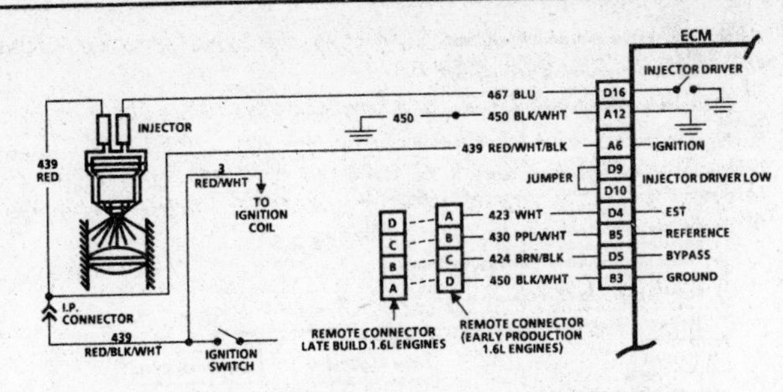
ECM
INJECTOR DRIVER
467 BLU
D16
450
450 BLK/WHT
A12
INJECTOR
439 RED/WHT/BLK
A6
IGNITION
439
RED
3
RED/WHT
TO
IGNITION
COIL
JUMPER
D9
D10
INJECTOR DRIVER LOW
423 WHT
D4
EST
430 PPL/WHT
B5
REFERENCE
424 BRN/BLK
D5
BYPASS
450 BLK/WHT
B3
GROUND
I.P.
CONNECTOR
439
RED/BLK/WHT
IGNITION
SWITCH
REMOTE CONNECTOR
LATE BUILD 1.6L ENGINES
REMOTE CONNECTOR
(EARLY PRODUCTION
1.6L ENGINES)

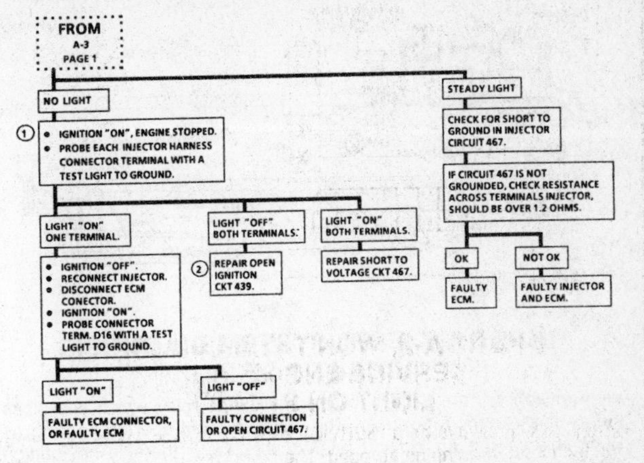
FROM
A-3
PAGE 1
NO LIGHT
STEADY LIGHT
1
• IGNITION "ON", ENGINE STOPPED.
• PROBE EACH INJECTOR HARNESS CONNECTOR TERMINAL WITH A TEST LIGHT TO GROUND.
CHECK FOR SHORT TO GROUND IN INJECTOR CIRCUIT 467.
IF CIRCUIT 467 IS NOT GROUNDED, CHECK RESISTANCE ACROSS TERMINALS INJECTOR, SHOULD BE OVER 1.2 OHMS.
LIGHT "ON" ONE TERMINAL.
LIGHT "OFF" BOTH TERMINALS.
LIGHT "ON" BOTH TERMINALS.
OK
NOT OK
• IGNITION "OFF".
• RECONNECT INJECTOR.
• DISCONNECT ECM CONECTOR.
• IGNITION "ON".
• PROBE CONNECTOR TERM. D16 WITH A TEST LIGHT TO GROUND.
2
REPAIR OPEN IGNITION CKT 439.
REPAIR SHORT TO VOLTAGE CKT 467.
FAULTY ECM.
FAULTY INJECTOR AND ECM.
LIGHT "ON"
LIGHT "OFF"
FAULTY ECM CONNECTOR, OR FAULTY ECM
FAULTY CONNECTION OR OPEN CIRCUIT 467.

## CHART A-3, ENGINE CRANKS BUT WILL NOT RUN (CHART 2 OF 2)

Ignition voltage is supplied to fuel injector on circuit No. 439. The injector will be pulsed (turned on and off) when ECM opens and grounds circuit No. 467.

**NOTE: Test numbers refer to test numbers on diagnostic chart.**

**1)** No blinking light indicates no ECM control of injector, or wiring problem.

**2)** There is a remote possibility the resistance across the injector terminals is less than 1.2 ohms and has resulted in a blown fuse for circuit No. 439. If this has happened, replace fuse and injector.

CLEAR CODES AND CONFIRM "CLOSED LOOP" OPERATION AND NO "SERVICE ENGINE SOON" LIGHT.

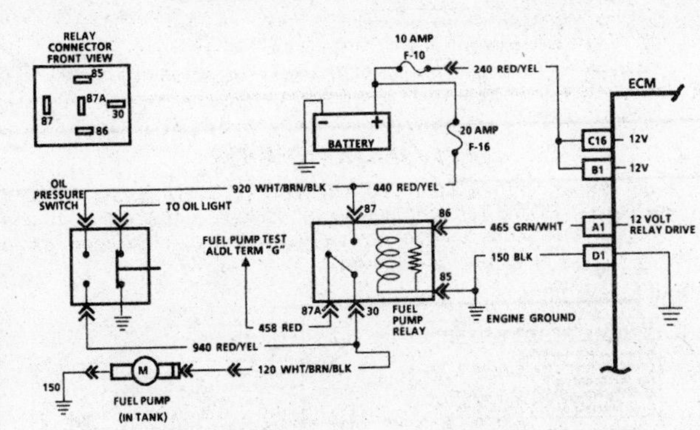
RELAY
CONNECTOR
FRONT VIEW
85
87
87A
30
86
10 AMP
F-10
240 RED/YEL
ECM
BATTERY
20 AMP
F-16
C16
12V
B1
12V
OIL
PRESSURE
SWITCH
920 WHT/BRN/BLK
440 RED/YEL
TO OIL LIGHT
87
86
465 GRN/WHT
A1
12 VOLT
RELAY DRIVE
FUEL PUMP TEST
ALDL TERM "G"
150 BLK
D1
85
87A
30
FUEL
PUMP
RELAY
458 RED
ENGINE GROUND
940 RED/YEL
M
120 WHT/BRN/BLK
150
FUEL PUMP
(IN TANK)

## CHART A-5, FUEL PUMP RELAY

With ignition on, the ECM activates fuel pump relay, which energizes the in-tank electric fuel pump. The fuel pump will operate as long as ECM is receiving an ignition reference pulse. If there is no ignition reference pulse, fuel pump will stop within 2 seconds. If the fuel pump relay or ECM fail while engine is running, the fuel pump will continue to run through an oil pressure switch back-up circuit.

## DIAGNOSTIC AIDS

An inoperative fuel pump relay can cause long crank times before engine start. The long crank period is caused by the time necessary for engine to build oil pressure during crank to energize fuel pump.

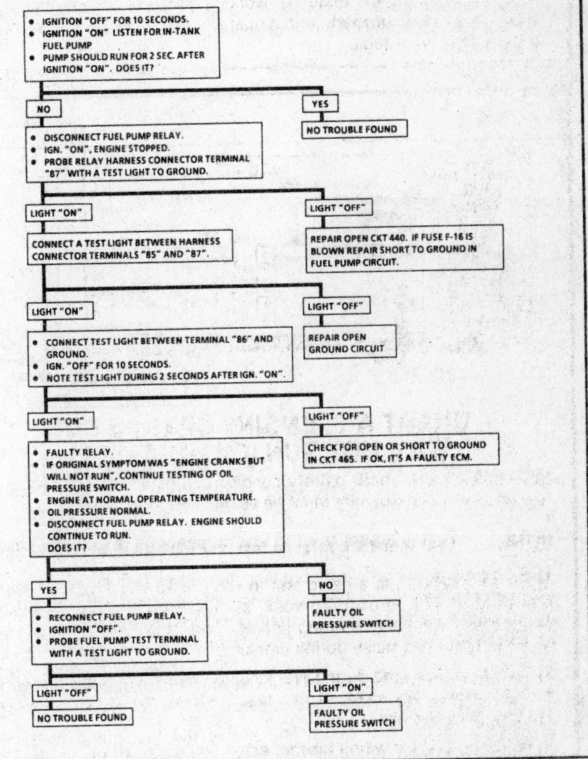
• IGNITION "OFF" FOR 10 SECONDS.
• IGNITION "ON" LISTEN FOR IN-TANK FUEL PUMP
• PUMP SHOULD RUN FOR 2 SEC. AFTER IGNITION "ON". DOES IT?
NO
YES
NO TROUBLE FOUND
• DISCONNECT FUEL PUMP RELAY.
• IGN. "ON", ENGINE STOPPED.
• PROBE RELAY HARNESS CONNECTOR TERMINAL "87" WITH A TEST LIGHT TO GROUND.
LIGHT "ON"
LIGHT "OFF"
CONNECT A TEST LIGHT BETWEEN HARNESS CONNECTOR TERMINALS "85" AND "87".
REPAIR OPEN CKT 440. IF FUSE F-16 IS BLOWN REPAIR SHORT TO GROUND IN FUEL PUMP CIRCUIT.
LIGHT "ON"
LIGHT "OFF"
• CONNECT TEST LIGHT BETWEEN TERMINAL "86" AND GROUND.
• IGN. "OFF" FOR 10 SECONDS.
• NOTE TEST LIGHT DURING 2 SECONDS AFTER IGN. "ON".
REPAIR OPEN GROUND CIRCUIT
LIGHT "ON"
LIGHT "OFF"
• FAULTY RELAY.
• IF ORIGINAL SYMPTOM WAS "ENGINE CRANKS BUT WILL NOT RUN", CONTINUE TESTING OF OIL PRESSURE SWITCH.
• ENGINE AT NORMAL OPERATING TEMPERATURE.
• OIL PRESSURE NORMAL.
• DISCONNECT FUEL PUMP RELAY. ENGINE SHOULD CONTINUE TO RUN. DOES IT?
CHECK FOR OPEN OR SHORT TO GROUND IN CKT 465. IF OK, IT'S A FAULTY ECM.
YES
NO
• RECONNECT FUEL PUMP RELAY.
• IGNITION "OFF".
• PROBE FUEL PUMP TEST TERMINAL WITH A TEST LIGHT TO GROUND.
FAULTY OIL PRESSURE SWITCH
LIGHT "OFF"
LIGHT "ON"
NO TROUBLE FOUND
FAULTY OIL PRESSURE SWITCH

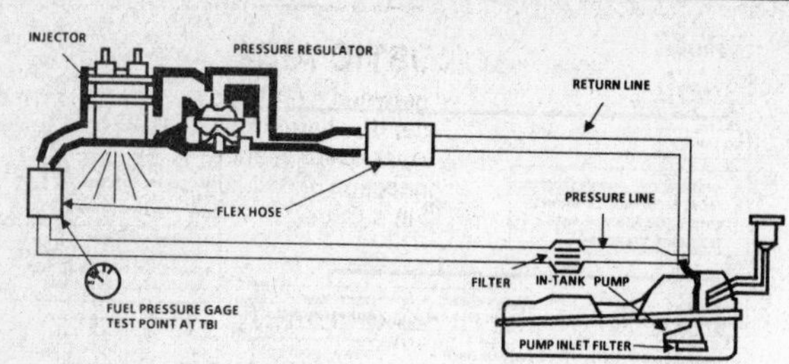
INJECTOR
PRESSURE REGULATOR
RETURN LINE
FLEX HOSE
PRESSURE LINE
FILTER
IN-TANK PUMP
FUEL PRESSURE GAGE TEST POINT AT TBI
PUMP INLET FILTER

## CHART A-7, FUEL SYSTEM DIAGNOSIS (CHART 1 OF 2)

With ignition on, the ECM activates fuel pump relay which energizes the in-tank electric fuel pump. The fuel pump will operate as long as ECM is receiving an ignition reference pulse. If there is no ignition reference pulse, fuel pump will stop within 2 seconds.
The fuel pump will deliver fuel to the TBI unit where pressure is controlled at 9-13 psi. Excess fuel is returned to fuel tank. The fuel pump test terminal is located on the right side of engine compartment. When engine is stopped, fuel pump can be turned on by applying battery voltage to test terminal.

### DIAGNOSTIC AIDS

Improper fuel pressure can result in one of the following conditions:

- Cranks, but won't run.
- Code 44.
- Code 45.
- Cuts out like an ignition problem.
- Poor fuel economy and loss of power.
- Hesitation on acceleration.

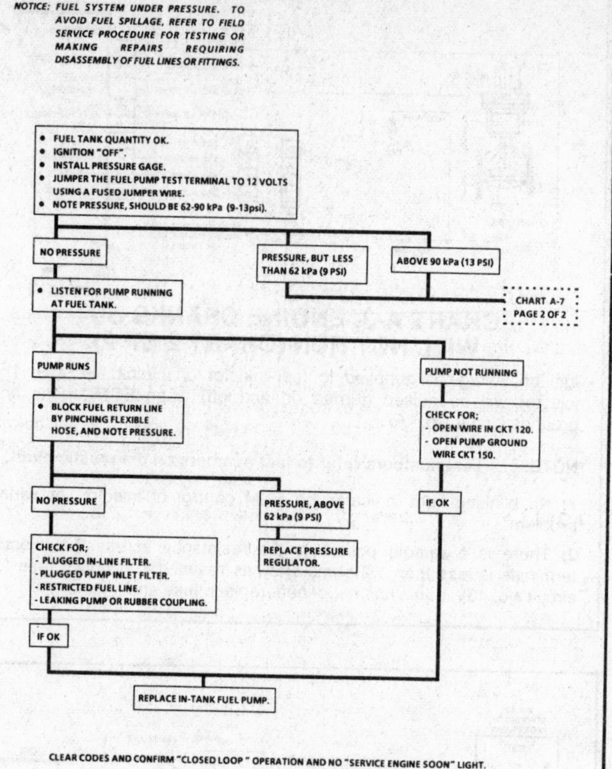
NOTICE: FUEL SYSTEM UNDER PRESSURE. TO AVOID FUEL SPILLAGE, REFER TO FIELD SERVICE PROCEDURE FOR TESTING OR MAKING REPAIRS REQUIRING DISASSEMBLY OF FUEL LINES OR FITTINGS.
• FUEL TANK QUANTITY OK.
• IGNITION "OFF".
• INSTALL PRESSURE GAGE.
• JUMPER THE FUEL PUMP TEST TERMINAL TO 12 VOLTS USING A FUSED JUMPER WIRE.
• NOTE PRESSURE, SHOULD BE 62-90 kPa (9-13psi).
NO PRESSURE
PRESSURE, BUT LESS THAN 62 kPa (9 PSI)
ABOVE 90 kPa (13 PSI)
CHART A-7 PAGE 2 OF 2
• LISTEN FOR PUMP RUNNING AT FUEL TANK.
PUMP RUNS
PUMP NOT RUNNING
• BLOCK FUEL RETURN LINE BY PINCHING FLEXIBLE HOSE, AND NOTE PRESSURE.
CHECK FOR;
- OPEN WIRE IN CKT 120.
- OPEN PUMP GROUND WIRE CKT 150.
NO PRESSURE
PRESSURE, ABOVE 62 kPa (9 PSI)
IF OK
REPLACE PRESSURE REGULATOR.
CHECK FOR;
- PLUGGED IN-LINE FILTER.
- PLUGGED PUMP INLET FILTER.
- RESTRICTED FUEL LINE.
- LEAKING PUMP OR RUBBER COUPLING.
IF OK
REPLACE IN-TANK FUEL PUMP.
CLEAR CODES AND CONFIRM "CLOSED LOOP" OPERATION AND NO "SERVICE ENGINE SOON" LIGHT.

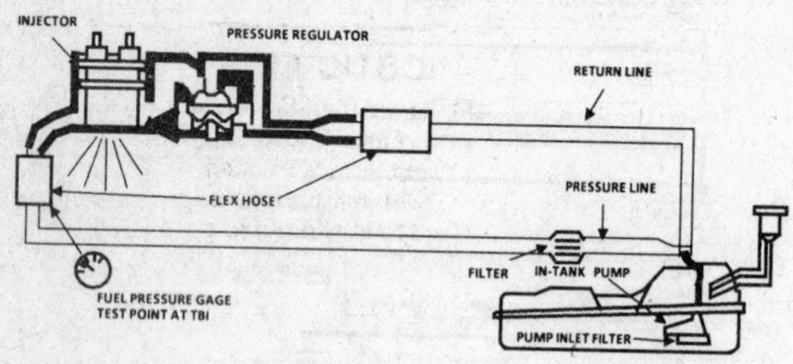
INJECTOR
PRESSURE REGULATOR
RETURN LINE
FLEX HOSE
PRESSURE LINE
FILTER
IN-TANK PUMP
FUEL PRESSURE GAGE TEST POINT AT TBI
PUMP INLET FILTER

## CHART A-7, FUEL SYSTEM DIAGNOSIS (CHART 2 OF 2)

**NOTE: Test numbers refer to test numbers on diagnostic chart.**

**1)** Fuel system has pressure, but less than 9 psi, falls into 2 areas:

- Fuel volume okay but pressure too low. System will run lean and may set a Code 44. Hard starting and poor performance.
- Check for restriction in fuel flow. Normally a vehicle with less than 9 psi fuel pressure at idle will not be driveable. However, if the pressure drop occurs only when driving, the engine will surge and then stop as pressure drops to zero.

**2)** Restricting the fuel return line allows the fuel pump to develop maximum pressure. When battery voltage is applied to fuel pump test terminal, pressure should be 13-18 psi.

**3)** This test determines if high fuel pressure is due to restricted fuel return line, or a TBI fuel pressure regulator problem.

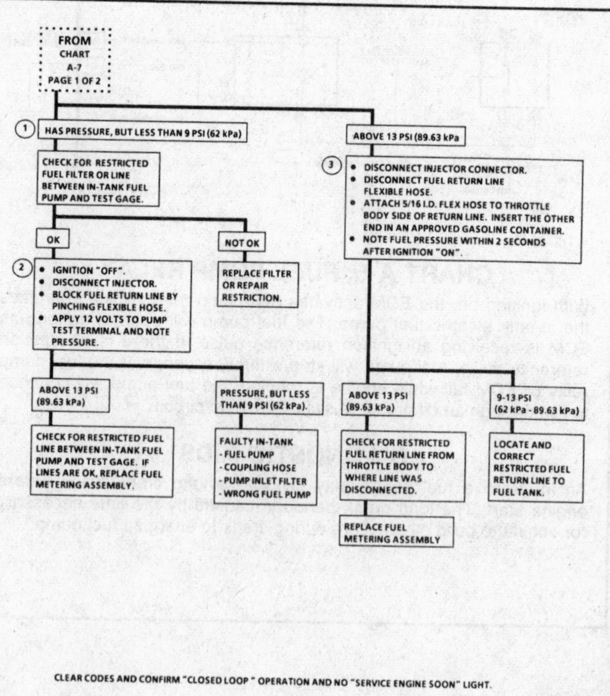
FROM CHART A-7 PAGE 1 OF 2
1 HAS PRESSURE, BUT LESS THAN 9 PSI (62 kPa)
ABOVE 13 PSI (89.63 kPa
CHECK FOR RESTRICTED FUEL FILTER OR LINE BETWEEN IN-TANK FUEL PUMP AND TEST GAGE.
3 • DISCONNECT INJECTOR CONNECTOR.
• DISCONNECT FUEL RETURN LINE FLEXIBLE HOSE.
• ATTACH 5/16 I.D. FLEX HOSE TO THROTTLE BODY SIDE OF RETURN LINE. INSERT THE OTHER END IN AN APPROVED GASOLINE CONTAINER.
• NOTE FUEL PRESSURE WITHIN 2 SECONDS AFTER IGNITION "ON".
OK
NOT OK
2 • IGNITION "OFF".
• DISCONNECT INJECTOR.
• BLOCK FUEL RETURN LINE BY PINCHING FLEXIBLE HOSE.
• APPLY 12 VOLTS TO PUMP TEST TERMINAL AND NOTE PRESSURE.
REPLACE FILTER OR REPAIR RESTRICTION.
ABOVE 13 PSI (89.63 kPa)
PRESSURE, BUT LESS THAN 9 PSI (62 kPa).
ABOVE 13 PSI (89.63 kPa)
9-13 PSI (62 kPa - 89.63 kPa)
CHECK FOR RESTRICTED FUEL LINE BETWEEN IN-TANK FUEL PUMP AND TEST GAGE. IF LINES ARE OK, REPLACE FUEL METERING ASSEMBLY.
FAULTY IN-TANK
- FUEL PUMP
- COUPLING HOSE
- PUMP INLET FILTER
- WRONG FUEL PUMP
CHECK FOR RESTRICTED FUEL RETURN LINE FROM THROTTLE BODY TO WHERE LINE WAS DISCONNECTED.
LOCATE AND CORRECT RESTRICTED FUEL RETURN LINE TO FUEL TANK.
REPLACE FUEL METERING ASSEMBLY
CLEAR CODES AND CONFIRM "CLOSED LOOP" OPERATION AND NO "SERVICE ENGINE SOON" LIGHT.

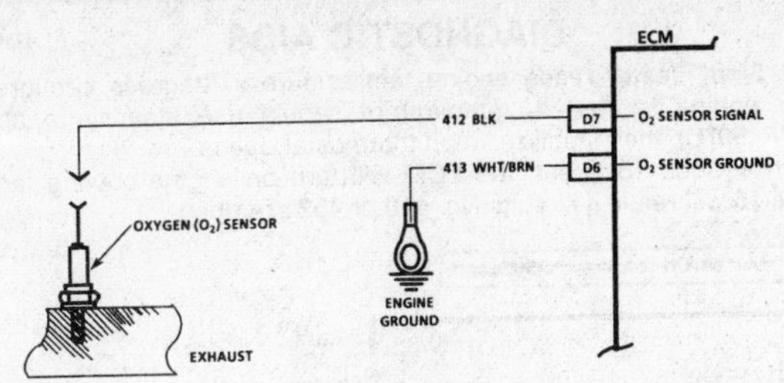

ECM
412 BLK
D7
O₂ SENSOR SIGNAL
413 WHT/BRN
D6
O₂ SENSOR GROUND
OXYGEN (O₂) SENSOR
ENGINE GROUND
EXHAUST


## CODE 13, OPEN OXYGEN SENSOR CIRCUIT

The ECM supplies a voltage of about .45 volt between terminals D7 and D6. If measured with 10-megohm voltmeter, this may read as low as .32 volt.

The oxygen sensor varies the voltage within a range of about one volt, if the exhaust is rich, down to about .10 volt if the exhaust is lean. The sensor is like an open circuit and produces no voltage when below 600°F (316°C). An open sensor circuit or cold sensor causes "open loop" operation.

**NOTE: Test numbers refer to test numbers on diagnostic chart.**

**1)** Code 13 will set if the following conditions occur:
- Code 21 or 22 is not being detected.
- Engine at normal operating temperature.
- At least 40 seconds engine run time.
- Oxygen signal steady between .35-.55 volt.
- Throttle angle more than 7 percent.
- All conditions must be met for 3 seconds.

**2)** This test determines if the oxygen sensor is the problem, or if the ECM or wiring is at fault.

**3)** When performing this test, use only a high impedence digital volt/ohmmeter. This test checks the continuity of circuits No. 412 and 413. If circuit No. 413 is open, the ECM voltage on circuit No. 412 will measure over .6 volt.

### DIAGNOSTIC AIDS

Normal "Scan" voltage varies between .1-1.0 volt, while in "closed loop". Code 13 sets in one minute, if voltage remains between .35-.55 volt, but the system will go into "open loop" in about 15 seconds. Verify a clean, tight ground connection for circuit No. 413. Open in circuits No. 412 or 413 will result in a Code 13.

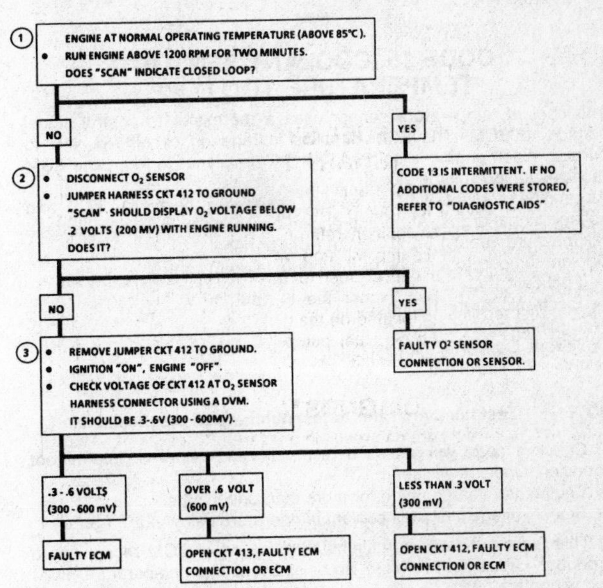

1 ENGINE AT NORMAL OPERATING TEMPERATURE (ABOVE 85°C).
• RUN ENGINE ABOVE 1200 RPM FOR TWO MINUTES.
DOES "SCAN" INDICATE CLOSED LOOP?
NO
YES
CODE 13 IS INTERMITTENT. IF NO ADDITIONAL CODES WERE STORED, REFER TO "DIAGNOSTIC AIDS"
2 • DISCONNECT O₂ SENSOR
• JUMPER HARNESS CKT 412 TO GROUND
"SCAN" SHOULD DISPLAY O₂ VOLTAGE BELOW .2 VOLTS (200 MV) WITH ENGINE RUNNING.
DOES IT?
NO
YES
FAULTY O² SENSOR CONNECTION OR SENSOR.
3 • REMOVE JUMPER CKT 412 TO GROUND.
• IGNITION "ON", ENGINE "OFF".
• CHECK VOLTAGE OF CKT 412 AT O₂ SENSOR HARNESS CONNECTOR USING A DVM.
IT SHOULD BE .3-.6V (300 - 600MV).
.3 - .6 VOLTS (300 - 600 mV)
OVER .6 VOLT (600 mV)
LESS THAN .3 VOLT (300 mV)
FAULTY ECM
OPEN CKT 413, FAULTY ECM CONNECTION OR ECM
OPEN CKT 412, FAULTY ECM CONNECTION OR ECM
CLEAR CODES AND CONFIRM "CLOSED LOOP" OPERATION AND NO "SERVICE ENGINE SOON" LIGHT.


THE ALDL CONNECTOR IS MOUNTED ON TOP OF THE ECM BEHIND THE PASSENGER SIDE KICK PAD.

COOLANT TEMPERATURE SENSOR
ECM
COOLANT SENSOR SIGNAL
410 YEL
C10
5V SIGNAL
452 BLK
A11
SENSOR GROUND
410
452
450 BLK/WHT
TO MAP SENSOR
COOLANT SENSOR CONNECTOR

## CODE 14, COOLANT SENSOR TEMPERATURE TOO HIGH

The coolant temperature sensor uses a thermistor to control signal voltage to ECM. The ECM supplies voltage on circuit No. 410 to sensor. When engine is cold, the sensor resistance is high, and ECM receives a high voltage signal.

As engine coolant warms, sensor resistance becomes less, and voltage signal drops. At normal engine operating temperature, voltage will measure about 1.5-2.0 volts at ECM terminal C10.

Coolant temperature is one of the inputs used to control:
- Fuel delivery.
- Electronic Spark Timing (EST).
- Radiator cooling fan.
- Torque Converter Clutch (TCC).
- Idle Air Control (IAC).

**NOTE: Test numbers refer to test numbers on diagnostic chart.**

**1)** Check if code will set as a result of hard failure or intermittent condition. Code 14 will set if CTS signal voltage indicates a coolant temperature above 275°F (135°C) for 2 seconds.

**2)** This test simulates conditions for a Code 15. If ECM recognizes an open circuit (high voltage), and displays a low temperature, the ECM and wiring are okay.

### DIAGNOSTIC AIDS

The "Scan" tester reads engine temperature in degrees centigrade. After engine is started, temperature should rise steadily to about 194°F (90°C), then stabilize when thermostat opens.

When a Code 14 is set, the ECM will turn on engine cooling fan. A Code 14 will result if circuit No. 410 is shorted to ground.

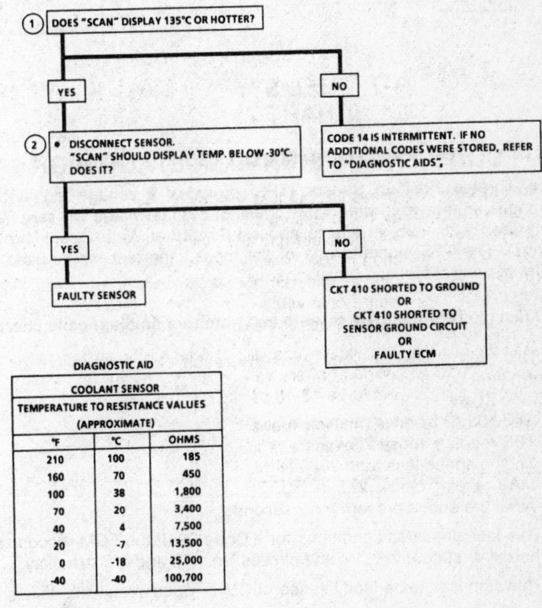

1 DOES "SCAN" DISPLAY 135°C OR HOTTER?
YES
NO
CODE 14 IS INTERMITTENT. IF NO ADDITIONAL CODES WERE STORED, REFER TO "DIAGNOSTIC AIDS".
2 • DISCONNECT SENSOR.
"SCAN" SHOULD DISPLAY TEMP. BELOW -30°C.
DOES IT?
YES
NO
FAULTY SENSOR
CKT 410 SHORTED TO GROUND OR CKT 410 SHORTED TO SENSOR GROUND CIRCUIT OR FAULTY ECM


DIAGNOSTIC AID

COOLANT SENSOR
TEMPERATURE TO RESISTANCE VALUES (APPROXIMATE)

| °F | °C | OHMS |
|---|---|---|
| 210 | 100 | 185 |
| 160 | 70 | 450 |
| 100 | 38 | 1,800 |
| 70 | 20 | 3,400 |
| 40 | 4 | 7,500 |
| 20 | -7 | 13,500 |
| 0 | -18 | 25,000 |
| -40 | -40 | 100,700 |

CLEAR CODES AND CONFIRM "CLOSED LOOP" OPERATION AND NO "SERVICE ENGINE SOON" LIGHT.

THE ALDL CONNECTOR IS MOUNTED ON TOP OF THE ECM BEHIND THE PASSENGER SIDE KICK PAD.

# 1988 COMPUTERIZED ENGINE CONTROLS
# General Motors LeMans 1.6L TBI (Cont.)

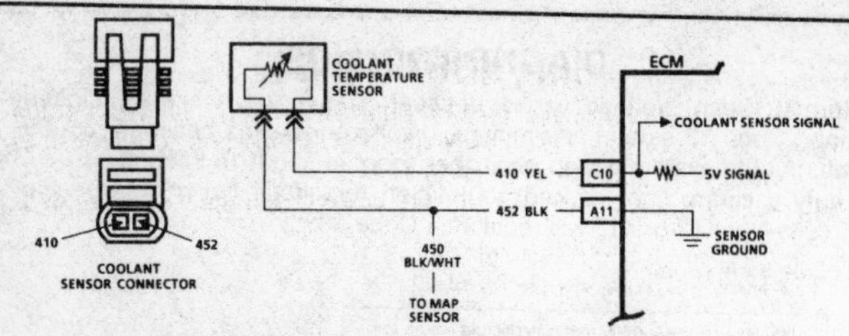

COOLANT TEMPERATURE SENSOR
ECM
COOLANT SENSOR SIGNAL
410 YEL
C10
5V SIGNAL
452 BLK
A11
SENSOR GROUND
410
452
COOLANT SENSOR CONNECTOR
450 BLK/WHT
TO MAP SENSOR


## CODE 15, COOLANT SENSOR TEMPERATURE TOO LOW

The coolant temperature sensor uses a thermistor to control signal voltage to ECM. The ECM supplies voltage on circuit No. 410 to sensor. When engine is cold, the sensor resistance is high, and ECM receives a high voltage signal.

As engine coolant warms, sensor resistance becomes less, and voltage signal drops. At normal engine operating temperature, voltage will measure about 1.5-2.0 volts at ECM terminal C10.

Coolant temperature is one of the inputs used to control:
- Fuel delivery.
- Electronic Spark Timing (EST).
- Radiator cooling fan.
- Torque Converter Clutch (TCC).
- Idle Air Control (IAC).

**NOTE: Test numbers refer to test numbers on diagnostic chart.**

**1)** Check if code will set as a result of hard failure or intermittent condition. Code 15 will set if:
- Engine has been running for more than one minute.
- Signal voltage indicates coolant temperature below -22°F (-30°C).

**2)** This tests simulates conditions for code 14. If ECM recognizes a grounded circuit (low voltage), and displays a high temperature, ECM and wiring are okay.

**3)** This test will determine if there is a wiring problem or defective ECM. If circuit No. 452 is open, there may also be a Code 33 stored.

## DIAGNOSTIC AIDS

The "Scan" tester reads engine temperature in degrees centigrade. After engine is started, temperature should rise steadily to about 194°F (90°C), then stabilize when thermostat opens.

When a Code 15 is set, the ECM will turn on engine cooling fan. A Code 15 will result if circuits No. 410 or 452 are open.

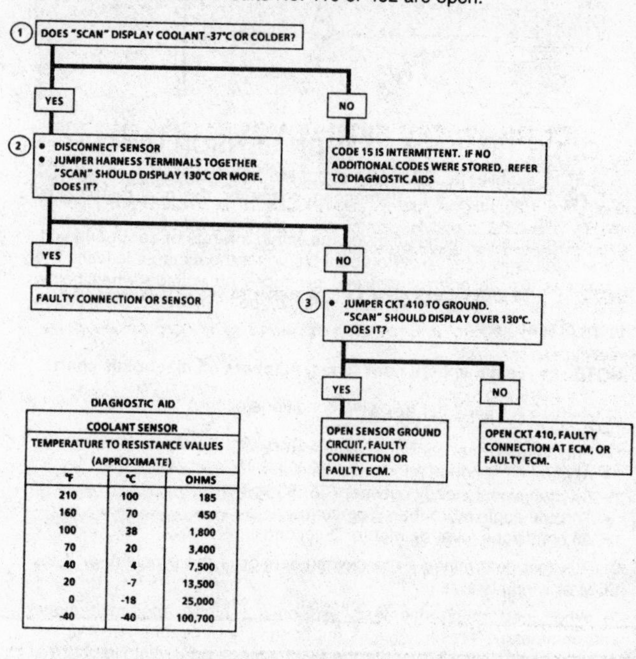

1 DOES "SCAN" DISPLAY COOLANT -37°C OR COLDER?
YES
NO
2 • DISCONNECT SENSOR
• JUMPER HARNESS TERMINALS TOGETHER "SCAN" SHOULD DISPLAY 130°C OR MORE. DOES IT?
CODE 15 IS INTERMITTENT. IF NO ADDITIONAL CODES WERE STORED, REFER TO DIAGNOSTIC AIDS
YES
NO
FAULTY CONNECTION OR SENSOR
3 • JUMPER CKT 410 TO GROUND. "SCAN" SHOULD DISPLAY OVER 130°C. DOES IT?
YES
NO
OPEN SENSOR GROUND CIRCUIT, FAULTY CONNECTION OR FAULTY ECM.
OPEN CKT 410, FAULTY CONNECTION AT ECM, OR FAULTY ECM.


DIAGNOSTIC AID

| COOLANT SENSOR TEMPERATURE TO RESISTANCE VALUES (APPROXIMATE) | | |
|---|---|---|
| °F | °C | OHMS |
| 210 | 100 | 185 |
| 160 | 70 | 450 |
| 100 | 38 | 1,800 |
| 70 | 20 | 3,400 |
| 40 | 4 | 7,500 |
| 20 | -7 | 13,500 |
| 0 | -18 | 25,000 |
| -40 | -40 | 100,700 |

CLEAR CODES AND CONFIRM "CLOSED LOOP" OPERATION AND NO "SERVICE ENGINE SOON" LIGHT.

THE ALDL CONNECTOR IS MOUNTED ON TOP OF THE ECM BEHIND THE PASSENGER SIDE KICK PAD.

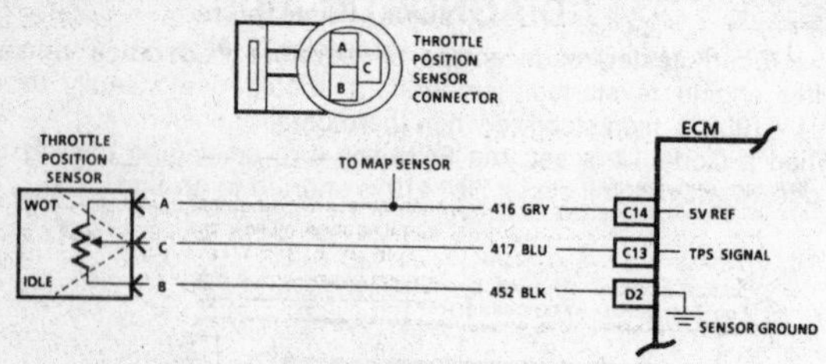

THROTTLE POSITION SENSOR CONNECTOR
A
B
C
THROTTLE POSITION SENSOR
WOT
IDLE
TO MAP SENSOR
ECM
416 GRY
C14
5V REF
417 BLU
C13
TPS SIGNAL
452 BLK
D2
SENSOR GROUND


## CODE 21, TPS SIGNAL VOLTAGE HIGH

The Throttle Position Sensor (TPS) provides a voltage signal that changes relative to throttle valve opening. Signal voltage will vary from less than 1.25 volts at idle to about 4.5 volts at Wide Open Throttle (WOT). The TPS signal is one of the most important inputs used by ECM to control fuel and emissions.

**NOTE: Test numbers refer to test numbers on diagnostic chart.**

**1)** This step checks if Code 21 is the result of a hard failure or an intermittent condition.

A Code 21 will set if:
- Code 33 or 34 have been detected.
- TPS reading above 2.5 volts.
- Engine speed less than 2000 RPM.
- MAP reading below 19.5 in. Hg.
- All of the above present for 2 seconds.

**2)** This test simulates conditions for a Code 22. If the ECM recognizes a change of state, the ECM and circuits No. 416 and 417 are okay.

**3)** This step isolates a faulty sensor, ECM or open circuit No. 452.

## DIAGNOSTIC AIDS

The "Scan" tester displays throttle position in volts. Closed throttle voltage should be less than 1.25 volts. TPS voltage should increase at a steady rate as throttle is moved to WOT.

A Code 21 will result if circuit No. 452 is open or if circuit No. 417 is shorted to voltage.

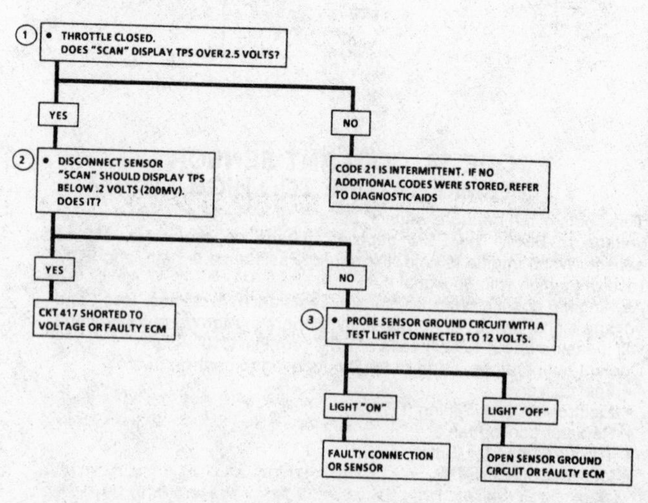

1 • THROTTLE CLOSED. DOES "SCAN" DISPLAY TPS OVER 2.5 VOLTS?
YES
NO
2 • DISCONNECT SENSOR "SCAN" SHOULD DISPLAY TPS BELOW .2 VOLTS (200MV). DOES IT?
CODE 21 IS INTERMITTENT. IF NO ADDITIONAL CODES WERE STORED, REFER TO DIAGNOSTIC AIDS
YES
NO
CKT 417 SHORTED TO VOLTAGE OR FAULTY ECM
3 • PROBE SENSOR GROUND CIRCUIT WITH A TEST LIGHT CONNECTED TO 12 VOLTS.
LIGHT "ON"
LIGHT "OFF"
FAULTY CONNECTION OR SENSOR
OPEN SENSOR GROUND CIRCUIT OR FAULTY ECM


CLEAR CODES AND CONFIRM "CLOSED LOOP" OPERATION AND NO "SERVICE ENGINE SOON" LIGHT.

THE ALDL CONNECTOR IS MOUNTED ON TOP OF THE ECM BEHIND THE PASSENGER SIDE KICK PAD.

# 1988 COMPUTERIZED ENGINE CONTROLS
## General Motors LeMans 1.6L TBI (Cont.)

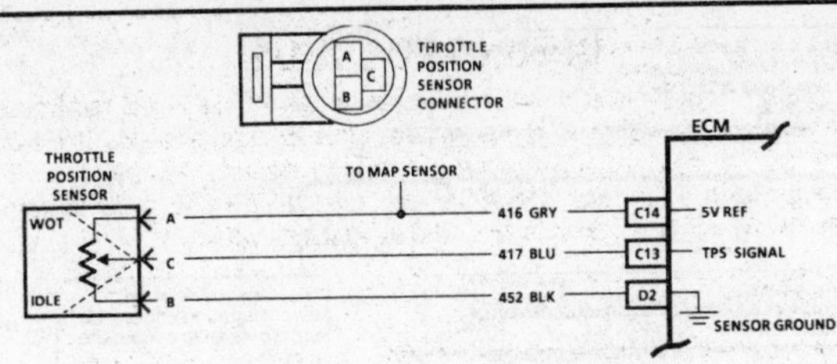
THROTTLE POSITION SENSOR CONNECTOR
A
B
C
ECM
THROTTLE POSITION SENSOR
TO MAP SENSOR
WOT
IDLE
416 GRY
417 BLU
452 BLK
C14
C13
D2
5V REF
TPS SIGNAL
SENSOR GROUND

### CODE 22, TPS SIGNAL VOLTAGE LOW

The Throttle Position Sensor (TPS) provides a voltage signal that changes relative to throttle valve opening. Signal voltage will vary from less than 1.25 volts at idle to about 4.5 volts at Wide Open Throttle (WOT). The TPS signal is one of the most important inputs used by ECM to control fuel and emissions.

**NOTE: Test numbers refer to test numbers on diagnostic chart.**

**1)** This step checks if Code 22 is a result of a hard failure or an intermittent condition.
A Code 22 will set if:
- The engine is running.
- TPS voltage is below .16 volt.

**2)** This test simulates conditions for a Code 21. If a Code 21 is set, or the "Scan" tester displays over 4 volts, the ECM and wiring are okay.

**3)** The "Scan" tester may not display 12 volts. The important thing is for ECM to recognize the voltage as over 4 volts, indicating circuit No. 417 and ECM are okay.

**4)** If circuit No. 416 is open or shorted to ground, there may also be a Code 34 stored.

### DIAGNOSTIC AIDS

The "Scan" tester displays throttle position in volts. Closed throttle voltage should be less than 1.25 volts. TPS voltage should increase at a steady rate as throttle is moved to WOT.
A Code 22 will result if circuits No. 416 and 417 are open or grounded.

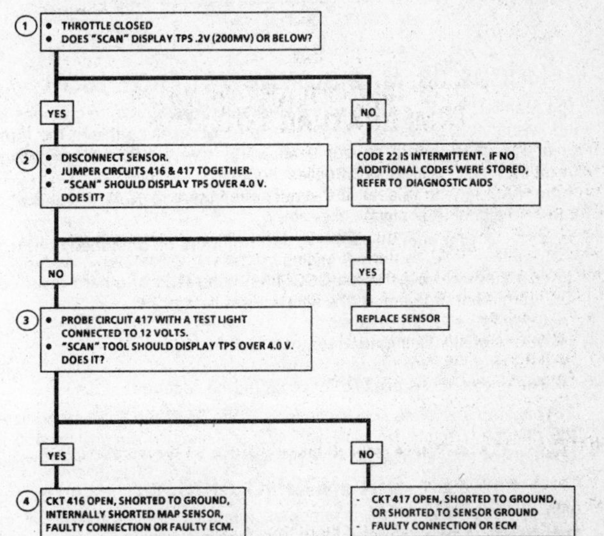
1 • THROTTLE CLOSED
• DOES "SCAN" DISPLAY TPS .2V (200MV) OR BELOW?
YES
NO
2 • DISCONNECT SENSOR.
• JUMPER CIRCUITS 416 & 417 TOGETHER.
• "SCAN" SHOULD DISPLAY TPS OVER 4.0 V. DOES IT?
CODE 22 IS INTERMITTENT. IF NO ADDITIONAL CODES WERE STORED, REFER TO DIAGNOSTIC AIDS
NO
YES
3 • PROBE CIRCUIT 417 WITH A TEST LIGHT CONNECTED TO 12 VOLTS.
• "SCAN" TOOL SHOULD DISPLAY TPS OVER 4.0 V. DOES IT?
REPLACE SENSOR
YES
NO
4 CKT 416 OPEN, SHORTED TO GROUND, INTERNALLY SHORTED MAP SENSOR, FAULTY CONNECTION OR FAULTY ECM.
CKT 417 OPEN, SHORTED TO GROUND, OR SHORTED TO SENSOR GROUND
FAULTY CONNECTION OR ECM

CLEAR CODES AND CONFIRM "CLOSED LOOP" OPERATION AND NO "SERVICE ENGINE SOON" LIGHT.

THE ALDL CONNECTOR IS MOUNTED ON TOP OF THE ECM BEHIND THE PASSENGER SIDE KICK PAD.

### CODE 24, VEHICLE SPEED SENSOR

The ECM applies and monitors 12 volts on circuit No. 437 to VSS. The VSS alternately grounds and opens circuit No. 437 when drive wheels are turning. The pulsing action is supplied to ECM. The ECM calculates vehicle speed based on time between pulses.

**NOTE: Test numbers refer to test numbers on diagnostic chart.**

**1)** This test uses the "Scan" tester to verify VSS operation.

**2)** The ECM supplies 12 volts to circuit No. 437, but this test should not light a test light. This test verifies circuit No. 437 is not shorted to a voltage source.

**3)** By probing circuit No. 437 with a test light several times a second, vehicle speed signal should be generated and displayed on the "Scan" tester.

**4)** This test must be done using a voltmeter and will check for 12 volts being supplied to circuit No. 437 by the ECM.

**5)** Circuit 439 is the ignition feed supplying operating power to VSS.

**6)** Circuit No. 450 supplies ground path for VSS operation. If circuit No. 450 is open, VSS cannot pulse circuit No. 437 to ground.

### DIAGNOSTIC AIDS

"Scan" should indicate a vehicle speed whenever drive wheels are turning greater than 3 MPH.
A faulty or misadjusted Park/Neutral switch can result in a false Code 24. Use "Scan" tester to check for properly adjusted Park/Neutral switch.

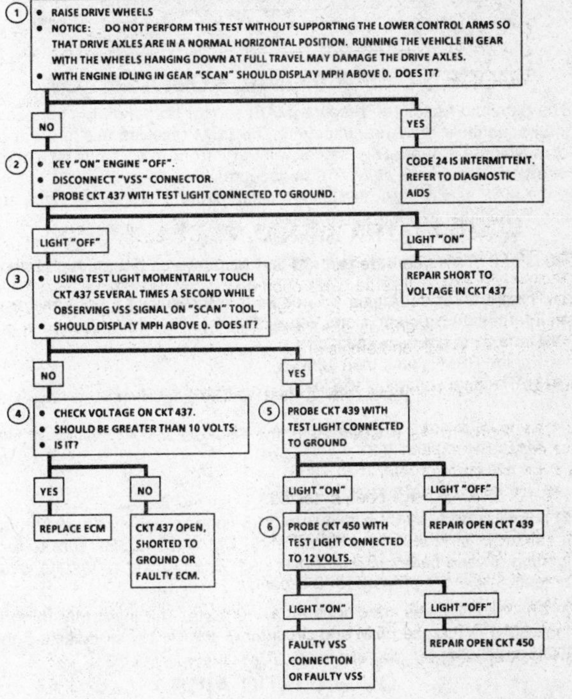
DISREGARD CODE 24, IF SET WHILE DRIVE WHEELS ARE NOT TURNING.
1 • RAISE DRIVE WHEELS
• NOTICE: DO NOT PERFORM THIS TEST WITHOUT SUPPORTING THE LOWER CONTROL ARMS SO THAT DRIVE AXLES ARE IN A NORMAL HORIZONTAL POSITION. RUNNING THE VEHICLE IN GEAR WITH THE WHEELS HANGING DOWN AT FULL TRAVEL MAY DAMAGE THE DRIVE AXLES.
• WITH ENGINE IDLING IN GEAR "SCAN" SHOULD DISPLAY MPH ABOVE 0. DOES IT?
NO
YES
2 • KEY "ON" ENGINE "OFF".
• DISCONNECT "VSS" CONNECTOR.
• PROBE CKT 437 WITH TEST LIGHT CONNECTED TO GROUND.
CODE 24 IS INTERMITTENT. REFER TO DIAGNOSTIC AIDS
LIGHT "OFF"
LIGHT "ON"
3 • USING TEST LIGHT MOMENTARILY TOUCH CKT 437 SEVERAL TIMES A SECOND WHILE OBSERVING VSS SIGNAL ON "SCAN" TOOL.
• SHOULD DISPLAY MPH ABOVE 0. DOES IT?
REPAIR SHORT TO VOLTAGE IN CKT 437
NO
YES
4 • CHECK VOLTAGE ON CKT 437.
• SHOULD BE GREATER THAN 10 VOLTS.
• IS IT?
5 PROBE CKT 439 WITH TEST LIGHT CONNECTED TO GROUND
YES
NO
LIGHT "ON"
LIGHT "OFF"
REPLACE ECM
CKT 437 OPEN, SHORTED TO GROUND OR FAULTY ECM.
6 PROBE CKT 450 WITH TEST LIGHT CONNECTED TO 12 VOLTS.
REPAIR OPEN CKT 439
LIGHT "ON"
LIGHT "OFF"
FAULTY VSS CONNECTION OR FAULTY VSS
REPAIR OPEN CKT 450

CLEAR CODES AND CONFIRM "CLOSED LOOP" OPERATION AND NO "SERVICE ENGINE SOON" LIGHT.

THE ALDL CONNECTOR IS MOUNTED ON TOP OF THE ECM BEHIND THE PASSENGER SIDE KICK PAD.

# 1988 COMPUTERIZED ENGINE CONTROLS
## General Motors LeMans 1.6L TBI (Cont.)

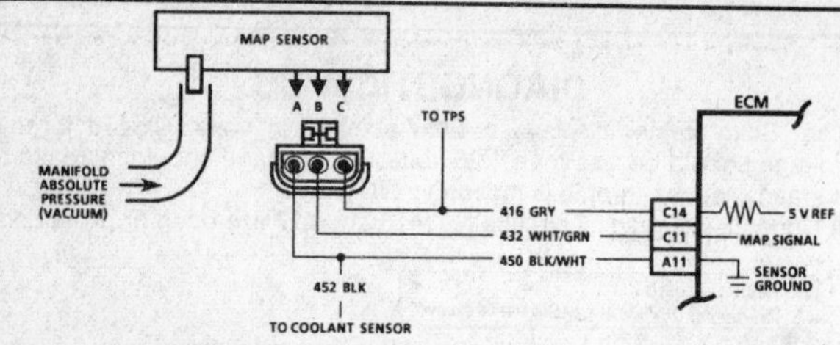
MAP SENSOR
A B C
MANIFOLD ABSOLUTE PRESSURE (VACUUM)
TO TPS
ECM
416 GRY
432 WHT/GRN
450 BLK/WHT
C14
C11
A11
5 V REF
MAP SIGNAL
SENSOR GROUND
452 BLK
TO COOLANT SENSOR

### CODE 33, MAP SIGNAL VOLTAGE HIGH

The Manifold Absolute Pressure (MAP) sensor responds to changes in intake manifold pressure (vacuum). The ECM receives this in the form of a voltage signal. This signal will vary from 1-1.5 volts at closed throttle to 4-4.5 volts at WOT (low vacuum).
If the MAP sensor fails, the ECM will substitute a fixed MAP value and use TPS signal to control fuel delivery.

**NOTE: Test numbers refer to test numbers on diagnostic chart.**

**1)** This step will determine if Code 33 is the result of a hard failure or an intermittent problem. A Code 33 will set if:

- Code 21 or 22 is not detected.
- MAP signal indicates greater than 19.5 In. Hg.
- TPS less than 1.6 percent.
- These conditions present for more than 5 seconds.

**2)** This step simulates conditions for a Code 34. If the ECM recognizes the change, circuits No. 416 and 432 are okay. If circuit No. 450 is open, there may also be a Code 15 stored.

### DIAGNOSTIC AIDS

With ignition on and engine stopped, manifold pressure is equal to atmospheric pressure and the signal will be high. MAP sensor is also used for altitude compensation. This information is used by ECM as an indication of vehicle altitude and referred to as barometric pressure. A Code 33 will result if circuit No. 450 is open, or if circuit No. 432 is shorted to voltage or shorted to circuit No. 416.

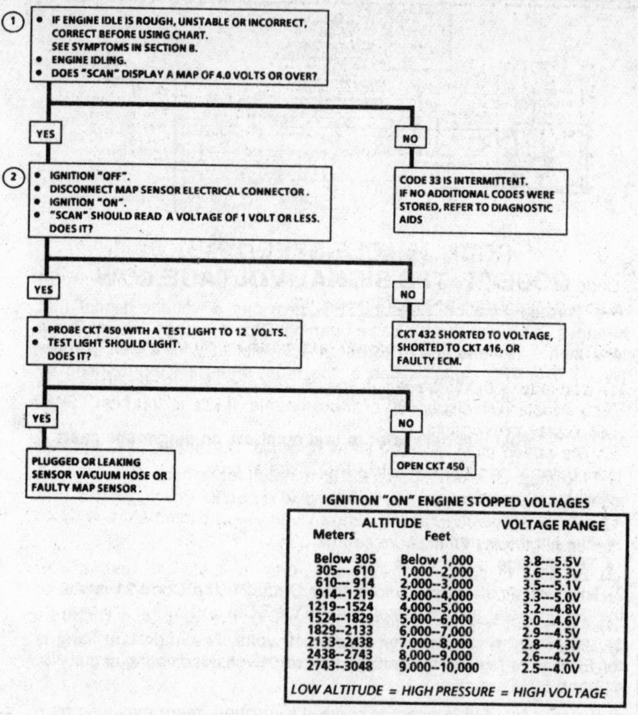
1
• IF ENGINE IDLE IS ROUGH, UNSTABLE OR INCORRECT, CORRECT BEFORE USING CHART. SEE SYMPTOMS IN SECTION B.
• ENGINE IDLING.
• DOES "SCAN" DISPLAY A MAP OF 4.0 VOLTS OR OVER?
YES
NO
CODE 33 IS INTERMITTENT. IF NO ADDITIONAL CODES WERE STORED, REFER TO DIAGNOSTIC AIDS
2
• IGNITION "OFF".
• DISCONNECT MAP SENSOR ELECTRICAL CONNECTOR.
• IGNITION "ON".
• "SCAN" SHOULD READ A VOLTAGE OF 1 VOLT OR LESS. DOES IT?
YES
NO
CKT 432 SHORTED TO VOLTAGE, SHORTED TO CKT 416, OR FAULTY ECM.
• PROBE CKT 450 WITH A TEST LIGHT TO 12 VOLTS.
• TEST LIGHT SHOULD LIGHT. DOES IT?
YES
NO
OPEN CKT 450
PLUGGED OR LEAKING SENSOR VACUUM HOSE OR FAULTY MAP SENSOR.

IGNITION "ON" ENGINE STOPPED VOLTAGES

| ALTITUDE Meters | Feet | VOLTAGE RANGE |
|---|---|---|
| Below 305 | Below 1,000 | 3.8---5.5V |
| 305--- 610 | 1,000--2,000 | 3.6---5.3V |
| 610--- 914 | 2,000--3,000 | 3.5---5.1V |
| 914--1219 | 3,000--4,000 | 3.3---5.0V |
| 1219--1524 | 4,000--5,000 | 3.2---4.8V |
| 1524--1829 | 5,000--6,000 | 3.0---4.6V |
| 1829--2133 | 6,000--7,000 | 2.9---4.5V |
| 2133--2438 | 7,000--8,000 | 2.8---4.3V |
| 2438--2743 | 8,000--9,000 | 2.6---4.2V |
| 2743--3048 | 9,000--10,000 | 2.5---4.0V |

*LOW ALTITUDE = HIGH PRESSURE = HIGH VOLTAGE*

CLEAR CODES AND CONFIRM "CLOSED LOOP" OPERATION AND NO "SERVICE ENGINE SOON" LIGHT.

THE ALDL CONNECTOR IS MOUNTED ON TOP OF THE ECM BEHIND THE PASSENGER SIDE KICK PAD.

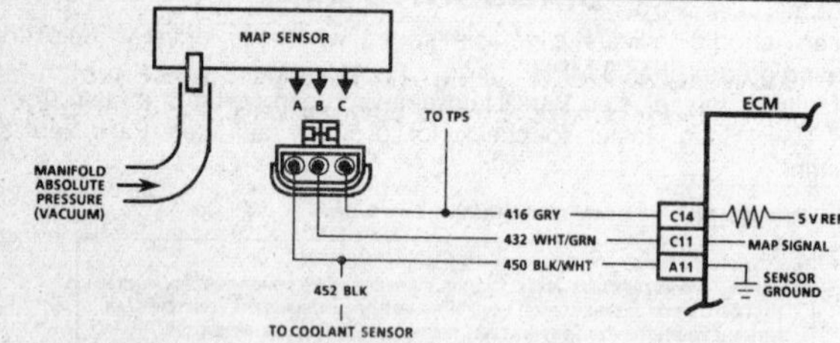
MAP SENSOR
A B C
MANIFOLD ABSOLUTE PRESSURE (VACUUM)
TO TPS
ECM
416 GRY
432 WHT/GRN
450 BLK/WHT
C14
C11
A11
5 V REF
MAP SIGNAL
SENSOR GROUND
452 BLK
TO COOLANT SENSOR

### CODE 34, MAP SIGNAL VOLTAGE LOW

The Manifold Absolute Pressure (MAP) sensor responds to changes in intake manifold pressure (vacuum). The ECM receives this in the form of a voltage signal. This signal will vary from 1-1.5 volts at closed throttle to 4-4.5 volts at WOT (low vacuum).
If the MAP sensor fails, the ECM will substitute a fixed MAP value and use TPS signal to control fuel delivery.

**NOTE: Test numbers refer to test numbers on diagnostic chart.**

**1)** This step will determine if Code 34 is the result of a hard failure or an intermittent problem. Code 34 will set if:

- Code 21 is not being detected.
- Engine RPM is less than 1200.
- MAP signal voltage is too low.

OR

- Code 21 is not being detected.
- MAP reading less than 4.2 In. Hg.
- Engine RPM greater than 1200.
- TPS less than 20 percent.

**2)** Jumping harness terminals B to C, (5 volts to signal), will determine if sensor is at fault, or if problem is in ECM or wiring. Be sure to turn ignition off and back on before checking "Scan" tester to update value of test.

**3)** The "Scan" tester may not display 12 volts. The important thing is that ECM recognizes the voltage is more than 4 volts, indicating the ECM and circuit No. 432 are okay.

### DIAGNOSTIC AIDS

With ignition on and engine stopped, manifold pressure is equal to atmospheric pressure and the signal will be high. MAP sensor is also used for altitude compensation. This information is used by ECM as an indication of vehicle altitude and referred to as barometric pressure. A Code 34 will result if circuits No. 416 or 432 are open or shorted to ground. An internally shorted TPS will cause a Code 34.

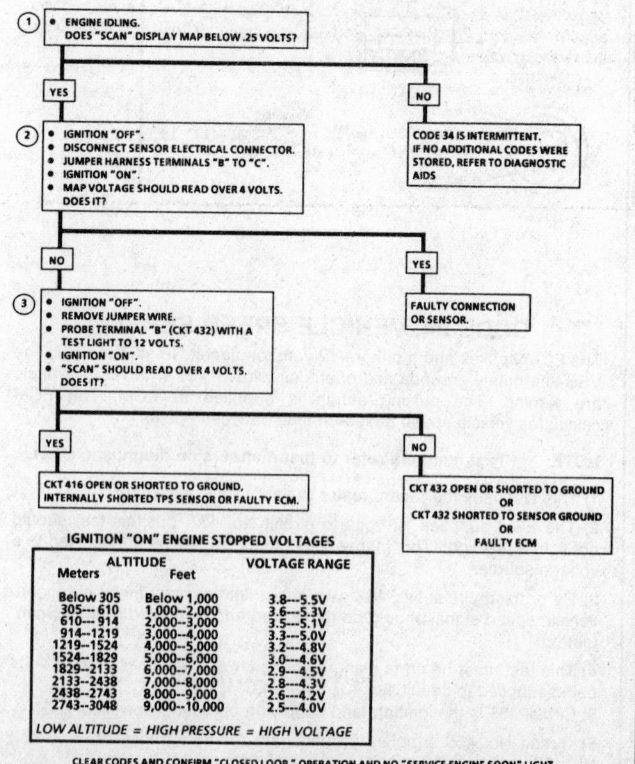
1
• ENGINE IDLING.
DOES "SCAN" DISPLAY MAP BELOW .25 VOLTS?
YES
NO
CODE 34 IS INTERMITTENT. IF NO ADDITIONAL CODES WERE STORED, REFER TO DIAGNOSTIC AIDS
2
• IGNITION "OFF".
• DISCONNECT SENSOR ELECTRICAL CONNECTOR.
• JUMPER HARNESS TERMINALS "B" TO "C".
• IGNITION "ON".
• MAP VOLTAGE SHOULD READ OVER 4 VOLTS. DOES IT?
NO
YES
FAULTY CONNECTION OR SENSOR.
3
• IGNITION "OFF".
• REMOVE JUMPER WIRE.
• PROBE TERMINAL "B" (CKT 432) WITH A TEST LIGHT TO 12 VOLTS.
• IGNITION "ON".
• "SCAN" SHOULD READ OVER 4 VOLTS. DOES IT?
YES
NO
CKT 416 OPEN OR SHORTED TO GROUND, INTERNALLY SHORTED TPS SENSOR OR FAULTY ECM.
CKT 432 OPEN OR SHORTED TO GROUND OR CKT 432 SHORTED TO SENSOR GROUND OR FAULTY ECM

IGNITION "ON" ENGINE STOPPED VOLTAGES

| ALTITUDE Meters | Feet | VOLTAGE RANGE |
|---|---|---|
| Below 305 | Below 1,000 | 3.8---5.5V |
| 305--- 610 | 1,000--2,000 | 3.6---5.3V |
| 610--- 914 | 2,000--3,000 | 3.5---5.1V |
| 914--1219 | 3,000--4,000 | 3.3---5.0V |
| 1219--1524 | 4,000--5,000 | 3.2---4.8V |
| 1524--1829 | 5,000--6,000 | 3.0---4.6V |
| 1829--2133 | 6,000--7,000 | 2.9---4.5V |
| 2133--2438 | 7,000--8,000 | 2.8---4.3V |
| 2438--2743 | 8,000--9,000 | 2.6---4.2V |
| 2743--3048 | 9,000--10,000 | 2.5---4.0V |

*LOW ALTITUDE = HIGH PRESSURE = HIGH VOLTAGE*

CLEAR CODES AND CONFIRM "CLOSED LOOP" OPERATION AND NO "SERVICE ENGINE SOON" LIGHT.

THE ALDL CONNECTOR IS MOUNTED ON TOP OF THE ECM BEHIND THE PASSENGER SIDE KICK PAD.

# 1988 COMPUTERIZED ENGINE CONTROLS
## General Motors LeMans 1.6L TBI (Cont.)

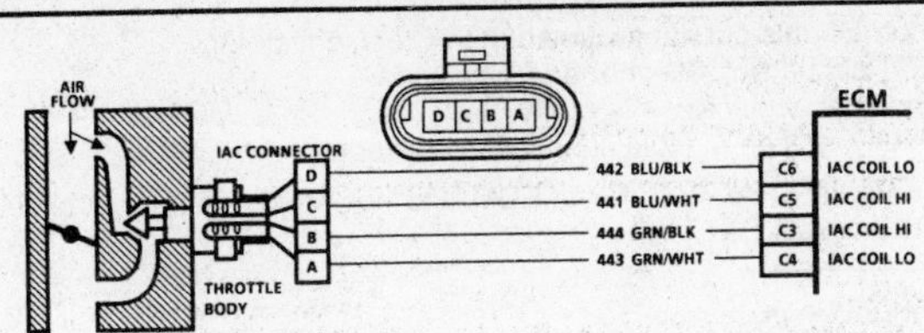
AIR FLOW
IAC CONNECTOR
D C B A
THROTTLE BODY
ECM
442 BLU/BLK
441 BLU/WHT
444 GRN/BLK
443 GRN/WHT
C6
C5
C3
C4
IAC COIL LO
IAC COIL HI
IAC COIL HI
IAC COIL LO

## CODE 35, IDLE SPEED ERROR

Code 35 will set if the closed throttle idle speed is 175 RPM above or below desired idle speed for 20 seconds.

**NOTE: Test numbers refer to test numbers on diagnostic chart.**

**1)** Continue with test, even if engine will not idle. If idle is too low, "Scan" tester will display 80 or more counts. If idle is too high, "Scan" will display zero counts.
Engine speed may vary 200 RPM or more. Disconnect IAC electrical connector. If condition remains, IAC is not at fault.

**2)** When engine was stopped, IAC valve retracted (more air) to a fixed "Park" position for increased airflow during next engine start. A "Scan" tester will display 75 or more counts.

**3)** Be sure to disconnect IAC valve prior to test. The test light will confirm the ECM signals by a steady or flashing light on all circuits.

**4)** There is a remote possibility that one of the circuits is shorted to voltage, which would have been indicated by a steady test light. Disconnect ECM and turn ignition on and probe terminals to check for this condition.

## DIAGNOSTIC AIDS

A slow or unstable idle may be caused by a system problem that cannot be overcome by IAC. If idle is too high, stop engine and plug IAC valve air inlet with Test Tool (BT-8528A). If idle speed is above 900 RPM, locate and correct vacuum leak.
If air/fuel ratio is too lean, "Scan" tester or voltmeter will read an Oxygen ($O_2$) sensor output less than .3 volt. Check for low fuel pressure or water in fuel. A lean air/fuel ratio with $O_2$ sensor output fixed above .8 volt indicates a contaminated $O_2$ sensor, usually silicone. This may also set a Code 45.
If air/fuel ratio is too rich, "Scan" tester or voltmeter will read an $O_2$ sensor output fixed above .8 volt. Check for high fuel pressure or fuel injector leaking. Remove IAC and inspect bore for foriegn material and evidence of valve dragging in bore.

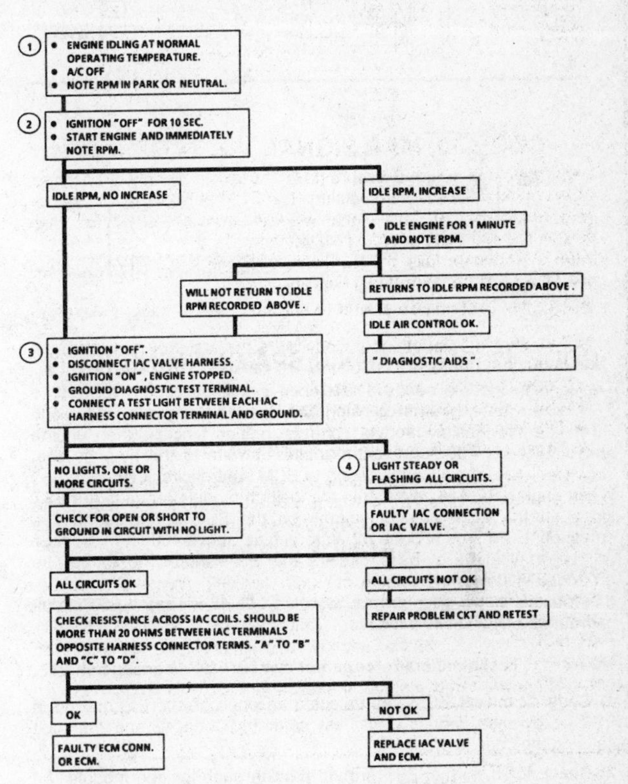
1
• ENGINE IDLING AT NORMAL OPERATING TEMPERATURE.
• A/C OFF
• NOTE RPM IN PARK OR NEUTRAL.
2
• IGNITION "OFF" FOR 10 SEC.
• START ENGINE AND IMMEDIATELY NOTE RPM.
IDLE RPM, NO INCREASE
IDLE RPM, INCREASE
• IDLE ENGINE FOR 1 MINUTE AND NOTE RPM.
WILL NOT RETURN TO IDLE RPM RECORDED ABOVE.
RETURNS TO IDLE RPM RECORDED ABOVE.
IDLE AIR CONTROL OK.
"DIAGNOSTIC AIDS".
3
• IGNITION "OFF".
• DISCONNECT IAC VALVE HARNESS.
• IGNITION "ON", ENGINE STOPPED.
• GROUND DIAGNOSTIC TEST TERMINAL.
• CONNECT A TEST LIGHT BETWEEN EACH IAC HARNESS CONNECTOR TERMINAL AND GROUND.
NO LIGHTS, ONE OR MORE CIRCUITS.
4
LIGHT STEADY OR FLASHING ALL CIRCUITS.
CHECK FOR OPEN OR SHORT TO GROUND IN CIRCUIT WITH NO LIGHT.
FAULTY IAC CONNECTION OR IAC VALVE.
ALL CIRCUITS OK
ALL CIRCUITS NOT OK
REPAIR PROBLEM CKT AND RETEST
CHECK RESISTANCE ACROSS IAC COILS. SHOULD BE MORE THAN 20 OHMS BETWEEN IAC TERMINALS OPPOSITE HARNESS CONNECTOR TERMS. "A" TO "B" AND "C" TO "D".
OK
NOT OK
FAULTY ECM CONN. OR ECM.
REPLACE IAC VALVE AND ECM.

CLEAR CODES AND CONFIRM "CLOSED LOOP" OPERATION AND NO "SERVICE ENGINE SOON" LIGHT.

THE ALDL CONNECTOR IS MOUNTED ON TOP OF THE ECM BEHIND THE PASSENGER SIDE KICK PAD.

# 1988 COMPUTERIZED ENGINE CONTROLS
## General Motors LeMans 1.6L TBI (Cont.)

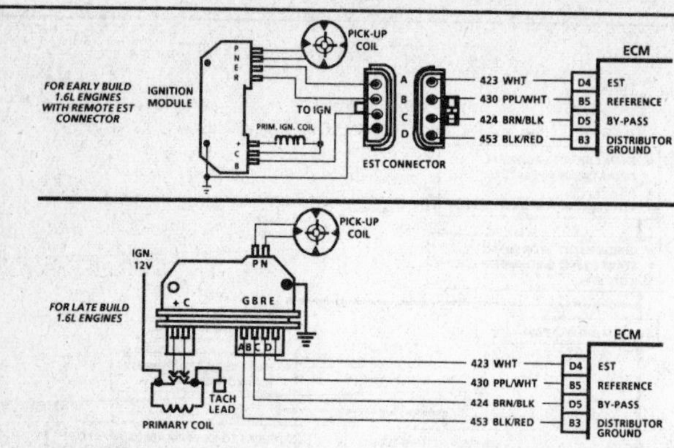
PICK-UP COIL
ECM
FOR EARLY BUILD 1.6L ENGINES WITH REMOTE EST CONNECTOR
IGNITION MODULE
TO IGN
PRIM. IGN. COIL
423 WHT
D4
EST
430 PPL/WHT
B5
REFERENCE
424 BRN/BLK
D5
BY-PASS
453 BLK/RED
B3
DISTRIBUTOR GROUND
EST CONNECTOR
PICK-UP COIL
IGN. 12V
FOR LATE BUILD 1.6L ENGINES
ECM
423 WHT
D4
EST
430 PPL/WHT
B5
REFERENCE
424 BRN/BLK
D5
BY-PASS
453 BLK/RED
B3
DISTRIBUTOR GROUND
TACH LEAD
PRIMARY COIL

## CODE 42, ELECTRONIC SPARK TIMING (EST)

The ignition module sends a reference signal on circuit No. 430 to ECM when the engine is cranking. While engine speed is under 400 RPM, the the ignition module controls ignition timing. When engine speed exceeds 400 RPM, ECM applies 5 volts to the by-pass line, circuit No. 424, to switch the timing to ECM control circuit No. 423. When engine RPM is below 400, the ignition module grounds the EST signal. If the ECM detects voltage on the EST circuit during this condition, ECM sets a Code 42. With engine above 400 RPM, voltage will be applied to by-pass circuit, and EST should no longer be grounded in ignition module.
If by-pass circuit is open or grounded, a Code 42 will set. If EST circuit is grounded, a Code 42 will set.

**NOTE:** **Test numbers refer to test numbers on diagnostic chart.**

**1)** Code 42 means ECM has detected an open or short to ground in EST or by-pass circuits. This test confirms Code 42 and the fault causing the code is present.

**2)** Check for a normal EST ground path through ignition module. An EST circuit No. 423 shorted to ground will also read less than 500 ohms.

**3)** As the test light voltage touches circuit No. 424, the module should switch, causing the ohmmeter to read above 5000 ohms. Ensure module switched, causing ohms to increase.

**4)** If the module did not switched in this test, check for:
- EST circuit No. 423 shorted to ground.
- By-pass circuit No. 424 open.
- Faulty ignition module connection or module.

**5)** Confirms Code 42 is faulty ECM and not an intermittent in circuits No. 423 or 424.

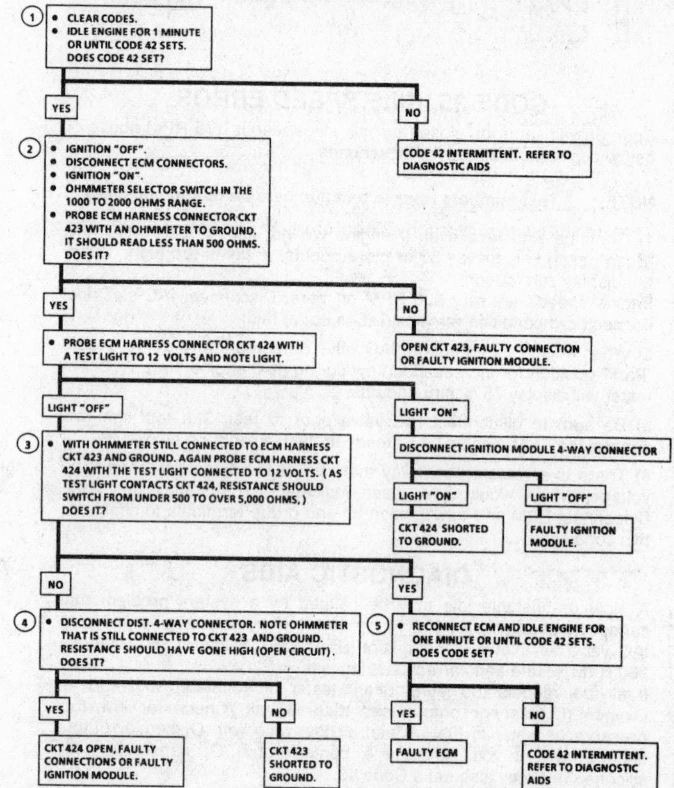
1
• CLEAR CODES.
• IDLE ENGINE FOR 1 MINUTE OR UNTIL CODE 42 SETS. DOES CODE 42 SET?
YES
NO
CODE 42 INTERMITTENT. REFER TO DIAGNOSTIC AIDS
2
• IGNITION "OFF".
• DISCONNECT ECM CONNECTORS.
• IGNITION "ON".
• OHMMETER SELECTOR SWITCH IN THE 1000 TO 2000 OHMS RANGE.
• PROBE ECM HARNESS CONNECTOR CKT 423 WITH AN OHMMETER TO GROUND. IT SHOULD READ LESS THAN 500 OHMS. DOES IT?
YES
NO
• PROBE ECM HARNESS CONNECTOR CKT 424 WITH A TEST LIGHT TO 12 VOLTS AND NOTE LIGHT.
OPEN CKT 423, FAULTY CONNECTION OR FAULTY IGNITION MODULE.
LIGHT "OFF"
LIGHT "ON"
3
• WITH OHMMETER STILL CONNECTED TO ECM HARNESS CKT 423 AND GROUND. AGAIN PROBE ECM HARNESS CKT 424 WITH THE TEST LIGHT CONNECTED TO 12 VOLTS. ( AS TEST LIGHT CONTACTS CKT 424, RESISTANCE SHOULD SWITCH FROM UNDER 500 TO OVER 5,000 OHMS. ) DOES IT?
DISCONNECT IGNITION MODULE 4-WAY CONNECTOR
LIGHT "ON"
LIGHT "OFF"
CKT 424 SHORTED TO GROUND.
FAULTY IGNITION MODULE.
NO
YES
4
• DISCONNECT DIST. 4-WAY CONNECTOR. NOTE OHMMETER THAT IS STILL CONNECTED TO CKT 423 AND GROUND. RESISTANCE SHOULD HAVE GONE HIGH (OPEN CIRCUIT). DOES IT?
5
• RECONNECT ECM AND IDLE ENGINE FOR ONE MINUTE OR UNTIL CODE 42 SETS. DOES CODE SET?
YES
NO
YES
NO
CKT 424 OPEN, FAULTY CONNECTIONS OR FAULTY IGNITION MODULE.
CKT 423 SHORTED TO GROUND.
FAULTY ECM
CODE 42 INTERMITTENT. REFER TO DIAGNOSTIC AIDS

CLEAR CODES AND CONFIRM "CLOSED LOOP" OPERATION AND NO "SERVICE ENGINE SOON" LIGHT.

THE ALDL CONNECTOR IS MOUNTED ON TOP OF THE ECM BEHIND THE PASSENGER SIDE KICK PAD.

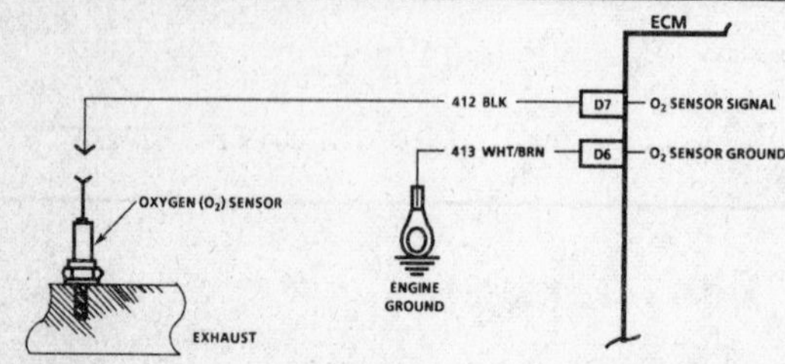
ECM
412 BLK
D7
$O_2$ SENSOR SIGNAL
413 WHT/BRN
D6
$O_2$ SENSOR GROUND
OXYGEN ($O_2$) SENSOR
ENGINE GROUND
EXHAUST

## CODE 44, LEAN EXHAUST INDICATION

The ECM supplies a voltage of about .45 volt between terminals D7 and D6. If measured with 10-megohm voltmeter, this may read as low as .32 volt.
The oxygen sensor varies the voltage within a range of about one volt, if the exhaust is rich, down to about .10 volt if the exhaust is lean. The sensor is like an open circuit and produces no voltage when below 600°F (316°C). An open sensor circuit or cold sensor causes "open loop" operation.

Code 44 is set when the oxygen ($O_2$) sensor signal voltage on circuit No. 412 remains below .2 volt for about one minute, and the system is operating in "open loop".

### DIAGNOSTIC AIDS

Using "Scan" tester, observe the block learn value at different engine RPM. If the condition for Code 44 exists, block learn value will be around 150.
- $O_2$ sensor wire pigtail may be mispositioned and contacting exhaust manifold.
- Check for ground in wire between connector and sensor.
- Even a small amount of water contamination near the in-tank fuel pump inlet can be delivered to the injector causing a lean exhaust and setting a Code 44.
- Low fuel pressure can cause a lean exhaust. It may be necessary to monitor fuel pressure while driving car at various road speeds and engine loads.
- Exhaust leaks ahead of $O_2$ sensor can dilute exhaust gases causing a false lean signal and a Code 44.

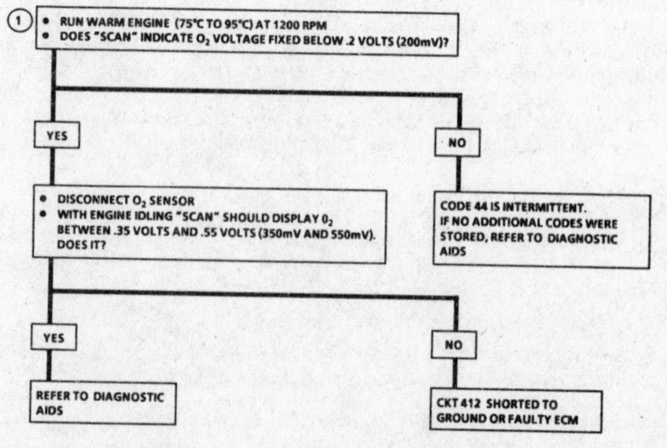
1
• RUN WARM ENGINE (75°C TO 95°C) AT 1200 RPM
• DOES "SCAN" INDICATE $O_2$ VOLTAGE FIXED BELOW .2 VOLTS (200mV)?
YES
NO
• DISCONNECT $O_2$ SENSOR
• WITH ENGINE IDLING "SCAN" SHOULD DISPLAY $O_2$ BETWEEN .35 VOLTS AND .55 VOLTS (350mV AND 550mV). DOES IT?
CODE 44 IS INTERMITTENT. IF NO ADDITIONAL CODES WERE STORED, REFER TO DIAGNOSTIC AIDS
YES
NO
REFER TO DIAGNOSTIC AIDS
CKT 412 SHORTED TO GROUND OR FAULTY ECM

CLEAR CODES AND CONFIRM "CLOSED LOOP" OPERATION AND NO "SERVICE ENGINE SOON" LIGHT.

THE ALDL CONNECTOR IS MOUNTED ON TOP OF THE ECM BEHIND THE PASSENGER SIDE KICK PAD.

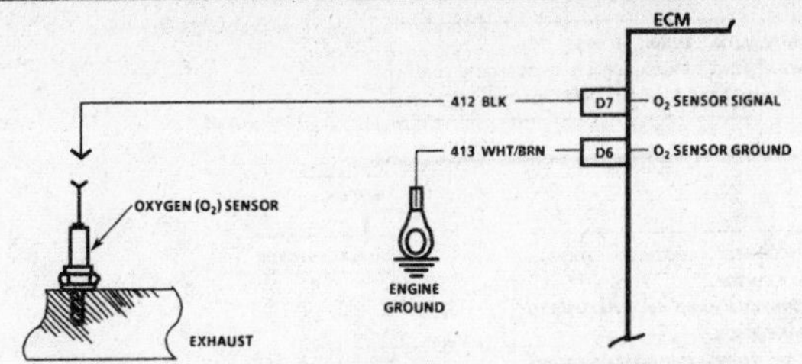
ECM
412 BLK
D7
$O_2$ SENSOR SIGNAL
413 WHT/BRN
D6
$O_2$ SENSOR GROUND
OXYGEN ($O_2$) SENSOR
ENGINE GROUND
EXHAUST

## CODE 45, RICH EXHAUST INDICATION

The ECM supplies a voltage of about .45 volt between terminals D7 and D6. If measured with 10-megohm digital voltmeter, this may read as low as .32 volt.

The oxygen sensor varies the voltage within a range of about one volt, if the exhaust is rich, down to about .10 volt if the exhaust is lean. The sensor is like an open circuit and produces no voltage when below 600°F (316°C). An open sensor circuit or cold sensor causes "open loop" operation.

Code 45 is set when $O_2$ sensor voltage on circuit No. 412 remains above .8 volt for one minute and system is in "closed loop".

### DIAGNOSTIC AIDS

Code 45 is most likely caused by:

- Fuel pressure too high. ECM can compensate for some increase in fuel pressure. However, if fuel pressure gets too high, a Code 45 will set.
- An open ground in circuit No. 450H may result in electrical noise interference causing faulty engine RPM signals to ECM. Engine tachometer will also show higher than actual readings.
- Check for fuel saturation of canister and for faulty canister purge control.
- A false MAP sensor signal indicating manifold vacuum lower than actual can cause system to have rich exhaust, setting a Code 45.
- An intermittent TPS signal giving false indication of engine acceleration will cause rich exhaust and Code 45 to set.
- A contaminated $O_2$ sensor will provide a false high reading to ECM. The ECM will reduce fuel delivery, causing a severe surge driveability problem.
- EGR valve leaking causing dilution of exhaust gases will cause ECM to drive fuel system rich.

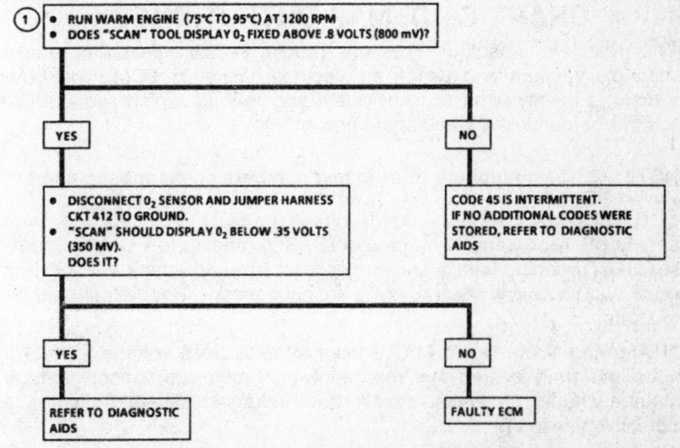
1
• RUN WARM ENGINE (75°C TO 95°C) AT 1200 RPM
• DOES "SCAN" TOOL DISPLAY $O_2$ FIXED ABOVE .8 VOLTS (800 mV)?
YES
NO
• DISCONNECT $O_2$ SENSOR AND JUMPER HARNESS CKT 412 TO GROUND.
• "SCAN" SHOULD DISPLAY $O_2$ BELOW .35 VOLTS (350 MV).
DOES IT?
CODE 45 IS INTERMITTENT. IF NO ADDITIONAL CODES WERE STORED, REFER TO DIAGNOSTIC AIDS
YES
NO
REFER TO DIAGNOSTIC AIDS
FAULTY ECM

CLEAR CODES AND CONFIRM "CLOSED LOOP" OPERATION AND NO "SERVICE ENGINE SOON" LIGHT.

THE ALDL CONNECTOR IS MOUNTED ON TOP OF THE ECM BEHIND THE PASSENGER SIDE KICK PAD.

## CODE 51, FAULTY MEM-CAL

Check that MEM-CAL is properly seated. If okay, replace MEM-CAL and recheck. If Code 51 reappears, replace ECM.

## CODE 53, SYSTEM OVERVOLTAGE

Code 53 will set if charging voltage at ECM terminal B2 is over 16.9 volts for more than 10 seconds. Check and repair charging system.

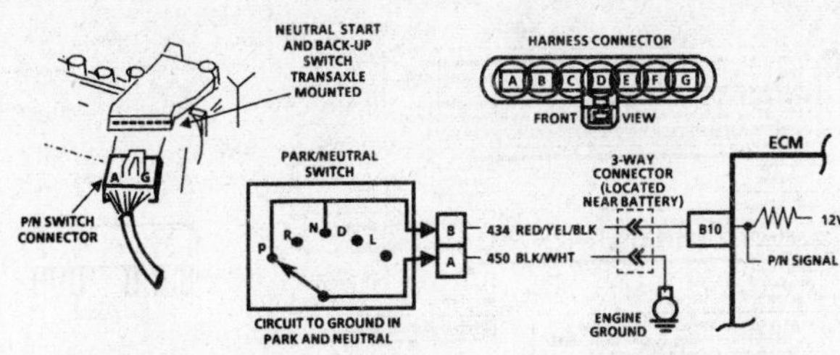
NEUTRAL START AND BACK-UP SWITCH TRANSAXLE MOUNTED
HARNESS CONNECTOR
A B C D E F G
FRONT VIEW
P/N SWITCH CONNECTOR
PARK/NEUTRAL SWITCH
P R N D L
CIRCUIT TO GROUND IN PARK AND NEUTRAL
3-WAY CONNECTOR (LOCATED NEAR BATTERY)
B
A
434 RED/YEL/BLK
450 BLK/WHT
ECM
B10
12V
P/N SIGNAL
ENGINE GROUND

## CHART C-1A, PARK/NEUTRAL SWITCH

The Park/Neutral switch contacts are closed to ground in Park or Neutral, and open in all other ranges. The ECM supplies ignition voltage through a current limiting resistor to circuit No. 434, and senses a closed switch when voltage in circuit No. 434 drops to less than one volt. The ECM uses the Park/Neutral switch signal as one of the inputs to control idle air control and spark timing.

**NOTE:** **Test numbers refer to test numbers on diagnostic chart.**

**1)** Checks for a closed switch to ground in Park position. Different makes of "Scan" testers will read value differently. Refer to tester operation manual for type of display used.

**2)** Checks for an open switch in Drive range.

**3)** Be sure "Scan" tester indicates drive, even while wiggling shifter to test for an intermittent or misadjusted switch in Drive range.

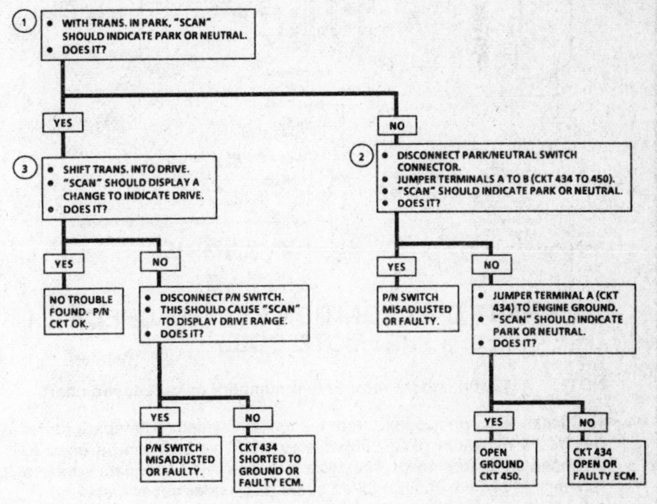
1
• WITH TRANS. IN PARK, "SCAN" SHOULD INDICATE PARK OR NEUTRAL.
• DOES IT?
YES
NO
3
• SHIFT TRANS. INTO DRIVE.
• "SCAN" SHOULD DISPLAY A CHANGE TO INDICATE DRIVE.
• DOES IT?
2
• DISCONNECT PARK/NEUTRAL SWITCH CONNECTOR.
• JUMPER TERMINALS A TO B (CKT 434 TO 450).
• "SCAN" SHOULD INDICATE PARK OR NEUTRAL.
• DOES IT?
YES
NO
NO TROUBLE FOUND. P/N CKT OK.
• DISCONNECT P/N SWITCH.
• THIS SHOULD CAUSE "SCAN" TO DISPLAY DRIVE RANGE.
• DOES IT?
YES
NO
P/N SWITCH MISADJUSTED OR FAULTY.
• JUMPER TERMINAL A (CKT 434) TO ENGINE GROUND.
• "SCAN" SHOULD INDICATE PARK OR NEUTRAL.
• DOES IT?
YES
NO
P/N SWITCH MISADJUSTED OR FAULTY.
CKT 434 SHORTED TO GROUND OR FAULTY ECM.
YES
NO
OPEN GROUND CKT 450.
CKT 434 OPEN OR FAULTY ECM.

CLEAR CODES AND CONFIRM "CLOSED LOOP" OPERATION AND NO "SERVICE ENGINE SOON" LIGHT.

THE ALDL CONNECTOR IS MOUNTED ON TOP OF THE ECM BEHIND THE PASSENGER SIDE KICK PAD.

# 1988 COMPUTERIZED ENGINE CONTROLS
## General Motors LeMans 1.6L TBI (Cont.)

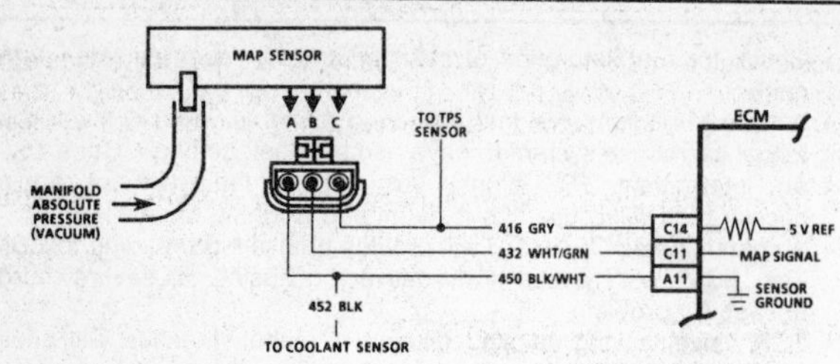

MAP SENSOR
A B C
TO TPS SENSOR
ECM
MANIFOLD ABSOLUTE PRESSURE (VACUUM)
416 GRY
432 WHT/GRN
450 BLK/WHT
C14
C11
A11
5 V REF
MAP SIGNAL
SENSOR GROUND
452 BLK
TO COOLANT SENSOR


### CHART C-1D, MAP OUTPUT CHECK

The Manifold Absolute Pressure (MAP) sensor measures intake manifold vacuum and sends an electrical signal to ECM. The MAP sensor is mainly used to to calculate engine load, which allows ECM to control fuel delivery and spark timing.

**NOTE: Test numbers refer to test numbers on diagnostic chart.**

**1)** Checks MAP sensor output voltage to ECM. This voltage, with engine off, represents a barometer (BARO) reading to ECM. Comparing BARO reading with a known good vehicle, with same sensor, is a good way to check accuracy of a suspect sensor. Reading should be the same ± .4 volt.

**2)** Applying 10 in. Hg to MAP sensor should cause voltage to be 1.2 volts less than in step **1**). When applying vacuum to sensor, voltage change should be immediate. A slow changing sensor indicates a defective sensor.

**3)** Check vacuum hose to sensor for leaks or restrictions. Ensure no other vacuum hoses are connected to MAP sensor vacuum hose. The engine must be running in this step or the "Scan" tester will not detect a change in voltage. It is normal for the SES light to come on and for a Code 33 to set in memory. Clear code when test is complete.

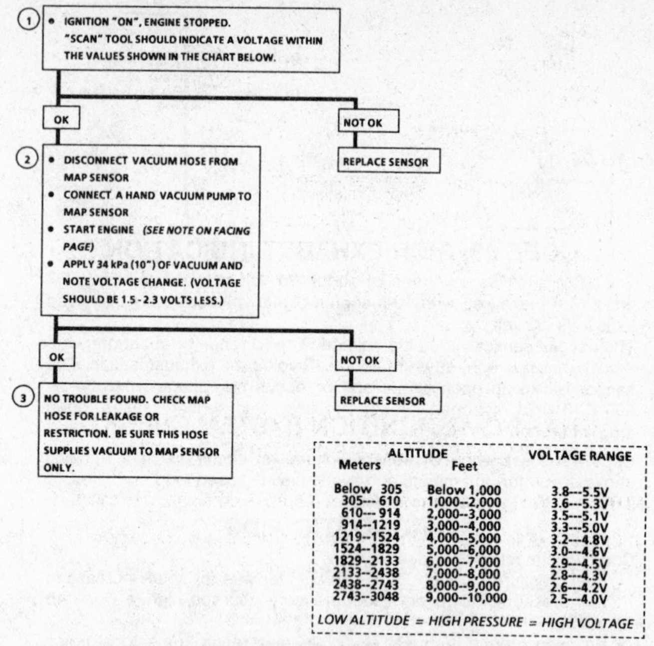

1
• IGNITION "ON", ENGINE STOPPED.
"SCAN" TOOL SHOULD INDICATE A VOLTAGE WITHIN THE VALUES SHOWN IN THE CHART BELOW.
OK
NOT OK
REPLACE SENSOR
2
• DISCONNECT VACUUM HOSE FROM MAP SENSOR
• CONNECT A HAND VACUUM PUMP TO MAP SENSOR
• START ENGINE (SEE NOTE ON FACING PAGE)
• APPLY 34 kPa (10") OF VACUUM AND NOTE VOLTAGE CHANGE. (VOLTAGE SHOULD BE 1.5 - 2.3 VOLTS LESS.)
OK
NOT OK
REPLACE SENSOR
3
NO TROUBLE FOUND. CHECK MAP HOSE FOR LEAKAGE OR RESTRICTION. BE SURE THIS HOSE SUPPLIES VACUUM TO MAP SENSOR ONLY.


| ALTITUDE Meters | Feet | VOLTAGE RANGE |
|---|---|---|
| Below 305 | Below 1,000 | 3.8---5.5V |
| 305--- 610 | 1,000--2,000 | 3.6---5.3V |
| 610--- 914 | 2,000--3,000 | 3.5---5.1V |
| 914--1219 | 3,000--4,000 | 3.3---5.0V |
| 1219--1524 | 4,000--5,000 | 3.2---4.8V |
| 1524--1829 | 5,000--6,000 | 3.0---4.6V |
| 1829--2133 | 6,000--7,000 | 2.9---4.5V |
| 2133--2438 | 7,000--8,000 | 2.8---4.3V |
| 2438--2743 | 8,000--9,000 | 2.6---4.2V |
| 2743--3048 | 9,000--10,000 | 2.5---4.0V |

*LOW ALTITUDE = HIGH PRESSURE = HIGH VOLTAGE*

CLEAR CODES AND CONFIRM "CLOSED LOOP" OPERATION AND NO "SERVICE ENGINE SOON" LIGHT.

THE ALDL CONNECTOR IS MOUNTED ON TOP OF THE ECM BEHIND THE PASSENGER SIDE KICK PAD.

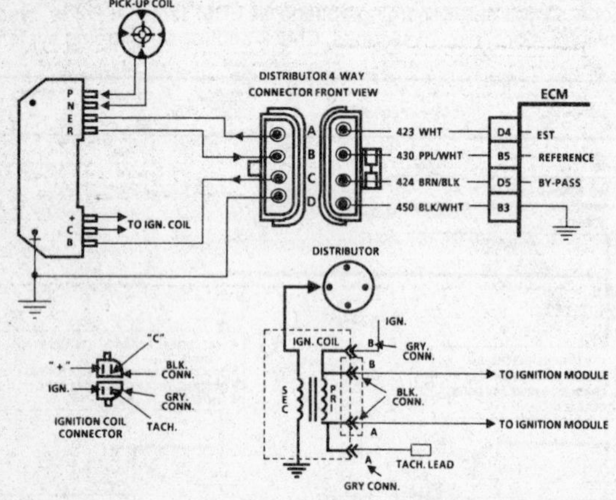

PICK-UP COIL
DISTRIBUTOR 4 WAY CONNECTOR FRONT VIEW
ECM
P N E R
C B
TO IGN. COIL
A B C D
423 WHT
430 PPL/WHT
424 BRN/BLK
450 BLK/WHT
D4
B5
D5
B3
EST
REFERENCE
BY-PASS
DISTRIBUTOR
IGN.
IGN. COIL
GRY. CONN.
BLK. CONN.
TO IGNITION MODULE
TO IGNITION MODULE
SEC
PRI
TACH. LEAD
GRY CONN.
"C"
"+"
IGN.
TACH.
IGNITION COIL CONNECTOR


### CHART C-4A, IGNITION SYSTEM CHECK (REMOTE COIL)

**NOTE: Test numbers refer to test numbers on diagnostic chart.**

**1)** Checks for proper output from the ignition system. The spark tester requires a minimum of 25,000 volts to fire. This test can be used to diagnose an ignition miss. The system may provide adequate spark to run engine, but not enough to fire spark plug under heavy load.

**1A)** If spark occurs with EST disconnected, pick-up coil output is too low for EST operation.

**2)** A spark indicates problem is a faulty distributor cap or rotor.

**3)** Normally there should be battery voltage at "+" terminal. Low voltage would indicate an open or high resistance circuit from distributor to coil or ignition switch.

**4)** Checks for a shorted module or grounded circuit from ignition coil to module. The distributor module should be turned off so normal voltage will be 12 volts. If the module is turned on, the voltage will drop but should be above one volt. Failure of this test can cause ignition coil to fail due to excessive heat. With an open ignition coil primary winding, a small amount of voltage will leak through the module from the "Bat." terminal to the tachometer terminal.

**5)** Checks for an open module or circuit. With 12 volts applied to the module "P" terminal, module should turn on and voltage should drop to 7-9 volts.

**6)** This should turn module off and cause a spark. If no spark occurs, the fault is most likely in ignition coil.

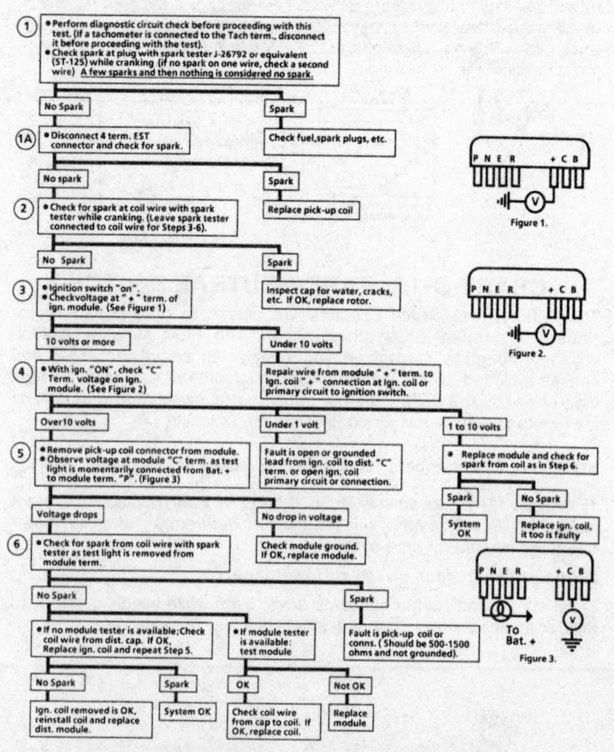

1
• Perform diagnostic circuit check before proceeding with this test. (If a tachometer is connected to the Tach term., disconnect it before proceeding with the test).
• Check spark at plug with spark tester J-26792 or equivalent (ST-125) while cranking (if no spark on one wire, check a second wire) A few sparks and then nothing is considered no spark.
No Spark
Spark
1A
• Disconnect 4 term. EST connector and check for spark.
Check fuel,spark plugs, etc.
No spark
Spark
2
• Check for spark at coil wire with spark tester while cranking. (Leave spark tester connected to coil wire for Steps 3-6).
Replace pick-up coil
No Spark
Spark
3
• Ignition switch "on".
• Checkvoltage at "+" term. of ign. module. (See Figure 1)
Inspect cap for water, cracks, etc. If OK, replace rotor.
10 volts or more
Under 10 volts
4
• With ign. "ON", check "C" Term. voltage on Ign. module. (See Figure 2)
Repair wire from module "+" term. to Ign. coil "+" connection at Ign. coil or primary circuit to ignition switch.
Over10 volts
Under 1 volt
1 to 10 volts
5
• Remove pick-up coil connector from module.
• Observe voltage at module "C" term. as test light is momentarily connected from Bat. + to module term. "P". (Figure 3)
Fault is open or grounded lead from ign. coil to dist. "C" term. or open ign. coil primary circuit or connection.
• Replace module and check for spark from coil as in Step 6.
Spark
No Spark
System OK
Replace ign. coil, it too is faulty
Voltage drops
No drop in voltage
6
• Check for spark from coil wire with spark tester as test light is removed from module term.
Check module ground. If OK, replace module.
No Spark
Spark
• If no module tester is available;Check coil wire from dist. cap. If OK, Replace ign. coil and repeat Step 5.
• If module tester is available: test module
Fault is pick-up coil or conns. ( Should be 500-1500 ohms and not grounded).
No Spark
Spark
OK
Not OK
Ign. coil removed is OK, reinstall coil and replace dist. module.
System OK
Check coil wire from cap to coil. If OK, replace coil.
Replace module
P N E R
+ C B
V
To Bat. +

Figure 1.
Figure 2.
Figure 3.

CLEAR CODES AND CONFIRM "CLOSED LOOP" OPERATION AND NO "SERVICE ENGINE SOON" LIGHT.

THE ALDL CONNECTOR IS MOUNTED ON TOP OF THE ECM BEHIND THE PASSENGER SIDE KICK PAD.

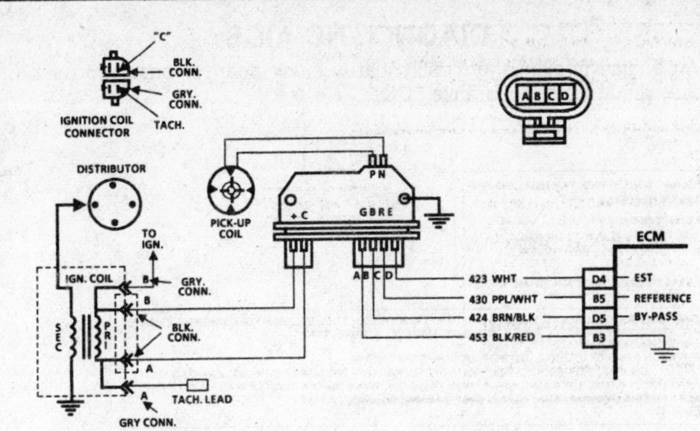
"C"
BLK. CONN.
GRY. CONN.
IGNITION COIL CONNECTOR
TACH.
A B C D
DISTRIBUTOR
PICK-UP COIL
P N
+ C
G B R E
TO IGN.
IGN. COIL
B
GRY. CONN.
B
S E C
P R I
BLK. CONN.
A
A
TACH. LEAD
GRY CONN.
A B C D
ECM
423 WHT
430 PPL/WHT
424 BRN/BLK
453 BLK/RED
D4
B5
D5
B3
EST
REFERENCE
BY-PASS

## CHART C-4B, IGNITION SYSTEM CHECK (REMOTE COIL-SEALED MODULE)

**NOTE:** **Test numbers refer to test numbers on diagnostic chart.**

**1)** Check 2 wires to ensure an open is not present in spark plug wire.

**1A)** If spark occurs with EST connector disconnected, pick-up coil output is too low for EST operation.

**2)** A spark indicates problem is in distributor cap or rotor.

**3)** Normally there should be battery voltage at "C" and "+" terminals. Low voltage would indicate an open or a high resistance circuit from the distributor to the coil or ignition switch. If "C" terminal voltage was low but "+" is 10 volts or more, circuit from from "C" terminal to ignition coil or ignition coil primary is open.

**4)** Checks for a shorted module or grounded circuit from the ignition coil to the module. The distributor module should be turned off so normal voltage (12 volts) is present. If module is turned on, the voltage would be low but above one volt. Failure of this test can cause ignition coil to fail due to excessive heat. With an open ignition coil primary winding, a small amount of voltage will leak through the module from the "Bat." terminal to the tachometer terminal.

**5)** Applying a voltage of 1.5-8 volts to module terminal "P" should turn module on and the tach terminal voltage will drop to 7-9 volts. This test will determine if the module or coil is faulty, or if the pick-up coil is not generating the proper signal to turn module on. This test can be performed by using a DC battery of 1.5-8 volts. The use of the test light is to allow the "P" terminal to be probed more easily.

Some digital multi-meters can be used to trigger the module by selecting ohms, usually the diode position. In this position the meter may have a voltage across it's terminals which can be used to trigger module.

**6)** This should turn off the module and cause a spark. If no spark occurs, The fault is most likely in the ignition coil.

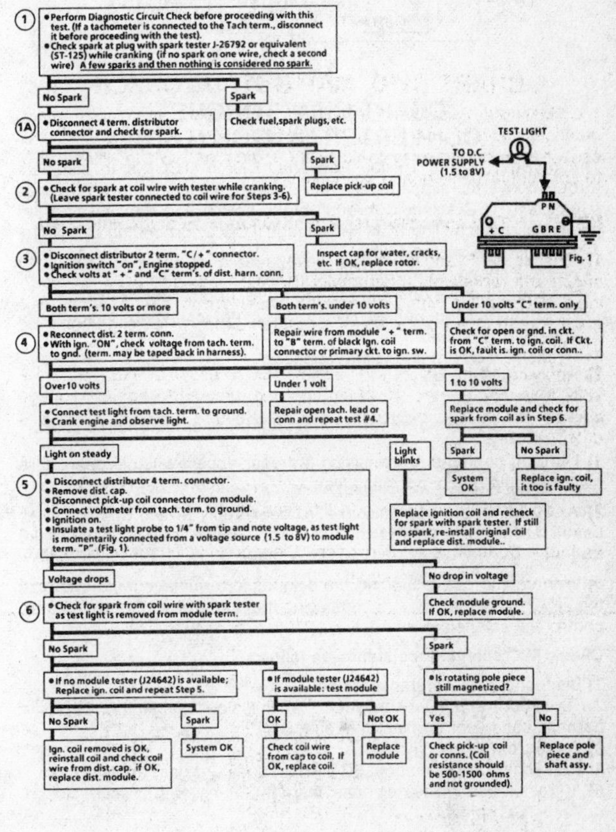
1
• Perform Diagnostic Circuit Check before proceeding with this test. (If a tachometer is connected to the Tach term., disconnect it before proceeding with the test).
• Check spark at plug with spark tester J-26792 or equivalent (ST-125) while cranking (if no spark on one wire, check a second wire) A few sparks and then nothing is considered no spark.
No Spark
Spark
1A
• Disconnect 4 term. distributor connector and check for spark.
Check fuel,spark plugs, etc.
No spark
Spark
2
• Check for spark at coil wire with tester while cranking. (Leave spark tester connected to coil wire for Steps 3-6).
Replace pick-up coil
TEST LIGHT
TO D.C. POWER SUPPLY (1.5 to 8V)
P N
+ C
G B R E
Fig. 1
No Spark
Spark
3
• Disconnect distributor 2 term. "C/+" connector.
• Ignition switch "on", Engine stopped.
• Check volts at "+" and "C" term's. of dist. harn. conn.
Inspect cap for water, cracks, etc. If OK, replace rotor.
Both term's. 10 volts or more
Both term's. under 10 volts
Under 10 volts "C" term. only
4
• Reconnect dist. 2 term. conn.
• With ign. "ON", check voltage from tach. term. to gnd. (term. may be taped back in harness).
Repair wire from module "+" term. to "B" term. of black Ign. coil connector or primary ckt. to ign. sw.
Check for open or gnd. in ckt. from "C" term. to ign. coil. If Ckt. is OK, fault is. ign. coil or conn..
Over10 volts
Under 1 volt
1 to 10 volts
• Connect test light from tach. term. to ground.
• Crank engine and observe light.
Repair open tach. lead or conn and repeat test #4.
Replace module and check for spark from coil as in Step 6.
Light on steady
Light blinks
Spark
No Spark
System OK
Replace ign. coil, it too is faulty
5
• Disconnect distributor 4 term. connector.
• Remove dist. cap.
• Disconnect pick-up coil connector from module.
• Connect voltmeter from tach. term. to ground.
• Ignition on.
• Insulate a test light probe to 1/4" from tip and note voltage, as test light is momentarily connected from a voltage source (1.5 to 8V) to module term. "P". (Fig. 1).
Replace ignition coil and recheck for spark with spark tester. If still no spark, re-install original coil and replace dist. module..
Voltage drops
No drop in voltage
6
• Check for spark from coil wire with spark tester as test light is removed from module term.
Check module ground. If OK, replace module.
No Spark
Spark
• If no module tester (J24642) is available; Replace ign. coil and repeat Step 5.
• If module tester (J24642) is available: test module
• Is rotating pole piece still magnetized?
No Spark
Spark
OK
Not OK
Yes
No
Ign. coil removed is OK, reinstall coil and check coil wire from dist. cap. if OK, replace dist. module.
System OK
Check coil wire from cap to coil. If OK, replace coil.
Replace module
Check pick-up coil or conns. (Coil resistance should be 500-1500 ohms and not grounded).
Replace pole piece and shaft assy.

# 1988 COMPUTERIZED ENGINE CONTROLS
## General Motors LeMans 1.6L TBI (Cont.)

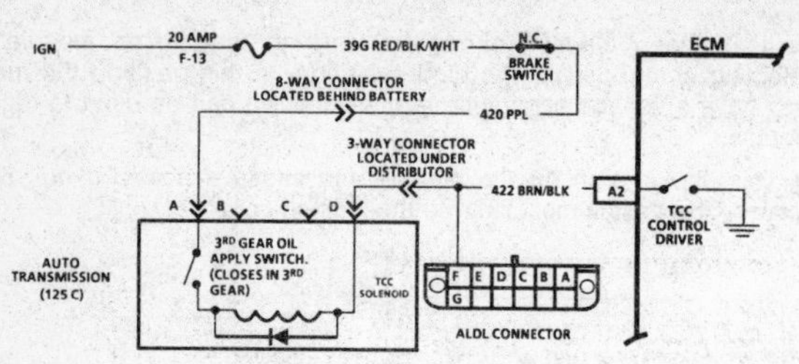

IGN
20 AMP
F-13
39G RED/BLK/WHT
N.C.
BRAKE SWITCH
ECM
8-WAY CONNECTOR LOCATED BEHIND BATTERY
420 PPL
3-WAY CONNECTOR LOCATED UNDER DISTRIBUTOR
422 BRN/BLK
A2
TCC CONTROL DRIVER
A B C D
3RD GEAR OIL APPLY SWITCH. (CLOSES IN 3RD GEAR)
AUTO TRANSMISSION (125 C)
TCC SOLENOID
F E D C B A
G
ALDL CONNECTOR


## CHART C-8A, TORQUE CONVERTER CLUTCH (TCC)

The purpose of the Torque Converter Clutch (TCC) is to eliminate torque converter slippage at cruise speed. Fused battery power is supplied to TCC solenoid through brake switch and transmission 3rd gear apply switch. The ECM will engage TCC by grounding circuit No. 422 to energize solenoid when:

- Vehicle speed is between 26-40 MPH.
- Engine at normal operating temperature, above 156°F (70°C).
- Throttle Position Sensor (TPS) output not changing, indicating a steady road speed.
- Transmission 3rd gear switch closed.
- Brake switch closed.

**NOTE: Test numbers refer to test numbers on diagnostic chart.**

**1)** Light off confirms transmission 3rd gear apply switch is open. This switch should be open for this test.

**2)** At 30 MPH, the transmission 3rd gear apply switch should close. Test light will come on and confirm voltage supply, and a closed brake switch.

**3)** With engine off, grounding the diagnostic terminal should energize the TCC solenoid. This test checks the capability of the ECM to control the solenoid.

**Check TCC solenoid resistance as follows:**

**1)** Disconnect TCC at transmission.
**2)** Connect ohmmeter between transmission connector, opposite harness connector terminals "A" and "D".
**3)** Raise front wheels.
**4)** Run engine in Drive about 30 MPH to close 3rd gear apply switch.
**5)** If resistance measures less than 20 ohms with switch closed, replace TCC solenoid.

### DIAGNOSTIC AIDS

An engine coolant thermostat that is stuck open or opens too soon may result in an inoperative TCC.

USING A "SCAN" TOOL, CHECK THE FOLLOWING AND CORRECT IF NECESSARY:
- COOLANT TEMPERATURE SHOULD BE ABOVE 65°C.
- TPS - BE SURE TPS SIGNAL IS NOT ERRATIC.
- VSS - SHOULD INDICATE VSS WITH WHEELS TURNING.
- CODES - IF 24 IS PRESENT, SEE CODE CHART 24.

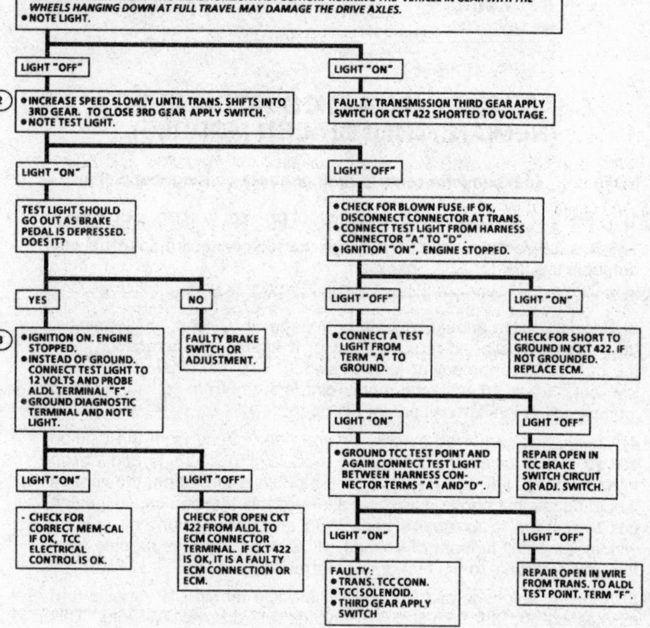

1
• PERFORM MECHANICAL CHECKS, SUCH AS LINKAGE, TRANS FLUID LEVEL, ETC., BEFORE USING THIS CHART.
• CONNECT TEST LIGHT FROM TCC TEST POINT, ALDL TERM "F" AND GROUND.
• RAISE DRIVE WHEELS.
• START AND IDLE ENGINE IN DRIVE. DO NOT DEPRESS BRAKE PEDAL.
• "NOTICE:" DO NOT PERFORM THIS TEST WITHOUT SUPPORTING THE LOWER CONTROL ARMS SO THAT THE DRIVE AXLES ARE IN A NORMAL HORIZONTAL POSITION. RUNNING THE VEHICLE IN GEAR WITH THE WHEELS HANGING DOWN AT FULL TRAVEL MAY DAMAGE THE DRIVE AXLES.
• NOTE LIGHT.
LIGHT "OFF"
LIGHT "ON"
2
• INCREASE SPEED SLOWLY UNTIL TRANS. SHIFTS INTO 3RD GEAR. TO CLOSE 3RD GEAR APPLY SWITCH.
• NOTE TEST LIGHT.
FAULTY TRANSMISSION THIRD GEAR APPLY SWITCH OR CKT 422 SHORTED TO VOLTAGE.
LIGHT "ON"
LIGHT "OFF"
TEST LIGHT SHOULD GO OUT AS BRAKE PEDAL IS DEPRESSED. DOES IT?
• CHECK FOR BLOWN FUSE. IF OK, DISCONNECT CONNECTOR AT TRANS.
• CONNECT TEST LIGHT FROM HARNESS CONNECTOR "A" TO "D".
• IGNITION "ON", ENGINE STOPPED.
YES
NO
LIGHT "OFF"
LIGHT "ON"
3
• IGNITION ON. ENGINE STOPPED.
• INSTEAD OF GROUND. CONNECT TEST LIGHT TO 12 VOLTS AND PROBE ALDL TERMINAL "F".
• GROUND DIAGNOSTIC TERMINAL AND NOTE LIGHT.
FAULTY BRAKE SWITCH OR ADJUSTMENT.
• CONNECT A TEST LIGHT FROM TERM "A" TO GROUND.
CHECK FOR SHORT TO GROUND IN CKT 422. IF NOT GROUNDED, REPLACE ECM.
LIGHT "ON"
LIGHT "OFF"
• GROUND TCC TEST POINT AND AGAIN CONNECT TEST LIGHT BETWEEN HARNESS CONNECTOR TERMS "A" AND "D".
REPAIR OPEN IN TCC BRAKE SWITCH CIRCUIT OR ADJ. SWITCH.
LIGHT "ON"
LIGHT "OFF"
- CHECK FOR CORRECT MEM-CAL IF OK, TCC ELECTRICAL CONTROL IS OK.
CHECK FOR OPEN CKT 422 FROM ALDL TO ECM CONNECTOR TERMINAL. IF CKT 422 IS OK, IT IS A FAULTY ECM CONNECTION OR ECM.
LIGHT "ON"
LIGHT "OFF"
FAULTY:
• TRANS. TCC CONN.
• TCC SOLENOID.
• THIRD GEAR APPLY SWITCH
REPAIR OPEN IN WIRE FROM TRANS. TO ALDL TEST POINT. TERM "F".


CLEAR CODES AND CONFIRM "CLOSED LOOP" OPERATION AND NO "SERVICE ENGINE SOON" LIGHT.

THE ALDL CONNECTOR IS MOUNTED ON TOP OF THE ECM BEHIND THE PASSENGER SIDE KICK PAD.

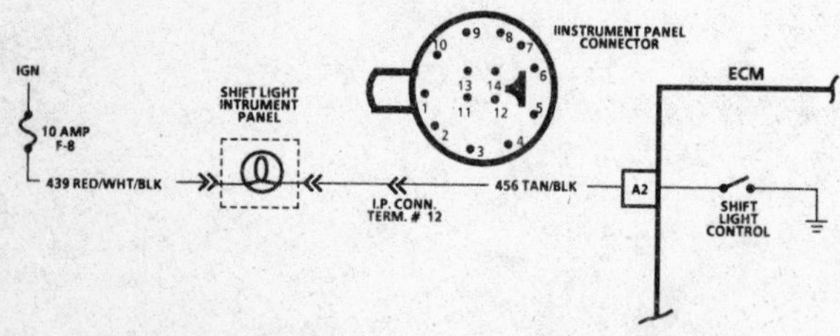

INSTRUMENT PANEL CONNECTOR
IGN
SHIFT LIGHT INTRUMENT PANEL
10 AMP
F-8
439 RED/WHT/BLK
I.P. CONN. TERM. # 12
456 TAN/BLK
A2
ECM
SHIFT LIGHT CONTROL


## CHART C-8B, SHIFT LIGHT CHECK

The shift light indicates the optimum shift point for manual transmission to achieve best fuel economy. The light is controlled by ECM by grounding circuit No. 456.
The ECM uses information from coolant temperature, TPS, VSS and engine RPM to determine when to turn light on.

**NOTE: Test numbers refer to test numbers on diagnostic chart.**

**1)** This should not turn on the shift light. If it does, there is a short to ground in circuit No. 456 or a fault in ECM.

**2)** When diagnostic terminal is grounded, the ECM should ground circuit No. 456, and shift light should come on.

**3)** This checks the shift light circuit up to ECM connector. If shift light comes on, ECM connector is faulty, or ECM does not have ability to ground circuit.

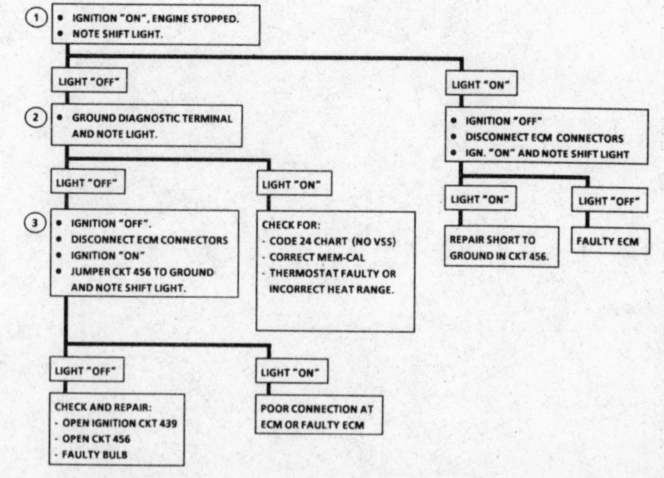

1
• IGNITION "ON", ENGINE STOPPED.
• NOTE SHIFT LIGHT.
LIGHT "OFF"
LIGHT "ON"
2
• GROUND DIAGNOSTIC TERMINAL AND NOTE LIGHT.
• IGNITION "OFF"
• DISCONNECT ECM CONNECTORS
• IGN. "ON" AND NOTE SHIFT LIGHT
LIGHT "OFF"
LIGHT "ON"
LIGHT "ON"
LIGHT "OFF"
3
• IGNITION "OFF".
• DISCONNECT ECM CONNECTORS
• IGNITION "ON"
• JUMPER CKT 456 TO GROUND AND NOTE SHIFT LIGHT.
CHECK FOR:
- CODE 24 CHART (NO VSS)
- CORRECT MEM-CAL
- THERMOSTAT FAULTY OR INCORRECT HEAT RANGE.
REPAIR SHORT TO GROUND IN CKT 456.
FAULTY ECM
LIGHT "OFF"
LIGHT "ON"
CHECK AND REPAIR:
- OPEN IGNITION CKT 439
- OPEN CKT 456
- FAULTY BULB
POOR CONNECTION AT ECM OR FAULTY ECM


CLEAR CODES AND CONFIRM "CLOSED LOOP" OPERATION AND NO "SERVICE ENGINE SOON" LIGHT.

THE ALDL CONNECTOR IS MOUNTED ON TOP OF THE ECM BEHIND THE PASSENGER SIDE KICK PAD.

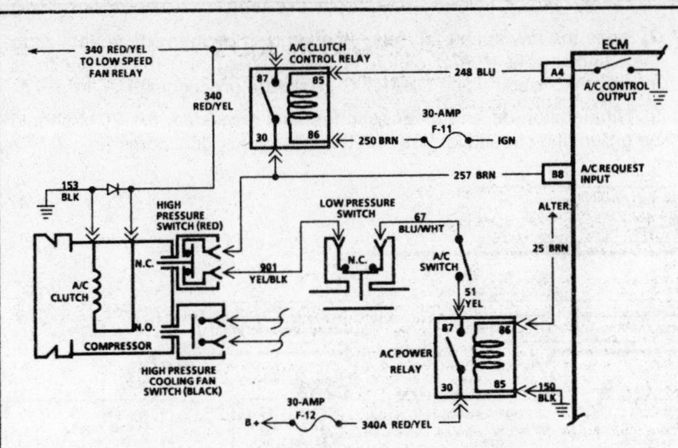

340 RED/YEL TO LOW SPEED FAN RELAY
A/C CLUTCH CONTROL RELAY
ECM
248 BLU
A4
A/C CONTROL OUTPUT
340 RED/YEL
87
85
30
86
30-AMP F-11
250 BRN
IGN
153 BLK
257 BRN
B8
A/C REQUEST INPUT
HIGH PRESSURE SWITCH (RED)
LOW PRESSURE SWITCH
67 BLU/WHT
ALTER.
N.C.
901 YEL/BLK
A/C SWITCH
25 BRN
A/C CLUTCH
51 YEL
N.O.
COMPRESSOR
AC POWER RELAY
HIGH PRESSURE COOLING FAN SWITCH (BLACK)
150 BLK
30-AMP F-12
B+
340A RED/YEL


## CHART C-10, AIR CONDITIONER (A/C) CLUTCH CONTROL

With the A/C on, alternator voltage is supplied actuating A/C power relay through the low pressure switch and high pressure switch to the A/C clutch relay.

If the system refrigerant level is okay, low pressure switch will be closed completing the circuit through the high pressure cut-off switch to circuit No. 257.

Circuit No. 257 supplies voltage to A/C control relay and ECM terminal "B8". The ECM will delay about 1/2 second then ground terminal "A4" and circuit No. 248. This will close the A/C relay allowing current to flow through the relay and circuit No. 340 to engage compressor clutch.

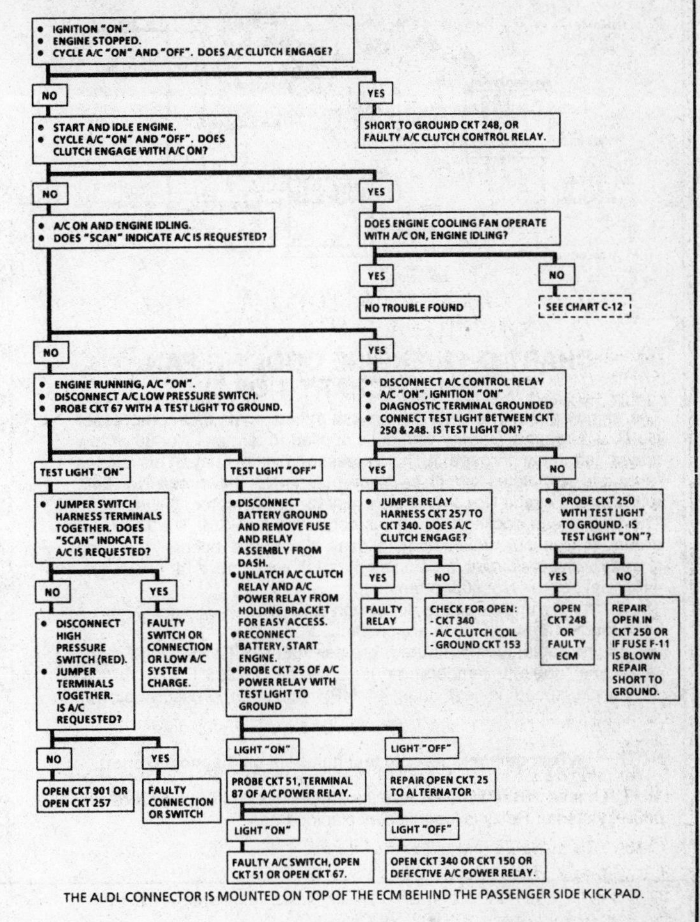

• IGNITION "ON".
• ENGINE STOPPED.
• CYCLE A/C "ON" AND "OFF". DOES A/C CLUTCH ENGAGE?
NO
YES
• START AND IDLE ENGINE.
• CYCLE A/C "ON" AND "OFF". DOES CLUTCH ENGAGE WITH A/C ON?
SHORT TO GROUND CKT 248, OR FAULTY A/C CLUTCH CONTROL RELAY.
NO
YES
• A/C ON AND ENGINE IDLING.
• DOES "SCAN" INDICATE A/C IS REQUESTED?
DOES ENGINE COOLING FAN OPERATE WITH A/C ON, ENGINE IDLING?
YES
NO
NO TROUBLE FOUND
SEE CHART C-12
NO
YES
• ENGINE RUNNING, A/C "ON".
• DISCONNECT A/C LOW PRESSURE SWITCH.
• PROBE CKT 67 WITH A TEST LIGHT TO GROUND.
• DISCONNECT A/C CONTROL RELAY
• A/C "ON", IGNITION "ON"
• DIAGNOSTIC TERMINAL GROUNDED
• CONNECT TEST LIGHT BETWEEN CKT 250 & 248. IS TEST LIGHT ON?
TEST LIGHT "ON"
TEST LIGHT "OFF"
YES
NO
• JUMPER SWITCH HARNESS TERMINALS TOGETHER. DOES "SCAN" INDICATE A/C IS REQUESTED?
• DISCONNECT BATTERY GROUND AND REMOVE FUSE AND RELAY ASSEMBLY FROM DASH.
• UNLATCH A/C CLUTCH RELAY AND A/C POWER RELAY FROM HOLDING BRACKET FOR EASY ACCESS.
• RECONNECT BATTERY, START ENGINE.
• PROBE CKT 25 OF A/C POWER RELAY WITH TEST LIGHT TO GROUND
• JUMPER RELAY HARNESS CKT 257 TO CKT 340. DOES A/C CLUTCH ENGAGE?
• PROBE CKT 250 WITH TEST LIGHT TO GROUND. IS TEST LIGHT "ON"?
NO
YES
YES
NO
YES
NO
• DISCONNECT HIGH PRESSURE SWITCH (RED).
• JUMPER TERMINALS TOGETHER. IS A/C REQUESTED?
FAULTY SWITCH OR CONNECTION OR LOW A/C SYSTEM CHARGE.
FAULTY RELAY
CHECK FOR OPEN:
- CKT 340
- A/C CLUTCH COIL
- GROUND CKT 153
OPEN CKT 248 OR FAULTY ECM
REPAIR OPEN IN CKT 250 OR IF FUSE F-11 IS BLOWN REPAIR SHORT TO GROUND.
NO
YES
LIGHT "ON"
LIGHT "OFF"
OPEN CKT 901 OR OPEN CKT 257
FAULTY CONNECTION OR SWITCH
PROBE CKT 51, TERMINAL 87 OF A/C POWER RELAY.
REPAIR OPEN CKT 25 TO ALTERNATOR
LIGHT "ON"
LIGHT "OFF"
FAULTY A/C SWITCH, OPEN CKT 51 OR OPEN CKT 67.
OPEN CKT 340 OR CKT 150 OR DEFECTIVE A/C POWER RELAY.
THE ALDL CONNECTOR IS MOUNTED ON TOP OF THE ECM BEHIND THE PASSENGER SIDE KICK PAD.

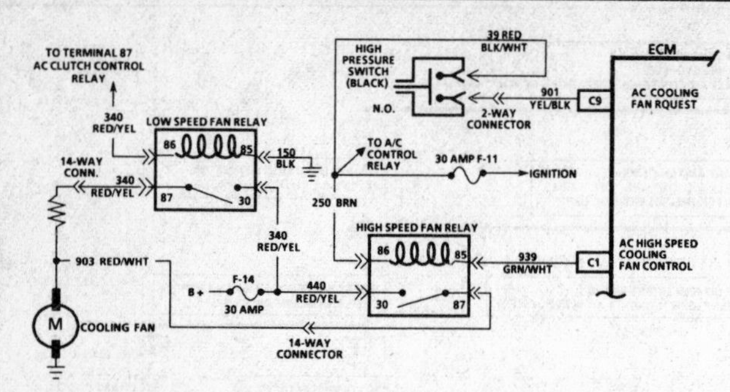
TO TERMINAL 87
AC CLUTCH CONTROL RELAY
340 RED/YEL
LOW SPEED FAN RELAY
14-WAY CONN.
340 RED/YEL
86
85
87
30
150 BLK
HIGH PRESSURE SWITCH (BLACK)
39 RED
BLK/WHT
N.O.
901 YEL/BLK
C9
2-WAY CONNECTOR
ECM
AC COOLING FAN RQUEST
TO A/C CONTROL RELAY
30 AMP F-11
IGNITION
250 BRN
340 RED/YEL
HIGH SPEED FAN RELAY
939 GRN/WHT
C1
AC HIGH SPEED COOLING FAN CONTROL
903 RED/WHT
F-14
30 AMP
B+
440 RED/YEL
M
COOLING FAN
14-WAY CONNECTOR

## CHART C-12, ENGINE COOLING FAN (WITH A/C) (CHART 1 OF 2)

The engine cooling fan will run on low speed when A/C compressor clutch is engaged. Battery voltage is applied to terminal No. 86 of low speed fan relay through A/C compressor clutch relay. This closes relay and completes circuit as follows: fuse No. 14, circuit No. 340, relay switch, circuit No. 340, .6 ohm resistor to fan motor.
The high speed cooling fan relay is controlled by ECM. The ECM will ground circuit No. 939 actuating relay. Once this occurs, the high speed fan motor circuit is completed as follows: fuse #14, circuit No. 440, relay, circuit No. 903 to fan motor.
The ECM will run the cooling fan at high speed if:

- Trouble Codes 14 or 15 are present.
- Engine coolant temperature is greater than 225°F (107°C).
- Engine coolant temperature is between 79-225°F (26-107°C), Vehicle speed is less than 44 MPH and high pressure blower switch is closed.

**NOTE: Test numbers refer to test numbers on diagnostic chart.**

**1)** High speed fan relay is located at center position in row of 5 relays on relay center. Relay is identified by black carrier.

**2)** Since the low speed fan relay is energized by the voltage applied to the clutch, note if A/C clutch is being energized. If A/C clutch is inoperative, repair using CHART C-10 before proceeding.

**3)** With ignition on and diagnostic terminal grounded, the ECM should be grounding circuit No. 939 and the test light should come on.

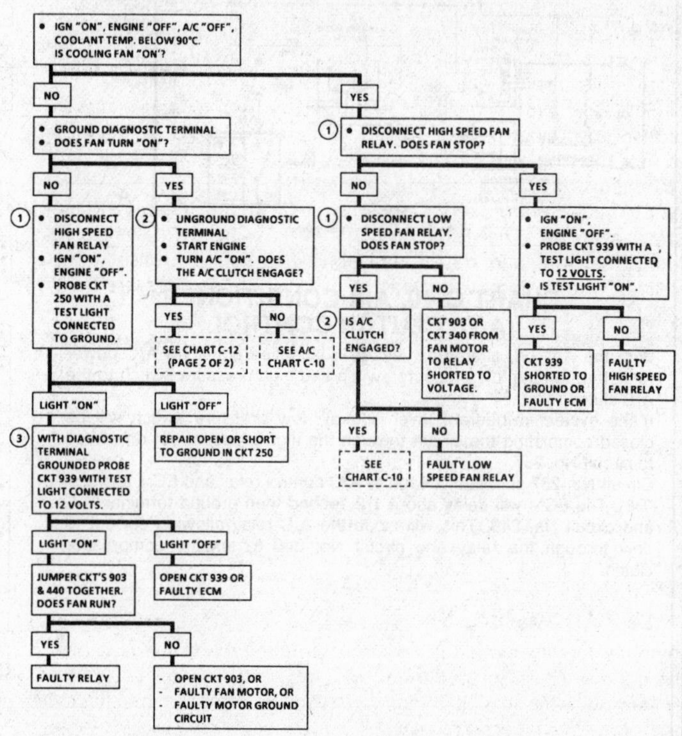
• IGN "ON", ENGINE "OFF", A/C "OFF", COOLANT TEMP. BELOW 90°C. IS COOLING FAN "ON"?
NO
YES
• GROUND DIAGNOSTIC TERMINAL
• DOES FAN TURN "ON"?
1 • DISCONNECT HIGH SPEED FAN RELAY. DOES FAN STOP?
NO
YES
NO
YES
1 • DISCONNECT HIGH SPEED FAN RELAY • IGN "ON", ENGINE "OFF". • PROBE CKT 250 WITH A TEST LIGHT CONNECTED TO GROUND.
2 • UNGROUND DIAGNOSTIC TERMINAL • START ENGINE • TURN A/C "ON". DOES THE A/C CLUTCH ENGAGE?
1 • DISCONNECT LOW SPEED FAN RELAY. DOES FAN STOP?
• IGN "ON", ENGINE "OFF". • PROBE CKT 939 WITH A TEST LIGHT CONNECTED TO 12 VOLTS. • IS TEST LIGHT "ON".
YES
NO
YES
NO
YES
NO
SEE CHART C-12 (PAGE 2 OF 2)
SEE A/C CHART C-10
2 IS A/C CLUTCH ENGAGED?
CKT 903 OR CKT 340 FROM FAN MOTOR TO RELAY SHORTED TO VOLTAGE.
CKT 939 SHORTED TO GROUND OR FAULTY ECM
FAULTY HIGH SPEED FAN RELAY
LIGHT "ON"
LIGHT "OFF"
YES
NO
3 WITH DIAGNOSTIC TERMINAL GROUNDED PROBE CKT 939 WITH TEST LIGHT CONNECTED TO 12 VOLTS.
REPAIR OPEN OR SHORT TO GROUND IN CKT 250
SEE CHART C-10
FAULTY LOW SPEED FAN RELAY
LIGHT "ON"
LIGHT "OFF"
JUMPER CKT'S 903 & 440 TOGETHER. DOES FAN RUN?
OPEN CKT 939 OR FAULTY ECM
YES
NO
FAULTY RELAY
- OPEN CKT 903, OR
- FAULTY FAN MOTOR, OR
- FAULTY MOTOR GROUND CIRCUIT

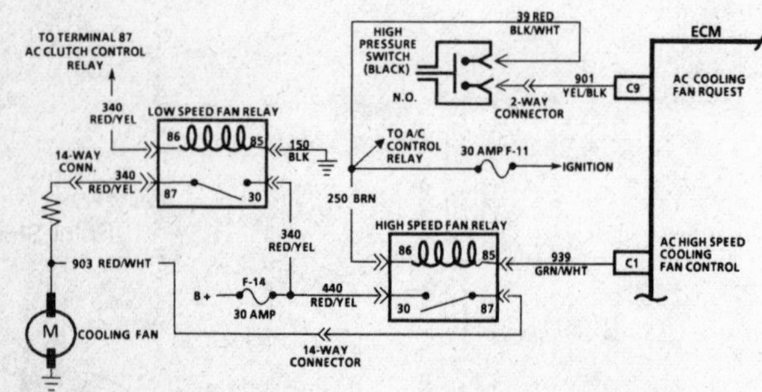
TO TERMINAL 87
AC CLUTCH CONTROL RELAY
340 RED/YEL
LOW SPEED FAN RELAY
14-WAY CONN.
340 RED/YEL
86
85
87
30
150 BLK
HIGH PRESSURE SWITCH (BLACK)
39 RED
BLK/WHT
N.O.
901 YEL/BLK
C9
2-WAY CONNECTOR
ECM
AC COOLING FAN RQUEST
TO A/C CONTROL RELAY
30 AMP F-11
IGNITION
250 BRN
340 RED/YEL
HIGH SPEED FAN RELAY
939 GRN/WHT
C1
AC HIGH SPEED COOLING FAN CONTROL
903 RED/WHT
F-14
30 AMP
B+
440 RED/YEL
M
COOLING FAN
14-WAY CONNECTOR

## CHART C-12, ENGINE COOLING FAN (WITH A/C) (CHART 2 OF 2)

The engine cooling fan will run on low speed when A/C compressor clutch is engaged. Battery voltage is applied to terminal No. 86 of low speed fan relay through A/C compressor clutch relay. This closes relay and completes circuit as follows: fuse No. 14, circuit No. 340, relay switch, circuit No. 340, .6 ohm resistor to fan motor.
The high speed cooling fan relay is controlled by ECM. The ECM will ground circuit No. 939 actuating relay. Once this occurs, the high speed fan motor circuit is completed as follows: fuse No. 14, circuit No. 440, relay, circuit No. 903 to fan motor.
The ECM will run the cooling fan at high speed if:

- Trouble Codes 14 or 15 are present.
- Engine coolant temperature is greater than 225°F (107°C).
- Engine coolant temperature is between 79-225°F (26-107°C). Vehicle speed is less than 44 MPH. High pressure blower switch is closed.

**NOTE: Test numbers refer to test numbers on diagnostic chart.**

**4)** When A/C clutch is engaged, cooling fan should be running on low speed.

**5)** As long as the high pressure fan circuit is not defective, or the engine is not overheating, ECM should not be commanding the fan on in this step.

**6)** If insufficient cooling is complaint, problem may be caused by high pressure fan switch circuit not operating properly. The "Scan" tester should indicate fan is requested before the A/C high pressure switch opens (see Mini-Schematic in CHART C-10). If high pressure fan switch does not close, check for open or short to ground in circuit No. 901 before replacing switch.

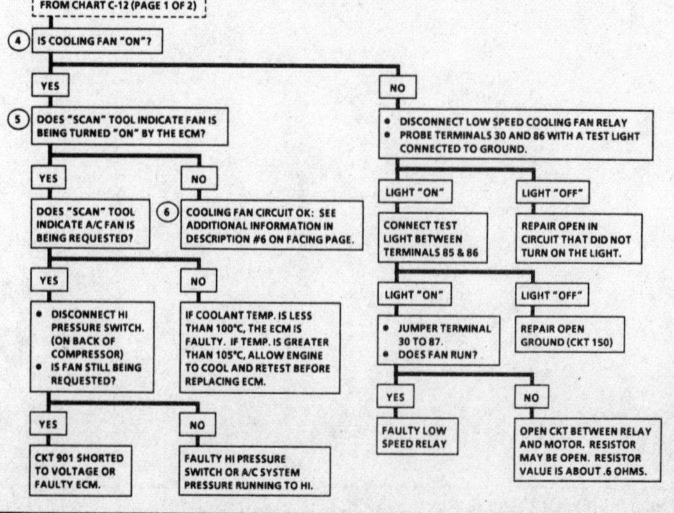
FROM CHART C-12 (PAGE 1 OF 2)
4 IS COOLING FAN "ON"?
YES
NO
5 DOES "SCAN" TOOL INDICATE FAN IS BEING TURNED "ON" BY THE ECM?
• DISCONNECT LOW SPEED COOLING FAN RELAY
• PROBE TERMINALS 30 AND 86 WITH A TEST LIGHT CONNECTED TO GROUND.
YES
NO
LIGHT "ON"
LIGHT "OFF"
DOES "SCAN" TOOL INDICATE A/C FAN IS BEING REQUESTED?
6 COOLING FAN CIRCUIT OK: SEE ADDITIONAL INFORMATION IN DESCRIPTION #6 ON FACING PAGE.
CONNECT TEST LIGHT BETWEEN TERMINALS 85 & 86
REPAIR OPEN IN CIRCUIT THAT DID NOT TURN ON THE LIGHT.
YES
NO
LIGHT "ON"
LIGHT "OFF"
• DISCONNECT HI PRESSURE SWITCH. (ON BACK OF COMPRESSOR)
• IS FAN STILL BEING REQUESTED?
IF COOLANT TEMP. IS LESS THAN 100°C, THE ECM IS FAULTY. IF TEMP. IS GREATER THAN 105°C, ALLOW ENGINE TO COOL AND RETEST BEFORE REPLACING ECM.
• JUMPER TERMINAL 30 TO 87.
• DOES FAN RUN?
REPAIR OPEN GROUND (CKT 150)
YES
NO
YES
NO
CKT 901 SHORTED TO VOLTAGE OR FAULTY ECM.
FAULTY HI PRESSURE SWITCH OR A/C SYSTEM PRESSURE RUNNING TO HI.
FAULTY LOW SPEED RELAY
OPEN CKT BETWEEN RELAY AND MOTOR. RESISTOR MAY BE OPEN. RESISTOR VALUE IS ABOUT .6 OHMS.

# Honda Electronic Control System

## Accord, Civic, Prelude

## DESCRIPTION & OPERATION

The Electronic Control Unit (ECU) receives input signals (data) from various sensors. The ECU processes input data and sends output signals to various control devices. This allows for precise control of air/fuel mixture and idle speed under most operating conditions.

The ECU is the main controlling device of the electronic control system. The basic injector duration is read from calibration tables built into ECU internal memory. The ECU modifies the basic injector duration according to input signals from various sensors to obtain the final injector duration. This allows the ECU to obtain optimum injector pulse.

The ECU also controls cold start system, electric fuel pump and fuel cut-off systems. The ECU also contains a fail-safe system to monitor sensors and detect any abnormality in ECU itself. This provides safe driving even if one or more of the sensors are faulty or ECU malfunctions.

The ECU has a self-diagnostic capability to help diagnose problems. This system uses a dash mounted PGM-FI or Check Engine warning light and one ECU mounted self-diagnostic LED. The PGM-FI warning light will glow for 2 seconds when ignition is turned on. The ECU is mounted below passenger seat (Accord), or under carpet below passenger side dash.

***NOTE: For additional information on fuel control portion of this system, see PGM-FI SYSTEM article in FUEL SYSTEMS section.***

## INPUT SIGNALS

Computer furnishes input sensors with a reference voltage (5 volts). This voltage signal is then modified by the resistance value of the sensors in each circuit. Some sensors are simple mechanical resistors, while others are temperature sensitive resistors (thermistors). ECU monitors either reference line or return signal to determine status of each sensor. Not all input signals are obtained from sensors. Some input signals are simply monitored circuits which either produce a voltage of their own ($O_2$ and pick-up coils) or already have a voltage signal present.

**Atmospheric Pressure (PA) Sensor** – The PA sensor converts atmospheric pressure into voltage signals and sends the signals to ECU.

**Battery Voltage Signal** – ECU uses the battery voltage signal (alternator FR terminal) to compensate for low voltage conditions which result in injector lag. ECU compensates by increasing injector opening time.

**Crank Angle Sensors** – On Accord models, the crank angle sensor consists of a combination TDC/CYL sensor mounted in the distributor housing. *See Fig. 2.* This sensor furnishes 2 separate

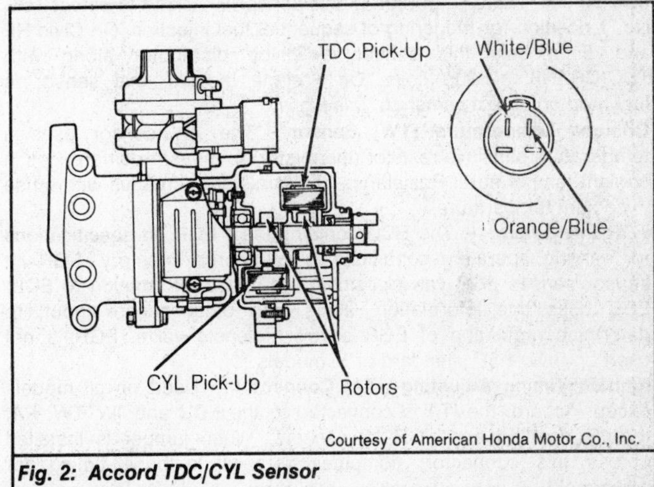

TDC Pick-Up
White/Blue
Orange/Blue
CYL Pick-Up
Rotors


Courtesy of American Honda Motor Co., Inc.

***Fig. 2: Accord TDC/CYL Sensor***

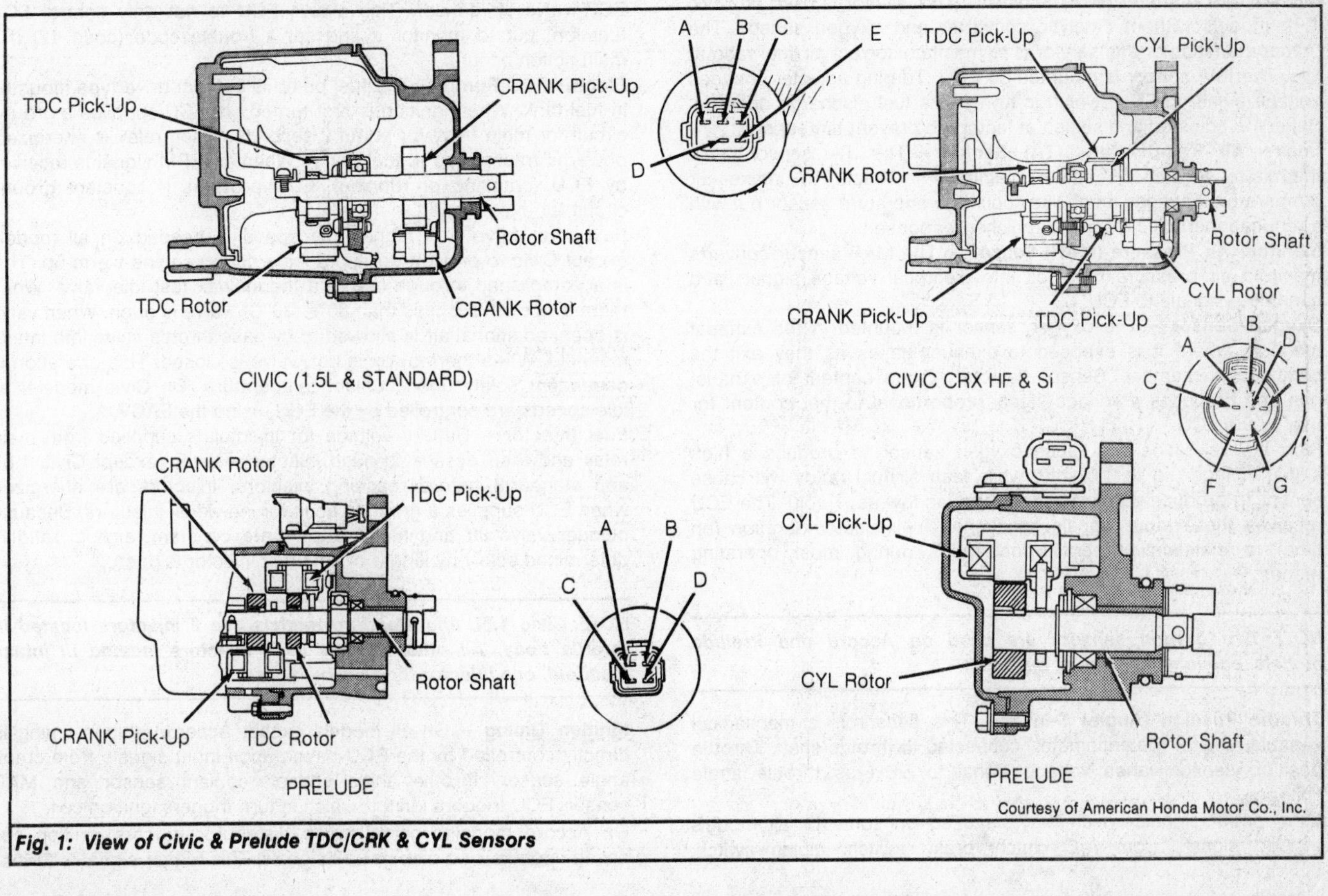

Courtesy of American Honda Motor Co., Inc.

***Fig. 1: View of Civic & Prelude TDC/CRK & CYL Sensors***

input signals to the ECU. The ECU uses the CYL signal to help determine No. 1 cylinder position as a base for sequential fuel injection. The ECU uses the TDC signal to determine injection timing for each cylinder. This sensor also furnishes an RPM signal to ECU.

On Prelude and Civic 1.5L and Std. models (TBI), the crank angle sensor consists of a combination TDC/Crank sensor mounted in the distributor housing. The ECU uses input from the crank pick-up coil portion of this sensor to help determine ignition and fuel injector timing for each cylinder. This sensor also furnishes an engine speed (RPM) signal to the ECU. The ECU uses the TDC pick-up coil portion of this sensor to initialize ignition timing upon start-up (cranking) and when crank angle signal is abnormal. *See Fig. 1.*

In addition to the TDC and Crank pick-up coils inside distributor housing, Prelude and Civic HF and Si models also utilize a CYL pick-up coil. The CYL portion of this sensor is utilized to detect TDC No. 1 position for triggering of sequential fuel injection. On Civic HF and Si models this sensor is inside distributor along with TDC/CRANK pick-up coils. On Prelude models, this sensor is mounted on end of camshaft. *See Fig. 1.*

**Coolant Temperature (TW) Sensor** – The TW sensor uses a temperature sensitive resistor (thermistor) to measure differences in coolant temperature. Resistance of thermistor decreases with a rise in coolant temperature.

**EGR Lift Sensor** – The ECU contains ideal EGR lift specifications for varying operating conditions in its internal memory. EGR lift sensor senses EGR valve position and relays information to ECU. ECU uses this information, along with other sensor input, to determine regulation of EGR control solenoid valve. EGR is not used on Civic 1.5L, standard or Si models.

**Ignition Timing Adjusting (ITA) Connector** – Used on all models except Accord, the ITA is connected to the ECU and TA, TW, PA, throttle position and EGR lift sensors. When jumper is installed across this connector, computer defaults to base timing for adjustment.

**Idle Mixture Adjuster (IMA) Sensor** – This sensor is used on Civic 1.6L models without catalytic converter and oxygen sensor. The primary function of this sensor is to maintain correct air/fuel ratio at idle. The IMA sensor is mounted on ECU. Turning adjuster changes voltage signal to ECU, which in turn alters fuel discharge duration. Sensor is adjusted and sealed at factory to prevent tampering.

**Intake Air Temperature (TA) Sensor** – The TA sensor is a thermistor located in intake manifold. It reacts to intake air temperature changes much like coolant temperature sensor but with a reduced thermal capacity for quicker response.

**Manifold Air Pressure (MAP) Sensor** – The MAP sensor converts manifold air pressure readings into electrical voltage signals and sends the signals to ECU.

**Oxygen Sensor** – The oxygen sensor is mounted in the exhaust manifold where it is exposed to exhaust gases as they exit the combustion chamber. Sensor detects oxygen content of exhaust gas and produces a voltage signal proportional to that content for use by the ECU.

Rich air/fuel ratios will cause oxygen sensor to produce a high signal voltage (up to 1.0 volt), while lean air/fuel ratios will cause sensor to produce a low signal voltage (as low as .1 volt). The ECU receives these input signals and varies fuel injector duration (on time) to maintain proper air/fuel ratios during most operating modes.

***NOTE:** Two oxygen sensors are used on Accord and Prelude models, one in each exhaust manifold.*

**Throttle Position (Angle) Sensor** – This sensor is a mechanical variable resistor (potentiometer) connected to throttle shaft. Throttle position sensor varies voltage signal to ECU as throttle angle changes.

Other input signals which may be used on some or all models include signals from A/C clutch, brake switch, clutch switch, cranking signal (fused starter switch), vehicle speed sensor, power steering pressure switch and/or gear position switch(es).

## CONTROL DEVICES

**By-Pass Control Solenoids (Accord & Prelude)** – Two air intake paths are provided in intake manifold. This allows ECU to select path length most favorable (power/performance) for a given engine speed. These air paths are selected by ECU based upon sensor input signals. ECU controls by-pass valves in intake manifold through use of 2 by-pass control solenoids and a by-pass valve control diaphragm. See PGM-FI SYSTEM article in FUEL SYSTEMS section.

**Dashpot Control Vacuum Solenoid (Civic Si)** – ECU controls solenoid which regulates vacuum to outer side of idle speed dashpot based upon coolant temperature. When solenoid is energized, vacuum signal to dashpot is blocked. This causes spring pressure to slightly open throttle valve, allowing for cold fast idle. The inner side of idle speed dashpot controls throttle closure speed using spring pressure and an orificed (restricted) manifold vacuum signal. ECU controls outer side of diaphragm only.

**EACV** – All models are equipped with an Electronic Air Control Valve (EACV). When idle speed is reduced due to electrical or other loads on engine, ECU opens this valve to by-pass additional air into intake manifold. This additional air will allow idle speed to increase to maintain normal idle.

After coolant temperature has reached 104°F (40°C), this valve lowers fast idle speed in steps during engine warm-up. To prevent erratic running after engine first fires, valve is opened during cranking and immediately after starting which by-passes additional air into intake manifold.

**EGR Control Solenoid** – Exhaust Gas Recirculation (EGR) is used on Accord, Prelude and Civic (HF) models. ECU controls ground circuit to EGR solenoid to regulate flow of recirculated exhaust gases into intake system. Accord and Prelude models also utilize an EGR valve lift sensor. This allows ECU to not only control EGR function, but to monitor it and set a trouble code (code 12) if a malfunction occurs.

**Electric Fuel Pump** – The fuel pump is a direct drive type mounted in fuel tank. When ignition is first turned on, ECU supplies a ground circuit for main relay for about 2 seconds. When relay is energized, power is transmitted to fuel pump. When an RPM signal is received by ECU (cranking or running), ECU provides a constant ground circuit for main relay.

**Fast Idle Valve** – A higher idle speed is needed on all models except Civic to prevent erratic running during engine warm-up. This is accomplished through use of a thermowax fast idle valve. When thermowax valve is less than 86°F (30°C), valve is open. When valve is open, additional air is allowed to by-pass throttle valve into intake manifold. When thermowax is hot, valve is closed. This operation is dependent solely upon coolant temperature. On Civic models, all idle speeds are controlled by the ECU, using the EACV.

**Fuel Injector** – Battery voltage for injector is supplied from main relay and then passes through injector resistor (except Civic 1.5L and standard) before reaching injectors. Injectors are energized when ECU supplies a ground circuit for individual injectors. Because plunger valve lift and fuel pressure are constant, air/fuel ratio is determined solely by length of time that injector is open.

***NOTE:** Civic 1.5L and standard models use 2 injectors located in throttle body. All other models have injectors located in intake manifold, one injector for each cylinder.*

**Ignition Timing** – On all models except Accord, ignition timing is directly controlled by the ECU based upon input signals from crank angle sensor, throttle angle sensor, coolant sensor and MAP sensor. ECU triggers ignitor, which in turn triggers ignition coil.

On Accord models, ignitor inside distributor triggers ignition coil based upon its own pick-up coil signals. This trigger signal is further modified by both vacuum and centrifugal advance mechanisms. The vacuum advance mechanism consists of a dual-diaphragm which operates on manifold vacuum. Vacuum to the outside diaphragm is controlled by an ECU-regulated vacuum solenoid. This solenoid will pass vacuum to outside diaphragm when vehicle is cold. This allows additional advance to improve cold engine performance.

**Main Relay** – One half of main relay is used by ECU to power electric fuel pump. ECU provides a ground for this part of relay when ignition is first turned on (2 seconds), or when an RPM signal is received by ECU (cranking or running). The second half of the main relay provides power from ignition for the ECU, injectors (through a resistor except on Civic) and power for the fuel pump part of relay.

**Purge Control Solenoid (Except Prelude)** – Purging evaporative emissions from charcoal canister is controlled by ECU using purge control solenoid. When solenoid is energized, manifold vacuum passes through solenid to open canister purge control valve diaphragm located on top of canister. Ported vacuum is then used to purge canister. Prelude models use a thermovalve instead of a solenoid to control purge diaphragm vacuum.

**Tandem Valve Control Solenoid (Civic 1.5L & Standard)** – The tandem valve is employed on throttle body injected Civic models to improve fuel atomization. This is accomplished by regulating venturi vacuum (to tandem valve actuating diaphragm) through an ECU controlled solenoid valve. This promotes a more complete atomization of fuel from main fuel injector, regardless of airflow rate. Solenoid is energized and venturi vacuum is allowed to activate diaphragm when coolant temperature is greater than 160°F (70°C) or engine speed is greater than 1500 RPM (auto. trans.) or 2000-2800 RPM (man. trans.), depending upon atmospheric pressure.

**Vacuum Control Solenoid Valve (Accord)** – Vacuum to the outside distributor advance diaphragm is controlled by ECU using a vacuum control solenoid. This solenoid will pass vacuum to outside diaphragm when vehicle is cold, supplying additional advance to improve cold engine performance.

Other control functions which may be used on some or all models include the PGM-FI or Check Engine warning light, economy driving indicator light and A/C clutch relay.

## TROUBLE SHOOTING

***NOTE: Observe PGM-FI or Check Engine warning light. If light is on and no codes are flashed by LED on ECU, this indicates that back-up system is in operation. See LED DOES NOT FLASH under CODE 0, NO CODES in TESTING section of this article.***

### ENGINE WON'T START

Check spark, fuel supply and EACV.

### DIFFICULT COLD START

Check coolant temperature sensor, TDC sensor and all other idle controls.

### FAST IDLE OUT OF SPECIFICATION

Check idle controls, coolant temperature sensor, throttle position sensor, TDC sensor, intake air temperature sensor and atmospheric pressure sensor.

### ROUGH IDLE WHEN WARM

Check EACV, MAP sensor, oxygen sensor, crank angle sensor, throttle position sensor, intake air temperature sensor, atmospheric pressure sensor and EGR and other emission control systems.

### IDLE RPM HIGH WHEN WARM

Check EACV and other idle controls. Check MAP sensor, atmospheric pressure sensor, air intake system and emission systems.

### IDLE RPM LOW WHEN WARM

Check EACV, air intake system, MAP sensor and other idle controls.

### STALLING DURING WARM-UP

Check EACV, air intake system, MAP sensor, crank angle sensor, coolant temperature sensor, throttle position sensor, other idle controls, fuel supply and EGR control system.

### STALLING AFTER WARM-UP

Check EGR control system, EACV, MAP sensor, throttle position sensor, crank angle sensor, vehicle speed sensor, air intake and fuel supply.

### MISFIRE OR ROUGH OPERATION

Using a stethoscope, check each injector for clicking at idle. Check fuel supply, MAP sensor. oxygen sensor, crank angle sensor, throttle position sensor, ignition output signal, EGR system and vehicle speed sensor.

### EMISSION TEST FAILURE

Check MAP sensor, oxygen sensor, all emission control systems, crank angle sensor and coolant temperature sensor.

### LACK OF POWER

Check for dragging/binding brakes. Check fuel supply, MAP sensor, crank angle sensor, coolant temperature sensor, atmospheric pressure sensor, vehicle speed sensor, air intake system and EGR control system.

## TESTING

***NOTE: Before starting testing, ensure engine is in good mechanical condition and adjusted to specifications.***

On all models, an LED is located on ECU for self-diagnostic codes. LED is used to read codes set due to component failure. See appropriate LED CODES table in this article. To obtain codes, turn ignition switch to the "ON" position and count flashes of LED on ECU.

***NOTE: If unlisted codes are flashed by ECU LED, clear codes and recheck. If code still appears, substitute a known good ECU. If condition is rectified, replace original ECU.***

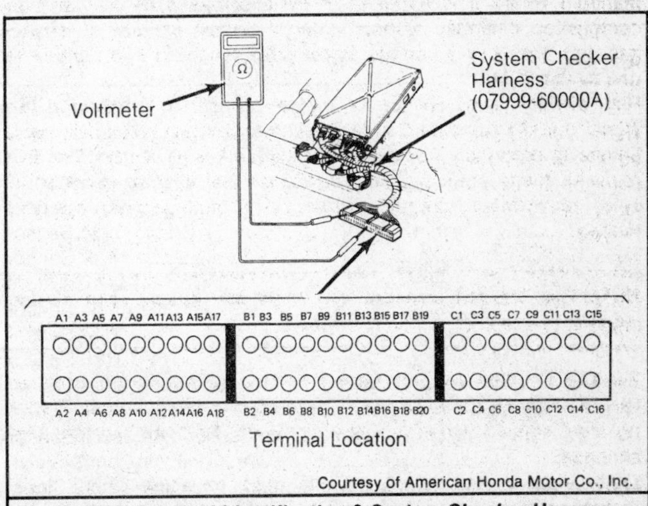
Voltmeter
System Checker Harness (07999-60000A)
A1 A3 A5 A7 A9 A11 A13 A15 A17
B1 B3 B5 B7 B9 B11 B13 B15 B17 B19
C1 C3 C5 C7 C9 C11 C13 C15
A2 A4 A6 A8 A10 A12 A14 A16 A18
B2 B4 B6 B8 B10 B12 B14 B16 B18 B20
C2 C4 C6 C8 C10 C12 C14 C16
Terminal Location
Courtesy of American Honda Motor Co., Inc.

***Fig. 3: ECU Terminal Identification & System Checker Harness Installation***

# Honda Electronic Control System (Cont.)

On all models, System Checker Harness (07999-PD60000A) is needed to test components. *See Fig. 3.* On Accord and Prelude models, an Inspection Harness (07GMJ-ML80100) is needed for testing specific 3-wire sensors. Both of these devices function as breakout boxes to access pin voltage signals while component is either in or out of circuit.

To reset ECU, remove hazard fuse in main fuse box for 10 seconds on Civic models. Remove clock (Prelude) or No. 11 (Accord) fuse in the under-hood relay box for 10 seconds to reset ECU.

## SELF-DIAGNOSTIC CODES

*CIVIC LED CODES*

| LED Blinks | System Code |
|---|---|
| 0 | ECU |
| 1 | Oxygen Sensor |
| 3 | MAP Sensor |
| 4 | Crank Angle Sensor |
| 5 | MAP Sensor |
| 6 | Coolant Temperature |
| 7 | Throttle Angle Sensor |
| 8 | TDC Sensor |
| 9 | No. 1 CYL Sensor (HF & Si) |
| 10 | Intake Air Temperature Sensor |
| 11 | IMA Sensor (Without $O_2$ & Catalyst) |
| 12 | EGR System (HF) |
| 13 | Atmospheric Pressure Sensor |
| 14 | Electronic Air Control Valve |
| 15 | Ignition Output Signal |
| 16 | Fuel Injector |
| 17 | Vehicle Speed Sensor |
| 19 | Lock-Up Solenoid Valve (Auto. Trans.) |
| 20 | Electric Load Detector |

*ACCORD LED CODES*

| LED Blinks | System Code |
|---|---|
| 0 | ECU |
| 1 | Oxygen Sensor A |
| 2 | Oxygen Sensor B |
| 3 | MAP Sensor |
| 5 | MAP Sensor |
| 6 | Coolant Temperature |
| 7 | Throttle Angle Sensor |
| 8 | TDC Sensor |
| 9 | No. 1 CYL Sensor |
| 10 | Intake Air Temperature Sensor |
| 12 | EGR System |
| 13 | Atmospheric Pressure Sensor |
| 14 | Electronic Air Control Valve |

*PRELUDE LED CODES*

| LED Blinks | System Code |
|---|---|
| 0 | ECU |
| 1 | Oxygen Sensor A |
| 2 | Oxygen Sensor B |
| 3 | MAP Sensor |
| 4 | Crank Angle Sensor |
| 5 | MAP Sensor |
| 6 | Coolant Temperature |
| 7 | Throttle Angle Sensor |
| 8 | TDC Sensor |
| 9 | No. 1 CYL Sensor |
| 10 | Intake Air Temperature Sensor |
| 12 | EGR System |
| 13 | Atmospheric Pressure Sensor |
| 14 | Electronic Air Control Valve |
| 15 | Ignition Output Signal |
| 16 | Fuel Injector |
| 17 | Vehicle Speed Sensor |

## CODE 0, NO CODES (ALL MODELS)

**No PGM-FI Warning Light – 1)** Turn ignition on. If oil pressure light is on, go to step **2)**. If light is off, inspect fuse No 1 (Civic), No. 2 (Accord) or No. 15 (Prelude). If fuse is okay, repair open circuit in Yellow wire between fuse and combination meter.

**2)** Turn ignition off. Connect system checker harness between ECU and connector. Connect terminal B6 to ground. Turn ignition on. If warning light is now on, go to step **3)**. If light is off, replace warning light bulb or repair open in wire between ECU terminal B6 and combination meter.

**3)** Individually, connect terminal A2 and then terminal A4 to terminal B6. If warning light fails to illuminate, repair open in Black A2 or A4 wires between ECU and ground.

**4)** If warning light illuminated in step **3)**, substitute a known good ECU. If condition is rectified, replace original ECU.

**PGM-FI Warning Light On, LED Does Not Flash Codes (Except Civic) – 1)** Turn ignition on. One at a time, disconnect the 3-wire connectors at MAP sensor, throttle angle sensor and EGR position sensor. If LED remains lit, go to step **2)**. If LED goes out, replace the sensor which caused LED to go out when unplugged.

**2)** Reconnect all connectors. Disconnect the 3-wire connector at Atmospheric Pressure (PA) sensor. If LED flashes code 13 when sensor is disconnected, replace faulty sensor. If code for disconnected sensor was not flashed, go to the next step.

**3)** Turn ignition off. Reconnect connector(s). Connect system checker harness between ECU and ECU harness. Disconnect "C" connector from ECU, not main harness. Check for continuity between ground and terminals C13 and C15. If continuity does not exist, go to step **4)**. If continuity exists, repair short to ground in Red/White wire from terminal C15 to MAP sensor or in Yellow/White wire from terminal C13 to PA sensor or EGR position sensor.

**4)** Reconnect "C" connector. Disconnect "B" connector from ECU only, not main harness. Turn ignition on. If LED is lit, repair short to ground in Yellow/Red (Prelude) or Green/Red (Accord) wire between ECU terminal B6 and combination meter. If LED is not lit, one at a time, connect terminal B6 to terminal A16 and then to terminal A18. If LED illuminates, go to step **5)**. If not, repair individual ground connections which did not make light come on (A18 or A16).

**5)** Measure voltage between terminal A15 (pos.) and A18 (neg.). If battery voltage is not present, repair open Yellow/Black (Prelude) or Yellow/White (Accord) A15 wire between ECU and main relay or repair main relay or relay wiring. If battery voltage is present, substitute a known good ECU. If condition is rectified, replace original ECU.

**Check Engine Light On, LED Does Not Flash (Civic) – 1)** Connect system checker harness between ECU and ECU connectors. Disconnect "B" connector from ECU only, not from main wire harness. Turn ignition on. If Check Engine light remains on, repair short to ground in Green/Orange wire between ECU terminal B6 and combination meter.

**2)** If Check Engine light goes out with ECU "B" connector unplugged, reconnect "B" connector. Individually, jumper terminal A2 to terminal A16 and then to terminal A18. If Check Engine light illuminates, go to step **3)**. If Check Engine light does not illuminate, repair open in Black/Red wire between ECU terminal A18 and ground or repair open in Brown/Black wire between ECU terminal A16 and ground.

**3)** Measure voltage between terminal A18 (neg.) and terminals A13 (pos.) and A15 (pos.). If battery voltage is present, go to step **4)**. If battery voltage is not present, repair open in Yellow/Black wires between ECU terminals A13 and A15 and main relay. Check main relay and wiring connectors at main relay.

**4)** Turn ignition off. Disconnect 3-wire connector at MAP sensor. Start engine. If LED does not indicate code for the disconnected sensor, replace sensor. Reconnect 3-wire connector. Repeat procedure with, throttle angle sensor, PA sensor, and finally idle mixture adjuster sensor (without catalyst). If all sensor codes are

displayed, turn ignition off. With system checker harness installed between ECU and ECU connector, disconnect "C" connector from ECU only, not from main harness.
**5)** Check for continuity between ground and terminal C13. Check for continuity between ground and terminal C15. If continuity exists, repair short to ground in Yellow/Red wire between ECU terminal C15 and MAP sensor, repair short to ground in Yellow/White wire between ECU terminal C13 and altitude sensor or throttle angle sensor, or repair short to ground in Yellow/White wire between ECU terminal C13 and idle mixture adjuster sensor (without catalyst).
**6)** If continuity did not exist in step **5)**, substitute a known good ECU. If condition is rectified, replace original ECU.

### CODE 1 &/OR CODE 2 OXYGEN SENSOR (ALL MODELS)

**1)** Turn off ignition. Reset ECU by removing hazard fuse in main fuse box on Civic models for 10 seconds or by removing clock (Prelude) or No. 11 (Accord) fuse in the under-hood relay box for 10 seconds. Start engine. Check fuel pressure at fuel filter. See appropriate FUEL INJECTION article in FUEL SYSTEMS section. Repair fuel system if not within specifications. If fuel pressure is within specifications, proceed to next step.
**2)** Bring engine to operating temperature (cooling fan comes on). Hold engine speed at 1500 RPM (minimum) for 15 minutes, without closing throttle completely during this time. Check if PGM-FI or Check Engine warning light is on. If not on, problem is intermittent. Test drive and check light again.
**3)** If light is on, disconnect indicated oxygen sensor connector. Attach voltmeter to vehicle ground and oxygen sensor connector. With engine at normal operating temperature, momentarily open throttle wide open, then close throttle.
**4)** Voltage at wide open throttle should be greater than .6 volt, and less than .4 volt at closed throttle. If not within specifications, replace oxygen sensor. If voltage is within specifications, proceed to next step.
**5)** Turn engine off and attach system checker harness between ECU and ECU connector. Using a voltmeter, connect negative lead to connector terminal A18.
**6)** On Civic models, attach positive voltmeter lead to connector terminal C16. On Accord and Prelude models, for oxygen sensor A, attach positive voltmeter lead to connector terminal C16 and attach to connector terminal B11 for oxygen sensor B.
**7)** Start engine and warm to operating temperature. Momentarily open throttle wide open, then close throttle. Voltage at wide open throttle should be greater than .6 volt, and less than .4 volt at closed throttle. If not within specifications, repair wire between ECU and oxygen sensor. If within specifications, substitute a known good ECU. If condition is rectified, replace original ECU.

### CODE 3, MAP SENSOR (CIVIC)

**1)** Turn off ignition. Remove hazard fuse in main fuse box for 10 seconds to reset ECU. Start engine and observe Check Engine light. If light is off, problem is intermittent. Test drive and check again.
**2)** If light is on, turn ignition off. Disconnect 3-wire MAP sensor connector. Turn ignition on. Measure voltage between Yellow/Red (pos.) and Green/White (neg.) terminals. Go to step **4)** if reading is about 5 volts. If not, measure voltage between Yellow/Red (pos.) terminal and ground. If voltage is still not 5 volts, go to step **3)**. If voltage is about 5 volts, repair open in Green/White wire between ECU terminal C14 and MAP sensor.
**3)** Turn ignition off. Connect system checker harness between ECU and ECU connector. Measure voltage between terminal C15 (pos.) and C14 (neg.) with ignition on. If voltage reading is about 5 volts, repair open Yellow/Red wire between ECU terminal C15 and MAP sensor. If voltage is not about 5 volts, substitute a known good ECU. If condition is rectified, replace original ECU.
**4)** Measure voltage between White (pos.) and Green/White (neg.) terminals. If reading is not about 5 volts, go to step **6)**. If measured voltage is about 5 volts, turn ignition off. Connect system checker harness between ECU and ECU connector. Reconnect 3-wire MAP connector. Turn ignition on. Measure voltage between terminal C11 (pos.) and C14 (neg.). If there is not about 3 volts present, replace MAP sensor.
**5)** If there is about 5 volts present between C11 and C14, substitute a known good ECU. If condition is rectified, replace original ECU.
**6)** If voltage measured between White (pos.) and Green/White (neg.) terminals in step **4)** was not about 5 volts, turn ignition off. Connect system checker harness between ECU and ECU connector. Turn ignition on. Measure voltage between terminal C11 (pos.) and C14 (neg.). If reading is not about 5 volts, repair short in White wire between ECU terminal C11 and MAP sensor. If voltage is about 5 volts, repair open in White wire between ECU terminal C11 and MAP sensor.

### CODE 3, MAP SENSOR (ACCORD & PRELUDE)

**1)** Turn ignition off. Remove clock (Prelude) or No. 11 (Accord) fuse in the under-hood relay box for 10 seconds to reset ECU. Start engine and observe PGM-FI warning light. If light is off, problem is intermittent. Test drive and check again.
**2)** If light is on, turn ignition off. Connect test harness between MAP sensor and sensor harness. Turn ignition on. Measure voltage between Red (pos.) and Green (neg.) terminals. If reading is about 5 volts, go to step **4)**. If not, measure voltage between Red (pos.) terminal and ground. If voltage is still not 5 volts, go to step **3)**. If voltage is about 5 volts, repair open in Green/White (Accord) or Blue/White (Prelude) wire between ECU terminal C14 and MAP sensor.
**3)** Turn ignition off. Connect system checker harness between ECU and ECU harness. Measure voltage between terminal C15 (pos.) and C14 (neg.) with ignition on. If voltage reading is about 5 volts, repair open Red/White wire between ECU terminal C15 and MAP sensor. If voltage is not about 5 volts, substitute a known good ECU. If condition is rectified, replace original ECU.
**4)** Measure voltage between White (pos.) and Green (neg.) terminals. If reading is not about 3 volts, replace MAP sensor or repair short in White/Blue wire between ECU terminal C11 and MAP sensor.
**5)** If measured voltage is about 3 volts, turn ignition off. Connect system checker harness between ECU and ECU connectors. Turn ignition on. Measure voltage between terminals C11 (pos.) and C14 (neg.). If there is not about 3 volts present, repair open White/Blue wire between ECU terminal C11 and MAP sensor.
**6)** If there are about 3 volts present, substitute a known good ECU. If condition is rectified, replace original ECU.

### CODE 4, TDC/CRANK SENSOR (CIVIC 1.5L & STANDARD)

**1)** Turn off ignition. Remove hazard fuse in main fuse box for 10 seconds to reset ECU. Start engine and observe Check Engine light. If light is off, problem is intermittent. Test drive and check again.
**2)** If light is on, turn ignition off. Disconnect 6-wire TDC/Crank sensor connector at distributor. Measure resistance between terminals "D" and "E". *See Fig. 1*. If resistance is not 350-550 ohms, replace distributor assembly. If resistance is within specification, check for continuity between ground and terminals "D" and "E". If continuity exists, sensor is shorted to ground. Replace distributor assembly.
**3)** If continuity to ground did not exist in step **2)**, reconnect 6-wire connector. Connect system checker harness between ECU and ECU connector. Measure resistance between terminals B10 and B12 (DOHC) or terminals C1 and C2 (1.5L). If resistance is not 350-550 ohms, repair Orange and/or White wires.
**4)** If resistance is within specification, substitute a known good ECU. If condition is rectified, replace original ECU.

## CODE 4, TDC/CRANK/CYL SENSOR (CIVIC HF & Si)

**1)** Turn off ignition. Remove hazard fuse in main fuse box for 10 seconds to reset ECU. Start engine and observe Check Engine light. If light is off, problem is intermittent. Test drive and check again.
**2)** If light is on, turn ignition off. Unplug 8-wire TDC/CRANK/CYL sensor connector at distributor. Measure resistance between terminals "C" and "D". *See Fig. 4*. If resistance is not 350-550 ohms, replace distributor assembly. If resistance is within specification, check for continuity between ground and terminals "C" and "D". If continuity exists, sensor is shorted to ground. Replace distributor assembly.
**3)** If continuity to ground did not exist in step **2)**, reconnect 8-wire connector. Connect system checker harness to main harness only, not to ECU. Measure resistance between terminals B10 and B12. If resistance is not 350-550 ohms, repair Orange and/or White wires.
**4)** If resistance is within specification, substitute a known good ECU. If condition is rectified, replace original ECU.

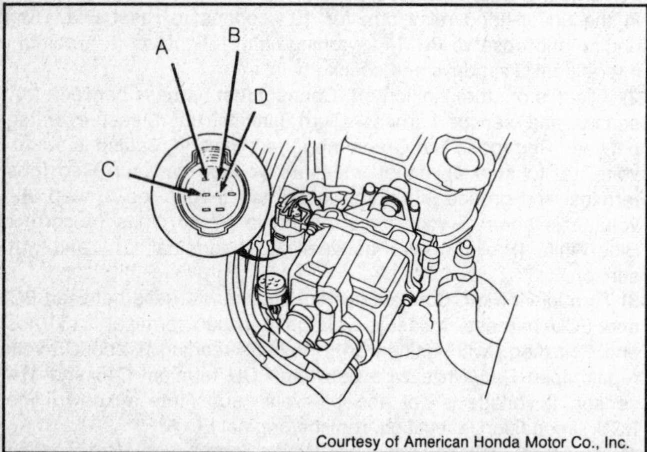
A
B
D
C
Courtesy of American Honda Motor Co., Inc.

*Fig. 4: Civic HF & Si TDC/CRANK/CYL Sensor Connector*

## CODE 4, TDC/CRANK SENSOR (PRELUDE)

**1)** Turn ignition off. Remove clock fuse in the under-hood relay box for 10 seconds to reset ECU. Start engine and observe PGM-FI warning light. If light is off, problem is intermittent. Test drive and check again.
**2)** If light is on, turn ignition off. Disconnect TDC/CRANK sensor connector nearest the sensor. Measure resistance across terminals "C" and "D" at sensor. *See Fig. 1*. If reading is not 700-1000 ohms, replace distributor assembly. If reading is within specification, proceed to next step.
**3)** Check continuity between ground and sensor terminals "C" and "D". If continuity exists, sensor is shorted to ground. Replace distributor assembly. If no continuity exists, proceed to next step.
**4)** Reconnect sensor connector. Attach system checker harness to main harness only, not to ECU. Check resistance between connector terminals B10 and B12. Resistance should be 700-1000 ohms.
**5)** If resistance is not within specification, repair open in Blue/Yellow and/or Blue/Green wire. If resistance is within specification, substitute a known good ECU. If condition is rectified, replace original ECU.

## CODE 5, MAP SENSOR (CIVIC)

**1)** Turn off ignition. Remove hazard fuse in main fuse box for 10 seconds to reset ECU. Start engine and observe Check Engine light. If light is off, problem is intermittent. Test drive and check again.
**2)** If light is on, turn ignition off. Connect hand-held vacuum pump/gauge to MAP hose at throttle body. Apply vacuum. If vacuum holds, go to step **3)**. If vacuum does not hold, attach vacuum pump/gauge directly to MAP sensor. Apply vacuum. If vacuum does not hold, replace MAP sensor. If vacuum holds, check MAP sensor vacuum hose for cracks. splits or looseness. Repair as necessary.
**3)** Check vacuum supply to MAP sensor with engine running. If vacuum is not present, repair hose or remove restriction from throttle body. If vacuum supply is okay, turn ignition off. Connect system checker harness between ECU and ECU connector. Measure voltage between terminals C11 (pos.) and C14 (neg.). If voltage reading is about 3 volts, go to next step. If voltage is not about 3 volts, check for open in White wire between MAP sensor and ECU. If wire is okay, replace MAP sensor.
**4)** Substitute a known good ECU. If condition is rectified, replace original ECU.

## CODE 5, MAP SENSOR (ACCORD & PRELUDE)

**1)** Turn ignition off. Remove clock (Prelude) or No. 11 (Accord) fuse in the under-hood relay box for 10 seconds to reset ECU. Start engine and observe PGM-FI warning light. If light is off, problem is intermittent. Test drive and check again.
**2)** If light is on, turn ignition off. Using a "T" fitting, connect a hand-held vacuum pump/gauge into vacuum hose between throttle body and MAP sensor. Start engine. If vacuum is not present, repair as necessary. If vacuum is present and holds, turn ignition off.
**3)** Connect inspection harness between MAP sensor and harness. Turn ignition on. Measure voltage between White (pos.) terminal and Green (neg.) terminal. If reading is not about 3 volts, replace MAP sensor. If voltage reading is about 3 volts, substitute a known good ECU. If condition is rectified, replace original ECU.

## CODE 6, COOLANT (TW) SENSOR (CIVIC)

**1)** Turn off ignition. Remove hazard fuse in main fuse box for 10 seconds to reset ECU. Start engine and observe Check Engine light. If light is off, problem is intermittent. Test drive and check again.
**2)** If light is on, warm engine to normal operating temperature (cooling fan on). Disconnect C101 (1.5L and standard) or C151 (HF and Si) connector from C210 connector. *See Fig. 5*. Measure resistance between Red/White wire terminal and Green/White wire terminal of C101 or C151 connector, on sensor side of harness. If resistance value is not 200-400 ohms, inspect for short or open in Red/White or Green/White wire between connector and coolant sensor. If wires are okay, replace coolant sensor.
**3)** If resistance values are within specification, reconnect connectors. Disconnect 2-wire connector directly from coolant sensor. Measure voltage between ground and Red/White wire on sensor harness. If voltage is not about 5 volts, go to step **5)**. If voltage reads about 5 volts, measure voltage between Red/White (pos.) and Green/White (neg.) wires. If about 5 volts is not present, repair open in Green/White wire between ECU and coolant sensor.
**4)** If voltage reading from Green/White wire to Red/White wire of coolant sensor harness was about 5 volts, substitute a known good ECU. If about 5 volts is now read, replace original ECU.

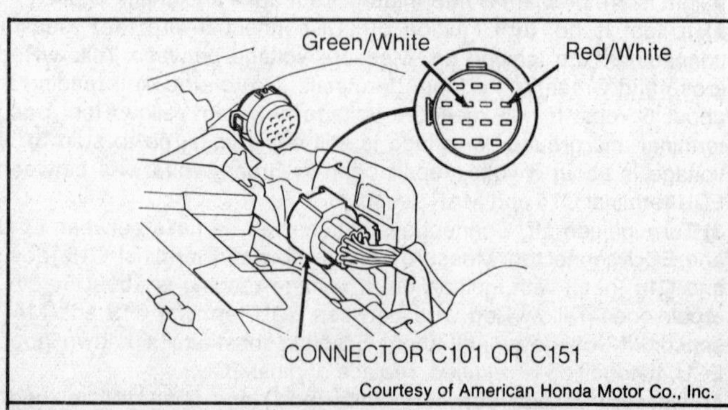
Green/White
Red/White
CONNECTOR C101 OR C151
Courtesy of American Honda Motor Co., Inc.

*Fig. 5: Civic Connector Identification*

**5)** If voltage reading from ground to Red/White wire of coolant sensor harness was not about 5 volts in step **3)**, turn ignition off. Connect system checker harness between ECU and ECU connector. Turn ignition on. Measure voltage between terminals C6 (pos.) and C12 (neg.). If about 5 volts is present, repair open in Red/White wire between ECU terminal C6 and coolant sensor.

**6)** If voltage reading is not about 5 volts, disconnect "C" connector from main wiring harness only, not at ECU. Measure voltage between terminals C6 (pos.) and C12 (neg.). If about 5 volts is now indicated, repair short in Red/White wire between ECU terminal C6 and sensor.

**7)** If about 5 volts is not indicated, substitute a known good ECU. If condition is rectified, replace original ECU.

## CODE 6, COOLANT (TW) SENSOR (ACCORD & PRELUDE)

**1)** Turn ignition off. Remove clock (Prelude) or No. 11 (Accord) fuse in the under-hood relay box for 10 seconds to reset ECU. Start engine and observe PGM-FI warning light. If light is off, problem is intermittent. Test drive and check again.

**2)** If light is on, warm engine to normal operating temperature (cooling fan comes on). Disconnect 2-wire coolant sensor connector. Measure resistance across sensor terminals.

**3)** If resistance is not 200-400 ohms, replace TW sensor. If resistance is within specification, measure voltage between ground and Yellow/Green wire of sensor harness. If reading is not about 5 volts, go to step **5)**. If reading is about 5 volts, measure voltage between Yellow/Green (pos.) and Green/White wires of connector harness.

**4)** If voltage is not about 5 volts, repair open Green/White (neg.) wire between ECU terminal C12 and sensor. If voltage reading is correct, substitute a known good ECU. If condition is rectified, replace original ECU.

**5)** If voltage between ground and Yellow/Green wire of sensor harness did not read 5 volts in step **3)**, turn ignition off. Connect system checker harness between ECU and ECU connector. Turn ignition on. Measure voltage between terminals C6 (pos.) and C12 (neg.) If voltage reading is about 5 volts, repair open Yellow/Green wire between ECU terminal C6 and TW sensor.

**6)** If reading is not about 5 volts, disconnect "C" connector from main wire harness only, not the ECU. Measure voltage between terminals C6 (pos.) and C12 (neg.). If reading is not about 5 volts, go to next step. If voltage reading is about 5 volts, repair short in Yellow/Green wire between ECU terminal C6 and sensor or repair short in Yellow/Green wire between TW sensor and automatic transmission control unit (Prelude).

**7)** If voltage reading is still not about 5 volts, substitute a known good ECU. If condition is rectified, replace original ECU.

## CODE 7, THROTTLE ANGLE SENSOR (ALL MODELS)

**1)** Turn off ignition. Remove hazard fuse in main fuse box for 10 seconds to reset ECU on Civic models. Remove clock (Prelude) or No. 11 (Accord) fuse in the under-hood relay box for 10 seconds to reset ECU. Start engine and observe PGM-FI warning light. If light is off, problem is intermittent. Test drive and check again.

**2)** If light is on, turn ignition off. Disconnect 3-wire connector at throttle position sensor. Turn ignition on. Measure voltage between Yellow/White (pos.) and Green/White (neg.) terminals. If voltage is not about 5 volts, go to step **5)**. If voltage is about 5 volts, turn ignition off. Reconnect sensor connector. Connect system checker harness between ECU and ECU connector.

**3)** Turn ignition on. measure voltage between terminals C7 (pos.) and C12 (neg.). Voltage should read .5 volt at closed throttle, and about 4.5 volts at wide open throttle, with a smooth transition between the lower and upper voltage specification as the throttle is depressed.

**4)** If sensor does not respond as indicated in step **3)**, replace throttle sensor or repair open or short in Red/Blue (Civic) or Red/Yellow (Accord and Prelude) wire between ECU terminal C7 and throttle sensor. On Prelude models, also check for short in Red/Yellow wire between throttle angle sensor and automatic transmission control unit. If throttle sensor responds as indicated, substitute a known good ECU. If condition is rectified, replace original ECU.

**5)** If voltage reading between Yellow/White (pos.) and Green/White (neg.) terminals in step **2)** was not about 5 volts, measure voltage between ground and Yellow/White wire terminal. If voltage is now about 5 volts, repair open in Green/White wire between ECU terminal C12 and throttle sensor. If about 5 volts is not present between ground and Yellow/White wire, turn ignition off.

**6)** Connect system checker harness between ECU and ECU connector. Turn ignition on. Measure voltage between terminals C13 (pos.) and C12 (neg.). If voltage is still not about 5 volts, go to next step. If voltage is about 5 volts, repair open Yellow/White wire between ECU terminal C13 and throttle sensor.

**7)** Substitute a known good ECU. If condition is rectified, replace original ECU.

## CODE 8, TDC/CRANK SENSOR (CIVIC)

**1)** Turn off ignition. Remove hazard fuse in main fuse box for 10 seconds to reset ECU. Start engine and observe Check Engine light. If light is off, problem is intermittent. Test drive and check again.

**2)** If light is on, turn ignition off. Disconnect sensor connector at distributor. Measure resistance between terminals "B" and "C" (standard and DOHC) or terminals "A" and "B" (HF and Si). *See Figs. 1 and 4*. If resistance is not 350-550 ohms, replace distributor assembly. If resistance value is within specification, individually check for continuity between ground and the same respective terminals. If continuity exists, sensor is shorted to ground. Replace distributor assembly.

**3)** Reconnect sensor connector. Connect system checker harness to main wiring harness only, not to ECU. Measure resistance between terminals C3 and C4. If resistance is not 350-550 ohms, repair open or short in Orange/Blue and/or White/Blue wire. If resistance value is within specification, substitute a known good ECU. If condition is rectified, replace original ECU.

## CODE 8, CYL SENSOR (ACCORD)

**1)** Turn ignition off. Remove No. 11 fuse in the under-hood relay box for 10 seconds to reset ECU. Start engine and observe PGM-FI warning light. If light is off, problem is intermittent. Test drive and check again.

**2)** If light is on, turn ignition off. Disconnect sensor connector at distributor. Using an ohmmeter, measure resistance between Orange/Blue and White/Blue terminals. If reading is not 650-850 ohms, replace crank angle sensor. If reading is within specification, proceed to next step.

**3)** Check continuity between ground and Orange/Blue wire terminal. Check continuity between ground and White/Blue wire terminal. If continuity exists, sensor is shorted to ground. Replace crank angle sensor. If no continuity exists, proceed to next step.

**4)** Reconnect sensor connector. Attach system checker harness to main wire harness only, not to ECU. Using an ohmmeter, check resistance between connector C3 and C4 terminals. Resistance should be 650-850 ohms.

**5)** If resistance is not within specification, repair open or short in Orange/Blue and/or White/Blue wire. If resistance is within specification, substitute a known good ECU. If condition is rectified, replace original ECU.

## CODE 8, TDC/CRANK SENSOR (PRELUDE)

**1)** Turn ignition off. Remove clock fuse in the under-hood relay box for 10 seconds to reset ECU. Start engine and observe PGM-FI warning light. If light is off, problem is intermittent. Test drive and check again.

**2)** If light is on, turn ignition off. Disconnect 4-wire sensor connector at distributor. Measure resistance between Orange/Blue and White/Blue terminals. If reading is not 700-1000 ohms, replace distributor assembly. If reading is within specification, proceed to next step.
**3)** Check continuity between ground and Orange/Blue wire terminal. Check continuity between ground and White/Blue wire terminal. If continuity exists, sensor is shorted to ground. Replace distributor assembly. If no continuity exists, proceed to next step.
**4)** Reconnect sensor connector. Attach system checker harness to main wire harness only, not to ECU. Using an ohmmeter, check resistance between connector C3 and C4 terminals. Resistance should be 700-1000 ohms.
**5)** If resistance is not within specification, repair open or short in Orange/Blue and/or White/Blue wire. If resistance is within specification, substitute a known good ECU. If condition is rectified, replace original ECU.

## CODE 9, TDC/CRANK/CYL SENSOR (CIVIC HF & Si)

**1)** Turn off ignition. Remove hazard fuse in main fuse box for 10 seconds to reset ECU. Start engine and observe Check Engine light. If light is off, problem is intermittent. Test drive and check again.
**2)** If light is on, turn ignition off. Disconnect 8-wire sensor connector nearest the sensor. Measure resistance between Blue/Green and Blue/Yellow wire of sensor. If reading is not 350-550 ohms, replace distributor assembly. If reading is within specification, proceed to next step.
**3)** Check continuity between ground and Blue/Green and Blue/Yellow wire sensor terminals. If continuity exists, replace distributor assembly. If no continuity exists, proceed to next step.
**4)** Reconnect sensor connector. Attach system checker harness to main wire harness only, not to ECU. Check resistance between connector terminals C1 and C2. Resistance should be 350-550 ohms.
**5)** If resistance is not within specification, repair open in Blue/Green and/or Blue/Yellow wires. If resistance is within specification, substitute a known good ECU. If condition is rectified, replace original ECU.

## CODE 9, CYL SENSOR (CIVIC STANDARD & PRELUDE)

**1)** Turn off ignition. Remove hazard fuse in main fuse box for 10 seconds to reset ECU on Civic standard. Remove clock fuse in the under-hood relay box for 10 seconds to reset ECU on Prelude models. Start engine and observe PGM-FI warning light. If light is off, problem is intermittent. Test drive and check again.
**2)** If light is on, turn ignition off. Disconnect 2-wire sensor connector. Measure resistance across sensor terminals. If reading is not 700-1000 ohms, replace CYL sensor assembly. If reading is within specification, proceed to next step.
**3)** Check continuity between ground and each sensor terminal. If continuity exists, replace CYL sensor assembly. If no continuity exists, proceed to next step.
**4)** Reconnect sensor connector. Attach system checker harness to main wire harness only, not to ECU. Check resistance between connector terminals C1 and C2. Resistance should be 700-1000 ohms.
**5)** If resistance is not within specification, repair open in Blue/Green and/or Blue/Yellow wires (Civic) or Orange and/or White wires (Prelude). If resistance is within specification, substitute a known good ECU. If condition is rectified, replace original ECU.

## CODE 9, CRK/CYL SENSOR (ACCORD)

**1)** Turn ignition off. Remove No. 11 fuse in the under-hood relay box for 10 seconds to reset ECU. Start engine and observe PGM-FI warning light. If light is off, problem is intermittent. Test drive and check again.
**2)** If light is on, turn ignition off. Disconnect 4-wire sensor connector near distributor. Measure resistance between White and Orange wire terminals at sensor. If reading is not 650-850, replace sensor. If reading is within specification, proceed to next step.
**3)** Check continuity between ground and White wire terminal. Check continuity between ground and Orange wire terminal. If continuity exists, sensor is shorted to ground. Replace sensor. If no continuity exists, proceed to next step.
**4)** Reconnect sensor connector. Attach system checker harness to main wire harness only, not to ECU. Check resistance between connector terminals C1 and C2. Resistance should be 650-850 ohms.
**5)** If resistance not within specification, repair open in Orange and/or White wire. If resistance is within specification, substitute a known good ECU. If condition is rectified, replace original ECU.

## CODE 10, AIR TEMPERATURE (TA) SENSOR (ALL MODELS)

**1)** Turn off ignition. Remove hazard fuse in main fuse box for 10 seconds (Civic) or remove clock (Prelude) or No. 11 (Accord) fuse in the under-hood relay box for 10 seconds to reset ECU. Start engine and observe PGM-FI warning light. If light is off, problem is intermittent. Test drive and check again.
**2)** If light is on, turn ignition off. Measure resistance across TA sensor terminals. If reading is not 1000-4000 ohms, replace sensor. If resistance is within specification, measure voltage between ground and White/Red (Accord and Prelude) or Red/Yellow (Civic) wire terminal. If reading is about 5 volts, go to step **3)**. If reading is not about 5 volts, go to step **4)**.
**3)** Measure voltage between same wire (pos.) and Green/White (neg.) wire terminal. If voltage is not about 5 volts, repair open in Green/White between ECU terminal C12 and sensor. If reading is about 5 volts, substitute a known good ECU. If condition is rectified, replace original ECU.
**4)** If voltage in step **2)** was not about 5 volts, turn ignition off. Connect system checker harness between ECU and ECU connector. Turn ignition on. Measure voltage between terminals C5 (pos.) and C12 (neg.). If voltage reading is about 5 volts, repair open in White/Red (Accord and Prelude) or Red/Yellow (Civic) wire between ECU terminal C5 and sensor.
**5)** If reading was not about 5 volts, disconnect "C" connector from the main wire harness only, not the ECU. Measure voltage between terminals C5 (pos.) and C12 (neg.). If voltage reading is about 5 volts, repair short in White/Red (Accord and Prelude) or Red/Yellow wire between ECU terminal C5 and sensor.
**6)** If voltage is not about 5 volts, substitute a known good ECU. If voltage is now correct, replace original ECU.

## CODE 11, IDLE MIXTURE ADJUSTER (IMA) (CIVIC WITHOUT CATALYST)

**1)** Turn off ignition. Remove hazard fuse in main fuse box for 10 seconds to reset ECU. Start engine and observe Check Engine light. If light is off, problem is intermittent. Test drive and check again.
**2)** If light is on, turn ignition off. Disconnect 3-wire connector at sensor. Measure resistance across Yellow/White and Green/White wires of sensor. If resistance is not 400-6000 ohms, replace sensor. Measure resistance across Yellow/White and Brown wires of sensor. If resistance is not 400-6000 ohms, replace sensor.
**3)** If resistance values are within specification, turn ignition on. Measure voltage between Yellow/White (pos.) and Green/White (neg.) terminals of sensor harness. If voltage is not about 5 volts, go to step **5)**. If voltage is about 5 volts, turn ignition off. Connect system checker harness between ECU and ECU connector.
**4)** Turn ignition on. Measure voltage between terminals B20 (pos.) and C12 (neg.) If voltage reading is not .5-4.5 volts, repair open or short in Brown wire between ECU terminal B20 and IMA sensor. If

voltage is within specification, substitute a known good ECU. If condition is rectified, replace original ECU.

**5)** Measure voltage between ground and Yellow/White wire of sensor harness. If voltage is now about 5 volts, repair open in Green/White wire between ECU terminal C12 and IMA sensor. If voltage is not about 5 volts, turn ignition off.

**6)** Connect system checker harness between ECU and ECU connector. Turn ignition on. Measure voltage between terminals C13 (pos.) and C12 (neg.). If voltage is now about 5 volts, repair open in Yellow/White wire between ECU terminal C13 and IMA sensor.

**7)** If voltage is not about 5 volts, substitute a known good ECU. If voltage reading is now correct, replace original ECU.

## CODE 12, EGR SYSTEM (CIVIC HF)

**1)** Check harness and connections between EGR valve and ECU. Verify vacuum supply to EGR control solenoid. Check vacuum hoses for cracks, splits or looseness. Repair as necessary. Warm engine to normal operating temperature (cooling fan on). Disconnect vacuum hose from EGR valve. Using a hand-held vacuum pump, apply vacuum to EGR valve. If vacuum does not hold and engine does not stall, replace faulty EGR valve or clean blocked EGR passages.

**2)** If vacuum held and engine stalled in step **1)**, remove control box cover. Disconnect vacuum hose between air chamber and solenoid valve. Connect vacuum gauge to air chamber. If there is not about 8 in. Hg, replace CVC. If vacuum is present, reconnect hose between vacuum chamber and EGR solenoid.

**3)** If vacuum is now present at EGR valve, check for short in Red wire between ECU terminal A10 and EGR control solenoid. If wire is okay, replace solenoid. If vacuum is not present, disconnect 4-wire connector from control box. *See Fig. 6.* Jumper battery voltage to terminal "D" and ground to terminal "C" at control box (solenoid side of harness). Check EGR valve for 8 in. Hg. If vacuum is present, go to step **5)**.

**4)** Connect and disconnect ground from terminal "C" of solenoid harness. If EGR solenoid does not click, replace solenoid. If solenoid does click, repair blockage in vacuum port of solenoid.

**5)** Measure voltage between ground and Black/Yellow wire terminal of harness. If battery voltage is not present, repair open in Black/Yellow wire between solenoid valve and No. 14 fuse. If battery voltage is present, turn ignition off. Connect test harness between EGR lift sensor and sensor connector.

**6)** Turn ignition on. Measure voltage between Red (pos.) and Green (neg.) terminals of harness. If about 5 volts is indicated, go to step **8)**. If 5 volts is not indicated, measure voltage between ground and Red (pos.) harness terminal. If 5 volts is indicated, repair open in Green/White wire between ECU terminal C12 and sensor.

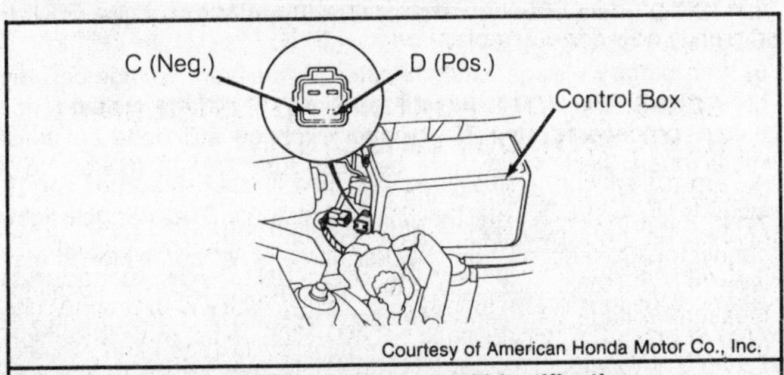
C (Neg.)
D (Pos.)
Control Box
Courtesy of American Honda Motor Co., Inc.

*Fig. 6: Civic (HF) EGR Solenoid terminal Identification*

**7)** If 5 volts is not indicated, turn ignition off. Connect system checker harness between ECU and ECU connector. Turn ignition on. Measure voltage between terminals C13 (pos.) and C12 (neg.). If voltage is about 5 volts, repair open in White/Yellow wire between ECU terminal C13 and sensor. If 5 volts is not indicated, substitute a known good ECU. If condition is rectified, replace original ECU.

**8)** Measure voltage between White (pos.) and Green (neg.) terminals of harness. If about one volt is not indicated, replace EGR valve or repair short in Yellow wire between ECU terminal C8 and EGR valve lift sensor. If about one volt is indicated, turn ignition off.

**9)** Connect system checker harness between ECU and ECU connector. Turn ignition on. Measure voltage between terminals C8 (pos.) and C12 (neg.). If about one volt is not indicated, repair open Yellow wire between ECU terminal C8 and sensor.

**10)** Disconnect "A" connector of system checker harness from ECU only, not main harness. Measure voltage between terminals A10 (pos.) and A2 (neg.). If battery voltage is not present, repair open Red wire between ECU terminal A10 and EGR control solenoid.

**11)** If battery voltage is indicated, substitute a known good ECU. If condition is rectified, replace original ECU.

## CODE 12, EGR SYSTEM (ACCORD)

**1)** Check harness and connections between EGR valve and ECU. Warm engine to normal operating temperature (cooling fan on). Disconnect vacuum hose from EGR valve. Using a hand-held vacuum pump, apply vacuum to EGR valve. If vacuum does not hold, and engine does not stall, replace faulty EGR valve or clean blocked EGR passages.

**2)** If vacuum held and engine stalled in step **1)**, restart engine. Open control box. Verify vacuum from intake manifold to CVC valve. Repair as necessary. Reconnect manifold vacuum hose. Disconnect vacuum hose between CVC valve and air chamber. Connect vacuum gauge and check for about 8 in. Hg.

**3)** If reading is not about 8 in. Hg, replace CVC valve. If vacuum is correct, reconnect vacuum hose. Install vacuum gauge at EGR valve hose. Disconnect electrical connector from control box. Jumper voltage to Black/Yellow wire terminal of box and ground to Red wire terminal of box. Reading at EGR valve hose should now be about 8 in. Hg.

**4)** If vacuum reading is not correct, replace EGR control solenoid. If reading is correct, measure voltage from ground to Black/Yellow wire of control box harness connector. If battery voltage is not present, repair open in Black/Yellow wire between No. 1 fuse and control box harness connector.

**5)** If battery voltage is present, turn ignition off. Connect test harness between EGR lift sensor and sensor harness connector. Turn ignition on. Measure voltage between Red (pos.) and Green (neg.) terminals. If voltage is about 5 volts, go to step **7)**. If voltage is not about 5 volts, measure voltage between ground and Red terminal. If voltage is now about 5 volts, repair open in Green/White wire between ECU terminal C12 and sensor.

**6)** If voltage is not about 5 volts, turn ignition off. Connect system checker harness between ECU and ECU connector. Measure voltage between terminals C13 (pos.) and C12 (neg.). If voltage is now about 5 volts, repair open in Yellow/White wire between ECU terminal C13 and sensor. If voltage is not about 5 volts, substitute a known good ECU. If condition is rectified, replace original ECU.

**7)** Measure voltage between White (pos.) and Green (neg.) terminals. If voltage reading is not about one volt, replace EGR valve or repair short in Red wire between ECU terminal A10 and EGR control solenoid. If about one volt is measured, turn ignition off. Connect system checker harness between ECU and ECU connector.

**8)** Turn ignition on. Measure voltage between terminals C8 (pos.) and C12 (neg.). If voltage is not about one volt, repair open in Yellow wire between ECU terminal C8 and sensor. If voltage is about one volt, disconnect "A" connector from ECU only, not from main harness.

**9)** Measure voltage between terminals A10 (pos.) and A18 (neg.). If battery voltage is not present, repair open or short in Red wire between ECU terminal A10 and EGR control solenoid. If battery voltage is present, substitute a known good ECU. If condition is rectified, replace original ECU.

## CODE 12, EGR SYSTEM (PRELUDE)

**1)** Check harness and connections between EGR valve and ECU. Verify vacuum supply to EGR control solenoid. Check vacuum hoses for cracks, splits or looseness. Repair as necessary. Warm engine to normal operating temperature (cooling fan on). Disconnect vacuum hose from EGR valve. Using a hand-held vacuum pump, apply vacuum to EGR valve. If vacuum does not hold and engine does not stall, replace faulty EGR valve or clean blocked EGR passages.

**2)** If vacuum held and engine stalled in step **1)**, remove control box cover. Disconnect vacuum hose between air chamber and solenoid valve. Connect vacuum gauge to air chamber. If there is not about 8 in. Hg, replace CVC. If correct vacuum is present, reconnect hose between vacuum chamber and EGR solenoid.

**3)** If vacuum is now present at EGR valve, check for short in Red wire between ECU terminal A10 and EGR control solenoid. If wire is okay, replace solenoid. If vacuum is not present, disconnect 4-wire connector from control box. Jumper battery voltage to Black/Yellow wire terminal and ground to Red wire terminal at control box (solenoid side of harness). Check EGR valve for about 8 in. Hg. If correct vacuum is present, go to step **5)**.

**4)** Connect and disconnect ground from Red terminal of solenoid harness. If EGR solenoid does not click, replace solenoid. If solenoid does click, repair blockage in vacuum port of solenoid.

**5)** Measure voltage between ground and Black/Yellow wire terminal of harness. If battery voltage is not present, repair open in Black/Yellow wire between solenoid valve and No. 12 fuse. If battery voltage is present, turn ignition off. Connect test harness between EGR lift sensor and sensor connector.

**6)** Turn ignition on. Measure voltage between Red (pos.) and Green (neg.) terminals of harness. Go to step **8)** if about 5 volts is indicated. If 5 volts is not indicated, measure voltage between ground and Red (pos.) harness terminal. If 5 volts is indicated, repair open in Green/White wire between ECU terminal C12 and sensor.

**7)** If 5 volts is not indicated, turn ignition off. Connect system checker harness between ECU and ECU connector. Turn ignition on. Measure voltage between terminals C13 (pos.) and C12 (neg.). If voltage is about 5 volts, repair open in White/Yellow wire between ECU terminal C13 and sensor. If 5 volts is not indicated, substitute a known good ECU. If condition is rectified, replace original ECU.

**8)** Measure voltage between White (pos.) and Green (neg.) terminals of harness. If about one volt is not indicated, replace EGR valve or repair short in Yellow wire between ECU terminal C8 and EGR valve lift sensor. If about one volt is indicated, turn ignition off.

**9)** Connect system checker harness between ECU and ECU connector. Turn ignition on. Measure voltage between terminals C8 (pos.) and C12 (neg.). If about one volt is not indicated, repair open Yellow wire between ECU terminal C8 and sensor.

**10)** If about one volt is not indicated, disconnect "A" connector of system checker harness from ECU only, not main harness. Measure voltage between terminals A10 (pos.) and A18 (neg.). If battery voltage is not present, repair open Red wire between ECU terminal A10 and EGR control solenoid.

**11)** If battery voltage is indicated, substitute a known good ECU. If condition is rectified, replace original ECU.

## CODE 13, ATMOSPHERIC (PA) SENSOR (ALL MODELS)

**1)** Turn off ignition. Remove hazard fuse in main fuse box (Civic), or remove clock (Prelude) or No. 11 (Accord) fuse in the under-hood relay box for 10 seconds to reset ECU. Start engine and observe PGM-FI warning light. If light is off, problem is intermittent. Test drive and check again.

**2)** If light is on, turn ignition off. Connect system checker harness between ECU and ECU connector. Turn ignition on. Measure voltage between terminals C13 (pos.) and C12 (neg.). If about 5 volts is read, go to step **3)**. If not, substitute a known good ECU. If correct voltage is now indicated, replace original ECU.

**3)** Measure voltage between terminals C9 (pos.) and C12 (neg.). If about 3 volts is not present, go to step **4)**. If about 3 volts is present, substitute a known good ECU. If condition is rectified, replace original ECU.

**4)** Disconnect connector from atmospheric pressure sensor. Measure voltage between terminals C9 (pos.) and C12 (neg.) on harness side. If about 5 volts is indicated, go to step **5)**. If about 5 volts is not indicated, repair short in Red (Red/White on Civic) wire between ECU terminal C9 and sensor.

**5)** Measure voltage between Yellow/White (White/Yellow on Prelude) and Green/White (neg.) wires. If reading is not about 5 volts, go to step **6)**. If about 5 volts is present, measure voltage between Red (Red/White on Civic) and Green/White (neg.) terminals. If about 5 volts is not read, repair open Red or Red/White wire between ECU terminal C9 and sensor. If about 5 volts is read, replace sensor.

**6)** Measure voltage between ground and Yellow/White (White/Yellow on Prelude) wire of harness. If about 5 volts is not present, repair open in White/Yellow or Yellow/White wire between ECU terminal C13 and sensor. If about 5 volts is present, repair open Green/White wire between ECU terminal C12 and sensor.

## CODE 14, IDLE CONTROL SYSTEM EACV (ALL MODELS)

**1)** Turn off ignition. Remove hazard fuse in main fuse box (Civic), or remove clock (Prelude) or No. 11 (Accord) fuse in the under-hood relay box for 10 seconds to reset ECU. Start engine and observe PGM-FI warning light. If light is off, problem is intermittent. Test drive and check again.

**2)** If light is on, turn ignition off. Disconnect Electronic Air Control Valve (EACV) connector. Check resistance between the 2 connector terminals on valve.

**3)** Resistance should be 8-15 ohms. If not within specification, replace EACV. If resistance is within specification, proceed to next step.

**4)** Check for continuity to ground on each EACV connector terminal. If continuity exists, replace EACV. If no continuity exists, turn ignition on. On Civic models, connect a voltmeter between Black/Yellow (pos.) and Blue/Yellow (neg.) terminals. On Accord models, connect voltmeter between Black/Yellow (pos.) and Black/Blue (neg.) terminals. On Prelude models, connect voltmeter between Black/Yellow (pos.) and Blue/Red (neg.) terminals.

**5)** Check for battery voltage. If no battery voltage exists, proceed to step **6)**. If battery voltage exists, disconnect connector from ECU and again check for battery voltage. If battery voltage still does not exist, substitute a known good ECU. If condition is rectified, replace original ECU. If battery voltage does exist, repair short in Blue/Yellow (Civic), Black/Blue (Accord) or Blue/Red (Prelude) wire between ECU terminal A11 and EACV.

**6)** If no battery voltage existed in step **5)**, measure voltage between ground and Black/Yellow wire terminal. If battery voltage now exists, proceed to step **7)**. If battery voltage still does not exist, repair open Black/Yellow wire between fuse No. 14 (Civic), No. 1 (Accord) or No. 12 (Prelude) and EACV.

**7)** If battery voltage exists, turn ignition off. Reconnect EACV connector. Connect system checker harness "A" connector to main wire harness only, not ECU. Turn ignition on. Using a voltmeter, measure voltage between connector terminals A11 (pos.) and A18 (neg.) on Accord and Prelude, or terminals A11 (pos.) and A2 (neg.) on Civic. If voltage does not exist, repair open in wire between ECU terminal A11 and EACV.

**8)** If battery voltage exists, connect and disconnect terminal A11 to A18 on Accord and Prelude, or terminal A11 to A2 on Civic. If EACV does not click when connector is connected and disconnected, replace EACV. If EAVC clicks, substitute a known good ECU. If condition is rectified, replace original ECU.

## CODE 15, IGNITION OUTPUT SIGNAL (CIVIC & PRELUDE)

**1)** Turn off ignition. Remove hazard fuse in main fuse box (Civic) or remove clock (Prelude) fuse in the under-hood relay box for 10 seconds to reset ECU. Start engine and observe PGM-FI warning light. If light is off, problem is intermittent. Test drive and check again.

**2)** If light is on, turn ignition off. Disconnect 2-wire (Civic) connector at distributor or 6-wire (Prelude) connector at ignitor. Turn ignition on. Measure voltage between ground and Black/Yellow wire terminal on ignition side of harness. If battery voltage is not present, repair open Black/Yellow wire between connector and ignition switch.

**3)** If battery voltage is present, turn ignition off. Reconnect 2-wire or 6-wire connector. Connect system checker harness between ECU and ECU connector. Turn ignition on. Individually, measure voltage between terminal A18 (neg.) and terminals B15 and B17. If battery voltage is present, go to step **4)**. If battery voltage is not present, on Prelude go to step **5)**, on Civic, repair open in wires between distributor and ECU terminals B15 or B17 or replace faulty ignitor unit.

**4)** Substitute a known good ECU. If condition is rectified, replace original ECU.

**5)** Turn ignition off. Disconnect 6-wire ignitor connector and connectors from ECU only, not main harness. Check for continuity between White wires and ECU terminals B15 and B17 and ignitor. If continuity does not exist, repair as necessary. If continuity does exist, check for continuity between ground and White wires of 6-wire connector. If continuity exists, repair short to ground. If continuity does not exist, replace ignitor.

## CODE 16, FUEL INJECTOR CIRCUIT (CIVIC HF & Si & PRELUDE)

**1)** Turn off ignition. Remove hazard fuse in main fuse box for 10 seconds to reset ECU. Attempt to start engine. If engine does not start, go to step **3)**. Start engine and observe Check Engine light. If light is off, problem is intermittent. Test drive and check again.

**2)** If light is on, turn ignition off. Test drive and check again. If light is on, using a stethescope, check for clicking sound at each injector while engine is idling. If all injectors click, substitute a known good ECU. If condition is rectified, replace original ECU.

**3)** Turn ignition off. If engine does not start, check resistance of all injectors. If engine does start, check resistance of injectors which did not click. If resistance value is not 1.5-2.5 ohms, replace injector(s). If resistance values are within specification, turn ignition on. Measure voltage between ground and Red/Black wire at injector.

**4)** If battery voltage is not present, go to step **7)**. If battery voltage is present, check voltage at the following terminals.

- Injector No. 1 – Red/Black (pos.) and Brown (neg.).
- Injector No. 2 – Red/Black (pos.) and Red (neg.).
- Injector No. 3 – Red/Black (pos.) and Light Blue (neg.).
- Injector No. 4 – Red/Black (pos.) and Yellow (neg.).

If battery voltage is not present, go to step **5)**. If battery voltage is present, disconnect ECU connector. If battery voltage is still present, repair short in wires A1 (injector 1), A3 (injector 2), A5 (injector 3) or A7 (injector 4) between ECU and injector. If battery voltage is not present, substitute a known good ECU. If battery voltage is now present, replace original ECU.

**5)** Reconnect injector connector(s). Connect system checker harness between ECU and ECU connector. Measure voltage between negative terminal A2 (Civic) or A18 (Prelude) and the following positive terminals.

- Injector No. 1 – A1
- Injector No. 2 – A3
- Injector No. 3 – A5
- Injector No. 4 – A7

**6)** If battery voltage is not present, repair open in wire A1 (injector 1), A3 (injector 2), A5 (injector 3) or A7 (injector 4) between ECU and injector. If battery voltage is present, substitute a known good ECU. If condition is rectified, replace original ECU.

**7)** Turn ignition off. Disconnect injector resistor connector. Turn ignition on. Measure voltage between ground and Yellow/Black wire terminal. If battery voltage is present, replace injector resistor. If battery voltage is not present, repair open in Yellow/Black wire between injector resistor and main relay.

## CODE 17, VEHICLE SPEED SENSOR (CIVIC)

**1)** Block drive wheels and set parking brake. Raise front of vehicle and support with safety stands. With ignition off, connect system checker harness between ECU and ECU connector. Turn ignition on.

**2)** Slowly rotate left front wheel while measuring voltage between terminals B16 (pos.) and A18 (neg.). If voltmeter pulses between zero and 5 volts, substitute a known good ECU. If condition is rectified, replace original ECU.

**3)** If voltmeter does not pulse between zero and 5 volts, repair open or short in Yellow/Red wire between ECU terminal B16 and speed sensor or replace faulty speed sensor.

## CODE 17, VEHICLE SPEED PULSER (PRELUDE)

**1)** Block rear wheels and set parking brake. Raise front of vehicle and support with stands. Connect system checker harness between ECU and connector. Turn ignition on.

**2)** Slowly rotate left front wheel and measure voltage between terminals B16 (pos.) and A18 (neg.). If voltage pulses from 0-5 volts, proceed to step **5)**. If voltage does not pulse, turn ignition off.

**3)** Disconnect connectors from ECU only, not from main harness. Turn ignition on. Slowly rotate left front wheel and measure voltage between terminals B16 (pos.) and A18 (neg.). If voltage pulses from 0-5 volts, substitute a known good ECU. If condition is rectified, replace original ECU.

**4)** If voltage does not pulse from 0-5 volts, repair open or short in White/Blue wire between ECU terminal B16 and speed sensor or replace faulty speed sensor.

**5)** Substitute a known good ECU. If condition is rectified, replace original ECU.

## CODE 19, LOCK-UP CONTROL SOLENOID AUTO. TRANS. (CIVIC)

**1)** Turn ignition off and remove hazard fuse in main fuse box for 10 seconds to reset ECU. Drive vehicle and observe Check Engine light. If light is off, problem is intermittent. Test drive and check again.

**2)** If light is on, turn ignition off. Connect system checker harness between ECU and ECU connector. Disconnect "A" connector from ECU only, not from main harness. Turn ignition on. Measure voltage between terminals A17 (pos.) and A18 (neg.). If battery voltage is present, go to step **4)**.

**3)** If battery voltage is not present, inspect No. 14 fuse. If fuse is okay, repair open in Black/Yellow wire between ECU terminal A17 and No. 14 fuse.

**4)** Turn ignition off. Disconnect connector from lock-up control solenoid valve. Check terminal A8 at ECU harness for continuity to ground. If continuity exists, repair short in wire between ECU and solenoid valve.

**5)** If continuity does not exist, reconnect solenoid connector. Measure resistance between terminal A8 and A18. If resistance is 14-25 ohms, substitute a known good ECU. If condition is rectified, replace original ECU.

**6)** If resistance is not to specification, unplug solenoid connector. Check for continuity in Yellow wire between ECU and solenoid connector. If continuity does not exist, repair open in Yellow wire. If continuity does exist, replace faulty lock-up solenoid valve.

## CODE 20, ELECTRICAL LOAD DETECTOR (CIVIC)

**1)** Turn ignition off and remove hazard fuse in main fuse panel for 10 seconds to reset ECU. Start engine and observe Check Engine light. If light is off, problem is intermittent. Test drive and check again.

**2)** If light is on, turn ignition off. Open lid of main fuse panel in engine compartment. Disconnect 3-wire electrical load detector. Turn ignition on. Measure voltage between Black/Yellow (pos.) and Black (neg.) wire terminals of harness. If battery voltage is present, go to step **4**).

**3)** If battery voltage is not present, measure voltage between Black/Yellow wire and ground. If battery voltage is now present, repair open in Black wire between connector and ground. If battery voltage is not present, repair open Black/Yellow wire between No. 14 fuse and connector.

**4)** Turn ignition off. Connect system checker harness between ECU and ECU connector. Disconnect "B" connector from ECU only, not main harness. Connect Green/Red terminal of load detector harness connector to ground. Check for continuity between ECU terminal B19 and ground. If continuity does not exist, repair open Green/Red wire between ECU connector terminal B19 and load detector connector.

**5)** Reconnect "B" connector to ECU. Turn ignition on. Measure voltage between Green/Red (pos.) and Black (neg.) terminals of load detector harness. If 4.5-5 volts is present, go to step **7**). If 4.5-5 volts is not present, disconnect "B" connector from main wiring harness, not ECU. Measure voltage between terminals B19 (pos.) and A18 (neg.)

**6)** If voltage is now 4.5-5 volts, repair short in Green/Red wire between ECU terminal B19 and load detector connector. If voltage is not 4.5-5 volts, substitute a known good ECU. If correct voltage is now available, replace original ECU.

**7)** Reconnect load detector connector. Measure voltage between terminals B19 (pos.) and A18 (neg.) under the following conditions.

- Headlight switch in first position – Voltage should be 2.5-3.5 volts.
- Headlight switch in second position – Voltage should be 1.5-2.5 volts.

**8)** If voltage is not as noted replace faulty electrical load detector. If voltage responds as indicated, substitute a known good ECU. If condition is rectified, replace original ECU.

# 1988 COMPUTERIZED ENGINE CONTROLS
## Honda Electronic Control System (Cont.)

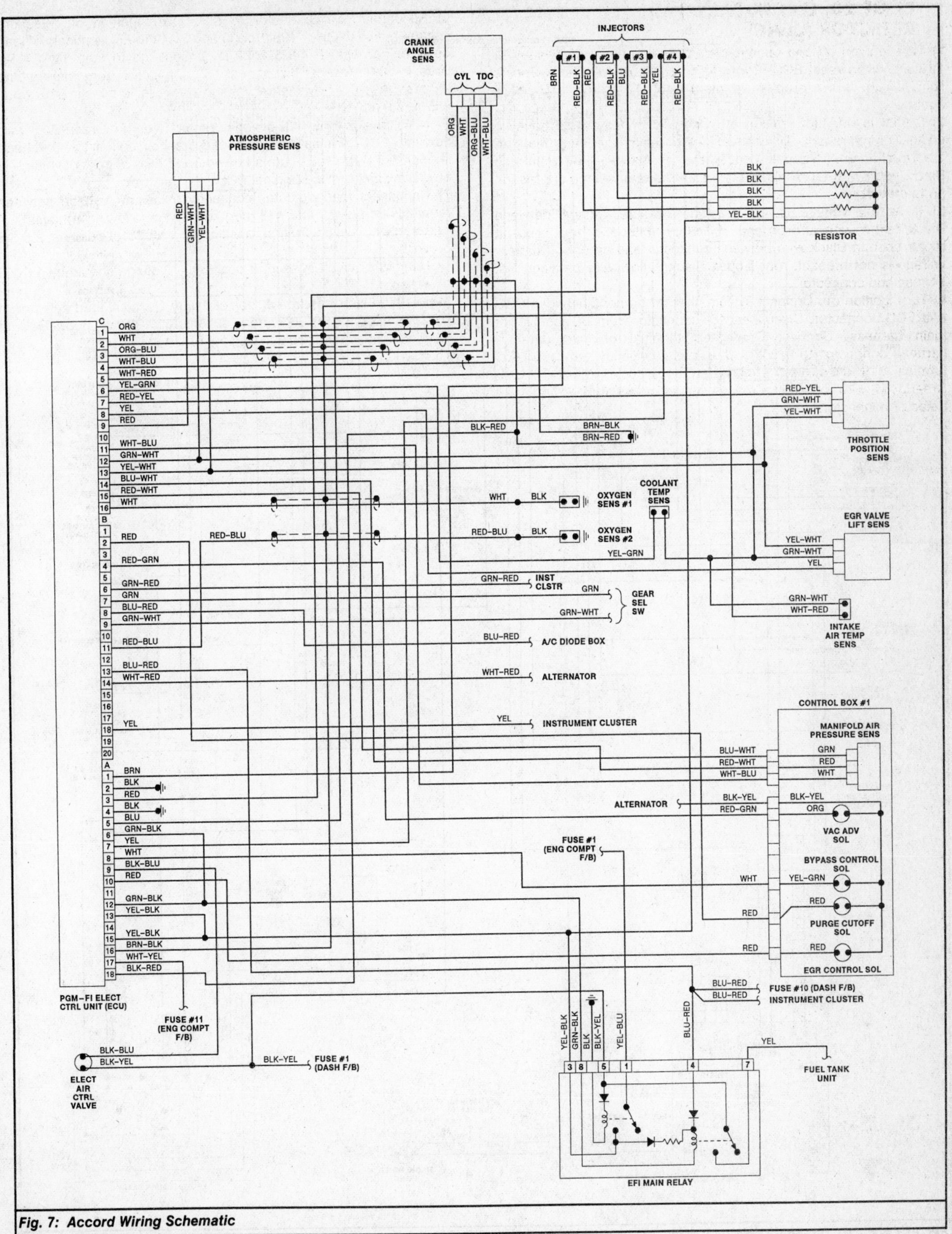

INJECTORS
CRANK ANGLE SENS
CYL
TDC
ATMOSPHERIC PRESSURE SENS
RESISTOR
THROTTLE POSITION SENS
COOLANT TEMP SENS
OXYGEN SENS #1
OXYGEN SENS #2
EGR VALVE LIFT SENS
INST CLSTR
GEAR SEL SW
INTAKE AIR TEMP SENS
A/C DIODE BOX
ALTERNATOR
INSTRUMENT CLUSTER
CONTROL BOX #1
MANIFOLD AIR PRESSURE SENS
VAC ADV SOL
BYPASS CONTROL SOL
PURGE CUTOFF SOL
EGR CONTROL SOL
FUSE #1 (ENG COMPT F/B)
FUSE #10 (DASH F/B)
FUSE #11 (ENG COMPT F/B)
FUSE #1 (DASH F/B)
PGM-FI ELECT CTRL UNIT (ECU)
ELECT AIR CTRL VALVE
FUEL TANK UNIT
EFI MAIN RELAY


*Fig. 7: Accord Wiring Schematic*

# 1988 COMPUTERIZED ENGINE CONTROLS
## Honda Electronic Control System (Cont.)

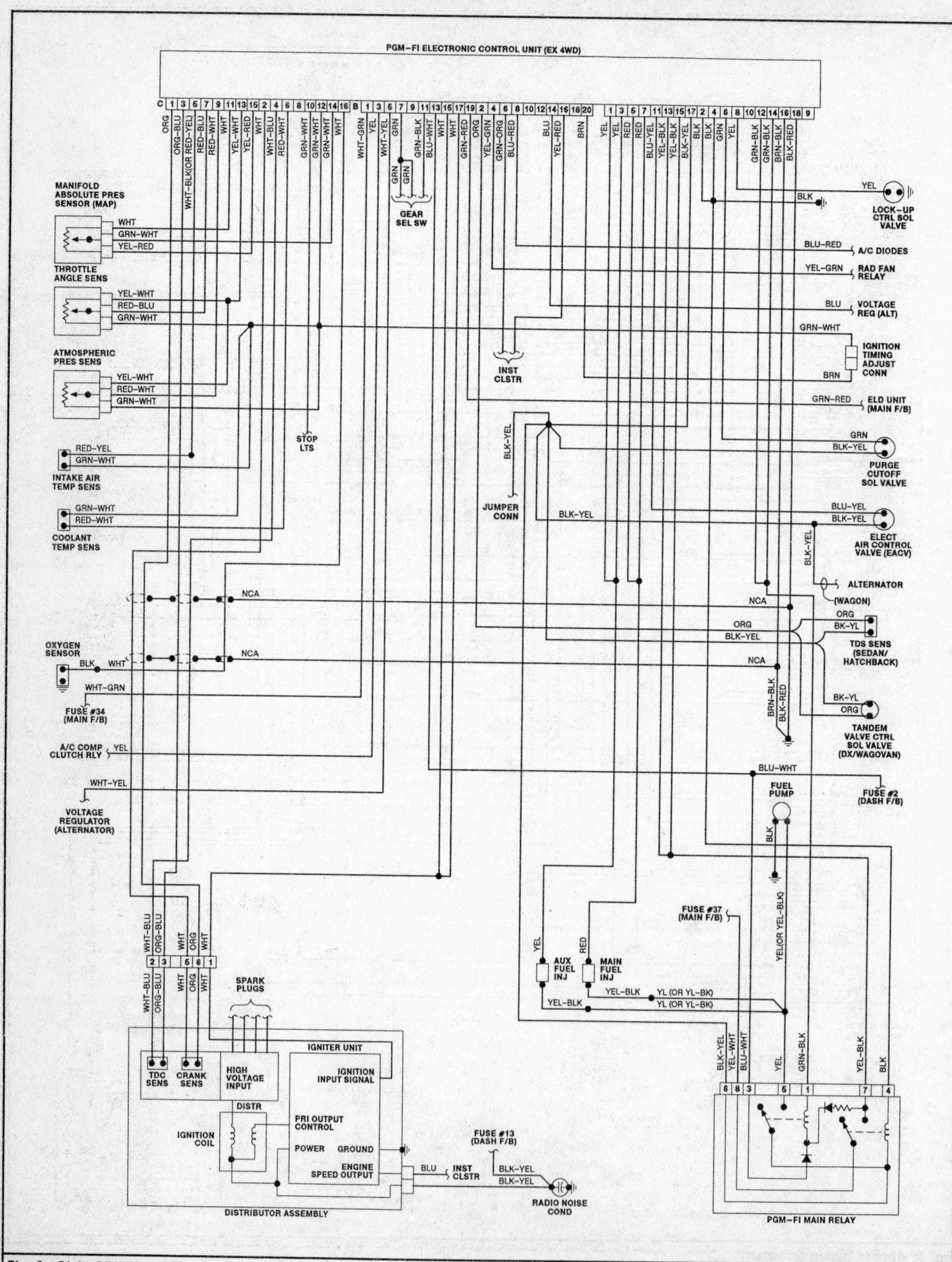

PGM-FI ELECTRONIC CONTROL UNIT (EX 4WD)
MANIFOLD ABSOLUTE PRES SENSOR (MAP)
THROTTLE ANGLE SENS
ATMOSPHERIC PRES SENS
INTAKE AIR TEMP SENS
COOLANT TEMP SENS
OXYGEN SENSOR
FUSE #34 (MAIN F/B)
A/C COMP CLUTCH RLY
VOLTAGE REGULATOR (ALTERNATOR)
GEAR SEL SW
STOP LTS
INST CLSTR
JUMPER CONN
LOCK-UP CTRL SOL VALVE
A/C DIODES
RAD FAN RELAY
VOLTAGE REG (ALT)
IGNITION TIMING ADJUST CONN
ELD UNIT (MAIN F/B)
PURGE CUTOFF SOL VALVE
ELECT AIR CONTROL VALVE (EACV)
ALTERNATOR
(WAGON)
TDS SENS (SEDAN/ HATCHBACK)
TANDEM VALVE CTRL SOL VALVE (DX/WAGOVAN)
FUSE #2 (DASH F/B)
FUEL PUMP
FUSE #37 (MAIN F/B)
AUX FUEL INJ
MAIN FUEL INJ
SPARK PLUGS
IGNITER UNIT
TDC SENS
CRANK SENS
HIGH VOLTAGE INPUT
IGNITION INPUT SIGNAL
DISTR
IGNITION COIL
PRI OUTPUT CONTROL
POWER
GROUND
ENGINE SPEED OUTPUT
DISTRIBUTOR ASSEMBLY
FUSE #13 (DASH F/B)
RADIO NOISE COND
PGM-FI MAIN RELAY


*Fig. 8: Civic CRX (Standard) Wiring Schematic*

# 1988 COMPUTERIZED ENGINE CONTROLS
## Honda Electronic Control System (Cont.)

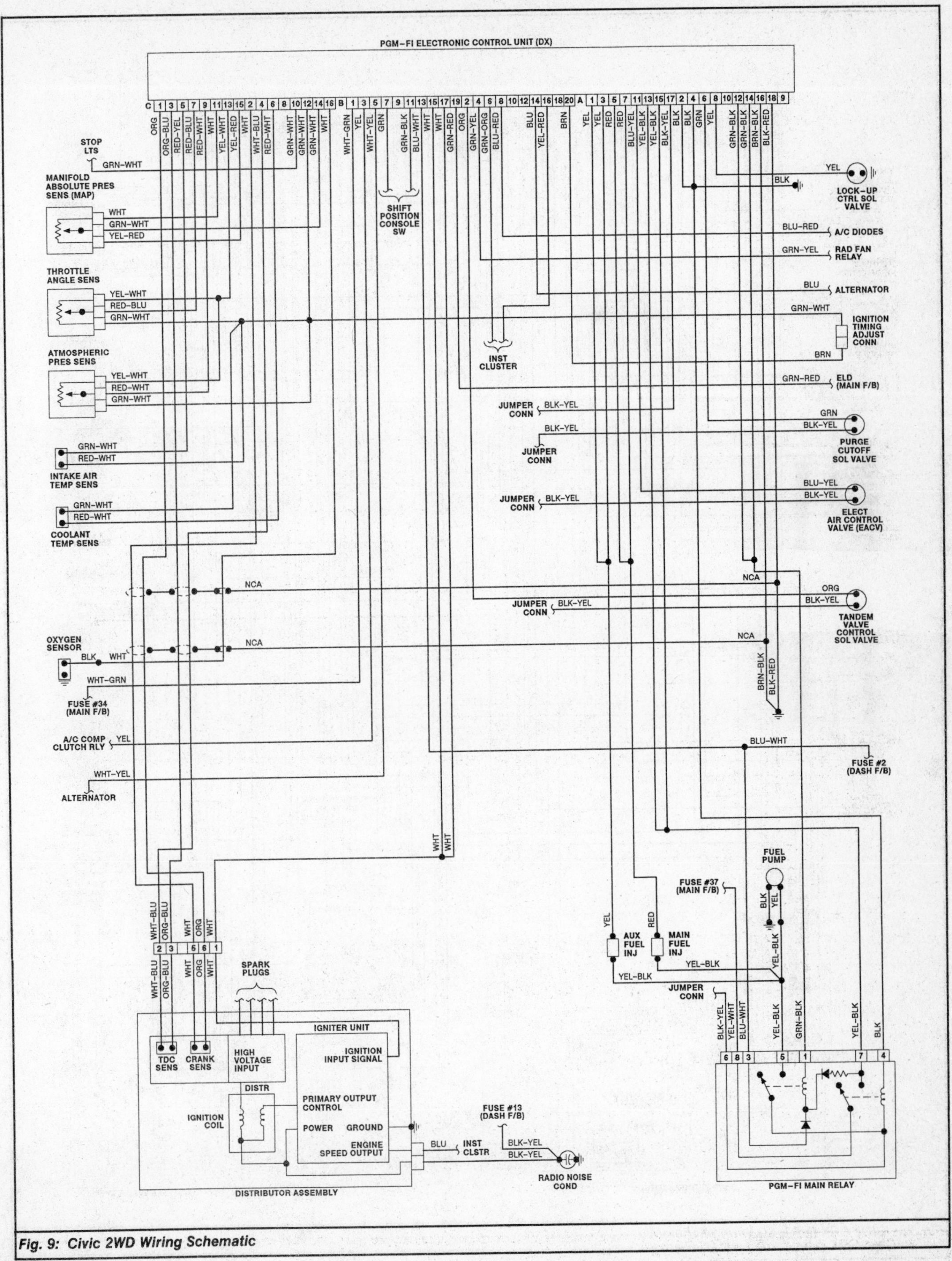
PGM-FI ELECTRONIC CONTROL UNIT (DX)
STOP LTS
MANIFOLD ABSOLUTE PRES SENS (MAP)
THROTTLE ANGLE SENS
ATMOSPHERIC PRES SENS
INTAKE AIR TEMP SENS
COOLANT TEMP SENS
OXYGEN SENSOR
FUSE #34 (MAIN F/B)
A/C COMP CLUTCH RLY
ALTERNATOR
SHIFT POSITION CONSOLE SW
LOCK-UP CTRL SOL VALVE
A/C DIODES
RAD FAN RELAY
ALTERNATOR
IGNITION TIMING ADJUST CONN
INST CLUSTER
ELD (MAIN F/B)
JUMPER CONN
PURGE CUTOFF SOL VALVE
ELECT AIR CONTROL VALVE (EACV)
TANDEM VALVE CONTROL SOL VALVE
FUSE #2 (DASH F/B)
FUEL PUMP
FUSE #37 (MAIN F/B)
AUX FUEL INJ
MAIN FUEL INJ
SPARK PLUGS
IGNITER UNIT
IGNITION INPUT SIGNAL
TDC SENS
CRANK SENS
HIGH VOLTAGE INPUT
DISTR
IGNITION COIL
PRIMARY OUTPUT CONTROL
POWER
GROUND
ENGINE SPEED OUTPUT
INST CLSTR
FUSE #13 (DASH F/B)
RADIO NOISE COND
DISTRIBUTOR ASSEMBLY
PGM-FI MAIN RELAY

*Fig. 9: Civic 2WD Wiring Schematic*

# 1988 COMPUTERIZED ENGINE CONTROLS
## Honda Electronic Control System (Cont.)

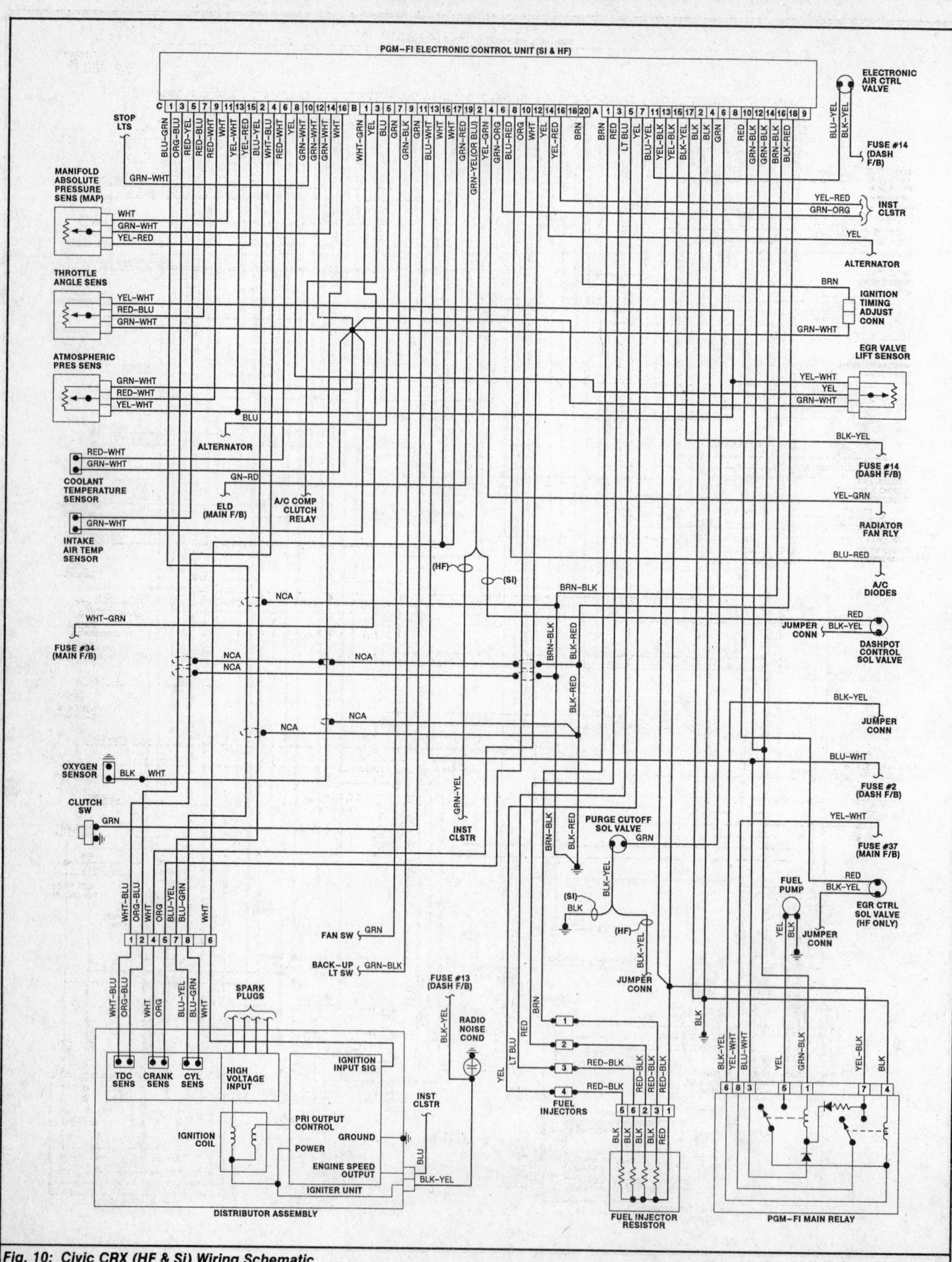

PGM-FI ELECTRONIC CONTROL UNIT (SI & HF)
STOP LTS
MANIFOLD ABSOLUTE PRESSURE SENS (MAP)
THROTTLE ANGLE SENS
ATMOSPHERIC PRES SENS
ALTERNATOR
COOLANT TEMPERATURE SENSOR
ELD (MAIN F/B)
A/C COMP CLUTCH RELAY
INTAKE AIR TEMP SENSOR
FUSE #34 (MAIN F/B)
OXYGEN SENSOR
CLUTCH SW
ELECTRONIC AIR CTRL VALVE
FUSE #14 (DASH F/B)
INST CLSTR
ALTERNATOR
IGNITION TIMING ADJUST CONN
EGR VALVE LIFT SENSOR
FUSE #14 (DASH F/B)
RADIATOR FAN RLY
A/C DIODES
JUMPER CONN
DASHPOT CONTROL SOL VALVE
JUMPER CONN
FUSE #2 (DASH F/B)
FUSE #37 (MAIN F/B)
PURGE CUTOFF SOL VALVE
FUEL PUMP
EGR CTRL SOL VALVE (HF ONLY)
JUMPER CONN
INST CLSTR
FAN SW
BACK-UP LT SW
FUSE #13 (DASH F/B)
RADIO NOISE COND
SPARK PLUGS
TDC SENS
CRANK SENS
CYL SENS
HIGH VOLTAGE INPUT
IGNITION INPUT SIG
IGNITION COIL
PRI OUTPUT CONTROL
GROUND
POWER
ENGINE SPEED OUTPUT
IGNITER UNIT
DISTRIBUTOR ASSEMBLY
FUEL INJECTORS
FUEL INJECTOR RESISTOR
PGM-FI MAIN RELAY


*Fig. 10: Civic CRX (HF & Si) Wiring Schematic*

# 1988 COMPUTERIZED ENGINE CONTROLS
## Honda Electronic Control System (Cont.)

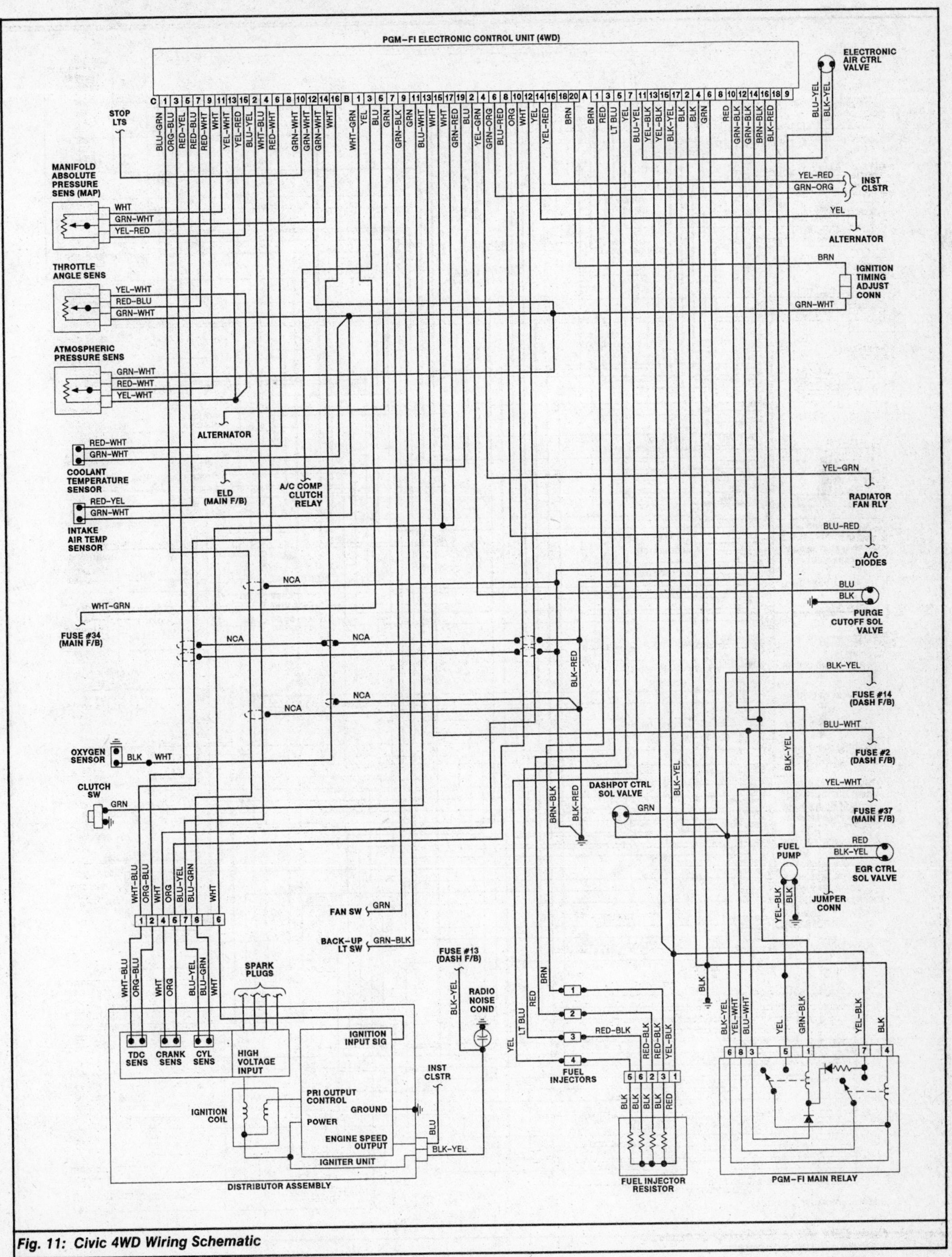

PGM-FI ELECTRONIC CONTROL UNIT (4WD)
ELECTRONIC AIR CTRL VALVE
STOP LTS
MANIFOLD ABSOLUTE PRESSURE SENS (MAP)
THROTTLE ANGLE SENS
ATMOSPHERIC PRESSURE SENS
ALTERNATOR
COOLANT TEMPERATURE SENSOR
ELD (MAIN F/B)
A/C COMP CLUTCH RELAY
INTAKE AIR TEMP SENSOR
INST CLSTR
IGNITION TIMING ADJUST CONN
RADIATOR FAN RLY
A/C DIODES
PURGE CUTOFF SOL VALVE
FUSE #34 (MAIN F/B)
NCA
FUSE #14 (DASH F/B)
FUSE #2 (DASH F/B)
OXYGEN SENSOR
CLUTCH SW
DASHPOT CTRL SOL VALVE
FUSE #37 (MAIN F/B)
FUEL PUMP
EGR CTRL SOL VALVE
JUMPER CONN
FAN SW
BACK-UP LT SW
FUSE #13 (DASH F/B)
RADIO NOISE COND
SPARK PLUGS
TDC SENS
CRANK SENS
CYL SENS
HIGH VOLTAGE INPUT
IGNITION INPUT SIG
PRI OUTPUT CONTROL
GROUND
POWER
ENGINE SPEED OUTPUT
IGNITION COIL
IGNITER UNIT
DISTRIBUTOR ASSEMBLY
FUEL INJECTORS
FUEL INJECTOR RESISTOR
PGM-FI MAIN RELAY


Fig. 11: Civic 4WD Wiring Schematic

# 1988 COMPUTERIZED ENGINE CONTROLS
## Honda Electronic Control System (Cont.)

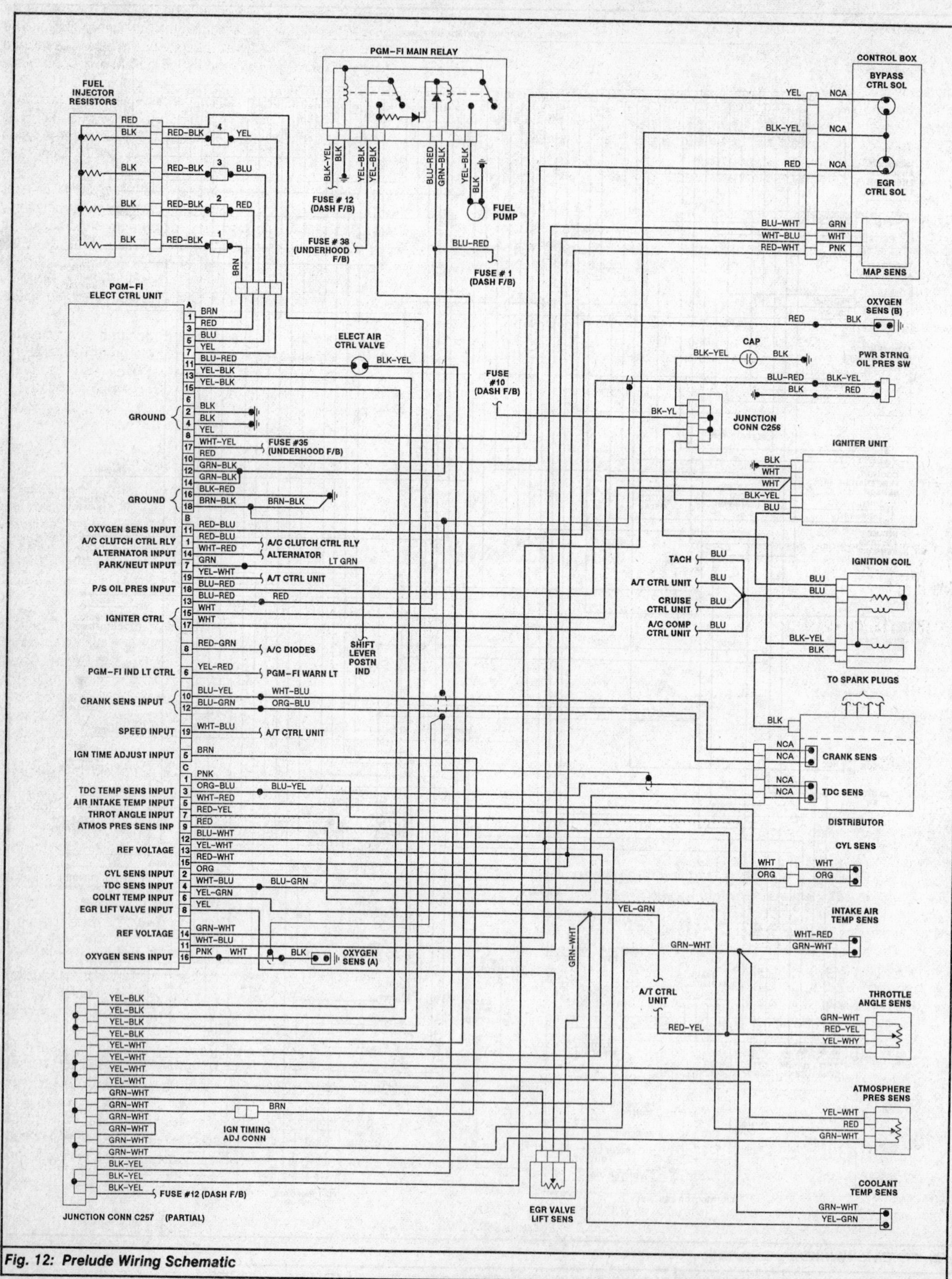
PGM-FI MAIN RELAY
CONTROL BOX
BYPASS CTRL SOL
EGR CTRL SOL
MAP SENS
FUEL INJECTOR RESISTORS
FUSE # 12 (DASH F/B)
FUSE # 38 (UNDERHOOD F/B)
FUSE # 1 (DASH F/B)
FUEL PUMP
PGM-FI ELECT CTRL UNIT
ELECT AIR CTRL VALVE
FUSE #10 (DASH F/B)
OXYGEN SENS (B)
CAP
PWR STRNG OIL PRES SW
JUNCTION CONN C256
IGNITER UNIT
GROUND
FUSE #35 (UNDERHOOD F/B)
OXYGEN SENS INPUT
A/C CLUTCH CTRL RLY
ALTERNATOR INPUT
ALTERNATOR
PARK/NEUT INPUT
A/T CTRL UNIT
P/S OIL PRES INPUT
IGNITER CTRL
A/C DIODES
SHIFT LEVER POSTN IND
PGM-FI IND LT CTRL
PGM-FI WARN LT
CRANK SENS INPUT
SPEED INPUT
IGN TIME ADJUST INPUT
TACH
CRUISE CTRL UNIT
A/C COMP CTRL UNIT
IGNITION COIL
TO SPARK PLUGS
CRANK SENS
TDC SENS
DISTRIBUTOR
TDC TEMP SENS INPUT
AIR INTAKE TEMP INPUT
THROT ANGLE INPUT
ATMOS PRES SENS INP
REF VOLTAGE
CYL SENS INPUT
TDC SENS INPUT
COLNT TEMP INPUT
EGR LIFT VALVE INPUT
CYL SENS
INTAKE AIR TEMP SENS
OXYGEN SENS (A)
THROTTLE ANGLE SENS
ATMOSPHERE PRES SENS
IGN TIMING ADJ CONN
FUSE #12 (DASH F/B)
JUNCTION CONN C257 (PARTIAL)
EGR VALVE LIFT SENS
COOLANT TEMP SENS

Fig. 12: Prelude Wiring Schematic

# 1988 COMPUTERIZED ENGINE CONTROLS
# Honda Feedback Carburetor System

### Accord

## DESCRIPTION

The Electronic Control Unit (ECU) uses sensor input signals in conjunction with vacuum and fuel regulating solenoids to maintain proper air/fuel ratio during most engine operating conditions. The ECU also controls an idle boost system which compensates for engine loads on vehicles equipped with automatic transmission and/or air conditioning. Vehicle is also equipped with a fuel cut-off system.

The feedback fuel system consists of 4 subsystems: "X", "M", idle feedback and fuel cut-off. The "X" subsystem consists of air control valve B, feedback control solenoid valve, frequency solenoid valve B, Constant Vacuum (CV) generator, check valve, pulse rectifier and silencer.

The "M" subsystem consists of air control valve A and frequency solenoid valve A. Frequency solenoid valve C is used only on vehicles equipped with automatic transmission.

The idle feedback subsystem consists of air bleed valve B and the air leak solenoid valve. To reduce idle emissions, both the air bleed valve B and the air leak solenoid valve operate when the air injection to the exhaust manifold is cut off.

The fuel cut-off subsystem consists of an ECU controlled primary slow mixture cut-off solenoid valve in the carburetor. Solenoid cuts off idle fuel mixture when ignition is turned off or vehicle is under deceleration.

## OPERATION

### INPUT SIGNALS

The ECU monitors several input signals in calculations to determine control of its output devices. Input signals include the following:

- A/C switch signal
- A/T shifter position signal
- Air temperature (TA) sensor
- Battery voltage (ignition fuse No. 1 and direct from battery)
- Clutch switch signal (M/T)
- Ignition coil signal (RPM)
- Oxygen sensor
- Starter signal
- Vacuum switches A, B and C
- Vehicle speed sensor

### OUTPUT DEVICES

Based upon input signals, the ECU maintains optimum vehicle operation for reduced emissions and improved performance and fuel economy. Output devices include the following:

- Air leak solenoid
- A/C idle boost solenoid
- A/T idle boost solenoid
- Air suction control solenoid
- Anti-afterburn control solenoid
- Cranking leak solenoid
- Early Fuel Evaporation (EFE) relay
- Feedback control solenoid
- Frequency solenoid valves A and B
- Frequency solenoid valve C (A/T only)
- Primary slow mixture cut-off solenoid
- Vacuum holding solenoid

### FEEDBACK SYSTEM

**"X" System** – This system regulates air/fuel mixtures by controlling opening of air control valve B according to the amount of vacuum present at the valve. Frequency solenoid valve B is modulated by the control unit, and controls the amount of vacuum to air control valve B.

The CV generator provides a stable vacuum level to the frequency solenoid valve, assisted by the accumulator and check valve. The pulse rectifier eliminates vacuum pulsations in the diaphragm chamber of air control valve B caused by the operation of frequency solenoid valve B.

The feedback control solenoid valve is provided to stop feedback operation at low engine speed (idling). Frequency solenoid B is controlled by the ECU based upon signals generated by the oxygen sensor. Air control valve B is opened only when air/fuel mixture is rich.

**"M" System** – After being controlled by the "X" system to near stoichiometric (14.7:1) air/fuel ratio, the mixture is more finely controlled based upon engine load. The diaphragm chamber of air control valve A receives the same carburetor vacuum as the EGR valve, while air is supplied to the intake manifold in proportion to carburetor intake air volume. Frequency solenoid valve A receives signals from the oxygen sensor through the control unit and opens the valve when air/fuel mixture is rich.

**Idle Feedback System** – Air bleed valve B (located in air cleaner) is a temperature sensitive bleed valve. As underhood temperatures increase, valve rises from its seat, introducing air into the intake manifold. The ECU controlled air leak solenoid valve (located in control box) supplies additional air to the intake manifold when the engine is idling with high intake air temperature.

### EARLY FUEL EVAPORATION (EFE)

The EFE system promotes improved engine operation while engine is warming. System consists of an EFE relay, EFE control unit and an EFE heater grid located below carburetor base plate. Maximum temperature of heater is regulated by internal resistance of heating element.

### IDLE BOOST SYSTEM

**A/T Idle Boost Solenoid** – The A/T idle boost solenoid valve is energized by the ECU when transmission is in gear (other than Park or Neutral) or engine is cold. Boost is accomplished when solenoid passes manifold vacuum to the inner diaphragm of the idle boost throttle controller. Vacuum to throttle controller is also regulated by frequency solenoid valve C which is energized by the ECU when engine speed is greater than or less than 730 RPM and coolant temperature is greater than 140°F (60°C).

**A/C Idle Boost Solenoid** – The A/C idle boost solenoid valve is energized by the ECU when A/C compressor is energized. Boost is accomplished when solenoid passes manifold vacuum to the outer diaphragm of the idle boost throttle controller.

## TESTING

### FEEDBACK CONTROL

### HOT ENGINE

**1)** Ensure engine is at normal operating temperature. Disconnect manifold vacuum hose from power valve at carburetor. Plug hose. Start engine and check frequency valves A and B for clicking at about 2500 RPM. *See Fig. 2.*

**2)** If either valve does not click, replace valve and retest. If both valves do not click, fault is in ECU control circuit. Go to TROUBLE SHOOTING. If both valves click, reconnect vacuum hose to power valve.

**3)** With air conditioning off, verify that solenoid valves do not click. If solenoid valves click, fault is in ECU control circuit. Go to TROUBLE SHOOTING. If solenoids do not click, system is functioning properly.

# 1988 COMPUTERIZED ENGINE CONTROLS
## Honda Feedback Carburetor System (Cont.)

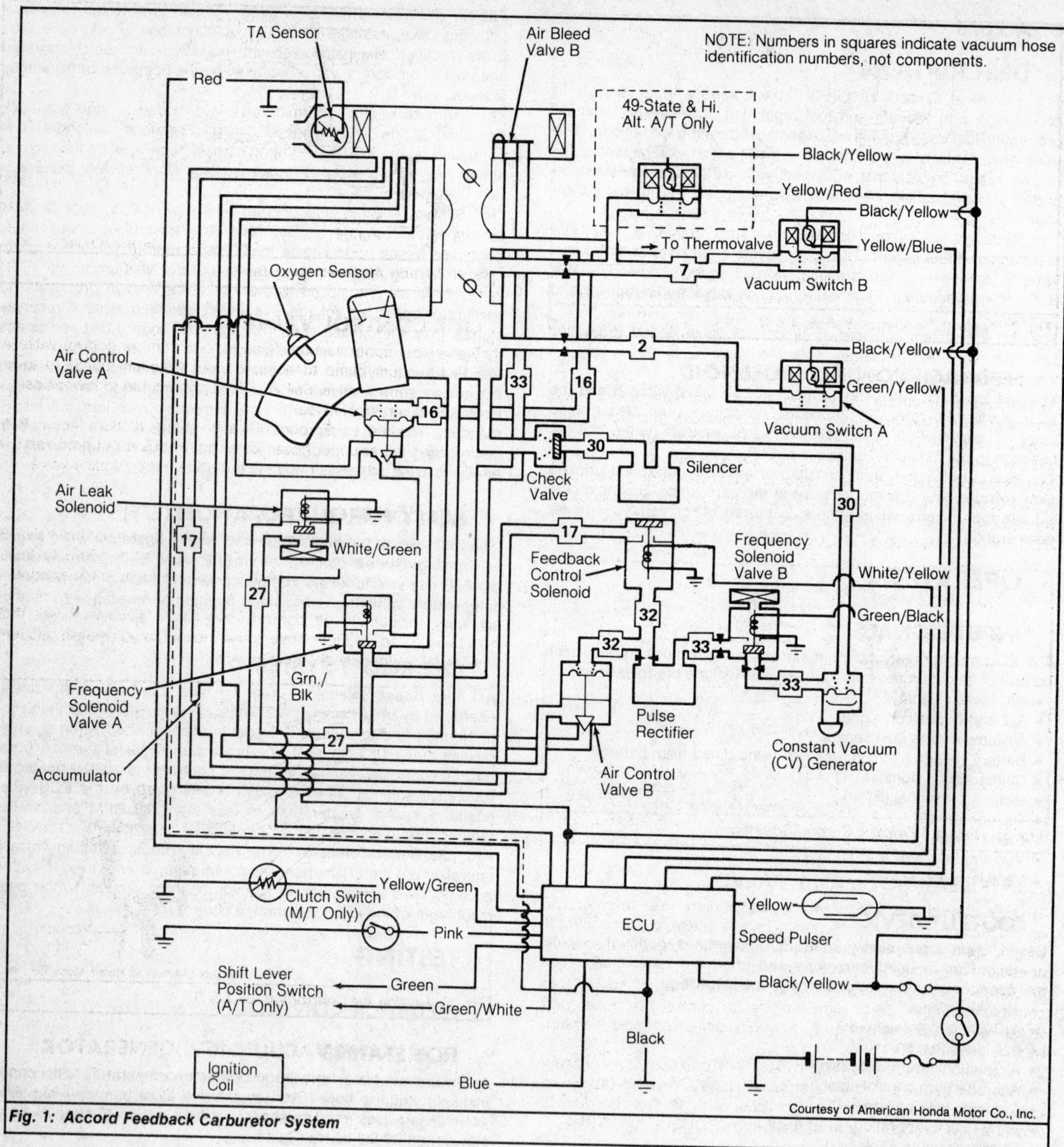
TA Sensor
Red
Air Bleed Valve B
NOTE: Numbers in squares indicate vacuum hose identification numbers, not components.
49-State & Hi. Alt. A/T Only
Black/Yellow
Yellow/Red
Black/Yellow
To Thermovalve
Yellow/Blue
7
Vacuum Switch B
Oxygen Sensor
2
Black/Yellow
Green/Yellow
Air Control Valve A
16
33
16
Vacuum Switch A
30
Check Valve
Silencer
Air Leak Solenoid
30
17
17
Feedback Control Solenoid
Frequency Solenoid Valve B
White/Green
White/Yellow
27
Green/Black
32
32
33
33
Frequency Solenoid Valve A
Grn./ Blk
Pulse Rectifier
Constant Vacuum (CV) Generator
27
Accumulator
Air Control Valve B
Yellow/Green
Clutch Switch (M/T Only)
ECU
Yellow
Pink
Speed Pulser
Shift Lever Position Switch (A/T Only)
Green
Black/Yellow
Green/White
Black
Ignition Coil
Blue
Courtesy of American Honda Motor Co., Inc.

*Fig. 1: Accord Feedback Carburetor System*

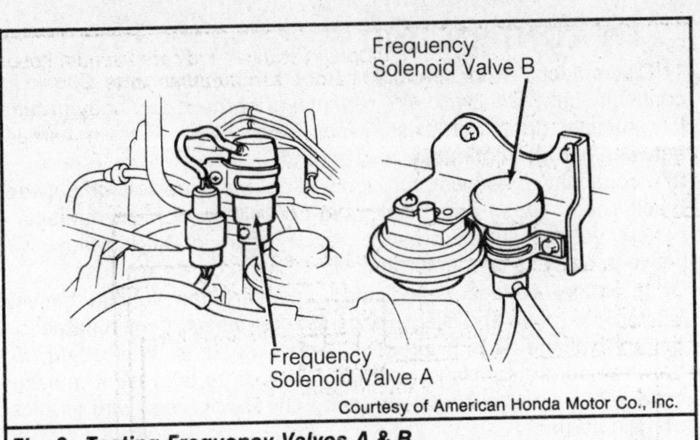
Frequency
Solenoid Valve B
Frequency
Solenoid Valve A
Courtesy of American Honda Motor Co., Inc.

*Fig. 2: Testing Frequency Valves A & B*

## FEEDBACK CONTROL SOLENOID

**1)** Disconnect upper No. 32 vacuum hose from feedback solenoid and plug hose. Connect vacuum pump to solenoid. *See Fig. 3.* Start engine and apply vacuum to valve. If solenoid holds vacuum, fault is in ECU control circuit. Go to TROUBLE SHOOTING.

**2)** If solenoid does not hold vacuum, increase engine speed to about 2500 RPM and apply vacuum. If vacuum holds, solenoid is functioning properly. If solenoid does not hold vacuum, fault is in ECU control circuit. Go to TROUBLE SHOOTING.

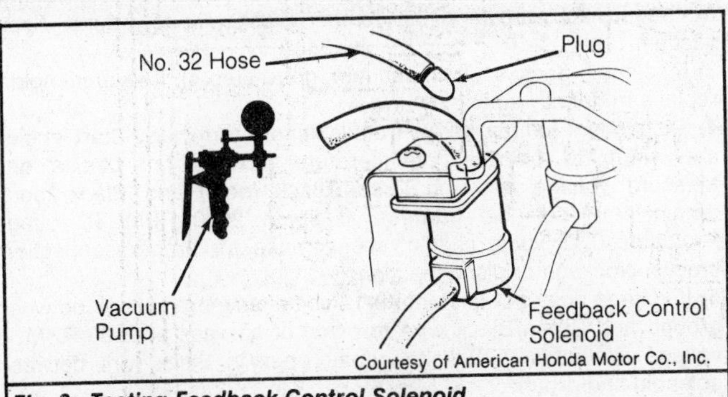
No. 32 Hose
Plug
Vacuum
Pump
Feedback Control
Solenoid
Courtesy of American Honda Motor Co., Inc.

*Fig. 3: Testing Feedback Control Solenoid*

## AIR LEAK SOLENOID VALVE

**1)** Open control box. Disconnect lower vacuum hose from air leak control solenoid. Connect vacuum pump to solenoid. Disconnect 8-wire connector at control box. Apply vacuum to solenoid. If solenoid does not hold vacuum, replace solenoid.

**2)** Jumper battery voltage to Gray wire terminal of control box connector. Jumper Black wire terminal of control box to ground. Apply vacuum to solenoid. If solenoid does not hold vacuum, replace solenoid.

**3)** If solenoid holds vacuum, inspect White/Green wire between control box harness and ECU terminal No. 18. Inspect Black wire between control box harness and ground. If no fault is found in wires, fault is in ECU control circuit. Go to TROUBLE SHOOTING.

## AIR BLEED VALVE B

**1)** Disconnect air bleed valve B No. 39 vacuum hose from intake manifold and connect vacuum pump. *See Fig. 4.* With ambient temperature less than 149°F (65°C), apply vacuum. If vacuum holds, go to next step. If vacuum does not hold, replace air bleed valve B and retest.

**2)** Warm air bleed valve with a heat gun to greater than 149°F (65°C). Apply vacuum. If vacuum holds, replace air bleed valve B. If vacuum does not hold, valve is functioning properly.

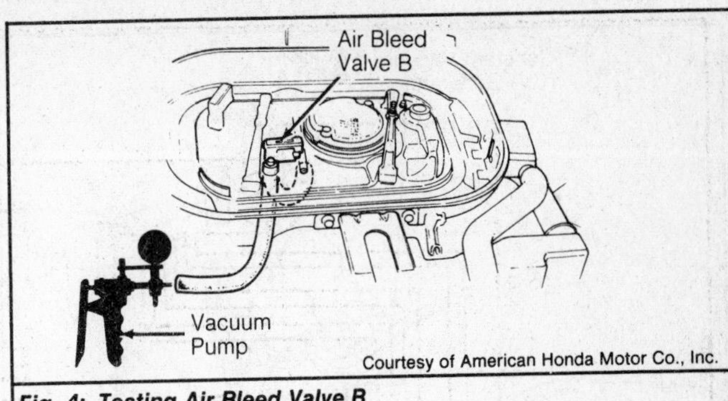
Air Bleed
Valve B
Vacuum
Pump
Courtesy of American Honda Motor Co., Inc.

*Fig. 4: Testing Air Bleed Valve B*

## AIR CONTROL VALVE A

**1)** Disconnect upper vacuum hose No. 16 from air control valve A. Connect vacuum pump to hose. Connect vacuum pump to lower hose of air control valve. *See Fig. 5.* Apply vacuum to lower hose. It should have a restricted leak.

**2)** Apply vacuum to air control valve upper vacuum hose. With vacuum applied at upper hose, lower hose should not hold vacuum at all (unrestricted leak). If valve fails either check, replace valve.

## AIR CONTROL VALVE B

**1)** Disconnect upper vacuum hose No. 32 from air control valve B. Connect vacuum pump to hose. Connect vacuum pump to lower hose of air control valve. *See Fig. 5.* Apply vacuum to lower hose. It should hold vacuum.

**2)** Apply vacuum to air control valve upper vacuum hose. With vacuum applied at upper hose, lower hose should release vacuum. If valve fails either check, replace valve.

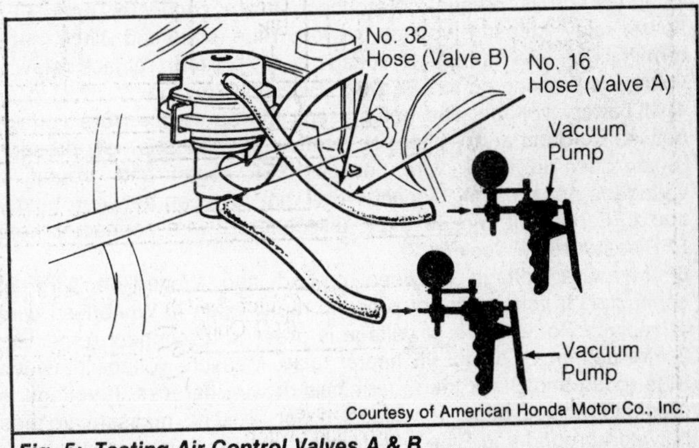
No. 32
Hose (Valve B)
No. 16
Hose (Valve A)
Vacuum
Pump
Vacuum
Pump
Courtesy of American Honda Motor Co., Inc.

*Fig. 5: Testing Air Control Valves A & B*

## CONSTANT VACUUM (CV) GENERATOR

**1)** Disconnect hose from frequency solenoid valve B and connect vacuum gauge to hose. Start engine and allow to run at idle. After vacuum stabilizes, reading should be 7-11 in. Hg (49-state and high altitude) or 5.9-9.8 in. Hg (California).

**2)** If vacuum stabilizes within range, constant vacuum generator is okay. Reconnect hose to frequency valve B. If vacuum stabilizes at a value greater or less than specification, replace CV generator.

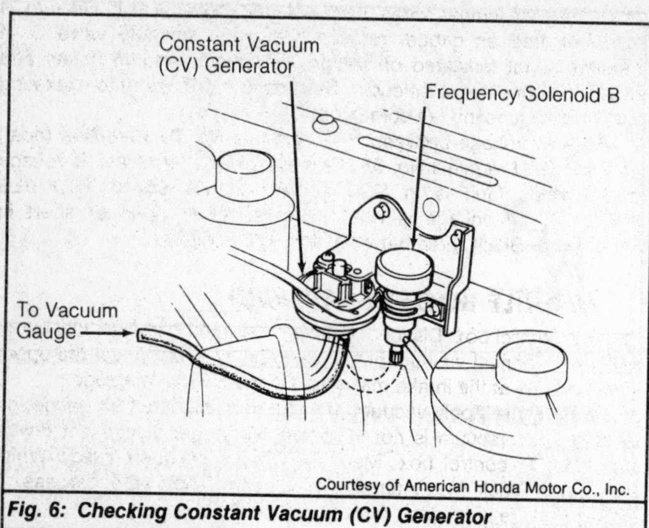
Constant Vacuum
(CV) Generator
Frequency Solenoid B
To Vacuum
Gauge
Courtesy of American Honda Motor Co., Inc.

*Fig. 6: Checking Constant Vacuum (CV) Generator*

## EFE HEATER

**1)** With engine coolant temperature less than 140°F (60°C), disconnect EGR heater connector. Measure resistance across heater connector terminals. If continuity does not exist, replace heater. If continuity exists, start engine. Measure voltage between White (pos.) and Black (neg.) terminals of heater harness. If battery voltage is not present, go to step **4)**.

**2)** If battery voltage is present, warm engine to operating temperature (cooling fan comes on). Measure voltage between White (pos.) and Black (neg.) terminals of heater harness. If battery voltage is not present, EFE system is functioning properly.

**3)** If voltage is present, disconnect 2-wire connector near EFE heater relay. Measure voltage between Blue (pos.) and Black (neg.) terminals of wire harness. If voltage is not present, replace relay. If voltage is present, go to EFE CONTROL UNIT testing.

**4)** If battery voltage was not present in step **1)**, measure voltage between ground and White wire terminal. If voltage is now present, repair open in Black wire between EFE heater and ground. If voltage is not present, Inspect White wire for open between heater and EFE relay. If wire is okay, disconnect 2-wire connector near EFE heater relay. *See Fig. 7.*

**5)** Measure voltage between ground and White/Red wire of connector. If voltage is not present, repair open in White/Red wire or replace No. 24 fuse. If voltage is present, disconnect remaining 2-wire connector near EFE heater relay. Measure voltage between Blue (pos.) and Black (neg.) terminals of wire harness. If voltage is present, replace relay. If voltage is not present, measure voltage between ground and Blue wire terminal. If voltage is present, repair open Black wire between relay and ground.

**6)** If voltage is not present, inspect Blue wire between EFE heater relay and EFE control unit. If wire is okay, go to EFE CONTROL UNIT testing.

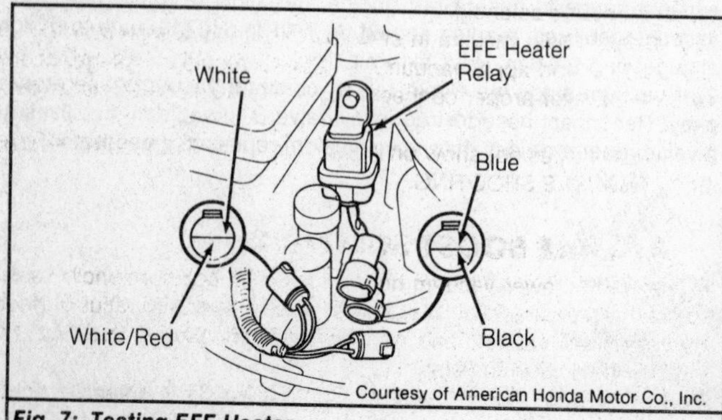
White
EFE Heater
Relay
Blue
White/Red
Black
Courtesy of American Honda Motor Co., Inc.

*Fig. 7: Testing EFE Heater*

## EFE CONTROL UNIT

**1)** Disconnect 7-wire connector from EFE control unit. Check for continuity between Black wire terminal of harness and body ground. If continuity does not exist, repair open Black wire in harness between harness connector and ground.

**2)** If continuity does exist, turn ignition on. Measure voltage between Black/Yellow (pos.) and Black (neg.) terminals of main harness. If battery voltage is not present, repair open in Black/Yellow wire between harness connector and No. 12 fuse, or replace fuse.

**3)** If battery voltage is indicated, measure the voltage between White/Blue (pos.) and Black (neg.) wire terminals of main harness. If battery voltage is not present, repair open in White/Blue wire between control unit and alternator. If voltage is present, measure voltage between Yellow/Green (pos.) and Black (neg.) wire terminals of main harness.

**4)** If battery voltage is present, replace EFE control unit and retest. If battery voltage is not present, inspect Yellow/Green wire between ECU and EFE control unit. If wire is okay, fault is in ECU control circuit. Go to TROUBLE SHOOTING.

## FREQUENCY SOLENOID VALVE A

**1)** Disconnect wire harness from frequency solenoid valve A. Disconnect vacuum hose from solenoid. Connect vacuum pump to solenoid. *See Fig. 8.*

**2)** Apply vacuum to solenoid valve A. If solenoid does not hold vacuum, replace solenoid. If vacuum holds, jumper battery voltage to Green/Black wire terminal. Jumper Black wire to ground. Apply vacuum.

**3)** If solenoid does not hold vacuum, go to step **4)**. If vacuum holds, replace frequency solenoid valve A.

**4)** Disconnect jumper wires from solenoid terminals. Start engine and warm to operating temperature (cooling fan comes on). Measure voltage between Green/Black (pos.) and Black (neg.) terminals of solenoid harness at about 2500 RPM. If voltage fluctuates 0-12 volts, check vacuum hose for proper connection, cracks, blockage or disconnection.

**5)** If voltage does not fluctuate 0-12 volts, measure voltage between ground and Green/Black wire terminal of harness at 2500 RPM. If voltage fluctuates 0-12 volts, repair open in Black wire between solenoid and ground.

**6)** If voltage does not fluctuate 0-12 volts, repair open in Green/Black wire between solenoid valve and control unit terminal No. 29. If wire is okay, fault is in ECU control circuit. Go to TROUBLE SHOOTING.

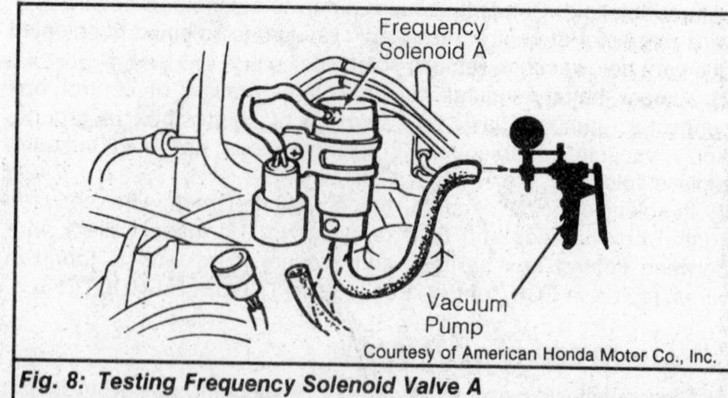
Frequency
Solenoid A
Vacuum
Pump
Courtesy of American Honda Motor Co., Inc.

*Fig. 8: Testing Frequency Solenoid Valve A*

## FREQUENCY SOLENOID B

**1)** Disconnect frequency solenoid B connector. Disconnect lower hose from frequency solenoid valve B and connect vacuum pump. Disconnect upper hose from frequency solenoid valve B and connect vacuum gauge. *See Fig. 9.*

**2)** Apply vacuum to solenoid valve B. If solenoid does not hold vacuum, replace solenoid. If vacuum holds, jumper battery voltage to Green/Black wire terminal of solenoid. Jumper Black wire terminal of solenoid to ground. Apply vacuum.

**3)** If vacuum is indicated on gauge connected to upper hose fitting, go to step **4)**. If vacuum is not indicated on gauge, replace frequency solenoid valve B.

**4)** Disconnect jumper wires from solenoid terminals. If vacuum is now indicated on gauge, replace frequency solenoid valve B. If vacuum is not indicated on gauge, reconnect vacuum hoses. Start engine and warm to operating temperature (cooling fan comes on).

**5)** Measure voltage between Green/Black (pos.) and Black (neg.) terminals of solenoid harness at about 2500 RPM. If voltage fluctuates 0-12 volts, check vacuum hose for proper connection, cracks, blockage or disconnection.

**6)** If voltage does not fluctuate 0-12 volts, measure voltage between ground and Green/Black wire terminal of harness at 2500 RPM. If voltage fluctuates 0-12 volts, repair open in Black wire between solenoid and ground.

**6)** If voltage does not fluctuate 0-12 volts, repair open in Green/Black wire between solenoid valve and control unit terminal No. 29. If wire is okay, fault is in ECU control circuit. Go to TROUBLE SHOOTING.

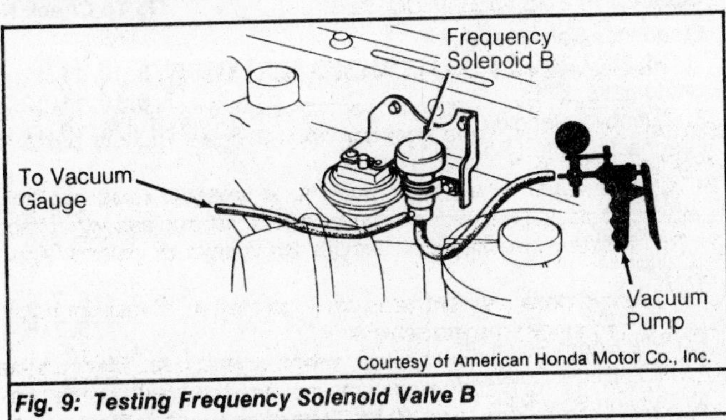
Frequency
Solenoid B
To Vacuum
Gauge
Vacuum
Pump
Courtesy of American Honda Motor Co., Inc.

*Fig. 9: Testing Frequency Solenoid Valve B*

## FREQUENCY SOLENOID C (AUTO. TRANS. ONLY)

**1)** Disconnect frequency solenoid C connector. Disconnect lower hose from frequency solenoid valve C and connect vacuum pump. Disconnect upper hose from frequency solenoid valve C. *See Fig. 10.*

**2)** Apply vacuum to solenoid valve C. If solenoid does not hold vacuum, replace solenoid. If vacuum holds, connect a vacuum gauge to upper frequency valve C hose. Jumper battery voltage to Blue/Red wire solenoid terminal. Jumper Black wire terminal to ground. Apply vacuum.

**3)** If vacuum is indicated on gauge connected to upper hose fitting, go to step **4)**. If vacuum is not indicated on gauge, replace frequency solenoid valve C.

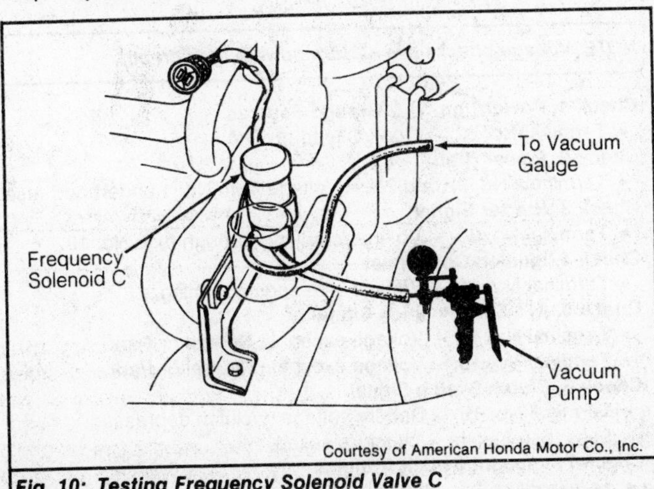
To Vacuum
Gauge
Frequency
Solenoid C
Vacuum
Pump
Courtesy of American Honda Motor Co., Inc.

*Fig. 10: Testing Frequency Solenoid Valve C*

**4)** Disconnect jumper wires from solenoid terminals. If vacuum is now indicated on gauge, replace frequency solenoid valve C. If vacuum is not indicated on gauge, reconnect vacuum hoses and electrical connector to solenoid. Start engine and warm to operating temperature (cooling fan comes on).

**5)** Measure voltage between ECU terminal No. 21 Blue/Red (pos.) wire and ECU terminal No. 32 Black (neg.) wire terminals. If voltage is 5-6 volts, fault is in ECU control circuit. Go to TROUBLE SHOOTING. If voltage is not 5-6 volts, repair open or short in Blue/Red or Black wires between solenoid and ECU.

## A/T IDLE BOOST SOLENOID

**1)** Open control box. Disconnect lower vacuum hose from idle boost solenoid. Connect vacuum pump. *See Fig. 11.* Disconnect the upper vacuum hose at the intake manifold. Connect vacuum gauge.

**2)** Start engine. Apply vacuum. If vacuum is indicated on gauge, go to step **5)**. If vacuum is not indicated on gauge, disconnect 8-wire connector at control box. Measure voltage between Yellow/White (pos.) and Black (neg.) terminals of control box wire harness. If battery voltage is present, replace solenoid.

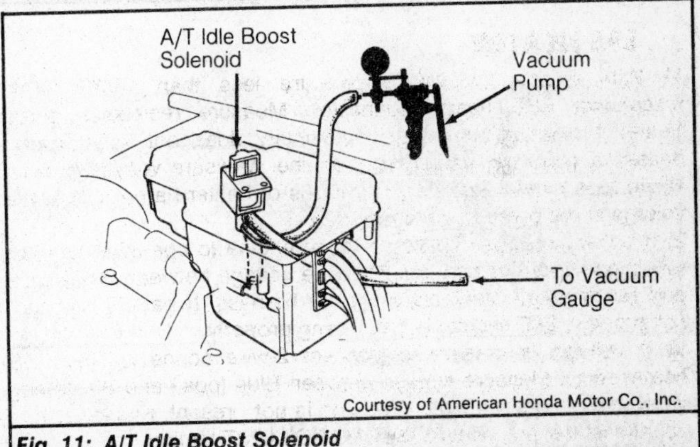
A/T Idle Boost
Solenoid
Vacuum
Pump
To Vacuum
Gauge
Courtesy of American Honda Motor Co., Inc.

*Fig. 11: A/T Idle Boost Solenoid*

**3)** If battery voltage is not present, measure voltage between ground and Yellow/White wire terminal of harness. If voltage is now present, repair open Black wire between harness connector and ground.

**4)** If battery voltage is not present, inspect Yellow/White wire of harness between harness connector and ECU terminal No. 19. If harness is okay, fault is in ECU control circuit. Go to TROUBLE SHOOTING.

**5)** If vacuum was indicated on gauge in step **2)**, warm engine to operating temperature (cooling fan comes on). Apply vacuum to solenoid in Neutral or Park. If solenoid holds vacuum go to step **7)**. If solenoid does not hold vacuum, disconnect 8-wire connector at control box.

**6)** Measure voltage between Yellow/White (pos.) and Black (neg.) terminals of control box harness. If voltage is present, fault is in ECU control circuit. Go to TROUBLE SHOOTING. If voltage is not present, replace solenoid.

**7)** If solenoid held vacuum in step **5)**, Shift transmission into "$D_3$" or "$D_4$" position and apply vacuum. If vacuum shows on gauge, check vacuum hose for proper connection, cracks, blockage or disconnection.

**8)** If vacuum does not show on gauge, fault is in ECU control circuit. Go to TROUBLE SHOOTING.

## A/C IDLE BOOST SOLENOID

**1)** Disconnect lower vacuum hose of A/C idle boost solenoid valve. Connect vacuum pump. Disconnect upper solenoid vacuum hose from manifold vacuum and connect vacuum gauge. *See Fig. 12.* Plug manifold vacuum fitting.

**2)** Start engine. Apply vacuum. Go to step **3)** if solenoid holds vacuum. If solenoid does not hold vacuum, disconnect 2-wire

# 1988 COMPUTERIZED ENGINE CONTROLS
# Honda Feedback Carburetor System (Cont.)

connector near solenoid. Measure voltage between Red (pos.) and Black (neg.) wire terminals of harness. If voltage is not present, replace solenoid. If voltage is present, fault is in ECU control circuit. Go to TROUBLE SHOOTING.

**3)** If solenoid held vacuum is step **2)**, turn A/C switch to "ON" position. Apply vacuum. If vacuum is not indicated on gauge, go to step **4)**. If vacuum is indicated on gauge, turn A/C switch to "OFF" position. If vacuum is still indicated on gauge, replace solenoid. If vacuum is not indicated on gauge, check vacuum hose for proper connection, cracks, blockage or disconnection.

**4)** If vacuum gauge did not indicate vacuum in step **3)**, disconnect 2-wire connector near solenoid. Measure voltage between Red (pos.) and Black (neg.) wire terminals of harness. If battery voltage is present, replace solenoid.

**5)** If battery voltage is not present, measure voltage between ground and Red wire terminal of solenoid harness. If battery voltage is present, repair open in Black wire between solenoid connector and ground. If battery voltage is not present, inspect Red wire between solenoid valve connector and ECU terminal No. 17. If wire is okay, fault is in ECU control circuit. Go to TROUBLE SHOOTING.

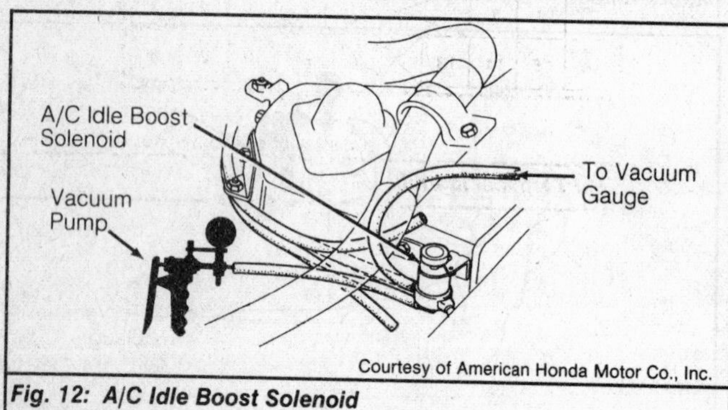
A/C Idle Boost Solenoid
To Vacuum Gauge
Vacuum Pump
Courtesy of American Honda Motor Co., Inc.

*Fig. 12: A/C Idle Boost Solenoid*

## PRIMARY SLOW MIXTURE CUT-OFF SOLENOID VALVE

**1)** Place a towel around solenoid valve to soak up any spilled fuel. Loosen solenoid screws and remove solenoid valve. Ground valve as far from carburetor as possible. Turn ignition on. If solenoid retracts, go to step **4)**.

**2)** If solenoid does not retract, turn ignition off. Disconnect solenoid connector. Turn ignition on. Measure voltage between ground and Green/Red wire of solenoid harness. If battery voltage is present, replace solenoid.

**3)** If battery voltage is not present, inspect Green/Red wire between solenoid valve connector and ECU terminal No. 28. If wire is okay, fault is in ECU control circuit. Go to TROUBLE SHOOTING.

**4)** If solenoid did retract in step **1)**, reinstall solenoid. Start engine and warm to operating temperature (cooling fan comes on). Block rear wheels and set parking brake. Raise front of vehicle and support with safety stands. Place transmission in 2nd or "2" position.

**5)** Accelerate to greater than 20 MPH. Suddenly release accelerator. Measure voltage between ECU Green/Red (pos.) wire terminal No. 28 and ECU Black wire terminal No. 32 during deceleration (above 12.5 MPH).

**6)** If voltage is not present, solenoid valve is okay. If voltage is present, fault is in ECU control circuit. Go to TROUBLE SHOOTING.

## CRANKING LEAK SOLENOID VALVE

For testing of cranking leak solenoid valve, see HONDA CHOKE CONTROL SYSTEM article in EXHAUST EMISSION SYSTEMS section.

## VACUUM HOLDING SOLENOID VALVE

For testing of vacuum holding solenoid valve, see ACURA & HONDA FUEL EVAPORATION article in EXHAUST EMISSION SYSTEMS section.

## AIR SUCTION SOLENOID VALVE

For testing of air suction solenoid valve, see ACURA & HONDA AIR INJECTION SYSTEM article in EXHAUST EMISSION SYSTEMS section.

## ANTI-AFTERBURN SOLENOID VALVE

For testing of anti-afterburn solenoid valve, see HONDA ANTI-AFTERBURN SYSTEM article in EXHAUST EMISSION SYSTEMS section.

## TROUBLE SHOOTING

If no faults were found during testing of individual components, fault may be in ECU control circuit. Inspect each input signal to ECU. If no faults are found in input signals, replace ECU.

***CONTROL UNIT INPUT CHECKS***

| Circuit | Go To Check No. |
|---|---|
| Frequency Solenoids A & B | |
| Manual | 1, 4, 6, 7, 8, 10, 11, 12, 13 |
| Automatic | 1, 4, 5, 7, 8, 10, 11, 12, 13 |
| Frequency Solenoid C | 1, 2, 4, 5, 10, 11, 14 |
| Feedback Control Solenoid | |
| 49-State | |
| Manual | 1, 4, 6, 8, 11 |
| Automatic | 1, 4, 5, 8, 9, 11 |
| California | |
| Manual | 1, 4, 6, 7, 8, 11 |
| Automatic | 1, 4, 5, 7, 8, 11 |
| A/T Idle Boost Solenoid | 1, 4, 5, 7, 10, 11, 14 |
| A/C Idle Boost Solenoid | 1, 4, 7, 10, 11, 14 |
| Air Suction Solenoid | |
| 49-State | |
| Manual | 1, 4, 7, 8, 10, 11, 12 |
| Automatic | 1, 4, 7, 9, 10, 11, 12 |
| California | 1, 4, 7, 8, 10, 11, 12 |
| Anti-Afterburn Solenoid | |
| Manual | 1, 10, 11 |
| Automatic | 1, 5, 11 |
| Cranking Leak Solenoid | 1, 3, 4, 10, 11, 12 |
| Primary Slow Mixture Cut-Off Solenoid | |
| Manual | 1, 4, 6, 7, 8, 10, 11 |
| Automatic | 1, 4, 5, 7, 8, 10, 11 |
| EFE Heater | 1, 11 |

## INPUT CHECKS

***NOTE: Voltage checks are performed with ignition on.***

**Check 1, Power (Ign. 1) & Ground Sources**
- Terminal No. 32 – Continuity to ground.

**Check 2, Power (Bat.)**
- Terminals No. 22 and 23 – Voltage from No. 1 underhood fuse.

**Check 3, Starter Signal**
- Terminal No. 30 – Voltage/cranking through fuse No. 10.

**Check 4, Ignition Coil Signal**
- Terminal No. 11 – Voltage with engine running.

**Check 5, A/T Shift Position Signal.**
- Terminal No. 14 – Voltage except in Neutral or Park.
- Terminal No. 15 – Voltage except in Neutral or Park.

**Check 6, Clutch Switch Signal**
- Terminal No. 16 – Battery voltage w/clutch depressed. Less than 3 volts w/clutch released.

**Check 7, Vacuum Switch A Signal**
- Terminal No. 1 – Battery voltage with no vacuum. Zero volts with greater than 3.1 in. Hg.

# 1988 COMPUTERIZED ENGINE CONTROLS
# Honda Feedback Carburetor System (Cont.)

**Check 8, Vacuum Switch B Signal**
- Terminal No. 8 – Battery voltage with no vacuum. Zero volts with greater than 1.2 in. Hg.

**Check 9, Vacuum Switch C Signal**
- Terminal No. 2 – Battery voltage with no vacuum. Zero volts with greater than 2.4 in. Hg.

**Check 10, Speed Pulser Signal (Man. Trans.).**
- Terminal No. 5 – Pulsing 0-5 volts with L/F wheel turned by hand and ignition on. If not, terminals No. 32 and 23 – Continuity/no continuity fluctuation with L/F wheel turned by hand and ignition on.

**Check 11, Coolant Sensor Signal.**
- Terminal No. 7 – One volt at operating temperature.

**Check 12, Air Temperature Sensor Signal**
- Terminal No. 3 – 2-4 volts at operating temperature.

**Check 13, Oxygen Sensor Signal**
- Terminal No. 31 – Voltage less than .4 volt at idle. Voltage greater than .6 volt at wide open throttle. Both at operating temperature.

**Check 14, A/C Switch Signal**
- Terminal No. 10 – Voltage less than 3 volts with switch on.

If no faults are found in these checks, replace ECU.

## INTAKE AIR TEMPERATURE (TA) SENSOR

Unplug air intake temperature sensor connector. Check resistance across sensor terminals when air temperature is less than 40°F (4.5°C). Resistance should be about 4000 ohms. Check resistance across sensor terminals when air temperature is greater than 140°F (60°C). Resistance should be 500-1000 ohms. Replace sensor if not within specification.

## COOLANT TEMPERATURE (TW) SENSOR

Unplug coolant temperature sensor connector. With cylinder head temperature less than 158°F (70°C), resistance should be 400-2000 ohms. With cylinder head temperature greater than 158°F (70°C), resistance across sensor terminals should be 200-400 ohms. If sensor does not operate as described, replace sensor.

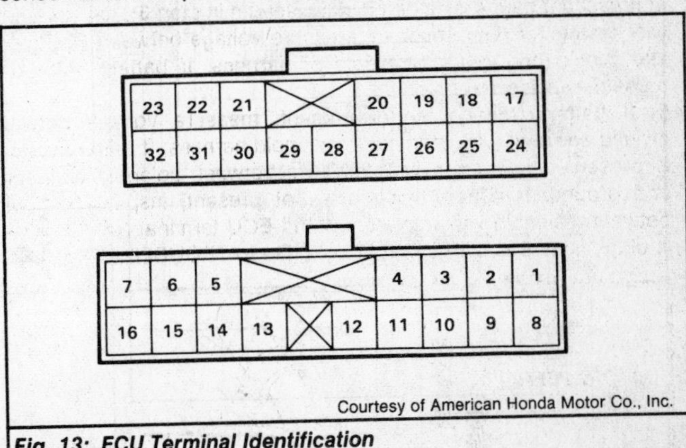
23
22
21
20
19
18
17
32
31
30
29
28
27
26
25
24
7
6
5
4
3
2
1
16
15
14
13
12
11
10
9
8
Courtesy of American Honda Motor Co., Inc.

*Fig. 13: ECU Terminal Identification*

# 1988 COMPUTERIZED ENGINE CONTROLS
## Honda Feedback Carburetor System (Cont.)

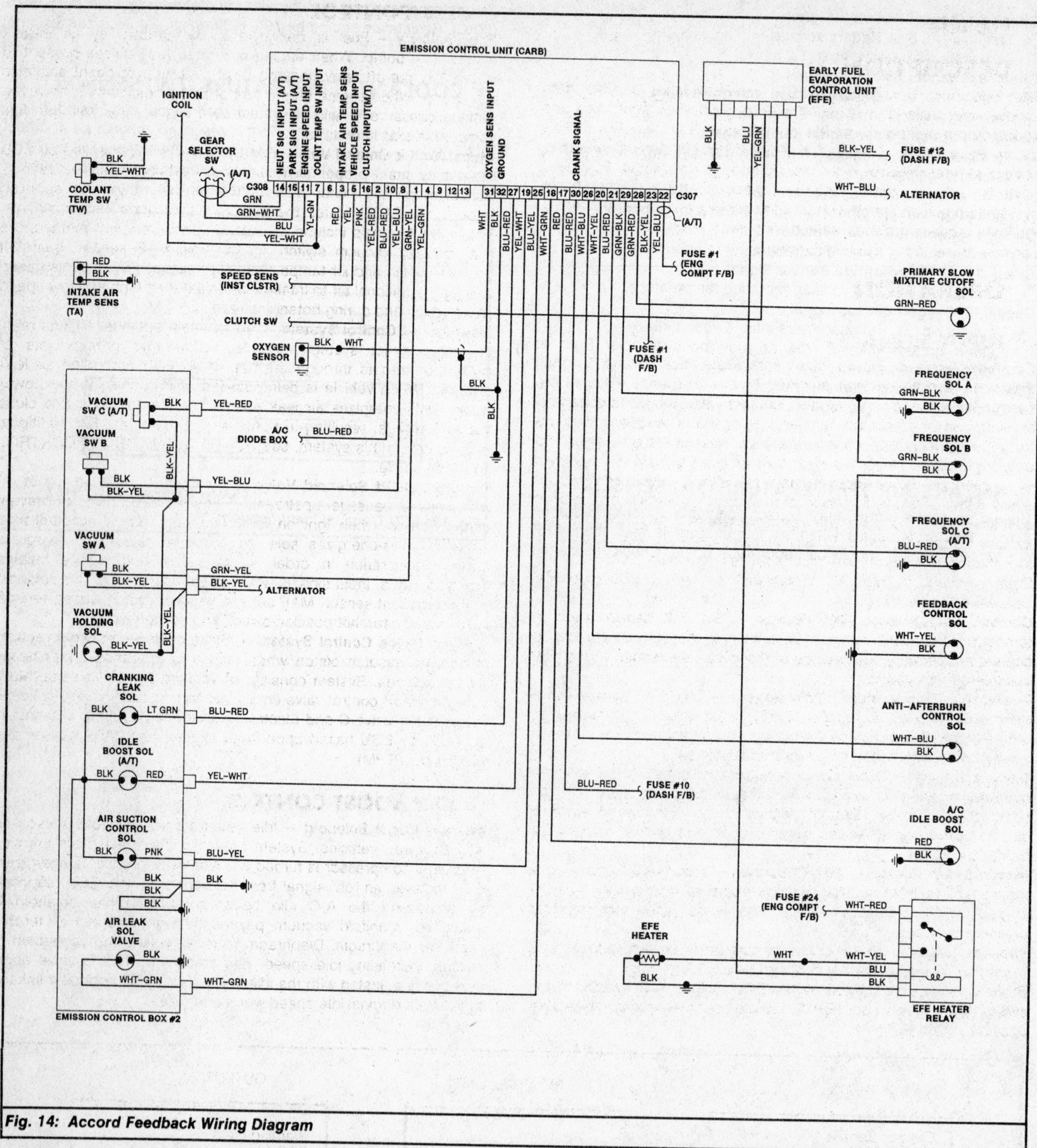

EMISSION CONTROL UNIT (CARB)
IGNITION COIL
GEAR SELECTOR SW
(A/T)
COOLANT TEMP SW (TW)
INTAKE AIR TEMP SENS (TA)
SPEED SENS (INST CLSTR)
CLUTCH SW
OXYGEN SENSOR
NEUT SIG INPUT (A/T)
PARK SIG INPUT (A/T)
ENGINE SPEED INPUT
COLNT TEMP SW INPUT
INTAKE AIR TEMP SENS
VEHICLE SPEED INPUT
CLUTCH INPUT(M/T)
OXYGEN SENS INPUT
GROUND
CRANK SIGNAL
C308
C307
EARLY FUEL EVAPORATION CONTROL UNIT (EFE)
FUSE #12 (DASH F/B)
ALTERNATOR
FUSE #1 (ENG COMPT F/B)
FUSE #1 (DASH F/B)
PRIMARY SLOW MIXTURE CUTOFF SOL
FREQUENCY SOL A
FREQUENCY SOL B
FREQUENCY SOL C (A/T)
FEEDBACK CONTROL SOL
ANTI-AFTERBURN CONTROL SOL
FUSE #10 (DASH F/B)
A/C IDLE BOOST SOL
FUSE #24 (ENG COMPT F/B)
EFE HEATER
EFE HEATER RELAY
VACUUM SW C (A/T)
VACUUM SW B
A/C DIODE BOX
VACUUM SW A
ALTERNATOR
VACUUM HOLDING SOL
CRANKING LEAK SOL
IDLE BOOST SOL (A/T)
AIR SUCTION CONTROL SOL
AIR LEAK SOL VALVE
EMISSION CONTROL BOX #2


Fig. 14: Accord Feedback Wiring Diagram

# COMPUTERIZED ENGINE CONTROLS
# Honda PGM-CARB Electronic Control System

## Prelude

## DESCRIPTION

The Electronic Control Unit (ECU) receives input signals from various sensors and switches. The ECU processes input data and sends output signals to various control solenoids. *See Fig. 1.* This allows Programmed Carburetion (PGM-CARB) system to precisely control air/fuel mixture under most operating conditions. ECU also controls self-diagnostic system, emissions system, idle boost system (models equipped with air conditioning) and fail-safe system. Fail-safe system provides safe driving even if one or more of the sensors are faulty or ECU malfunctions.

## OPERATION

### INPUT SIGNALS

Computer furnishes input sensors with a reference voltage (5 volts). This voltage signal is then modified by the resistance value of the sensor in each circuit. Some sensors are simple mechanical resistors, while others are temperature sensitive resistors (thermistors). ECU monitors either reference line or return signal to determine status of each sensor. Not all input signals are obtained from sensors. Some input signals are simply monitored circuits which either produce a voltage of their own ($O_2$ sensor and ignition coil) or already have a voltage signal present (A/T gearshift switch).

**Battery Voltage Signal** – ECU uses the battery voltage signal from the 10-amp fuse in underhood relay box to retain ECU memory. Battery voltage through "IG. 1" terminal is used by ECU to power sensors and solenoids.

**Coolant Temperature (TW) Sensor** – The TW sensor uses a temperature sensitive resistor (thermistor) to measure differences in coolant temperature. Resistance of thermistor decreases with a rise in coolant temperature.

**Intake Air Temperature (TA) Sensor** – The TA sensor is a thermistor located in intake manifold. It reacts to intake air temperature changes much like coolant temperature sensor but with a reduced thermal capacity for quicker response.

**Oxygen Sensor** – The oxygen sensor is mounted in the exhaust manifold where it is exposed to exhaust gases as they exit the combustion chamber. Sensor detects oxygen content of exhaust gas and produces a voltage signal proportional to that content for use by the ECU.

**Manifold Air Pressure (MAP) Sensor** – The MAP sensor is a mechanical variable resistor. Voltage signal sent to sensor by ECU is modified by internal resistance. Resistance varies with manifold pressure changes.

**Vacuum Switch** – Switch converts carburetor ported vacuum to a simple on/off signal. Switch is closed below 1.2 in. Hg.

Other input signals utilized by the ECU include A/C switch, clutch switch (M/T), ignition coil (RPM), vehicle speed sensor and gearshift position switch (A/T).

### FUEL CONTROL

**Fuel Delivery** – Fuel is delivered to carburetors by an in-tank electric fuel pump. When engine is started (coil pulses present at relay), fuel cut-off relay (located under left side of dash) activates fuel pump. When engine stops, fuel pump is deactivated, however, residual pressure is held in system by a check valve built into fuel pump. This aids in restarts.

**Electronic Air Control Valve (EACV)** – EACV is controlled by ECU to help maintain proper air/fuel ratios. Carburetor air/fuel ratio is calibrated on the richer side of the air/fuel range. Air supplied through the EACV dilutes the mixture based upon sensor signals. These input signals include the speed sensor, coolant temperature (TW) sensor, vacuum switch, igniton coil, MAP sensor, gearshift position switch and air temperature (TA) sensor. EACV is also used to supply additional air to intake manifold during high and low speed deceleration and during hotengine restart.

**Slow Air-Jet Control System** – To maintain optimum air/fuel ratio, the slow air-jet system controls airflow into primary jets of carburetor throats through the use of an ECU controlled air leak solenoid. When vehicle is being started or is running in the power mode, ECU energizes air leak solenoid in the air cleaner to close the air passage, resulting in richer air/fuel mixtures. For additional information on this system, see HONDA SLOW AIR JET CONTROL SYSTEM article.

**Mixture Cut-Off Solenoid Valve** – Solenoid is provided to cut off idle mixture passage upstream of the by-pass port to prevent engine run-on when ignition is turned off. This is accomplished when ECU de-energizes solenoid. Solenoid is also de-energized during deceleration in order to save fuel and reduce tailpipe emission levels. Input signals which affect operation of this solenoid include, coolant sensor, MAP sensor, vacuum switch, speed sensor, ignition coil, gearshift position switch and ignition switch.

**Vacuum Piston Control System** – System allows manifold vacuum to activate vacuum piston when engine is operating under heavy load conditions. System consists of vacuum piston (in carburetor), vacuum piston control valve (in air cleaner), vacuum piston solenoid valve, check valve C and Electronic Control Unit (ECU). Solenoid is activated by ECU based upon input signals from MAP sensor and ignition coil (RPM).

### IDLE BOOST CONTROL

**A/C Idle Boost Solenoid** – Idle boost control solenoid is used on A/C equipped vehicles. System prevents idle speed from dripping when A/C compressor is turned on. When compressor is energized, ECU recieves an "on" signal from the control switch. ECU responds by energizing the A/C idle boost solenoid. When solenoid is energized, manifold vacuum passes through solenoid to throttle controller diaphragm. Diaphragm retracts, pulling rod connected to linkage, increasing idle speed. The amount of throttle valve angle increase is adjusted with the idle control screw on controller linkage to maintain original idle speed when energized.

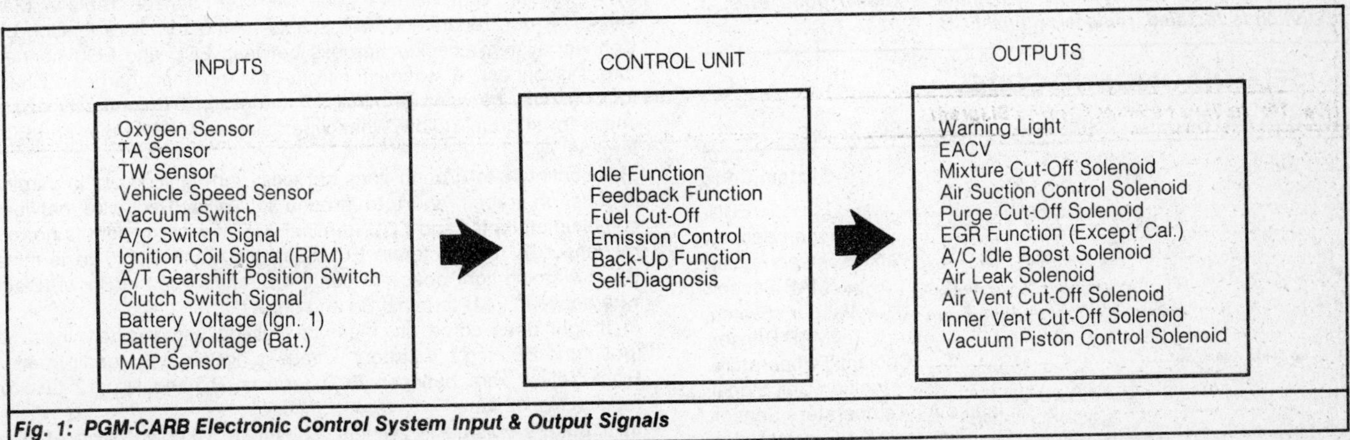
INPUTS
Oxygen Sensor
TA Sensor
TW Sensor
Vehicle Speed Sensor
Vacuum Switch
A/C Switch Signal
Ignition Coil Signal (RPM)
A/T Gearshift Position Switch
Clutch Switch Signal
Battery Voltage (Ign. 1)
Battery Voltage (Bat.)
MAP Sensor
CONTROL UNIT
Idle Function
Feedback Function
Fuel Cut-Off
Emission Control
Back-Up Function
Self-Diagnosis
OUTPUTS
Warning Light
EACV
Mixture Cut-Off Solenoid
Air Suction Control Solenoid
Purge Cut-Off Solenoid
EGR Function (Except Cal.)
A/C Idle Boost Solenoid
Air Leak Solenoid
Air Vent Cut-Off Solenoid
Inner Vent Cut-Off Solenoid
Vacuum Piston Control Solenoid

*Fig. 1: PGM-CARB Electronic Control System Input & Output Signals*

# Honda PGM-CARB Electronic Control System (Cont.)

## EMISSION CONTROL

**Purge Control Solenoid** – Purging evaporative emissions from charcoal canister is controlled by ECU using purge control solenoid. When solenoid is energized, manifold vacuum passes through soleniod to open canister purge control valve diaphragm located on top of canister. Ported vacuum is then used to purge canister. For additional information on this system, see ACURA & HONDA FUEL EVAPORATION article.

**Inner Vent Solenoid Valve** – Inner vent solenoid controls venting of the carburetor float bowl. During cranking the inner vent solenoid valve remains closed to prevent vapor from being drawn into intake manifold. When engine starts, solenoid is energized, opening the passage between the air cleaner and float bowl. For additional information on this system, see ACURA & HONDA FUEL EVAPORATION article.

**Air Suction Control Solenoid** – When air suction control solenoid is activated by ECU, manifold vacuum lifts suction valve diaphragm, routing fresh air from air cleaner to exhaust manifold through the integral reed valve of the suction valve. For additional information on this system, see ACURA & HONDA AIR INJECTION SYSTEM article.

**EGR Cut-Off Solenoid (Except Calif.)** – When engine is cold, vacuum signal to EGR valve is bled off to atmosphere through EGR cut-off solenoid. For additional information on this system see ACURA & HONDA EGR article.

## SELF DIAGNOSTIC SYSTEM

The ECU has a self-diagnostic capability to help diagnose problems in sensor or in ECU itself. This system uses a dash mounted Check Engine warning light and one ECU mounted self-diagnostic LED. As a bulb check, warning light on dash will glow for 2 seconds when ignition is turned on. Warning light will also illuminate if ECU has detected a system malfunction. The ECU is mounted under access panel under carpet, below passenger side of dash.

ECU mounted LED is used to indicate trouble codes stored in ECU memory. Control unit can indicate any number of simultaneous component problems by blinking separate codes, one after another.

## TESTING

***NOTE: Before starting testing, ensure engine is in good mechanical condition and adjusted to specifications.***

## TROUBLE CODES

LED located on ECU is used to read codes set due to component failure. To obtain codes, turn ignition switch to the "ON" position and count flashes of LED on ECU. See appropriate LED CODES table in this article.

***NOTE: If unlisted codes are flashed by ECU LED, clear codes and recheck. If code still appears, substitute a known good ECU. If condition is rectified, replace original ECU.***

## SELF-DIAGNOSTIC CODES

*ACCORD LED CODES*

| LED Blinks | System Code |
|---|---|
| 0 | ECU. |
| 1 | Oxygen Sensor. |
| 2 | Vehicle Speed Pulser. |
| 3 | MAP Sensor. |
| 4 | Vacuum Switch. |
| 5 | MAP Sensor. |
| 6 | Coolant Temperature. |
| 8 | Ignition Coil Signal. |
| 10 | Intake Air Temperature Sensor. |
| 14 | Electronic Air Control Valve. |

System Checker Harnesses (07HAZ-PJ7010A and 07HAZ-PJ7000A) and Test Harness (07GMJ-ML80100) are needed to test harness and specific components. These function as a breakout box to access pin voltage signals while component is either in or out of circuit. To reset ECU and clear codes from memory, remove 10-amp "EFI/ECU" fuse in the under-hood relay box for 10 seconds.

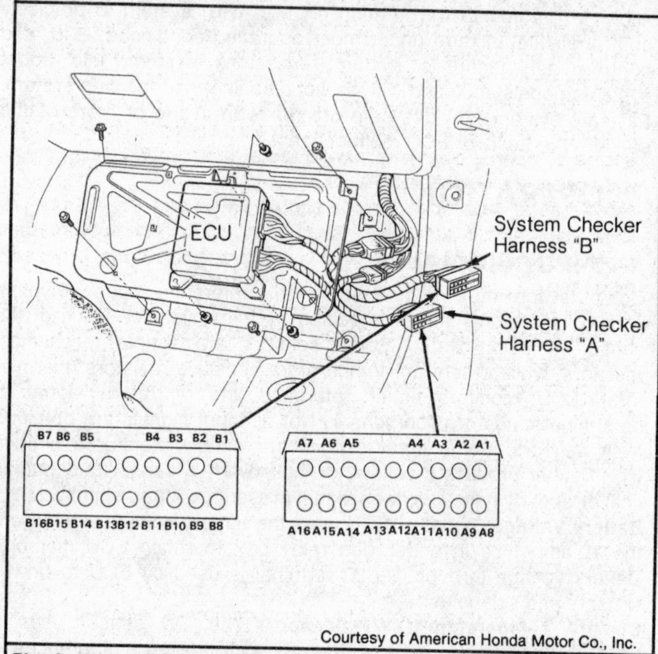
ECU
System Checker Harness "B"
System Checker Harness "A"
B7 B6 B5 B4 B3 B2 B1
B16 B15 B14 B13 B12 B11 B10 B9 B8
A7 A6 A5 A4 A3 A2 A1
A16 A15 A14 A13 A12 A11 A10 A9 A8
Courtesy of American Honda Motor Co., Inc.

***Fig. 2: ECU System Checker Harness & Terminal Identification***

## CODE 0, NO CODES

**No Warning Light** – **1)** Turn ignition on. If oil pressure light is on, go to step **2)**. If light is off, inspect fuse No 13. If fuse is okay, repair open circuit in Yellow wire between fuse and combination meter.

**2)** Turn ignition off. Connect system checker harness between ECU and connectors. Connect terminal A15 to ground. Turn ignition on. If warning light is now on, go to step **3)**. If light is off, replace warning light bulb or repair open in wire between ECU terminal A15 and combination meter.

**3)** Connect terminal A15 to terminal A16. If warning light fails to illuminate, repair open in Black wire between ECU terminal B16 and ground.

**4)** If warning light illuminated in step **3)**, substitute a known good ECU. If condition is rectified, replace original ECU.

**Warning Light On, LED Does Not Flash Codes** – **1)** Turn ignition on. Disconnect MAP sensor 3-wire connector. If warning light is still illuminated, go to step **2)**. If light is not on, replace MAP sensor.

**2)** If warning light flashes code for MAP sensor, replace MAP sensor. If not, reconnect MAP sensor connector. Turn ignition off. Connect system checker harness between ECU and ECU connectors. Disconnect "A" connector from ECU, not main harness. Check for continuity between terminal A7 and ground. If continuity exists, check for short in Yellow/White wire between MAP sensor and ECU terminal A7.

**3)** If continuity to ground does not exist, turn ignition on. If warning light is on, repair short to ground in Yellow/Red wire between combination meter and ECU terminal A15. If warning light is not on, reconnect "A" connector to ECU. Jumper terminal A15 to terminal B8. If warning light does not come on, repair open in Brown/Black wire between ECU terminal B8 and ground.

**4)** If light does come on, measure voltage between terminals B7 (pos.) and B8 (neg.). If battery voltage is not present, repair open in Black/Yellow wire between ECU terminal B7 and No. 12 fuse or replace No. 12 fuse.

**5)** If battery voltage is present, substitute a known good ECU. If condition is rectified, replace original ECU.

# COMPUTERIZED ENGINE CONTROLS
# Honda PGM-CARB Electronic Control System (Cont.)

## CODE 1, OXYGEN SENSOR

**1)** Warm engine to operating temperature (cooling fan comes on). Turn off ignition. Remove "EFI/ECU" fuse in under-hood relay panel for 10 seconds to reset ECU. Remove No. 2 vacuum hose from manifold vacuum fitting. Plug fitting. *See Fig. 3.* Start engine and slowly apply 13 in. Hg. Hold engine speed at 2500 RPM (minimum) for 30 seconds (late models) or 3 minutes (early models), without closing throttle completely during this time. Check if warning light is on. If not on, problem is intermittent. Check and seat connectors at sensor, battery and control unit. Test drive and check light again.

**3)** If light is on, disconnect oxygen sensor connector. Attach voltmeter to vehicle ground and oxygen sensor connector. With engine at normal operating temperature, momentarily open throttle wide open, then close throttle.

**4)** Voltage at wide open throttle should be greater than .6 volt, and less than .4 volt at closed throttle. If not within specifications, replace oxygen sensor. If voltage is within specifications, proceed to next step.

**5)** Turn engine off and reconnect oxygen sensor connector. Attach system checker harness between ECU and ECU connectors. Using a voltmeter, connect negative lead to connector terminal B8.

**6)** Attach positive voltmeter lead to connector terminal B1. Start engine and warm to operating temperature. Momentarily open throttle wide open, then close throttle. Voltage at wide open throttle should be greater than .6 volt, and less than .4 volt at closed throttle. If not within specifications, repair wire between ECU terminal B1 and oxygen sensor.

**7)** If within specifications, hold engine speed at about 2000 RPM. If voltage does not fluctuate from less than .4 volt to greater than .6 volt, perform EACV FUNCTIONAL TEST. If voltage does fluctuate, substitute a known good ECU. If condition is rectified, replace original ECU.

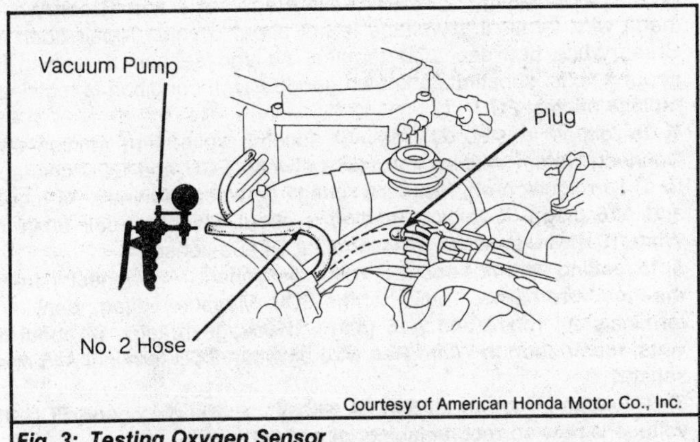
Vacuum Pump
Plug
No. 2 Hose
Courtesy of American Honda Motor Co., Inc.

***Fig. 3: Testing Oxygen Sensor***

## CODE 2, VEHICLE SPEED SENSOR

**1)** Block rear wheels and set parking brake. Raise front of vehicle and support with stands. Connect system checker harness between ECU and connectors. Turn ignition on.

**2)** Slowly rotate left front wheel and measure voltage between terminals A5 (pos.) and B8 (neg.). If voltage pulses from 0-5 volts, proceed to step **5)**. If voltage does not pulse, turn ignition off.

**3)** Disconnect connectors from ECU only, not from main harness. Turn ignition on. Slowly rotate left front wheel and measure voltage between terminals B7 (pos.) and A5 (neg.). If voltage pulses from 0-12 volts, substitute a known good ECU. If condition is rectified, replace original ECU.

**4)** If voltage does not pulse from 0-12 volts, repair open or short in White/Blue wire between ECU terminal A5 and speed sensor or replace faulty speed sensor.

**5)** Increase engine speed to 3000 RPM with no load. If code is reset, check No. 7 vacuum hose and vacuum switch for leaks. If hose and switch are okay, substitute a known good ECU. If condition is rectified, replace original ECU.

## CODE 3, MAP SENSOR

**1)** Turn off ignition. Remove "EFI/ECU" fuse in under-hood relay panel for 10 seconds to reset ECU. Start engine. Warm engine to operating temperature (cooling fan comes on). Check if warning light is on. If not on, problem is intermittent. Test drive and check light again.

**2)** If light is on, turn ignition off. Connect test harness between MAP sensor and sensor harness. Turn ignition on. Measure voltage between Red (pos.) and Green (neg.) terminals. If reading is about 5 volts, go to step **4)**. If not, measure voltage between Red (pos.) terminal and ground. If voltage is still not 5 volts, go to step **3)**. If voltage is about 5 volts, repair open in Green/White wire between ECU terminal A16 and MAP sensor.

**3)** Turn ignition off. Connect system checker harness between ECU and ECU connectors. Measure voltage between terminal A7 (pos.) and A16 (neg.) with ignition on. If voltage reading is about 5 volts, repair open Yellow/White wire between ECU terminal A7 and MAP sensor. If voltage is not about 5 volts, substitute a known good ECU. If condition is rectified, replace original ECU.

**4)** Measure voltage between White (pos.) and Green (neg.) terminals. If reading is not about 3 volts, replace MAP sensor or repair short in White/Blue wire between ECU terminal A6 and MAP sensor.

**5)** If measured voltage is about 3 volts, turn ignition off. Connect system checker harness between ECU and ECU connectors. Turn ignition on. Measure voltage between terminals A6 (pos.) and A16 (neg.). If there is not about 3 volts present, repair open White/Blue wire between ECU terminal A6 and MAP sensor.

**6)** If there is about 3 volts present, substitute a known good ECU. If condition is rectified, replace original ECU.

## CODE 4, VACUUM SWITCH

**1)** Turn off ignition. Remove "EFI/ECU" fuse in under-hood relay panel for 10 seconds to reset ECU. Start engine and allow to idle for 30 seconds. Check if warning light is on. If not on, problem is intermittent. Test drive and check light again.

**2)** If light is on, turn ignition off. Disconnect 8-wire connector at control box. Check for continuity between terminals No. 3 and 4 of control box. *See Fig. 4.* If continuity exists, go to step **4)**. If continuity does not exist, install "T" fittin in manifold vacuum hose between manifold and vacuum switch (located inside control box). Connect vacuum gauge to "T" fitting.

**3)** Start engine. If vacuum is less than 1.2 in. Hg, check vacuum hose routing. If vacuum is greater than 1.2 in. Hg, replace vacuum switch or repair open in Black/Yellow or White wrie in control box.

**4)** If continuity existed in step **2)**, turn ignition on. Measure voltage between Black/Yellow harness terminal and ground. If vattery voltage is not present, repair open in Black/Yellow wire between 8-wire harness connector and No. 12 fuse.

**5)** If battery voltage is present, turn ignition off. Reconnect 8-wire connector to control box. Connect system checker harness between ECU and ECU connectors. Turn ignition on. Measure voltage between terminals A10 (pos.) and B8 (neg.). If battery voltage is not present, repair open in Light Blue wire between ECU terminal A10 and vacuum switch.

**6)** If battery voltage is not present, substitute a known good ECU. If condition is rectified, replace original ECU.

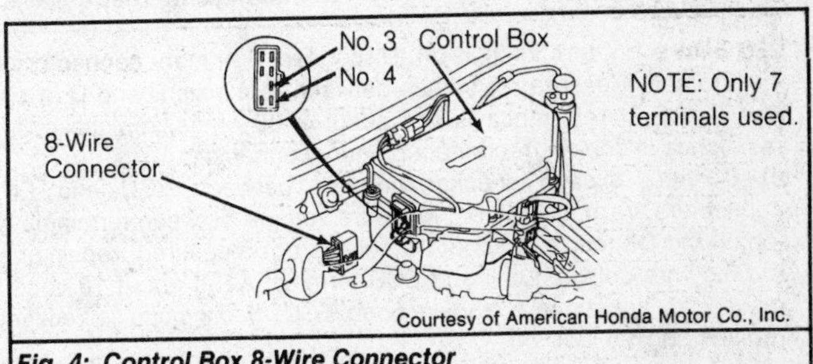
No. 3
Control Box
No. 4
NOTE: Only 7 terminals used.
8-Wire Connector
Courtesy of American Honda Motor Co., Inc.

***Fig. 4: Control Box 8-Wire Connector***

# COMPUTERIZED ENGINE CONTROLS
# Honda PGM-CARB Electronic Control System (Cont.)

## CODE 5, MAP SENSOR

**1)** Turn off ignition. Remove "EFI/ECU" fuse in under-hood relay panel for 10 seconds to reset ECU. Start engine and hold at idle. Check if warning light is on. If not on, problem is intermittent. Test drive and check light again.
**2)** If light is on, turn ignition off. Using a "T" fitting, connect a hand-held vacuum pump/gauge into vacuum hose between throttle body and MAP sensor (located inside control box). Start engine. If vacuum is not present, repair as necessary. If vacuum is present and holds, turn ignition off.
**3)** Connect vacuum pump to MAP sensor and apply vacuum. If vacuum does not hold, replace MAP sensor. Also check vacuum hose for leaks or blackage. If vacuum does hold, turn ignition off. Connect test harness between MAP sensor and harness. Turn ignition on. Measure voltage between White (pos.) terminal and Green (neg.) terminal. If reading is not about 3 volts, replace MAP sensor. If voltage reading is about 3 volts, substitute a known good ECU. If condition is rectified, replace original ECU.

## CODE 6, COOLANT (TW) SENSOR

**1)** Turn off ignition. Remove "EFI/ECU" fuse in under-hood relay panel for 10 seconds to reset ECU. Start engine. Check if warning light is on. If not on, problem is intermittent. Test drive and check light again.
**2)** If light is on, warm engine to normal operating temperature (cooling fan comes on). Disconnect 2-wire coolant sensor connector. Measure resistance across sensor terminals.
**3)** If resistance is not 200-400 ohms, replace TW sensor. If resistance is within specification, measure voltage between ground and Yellow/Green wire of sensor harness. If reading is not about 5 volts, go to step **5)**. If reading is about 5 volts, measure voltage between Yellow/Green (pos.) and Green/White wires of connector harness.
**4)** If voltage is not about 5 volts, repair open Green/White (neg.) wire between ECU terminal A16 and sensor. If voltage reading is correct, substitute a known good ECU. If condition is rectified, replace original ECU.
**5)** If voltage reading between ground and Yellow/Green wire of sensor harness in step **3)** was not about 5 volts, turn ignition off. Connect system checker harness between ECU and ECU connectors. Turn ignition on. Measure voltage between terminals A3 (pos.) and A16 (neg.) If voltage reading is about 5 volts, repair open Yellow/Green wire between ECU terminal A3 and TW sensor.
**6)** If reading is not about 5 volts, disconnect "A" connector from main wire harness only, not the ECU. Measure voltage between terminals A3 (pos.) and A16 (neg.). If reading is not about 5 volts, go to step **7)**. If voltage reading is about 5 volts, repair short in Yellow/Green wire between ECU terminal A3 and sensor or repair short in Yellow/Green wire between TW sensor and automatic transmission control unit.
**7)** If voltage reading is still not about 5 volts, substitute a known good ECU. If condition is rectified, replace original ECU.

## CODE 8, IGNITION OUTPUT SIGNAL

**1)** Turn off ignition. Remove "EFI/ECU" fuse in under-hood relay panel for 10 seconds to reset ECU. Start engine and observe warning light. If light is off, problem is intermittent. Test drive and check again.
**2)** If light is on, turn ignition off. Disconnect 2 primary connectors at ignition coil. Measure resistance between terminals B and D of coil. *See Fig. 5.* If resistance is not about 2000 ohms, replace coil. If resistance is correct, reconnect primary connectors.
**3)** Connect system checker harness between ECU and ECU connectors. Turn ignition on. Measure voltage between terminals A1 (pos.) and B8 (neg.). If about 10 volts is not measured, repair open in Blue wire between coil and ECU terminal A1. If about 10 volts is measured, substitute a known good ECU. If condition is rectified, replace original ECU.

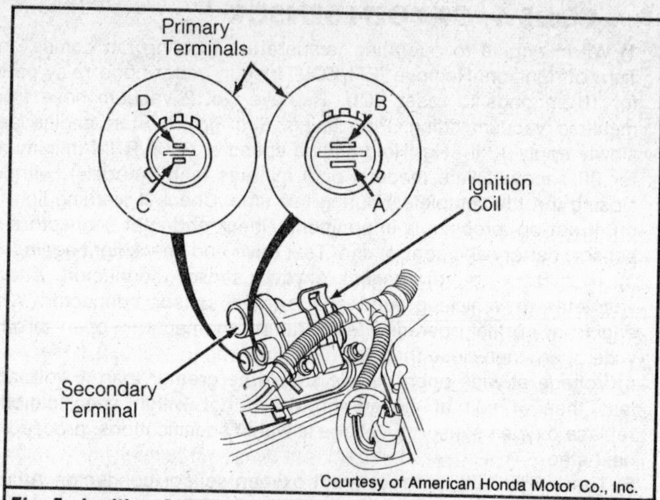
Primary
Terminals
D
B
C
A
Ignition
Coil
Secondary
Terminal
Courtesy of American Honda Motor Co., Inc.
***Fig. 5: Ignition Coil Terminal Identification***

## CODE 10, AIR TEMPERATURE (TA) SENSOR

**1)** Turn off ignition. Remove "EFI/ECU" fuse in under-hood relay panel for 10 seconds to reset ECU. Start engine and observe warning light. If light is off, problem is intermittent. Test drive and check again.
**2)** If light is on, turn ignition off. Measure resistance across TA sensor terminals. If reading is not 1000-4000 ohms, replace sensor. If resistance is within specification, measure voltage between ground and White/Red wire terminal. If reading is about 5 volts, go to step **3)**. If reading is not about 5 volts, go to step **4)**.
**3)** Measure voltage between White/Red (pos.) and Green/White (neg.) wire terminal. If voltage is not about 5 volts, repair open in Green/White between ECU terminal A4 and sensor. If reading is about 5 volts, substitute a known good ECU. If condition is rectified, replace original ECU.
**4)** If voltage in step **2)** was not about 5 volts, turn ignition off. Connect system checker harness between ECU and ECU connectors. Turn ignition on. Measure voltage between terminals A4 (pos.) and A16 (neg.). If voltage reading is about 5 volts, repair open in White/Red wire between ECU terminal A4 and sensor.
**5)** If reading was not about 5 volts, disconnect "A" connector from the main wire harness only, not the ECU. Measure voltage between terminals A4 (pos.) and A16 (neg.). If voltage reading is about 5 volts, repair short in White/Red wire between ECU terminal A45 and sensor.
**6)** If voltage is not about 5 volts, substitute a known good ECU. If voltage is now correct replace original ECU.

## CODE 14, ELECTRONIC AIR CONTROL VALVE (EACV)

**1)** Turn off ignition. Remove "EFI/ECU" fuse in under-hood relay panel for 10 seconds to reset ECU. Start engine and observe warning light. If light is off, problem is intermittent. Test drive and check again.
**2)** If light is on, turn ignition off. Disconnect Electronic Air Control Valve (EACV) connector. Check resistance between the 2 connector terminals on valve.
**3)** Resistance should be 8-15 ohms. If not within specification, replace EACV. If resistance is within specification, proceed to next step.
**4)** Check for continuity to ground on each EACV connector terminal. If continuity exists, replace EACV. If no continuity exists, reconnect EACV connector. Connect system checker harness between ECU and ECU connectors. Start engine. Measure voltage between terminals B3 (pos.) and B16 (neg.). If voltage is present, substitute a known good ECU. If condition is rectified, replace original ECU.

**5)** If voltage is not present, measure voltage between terminals B2 (pos.) and B16 (neg.). If voltage is present, substitute a known good ECU. If condition is rectified, replace original ECU. If battery voltage is not present, repair open in Blue/Red wire between ECU terminal B3 and EACV or Yellow/Black wire between ECU terminal B2 and EACV.

## EACV FUNCTIONAL TEST

**1)** Start engine and warm to operating temperature (cooling fan comes on). Disconnect EACV hose from air cleaner. Increase engine speed to 3500 RPM and check for vacuum. If vacuum is not present, check warning light on dash and self-diagnosis LED on ECU. If light is not illuminated, replace EACV.
**2)** If vacuum is present, increase engine speed to 3500 RPM and suddenly close throttle. If vacuum is not present, check warning light on dash and self-diagnosis LED on ECU. If light is illuminated and code 14 is displayed, go to CODE 14, EACV. If dash warning light is not illuminated and ECU LED is not displayinbg codes, chedck EACV hose for proper connection, cracks, blockage or disconnection. If hose is okay, replace EACV.

## MIXTURE CUT-OFF SOLENOID

**1)** Turn ignition on and off while listening to cut-off solenoids at carburetors. Solenoids should click. If both solenoids click, go to step **4)**. If either solenoid does not click, turn ignition off. Connect system checker harness between ECU and ECU connectors. Turn ignition on.
**2)** Measure voltage between terminals B4 (pos.) and B16 (neg.). If battery voltage is not present, go to step **3)**. If battery voltage is present, repair open or short in Black/Yellow wire between solenoid valve and ECU terminal B4. If wire is okay, replace solenoid valve which did not click. Also check Black wire from left solenoid valve to ground.
**3)** If battery voltage was not present at terminals B4 (pos.) and B16 (neg.), check warning light on dash and self-diagnosis LED on ECU. If okay, go to ECU INPUT SIGNALS.
**4)** Start engine and warm to operating temperature (cooling fan comes on). Block rear wheels and raise front of vehicle. Support with safety stands. Place transmission in 2nd (man. trans.) or "2" (auto. trans.). Accelerate and suddenly release throttle.
**5)** Check for clicking sound at each solenoid. If solenoids click, they are functioning properly. If solenoids do not click, turn ignition off. Connect system checker harness between ECU and ECU connectors. Start engine. Measure voltage between terminals B4 (pos.) and B16 (neg.) while decelerating from greater than 12.5 MPH and 4000 RPM.
**6)** If voltage goes away briefly, replace solenoid valve which does not click. If voltage does not go away briefly, check warning light on dash and ECU LED for codes. If okay, go to ECU INPUT SIGNALS.

## VACUUM PISTON CONTROL SYSTEM

**1)** Remove control box cover. Disconnect lower vacuum hose from vacuum piston control solenoid at 3-way joint. Connect vacuum pump. Disconnect upper vacuum hose at manifold vacuum port. Connect a vacuum gauge.
**2)** Start engine and warm to operating temperature (cooling fan comes on). Apply vacuum to solenoid. If vacuum is indicated on gauge, go to step **5)**. If vacuum is not indicated on gauge, turn ignition off. Disconnect 8-wire connector at control box.
**3)** Start engine. Measure voltage between Yellow (pos.) and Black (neg.) terminals of wire harness. If battery voltage is present, replace solenoid valve. If battery voltage is not present, measure voltage between ground and Yellow wire terminal. If battery voltage is present, repair open in Black wire between control box connector and ground.
**4)** If battery voltage is not present, check warning light on dash and self-diagnosis LED on ECU. If okay, check for open in Yellow wire between control box connector harness and ECU terminal B14.
**5)** If vacuum was indicated on gauge in step **1)**, quickly increase engine speed to 3000 RPM. Close throttle suddenly. If vacuum indication on gauge briefly decrease, vacuum piston solenoid valve is operating properly. If vacuum does not briefly decrease, turn ignition off.
**6)** Disconnect 8-wire connector at control box. Start engine. While measuring voltage at Yellow (pos.) and Black (neg.) terminals of contrl box harness, increase engine speed to 3000 RPM and close throttle suddenly. If battery voltage does not decrease momentarily, replace solenoid valve.
**7)** If battery voltage does decrease momentarily, check warning light on dash and self-diagnosis LED on ECU. If okay, substitute a known good ECU. If condition is rectified, replace original ECU.

## ECU INPUT SIGNALS

**Clutch Switch Signal (Man. Trans.) – 1)** Connect system checker harness between ECU and ECU connectors. Turn ignition on. Measure voltage between terminal A12 (pos.) and B8 (neg.). If battery voltage is not present, go to step **4)**.
**2)** If battery voltage is present, depress clutch pedal and again measure voltage as in step **1)**. If battery voltage is not present, clutch switch is functionoing properly.
**3)** If battery voltage is present with clutch pedal depressed, turn ignition off. Disconnect clutch switch 2-wire connector. Check for continuity between 2 clutch switch terminals while depressing and releasing clutch. If continuity does not fluctuate between zero and infinity, replace clutch switch.
**4)** If battery voltage was not present in step **1)**, turn ignition off. Disconnect 2-wire clutch switch connector. Check for continuity between 2 clutch switch terminals while depressing and releasing clutch. If continuity does not fluctuate between zero and infinity, replace clutch switch.
**5)** If continuity does fluctuate, turn igniton on. Measure voltage between Pink clutch switch wire and ground. If battery voltage is not present, repair open in Pink wire between ECU terminal A12 and clutch switch. If battery voltage is present, repair open in Black wire between clutch switch and ground.
**Gearshift Position Signal (Auto. Trans.) – 1)** Verify gearshift selector indicator light functions properly. Turn ignition off. Install system checker harness between ECU and ECU connectors. Disconnect "A" connector from harness only, not ECU.
**2)** Turn ignition on. Measure boltage between terminals A11 (pos.) and B8 (neg.). If battery voltage is not indicated, substitute a known good ECU. If condition is rectified, replace original ECU. If battery voltage is indicated, reconnect "A" connector to main wire harness. Measure voltage between A11 (pos.) and B8 (neg.) with gearshift in Neutral. If voltage is not present, go to step **4)**.
**3)** If voltage is present, repair open in Light Green wire between ECU terminal A11 and combination meter or repair open in Green wire between combination meter and gearshift selector switch.
**4)** Measure voltage between ECU terminals A11 (pos.) and B8 (neg.) in all other gearshift positions except Neutral. If battery voltage is present, shift position signal is okay. If battery voltage is not present, repair short in Light Green wire between combination meter and ECU.
**A/C Clutch Signal – 1)** Connect system checker harness between ECU and ECU connectors. Start engine. Measure voltage between terminals A2 (pos.) and B8 (neg.). If battery voltage is not present, go to step **3)**.
**2)** If battery voltage is present, repair short in Red/Green wire between ECU terminal A2 and compressor control unit. If wire is okay, inspect compressor control unit. Replace if necessary.
**3)** Turn A/C switch to "ON" position. If A/C does not operate, service A/C system. If A/C system functions properly, measure voltage between terminals A2 (pos.) and B8 (neg.). If battery voltage is present, A/C clutch signal is okay. If battery voltage is not present, repair open in Red/Green wire between ECU terminal A2 and compressor control unit. If wire is okay, inspect compressor control unit. Replace if necessary.

# Honda PGM-CARB Electronic Control System (Cont.)

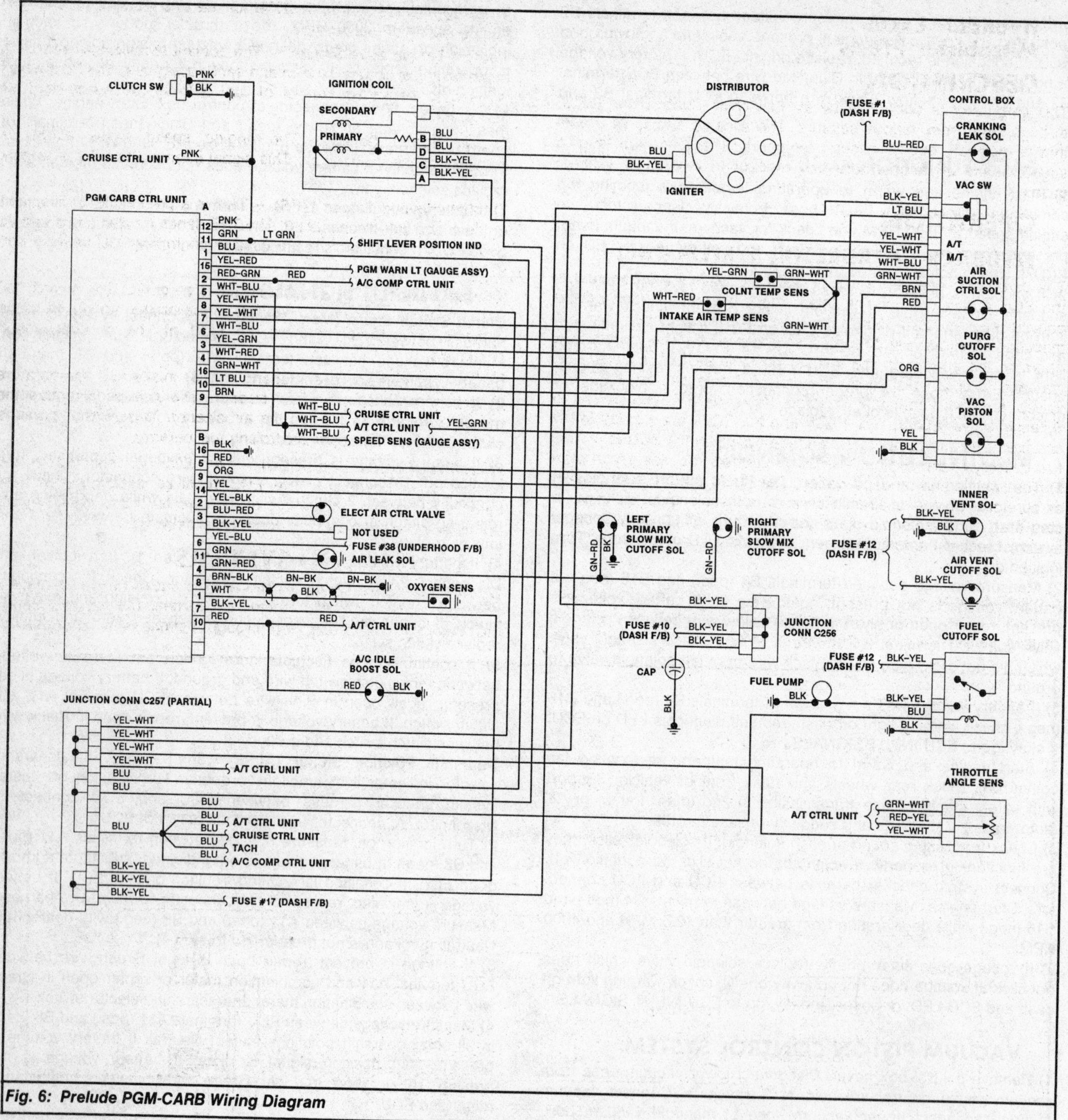
CLUTCH SW
PNK
BLK
CRUISE CTRL UNIT
PNK
IGNITION COIL
SECONDARY
PRIMARY
B
D
C
A
BLU
BLU
BLK-YEL
BLK-YEL
DISTRIBUTOR
BLU
BLK-YEL
IGNITER
FUSE #1 (DASH F/B)
BLU-RED
CONTROL BOX
CRANKING LEAK SOL
VAC SW
BLK-YEL
LT BLU
YEL-WHT
YEL-WHT
WHT-BLU
A/T
M/T
GRN-WHT
BRN
RED
AIR SUCTION CTRL SOL
PURG CUTOFF SOL
ORG
VAC PISTON SOL
YEL
BLK
PGM CARB CTRL UNIT
A
PNK
GRN
LT GRN
BLU
SHIFT LEVER POSITION IND
YEL-RED
RED-GRN
RED
PGM WARN LT (GAUGE ASSY)
WHT-BLU
A/C COMP CTRL UNIT
YEL-WHT
YEL-WHT
WHT-BLU
YEL-GRN
WHT-RED
GRN-WHT
LT BLU
BRN
YEL-GRN
GRN-WHT
COLNT TEMP SENS
WHT-RED
INTAKE AIR TEMP SENS
GRN-WHT
WHT-BLU
WHT-BLU
CRUISE CTRL UNIT
WHT-BLU
A/T CTRL UNIT
YEL-GRN
WHT-BLU
SPEED SENS (GAUGE ASSY)
B
BLK
RED
ORG
YEL
YEL-BLK
BLU-RED
ELECT AIR CTRL VALVE
BLK-YEL
YEL-BLU
NOT USED
GRN
FUSE #38 (UNDERHOOD F/B)
GRN-RED
AIR LEAK SOL
BRN-BLK
BN-BK
BN-BK
WHT
BLK
OXYGEN SENS
BLK-YEL
RED
RED
A/T CTRL UNIT
A/C IDLE BOOST SOL
RED
BLK
LEFT PRIMARY SLOW MIX CUTOFF SOL
GN-RD
BK
RIGHT PRIMARY SLOW MIX CUTOFF SOL
GN-RD
INNER VENT SOL
BLK-YEL
BLK
FUSE #12 (DASH F/B)
AIR VENT CUTOFF SOL
BLK-YEL
BLK-YEL
FUSE #10 (DASH F/B)
BLK-YEL
BLK-YEL
JUNCTION CONN C256
CAP
BLK
FUEL CUTOFF SOL
FUSE #12 (DASH F/B)
BLK-YEL
FUEL PUMP
BLK
BLK-YEL
BLU
BLK
JUNCTION CONN C257 (PARTIAL)
YEL-WHT
YEL-WHT
YEL-WHT
YEL-WHT
A/T CTRL UNIT
BLU
BLU
BLU
BLU
BLU
A/T CTRL UNIT
BLU
CRUISE CTRL UNIT
BLU
TACH
BLU
A/C COMP CTRL UNIT
BLK-YEL
BLK-YEL
BLK-YEL
FUSE #17 (DASH F/B)
THROTTLE ANGLE SENS
A/T CTRL UNIT
GRN-WHT
RED-YEL
YEL-WHT

*Fig. 6: Prelude PGM-CARB Wiring Diagram*

# 1988 COMPUTERIZED ENGINE CONTROLS
# Hyundai & Mitsubishi FBC System

**Hyundai: Excel**
**Mitsubishi: Precis**

## DESCRIPTION

This carburetor is controlled by an Electronic Control Unit (ECU) through input from various sensors. The sensors supply ECU with throttle position, engine coolant temperature, engine load, engine speed, intake air temperature and amount of oxygen in exhaust gases.

## OPERATION

### FEEDBACK CARBURETOR SYSTEM (FBC)

The carburetor operates on a preset fuel delivery programmed in the ECU during cold engine (open loop) operation. When engine coolant reaches 122°F (50°C) the ECU switches to closed loop and modulates fuel delivery through 2 solenoid valves The system now operates the engine on the leanest possible air/fuel mixture. Fuel metering is accomplished by the use of 2 solenoid valves. The 2 valves are the Feedback Solenoid Valve (FBSV) and Slow-Cut Solenoid Valve (SCSV). The FBSV and the SCSV are located in the carburetor float chamber cover and are cycled by the ECU to control fuel delivery to the engine. The SCSV controls fuel delivery at slow engine speeds and on deceleration. The FBCV controls fuel delivery at all other engine speeds. Activation of each solenoid valve is controlled by the duty cycle signal from the ECU. Duty cycle is length of time the electrical current is supplied to each solenoid. *See Fig. 1.*

**Oxygen Sensor** – The oxygen sensor is mounted in exhaust manifold ahead of catalytic converter. Output signals from the oxygen sensor vary with percent of oxygen in the exhaust gas. These signals are sent to the ECU for use in controlling closed loop compensation of fuel delivery.

**Coolant Temperature Sensor** – The coolant temperature sensor is mounted in the cooling system and sends a signal to the ECU which is used to determine control of fuel delivery and secondary air management.

**Engine Speed Sensor** – The engine speed signal (RPM) is supplied by the ignition coil. This signal informs the ECU of engine speed.

**Throttle Position Sensor (TPS)** – This is a potentiometer mounted to the carburetor throttle shaft. The TPS sends throttle angle signals to the ECU. These signals are used in controlling fuel delivery and secondary air management.

**Vacuum Switch** – The vacuum switch is a contact type switch that uses manifold vacuum to override a calibrated spring to close contacts. This switch informs the ECU of idle or deceleration conditions.

**Intake Air Temperature Sensor** – The intake air temperature sensor is mounted in the air cleaner. The sensor measures the temperature of intake air in the air cleaner. This sensor signal is sent to the ECU for use in controlling fuel delivery.

**Electronic Control Unit (ECU)** – The ECU is mounted in the passenger compartment. The ECU receives analog inputs from sensors and converts them into digital signals. These digital signals are processed by the ECU to control fuel delivery.

## CONTROLLED SYSTEMS

**Electric Controlled Choke** – The electric choke uses a bi-metallic spring to close choke. An electric choke heater is incorporated in the choke cap and is operated through a choke relay, energized by

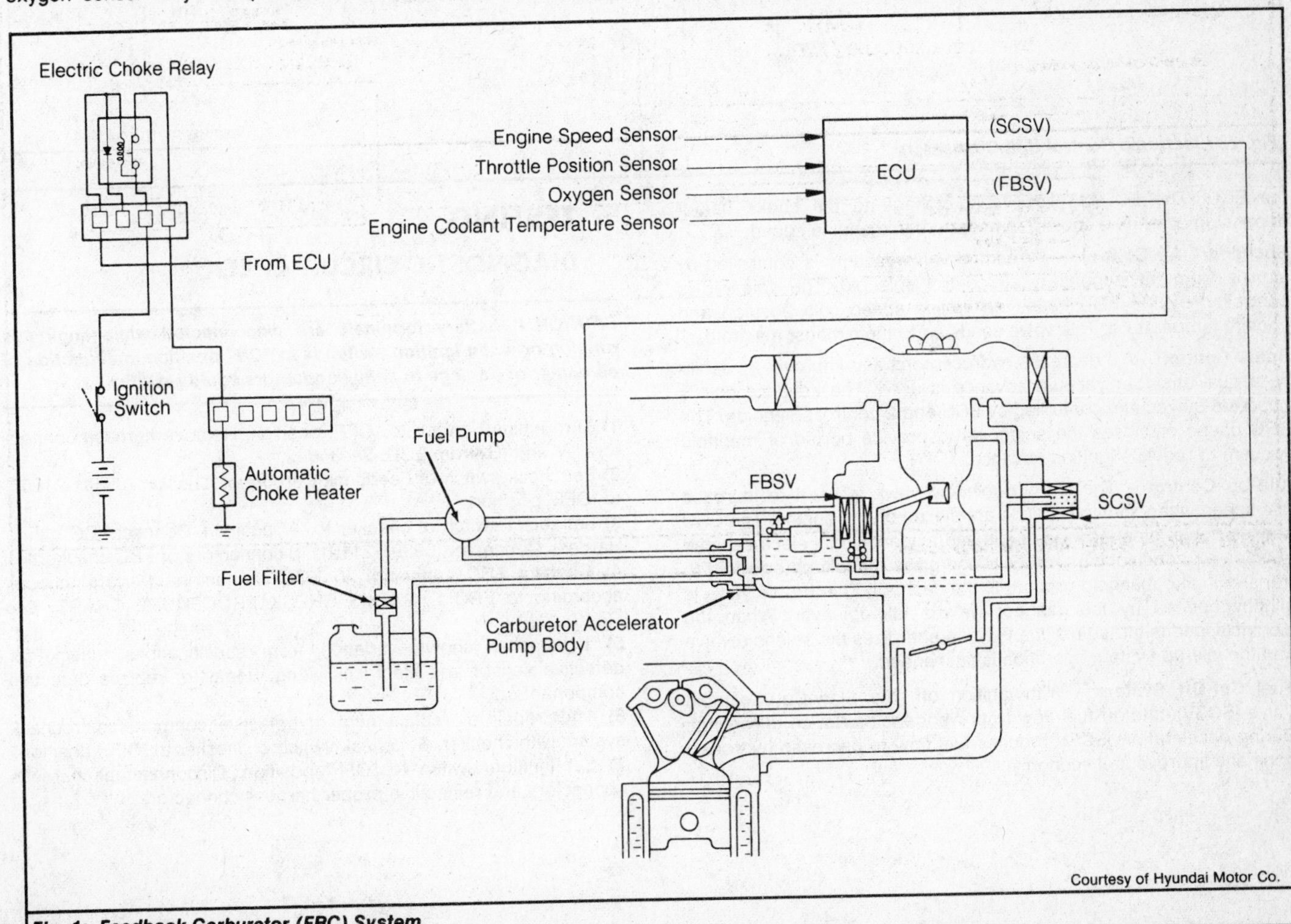

Electric Choke Relay
Engine Speed Sensor
Throttle Position Sensor
Oxygen Sensor
Engine Coolant Temperature Sensor
ECU
(SCSV)
(FBSV)
From ECU
Ignition Switch
Fuel Pump
Automatic Choke Heater
FBSV
SCSV
Fuel Filter
Carburetor Accelerator Pump Body
Courtesy of Hyundai Motor Co.


*Fig. 1: Feedback Carburetor (FBC) System*

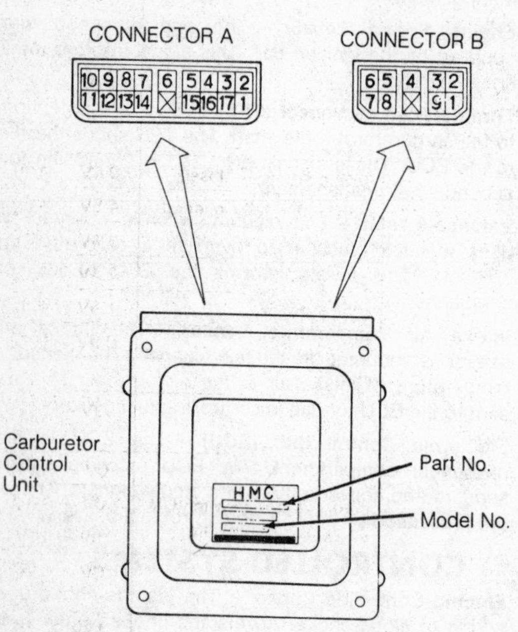
CONNECTOR A
10 9 8 7 6 5 4 3 2
11 12 13 14 15 16 17 1
CONNECTOR B
6 5 4 3 2
7 8 9 1
Carburetor Control Unit
HMC
Part No.
Model No.

CONNECTOR A
Pin 1: Battery Back-Up
Pin 2: Power Source
Pin 3: Power Source
Pin 4: Ground
Pin 5: Cold Spark Advance Solenoid Valve
Pin 6: Vacuum Switch
Pin 7: Blank
Pin 8: Air Conditioning Cut Relay
Pin 9: Secondary Air Control Solenoid
Pin 10: Slow-Cut Solenoid Valve
Pin 11: Feedback Solenoid Valve
Pin 12: Idle-Up Control Solenoid Valve
Pin 13: Distributor Advance Solenoid Valve
Pin 14: Electric Choke Relay
Pin 15: Ignition Coil (RPM)
Pin 16: Ground
Pin 17: Blank

CONNECTOR B
Pin 1: Sensor Power Source (Positive)
Pin 2: Ground for Sensor
Pin 3: Coolant Temperature Sensor
Pin 4: Blank
Pin 5: Oxygen Sensor (Output)
Pin 6: Blank
Pin 7: Cold Mixture Heater Relay (Negative)
Pin 8: Blank
Pin 9: Throttle Position Sensor (Output)

Courtesy of Hyundai Motor Co.

***Fig. 2: Electronic Control Unit Connectors***

the ECU. The ECU applies varing voltage to the choke heater depending on engine coolant temperature and engine speed.

**Secondary Air Control** – Air control valve vacuum is controlled by signals from the secondary air control solenoid. The solenoid is controlled by the ECU based on engine speed, idle position and coolant temperature. This valve sends air to the exhaust manifold.

**Spark Control** – To decrease hydrocarbons and improve driveability, a dual chamber vacuum advance is used. The advance unit is operated by vacuum controlled by ECU and 2 control solenoids. The ECU opens or closes the solenoids to provide ported or manifold vacuum to regulate ignition advance.

**Idle-Up Control** – The idle-up solenoid valve is used to increase idle speed when additional loads are placed on the engine. The ECU senses power steering load at idle and any additional electrical load such as air conditioning. The ECU energizes the idle-up solenoid to transfer intake manifold vacuum to the dashpot. The throttle valve is slightly opened by the dashpot via the idle-up lever. When the electrical load is turned off, the ECU de-energizes the solenoid valve and the idle-up system operation is suspended.

**Fuel Cut-Off System** – With ignition off, the Slow-Cut Solenoid Valve (SCSV) cuts off fuel flow to prevent engine run-on (dieseling). During deceleration, SCSV reduces fuel flow to decrease hydrocarbons and improve fuel economy.

# TESTING

## DIAGNOSTIC CIRCUIT CHECK

***CAUTION: If battery terminals are disconnected while engine is running or when ignition switch is in "ON" position, malfunction of computer or damage to semi-conductors could result.***

**1)** Turn ignition switch to "OFF" position. Remove harness connectors "A" and "B" from ECU. *See Fig. 2.*
**2)** Set check switch of Feedback Carburetor Checker (09341-21000) to "OFF" position.
**3)** Set select switch of checker to "A" position. Connect FBC Wiring Harness Connector (09391-21101) to connectors of FBC checker.
**4)** Connect FBC connector to ECU connectors. Perform checks according to FBC SYSTEMS CHECK PROCEDURE CHART. *See Fig. 3.*
**5)** If checker shows variation from specifications, check for defective sensor and electrical wiring. Repair or replace defective components.
**6)** After repair or replacement of defective components, recheck system with checker. Set check switch of checker to "OFF" position.
**7)** Set ignition switch to "OFF" position. Disconnect all harness connectors and reinstall in proper harness connectors.

# 1988 COMPUTERIZED ENGINE CONTROLS
## Hyundai & Mitsubishi FBC System (Cont.)

| FBC checker setting | | Check item | ECU Terminal# checked | Condition | | Test specification |
|---|---|---|---|---|---|---|
| Select switch | Check switch | | | | | |
| "A" | 1 | Power supply | A — 2 | Ignition switch "LOCK" → "ON" | | 11V — 13V |
| | 2 | Spark advance control solenoid valve | A — 13 | Idling (warm engine) | | 0V — 0.6V |
| | | | | Start engine. Drive vehicle at a speed higher than 8 km/h (5 mph), then hold 2,000 rpm (warm engine) | | 13V — 15V |
| | 3 | Throttle position sensor (TPS) | B — 9 | Ignition switch "LOCK"→"ON" (warm engine) | Accelerator fully closed | 0.4V — 0.7V |
| | | | | | Accelerator fully opened | 4.5V — 5.5V |
| | 4 | Engine coolant temperature sensor | B — 3 | Ignition switch "LOCK" → "ON" | 0°C (32°F) | 3.4V — 3.6V |
| | | | | | 20°C (68°F) | 2.4V — 2.7V |
| | | | | | 40°C (104°F) | 1.5V — 1.8V |
| | | | | | 80°C (176°C) | 0.5V — 0.7V |
| | 5 | | | | | |
| | 6 | Vacuum switch for idle position | A — 6 | Ignition switch "LOCK" → "ON" | | 9V — 13V |
| | | | | Idling (warm engine) | | 0V — 0.6 V |
| | 7 | Idle up (throttle opener) control solenoid valve | A — 12 | Idling | Power steering switch ON or lighting switch ON | 0V — 0.6V |
| | | | | 2,000 rpm | | 9V — 15V |
| | 8 | Electric choke relay | A — 14 | Ignition switch "LOCK"→"ON" | | 0V — 0.6V |
| | | | | Idling | | 13V — 15V |
| | 9 | Air conditioner cut-off | A — 8 | Ignition switch "LOCK"→"ON" and air conditioner switch "ON"*1 | Accelerator fully closed | 0V — 0.6V |
| | | | | | Accelerator fully opened | M/T 0V—0.6V |
| | | | | | | A/T 13V—15V |
| | 10 | Power supply for sensor | B — 1 | Ignition switch "LOCK" → "ON" | | 4.5V — 5.5V |
| | 11 | | | | | |
| | 12 | Secondary air control solenoid valve | A — 9 | Idling, 70 seconds after start of warm engine | | 0V — 0.6V then 13V — 15V |
| | | | | Quick deceleration from above 2,000 rpm to idling with gear in "N" position | | Momentarily drop |
| "B" | 1 | | | | | |
| | 2 | Feed back solenoid valve (FBSV) | A—11 | Ignition switch "LOCK" → "ON" | | 11V — 13V |
| | | | | Idling (warm engine) | | 2V — 12V |
| | 3 | | | | | |
| | 4 | Ignition pulse | A—15 | Ignition switch "LOCK"→"START" | | 2V — 8V |
| | 5 | | | | | |
| | 6 | | | | | |
| | 7 | Slow cut solenoid valve | A—10 | Idling | | 0V — 0.6V |
| | | | | Quick deceleration from above 4,000 rpm to idle with transmission in position | | Momentarily 13V — 15V |
| | 8 | Oxygen sensor | B — 5 | Hold speed constant above 1,300 rpm, 70 seconds after start of warm engine | | 0V — 1V ↑ (Pulsates) ↓ 2V — 3V |
| | 9 | | | | | |
| | 10 | | | | | |
| | 11 | | | | | |
| | 12 | | | | | |

Courtesy of Hyundai Motor Co.

***Fig. 3: FBC Systems Check Procedure Chart***

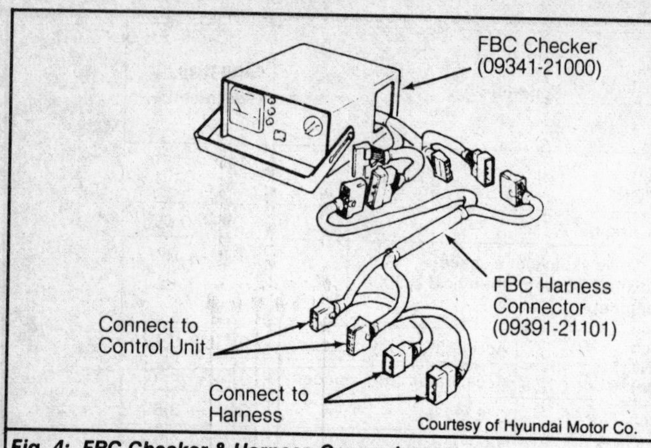
FBC Checker
(09341-21000)
FBC Harness
Connector
(09391-21101)
Connect to
Control Unit
Connect to
Harness
Courtesy of Hyundai Motor Co.

*Fig. 4: FBC Checker & Harness Connectors*

## THROTTLE POSITION SENSOR (TPS)

Disconnect TPS connector. Connect a digital voltmeter between terminals No. 2 and 3. *See Fig. 5.* Ensure voltage output matches specifications in FBC System Check Procedures Chart. *See Fig. 3.* If voltage readings are improper adjust TPS by loosening 2 screws and rotating TPS. *See Fig. 6.* If adjusting will not provide proper voltage, replace TPS.

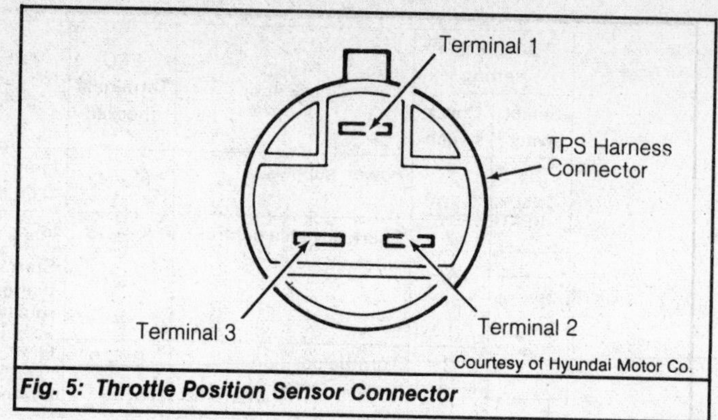
Terminal 1
TPS Harness
Connector
Terminal 3
Terminal 2
Courtesy of Hyundai Motor Co.

*Fig. 5: Throttle Position Sensor Connector*

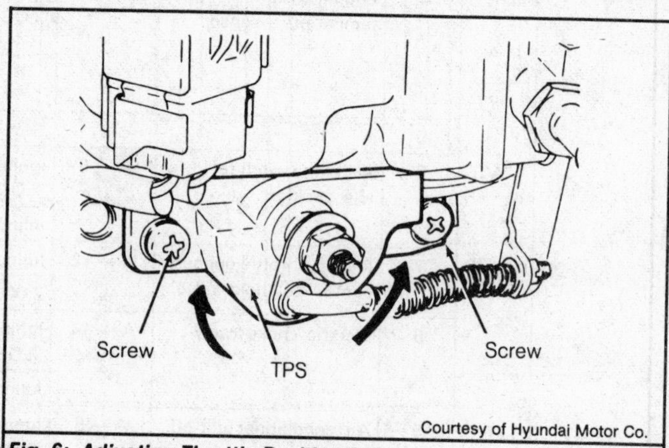
Screw
TPS
Screw
Courtesy of Hyundai Motor Co.

*Fig. 6: Adjusting Throttle Position Sensor*

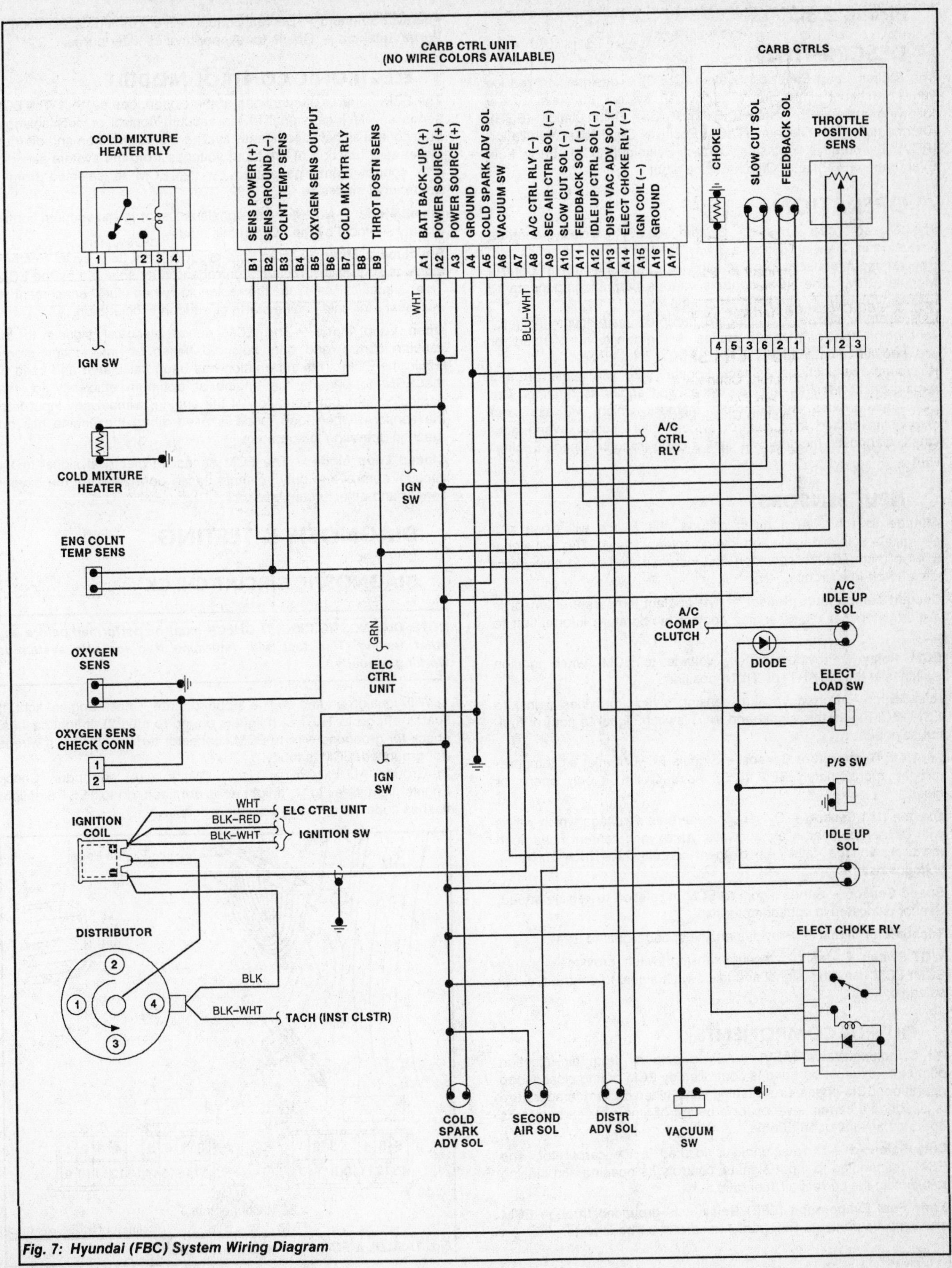
CARB CTRL UNIT
(NO WIRE COLORS AVAILABLE)
CARB CTRLS
COLD MIXTURE HEATER RLY
SENS POWER (+)
SENS GROUND (−)
COLNT TEMP SENS
OXYGEN SENS OUTPUT
COLD MIX HTR RLY
THROT POSTN SENS
BATT BACK-UP (+)
POWER SOURCE (+)
POWER SOURCE (+)
GROUND
COLD SPARK ADV SOL
VACUUM SW
A/C CTRL RLY (−)
SEC AIR CTRL SOL (−)
SLOW CUT SOL (−)
FEEDBACK SOL (−)
IDLE UP CTRL SOL (−)
DISTR VAC ADV SOL (−)
ELECT CHOKE RLY (−)
IGN COIL (−)
GROUND
CHOKE
SLOW CUT SOL
FEEDBACK SOL
THROTTLE POSITION SENS
B1 B2 B3 B4 B5 B6 B7 B8 B9
A1 A2 A3 A4 A5 A6 A7 A8 A9 A10 A11 A12 A13 A14 A15 A16 A17
WHT
BLU-WHT
IGN SW
A/C CTRL RLY
COLD MIXTURE HEATER
IGN SW
ENG COLNT TEMP SENS
A/C IDLE UP SOL
A/C COMP CLUTCH
GRN
ELC CTRL UNIT
DIODE
OXYGEN SENS
ELECT LOAD SW
OXYGEN SENS CHECK CONN
IGN SW
P/S SW
IGNITION COIL
WHT
BLK-RED
BLK-WHT
ELC CTRL UNIT
IGNITION SW
IDLE UP SOL
DISTRIBUTOR
ELECT CHOKE RLY
BLK
BLK-WHT
TACH (INST CLSTR)
COLD SPARK ADV SOL
SECOND AIR SOL
DISTR ADV SOL
VACUUM SW

*Fig. 7: Hyundai (FBC) System Wiring Diagram*

# 1988 COMPUTERIZED ENGINE CONTROLS
# Isuzu Closed Loop Emission System

## Pickup 2.3L

## DESCRIPTION

The Closed Loop Emission System (CLES) is designed to reduce vehicle eshaust emissions. The overall system consists of the following major sub-systems: Exhaust Gas Recirculation (EGR), Thermostatic Air Cleaner (TAC), Positive Crankcase Ventilation (PCV), Evaporative Emission Control System (EECS), Early Fuel Evaporation (EFE), and "Check Engine" light.

## OPERATION

The Closed Loop Emission System (CLES) precisely controls air/fuel ratio, allowing use of a 3-way catalyst to reduce emissions. Several input sensors provide signals to the Electronic Control Module (ECM). The ECM controls various output components to maintain driveablility and keep emissions low.

This system utilizes a dashboard mounted malfunction indicator light which, for some failure modes, will inform driver of need for unscheduled maintenance.

If system malfunctions, "Check Engine" light will come on and remain on as long as fault continues and engine is running. The ECM incorporates a diagnostic memory which will assist in diagnosing closed loop control system malfunctions. When activated, diagnostic memory will flash a code through "Check Engine" light.

### INPUT SENSORS

**Altitude Switch** – At a given altitude, the switch will close and energize a solenoid valve and idle-up solenoid valve. This will signal ECM of high altitude condition and increase air flow to carburetor idle and off-idle circuits.

**Coolant Temperature Sensor** – The coolant temperature sensor is a thermistor that relays engine coolant temperature information to ECM.

**ECM Relay** – Provides battery voltage to ECM, when ignition switch is in the "START" or "RUN" position.

**Idle Switch** – Ported vacuum sensing switch, provides signal to ECM. ECM uses this signal and WOT switch signal to control fuel-cut solenoid.

**Inlet Air Temperature Sensor** – Signals ECM of inlet air temperature at approximately 32°F (0°C). As a switch, it only opens or closes.

**Oxygen ($O_2$) Sensor** – $O_2$ sensor generates a voltage which varies with oxygen content in exhaust gas. As oxygen content rises (lean mixture), voltage falls. As oxygen content falls (rich mixture), voltages rises.

**Speed Sensor** – Sends signal to ECM in relation to vehicle speed. Sensor is located in speedometer head.

**Tachometer Signal** – Provides engine speed signal to ECM.

**WOT Switch** – Manifold vacuum sensing switch, provides signal to ECM. ECM uses this signal and idle switch signal to control fuel-cut solenoid.

### OUTPUT COMPONENTS

**Air Switching Valve (ASV)** – ASV directs air from air injection pump into exhaust port and is controlled by ECM during closed loop operation. ECM opens air switching valve when coolant temperature is less than a certain level or for a period of time after carburetor is operated at wide open throttle.

**Duty Solenoid** – Duty solenoid is located in the carburetor. The ECM, responding to input signals, controls its opening and closing to maintain the correct air/fuel ratio.

**Early Fuel Evaporation (EFE) Relay** – Is grounded through ECM and supplies power to EFE heater in carburetor base plate.

**Fuel-Cut Solenoid** – Decreases fuel delivery during deceleration.

**Purge Solenoid** – Opens for evaporative canister purge.

### ELECTRONIC CONTROL MODULE

The ECM controls all functions of the closed loop system. The ECM sends an electrical signal to the vacuum control or duty solenoid. This control signal is constantly cycling the solenoid on and off (duty cycle) as a function of the input voltages from the system sensors. The control signal generated by the ECM is selected from 4 operational modes.

**Inhibit Mode** – No electrical signals are sent to the vacuum control or duty solenoid by the ECM in this mode.

**Enrichment Mode** – Fixed, pre-programmed duty cycle electrical signal is sent to the vacuum control and duty solenoid by the ECM. This signal is sent to the solenoid when fuel enrichment is necessary for cold engine starts or sudden acceleration.

**Open Loop Mode** – The ECM sends electrical signals to the vacuum control and duty solenoid based on information stored within the ECM. This information has been calculated and used by the ECM to operate the engine at optimum efficiency for that particular operating condition of the engine, without any input from the sensors. Open loop mode is used when the engine has not reached operating temperature.

**Closed Loop Mode** – The ECM sends an electrical signal to the vacuum control and duty solenoid based on input from the oxygen sensor and other system sensors.

## DIAGNOSIS & TESTING

### DIAGNOSTIC CIRCUIT CHECK

***NOTE: DIAGNOSTIC CIRCUIT CHECK must be performed before any other testing. This test will determine if diagnostic system is working properly.***

**1)** With ignition on and engine stopped, note "Check Engine" light. If light is off, go to TEST 5. If light is on, go to step **2)**. If light flashes, check for grounded wire to ECM connector terminal C45-1. If wire is not grounded, ECM is faulty.

**2)** Ground ALDL terminal No. 1 (White wire) and note "Check Engine" light. *See Fig. 1.* If light does not flash, go to TEST 6. If light flashes code 12, note any additional codes.

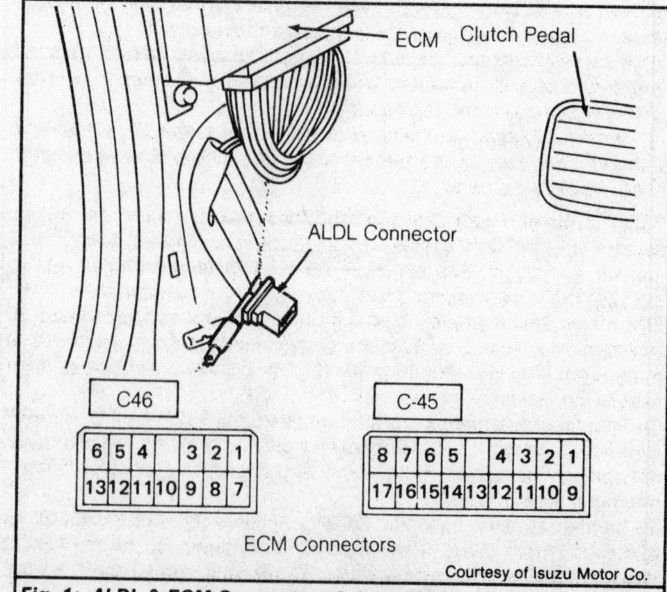
ECM
Clutch Pedal
ALDL Connector
C46
C-45
6 5 4 3 2 1
13 12 11 10 9 8 7
8 7 6 5 4 3 2 1
17 16 15 14 13 12 11 10 9
ECM Connectors
Courtesy of Isuzu Motor Co.

***Fig. 1: ALDL & ECM Connectors & Location***

**3)** If code 52 or 55 flashes, replace ECM. If no additional codes flash, turn ignition off, clear codes and remove ground from ALDL terminal No. 1.
**4)** Set parking brake and run engine for 2 minutes. Note "Check Engine" light. If light is off, go to step **6)**. If light is on, ground ALDL terminal No. 1.
**5)** If code flashes, go to appropriate code information. If light flashes, but no code is noted, replace ECM.
**6)** Refer to additional codes in step **2)**. If no additional codes, verify customers complaint. If additional codes are 13, 15, 21, 22, 31, 44 or 45, go to appropriate code information. For all others, trouble is intermittent. Make physical check of circuits indicated by code.

**Clearing Trouble Codes** – To clear memory of trouble codes, remove ECM fuse for 10 seconds.

**Exiting Diagnostic Mode** – To exit diagnostic mode, turn ignition off. Disconnect diagnostic terminals.

### SYSTEM PERFORMANCE CHECK

**1)** Set parking brake with transmission in "N" and block wheels. Disconnect purge hose from canister and plug. Connect tachometer and start engine. Disconnect carburetor duty solenoid and ground duty solenoid dwell terminal.
**2)** Run engine at 3000 RPM. Keep throttle constant and reconnect duty solenoid. Note RPM. Remove ground from duty solenoid dwell terminal before returning to idle. If RPM decreases more than 100 RPM, go to step **3)**. If RPM decreases less than 100 RPM or increases, check duty solenoid connections. If connections are okay, repair carburetor.
**3)** Connect dwell meter (4-cyl. scale) to duty solenoid dwell terminal. Warm engine at part throttle until upper radiator hose is warm. Return engine to idle and note dwell.
**4)** If dwell is varying, go to step **5)**. If dwell is fixed under 10 degrees, go to TEST 1. If the dwell is fixed 10-80 degrees, go to TEST 2. If dwell is fixed over 80 degrees, go to TEST 3.
**5)** Check dwell at 3000 RPM. If dwell is between 10-80 degrees, go to step **6)**. If dwell is not between 10-80 degrees, repair carburetor.
**6)** Check duty solenoid connector connections. If okay, check AIR management system. If no trouble found, clear codes.

**TEST 1 (Dwell Fixed Under 10 Degrees)** – **1)** Check vacuum hose connections at switches. If okay, disconnect switch connectors and run engine at part throttle. Note dwell. If dwell is under 10 degrees, go to step **2)**. If dwell varies, replace vacuum switch assembly.
**2)** Check for shorted or grounded wires between WOT switch and idle switch wires and ECM connector. If okay, run engine at part throttle and choke engine. If dwell increases, go to step **4)**. If dwell does not change, disconnect $O_2$ sensor and note dwell.
**3)** If dwell increases, replace $O_2$ sensor. If dwell is less than 10 degrees, check for grounded Violet wire to ECM connector terminal C45-8. If not grounded, replace ECM.
**4)** Check for intake vacuum leak, exhaust leak before $O_2$ sensor and vacuum hose routing. If no leaks are found, check duty solenoid. If okay, repair carburetor.

**TEST 2 (Dwell Fixed Between 10-80 Degrees)** – **1)** Warm engine at part throttle. With engine idling, disconnect coolant sensor and jumper connector. Note dwell. If the dwell does not change, go to step **3)**. If dwell is varying, check coolant sensor resistance.
**2)** If resistance is greater than 800 ohms, replace coolant sensor. If resistance is less than 800 ohms, reconnect coolant sensor and note dwell. If dwell is fixed, go to step **3)**. If dwell is varying, coolant sensor connection was poor.
**3)** Reconnect coolant sensor and remove connector from $O_2$ sensor. Ground $O_2$ sensor to ECM connector and note dwell. If dwell does not change, go to step **4)**. If dwell is less than 10 degrees, $O_2$ sensor or connection is faulty.
**4)** Connect jumper between ECM connector terminals C45-16 to C45-8 and note dwell. If dwell does not change, go to step **5)**. If dwell is less than 10 degrees after 30 seconds, repair open in wire from ECM connector terminal C45-8 to $O_2$ sensor.
**5)** Connect jumper between ECM connector terminals C45-15 to C45-7 and note dwell. If dwell varies, repair open in wire to coolant sensor. If dwell does not change, ECM or connection is faulty.

**TEST 3 (Dwell Fixed Over 80 Degrees)** – **1)** Run engine at part throttle for one minute. Return engine to idle and remove large vacuum hose. Do not stall engine. Note dwell. If dwell decreases, go to step **3)**. If dwell does not change, go to step **2)**.
**2)** Disconnect $O_2$ sensor and ground $O_2$ sensor to ECM terminal. If dwell decreases to less than 10 degrees, $O_2$ sensor or connector is faulty. If dwell does not change, ECM or connector is faulty.
**3)** Check canister and purge valve for leaks or excess fuel. If okay, check carburetor duty solenoid. If duty solenoid is okay, repair carburetor.

**TEST 4 (Idle & WOT Switch Circuit Check)** – **1)** Connect dwell meter (4-cyl. scale) and warm engine until dwell starts to vary. Pinch hoses at idle and WOT switch and remove. Note dwell. If dwell is greater than 10 degrees, go to step **2)**. If dwell is less than 10 degrees, enrichment system is okay. Perform SYSTEM PERFORMANCE CHECK.
**2)** Disconnect idle and WOT switches. Connect jumpers between harness connector terminals C31-1 to C31-3 and C31-2 to C31-4. Note dwell. If dwell is greater than 10 degrees, go to step **3)**. If dwell is less than 10 degrees, switch or connection is faulty.
**3)** Connect jumper between ECM connector terminals C45-3 to C46-9 and C45-2 to C46-2. If dwell is greater than 10 degrees, ECM is faulty. If dwell is less than 10 degrees, check for open wire to ECM connector terminals C45-3, C46-9, C45-2 and C46-2. If okay, ECM is faulty.

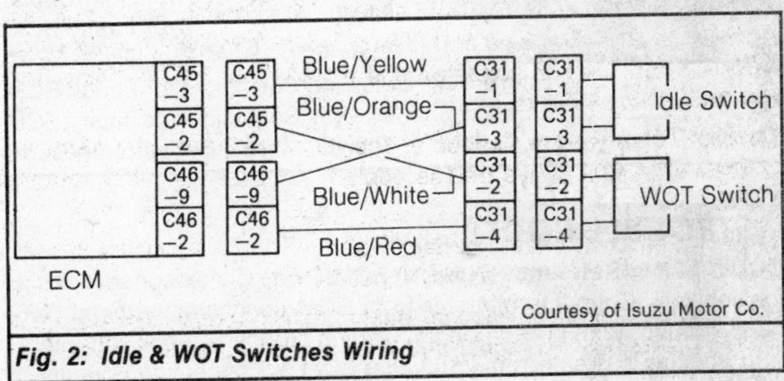
C45 –3
C45 –2
C46 –9
C46 –2
ECM
Blue/Yellow
Blue/Orange
Blue/White
Blue/Red
C31 –1
C31 –3
C31 –2
C31 –4
Idle Switch
WOT Switch
Courtesy of Isuzu Motor Co.

*Fig. 2: Idle & WOT Switches Wiring*

**TEST 5 ("Check Engine" Light Inoperative)** – **1)** Check ECM fuse. Inspect "Check Engine" light connector for proper connection. With ignition on and engine off, check voltage at "Check Engine" light connector Blue wire and ground. If voltage is greater than 9 volts, go to step **3)**. If voltage is less than 9 volts, check voltage from "Check Engine" light connector Yellow wire and ground.
**2)** If voltage is greater than 9 volts, check bulb and connection. If voltage is less than 9 volts, repair open in Yellow wire.
**3)** Check voltage from ECM connector terminal C46-4 to ground. If voltage is greater than 9 volts, go to step **4)**. If voltage is less than 9 volts, repair open in wire to ECM connector terminal C46-4.
**4)** Check voltage from ECM connector terminal C46-7 to ground. If voltage is less than one volt, ECM or connection is faulty. If voltage is greater than one volt, repair ECM ground.

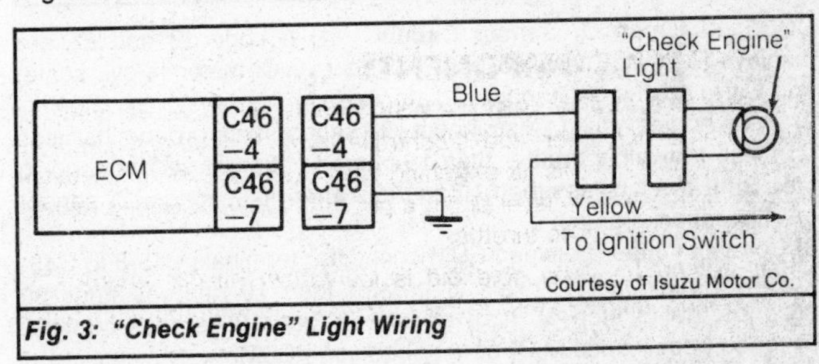
"Check Engine" Light
Blue
ECM
C46 –4
C46 –7
Yellow
To Ignition Switch
Courtesy of Isuzu Motor Co.

*Fig. 3: "Check Engine" Light Wiring*

**TEST 6 (Will Not Flash Code 12)** – **1)** Check ECM fuse. With ignition on and engine stopped, ground ALDL terminal No. 1. Ground ECM connector terminal C45-1 and note "Check Engine" light. If "Check Engine" light does not flash code 12, go to step **2)**. If code 12 flashes, repair open in ALDL terminal No. 1 wire.

**2)** Disconnect ECM connector C46. If light is off, replace ECM and repeat DIAGNOSTIC CIRCUIT CHECK. If light is on, repair grounded lead from "Check Engine" light and ECM connector terminal C46-4. Repeat DIAGNOSTIC CIRCUIT CHECK.

### *ECM TROUBLE CODE IDENTIFICATION*

| Code | Problem |
|---|---|
| 12 | No Ignition Reference Pulse to ECM |
| 13 | Oxygen ($O_2$) Sensor Circuit |
| 14 | Shorted Coolant Sensor Circuit |
| 15 | Open Coolant Sensor Circuit |
| 21 | Idle Switch Circuit Open or WOT Switch Circuit Shorted |
| 22 | Fuel Cut Solenoid Circuit Open or Grounded |
| 23 | Duty Solenoid Circuit Open or Grounded |
| 25 | Air Switching Solenoid Circuit Open or Grounded |
| 26 | Canister Purge Vacuum Switching Valve Circuit Open or Grounded |
| 27 | Constant High Voltage from VSV to ECM |
| 31 | No Ignition Reference Pulse to ECM at Part Throttle, Under Road Load |
| 32 | EGR or Sensor Circuit Failure |
| 34 | EGR Sensor Circuit Failure |
| 44 | Oxygen ($O_2$) Sensor Lean Indication |
| 45 | Oxygen ($O_2$) Sensor Rich Indication |
| 51 | Shorted Fuel-Cut Solenoid Circuit &/or Faulty ECM |
| 52 | Faulty ECM (RAM Problem in ECM) |
| 53 | Shorted Air Switching Solenoid &/or Faulty ECM |
| 54 | Shorted Duty Solenoid &/or Faulty ECM |
| 55 | Faulty ECM (A/D Converter in ECM) |

## TROUBLE CODES

**CODE 12 (No Reference Pulse to ECM) – 1)** Check connections at ignition coil. Connect voltmeter from ECM connector terminal C46-10 to ground. With ignition on and engine stopped, check voltage.

**2)** If voltage is greater than 10 volts, ECM or connection is faulty. If voltage is less than 10 volts, check for open from ignition coil to ECM.

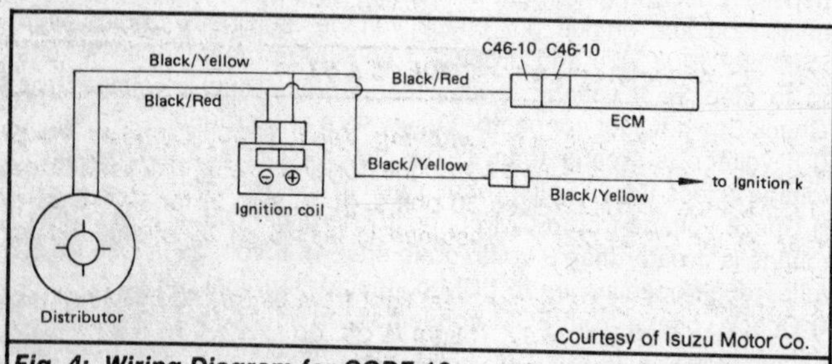
Black/Yellow
Black/Red
C46-10 C46-10
Black/Red
ECM
Black/Yellow
Black/Yellow
to Ignition k
Ignition coil
Distributor
Courtesy of Isuzu Motor Co.

*Fig. 4: Wiring Diagram for CODE 12*

**CODE 13 (Open $O_2$ Sensor Circuit) – 1)** If code 13 and 23 are displayed, go to CODE 23 first. Connect dwell meter (4-cyl. scale) and warm engine until upper radiator hose is warm.

**2)** With engine idling, disconnect $O_2$ sensor and ground harness terminal. If dwell is greater than 10 degrees after 30 seconds, go to step **3)**. If dwell is less than 10 degrees after 30 seconds, $O_2$ sensor or connection is faulty.

**3)** Connect jumper between ECM connector terminals C45-8 to C45-16 and note dwell. If dwell is greater than 10 degrees after 30 seconds, go to step **4)**. If dwell is less than 10 degrees after 30 seconds, repair open in $O_2$ sensor harnss to ECM.

**4)** Ensure ECM connector terminal C45-16 is grounded with ignition off. If okay, ECM or connector is faulty.

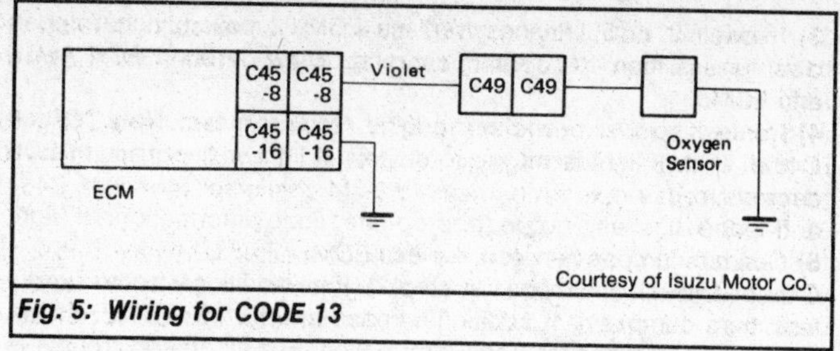
C45 -8
C45 -8
Violet
C49
C49
C45 -16
C45 -16
Oxygen Sensor
ECM
Courtesy of Isuzu Motor Co.

*Fig. 5: Wiring for CODE 13*

**CODE 14 (Shorted Coolant Sensor Circuit) – 1)** With ECM connector disconnected, check resistance between ECM harness connector terminals C45-7 to C45-15. If resistance is less than 70 ohms, go to step **3)**. If resistance is greater than 70 ohms, check resistance between ECM harness connector terminal C45-7 to ground.

**2)** If resistance is greater than 100,000 ohms, ECM or connection is faulty. If resistance is less than 100,000 ohms, check for grounded wire from coolant sensor to ECM connector terminal C45-7. If not grounded, replace coolant sensor.

**3)** With coolant sensor disconnected, check resistance between ECM harness connector terminal C45-7 to C45-15. If resistance is less than 100,000 ohms, go to step **4)**. If resistance is greater than 100,000, replace coolant sensor.

**4)** Repair short between coolant sensor and ECM connector. Connect coolant sensor and check resistance between ECM harness connector terminals C45-7 to C45-15. If resistance is less than 100,000 ohms, replace coolant sensor.

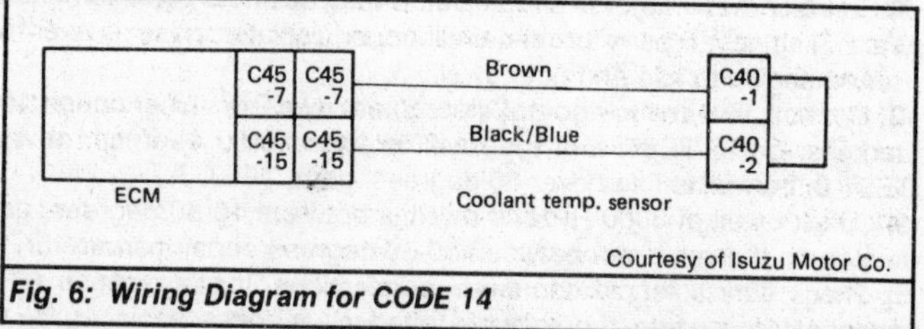
C45 -7
C45 -7
Brown
C40 -1
C45 -15
C45 -15
Black/Blue
C40 -2
ECM
Coolant temp. sensor
Courtesy of Isuzu Motor Co.

*Fig. 6: Wiring Diagram for CODE 14*

**CODE 15 (Open Coolant Sensor Circuit) – 1)** With coolant sensor disconnected, ignition on and engine stopped, check voltage between coolant sensor connector terminals. If voltage is greater than 2 volts, go to step **3)**. If the voltage is less than 2 volts, go to the next step.

**2)** Check voltage from ECM connector terminals C45-7 to C45-15. If voltage is less than 2 volts, ECM or connection is faulty. If voltage is greater than 2 volts, check for open in wires from ECM connector terminals C45-7 and C45-15.

**3)** Check resistance of coolant sensor. If resistance is less than 800 ohms, connection at coolant sensor is poor or coolant level is low. If resistance is greater than 800 ohms, replace coolant sensor.

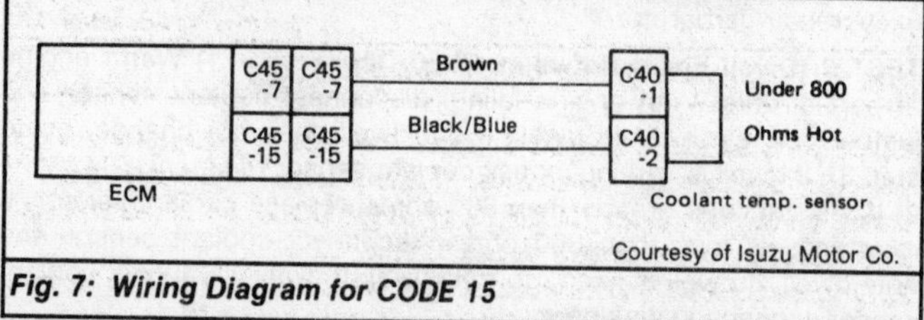
C45 -7
C45 -7
Brown
C40 -1
Under 800
C45 -15
C45 -15
Black/Blue
C40 -2
Ohms Hot
ECM
Coolant temp. sensor
Courtesy of Isuzu Motor Co.

*Fig. 7: Wiring Diagram for CODE 15*

**CODE 21 (Idle Switch Circuit Open or WOT Switch Circuit Shorted) – 1)** If CODE 21 and 23 are displayed, go to CODE 23 first. With dwell meter connected (4-cyl. scale), run engine at part throttle until dwell starts to vary. Disconnect switches. Jumper harness connector C31-1 to C31-3 and C31-2 to C31-4.

**2)** Run engine at part throttle and note dwell. If dwell is varying, go to step **4)**. If dwell is less than 10 degrees, disconnect jumper between harness connector terminals C31-2 to C31-4.

# 1988 COMPUTERIZED ENGINE CONTROLS
## Isuzu Closed Loop Emission System (Cont.)

**3)** If dwell is now varying, WOT switch or connection is faulty. If dwell is less than 10 degrees, check for short between WOT switch and ECM.
**4)** Connect jumper between the ECM connector terminals C45-3 to C46-9. If dwell is varying, go to step **5)**. If dwell is less than 10 degrees, repair open in harness to ECM connector terminals C45-3 and C46-9.
**5)** Connect jumper between the ECM connector terminals C45-2 to C46-2. If dwell is varying, ECM or connection is faulty. If dwell is less than 10 degrees, repair open in harness to ECM connector terminals C45-2 and C46-2.

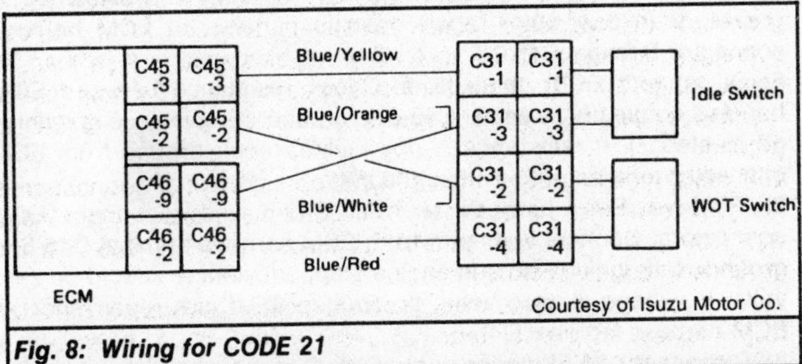
C45 -3
C45 -2
C46 -9
C46 -2
Blue/Yellow
Blue/Orange
Blue/White
Blue/Red
C31 -1
C31 -3
C31 -2
C31 -4
Idle Switch
WOT Switch
ECM
Courtesy of Isuzu Motor Co.
*Fig. 8: Wiring for CODE 21*

**CODE 22 & 51 (Fuel-Cut Solenoid Circuit Failure) – 1)** Disconnect fuel-cut solenoid and check resistance. If resistance is greater than 15 ohms, go to step **2)** for CODE 22 or **5)** for CODE 51. If resistance is less than 15 ohms, replace fuel-cut solenoid.
**2)** With ECM connetors disconnected, connect test light from battery to ECM harness connector terminal C46-5. If test light is off, go to step **3)**. If test light is on, repair short in Light Green wire to ECM connector terminal C46-5.
**3)** Connect fuel-cut solenoid. Connect test light from ECM connector terminal C46-5 to ground. If light is off, go to step **4)**. If light is on, ECM or connector is faulty.
**4)** Disconnect fuel-cut solenoid. Connect test light from fuel-cut solenoid harness connector White/Yellow wire to ground. Turn ignition on with engine stopped. If light is on, repair open in wire from ECM to fuel-cut solenoid. If light is off, repair open in White/Yellow wire.
**5)** Disconnect ECM connectors. Connect test light from ground to ECM harness connector C46-5. Turn ignition on with engine stopped. If light is on, repair short in Light Green wire to ECM. If light is off, ECM or connection is faulty.

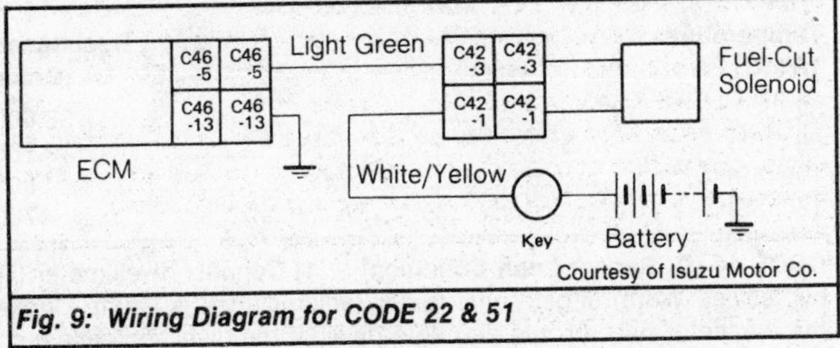
C46 -5
C46 -13
Light Green
C42 -3
C42 -1
Fuel-Cut Solenoid
ECM
White/Yellow
Key
Battery
Courtesy of Isuzu Motor Co.
*Fig. 9: Wiring Diagram for CODE 22 & 51*

**CODE 23 & 54 (Duty Solenoid Circuit Failure) – 1)** Disconnect duty solenoid and check resistance. If resistance is greater than 20 ohms, go to step **2)** for CODE 23 or **5)** for CODE 54. If resistance is less than 20 ohms, replace duty solenoid.
**2)** Disconnect ECM. Connect test light from battery to ECM harness connector terminal C46-6. If light is off, go to step **3)**. If light is on, repair short in Light Green wire to ECM.
**3)** Connect duty solenoid. Connect test light from ECM harness connector terminal C46-6 to ground. Turn ignition on with engine stopped. If light is off, go to step **4)**. If light is on, ECM or connector is faulty.
**4)** With duty solenoid disconnected, connect test light from White/Yellow wire to ground. Turn ignition on with engine stopped. If light is on, repair open in wire from duty solenoid to ECM. If light is off, repair open in White/Yellow wire.
**5)** Disconnect ECM connectors. Connect test light from ground to ECM harness connector terminal C46-6. Turn ignition on with engine stopped. If light is on, repair short in Light Green wire to ECM. If light is off, ECM or connection is faulty.

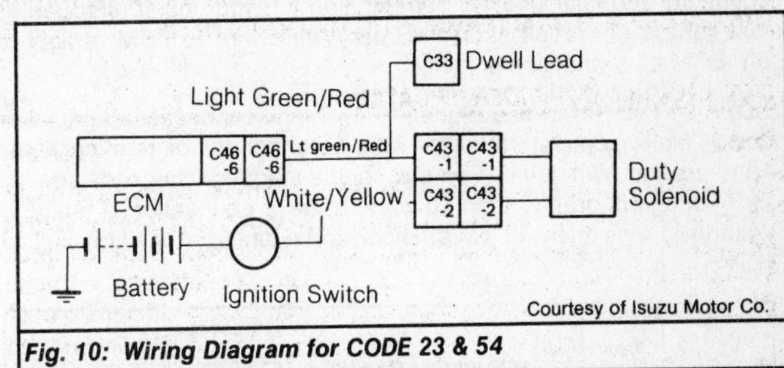
C33
Dwell Lead
Light Green/Red
C46 -6
Lt green/Red
C43 -1
C43 -2
Duty Solenoid
ECM
White/Yellow
Battery
Ignition Switch
Courtesy of Isuzu Motor Co.
*Fig. 10: Wiring Diagram for CODE 23 & 54*

**CODE 25 & 53 (AIR Vacuum Switching Valve (VSV) Failure) – 1)** Disconnect VSV and check VSV resistance. If resistance is greater than 20 ohms, go to step **2)** for CODE 25 or step **5)** for CODE 53. If resistance is less than 20 ohms, replace VSV.
**2)** Disconnect ECM connectors. Connect test light from battery to ECM harness connector terminal C46-11. If light is off, go to step **3)**. If light is on, repair short in Light Green/Black wire to ECM.
**3)** Connect VSV. Connect test light from ECM harness connector terminal C46-11 to ground. Turn ignition on with enigne stopped. If light is off, go to step **4)**. If light is on, ECM or connection is faulty.
**4)** Disconnect VSV and connect test light from White/Yellow wire to ground. Turn ignition on with engine off. If light is on, repair open in wire from VSV to ECM. If light is off, repair open in White/Yellow wire.
**5)** Disconnect ECM connectors. Connect test light from ground to ECM harness connector terminal C46-11. Turn ignition on with engine stopped. If test light is on, repair short in Light Green/Black wire to ECM. If light is off, ECM or connection is faulty.

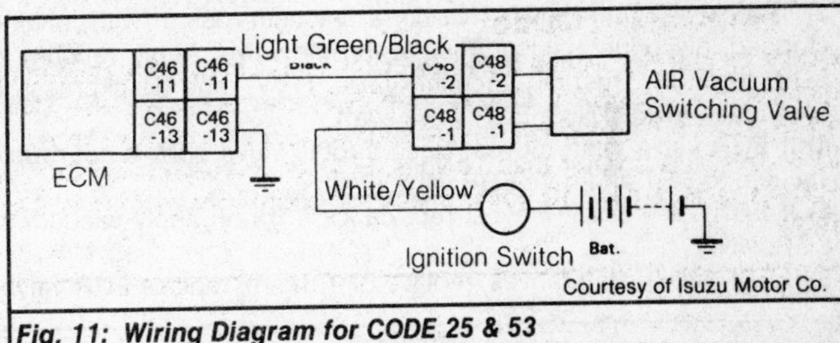
Light Green/Black
C46 -11
C46 -13
C48 -2
C48 -1
AIR Vacuum Switching Valve
ECM
White/Yellow
Ignition Switch
Bat.
Courtesy of Isuzu Motor Co.
*Fig. 11: Wiring Diagram for CODE 25 & 53*

**CODE 26 & 27 (Vacuum Switching Valve (VSV) Canister Purge Failure) – 1)** Disconnect VSV connector and check VSV resistance. If resistance is greater than 30 ohms, go to step **2)** for CODE 26 or step **5)** for CODE 27. If resistance is less than 30 ohms, replace VSV.
**2)** Disconnect ECM. Connect test light from battery to ECM harness connector terminal C45-12. If light is off, go to step **3)**. If light is on, repair short in Green/White wire to ECM.
**3)** Connect VSV and connect test light from ECM harness connector terminal C45-12 to ground. If light is off, go to step **4)**. If light is on, ECM or connection is faulty.

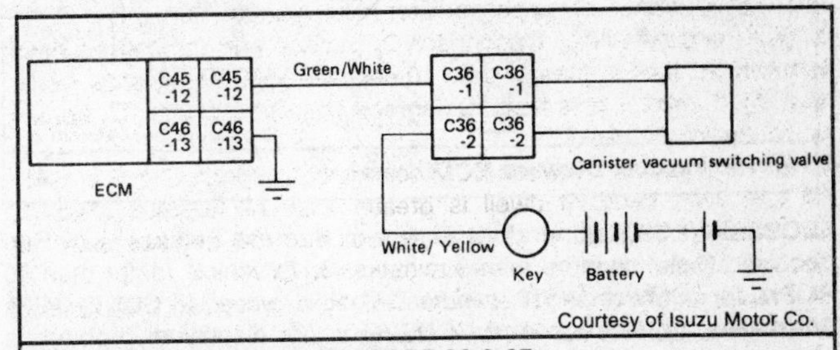
C45 -12
C46 -13
Green/White
C36 -1
C36 -2
Canister vacuum switching valve
ECM
White/ Yellow
Key
Battery
Courtesy of Isuzu Motor Co.
*Fig. 12: Wiring Diagram for CODE 26 & 27*

**4)** Disconnect VSV and connect test light from White/Yellow wire to ground. If light is on, repair open in wire to ECM. If light is off, repair open in White/Yellow wire.
**5)** Disconnect ECM. Connect test light from ground to ECM harness connector terminal C45-12. Turn ignition on with engine stopped. If test light is on, repair short in Green/White wire to ECM. If light is off, ECM or connection is faulty.

**CODE 31 (No Reference Signal) – 1)** Check connections at ignition coil. If okay, connect voltmeter from ECM connector terminal C46-10 to ground. With ignition on and engine stopped, check voltage.
**2)** If voltage is greater than 10 volts, ECM or connection is faulty. If voltage is less than 10 volts, check for open from ignition coil to ECM.

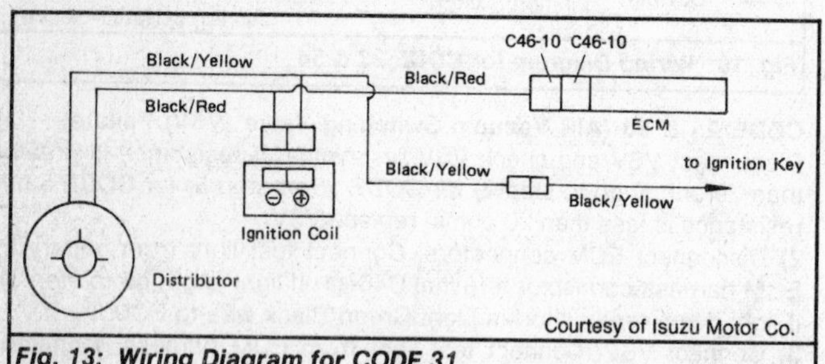
C46-10 C46-10
Black/Yellow
Black/Red
Black/Red
ECM
Black/Yellow
to Ignition Key
Black/Yellow
Ignition Coil
Distributor
Courtesy of Isuzu Motor Co.
*Fig. 13: Wiring Diagram for CODE 31*

**CODE 32 (EGR System Failure & Sensor Circuit Failure) – 1)** If CODE 34 is displayed, go to CODE 34. If not, run engine at idle for more than 10 seconds. Drive vehicle at 20 MPH. Accelerate for 10 seconds to at least 40 MPH. Decelerate to a stop within 30 seconds. Repeat this procedure several times. Recheck codes.
**2)** If CODE 34 is now displayed, go to CODE 34. If CODE 32 is displayed, run engine at 1/4 to 1/2 throttle. Check action of EGR valve shaft. If EGR shaft does not lift, go to step **3)**. If EGR does lift, EGR is defective or passage is clogged.
**3)** Check vacuum hoses. Using a vacuum pump with engine stopped, disconnect signal hose at throttle valve. Apply vacuum to EGR through Thermal Vacuum Valve (TVV) and Backpressure Transducer (BPT). Note EGR valve shaft.
**4)** If EGR valve shaft moves, clean throttle valve port. If not, apply vacuum to BPT and note EGR valve shaft.
**5)** If EGR valve shaft moves, replace TVV. If not, apply vacuum to EGR valve.
**6)** If EGR valve shaft moves, replace BPT. If not, replace EGR valve.

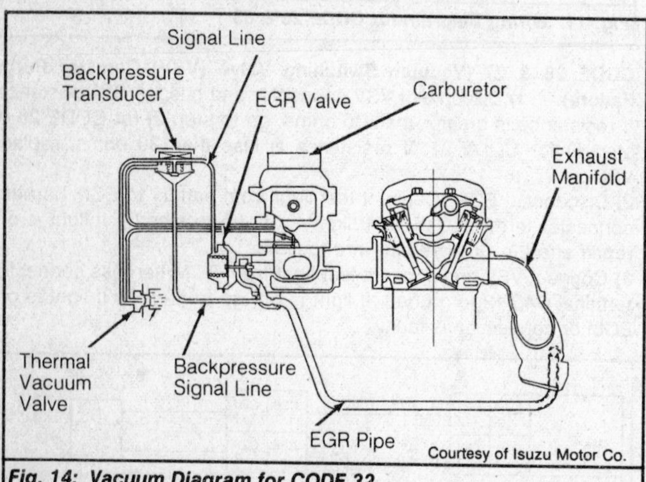
Signal Line
Backpressure Transducer
EGR Valve
Carburetor
Exhaust Manifold
Thermal Vacuum Valve
Backpressure Signal Line
EGR Pipe
Courtesy of Isuzu Motor Co.
*Fig. 14: Vacuum Diagram for CODE 32*

**CODE 34 (EGR Temperature Sensor or Harness Failure) – 1)** Run engine at idle for more than 5 minutes. Drive vehicle faster than 40 MPH for more than 10 minutes. Check codes. If CODE 34 is displayed, go to step **2)**. If CODE 34 is not displayed, problem is intermittent.
**2)** With ignition off, inspect EGR gas temperature sensor for loose fit, contamination or deformation of terminals or housing. If okay, disconnect EGR temperature sensor connector.
**3)** Check resistance from EGR temperature sensor connector terminal (Black/Blue) to ground. If resistance is less than one ohm, go to step **6)**. If resistance is greater than one ohm, check resistance between ECM connector terminal C46-7 to ground.
**4)** If resistance is less than one ohm, go to step **5)**. If resistance is greater than one ohm, repair open in harness to ECM.
**5)** Disconnect ECM harness connectors. Check resistance between ECM harness connector terminals C45-15 to C38-2. If resistance is less than 1 ohm, ECM or connection is faulty. If resistance is greater than one ohm, repair open is harness to ECM harness connector terminal C45-15.
**6)** Disconnect ECM connectors. Check resistance between ECM harness connector terminal C45-6 to ground. If resistance is infinite, go to step **7)**. If resistance is not infinite, repair ground from ECM connector terminal C45-16 to sensor.
**7)** Remove ECM harness terminal C45-6 and reconnect ECM connectors. Connect voltmeter from ECM harness terminal C45-6 to ground. With ignition on and engine stopped, voltage should be zero volts. If voltage is zero volts, go to step **8)**. If not, repair short in ECM harness terminal C45-6.
**8)** Disconnect ECM connectors. Check resistance between ECM harness terminal C45-6 to EGR gas temperature sensor terminal C38-1 (Yellow/Green). If resistance is less than one ohm, go to step **9)**. If resistance is greater than one ohm, repair open in harness.
**9)** Remove EGR gas temperature sensor and measure resistance. Refer to EGR TEMPERATURE SENSOR RESISTANCE table. If resistance is okay, ECM or connection is faulty.

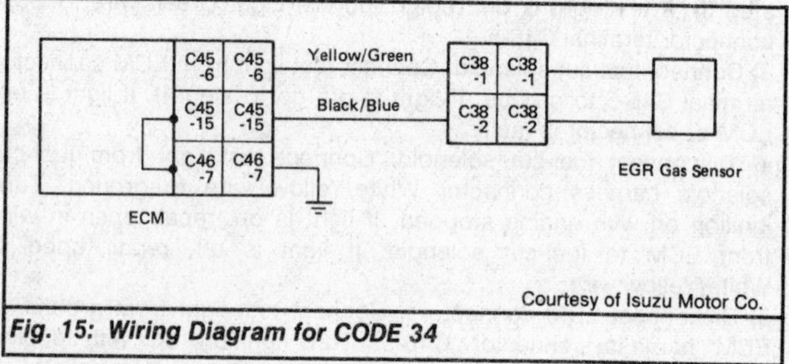
C45 -6
C45 -6
Yellow/Green
C38 -1
C38 -1
C45 -15
C45 -15
Black/Blue
C38 -2
C38 -2
C46 -7
C46 -7
EGR Gas Sensor
ECM
Courtesy of Isuzu Motor Co.
*Fig. 15: Wiring Diagram for CODE 34*

***EGR TEMPERATURE SENSOR RESISTANCE***

| Temperature °F (°C) | Resistance Ohms |
|---|---|
| 32 (0) | 28,000 |
| 68 (20) | 12,100 |
| 109 (40) | 5800 |
| 176 (80) | 1700 |

**CODE 44 ($O_2$ Sensor Lean Condition) – 1)** Connect dwell meter (4-cyl. scale). Warm engine until upper radiator hose is warm. Choke the engine at part throttle and note dwell. If the dwell increases, go to step **4)**. If dwell does not change, disconnect $O_2$ sensor.
**3)** Connect 1.5-volt dry cell battery positive side to $O_2$ sensor wire to ECM. Connect negative side of dry cell battery to ground. If dwell

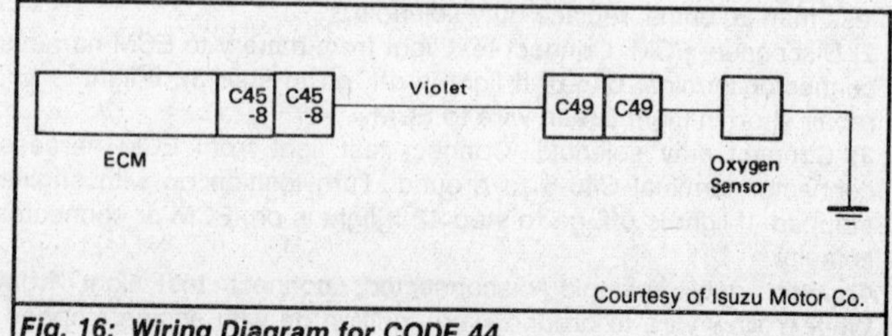
C45 -8
C45 -8
Violet
C49
C49
ECM
Oxygen Sensor
Courtesy of Isuzu Motor Co.
*Fig. 16: Wiring Diagram for CODE 44*

increases, replace $O_2$ sensor. If dwell is less than 10 degrees, Violet wire to ECM is grounded or ECM is faulty.
**4)** Check for intake air leak or exhaust leak ahead of $O_2$ sensor. If no leaks, repair carburetor.

**CODE 45 ($O_2$ Sensor Rich Condition) - 1)** Check condition of air filter. With dwell meter connected, run engine at part throttle until dwell varies. Idle engine and note dwell.
**2)** Remove large vacuum hose to cause an air leak. Note dwell. If dwell does not change, go to step **3)**. If dwell decreases, check carburetor duty solenoid.
**3)** Disconnect $O_2$ sensor and ground $O_2$ sensor ECM connector. If dwell drops to less than 10 degrees, $O_2$ sensor or connection is faulty. If dwell does not change, ECM or connection is faulty.

**CODE 52 & 55 (Internal ECM Problem) - 1)** Check connections at ECM. Ensure ground at ECM connector terminals C46-13, C46-7 and C45-16. If okay, clear codes, start engine and recheck for codes. If codes including CODE 52 reappear, go to step **2)**. If codes other than CODE 52 appear, go to specific code test. If no codes appear, perform SYSTEM PERFORMANCE CHECK.
**2)** Clear codes, start engine and recheck for codes again. If no codes reappear, perform SYSTEM PERFORMANCE CHECK. If other codes reappear, go to specific code test. If codes including CODE 52 reappear, replace ECM.

## COMPONENT TESTING

**AIR Management System - 1)** Check vacuum hose routing and connections. With engine at normal operating temperature, disconnect rubber hoses to check valve, air cleaner and air switching valve. With engine running at part throttle, ensure that air is diverted to air cleaner. Pinch rubber hoses at idle and WOT switches, air should be pumped to check valve for about 10 seconds. After 10 seconds, air should be pumped to air cleaner. If system does not operate in this manner, go to step **2)**. If system does operate in this manner, system is okay.
**2)** Reconnect hoses at idle and WOT switches. Remove vacuum hose from port "C" of vacuum switching solenoid. With engine running and ECM terminal C46-11 not grounded, pumped air should be supplied to port "C". With engine running and ECM terminal C46-11 grounded, vacuum should be supplied to port "C". If okay, go to step **3)**. If not okay, replace vacuum switching solenoid.
**3)** Connect vacuum pump to vacuum hose removed from port "C" and apply 5 in. Hg. Note gauge reading and pumped air flow. Vacuum should not decrease and air should be pumped to check valve. If okay, go to step **4)**. If not okay, replace air switching valve.
**4)** Disconnect vacuum pump and check pumped air flow. If air is pumped to air cleaner, replace ECM. If air is not pumped to air cleaner, replace air switching valve.

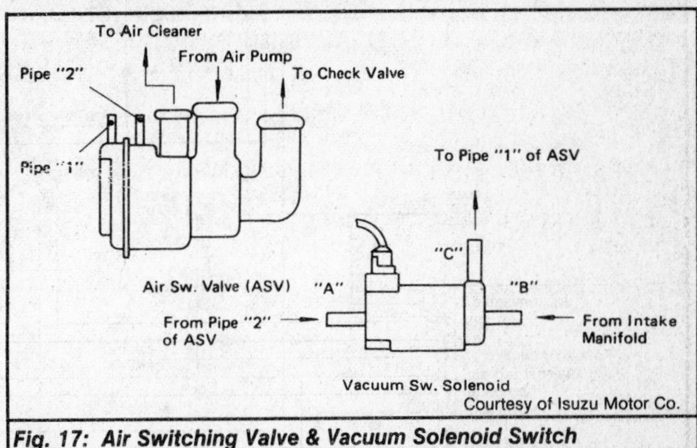
To Air Cleaner
From Air Pump
Pipe "2"
To Check Valve
Pipe "1"
To Pipe "1" of ASV
"C"
Air Sw. Valve (ASV)
"A"
"B"
From Pipe "2" of ASV
From Intake Manifold
Vacuum Sw. Solenoid
Courtesy of Isuzu Motor Co.

***Fig. 17: Air Switching Valve & Vacuum Solenoid Switch***

**Coolant Temperature Sensor -** With coolant temperature sensor at 68°F (20°C), measure resistance. Resistance should be 2100-2900 ohms.

**Duty Solenoid - 1)** Disconnect $O_2$ sensor and vacuum switch. With ignition on and engine stopped, check for repeated clicks from duty solenoid.
**2)** If duty solenoid clicks, repair carburetor. If duty solenoid does not click, replace duty solenoid.

**Idle & WOT Switches - 1)** With engine stopped, disconnect idle and WOT switch connectors. Check resistance between terminals C31-1 to C31-3 and C31-2 to C31-4 of switch side of connector. If resistance of both switches is zero ohms, go to step **2)**. If resistance of either or both switches is not zero ohms, replace switch assembly and perform SYSTEM PERFORMANCE CHECK.
**2)** Disconnect vacuum hoses from switches. Connect vacuum pump to switches and apply 4 in. Hg. Check resistance between terminals C31-1 to C31-3 and C31-2 to C31-4. If resistance is less than 100,000 ohms or vacuum decreases, replace switch assembly. If resistance is greater than 100,000 ohms and vacuum does not decrease, switches are okay. Check for shorted or grounded wires to ECM and perform SYSTEM PERFORMACE CHECK.

**Inlet Air Temperature Sensor -** Inlet air temperature should have continuity at temperature between 25-39°F (-4-4°C).

# 1988 COMPUTERIZED ENGINE CONTROLS
## Isuzu Closed Loop Emission System (Cont.)

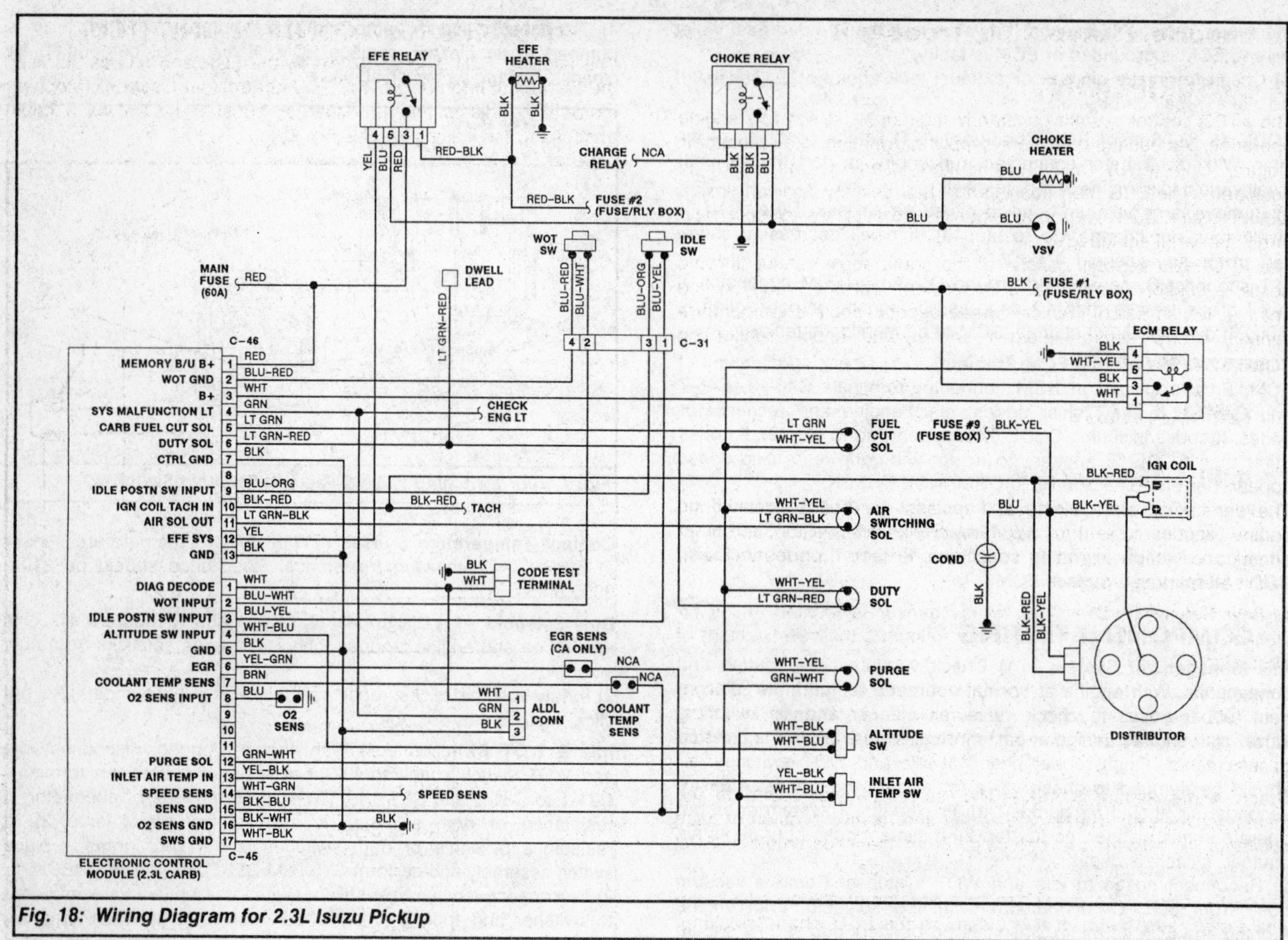
EFE RELAY
EFE HEATER
CHOKE RELAY
CHOKE HEATER
4 5 3 1
YEL
BLU
RED
RED-BLK
BLK
CHARGE RELAY
NCA
FUSE #2 (FUSE/RLY BOX)
BLU
VSV
WOT SW
IDLE SW
MAIN FUSE (60A)
RED
DWELL LEAD
LT GRN-RED
BLU-RED
BLU-WHT
BLU-ORG
BLU-YEL
FUSE #1 (FUSE/RLY BOX)
C-46
C-31
ECM RELAY
WHT-YEL
WHT
MEMORY B/U B+
WOT GND
B+
SYS MALFUNCTION LT
CARB FUEL CUT SOL
DUTY SOL
CTRL GND
IDLE POSTN SW INPUT
IGN COIL TACH IN
AIR SOL OUT
EFE SYS
GND
GRN
LT GRN
BLK-RED
LT GRN-BLK
CHECK ENG LT
TACH
FUEL CUT SOL
FUSE #9 (FUSE BOX)
BLK-YEL
IGN COIL
AIR SWITCHING SOL
COND
CODE TEST TERMINAL
DUTY SOL
DIAG DECODE
WOT INPUT
IDLE POSTN SW INPUT
ALTITUDE SW INPUT
GND
EGR
COOLANT TEMP SENS
O2 SENS INPUT
WHT-BLU
YEL-GRN
BRN
EGR SENS (CA ONLY)
PURGE SOL
GRN-WHT
O2 SENS
ALDL CONN
COOLANT TEMP SENS
DISTRIBUTOR
WHT-BLK
ALTITUDE SW
PURGE SOL
INLET AIR TEMP IN
SPEED SENS
SENS GND
O2 SENS GND
SWS GND
YEL-BLK
WHT-GRN
BLK-BLU
BLK-WHT
INLET AIR TEMP SW
C-45
ELECTRONIC CONTROL MODULE (2.3L CARB)

*Fig. 18: Wiring Diagram for 2.3L Isuzu Pickup*

# Isuzu I-TEC Control System

### Impulse, Pickup 2.6L, Trooper II

## DESCRIPTION

The I-TEC control system constantly monitors and controls engine operation. Various input sensors supply information to an Electronic Control Unit (ECU), and Turbocharger Control Unit (TCU) (if equipped). The ECU then controls the fuel delivery, ignition timing, fuel pressure, fuel evaporative purge, exhaust air injection and turbocharger (if equipped).

The ECU input sensors consist of the crank angle sensor, throttle position sensor (automatic transmission), throttle valve switch (manual transmission), vehicle speed sensor, coolant temperature sensor, airflow sensor, oxygen sensor and knock sensor on Impulse models.

## OPERATION

### INPUT SENSORS

The sensors provide electrical impulses to ECU by monitoring engine vacuum, coolant temperature, crankshaft position, and other engine and vehicle operating conditions. Location and operation of each sensor is as follows:

**Airflow Sensor (AFS)** - The airflow sensor is located in the air cleaner housing. The airflow sensor measures the rate (volume) of air intake.

**Oxygen Sensor ($O_2$)** - This sensor is threaded into the exhaust manifold. The oxygen sensor measures and produces an electrical signal proportional to the amount of oxygen present in the exhaust gases.

**Crank Angle Sensor (CAS)** - This sensor is located inside the distributor housing. The engine speed and relative position of each piston in its cylinder are detected. From these parameters, ECU calculates proper ignition timing and dwell angle.

**Knock Sensor** - The knock sensor is located on the cylinder head. The sensor sends electrical impulses to the ECU when "knocking" occurs. The ECU retards timing to reduce detonation.

**Coolant Temperature Sensor (CTS)** - This sensor is located on the engine block, under the intake manifold. It sends coolant temperature information to ECU. This information is used by ECU to calculate required air/fuel mixture and ignition timing.

**Throttle Valve Switch (TVS)** - The throttle valve switch is used on manual transmission equipped vehicles. It detects throttle position at idle, wide open throttle, or not idle or wide open throttle. This switch is used to control the fuel-cut system.

**Throttle Position Sensor (TPS)** - The TPS is used on automatic transmission vehicles and informs ECU of any throttle position change for ECU to provide proper fuel delivery and ignition timing under all driving conditions. The TPS also contains an idle switch for control of fuel-cut system.

**Vehicle Speed Sensor (VSS)** - This sensor is built into the speedometer and supplies ECU with vehicle speed information.

**EGR Temperature Sensor** - The EGR temperature sensor is mounted in the engine exhaust passage next to the EGR valve. It provides the ECU with EGR flow information.

### ELECTRONIC CONTROL UNIT (ECU)

The ECU is located under instrument panel left of steering column on Impulse and Pickup. On Trooper II, ECU is located under center console. The ECU analyzes all electrical data signals from the sensors. It controls the fuel injection system, the ignition system, various emission devices and the turbocharger control system (if used). The ECU includes back-up, self-diagnostics and fail-safe control systems.

### TURBOCHARGER CONTROL UNIT (TCU)

The Impulse TCU is located next to the ECU and shares some of the ECU input information. The TCU controls an electronic stepping motor that adjusts the turbocharger boost pressure via a cable attached to the wastegate. *See Fig. 1.*

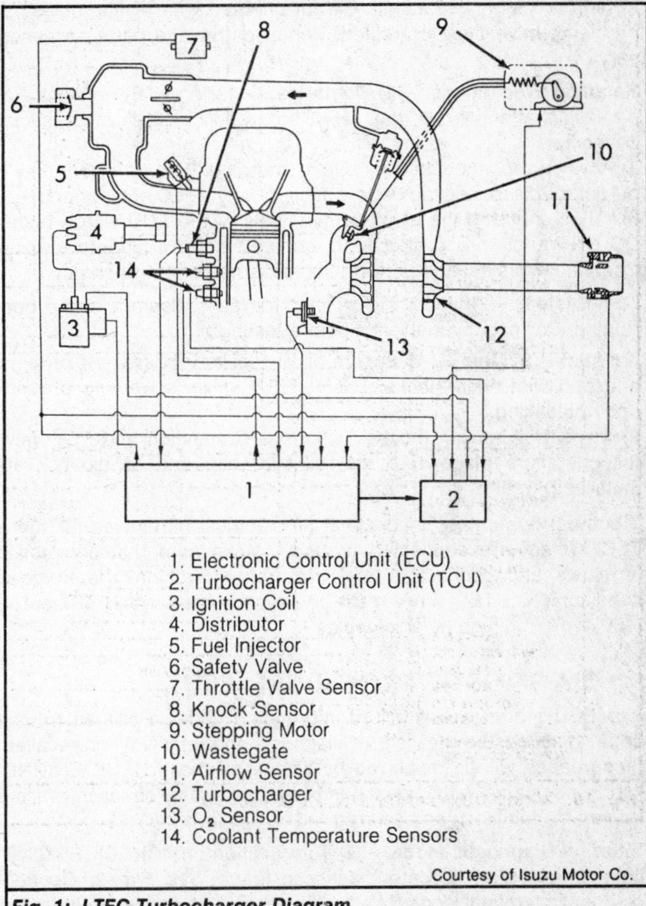

8
9
7
6
5
10
11
4
14
3
13
12
1
2
1. Electronic Control Unit (ECU)
2. Turbocharger Control Unit (TCU)
3. Ignition Coil
4. Distributor
5. Fuel Injector
6. Safety Valve
7. Throttle Valve Sensor
8. Knock Sensor
9. Stepping Motor
10. Wastegate
11. Airflow Sensor
12. Turbocharger
13. O₂ Sensor
14. Coolant Temperature Sensors
Courtesy of Isuzu Motor Co.


***Fig. 1: I-TEC Turbocharger Diagram***

### BACK-UP CONTROL SYSTEM

In the event a malfunction has developed in the microcomputer within the ECU, the back-up control system works to maintain the necessary functions of the control unit to permit continuous operation of the vehicle.

### DIAGNOSTIC SYSTEM

The ECU is equipped with a self-diagnostic system which detects system failures or abnormalities. When a malfunction occurs, the ECU will store a code in its memory. ECU will also turn on a "CHECK ENGINE" light located on the instrument panel.

As a bulb and system check, the "CHECK ENGINE" light will glow when ignition switch is on and engine is not running. When engine is started, the light should go out after 4 seconds. If not, a malfunction has been detected in the I-TEC system.

### FAIL-SAFE SYSTEM

If a failure takes place in the oxygen sensor, coolant temperature sensor circuit, throttle valve switch, airflow sensor, or the knock sensor circuit, the output of the electronic control unit will switch automatically to the fail-safe mode.

### FUEL-CUT SYSTEM

When signaled by the TPS or TVS, the ECU decreases fuel delivery to the engine on deceleration, and increases fuel delivery at wide open throttle.

## DIAGNOSIS & TESTING

### PRELIMINARY INSPECTION

Perform the following inspection before diagnosing the I-TEC control system. Ensure all engine systems NOT related to the system are fully operational. Do not proceed with testing unless all problems have been corrected. Repair or replace parts as necessary.

**Handling Precautions** – **1)** Do not get water on I-TEC system. Pay particular attention to the relay box and throttle valve switch connector.
**2)** Always disconnect battery before charging. Ensure ignition key is off before disconnecting battery cable or any I-TEC component.
**3)** When checking the electrical terminals of the ECU with a tester, DO NOT apply probe directly to terminal. Insert a pin into terminal from harness side, and perform the measurement through pin.

**Fuel System** – Inspect all fuel lines for leaks, damage and proper routing. Correct any fuel leaks before testing.

**Air Intake System** – **1)** Ensure all air delivery hoses are properly attached with no air leaks. Ensure EGR valve is working properly and not leaking.
**2)** Inspect all vacuum hoses for proper connection and PCV valve for operation. Make sure that oil filler cap and oil dipstick are installed properly.

**Electrical System** – Ensure that all electrical harnesses for the I-TEC system are connected properly. Make sure that connecting terminals and connectors are free from corrosion and in good condition. All I-TEC wires must be properly routed and at least 4" (100 mm) from high tension cables.

### DIAGNOSTIC PROCEDURE (ECU)

The ECU stores circuit failure information under a related trouble code which can be recalled for diagnosis and repair. When recalled, these codes will be displayed by flashes of the "CHECK ENGINE" light. Codes start with lowest numbered code. Only codes in which a related malfunction has occurred will be displayed.

**Entering Diagnostic Mode** – **1)** Turn ignition on. "CHECK ENGINE" light should glow. Locate diagnostic leads. *See Fig. 2.* Connect diagnostic terminal leads together. If any trouble codes are stored in ECU memory, the "CHECK ENGINE" light will flash 2-digit codes. *See Fig 3.*
**2)** The trouble codes will be displayed from lowest to highest numbered code. Each code is repeated 3 times before the next code sequence is displayed. The trouble codes will be repeated as long as the diagnostic terminals are connected and the ignition is on.

### CLEARING TROUBLE CODES

After completion of service, clear memory of trouble codes by removing fuse No. 4 on Impulse, main fuse (60A) on Pickup, or fuse No. 13 on Trooper II. Make sure only code 12 is displayed.

### DIAGNOSTIC PROCEDURE (TCU)

**1)** The TCU will store up to 7 fault codes. These codes are displayed by an LED light in the cover of TCU.
**2)** To access trouble codes, turn ignition on. Signal codes 2 and 6 (stored in memory) are displayed. Depress accelerator fully and let return. Signal code 6 is cleared. Start engine. Signal code 2 is cleared. Any trouble codes stored in TCU will now be displayed. *See Fig. 3.*
**3)** To clear codes after repair. Repeat step **2)**.

### DIAGNOSTIC TOOLS

The I-TEC system requires special tools for diagnosis: a multimeter, 2 jumper wires 6" long, a 1.5 volt battery, a jumper wire 10 ft. long fitted at ends with a pin and an alligator clip.

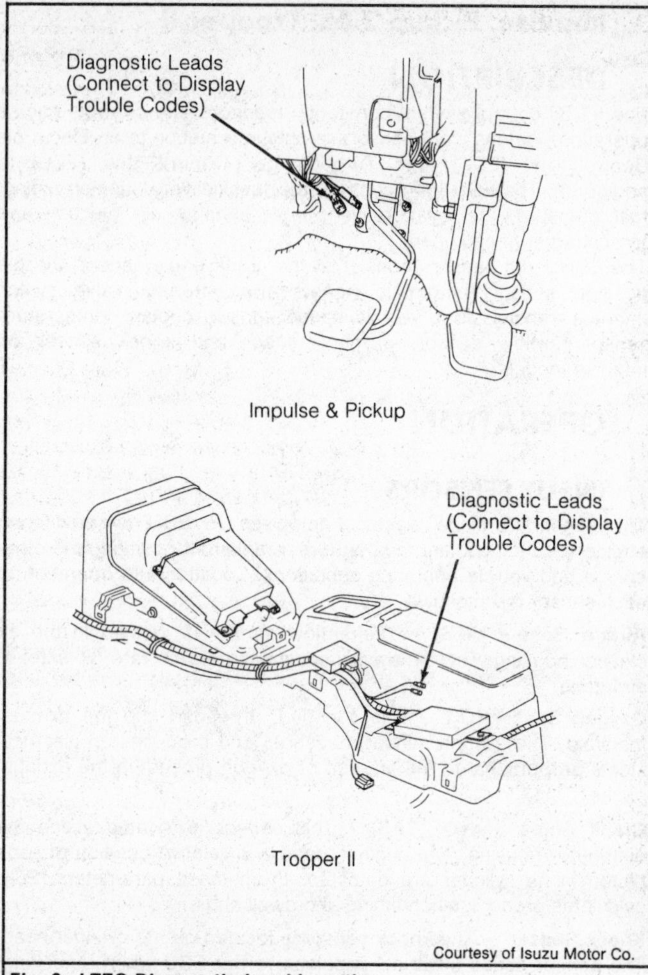
Diagnostic Leads
(Connect to Display
Trouble Codes)
Impulse & Pickup
Diagnostic Leads
(Connect to Display
Trouble Codes)
Trooper II
Courtesy of Isuzu Motor Co.

*Fig. 2: I-TEC Diagnostic Lead Location*

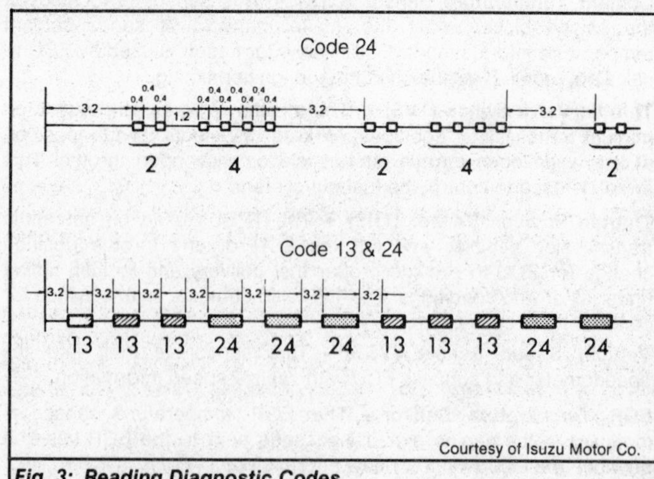
Code 24
3.2
0.4
1.2
2
4
2
4
2
Code 13 & 24
3.2
13 13 13 24 24 24 13 13 13 24 24
Courtesy of Isuzu Motor Co.

*Fig. 3: Reading Diagnostic Codes*

*TCU TROUBLE CODE IDENTIFICATION*

| Code | Problem |
|---|---|
| 1 | Faulty Knock Sensor Signal |
| 2 | Interruption of Ignition Signal |
| 3 | Short or Open Coolant Sensor |
| 4 | Faulty Stepping Motor |
| 5 | Shorted TPS |
| 6 | No Signal From TPS |
| 7 | Improper Voltage Supply |

### ECU TROUBLE CODE IDENTIFICATION

| Code | Problem |
|---|---|
| 12 | No Ignition - Normal condition |
| 13 | Open Oxygen Sensor Circuit |
| 14 | Shorted Coolant Sensor Circuit |
| 15 | Open Coolant Sensor Circuit |
| 21 | Faulty Throttle Valve Switch Circuits |
| 22 | Starter Signal Circuit |
| 23 | Output Terminal to Ignition Coil Grounded |
| 25 | Output Terminal to Vacuum Switching Solenoid Circuit Open or Grounded |
| 26 | Canister Purge Vacuum Switching Valve Shorted |
| 27 | Canister Purge Vacuum Switching Valve Grounded |
| 32 | EGR Temperature Sensor Malfunction |
| 33 | Open or Shorted Fuel Injector Circuit |
| 34 | EGR Temperature Sensor Grounded |
| 35 | Ignition Power Transistor Open |
| 41 | Bad Signal From Crank Angle Sensor |
| 43 | No Idle Position Signal |
| 44 | Lean Oxygen Sensor Indication |
| 45 | Rich Oxygen Sensor Indication |
| 51 | Faulty ECU |
| 52 | Faulty ECU |
| 53 | Faulty Vacuum Switching Valve |
| 54 | Bad Ignition Transistor or Ground |
| 55 | Faulty ECU |
| 61 | Circuit to Airflow Sensor Signal Low |
| 62 | Circuit to Airflow Sensor Signal High |
| 63 | No Vehicle Speed Sensor Signal |
| 64 | Fuel Injector Transistor or Ground |
| 65 | Continuous Signal From Throttle Position Switch |
| 66 | Open or Shorted Knock Sensor Circuit |
| 71 | Abnormal Signal from TPS |
| 72 | Output Terminal to EGR Vacuum Switching Valve Open or Grounded |
| 73 | EGR Vacuum Switching Valve or Ground |

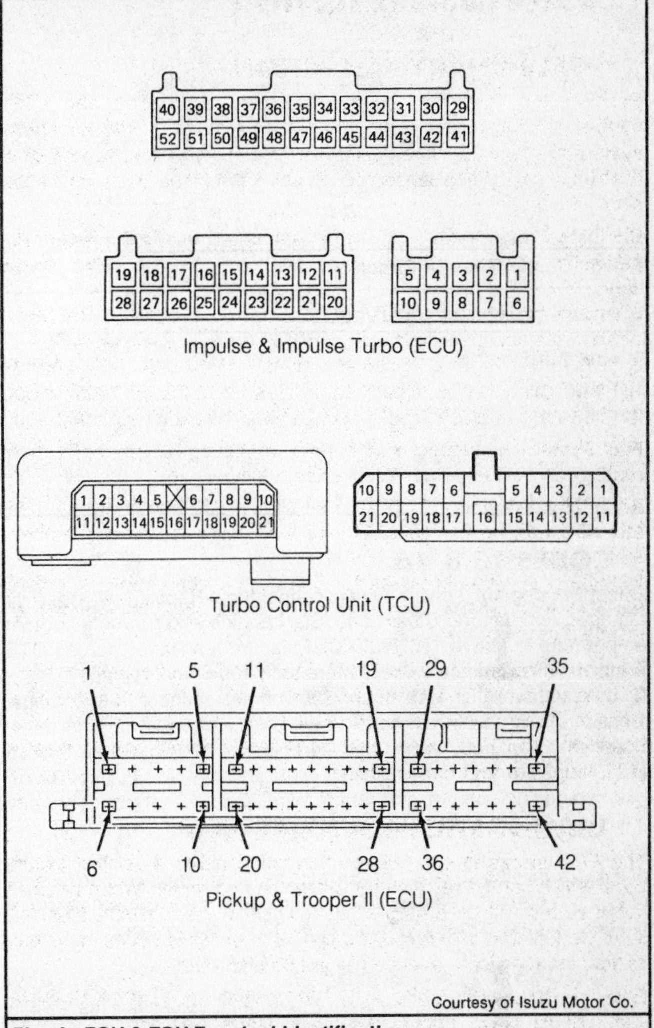

Impulse & Impulse Turbo (ECU)
Turbo Control Unit (TCU)
Pickup & Trooper II (ECU)
Courtesy of Isuzu Motor Co.


*Fig. 4: ECU & TCU Terminal Identification*

## CIRCUIT INSPECTION

**1)** The ECU harnesses are connected with 3 types of connectors, each of which has specific numbers. Inspection procedures will be described with reference made to specific numbers.

**2)** When checking the system, carefully note the terminal number to avoid a direct battery connection when ignition switch is turned on.

**3)** The inspection based on the trouble codes should be performed in the following steps: Check continuity of sensor(s). Check continuity of sensor circuit(s). Check ECU.

**4)** Disconnect wiring at ECU, sensor or output device when testing for shorts or continuity. When checking control unit harness connector terminals, make connection by inserting a pin into terminal from harness side. Avoid connecting tester probe directly to control unit terminal.

**5)** If trouble is not found in sensor(s) or in circuit(s), clear the memory and reconnect circuit(s). Road test vehicle. Obtain code display to see if trouble has been corrected. If trouble persists, replace the control unit.

## ECU TROUBLE CODES

### CODE 12

Indicates no problem in I-TEC system

### CODE 13

**1)** Inspect $O_2$ sensor wiring and connectors. Correct any problem and clear trouble code. Start engine and run at 2500 RPM until normal operating temperature. Access trouble codes. If trouble code is still present, clear code.

**2)** Disconnect $O_2$ sensor and apply 1.5 volts to ECU. Start engine and run at 2500 RPM for 2 minutes. Access trouble code. If code 13 does not exist, replace $O_2$ sensor.

**3)** If trouble code 13 is present, check continuity between ECU harness connector terminal No. 30 (No. 27 on Pickup and Trooper II) and $O_2$ sensor connector. If continuity does not exist, repair or replace harness. If continuity exists, replace ECU. Clear codes and run engine for 2 minutes. Access codes to ensure code 13 is not present.

### CODE 14

**1)** Check CTS wiring and correct any problems. Clear trouble code. Start engine and run for 2 minutes. Access trouble codes. If code 14 is present, inspect wiring harness. Check that no continuity exists between ECU harness pin No. 33 (No. 36 on Pickup and Trooper II) and Black wire, and pin No. 33 (No. 36 on Pickup and Trooper II) and ground. *See Fig. 5.* If continuity exists, replace or repair harness. Clear trouble code.

**2)** Start engine and run for 2 minutes. Access trouble codes. If code 14 exists, remove connector at CTS and check for proper resistance. See COOLANT SENSOR RESISTANCE table.

**3)** If resistance values are not correct, replace CTS. If resistance values are correct, replace ECU. Clear codes and run engine for 2 minutes. Access codes to ensure code 14 is not present.

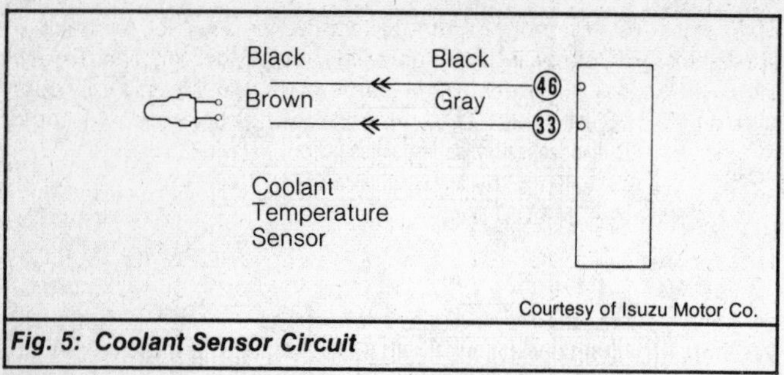
Black
Black
Brown
Gray
46
33
Coolant
Temperature
Sensor
Courtesy of Isuzu Motor Co.

*Fig. 5: Coolant Sensor Circuit*

**COOLANT SENSOR RESISTANCE**

| Temperature | Ohms |
|---|---|
| 14°F (-10°C) | 7000-12,000 |
| 50°F (10°C) | 3000-5000 |
| 68°F (20°C) | 2000-3000 |
| 122°F (50°C) | 700-1000 |
| 176°F (80°C) | 200-400 |

## CODES 15 & 16

**1)** Inspect coolant sensor wiring connectors. Repair any loose or damaged connectors. Clear code. Start engine and run until coolant temperature is above 176°F (80°C). Measure resistance across CTS terminals. If resistance value is more than 700 ohms, replace CTS.
**2)** If resistance is less than 700 ohms, recheck all terminal connections and wiring. If code 15 still exists, check wiring harness. Check that continuity exists between pin No. 33 (No. 36 on Pickup and Trooper II) and Green/Yellow wire, and pin No. 46 (No. 37 on Pickup and Trooper II) and Black Wire. Check that no continuity exists between pin No. 46 (No. 37 on Pickup and Trooper II) and ground.
**3)** If tests in step **2)** are not correct, repair or replace harness. If tests were correct, replace ECU. Clear codes and run engine for 2 minutes. Access codes to ensure code 15 is not present.

## CODES 21, 43 & 65

**1)** Check TVS terminals for proper continuity. With throttle at idle, there should be continuity between terminals I and P, but not between terminals P and F. At wide open throttle there should be continuity between terminals P and F, but not between terminals I and P. There should be no continuity between terminals I and P or P and F with throttle between idle and wide open. *See Fig. 6.*

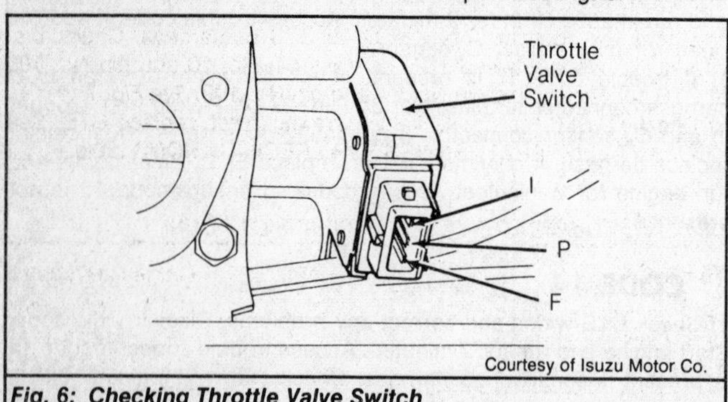
Throttle
Valve
Switch
I
P
F
Courtesy of Isuzu Motor Co.

*Fig. 6: Checking Throttle Valve Switch*

**2)** Check wiring harness by disconnecting harness at ECU and checking for continuity. Check between ECU terminal No. 27 (No. 14 on Pickup and Trooper II) and Green wire (Blue/White wire on Pickup and Trooper II), and terminal No. 18 (No. 17 on Pickup and Trooper II) and Blue/Yellow wire. If continuity exists in either test, repair or replace harness.
**3)** Clear trouble code. Start engine and operate throttle through full travel. Access trouble codes to ensure code 21 is not present.

## CODE 22

**1)** Check voltage between terminal No. 16 at ECU harness connector and terminal No. 4 at ignition switch or at starter relay. If voltage is less than 5 volts, correct power feed fault.
**2)** If voltage is over 5 volts, check for faulty ECU harness connector. Repair connector or replace ECU. Clear code and run engine. Access trouble codes to ensure code 22 is not present.

## CODES 23, 35 & 54

**1)** Disconnect ignition coil wire at distributor cap and provide approximately a 1/4" air gap to ground. Disconnect power transistor harness and turn ignition on. Connect positive side of a 1.5 volt battery to Y terminal of power transistor at ignition coil. Connect negative side of 1.5 volt battery to ground. A spark should jump air gap when 1.5 volt battery lead is disconnected. Repeat test several times to ensure accuracy. Replace power transistor and bracket if no spark exists.
**2)** If spark exists, check wiring harness. Disconnect harness at ECU and check for continuity between harness terminal No. 5 and Blue wire, and terminal No. 10 and ground. If continuity does not exist, repair or replace harness. No continuity should exist between terminal No. 5 and ground. Clear code. Start engine and access codes to ensure faults are corrected.

## CODES 25 & 53

**1)** Apply battery voltage to vacuum switching valve to check operation. Replace valve if not operating. Disconnect wiring harness at vacuum switch. Check for 12 volts between Black/White wire and ground. Repair or replace harness if 12 volts are not present.
**2)** Disconnect harness at ECU and check for continuity between harness terminal No. 13 (No. 4 on Pickup and Trooper II) and Light Green/Yellow wire, and terminal No. 10 and ground. If continuity does not exist, repair or replace harness. Clear codes. Start engine and access codes to ensure fault is corrected.

## CODES 32 & 34

**1)** Remove the EGR temperature sensor. Place sensor tip in hot water and check resistance across sensor terminals. See EGR TEMPERATURE SWITCH SPECIFICATIONS table. If sensor is not within specifications, replace sensor.
**2)** Check for continuity between ECU harness connector pin No. 45 (No. 26 on Pickup and Trooper II) and Gray wire, pin No. 47 (No. 38 on Pickup and Trooper II) and Black wire, and pin No. 47 (No. 38 on Pickup and Trooper II) and ground. If continuity does not exist in these tests, repair or replace harness.

**EGR TEMPERATURE SWITCH SPECIFICATIONS**

| Temperature | Ohms Resistance |
|---|---|
| 32°F (0°C) | 28,000 |
| 68°F (20°C) | 12,100 |
| 109°F (40°C) | 5800 |
| 176°F (80°C) | 1700 |
| 248°F (120°C) | 600 |

## CODE 33

**1)** Check voltage in fuel injector circuit. Disconnect harness connector ay ECU. Turn ignition on and check for battery voltage at harness pins No. 1, 2, 3 and 8 (No. 6 and 7 on Pickup and Trooper II).
**2)** If battery voltage is not present at terminals, disconnect fuel injector harnesses and check for battery voltage at either terminal. If battery is no present replace dropping resistor, main relay or ignition switch. Clear code. Start engine and run for 2 minutes. Access trouble codes to ensure fault is corrected.

## CODE 41

**1)** Disconnect harness at ECU and at CAS. Check that continuity exists between ECU harness connector pin No. 32 (No. 34 on Pickup and Trooper II) and White wire, pin No. 31 (No. 35 on Pickup and Trooper II) and Green wire, and Black wire and ground. There should be no voltage at these terminals. Check voltage in Red wire (Green/Black on Pickup, Red/White on Trooper II) to ground. Voltage should be 10-14 volts. Repair or replace harness as required.
**2)** Check voltage at CAS connector. Voltage should be 1-3 volts between White wire (Black/White wire on Pickup and Trooper II) and ground, and 2-3 volts between Green wire (Gray wire on Pickup and Trooper II) and ground. If voltage is incorrect, replace CAS. If voltage is correct, replace ECU. Clear code. Start engine and access trouble codes to ensure fault is corrected.

## CODES 44 & 45

**1)** Check that continuity exists between ECU harness connector terminal No. 30 (No. 27 on Pickup and Trooper II) and $O_2$ harness connector. If no continuity exists, repair or replace harness.
**2)** Check voltage output of $O_2$ sensor. Insert a jumper wire with wire exposed between sensor and harness. Set voltmeter to 2-volt scale. Connect positive lead of voltmeter to jumper and ground negative voltmeter lead. Start and run engine until closed loop is achieved. Voltage should be between .5 and .8 volts. If not, replace $O_2$ sensor.
**3)** Check $O_2$ sensor voltage output at ECU. Check voltage between pin No. 27 and ground with engine running above idle and in closed loop. If voltage reading moves back and forth to less than .35 volts and more than .50 volts, repair ECU connector or replace ECU. Clear codes. Start engine and run at high idle for 2 minutes. Access trouble codes to ensure fault is corrected.

## CODES 51, 52 & 55

Disconnect ECU harness connector and ensure terminals are clean and make good contact. Clear codes. If vehicle will not start, replace ECU. Road test vehicle and access trouble codes to ensure fault is corrected. If trouble code persists, replace ECU.

## CODES 61 & 62

**1)** Slide waterproof connector cap partially off AFS connector. Start engine and idle. Check voltage between Red and Black terminals. Voltage should be 8 volts or more. If less than 8 volts, inspect harness and replace ECU as required.
**2)** If voltage is 8 volts or more, check voltage between White terminal and Black terminal. With engine idling, the voltage should be between .3 and 5 volts. If voltage out of range, repair harness or replace airflow sensor.
**3)** Check AFS harness. Check that continuity exists between ECU harness connector pin No. 36 and White wire (No. 31 and Light Green/White wire on Pickup and Trooper II), pin No. 37 and Red wire (No. 32 and Light Green/Red wire on Pickup and Trooper II), and pin No. 49 and Black wire (No. 40 on Pickup and Trooper II).
**4)** Check that there is no continuity between White wire (Light Green/White wire on Pickup and Trooper II) and ground, and Red wire (Light Green/Red wire on Pickup and Trooper II) and ground. If continuity is incorrect, repair or replace harness.
**5)** If steps **1)**, **2)**, **3)** and **4)** all check proper, replace ECU. Clear codes. Test drive vehicle. Access trouble codes to ensure fault is corrected.

## CODE 63

**1)** Disconnect harness at ECU. Connect an ohmmeter between harness connector pin No. 25 (No. 41 on Pickup and Trooper II) and ground. Disconnect speedometer drive cable at transmission. Ohmmeter should read continuity and open at rate of 4 signals per revolution of speedometer cable. If signal is proper, replace ECU.
**2)** If signal is not proper, remove connector at VSS on back of speedometer. Connecting ohmmeter across connector pins. Repeat step **1)**. If signal is correct, repair harness. If signal is still improper, replace VSS. Clear code. Test drive vehicle. Access trouble codes to ensure fault is corrected

## CODE 66 (IMPULSE)

**1)** Disconnect ECU harness connector and check that no continuity exists between harness connector pin No. 29 and ground. If continuity exists, check knock sensor harness.
**2)** Continuity should exist between ECU harness connector pin No. 29 and White wire, and between pin No. 41 and Black wire. No continuity should exist between pin No. 29 and ground. If continuity tests are proper, replace knock sensor. Clear code. Test drive vehicle. Access trouble codes to ensure fault is corrected.

## CODE 71

See (TCU) TROUBLE CODE 6.

## CODES 72 & 73

Check EGR vacuum switching valve connector for damage and corrosion. Check operation of vacuum switching valve. Replace valve or ECU as required. Clear codes. Test drive vehicle. Access trouble codes to ensure fault is corrected.

# TCU TROUBLE CODES

## CODE 1

**1)** Check for short between ECU and TCU harness. Disconnect harness connectors at ECU and TCU. Check that continuity exists between pin No. 23 on ECU and pin No. 20 on TCU. Check that no continuity exists between pin No. 20 on TCU and ground. If tests are not proper, repair or replace harness.
**2)** If tests in step **1)** are proper, go to ECU TROUBLE CODE 66.

## CODE 2

Check harness from negative side of ignition coil to pin No. 19 on TCU. Check for continuity between pin No. 19 and Brown wire at coil. Check all connections. Check that no continuity exists between pin No. 19 and ground. Repair or replace harness as required.

## CODE 3

**1)** Check for open or short circuit in CTS or harness. Check that continuity exists between TCU harness pin No. 10 and pin No. 106 at CTS connector, and pin No. 21 and pin No. 109. *See Fig. 7.*
**2)** Check CTS. If resistance values are incorrect, replace CTS. See COOLANT TEMPERATURE SENSOR SPECIFICATIONS table.

***COOLANT TEMPERATURE SENSOR SPECIFICATIONS***

| Temperature | Ohms Resistance |
|---|---|
| 68°F (20°C) | 2210-2690 |
| 86°F (30°C) | 1570-1730 |
| 140°F (60°C) | 550-610 |

## CODE 4

**1)** With all harnesses connected, check that continuity exists between TCU connector pins No. 8 and 13. Turbocharger stepping motor cable lever must be in relaxed position so internal micro switch is on. Now check that no continuity exists between pins No. 8 and 13 when turbocharger stepping motor cable lever is turned manually.
**2)** If tests results in step **1)** are correct, replace TCU. If either test result in step **1)** is incorrect, check for continuity at stepping motor and replace harness or stepping motor. *See Fig. 8.*

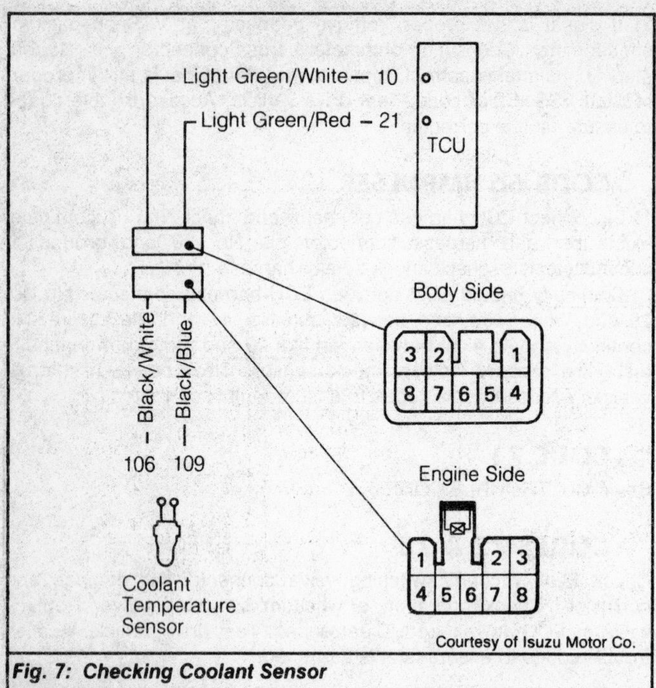
Light Green/White — 10
Light Green/Red – 21
TCU
Body Side
3 2 1
8 7 6 5 4
Black/White
Black/Blue
106 109
Engine Side
1 2 3
4 5 6 7 8
Coolant Temperature Sensor
Courtesy of Isuzu Motor Co.

*Fig. 7: Checking Coolant Sensor*

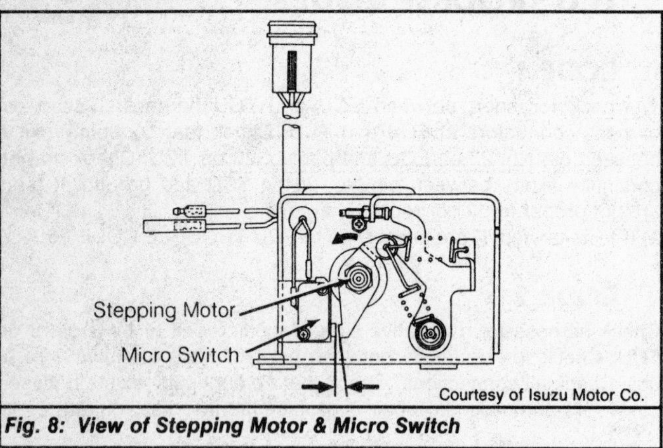
Stepping Motor
Micro Switch
Courtesy of Isuzu Motor Co.

*Fig. 8: View of Stepping Motor & Micro Switch*

## CODE 5

**1)** Check for short or open in TCU to TPS harness. Check that continuity exists between TCU harness connector pin No. 9 and pin B, pin No. 10 and pin A, and pin No. 7 and pin C. *See Fig. 9.*

**2)** Check that continuity does not exist between pin No. 9 and ground, and pin No. 6 and ground. Repair or replace harness as necessary.

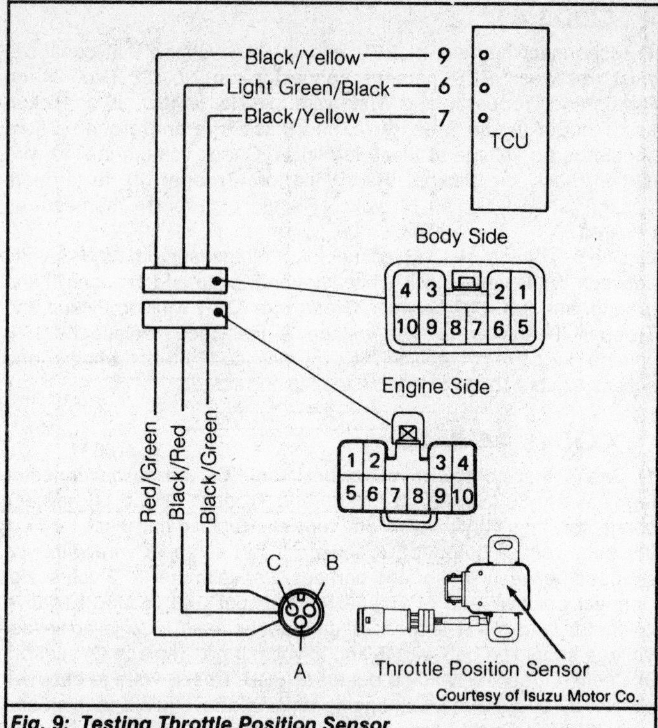
Black/Yellow — 9
Light Green/Black — 6
Black/Yellow — 7
TCU
Body Side
4 3 2 1
10 9 8 7 6 5
Engine Side
1 2 3 4
5 6 7 8 9 10
Red/Green
Black/Red
Black/Green
C
B
A
Throttle Position Sensor
Courtesy of Isuzu Motor Co.

*Fig. 9: Testing Throttle Position Sensor*

## CODE 6

**1)** Pull water shield cover back from TPS connector. Do not disconnect. With ignition on, check voltage between Red wire and Black wire. Voltage should be 4.5-5.5 volts.

**2)** Switch positive lead of voltmeter to White wire. With throttle at idle, reading should be higher than 4 volts. At wide open throttle the reading should be less than 2 volts. Difference of readings between idle and wide open throttle should be 2.6-4.6 volts.

**3)** TPS is adjustable. If adjustment will not bring correct voltage readings, replace TPS.

## CODE 7

This code will appear if charging voltage is below 9.5 volts or over 16.5 volts. Check and repair charging system.

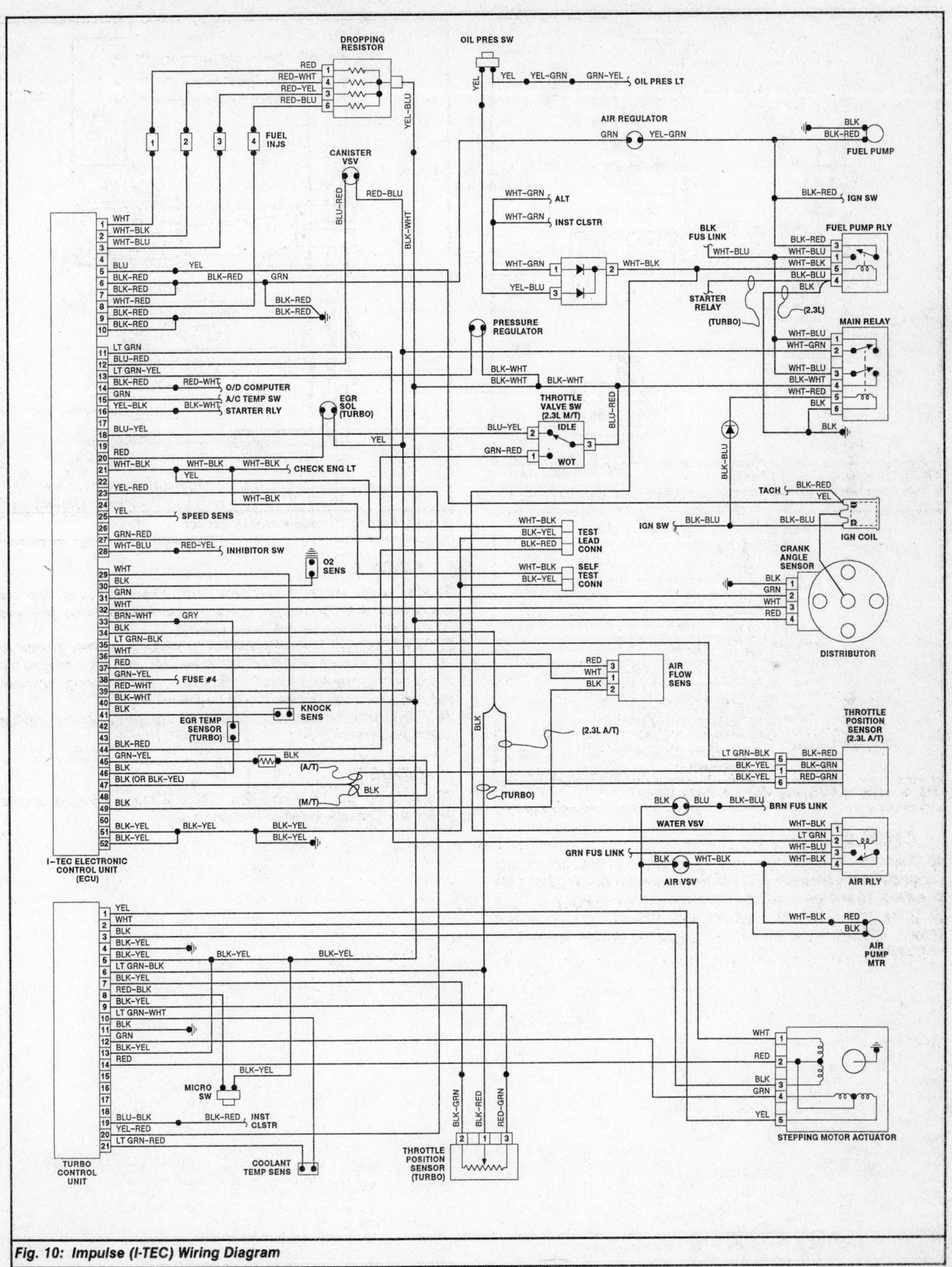

Fig. 10: Impulse (I-TEC) Wiring Diagram

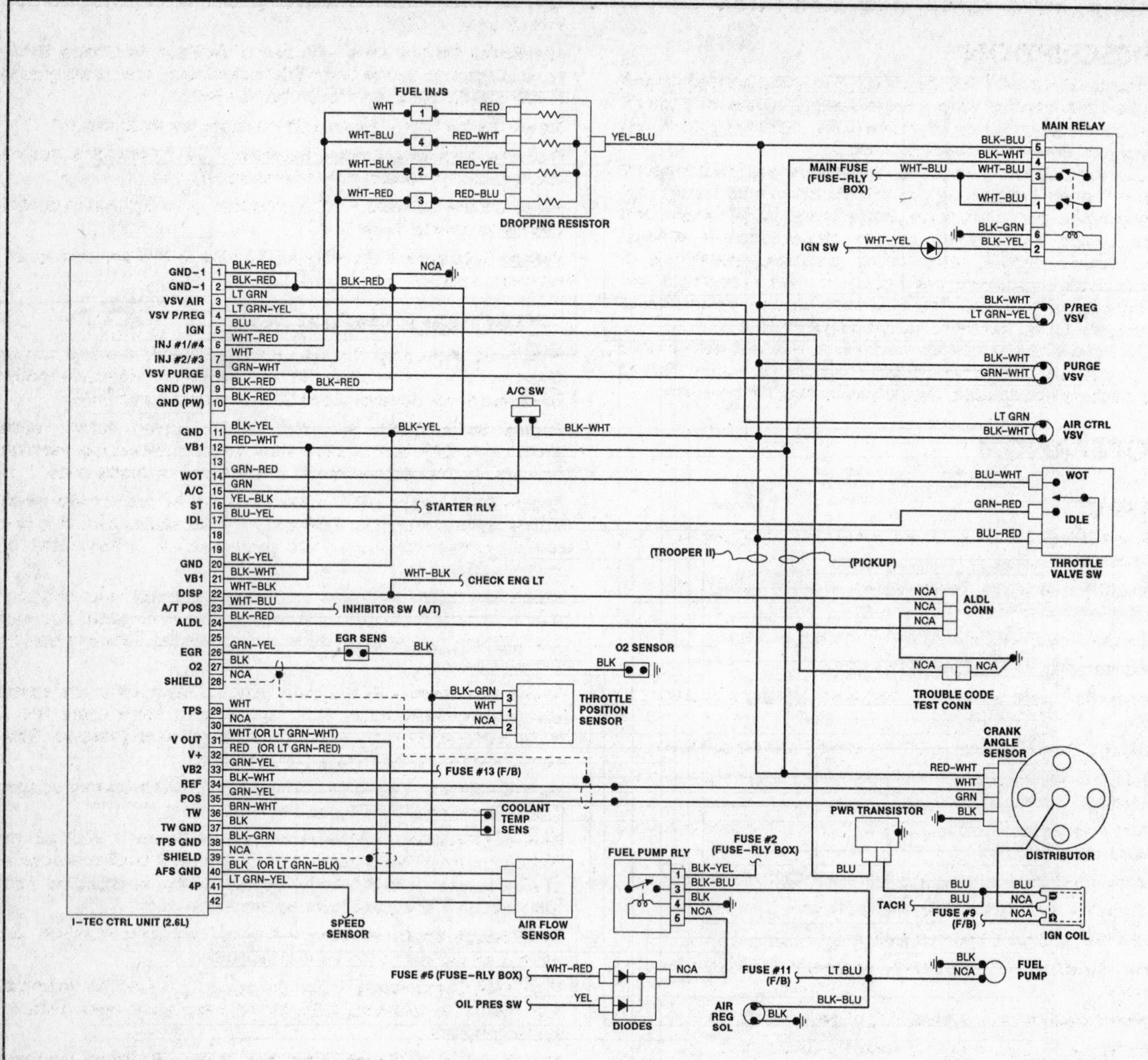
FUEL INJS
WHT
RED
WHT-BLU
RED-WHT
WHT-BLK
RED-YEL
WHT-RED
RED-BLU
DROPPING RESISTOR
YEL-BLU
MAIN RELAY
BLK-BLU
BLK-WHT
MAIN FUSE
(FUSE-RLY BOX)
WHT-BLU
BLK-GRN
IGN SW
WHT-YEL
BLK-YEL
GND-1
GND-1
VSV AIR
VSV P/REG
IGN
INJ #1/#4
INJ #2/#3
VSV PURGE
GND (PW)
GND (PW)
GND
VB1
WOT
A/C
ST
IDL
GND
VB1
DISP
A/T POS
ALDL
EGR
O2
SHIELD
TPS
V OUT
V+
VB2
REF
POS
TW
TW GND
TPS GND
SHIELD
AFS GND
4P
I-TEC CTRL UNIT (2.6L)
BLK-RED
LT GRN
LT GRN-YEL
BLU
WHT-RED
GRN-WHT
NCA
A/C SW
BLK-YEL
RED-WHT
GRN-RED
GRN
YEL-BLK
BLU-YEL
STARTER RLY
WHT-BLK
CHECK ENG LT
INHIBITOR SW (A/T)
GRN-YEL
EGR SENS
BLK
O2 SENSOR
BLK-GRN
THROTTLE POSITION SENSOR
WHT (OR LT GRN-WHT)
RED (OR LT GRN-RED)
FUSE #13 (F/B)
BRN-WHT
COOLANT TEMP SENS
BLK (OR LT GRN-BLK)
SPEED SENSOR
AIR FLOW SENSOR
P/REG VSV
PURGE VSV
AIR CTRL VSV
BLU-WHT
WOT
IDLE
BLU-RED
THROTTLE VALVE SW
(TROOPER II)
(PICKUP)
ALDL CONN
TROUBLE CODE TEST CONN
CRANK ANGLE SENSOR
DISTRIBUTOR
PWR TRANSISTOR
FUSE #2
(FUSE-RLY BOX)
FUEL PUMP RLY
BLK-BLU
TACH
FUSE #9 (F/B)
IGN COIL
FUEL PUMP
FUSE #5 (FUSE-RLY BOX)
OIL PRES SW
YEL
DIODES
FUSE #11 (F/B)
LT BLU
AIR REG SOL

Fig. 11: Pickup 2.6L & Trooper II (I-TEC) Wiring Diagram

# 1988 COMPUTERIZED ENGINE CONTROLS
# Mazda – MX-6 & 626 EGI

## MX-6, MX-6 Turbo, 626, 626 Turbo

## DESCRIPTION

The Mazda Electronic Gas Injection (EGI) computerized engine control system monitors various engine/vehicle functions to control engine operation and lower emissions while maintaining good fuel economy and driveability. *See Figs. 1 and 2.*

The Electronic Control Unit (ECU), through various input sensors, monitors battery voltage, engine RPM, amount of intake air, cranking signal, crankshaft angle, intake temperature, radiator and engine coolant temperatures, oxygen concentration in exhaust gases, throttle opening, atmospheric pressure, gearshift lever position, clutch engagement, braking, power steering operation, and A/C compressor operation. The ECU uses all input information to control spark timing, fuel injection, and output devices.

The ECU has a built-in fail-safe mechanism. If a fault occurs while driving, the ECU will substitute pre-programmed values. Driving performance will be affected, but the vehicle may still be driven.

## OPERATION

### INPUTS

**Air Conditioning Switch** – Closes when A/C or blower is in the "ON" position.

**Airflow Meter (Inlet Air Temperature)** – Varies voltage signal to ECU in relation to inlet air temperature.

**Airflow Meter (Vc)** – Corrected airflow meter voltage.

**Airflow Meter (Vs)** – Airflow position signal.

**Atmospheric Pressure Sensor** – Varies voltage signal according to altitude.

**Brake Light Switch** – Signals ECU of vehicle braking condition.

**Coolant Temperature Sensor** – Varies input voltage signal according to engine coolant temperature.

**Coolant Temperature Switch** – Switch opens and closes according to radiator temperature.

**Electrical Load Control** – Signals ECU of additional electrical load.

**Idle Switch** – Indicates throttle closed position.

**Ignition Coil** – Signals engine speed.

**Ignition Switch** – Supplies battery voltage to ECU during engine cranking.

**Inhibitor Switch (A/T)** – Signals ECU of gear selection.

**Knock Sensor** – Signals ECU of knocking condition.

**Main Relay** – Provides battery voltage to ECU.

**Neutral/Clutch Switch (M/T)** – Signals ECU of clutch operation and transaxle gear selection.

**Oxygen ($O_2$) Sensor** – Generates voltage signal depending on oxygen content of exhaust.

**Power Steering Switch** – Provides signal to ECU when vehicle is turning.

**Speed Sensor** – Signals ECU of vehicle speed. Located in speedometer.

**Throttle Position Sensor (TPS)** – Provides voltage signal in response to throttle position.

### OUTPUTS

**Air Conditioning Relay** – ECU completes ground circuit for A/C operation.

**"Check Engine" Light** – Lights during engine start up and monitored component malfunction. Is also referred to as MIL or Malfunction Indicator Light. Is used to read trouble codes.

**EGR Solenoid** – ECU completes ground circuit to control vacuum to EGR valve.

**Fuel Injectors** – ECU completes ground circuit to control fuel injector pulse.

**Idle Speed Control Valve** – Is part of By-Pass Air Control (BAC) valve attached to throttle body. ECU intermittently completes ground to idle speed control valve for proper idle RPM.

**Knock Control Unit** – Retards timing during knock condition.

**Pressure Regulator Control Solenoid** – ECU completes ground circuit to control vacuum to fuel pressure regulator.

**Purge Control Solenoid** – ECU completes ground circuit to control vacuum to canister purge.

**Voltage Reference** – Provides 4.5-5.5 volts to TPS and atmospheric pressure sensor.

## TROUBLE SHOOTING

**Hard Start or No Start (Cranks Okay)** – Incorrect fuel injection or pressure. Poor connections at airflow meter or throttle body. Electronic Spark Advance (ESA) Control system (turbo only).

**Engine Stalls Cold** – Air valve or idle speed control valve malfunction. EGR control valve stuck open. Incorrect fuel injection or pressure. Poor connections at airflow meter or throttle body.

**Engine Stalls Warm** – PCV system clogged. Air valve or idle speed control valve malfunction. EGR control valve stuck open. Incorrect fuel injection or pressure. Poor connections at airflow meter or throttle body.

**Rough Idle Cold** – Air valve or idle speed control valve malfunction. PCV system clogged. EGR control valve stuck open. Incorrect fuel injection or pressure. Poor connections at airflow meter or throttle body.

**Rough Idle Warm** – PCV system clogged. Air valve or idle speed control valve malfunction. EGR control valve stuck open. No. 1 purge valve malfunction. Incorrect fuel injection or pressure. Poor connections at airflow meter or throttle body.

**High Idle Speed** – Air valve or idle speed control valve malfunction. Poor connection at airflow meter or throttle body.

**Poor Acceleration, Hesistation or Lack of Power** – EGR control valve stuck open. No. 1 purge valve malfunction. Poor connections at airflow meter or throttle body. Exhaust system clogged. Incorrect fuel injection or pressure. Turbo system malfunction.

**Runs Rough on Deceleration** – Fuel-cut system malfunction. Air valve or idle speed control valve malfunction.

**High Fuel Consumption** – Fuel-cut system malfunction. Incorrect fuel injection or pressure. EGR control valve stuck open. Exhaust system clogged.

**Engine Stalls or Rough After Hot Start** – Pressure regulator control system malfunction. Incorrect fuel injection or pressure.

**Excessive Oil Consumption** – Turbo system malfunction.

**Knocking (Turbo Only)** – ESA malfunction. Incorrect fuel injection or pressure.

**Abnormal Noise or Vibration** – Turbo system malfunction.

**Fails Emission Test** – Exhaust system clogged. EGR control valve stuck open. Fuel-cut system malfunction. Air valve or idle speed control valve malfunction. No. 1 purge valve malfunction. Poor connections at airflow meter or throttle body. Incorrect fuel injection or pressure.

## DIAGNOSIS & TESTING

### WITH SELF-DIAGNOSTIC CHECKER

**Trouble Code Access – 1)** Connect Self-Diagnostic Checker (49 H018 9A1) to Green 6-pin connector and negative battery terminal. *See Fig. 3.* Connector is located at back of left front wheelwell. Select position "A" on checker.

**2)** Ground Green 1-pin connector with jumper wire. With ignition on and engine stopped, verify code 88 flashes and buzzer sounds for 3

# 1988 COMPUTERIZED ENGINE CONTROL
## Mazda – MX-6 & 626 EGI (Cont.)

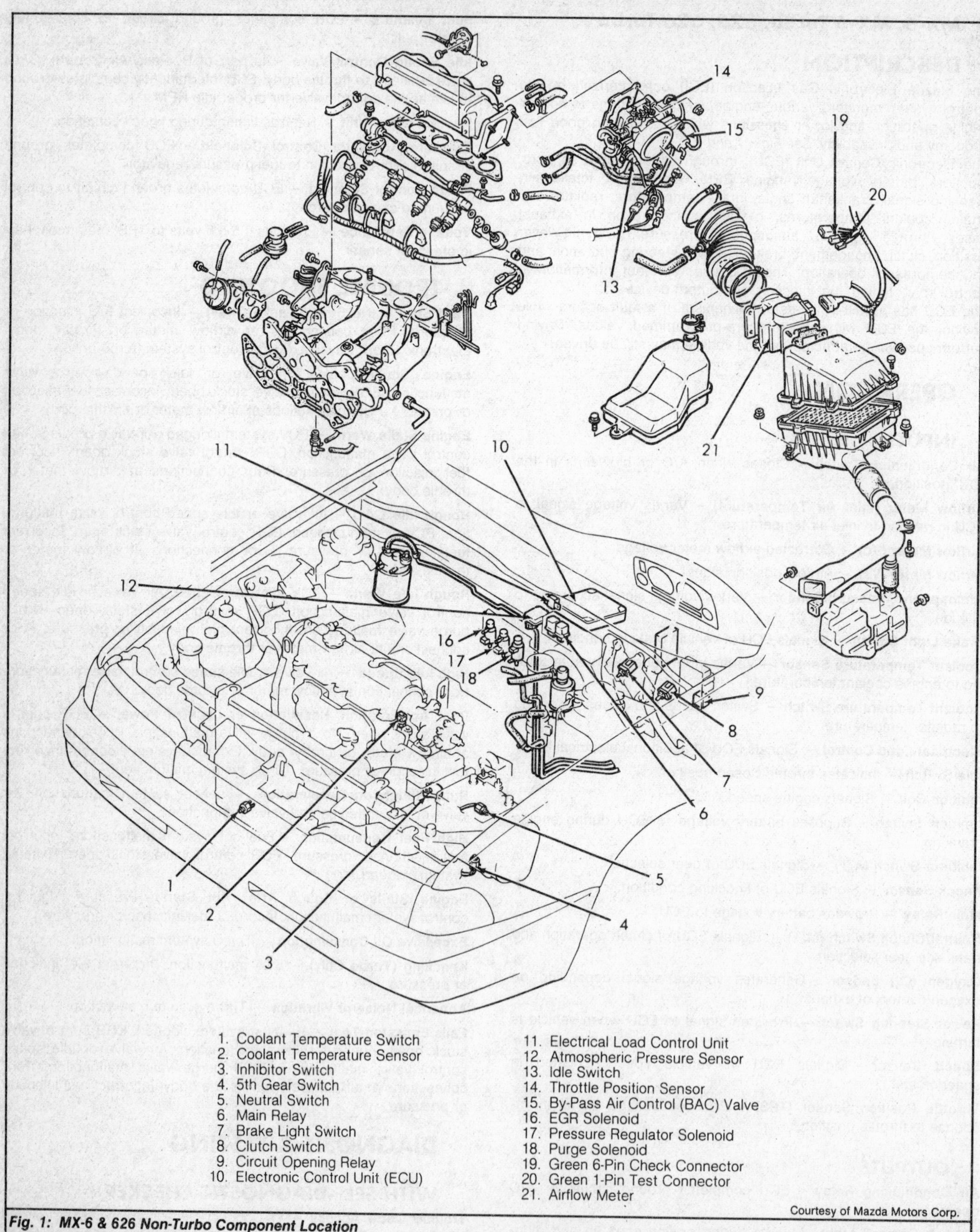

1
2
3
4
5
6
7
8
9
10
11
12
13
14
15
16
17
18
19
20
21
1. Coolant Temperature Switch
2. Coolant Temperature Sensor
3. Inhibitor Switch
4. 5th Gear Switch
5. Neutral Switch
6. Main Relay
7. Brake Light Switch
8. Clutch Switch
9. Circuit Opening Relay
10. Electronic Control Unit (ECU)
11. Electrical Load Control Unit
12. Atmospheric Pressure Sensor
13. Idle Switch
14. Throttle Position Sensor
15. By-Pass Air Control (BAC) Valve
16. EGR Solenoid
17. Pressure Regulator Solenoid
18. Purge Solenoid
19. Green 6-Pin Check Connector
20. Green 1-Pin Test Connector
21. Airflow Meter
Courtesy of Mazda Motors Corp.


*Fig. 1: MX-6 & 626 Non-Turbo Component Location*

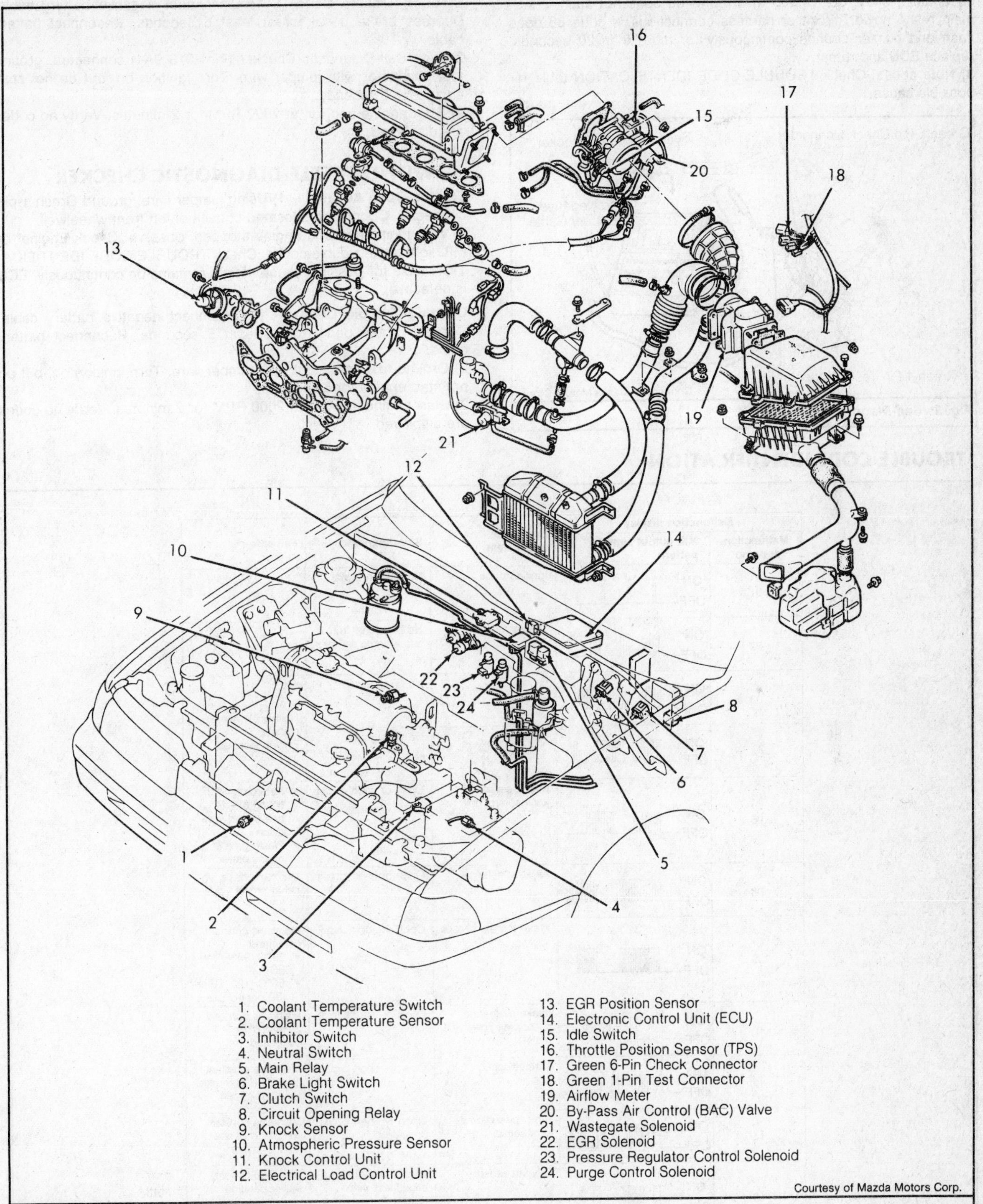
1
2
3
4
5
6
7
8
9
10
11
12
13
14
15
16
17
18
19
20
21
22
23
24

1. Coolant Temperature Switch
2. Coolant Temperature Sensor
3. Inhibitor Switch
4. Neutral Switch
5. Main Relay
6. Brake Light Switch
7. Clutch Switch
8. Circuit Opening Relay
9. Knock Sensor
10. Atmospheric Pressure Sensor
11. Knock Control Unit
12. Electrical Load Control Unit
13. EGR Position Sensor
14. Electronic Control Unit (ECU)
15. Idle Switch
16. Throttle Position Sensor (TPS)
17. Green 6-Pin Check Connector
18. Green 1-Pin Test Connector
19. Airflow Meter
20. By-Pass Air Control (BAC) Valve
21. Wastegate Solenoid
22. EGR Solenoid
23. Pressure Regulator Control Solenoid
24. Purge Control Solenoid

Courtesy of Mazda Motors Corp.

*Fig. 2: MX-6 & 626 Turbo Component Location*

seconds. If okay, go to step **3)**. If code 88 does not flash, check main relay, power circuit or harness connections. If code 88 does flash and buzzer sounds continuously for more than 20 seconds, replace ECU and retest.

**3)** Note codes. Check TROUBLE CODE IDENTIFICATION table for possible cause.

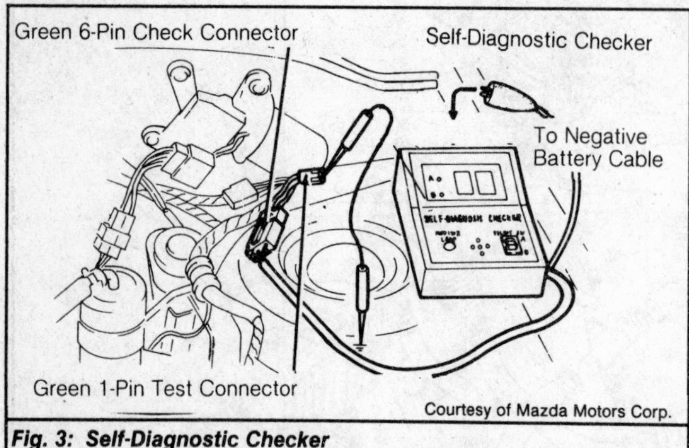
Green 6-Pin Check Connector
Self-Diagnostic Checker
To Negative Battery Cable
Green 1-Pin Test Connector
Courtesy of Mazda Motors Corp.

*Fig. 3: Self-Diagnostic Checker*

**Clearing Trouble Codes – 1)** Disconnect negative battery cable. Depress brake pedal for at least 5 seconds. Reconnect battery cable.

**2)** With Self-Diagnostic Checker (49 H018 9A1) connected, ground test connector with jumper wire. Turn ignition on, but do not start engine for 6 seconds.

**3)** Start engine and run at 2000 RPM for 2 minutes. Verify no codes are displayed.

## WITHOUT SELF-DIAGNOSTIC CHECKER

**Trouble Code Access – 1)** Using jumper wire, ground Green 1-pin connector. Connector is located at back of left front wheelwell.

**2)** With ignition on and engine stopped, observe "Check Engine" or MIL light. Note trouble codes. Check TROUBLE CODE IDENTIFICATION table for possible cause. If light remains on continuously, ECU is defective.

**Clearing Trouble Codes – 1)** Disconnect negative battery cable. Depress brake pedal for at least 5 seconds. Reconnect battery cable.

**2)** Ground test connector with jumper wire. Turn ignition on, but do not start engine for 6 seconds.

**3)** Start engine and run at 2000 RPM for 2 minutes. Verify no codes are displayed.

## TROUBLE CODE IDENTIFICATION

| Malfunction display | | Sensor or subsystem | Self-diagnosis | Fail-safe |
|---|---|---|---|---|
| Malfunction code no. | MIL output signal pattern | | | |
| 01 | ON / OFF | Ignition pulse | No ignition signal | — |
| 02 | ON / OFF | Ne signal | No Ne signal from crank angle sensor | — |
| 03 | ON / OFF | $G_1$ signal | No $G_1$ signal | Neither $G_1$ nor $G_2$ signal: Engine stopped |
| 04 | ON / OFF | $G_2$ signal | No $G_2$ signal | |
| 05 | ON / OFF | Knock sensor and kock control unit | Open or short circuit | • Retards ignition timing 6° in heavy-load condition<br>• Waste gate opens earlier |
| 08 | ON / OFF | Air flow meter | Open or short circuit | Maintains basic signal at preset value |
| 09 | ON / OFF | Water thermo sensor | Open or short circuit | Maintains constant command<br>• 35°C (95°F) for EGI<br>• 50°C (122°F) for ISC control use |
| 10 | ON / OFF | Intake air thermo sensor (air flow meter) | Open or short circuit | Maintains constant 20°C (68°F) command |
| 12 | ON / OFF | Throttle sensor | Open or short circuit | Maintains constant command of throttle valve fully open |
| 14 | ON / OFF | Atmospheric pressure sensor | Open or short circuit | Maintains constant command of sea level pressure |
| 15 | ON / OFF | Oxygen sensor | Sensor output continues less than 0.55V 120 sec. after engine starts (1,500 rpm) | Cancels EGI feedback operation |

Courtesy of Mazda Motors Corp.

## TROUBLE CODE IDENTIFICATION (Cont.)

| Malfunction display | | Sensor or subsystem | Self-diagnosis | Fail-safe |
|---|---|---|---|---|
| Malfunction code no. | MIL output signal pattern | | | |
| 16 | ON OFF | EGR position sensor | Open or short circuit | Cuts off EGR |
| | | | Sensor output does not match target value (incorrect output) | — |
| 17 | ON OFF | Feedback system | Sensor output not changed 20 sec. after engine exceeds 1,500 rpm | Cancels EGI feedback operation |
| 25 | ON OFF | Solenoid valve (pressure regulator) | Open or short circuit | — |
| 26 | ON OFF | Solenoid valve (purge control) | | — |
| 28 | ON OFF | Solenoid valve (EGR-vacuum) | | — |
| 29 | ON OFF | Solenoid valve (EGR-vent) | | — |
| 34 | ON OFF | Solenoid valve (Idle speed control) | | — |
| 42 | ON OFF | Solenoid valve (waste gate) | | — |

Courtesy of Mazda Motors Corp.

## NON-TURBO TROUBLE CODES

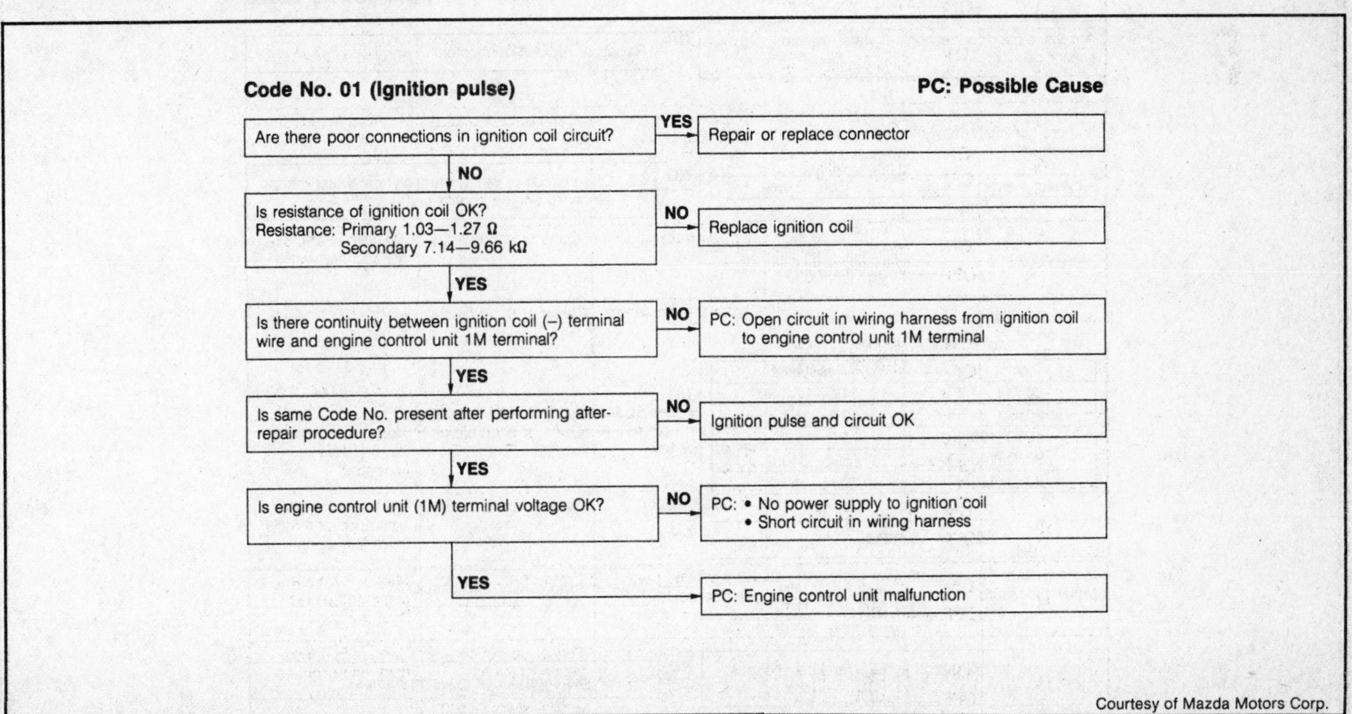
Code No. 01 (Ignition pulse)
PC: Possible Cause
Are there poor connections in ignition coil circuit?
YES
Repair or replace connector
NO
Is resistance of ignition coil OK?
Resistance: Primary 1.03—1.27 Ω
Secondary 7.14—9.66 kΩ
NO
Replace ignition coil
YES
Is there continuity between ignition coil (–) terminal wire and engine control unit 1M terminal?
NO
PC: Open circuit in wiring harness from ignition coil to engine control unit 1M terminal
YES
Is same Code No. present after performing after-repair procedure?
NO
Ignition pulse and circuit OK
YES
Is engine control unit (1M) terminal voltage OK?
NO
PC: • No power supply to ignition coil
• Short circuit in wiring harness
YES
PC: Engine control unit malfunction

Courtesy of Mazda Motors Corp.

## NON-TURBO TROUBLE CODES (Cont.)

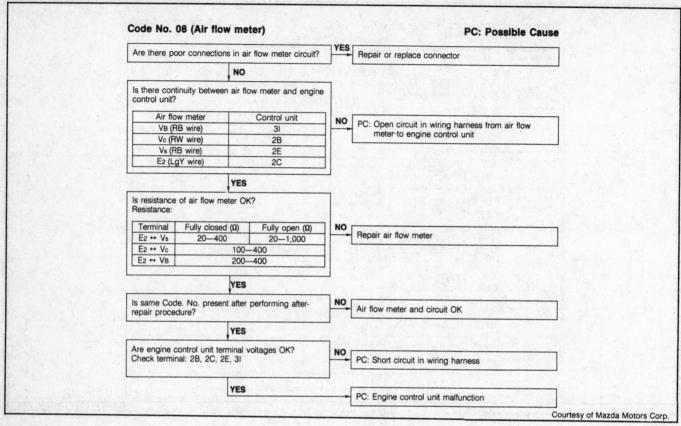

**Code No. 08 (Air flow meter)**

**PC: Possible Cause**

Are there poor connections in air flow meter circuit?
- YES → Repair or replace connector
- NO ↓

Is there continuity between air flow meter and engine control unit?

| Air flow meter | Control unit |
|---|---|
| $V_B$ (RB wire) | 3I |
| $V_C$ (RW wire) | 2B |
| $V_S$ (RB wire) | 2E |
| $E_2$ (LgY wire) | 2C |

- NO → PC: Open circuit in wiring harness from air flow meter to engine control unit
- YES ↓

Is resistance of air flow meter OK?
Resistance:

| Terminal | Fully closed (Ω) | Fully open (Ω) |
|---|---|---|
| $E_2 \leftrightarrow V_S$ | 20—400 | 20—1,000 |
| $E_2 \leftrightarrow V_C$ | 100—400 | |
| $E_2 \leftrightarrow V_B$ | 200—400 | |

- NO → Repair air flow meter
- YES ↓

Is same Code. No. present after performing after-repair procedure?
- NO → Air flow meter and circuit OK
- YES ↓

Are engine control unit terminal voltages OK?
Check terminal: 2B, 2C, 2E, 3I
- NO → PC: Short circuit in wiring harness
- YES → PC: Engine control unit malfunction

Courtesy of Mazda Motors Corp.

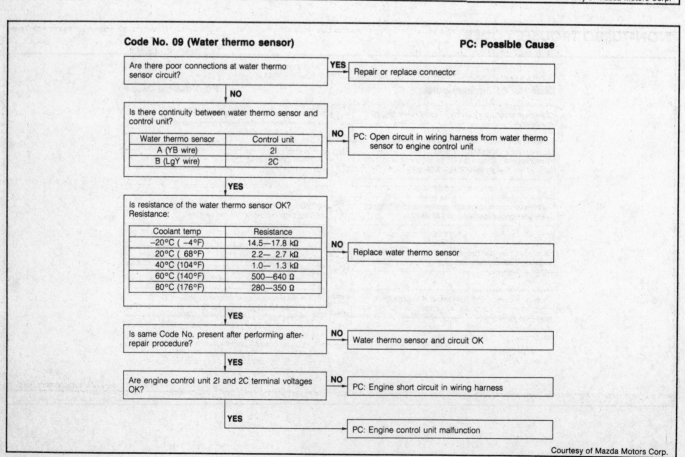

**Code No. 09 (Water thermo sensor)**

**PC: Possible Cause**

Are there poor connections at water thermo sensor circuit?
- YES → Repair or replace connector
- NO ↓

Is there continuity between water thermo sensor and control unit?

| Water thermo sensor | Control unit |
|---|---|
| A (YB wire) | 2I |
| B (LgY wire) | 2C |

- NO → PC: Open circuit in wiring harness from water thermo sensor to engine control unit
- YES ↓

Is resistance of the water thermo sensor OK?
Resistance:

| Coolant temp | Resistance |
|---|---|
| −20°C ( −4°F) | 14.5—17.8 kΩ |
| 20°C ( 68°F) | 2.2— 2.7 kΩ |
| 40°C (104°F) | 1.0— 1.3 kΩ |
| 60°C (140°F) | 500—640 Ω |
| 80°C (176°F) | 280—350 Ω |

- NO → Replace water thermo sensor
- YES ↓

Is same Code No. present after performing after-repair procedure?
- NO → Water thermo sensor and circuit OK
- YES ↓

Are engine control unit 2I and 2C terminal voltages OK?
- NO → PC: Engine short circuit in wiring harness
- YES → PC: Engine control unit malfunction

Courtesy of Mazda Motors Corp.

## NON-TURBO TROUBLE CODES (Cont.)

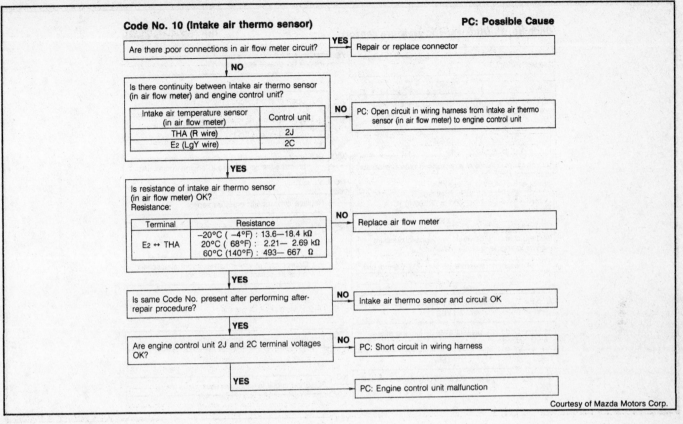

**Code No. 10 (Intake air thermo sensor)**

**PC: Possible Cause**

- Are there poor connections in air flow meter circuit?
  - **YES** → Repair or replace connector
  - **NO** ↓
- Is there continuity between intake air thermo sensor (in air flow meter) and engine control unit?

| Intake air temperature sensor (in air flow meter) | Control unit |
|---|---|
| THA (R wire) | 2J |
| $E_2$ (LgY wire) | 2C |

  - **NO** → PC: Open circuit in wiring harness from intake air thermo sensor (in air flow meter) to engine control unit
  - **YES** ↓
- Is resistance of intake air thermo sensor (in air flow meter) OK?
  Resistance:

| Terminal | Resistance |
|---|---|
| $E_2$ ↔ THA | −20°C (−4°F) : 13.6—18.4 kΩ<br>20°C (68°F) : 2.21— 2.69 kΩ<br>60°C (140°F) : 493— 667 Ω |

  - **NO** → Replace air flow meter
  - **YES** ↓
- Is same Code No. present after performing after-repair procedure?
  - **NO** → Intake air thermo sensor and circuit OK
  - **YES** ↓
- Are engine control unit 2J and 2C terminal voltages OK?
  - **NO** → PC: Short circuit in wiring harness
  - **YES** → PC: Engine control unit malfunction

Courtesy of Mazda Motors Corp.

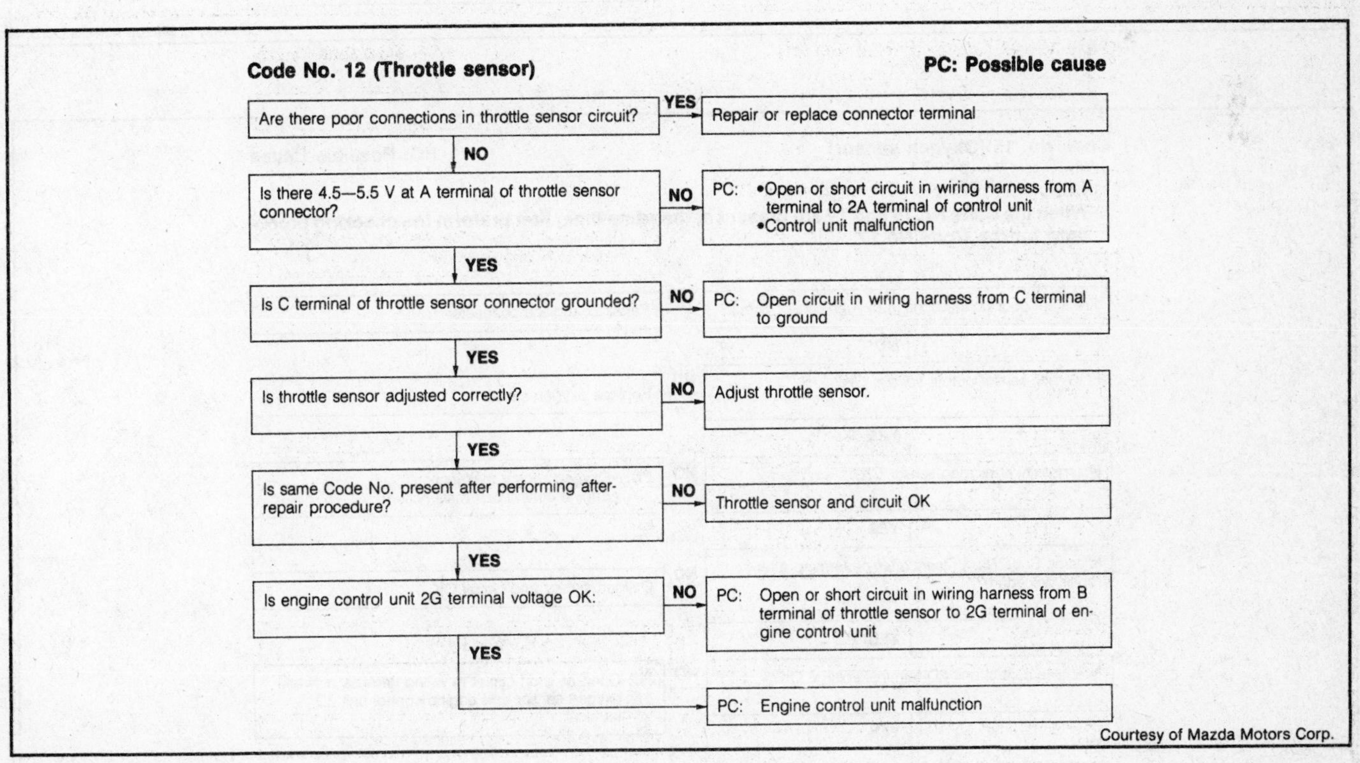
Code No. 12 (Throttle sensor)
PC: Possible cause
Are there poor connections in throttle sensor circuit?
YES
Repair or replace connector terminal
NO
Is there 4.5—5.5 V at A terminal of throttle sensor connector?
NO
PC: •Open or short circuit in wiring harness from A terminal to 2A terminal of control unit
•Control unit malfunction
YES
Is C terminal of throttle sensor connector grounded?
NO
PC: Open circuit in wiring harness from C terminal to ground
YES
Is throttle sensor adjusted correctly?
NO
Adjust throttle sensor.
YES
Is same Code No. present after performing after-repair procedure?
NO
Throttle sensor and circuit OK
YES
Is engine control unit 2G terminal voltage OK:
NO
PC: Open or short circuit in wiring harness from B terminal of throttle sensor to 2G terminal of engine control unit
YES
PC: Engine control unit malfunction

Courtesy of Mazda Motors Corp.

## NON-TURBO TROUBLE CODES (Cont.)

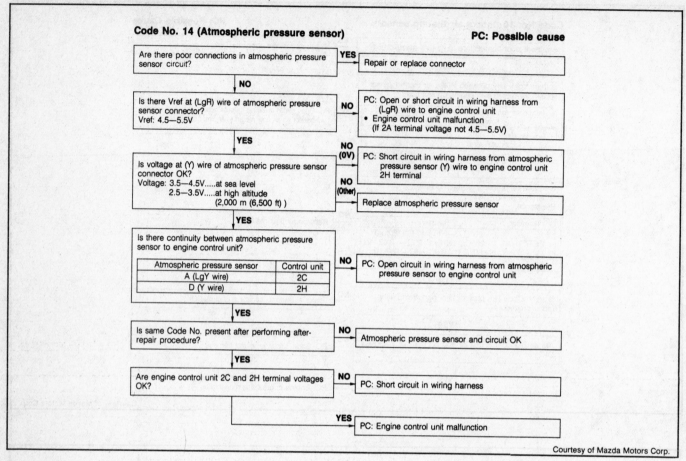

**Code No. 14 (Atmospheric pressure sensor)**

**PC: Possible cause**

Are there poor connections in atmospheric pressure sensor circuit?
- YES → Repair or replace connector
- NO ↓

Is there Vref at (LgR) wire of atmospheric pressure sensor connector? Vref: 4.5—5.5V
- NO → PC: Open or short circuit in wiring harness from (LgR) wire to engine control unit
  - Engine control unit malfunction (If 2A terminal voltage not 4.5—5.5V)
- YES ↓

Is voltage at (Y) wire of atmospheric pressure sensor connector OK?
Voltage: 3.5—4.5V.....at sea level
2.5—3.5V.....at high altitude (2,000 m (6,500 ft) )
- NO (0V) → PC: Short circuit in wiring harness from atmospheric pressure sensor (Y) wire to engine control unit 2H terminal
- NO (Other) → Replace atmospheric pressure sensor
- YES ↓

Is there continuity between atmospheric pressure sensor to engine control unit?

| Atmospheric pressure sensor | Control unit |
|---|---|
| A (LgY wire) | 2C |
| D (Y wire) | 2H |

- NO → PC: Open circuit in wiring harness from atmospheric pressure sensor to engine control unit
- YES ↓

Is same Code No. present after performing after-repair procedure?
- NO → Atmospheric pressure sensor and circuit OK
- YES ↓

Are engine control unit 2C and 2H terminal voltages OK?
- NO → PC: Short circuit in wiring harness
- YES → PC: Engine control unit malfunction

Courtesy of Mazda Motors Corp.

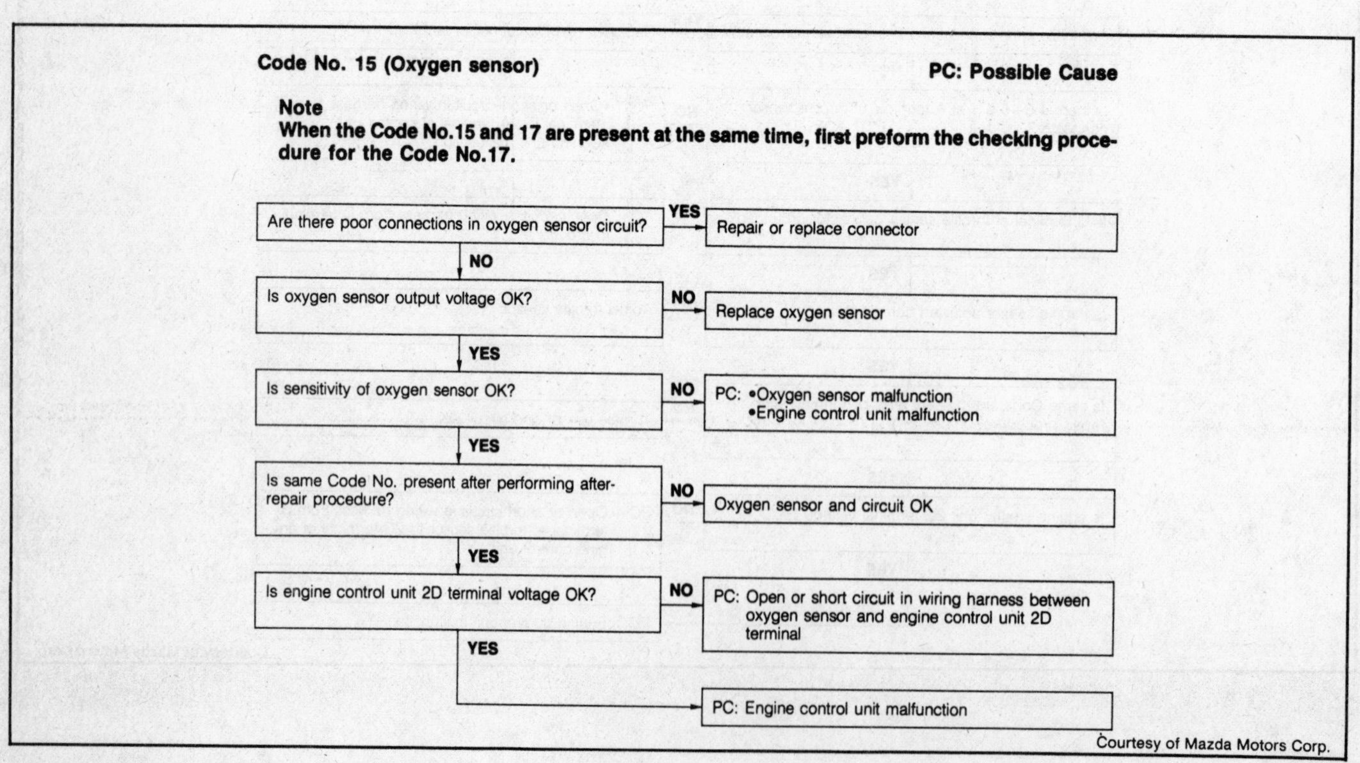
Code No. 15 (Oxygen sensor)
PC: Possible Cause
Note
When the Code No.15 and 17 are present at the same time, first preform the checking procedure for the Code No.17.
Are there poor connections in oxygen sensor circuit?
YES
Repair or replace connector
NO
Is oxygen sensor output voltage OK?
NO
Replace oxygen sensor
YES
Is sensitivity of oxygen sensor OK?
NO
PC: •Oxygen sensor malfunction
•Engine control unit malfunction
YES
Is same Code No. present after performing after-repair procedure?
NO
Oxygen sensor and circuit OK
YES
Is engine control unit 2D terminal voltage OK?
NO
PC: Open or short circuit in wiring harness between oxygen sensor and engine control unit 2D terminal
YES
PC: Engine control unit malfunction
Courtesy of Mazda Motors Corp.

## NON-TURBO TROUBLE CODES (Cont.)

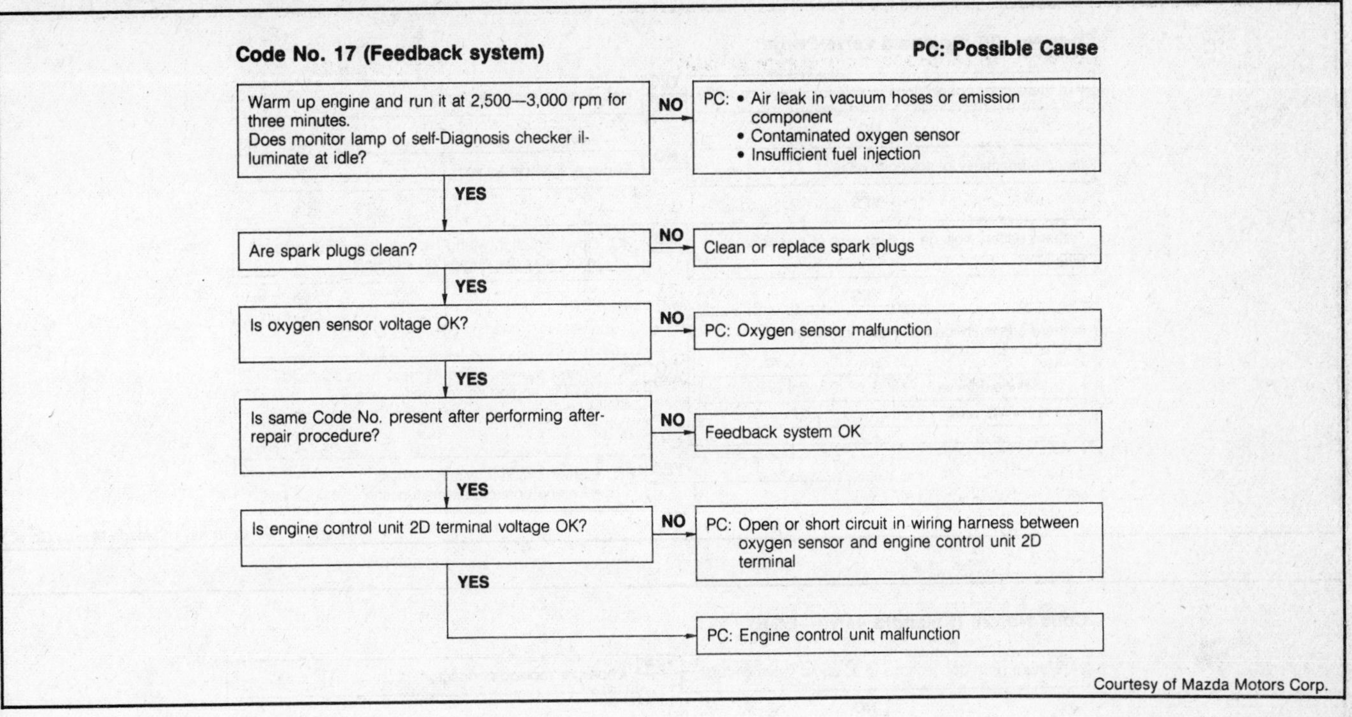
Code No. 17 (Feedback system)
PC: Possible Cause
Warm up engine and run it at 2,500—3,000 rpm for three minutes. Does monitor lamp of self-Diagnosis checker illuminate at idle?
NO
PC: • Air leak in vacuum hoses or emission component
• Contaminated oxygen sensor
• Insufficient fuel injection
YES
Are spark plugs clean?
NO
Clean or replace spark plugs
YES
Is oxygen sensor voltage OK?
NO
PC: Oxygen sensor malfunction
YES
Is same Code No. present after performing after-repair procedure?
NO
Feedback system OK
YES
Is engine control unit 2D terminal voltage OK?
NO
PC: Open or short circuit in wiring harness between oxygen sensor and engine control unit 2D terminal
YES
PC: Engine control unit malfunction

Courtesy of Mazda Motors Corp.

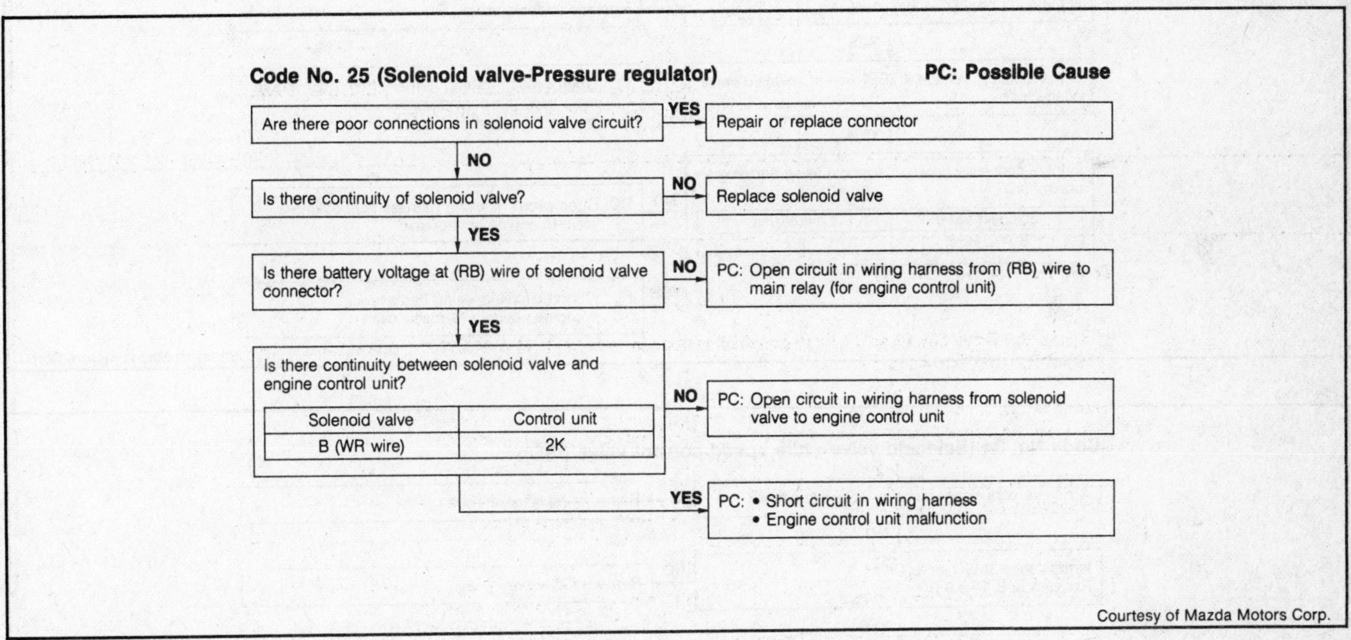
Code No. 25 (Solenoid valve-Pressure regulator)
PC: Possible Cause
Are there poor connections in solenoid valve circuit?
YES
Repair or replace connector
NO
Is there continuity of solenoid valve?
NO
Replace solenoid valve
YES
Is there battery voltage at (RB) wire of solenoid valve connector?
NO
PC: Open circuit in wiring harness from (RB) wire to main relay (for engine control unit)
YES
Is there continuity between solenoid valve and engine control unit?
Solenoid valve | Control unit
B (WR wire) | 2K
NO
PC: Open circuit in wiring harness from solenoid valve to engine control unit
YES
PC: • Short circuit in wiring harness
• Engine control unit malfunction

Courtesy of Mazda Motors Corp.

## NON-TURBO TROUBLE CODES (Cont.)

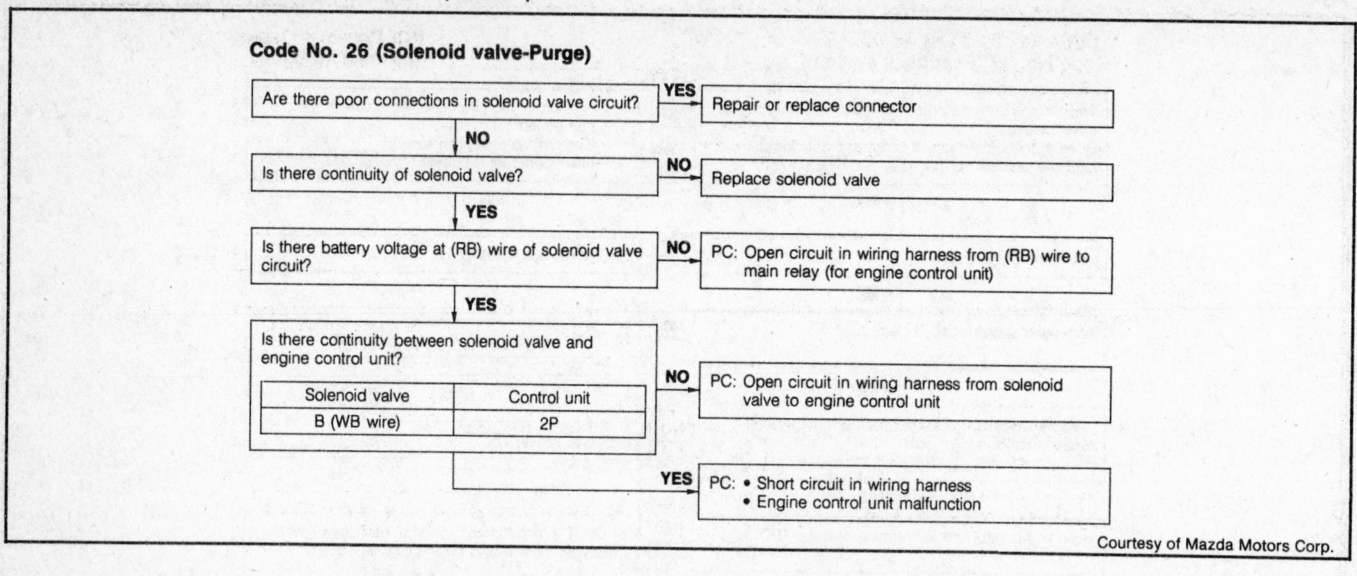
Code No. 26 (Solenoid valve-Purge)
Are there poor connections in solenoid valve circuit?
YES
Repair or replace connector
NO
Is there continuity of solenoid valve?
NO
Replace solenoid valve
YES
Is there battery voltage at (RB) wire of solenoid valve circuit?
NO
PC: Open circuit in wiring harness from (RB) wire to main relay (for engine control unit)
YES
Is there continuity between solenoid valve and engine control unit?
Solenoid valve
Control unit
B (WB wire)
2P
NO
PC: Open circuit in wiring harness from solenoid valve to engine control unit
YES
PC: • Short circuit in wiring harness
• Engine control unit malfunction
Courtesy of Mazda Motors Corp.

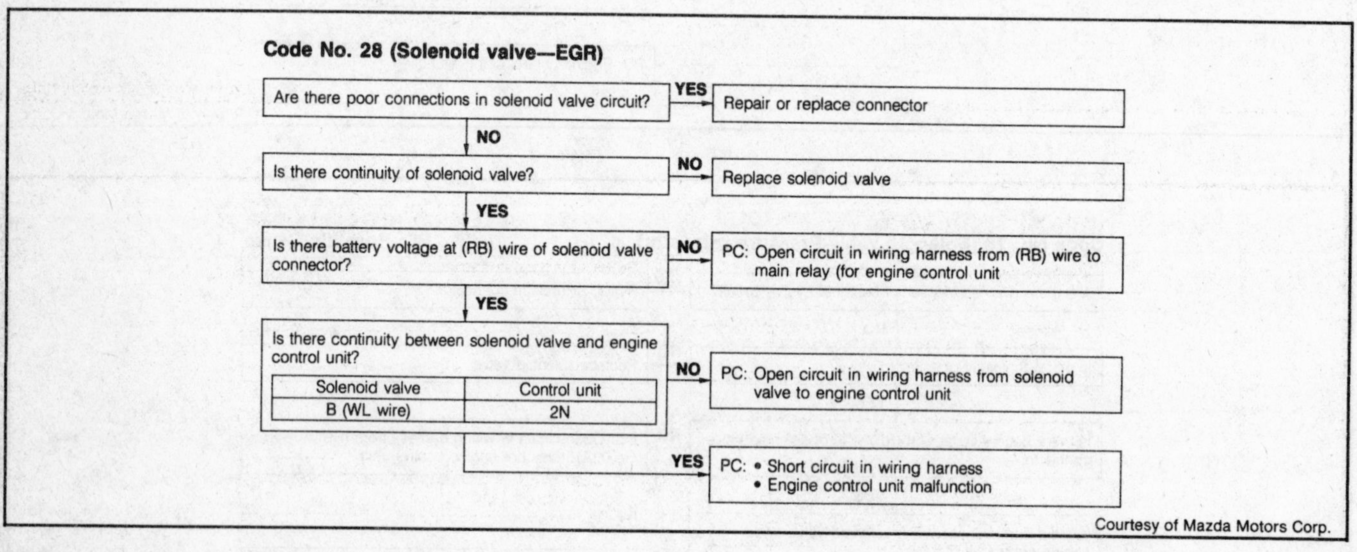
Code No. 28 (Solenoid valve—EGR)
Are there poor connections in solenoid valve circuit?
YES
Repair or replace connector
NO
Is there continuity of solenoid valve?
NO
Replace solenoid valve
YES
Is there battery voltage at (RB) wire of solenoid valve connector?
NO
PC: Open circuit in wiring harness from (RB) wire to main relay (for engine control unit
YES
Is there continuity between solenoid valve and engine control unit?
Solenoid valve
Control unit
B (WL wire)
2N
NO
PC: Open circuit in wiring harness from solenoid valve to engine control unit
YES
PC: • Short circuit in wiring harness
• Engine control unit malfunction
Courtesy of Mazda Motors Corp.

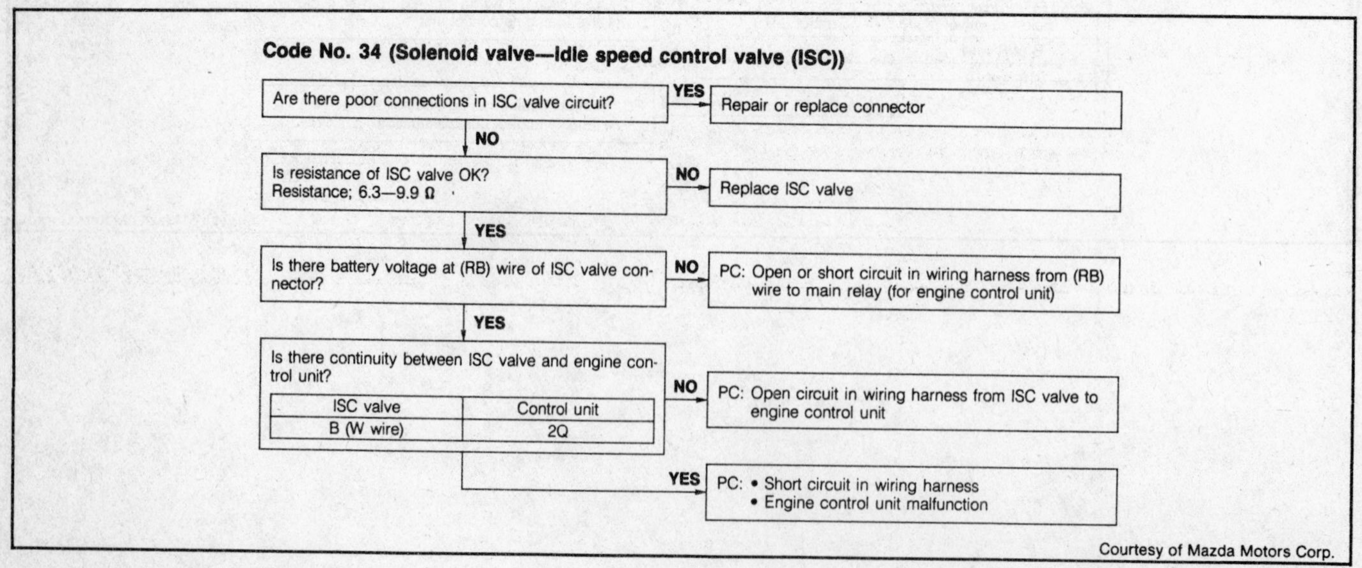
Code No. 34 (Solenoid valve—idle speed control valve (ISC))
Are there poor connections in ISC valve circuit?
YES
Repair or replace connector
NO
Is resistance of ISC valve OK?
Resistance; 6.3—9.9 Ω
NO
Replace ISC valve
YES
Is there battery voltage at (RB) wire of ISC valve connector?
NO
PC: Open or short circuit in wiring harness from (RB) wire to main relay (for engine control unit)
YES
Is there continuity between ISC valve and engine control unit?
ISC valve
Control unit
B (W wire)
2Q
NO
PC: Open circuit in wiring harness from ISC valve to engine control unit
YES
PC: • Short circuit in wiring harness
• Engine control unit malfunction
Courtesy of Mazda Motors Corp.

## TURBO TROUBLE CODES

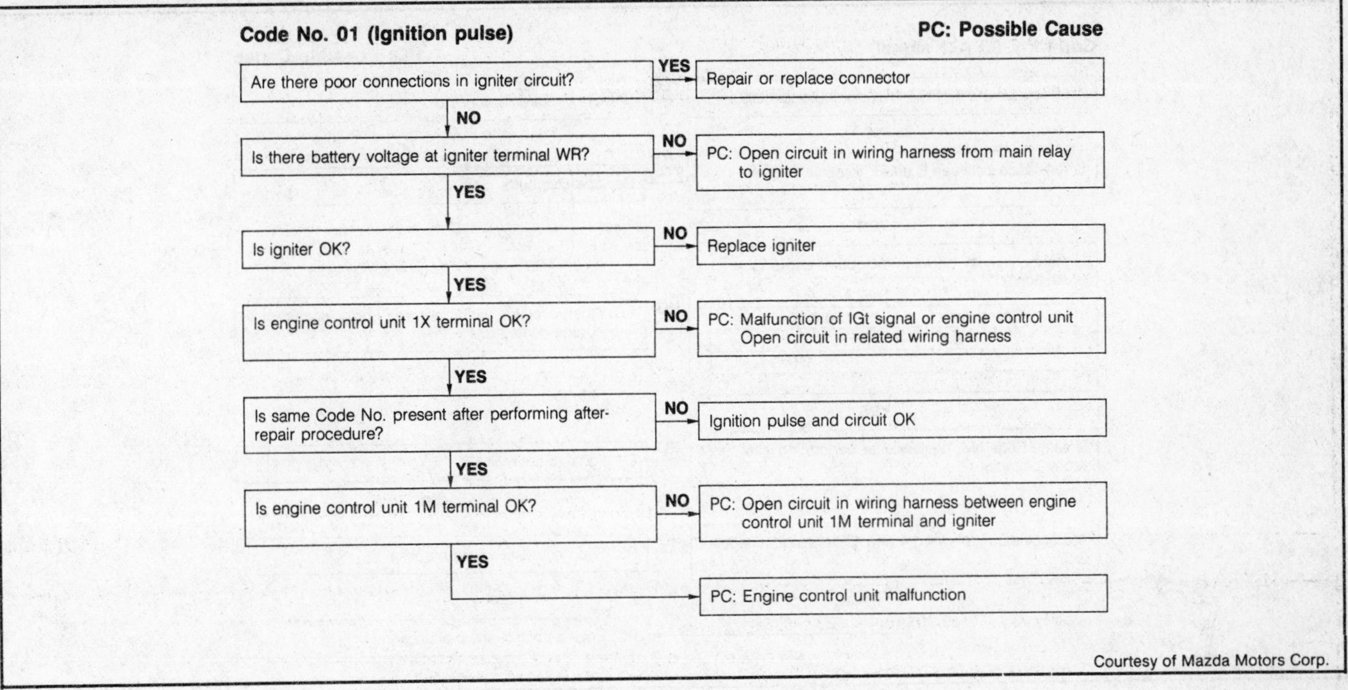
Code No. 01 (Ignition pulse)
PC: Possible Cause
Are there poor connections in igniter circuit?
YES
Repair or replace connector
NO
Is there battery voltage at igniter terminal WR?
NO
PC: Open circuit in wiring harness from main relay to igniter
YES
Is igniter OK?
NO
Replace igniter
YES
Is engine control unit 1X terminal OK?
NO
PC: Malfunction of IGt signal or engine control unit Open circuit in related wiring harness
YES
Is same Code No. present after performing after-repair procedure?
NO
Ignition pulse and circuit OK
YES
Is engine control unit 1M terminal OK?
NO
PC: Open circuit in wiring harness between engine control unit 1M terminal and igniter
YES
PC: Engine control unit malfunction

Courtesy of Mazda Motors Corp.

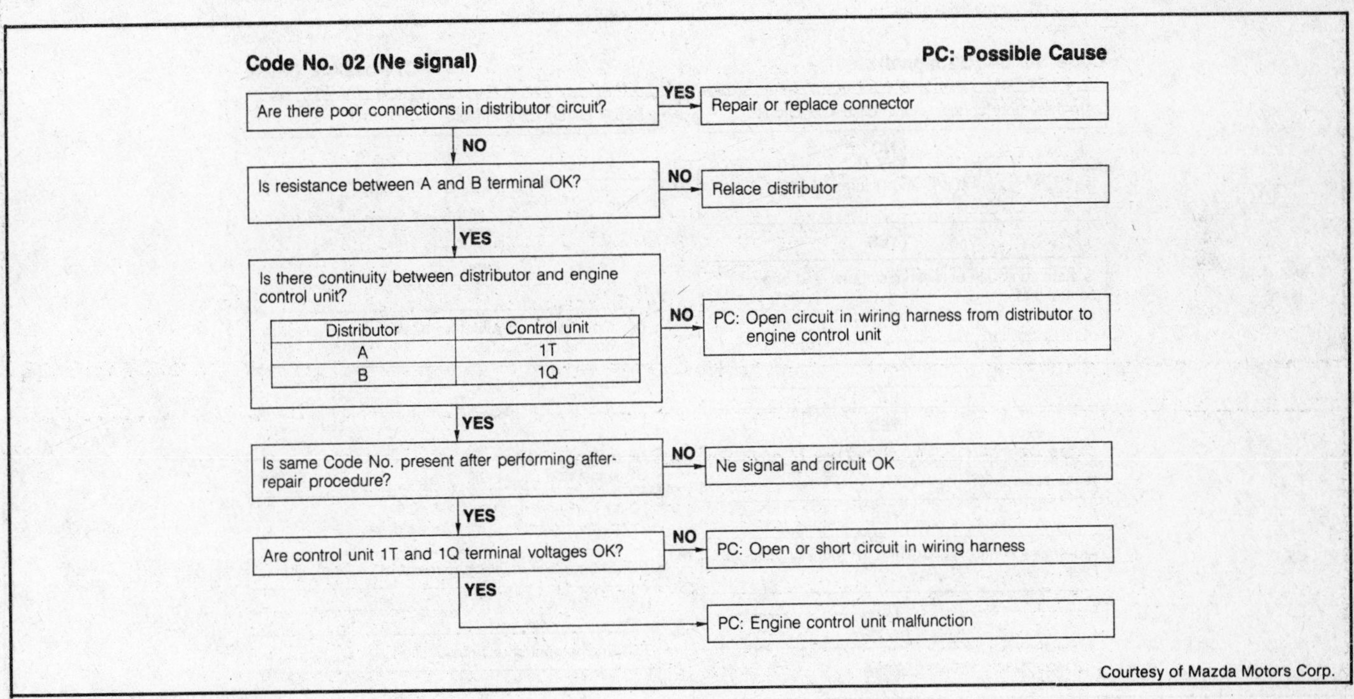
Code No. 02 (Ne signal)
PC: Possible Cause
Are there poor connections in distributor circuit?
YES
Repair or replace connector
NO
Is resistance between A and B terminal OK?
NO
Relace distributor
YES
Is there continuity between distributor and engine control unit?
Distributor | Control unit
A | 1T
B | 1Q
NO
PC: Open circuit in wiring harness from distributor to engine control unit
YES
Is same Code No. present after performing after-repair procedure?
NO
Ne signal and circuit OK
YES
Are control unit 1T and 1Q terminal voltages OK?
NO
PC: Open or short circuit in wiring harness
YES
PC: Engine control unit malfunction

Courtesy of Mazda Motors Corp.

## TURBO TROUBLE CODES (Cont.)

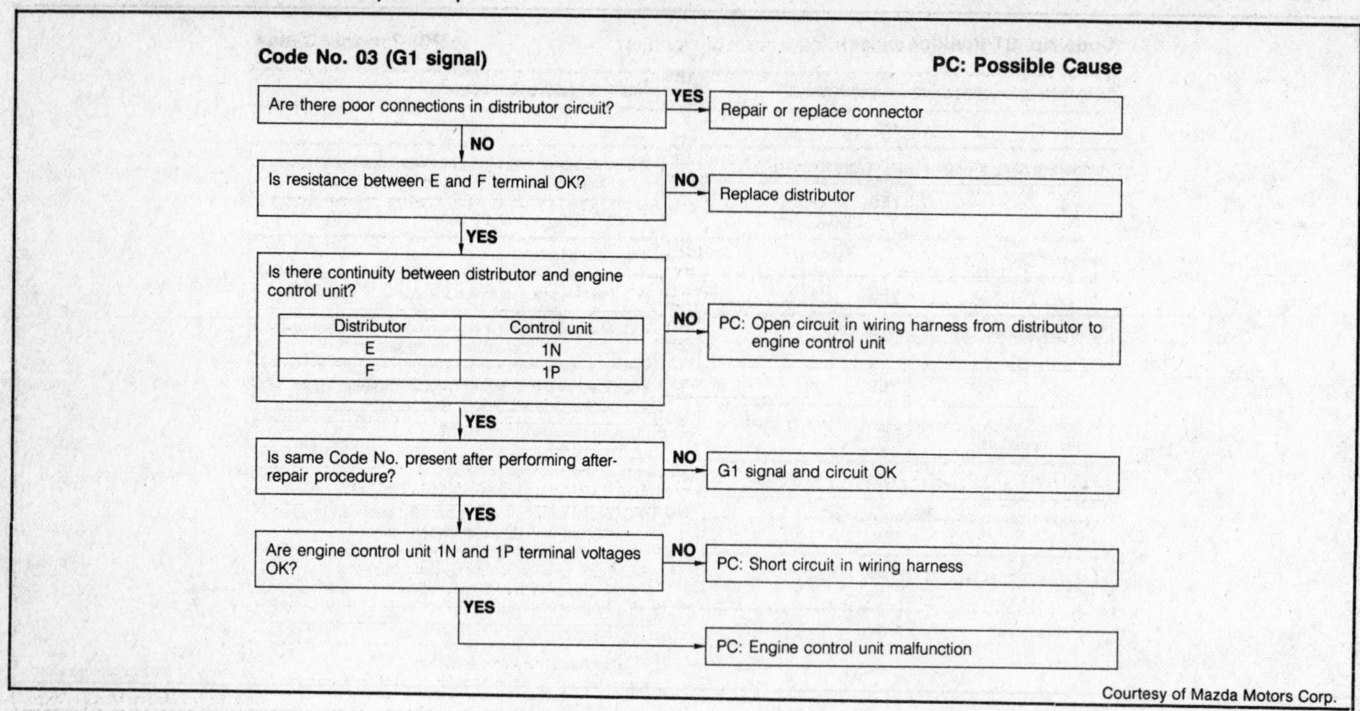
Code No. 03 (G1 signal)
PC: Possible Cause
Are there poor connections in distributor circuit?
YES
Repair or replace connector
NO
Is resistance between E and F terminal OK?
NO
Replace distributor
YES
Is there continuity between distributor and engine control unit?
Distributor | Control unit
E | 1N
F | 1P
NO
PC: Open circuit in wiring harness from distributor to engine control unit
YES
Is same Code No. present after performing after-repair procedure?
NO
G1 signal and circuit OK
YES
Are engine control unit 1N and 1P terminal voltages OK?
NO
PC: Short circuit in wiring harness
YES
PC: Engine control unit malfunction
Courtesy of Mazda Motors Corp.

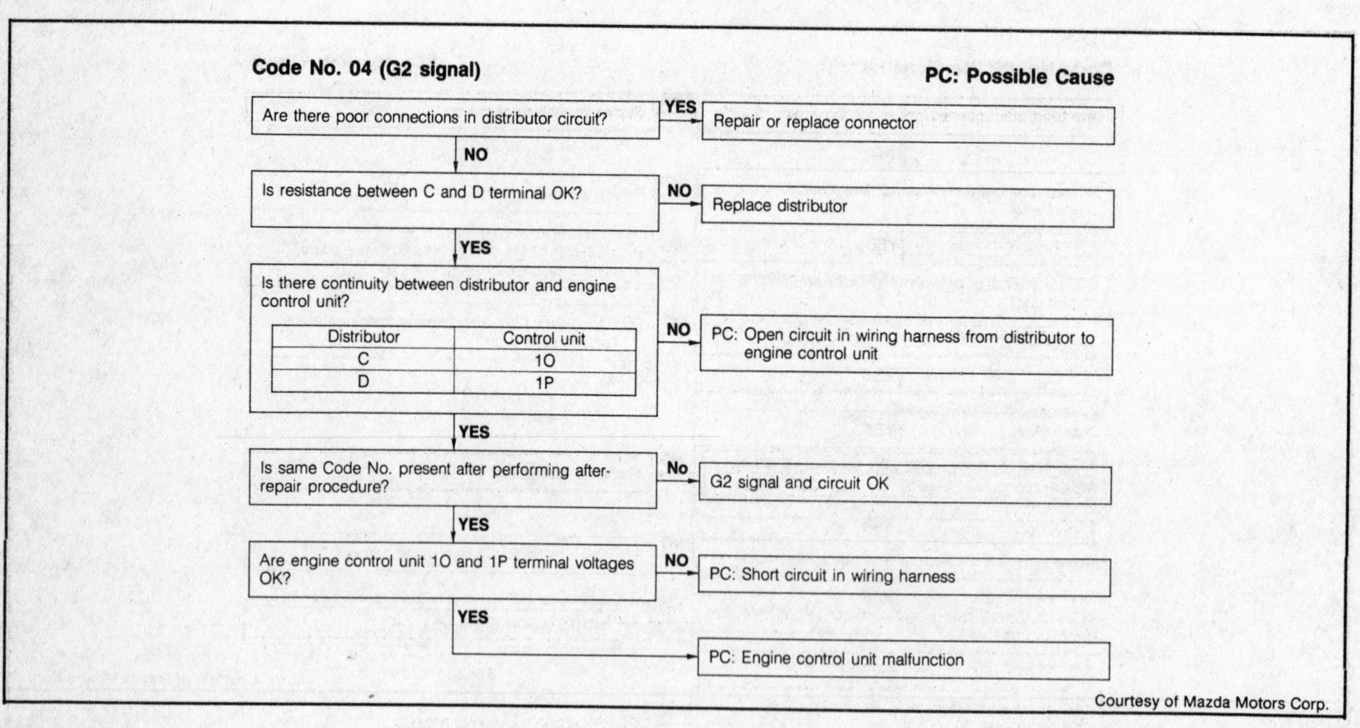
Code No. 04 (G2 signal)
PC: Possible Cause
Are there poor connections in distributor circuit?
YES
Repair or replace connector
NO
Is resistance between C and D terminal OK?
NO
Replace distributor
YES
Is there continuity between distributor and engine control unit?
Distributor | Control unit
C | 1O
D | 1P
NO
PC: Open circuit in wiring harness from distributor to engine control unit
YES
Is same Code No. present after performing after-repair procedure?
No
G2 signal and circuit OK
YES
Are engine control unit 1O and 1P terminal voltages OK?
NO
PC: Short circuit in wiring harness
YES
PC: Engine control unit malfunction
Courtesy of Mazda Motors Corp.

## TURBO TROUBLE CODES (Cont.)

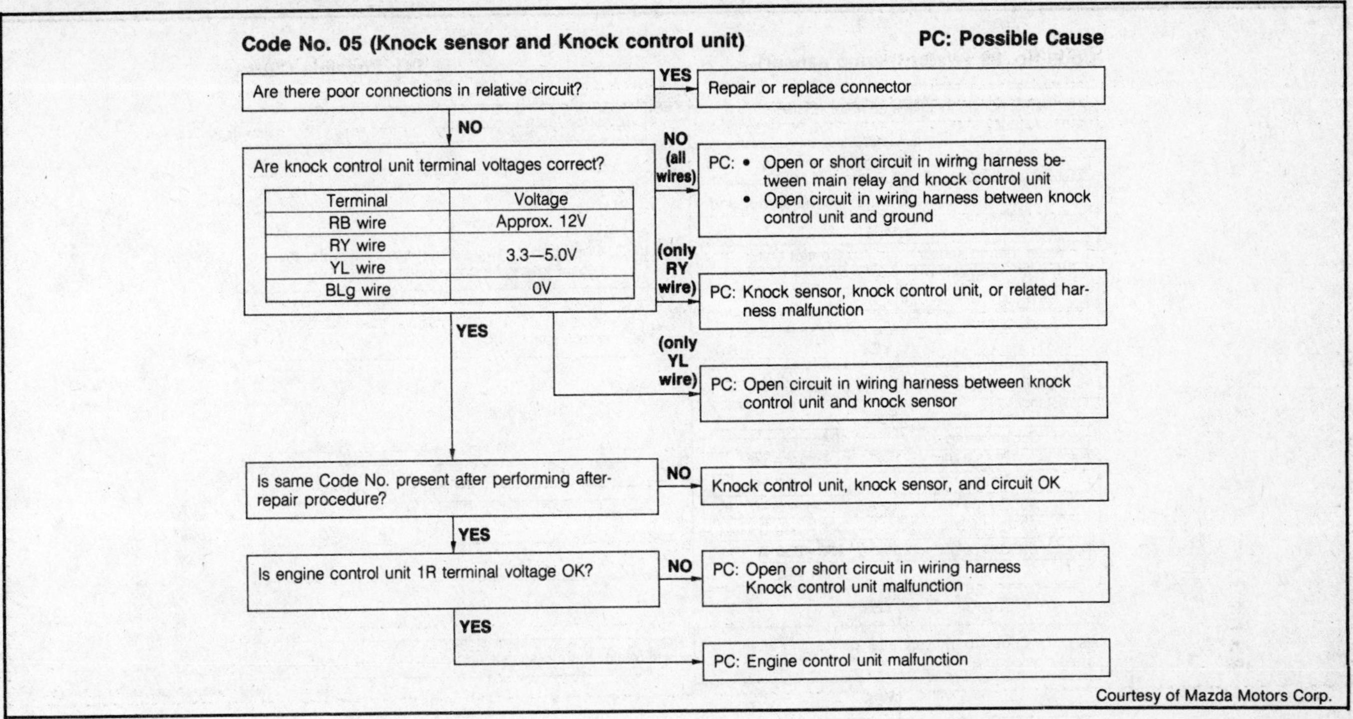

Code No. 05 (Knock sensor and Knock control unit)
PC: Possible Cause
Are there poor connections in relative circuit?
YES
Repair or replace connector
NO
Are knock control unit terminal voltages correct?
Terminal
Voltage
RB wire
Approx. 12V
RY wire
YL wire
3.3—5.0V
BLg wire
0V
NO (all wires)
PC: • Open or short circuit in wiring harness between main relay and knock control unit
• Open circuit in wiring harness between knock control unit and ground
(only RY wire)
PC: Knock sensor, knock control unit, or related harness malfunction
(only YL wire)
PC: Open circuit in wiring harness between knock control unit and knock sensor
YES
Is same Code No. present after performing after-repair procedure?
NO
Knock control unit, knock sensor, and circuit OK
YES
Is engine control unit 1R terminal voltage OK?
NO
PC: Open or short circuit in wiring harness
Knock control unit malfunction
YES
PC: Engine control unit malfunction


Courtesy of Mazda Motors Corp.

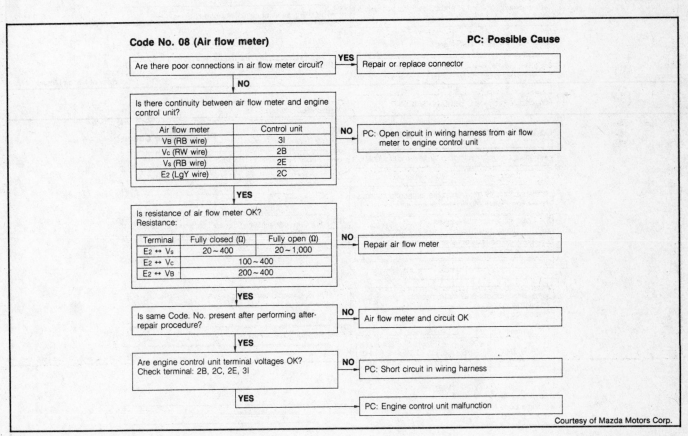

**Code No. 08 (Air flow meter)** — **PC: Possible Cause**

Are there poor connections in air flow meter circuit?
- YES → Repair or replace connector
- NO ↓

Is there continuity between air flow meter and engine control unit?

| Air flow meter | Control unit |
|---|---|
| $V_B$ (RB wire) | 3I |
| $V_C$ (RW wire) | 2B |
| $V_S$ (RB wire) | 2E |
| $E_2$ (LgY wire) | 2C |

- NO → PC: Open circuit in wiring harness from air flow meter to engine control unit
- YES ↓

Is resistance of air flow meter OK?
Resistance:

| Terminal | Fully closed (Ω) | Fully open (Ω) |
|---|---|---|
| $E_2 \leftrightarrow V_S$ | 20 ~ 400 | 20 ~ 1,000 |
| $E_2 \leftrightarrow V_C$ | 100 ~ 400 | |
| $E_2 \leftrightarrow V_B$ | 200 ~ 400 | |

- NO → Repair air flow meter
- YES ↓

Is same Code. No. present after performing after-repair procedure?
- NO → Air flow meter and circuit OK
- YES ↓

Are engine control unit terminal voltages OK?
Check terminal: 2B, 2C, 2E, 3I
- NO → PC: Short circuit in wiring harness
- YES → PC: Engine control unit malfunction

Courtesy of Mazda Motors Corp.

## TURBO TROUBLE CODES (Cont.)

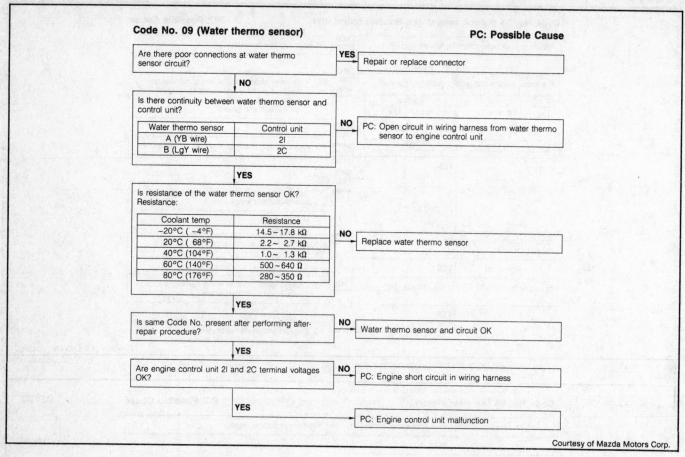

### Code No. 09 (Water thermo sensor)

**PC: Possible Cause**

Are there poor connections at water thermo sensor circuit?
- **YES** → Repair or replace connector
- **NO** ↓

Is there continuity between water thermo sensor and control unit?

| Water thermo sensor | Control unit |
|---|---|
| A (YB wire) | 2I |
| B (LgY wire) | 2C |

- **NO** → PC: Open circuit in wiring harness from water thermo sensor to engine control unit
- **YES** ↓

Is resistance of the water thermo sensor OK?
Resistance:

| Coolant temp | Resistance |
|---|---|
| −20°C ( −4°F) | 14.5 ~ 17.8 kΩ |
| 20°C ( 68°F) | 2.2 ~ 2.7 kΩ |
| 40°C (104°F) | 1.0 ~ 1.3 kΩ |
| 60°C (140°F) | 500 ~ 640 Ω |
| 80°C (176°F) | 280 ~ 350 Ω |

- **NO** → Replace water thermo sensor
- **YES** ↓

Is same Code No. present after performing after-repair procedure?
- **NO** → Water thermo sensor and circuit OK
- **YES** ↓

Are engine control unit 2I and 2C terminal voltages OK?
- **NO** → PC: Engine short circuit in wiring harness
- **YES** → PC: Engine control unit malfunction

Courtesy of Mazda Motors Corp.

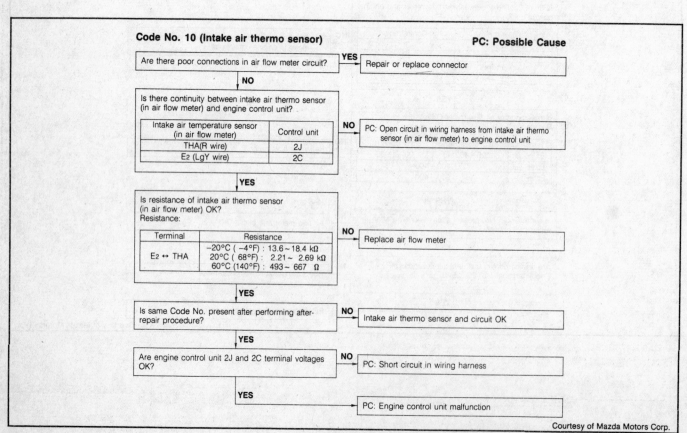

### Code No. 10 (Intake air thermo sensor)

**PC: Possible Cause**

Are there poor connections in air flow meter circuit?
- **YES** → Repair or replace connector
- **NO** ↓

Is there continuity between intake air thermo sensor (in air flow meter) and engine control unit?

| Intake air temperature sensor (in air flow meter) | Control unit |
|---|---|
| THA(R wire) | 2J |
| $E_2$ (LgY wire) | 2C |

- **NO** → PC: Open circuit in wiring harness from intake air thermo sensor (in air flow meter) to engine control unit
- **YES** ↓

Is resistance of intake air thermo sensor (in air flow meter) OK?
Resistance:

| Terminal | Resistance |
|---|---|
| $E_2$ ↔ THA | −20°C ( −4°F) : 13.6 ~ 18.4 kΩ<br>20°C ( 68°F) : 2.21 ~ 2.69 kΩ<br>60°C (140°F) : 493 ~ 667 Ω |

- **NO** → Replace air flow meter
- **YES** ↓

Is same Code No. present after performing after-repair procedure?
- **NO** → Intake air thermo sensor and circuit OK
- **YES** ↓

Are engine control unit 2J and 2C terminal voltages OK?
- **NO** → PC: Short circuit in wiring harness
- **YES** → PC: Engine control unit malfunction

Courtesy of Mazda Motors Corp.

# 1988 COMPUTERIZED ENGINE CONTROL
# Mazda – MX-6 & 626 EGI (Cont.)

## TURBO TROUBLE CODES (Cont.)

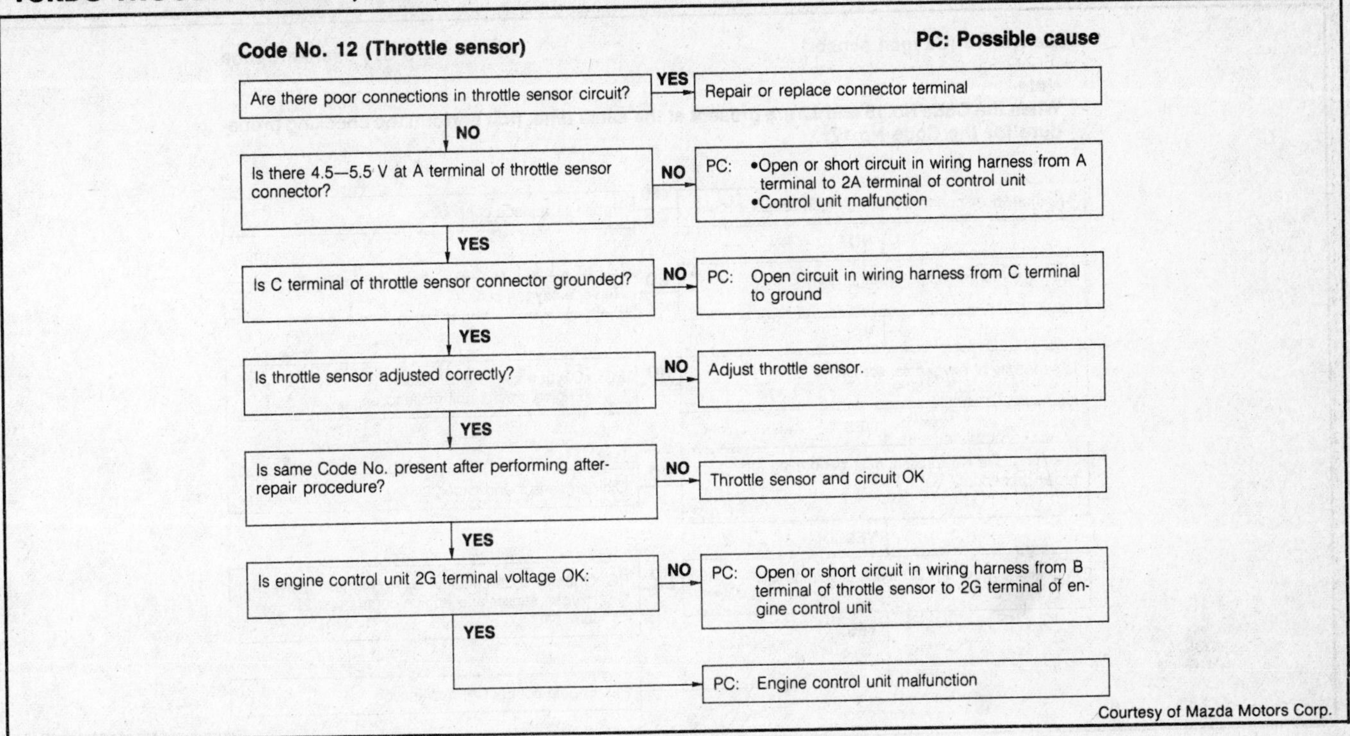
Code No. 12 (Throttle sensor)
PC: Possible cause
Are there poor connections in throttle sensor circuit?
YES
Repair or replace connector terminal
NO
Is there 4.5—5.5 V at A terminal of throttle sensor connector?
NO
PC: •Open or short circuit in wiring harness from A terminal to 2A terminal of control unit
•Control unit malfunction
YES
Is C terminal of throttle sensor connector grounded?
NO
PC: Open circuit in wiring harness from C terminal to ground
YES
Is throttle sensor adjusted correctly?
NO
Adjust throttle sensor.
YES
Is same Code No. present after performing after-repair procedure?
NO
Throttle sensor and circuit OK
YES
Is engine control unit 2G terminal voltage OK:
NO
PC: Open or short circuit in wiring harness from B terminal of throttle sensor to 2G terminal of engine control unit
YES
PC: Engine control unit malfunction

Courtesy of Mazda Motors Corp.

**Code No. 14 (Atmospheric pressure sensor)**

**PC: Possible cause**

Are there poor connections in atmospheric pressure sensor circut?
- **YES** → Repair or replace connector
- **NO** ↓

Is there Vref at (LgR) wire of atmospheric pressure sensor connector? Vref: 4.5—5.5V
- **NO** → PC: Open or short circuit in wiring harness from (LgR) wire to engine control unit
  - Engine control unit malfunction (If 2A terminal voltage not 4.5—5.5V)
- **YES** ↓

Is voltage at (Y) wire of atmospheric pressure sensor connector OK?
Voltage: 3.5—4.5V.....at sea level
2.5—3.5V.....at high altitude (2,000 m (6,500 ft) )
- **NO (0V)** → PC: Short circuit in wiring harness from atmospheric pressure sensor (Y) wire to engine control unit (2H) terminal.
- **NO (Others)** → Replace atmospheric pressure sensor.
- **YES** ↓

Is there continuity between atmospheric pressure sensor to engine control unit?

| Atmospheric pressure sensor | Control unit |
|---|---|
| A (LgY wire) | 2C |
| D (Y wire) | 2H |

- **NO** → PC: Open circuit in wiring harness from atmospheric pressure sensor to engine control unit
- **YES** ↓

Is same Code No. present after performing after-repair procedure?
- **NO** → Atmospheric pressure sensor and circuit OK
- **YES** ↓

Are engine control unit 2C and 2H terminal voltages OK?
- **NO** → PC: Short circuit in wiring harness
- **YES** → PC: Engine control unit malfunction

Courtesy of Mazda Motors Corp.

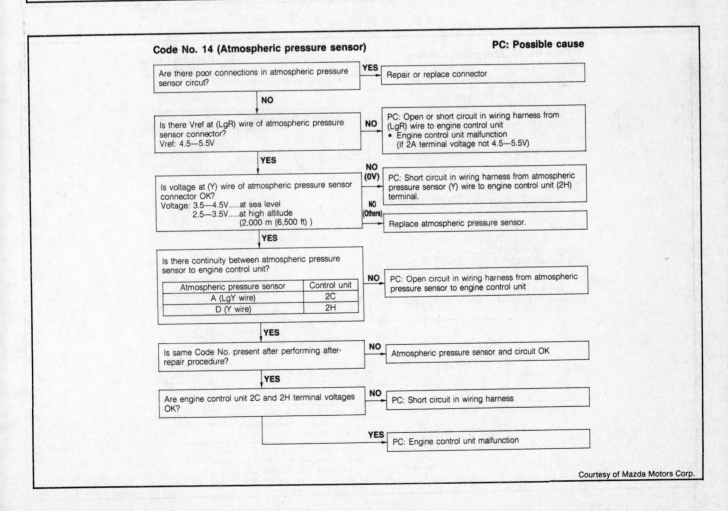

## TURBO TROUBLE CODES (Cont.)

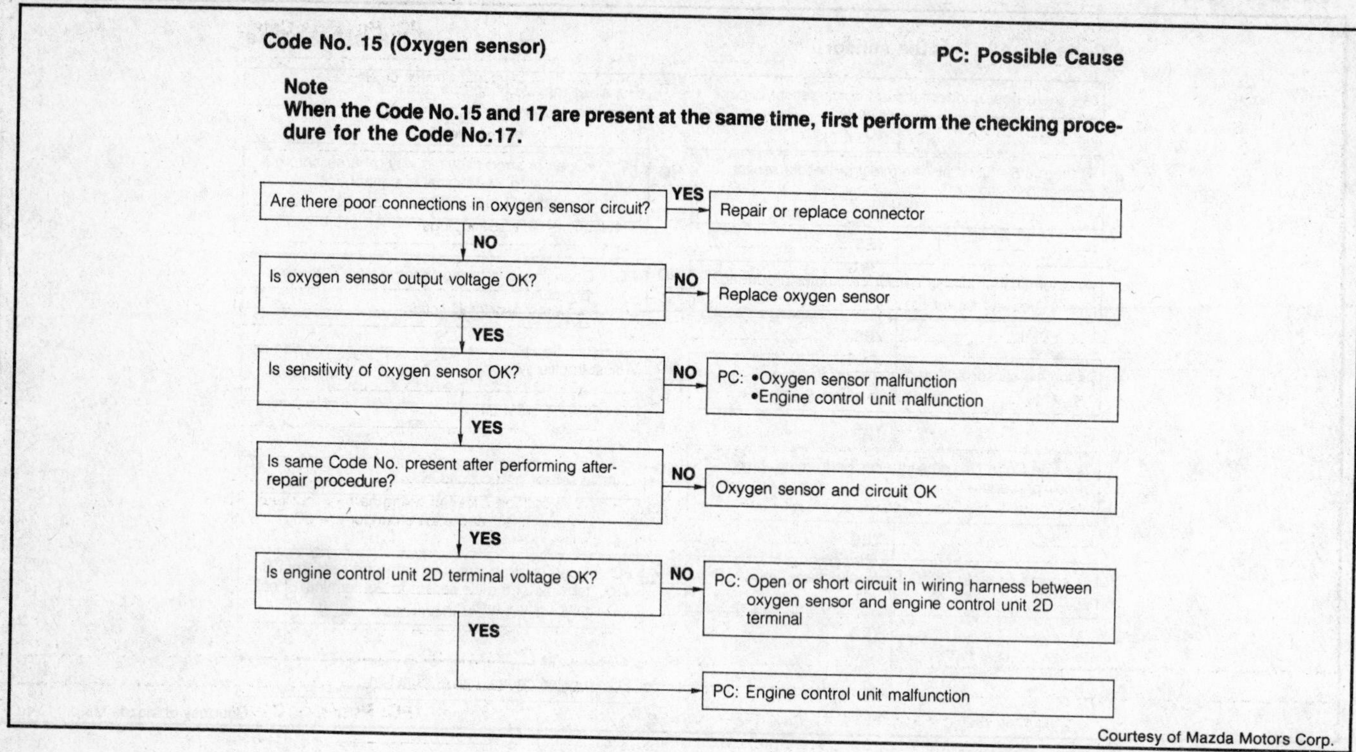
Code No. 15 (Oxygen sensor)
PC: Possible Cause
Note
When the Code No.15 and 17 are present at the same time, first perform the checking procedure for the Code No.17.
Are there poor connections in oxygen sensor circuit?
YES
Repair or replace connector
NO
Is oxygen sensor output voltage OK?
NO
Replace oxygen sensor
YES
Is sensitivity of oxygen sensor OK?
NO
PC: •Oxygen sensor malfunction
•Engine control unit malfunction
YES
Is same Code No. present after performing after-repair procedure?
NO
Oxygen sensor and circuit OK
YES
Is engine control unit 2D terminal voltage OK?
NO
PC: Open or short circuit in wiring harness between oxygen sensor and engine control unit 2D terminal
YES
PC: Engine control unit malfunction

Courtesy of Mazda Motors Corp.

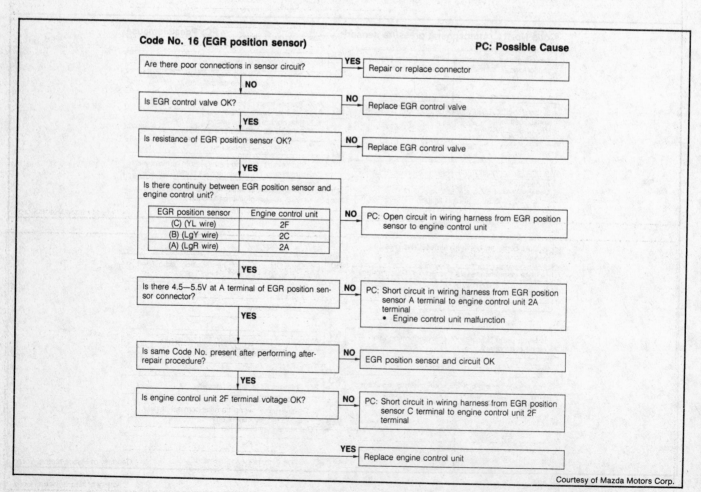

**Code No. 16 (EGR position sensor)**

PC: Possible Cause

- Are there poor connections in sensor circuit?
  - YES → Repair or replace connector
  - NO ↓
- Is EGR control valve OK?
  - NO → Replace EGR control valve
  - YES ↓
- Is resistance of EGR position sensor OK?
  - NO → Replace EGR control valve
  - YES ↓
- Is there continuity between EGR position sensor and engine control unit?

| EGR position sensor | Engine control unit |
|---|---|
| (C) (YL wire) | 2F |
| (B) (LgY wire) | 2C |
| (A) (LgR wire) | 2A |

  - NO → PC: Open circuit in wiring harness from EGR position sensor to engine control unit
  - YES ↓
- Is there 4.5—5.5V at A terminal of EGR position sensor connector?
  - NO → PC: Short circuit in wiring harness from EGR position sensor A terminal to engine control unit 2A terminal
    • Engine control unit malfunction
  - YES ↓
- Is same Code No. present after performing after-repair procedure?
  - NO → EGR position sensor and circuit OK
  - YES ↓
- Is engine control unit 2F terminal voltage OK?
  - NO → PC: Short circuit in wiring harness from EGR position sensor C terminal to engine control unit 2F terminal
  - YES → Replace engine control unit

Courtesy of Mazda Motors Corp.

## TURBO TROUBLE CODES (Cont.)

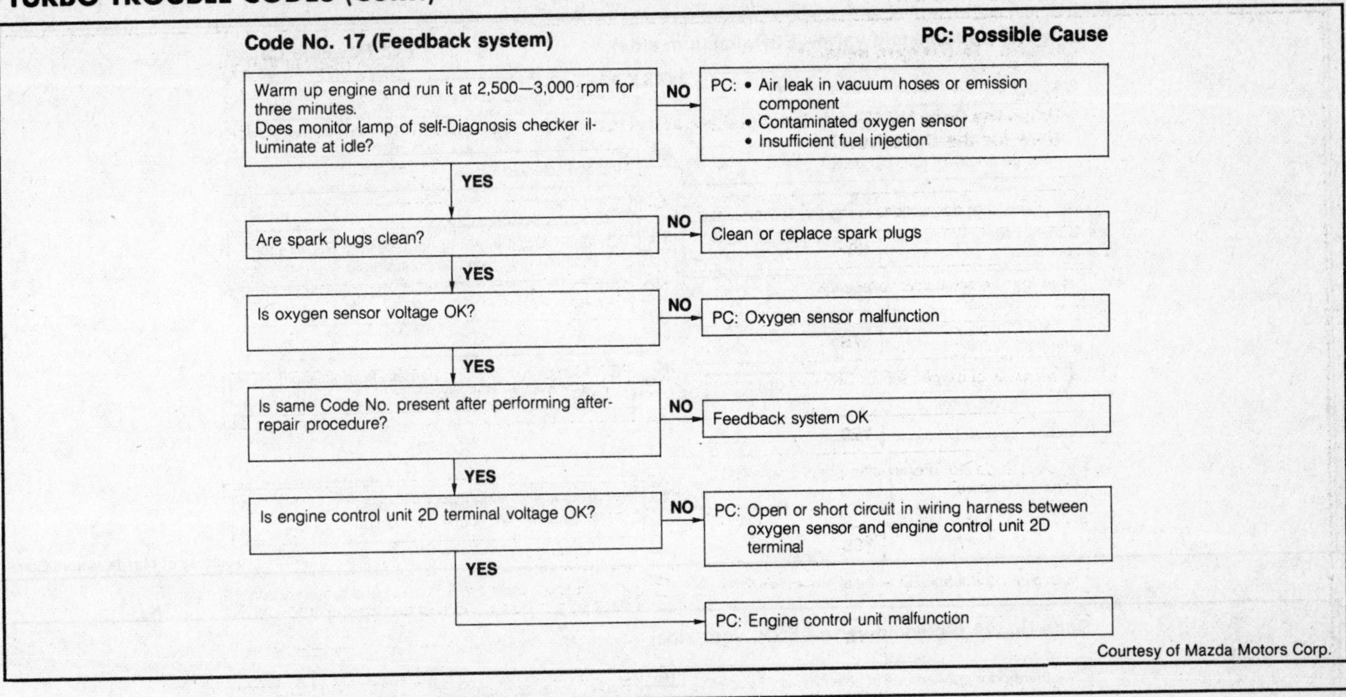
Code No. 17 (Feedback system)
PC: Possible Cause
Warm up engine and run it at 2,500—3,000 rpm for three minutes.
Does monitor lamp of self-Diagnosis checker illuminate at idle?
NO
PC: • Air leak in vacuum hoses or emission component
• Contaminated oxygen sensor
• Insufficient fuel injection
YES
Are spark plugs clean?
NO
Clean or replace spark plugs
YES
Is oxygen sensor voltage OK?
NO
PC: Oxygen sensor malfunction
YES
Is same Code No. present after performing after-repair procedure?
NO
Feedback system OK
YES
Is engine control unit 2D terminal voltage OK?
NO
PC: Open or short circuit in wiring harness between oxygen sensor and engine control unit 2D terminal
YES
PC: Engine control unit malfunction
Courtesy of Mazda Motors Corp.

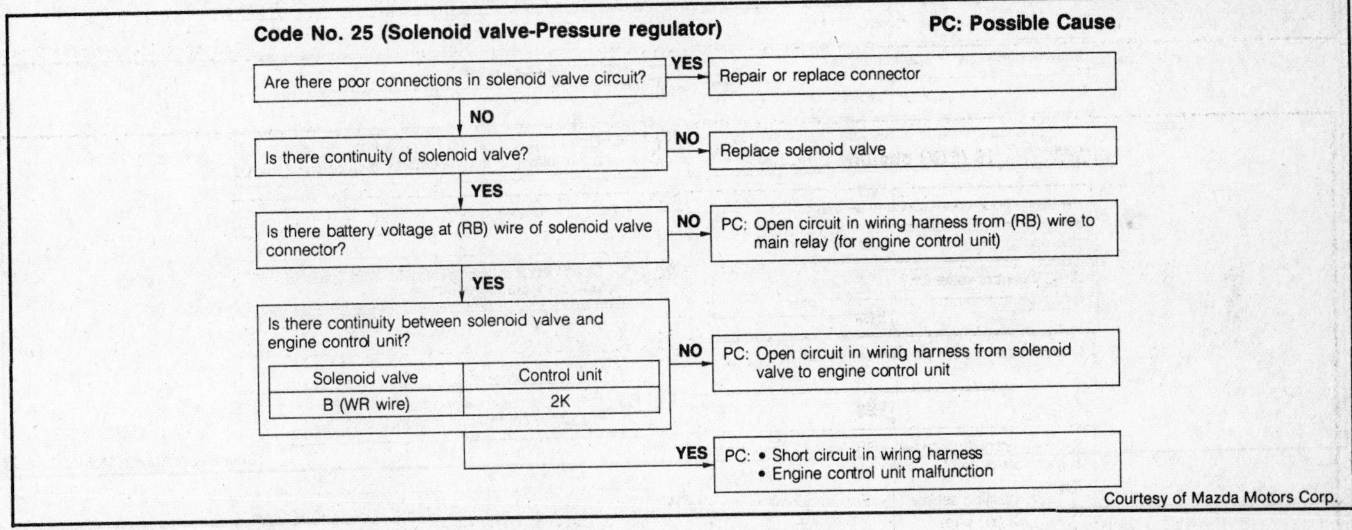
Code No. 25 (Solenoid valve-Pressure regulator)
PC: Possible Cause
Are there poor connections in solenoid valve circuit?
YES
Repair or replace connector
NO
Is there continuity of solenoid valve?
NO
Replace solenoid valve
YES
Is there battery voltage at (RB) wire of solenoid valve connector?
NO
PC: Open circuit in wiring harness from (RB) wire to main relay (for engine control unit)
YES
Is there continuity between solenoid valve and engine control unit?
Solenoid valve | Control unit
B (WR wire) | 2K
NO
PC: Open circuit in wiring harness from solenoid valve to engine control unit
YES
PC: • Short circuit in wiring harness
• Engine control unit malfunction
Courtesy of Mazda Motors Corp.

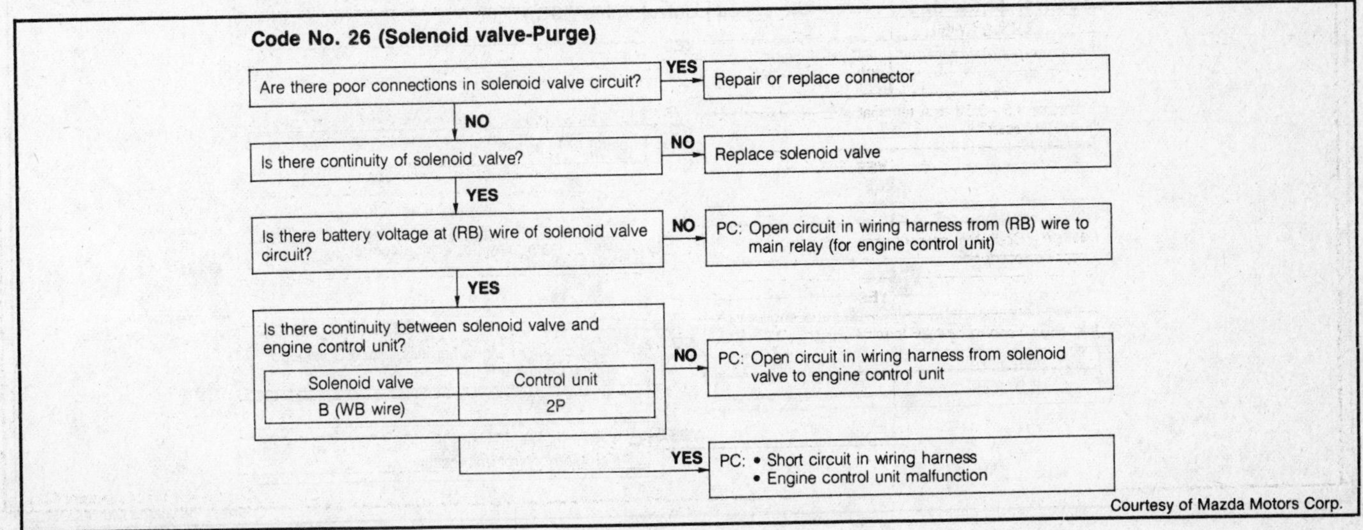
Code No. 26 (Solenoid valve-Purge)
Are there poor connections in solenoid valve circuit?
YES
Repair or replace connector
NO
Is there continuity of solenoid valve?
NO
Replace solenoid valve
YES
Is there battery voltage at (RB) wire of solenoid valve circuit?
NO
PC: Open circuit in wiring harness from (RB) wire to main relay (for engine control unit)
YES
Is there continuity between solenoid valve and engine control unit?
Solenoid valve | Control unit
B (WB wire) | 2P
NO
PC: Open circuit in wiring harness from solenoid valve to engine control unit
YES
PC: • Short circuit in wiring harness
• Engine control unit malfunction
Courtesy of Mazda Motors Corp.

## TURBO TROUBLE CODES (Cont.)

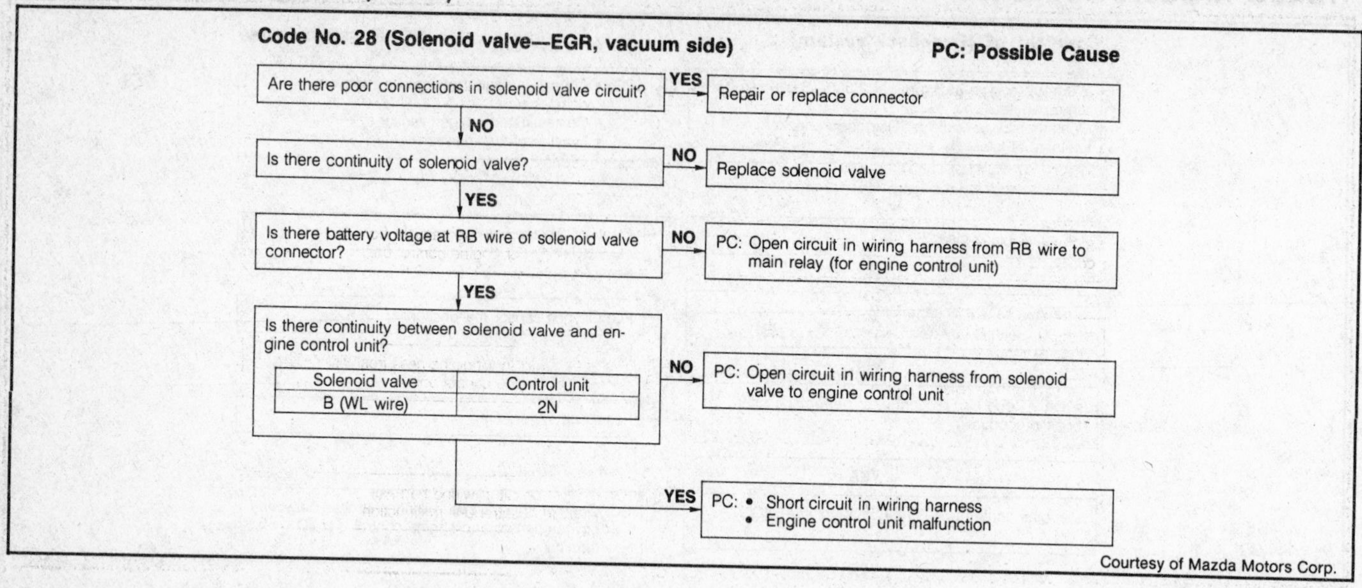
Code No. 28 (Solenoid valve—EGR, vacuum side)
PC: Possible Cause
Are there poor connections in solenoid valve circuit?
YES
Repair or replace connector
NO
Is there continuity of solenoid valve?
NO
Replace solenoid valve
YES
Is there battery voltage at RB wire of solenoid valve connector?
NO
PC: Open circuit in wiring harness from RB wire to main relay (for engine control unit)
YES
Is there continuity between solenoid valve and engine control unit?
Solenoid valve | Control unit
B (WL wire) | 2N
NO
PC: Open circuit in wiring harness from solenoid valve to engine control unit
YES
PC: • Short circuit in wiring harness
• Engine control unit malfunction
Courtesy of Mazda Motors Corp.

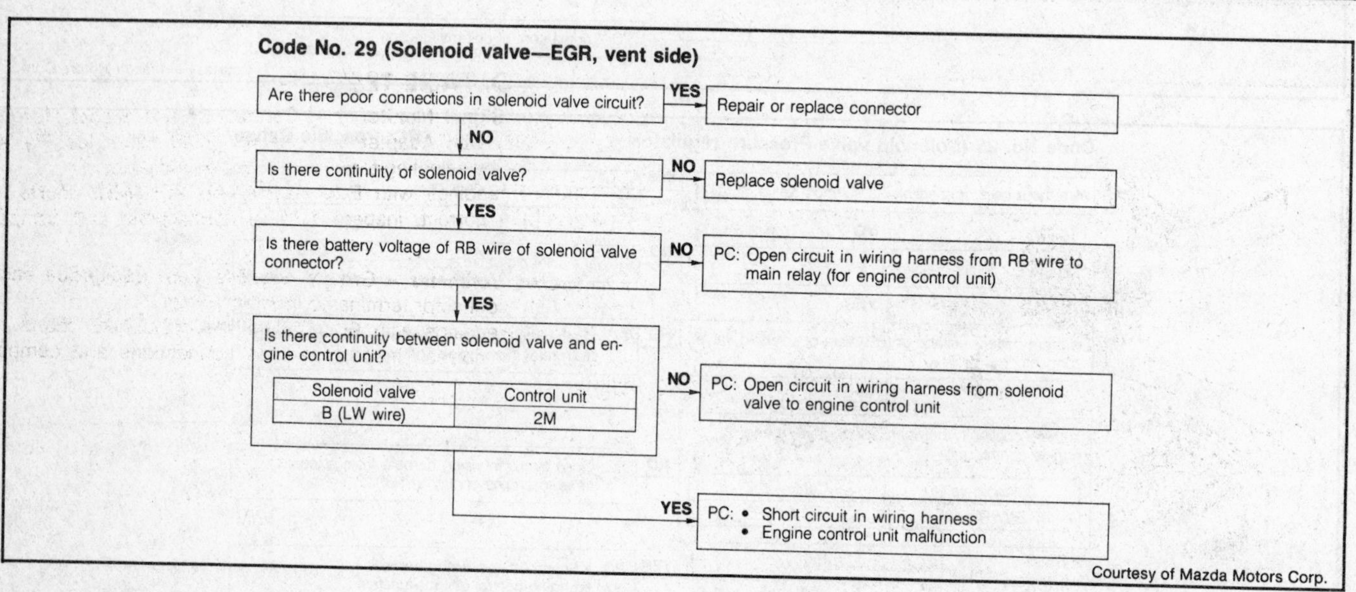
Code No. 29 (Solenoid valve—EGR, vent side)
Are there poor connections in solenoid valve circuit?
YES
Repair or replace connector
NO
Is there continuity of solenoid valve?
NO
Replace solenoid valve
YES
Is there battery voltage of RB wire of solenoid valve connector?
NO
PC: Open circuit in wiring harness from RB wire to main relay (for engine control unit)
YES
Is there continuity between solenoid valve and engine control unit?
Solenoid valve | Control unit
B (LW wire) | 2M
NO
PC: Open circuit in wiring harness from solenoid valve to engine control unit
YES
PC: • Short circuit in wiring harness
• Engine control unit malfunction
Courtesy of Mazda Motors Corp.

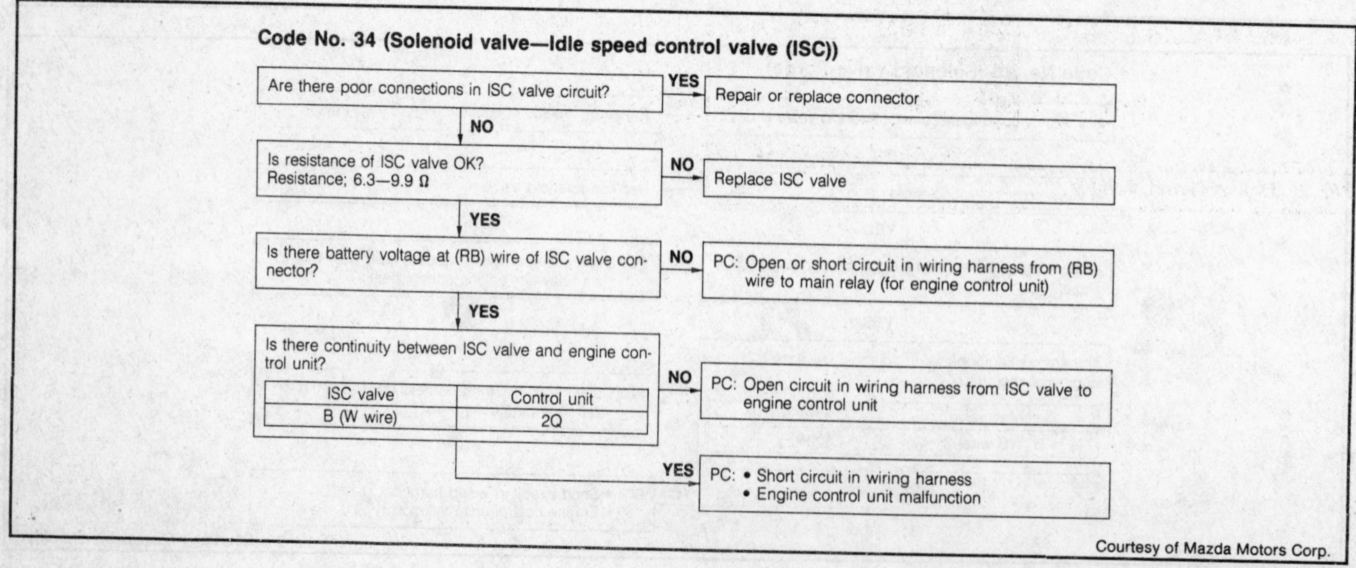
Code No. 34 (Solenoid valve—Idle speed control valve (ISC))
Are there poor connections in ISC valve circuit?
YES
Repair or replace connector
NO
Is resistance of ISC valve OK?
Resistance; 6.3—9.9 Ω
NO
Replace ISC valve
YES
Is there battery voltage at (RB) wire of ISC valve connector?
NO
PC: Open or short circuit in wiring harness from (RB) wire to main relay (for engine control unit)
YES
Is there continuity between ISC valve and engine control unit?
ISC valve | Control unit
B (W wire) | 2Q
NO
PC: Open circuit in wiring harness from ISC valve to engine control unit
YES
PC: • Short circuit in wiring harness
• Engine control unit malfunction
Courtesy of Mazda Motors Corp.

## TURBO TROUBLE CODES (Cont.)

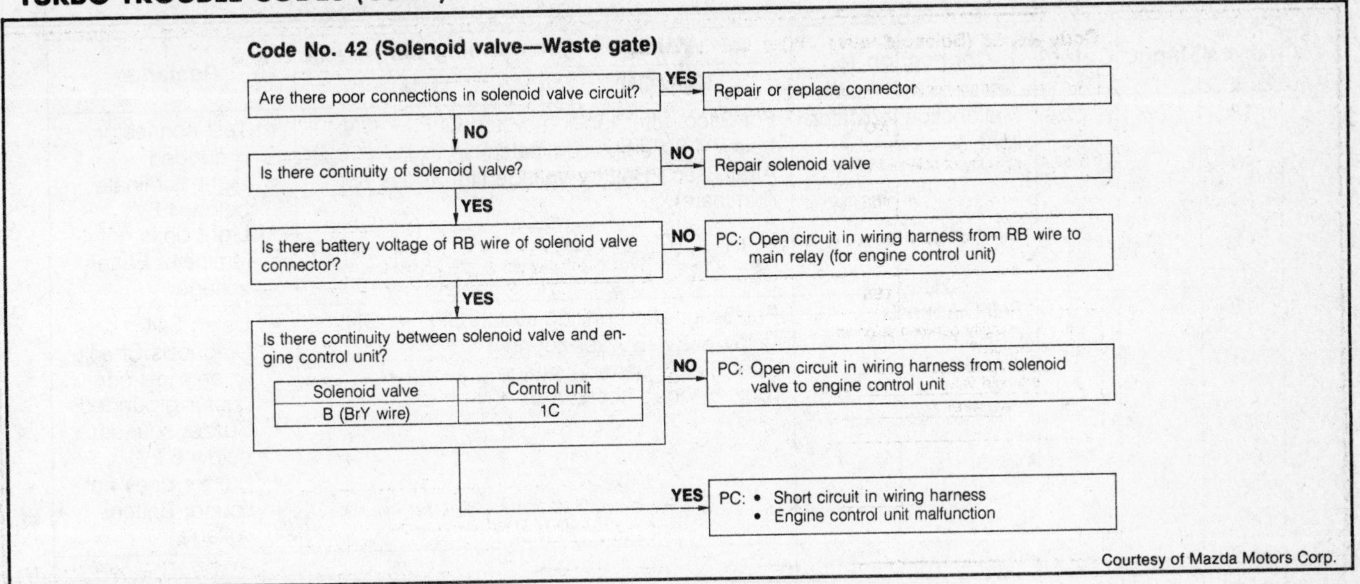
Code No. 42 (Solenoid valve—Waste gate)
Are there poor connections in solenoid valve circuit?
YES
Repair or replace connector
NO
Is there continuity of solenoid valve?
NO
Repair solenoid valve
YES
Is there battery voltage of RB wire of solenoid valve connector?
NO
PC: Open circuit in wiring harness from RB wire to main relay (for engine control unit)
YES
Is there continuity between solenoid valve and engine control unit?
Solenoid valve
Control unit
B (BrY wire)
1C
NO
PC: Open circuit in wiring harness from solenoid valve to engine control unit
YES
PC: • Short circuit in wiring harness
• Engine control unit malfunction

Courtesy of Mazda Motors Corp.

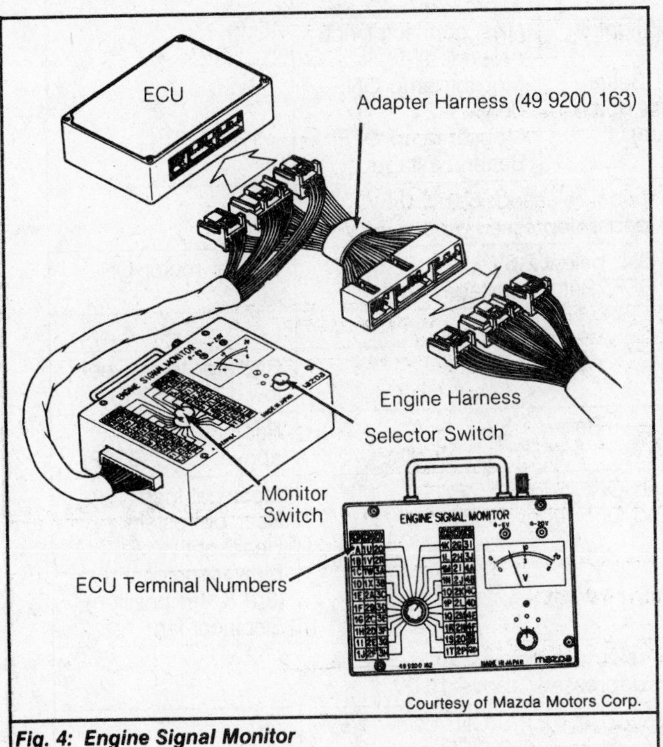
ECU
Adapter Harness (49 9200 163)
Engine Harness
Selector Switch
Monitor Switch
ECU Terminal Numbers
ENGINE SIGNAL MONITOR

Courtesy of Mazda Motors Corp.

*Fig. 4: Engine Signal Monitor*

## ECU VOLTAGE TESTING

**With Engine Signal Monitor** – **1)** Connect Engine Signal Monitor (49 9200 162) with Adapter Harness (49 9200 163). *See Fig. 4.* Check voltage by selecting terminal number on monitor.

**2)** Compare readings with ECU TERMINAL VOLTAGE charts. If voltage is not correct, inspect harness connections and components.

**With Analog Voltmeter** – Ground negative lead. Backprobe each specific ECU connector terminal to monitor voltage.

**2)** Compare readings with ECU TERMINAL VOLTAGE charts. If voltage is not correct, inspect harness connections and components.

## NON-TURBO ECU TERMINAL VOLTAGE

| Terminal | Input | Output | Connection to | Voltage (After warming-up) | | Remarks |
|---|---|---|---|---|---|---|
| | | | | IGN: ON | Idle | |
| 1A | | ○ | Malfunction indicator light | For 3sec. after ignition switch OFF → ON: below 4.8V (light illuminates) After 3sec.: Battery voltage (light does not illuminate) | | • Test connector grounded • Light illuminate: below 4.8V • Light does not illuminate: Battery voltage |
| 1B | | ○ | Self-Diagnosis Checker (Code number) | For 3sec. after ignition switch OFF → ON: below 6.2V (Buzzer sounds) After 3sec.: Battery voltage (Buzzer does not sound) | | • Using Self-Diagnosis Checker and test connector grounded • Buzzer sounds: below 6.2V • Buzzer does not sound: Battery voltage |
| 1C | — | — | — | — | | — |
| 1D | | ○ | Self-Diagnosis Checker (Monitor lamp) | For 3sec. after ignition switch OFF → ON: below 6.2V (light illuminates) After 3sec.: Battery voltage (light does not illuminate) | (Test connector grounded) approx. 5V (Test connector not grounded) Monitor lamp ON: below 6.2V Monitor lamp OFF: Battery voltage | With Self-Diagnosis Checker |
| 1E | ○ | | Idle switch | Accelerator pedal released: below 0.5V Accelerator pedal depressed: above 7.7V | | |
| 1F | | ○ | A/C relay | A/C switch ON: below 2.5V A/C switch OFF: Battery voltage | | Blower motor ON |
| 1G | — | — | — | — | | — |
| 1H | ○ | | Water thermo switch | Above 7.3V | | Radiator temp.: below 17°C (63°F) |
| | | | | Below 1.5V | | Radiator temp.: above 17°C (63°F) |
| 1I | ○ | | Electrical load control unit | Electrical load ON: below 1.5V Electrical load OFF: above 7.3V | | Electrical load: Rear defroster Headlight Blower motor (3rd & 4th position) Electrical fan |
| 1J | ○ | | Brake light switch | Brake pedal released: below 3.6V Brake pedal depressed: above 10.0V | | |
| 1K | ○ | | P/S pressure switch | Constant above 10.5v | P/S ON: below 1.5V P/S OFF: above 10.5V | |
| 1L | ○ | | A/C switch | A/C switch ON: below 1.5V A/C switch OFF: above 10.0V | | Blower motor: ON |
| 1M | ○ | | Ignition coil ⊖ terminal | Battery voltage | *1 Battery voltage | *1 Engine Signal Monitor: green and red lights flash |
| 1N | — | — | — | — | | — |
| 1O | — | — | — | — | | — |

Courtesy of Mazda Motors Corp.

# 1988 COMPUTERIZED ENGINE CONTROLS
# Mazda – MX-6 & 626 EGI (Cont.)

## NON-TURBO ECU TERMINAL VOLTAGE (Cont.)

| Terminal | Input | Output | Connection to | Voltage (After warming-up) IGN: ON | Voltage (After warming-up) Idle | Remarks |
|---|---|---|---|---|---|---|
| 1P | — | — | — | — | | — |
| 1Q | — | — | — | — | | — |
| 1R | — | — | — | — | | — |
| 1S | | ○ | Shift indicator light (MTX) | Battery voltage | | Shift indicator light illuminates: below 4.8V |
| 1T | — | — | — | — | | — |
| 1U | — | — | — | — | | — |
| 1V | ○ | | — | Constant below 1.5V | | MTX |
| | | | | Constant above 10.5V | | ATX |
| 1W | ○ | | Test connector | Test connector grounded: below 0.5V<br>Test connector not grounded: above 10.5V | | Green connector, 1-pin |
| 1X | — | — | — | — | | — |
| 2A | | ○ | V ref | 4.5—5.5V | | |
| 2B | ○ | | Air flow meter (Vc) | 7—9V | | |
| 2C | — | — | Ground (E2) | 0V | | |
| 2D | ○ | | Oxygen sensor | 0V | 0—1.0V | • Cold engine: 0V at idle<br>• After warming-up: Increase engine speed: 0.5—1.0V Deceleration: 0—0.4V |
| 2E | ○ | | Air flow meter (Vs) | Approx. 1.7V | Approx. 4—5V | Increase engine speed: voltage increases |
| 2F | — | — | — | | | — |
| 2G | ○ | | Throttle sensor | Accelerator pedal released: 0.36—0.66 V (depends on 2A terminal voltage) | | Max. voltage (Throttle valve fully open): approx. 4.0V |
| 2H | ○ | | Atmospheric pressure sensor | At sea level: approx. 4.0V | | |
| 2I | ○ | | Water thermo sensor | 0.3—0.6 V | | Engine coolant temp. 20°C (68°F): approx. 2.5V |
| 2J | ○ | | Air flow meter (Intake air thermo sensor) | Approx. 2.5V at 20°C (68°F) | | |
| 2K | | ○ | Solenoid valve (Pressure regulator control) | For 120 sec. after ignition switch OFF → ON: below 3.5V | For 120 sec. after starting: below 3.5V | Hot condition: Coolant temp. above 70°C (158°F) Intake air temp. above 20°C (63°F) |
| | | | | Battery voltage | | Other conditions |
| 2L | ○ | | Speedometer | Battery voltage | | • Above 113 mph (180 km/h): below 1.0V |
| 2M | — | — | — | — | | — |

Courtesy of Mazda Motors Corp.

## NON-TURBO ECU TERMINAL VOLTAGE (Cont.)

| Terminal | Input | Output | Connection to | Voltage (After warming-up) | | Remarks |
|---|---|---|---|---|---|---|
| | | | | IGN: ON | Idle | |
| 2N | | ○ | Solenoid valve (EGR) | Below 3.5V | | • Cold engine: below 3.5V Radiator coolant temp.—below 17°C (63°F) or Engine coolant temp.—below 70°C (158°F) • Engine above approx. 1,500 rpm: Battery voltage |
| 2O | — | — | — | — | | — |
| 2P | | ○ | Solenoid valve (Purge control valve) | Battery voltage | | • Medium and high load: below 3.5V |
| 2Q | | ○ | Solenoid valve (Idle speed control valve) | Approx. 1.7—11V | | |
| 2R | — | — | Ground ($E_{02}$) | 0V | | |
| 3A | — | — | Ground ($E_{01}$) | 0V | | |
| 3B | ○ | | Ignition switch (Start position) | Below 2.5V | | While cranking: battery voltage |
| 3C | | ○ | Injector (No. 4 and No. 2) | Battery voltage | *1 Battery voltage | *1 Engine Signal Monitor green and red lights flash |
| 3D | ○ | | Inhibitor switch through EC-AT unit | "N" or "P" range: below 0.5V Other ranges: battery voltage | | ATX |
| | | | Neutral and clutch switch | In-gear condition Clutch pedal depressed: battery voltage Clutch pedal released: below 0.5V | | MTX (Neutral: constant battery voltage) |
| 3E | | ○ | Injector (No. 1 and No. 3) | Battery voltage | *1 Battery voltage | *1 Engine Signal Monitor: green and red lights flash |
| 3F | — | — | — | — | | — |
| 3G | — | — | Ground ($E_1$) | 0V | | |
| 3H | — | — | — | — | | — |
| 3I | ○ | — | Main relay | Battery voltage | | |
| 3J | — | — | Battery | Battery voltage | | For back-up |

Courtesy of Mazda Motors Corp.

## NON-TURBO ECU TERMINAL IDENTIFICATION

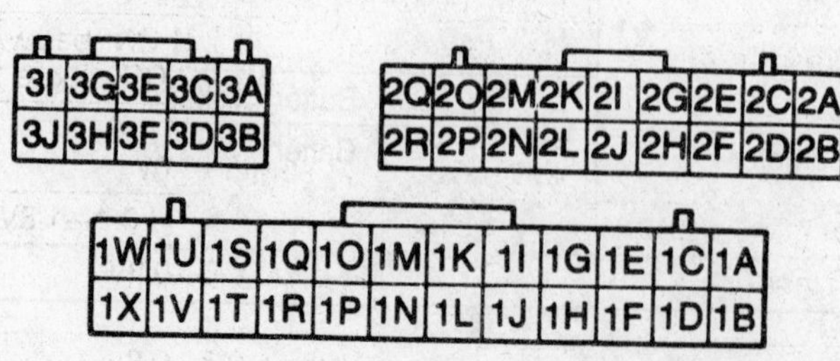
3I 3G 3E 3C 3A
3J 3H 3F 3D 3B
2Q 2O 2M 2K 2I 2G 2E 2C 2A
2R 2P 2N 2L 2J 2H 2F 2D 2B
1W 1U 1S 1Q 1O 1M 1K 1I 1G 1E 1C 1A
1X 1V 1T 1R 1P 1N 1L 1J 1H 1F 1D 1B

Courtesy of Mazda Motors Corp.

# 1988 COMPUTERIZED ENGINE CONTROLS
# Mazda – MX-6 & 626 EGI (Cont.)

## TURBO ECU TERMINAL VOLTAGE

| Terminal | Input | Output | Connection to | Voltage (After warming-up) | | Remarks |
|---|---|---|---|---|---|---|
| | | | | IGN: ON | Idle | |
| 1A | | ○ | Malfunction indicator light | For 3 sec. after ignition switch OFF → ON: below 4.8V (Light illuminates) After 3 sec.: Battery voltage (Light does not illuminate) | | • Test connector grounded • Light illuminates: below 4.8V • Light does not illuminate: Battery voltage |
| 1B | | ○ | Self-Diagnosis Checker (Code number) | For 3 sec. after ignition switch OFF → ON: below 6.2V (Buzzer sounds) After 3 sec.: Battery voltage (Buzzer does not sound) | | • Using Self-Diagnosis Checker and test connector grounded • Buzzer sounds: below 6.2V • Buzzer does not sound: Battery voltage |
| 1C | | ○ | Solenoid valve (Waste gate) | Battery voltage | | • Suddenly increase engine speed to above 4,500 rpm: below 3.5V |
| 1D | | ○ | Self-Diagnosis Checker (Monitor lamp) | For 3 sec. after ignition switch OFF → ON: below 6.2V (Light illuminates) After 3 sec.: Battery voltage (light does not illuminate) | (Test connector grounded) approx. 5V (Test connector not grounded) Monitor lamp ON: below 6.2V Monitor lamp OFF: Battery voltage | With Self-Diagnosis Checker |
| 1E | ○ | | Idle switch | Accelerator pedal released: below 0.5V Accelerator pedal depressed: above 7.7V | | |
| 1F | | ○ | A/C relay | A/C switch ON: below 2.5V A/C switch OFF: battery voltage | | Blower motor: ON |
| 1G | — | — | — | — | | — |
| 1H | ○ | | Water thermo switch | Above 7.3V | | Radiator temp.: below 17°C (63°F) |
| | | | | Below 1.5V | | Radiator temp.: above 17°C (63°F) |
| 1I | ○ | | Electrical load control unit | Electrical load ON: below 1.5V Electrical load OFF: above 7.3V | | Electrical load: Rear defroster Headlight Blower motor (3rd & 4th position) Electrical fan |
| 1J | ○ | | Brake light switch | Brake pedal released: below 3.6V Brake pedal depressed: above 10.0V | | |
| 1K | ○ | | P/S pressure switch | Constant above 10.5V | P/S ON: below 1.5V P/S OFF: above 10.5V | |
| 1L | ○ | | A/C switch | A/C switch ON: below 1.5V A/C switch OFF: above 10.0V | | Blower motor: ON |
| 1M | ○ | | Igniter (IGf signal) | Below 1.0V | 0.1—1.8V | |
| 1N | ○ | | Distributor (G1 ⊕ signal) | Approx. 0.6—0.8V | | |
| 1O | ○ | | Distributor (G2 ⊕ signal) | Approx. 0.6—0.8V | | |

# 1988 COMPUTERIZED ENGINE CONTROLS
# Mazda – MX-6 & 626 EGI (Cont.)

## TURBO ECU TERMINAL VOLTAGE (Cont.)

| Terminal | Input | Output | Connection to | Voltage (After warming-up) IGN: ON | Voltage (After warming-up) Idle | Remarks |
|---|---|---|---|---|---|---|
| 1P | ○ | | Distributor (G1, G2 ⊖ signal) | Approx. 0.6—0.8V | | |
| 1Q | ○ | | Distributor (Ne ⊖ signal) | Approx. 0.6—0.8V | | |
| 1R | ○ | | Knock control unit | 3.3—5.0V | | Knocking: 1.3—2.6V |
| 1S | | ○ | Warning buzzer Overboost | Approx. 5.0V | | Buzzer sounds: below 4.8V |
| 1T | ○ | | Distributor (Ne ⊕ signal) | Approx. 0.6—0.8V | | |
| 1U | — | — | — | — | | — |
| 1V | ○ | | — | Constant below 1.5V | | MTX |
| | | | | Constant above 10.5V | | ATX |
| 1W | ○ | | Test connector | Test connector grounded: below 0.5V<br>Test connector not grounded: above 10.5V | | Green connector, 1-pin |
| 1X | | ○ | Igniter (IGt signal) | Approx. 0V | Approx. 0.6—0.8V | |
| 2A | | ○ | V ref | 4.5—5.5V | | |
| 2B | ○ | | Air flow meter (Vc) | 7—9V | | |
| 2C | — | — | Ground (E2) | 0V | | |
| 2D | ○ | | Oxygen sensor | 0V | 0—1.0V | • Cold engine: 0V at idle<br>• After warming-up: Increase engine speed: 0.5—1.0V Deceleration: 0—0.4V |
| 2E | ○ | | Air flow meter (Vs) | Approx. 1.7V | Approx. 5—6V | Increase engine speed: voltage increases |
| 2F | ○ | | EGR position sensor | 0.25—0.95V | | |
| 2G | ○ | | Throttle sensor | Accelerator pedal released: 0.36—0.66V (depends on 2A terminal voltage) | | Max. voltage (Throttle valve fully opened): approx. 4.3V |
| 2H | ○ | | Atmospheric pressure sensor | At sea level: approx. 4.0V | | |
| 2I | ○ | | Water thermo sensor | 0.3—0.6V | | Engine coolant temp. 20°C (68°F): approx. 2.5V |
| 2J | ○ | | Air flow meter (Intake air thermo sensor) | Approx. 2.5V at 20°C (68°F) | | |
| 2K | | ○ | Solenoid valve (Pressure regulator control) | For 120 sec. after ignition switch OFF → ON: below 3.5V | For 120 sec. after starting: below 3.5V | Hot condition: Coolant temp. above 70°C (158°F) and Intake air temp. above 20°C (68°F) |
| | | | | Battery voltage | | Other conditions |
| 2L | — | — | — | — | | — |

Courtesy of Mazda Motors Corp.

## TURBO ECU TERMINAL VOLTAGE (Cont.)

| Terminal | Input | Output | Connection to | Voltage (After warming-up) | | Remarks |
|---|---|---|---|---|---|---|
| | | | | IGN: ON | Idle | |
| 2M | | ○ | Solenoid valve (EGR-Vent side) | Battery voltage | | • Voltages change depending on driving condition (EGR amount) • Cold engine: battery voltage (Radiator coolant temp-below 17°C (63°F) or Engine coolant temp-below 40°C (104°F)) |
| 2N | | ○ | Solenoid valve (EGR-vacuum side) | Battery voltage | | |
| 2O | | ○ | Circuit opening relay | Battery voltage | Below 3.5V | |
| 2P | | ○ | Solenoid valve (Purge control valve) | Battery voltage | | Medium and high load: below 3.5V |
| 2Q | | ○ | Solenoid valve (Idle speed control valve) | Approx. 1.7–11V | | |
| 2R | — | — | Ground (E02) | 0V | | |
| 3A | — | — | Ground (E01) | 0V | | |
| 3B | ○ | | Ignition switch (Start position) | Below 2.5V | | While cranking: battery voltage |
| 3C | | ○ | Injector (No. 4 and No. 2) | Battery voltage | *1 Battery voltage | *1 Engine Signal Monitor green and red lights flash |
| 3D | ○ | | Inhibitor switch through EC-AT unit | "N" or "P" range: below 0.5V<br>Other ranges: Battery voltage | | ATX |
| | | | Neutral and clutch switch | In-gear condition<br>Clutch pedal depressed: Battery voltage<br>Clutch pedal released: below 0.5V | | MTX (Neutral: constant Battery voltage) |
| 3E | | ○ | Injector (No. 1 and No. 3) | Battery voltage | *1 Battery voltage | *1 Engine Signal Monitor: green and red lights flash |
| 3F | — | — | — | — | | — |
| 3G | — | — | Ground (E1) | 0V | | |
| 3H | — | — | — | — | | — |
| 3I | ○ | — | Main relay | Battery voltage | | |
| 3J | — | — | Battery | Battery voltage | | For back-up |

Courtesy of Mazda Motors Corp.

## TURBO ECU TERMINAL IDENTIFICATION

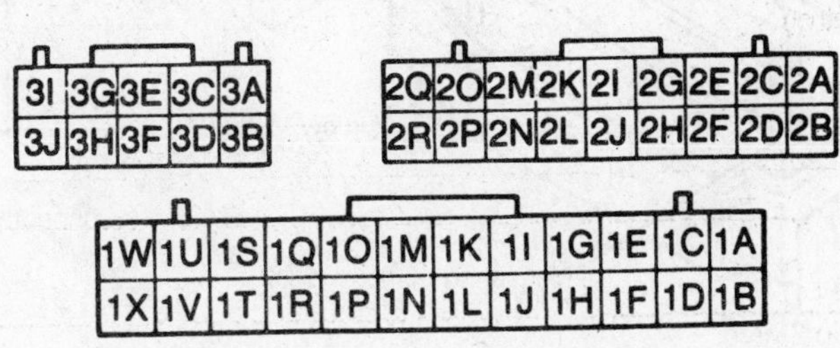
3I 3G 3E 3C 3A
3J 3H 3F 3D 3B
2Q 2O 2M 2K 2I 2G 2E 2C 2A
2R 2P 2N 2L 2J 2H 2F 2D 2B
1W 1U 1S 1Q 1O 1M 1K 1I 1G 1E 1C 1A
1X 1V 1T 1R 1P 1N 1L 1J 1H 1F 1D 1B

Courtesy of Mazda Motors Corp.

## DECELERATION CONTROL SYSTEM

Deceleration control system is a function of ECU. It provides fuel cut during deceleration.

1) Connect Engine Signal Monitor (49 9200 162) or backprobe ECU connector terminals No. 3C or 3E. Start engine. Voltage should pulsate.

2) Increase engine speed to 4000 RPM. Suddenly decrease engine speed. Voltage should become constant during deceleration. If not, check idle switch, coolant temperature switch and all ECU connections.

## COMPONENT TESTING

**Airflow Meter** – Inspect airflow meter for damage and ensure measuring plate moves smoothly. Disconnect airflow meter connector. *See Fig. 5.* Measure resistance using AIRFLOW METER TERMINAL RESISTANCE table.

***AIRFLOW METER TERMINAL RESISTANCE***

| Terminal | Fully Closed Ohms | Fully Open Ohms |
|---|---|---|
| E2-Vs | 20-400 | 20-1000 |
| E2-Vc | 100-400 | 100-400 |
| E2-Vb | 200-400 | 200-400 |
| E2-THA | -4°F (-20°C) 13.6-18.4 | -4°F (-20°C) 13.6-18.4 |
| | 68°F (20°C) 2.21-2.69 | 68°F (20°C) 2.21-2.69 |
| | 140°F (60°C) 493-667 | 140°F (60°C) 493-667 |
| E1-Fc | Infinite | 0 |

**Atmospheric Pressure Sensor** – 1) Connect voltmeter to terminal D. Turn ignition on and note voltage. *See Fig. 6.*

2) Voltage at sea level should be 3.5-4.5 volts. Voltage at 6500 feet should be 2.5-3.5 volts. Replace if not to specification.

**Brake Light Switch** – 1) Disconnect brake light switch connector. Measure resistance between Green/White wire and White/Green wire terminals of brake light switch.

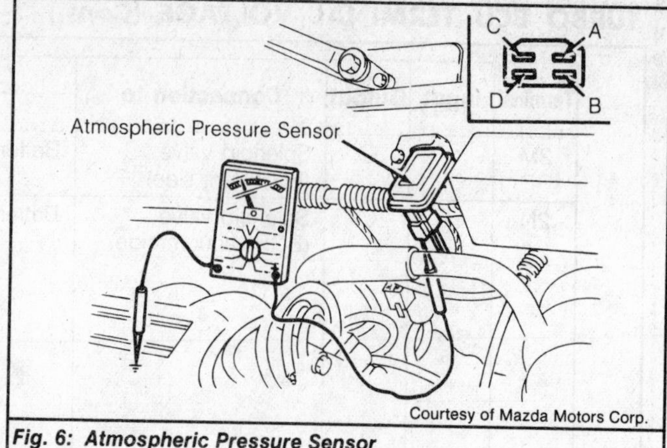
C
A
D
B
Atmospheric Pressure Sensor
Courtesy of Mazda Motors Corp.

***Fig. 6: Atmospheric Pressure Sensor***

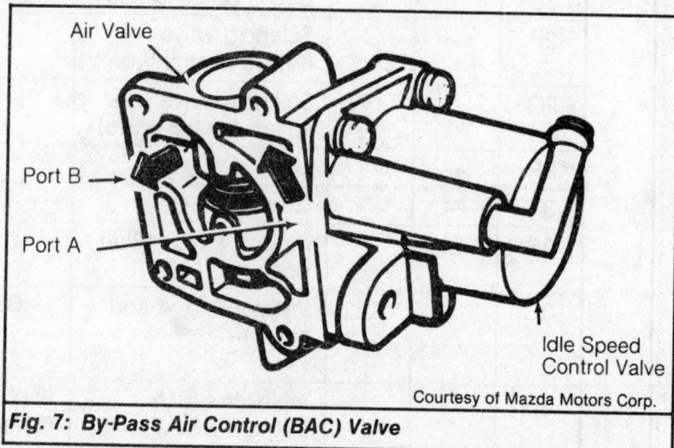
Air Valve
Port B
Port A
Idle Speed
Control Valve
Courtesy of Mazda Motors Corp.

***Fig. 7: By-Pass Air Control (BAC) Valve***

2) With brake pedal released, resistance should be infinite. With brake pedal depressed, resistance should be zero ohms.

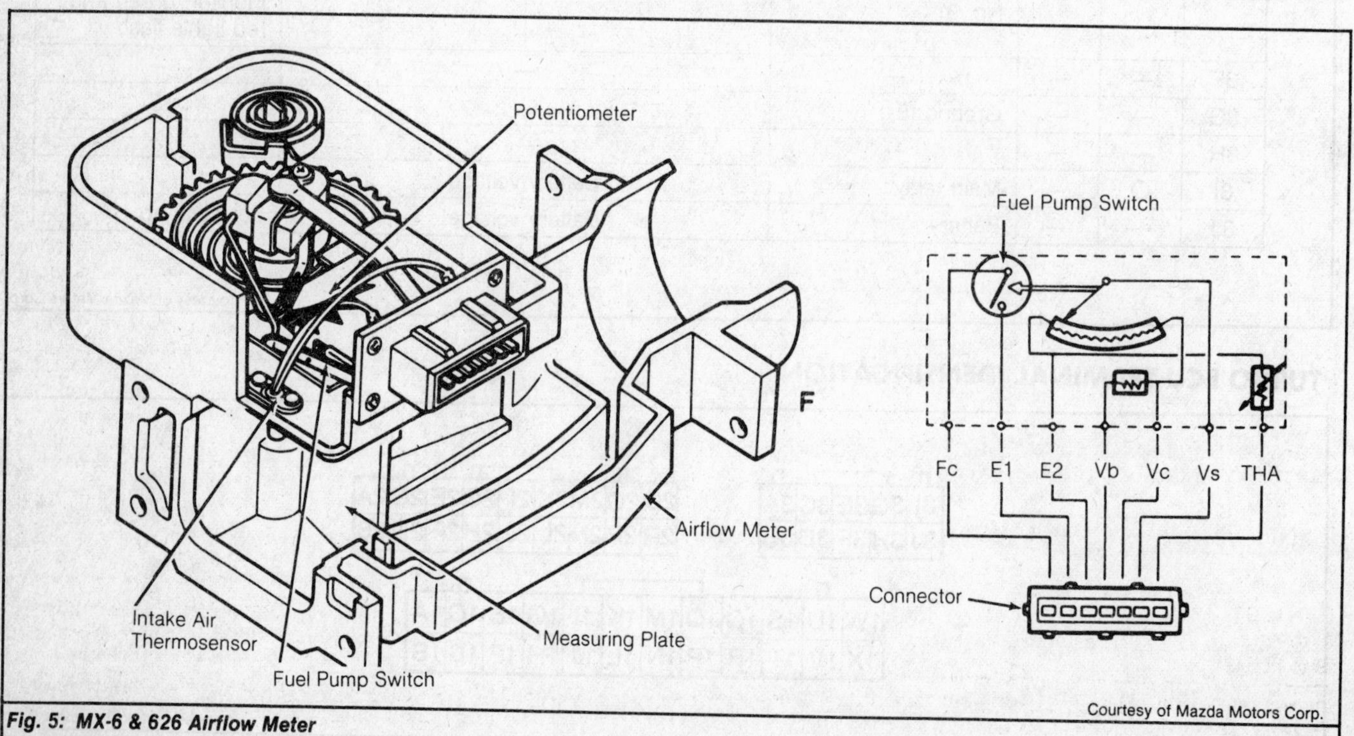
Potentiometer
F
Airflow Meter
Intake Air
Thermosensor
Measuring Plate
Fuel Pump Switch
Fuel Pump Switch
Fc
E1
E2
Vb
Vc
Vs
THA
Connector
Courtesy of Mazda Motors Corp.

***Fig. 5: MX-6 & 626 Airflow Meter***

# 1988 COMPUTERIZED ENGINE CONTROLS Mazda – MX-6 & 626 EGI (Cont.)

**By-Pass Air Control (BAC) Valve – 1)** Remove BAC valve from throttle body. Blow air through port "A". Ensure air exhausts through port "B" when valve is cold. If not, replace BAC valve. *See Fig. 7.*
**2)** Measure resistance of Idle Speed Control (ISC) valve at 2 wire connector of BAC valve. Resistance should be between 6.3-9.9 ohms, at normal operating temperature. If not, replace BAC valve.

**Circuit Opening Relay – 1)** Remove circuit opening relay from fuse block panel. *See Fig. 8.* Check circuit opening relay circuits with CIRCUIT OPENING RELAY TERMINAL CIRCUITS table.

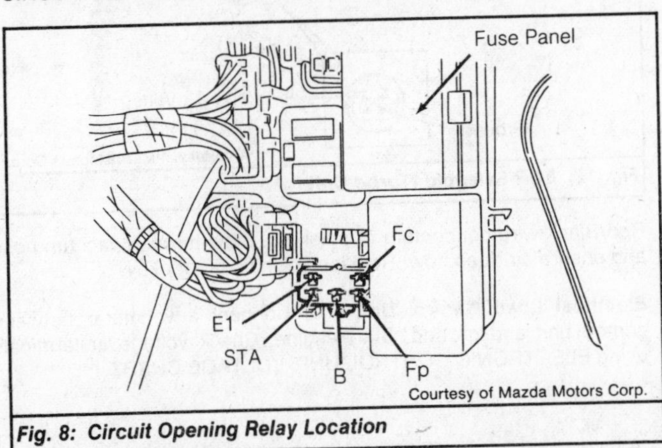

Fuse Panel
Fc
E1
STA
B
Fp
Courtesy of Mazda Motors Corp.


*Fig. 8: Circuit Opening Relay Location*

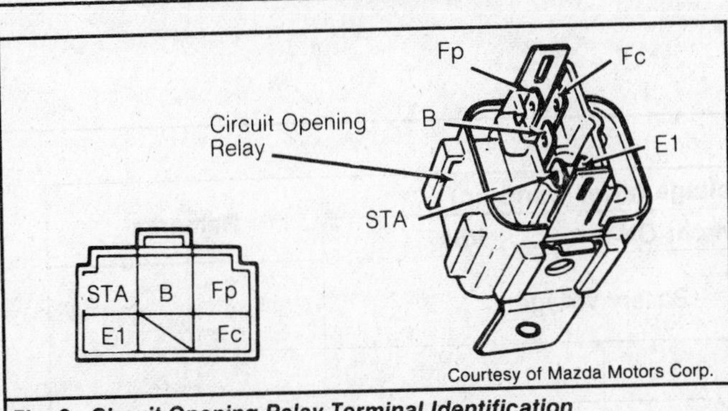

Fp
Fc
Circuit Opening Relay
B
E1
STA
STA
B
Fp
E1
Fc
Courtesy of Mazda Motors Corp.


*Fig. 9: Circuit Opening Relay Terminal Identification*

### CIRCUIT OPENING RELAY TERMINAL CIRCUITS

| Terminal | Condition | Specifications |
|---|---|---|
| Fp | Resistance to Ground | 0.2-30 Ohms |
| Fc | Resistance to Ground (Cranking) | Infinite |
| B | Voltage to Ground (Ign. On) | Battery Voltage |
| STA | Voltage to Ground (Cranking) | Approx. 9 Volts |
| E1 | Resistance to Ground | Infinite |

**2)** With circuit opening relay removed, apply 12 volts to terminal STA of relay. *See Fig. 9.* Ground terminal E1. Ensure continuity from relay terminals B to FP.
**3)** Apply 12 volts to terminal B of relay. Ground terminal Fc. Ensure battery voltage is at relay terminal Fp.
**4)** Ensure that relay has correct resistance between terminal with CIRCUIT OPENING RELAY RESISTANCE table.

### CIRCUIT OPENING RELAY RESISTANCE

| Terminals | Resistance |
|---|---|
| STA to E1 | 15-30 Ohms |
| B to Fc | 80-150 Ohms |
| B to Fp | Infinite |

**Clutch Switch (M/T) – 1)** Disconnect clutch switch connector. Measure resistance across Red/Green wire and Light Green/Black wire terminals on switch.
**2)** With clutch pedal released, resistance should be 0 ohms. With clutch pedal depressed, resistance should be infinite.

**Coolant Temperature Sensor –** Disconnect and remove coolant temperature sensor. Check resistance using COOLANT TEMPERATURE SENSOR RESISTANCE table.

### COOLANT TEMPERATURE SENSOR RESISTANCE

| Temperature °F (°C) | Ohms |
|---|---|
| -4 (-20) | 14,500-17,800 |
| 68 (20) | 2200-2700 |
| 104 (40) | 1000-1300 |
| 140 (60) | 500-640 |
| 176 (80) | 280-350 |

**Coolant Temperature Switch –** Remove switch from radiator. Switch should have continuity at temperatures greater than 63°F (17°C).

**EGR Position Sensor (Turbo Only) – 1)** If adapter is available, disconnect EGR position sensor connector and connect Adapter (49 G018 901) in harness. *See Fig. 10.* If adapter is not available, back probe connector with voltmeter.
**2)** With EGR vacuum hose disconnected, connect vacuum pump. Turn ignition on and check voltages at connector. Use EGR POSITION SENSOR VOLTAGE table to compare results.

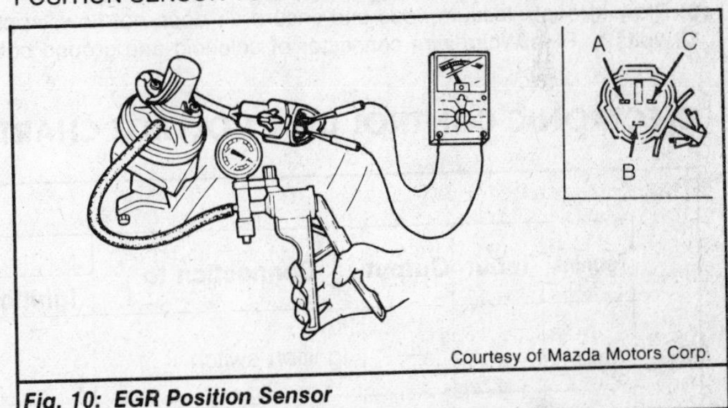

A
C
B
Courtesy of Mazda Motors Corp.


*Fig. 10: EGR Position Sensor*

### EGR POSITION SENSOR VOLTAGE

| Terminal | Voltage |
|---|---|
| A | 4.5-5.5 |
| B | Less Than 1.5 |
| C | |
| (Without Vacuum) | .25-.95 |
| (With Vacuum) | Approx. 4 |

**3)** If voltage is not correct at terminals A and B, check harness and connection at ECU connector terminals No. 2A and 2C. If voltage is not correct at terminal C, check sensor resistance, harness and ECU connector terminal No. 2F.
**4)** Check sensor resistance according to EGR POSITION SENSOR RESISTANCE table. If resistance is not within specifications, replace sensor.

### EGR POSITION SENSOR RESISTANCE

| Terminals | Ohms |
|---|---|
| A-B | 5000 |
| A-C | 700-5000 |
| B-C | 700-5000 |

**EGR Solenoid (Non-Turbo) – 1)** Disconnect vacuum hose from solenoid. *See Fig. 11.* Blow through port "A". Ensure air exhausts through port "B".
**2)** Disconnect 2 wire connector from solenoid. Connect 12 volts to one terminal and ground other terminal of solenoid. Blow air though port "A". Ensure air exhausts through air filter.

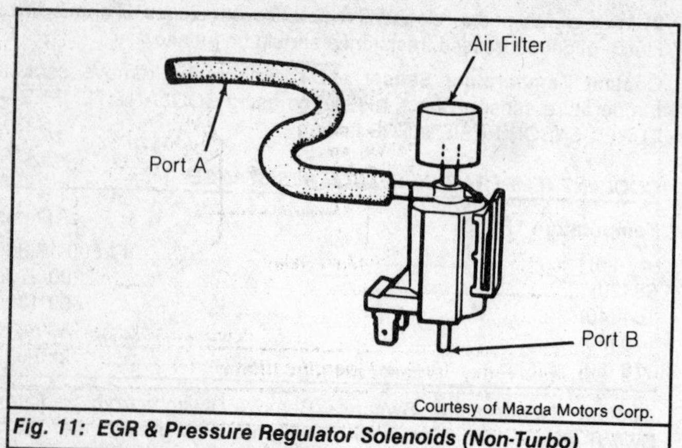
Air Filter
Port A
Port B
Courtesy of Mazda Motors Corp.

*Fig. 11: EGR & Pressure Regulator Solenoids (Non-Turbo)*

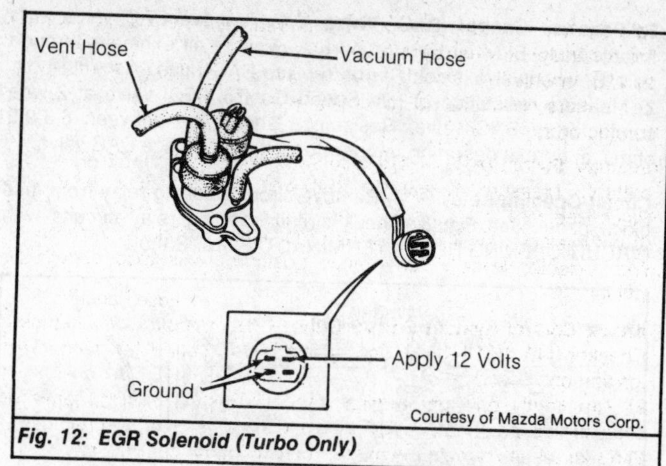
Vent Hose
Vacuum Hose
Apply 12 Volts
Ground
Courtesy of Mazda Motors Corp.

*Fig. 12: EGR Solenoid (Turbo Only)*

**EGR Solenoid (Turbo) – 1)** Disconnect vacuum hoses and blow through vent hose. *See Fig. 12.* Ensure air flows. Disconnect solenoid connector.

**2)** Apply 12 volts to White/Blue wire connector of solenoid and ground both Red/Black wire connectors of solenoid. Blow through vent hose and ensure air does not flow. Replace solenoid if not okay.

**3)** Blow through vacuum hose and ensure air does not flow. Apply 12 volts to Blue/White wire connector of solenoid and ground both Red/Black wire connectors of solenoid. Blow through vacuum hose and ensure air does flow. Replace solenoid if not okay.

**Electrical Load Control Unit – 1)** Connect a voltmeter between control unit and ground. Start engine. Check voltage at terminals using ELECTRONIC CONTROL UNIT VOLTAGE CHART.

## ELECTRONIC CONTROL UNIT VOLTAGE CHART

| Terminal | Input | Output | Connection to | Voltage (after warm-up) Ignition switch: ON | Voltage (after warm-up) Idle | Remarks |
|---|---|---|---|---|---|---|
| A (BW) | — | — | Ignition switch | Battery voltage | | |
| B | — | — | — | — | — | — |
| C (B) | — | — | Ground | 0V | | |
| D (LY) | ○ | | Electrical fan relay | Battery voltage | | Coolant temp.: below 97°C (207°F) |
| | | | | Below 1.5V | | Coolant temp.: above 97°C (207°F) |
| E (GY) | | ○ | Control unit (1I) | 0V | | E/L: ON |
| | | | | Battery voltage | | E/L: OFF |
| F (W) | ○ | | Headlight switch | Battery voltage | | Headlight switch: ON |
| | | | | Below 1.5V | | Headlight switch: OFF |
| G (LB) | ○ | | Blower motor switch | Below 1.5V | | Blower motor switch: ON (3rd or 4th position) |
| | | | | Approx. 5V | | Others |
| H (BL) | ○ | | Rear defroster switch | Below 1.5V | | Rear defroster switch: ON |
| | | | | Battery voltage | | Rear defroster switch: OFF |

Courtesy of Mazda Motors Corp.

**Idle Switch – 1)** Disconnect 1-pin connector at idle switch. Check for continuity between switch and ground.
**2)** With throttle fully closed, there should be continuity. With throttle open, there should be no continuity. If switch is not correct, replace throttle body.

**Inhibitor Switch (A/T) – 1)** Disconnect White 3-pin connector near battery. Measure resistance between Black/Yellow wire and Black/Red wire.
**2)** With selector lever in "P" or "N", resistance should be zero ohms. With selector lever in any other position, resistance should be infinite.

**Knock Control System (Turbo Only) – 1)** Connect Self-Diagnostic Checker (49 H018 9A1) and ground test connector lead. Turn ignition on.
**2)** Tap lightly on right engine hanger. Ensure monitor lamp on checker flashes. If not, connect a good knock sensor and recheck.
**3)** If test results remain the same, replace knock control unit.

**Main Relay – 1)** Ensure a clicking sound is heard at main relay when turning ignition on and off. *See Fig. 13.* Disconnect main relay. Apply 12 volts to terminal A and ground terminal B.
**2)** Ensure there is continuity between main relay terminals C and D, when voltage is applied. There should be no continuity when voltage is not applied.

**Neutral Switch (M/T) – 1)** Disconnect Black 3-pin connector (only 2 wires) behind battery. Measure resistance between Black wire and ground. If resistance is zero ohms, use other side of connector.
**2)** Place transaxle in neutral position. Resistance between the Red/Green wire and Black wire should be infinite.
**3)** Place transaxle in any gear. Resistance between Red/Green wire and Black wire should be zero ohms.

**Power Steering Switch – 1)** Disconnect power steering connector at power steering gear. Connect an ohmmeter to switch.
**2)** Start engine. When turning, resistance should be 0 ohms. When not turning, resistance should be infinite.

**Pressure Regulator Control Solenoid – 1)** Disconnect vacuum hose from solenoid. Blow through port "A". Ensure air exhausts through port "B".
**2)** Disconnect 2 wire connector from solenoid. Connect 12 volts to one terminal and ground the other terminal of solenoid. Blow air though port "A". Ensure air exhausts through air filter.

**Purge Solenoid – 1)** Disconnect vacuum hose from solenoid. *See Fig. 14.* Blow through port "A". Ensure air exhausts through air filter.
**2)** Disconnect 2 wire connector from solenoid. Connect 12 volts to one terminal and ground the other terminal of solenoid. Blow air though port "A". Ensure air exhausts through port "B".

**Wastegate Solenoid (Turbo Only) – 1)** Disconnect small air tube from air hose. *See Fig. 15.* Disconnect solenoid connector. Blow air though air tube, ensure air does not flow. If not okay, replace turbo and solenoid as an assembly.
**2)** Apply 12 volts to one side of solenoid and ground the other. Blow air through air tube, ensure air does flow. If not, replace turbo and solenoid as an assembly.

**5th Gear Switch (M/T) – 1)** Disconnect White 2-pin connector near battery. Measure resistance between Blue wires.
**2)** With transaxle in 5th gear, resistance should be infinite. With transaxle in any other gear, resistance should be zero ohms.

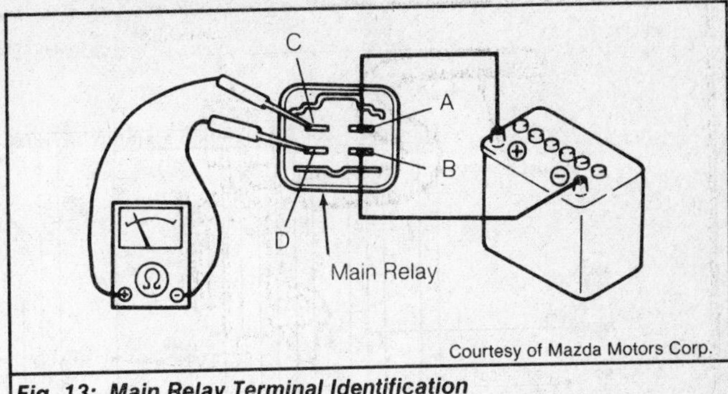
C
A
B
D
Main Relay
Courtesy of Mazda Motors Corp.
*Fig. 13: Main Relay Terminal Identification*

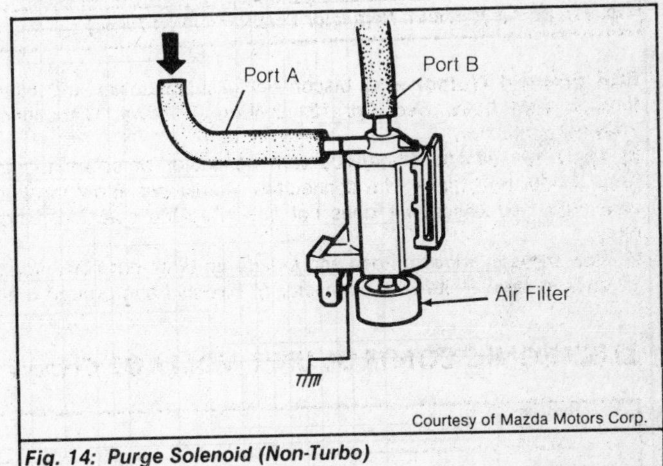
Port A
Port B
Air Filter
Courtesy of Mazda Motors Corp.
*Fig. 14: Purge Solenoid (Non-Turbo)*

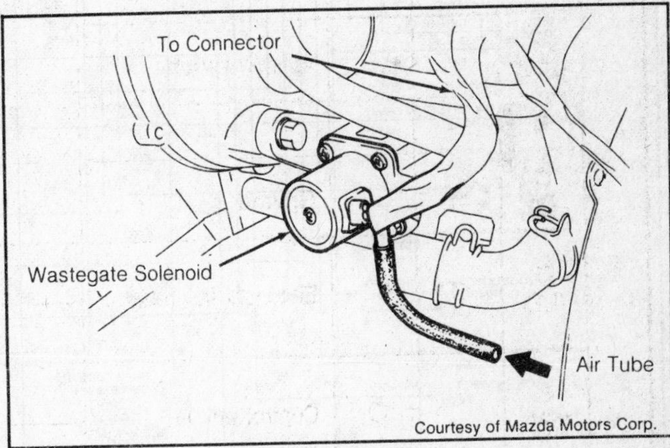
To Connector
Wastegate Solenoid
Air Tube
Courtesy of Mazda Motors Corp.
*Fig. 15: Wastegate Solenoid (Turbo Only)*

# 1988 COMPUTERIZED ENGINE CONTROLS
## Mazda – MX-6 & 626 EGI (Cont.)

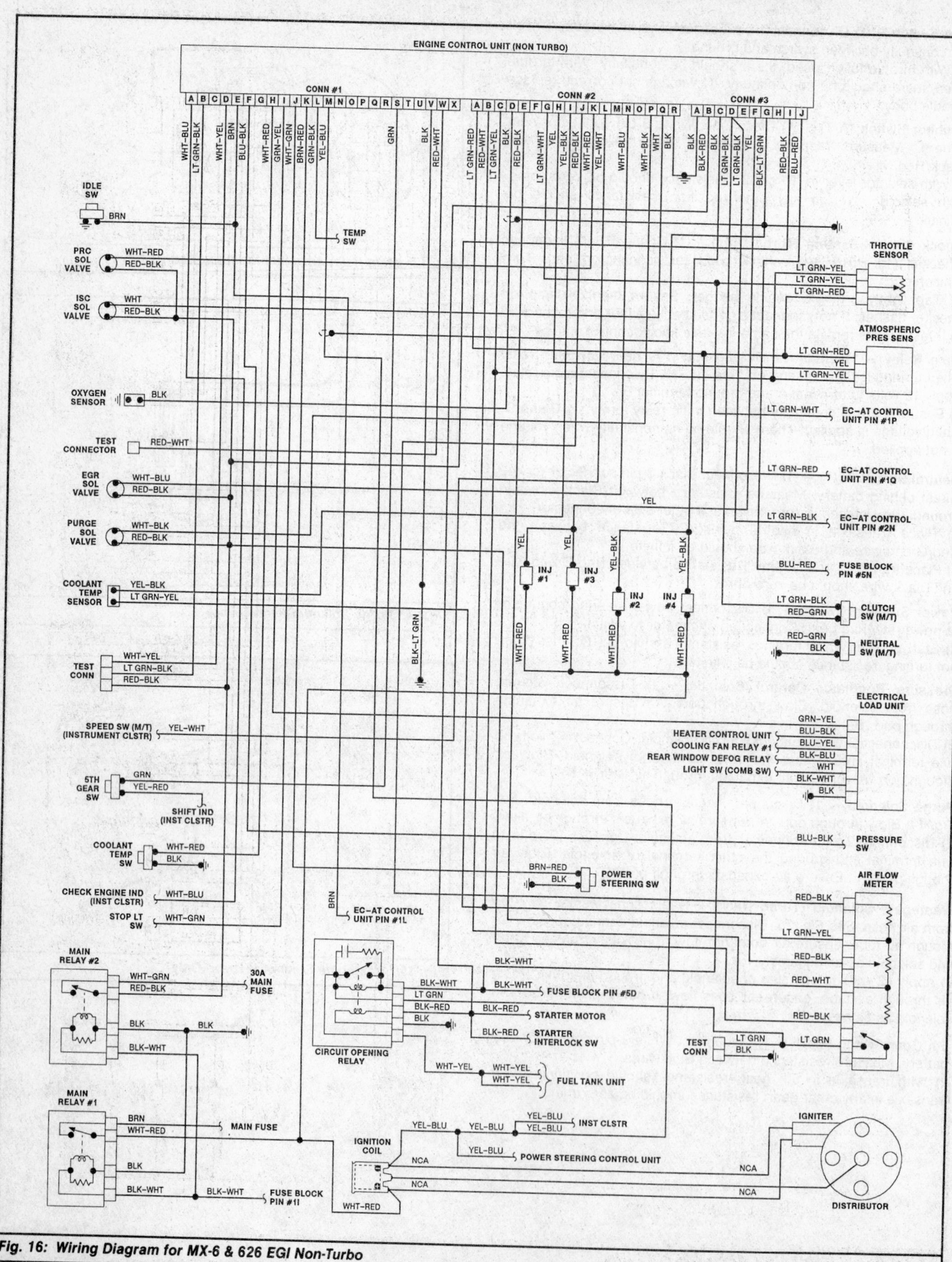
ENGINE CONTROL UNIT (NON TURBO)
CONN #1
CONN #2
CONN #3
IDLE SW
TEMP SW
PRC SOL VALVE
ISC SOL VALVE
THROTTLE SENSOR
ATMOSPHERIC PRES SENS
OXYGEN SENSOR
TEST CONNECTOR
EC-AT CONTROL UNIT PIN #1P
EGR SOL VALVE
EC-AT CONTROL UNIT PIN #1Q
PURGE SOL VALVE
EC-AT CONTROL UNIT PIN #2N
FUSE BLOCK PIN #5N
COOLANT TEMP SENSOR
INJ #1
INJ #2
INJ #3
INJ #4
CLUTCH SW (M/T)
NEUTRAL SW (M/T)
TEST CONN
ELECTRICAL LOAD UNIT
HEATER CONTROL UNIT
COOLING FAN RELAY #1
REAR WINDOW DEFOG RELAY
LIGHT SW (COMB SW)
SPEED SW (M/T) (INSTRUMENT CLSTR)
5TH GEAR SW
SHIFT IND (INST CLSTR)
COOLANT TEMP SW
PRESSURE SW
POWER STEERING SW
AIR FLOW METER
CHECK ENGINE IND (INST CLSTR)
STOP LT SW
EC-AT CONTROL UNIT PIN #1L
MAIN RELAY #2
30A MAIN FUSE
FUSE BLOCK PIN #5D
STARTER MOTOR
STARTER INTERLOCK SW
CIRCUIT OPENING RELAY
TEST CONN
FUEL TANK UNIT
MAIN RELAY #1
MAIN FUSE
INST CLSTR
IGNITER
IGNITION COIL
POWER STEERING CONTROL UNIT
FUSE BLOCK PIN #1I
DISTRIBUTOR

*Fig. 16: Wiring Diagram for MX-6 & 626 EGI Non-Turbo*

# 1988 COMPUTERIZED ENGINE CONTROLS
## Mazda – MX-6 & 626 EGI (Cont.)

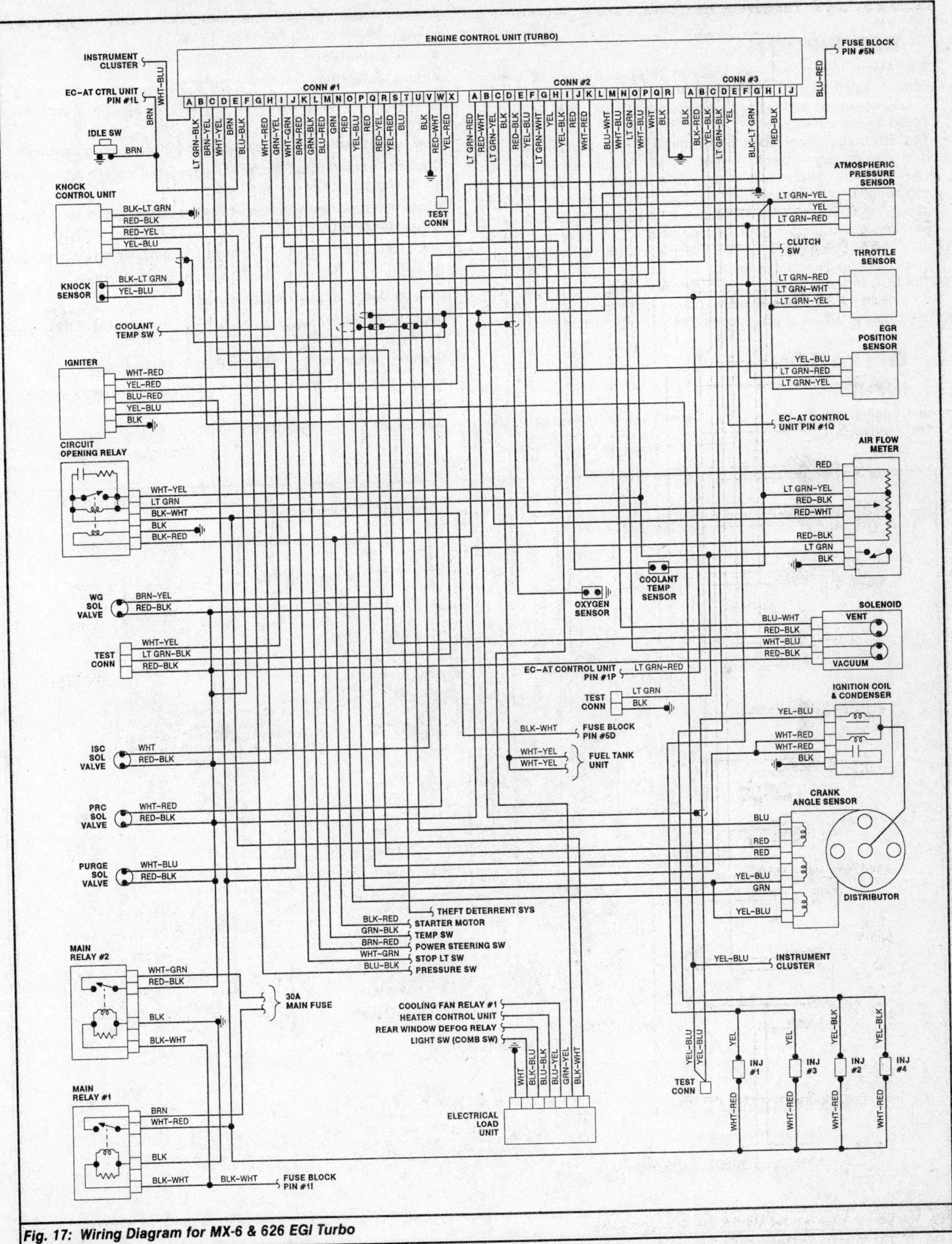
ENGINE CONTROL UNIT (TURBO)
CONN #1
CONN #2
CONN #3
FUSE BLOCK PIN #5N
INSTRUMENT CLUSTER
EC-AT CTRL UNIT PIN #1L
IDLE SW
KNOCK CONTROL UNIT
TEST CONN
ATMOSPHERIC PRESSURE SENSOR
CLUTCH SW
THROTTLE SENSOR
KNOCK SENSOR
COOLANT TEMP SW
EGR POSITION SENSOR
IGNITER
EC-AT CONTROL UNIT PIN #1Q
CIRCUIT OPENING RELAY
AIR FLOW METER
COOLANT TEMP SENSOR
OXYGEN SENSOR
WG SOL VALVE
SOLENOID
VENT
VACUUM
TEST CONN
EC-AT CONTROL UNIT PIN #1P
IGNITION COIL & CONDENSER
FUSE BLOCK PIN #5D
ISC SOL VALVE
FUEL TANK UNIT
CRANK ANGLE SENSOR
PRC SOL VALVE
PURGE SOL VALVE
DISTRIBUTOR
THEFT DETERRENT SYS
STARTER MOTOR
TEMP SW
POWER STEERING SW
STOP LT SW
PRESSURE SW
MAIN RELAY #2
INSTRUMENT CLUSTER
30A MAIN FUSE
COOLING FAN RELAY #1
HEATER CONTROL UNIT
REAR WINDOW DEFOG RELAY
LIGHT SW (COMB SW)
INJ #1
INJ #3
INJ #2
INJ #4
MAIN RELAY #1
ELECTRICAL LOAD UNIT
FUSE BLOCK PIN #1I

*Fig. 17: Wiring Diagram for MX-6 & 626 EGI Turbo*

## 323, 323 Turbo

# DESCRIPTION

The Mazda Electronic Gas Injection (EGI) computerized engine control system monitors various engine/vehicle functions to control engine operation and lower emissions while maintaining good fuel economy and driveability.

The Electronic Control Unit (ECU), through various input sensors, monitors battery voltage, engine RPM, amount of intake air, cranking signal, crankshaft angle, intake temperature, radiator and engine coolant temperatures, oxygen concentration in exhaust gases, throttle opening, atmospheric pressure, gearshift lever position, clutch engagement, braking, and A/C compressor operation. The ECU uses all input information to control fuel injection, and output devices. *See Figs. 1 and 2.*

The ECU has a built-in fail-safe mechanism. If a fault occurs while driving, the ECU will substitute pre-programmed values. Driving performance will be affected, but the vehicle may still be driven.

# OPERATION

## INPUTS

**Air Conditioning Switch** – Closes when A/C or blower is in the "ON" position.

**Airflow Meter (Inlet Air Temperature)** – Varies voltage signal to ECU in relation to inlet air temperature.

**Airflow Meter (Vc)** – Corrected airflow meter voltage.

**Airflow Meter (Vs)** – Airflow position signal.

**Atmospheric Pressure Sensor** – Varies voltage signal according to altitude.

**Brake Light Switch** – Signals ECU of vehicle braking condition.

**Coolant Temperature Sensor** – Varies input voltage signal according to engine coolant temperature.

**Coolant Temperature Switch** – Switch opens and closes according to radiator temperature.

**Electrical Load Control** – Signals ECU of additional electrical load.

**Idle Switch** – Indicates throttle open or closed position.

**Ignition Coil** – Signals engine speed.

**Ignition Switch** – Supplies battery voltage to ECU during engine cranking.

**Inhibitor Switch (A/T)** – Signals ECU of gear selection.

**Knock Sensor (Turbo)** – Retards ignition timing when knocking occurs.

**Main Relay** – Provides battery voltage to ECU.

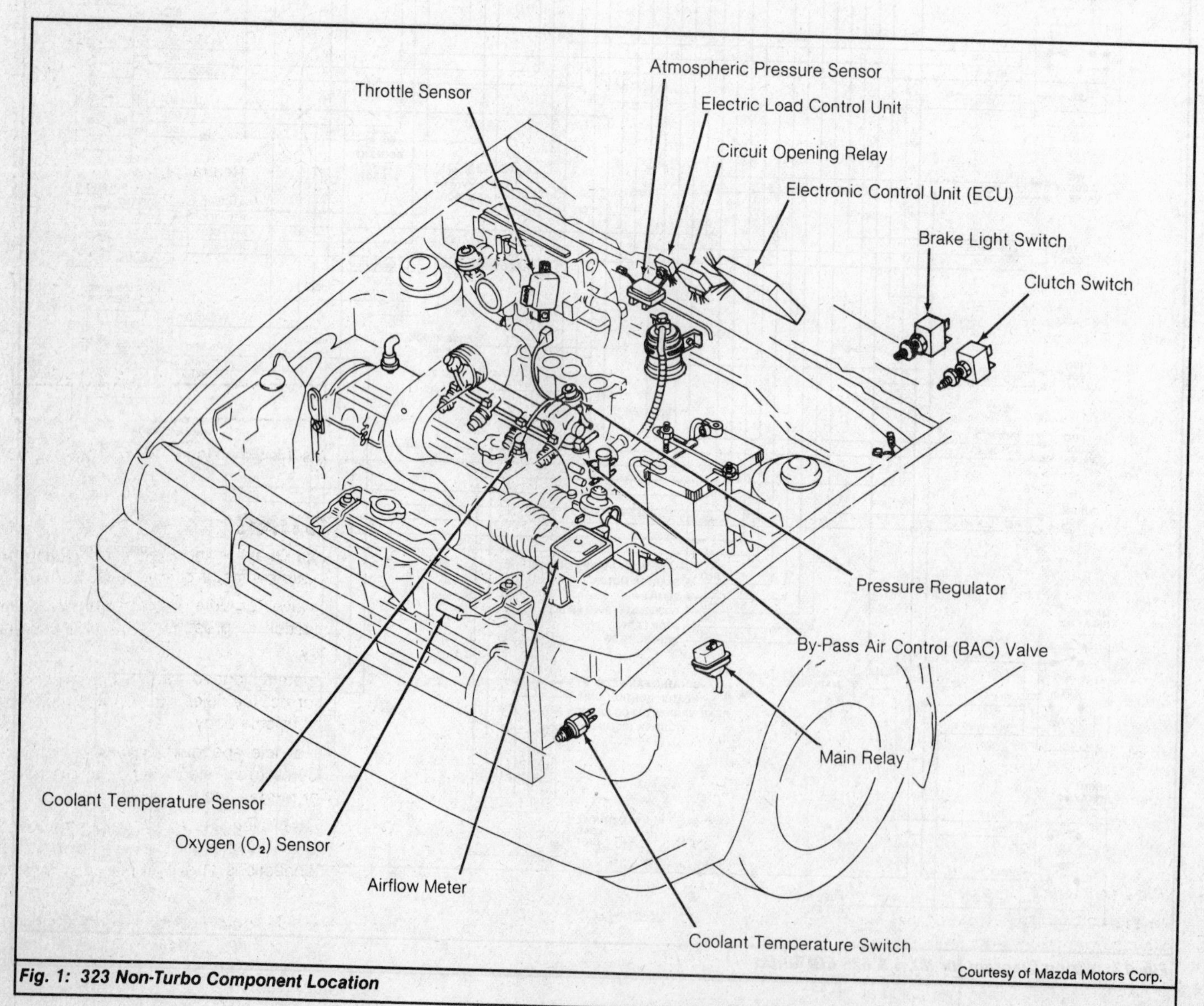
Atmospheric Pressure Sensor
Throttle Sensor
Electric Load Control Unit
Circuit Opening Relay
Electronic Control Unit (ECU)
Brake Light Switch
Clutch Switch
Pressure Regulator
By-Pass Air Control (BAC) Valve
Main Relay
Coolant Temperature Sensor
Oxygen (O2) Sensor
Airflow Meter
Coolant Temperature Switch

*Fig. 1: 323 Non-Turbo Component Location*

Courtesy of Mazda Motors Corp.

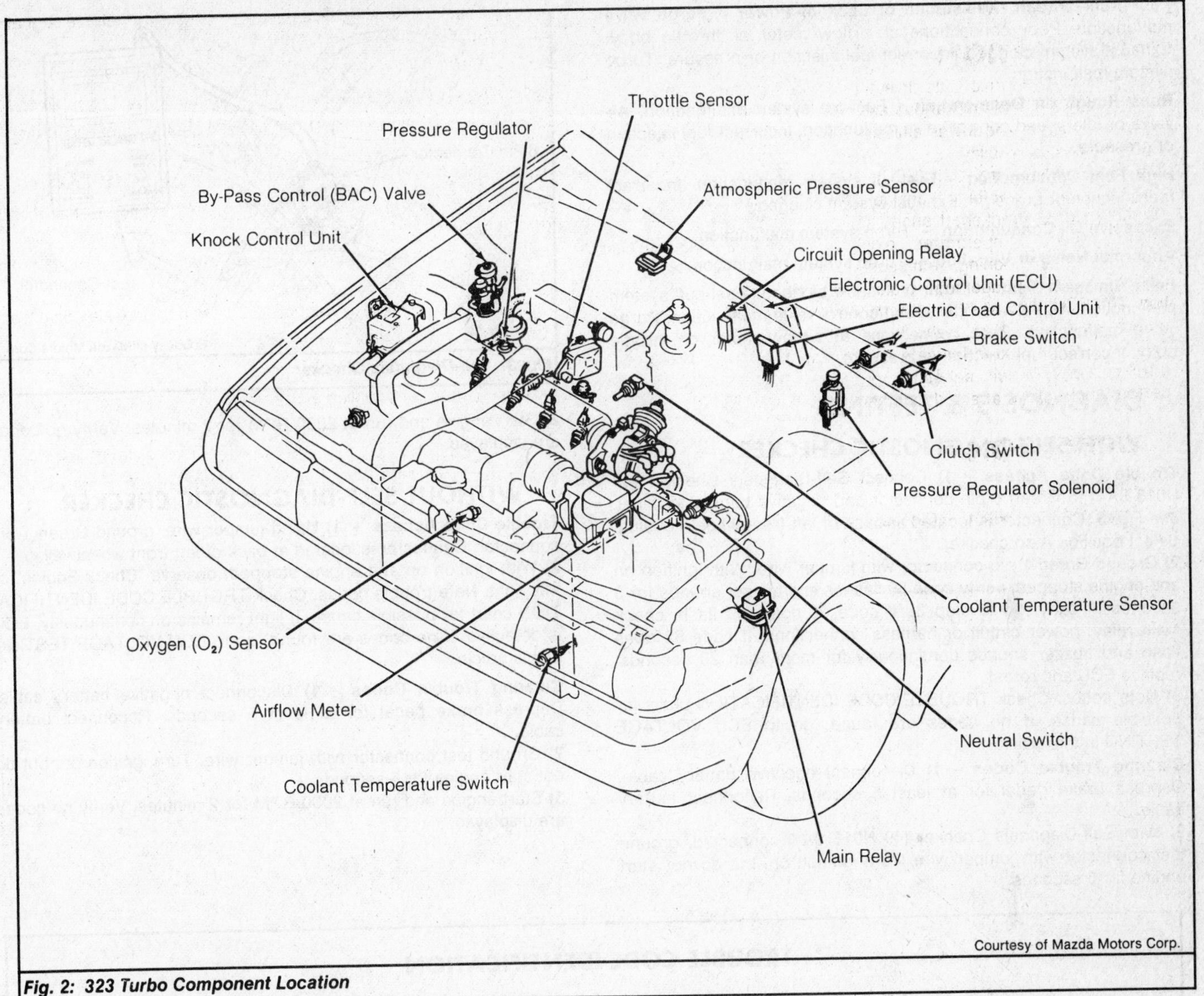
Throttle Sensor
Pressure Regulator
By-Pass Control (BAC) Valve
Atmospheric Pressure Sensor
Knock Control Unit
Circuit Opening Relay
Electronic Control Unit (ECU)
Electric Load Control Unit
Brake Switch
Clutch Switch
Pressure Regulator Solenoid
Coolant Temperature Sensor
Oxygen (O2) Sensor
Airflow Meter
Neutral Switch
Coolant Temperature Switch
Main Relay
Courtesy of Mazda Motors Corp.

*Fig. 2: 323 Turbo Component Location*

**Neutral/Clutch Switch (M/T)** – Signals ECU of clutch operation and transaxle gear selection.

**Oxygen ($O_2$) Sensor** – Generates voltage signal depending on oxygen content of exhaust.

**Throttle Sensor** – Referred to as PSW switch. Provides signal in response to wide open throttle position.

## OUTPUTS

**Air Conditioning Relay** – ECU completes ground circuit for A/C operation.

**"Check Engine" Light** – Lights during engine start up and monitored component malfunction. Is also referred to as MIL or Malfunction Indicator Light. Is used to read trouble codes.

**Fuel Injectors** – ECU completes ground circuit to control fuel injector pulse.

**Idle Speed Control Valve** – Is part of By-Pass Air Control (BAC) valve attached to throttle body. ECU intermittently completes ground to idle speed control valve for proper idle RPM.

**Pressure Regulator Control Solenoid** – ECU completes ground circuit to control vacuum to fuel pressure regulator.

**No. 1 & 2 Purge Control Solenoid** – ECU completes ground circuit to control vacuum to canister purge.

**Voltage Reference** – Provides 4.5-5.5 volts to TPS and atmospheric pressure sensor.

## TROUBLE SHOOTING

**Hard Start or No Start (Cranks Okay)** – Incorrect fuel injection or pressure. Poor connections at airflow meter or throttle body.

**Engine Stalls Cold** – Air valve or idle speed control valve malfunction. Incorrect fuel injection or pressure. Poor connections at airflow meter or throttle body.

**Engine Stalls Warm** – PCV system clogged. Air valve or idle speed control valve malfunction. Incorrect fuel injection or pressure. Poor connections at airflow meter or throttle body.

**Rough Idle Cold** – Air valve or idle speed control valve malfunction. PCV system clogged. Incorrect fuel injection or pressure. Poor connections at airflow meter or throttle body.

**Rough Idle Warm** – PCV system clogged. Air valve or idle speed control valve malfunction. Purge valve malfunction. Incorrect fuel injection or pressure. Poor connections at airflow meter or throttle body.

**High Idle Speed** – Air valve or idle speed control valve malfunction. Poor connection at airflow meter or throttle body.

**Poor Acceleration, Hesistation or Lack of Power** - Purge valve malfunction. Poor connections at airflow meter or throttle body. Exhaust system clogged. Incorrect fuel injection or pressure. Turbo system malfunction.

**Runs Rough on Deceleration** - Fuel-cut system malfunction. Air valve or idle speed control valve malfunction. Incorrect fuel injection or pressure.

**High Fuel Consumption** - Fuel-cut system malfunction. Incorrect fuel injection or pressure. Exhaust system clogged.

**Excessive Oil Consumption** - Turbo system malfunction.

**Abnormal Noise or Vibration** - Turbo system malfunction.

**Fails Emission Test** - Exhaust system clogged. Fuel-cut system malfunction. Air valve or idle speed control valve malfunction. Purge valve malfunction. Poor connections at airflow meter or throttle body. Incorrect fuel injection or pressure.

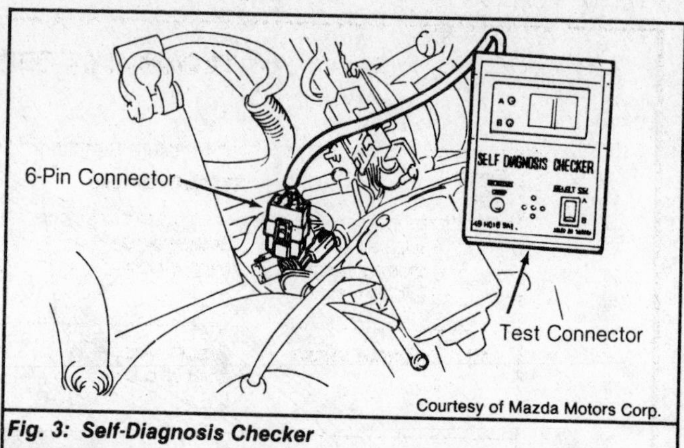
6-Pin Connector
SELF DIAGNOSIS CHECKER
Test Connector
Courtesy of Mazda Motors Corp.

*Fig. 3: Self-Diagnosis Checker*

## DIAGNOSIS & TESTING

### WITH SELF-DIAGNOSTIC CHECKER

**Trouble Code Access - 1)** Connect Self-Diagnosis Checker (49 H018 9A1) to Green 6-pin connector and negative battery terminal. *See Fig. 3.* Connector is located at back of left front wheel housing. Select position A on checker.

**2)** Ground Green 1-pin connector with jumper wire. With ignition on and engine stopped, verify code 88 flashes and buzzer sounds for 3 seconds. If okay, go to step **3)**. If code 88 does not flash, check main relay, power circuit or harness connections. If code 88 does flash and buzzer sounds continuously for more than 20 seconds, replace ECU and retest.

**3)** Note codes. Check TROUBLE CODE IDENTIFICATION chart for possible cause. If no codes are found, go to ECU VOLTAGE TESTING in this article.

**Clearing Trouble Codes - 1)** Disconnect negative battery cable. Depress brake pedal for at least 5 seconds. Reconnect battery cable.

**2)** With Self-Diagnosis Checker (49 H018 9A1) connected, ground test connector with jumper wire. Turn ignition on, but do not start engine for 6 seconds.

**3)** Start engine and run at 2000 RPM for 2 minutes. Verify no codes are displayed.

### WITHOUT SELF-DIAGNOSTIC CHECKER

**Trouble Code Access - 1)** Using jumper wire, ground Green 1-pin connector. Connector is located at back of left front wheelwell.

**2)** With ignition on and engine stopped, observe "Check Engine" or MIL light. Note trouble codes. Check TROUBLE CODE IDENTIFICATION chart for possible cause. If light remains on continuously, ECU is defective. If no codes are found, go to ECU VOLTAGE TESTING in this article.

**Clearing Trouble Codes - 1)** Disconnect negative battery cable. Depress brake pedal for at least 5 seconds. Reconnect battery cable.

**2)** Ground test connector with jumper wire. Turn ignition on, but do not start engine for 6 seconds.

**3)** Start engine and run at 2000 RPM for 2 minutes. Verify no codes are displayed.

#### TROUBLE CODE IDENTIFICATION

| Code No. | Input devices | Malfunction | Fail-safe function | Pattern of output signals (Self-Diagnosis Checker or MIL) |
|---|---|---|---|---|
| 01 | Ignition pulse (Igniter) | Broken wire, Short circuit | — | ON / OFF |
| 03 | Distributor (G signal) | Broken wire, short circuit | — | ON / OFF |
| 08 | Air flow meter | Broken wire, short circuit | Basic fuel injection amount fixed as for 2 driving modes 1) Idle switch: ON 2) Idle switch: OFF | ON / OFF |
| 09 | Water thermo sensor | Broken wire, short circuit | Coolant temp input fixed at 80°C (176°F) ...for ISC at 60°C (14°F) ...for fuel injection | ON / OFF |

Courtesy of Mazda Motors Corp.

# 1988 COMPUTERIZED ENGINE CONTROLS
# Mazda – 323 EGI (Cont.)

## TROUBLE CODE IDENTIFICATION (Cont.)

| Code No. | Output devices | | | Pattern of output signals (Self-Diagnosis Checker or MIL) |
|---|---|---|---|---|
| 10 | Intake air thermo sensor (air flow meter) | Broken wire, short circuit | Intake air temp input fixed at 20°C (68°F) | ON / OFF |
| 12 | Throttle sensor | Broken wire, short circuit | Throttle valve opening angle signal input fixed at full open | ON / OFF |
| 14 | Atmospheric preassure sensor | Broken wire, short circuit | Atmospheric pressure input fixed at 760 mmHg (29.9 inHg) | ON / OFF |
| 15 | Oxygen sensor | Oxygen sensor output below 0.55V 120 sec after engine at 1,500 rpm | Cancels EGI feedback operation | ON / OFF |
| 17 | Feedback system | $O_2$ sensor output below 0.45V 20 sec after engine exceeds 1,500 rpm | Cancels EGI feedback operation | ON / OFF |
| 25 | Solenoid valve (for pressure regulator) | | | ON / OFF |
| 26 | Solenoid valve (for vacuum switch valve) | | | ON / OFF |
| 27 | Solenoid valve (for No.1 purge control valve) | | | ON / OFF |
| 34 | Solenoid valve (for idle speed) | | | ON / OFF |

Courtesy of Mazda Motors Corp.

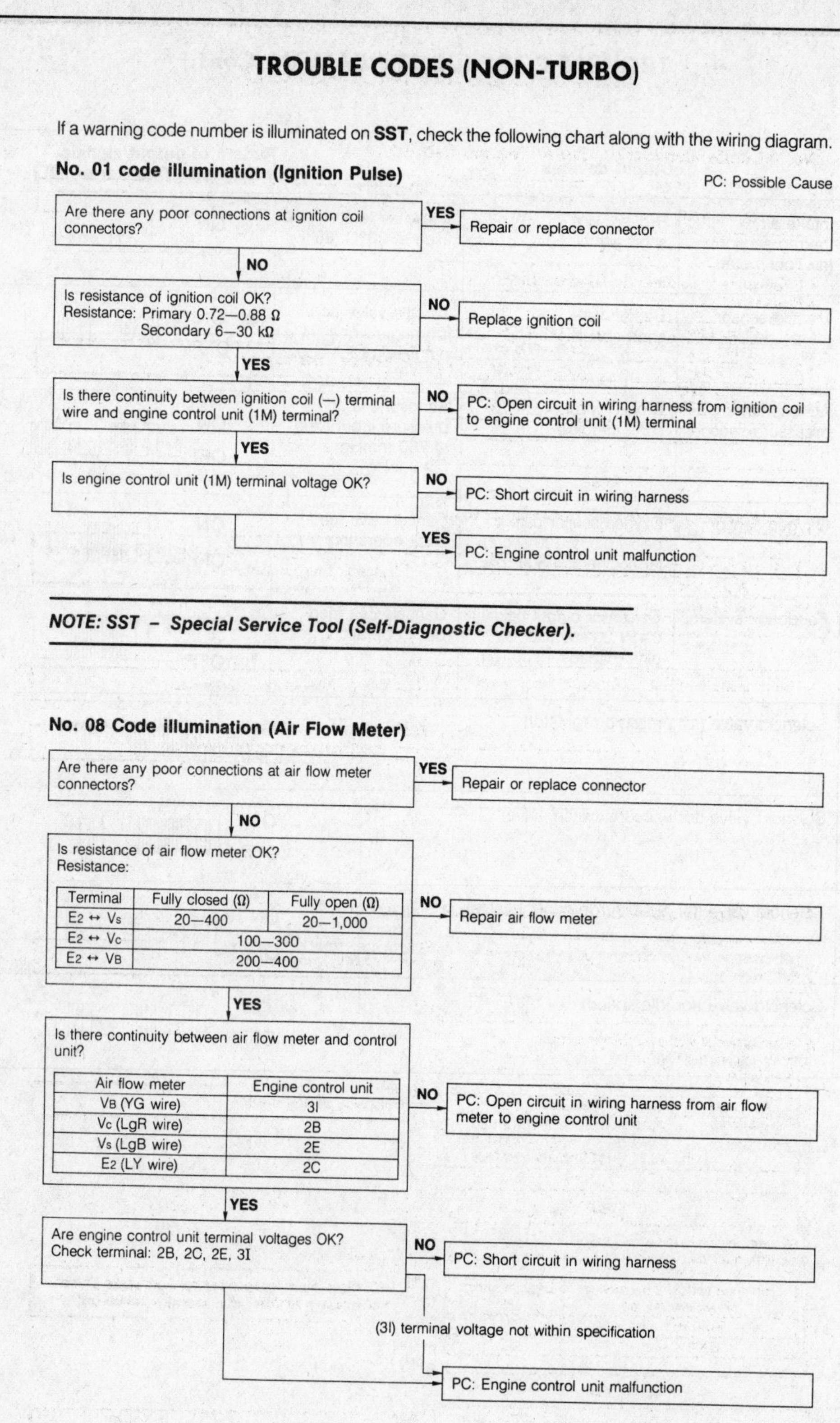
TROUBLE CODES (NON-TURBO)
If a warning code number is illuminated on SST, check the following chart along with the wiring diagram.
No. 01 code illumination (Ignition Pulse)
PC: Possible Cause
Are there any poor connections at ignition coil connectors?
YES
Repair or replace connector
NO
Is resistance of ignition coil OK?
Resistance: Primary 0.72—0.88 Ω
Secondary 6—30 kΩ
NO
Replace ignition coil
YES
Is there continuity between ignition coil (—) terminal wire and engine control unit (1M) terminal?
NO
PC: Open circuit in wiring harness from ignition coil to engine control unit (1M) terminal
YES
Is engine control unit (1M) terminal voltage OK?
NO
PC: Short circuit in wiring harness
YES
PC: Engine control unit malfunction
NOTE: SST – Special Service Tool (Self-Diagnostic Checker).
No. 08 Code illumination (Air Flow Meter)
Are there any poor connections at air flow meter connectors?
YES
Repair or replace connector
NO
Is resistance of air flow meter OK?
Resistance:
Terminal | Fully closed (Ω) | Fully open (Ω)
$E_2 \leftrightarrow V_S$ | 20—400 | 20—1,000
$E_2 \leftrightarrow V_C$ | 100—300
$E_2 \leftrightarrow V_B$ | 200—400
NO
Repair air flow meter
YES
Is there continuity between air flow meter and control unit?
Air flow meter | Engine control unit
$V_B$ (YG wire) | 3I
$V_C$ (LgR wire) | 2B
$V_S$ (LgB wire) | 2E
$E_2$ (LY wire) | 2C
NO
PC: Open circuit in wiring harness from air flow meter to engine control unit
YES
Are engine control unit terminal voltages OK?
Check terminal: 2B, 2C, 2E, 3I
NO
PC: Short circuit in wiring harness
(3I) terminal voltage not within specification
PC: Engine control unit malfunction

Courtesy of Mazda Motors Corp.

## TROUBLE CODES (NON-TURBO)

### No. 09 Code illumination (Water Thermo Sensor)

Are there any poor connections at water thermo sensor connectors?

- YES → Repair or replace connector
- NO ↓

Is resistance of the water thermo sensor OK?
Resistance:

| Coolant temp | Resistance |
| --- | --- |
| –20°C (–4°F) | 14.6—17.8 kΩ |
| 20°C (68°F) | 2.21—2.69 kΩ |
| 40°C (104°F) | 1.0—1.3 kΩ |
| 60°C (140°F) | 0.49—0.67 kΩ |
| 80°C (176°F) | 0.29—0.35 kΩ |

- NO → Replace water thermo sensor
- YES ↓

Is there continuity between water thermo sensor and engine control unit?

| Water thermo sensor | Engine control unit |
| --- | --- |
| A (LR wire) | 2I |
| B (LY wire) | 2C |

- NO → PC: Open circuit in wiring harness from water thermo sensor to engine control unit
- YES ↓

Are engine control unit (2I) and (2C) terminal voltages OK?

- NO → PC: Short circuit in wiring harness
- YES → PC: Engine control unit malfunction

### No. 10 Code illumination (Intake Air Thermo Sensor)

Are there any poor connections at air flow meter connectors?

- YES → Repair or replace connector
- NO ↓

Is resistance of intake air thermo sensor (in air flow meter) OK?
Resistance:

| Terminal | Resistance |
| --- | --- |
| $E_2$ ↔ THA | –20°C (–4°F) : 14.6—17.8 kΩ<br>20°C (68°F) : 2.21—2.69 kΩ<br>60°C (140°F): 0.49—0.67 kΩ |

- NO → Replace air flow meter
- YES ↓

Is there continuity between intake air thermo sensor (in air flow meter) and engine control unit?

| Intake air temperature sensor (in air flow meter) | Engine control unit |
| --- | --- |
| THA (BrY wire) | 2J |
| $E_2$ (LY wire) | 2C |

- NO → PC: Open circuit in wiring harness from intake air thermo sensor (in air flow meter) to engine control unit
- YES ↓

Are engine control unit (2J) and (2C) terminal voltages OK?

- NO → PC: Short circuit in wiring harness
- YES → PC: Engine control unit malfunction

Courtesy of Mazda Motors Corp.

## TROUBLE CODES (NON-TURBO)

### No. 14 Code illumination (Atmospheric Pressure Sensor)

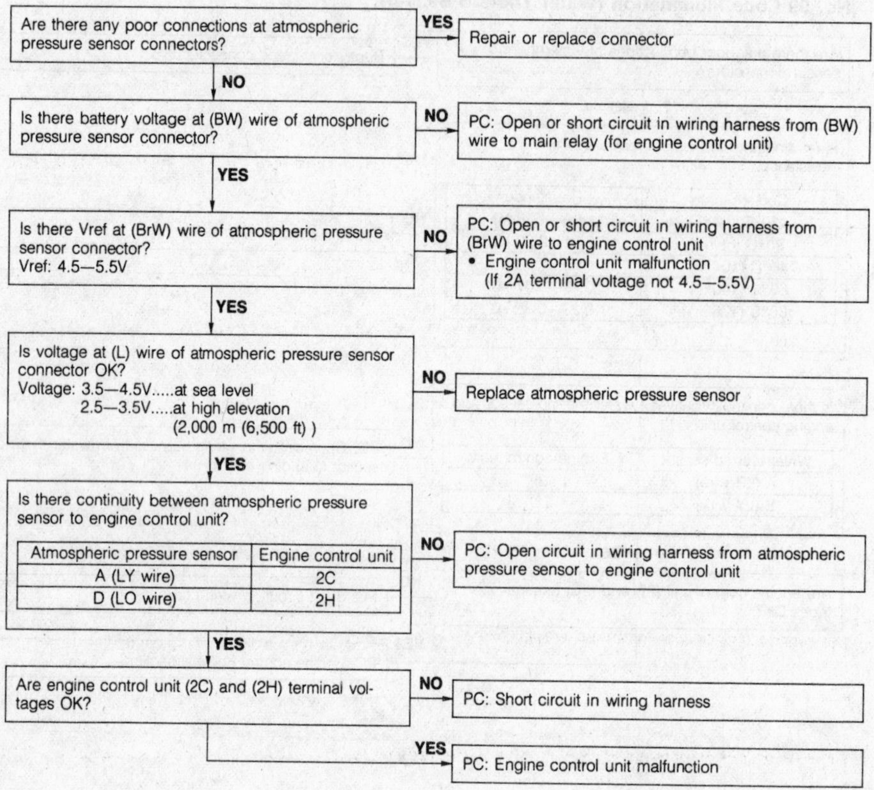
Are there any poor connections at atmospheric pressure sensor connectors?
YES
Repair or replace connector
NO
Is there battery voltage at (BW) wire of atmospheric pressure sensor connector?
NO
PC: Open or short circuit in wiring harness from (BW) wire to main relay (for engine control unit)
YES
Is there Vref at (BrW) wire of atmospheric pressure sensor connector?
Vref: 4.5—5.5V
NO
PC: Open or short circuit in wiring harness from (BrW) wire to engine control unit
• Engine control unit malfunction
(If 2A terminal voltage not 4.5—5.5V)
YES
Is voltage at (L) wire of atmospheric pressure sensor connector OK?
Voltage: 3.5—4.5V.....at sea level
2.5—3.5V.....at high elevation
(2,000 m (6,500 ft) )
NO
Replace atmospheric pressure sensor
YES
Is there continuity between atmospheric pressure sensor to engine control unit?
Atmospheric pressure sensor
Engine control unit
A (LY wire)
2C
D (LO wire)
2H
NO
PC: Open circuit in wiring harness from atmospheric pressure sensor to engine control unit
YES
Are engine control unit (2C) and (2H) terminal voltages OK?
NO
PC: Short circuit in wiring harness
YES
PC: Engine control unit malfunction

### No. 15 Code illumination (Oxygen Sensor)

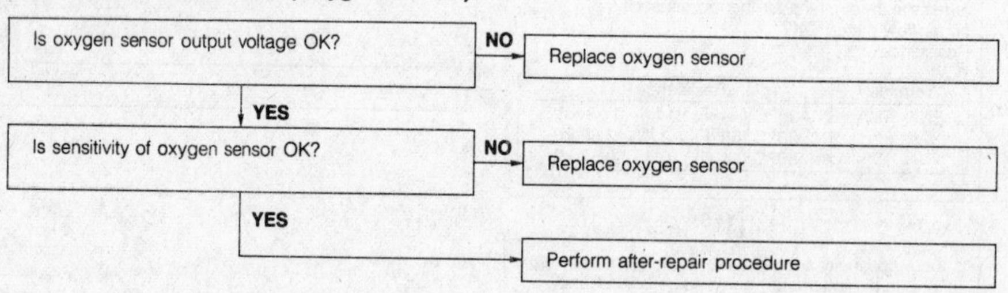
Is oxygen sensor output voltage OK?
NO
Replace oxygen sensor
YES
Is sensitivity of oxygen sensor OK?
NO
Replace oxygen sensor
YES
Perform after-repair procedure

Courtesy of Mazda Motors Corp.

## TROUBLE CODES (NON-TURBO)

### No. 17 Code illumination (Feedback System)

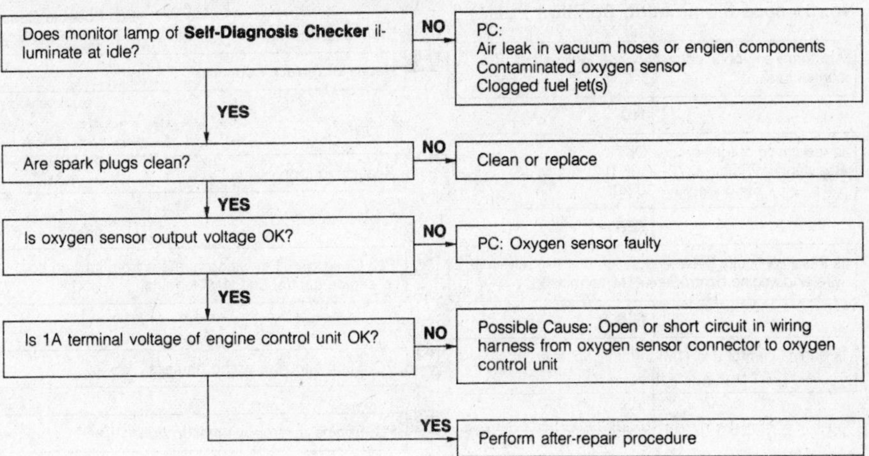
Does monitor lamp of **Self-Diagnosis Checker** illuminate at idle?
NO
PC:
Air leak in vacuum hoses or engien components
Contaminated oxygen sensor
Clogged fuel jet(s)
YES
Are spark plugs clean?
NO
Clean or replace
YES
Is oxygen sensor output voltage OK?
NO
PC: Oxygen sensor faulty
YES
Is 1A terminal voltage of engine control unit OK?
NO
Possible Cause: Open or short circuit in wiring harness from oxygen sensor connector to oxygen control unit
YES
Perform after-repair procedure

### No. 26, 27 Code illuminate (Solenoid Valve)

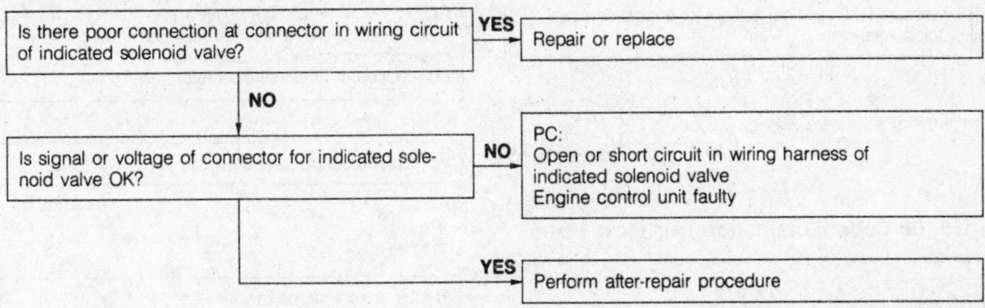
Is there poor connection at connector in wiring circuit of indicated solenoid valve?
YES
Repair or replace
NO
Is signal or voltage of connector for indicated solenoid valve OK?
NO
PC:
Open or short circuit in wiring harness of indicated solenoid valve
Engine control unit faulty
YES
Perform after-repair procedure

### No. 34 Code illuminate (BAC valve)

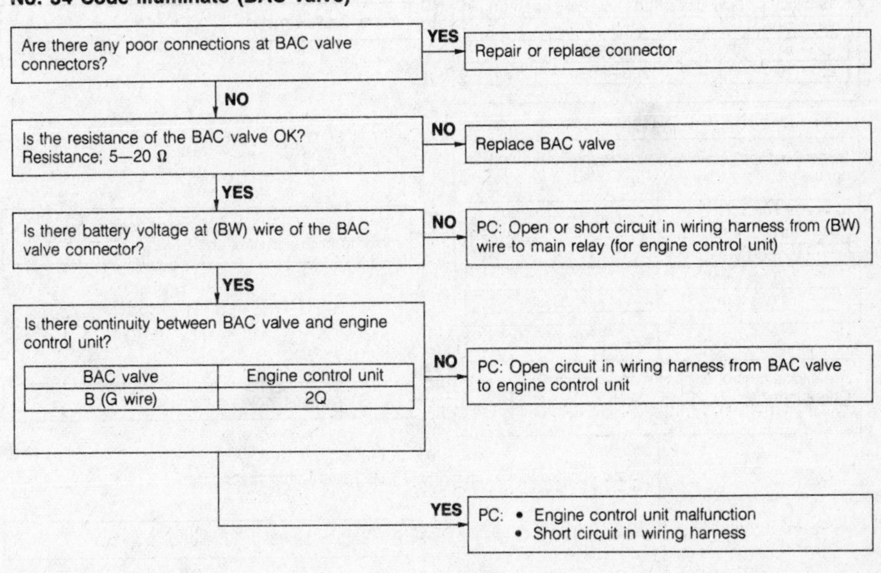
Are there any poor connections at BAC valve connectors?
YES
Repair or replace connector
NO
Is the resistance of the BAC valve OK? Resistance; 5—20 Ω
NO
Replace BAC valve
YES
Is there battery voltage at (BW) wire of the BAC valve connector?
NO
PC: Open or short circuit in wiring harness from (BW) wire to main relay (for engine control unit)
YES
Is there continuity between BAC valve and engine control unit?
BAC valve | Engine control unit
B (G wire) | 2Q
NO
PC: Open circuit in wiring harness from BAC valve to engine control unit
YES
PC: • Engine control unit malfunction
• Short circuit in wiring harness

Courtesy of Mazda Motors Corp.

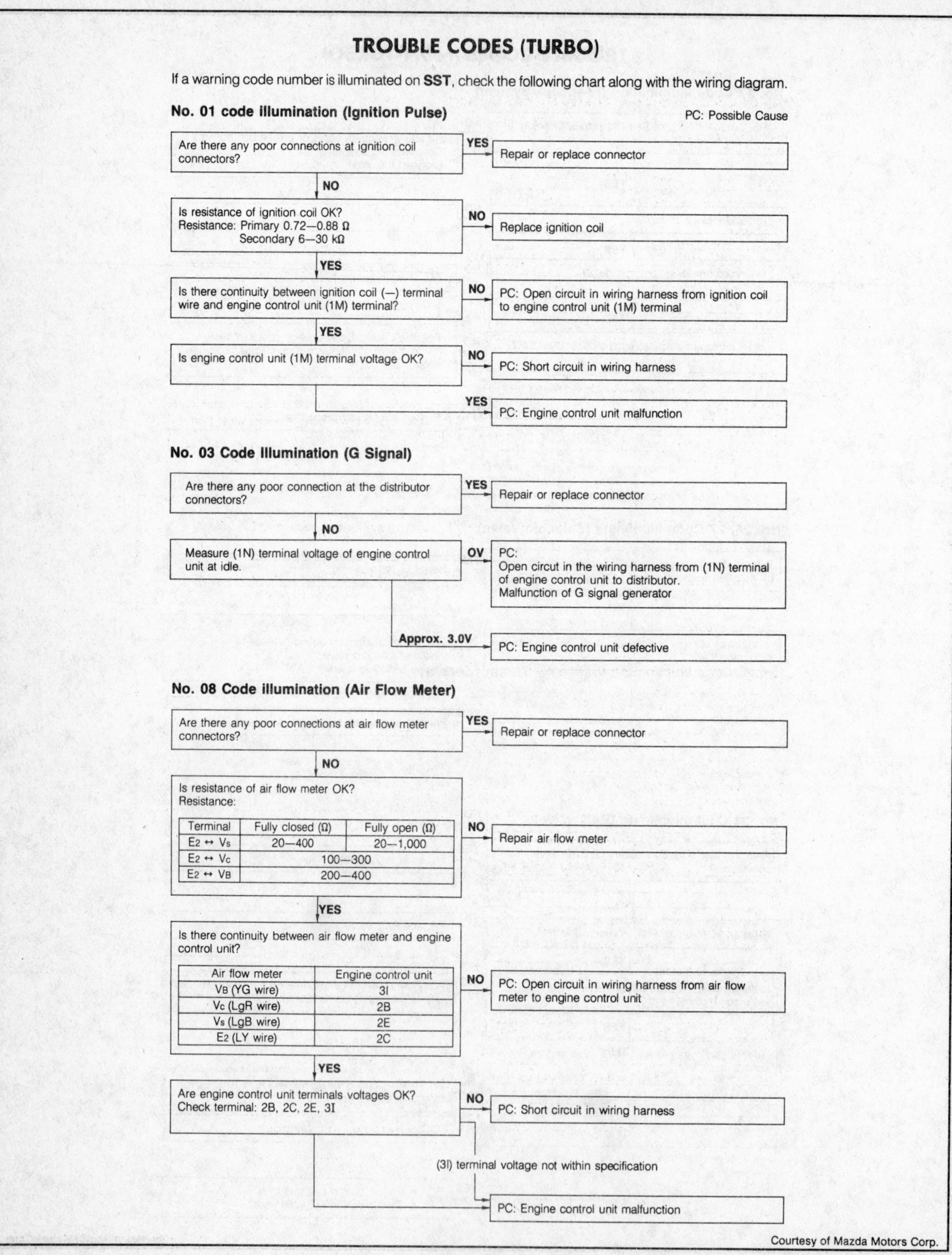
TROUBLE CODES (TURBO)
If a warning code number is illuminated on SST, check the following chart along with the wiring diagram.
No. 01 code illumination (Ignition Pulse)
PC: Possible Cause
Are there any poor connections at ignition coil connectors?
YES
Repair or replace connector
NO
Is resistance of ignition coil OK? Resistance: Primary 0.72—0.88 Ω Secondary 6—30 kΩ
NO
Replace ignition coil
YES
Is there continuity between ignition coil (—) terminal wire and engine control unit (1M) terminal?
NO
PC: Open circuit in wiring harness from ignition coil to engine control unit (1M) terminal
YES
Is engine control unit (1M) terminal voltage OK?
NO
PC: Short circuit in wiring harness
YES
PC: Engine control unit malfunction
No. 03 Code Illumination (G Signal)
Are there any poor connection at the distributor connectors?
YES
Repair or replace connector
NO
Measure (1N) terminal voltage of engine control unit at idle.
OV
PC: Open circuit in the wiring harness from (1N) terminal of engine control unit to distributor. Malfunction of G signal generator
Approx. 3.0V
PC: Engine control unit defective
No. 08 Code illumination (Air Flow Meter)
Are there any poor connections at air flow meter connectors?
YES
Repair or replace connector
NO
Is resistance of air flow meter OK? Resistance:
Terminal | Fully closed (Ω) | Fully open (Ω)
E2 ↔ Vs | 20—400 | 20—1,000
E2 ↔ Vc | 100—300
E2 ↔ VB | 200—400
NO
Repair air flow meter
YES
Is there continuity between air flow meter and engine control unit?
Air flow meter | Engine control unit
VB (YG wire) | 3I
Vc (LgR wire) | 2B
Vs (LgB wire) | 2E
E2 (LY wire) | 2C
NO
PC: Open circuit in wiring harness from air flow meter to engine control unit
YES
Are engine control unit terminals voltages OK? Check terminal: 2B, 2C, 2E, 3I
NO
PC: Short circuit in wiring harness
(3I) terminal voltage not within specification
PC: Engine control unit malfunction
Courtesy of Mazda Motors Corp.

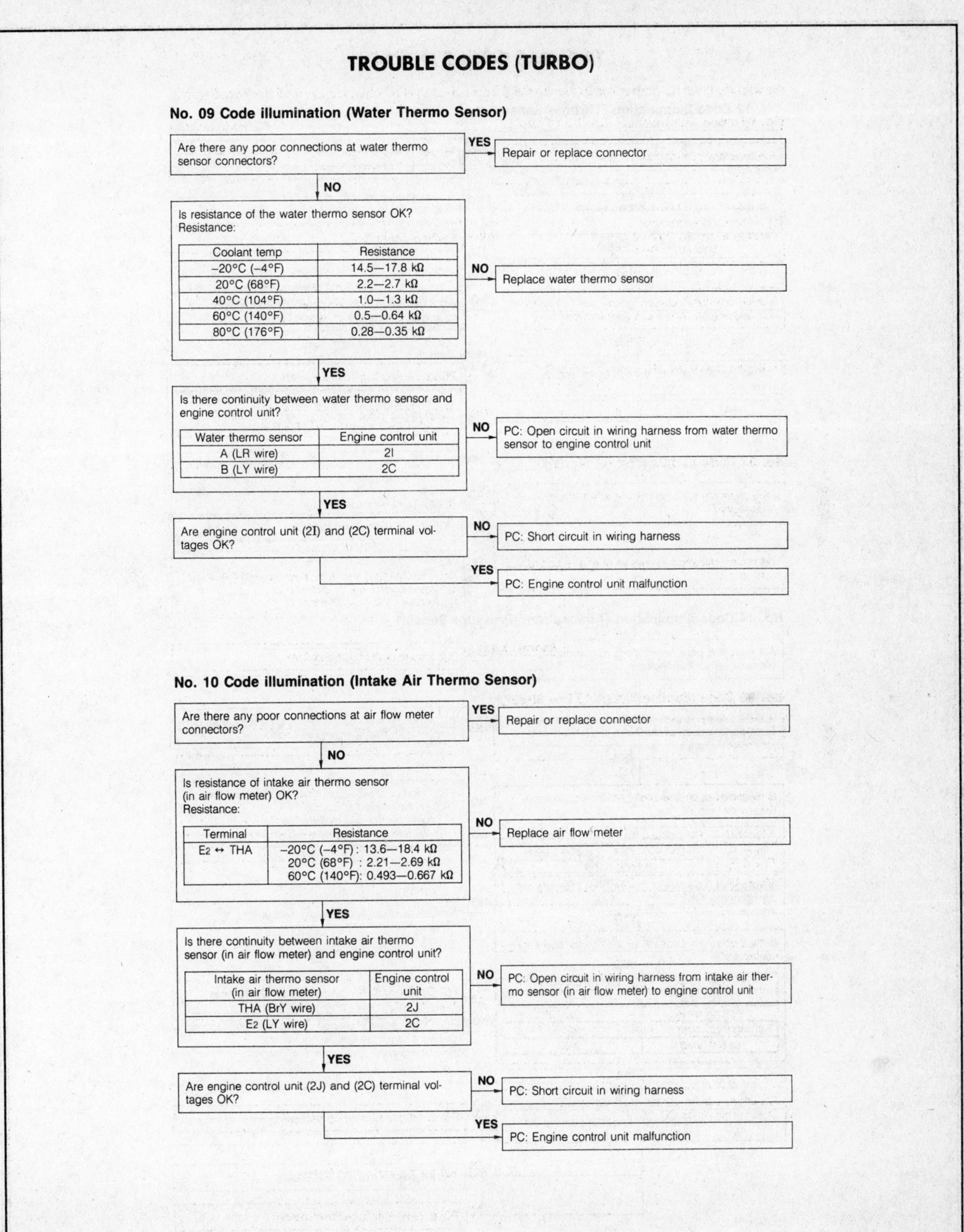

## TROUBLE CODES (TURBO)

### No. 09 Code illumination (Water Thermo Sensor)

Are there any poor connections at water thermo sensor connectors?
- YES → Repair or replace connector
- NO ↓

Is resistance of the water thermo sensor OK?
Resistance:

| Coolant temp | Resistance |
|---|---|
| −20°C (−4°F) | 14.5—17.8 kΩ |
| 20°C (68°F) | 2.2—2.7 kΩ |
| 40°C (104°F) | 1.0—1.3 kΩ |
| 60°C (140°F) | 0.5—0.64 kΩ |
| 80°C (176°F) | 0.28—0.35 kΩ |

- NO → Replace water thermo sensor
- YES ↓

Is there continuity between water thermo sensor and engine control unit?

| Water thermo sensor | Engine control unit |
|---|---|
| A (LR wire) | 2I |
| B (LY wire) | 2C |

- NO → PC: Open circuit in wiring harness from water thermo sensor to engine control unit
- YES ↓

Are engine control unit (2I) and (2C) terminal voltages OK?
- NO → PC: Short circuit in wiring harness
- YES → PC: Engine control unit malfunction

### No. 10 Code illumination (Intake Air Thermo Sensor)

Are there any poor connections at air flow meter connectors?
- YES → Repair or replace connector
- NO ↓

Is resistance of intake air thermo sensor (in air flow meter) OK?
Resistance:

| Terminal | Resistance |
|---|---|
| $E_2$ ↔ THA | −20°C (−4°F): 13.6—18.4 kΩ<br>20°C (68°F) : 2.21—2.69 kΩ<br>60°C (140°F): 0.493—0.667 kΩ |

- NO → Replace air flow meter
- YES ↓

Is there continuity between intake air thermo sensor (in air flow meter) and engine control unit?

| Intake air thermo sensor (in air flow meter) | Engine control unit |
|---|---|
| THA (BrY wire) | 2J |
| $E_2$ (LY wire) | 2C |

- NO → PC: Open circuit in wiring harness from intake air thermo sensor (in air flow meter) to engine control unit
- YES ↓

Are engine control unit (2J) and (2C) terminal voltages OK?
- NO → PC: Short circuit in wiring harness
- YES → PC: Engine control unit malfunction

Courtesy of Mazda Motors Corp.

## TROUBLE CODES (TURBO)

### ,. 12 Code Illumination (Throttle Sensor)

- Are there any poor connections at throttle sensor connectors?
  - YES → Repair or replace connector the terminal
  - NO ↓
- Is the resistance of the throttle sensor O.K?
  - NO → Replace the throttle sensor
  - YES ↓
- Is there 4.5—5.5V at the (1C) terminal of the throttle sensor connector?
  - NO → PC: Open or short circuit in the wiring harness from the (1C) terminal to the throttle senser to engine control unit. Engine control unit defective
  - YES ↓
- Measure (2G) terminal voltage of the engine control unit
  - More than 4.5V → PC: Open circuit in the wiring harness from (1A) terminal of throttle sensor to engine control unit. Open circuit in the wiring harness of gound
  - Less than 0.25V → PC: Short circuit in the wiring harness from (1A) terminal of throttle sensor to engine control unit.
  - 0.25—4.5V → PC: Engine control unit defective

### No. 14 Code illumination (Atmospheric Pressure Sensor)

- Are there any poor connections at atmospheric pressure sensor connectors?
  - YES → Repair or replace connector
  - NO ↓
- Is there battery voltage at (WB) wire of atmospheric pressure sensor connector?
  - NO → PC: Open or short circuit in wiring harness from (WB) wire to main relay (for engine control unit)
  - YES ↓
- Is there Vref at (YG) wire of atmospheric pressure sensor connector? Vref: 4.5—5.5V
  - NO → PC: Open or short circuit in wiring harness from (YG) wire to control unit
    - Engine control unit malfunction (If 2A terminal voltage not 4.5—5.5V)
  - YES ↓
- Is voltage at (LO) wire of atmospheric pressure sensor connector OK? Voltage: 3.5—4.5V.....at sea level; 2.5—3.5V.....at high elevation (2,000 m (6,500 ft) )
  - NO → Replace atmospheric pressure sensor
  - YES ↓
- Is there continuity between atmospheric pressure sensor to engine control unit?

| Atmospheric pressure sensor | Engine control unit |
|---|---|
| A (LY wire) | 2C |
| D (LO wire) | 2H |

  - NO → PC: Open circuit in wiring harness from atmospheric pressure sensor to engine control unit
  - YES ↓
- Are engine control unit (2C) and (2H) terminal voltages OK?
  - NO → PC: Short circuit in wiring harness
  - YES → PC: Engine control unit malfunction

Courtesy of Mazda Motors Corp.

## TROUBLE CODES (TURBO)

**No. 15 code display illumination (Oxygen Sensor)**

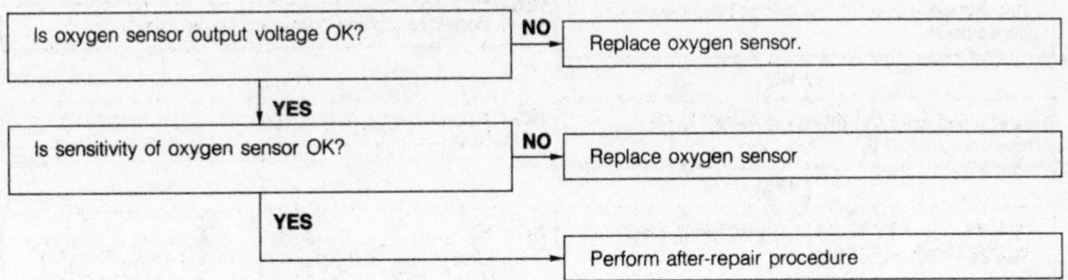
Is oxygen sensor output voltage OK?
NO
Replace oxygen sensor.
YES
Is sensitivity of oxygen sensor OK?
NO
Replace oxygen sensor
YES
Perform after-repair procedure

**No. 17 code display illumination (Feedback System)**

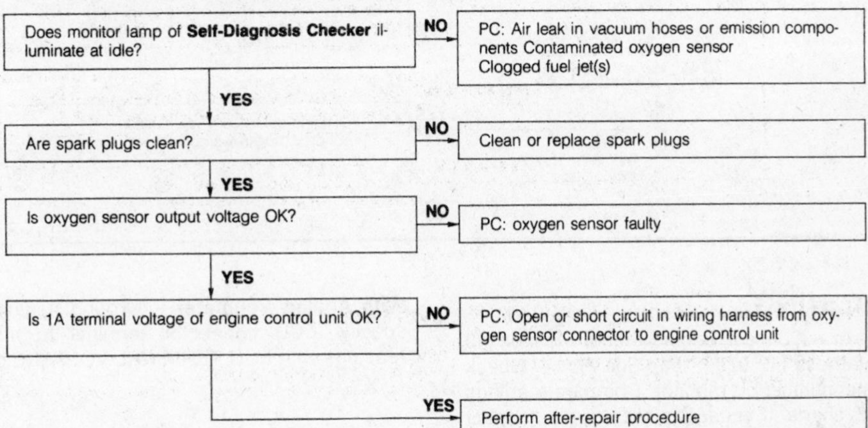
Does monitor lamp of Self-Diagnosis Checker illuminate at idle?
NO
PC: Air leak in vacuum hoses or emission components Contaminated oxygen sensor Clogged fuel jet(s)
YES
Are spark plugs clean?
NO
Clean or replace spark plugs
YES
Is oxygen sensor output voltage OK?
NO
PC: oxygen sensor faulty
YES
Is 1A terminal voltage of engine control unit OK?
NO
PC: Open or short circuit in wiring harness from oxygen sensor connector to engine control unit
YES
Perform after-repair procedure

**No. 25, 26, 27 code illumination (Solenoid Valve)**

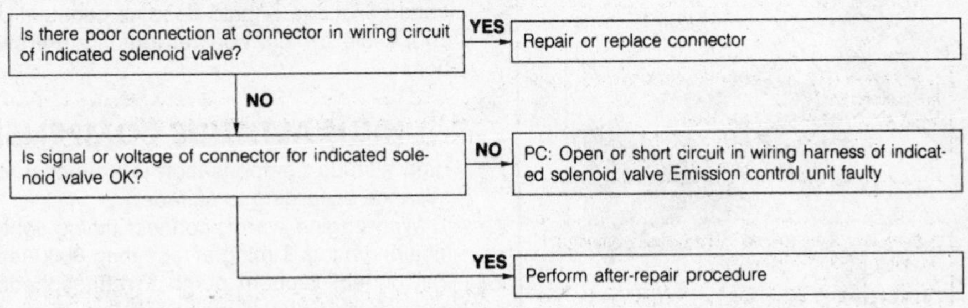
Is there poor connection at connector in wiring circuit of indicated solenoid valve?
YES
Repair or replace connector
NO
Is signal or voltage of connector for indicated solenoid valve OK?
NO
PC: Open or short circuit in wiring harness of indicated solenoid valve Emission control unit faulty
YES
Perform after-repair procedure

Courtesy of Mazda Motors Corp.

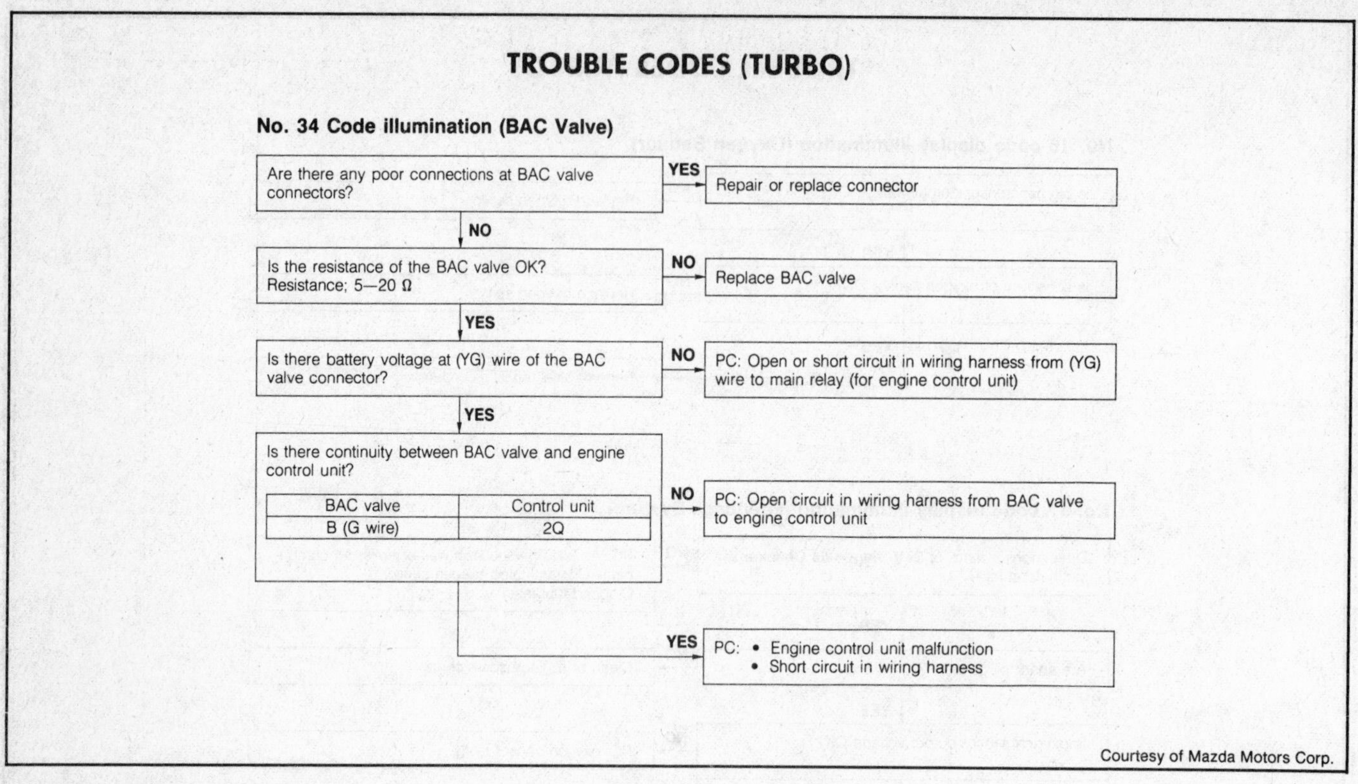
TROUBLE CODES (TURBO)
No. 34 Code illumination (BAC Valve)
Are there any poor connections at BAC valve connectors?
YES
Repair or replace connector
NO
Is the resistance of the BAC valve OK? Resistance; 5—20 Ω
NO
Replace BAC valve
YES
Is there battery voltage at (YG) wire of the BAC valve connector?
NO
PC: Open or short circuit in wiring harness from (YG) wire to main relay (for engine control unit)
YES
Is there continuity between BAC valve and engine control unit?
BAC valve
Control unit
B (G wire)
2Q
NO
PC: Open circuit in wiring harness from BAC valve to engine control unit
YES
PC: • Engine control unit malfunction
• Short circuit in wiring harness
Courtesy of Mazda Motors Corp.

## ECU VOLTAGE TESTING

**With Engine Signal Monitor** – Connect Engine Signal Monitor (49 9200 162) with Adapter Harness (49 9200 163). *See Fig. 4.* Check voltage by selecting terminal number on monitor. Compare readings with TERMINAL VOLTAGE charts. If voltage is not correct, inspect components or harness. If no trouble is found, replace ECU.

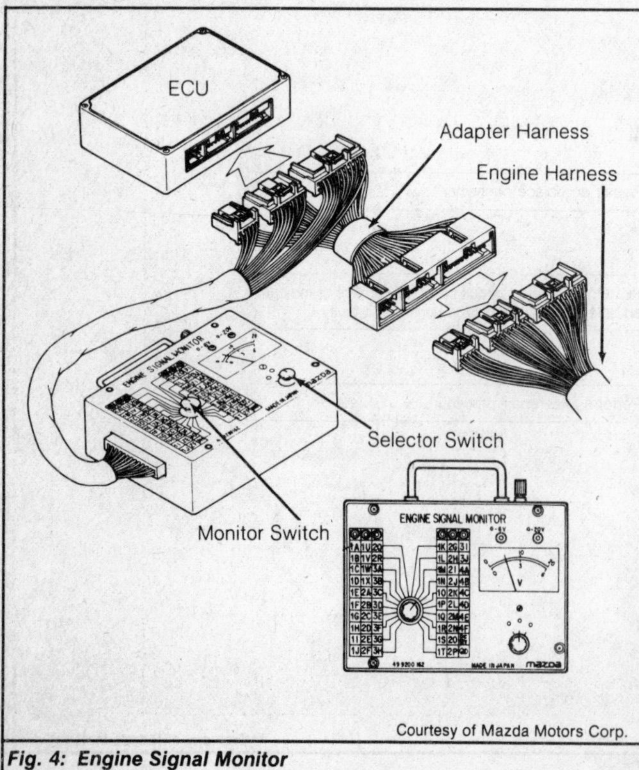
ECU
Adapter Harness
Engine Harness
Selector Switch
Monitor Switch
ENGINE SIGNAL MONITOR
Courtesy of Mazda Motors Corp.

*Fig. 4: Engine Signal Monitor*

**With Analog Voltmeter** – Ground negative lead. Backprobe each specific ECU connector terminal to monitor voltage. Compare readings with ECU TERMINAL VOLTAGE charts.

## DECELERATION CONTROL SYSTEM

Deceleration control system is a function of ECU. It provides fuel cut during deceleration.

**1)** Connect Engine Signal Monitor (49 9200 162) or backprobe ECU connector terminals No. 3C or 3E with voltmeter. Start engine. Voltage should pulsate.

**2)** Increase engine speed to 4000 RPM. Suddenly decrease engine speed. Voltage should become constant during deceleration. If not, check idle switch, coolant temperature switch and all ECU connections.

## HIGH ALTITUDE COMPENSATION SYSTEM

High altitude compensation is a function of ECU. It provides timing advance according to altitude.

**1)** With engine warm, connect timing light to No. 1 cylinder. Check ignition timing. Timing at less than 3000 feet should be 7° BTDC.

**2)** Connect vacuum pump to atmospheric pressure sensor. Apply vacuum and check ignition timing. Timing should advance to 13° BTDC.

**3)** If not, inspect atmospheric pressure sensor and ECU. Ensure altitude is not greater than 3000 feet.

## COMPONENT TESTING

**Airflow Meter** – Inspect airflow meter for damage and ensure measuring plate moves smoothly. Disconnect airflow meter connector. *See Fig. 5.* Measure resistance using AIRFLOW METER TERMINAL RESISTANCE table.

### ECU TERMINAL VOLTAGE TURBO

| Terminal | Connected to | Voltage | Condition | Remark |
|---|---|---|---|---|
| 1A (Output) | MIL | Below 2.5V | Ignition switch OFF → ON for 3 sec. | Test connector grounded |
| | | Approx. 12V | After 3 sec. | |
| 1B (Output) | Self-Diagnosis Checker (for Code No.) | Below 2.5V | Ignition switch OFF → ON for 3 sec. | Test connector grounded Checker connected |
| | | Approx. 12V | After 3 sec. | |
| 1C | — | — | — | — |
| 1D (Output) | Self-Diagnosis Checker (for Monitor lamp) | Approx. 5V | Ignition switch OFF → ON for 3 sec. | Test connector grounded Checker connected |
| | | Approx. 10V | After 3 sec. | |
| 1E (Input) | Throttle sensor (IDL switch) | Approx. 12V | Accelerator pedal depressed | |
| | | Below 1.5V | Accelerator pedal released | |
| 1F (Output) | A/C control relay | Approx. 12V | Ignition switch ON | |
| | | Below 1.5V | A/C switch ON (at idle) | |
| 1G (Input) | Neutral/clutch switch | Approx. 12V | Clutch pedal depressed | In-gear condition (Neutral switch: Constant 12V) |
| | | Below 1.5V | Clutch pedal released | |
| 1H (Input) | Water thermo switch (Radiator) | Approx. 12V | Below 17°C (63°F) | |
| | | Below 1.5V | Above 17°C (63°F) | |
| 1I (Input) | Electrical load (E/L) switch | Approx. 2.5V | E/L switch ON | |
| | | Approx. 10V | E/L switch OFF | |
| 1J (Input) | Brake light switch | Approx. 12V | Brake pedal depressed | |
| | | Below 1.5V | Brake pedal released | |
| 1K (Input) | Power steering switch | Approx. 12V | Power steering switch OFF | |
| | | Below 1.5V | Power steering switch ON | |
| 1L (Input) | A/C switch | Approx. 12V | A/C switch OFF | Blower motor ON |
| | | Below 2.5V | A/C switch ON | |
| 1M (Input) | Ignition coil | Approx. 12V | Ignition switch ON | (When engine running) Engine Signal Monitor: Green and red light flash |
| | | Approx. 12V | At idle | |
| 1N | G sensor (Distributor) | Below 1.5V | Ignition switch ON | |
| | | Approx. 3V | At idle | |
| 1O | — | — | — | — |
| 1P | — | — | — | — |
| 1Q | — | — | — | — |
| 1R | — | — | — | — |
| 1S | — | — | — | — |
| 1T | — | — | — | — |
| 1U (Output) | Knock control unit (I terminal) | Below 1.5V | Ignition switch ON | |
| | | Approx. 12V | At idle | |
| 1V (Input) | FF switch (ground) | Below 1.5V | 4x4 | |
| | | Approx. 12V | FF | |
| 1W (Input) | Test connector | Below 1.5V | Test connector grounded | |
| | | Approx. 12V | Test connector not grounded | |
| 1X | — | — | — | — |
| 2A (Output) | Vref | 4.5—5.5V | — | — |
| 2B (Input) | Air flow meter (Vc) | 7—9V | — | — |
| 2C | Ground ($E_2$) | Below 1.5V | — | — |
| 2D (Input) | Oxygen sensor | 0.3—0.7V | At idle | |
| | | More than 0.45V | During acceleration | |
| | | Less than 0.45V | During deceleration | |

Courtesy of Mazda Motors Corp.

## ECU TERMINAL VOLTAGE TURBO (Cont.)

| Terminal | Connected to | Voltage | Condition | Remark |
|---|---|---|---|---|
| 2E (Input) | Air flow meter (Vs) | Approx. 2V | Ignition switch ON | |
| | | 4—5V | At idle | |
| 2F | — | — | — | — |
| 2G (Input) | Throttle sensor | Approx. 0.5V | Accelerator pedal released | |
| | | Approx. 12V | Accelerator pedal depressed | |
| 2H (Input) | Atmospheric pressure sensor | Approx. 4V | — | At sea level |
| 2I (Input) | Water thermo sensor | Approx. 0.5V | Normal operating temperature | |
| 2J (Input) | Intake air thermo sensor (Air flow meter) | 2—3V | Intake air temperature: 20°C (68°F) | |
| 2K (Output) | Pressure regulator control valve (PRCV) solenoid | Below 2.5V | Intake air temp. more than 58°C (136°F) Water temp. more than 90°C (194°F) | |
| | | Approx. 12V | Other | |
| 2L (Output) | Pressure switch | Approx. 12V | At idle | Air pressure 71.8—79.8 kPa (0.73—0.81 kg/cm$^2$, 10.4—11.6 psi) |
| | | Below 1.5V | At overboost | |
| 2M (Output) | Knock control unit (f terminal) | Below 1.5V | At idle | Coolant temp: More than 80°C (176°F) Intake air temp: More than 0°C (32°F) |
| | | Approx. 12V | Engine speed 1,000 rpm (Positive pressure) | |
| 2N (Output) | Indicator light | Approx. 12V | At idle | 71.8—79.8 kPa (0.73—0.81 kg/cm$^2$, 10.4—11.6 psi) |
| | | Below 1.5V | At overboost | |
| 2O | No.2 purge control solenoid | Approx. 12V | Less than 1,500 rpm | |
| | | Below 1.5V | More than 1,500 rpm | |
| 2P | No.1 purge control valve solenoid | Below 1.5V | Intake air temp. more than 50°C (122°F) Water temp. more than 50°C (122°F) | In-gear condition. Jumper wire connect to the Neutral switch |
| | | Approx. 12V | Other | |
| 2Q | Idle speed control (ISC) valve | 1.5—11.6V | At idle | Engine Signal Monitor: Green and red light flash |
| 2R | Ground | Below 1.5V | — | — |
| 3A | Ground | Below 1.5V | — | — |
| 3B | Starter switch | Below 2.5V | Ignition switch ON | |
| | | 7—9V | While cranking | |
| 3C | Injector No.2, No.4 | Approx. 12V | At idle | Engine Signal Monitor: Green and red light flash |
| 3D | — | — | — | — |
| 3E | Injector No.1, No.3 | Approx. 12V | At idle | Engine signal Monitor: Green and red light flash |
| 3F | — | — | — | — |
| 3G | Ground | Below 1.5V | — | — |
| 3H | — | — | — | — |
| 3I | Main relay | Approx. 12V | Ignition switch ON | |
| 3J | Battery | Approx. 12V | — | — |

**EGI control unit connector**

| 3I | 3G | 3E | 3C | 3A | 2Q | 2O | 2M | 2K | 2I | 2G | 2E | 2C | 2A | 1W | 1U | 1S | 1Q | 1O | 1M | 1K | 1I | 1G | 1E | 1C | 1A |
|---|---|---|---|---|---|---|---|---|---|---|---|---|---|---|---|---|---|---|---|---|---|---|---|---|---|
| 3J | 3H | 3F | 3D | 3B | 2R | 2P | 2N | 2L | 2J | 2H | 2F | 2D | 2B | 1X | 1V | 1T | 1R | 1P | 1N | 1L | 1J | 1H | 1F | 1D | 1B |

# 1988 COMPUTERIZED ENGINE CONTROLS
# Mazda – 323 EGI (Cont.)

## ECU TERMINAL VOLTAGE NON-TURBO

| Terminal | Connected to | Voltage | Condition | Remark |
|---|---|---|---|---|
| 1A (Output) | MIL | Below 2.5V | Ignition switch OFF → ON for 3 sec. | Test connector grounded |
| | | Approx. 12V | After 3 sec. | |
| 1B (Output) | Self-Diagnosis Checker (for Code No.) | Below 2.5V | Ignition switch OFF → ON for 3 sec. | • Test connector grounded • Checker connected |
| | | Approx. 12V | After 3 sec. | |
| 1C | — | — | — | — |
| 1D (Output) | Self-Diagnosis Checker (for Monitor lamp) | Approx. 5V | Ignition switch OFF → ON for 3 sec. | • Test connector grounded • Checker connected |
| | | Approx. 10V | After 3 sec. | |
| 1E (Input) | Throttle sensor (IDL switch) | Approx. 12V | Accelerator pedal depressed | |
| | | Below 1.5V | Accelerator pedal released | |
| 1F (Output) | A/C control relay | Approx. 12V | Ignition switch ON | |
| | | Below 1.5V | A/C switch ON (at idle) | |
| 1G (Input) | Neutral/clutch switch | Approx. 12V | Clutch pedal depressed | In-gear condition |
| | | Below 1.5V | Clutch pedal released | |
| 1H (Input) | Water thermo switch (Radiator) | Approx. 12V | Below 17°C (63°F) | |
| | | Below 1.5V | Above 17°C (63°F) | |
| 1I (Input) | Electrical load (E/L) switch | Approx. 2.5V | E/L switch ON | |
| | | Approx. 10V | E/L switch OFF | |
| 1J (Input) | Brake light switch | Approx. 12V | Brake pedal depressed | |
| | | Below 1.5V | Brake pedal released | |
| 1K (Input) | Power steering switch | Approx. 12V | Power steering switch OFF | |
| | | Below 1.5V | Power steering switch ON | |
| 1L (Input) | A/C switch | Approx. 12V | A/C switch OFF | Blower motor ON |
| | | Below 2.5V | A/C switch ON | |
| 1M (Input) | Ignition coil | Approx. 12V | Ignition switch ON | (When engine running) Engine Signal Monitor: Green and red light flash |
| | | Approx. 12V | At idle | |
| 1N | — | — | — | — |
| 1O | — | — | — | — |
| 1P | — | — | — | — |
| 1Q | — | — | — | — |
| 1R | — | — | — | — |
| 1S | — | — | — | — |
| 1T | — | — | — | — |
| 1U (Output) | Igniter | Below 1.5V | Ignition switch ON | |
| | | Approx. 12V | At idle | |
| 1V (Input) | MT switch (ground) | Below 1.5V | — | AT constant 12V |
| 1W (Input) | Test connector | Below 1.5V | Test connector grounded | |
| | | Approx. 12V | Test connector not grounded | |
| 1X | — | — | — | — |
| 2A (Output) | Vref | 4.5—5.5V | — | — |
| 2B (Input) | Air flow meter (Vc) | 7—9V | — | — |
| 2C | Ground (E2) | Below 1.5V | — | — |
| 2D (Input) | Oxygen sensor | 0.3—0.7V | At idle | |
| | | More than 0.45V | During acceleration | |
| | | Less than 0.45V | During acceleration | |
| 2E (Input) | Air flow meter (Vs) | Approx. 2V | Ignition switch ON | |
| | | 4—5V | At idle | |
| 2F | — | — | — | — |
| 2G (Input) | Throttle sensor (PSW switch) | Approx. 12V | Accelerator pedal released | |
| | | Below 1.5V | Accelerator pedal depressed (fully open throttle) | |
| 2H (Input) | Atmospheric pressure sensor | Approx. 4V | — | At sea level |
| 2I (Input) | Water thermo sensor | Approx. 0.5V | Normal operating temperature | |
| 2J (Input) | Intake air thermo sensor (Air flow meter) | 2—3V | Intake air temperature: 20°C (68°F) | |

Courtesy of Mazda Motors Corp.

## ECU TERMINAL VOLTAGE NON-TURBO (Cont.)

| Terminal | Connected to | Voltage | Condition | Remark |
|---|---|---|---|---|
| 2K (Output) | Pressure regulator control valve (PRCV) solenoid | Below 1.5V | Intake air temp. more than 58°C (136°F) Water temp. more than 90°C (194°F) | If PRCV solenoid is equipped. |
| | | Approx. 12V | Other | |
| 2L | — | — | — | — |
| 2M | — | — | — | — |
| 2N | — | — | — | — |
| 2O | No.2 purge control solenoid | Approx. 12V | Less than 1,500 rpm | |
| | | Below 1.5V | More than 1,500 rpm | |
| 2P | No.1 purge control valve solenoid | Below 1.5V | Intake air temp. more than 50°C (122°F) Water temp. more than 50°C (122°F) | In-gear condition. • Jumper wire connect to the Neutral switch (MTX) • Disconnect the inhibitor switch connector (ATV) |
| | | Approx. 12V | Other | |
| 2Q | Idle speed control (ISC) valve | 1.5—11.6V | At idle | Engine Signal Monitor: Green and red light flash |
| 2R | Ground | Below 1.5V | — | — |
| 3A | Ground | Below 1.5V | — | — |
| 3B | Starter switch | Below 2.5V | Ignition switch ON | |
| | | 7—9V | While cranking | |
| 3C | Injector No.2, No.4 | Approx. 12V | At idle | Engine Signal Monitor: Green and red light flash |
| 3D | Inhibitor switch | Below 1.5V | "N" or "P" range | MTX constant 0V |
| | | Approx. 12V | Other range | |
| 3E | Injector No.1 and No.3 | Approx. 12V | At idle | Engine Signal Monitor: Green and red light flash |
| 3F | — | — | — | — |
| 3G | Ground | Below 1.5V | — | — |
| 3H | — | — | — | — |
| 3I | Main relay | Approx. 12V | Ignition switch ON | |
| 3J | Battery | Approx. 12V | — | — |

### EGI control unit connector

| 3I | 3G | 3E | 3C | 3A | 2Q | 2O | 2M | 2K | 2I | 2G | 2E | 2C | 2A | 1W | 1U | 1S | 1Q | 1O | 1M | 1K | 1I | 1G | 1E | 1C | 1A |
|---|---|---|---|---|---|---|---|---|---|---|---|---|---|---|---|---|---|---|---|---|---|---|---|---|---|
| 3J | 3H | 3F | 3D | 3B | 2R | 2P | 2N | 2L | 2J | 2H | 2F | 2D | 2B | 1X | 1V | 1T | 1R | 1P | 1N | 1L | 1J | 1H | 1F | 1D | 1B |

Courtesy of Mazda Motors Corp.

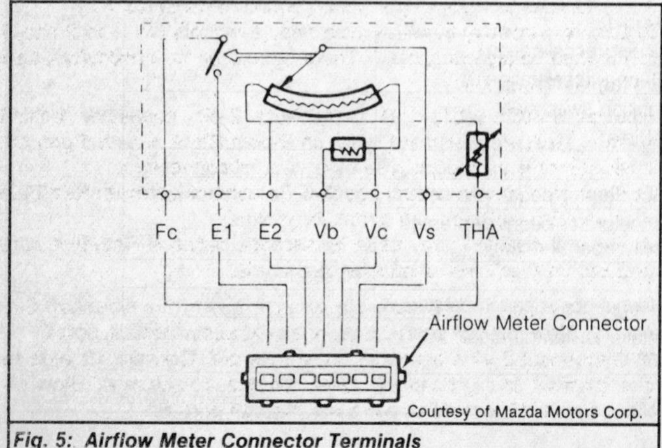
Fc
E1
E2
Vb
Vc
Vs
THA
Airflow Meter Connector
Courtesy of Mazda Motors Corp.

*Fig. 5: Airflow Meter Connector Terminals*

***AIRFLOW METER TERMINAL RESISTANCE***

| Terminal | Fully Closed Ohms | Fully Open Ohms |
|---|---|---|
| E2-Vs | 20-400 | 20-1000 |
| E2-Vc | 100-300 | 100-300 |
| E2-Vb | 200-400 | 200-400 |
| E2-THA | -4°F (-20°C) 10-20k | -4°F (-20°C) 10-20k |
| | 68°F (20°C) 2.0-3.0k | 68°F (20°C) 2.0-3.0k |
| | 140°F (60°C) 400-700 | 140°F (60°C) 400-700 |
| E1-Fc | Infinite | 0 |

**Atmospheric Pressure Sensor – 1)** Connect voltmeter to terminal B. Turn ignition on and note voltage. *See Fig. 6.*
**2)** Voltage at sea level should be 3.5-4.5 volts. Voltage at 6500 feet should be 2.5-3.5 volts. Replace if not to specification.

**Brake Light Switch – 1)** Disconnect brake light switch connector. Measure resistance between terminals of brake light switch.

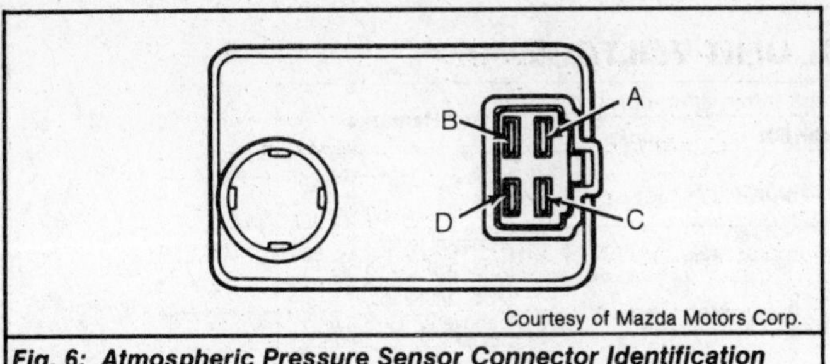
A
B
D
C
Courtesy of Mazda Motors Corp.

*Fig. 6: Atmospheric Pressure Sensor Connector Identification*

**2)** With brake pedal released, resistance should be infinite. With brake pedal depressed, resistance should be zero ohms.

**By-Pass Air Control (BAC) Valve – 1)** Remove BAC valve hose from throttle body. *See Fig. 7.* Blow air through port "A". Ensure air flows when valve is cold. If not, replace BAC valve.
**2)** Measure resistance of Idle Speed Control (ISC) Valve at 2 wire connector of BAC valve. Resistance should be between 5-20 ohms, at normal operating temperature. If not, replace BAC valve.

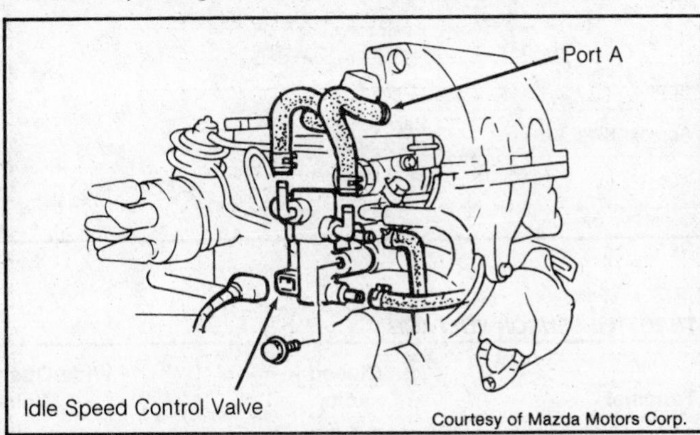
Port A
Idle Speed Control Valve
Courtesy of Mazda Motors Corp.

*Fig. 7: By-Pass Air Control (BAC) Valve*

**Circuit Opening Relay – 1)** Remove circuit opening relay from fuse block panel. *See Fig. 8.* Check circuit opening relay circuits with CIRCUIT OPENING RELAY TERMINAL CIRCUITS table.

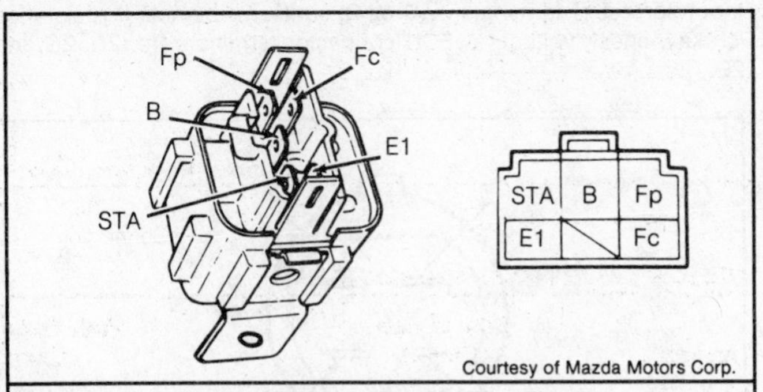
Fp
Fc
B
E1
STA
STA
B
Fp
E1
Fc
Courtesy of Mazda Motors Corp.

*Fig. 8: Circuit Opening Relay Connector Identification*

***CIRCUIT OPENING RELAY TERMINAL CIRCUITS***

| Terminal | Condition | Specifications |
|---|---|---|
| Fp | Resistance to Ground | 0.2-30 ohms |
| Fc | Resistance to Ground (Cranking) | Infinite |
| B | Voltage to Ground (Ign. On) | Battery Voltage |
| STA | Voltage to Ground (Cranking) | Approx. 9 Volts |
| E1 | Resistance to Ground | Infinite |

**2)** With circuit opening relay removed, apply 12 volts to terminal STA of relay. Ground terminal E1. Ensure continuity from relay terminals B to FP.

**3)** Apply 12 volts to terminal B of relay. Ground terminal Fc. Ensure battery voltage is at relay terminal Fp.
**4)** Ensure that relay has correct resistance between terminal with CIRCUIT OPENING RELAY RESISTANCE table.

***CIRCUIT OPENING RELAY RESISTANCE***

| Terminals | Resistance |
|---|---|
| STA to E1 | 15-30 ohms |
| B to Fc | 80-150 ohms |
| B to Fp | Infinite |

**Clutch Switch (M/T) –** Disconnect clutch switch connector. Check for continuity across switch. With clutch pedal released, resistance should be zero ohms. With clutch pedal depressed, resistance should be infinite.

**Coolant Temperature Sensor –** Disconnect and remove water thermo sensor. Check resistance using COOLANT TEMPERATURE SENSOR RESISTANCE table.

***COOLANT TEMPERATURE SENSOR RESISTANCE***

| Temperature °F (°C) | Ohms |
|---|---|
| -4 (-20) | 14.6-17.8K |
| 68 (20) | 2.2-2.7K |
| 176 (80) | 280-350 |

**Coolant Temperature Switch –** Remove switch from radiator. Switch should have continuity at temperatures greater than 63°F (17°C).

**Electrical Load Control Unit –** Connect a voltmeter between control unit and ground. Start engine. Check voltage at terminals using ELECTRICAL CONTROL UNIT VOLTAGE chart.

**Inhibitor Switch (A/T) – 1)** Disconnect 4-pin connector near battery. Measure resistance between terminal on 2 wire side of connnector.
**2)** With selector lever in "P" or "N", resistance should be zero ohms. With selector lever in any other position, resistance should be infinite.

**Knock Control System – 1)** With engine at normal operating temperature, check ignition timing. Ensure voltage at ECU connector terminal No. 1U is approximately 12 volts.
**2)** Disconnect single wire service connector at ECU. Tap engine hanger and note ignition timing. If timing does not retard, replace knock sensor and retest.
**3)** If timing retards, connect single wire service connector and retest. If timing retards, replace knock control unit. If timing does not, system is okay.

**Main Relay – 1)** Ensure a clicking sound is heard at main relay when turning ignition on and off. *See Fig. 9.* Disconnect main relay. Apply 12 volts to terminal No. 5 and ground terminal No. 6.
**2)** Ensure continuity between main relay terminals No. 1 to 2 and 3 to 4, when voltage is applied. There should be no continuity when voltage is not applied.

**Neutral Switch (M/T) – 1)** Disconnect 2-pin connector behind battery. Measure resistance between Brown/Black wire and ground. If resistance is zero ohms, use other side of connector.
**2)** Place transaxle in neutral position. Resistance between Red/Blue wire and Brown/Black wire should be infinite.
**3)** Place transaxle in any gear. Resistance between Red/Blue wire and Brown/Black wire should be zero ohms.

**Purge Solenoid – 1)** Disconnect vacuum hose from solenoid. *See Fig. 10.* Blow through port A. Ensure air exhausts through port C.
**2)** Disconnect 2 wire connector from solenoid. Connect 12 volts to one terminal and ground the other terminal of solenoid. Blow air though port "A". Ensure air exhausts through port "B".

## ELECTRICAL CONTROL UNIT VOLTAGE

| Terminal | Input | Output | Connection to | Voltage (after warm-up) Ignition switch: ON | Voltage (after warm-up) Idle | Remarks |
|---|---|---|---|---|---|---|
| A (YG) | — | — | Main relay | Approx. 12V | | |
| B (YG) | ○ | | Electrical fan relay | Approx. 12V | | Coolant temp.: below 97°C (206.6°F) |
| | | | | Below 1.5V | | Coolant temp.: above 97°C (206.6°F) |
| C (B) | — | — | Ground | 0V | | |
| D | — | — | — | — | — | — |
| E (L) | | ○ | Control unit (1H) | Below 1.5V | | E/L: ON |
| | | | | Approx. 12V | | E/L: OFF |
| F (RB) | ○ | | Combination switch | Approx. 12V | | Combination switch: ON |
| | | | | Below 1.5V | | Combination switch: OFF |
| G (LG) | ○ | | Blower motor switch | Below 1.5V | | Blower motor switch: ON (2nd, 3rd or 4th position) |
| | | | | Approx. 12V | | Others |
| H (BY) | ○ | | Rear defroster switch | Approx. 12V | | Rear defroster switch: ON |
| | | | | Below 1.5V | | Rear defroster switch: OFF |

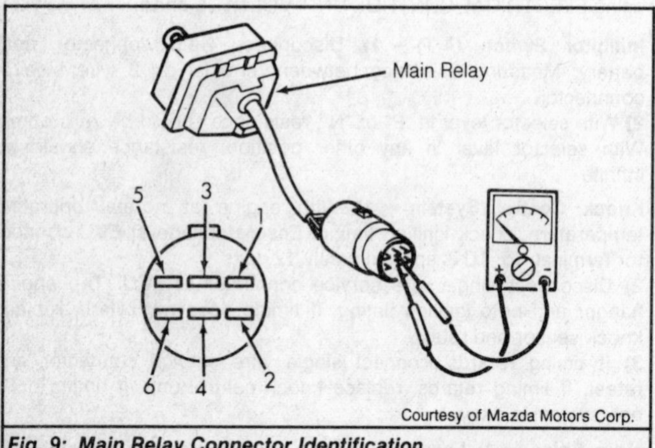
Main Relay
5
3
6
4
2
Courtesy of Mazda Motors Corp.

*Fig. 9: Main Relay Connector Identification*

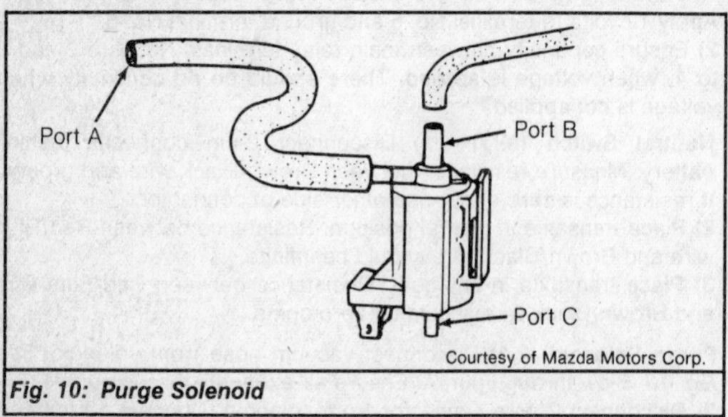
Port A
Port B
Port C
Courtesy of Mazda Motors Corp.

*Fig. 10: Purge Solenoid*

**Throttle Sensor (Turbo) – 1)** Remove rubber boot from throttle sensor. *See Fig. 11.* With ignition on, check voltage between each terminal and ground. See THROTTLE SENSOR VOLTAGE table. Repeat test with throttle wide open.

### THROTTLE SENSOR VOLTAGE

| Terminal | Closed Volts | Wide Open Volts |
|---|---|---|
| A | 0.3-0.7 | Approx. 4.0 |
| B | Less Than 1.5 | Less Than 1.5 |
| C | 4.5-5.5 | 4.5-5.5 |
| D | Less Than 1.5 | Approx. 12.0 |

**2)** If not correct at terminal D only, check throttle sensor adjustment. If not correct at terminals A, B or C, check resistance. If resistance is okay, check voltage at ECU connector terminals No. 2A, 2C and 2E.

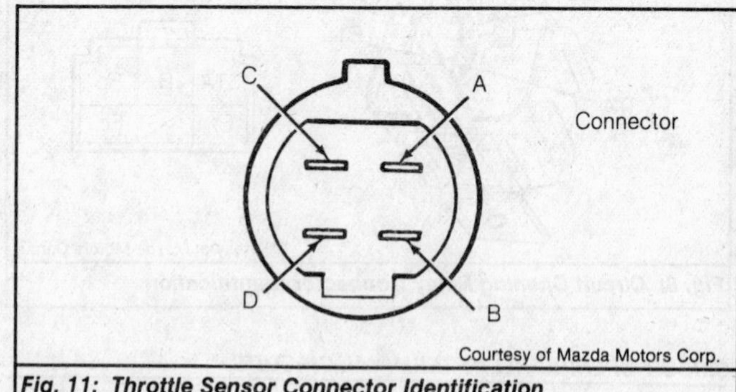
C
A
Connector
D
B
Courtesy of Mazda Motors Corp.

*Fig. 11: Throttle Sensor Connector Identification*

### THROTTLE SENSOR RESISTANCE

| Terminal | Closed Throttle | Wide Open Throttle |
|---|---|---|
| A-B | Approx. 500 ohms | Approx. 4500 ohms |
| B-C | 3000-7000 ohms | 7000 |

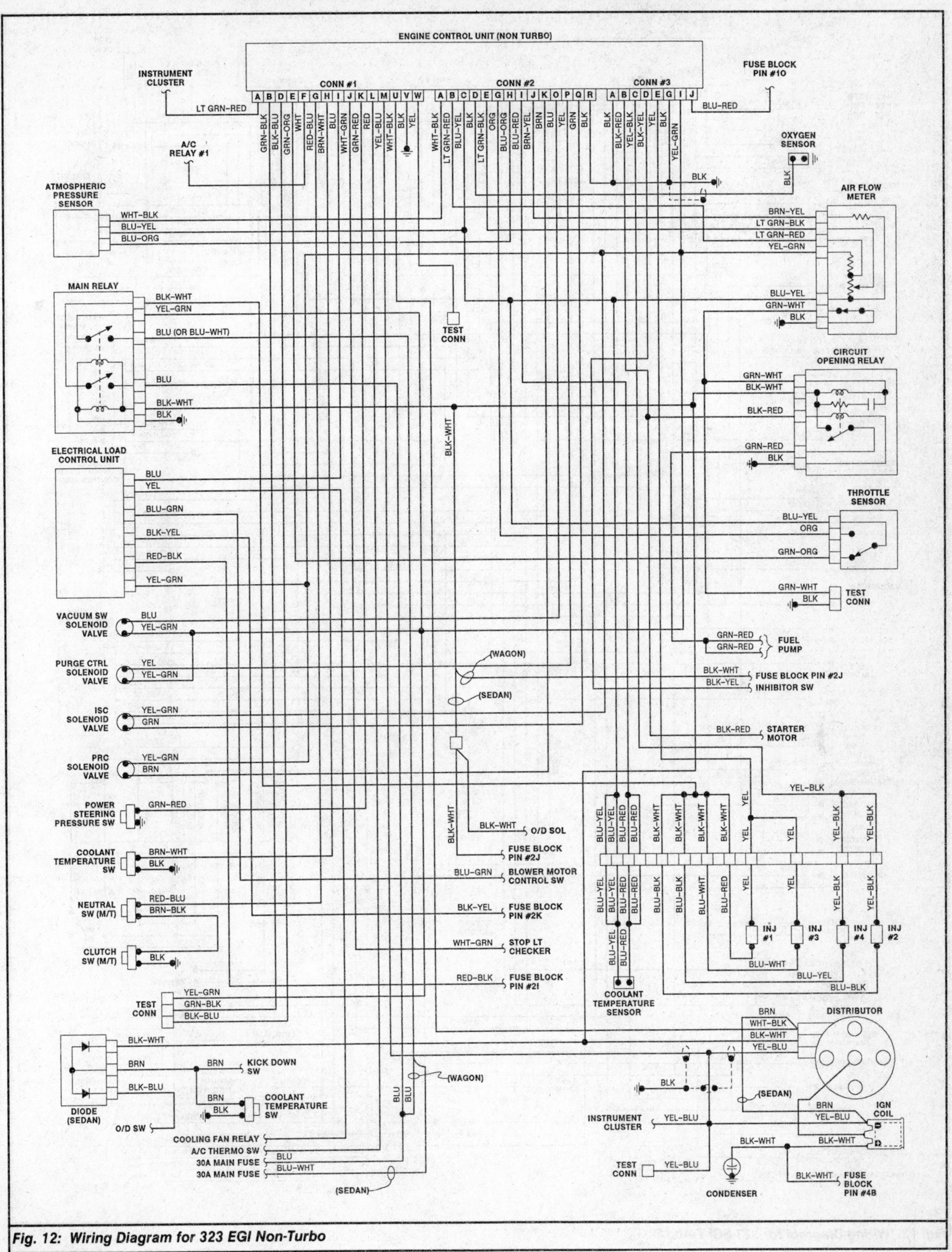
ENGINE CONTROL UNIT (NON TURBO)
CONN #1
CONN #2
CONN #3
INSTRUMENT CLUSTER
FUSE BLOCK PIN #10
LT GRN-RED
BLU-RED
A/C RELAY #1
OXYGEN SENSOR
ATMOSPHERIC PRESSURE SENSOR
WHT-BLK
BLU-YEL
BLU-ORG
AIR FLOW METER
BRN-YEL
LT GRN-BLK
LT GRN-RED
YEL-GRN
GRN-WHT
BLK
MAIN RELAY
BLK-WHT
YEL-GRN
BLU (OR BLU-WHT)
BLU
TEST CONN
CIRCUIT OPENING RELAY
BLK-RED
GRN-RED
ELECTRICAL LOAD CONTROL UNIT
YEL
BLU-GRN
BLK-YEL
RED-BLK
THROTTLE SENSOR
ORG
GRN-ORG
VACUUM SW SOLENOID VALVE
PURGE CTRL SOLENOID VALVE
FUEL PUMP
(WAGON)
(SEDAN)
FUSE BLOCK PIN #2J
INHIBITOR SW
ISC SOLENOID VALVE
GRN
STARTER MOTOR
PRC SOLENOID VALVE
BRN
POWER STEERING PRESSURE SW
YEL-BLK
O/D SOL
COOLANT TEMPERATURE SW
BRN-WHT
BLOWER MOTOR CONTROL SW
NEUTRAL SW (M/T)
RED-BLU
BRN-BLK
FUSE BLOCK PIN #2K
INJ #1
INJ #3
INJ #4
INJ #2
CLUTCH SW (M/T)
WHT-GRN
STOP LT CHECKER
BLU-WHT
BLU-BLK
FUSE BLOCK PIN #2I
COOLANT TEMPERATURE SENSOR
DISTRIBUTOR
GRN-BLK
BLK-BLU
YEL-BLU
DIODE (SEDAN)
KICK DOWN SW
O/D SW
COOLING FAN RELAY
A/C THERMO SW
30A MAIN FUSE
30A MAIN FUSE
IGN COIL
CONDENSER
FUSE BLOCK PIN #4B

Fig. 12: Wiring Diagram for 323 EGI Non-Turbo

# 1988 COMPUTERIZED ENGINE CONTROLS
## Mazda – 323 EGI (Cont.)

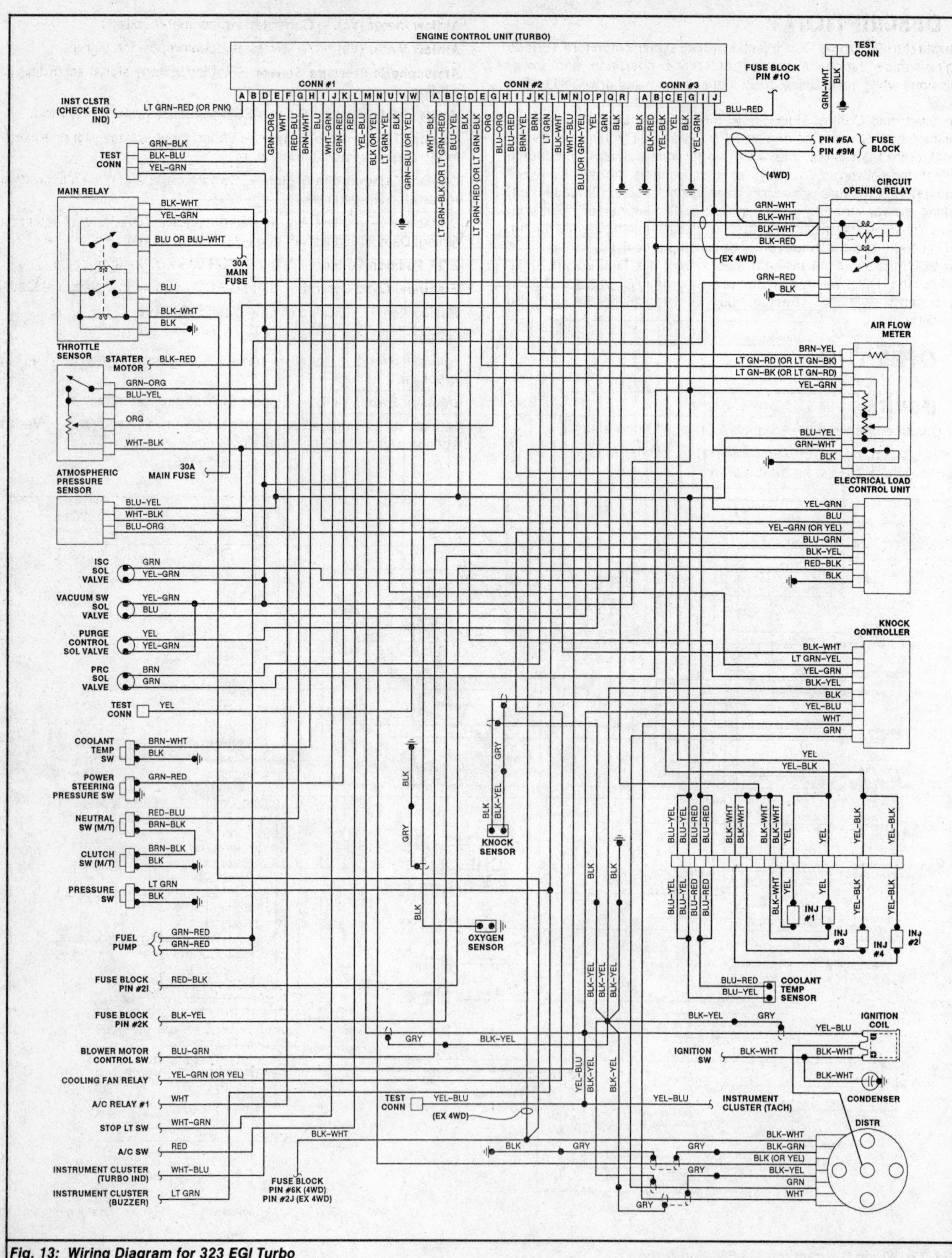
ENGINE CONTROL UNIT (TURBO)
CONN #1
CONN #2
CONN #3
INST CLSTR (CHECK ENG IND)
TEST CONN
MAIN RELAY
30A MAIN FUSE
THROTTLE SENSOR
STARTER MOTOR
ATMOSPHERIC PRESSURE SENSOR
ISC SOL VALVE
VACUUM SW SOL VALVE
PURGE CONTROL SOL VALVE
PRC SOL VALVE
COOLANT TEMP SW
POWER STEERING PRESSURE SW
NEUTRAL SW (M/T)
CLUTCH SW (M/T)
PRESSURE SW
FUEL PUMP
FUSE BLOCK PIN #2I
FUSE BLOCK PIN #2K
BLOWER MOTOR CONTROL SW
COOLING FAN RELAY
A/C RELAY #1
STOP LT SW
A/C SW
INSTRUMENT CLUSTER (TURBO IND)
INSTRUMENT CLUSTER (BUZZER)
FUSE BLOCK PIN #6K (4WD) PIN #2J (EX 4WD)
FUSE BLOCK PIN #10
PIN #5A
PIN #9M
FUSE BLOCK
(4WD)
(EX 4WD)
CIRCUIT OPENING RELAY
AIR FLOW METER
ELECTRICAL LOAD CONTROL UNIT
KNOCK CONTROLLER
KNOCK SENSOR
OXYGEN SENSOR
INJ #1
INJ #2
INJ #3
INJ #4
COOLANT TEMP SENSOR
IGNITION COIL
IGNITION SW
CONDENSER
INSTRUMENT CLUSTER (TACH)
DISTR

*Fig. 13: Wiring Diagram for 323 EGI Turbo*

# Mazda – 929 EGI

## DESCRIPTION

The Mazda Electronic Gas Injection (EGI) system monitors various engine/vehicle functions to control engine operation and lower emissions while maintaining good fuel economy and driveability. *See Fig. 1.*

The Electronic Control Unit (ECU), through various input sensors, monitors battery voltage, engine RPM, intake air volume, cranking signal, crankshaft angle, intake air temperature, radiator and engine coolant temperatures, exhaust oxygen content, throttle position, atmospheric pressure, gearshift lever position, clutch engagement, braking, power steering operation, and A/C compressor operation. The ECU uses this input information in determining spark timing, fuel injection, and the actuation of other output devices.

The ECU has a built-in fail-safe mechanism. If a fault occurs while driving, the ECU will substitute pre-programmed values. Driving performance will be affected, but vehicle driveability will be maintained.

## OPERATION

### INPUTS

**Air Conditioning Switch** – Signals ECU of A/C operation.

**Airflow Meter (Inlet Air Temperature)** – Varies voltage signal to ECU in relation to inlet air temperature.

**Airflow Meter (Vc)** – Corrected airflow meter voltage.

**Airflow Meter (Vs)** – Airflow plate opening position signal.

**Atmospheric Pressure Sensor** – Varies voltage signal according to altitude.

**Brake Light Switch** – Signals ECU of vehicle braking condition.

**Coolant Temperature Sensor** – Varies input voltage signal according to engine coolant temperature.

**Coolant Temperature Switch** – Switch opens and closes according to radiator temperature.

**Distributor** – Signals No. 1 and 4 cylinder TDC for fuel injection timing. Detects crankshaft angle at 30 degree intervals.

**EGR Position Sensor** – Signals EGR valve opening quantity.

**Electrical Load Control** – Signals ECU of additional electrical load.

**Idle Switch** – Indicates throttle closed position.

**Ignitor** – Signals engine speed.

**Ignition Switch** – Supplies battery voltage to ECU during engine cranking.

**Inhibitor Switch (A/T)** – Signals ECU of gear selection.

**Intake Air Temperature Sensor (Dynamic Chamber)** – Varies voltage signal to ECU in relation to engine air temperature.

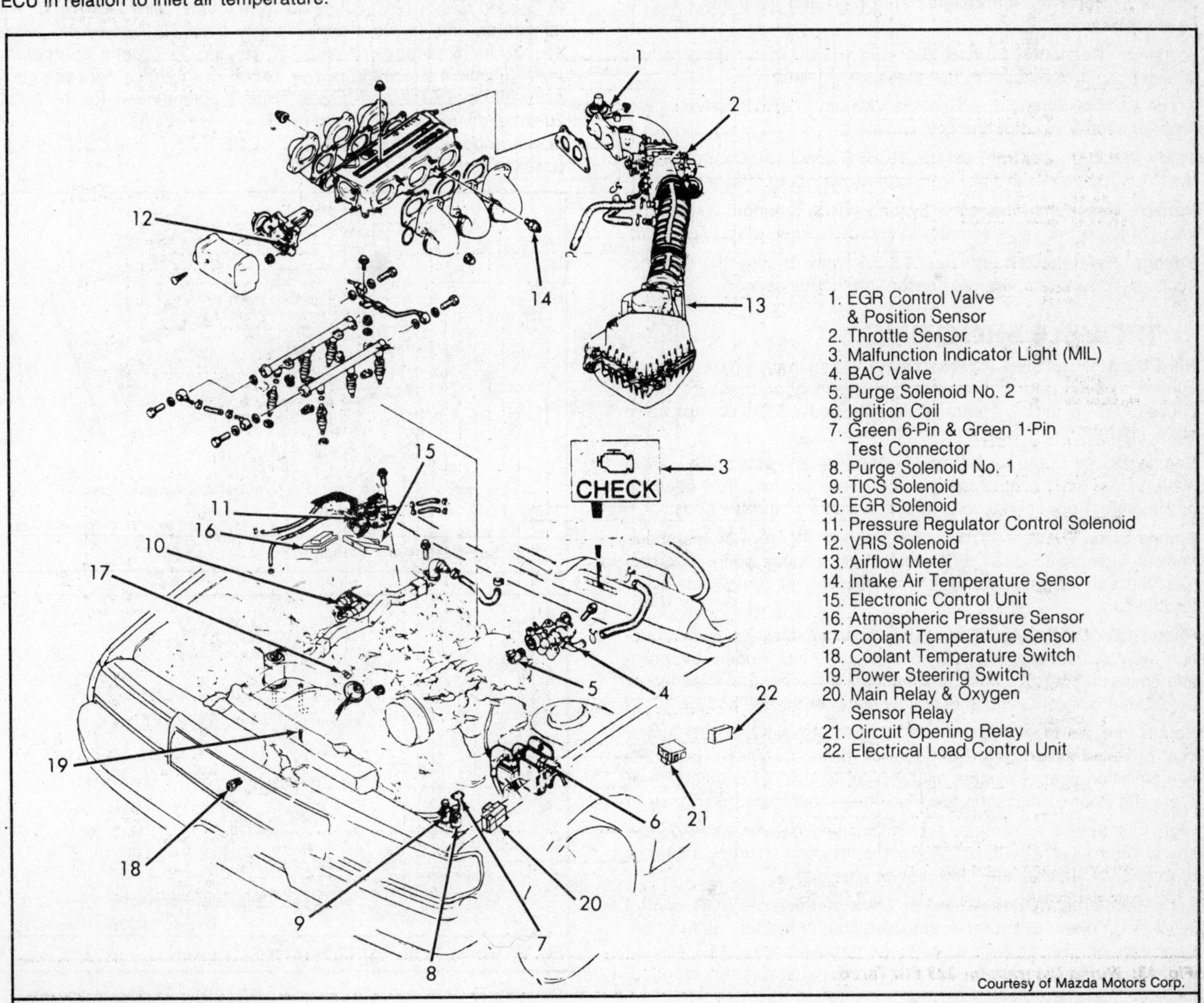
CHECK
1. EGR Control Valve & Position Sensor
2. Throttle Sensor
3. Malfunction Indicator Light (MIL)
4. BAC Valve
5. Purge Solenoid No. 2
6. Ignition Coil
7. Green 6-Pin & Green 1-Pin Test Connector
8. Purge Solenoid No. 1
9. TICS Solenoid
10. EGR Solenoid
11. Pressure Regulator Control Solenoid
12. VRIS Solenoid
13. Airflow Meter
14. Intake Air Temperature Sensor
15. Electronic Control Unit
16. Atmospheric Pressure Sensor
17. Coolant Temperature Sensor
18. Coolant Temperature Switch
19. Power Steering Switch
20. Main Relay & Oxygen Sensor Relay
21. Circuit Opening Relay
22. Electrical Load Control Unit
Courtesy of Mazda Motors Corp.

*Fig. 1: 929 Component Location*

**Main Relay** – Provides battery voltage to ECU.

**Neutral/Clutch Switch (M/T)** – Signals ECU of clutch operation and transmission gear position.

**Oxygen ($O_2$) Sensor** – Generates voltage signal depending on oxygen content of exhaust.

**Power Steering Switch** – Provides signal to ECU when vehicle is turning.

**Throttle Sensor** – Provides voltage signal in response to throttle opening angle.

## OUTPUTS

**Air Conditioning Relay** – ECU controls circuit for A/C operation.

**"CHECK ENGINE" Light** – Lights during engine start up and monitored component malfunction. Referred to as MIL or Malfunction Indicator Light and is used to read trouble codes.

**EGR Solenoid** – Controls EGR control valve operation.

**Fuel Injectors** – ECU controls ground circuit to control fuel injector pulse.

**Idle Speed Control Valve** – Is part of By-Pass Air Control (BAC) valve attached to throttle body. ECU intermittently completes ground to idle speed control valve for proper idle RPM.

**Ignitor** – Receives spark signal from ECU and generates secondary voltage in coil.

**Pressure Regulator Control Solenoid** – ECU completes ground circuit to control vacuum to fuel pressure regulator.

**Purge Control Solenoid** – Controls vacuum to switch valve or No. 1 purge control valve of charcoal canister.

**Triple Induction Control System (TICS) Solenoid** – Controls vacuum to swirl control valve actuator to improve intake efficiency.

**Variable Resonance Induction System (VRIS) Solenoid** – Controls vacuum to shutter valve actuator to improve torque at low speed.

**Voltage Reference** – Provides 4.5-5.5 volts to specific sensors such as, coolant temperature sensor and throttle sensor.

## TROUBLE SHOOTING

**Hard Start or No Start (Cranks Okay)** – Electronic spark advance control system failure. Incorrect fuel injection or pressure. Poor connections at airflow meter or throttle body. EGR control valve stuck open.

**Engine Stalls Cold** – Air valve or idle speed control valve malfunction. EGR control valve stuck open. Incorrect fuel injection or pressure. Poor connections at airflow meter or throttle body.

**Engine Stalls Warm** – PCV system clogged. Air valve or idle speed control valve malfunction. EGR control valve stuck open. Incorrect fuel injection or pressure. Poor connections at airflow meter or throttle body.

**Rough Idle Cold** – Air valve or idle speed control valve malfunction. PCV system clogged. EGR control valve stuck open. Evaporative emission control system malfunction. Incorrect fuel injection or pressure. Poor connections at airflow meter or throttle body.

**Rough Idle Warm** – PCV system clogged. Air valve or idle speed control valve malfunction. EGR control valve stuck open. Evaporative emission control system malfunction. Incorrect fuel injection or pressure. Poor connections at airflow meter or throttle body.

**High Idle Speed** – Fuel-cut system malfunction. Air valve or idle speed control valve malfunction. Poor connection at airflow meter or throttle body. Incorrect fuel injection or pressure.

**Poor Acceleration, Hesistation or Lack of Power** – EGR control valve stuck open. Evaporative emission control system malfunction. Poor connections at airflow meter or throttle body. VRIS system malfunction. TICS system malfunction. Exhaust system clogged. Incorrect fuel injection or pressure.

**Runs Rough on Deceleration** – Fuel-cut system malfunction. Air valve or idle speed control valve malfunction. Incorrect fuel injection or pressure.

**High Fuel Consumption** – Fuel-cut system malfunction. TICS system malfunction. Incorrect fuel injection or pressure. EGR control valve stuck open. Exhaust system clogged.

**Engine Stalls or Rough After Hot Start** – Pressure regulator control system malfunction. Incorrect fuel injection or pressure.

**Excessive Oil Consumption** – PCV system clogged.

**Fails Emission Test** – Exhaust system clogged. EGR control valve stuck open. Fuel-cut system malfunction. Air valve or idle speed control valve malfunction. Evaporative emission control system malfunction. Poor connections at airflow meter or throttle body. Incorrect fuel injection or pressure.

# DIAGNOSIS & TESTING

## WITH SELF-DIAGNOSTIC CHECKER

**Trouble Code Access** – **1)** Connect Self-Diagnostic Checker (49 H018 9A1) to Green 6-pin connector and negative battery terminal. *See Fig. 2.* Connector is located at left front wheelwell. Select position "A" on checker.

**2)** Ground Green 1-pin connector with jumper wire. *See Fig. 3.* With ignition on and engine stopped, verify code 88 flashes and buzzer sounds for 3 seconds. If okay, go to step **3)**. If code 88 does not flash, check main relay, power circuit or harness connections. If code 88 does flash and buzzer sounds continuously for more than 20 seconds, replace ECU and retest.

**3)** Note codes. Check TROUBLE CODE IDENTIFICATION chart for possible cause.

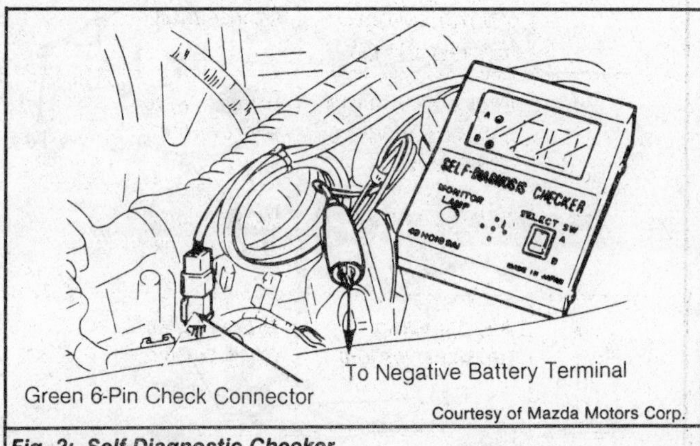
SELF-DIAGNOSIS CHECKER
MONITOR LAMP
SELECT SW
A
B
To Negative Battery Terminal
Green 6-Pin Check Connector
Courtesy of Mazda Motors Corp.

*Fig. 2: Self-Diagnostic Checker*

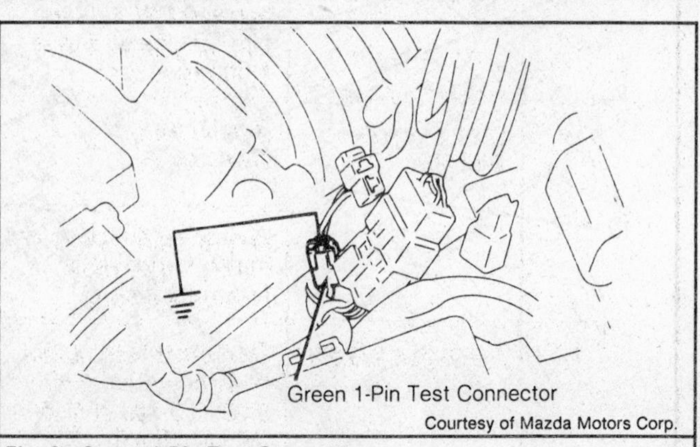
Green 1-Pin Test Connector
Courtesy of Mazda Motors Corp.

*Fig. 3: Green 1-Pin Test Connector*

# Mazda – 929 EGI (Cont.)

## TROUBLE CODE IDENTIFICATION

| Malfunction code No. | Input devices | Malfunction | Fail-safe function | Pattern of output signals (Self-Diagnosis Checker or MIL) |
|---|---|---|---|---|
| 01 | Ignition pulse (Igniter, ignition coil) | Broken wire, Short circuit | — |  |
| 02 | Distributor (Ne signal) | Ne signal not input for 1.5 sec during cranking | — | 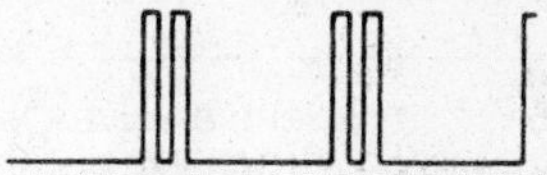 |
| 03 | Distributor (G1 signal) | Broken wire, short circuit | — | 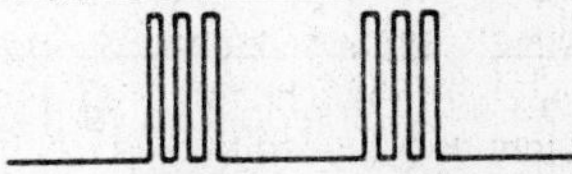 |
| 04 | Distributor (G2 signal) | Broken wire, short circuit | — |  |
| 08 | Air flow meter | Broken wire, short circuit | Basic fuel injection amount fixed as for 2 driving modes 1) Idle switch: ON 2) Idle switch: OFF |  |
| 09 | Water thermo sensor | Broken wire, short circuit | Coolant temp input fixed at 80°C (176°F) |  |
| 10 | Intake air thermo sensor (air flow meter) | Broken wire, short circuit | Intake air temp input fixed at 20°C (68°F) |  |
| 11 | Intake air thermo sensor (Dynamic chamber) | Broken wire, short circuit | Intake air temp input fixed at 20°C (68°F) | 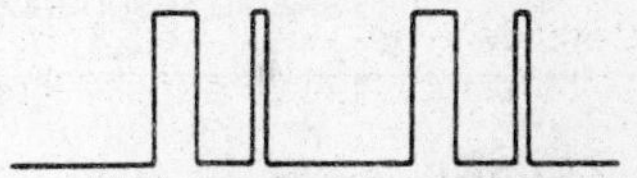 |
| 12 | Throttle sensor | Broken wire, short circuit | Throttle valve opening angle signal input fixed at full open |  |
| 14 | Atmospheric pressure sensor | Broken wire, short circuit | Atmospheric pressure input fixed at 760 mm Hg (29.9 in Hg) |  |
| 15 | Oxygen sensor | Oxygen sensor output below 0.55V 120 sec after engine at above 1,500 rpm | Feedback system cancelled (for EGI) |  |
| 16 | EGR position sensor | Broken wire, short circuit | EGR position signal input fixed at full closed | |
| | | Sensor output does not match target value (incorrect output) | — |  |
| 17 | Feedback system | Oxygen sensor output does not change at 0.55V 60 sec after engine at above 1,500 rpm | Feedback system cancelled (for EGI) |  |

Courtesy of Mazda Motors Corp.

## TROUBLE CODE IDENTIFICATION (Cont.)

| Malfunction code | Output devices | Pattern of output signals (Self-Diagnosis Checker or MIL) |
|---|---|---|
| 25 | Solenoid valve (Pressure regulator control) | |
| 26 | Solenoid valve (No. 2 purge control) | |
| 27 | Solenoid valve (No. 1 purge control) | |
| 28 | Solenoid valve (EGR, vacuum side) | |
| 29 | Solenoid valve (EGR, vent side) | |
| 34 | Idle speed control valve (ISC valve) | |
| 40 | Solenoid valve (Triple induction control system) and oxygen sensor relay | |
| 41 | Solenoid valve (Variable resonance induction system) | |

Courtesy of Mazda Motors Corp.

## TROUBLE CODES

### No. 01 Code

- Are there poor connections at ignition coil connectors ?
  - YES → Repair or replace connector
  - NO ↓
- Is resistance of ignition coil OK ? Resistance: Primary 0.72—0.88 Ω, Secondary 10—30 kΩ
  - NO → Replace ignition coil
  - YES ↓
- Is operation of igniter OK ?
  - NO → Replace igniter
  - YES ↓
- Is there continuity between IGf terminal of igniter connector (wiring harness side) and engine control unit (1M) terminal ?
  - NO → PC: Open circuit in wiring harness from igniter to engine control unit (1M) terminal
  - YES ↓
- Is engine control unit (1M) terminal voltage OK ?
  - NO → PC: Short circuit wiring harness
  - YES → Replace engine control unit

---

### No. 02 Code

- Are there poor connections at distributor connectors ?
  - YES → Repair or replace connector
  - NO ↓
- Is resistance of distributor OK ?
  - NO → Replace distributor
  - YES ↓
- Is there continuity between distributor connector (wiring harness side) and engine control unit ?

| Distributor | Engine control unit |
|---|---|
| Ne ① W | 1T |
| Ne ② G | 1Q |

  - NO → PC: Open circuit in wiring harness
  - YES ↓
- Are engine control unit (1T) and (1Q) terminal voltage OK ?
  - NO → PC: Short circuit in wiring harness
  - YES → Replace engine control unit

Courtesy of Mazda Motors Corp.

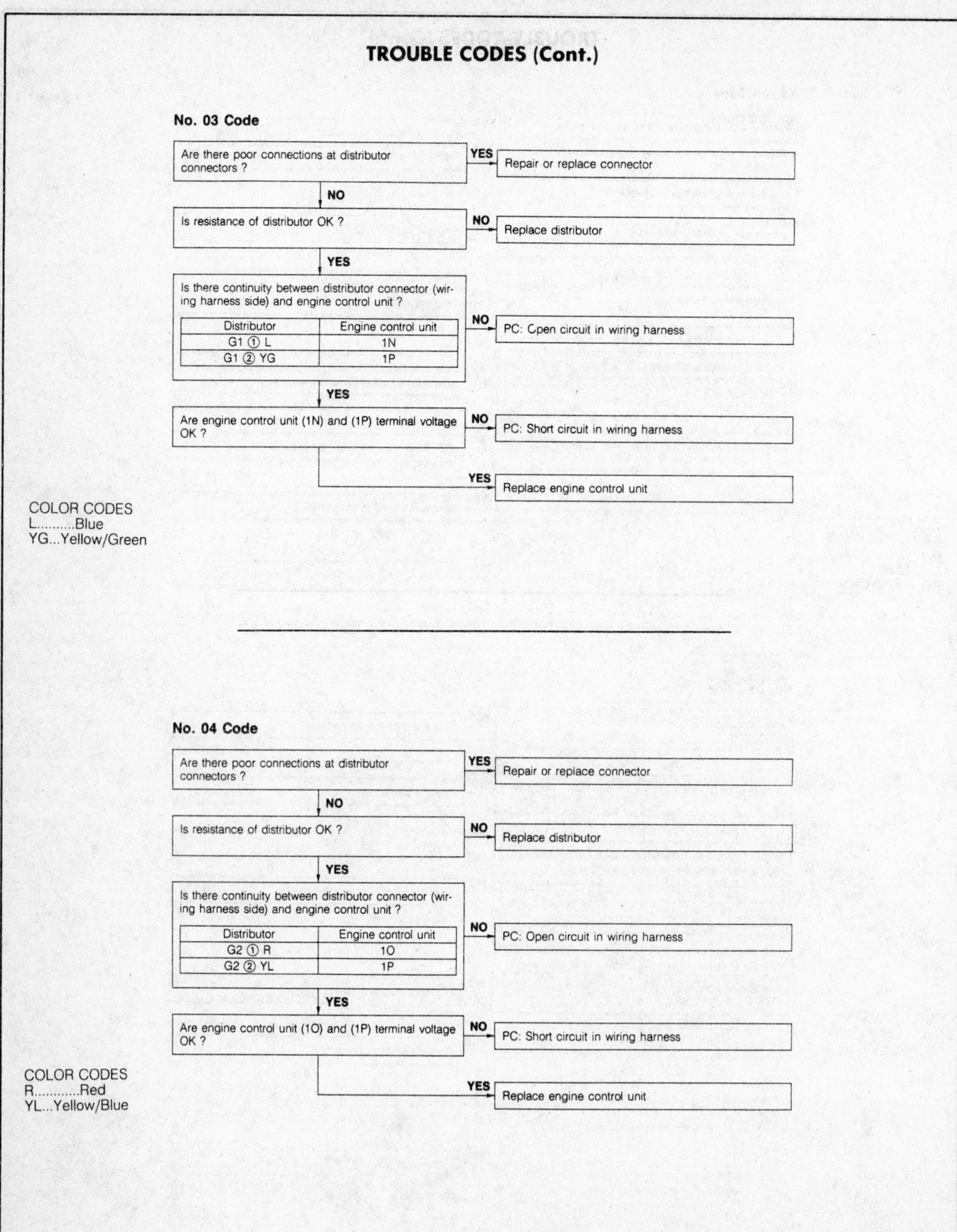
TROUBLE CODES (Cont.)
No. 03 Code
Are there poor connections at distributor connectors ?
YES
Repair or replace connector
NO
Is resistance of distributor OK ?
NO
Replace distributor
YES
Is there continuity between distributor connector (wiring harness side) and engine control unit ?
Distributor
Engine control unit
G1 ① L
1N
G1 ② YG
1P
NO
PC: Open circuit in wiring harness
YES
Are engine control unit (1N) and (1P) terminal voltage OK ?
NO
PC: Short circuit in wiring harness
YES
Replace engine control unit
COLOR CODES
L..........Blue
YG...Yellow/Green
No. 04 Code
Are there poor connections at distributor connectors ?
YES
Repair or replace connector
NO
Is resistance of distributor OK ?
NO
Replace distributor
YES
Is there continuity between distributor connector (wiring harness side) and engine control unit ?
Distributor
Engine control unit
G2 ① R
1O
G2 ② YL
1P
NO
PC: Open circuit in wiring harness
YES
Are engine control unit (1O) and (1P) terminal voltage OK ?
NO
PC: Short circuit in wiring harness
YES
Replace engine control unit
COLOR CODES
R............Red
YL...Yellow/Blue
Courtesy of Mazda Motors Corp.

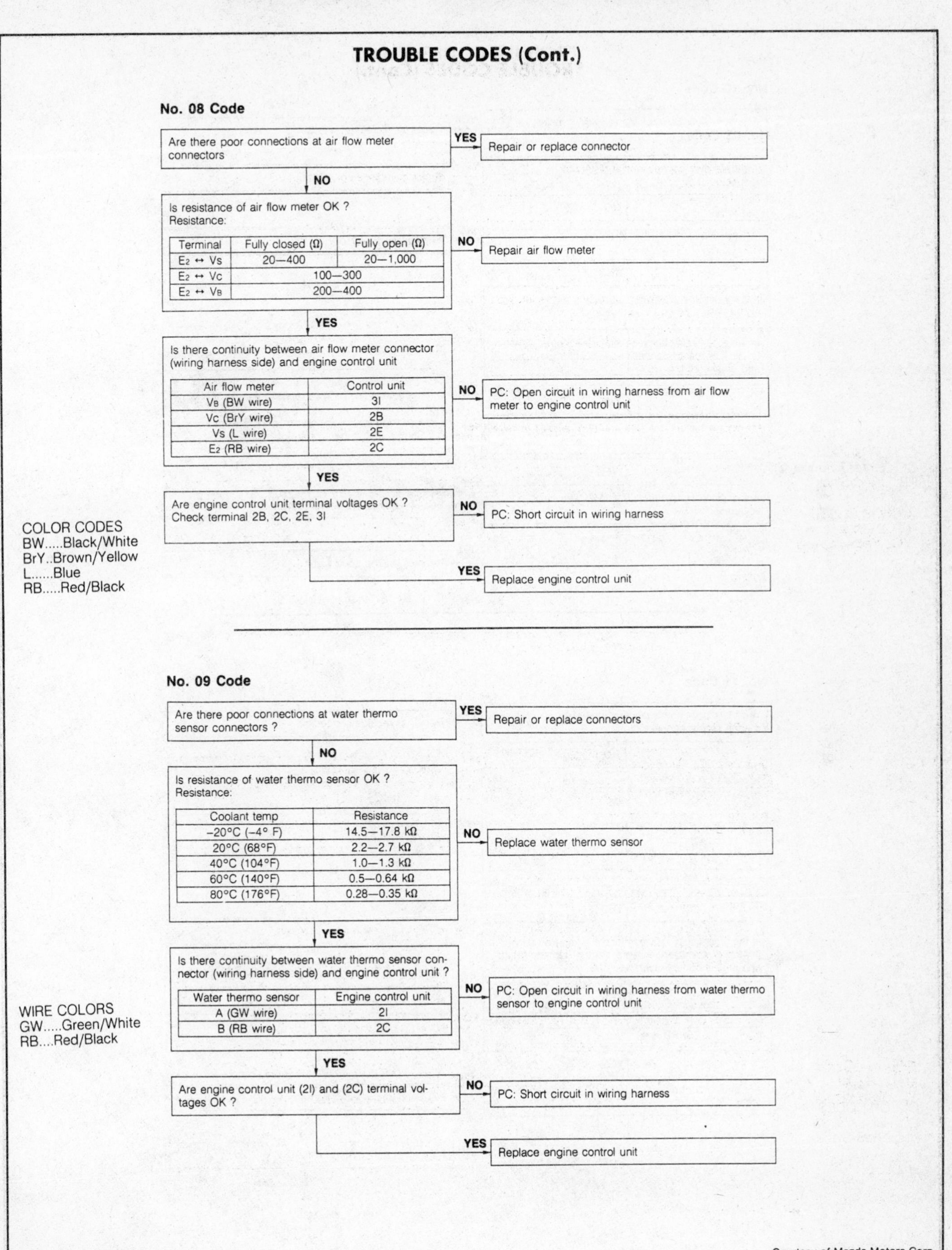
TROUBLE CODES (Cont.)
No. 08 Code
Are there poor connections at air flow meter connectors
YES
Repair or replace connector
NO
Is resistance of air flow meter OK ?
Resistance:
Terminal | Fully closed (Ω) | Fully open (Ω)
E2 ↔ Vs | 20—400 | 20—1,000
E2 ↔ Vc | 100—300
E2 ↔ VB | 200—400
NO
Repair air flow meter
YES
Is there continuity between air flow meter connector (wiring harness side) and engine control unit
Air flow meter | Control unit
VB (BW wire) | 3I
Vc (BrY wire) | 2B
Vs (L wire) | 2E
E2 (RB wire) | 2C
NO
PC: Open circuit in wiring harness from air flow meter to engine control unit
YES
Are engine control unit terminal voltages OK ? Check terminal 2B, 2C, 2E, 3I
NO
PC: Short circuit in wiring harness
YES
Replace engine control unit
COLOR CODES
BW.....Black/White
BrY..Brown/Yellow
L......Blue
RB.....Red/Black
No. 09 Code
Are there poor connections at water thermo sensor connectors ?
YES
Repair or replace connectors
NO
Is resistance of water thermo sensor OK ?
Resistance:
Coolant temp | Resistance
−20°C (−4° F) | 14.5—17.8 kΩ
20°C (68°F) | 2.2—2.7 kΩ
40°C (104°F) | 1.0—1.3 kΩ
60°C (140°F) | 0.5—0.64 kΩ
80°C (176°F) | 0.28—0.35 kΩ
NO
Replace water thermo sensor
YES
Is there continuity between water thermo sensor connector (wiring harness side) and engine control unit ?
Water thermo sensor | Engine control unit
A (GW wire) | 2I
B (RB wire) | 2C
NO
PC: Open circuit in wiring harness from water thermo sensor to engine control unit
WIRE COLORS
GW.....Green/White
RB....Red/Black
YES
Are engine control unit (2I) and (2C) terminal voltages OK ?
NO
PC: Short circuit in wiring harness
YES
Replace engine control unit
Courtesy of Mazda Motors Corp.

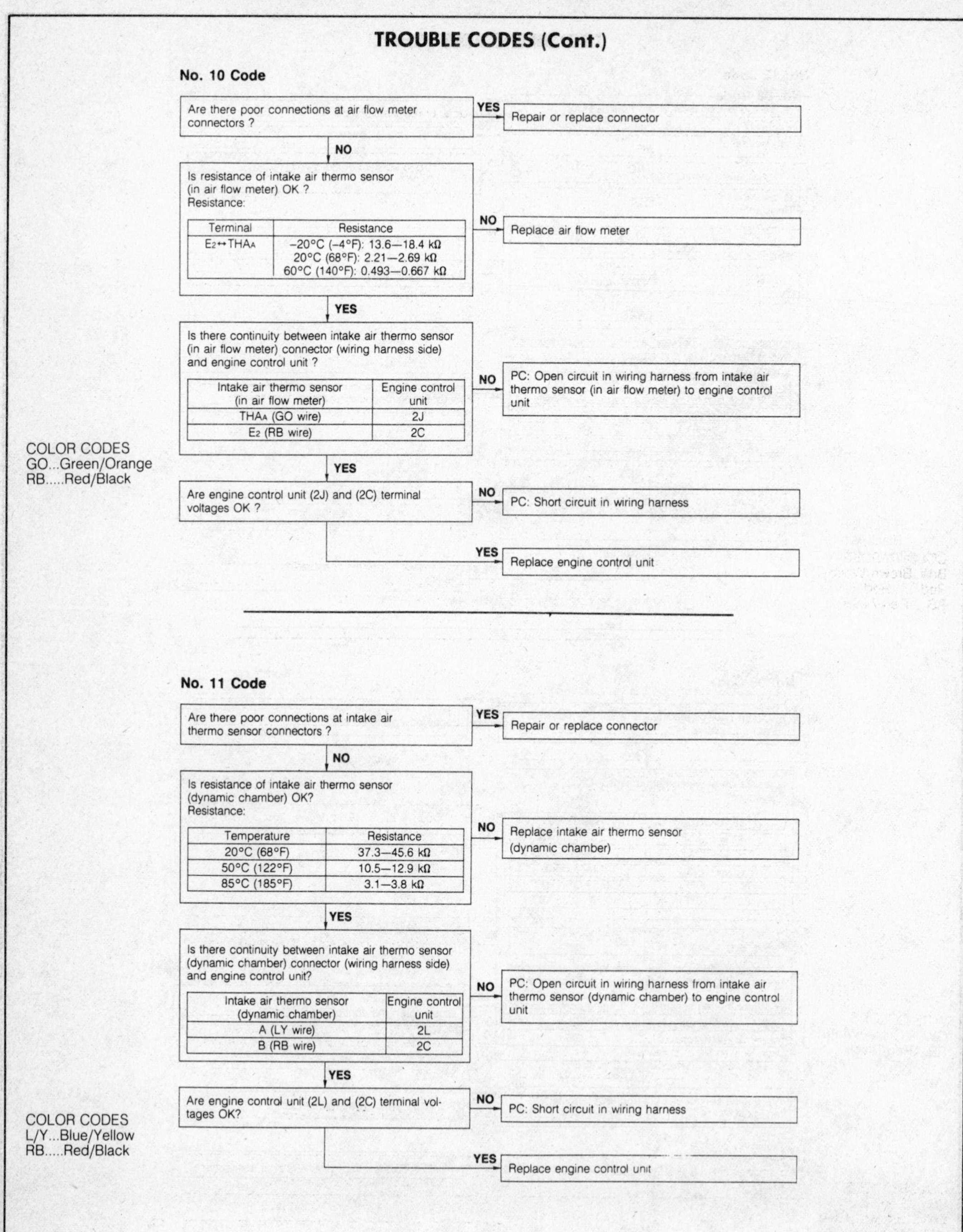

## TROUBLE CODES (Cont.)

### No. 10 Code

Are there poor connections at air flow meter connectors ?
- YES → Repair or replace connector
- NO ↓

Is resistance of intake air thermo sensor (in air flow meter) OK ?
Resistance:

| Terminal | Resistance |
|---|---|
| $E_2$↔$THA_A$ | −20°C (−4°F): 13.6—18.4 kΩ<br>20°C (68°F): 2.21—2.69 kΩ<br>60°C (140°F): 0.493—0.667 kΩ |

- NO → Replace air flow meter
- YES ↓

Is there continuity between intake air thermo sensor (in air flow meter) connector (wiring harness side) and engine control unit ?

| Intake air thermo sensor (in air flow meter) | Engine control unit |
|---|---|
| $THA_A$ (GO wire) | 2J |
| $E_2$ (RB wire) | 2C |

- NO → PC: Open circuit in wiring harness from intake air thermo sensor (in air flow meter) to engine control unit
- YES ↓

Are engine control unit (2J) and (2C) terminal voltages OK ?
- NO → PC: Short circuit in wiring harness
- YES → Replace engine control unit

COLOR CODES
GO...Green/Orange
RB.....Red/Black

### No. 11 Code

Are there poor connections at intake air thermo sensor connectors ?
- YES → Repair or replace connector
- NO ↓

Is resistance of intake air thermo sensor (dynamic chamber) OK?
Resistance:

| Temperature | Resistance |
|---|---|
| 20°C (68°F) | 37.3—45.6 kΩ |
| 50°C (122°F) | 10.5—12.9 kΩ |
| 85°C (185°F) | 3.1—3.8 kΩ |

- NO → Replace intake air thermo sensor (dynamic chamber)
- YES ↓

Is there continuity between intake air thermo sensor (dynamic chamber) connector (wiring harness side) and engine control unit?

| Intake air thermo sensor (dynamic chamber) | Engine control unit |
|---|---|
| A (LY wire) | 2L |
| B (RB wire) | 2C |

- NO → PC: Open circuit in wiring harness from intake air thermo sensor (dynamic chamber) to engine control unit
- YES ↓

Are engine control unit (2L) and (2C) terminal voltages OK?
- NO → PC: Short circuit in wiring harness
- YES → Replace engine control unit

COLOR CODES
L/Y...Blue/Yellow
RB.....Red/Black

Courtesy of Mazda Motors Corp.

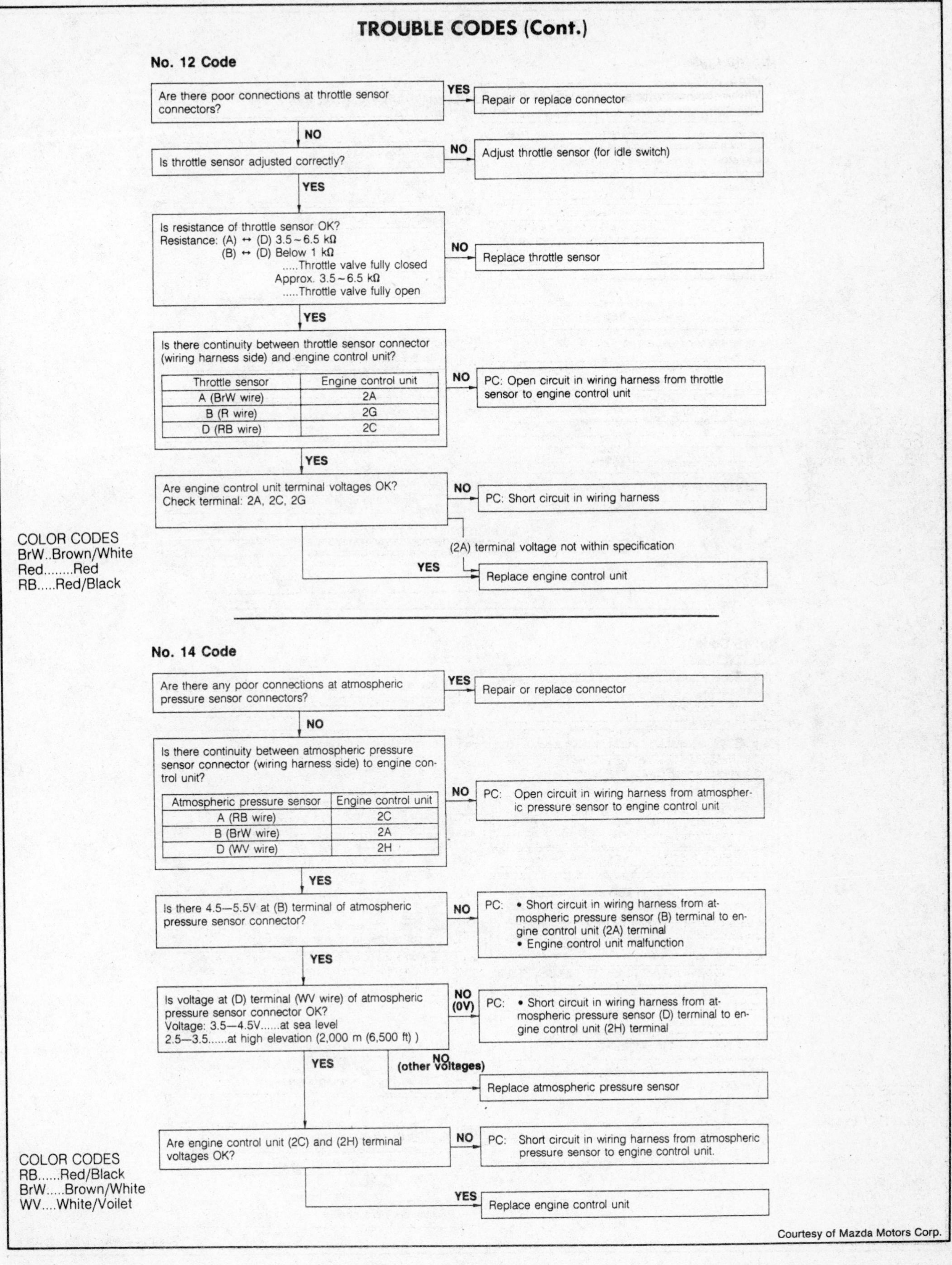
TROUBLE CODES (Cont.)
No. 12 Code
Are there poor connections at throttle sensor connectors?
YES
Repair or replace connector
NO
Is throttle sensor adjusted correctly?
NO
Adjust throttle sensor (for idle switch)
YES
Is resistance of throttle sensor OK?
Resistance: (A) ↔ (D) 3.5 ~ 6.5 kΩ
(B) ↔ (D) Below 1 kΩ
.....Throttle valve fully closed
Approx. 3.5 ~ 6.5 kΩ
.....Throttle valve fully open
NO
Replace throttle sensor
YES
Is there continuity between throttle sensor connector (wiring harness side) and engine control unit?
Throttle sensor
Engine control unit
A (BrW wire)
2A
B (R wire)
2G
D (RB wire)
2C
NO
PC: Open circuit in wiring harness from throttle sensor to engine control unit
YES
Are engine control unit terminal voltages OK?
Check terminal: 2A, 2C, 2G
NO
PC: Short circuit in wiring harness
(2A) terminal voltage not within specification
YES
Replace engine control unit
COLOR CODES
BrW..Brown/White
Red........Red
RB.....Red/Black
No. 14 Code
Are there any poor connections at atmospheric pressure sensor connectors?
YES
Repair or replace connector
NO
Is there continuity between atmospheric pressure sensor connector (wiring harness side) to engine control unit?
Atmospheric pressure sensor
Engine control unit
A (RB wire)
2C
B (BrW wire)
2A
D (WV wire)
2H
NO
PC: Open circuit in wiring harness from atmospheric pressure sensor to engine control unit
YES
Is there 4.5—5.5V at (B) terminal of atmospheric pressure sensor connector?
NO
PC: • Short circuit in wiring harness from atmospheric pressure sensor (B) terminal to engine control unit (2A) terminal
• Engine control unit malfunction
YES
Is voltage at (D) terminal (WV wire) of atmospheric pressure sensor connector OK?
Voltage: 3.5—4.5V......at sea level
2.5—3.5......at high elevation (2,000 m (6,500 ft) )
NO (0V)
PC: • Short circuit in wiring harness from atmospheric pressure sensor (D) terminal to engine control unit (2H) terminal
YES
NO (other voltages)
Replace atmospheric pressure sensor
Are engine control unit (2C) and (2H) terminal voltages OK?
NO
PC: Short circuit in wiring harness from atmospheric pressure sensor to engine control unit.
YES
Replace engine control unit
COLOR CODES
RB......Red/Black
BrW.....Brown/White
WV....White/Voilet
Courtesy of Mazda Motors Corp.

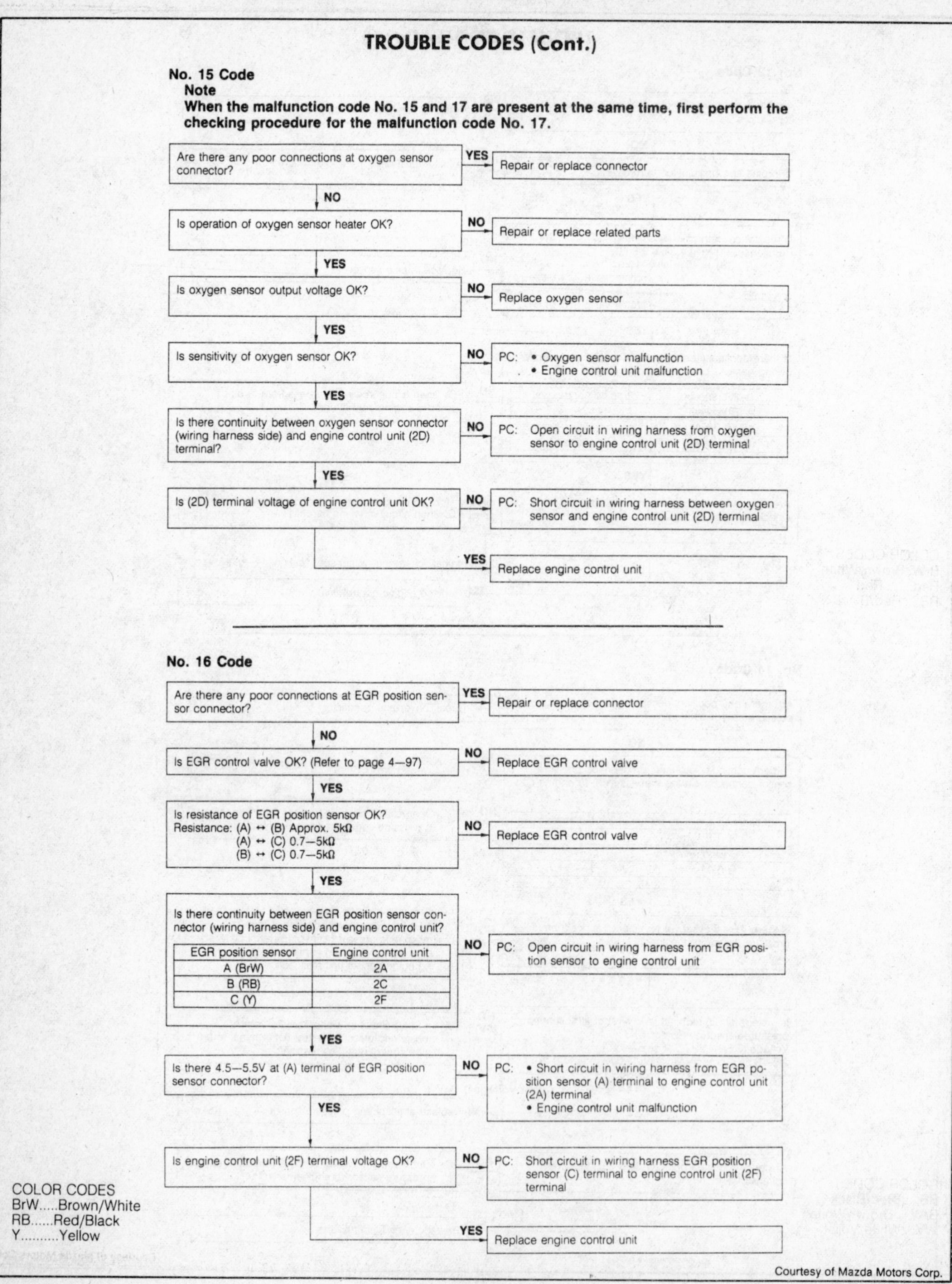
TROUBLE CODES (Cont.)
No. 15 Code
Note
When the malfunction code No. 15 and 17 are present at the same time, first perform the checking procedure for the malfunction code No. 17.
Are there any poor connections at oxygen sensor connector?
YES
Repair or replace connector
NO
Is operation of oxygen sensor heater OK?
NO
Repair or replace related parts
YES
Is oxygen sensor output voltage OK?
NO
Replace oxygen sensor
YES
Is sensitivity of oxygen sensor OK?
NO
PC: • Oxygen sensor malfunction
• Engine control unit malfunction
YES
Is there continuity between oxygen sensor connector (wiring harness side) and engine control unit (2D) terminal?
NO
PC: Open circuit in wiring harness from oxygen sensor to engine control unit (2D) terminal
YES
Is (2D) terminal voltage of engine control unit OK?
NO
PC: Short circuit in wiring harness between oxygen sensor and engine control unit (2D) terminal
YES
Replace engine control unit
No. 16 Code
Are there any poor connections at EGR position sensor connector?
YES
Repair or replace connector
NO
Is EGR control valve OK? (Refer to page 4—97)
NO
Replace EGR control valve
YES
Is resistance of EGR position sensor OK?
Resistance: (A) ↔ (B) Approx. 5kΩ
(A) ↔ (C) 0.7—5kΩ
(B) ↔ (C) 0.7—5kΩ
NO
Replace EGR control valve
YES
Is there continuity between EGR position sensor connector (wiring harness side) and engine control unit?
EGR position sensor | Engine control unit
A (BrW) | 2A
B (RB) | 2C
C (Y) | 2F
NO
PC: Open circuit in wiring harness from EGR position sensor to engine control unit
YES
Is there 4.5—5.5V at (A) terminal of EGR position sensor connector?
NO
PC: • Short circuit in wiring harness from EGR position sensor (A) terminal to engine control unit (2A) terminal
• Engine control unit malfunction
YES
Is engine control unit (2F) terminal voltage OK?
NO
PC: Short circuit in wiring harness EGR position sensor (C) terminal to engine control unit (2F) terminal
YES
Replace engine control unit
COLOR CODES
BrW.....Brown/White
RB......Red/Black
Y..........Yellow
Courtesy of Mazda Motors Corp.

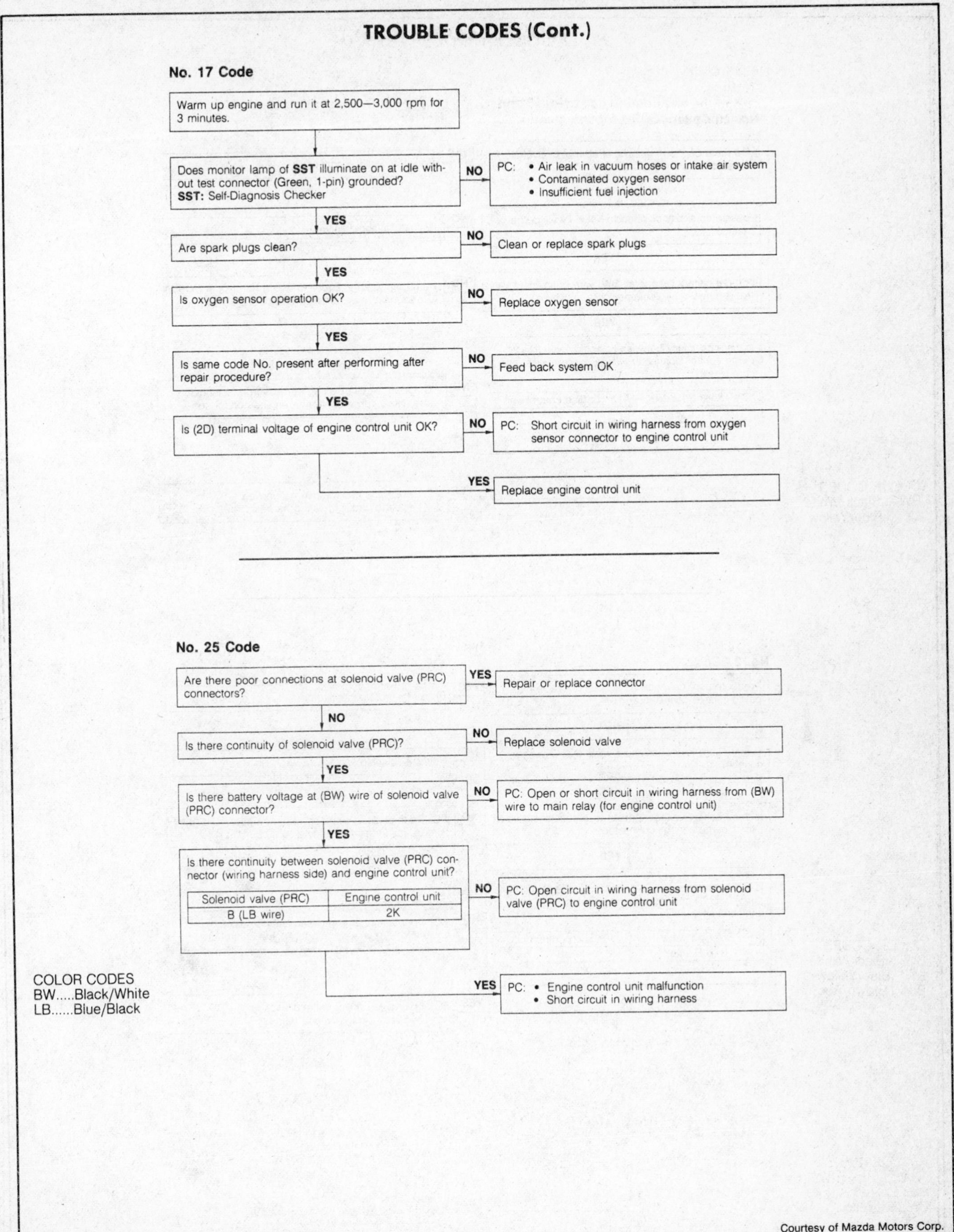
TROUBLE CODES (Cont.)
No. 17 Code
Warm up engine and run it at 2,500—3,000 rpm for 3 minutes.
Does monitor lamp of SST illuminate on at idle without test connector (Green, 1-pin) grounded?
SST: Self-Diagnosis Checker
NO
PC: • Air leak in vacuum hoses or intake air system
• Contaminated oxygen sensor
• Insufficient fuel injection
YES
Are spark plugs clean?
NO
Clean or replace spark plugs
YES
Is oxygen sensor operation OK?
NO
Replace oxygen sensor
YES
Is same code No. present after performing after repair procedure?
NO
Feed back system OK
YES
Is (2D) terminal voltage of engine control unit OK?
NO
PC: Short circuit in wiring harness from oxygen sensor connector to engine control unit
YES
Replace engine control unit
No. 25 Code
Are there poor connections at solenoid valve (PRC) connectors?
YES
Repair or replace connector
NO
Is there continuity of solenoid valve (PRC)?
NO
Replace solenoid valve
YES
Is there battery voltage at (BW) wire of solenoid valve (PRC) connector?
NO
PC: Open or short circuit in wiring harness from (BW) wire to main relay (for engine control unit)
YES
Is there continuity between solenoid valve (PRC) connector (wiring harness side) and engine control unit?
Solenoid valve (PRC) | Engine control unit
B (LB wire) | 2K
NO
PC: Open circuit in wiring harness from solenoid valve (PRC) to engine control unit
YES
PC: • Engine control unit malfunction
• Short circuit in wiring harness
COLOR CODES
BW.....Black/White
LB......Blue/Black
Courtesy of Mazda Motors Corp.

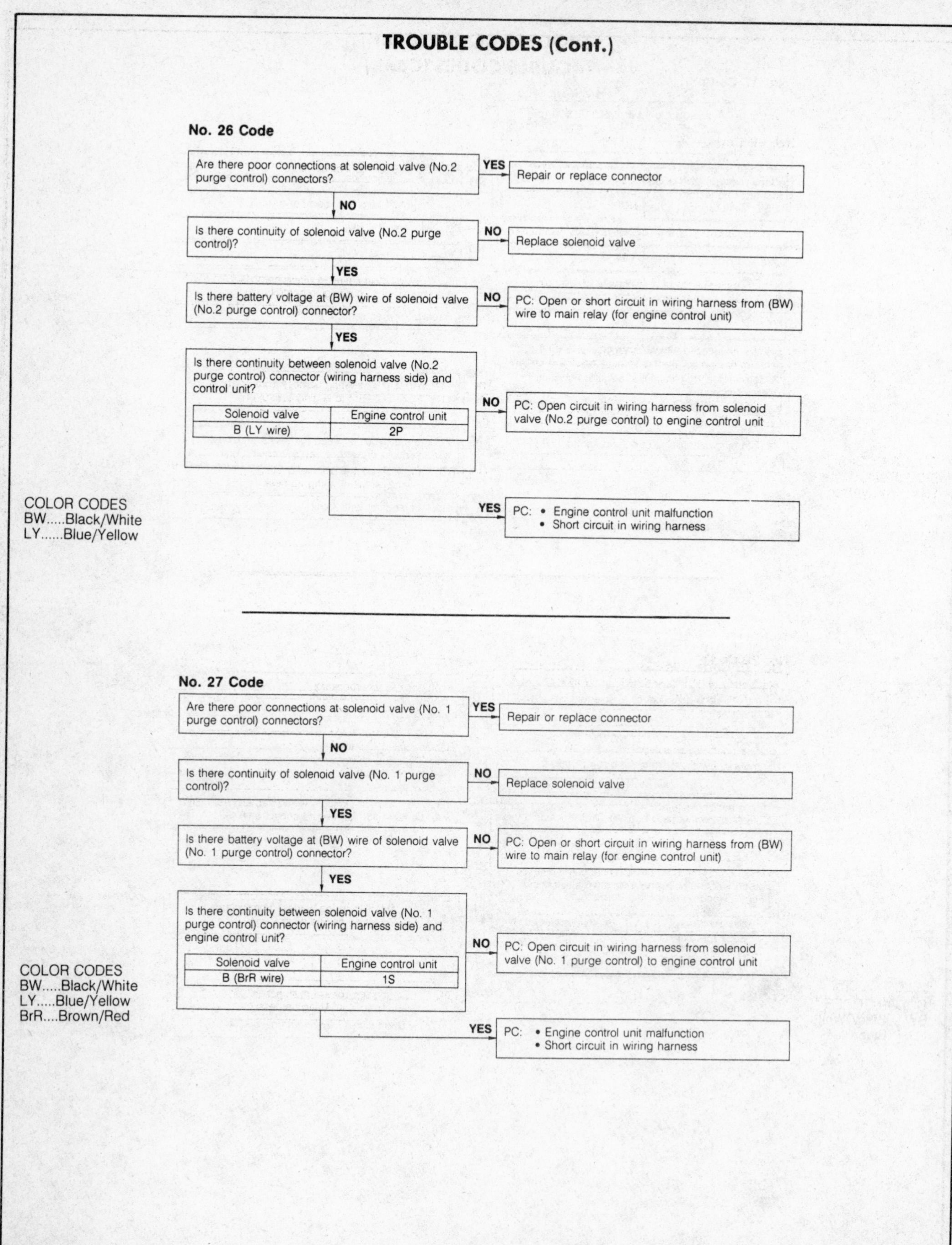
TROUBLE CODES (Cont.)
No. 26 Code
Are there poor connections at solenoid valve (No.2 purge control) connectors?
YES
Repair or replace connector
NO
Is there continuity of solenoid valve (No.2 purge control)?
NO
Replace solenoid valve
YES
Is there battery voltage at (BW) wire of solenoid valve (No.2 purge control) connector?
NO
PC: Open or short circuit in wiring harness from (BW) wire to main relay (for engine control unit)
YES
Is there continuity between solenoid valve (No.2 purge control) connector (wiring harness side) and control unit?
Solenoid valve
Engine control unit
B (LY wire)
2P
NO
PC: Open circuit in wiring harness from solenoid valve (No.2 purge control) to engine control unit
YES
PC: • Engine control unit malfunction
• Short circuit in wiring harness
COLOR CODES
BW.....Black/White
LY......Blue/Yellow
No. 27 Code
Are there poor connections at solenoid valve (No. 1 purge control) connectors?
YES
Repair or replace connector
NO
Is there continuity of solenoid valve (No. 1 purge control)?
NO
Replace solenoid valve
YES
Is there battery voltage at (BW) wire of solenoid valve (No. 1 purge control) connector?
NO
PC: Open or short circuit in wiring harness from (BW) wire to main relay (for engine control unit)
YES
Is there continuity between solenoid valve (No. 1 purge control) connector (wiring harness side) and engine control unit?
Solenoid valve
Engine control unit
B (BrR wire)
1S
NO
PC: Open circuit in wiring harness from solenoid valve (No. 1 purge control) to engine control unit
YES
PC: • Engine control unit malfunction
• Short circuit in wiring harness
COLOR CODES
BW.....Black/White
LY.....Blue/Yellow
BrR....Brown/Red

Courtesy of Mazda Motors Corp.

## TROUBLE CODES (Cont.)

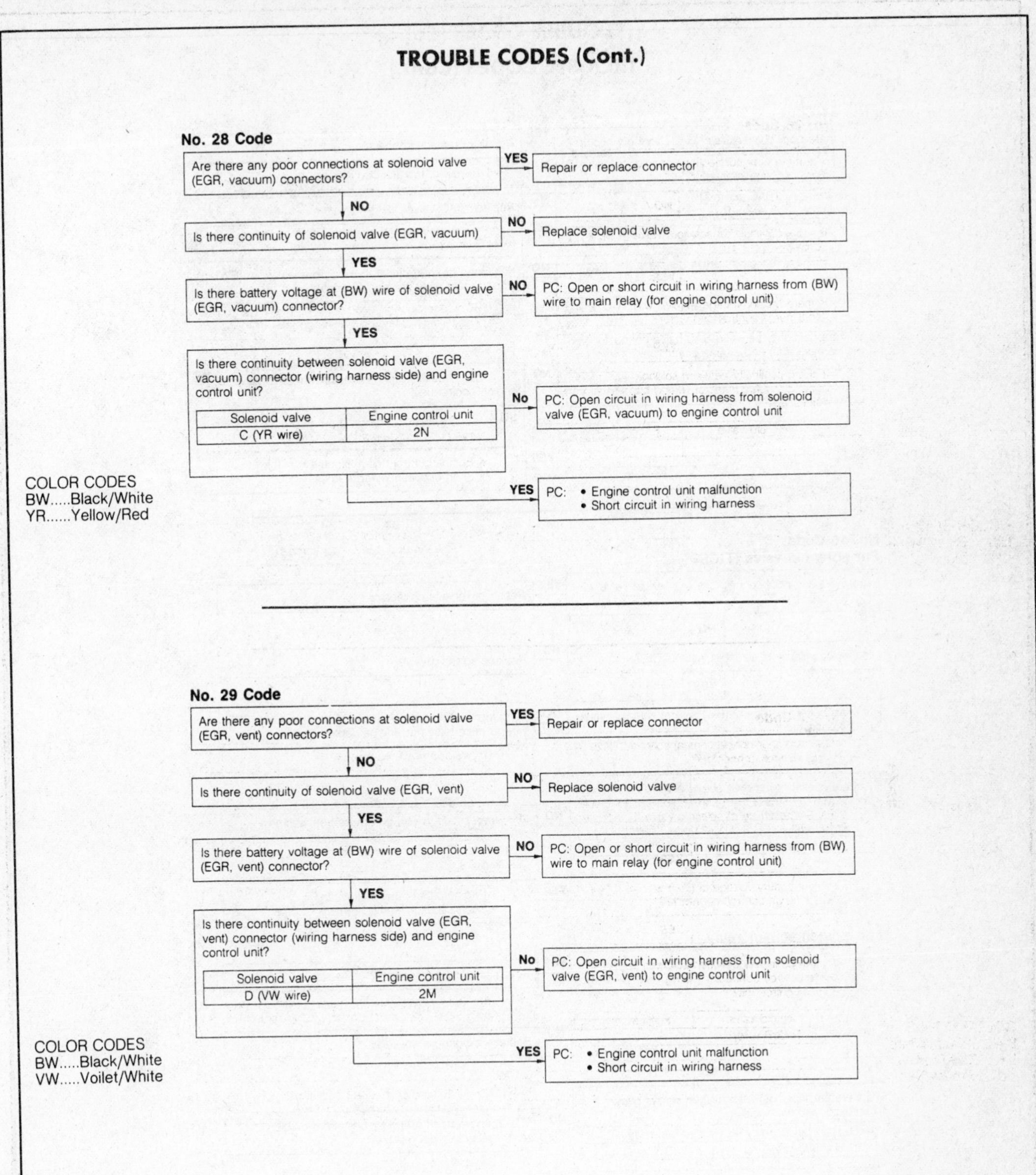

No. 28 Code
Are there any poor connections at solenoid valve (EGR, vacuum) connectors?
YES
Repair or replace connector
NO
Is there continuity of solenoid valve (EGR, vacuum)
NO
Replace solenoid valve
YES
Is there battery voltage at (BW) wire of solenoid valve (EGR, vacuum) connector?
NO
PC: Open or short circuit in wiring harness from (BW) wire to main relay (for engine control unit)
YES
Is there continuity between solenoid valve (EGR, vacuum) connector (wiring harness side) and engine control unit?
Solenoid valve
Engine control unit
C (YR wire)
2N
No
PC: Open circuit in wiring harness from solenoid valve (EGR, vacuum) to engine control unit
YES
PC: • Engine control unit malfunction
• Short circuit in wiring harness
COLOR CODES
BW.....Black/White
YR......Yellow/Red
No. 29 Code
Are there any poor connections at solenoid valve (EGR, vent) connectors?
YES
Repair or replace connector
NO
Is there continuity of solenoid valve (EGR, vent)
NO
Replace solenoid valve
YES
Is there battery voltage at (BW) wire of solenoid valve (EGR, vent) connector?
NO
PC: Open or short circuit in wiring harness from (BW) wire to main relay (for engine control unit)
YES
Is there continuity between solenoid valve (EGR, vent) connector (wiring harness side) and engine control unit?
Solenoid valve
Engine control unit
D (VW wire)
2M
No
PC: Open circuit in wiring harness from solenoid valve (EGR, vent) to engine control unit
YES
PC: • Engine control unit malfunction
• Short circuit in wiring harness
COLOR CODES
BW.....Black/White
VW.....Voilet/White


Courtesy of Mazda Motors Corp.

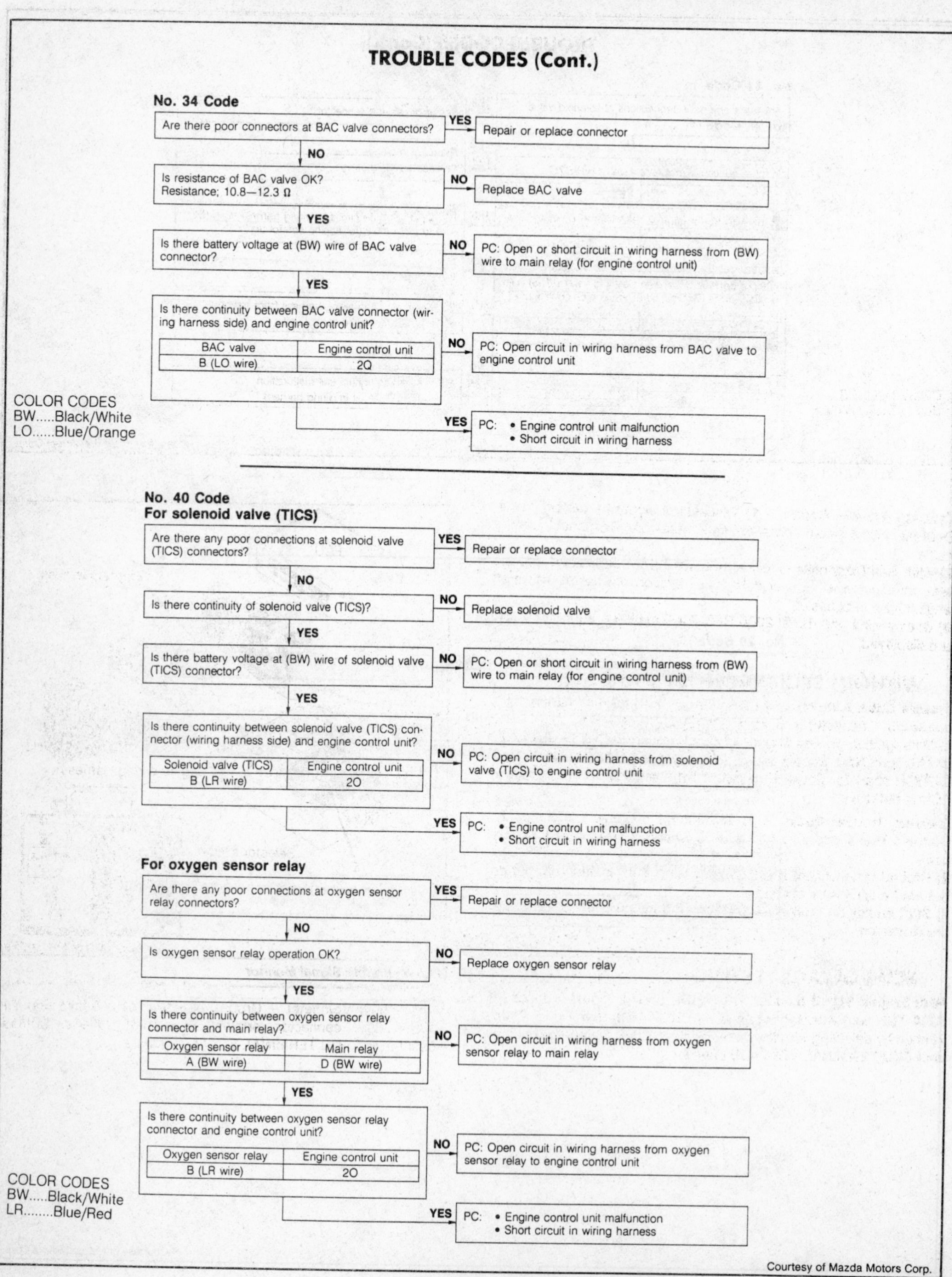
TROUBLE CODES (Cont.)
No. 34 Code
Are there poor connectors at BAC valve connectors?
YES
Repair or replace connector
NO
Is resistance of BAC valve OK?
Resistance; 10.8—12.3 Ω
NO
Replace BAC valve
YES
Is there battery voltage at (BW) wire of BAC valve connector?
NO
PC: Open or short circuit in wiring harness from (BW) wire to main relay (for engine control unit)
YES
Is there continuity between BAC valve connector (wiring harness side) and engine control unit?
BAC valve
Engine control unit
B (LO wire)
2Q
NO
PC: Open circuit in wiring harness from BAC valve to engine control unit
YES
PC: • Engine control unit malfunction
• Short circuit in wiring harness
COLOR CODES
BW.....Black/White
LO......Blue/Orange
No. 40 Code
For solenoid valve (TICS)
Are there any poor connections at solenoid valve (TICS) connectors?
YES
Repair or replace connector
NO
Is there continuity of solenoid valve (TICS)?
NO
Replace solenoid valve
YES
Is there battery voltage at (BW) wire of solenoid valve (TICS) connector?
NO
PC: Open or short circuit in wiring harness from (BW) wire to main relay (for engine control unit)
YES
Is there continuity between solenoid valve (TICS) connector (wiring harness side) and engine control unit?
Solenoid valve (TICS)
Engine control unit
B (LR wire)
2O
NO
PC: Open circuit in wiring harness from solenoid valve (TICS) to engine control unit
YES
PC: • Engine control unit malfunction
• Short circuit in wiring harness
For oxygen sensor relay
Are there any poor connections at oxygen sensor relay connectors?
YES
Repair or replace connector
NO
Is oxygen sensor relay operation OK?
NO
Replace oxygen sensor relay
YES
Is there continuity between oxygen sensor relay connector and main relay?
Oxygen sensor relay
Main relay
A (BW wire)
D (BW wire)
NO
PC: Open circuit in wiring harness from oxygen sensor relay to main relay
YES
Is there continuity between oxygen sensor relay connector and engine control unit?
Oxygen sensor relay
Engine control unit
B (LR wire)
2O
NO
PC: Open circuit in wiring harness from oxygen sensor relay to engine control unit
YES
PC: • Engine control unit malfunction
• Short circuit in wiring harness
COLOR CODES
BW.....Black/White
LR........Blue/Red

Courtesy of Mazda Motors Corp.

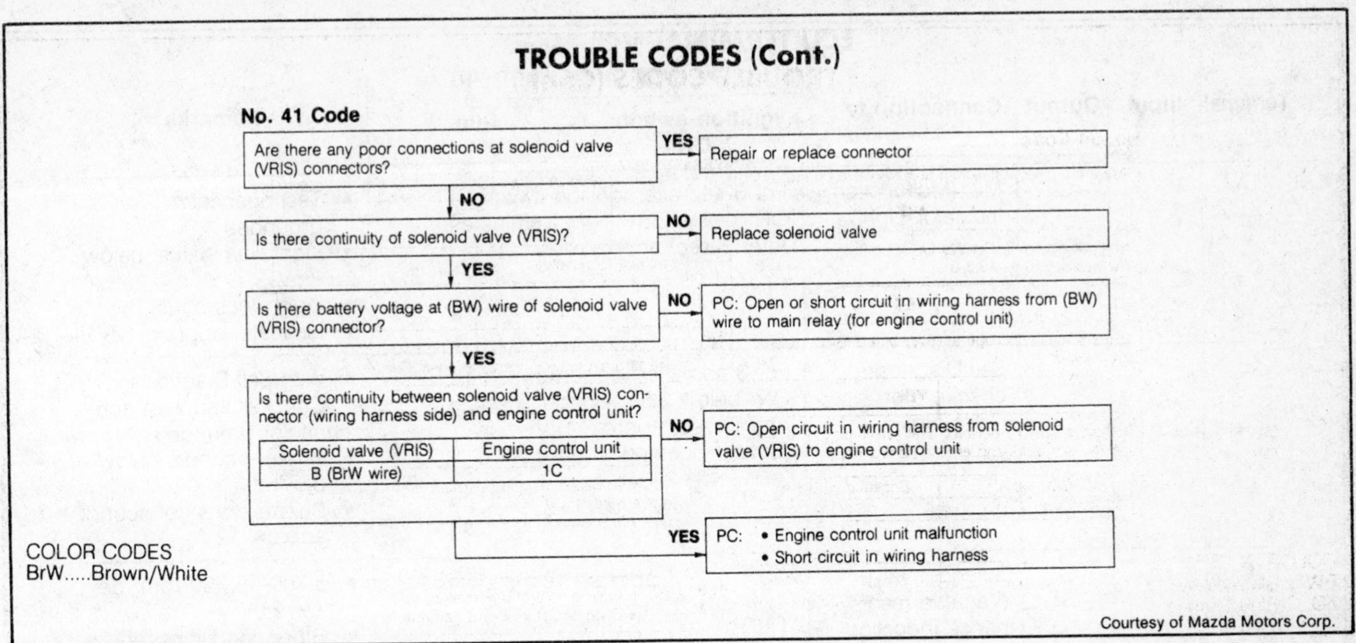
TROUBLE CODES (Cont.)
No. 41 Code
Are there any poor connections at solenoid valve (VRIS) connectors?
YES
Repair or replace connector
NO
Is there continuity of solenoid valve (VRIS)?
NO
Replace solenoid valve
YES
Is there battery voltage at (BW) wire of solenoid valve (VRIS) connector?
NO
PC: Open or short circuit in wiring harness from (BW) wire to main relay (for engine control unit)
YES
Is there continuity between solenoid valve (VRIS) connector (wiring harness side) and engine control unit?
Solenoid valve (VRIS) | Engine control unit
B (BrW wire) | 1C
NO
PC: Open circuit in wiring harness from solenoid valve (VRIS) to engine control unit
YES
PC: • Engine control unit malfunction
• Short circuit in wiring harness
COLOR CODES
BrW.....Brown/White
Courtesy of Mazda Motors Corp.

**Clearing Trouble Codes** – **1)** Disconnect negative battery cable. Depress brake pedal for at least 5 seconds. Reconnect battery cable.
**2)** With Self-Diagnostic Checker (49 H018 9A1) connected, ground test connector with jumper wire. Turn ignition on, but do not start engine for 6 seconds.
**3)** Start engine and run at 2000 RPM for 2 minutes. Verify no codes are displayed.

## WITHOUT SELF-DIAGNOSTIC CHECKER

**Trouble Code Access** – **1)** Using jumper wire, ground Green 1-pin connector. Connector is located at left front wheelwell.
**2)** With ignition on and engine stopped, observe "CHECK ENGINE" or MIL light. Note trouble codes. Check TROUBLE CODE IDENTIFICATION chart for possible cause. If light remains on continuously, ECU is defective.

**Clearing Trouble Codes** – **1)** Disconnect negative battery cable. Depress brake pedal for at least 5 seconds. Reconnect battery cable.
**2)** Ground test connector with jumper wire. Turn ignition on, but do not start engine for 6 seconds.
**3)** Start engine and run at 2000 RPM for 2 minutes. Verify no codes are displayed.

## ECU VOLTAGE TESTING

**With Engine Signal Monitor** – Connect Engine Signal Monitor (49 9200 162) with Adapter Harness (49 9200 163). *See Fig. 4* Check voltage by selecting terminal number on monitor. Compare readings with ECU TERMINAL VOLTAGE charts.

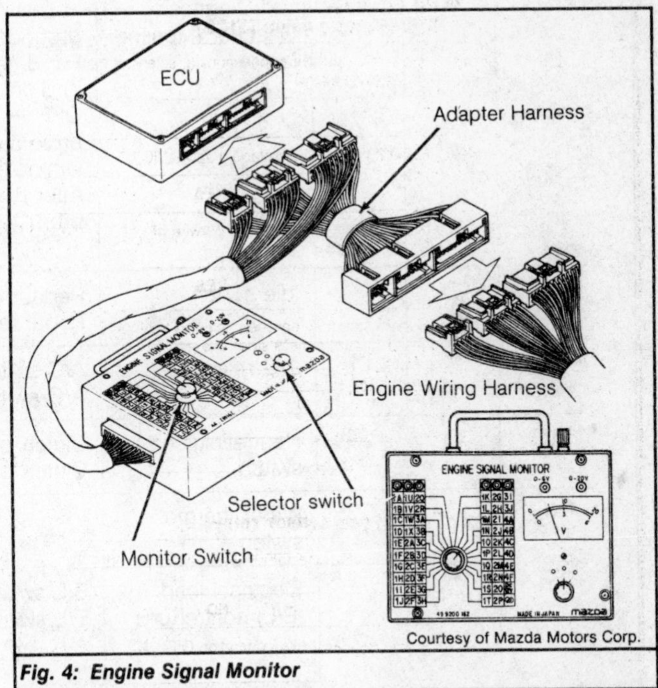
ECU
Adapter Harness
Engine Wiring Harness
ENGINE SIGNAL MONITOR
Selector switch
Monitor Switch
mazda
Courtesy of Mazda Motors Corp.

*Fig. 4: Engine Signal Monitor*

**With Analog Voltmeter** – Ground negative lead. Backprobe each specific ECU connector terminal to monitor voltage. Compare readings with ECU TERMINAL VOLTAGE charts.

# 1988 COMPUTERIZED ENGINE CONTROLS
# Mazda – 929 EGI (Cont.)

## ECU TERMINAL VOLTAGE

| Terminal | Input | Output | Connection to | Voltage (after warm-up) | | Remarks |
|---|---|---|---|---|---|---|
| | | | | Ignition switch: ON | Idle | |
| 1A | | ○ | MIL (Malfunction Indicator Light) | For 3 sec after ignition switch OFF → ON: below 2.5V (light illuminates)<br>After 3 sec: approx. 12V | | • Test connector grounded<br>• Light illuminates: below 2.5V<br>• Light does not illuminate: approx. 12V |
| 1B | | ○ | Self-Diagnosis checker (for Code No) | For 3 sec after ignition switch OFF → ON: below 2.5V (Buzzer sounds)<br>After 3 sec: approx. 12V (Buzzer does not sound) | | • With Self-Diagnosis Checker and Test connector grounded<br>• Buzzer sounds: below 2.5V<br>• Buzzer does not sound: approx. 12V |
| 1C | | ○ | Solenoid valve (Variable resonance induction system (VRIS) ) | approx. 12V | | • 3,700—5,750 rpm: below 2.0V<br>• Other conditions: approx. 12V |
| 1D | | ○ | Self-Diagnosis Checker (Monitor lamp) | <Test connector grounded><br>For 3 sec after ignition switch OFF → ON: approx. 5V (lamp illuminates)<br>After 3 sec: approx. 12V | <Test connector grounded><br>approx. 5V<br><Test connector is not grounded><br>Monitor lamp ON; Below 6V<br>Monitor lamp OFF: approx. 12V | With Self-Diagnosis Checker |
| 1E | ○ | | Idle switch | Pedal depressed: approx. 10V<br>Pedal released: 0V | | |
| 1F | | ○ | A/C relay | A/C switch ON; below 2.5V<br>A/C switch OFF; approx. 12V | | Blower motor: ON |
| 1G | ○ | | Neutral/clutch switch | Clutch pedal depressed: approx. 12V<br>Clutch pedal released: 0V | | In-gear condition (Neutral: constant 12V) |
| 1H | ○ | | Water thermo switch | 0V | | Radiator temp below 17°C (62.6°F): approx. 12V |
| 1I | ○ | | Electrical load (E/L) control unit | E/L switch ON: below 2.5V<br>E/L switch OFF: approx. 10—12V | | Electrical load switch:<br>Blow motor switch<br>Rear defroster switch<br>Headlight switch |
| 1J | ○ | | Brake light switch | Brake pedal depressed: approx. 12V<br>Brake pedal released: 0V | | |
| 1K | ○ | | Power steering (P/S) switch | Constant approx. 12V | P/S: ON: 0V<br>P/S: OFF: approx. 12V | |
| 1L | ○ | | A/C switch | A/C switch ON: below 2.5V<br>A/C switch OFF: approx. 12V | | Blower motor: ON |
| 1M | ○ | | Igniter | 0V | Approx. 0.6—0.8V | Engine Signal Monitor green and red lights flash |
| 1N | ○ | | Distributor (G1 signal) | Approx. 0.6—0.8V | | G1: Group 1 |

Courtesy of Mazda Motors Corp.

# 1988 COMPUTERIZED ENGINE CONTROLS
# Mazda – 929 EGI (Cont.)

## ECU TERMINAL VOLTAGE (Cont.)

| Terminal | Input | Output | Connection to | Voltage (after warm-up) Ignition switch: ON | Voltage (after warm-up) Idle | Remarks |
|---|---|---|---|---|---|---|
| 1O | ○ | | Distributor (G2 signal) | Approx. 0.6—0.8V | | G2: Group 2 |
| 1P | ○ | | Distributor (G1, G2 ground) | Approx. 0.6—0.8V | | |
| 1Q | ○ | | Distributor (Ne ground) | Approx. 0.6—0.8V | | Ne: Number of engine speed |
| 1S | | ○ | Solenoid valve (No. 1 purge control) | Approx. 12V | Approx. 12V | No-load condition |
| | | | | | Initial of acceleration or<br>Above 900 rpm: below 2.5V<br>Other condition: Approx. 12V | <Load condition><br>M/T: Disconnect neutral switch connector and connect jumper wire to connector<br>EC-AT: Disconnect EC-AT control unit connector (20-pin) |
| 1T | ○ | | Distributor (Ne signal) | Approx. 0.6—0.8V | | Ne: Number of engine speed |
| 1U | — | — | — | For 180 sec after ignition switch OFF → ON: Approx. 12V | For 180 sec after starting: Approx. 12V | During hot condition: Coolant temp.: above 90°C (194°F) and engine air temp.: above 85°C (185°F) |
| | | | | Below 2.5V | | Other condition |
| 1V | ○ | | — | Below 1.5V | | M/T |
| | | | | Approx. 12V | | EC-AT |
| 1W | ○ | | Test Connector | Test connector: grounded 0v<br>Test connector: Not grounded approx. 12V | | Green connector, 1-pin |
| 1X | | ○ | Igniter | 0V | Approx. 0.8V | |
| 2A | | ○ | Vref | 4.5—5.5V | | |
| 2B | ○ | | Air flow meter (Vc) | 7—9V | | |
| 2C | — | — | Ground (E2) | 0V | | |
| 2D | ○ | | Oxygen sensor | 0V | 0—1V | • Cold engine: 0V at idle<br>• After warming-up: Acceleration: 0.7—1.0V Deceleration: 0—0.2V |
| 2E | ○ | | Air flow meter (Vs) | Approx. 2.0V | Approx. 3.5—5V | |
| 2F | ○ | | EGR position sensor | Approx. 0.25—0.9V | | |
| 2G | ○ | | Throttle sensor | Throttle valve fully closed: approx. 0.3V<br>Throttle valve fully open: approx. 4V | | |
| 2H | ○ | | Atmospheric pressure sensor | Approx. 3.5—4.5V at sea level | | |

Courtesy of Mazda Motors Corp.

# 1988 COMPUTERIZED ENGINE CONTROLS
# Mazda – 929 EGI (Cont.)

**ECU TERMINAL VOLTAGE (Cont.)**

| Terminal | Input | Output | Connection to | Voltage (after warm-up): Ignition switch: ON | Voltage (after warm-up): Idle | Remarks |
|---|---|---|---|---|---|---|
| 2I | ○ | | Water thermo sensor | Approx. 0.3—0.6V | | |
| 2J | ○ | | Intake air thermo sensor (air flow meter) | Approx. 2—3V at 20°C (68°F) | | |
| 2K | | ○ | Solenoid valve (Pressure regulator control) | For 240 sec after ignition switch OFF → ON: below 2.5V | For 240 sec after starting: below 2.5V | During hot condition: coolant temp.: above 80°C (176°F) and engine air temp.: above 75°C (167°F) |
| | | | | Approx. 12V | | Other conditions |
| 2L | ○ | | Intake air thermo sensor (Dynamic chamber) | Approx. 1—2V at 80°C (176°F) | | |
| 2M | | ○ | Solenoid valve (EGR, vent side) | Approx. 12V | | Initial of acceleration; Engine Signal Monitor green and red light flash |
| 2N | | ○ | Solenoid valve (EGR, vacuum side) | Approx. 12V | | Initial of acceleration; Engine Signal Monitor green and red light flash |
| 2O | | ○ | Solenoid valve (Triple induction control system (TICS) ) and oxygen sensor relay | Below 2.5V | | Above approx. 4,000 rpm: approx. 12V |
| 2P | | ○ | Solenoid valve (No.2 purge control) | Approx. 12V | | Acceleration over 1,500 rpm: below 2.5V |
| 2Q | | ○ | Idle speed control (ISC) valve | Approx. 2—5V | Approx. 9—11V | Engine Signal Monitor green and red lights flash |
| 2R | — | — | Ground (E02) | 0V | | |
| 3A | — | — | Ground (E01) | 0V | | |
| 3B | ○ | | Ignition switch (START position) | Below 2.5V | | While cranking: 6—11V |
| 3C | | ○ | Injector (No.3 and No.4) | Approx. 12V | | Engine Signal Monitor green and red lights flash |
| 3D | ○ | | Inhibitor switch | "N" or "P" range: 0V<br>Other ranges: approx. 12V | | M/T: constant 0V |
| 3E | | ○ | Injector (No.1 and No.2) | Approx. 12V | | Engine Signal Monitor green and red lights flash |
| 3F | | ○ | Injector (No.5 and No.6) | Approx. 12V | | Engine Signal Monitor green and red lights flash |
| 3G | — | — | Ground (E1) | 0V | | — |
| 3I | ○ | | Main relay | Approx. 12V | | |
| 3J | — | — | Battery | Approx. 12V | | For back-up |

Courtesy of Mazda Motors Corp.

## ECU TERMINAL VOLTAGE (Cont.)

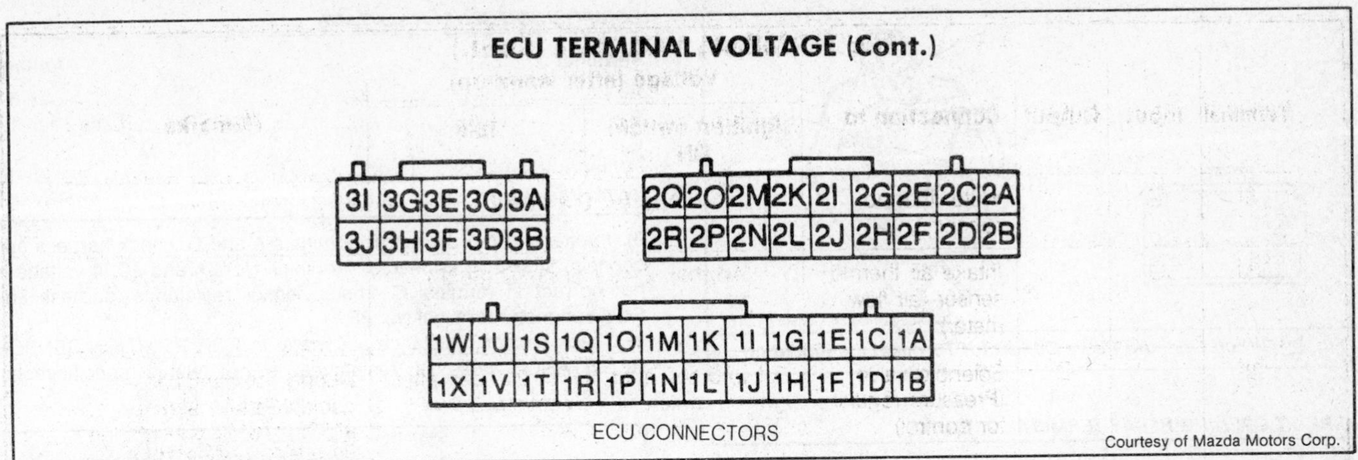
3I 3G 3E 3C 3A
3J 3H 3F 3D 3B
2Q 2O 2M 2K 2I 2G 2E 2C 2A
2R 2P 2N 2L 2J 2H 2F 2D 2B
1W 1U 1S 1Q 1O 1M 1K 1I 1G 1E 1C 1A
1X 1V 1T 1R 1P 1N 1L 1J 1H 1F 1D 1B
ECU CONNECTORS
Courtesy of Mazda Motors Corp.

## DECELERATION CONTROL SYSTEM

Deceleration control system is a function of ECU. It provides fuel cut during deceleration.

**1)** Connect Engine Signal Monitor (49 9200 162) or backprobe ECU connector terminals No. 3C, 3E or 3F. Start engine. Voltage should pulsate.

**2)** Increase engine speed to 4500 RPM. Suddenly decrease engine speed. Voltage should become constant during deceleration. If not, check idle switch, coolant temperature sensor, dashpot and all ECU connections.

## COMPONENT TESTING

**Airflow Meter** – Inspect airflow meter for damage and ensure measuring plate moves smoothly. *See Fig. 5.* Disconnect airflow meter connector. Measure resistance using AIRFLOW METER TERMINAL RESISTANCE table.

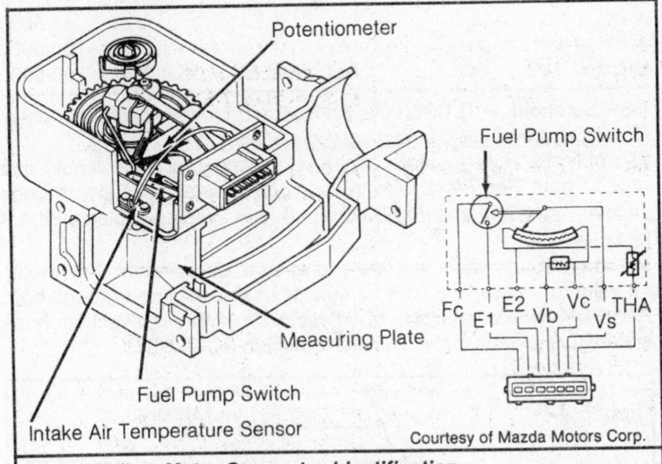
Potentiometer
Fuel Pump Switch
Fc
E1
E2
Vb
Vc
Vs
THA
Measuring Plate
Fuel Pump Switch
Intake Air Temperature Sensor
Courtesy of Mazda Motors Corp.

***Fig. 5: Airflow Meter Connector Identification***

***AIRFLOW METER TERMINAL RESISTANCE***

| Terminal | Fully Closed Ohms | Fully Open Ohms |
|---|---|---|
| E2-Vs | 20-400 | 20-1000 |
| E2-Vc | 100-300 | 100-300 |
| E2-Vb | 200-400 | 200-400 |
| E2-THA | -4°F (-20°C) 13.6-18.4k | -4°F (-20°C) 13.6-18.4k |
| | 68°F (20°C) 2.21-2.69k | 68°F (20°C) 2.21-2.69k |
| | 140°F (60°C) 493-667 | 140°F (60°C) 493-667 |
| E1-Fc | Infinite | 0 |

**Atmospheric Pressure Sensor** – **1)** Connect voltmeter to terminal D. Turn ignition on and note voltage. *See Fig. 6.*

**2)** Voltage at sea level should be 3.5-4.5 volts. Voltage at 6500 feet should be 2.5-3.5 volts. Replace if not to specification.

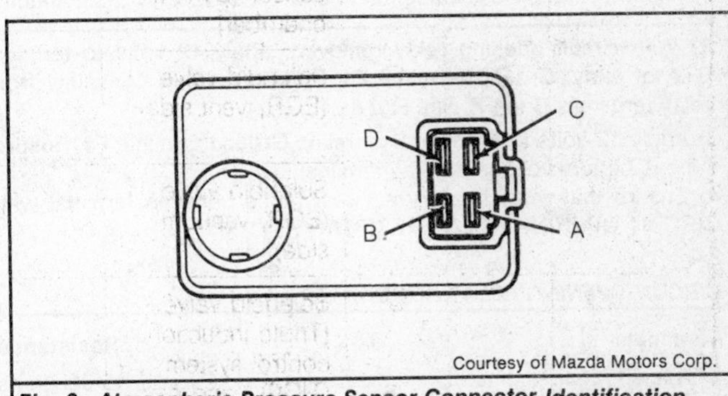
C
D
B
A
Courtesy of Mazda Motors Corp.

***Fig. 6: Atmospheric Pressure Sensor Connector Identification***

**Brake Light Switch** – **1)** Disconnect brake light switch connector. Measure resistance across terminals of brake light switch.

**2)** With brake pedal released, resistance should be infinite. With brake pedal depressed, resistance should be zero ohms.

**By-Pass Air Control (BAC) Valve** – **1)** Ensure air flows through port A when valve is cold. *See Fig. 7.* If not, replace BAC valve.

**2)** Measure resistance of Idle Speed Control (ISC) valve at 2 wire connector of BAC valve. Resistance should be between 10.8-12.3 ohms, at normal operating temperature. If not, replace BAC valve.

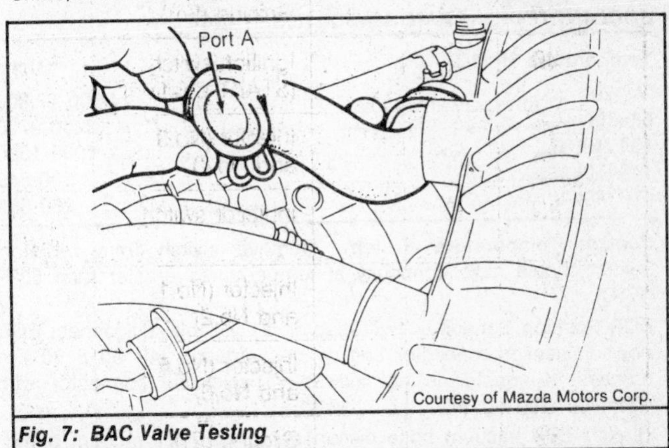
Port A
Courtesy of Mazda Motors Corp.

***Fig. 7: BAC Valve Testing***

**Circuit Opening Relay** – **1)** Remove circuit opening relay. Check circuit opening relay circuits with CIRCUIT OPENING RELAY TERMINAL CIRCUITS table.

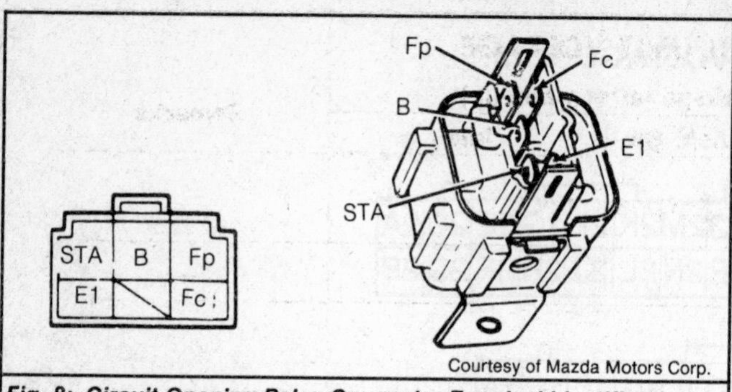
Fp
Fc
B
E1
STA
STA
B
Fp
E1
Fc
Courtesy of Mazda Motors Corp.

*Fig. 8: Circuit Opening Relay Connector Terminal Identification*

***CIRCUIT OPENING RELAY TERMINAL CIRCUITS***

| Terminal | Condition | Results |
|---|---|---|
| Fp | Resistance to Ground | 0.2-30 Ohms |
| Fc | Resistance to Ground (Cranking) | Infinite |
| B | Voltage to Ground (Ign. On) | Battery Voltage |
| STA | Voltage to Ground (Cranking) | Approx. 9 Volts |
| E1 | Resistance to Ground | Infinite |

**2)** With circuit opening relay removed, apply 12 volts to terminal STA of relay. Ground terminal E1. Ensure there is continuity from relay terminals B to FP. *See Fig. 8.*

**3)** Apply 12 volts to terminal B of relay. Ground terminal Fc. Ensure there is battery voltage at relay terminal Fp.

**4)** Ensure that relay has correct resistance between terminal with CIRCUIT OPENING RELAY RESISTANCE table.

***CIRCUIT OPENING RELAY RESISTANCE***

| Terminals | Resistance |
|---|---|
| STA to E1 | 15-30 Ohms |
| B to Fc | 80-150 Ohms |
| B to Fp | Infinite |

**Clutch Switch (M/T) – 1)** Disconnect clutch switch connector. Measure resistance across terminals on switch.

**2)** With clutch pedal released, resistance should be zero ohms. With clutch pedal depressed, resistance should be infinite.

**Coolant Temperature Sensor** – Disconnect and remove coolant temperature sensor. Check resistance using COOLANT TEMPERATURE SENSOR RESISTANCE table.

***COOLANT TEMPERATURE SENSOR RESISTANCE***

| Temperature °F (°C) | Ohms |
|---|---|
| -4 (-20) | 14,500-17,800 |
| 68 (20) | 2200-2700 |
| 104 (40) | 1000-1300 |
| 140 (60) | 500-640 |
| 176 (80) | 280-350 |

**Coolant Temperature Switch** – Remove switch from radiator. Switch should have continuity at temperatures greater than 63°F (17°C).

**EGR Position Sensor – 1)** If adapter is available, disconnect EGR position sensor connector and connect Adapter (49 G018 901) in harness. If adapter is not available, backprobe connector with voltmeter. *See Fig. 9.*

**2)** With EGR vacuum hose disconnected, connect vacuum pump. Turn ignition on and check voltages at connector. Use EGR POSITION SENSOR VOLTAGE table to compare results.

***EGR POSITION SENSOR VOLTAGE***

| Terminal | Voltage |
|---|---|
| A | 4.5-5.5 |
| B | Less Than 1.5 |
| C | |
| Without Vacuum | .25-.95 |
| With Vacuum | Approx. 4.0 |

**3)** If voltage is not correct at terminals A and B, check harness and connection at ECU connector terminals No. 2A and 2C. If voltage is not correct at terminal C, check sensor resistance, harness and ECU connector terminal No. 2F.

**4)** Check sensor resistance according to EGR POSITION SENSOR RESISTANCE table. If resistance is not within specifications, replace sensor.

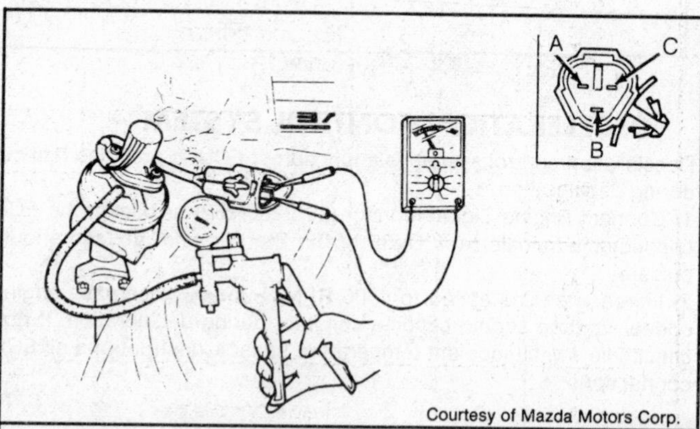
A
C
B
Courtesy of Mazda Motors Corp.

*Fig. 9: EGR Position Sensor Connector Terminal Identification*

***EGR POSITION SENSOR RESISTANCE***

| Terminals | Ohms |
|---|---|
| A-B | 5000 |
| A-C | 700-5000 |
| B-C | 700-5000 |

**EGR Solenoid – 1)** Disconnect hoses and blow through vent hose. Ensure air flows. Disconnect solenoid connector.

**2)** Apply 12 volts to Violet/White wire connector of solenoid and ground both Red/Black wire connectors of solenoid. Blow through vacuum hose and ensure air does not flow. Replace solenoid if not okay. *See Fig. 10.*

**3)** Blow through vacuum hose and ensure air does not flow. Apply 12 volts to Yellow/Red wire connector of solenoid and ground both Red/Black wire connectors of solenoid. Blow through vacuum hose and ensure air does flow. Replace solenoid if not okay.

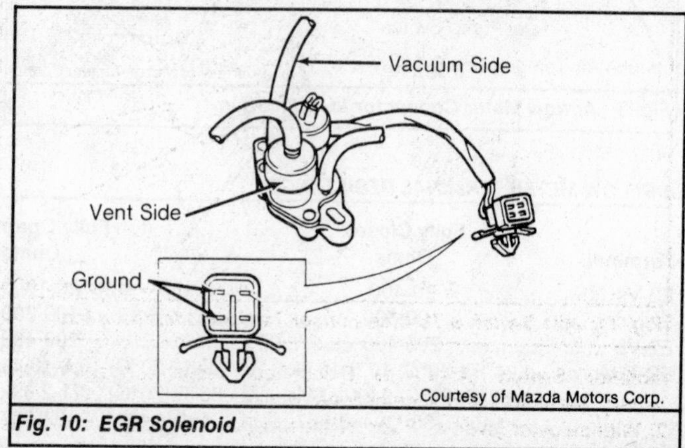
Vacuum Side
Vent Side
Ground
Courtesy of Mazda Motors Corp.

*Fig. 10: EGR Solenoid*

# 1988 COMPUTERIZED ENGINE CONTROLS
# Mazda – 929 EGI (Cont.)

**ELECTRONIC CONTROL UNIT VOLTAGE**

| Terminal | Input | Output | Connection to | Voltage (after warm-up) Ignition switch: ON | Voltage (after warm-up) Idle | Remarks |
|---|---|---|---|---|---|---|
| A (BW) | — | — | Ignition switch | Approx. 12V | | |
| B | — | — | — | — | — | — |
| C (B) | — | — | Ground | 0V | | |
| D | — | — | — | — | | |
| E (PB) | | ○ | Engine control unit (1I) | 0V | | E/L: ON |
| | | | | Approx. 12V | | E/L: OFF |
| F (RG) | ○ | | Headlight switch | Approx. 12V | | Headlight switch: ON |
| | | | | Below 1.5V | | Headlight switch: OFF |
| G (G) | ○ | | Blower motor switch | Below 1.5V | | Fan speed control: ON (5th—8th position) |
| | | | | Approx. 5V | | Others |
| H (RW) | ○ | | Rear defroster switch | Below 1.5V | | Rear defroster switch: ON |
| | | | | Approx. 5V | | Rear defroster switch: OFF |

**Electrical Load Control Unit** – Connect a voltmeter between electrical load control unit connector terminal and ground. Start engine. Check voltage at terminals using ELECTRONIC CONTROL UNIT VOLTAGE chart.

**Idle Switch** – **1)** Disconnect throttle sensor connector. Connect an ohmmeter between terminals C and D. With a .02" (.5 mm) feeler gauge between throttle stop and throttle lever, resistance should be zero ohms. *See Fig. 11.*

**2)** With a .028" (.7 mm) feeler gauge between throttle stop and throttle lever, resistance should be infinite. If not within specifications, adjust throttle sensor.

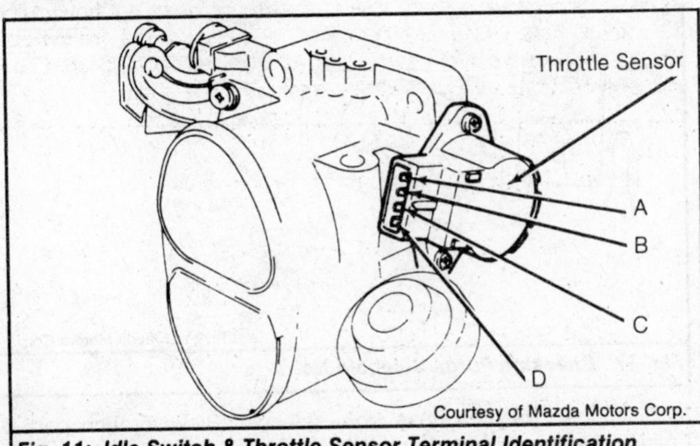
Throttle Sensor
A
B
C
D
Courtesy of Mazda Motors Corp.

*Fig. 11: Idle Switch & Throttle Sensor Terminal Identification*

**Inhibitor Switch (A/T)** – **1)** Disconnect 3-pin connector near battery. Measure resistance between wires.

**2)** With selector lever in "P" or "N", resistance should be zero ohms. With selector lever in any other position, resistance should be infinite.

**Intake Air Temperature Sensor (Dynamic Chamber)** – Disconnect intake air temperature sensor connector. Measure resistance of sensor using INTAKE AIR TEMPERATURE SENSOR RESISTANCE table. *See Fig. 12.*

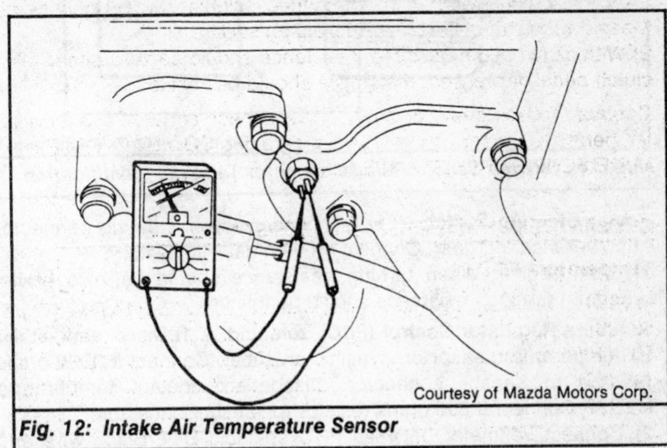
Courtesy of Mazda Motors Corp.

*Fig. 12: Intake Air Temperature Sensor*

***INTAKE AIR TEMPERATURE SENSOR RESISTANCE***

| Temperature °F (°C) | Ohms |
|---|---|
| 68 (20) | 37,300-45,600 |
| 122 (50) | 10,500-12,900 |
| 185 (85) | 3100-3800 |

**Main Relay** – **1)** Ensure a clicking sound is heard at main relay when turning ignition on and off. Disconnect main relay. Apply 12 volts to terminal A and ground terminal B. *See Fig. 13.*

**2)** Ensure there is continuity between main relay terminals C and D, when voltage is applied. There should be no continuity when voltage is not applied.

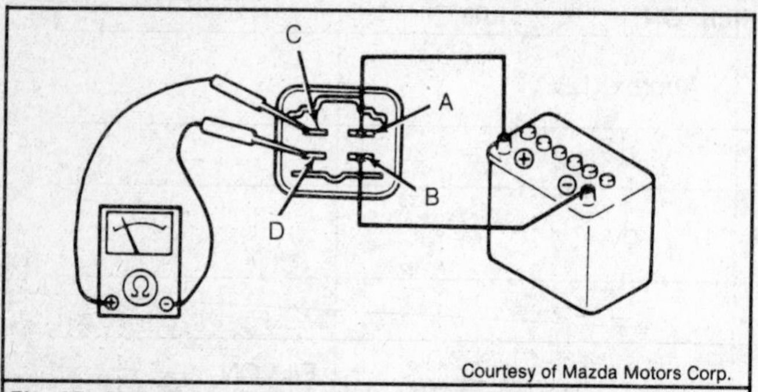
C
A
B
D
Courtesy of Mazda Motors Corp.

*Fig. 13: Main Relay Connector Terminal Identification*

**Neutral Switch (M/T) – 1)** Disconnect connector near transmission. Place transmission in Neutral position. Resistance across switch should be infinite.

**2)** Place transmission in any gear. Resistance across switch should be zero ohms.

**Oxygen Sensor Relay – 1)** Ensure there is a clicking sound heard at oxygen sensor relay when ignition is turned on and off. Apply 12 volts to terminal A and ground terminal B. *See Fig. 14.*

**2)** Measure resistance between terminals C and D. With 12 volts applied, resistance should be zero ohms. With no voltage applied, resistance should be infinite.

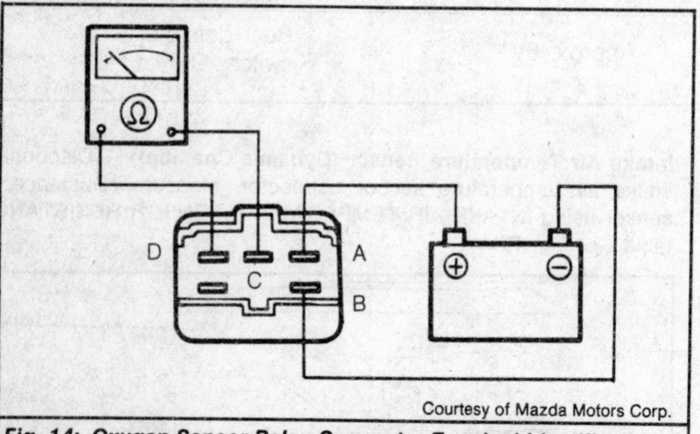
D
A
C
B
Courtesy of Mazda Motors Corp.

*Fig. 14: Oxygen Sensor Relay Connector Terminal Identification*

**Power Steering Switch – 1)** Disconnect power steering connector at power steering gear. Connect an ohmmeter to switch.

**2)** Start engine. When turning, resistance should be zero ohms. When not turning, resistance should be infinite.

**Pressure Regulator Control (PRC) Solenoid – 1)** Disconnect intake air temperature sensor on dynamic chamber. Connect a 3000 ohms resistor to sensor connector. Disconnect coolant temperature sensor. Connect a 200 ohms resistor to sensor connector.

**2)** Connect voltmeter between PRC solenoid Blue/Black wire and ground. With engine running, voltage should be less than 2.5 volts for 4 minutes after starting. After 4 minutes, voltage should be 12 volts. If not repair wiring or connection. *See Fig. 15.*

**3)** Disconnect vacuum hose from solenoid. Blow through port A. Ensure air exhausts through port B. *See Fig. 16.*

**4)** Disconnect 2 wire connector from solenoid. Connect 12 volts to one terminal and ground the other terminal of solenoid. Blow air though port A. Ensure air exhausts through air filter.

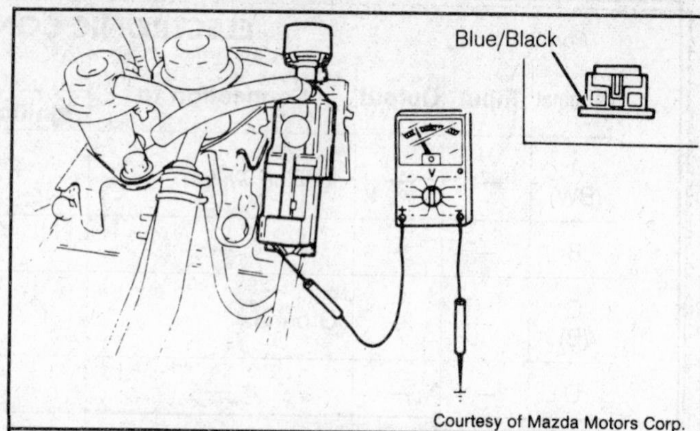
Blue/Black
Courtesy of Mazda Motors Corp.

*Fig. 15: Checking Pressure Regulator Control Solenoid*

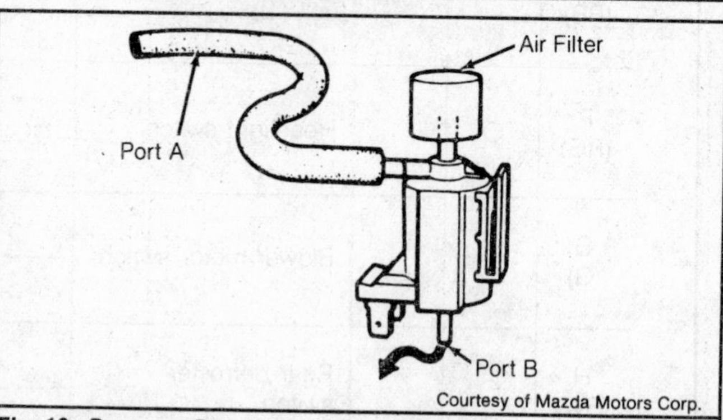
Air Filter
Port A
Port B
Courtesy of Mazda Motors Corp.

*Fig. 16: Pressure Regulator Control Solenoid*

**Purge Solenoid No. 1 – 1)** For manual transmissions, disconnect neutral switch connector (M/T), jumper connector and start engine. For automatic transmissions, disconnect ECAT control unit after starting engine.

**2)** Connect voltmeter between Brown/Red solenoid wire and ground. With engine temperature less than 131°F (55°C), voltage should be 12 volts. With engine temperature greater than 131°F (55°C) and engine RPM less than 900, voltage should be 12 volts. With engine warm and engine RPM greater than 900, voltage should be less than 2.5 volts. *See Fig. 17.*

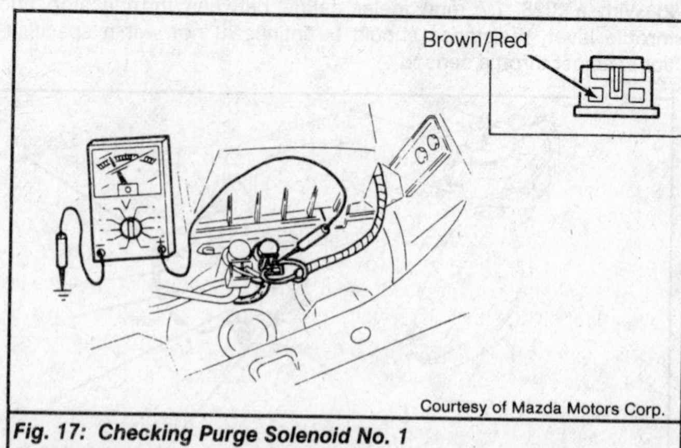
Brown/Red
Courtesy of Mazda Motors Corp.

*Fig. 17: Checking Purge Solenoid No. 1*

**3)** Disconnect vacuum hose from solenoid. Blow through port B. Ensure air exhaust through air filter.

**4)** Disconnect 2 wire connector from solenoid. Connect 12 volts to one terminal and ground the other terminal of solenoid. Blow air through port B. Ensure air exhaust through port A.

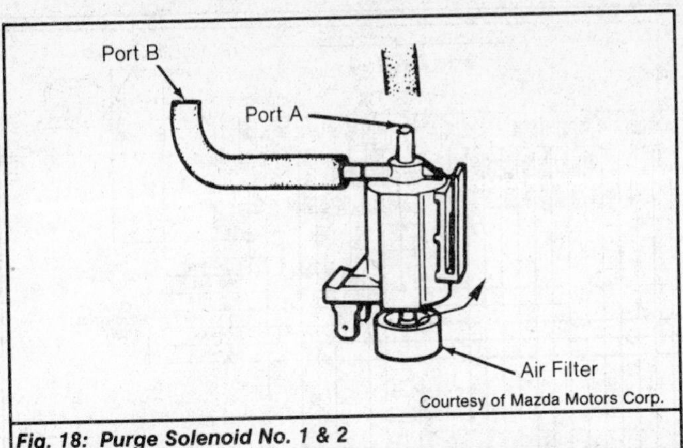
Port B
Port A
Air Filter
Courtesy of Mazda Motors Corp.
*Fig. 18: Purge Solenoid No. 1 & 2*

**Purge Solenoid No. 2 – 1)** Connect voltmeter between Blue/Yellow solenoid wire and ground. *See Fig. 19.* With engine temperature less than 158°F (70°C), start engine and note voltage. Voltage should be 12 volts.

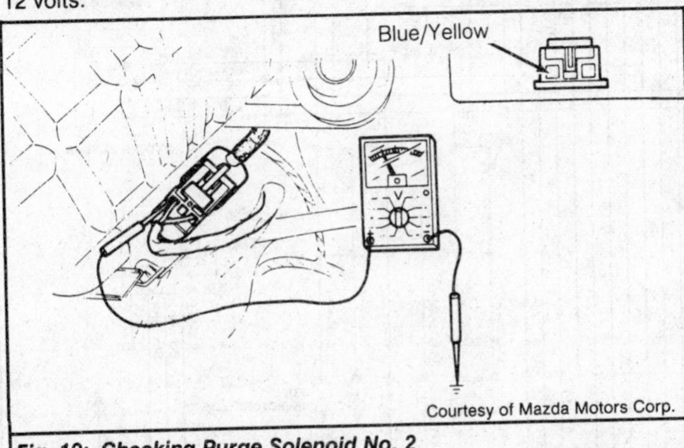
Blue/Yellow
Courtesy of Mazda Motors Corp.
*Fig. 19: Checking Purge Solenoid No. 2*

**2)** Warm engine to normal operating temperature. With engine RPM less than 1500, voltage should be 12 volts. During acceleration with engine RPM greater than 1500, voltage should be less than 2.5 volts. Any time except acceleration, with engine RPM is greater than 1500, voltage should be 12 volts.
**3)** Disconnect vacuum hose from solenoid. Blow through port B. Ensure air exhausts through air filter. *See Fig. 18.*
**4)** Disconnect 2 wire connector from solenoid. Connect 12 volts to one terminal and ground the other terminal of solenoid. Blow air though port B. Ensure air exhausts through port A.

**Throttle Sensor – 1)** Disconnect throttle sensor connector. Connect an ohmmeter between throttle sensor terminals A and D. Resistance should be 3500-6500 ohms. *See Fig. 11.*
**2)** Connect ohmmeter between throttle sensor terminals B and D. Gradually open throttle valve and note resistance. With throttle valve closed, resistance should be less than 1000 ohms. With throttle valve fully open, resistance should be 3500-6500 ohms. If not within specifications, check adjustment.

**TICS Solenoid – 1)** Connect voltmeter between solenoid valve Blue/Red wire and ground. *See Fig. 20.* Start engine and note voltage.
**2)** With engine RPM less than 4000, voltage should be less than 2 volts. With engine RPM greater than 4000, voltage should be approximately 12 volts.
**3)** Disconnect vacuum hose from solenoid. Blow through port B. Ensure exhaust through air filter.
**4)** Disconnect solenoid connector. Apply 12 volts to one solenoid terminal and ground the other. Blow through port B. Ensure air exhaust through port A. *See Fig. 21.*

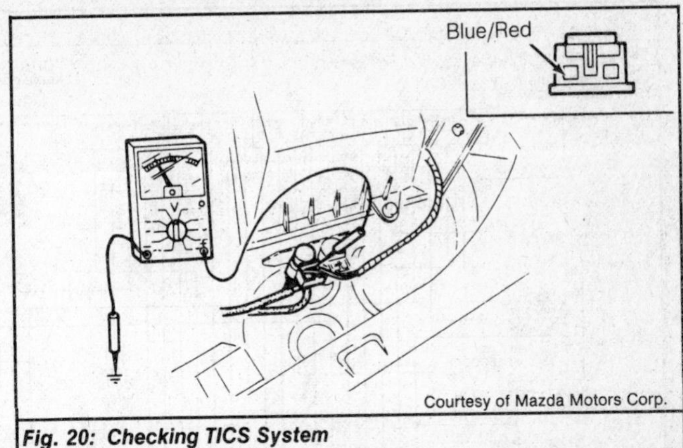
Blue/Red
Courtesy of Mazda Motors Corp.
*Fig. 20: Checking TICS System*

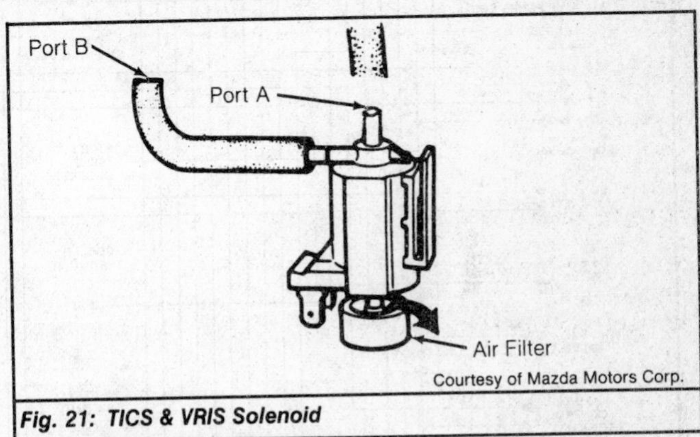
Port B
Port A
Air Filter
Courtesy of Mazda Motors Corp.
*Fig. 21: TICS & VRIS Solenoid*

**VRIS Solenoid – 1)** Connect voltmeter between solenoid valve Brown/White wire and ground. *See Fig. 22.* Start engine and note voltage. If voltage is not to specifications, check ECU terminal voltage and connections.

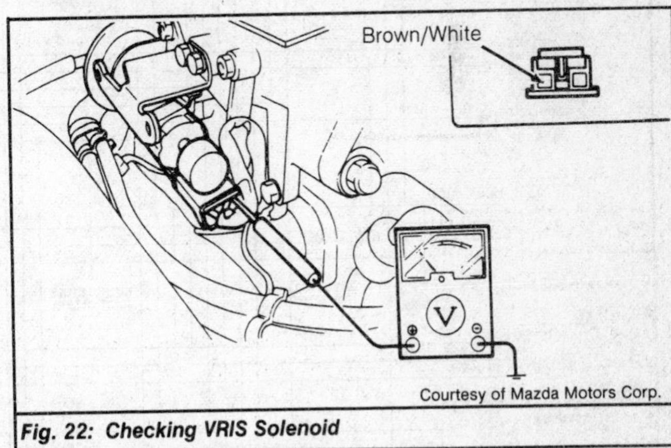
Brown/White
Courtesy of Mazda Motors Corp.
*Fig. 22: Checking VRIS Solenoid*

***VRIS OPERATING VOLTAGE***

| Engine RPM | Volts |
|---|---|
| Less Than 3700 | Approx. 12 |
| 3700-5750 | Less Than 2 |
| Greater Than 5750 | Approx. 12 |

**2)** Disconnect vacuum hoses from solenoid. Blow through port B. Ensure air exhaust through air filter.
**3)** Disconnect solenoid connector. Apply 12 volts to one solenoid terminal and ground the other. Blow through port B. Ensure air exhaust through port A. *See Fig. 21.*

# 1988 COMPUTERIZED ENGINE CONTROLS
## Mazda – 929 EGI (Cont.)

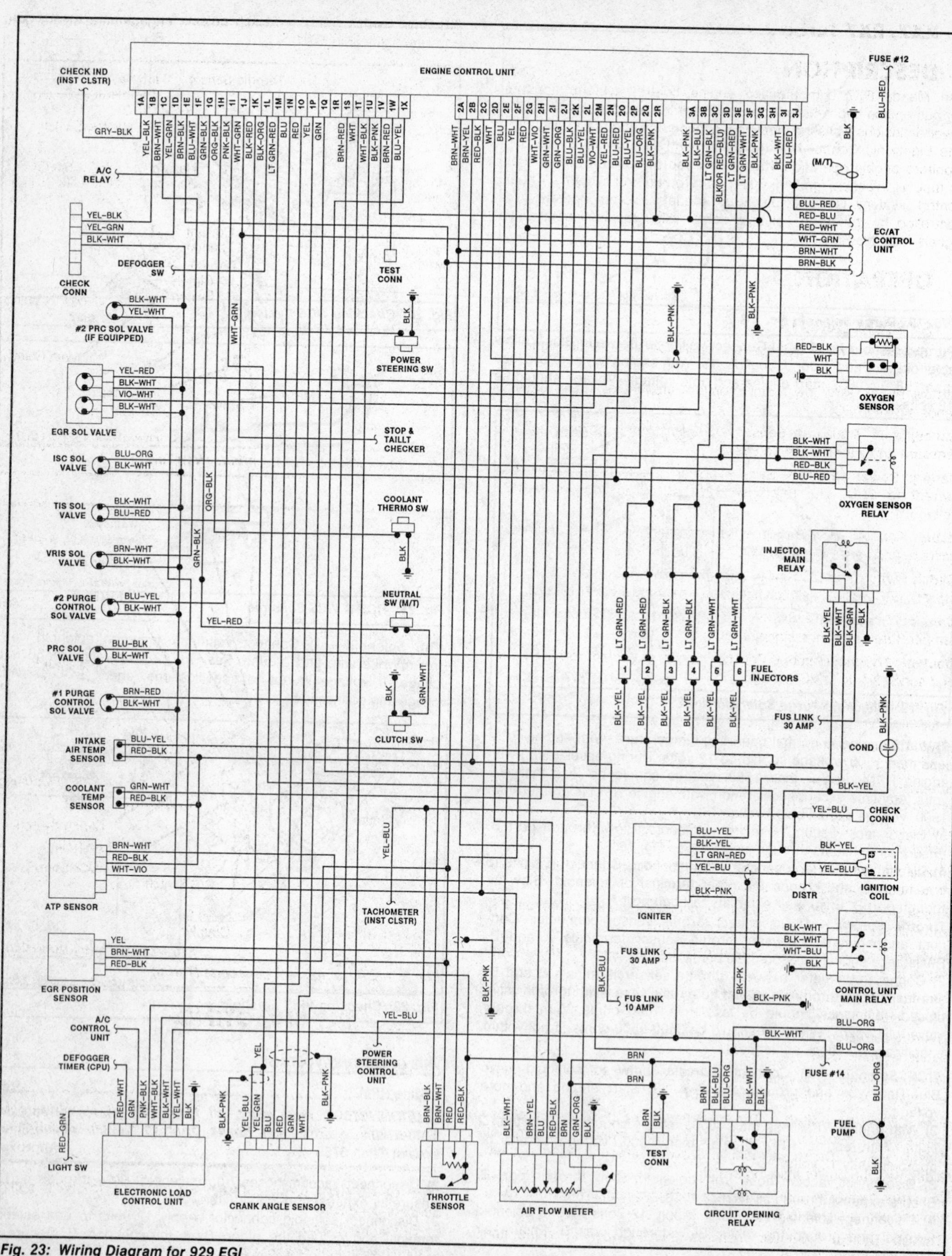
ENGINE CONTROL UNIT
CHECK IND (INST CLSTR)
FUSE #12
GRY-BLK
A/C RELAY
CHECK CONN
DEFOGGER SW
TEST CONN
#2 PRC SOL VALVE (IF EQUIPPED)
POWER STEERING SW
EGR SOL VALVE
STOP & TAILLT CHECKER
ISC SOL VALVE
TIS SOL VALVE
COOLANT THERMO SW
VRIS SOL VALVE
#2 PURGE CONTROL SOL VALVE
NEUTRAL SW (M/T)
PRC SOL VALVE
#1 PURGE CONTROL SOL VALVE
CLUTCH SW
INTAKE AIR TEMP SENSOR
COOLANT TEMP SENSOR
ATP SENSOR
TACHOMETER (INST CLSTR)
EGR POSITION SENSOR
A/C CONTROL UNIT
DEFOGGER TIMER (CPU)
POWER STEERING CONTROL UNIT
LIGHT SW
ELECTRONIC LOAD CONTROL UNIT
CRANK ANGLE SENSOR
THROTTLE SENSOR
AIR FLOW METER
TEST CONN
CIRCUIT OPENING RELAY
FUSE #14
FUEL PUMP
FUS LINK 10 AMP
FUS LINK 30 AMP
CONTROL UNIT MAIN RELAY
IGNITER
DISTR
IGNITION COIL
CHECK CONN
COND
FUS LINK 30 AMP
FUEL INJECTORS
INJECTOR MAIN RELAY
OXYGEN SENSOR RELAY
OXYGEN SENSOR
EC/AT CONTROL UNIT
(M/T)

*Fig. 23: Wiring Diagram for 929 EGI*

# Mazda RX7 Engine Control System

## RX7, RX7 Turbo

## DESCRIPTION

The Mazda RX7 computerized engine control system monitors various engine and vehicle functions to control engine operation and lower emissions while maintaining fuel economy and driveability.

The Electronic Control Unit (ECU), through various input sensors, monitors engine operation through the use of output devices such as fuel, air injection, ignition, EGR and turbo control systems. Knock control system is used on turbo models. Turbo operation is controlled by the turbo solenoid valve which receives controlling signals from the ECU.

## OPERATION

### SYSTEM INPUTS

**A/C Switch** – Switch detects A/C operation and sends signal to ECU.

**Airflow Meter** – Airflow meter monitors amount of intake air and sends signal to ECU.

**Atmospheric Pressure Sensor** – Sensor monitors atmospheric pressure and sends signal to ECU.

**Battery Power Circuit** – Battery power circuit provides electric current to ECU. The ECU uses this circuit to monitor battery voltage.

**Boost Sensor (Non-Turbo)** – Sensor monitors intake manifold vacuum and sends signal to ECU.

**Clutch Switch** – Clutch switch detects clutch operation and sends signal to ECU. Clutch switch is closed when pedal is depressed.

**Coolant Temperature Switch** – Switch monitors radiator coolant temperature and sends signal to ECU.

**Coolant Thermosensor** – Sensor monitors coolant temperature and sends signal to ECU.

**Crank Angle Sensor** – Sensor detects eccentric shaft and front rotor position and sends signal to ECU.

**Heat Hazard Sensor** – Sensor detects floor temperature and sends signal to ECU.

**Inhibitor Switch (A/T)** – Switch detects position of selector lever and sends signal to ECU.

**Initial Set Coupler** – Set coupler is used to deliver an initial set signal to ECU for idle mixture adjustment procedures.

**Intake Air Temperature Sensor** – Sensor monitors intake manifold air temperature and sends signal to ECU.

**Knock Sensor (Turbo)** – Sensor monitors engine knock conditions and sends signal to engine knock control unit.

**Mileage Switch** – Switch determines vehicle mileage and sends signal to ECU.

**Neutral Switch** – Switch detects gearshift Neutral position and sends signal to ECU.

**Overdrive Switch (A/T)** – Switch detects overdrive operation and sends signal to ECU.

**Oxygen Sensor** – Oxygen sensor ($O_2$) monitors oxygen content of exhaust gases and sends signal to ECU.

**Power Steering Switch** – The Power Steering (P/S) switch determines when pressure is required to turn the wheels and sends a signal to ECU. On turbo models, a power steering relay is used along with the power steering switch.

**Pressure Sensor (Turbo)** – Sensor monitors intake manifold vacuum and sends signal to ECU.

**Throttle Sensor** – Sensor monitors throttle opening angle and sends signal to ECU.

**Variable Resistor** – Variable resistor adjusts air/fuel ratio and sends signal to ECU.

**5th Gear Switch (M/T)** – Switch detects engagement of 5th gear and sends signal to ECU.

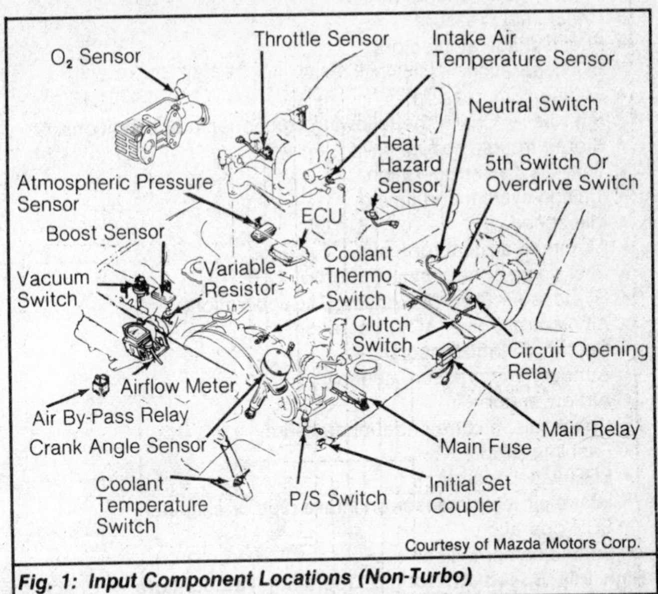
$O_2$ Sensor
Throttle Sensor
Intake Air Temperature Sensor
Neutral Switch
Heat Hazard Sensor
5th Switch Or Overdrive Switch
Atmospheric Pressure Sensor
ECU
Boost Sensor
Vacuum Switch
Variable Resistor
Coolant Thermo Switch
Clutch Switch
Circuit Opening Relay
Airflow Meter
Air By-Pass Relay
Main Relay
Crank Angle Sensor
Main Fuse
Coolant Temperature Switch
P/S Switch
Initial Set Coupler
Courtesy of Mazda Motors Corp.

*Fig. 1: Input Component Locations (Non-Turbo)*

$O_2$ Sensor
Throttle Sensor
Intake Air Temperature Sensor
Intercooler
Heat Hazard Sensor
Knock Control Unit
Atmospheric Pressure Sensor
Neutral Switch
5th Switch
ECU
Pressure Sensor
Variable Resistor
Circuit Opening Relay
Airflow Meter
Clutch Switch
Coolant Thermo switch
Main Relay
Knock Sensor
P/S Switch
Crank Angle Sensor
Initial Set Coupler
Coolant Temperature Switch
Courtesy of Mazda Motors Corp.

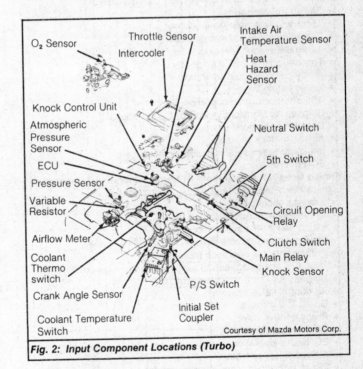

*Fig. 2: Input Component Locations (Turbo)*

## TROUBLE SHOOTING

### DRIVEABILITY

***CAUTION: Inspect main relay, all fuses, circuit operating relay, connections and vacuum hoses prior to trouble shooting the system.***

**Hard Or No Start (Cranks Okay)** – Check the following components or conditions:

- Stored trouble codes.
- Ignition system operation.
- Primary injector operation (non-turbo).
- Main fuel line pulsations to indicate operation (turbo).

- Coolant thermosensor.
- Fuel pump switch.
- Airflow meter operation.
- Check fuel pressure.
- Fuel leakage at injectors.
- ECU operation.
- Engine compression.

**Rough Idle** – Check the following components or conditions:

- Stored trouble codes.
- Throttle sensor operation.
- Ignition system and timing.
- Idle speed.
- Air intake system for leaks.
- Fuel pump control system (turbo).
- By-pass Air Control System (BAC) operation.
- Air Control Valve (ACV) operation.
- Coolant thermosensor.
- Atmospheric pressure sensor.
- Airflow meter.
- Check idle mixture and fuel pressure.
- Fast idle RPM.
- EGR valve operation.
- Intake air temp. sensor on intake pipe or chamber.
- ECU operation.
- Engine compression.

**High Idle Speed At Normal Operating Temperature** – Check the following components or conditions:

- Stored trouble codes.
- Throttle valves operate smoothly.
- Fast idle cam releases from roller.
- Air intake system for leaks.
- Throttle sensor and idle speed.
- Air by-pass solenoid operation.
- Ignition timing.
- Anti-afterburn valve operation.
- By-pass Air Control System (BAC) operation.
- Dashpot operation.
- Airflow meter operation.
- Intake air temp. sensor in airflow meter.
- ECU operation.

**Engine Does Not Run Smooth At Normal Operating Temperature** – Check the following components or conditions:

- Stored trouble codes.
- Ignition system and timing.
- Inspect air intake system for leaks.
- Idle speed and throttle sensor.
- Primary injector operation (non-turbo).
- Main fuel line pulsations to indicate operation (turbo).
- By-pass Air Control System (BAC).
- Air control valve operation.
- Check idle mixture.
- Purge control valve.
- Coolant thermosensor.
- EGR valve operation.
- Airflow meter operation.
- Intake air temp. sensor in airflow meter.
- Fuel pressure and fuel leaks.
- ECU operation.
- Engine compression.

**Engine Does Not Run Smooth At Cold Condition** – Check the following components or conditions:

- Stored trouble codes.
- Ignition system and timing.
- Inspect air intake system for leaks.
- Idle speed and throttle sensor.
- Check fast idle system.
- Primary injector operation (non-turbo).
- Main fuel line pulsations to indicate operation (turbo).
- Check double throttle system (turbo).
- By-pass Air Control System (BAC).
- Air control valve operation.
- Fuel pump control system (turbo).
- Check variable resistor.
- Purge control valve.
- Coolant thermosensor.
- EGR valve operation.
- Airflow meter operation.
- Intake air temp. sensor in airflow meter.
- Fuel pressure and fuel leaks.
- ECU operation.
- Engine compression.
- Check injection volume.

**Engine Does Not Run Smooth At Hot Condition** – Check the following components or conditions:

- Stored trouble codes.
- Ignition system and timing.
- Inspect air intake system for leaks.
- Idle speed and throttle sensor.
- Pressure regulator control solenoid operation.
- Primary injector operation (non-turbo).
- Main fuel line pulsations to indicate operation (turbo).
- By-pass Air Control System (BAC).
- Air control valve operation.
- Intake air temp. sensor on intake pipe or chamber.
- Fuel pump control system (turbo).
- Check idle mixture.
- Purge control valve.
- Coolant thermosensor.
- Airflow meter operation.
- Fuel pressure and fuel leaks.
- ECU operation.
- Engine compression.
- Check injection volume.

**Lack Of Power** – Check the following components or conditions:

- Stored trouble codes.
- Ignition system and timing.
- Initial set coupler jumper wire removed (non-turbo).
- Inspect air intake system for leaks.
- Air control valve operation.
- Air filter condition.
- Airflow meter operation.
- Intake air temp. sensor in airflow meter.
- Check auxiliary port valve (non-turbo).
- Intake air temperature sensor.
- Injector operating sound (non-turbo).
- Check double throttle system operation.
- Check pressure or boost sensor.
- Main fuel line pulsations to indicate operation (turbo).
- Throttle sensor operation.
- Coolant thermosensor.
- Fuel pressure and fuel leaks.
- ECU operation.
- Check feedback system.
- Engine compression.
- Check injection volume.
- Check knock control (turbo).
- Check turbo and wastegate valve.
- Check turbo control system.
- Check accelerator cable.

**Afterburn** – Check the following components or conditions:

- Stored trouble codes.
- Ignition system and timing.
- Air intake for leaks.
- Check idle speed.
- Air control valve operation.
- Check throttle sensor.
- Dashpot operation.
- Anti-afterburn valve operation.
- By-pass Air Control System (BAC).
- Injector operating sound.
- Coolant thermosensor.
- Intake air temp. sensor in airflow meter.

- Airflow meter operation.
- Check injector leakage.
- ECU operation.
- Engine compression.
- Check fuel pump control system (turbo).
- Check idle mixture.
- EGR valve operation.

**Runs Rough On Deceleration** – Check the following components or conditions:

- Stored trouble codes.
- Ignition system and timing.
- Air intake for leaks.
- Check idle speed.
- Check throttle sensor.
- Dashpot operation.
- Air control valve operation.
- By-pass Air Control System (BAC).
- Injector operating sound.
- Coolant thermosensor.
- Intake air temp. sensor in airflow meter.
- EGR valve operation.
- Clutch and neutral switch.
- ECU operation.
- Engine compression.
- Fuel leakage at injectors.

## SELF-DIAGNOSIS

Obtain trouble codes. See TROUBLE CODES under TESTING in this article.

**Trouble Code No. 01 – 1)** Check all connections and repair as necessary. Check crank angle sensor resistance. See CRANK ANGLE SENSOR under COMPONENT TESTING in this article. If resistance is okay, check for continuity between proper terminals of crank angle sensor and ECU. See ECU & SENSOR TERMINAL USAGE table. Determine terminal identification. *See Fig. 3.*

***ECU & SENSOR TERMINAL USAGE***

| Sensor Terminal | ECU Terminal |
|---|---|
| G1 | 1N |
| G2 | 1P |
| NE1 | 1T |
| NE2 | 1Q |

**2)** If continuity did not exist at proper terminals, check wiring circuit. If continuity exists, ECU is defective.

**Trouble Code No. 02 – 1)** Check all connections and repair as necessary. Check airflow meter resistance. See AIRFLOW METER under COMPONENT TESTING in this article.

**2)** If resistance is okay, check for voltage at BRN/WHT wire of airflow connector. Voltage should be 4.5-5.5 volts. If voltage is not within specification, check for faulty wiring circuit or defective ECU.

**3)** If voltage is correct, check for continuity between proper terminals of airflow meter and ECU. See ECU & AIRFLOW METER TERMINAL USAGE table. Determine terminal identification. *See Figs. 3 and 4.* If continuity does not exist, check wiring circuit. If continuity exists, ECU is defective.

***ECU & AIRFLOW METER TERMINAL USAGE***

| Airflow Meter Terminal | ECU Terminal |
|---|---|
| Vs | 2E |
| E2 | 2C |

**Trouble Code No. 03 – 1)** Check all connections and repair as necessary. Check coolant thermosensor resistance. See COOLANT THERMOSENSOR under COMPONENT TESTING in this article.

**2)** If resistance is okay, check for continuity between coolant thermosensor and ECU. Check continuity between BLK or BLK/BRN wire of coolant thermosensor and terminal "2C" of ECU and Green wire of coolant thermosensor and terminal "2I" of ECU. Determine proper ECU terminal identification. *See Fig. 3.*

**3)** If no continuity exists, check for open wiring circuit. If continuity exists, check for shorted circuit or defective ECU.

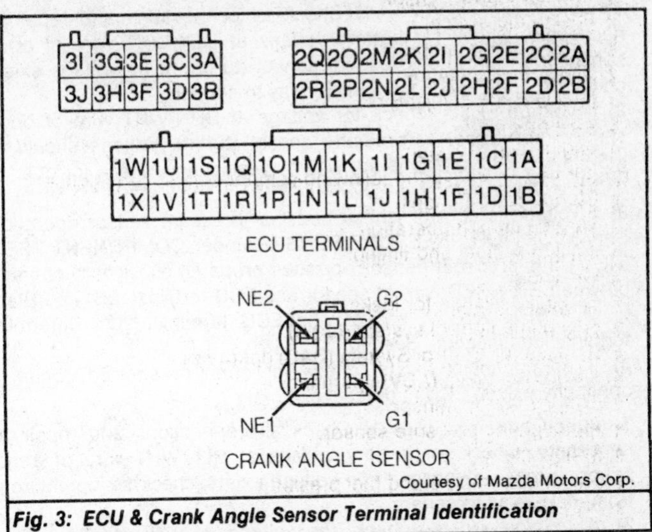
3I 3G 3E 3C 3A
3J 3H 3F 3D 3B
2Q 2O 2M 2K 2I 2G 2E 2C 2A
2R 2P 2N 2L 2J 2H 2F 2D 2B
1W 1U 1S 1Q 1O 1M 1K 1I 1G 1E 1C 1A
1X 1V 1T 1R 1P 1N 1L 1J 1H 1F 1D 1B
ECU TERMINALS
NE2
G2
NE1
G1
CRANK ANGLE SENSOR
Courtesy of Mazda Motors Corp.

*Fig. 3: ECU & Crank Angle Sensor Terminal Identification*

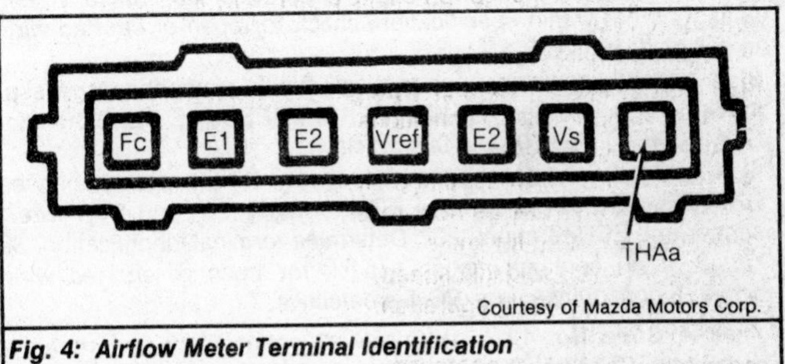
Fc
E1
E2
Vref
E2
Vs
THAa
Courtesy of Mazda Motors Corp.

*Fig. 4: Airflow Meter Terminal Identification*

**Trouble Code No. 04 – 1)** Check all connections and repair as necessary. Check air intake temperature sensor resistance. See AIR INTAKE TEMPERATURE SENSOR under COMPONENT TESTING in this article.

**2)** If resistance is okay, check for continuity between airflow meter terminal "THAa" and ECU terminal "2J". Determine terminal identification. *See Figs. 3 and 4.*

**3)** If no continuity exists, check for open wiring circuit. If continuity exists, check for shorted circuit or defective ECU.

**Trouble Code No. 05 – 1)** Check all connections and repair as necessary. Check for continuity between oxygen sensor terminal and ECU terminal "2D". *See Fig. 3.* If no continuity exists, check for open or shorted circuit.

**2)** If continuity exists, check feedback system operation. See FEEDBACK SYSTEM under TESTING in this article. DO NOT perform step **3)** under FEEDBACK SYSTEM. Repair as necessary.

**Trouble Code No. 06 – 1)** Check all connections and repair as necessary. Ensure throttle sensor is properly adjusted. See THROTTLE SENSOR under ADJUSTMENTS in this article.

**2)** If correctly adjusted, check throttle sensor resistance. See THROTTLE SENSOR under COMPONENT TESTING in this article.

**3)** If resistance is correct, check voltage at BRN/WHT wire of throttle sensor connector. Voltage should be 4.5-5.5 volts. If voltage is not within specification, check for open or shorted circuit or defective ECU.

**4)** If voltage is correct, check for continuity between GRN/RED wire at throttle sensor and ECU terminal "2G" and Black wire at throttle sensor and ECU terminal "2C". If no continuity exists, check for open wiring circuit. If continuity exists, ECU is defective.

**Trouble Code No. 07 – 1)** Check all connections and repair as necessary. Check for battery voltage at BLK/WHT wire of boost sensor (non-turbo) or pressure sensor (turbo). If no voltage exists, check for open circuit from main relay to sensor.
**2)** If voltage exists, check for voltage at BRN/WHT wire of boost sensor (non-turbo) or pressure sensor (turbo). Voltage should be 4.5-5.5 volts. If voltage is not within specification, check for open or short circuit or defective ECU.
**3)** If voltage is correct, check boost or pressure sensor operation. See BOOST OR PRESSURE SENSOR under COMPONENT TESTING in this article. If sensor operates properly, check for continuity between BRN/RED wire at sensor and ECU terminal "2B" and Black or BLK/BRN wire at sensor and ECU terminal "2C". Determine terminal identification. *See Fig. 3.*
**4)** If no continuity exists, check for open or shorted circuit. If continuity exists, ECU is defective.

**Trouble Code No. 09 – 1)** Check all connections and repair as necessary. Check for battery voltage at BLK/WHT wire of atmospheric pressure sensor. If no voltage exists, check for open circuit from main relay to sensor.
**2)** If voltage exists, check for voltage at BRN/WHT wire of atmospheric pressure sensor. Voltage should be 4.5-5.5 volts. If voltage is not within specification, check for open or shorted wiring circuit or defective ECU.
**3)** If voltage is within specification, check atmospheric pressure sensor operation. See ATMOSPHERIC PRESSURE SENSOR under COMPONENT TESTING in this article.
**4)** If sensor operates properly, check for continuity between GRN/YEL wire at sensor and ECU terminal "2H" and BLK wire at sensor and ECU terminal "2C". Determine terminal identification. *See Fig. 3.* If no continuity exists, check for open or shorted wiring circuit. If continuity exists, ECU is defective.

**Trouble Code No. 12 – 1)** Check all connections and repair as necessary. Check for battery voltage at BLK/WHT wire of connector of coil with ignitor (trailing side). If no voltage exists, check for open circuit from main relay to connector.
**2)** If voltage exists, check coil with ignitor operation. See appropriate DISTRIBUTOR & IGNITION SYSTEMS article for test procedures. If coil operates properly, check for voltage at terminal "1M" of ECU with engine at idle. If voltage exists, ECU is defective.
**3)** If no voltage exists with engine at idle, check for voltage at BLU/RED wire of coil with ignitor. If no voltage exists, coil with ignitor is defective. If voltage exists, ECU is defective.

**Trouble Code No. 15 – 1)** Check all connections and repair as necessary. Check intake air temperature sensor resistance. See INTAKE AIR TEMPERATURE SENSOR under COMPONENT TESTING in this article.
**2)** If resistance is correct, check continuity between ECU terminal "2L" and GRN wire of intake air temperature sensor connector and ECU terminal "2C" and BLK or BRN/BLK wire of connector.
**3)** Check for open or shorted circuits if continuity did not exist. If continuity did exist, check for short in wiring harness circuit or defective ECU.

# TESTING

## TROUBLE CODES

**1)** Self-Diagnosis Checker (49 H018 9A1) must be used to obtain trouble codes. Warm engine to normal operating temperature. Connect self-diagnosis checker to connector. *See Fig. 5.*
**2)** Place select switch in the "B" position. Check trouble code number indicated. Compare trouble code to that listed. See TROUBLE CODE USAGE table. See SELF-DIAGNOSIS under TROUBLE SHOOTING in this article for trouble shooting procedure.

***NOTE: Self-diagnosis checker buzzer will activate for approximately 3 seconds after the ignition is turned on.***

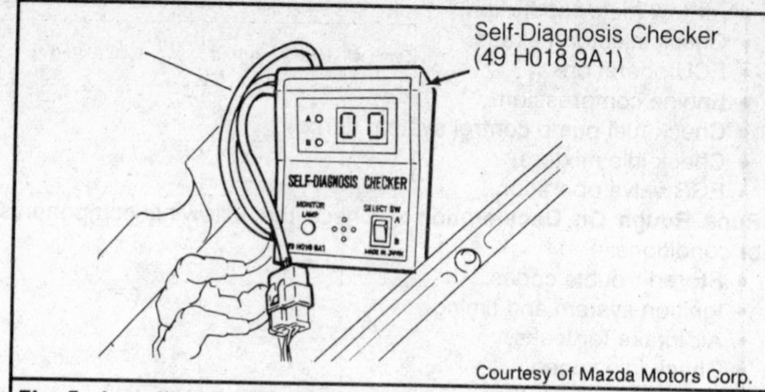
Self-Diagnosis Checker
(49 H018 9A1)
SELF-DIAGNOSIS CHECKER
Courtesy of Mazda Motors Corp.

***Fig. 5: Installing Self-Diagnosis Checker***

***TROUBLE CODE USAGE***

| Code | Probable Cause |
|---|---|
| 01 | Crank Angle Sensor |
| 02 | Airflow Meter |
| 03 | Coolant Thermosensor |
| 04 | [1] Intake Air Temp. Switch |
| 05 | Oxygen Sensor |
| 06 | Throttle Sensor |
| 07 | Boost or Pressure Sensor |
| 09 | Atmospheric Pressure Sensor |
| 12 | Coil W/Ignitor (Trailing Side) |
| 15 | [2] Intake Air Temp. Switch |

[1] – Located in airflow meter.
[2] – Located in intake pipe or dynamic chamber.

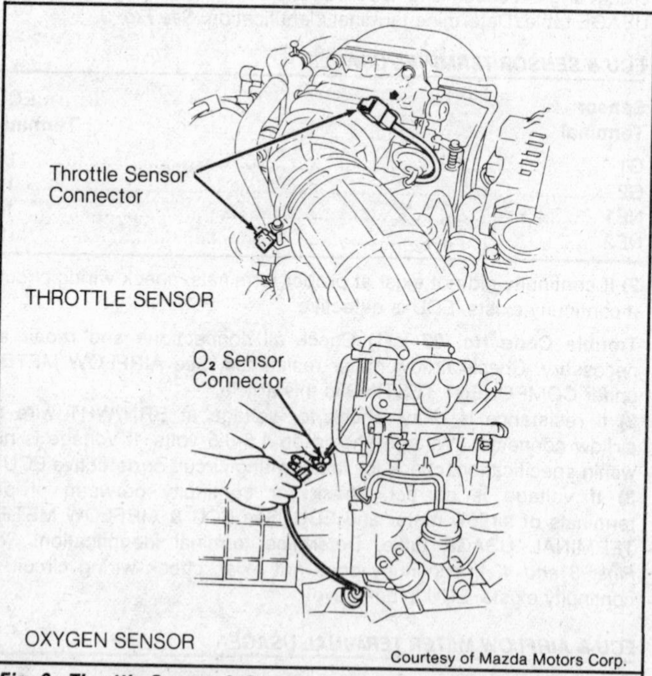
Throttle Sensor
Connector
THROTTLE SENSOR
$O_2$ Sensor
Connector
OXYGEN SENSOR
Courtesy of Mazda Motors Corp.

***Fig. 6: Throttle Sensor & Oxygen Sensor Connector Locations***

**3)** Monitor light on self-diagnosis checker will test $O_2$ sensor signal. Note light operation. Determine if air/fuel ratio is correct. See MONITOR LIGHT INDICATIONS table. Check feedback system if incorrect air/fuel ratio is indicated.

# 1988 COMPUTERIZED ENGINE CONTROLS
## Mazda RX7 Engine Control System (Cont.)

| Terminal | Input | Output | Connected to | Voltage (after warming up) | | Remark |
|---|---|---|---|---|---|---|
| | | | | Ignition switch: ON | Idle | |
| 1A | | ○ | Self-Diagnosis Checker | Ignition switch OFF → ON for 3 sec. below 5V, after 3 sec. approx. 12V | | with Self-Diagnosis Checker |
| 1B | | ○ | Self-Diagnosis Checker | Ignition switch OFF → ON for 3 sec. below 5V, after 3 sec. approx. 12V | | with Self-Diagnosis Checker |
| 1C | | ○ | Air by-pass relay | approx. 12V | | |
| 1D | | ○ | Self-Diagnosis Checker (Monitor lamp) | Ignition switch OFF → ON for 3 sec. below 5V, after 3 sec. approx. 12V | | with Self-Diagnosis Checker |
| 1E | ○ | | A/C switch | below 2.5V (A/C: ON), approx. 12V (A/C: OFF) | | Blower motor ON |
| 1F | | ○ | A/C main relay | approx. 12V (A/C: OFF) | | Blower motor ON |
| 1G | ○ | | Neutral switch | below 1.5V (in neutral) approx. 12V (others) | | A/T: always below 1.5V |
| 1H | ○ | | Coolant Temp. Switch | below 1.5V (Radiator coolant temperature above 17°C (62.6°F)) | | |
| 1I | ○ | | 5th switch | approx. 12V (M/T; 5th gear, A/T; others) below 1.5V (M/T; others, A/T; over drive) | | |
| 1J | ○ | | Initial set coupler | approx. 4—7V (Initial set coupler: OFF), below 1.5V (Initial set coupler: ON) | | |
| 1K | | ○ | Shift indicator light | below 1.5V | approx. 12V | |
| 1L | ○ | | Clutch switch | below 1.5V (clutch pedal; released) approx. 12V (clutch pedal; depressed, A/T) | | |
| 1M | | ○ | Coil with igniter (Trailing) IGf-T | below 2V | [1] | |
| 1N | ○ | | Crank angle sensor (G) | below 1.0V | | |
| 1O | ○ | | Mileage switch | approx. 12V (below 20,000 miles) below 1.5V (above 20,000 miles) | | |
| 1P | ○ | | Crank angle sensor G | below 1.0V | | |
| 1Q | ○ | | Crank angle sensor (Ne) | below 1.0V | | |
| 1R | ○ | | P/S switch | 10—12V | below 1.5V (Steering wheel turned) approx. 10—12V (Straight ahead) | |
| 1S | | ○ | Port air solenoid valve | below 2.5V | | Mileage switch ON; below 1.5V |
| 1T | ○ | | Crank angle sensor (Ne) | below 1.0V | | |
| 1U | | ○ | Coil with igniter (Trailing) IGs-T (Select signal) | approx. 4.4V | approx. 2.2V | |
| 1V | | ○ | Coil with igniter (Leading) IGT-L (Ignition timing signal) | 0V | approx. 0.8V | |
| 1W | ○ | | Heat hazard sensor | below 1.5V | approx. 12V | Floor Temp.: below 110°C (230°F) |
| 1X | | ○ | Coil with igniter (Trailing) IGT-T (Ignition timing signal) | 0V | approx. 0.8V | |
| 2A | | ○ | V ref | 4.5—5.5V | | |
| 2B | ○ | | Boost sensor | 3.5—4.0V | | Disconnect the vacuum hose |
| 2C | — | — | Ground | 0V | | |
| 2D | ○ | | $O_2$ sensor | below 1.0V | | Acceleration: 0.5—1.0V Deceleration: 0—0.4V |
| 2E | ○ | | Airflow meter (Vs) | approx. 4V | 2.5—3.5V | |
| 2F | ○ | | Variable resistor | 1—4V (varies according to the variable resistor adjustment) | | |
| 2G | ○ | | Throttle sensor (TVO) | approx. 1V (throttle sensor adjusted properly) | | |
| 2H | ○ | | Atmospheric pressure sensor | 3.5—4.5V (at sea level) 2.5—3.5V (at 2,000 m (6,500ft)) | | |
| 2I | ○ | | Coolant sensor | approx. 0.4—1.8V | | |
| 2J | ○ | | Airflow meter | 2—3V at 20°C (68°F) | | |
| 2K | | ○ | Split air solenoid valve | below 2.5V (M/T; in 5th gear, A/T; in overdrive) | | Others: approx. 12V |
| 2L | ○ | | Intake air temperature sensor (dynamic chamber) | 1—2V at 80°C (176°F) | | |
| 2M | | ○ | Pressure regulator control solenoid valve | below 2.0V | approx. 12V | |
| 2N | | ○ | EGR solenoid valve | approx. 12V | | |
| 2O | | ○ | Switching solenoid valve | approx. 12V (throttle sensor adjusted properly) | approx. 12V | |

[1] Engine signal monitor Green and Red light flashes.

Courtesy of Mazda Motors Corp.

***Fig. 7: Non-Turbo ECU Terminal Voltages***

| Terminal | Input | Output | Connected to | Voltage (after warming up) | | Remark |
|---|---|---|---|---|---|---|
| | | | | Ignition switch: ON | Idle | |
| 2P | | ○ | Relief solenoid valve | below 2.0V (throttle sensor adjusted properly) | below 2.0V | |
| 2Q | | ○ | By-pass air control valve | 8—12V Engine signal monitor green and red light flash | | |
| 2R | — | — | Ground | 0V | | |
| 3A | — | — | Ground | 0V | | |
| 3B | ○ | | Starter switch | below 1.5V | | approx 10V (at cranking) |
| 3C | | ○ | Injector (Rear primary) | approx. 12V | approx. 12V*[1] | |
| 3D | ○ | | Inhibitor switch | below 1.5V (A/T; N,P range) approx. 12V (A/T; others) | | M/T; always below 1.5V |
| 3E | | ○ | Injector (Front primary) | approx. 12V | approx. 12V*[1] | |
| 3F | | ○ | Injector (Rear secondary) | approx. 12V | | |
| 3G | — | — | Ground | 0V | | |
| 3H | | ○ | Injector (Front secondary) | approx. 12V | | |
| 3I | — | — | Main relay | approx. 12V | | |
| 3J | ○ | | Battery | approx. 12V | | |

[1] Engine signal monitor Green and Red light flashes.

Courtesy of Mazda Motors Corp.

*Fig. 8: Non-Turbo ECU Terminal Voltages (Cont.)*

***MONITOR LIGHT INDICATIONS***

| Light Operation | Air/Fuel Ratio |
|---|---|
| On | Too Rich |
| Off | Too Lean |
| Flashing | Best |

## FEEDBACK SYSTEM

**1)** Connect self-diagnosis checker to connector. *See Fig. 5.* Place select switch in the "B" position. Disconnect neutral switch connector. Operate engine at idle to normal operating temperature. Shut off engine. On turbo models, remove intercooler. *See Fig. 2.*
**2)** On all models, disconnect throttle sensor connector. *See Fig. 6.* On turbo models, reinstall intercooler. On all models, start engine and allow to idle. Self-diagnosis checker should read trouble code 06 with monitor light on.
**3)** Increase engine speed to 1500-2000 RPM and note that monitor light starts to flash within 10 seconds after increasing engine speed. Trouble code 06 should be indicated with monitor light flashing more than 8 times per 10 seconds.
**4)** Maintain engine speed at 1750 RPM and disconnect oxygen sensor connector. *See Fig. 6.* Monitor light should be off and trouble code 05 should exist. Replace ECU if any deviation from normal readings exists.

## ELECTRONIC CONTROL UNIT (ECU)

**1)** Operate engine to normal operating temperature. Connect Engine Signal Monitor (49 9200 162) and Adapter (49 9200 163) to ECU and wiring harness. Place selector switch and monitor switch on terminal voltage to be tested.
**2)** Turn ignition on. Note voltage of designated terminals. *See Figs. 7 through 10.* If voltage is not within specification, check wiring circuit and individual component.

## TURBO CONTROL SYSTEM

**1)** Warm engine to normal operating temperature. Shut engine off. Start engine and note if turbo actuator rod moves. On vehicles with Anti-Lock Brakes (ABS), it may be necessary to move air control valve and air silencer toward engine to gain access to actuator rod.
**2)** Disconnect Green turbo solenoid valve connector. Actuator rod should return. Reinstall valve connector. Increase engine speed and note that actuator rod starts to move at approximately 2700 RPM.

## TURBO SOLENOID VALVE SIGNAL

Warm engine to normal operating temperature. Connect voltmeter to LT. BLU wire of solenoid valve. Increase engine speed and note voltage. Voltage should be within specification. See TURBO SOLENOID VALVE VOLTAGE SPECIFICATIONS table.

***TURBO SOLENOID VALVE VOLTAGE SPECIFICATIONS***

| Engine RPM | Voltage |
|---|---|
| Below 2700 | Below 2 Volts |
| Above 2700 RPM | 12 Volts |

## COMPONENT TESTING

**A/C Switch –** Information not available from manufacturer.

**Airflow Meter – 1)** Intake air temperature sensor and fuel pump switch are contained in the airflow meter. Determine terminal identification. *See Fig. 11.*
**2)** Using ohmmeter, measure resistance between designated terminals. See AIRFLOW METER RESISTANCE SPECIFICATIONS table. Reading must be within specification.
**3)** Ensure measuring plate moves freely in airflow meter. Remaining terminals must be checked for fuel pump switch and measuring plate resistances. *See Fig. 11.* Attach ohmmeter to specified terminals to check fuel pump switch and measuring plate resistance. See FUEL PUMP SWITCH & PLATE RESISTANCE SPECIFICATIONS table.

***AIRFLOW METER RESISTANCE SPECIFICATIONS***

| Terminals | Ohms | Temperature |
|---|---|---|
| E2 & Vs | | |
| Non-Turbo | 50-500 | |
| Turbo | 200-600 | |
| E2 & Vref | | |
| Non-Turbo | 200-500 | |
| Turbo | 200-400 | |
| E2 & THAa [1] | 10,000-20,000 | -4°F (-20°C) |
| | 4000-7000 | 32°F (0°C) |
| | 2000-3000 | 68°F (20°C) |
| | 900-1300 | 104°F (40°C) |
| | 400-700 | 140°F (60°C) |
| E1 & Fc | Infinity | .... |

[1] – Intake air temperature sensor.

# 1988 COMPUTERIZED ENGINE CONTROLS
# Mazda RX7 Engine Control System (Cont.)

| Terminal | Input | Output | Connection to | Voltage (after warming up) | | Remark |
|---|---|---|---|---|---|---|
| | | | | Ignition switch: ON | Idle | |
| 1A | | ○ | Self-Diagnosis Checker | Ignition switch OFF → ON for 3 sec. below 5V, after 3sec. approx. 12V | | with Self-Diagnosis Checker |
| 1B | | ○ | Self-Diagnosis Checker | Ignition switch OFF → ON for 3 sec. below 5V after 3 sec. approx. 12V | | with Self-Diagnosis Checker |
| 1C | | ○ | Air by-pass solenoid valve | Approx. 12V | | |
| 1D | | ○ | Self-Diagnosis Checker (Monitor lamp) | Ignition switch OFF → ON for 3 sec. below 5V after 3 sec. approx. 12V | | with Self-Diagnosis Checker |
| 1E | ○ | | A/C switch | below 2.5V (A/C: ON), approx. 12V (A/C: OFF) | | Blower motor ON |
| 1F | | ○ | A/C main relay | approx. 12V (A/C: OFF) | | Blower motor ON |
| 1G | ○ | | Neutral switch | below 1.5V (in neutral), approx. 12V (others) | | |
| 1H | ○ | | Coolant Temp. Switch | below 1.5V (water temperature; above 17°C (62.6°F)) | | |
| 1I | ○ | | 5th switch | below 1.5V; (Others), approx. 12V (5th gear) | | |
| 1J | ○ | | Initial set coupler | approx. 4—7V (Initial set coupler: OFF), below 1.5V (Initial set coupler: ON) | | |
| 1K | | ○ | Shift indicator light | below 1.5V | approx. 12V | |
| 1L | ○ | | Clutch switch | below 1.5V (clutch pedal; released) approx. 12V (clutch pedal; depressed) | | |
| 1M | ○ | | Coil with igniter (Trailing) IGf-T | below 2V | *1 | |
| 1N | ○ | | Crank angle sensor G ① | below 1.0V | | |
| 1O | ○ | | Mileage switch | approx. 12V (below 20,000 miles), below 1.5V (above 20,000 miles) | | |
| 1P | ○ | | Crank angle sensor G ② | below 1.0V | | |
| 1Q | ○ | | Crank angle sensor Ne ② | below 1.0V | | |
| 1R | ○ | | Knock control unit | 3—5V | | |
| 1S | | ○ | Port air solenoid valve | approx. 12V | | Mileage switch ON: below 2.5V |
| 1T | ○ | | Crank angle sensor Ne ① | below 1.0V | | |
| 1U | | ○ | Coil with igniter (Trailing) IGs-T (Select signal) | approx. 4.4V | approx. 2.2V | |
| 1V | | ○ | Coil with igniter (Leading) IGT-L (Ignition timing signal) | 0V | approx. 0.8V | |
| 1W | ○ | | Heat hazard sensor | below 1.5V | approx. 12V | Floor Temp.: below 110°C (230°F) |
| 1X | | ○ | Coil with igniter (Trailing) IGT-T (Ignition timing signal) | 0V | approx. 0.8V | |
| 2A | | ○ | V ref | 4.5—5.5V | | |
| 2B | ○ | | Pressure sensor | 2.3—2.7V | | Disconnect vacuum hose |
| 2C | — | — | Ground | 0V | | |
| 2D | ○ | | $O_2$ sensor | below 1.0V | | Acceleration: 0.5—1.0 V Deceleration: 0—0.4 V |
| 2E | ○ | | Airflow meter (Vs) | approx. 4V | 2.5—3.5V | |
| 2F | ○ | | Variable resistor | 1—4V (varies according to the variable resistor adjustment) | | |
| 2G | ○ | | Throttle sensor (TVO) | approx. 1V (throttle sensor adjusted properly) | | |
| 2H | ○ | | Atmospheric pressure sensor | 3.5—4.5V (at sea level) 2.5—3.5V (at 2,000 m (6,500 ft)) | | |
| 2I | ○ | | Coolant sensor | approx. 0.4—1.8V | | Warm engine |
| 2J | ○ | | Airflow meter | 2—3V at 20°C (68°F) | | |
| 2K | | ○ | Twin-scroll turbocharger solenoid valve | below 2.0V | | above 2,700 rpm: approx. 12V |
| 2L | ○ | | Intake air temperature sensor (inlet air pipe) | 1—2V at 80°C (176°F) | | |
| 2M | | ○ | Pressure regulator control solenoid valve | below 2.0V | approx. 12V | Cranking: below 2.0V |
| 2N | | ○ | EGR solenoid valve | approx. 12V | | |
| 2O | | ○ | Switching solenoid valve | approx. 12V (throttle sensor is adjusted properly) | approx. 12V | |

[1] Engine signal monitor Green and Red light flashes.

Courtesy of Mazda Motors Corp.

*Fig. 9: Turbo ECU Terminal Voltages*

# Mazda RX7 Engine Control System (Cont.)

| Terminal | Input | Output | Connection to | Voltage (after warming up) | | Remark |
|---|---|---|---|---|---|---|
| | | | | Ignition switch: ON | Idle | |
| 2P | | ○ | Relief solenoid valve | below 2V (throttle sensor is adjusted properly) | below 2.0V | |
| 2Q | | ○ | By-pass air control (BAC) valve | 8—12V Engine signal monitor green and red light flash | | |
| 2R | — | — | Ground | 0V | | |
| 3A | — | — | Ground | 0V | | |
| 3B | ○ | | Starter switch | below 1.5V | | approx. 10V (at cranking) |
| 3C | | ○ | Injector (Rear primary) | approx. 12V | approx. 12V*[1] | |
| 3D | | ○ | Fuel pump resistor relay | approx. 12V | below 2.0V | |
| 3E | | ○ | Injector (Front primary) | approx. 12V | approx. 12V*[1] | |
| 3F | | ○ | Injector (Rear secondary) | approx. 12V | | |
| 3G | — | — | Ground | 0V | | |
| 3H | | ○ | Injector (Front secondary) | approx. 12V | | |
| 3I | — | — | Main relay | approx. 12V | | |
| 3J | ○ | | Battery | approx. 12V | | |

[1] Engine signal monitor Green and Red light flashes.

Courtesy of Mazda Motors Corp.

*Fig. 10: Turbo ECU Terminal Voltages (Cont.)*

### FUEL PUMP SWITCH & PLATE RESISTANCE SPECIFICATIONS

| Terminals | Ohms | Plate Position |
|---|---|---|
| E1 & Fc | Infinity | Fully Closed |
| E1 & Fc | 0 | Fully Open |
| E2 & Vs | 50-500 | Fully Closed |
| E2 & Vs | 50-500 | Fully Open |

**Atmospheric Pressure Sensor** – Connect voltmeter to "D" terminal of atmospheric pressure sensor and ground. *See Fig. 12.* Turn ignition and note voltage. Voltage should be within specfication. See ATMOSPHERIC PRESSURE SENSOR SPECIFICATIONS table. Replace sensor if not within specification.

### ATMOSPHERIC PRESSURE SENSOR SPECIFICATIONS

| Application | Voltage |
|---|---|
| Below 6500 Ft. | 3.5-4.5 |
| Above 6500 Ft. | 2.5-3.5 |

**Boost Or Pressure Sensor** – **1)** Disconnect vacuum hose from sensor. Connect voltmeter to "D" terminal. *See Fig. 13.* Using vacuum pump, apply 3.9 in. Hg to sensor.

**2)** Turn ignition on and note voltage reading. Voltage should be within 2.5-3.5 volts for non-turbo or 2.0-2.5 volts for turbo models. Replace sensor if not within specification.

**Clutch Switch** – Remove connector from switch. Connect ohmmeter to switch terminals. Check that continuity exists with clutch pedal depressed and no continuity exists with pedal released. Replace switch if continuity is not correct.

**Coolant Temperature Switch** – **1)** Remove switch from radiator. Place switch in container of heated coolant with thermometer.

**2)** Connect ohmmeter to switch terminals. Note temperature at which continuity exists between switch terminals. Continuity should exist with coolant temperature at 59-66.2°F (15-19°C). Replace switch if not within specification.

**Coolant Thermosensor** – **1)** Remove thermosensor. Place thermosensor in container of heated coolant with thermometer.

**2)** Connect ohmmeter to thermosensor terminals. Note resistance at specified temperatures. See COOLANT THERMOSENSOR RESISTANCE SPECIFICATIONS table. Replace if not within specification.

### COOLANT THERMOSENSOR RESISTANCE SPECIFICATIONS

| Coolant Temperature | Ohms |
|---|---|
| -4°F (-20°C) | 14,580-17,820 |
| 68°F (20°C) | 2210-2690 |
| 176°F (80°C) | 288-352 |

**Crank Angle Sensor** – **1)** Remove sensor connector. Note terminal identification. *See Fig. 3.* Using ohmmeter, check resistance at specified terminals. Resistance must be within specification. See CRANK ANGLE SENSOR RESISTANCE SPECIFICATIONS table.

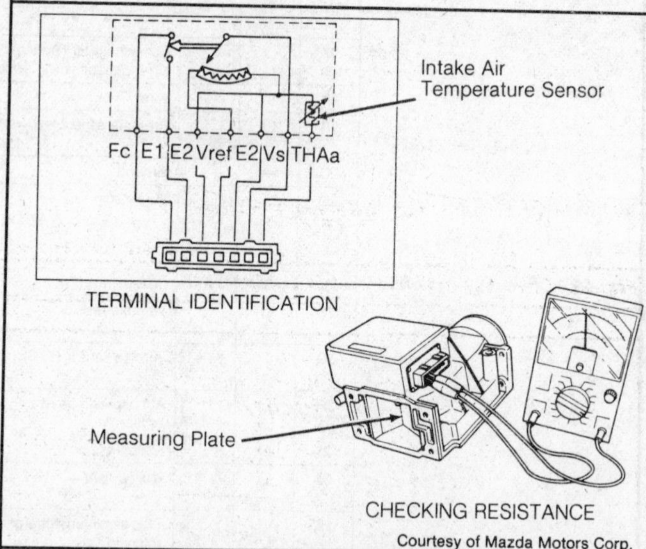
Intake Air Temperature Sensor
Fc E1 E2 Vref E2 Vs THAa
TERMINAL IDENTIFICATION
Measuring Plate
CHECKING RESISTANCE

Courtesy of Mazda Motors Corp.

*Fig. 11: Check Airflow Meter Resistance & Terminal Identication*

### CRANK ANGLE SENSOR RESISTANCE SPECIFICATIONS

| Terminal | Ohms |
|---|---|
| G1 & G2 | 110-210 |
| NE1 & NE2 | 110-210 |

**Inhibitor Switch (Non-Turbo A/T)** – Remove connector from switch. Connect ohmmeter to switch terminals "C" and "D". *See Fig. 14.* Continuity should exist with gearshift in Park and Neutral. No continuity should exist in all other ranges.

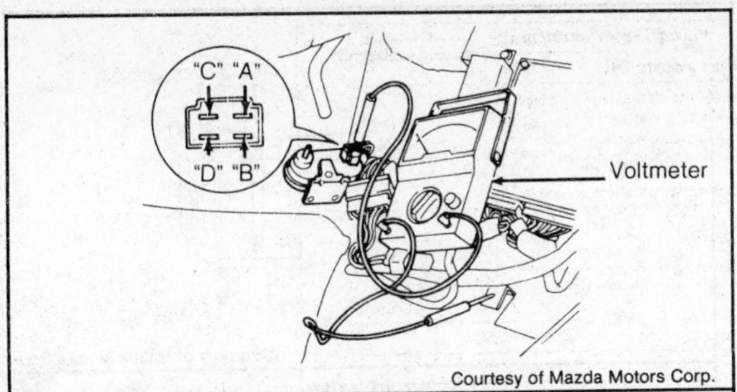
"C" "A"
"D" "B"
Voltmeter
Courtesy of Mazda Motors Corp.

*Fig. 12: Checking Atmospheric Pressure Sensor*

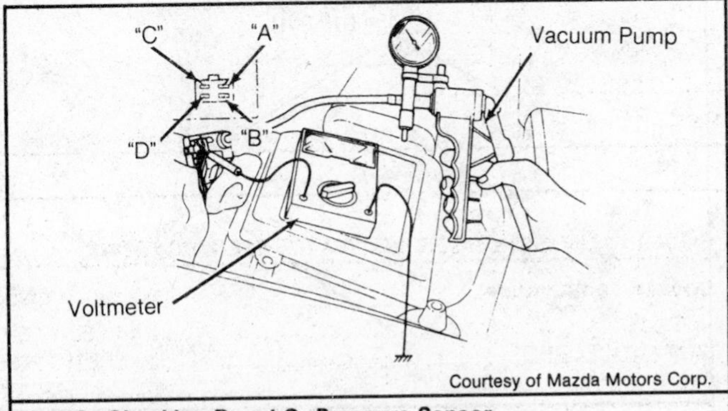
"C"
"A"
Vacuum Pump
"D"
"B"
Voltmeter
Courtesy of Mazda Motors Corp.

*Fig. 13: Checking Boost Or Pressure Sensor*

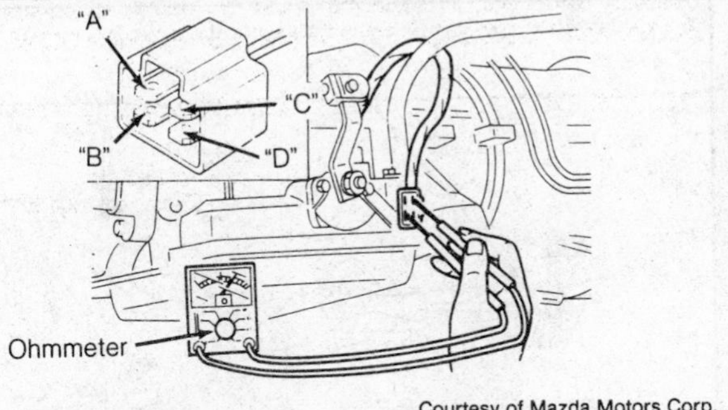

*Fig. 14: Checking Inhibitor Switch Continuity*

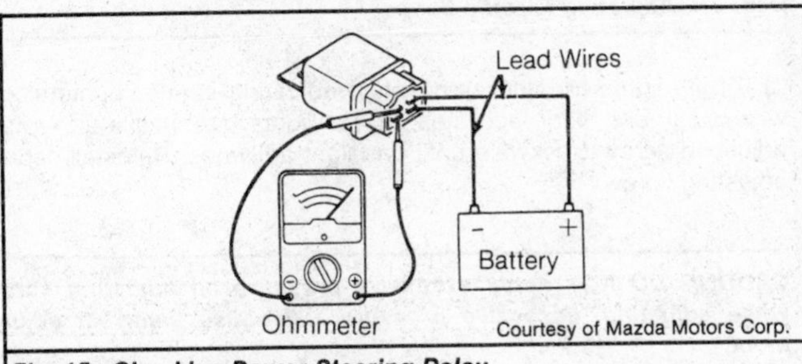
Lead Wires
Battery
Ohmmeter
Courtesy of Mazda Motors Corp.

*Fig. 15: Checking Power Steering Relay*

**Neutral Switch** – Remove connector from switch. Connect ohmmeter to switch terminals. Check that continuity exists with transmission in Neutral and no continuity exists in all other ranges. Replace switch if continuity is not correct.

**Power Steering Relay (Turbo)** – **1)** Connect battery leads to proper terminals. *See Fig. 15.* Using ohmmeter, check for continuity at remaining terminals.

**2)** Continuity should exist with battery voltage applied and not exist with battery disconnected. Replace relay if necessary.

**Power Steering Switch** – **1)** Start engine and allow to idle. Remove connector from switch. Connect ohmmeter to switch terminals. Turn steering wheel from side to side and note continuity reading.

**2)** Continuity should exist with wheels turned but should not exist with wheel straight ahead. Replace switch if continuity is not correct.

**Heat Hazard Sensor** – **1)** To check system operation, turn ignition on. The "OVER HEAT EXH SYSTEM" light should activate. Start engine and light should go out.

**2)** Remove right seat and lift up floor mat. Disconnect heat hazard sensor connector. Connect jumper wire between connector terminals. Check that "OVER HEAT EXH SYSTEM" light activates.

**3)** To check heat hazard sensor, remove sensor. Wrap sensor and thermometer with aluminum foil to prevent oil penetration. Place thermometer and sensor in container of oil.

**4)** Connect test light and battery to sensor terminals. *See Fig. 16.* Heat oil and note temperature in the aluminum foil when the test light activates. Test light should activate when temperature reaches 221-239°F (105-115°C). Replace sensor if not within specification.

***CAUTION: DO NOT allow oil temperature to exceed 302°F (150°C).***

**Knock Sensor** – Information not available from manufacturer.

**Intake Air Temperature Sensor** – See AIRFLOW METER under COMPONENT TESTING for test procedure.

**Mileage Switch** – Information not available from manufacturer.

**Overdrive Switch** – Information not available from manufacturer.

**5th Gear Switch** – Information not available from manufacturer.

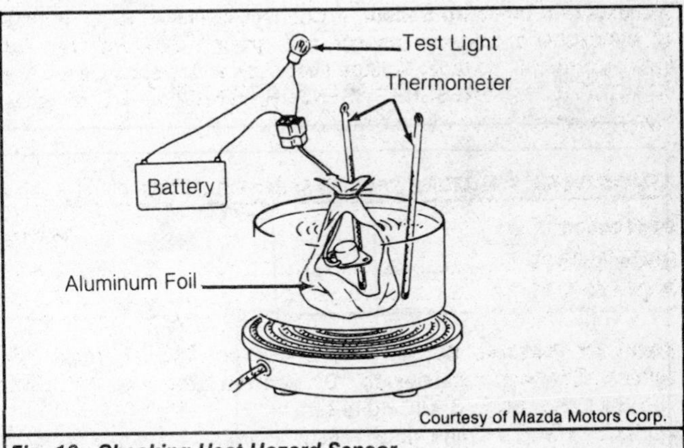
Test Light
Thermometer
Battery
Aluminum Foil
Courtesy of Mazda Motors Corp.

*Fig. 16: Checking Heat Hazard Sensor*

**Variable Resistor** – Remove resistor connector. Note terminal identification. *See Fig. 17.* Using ohmmeter, check resistance at specified terminals. See VARIABLE RESISTOR SPECIFICATIONS table. Replace resistor if not within specification.

***NOTE: Idle mixture must be adjusted if variable resistor is replaced.***

***VARIABLE RESISTOR SPECIFICATIONS***

| Terminal | k/Ohms |
|---|---|
| A & C | .5-4.5 |
| B & C | .5-4.5 |

**Coil With Ignitor** – See appropriate DISTRIBUTOR & IGNITION SYSTEMS article for test procedures.

# Mazda RX7 Engine Control System (Cont.)

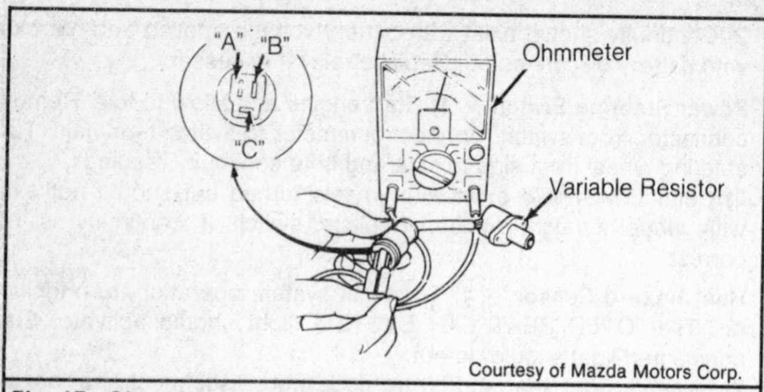

"A" "B"
"C"
Ohmmeter
Variable Resistor
Courtesy of Mazda Motors Corp.


*Fig. 17: Checking Variable Resistor*

**Throttle Sensor – 1)** On turbo models, remove intercooler. On all models, remove sensor connector. Connect ohmmeter to terminals "A" and "B". *See Fig. 18.* Open throttle valve and note resistance readings.

**2)** On non-turbo models, repeat procedure on terminals "A" and "C". Resistance readings must be within specification. See THROTTLE SENSOR RESISTANCE SPECIFICATIONS table. Install sensor connector. On turbo models, reinstall intercooler.

**Turbo Solenoid Valve – 1)** Disconnect vacuum hoses from solenoid valve. Blow through port "B". *See Fig. 19.* Air should flow from air filter. Remove connector from solenoid valve.

**2)** Apply battery voltage and ground to proper terminals. *See Fig. 19.* Blow through port "B". Air should flow from port "A".

***THROTTLE SENSOR RESISTANCE SPECIFICATIONS***

| Terminal | k/Ohms |
|---|---|
| A & B | |
| Idle Position | 1 |
| Fully Open | 4-6 |
| A & C (Non-Turbo Only) | |
| Idle Position | 4-6 |
| Fully Open | 4-6 |

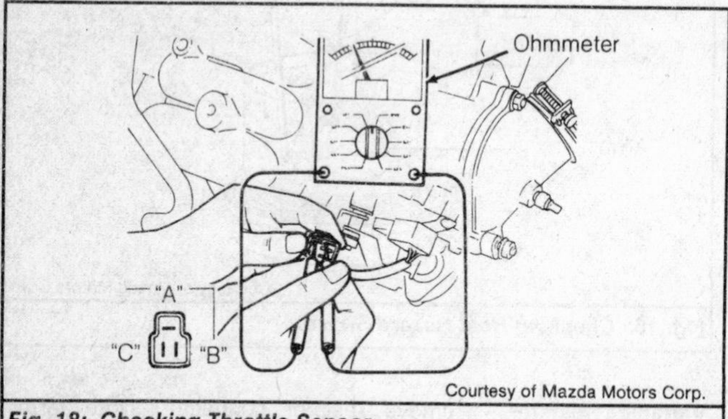

Ohmmeter
"A"
"C"
"B"
Courtesy of Mazda Motors Corp.


*Fig. 18: Checking Throttle Sensor*

## ADJUSTMENTS

**Throttle Sensor – 1)** Operate engine to normal operating temperature. With engine off, install Checker Light (49 F018 001) to the Green check connector. *See Fig. 20.*

**2)** Turn ignition on and note checker light. One light should activate on checker light. If none or both lights activate, remove cap and rotate throttle sensor adjusting screw until only one light activates. *See Fig. 21.*

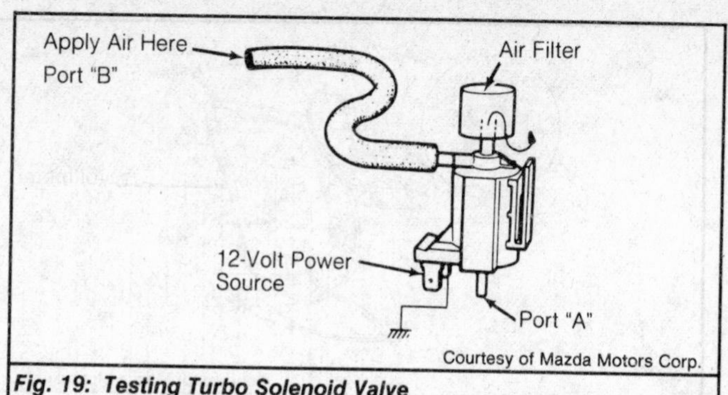

Apply Air Here
Port "B"
Air Filter
12-Volt Power
Source
Port "A"
Courtesy of Mazda Motors Corp.


*Fig. 19: Testing Turbo Solenoid Valve*

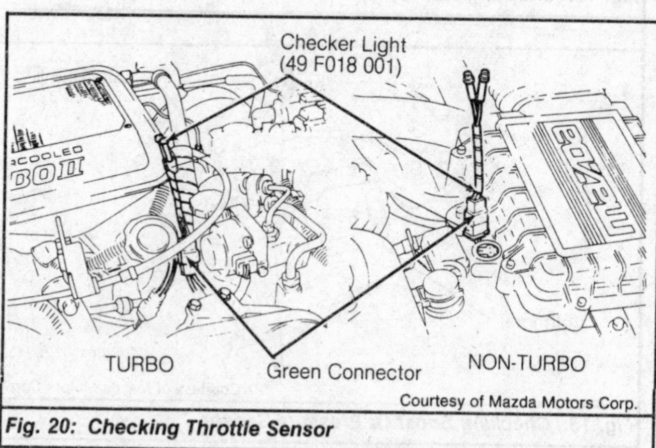

Checker Light
(49 F018 001)
TURBO
Green Connector
NON-TURBO
Courtesy of Mazda Motors Corp.


*Fig. 20: Checking Throttle Sensor*

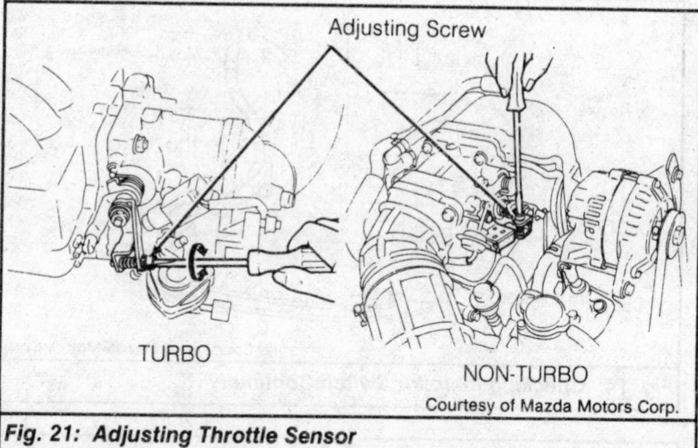

Adjusting Screw
TURBO
NON-TURBO
Courtesy of Mazda Motors Corp.


*Fig. 21: Adjusting Throttle Sensor*

**3)** If both lights are activated, rotate adjusting screw counterclockwise until one light activates. If no lights are activated, rotate adjusting screw clockwise until one light activates. Reinstall cap on adjusting screw.

***CAUTION: DO NOT apply excessive pressure on adjusting screw while adjusting. Excessive pressure will cause incorrect adjustment.***

# Mazda RX7 Engine Control System (Cont.)

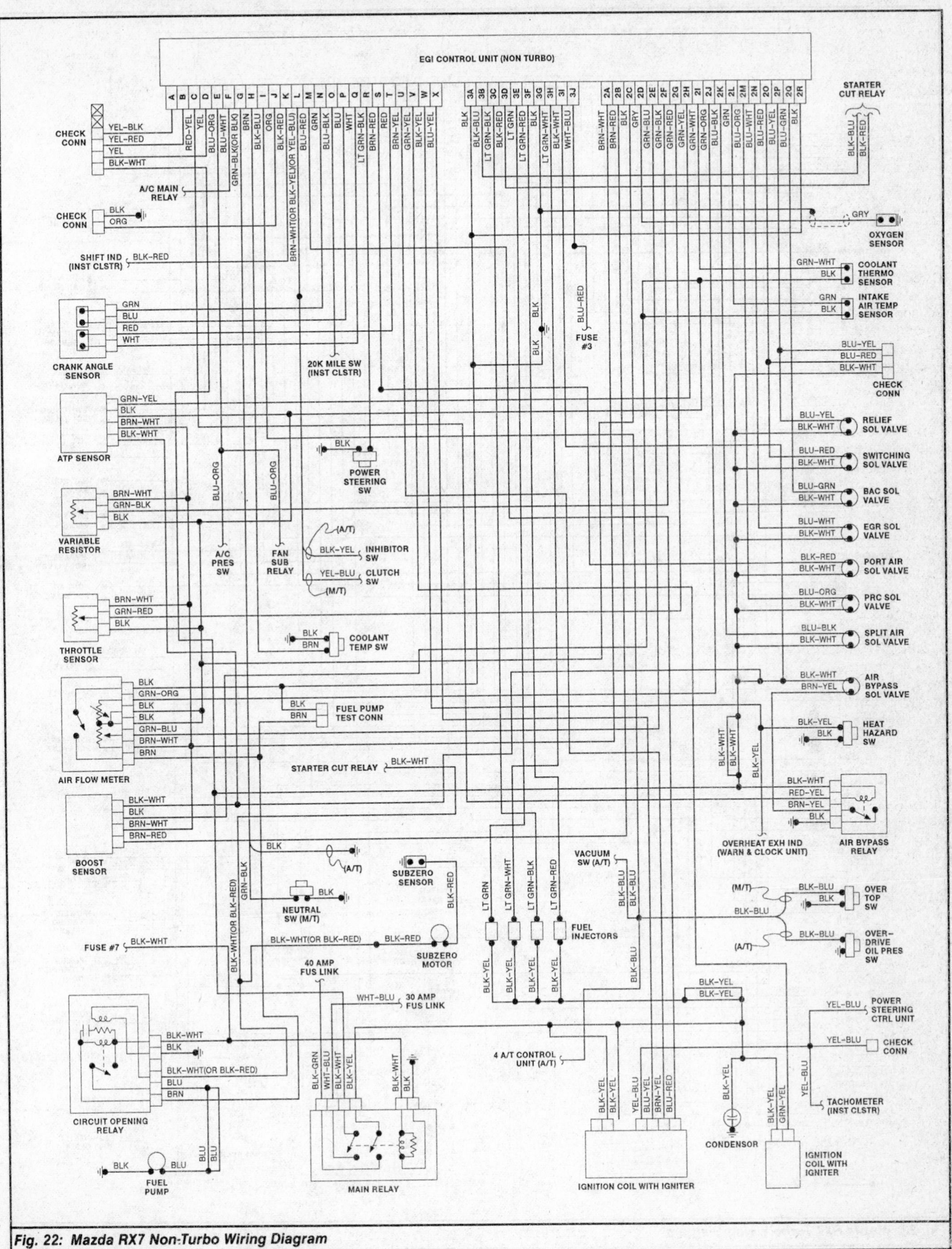
EGI CONTROL UNIT (NON TURBO)
CHECK CONN
A/C MAIN RELAY
SHIFT IND (INST CLSTR)
CRANK ANGLE SENSOR
ATP SENSOR
VARIABLE RESISTOR
A/C PRES SW
FAN SUB RELAY
20K MILE SW (INST CLSTR)
POWER STEERING SW
INHIBITOR SW
CLUTCH SW
THROTTLE SENSOR
COOLANT TEMP SW
AIR FLOW METER
FUEL PUMP TEST CONN
STARTER CUT RELAY
BOOST SENSOR
NEUTRAL SW (M/T)
SUBZERO SENSOR
SUBZERO MOTOR
FUSE #7
40 AMP FUS LINK
30 AMP FUS LINK
CIRCUIT OPENING RELAY
FUEL PUMP
MAIN RELAY
FUEL INJECTORS
VACUUM SW (A/T)
4 A/T CONTROL UNIT (A/T)
IGNITION COIL WITH IGNITER
CONDENSOR
FUSE #3
OXYGEN SENSOR
COOLANT THERMO SENSOR
INTAKE AIR TEMP SENSOR
RELIEF SOL VALVE
SWITCHING SOL VALVE
BAC SOL VALVE
EGR SOL VALVE
PORT AIR SOL VALVE
PRC SOL VALVE
SPLIT AIR SOL VALVE
AIR BYPASS SOL VALVE
HEAT HAZARD SW
OVERHEAT EXH IND (WARN & CLOCK UNIT)
AIR BYPASS RELAY
OVER TOP SW
OVER-DRIVE OIL PRES SW
POWER STEERING CTRL UNIT
TACHOMETER (INST CLSTR)

*Fig. 22: Mazda RX7 Non-Turbo Wiring Diagram*

## Mazda RX7 Engine Control System (Cont.)

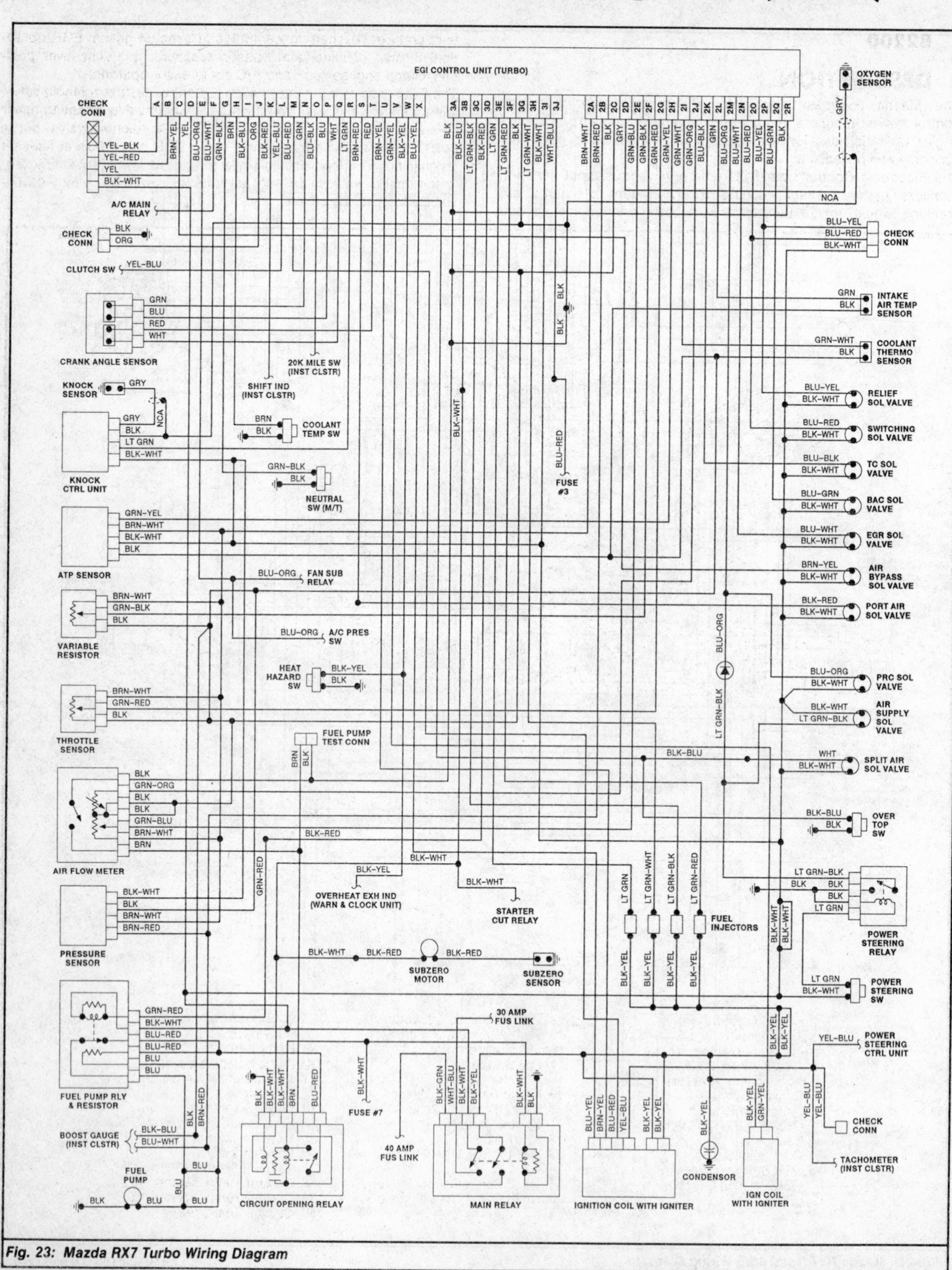
EGI CONTROL UNIT (TURBO)
CHECK CONN
OXYGEN SENSOR
A/C MAIN RELAY
CHECK CONN
CLUTCH SW
CHECK CONN
INTAKE AIR TEMP SENSOR
CRANK ANGLE SENSOR
COOLANT THERMO SENSOR
20K MILE SW (INST CLSTR)
KNOCK SENSOR
SHIFT IND (INST CLSTR)
RELIEF SOL VALVE
COOLANT TEMP SW
SWITCHING SOL VALVE
KNOCK CTRL UNIT
NEUTRAL SW (M/T)
FUSE #3
TC SOL VALVE
BAC SOL VALVE
EGR SOL VALVE
ATP SENSOR
FAN SUB RELAY
AIR BYPASS SOL VALVE
PORT AIR SOL VALVE
VARIABLE RESISTOR
A/C PRES SW
HEAT HAZARD SW
PRC SOL VALVE
AIR SUPPLY SOL VALVE
THROTTLE SENSOR
FUEL PUMP TEST CONN
SPLIT AIR SOL VALVE
OVER TOP SW
AIR FLOW METER
OVERHEAT EXH IND (WARN & CLOCK UNIT)
STARTER CUT RELAY
FUEL INJECTORS
POWER STEERING RELAY
PRESSURE SENSOR
SUBZERO MOTOR
SUBZERO SENSOR
POWER STEERING SW
30 AMP FUS LINK
FUEL PUMP RLY & RESISTOR
POWER STEERING CTRL UNIT
FUSE #7
BOOST GAUGE (INST CLSTR)
40 AMP FUS LINK
CHECK CONN
FUEL PUMP
TACHOMETER (INST CLSTR)
CONDENSOR
CIRCUIT OPENING RELAY
MAIN RELAY
IGNITION COIL WITH IGNITER
IGN COIL WITH IGNITER

*Fig. 23: Mazda RX7 Turbo Wiring Diagram*

# Mazda Feedback Carburetor System

## B2200

## DESCRIPTION

The Mazda Feedback Carburetor (FBC) computerized engine control system monitors various engine/vehicle functions to control engine operation and lower emissions while maintaining good fuel economy and driveability.

The Electronic Control Unit (ECU), through various input sensors, monitors battery voltage, engine RPM, amount of intake air, cranking signal, intake temperature, radiator and engine coolant temperatures, oxygen concentration in exhaust gases, EGR operation, throttle opening, atmospheric pressure, gearshift lever position, clutch engagement, and A/C compressor operation.

The ECU uses all input information to control air/fuel solenoid valve, idle-up solenoid valves, slow fuel-cut solenoid valve, coasting richer solenoid valve, vacuum solenoid valve, ACV solenoid valve, purge solenoid valve, and duty solenoid valve. ECU has a built-in fail-safe mechanism. If a fault occurs while driving, ECU will substitute pre-programmed values. Driving performance will be affected, but vehicle may still be driven.

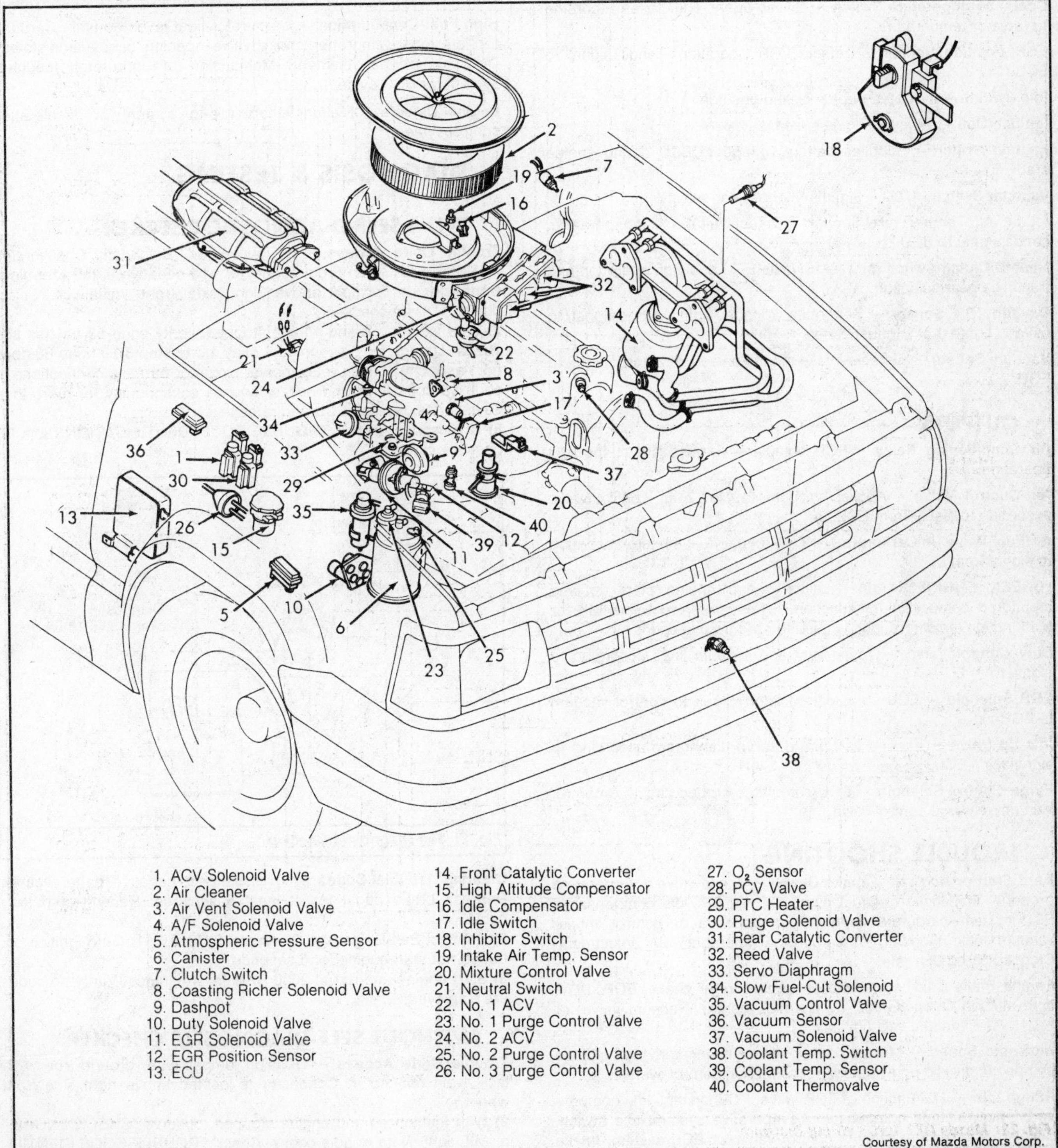

1. ACV Solenoid Valve
2. Air Cleaner
3. Air Vent Solenoid Valve
4. A/F Solenoid Valve
5. Atmospheric Pressure Sensor
6. Canister
7. Clutch Switch
8. Coasting Richer Solenoid Valve
9. Dashpot
10. Duty Solenoid Valve
11. EGR Solenoid Valve
12. EGR Position Sensor
13. ECU
14. Front Catalytic Converter
15. High Altitude Compensator
16. Idle Compensator
17. Idle Switch
18. Inhibitor Switch
19. Intake Air Temp. Sensor
20. Mixture Control Valve
21. Neutral Switch
22. No. 1 ACV
23. No. 1 Purge Control Valve
24. No. 2 ACV
25. No. 2 Purge Control Valve
26. No. 3 Purge Control Valve
27. $O_2$ Sensor
28. PCV Valve
29. PTC Heater
30. Purge Solenoid Valve
31. Rear Catalytic Converter
32. Reed Valve
33. Servo Diaphragm
34. Slow Fuel-Cut Solenoid
35. Vacuum Control Valve
36. Vacuum Sensor
37. Vacuum Solenoid Valve
38. Coolant Temp. Switch
39. Coolant Temp. Sensor
40. Coolant Thermovalve
Courtesy of Mazda Motors Corp.


*Fig. 1: B2200 Pickup Component Location*

## OPERATION

### INPUTS

**Air Conditioning Switch** – Closes when A/C or blower switch is in the "ON" position.

**Atmospheric Pressure Sensor** – Varies voltage signal according to altitude.

**Coolant Temperature Sensor** – Varies input voltage signal according to engine coolant temperature.

**Coolant Temperature Switch** – Switch opens and closes according to radiator temperature.

**EGR Position Sensor** – Detects EGR operation, sends signal to ECU.

**Idle Switch** – Indicates throttle closed position.

**Ignition Coil** – Signals engine speed.

**Ignition Switch** – Supplies battery voltage to ECU during engine cranking.

**Inhibitor Switch (A/T)** – Signals ECU of gear selection.

**Intake Air Temperature Sensor** – Detects intake air temperature, sends signal to ECU.

**Neutral/Clutch Switch (M/T)** – Signals ECU of clutch operation and transaxle gear selection.

**Oxygen ($O_2$) Sensor** – Generates voltage signal proportional to oxygen content of exhaust gases.

**Vacuum Sensor** – Detects intake manifold vacuum, sends signal to ECU.

### OUTPUTS

**Air Conditioning Relay** – ECU completes ground circuit for A/C operation.

**Air Control Valve** – Applies vacuum to No. 2 air control valve according to signal from ECU.

**Air/Fuel Valve (In Carburetor)** – Controls air/fuel mixture according to signal from ECU.

**"CHECK ENGINE" Light** – Lights during engine start up and monitored component malfunction. Is also referred to as MIL or Malfunction Indicator Light. Is used to read trouble codes.

**Duty Control Valve** – Opens vent and vacuum lines according to signal from ECU.

**EGR Solenoid** – ECU completes ground circuit to control vacuum to EGR valve.

**Idle-Up Valve** – Applies vacuum to servo diaphragm according to signal from ECU.

**Purge Control Solenoid** – ECU completes ground circuit to control vacuum to purge control valve.

## TROUBLE SHOOTING

**Hard Start or No Start (Cranks Okay)** – Choke valve not operating properly. Malfunction of fuel pump, PCV, EGR, idle compensator, ECU system, carburetor feedback, or deceleration control. Intake vacuum leak. Flooding of carburetor. Improper idle adjustment. Clogged carburetor jets.

**Engine Stalls Cold** – Malfunction of carburetor choke, EGR, PCV, high altitude compensator, deceleration control, vacuum valve, or ECU system. Intake vacuum leak.

**High Idle Speed** – Malfunction of idle compensator, high altitude compensator, idle-up system, or deceleration control system.

**Rough Idle** – Malfunction of EGR valve, PCV system, idle compensator, high altitude compensator, evaporative system, idle switch, deceleration system, vacuum control valve, or ECU system. Intake vacuum leak. Improper idle adjustment. Carburetor flooding. Damaged carburetor mixture adjusting screw. Clogged carburetor idle port or main jet. Poor or damaged intake manifold gasket or carburetor insulator seal. Improper throttle valve closing or float level adjustment.

**Poor Acceleration, Hesistation or Lack of Power** – Malfunction of EGR system, high altitude compensator, evaporative system, carburetor accelerator pump, throttle valve not fully opening, or ECU system. Clogged carburetor jets.

**Poor High Speed Operation** – Clogged carburetor main jet. Carburetor float level too low. Clogged fuel filter or fuel line. Dirty air cleaner element. Insufficent fuel pump output. Improper secondary valve opening. Malfunction of vacuum control valve, or ECU system.

**High Fuel Consumption** – Carburetor float level too high. Carburetor jets loose. Improper choke valve opening or idle adjustment. Dirty air cleaner element. Malfunction of carburetor feedback system, or ECU system.

**Engine Diesels** – Malfunction of idle-up system, or deceleration control system.

## DIAGNOSIS & TESTING

### WITH SELF-DIAGNOSTIC CHECKER

**Trouble Code Access – 1)** Connect Self-Diagnostic Checker (49 H018 9A1) to Green 6-pin connector and negative battery terminal. Connector is located above right side front wheelwell. Select position "A" on checker.

**2)** With ignition on and engine stopped, verify code 88 flashes and buzzer sounds for 3 seconds. If okay, go to step **3)**. If code 88 does not flash, check main relay, power circuit or harness connections. If code 88 does flash and buzzer sounds continuously for more than 20 seconds, replace ECU and retest.

**3)** Note codes. Check TROUBLE CODE IDENTIFICATION table for possible cause.

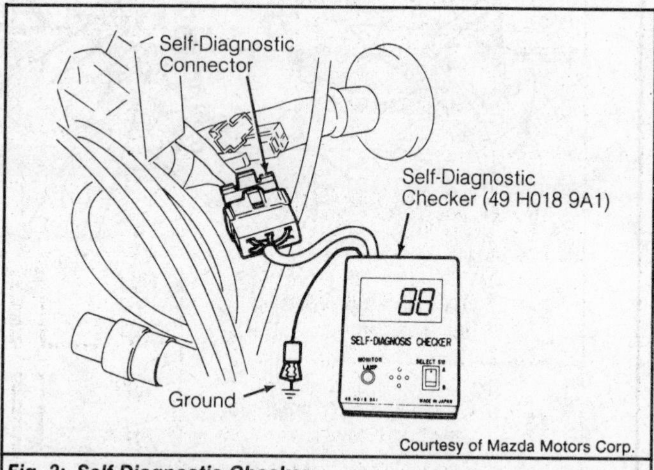
Self-Diagnostic
Connector
Self-Diagnostic
Checker (49 H018 9A1)
88
SELF-DIAGNOSIS CHECKER
Ground
Courtesy of Mazda Motors Corp.

*Fig. 2: Self-Diagnostic Checker*

**Clearing Trouble Codes – 1)** Disconnect negative battery cable. Depress brake pedal for at least 5 seconds. Reconnect battery cable.

**2)** Connect Self-Diagnostic Checker (49 H018 9A1). Turn ignition on, but do not start engine for 6 seconds.

**3)** Start engine and run at 2000 RPM for 4 minutes. Verify no codes are displayed.

### WITHOUT SELF-DIAGNOSTIC CHECKER

**Trouble Code Access – 1)** Using jumper wire, ground Yellow/Black 1-pin connector. Connector is located above right side front wheelwell.

**2)** With ignition on and engine stopped, observe "CHECK ENGINE" or MIL light. Note trouble codes. Check TROUBLE CODE IDENTIFICATION table for possible cause. If light remains on continuously, ECU is defective.

# 1988 COMPUTERIZED ENGINE CONTROLS
# Mazda Feedback Carburetor System

**Clearing Trouble Codes – 1)** Disconnect negative battery cable. Depress brake pedal for at least 5 seconds. Reconnect battery cable.

**2)** Ground test connector with jumper wire. Turn ignition on, but do not start engine for 6 seconds.

**3)** Start engine and run at 2000 RPM for 2 minutes. Verify no codes are displayed.

| Code No. | Location of malfunction | Buzzer | Control unit fail-safe function |
|---|---|---|---|
| 01 | IG pulse circuit | ON / OFF | — |
| 09 | Water thermo sensor or circuit | ON / OFF | Maintains constant **80°C (176°F)** signal |
| 13 | Vacuum sensor or circuit | ON / OFF | Holds A/F solenoid valve to **0%** duty and cuts off EGR |
| 14 | Atmospheric pressure sensor or circuit | ON / OFF | Maintains constant signal of sea-level pressure |
| 15 | $O_2$ sensor or circuit | ON / OFF | Holds A/F solenoid valve to **20%** duty |
| 16 | EGR control system | ON / OFF | — |
| | EGR position sensor or circuit | | Cuts off EGR |
| 17 | Feedback system | ON / OFF | Holds A/F solenoid valve to **30%** duty |
| 18 | A/F solenoid valve or circuit | ON / OFF | |
| 22 | Slow fuel cut solenoid valve or circuit | ON / OFF | — |
| 23 | Coasting richer solenoid valve or circuit | ON / OFF | — |
| 26 | Purge solenoid valve or circuit | ON / OFF | — |
| 28 | Duty solenoid vacuum valve or circuit | ON / OFF | — |

Courtesy of Mazda Motors Corp.

## TROUBLE CODE IDENTIFICATION (Cont.)

| Code No. | Location of malfunction | Buzzer | Control unit fail-safe function |
|---|---|---|---|
| 29 | Duty solenoid vent valve or circuit | ON / OFF | — |
| 30 | ACV solenoid valve or circuit | ON / OFF | — |
| 34 | Idle-up solenoid valve (for A/C) or circuit | ON / OFF | — |
| 35 | Idle-up solenoid valve (for A/T) or circuit | ON / OFF | — |
| 45 | Vacuum solenoid valve or circuit | ON / OFF | — |

## TROUBLE CODE NO. 1 (IGNITION PULSE)

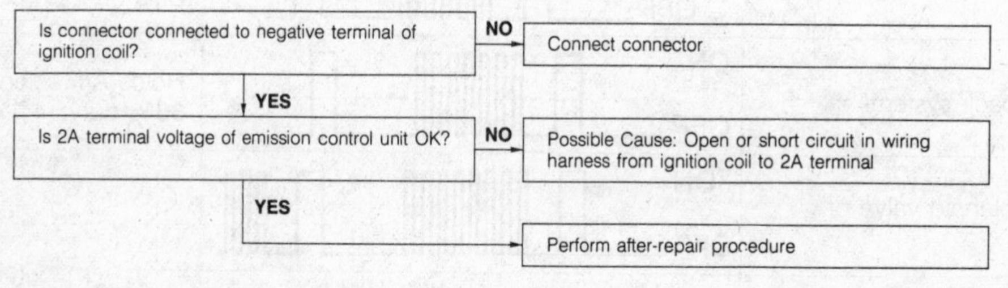
Is connector connected to negative terminal of ignition coil?
NO
Connect connector
YES
Is 2A terminal voltage of emission control unit OK?
NO
Possible Cause: Open or short circuit in wiring harness from ignition coil to 2A terminal
YES
Perform after-repair procedure

## TROUBLE CODE NO. 9 (COOLANT THERMOSENSOR)

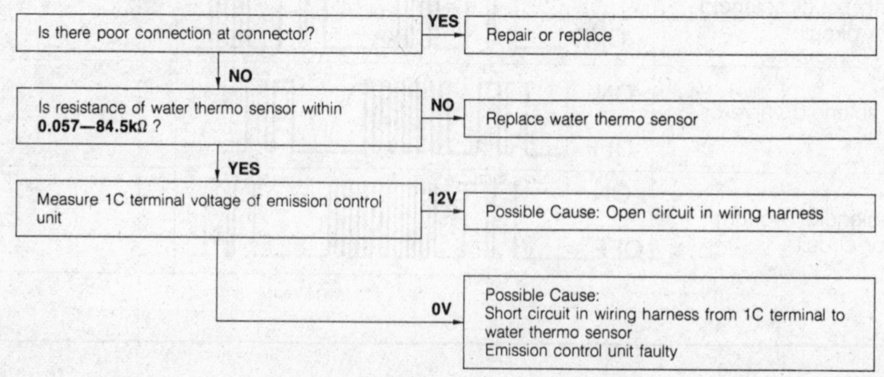
Is there poor connection at connector?
YES
Repair or replace
NO
Is resistance of water thermo sensor within 0.057—84.5kΩ ?
NO
Replace water thermo sensor
YES
Measure 1C terminal voltage of emission control unit
12V
Possible Cause: Open circuit in wiring harness
0V
Possible Cause:
Short circuit in wiring harness from 1C terminal to water thermo sensor
Emission control unit faulty

Courtesy of Mazda Motors Corp.

## TROUBLE CODE NO. 13 (VACUUM SENSOR)

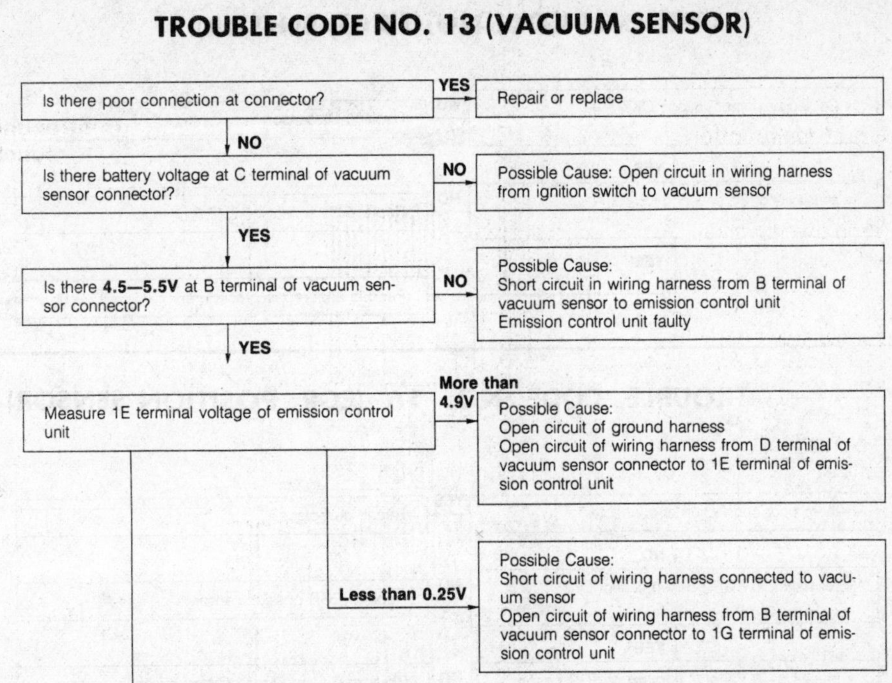
Is there poor connection at connector?
YES
Repair or replace
NO
Is there battery voltage at C terminal of vacuum sensor connector?
NO
Possible Cause: Open circuit in wiring harness from ignition switch to vacuum sensor
YES
Is there 4.5—5.5V at B terminal of vacuum sensor connector?
NO
Possible Cause:
Short circuit in wiring harness from B terminal of vacuum sensor to emission control unit
Emission control unit faulty
YES
Measure 1E terminal voltage of emission control unit
More than 4.9V
Possible Cause:
Open circuit of ground harness
Open circuit of wiring harness from D terminal of vacuum sensor connector to 1E terminal of emission control unit
Less than 0.25V
Possible Cause:
Short circuit of wiring harness connected to vacuum sensor
Open circuit of wiring harness from B terminal of vacuum sensor connector to 1G terminal of emission control unit
0.25—4.9V
Perform after-repair procedure

## TROUBLE CODE NO. 14 (ATMOSPHERIC PRESSURE SENSOR)

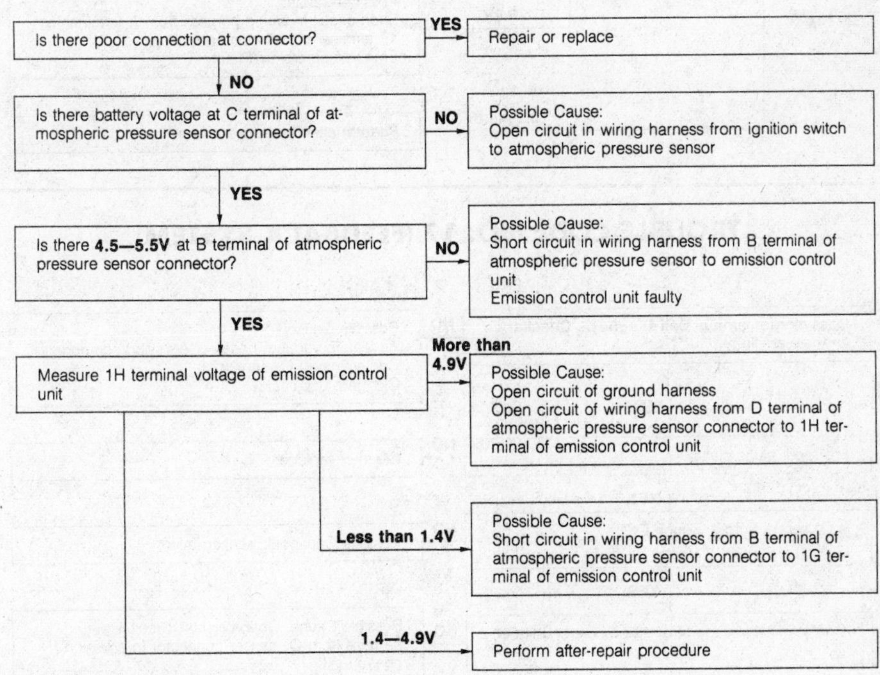
Is there poor connection at connector?
YES
Repair or replace
NO
Is there battery voltage at C terminal of atmospheric pressure sensor connector?
NO
Possible Cause:
Open circuit in wiring harness from ignition switch to atmospheric pressure sensor
YES
Is there 4.5—5.5V at B terminal of atmospheric pressure sensor connector?
NO
Possible Cause:
Short circuit in wiring harness from B terminal of atmospheric pressure sensor to emission control unit
Emission control unit faulty
YES
Measure 1H terminal voltage of emission control unit
More than 4.9V
Possible Cause:
Open circuit of ground harness
Open circuit of wiring harness from D terminal of atmospheric pressure sensor connector to 1H terminal of emission control unit
Less than 1.4V
Possible Cause:
Short circuit in wiring harness from B terminal of atmospheric pressure sensor connector to 1G terminal of emission control unit
1.4—4.9V
Perform after-repair procedure

Courtesy of Mazda Motors Corp.

## TROUBLE CODE NO. 15 ($O_2$ SENSOR)

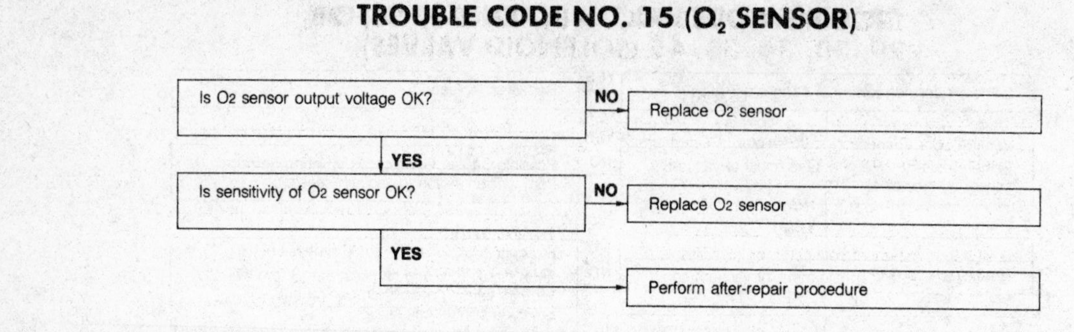
Is O2 sensor output voltage OK?
NO
Replace O2 sensor
YES
Is sensitivity of O2 sensor OK?
NO
Replace O2 sensor
YES
Perform after-repair procedure

## TROUBLE CODE NO. 16 (EGR POSITION SENSOR)

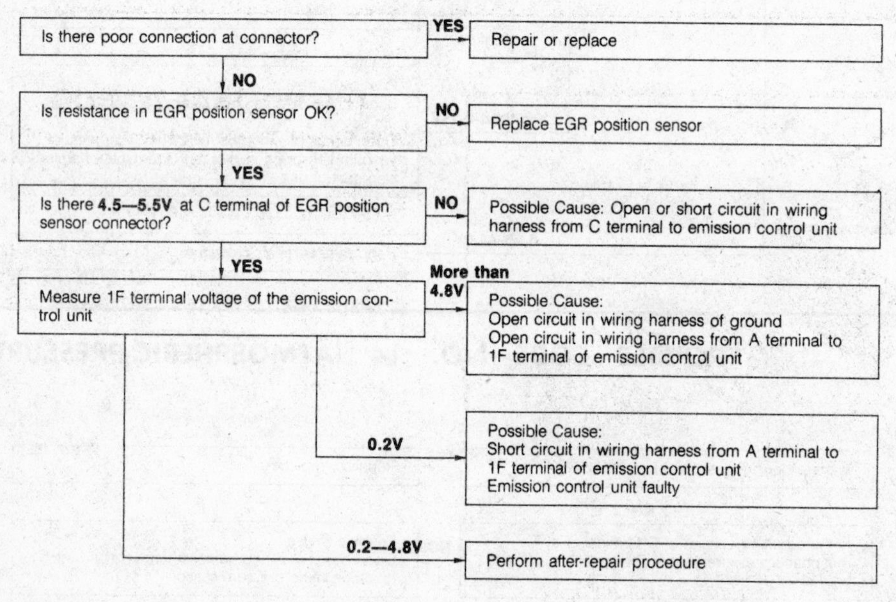
Is there poor connection at connector?
YES
Repair or replace
NO
Is resistance in EGR position sensor OK?
NO
Replace EGR position sensor
YES
Is there 4.5—5.5V at C terminal of EGR position sensor connector?
NO
Possible Cause: Open or short circuit in wiring harness from C terminal to emission control unit
YES
Measure 1F terminal voltage of the emission control unit
More than 4.8V
Possible Cause:
Open circuit in wiring harness of ground
Open circuit in wiring harness from A terminal to 1F terminal of emission control unit
0.2V
Possible Cause:
Short circuit in wiring harness from A terminal to 1F terminal of emission control unit
Emission control unit faulty
0.2—4.8V
Perform after-repair procedure

## TROUBLE CODE NO. 17 (FEEDBACK SYSTEM)

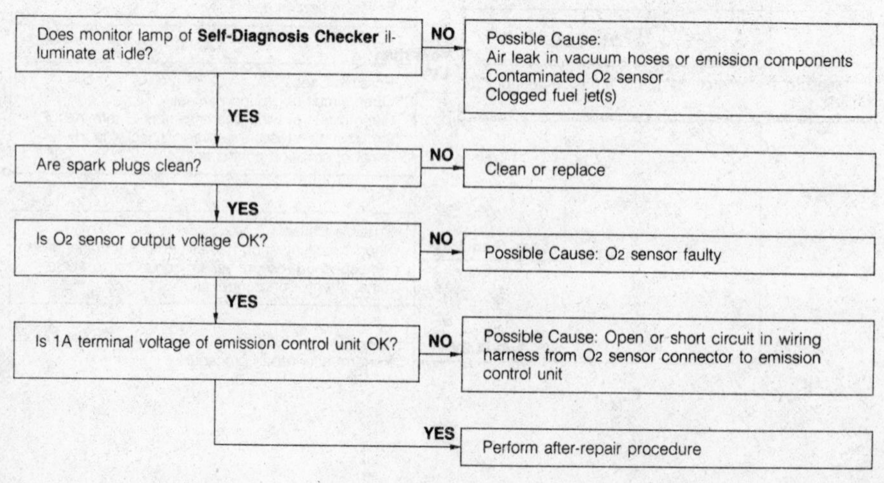
Does monitor lamp of Self-Diagnosis Checker illuminate at idle?
NO
Possible Cause:
Air leak in vacuum hoses or emission components
Contaminated O2 sensor
Clogged fuel jet(s)
YES
Are spark plugs clean?
NO
Clean or replace
YES
Is O2 sensor output voltage OK?
NO
Possible Cause: O2 sensor faulty
YES
Is 1A terminal voltage of emission control unit OK?
NO
Possible Cause: Open or short circuit in wiring harness from O2 sensor connector to emission control unit
YES
Perform after-repair procedure

Courtesy of Mazda Motors Corp.

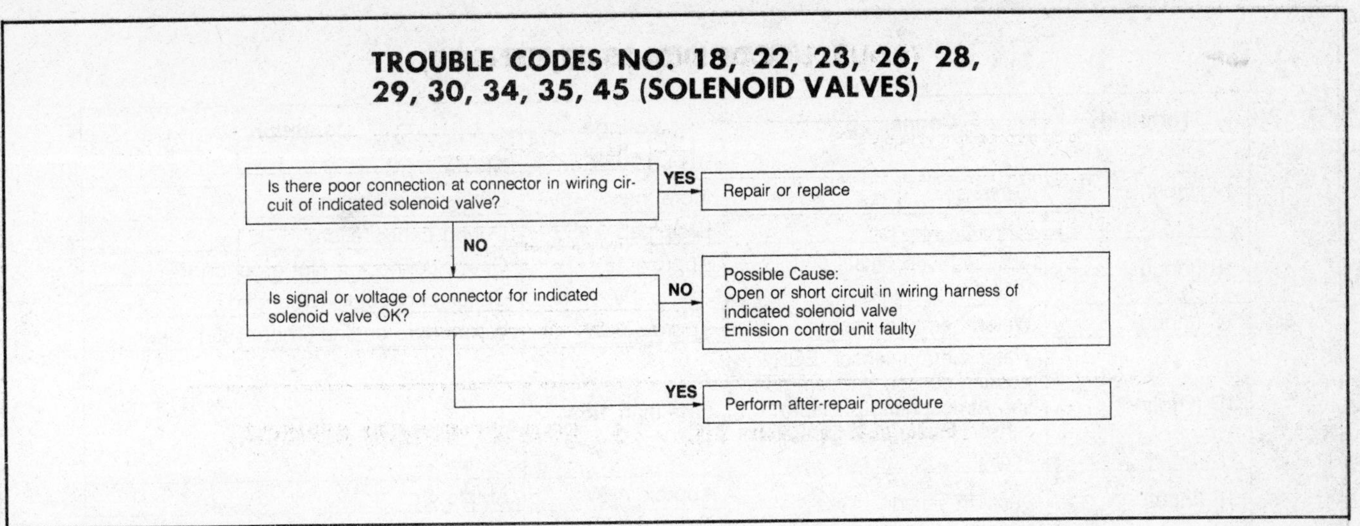
TROUBLE CODES NO. 18, 22, 23, 26, 28, 29, 30, 34, 35, 45 (SOLENOID VALVES)
Is there poor connection at connector in wiring circuit of indicated solenoid valve?
YES
Repair or replace
NO
Is signal or voltage of connector for indicated solenoid valve OK?
NO
Possible Cause:
Open or short circuit in wiring harness of indicated solenoid valve
Emission control unit faulty
YES
Perform after-repair procedure

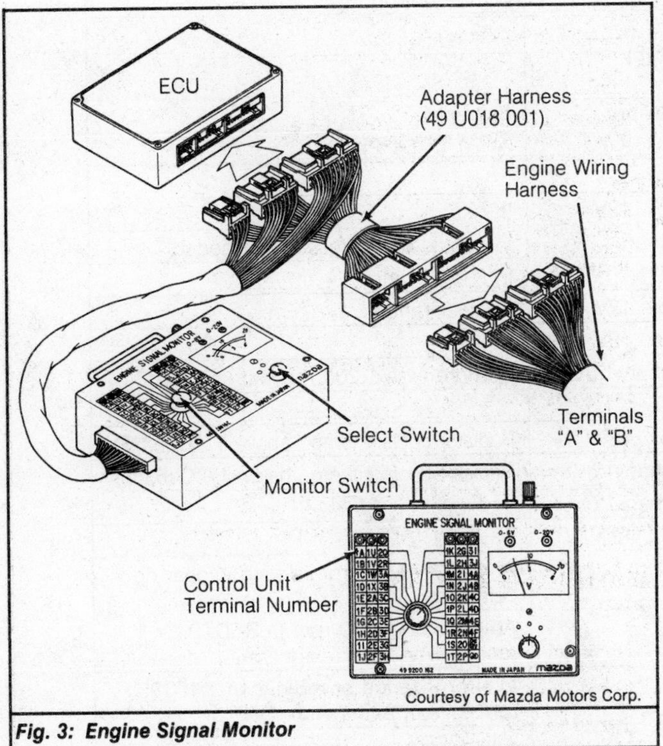
ECU
Adapter Harness
(49 U018 001)
Engine Wiring
Harness
Select Switch
Terminals
"A" & "B"
Monitor Switch
Control Unit
Terminal Number
ENGINE SIGNAL MONITOR
Courtesy of Mazda Motors Corp.

*Fig. 3: Engine Signal Monitor*

## ECU VOLTAGE TESTING

**With Engine Signal Monitor** - Connect Engine Signal Monitor (49 9200 162) with Adapter Harness (49 U018 001). Check voltage by selecting terminal number on monitor. Compare readings with ECU TERMINAL VOLTAGE CHARTS.

**With Analog Voltmeter** - Ground negative lead. Backprobe each specific ECU connector terminal to monitor voltage. Compare readings with TERMINAL VOLTAGE charts.

# 1988 COMPUTERIZED ENGINE CONTROLS
## Mazda Feedback Carburetor System (Cont.)

### ECU TERMINAL VOLTAGE

| Terminal | Connected to | Voltage | Condition |
|---|---|---|---|
| 1A (Input) | $O_2$ sensor | 0.3—0.7V | At idle |
| | | More than 0.45V | During acceleration |
| | | Less than 0.45V | During deceleration |
| 1B (Input) | Self-diagnosis check connector | Approx. 12V | Check connector; Not grounded |
| | | 0V | Check connector; Grounded |
| 1C (Input) | Water thermo sensor | Approx. 0.5V | Warmed-up engine (Thermostat: Open) |
| 1D (Ground) | Water thermo sensor, EGR position sensor, Vacuum sensor, Atmospheric pressure sensor, Intake air temperature sensor | Less than 1.5V | — |
| 1E (Input) | Vacuum sensor | Approx. 1.3V | At idle |
| | | Approx. 4.0V | Engine stopped (Atmospheric pressure) |
| 1F (Input) | EGR position sensor | Approx. 0.7V | At idle |
| | | 0.7—4.7V | During driving |
| 1G (Power supply) | EGR position sensor, Vacuum sensor, Atmospheric pressure sensor | 4.5—5.5V | — |
| 1H (Input) | Atmospheric pressure sensor | Approx. 4V | Sea level |
| 1J (Input) | Intake air temperature sensor | Approx. 4.1V | At 20°C (68°F) |
| 1L (Memory power) | Battery | Approx. 12V | — |
| 1N (Input) | Neutral and clutch switch | Approx. 12V | In gear |
| | | Less than 1.5V | In neutral or depress clutch pedal |
| | Inhibitor switch | Less than 1.5V | In N or P range |
| | | Approx. 12V | In other ranges |
| 1O (Input) | Idle switch | Approx. 12V | At idle |
| | | Less than 1.5V | At more than 1,200 rpm with no load |
| 1P (Ground) | Idle switch | Less than 1.5V | — |
| 1Q (Input) | Water temperature switch | Approx. 12V | Radiator coolant temp.: above 17°C (63°F) |
| | | Less than 1.5V | Radiator coolant temp.: below 17°C (63°F) |
| 1R (Ground) | Engine ground | Less than 1.5V | — |
| 1S (Output) | Coasting advance solenoid valve | Approx. 12V | At idle |
| | | Less than 1.5V | At 1,700—2,500 rpm during in-gear deceleration |
| 1T (Output) | Idle-up solenoid valve (A/T) | Less than 1.5V | At less than 1,000 rpm in R, D, 2, or 1 range |
| | | Approx. 12V | In N or P range or more than 1,100 rpm without A/C switch: ON |
| 1U (Output) | Malfunction indicator light | Approx. 12V | light: OFF |
| | | Less than 1.5V | light: ON |
| 1V (Output) | Purge solenoid valve | Approx. 12V | At idle |
| | | Less than 1.5V | At 1,400 rpm with warmed-up engine |
| 2A (Input) | Ignition coil negative terminal | Approx. 12V | — |
| 2B (Battery power) | Ignition switch (ON) | Approx. 12V | Ignition switch: ON |
| | | 0V | Ignition switch: OFF |
| 2C (Input) | Air-conditioner magnetic clutch circuit | Approx. 12V | Air conditioner: ON |
| | | 0V | Air conditioner: OFF |
| 2D (Output) | Slow fuel cut solenoid valve | Less than 1.5V | At idle |
| | | Approx. 12V | At 2,500 rpm or more during in-gear deceleration |

Courtesy of Mazda Motors Corp.

## ECU TERMINAL VOLTAGE (CONT.)

| Terminal | Connected to | Voltage | Condition |
|---|---|---|---|
| 2E (Output) | Self-Diagnosis Checker (Digital display) | Approx. 12V | Buzzer: OFF |
| | | Less than 1.5V | Buzzer: ON |
| | | Code signal | When self-diagnosis check connector grounded |
| 2F (Output) | Air/fuel (A/F) solenoid valve | Monitor reading: 1.5—3.8V (fluctuating) Actual voltage: 3.5—12V (fluctuating) | At idle |
| | | 0—14V (fluctuating or fixed) | During running |
| 2H (Output) | Coasting richer solenoid valve | Approx. 12V | At idle |
| | | Less than 1.5V | At 2,500—1,400 rpm with in-gear deceleration (Voltage indicated one second after conditions met) |
| 2I (Output) | Self-Diagnosis Checker (Monitor lamp) | Less than 1.5V | Monitor lamp: ON |
| | | Approx. 12V | Monitor lamp: OFF |
| 2J (Output) | ACV solenoid valve | Approx. 12V | At idle |
| | | Less than 1.5V | At 1,500 rpm or more, warmed up, no load |
| 2K (Output) | Duty solenoid valve (Vent) | Approx. 12V | At idle |
| | | Voltage decreases | During acceleration |
| 2L (Output) | Duty solenoid valve (Vacuum) | Approx. 12V | At idle |
| | | Voltage decreases | During acceleration |
| 2M (Output) | Idle-up solenoid valve (A/C) | Less than 1.5V | At idle (A/C: ON) |
| | | Approx. 12V | At 1,400 rpm or below (A/C: ON) |
| 2N (Ground) | Engine ground | Less than 1.5V | — |

**Connectors**

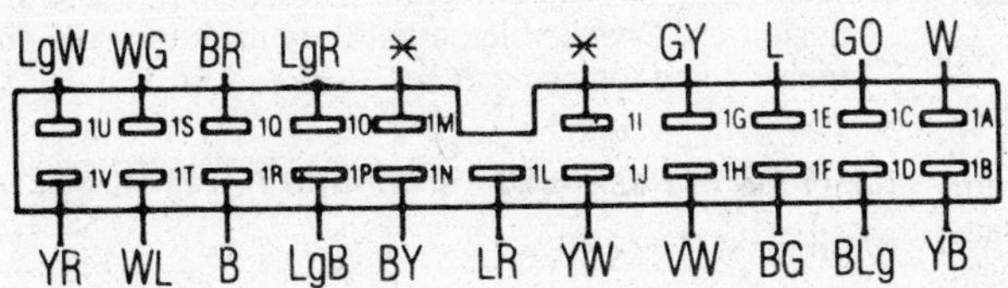
LgW WG BR LgR * * GY L GO W
1U 1S 1Q 1O 1M 1I 1G 1E 1C 1A
1V 1T 1R 1P 1N 1L 1J 1H 1F 1D 1B
YR WL B LgB BY LR YW VW BG BLg YB

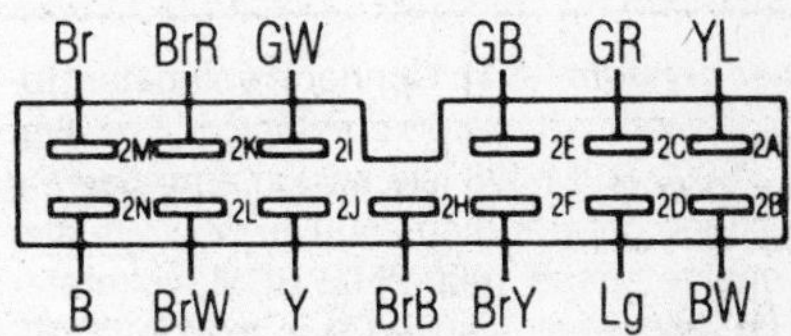
Br BrR GW GB GR YL
2M 2K 2I 2E 2C 2A
2N 2L 2J 2H 2F 2D 2B
B BrW Y BrB BrY Lg BW

Courtesy of Mazda Motors Corp.

## DECELERATION CONTROL SYSTEM

Warm engine to normal operating temperature and run at idle speed. Disconnect neutral or inhibitor switch connectors. Remove air cleaner housing assembly.

**Slow Fuel-Cut System - 1)** Connect a voltmeter to terminal "F" (Light Green wire) of carburetor connector. *See Fig. 4.* Increase engine speed to 3000 RPM. Lift idle switch arm. *See Fig. 5.*

**2)** With engine speed greater than 2500 RPM, voltmeter should read 12 volts. With engine speed less than 2500 RPM, voltmeter should read less than 1.5 volt. If voltmeter readings are not as specified, check ECU connector terminal 2D and slow fuel-cut solenoid valve.

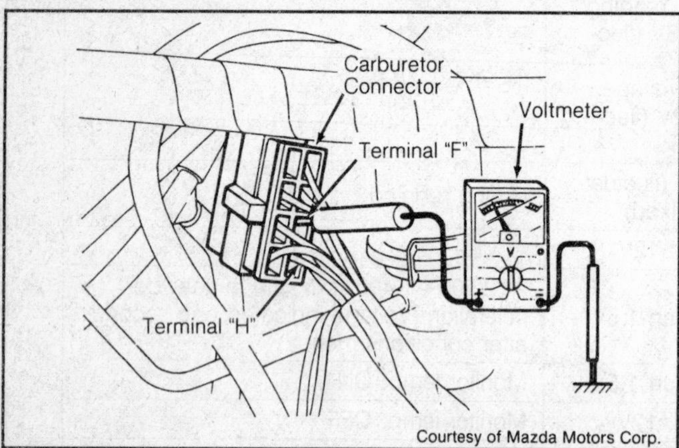
Carburetor Connector
Voltmeter
Terminal "F"
Terminal "H"
Courtesy of Mazda Motors Corp.

*Fig. 4: Carburetor Connector Terminal Identification*

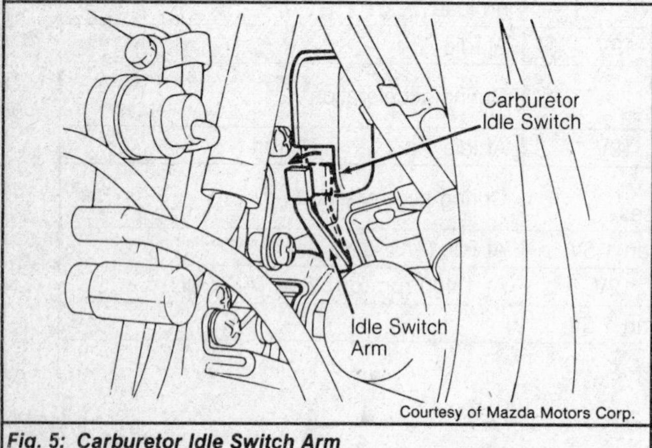
Carburetor Idle Switch
Idle Switch Arm
Courtesy of Mazda Motors Corp.

*Fig. 5: Carburetor Idle Switch Arm*

**Coasting Richer System - 1)** Connect voltmeter to terminal "H" (Brown/Black wire) of carburetor connector. *See Fig. 4.* Increase engine speed to 3000 RPM. Lift idle switch arm. *See Fig. 5.*

**2)** With engine speed greater than 2500 RPM, voltmeter should read 12 volts. With engine speed 1400-2500 RPM, voltmeter should read less than 1.5 volt. With engine speed less than 1400 RPM, voltmeter should read 12 volts.

**3)** If voltmeter readings are not as specified, check ECU connector terminal 2H and coasting richer solenoid valve.

**Coasting Advance System - 1)** Connect voltmeter to terminal "WG" of coasting advance solenoid valve. *See Fig. 6.* Increase engine speed to 3000 RPM. Lift idle switch arm. *See Fig. 5.*

**2)** With engine speed greater than 2500 RPM, voltmeter should read 12 volts. With engine speed 1700-2500 RPM, voltmeter should read less than 1.5 volt. With engine speed less than 1700 RPM, voltmeter reading should read 12 volts.

**3)** If voltmeter readings are not as specified, check ECU connector terminal 1S and vacuum solenoid valve.

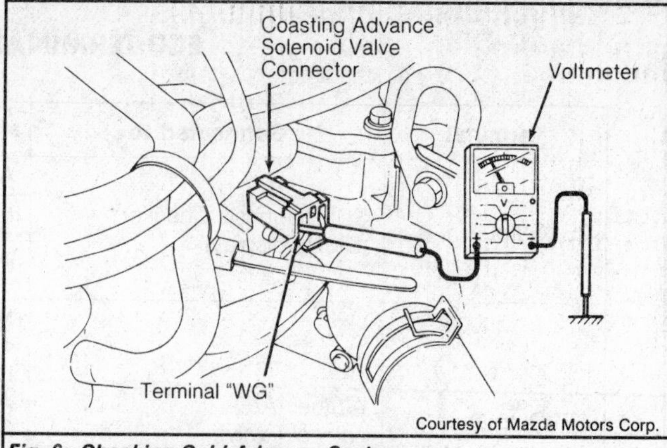
Coasting Advance Solenoid Valve Connector
Voltmeter
Terminal "WG"
Courtesy of Mazda Motors Corp.

*Fig. 6: Checking Cold Advance System*

## COMPONENT TESTING

**Air Conditioner Switch -** With transmission in Neutral and blower motor on, check self-diagnostic checker monitor light while operating A/C switch. With A/C off, monitor light should be off. With A/C on, monitor light should be on. If monitor light does not operate as specified, check ECU terminal 2C.

**Air Control Valve (ACV) Solenoid -** Warm engine to normal operating temperature and turn engine off. Connect coolant temperature switch using a jumper wire. Connect a voltmeter between ACV Yellow wire terminal and ground. Voltmeter should read zero volt at 1500 RPM or higher. If voltage is not as specified, check ECU terminal 2J.

**Air/Fuel (A/F) Solenoid Valve - 1)** Warm engine to normal operating temperature and run engine at idle speed. Connect a dwell meter (set on 6-cylinder scale) to A/F check connector terminal Brown/Yellow wire on side of carburetor.

**2)** Disconnect vacuum hose from vacuum sensor and plug. Connect a vacuum pump to vacuum sensor. Apply 20 in. Hg and check that dwell meter reads 20-70 degrees.

**3)** Release vacuum and check that dwell meter reads zero degrees. If dwell meter does not read as specified, check ECU terminal IE and vacuum sensor. Remove vacuum pump and reconnect vacuum hose.

**4)** Increase engine speed to 4500 RPM and check that dwell meter reads a fixed zero degrees. If dwell meter reading is 72 degrees, check idle and neutral switches. If reading is other than zero degrees or 72 degrees, replace ECU.

**Atmospheric Pressure Sensor - 1)** Remove left side kick panel. Remove rubber cap and attach a vacuum pump to sensor port. Turn ignition on. Check voltage between each terminal and ground while applying and releasing 30 in. Hg to sensor. *See Fig. 7.*

***ATMOSPHERIC PRESSURE SENSOR TERMINAL VOLTAGE***

| Terminal | Voltage |
|---|---|
| "A" | Less Than 1.5 |
| "B" | 4.5-5.5 |
| "C" | 12 |
| "D" | 1.4-4.9 |

**2)** If voltages at terminal "A", "B", or "C" is not within specification, check wiring harness to sensor. If voltages at terminal "A", "B", or "C" is within specification, but terminal "D" is not within specification, replace atmospheric pressure sensor.

**Clutch Switch (M/T) - 1)** Disconnect clutch switch connector. Measure resistance across Blue/Green wire and Black wire terminals on switch. With clutch pedal released, resistance should be present.

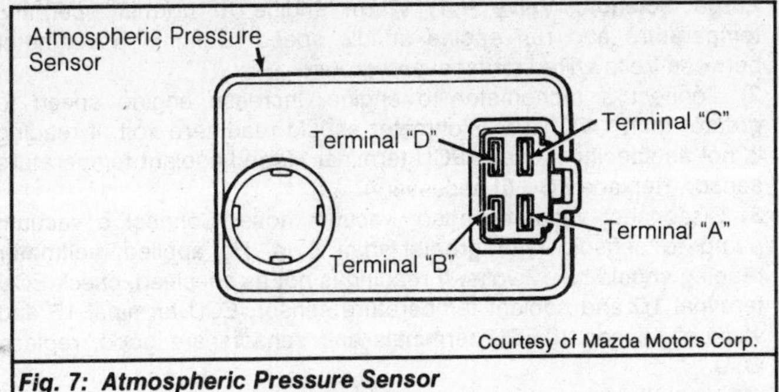
Atmospheric Pressure Sensor
Terminal "D"
Terminal "C"
Terminal "A"
Terminal "B"
Courtesy of Mazda Motors Corp.

*Fig. 7: Atmospheric Pressure Sensor*

**2)** With clutch pedal depressed, resistance should not be present. If resistance is not as specified, turn clutch switch to adjust.
**3)** When using Self-Diagnostic Checker (49 H018 9A1) and with transmission in gear, check self-diagnostic checker monitor light while depressing clutch pedal. With clutch pedal released, monitor light should be on. With clutch pedal depressed, monitor light should be off. If monitor light does not operate as specified, check ECU terminal 1N and clutch switch.

**Coasting Richer Solenoid Valve** – Run engine at idle speed. Ground terminal "H" (Brown/Black wire) of carburetor connector. Engine RPM should increase. If engine RPM does not increase, replace coasting richer solenoid valve.

**Coolant Temperature Switch** – Remove coolant temperature switch from radiator. Switch should have continuity at temperatures greater than 63°F (17°C). If continuity is not present, replace coolant temperature switch.

**Coolant Temperature Sensor** – Warm engine to normal operating temperature and run engine at idle. Turn ignition on. Check for 5 volts between sensor terminal and ground. If voltage is not as specified, check wiring harness for open or short circuit, and check resistance using COOLANT TEMPERATURE SENSOR RESISTANCE table.

***COOLANT TEMPERATURE SENSOR RESISTANCE***

| Temperature °F (°C) | Ohms |
|---|---|
| -4 (-20) | 14,600-17,800 |
| 68 (20) | 2200-2700 |
| 176 (80) | 290-350 |

**EGR Control Valve** – **1)** Warm engine to normal operating temperature and run engine at idle speed. Disconnect EGR control valve vacuum hose and plug hose.
**2)** Ensure engine idles smoothly. If engine does not idle smoothly, clean exhaust gas passage in EGR valve or replace EGR valve. Before replacing EGR valve, check intake air and control systems.
**3)** Connect a vacuum pump and apply 1.6-2.4 in. Hg to EGR valve. Ensure engine idles rough or stalls at greater than specified vacuum. If engine does not run rough or stall, replace EGR valve or check EGR passage for blockage.

**EGR Position Sensor** – **1)** Disconnect vacuum hose from EGR valve and connect a vacuum pump. Disconnect EGR position sensor connector. Turn ignition on. Using a voltmeter, check voltage of each terminal. *See Fig. 8.* See EGR POSITION SENSOR VOLTAGE table.

***EGR POSITION SENSOR VOLTAGE***

| Terminal | Voltage (No Vacuum) | Voltage (6 in. Hg Vac.) |
|---|---|---|
| "A" | .7 | 4.7 |
| "B" | 1.5 or less | 1.5 or less |
| "C" | 4.5-5.5 | 4.5-5.5 |

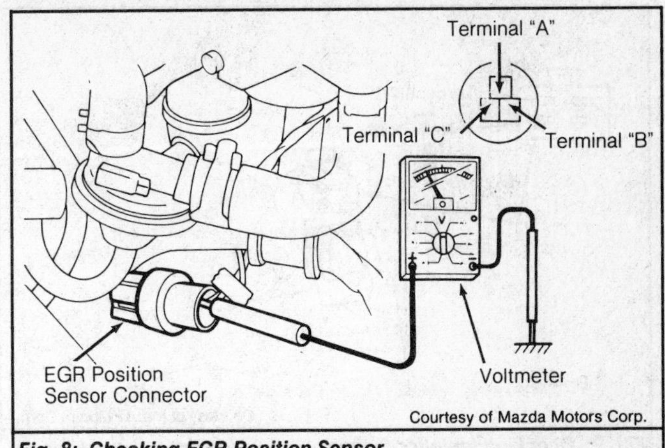
Terminal "A"
Terminal "C"
Terminal "B"
EGR Position Sensor Connector
Voltmeter
Courtesy of Mazda Motors Corp.

*Fig. 8: Checking EGR Position Sensor*

**2)** If voltage reading is not as specified at terminals "B" and "C", check wiring harness and ECU terminals 1D, 1F, and 1G.
**3)** If voltage is not as specified at terminal "A", check wiring harness, ECU, and sensor resistance. Disconnect sensor connector. Using an ohmmeter, check resistance between terminals while applying 6 in. Hg to EGR control valve. Check resistance using EGR POSITION SENSOR RESISTANCE table.

***EGR POSITION SENSOR RESISTANCE***

| Terminals | Ohms |
|---|---|
| "B"-"C" | 5000 |
| "A"-"C" | 0-5500 |
| "A"-"B" | 700-6000 |

**EGR Duty Solenoid Valve** – Turn ignition on. Using a voltmeter, ensure that 12 volts is present at each solenoid terminal. If 12 volts are not present at any terminal, check duty solenoid valve, valve wiring, and ECU terminals 2C and 2D.

**Idle Switch** – **1)** Warm engine to normal operating temperature and run engine at idle speed. Connect tachometer to engine. Connect voltmeter to idle switch terminal Lt. Green/Red wire.
**2)** Increase engine speed to greater than 2000 RPM. Decelerate gradually and note voltmeter reading. With engine speed at 1000-1200 RPM, reading should be less than 1.5 volt.
**3)** With engine speed at idle, reading should be 12 volts. If voltage reading is not as specified, turn idle switch adjustment screw to adjust.
**4)** Using Self-Diagnostic Checker (49 H018 9A1) and with shift lever in Neutral, check self-diagnostic checker monitor light while depressing accelerator pedal.
**5)** With accelerator pedal released, monitor light should be off. With accelerator pedal depressed, monitor light should be on. If monitor light does not operate as specified, check ECU terminal 1D and idle switch.

**Inhibitor Switch (A/T)** – **1)** Disconnect switch connector. Using an ohmmeter, check for continuity between terminals "A" and "B". *See Fig. 9.* With shift lever in "N" or "P" range, continuity should be present.
**2)** With shift lever in other ranges, continuity should not be present. If ohmmeter readings are not as specified, replace inhibitor switch.
**3)** Using Self-Diagnostic Checker (49 H018 9A1), check self-diagnostic checker monitor light while moving shift lever. With shifter in "P" or "N" position, monitor light should be off. With shifter in other positions, monitor light should be on. If monitor light does not operate as specified, check ECU terminal 1N and inhibitor switch.

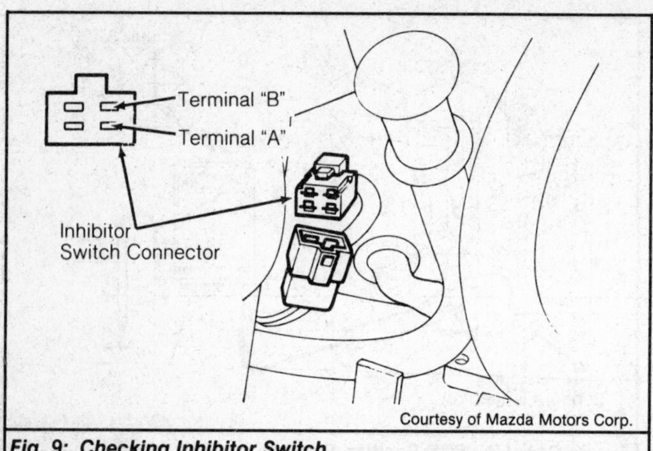
Terminal "B"
Terminal "A"
Inhibitor Switch Connector
Courtesy of Mazda Motors Corp.

*Fig. 9: Checking Inhibitor Switch*

**Intake Air Temperature Sensor** – Remove air cleaner cover. Heat intake air temperature sensor and note temperature. Using an ohmmeter, check resistance between intake air temperature sensor Black/Lt. Green and Yellow/White terminals. Check resistance using INTAKE AIR TEMPERATURE SENSOR RESISTANCE table.

***INTAKE AIR TEMPERATURE SENSOR RESISTANCE***

| Temperature °F (°C) | Ohms |
|---|---|
| -4 (-20) | 14,600-17,800 |
| 68 (20) | 2200-2700 |
| 176 (80) | 290-350 |

**Mixture Control Valve** – Start engine. Plug intake port of mixture control valve and ensure engine speed does not decrease. Increase engine speed and quickly decelerate. Ensure air is pulled into intake port for 1-2 seconds after accelerator is released.

**Neutral Switch – 1)** Disconnect switch connector. Using an ohmmeter, check continuity between switch Blue/Green and Black terminals. With shift lever in Neutral, no continuity should be present.

**2)** With shift lever in other positions, continuity should be present. If ohmmeter readings are not as specified, replace neutral switch.

**3)** Using Self-Diagnostic Checker (49 H018 9A1), check self-diagnostic checker monitor light while moving shift lever. On vehicles with automatic transmissions, with shifter in "P" or "N" position, monitor light should be off. With shifter in other positions, monitor light should be on.

**4)** On vehicles with manual transmissions, with shifter in Neutral, monitor light should be off. With shifter in gear, monitor light should be on. If monitor light does not operate as specified, check ECU terminal 1N and neutral or inhibitor switch.

**$O_2$ Sensor – 1)** Warm engine to normal operating temperature and run engine at idle speed. Connect a voltmeter between $O_2$ sensor connector and ground.

**2)** Increase engine speed to 4000 RPM until voltmeter reads .7 volt. Increase and decrease engine RPM suddenly several times. When engine RPM is increased, voltmeter should read .5-1.0 volt.

**3)** When engine RPM is decreased, voltmeter should read 0-.4 volt. If voltmeter readings are not as specified, replace $O_2$ sensor.

**4)** When using Self-Diagnostic Checker (49 H018 9A1), warm engine to normal operating temperature and run engine at idle speed. Increase engine speed to 2000-3000 RPM. Ensure self-diagnostic checker monitor light flashes more than 8 times in 10 seconds.

**Purge Solenoid Valve – 1)** Warm engine to normal operating temperature and run engine at idle speed. Connect a voltmeter between Yellow/Red terminal and ground.

**2)** Connect a tachometer to engine. Increase engine speed to greater than 1400 RPM. Voltmeter should read zero volt. If reading is not as specified, check ECU terminal 1C and coolant temperature sensor. Replace ECU (if necessary).

**3)** Disconnect vacuum sensor vacuum hose. Connect a vacuum pump to sensor. With greater than 6 in. Hg applied, voltmeter reading should be 12 volts. If reading is not as specified, check ECU terminal 1C and coolant temperature sensor, ECU terminal 1E and vacuum sensor. If ECU terminals and sensors are good, replace ECU.

**Slow Fuel-Cut Solenoid Valve** – Run engine at idle speed. Disconnect carburetor connector. Engine should stop running. If engine continues to run, replace slow fuel-cut solenoid valve.

**Vacuum Solenoid Valve** – Remove vacuum solenoid valve. Connect vacuum hoses to valve. *See Fig. 10.* Blow air through valve from hose "A" and ensure air comes out valve air filter. Using jumper wires, apply battery voltage and ground solenoid valve. *See Fig. 10.* Blow air through valve from hose "A" and ensure air comes out of port "B". If vacuum solenoid valve does not operate as specified, replace vacuum solenoid valve.

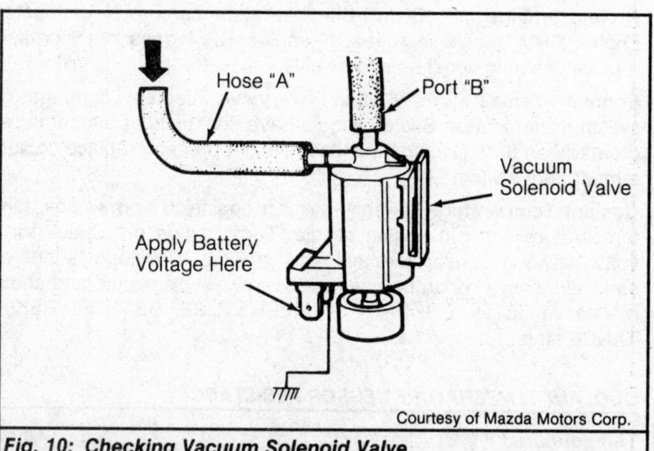
Hose "A"
Port "B"
Vacuum Solenoid Valve
Apply Battery Voltage Here
Courtesy of Mazda Motors Corp.

*Fig. 10: Checking Vacuum Solenoid Valve*

**Vacuum Sensor – 1)** Remove vacuum hose and attach a vacuum pump to sensor. Turn ignition on. Check voltage between each terminal and ground while applying and releasing 30 in. Hg to sensor. *See Fig. 7.*

***VACUUM SENSOR TERMINAL VOLTAGE***

| Terminal | Voltage |
|---|---|
| "A" | Less Than 1.5 |
| "B" | 4.5-5.5 |
| "C" | 12 |
| "D" | 1.4-4.9 |

**2)** If voltages at terminal "A", "B", or "C" is not within specifications, check wiring harness to sensor. If voltages at terminal "A", "B", or "C" is within specifications, but terminal "D" is not within specifications, replace vacuum sensor.

# 1988 COMPUTERIZED ENGINE CONTROLS
## Mazda Feedback Carburetor System (Cont.)

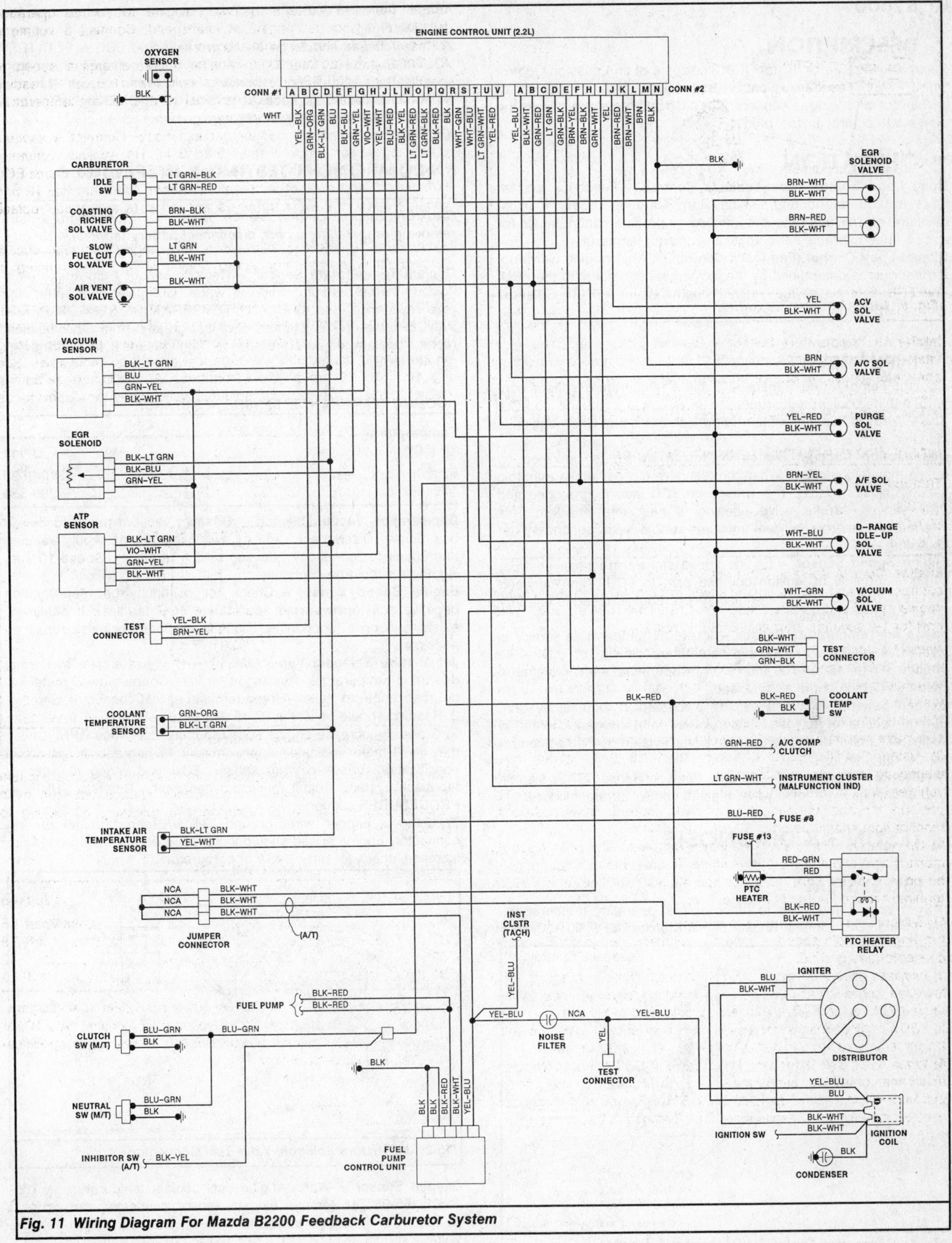
ENGINE CONTROL UNIT (2.2L)
OXYGEN SENSOR
BLK
WHT
CONN #1
A B C D E F G H J L N O P Q R S T U V
YEL-BLK
GRN-ORG
BLK-LT GRN
BLU
BLK-BLU
GRN-YEL
VIO-WHT
YEL-WHT
BLU-RED
BLK-YEL
LT GRN-RED
LT GRN-BLK
BLK-RED
BLK
WHT-GRN
WHT-BLU
LT GRN-WHT
YEL-RED
CONN #2
A B C D E F H I J K L M N
YEL-BLU
BLK-WHT
GRN-RED
LT GRN
GRN-BLK
BRN-YEL
BRN-BLK
GRN-WHT
YEL
BRN-RED
BRN-WHT
BRN
BLK
CARBURETOR
IDLE SW
LT GRN-BLK
LT GRN-RED
COASTING RICHER SOL VALVE
BRN-BLK
BLK-WHT
SLOW FUEL CUT SOL VALVE
LT GRN
BLK-WHT
AIR VENT SOL VALVE
BLK-WHT
VACUUM SENSOR
BLK-LT GRN
BLU
GRN-YEL
BLK-WHT
EGR SOLENOID
BLK-LT GRN
BLK-BLU
GRN-YEL
ATP SENSOR
BLK-LT GRN
VIO-WHT
GRN-YEL
BLK-WHT
TEST CONNECTOR
YEL-BLK
BRN-YEL
COOLANT TEMPERATURE SENSOR
GRN-ORG
BLK-LT GRN
INTAKE AIR TEMPERATURE SENSOR
BLK-LT GRN
YEL-WHT
NCA
NCA
NCA
BLK-WHT
BLK-WHT
BLK-WHT
JUMPER CONNECTOR
(A/T)
FUEL PUMP
BLK-RED
BLK-RED
CLUTCH SW (M/T)
BLU-GRN
BLK
BLU-GRN
NEUTRAL SW (M/T)
BLU-GRN
BLK
INHIBITOR SW (A/T)
BLK-YEL
BLK
BLK
BLK
BLK-RED
BLK-WHT
YEL-BLU
FUEL PUMP CONTROL UNIT
INST CLSTR (TACH)
YEL-BLU
YEL-BLU
NCA
NOISE FILTER
YEL
TEST CONNECTOR
YEL-BLU
EGR SOLENOID VALVE
BRN-WHT
BLK-WHT
BRN-RED
BLK-WHT
ACV SOL VALVE
YEL
BLK-WHT
A/C SOL VALVE
BRN
BLK-WHT
PURGE SOL VALVE
YEL-RED
BLK-WHT
A/F SOL VALVE
BRN-YEL
BLK-WHT
D-RANGE IDLE-UP SOL VALVE
WHT-BLU
BLK-WHT
VACUUM SOL VALVE
WHT-GRN
BLK-WHT
TEST CONNECTOR
BLK-WHT
GRN-WHT
GRN-BLK
BLK-RED
COOLANT TEMP SW
BLK-RED
BLK
A/C COMP CLUTCH
GRN-RED
INSTRUMENT CLUSTER (MALFUNCTION IND)
LT GRN-WHT
FUSE #8
BLU-RED
FUSE #13
RED-GRN
RED
PTC HEATER
BLK-RED
BLK-WHT
PTC HEATER RELAY
IGNITER
BLU
BLK-WHT
DISTRIBUTOR
YEL-BLU
BLU
BLK-WHT
BLK-WHT
IGNITION SW
IGNITION COIL
BLK
CONDENSER

*Fig. 11 Wiring Diagram For Mazda B2200 Feedback Carburetor System*

## B2600

## DESCRIPTION

Feedback Carburetor System (FBC) consists of an Emission Control Unit (ECU), Feedback Control Unit (FCU), 2-barrel downdraft carburetor and various sensors. The FCU utilizes signals from the sensors to control air/fuel ratio.

## OPERATION

**Open Loop Control (No Feedback Control)** – Feedback system does not operate during engine start, warm-up, heavy load or deceleration. Air/fuel ratio is controlled by predetermined values for engine speed, throttle valve angle and coolant temperature.

**Closed Loop Control (Feedback Control)** – After engine warm-up, air/fuel ratio is determined by the oxygen sensor signal to the FCU. The FCU controls air/fuel ratio through the Jet Mixture Solenoid Valve (JMSV).

## INPUT DEVICES

**Coolant Temperature Sensor** – Coolant temperature sensor converts engine coolant temperature to an electrical signal for the FCU. The FCU uses this information to provide extra fuel when engine is cold.

**Deceleration Vacuum Switch** – Vacuum switch is operated by intake manifold vacuum. When throttle valve closes, intake manifold vacuum closes switch. The voltage on FCU side is grounded and FCU senses throttle valve opening is near idle position. This information controls air/fuel mixture at idle with secondary air control.

**Engine Speed Sensor** – Engine speed signals are received from negative terminal of ignition coil and sent to FCU. Time between signals is used to calculate engine speed. Engine speed is used by ECU to control air/fuel ratio.

**Intake Air Temperature Sensor** – Intake air temperature sensor is located in air cleaner. Sensor determines density of intake air through temperature. The intake air temperature sensor signal is used by FCU to control air/fuel ratio.

**Oxygen Sensor** – Oxygen sensor is located in exhaust system. Output voltage of oxygen sensor varies with oxygen content in engine exhaust. The oxygen sensor signal is used by FCU to control air/fuel ratio.

**Throttle Position Sensor** – Throttle Position Sensor (TPS) signals FCU of changes in throttle valve angle to control air/fuel mixture.

## TESTING & DIAGNOSIS

### FBC SYSTEM

**1)** Start engine and allow to reach normal operating temperature. With ignition off, connect Engine Signal Monitor (49 9200 162) and Adapter (49 U018 002) to emission control unit and feedback control unit. *See Fig. 1.*

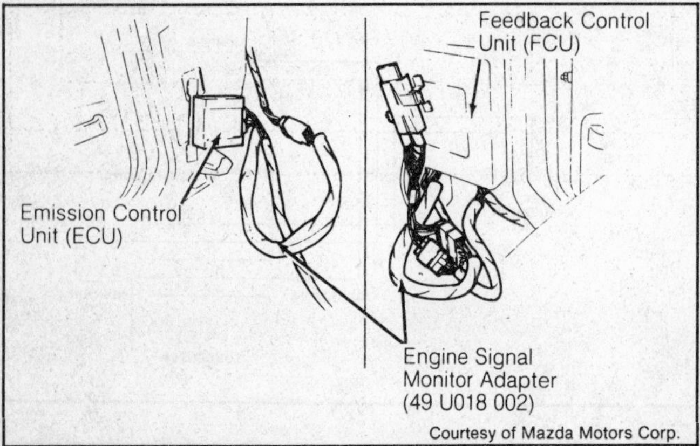
Feedback Control Unit (FCU)
Emission Control Unit (ECU)
Engine Signal Monitor Adapter (49 U018 002)
Courtesy of Mazda Motors Corp.

***Fig. 1: Connecting Engine Signal Monitor & Adapter***

**2)** Test voltages should be as shown in B2600 ECU & FCU TEST VOLTAGE tables. *See Figs. 4 and 6.* If voltages vary from specifications, check corresponding sensor and related electrical wiring, and repair as necessary. See COMPONENT TESTING & INSPECTION. Recheck with engine signal monitor to confirm repair has corrected problem.

## COMPONENT TESTING & INSPECTION

***CAUTION: Ensure ignition switch is in "OFF" position. Before removing or installing a part, disconnect battery terminal.***

**Coolant Temperature Sensor** – Remove sensor from intake manifold. Immerse sensor portion in water. Gradually heat water and read resistance. See COOLANT TEMPERATURE SENSOR RESISTANCE table. If resistance deviates greatly from specification, replace coolant temperature sensor. Tighten sensor to 14-29 ft. lbs. (20-40 N.m).

***COOLANT TEMPERATURE SENSOR RESISTANCE***

| Temperature °F (°C) | Ohms |
|---|---|
| 68 (20) | 2210-2690 |
| 176 (80) | 290-354 |

**Deceleration Vacuum Switch** – Connect vacuum pump to device box nipple. Disconnect vacuum switch connector. Apply vacuum and check for continuity between switch terminals. Above 10.6 in. Hg, there should be continuity.

**Engine Speed Sensor** – Check for continuity between ignition negative coil terminal and appropriate FCU terminal. If continuity exists, sensor is functioning. If continuity does not exist, repair as necessary.

**Jet Mixture Solenoid Valve (JMSV) – 1)** Warm engine to normal operating temperature, run engine at idle. Connect dwell meter (4-cylinder range) to Yellow/Green terminal of test connector. *See Fig. 2.* Reading should be within 27-45 degrees.

**2)** Gradually increase engine speed to more than 4000 RPM. Check that dwell meter indicates approximately 18 degrees. If not within specification, check oxygen sensor, FCU and wiring harness of feedback system. Adjust mixture if necessary. Refer to TUNE-UP PROCEDURES section.

**3)** Using a jumper wire, ground Yellow/Green terminal of test connector. Engine speed should increase. If engine speed does not increase, check for dirty JMSV or carburetor.

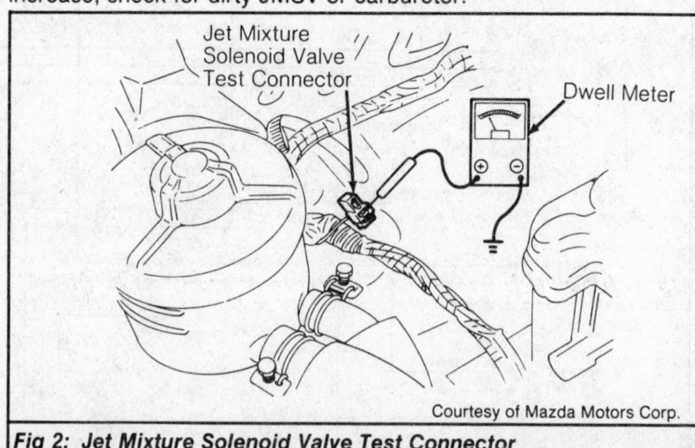
Jet Mixture Solenoid Valve Test Connector
Dwell Meter
Courtesy of Mazda Motors Corp.

***Fig 2: Jet Mixture Solenoid Valve Test Connector***

**Oxygen Sensor** – Warm engine until coolant temperature is 185-205°F (85-95°C). Remove oxygen sensor connector and connect voltmeter. With engine above 1300 RPM, measure output voltage. Voltage should be .1-.8 volt. If not, replace oxygen sensor.

**Throttle Position Sensor – 1)** Before checking TPS voltage, ensure that throttle cable is properly adjusted and that idle speed is 825 RPM.

**2)** Turn ignition switch to "ON" position. Connect voltmeter to Yellow/Red terminal of TPS connector (located on side of air cleaner housing). *See Fig. 3.*

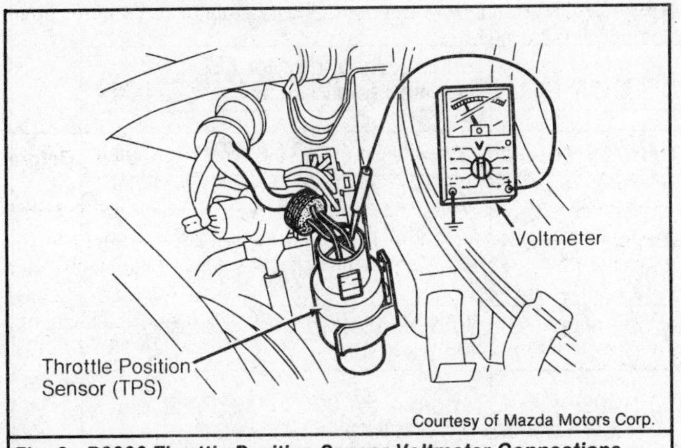
Voltmeter
Throttle Position
Sensor (TPS)
Courtesy of Mazda Motors Corp.

***Fig. 3: B2600 Throttle Position Sensor Voltmeter Connections***

**3)** Check voltage reading while slowly opening and closing throttle valve. See B2600 THROTTLE POSITION SENSOR VOLTAGE SPECIFICATIONS table.

**4)** If voltage is not to specification, adjust TPS setting by turning adjusting screw. *See Fig. 5.* If TPS cannot be adjusted to specifications, replace TPS unit.

***B2600 THROTTLE POSITION SENSOR VOLTAGE SPECIFICATIONS***

| Throttle Position | Voltage |
|---|---|
| Full Throttle | 4.7-5.1 |
| Idle Position | .4-.6 |

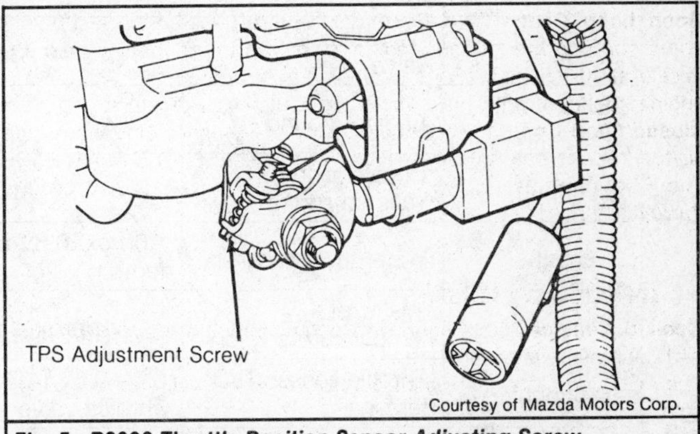
TPS Adjustment Screw
Courtesy of Mazda Motors Corp.

***Fig. 5: B2600 Throttle Position Sensor Adjusting Screw***

| Terminal | Connection to | Voltage with ignition ON | Voltage with various conditions |
|---|---|---|---|
| 1A (output) | No.1 EGR solenoid valve | Approx. 12V (at normal operating temp.) | Approx. 12V at idle |
| 1B (ground) | | 0V | 0V at idle |
| 1C (input) | No. 1 EGR vacuum switch | 0—0.6V | 0—0.6V at idle<br>Approx. 12V momentarily during quick acceleration above 1,500 rpm |
| 1D (input) | Ignition coil | Approx. 0.9V | Engine signal monitor auto range LEDs will pulsate rapidly at idle |
| 1E (output) | No. 2 EGR solenoid valve | 0—0.6V at operating temperature | 0—0.6 V at idle<br>Approx. 12V momentarily during quick acceleration above 1,500 rpm |
| 1F (input) | Battery | Approx. 12V | Approx. 12V at idle |
| 1H (output) | EEC solenoid valve | 0V | Approx. 12V at idle |
| 1J (input) | Water temp. switch | 0V (12—13V: below 17°C (63°F)) | 0V (12—13V: below 17°C (63°F)) at idle |
| 1K (input) | No. 2 EGR vacuum switch (M/T only) | Approx. 12V | 0—0.6V at idle |
| 1L (output) | No. 3 AIS solenoid valve | 0—0.6V | 0V at idle |

Courtesy of Mazda Motors Corp.

***Fig. 4: B2600 ECU & FCU Test Voltage Table (Part 1 of 2)***

| Terminal | Connection to | Voltage with ignition ON | Voltage with various conditions |
|---|---|---|---|
| 2A | Battery | 12V | 12—15V at idle |
| 2B (power supply) | Air vent solenoid valve | Approx. 12V | 12—15V at idle |
| 2C (input) | Ignition coil (—) terminal | Approx. 0.9V | Engine signal monitor LEDs will pulsate rapidly at idle |
| 2D (power supply) | Air vent solenoid valve | Approx. 12V | 12—15V at idle |
| 2E (ground) 2F | Engine ground | 0V | 0V at idle |
| 2H (input) | Deceleration vacuum switch | Approx. 10V | 0—1V at idle |
| 2I (input) | Water thermo sensor | Approx. 0.6V (normal operating temp.) | Approx. 0.6V (normal operating temp.) at idle |
| 2J (input) | Intake air temperature sensor | Approx. 1V (60°C (140°F)) | Approx. 1V (60°C (140°F)) at idle |
| 2K (input) | Throttle sensor TVO terminal | 0.4—0.6V (4.7—5.1V: Throttle valve full open) | 0.4—0.6V at idle |
| 2L (input) | Throttle sensor Vref terminal | Approx. 5V | Approx. 5V at idle |
| 2M (input) | $O_2$ sensor | 0V | 0—1V at idle |
| 2N (ground) | Water thermo sensor<br>Intake air temp. sensor<br>Throttle sensor | 0V | 0V at idle |
| 3A (output) | A/C cut relay | 0—0.6V | 0—0.6V at idle |
| 3B (output) | Enrichment solenoid valve | Approx. 12V | 12—15V at idle<br>Approx. 5V during quick acceleration |
| 3C (output) | Distributor vacuum solenoid valve | 0V | 0V at idle<br>13—15V at above 1,300 rpm |
| 3D (output) | No. 1 AIS solenoid valve | 0—0.6V (normal operating temp.) | 11—13V at idle; after warm up 0.6V above 1,100 rpm with 280 mmHg (11 in Hg) vacuum applied to the deceleration vacuum switch) |
| 3F (output) | Idle-up solenoid valve | 0—0.6 V | 13—15V 2,000 rpm with A/C switch ON |
| 3G (output) | Jet mixture solenoid valve | Approx. 12V | Engine signal monitor LEDs will pulsate rapidly at idle |
| 3H (output) | Slow fuel cut solenoid valve | 0—0.6V | 0—0.6V at idle<br>Approx 12V above 1,900 rpm with 280 mmHg (11 inHg) vacuum applied to the deceleration vacuum switch |

Connector

Feedback control unit

| 2M | 2K | 2I | | 2E | 2C | 2A | | 3G | | 3C | 3A |
|---|---|---|---|---|---|---|---|---|---|---|---|
| 2N | 2L | 2J | 2H | 2F | 2D | 2B | | 3H | 3F | 3D | 3B |

Emission control unit

| 1K | 1I | | 1E | 1C | 1A |
|---|---|---|---|---|---|
| 1L | 1J | 1H | 1F | 1D | 1B |

Courtesy of Mazda Motors Corp.

*Fig. 6: B2600 ECU & FCU Test Voltage Table (Part 2 of 2)*

# 1988 COMPUTERIZED ENGINE CONTROLS
## Mazda Feedback Carburetor System (Cont.)

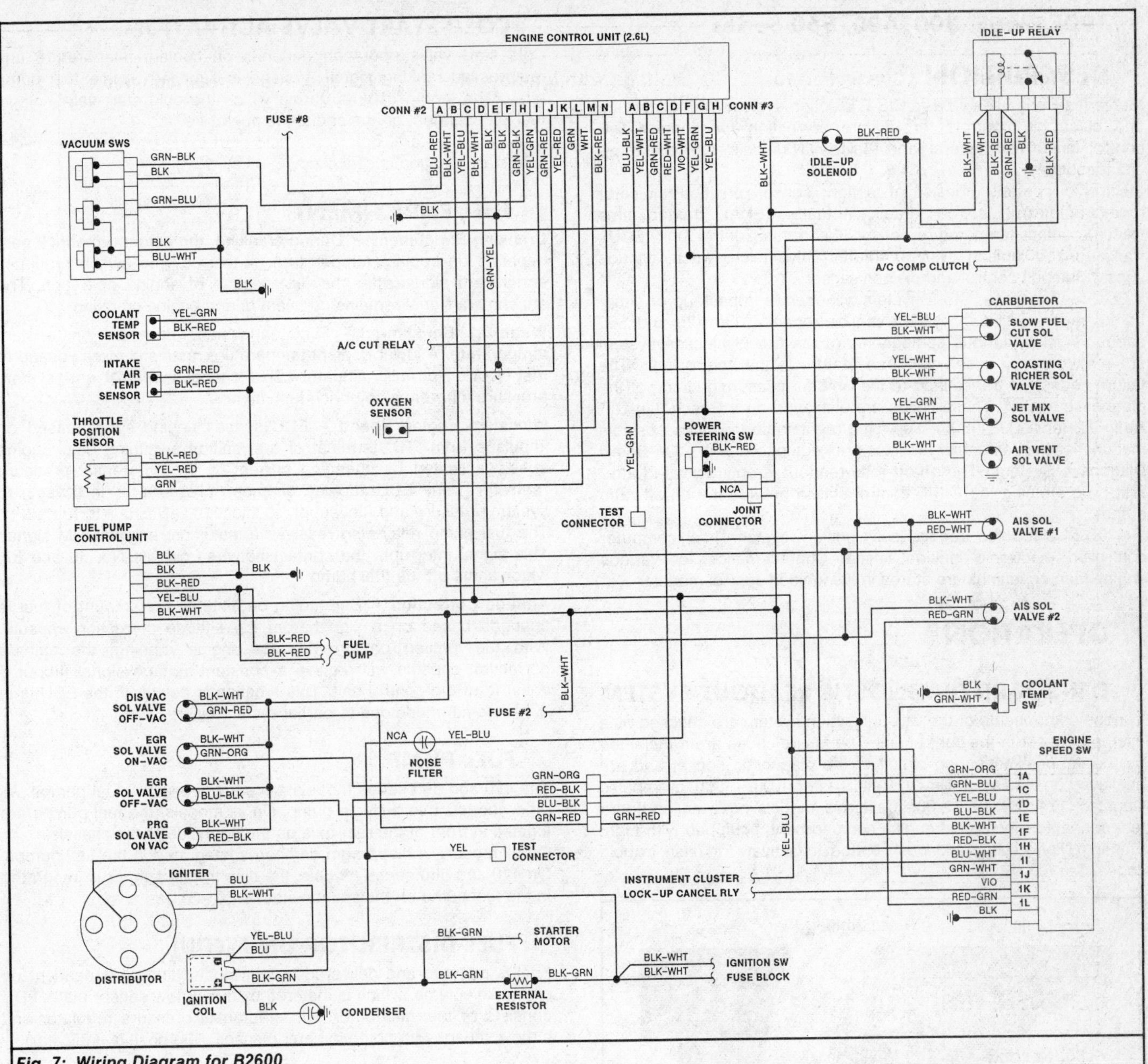

ENGINE CONTROL UNIT (2.6L)
CONN #2
CONN #3
IDLE-UP RELAY
FUSE #8
VACUUM SWS
IDLE-UP SOLENOID
A/C COMP CLUTCH
CARBURETOR
SLOW FUEL CUT SOL VALVE
COASTING RICHER SOL VALVE
JET MIX SOL VALVE
AIR VENT SOL VALVE
COOLANT TEMP SENSOR
INTAKE AIR TEMP SENSOR
A/C CUT RELAY
OXYGEN SENSOR
THROTTLE POSITION SENSOR
POWER STEERING SW
TEST CONNECTOR
JOINT CONNECTOR
AIS SOL VALVE #1
AIS SOL VALVE #2
FUEL PUMP CONTROL UNIT
FUEL PUMP
DIS VAC SOL VALVE OFF-VAC
FUSE #2
COOLANT TEMP SW
EGR SOL VALVE ON-VAC
NOISE FILTER
ENGINE SPEED SW
EGR SOL VALVE OFF-VAC
PRG SOL VALVE ON VAC
IGNITER
INSTRUMENT CLUSTER
LOCK-UP CANCEL RLY
STARTER MOTOR
IGNITION SW FUSE BLOCK
DISTRIBUTOR
EXTERNAL RESISTOR
IGNITION COIL
CONDENSER


*Fig. 7: Wiring Diagram for B2600*

# 1988 COMPUTERIZED ENGINE CONTROLS
# Mercedes-Benz CIS-E System

### 190E, 260E, 300, 420, 560 Series

## DESCRIPTION

Mercedes-Benz uses a basic CIS-E injection system for fuel delivery and electronic controls for mixture correction functions. CIS-E control units for Federal and California models are not interchangeable.

Electronic controls consist of airflow sensor position indicator (potentiometer), Electro-Hydraulic Actuator (EHA), thermo time switch, coolant temperature sensor, Electronic Control Unit (ECU), transistorized ignition system, throttle valve microswitch, altitude sensor, lambda control and oxygen sensor.

If ECU malfunctions, CIS-E system will operate in back-up or "limp-home" mode until fuel system can be repaired. On 420 and 560 series vehicles, various components of the CIS-E injection system are monitored by a self-diagnosis feature in the control unit. The failure codes are transmitted to the lambda measuring circuit of the diagnostic socket. These codes are displayed on a Bosch "On-Off" Ratio Tester (KDJE-P600). The fixed on-off ratio indicates possible malfunctions. California models are equipped with "On-Board Diagnostic System". The on-off ratio readout is only activated after first programming the CIS-E control unit to provide the on-off ratio output.

The EZL electronic breakerless ignition system has computer controlled electronic ignition timing. Characteristics for various engine load conditions are stored in the ignition control module.

## OPERATION

### ON-BOARD DIAGNOSTIC READOUT SYSTEM

Various components of the CIS-E injection system are checked by a microprocessor in the control unit. The failure codes are transmitted by the lambda measuring circuit of the diagnostic socket and are displayed on the Bosch On-Off Ratio Tester (KDJE-P600) or Impulse Counter (124 589 19 21 00). California models have an on-board test connector, located in engine compartment, equipped with Light Emitting Diode (LED) and push button to activate or flash trouble codes. *See Fig. 1.*

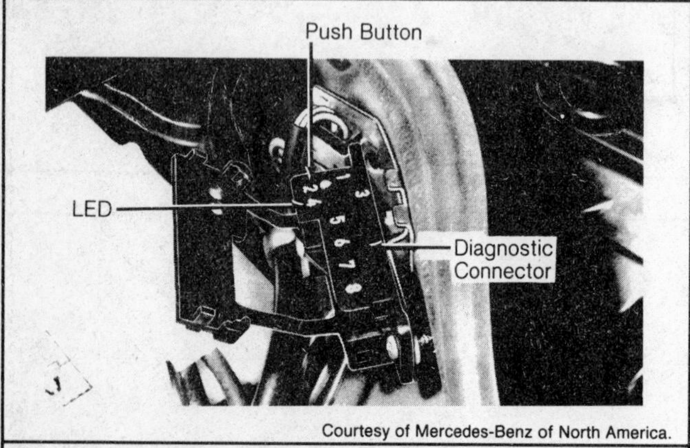
Push Button
LED
Diagnostic Connector

Courtesy of Mercedes-Benz of North America.

***Fig. 1: On-Board Diagnostic Connector (California)***

### FUEL PUMP RELAY

The fuel pump relay on 560SL models is located behind the glove compartment. For 420 and all other 560 series, the relay is located on the left rear side of the engine compartment, on the relay panel. For 190E, 260E and 300 series, the fuel pump relay is located in the engine compartment on the right rear firewall.

The fuel pump relay also controls: cold start valve activation, RPM limitation and kick-down shutoff.

### COLD START VALVE ACTIVATION

Cold start valve operation depends on coolant temperature and requires a cranking signal. Voltage is supplied by the fuel pump relay. The length of time during which the cold start valve injects fuel is dependent on the coolant temperature.

If the engine starts before the cold start valve completes its cycle, cold start injection is cancelled.

### FUEL ENRICHMENT

**Cranking Enrichment** – During cranking, the amount of enrichment depends on coolant temperature. A thermo time switch regulates enrichment signal after the first second of engine operation. The enrichment signal remains constant during engine cranking.

**Warm-Up Enrichment** – Fuel enrichment depends on coolant temperature. A lower coolant temperature results in more voltage to the electro-hydraulic actuator. This changes control and system pressure differential to enrich fuel mixture.

**Maximum Engine Speed** – ECU senses engine speed based on impulses from "TD" terminal of the ignition switching unit. Engine speed is limited by changing current to the differential pressure regulator from ECU. Lower chamber pressure is increased to system pressure and fuel supply to injection valves is interrupted.

The fuel pump relay also receives a maximum engine RPM signal. This signal interrupts the contact between circuits No. 30 and 87, which shuts off the fuel pump.

**Altitude Correction** – Depending on altitude, the amount of fuel is changed based on a signal from the altitude correction capsule. With the ignition on or with the engine running, the altitude correction capsule will receive a constant voltage signal (about 5 volts) from the control unit. This function is deleted if the ECU is in "Limp Home" mode due to partial system failure.

### FUEL PUMP

The 420 and 560 series models are equipped with 2 fuel pumps. All other models use a single pump. On all models, the fuel pumps are located in front of the rear axle on the right side of the chassis.

On all models, a diaphragm damper is integrated in the fuel pumps. On 420 and 560 series models, the diaphragm damper is integrated in the fuel pump on the suction side.

### FUEL DISTRIBUTOR UNIT (FDU)

Fuel is metered and delivered to individual cylinders dependent on air intake volume, which is metered by the airflow sensor plate. FDU consists of fuel distributor with differential pressure regulator and airflow sensor with potentiometer (sensor plate position indicator).

### COOLANT TEMPERATURE SENSOR

The coolant temperature sensor is located on the cylinder head. On Federal models, sensor has a 2-pin connector, one for Electronic Ignition System (EZL) and one for the CIS-E injection system. On California models, sensor has 4-pin connector, 2 for ground connections (CIS-E control unit and engine ground) and one connection each for the temperature signals to the CIS-E control unit and the EZL module.

### ELECTRONIC CONTROL UNIT (ECU)

On 190E, 260E and other 300 models, the ECU is located on right side of engine, behind the battery in engine compartment. On 300SE, 300SEL, 420 and 560 sedan models, ECU is located behind the right kick panel. On 560SL models, ECU is located under the right kick panel on the passenger side.

The ignition switch supplies battery voltage to the ECU. A voltage protection relay prevents current surges from damaging the ECU.

The ECU utilizes various input signals to control fuel delivery and exhaust emissions. Input signals control output current to the differential pressure regulator, and idle speed air valve.

# 1988 COMPUTERIZED ENGINE CONTROLS
## Mercedes-Benz CIS-E System (Cont.)

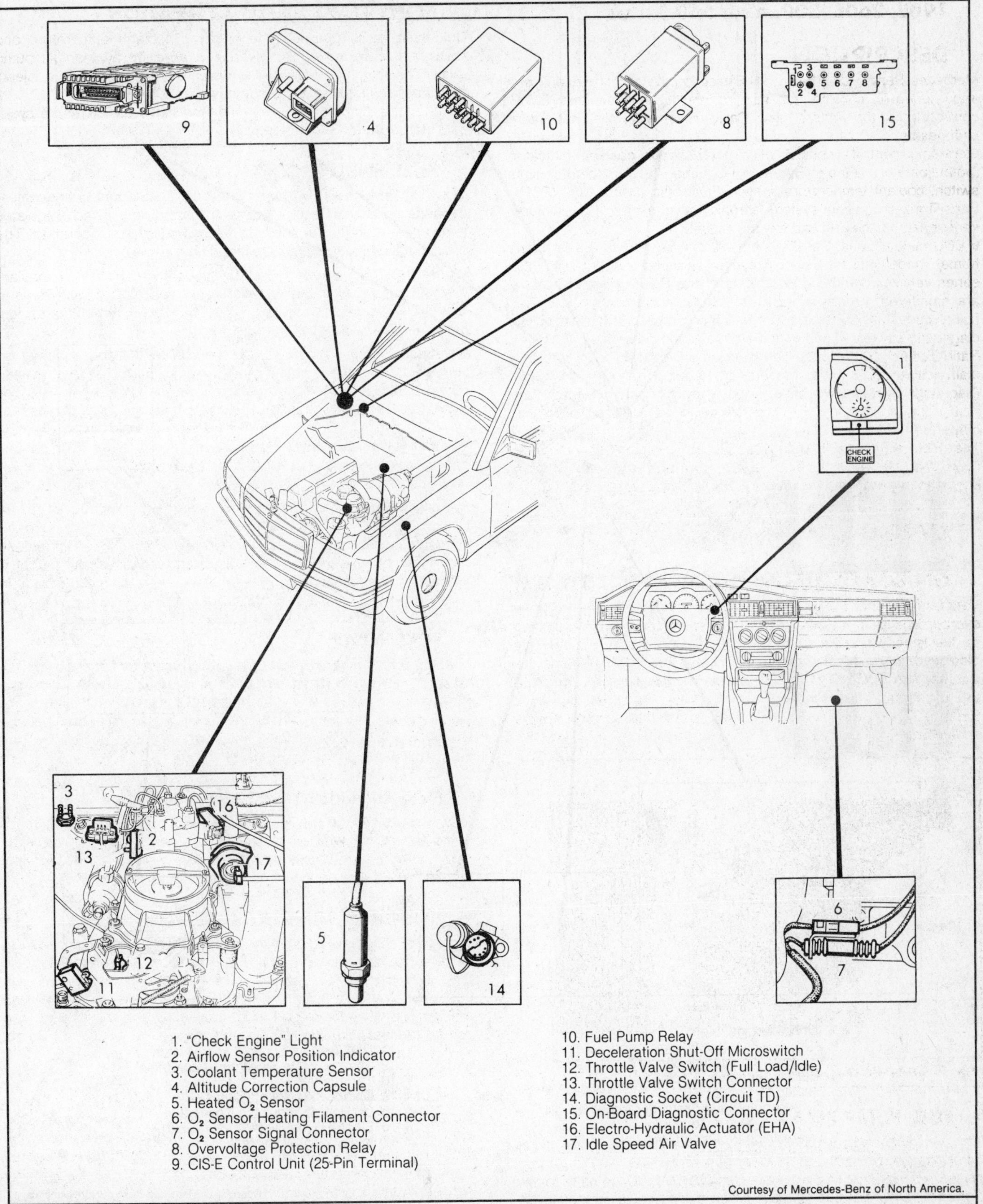
9
4
10
8
15
1
CHECK ENGINE
3
16
2
13
17
12
11
5
14
6
7
1. "Check Engine" Light
2. Airflow Sensor Position Indicator
3. Coolant Temperature Sensor
4. Altitude Correction Capsule
5. Heated $O_2$ Sensor
6. $O_2$ Sensor Heating Filament Connector
7. $O_2$ Sensor Signal Connector
8. Overvoltage Protection Relay
9. CIS-E Control Unit (25-Pin Terminal)
10. Fuel Pump Relay
11. Deceleration Shut-Off Microswitch
12. Throttle Valve Switch (Full Load/Idle)
13. Throttle Valve Switch Connector
14. Diagnostic Socket (Circuit TD)
15. On-Board Diagnostic Connector
16. Electro-Hydraulic Actuator (EHA)
17. Idle Speed Air Valve

Courtesy of Mercedes-Benz of North America.

*Fig. 2: 190E 2.3L Component Locations*

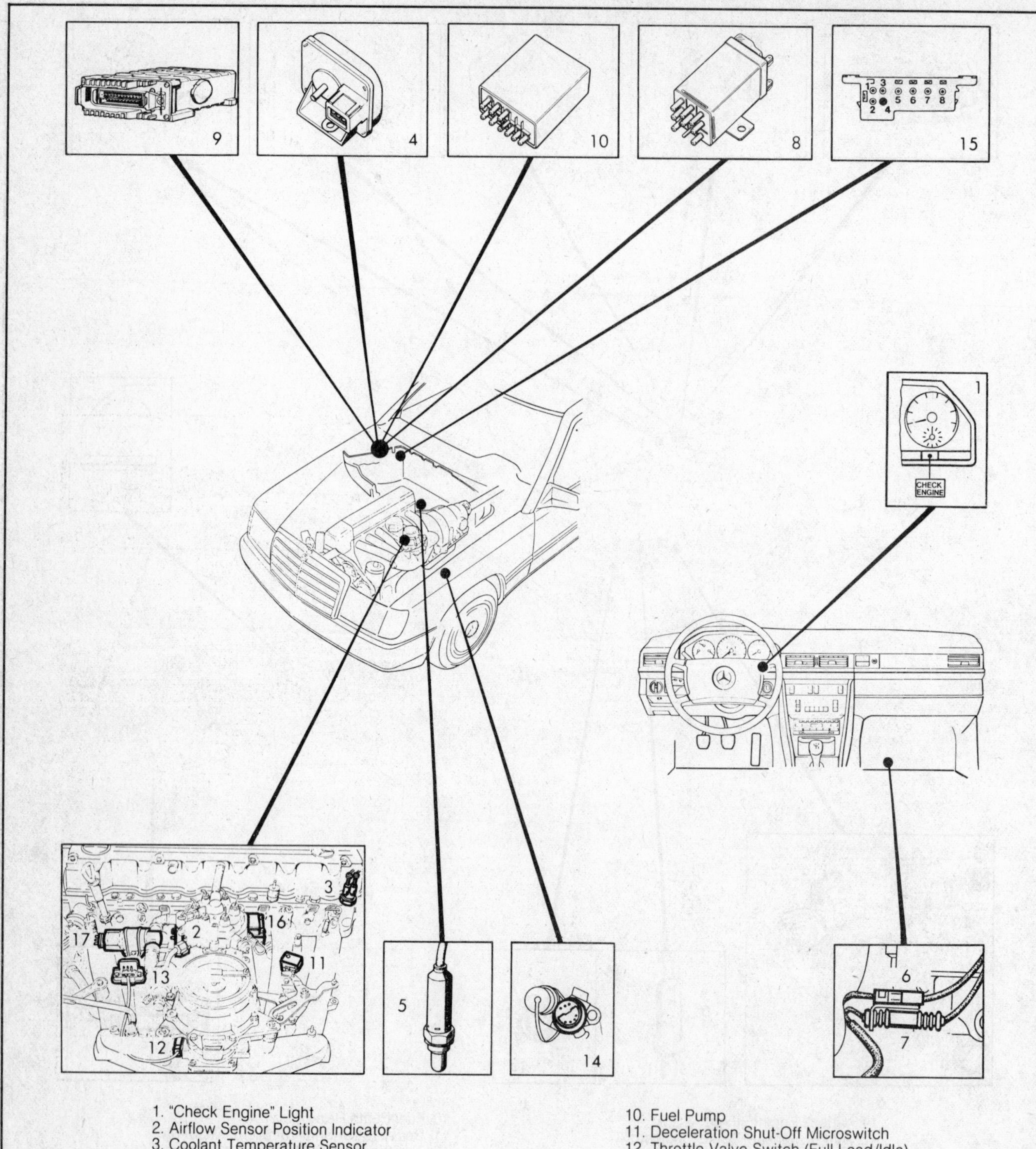
9
4
10
8
15
1
CHECK ENGINE
3
16
17
2
11
13
12
5
14
6
7

1. "Check Engine" Light
2. Airflow Sensor Position Indicator
3. Coolant Temperature Sensor
4. Altitude Correction Capsule
5. Heated $O_2$ Sensor
6. $O_2$ Sensor Heating Filament Connector
7. $O_2$ Sensor Signal Connector
8. Overvoltage Protection Relay
9. CIS-E Control Unit
10. Fuel Pump
11. Deceleration Shut-Off Microswitch
12. Throttle Valve Switch (Full Load/Idle)
13. Throttle Valve Switch Connector
14. Diagnostic Socket (Circuit TD)
15. On-Board Diagnostic Connector
16. Electro-Hydraulic Actuator (EHA)
17. Idle Speed Air Valve

Courtesy of Mercedes-Benz of North America.

***Fig. 3: 190E 2.6L, 260E, 300CE, 300E & 300TE Component Locations***

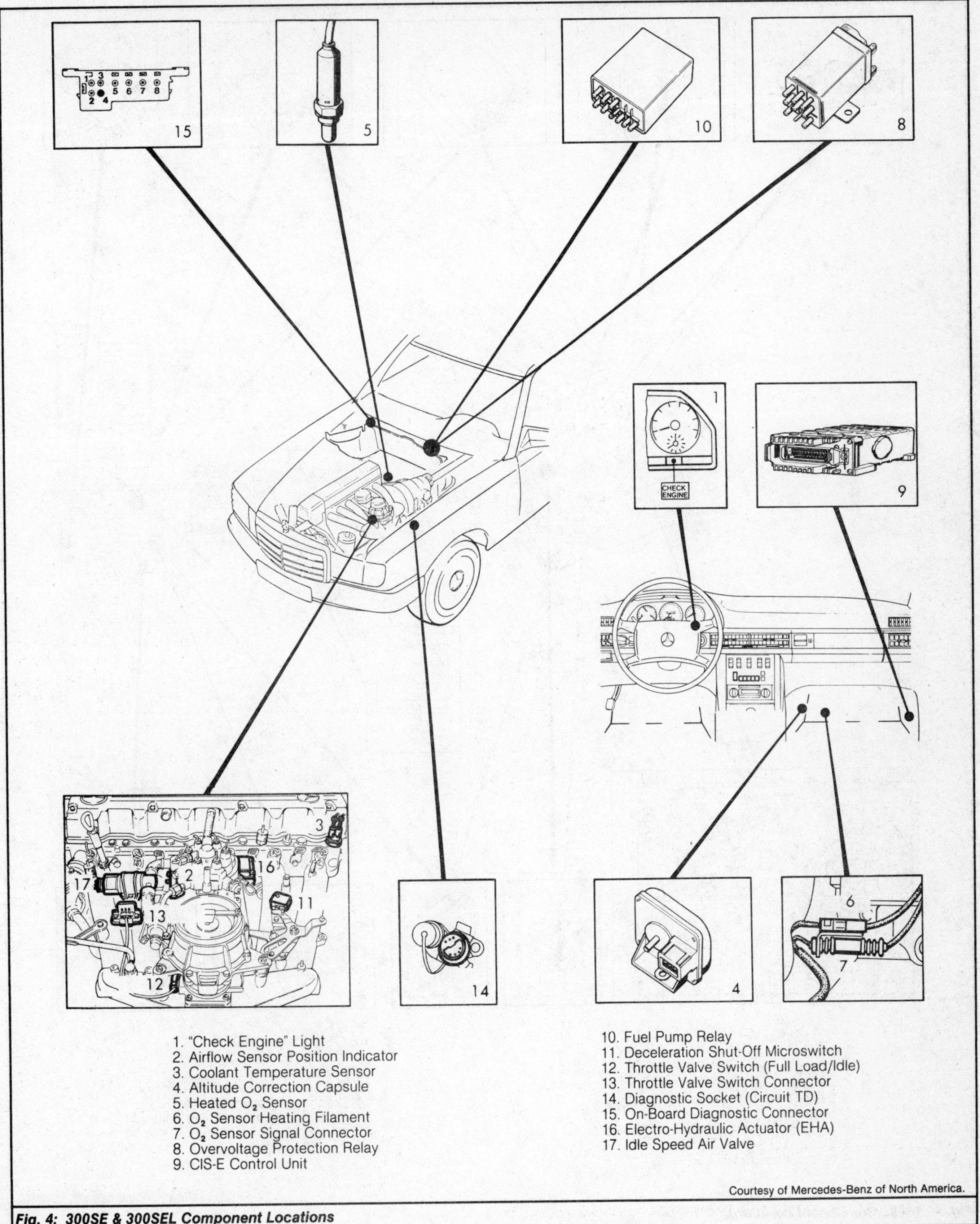
15
5
10
8
1
CHECK ENGINE
9
3
2
16
17
11
13
12
14
4
6
7
1. "Check Engine" Light
2. Airflow Sensor Position Indicator
3. Coolant Temperature Sensor
4. Altitude Correction Capsule
5. Heated $O_2$ Sensor
6. $O_2$ Sensor Heating Filament
7. $O_2$ Sensor Signal Connector
8. Overvoltage Protection Relay
9. CIS-E Control Unit
10. Fuel Pump Relay
11. Deceleration Shut-Off Microswitch
12. Throttle Valve Switch (Full Load/Idle)
13. Throttle Valve Switch Connector
14. Diagnostic Socket (Circuit TD)
15. On-Board Diagnostic Connector
16. Electro-Hydraulic Actuator (EHA)
17. Idle Speed Air Valve
Courtesy of Mercedes-Benz of North America.

***Fig. 4: 300SE & 300SEL Component Locations***

# 1988 COMPUTERIZED ENGINE CONTROLS
## Mercedes-Benz CIS-E System (Cont.)

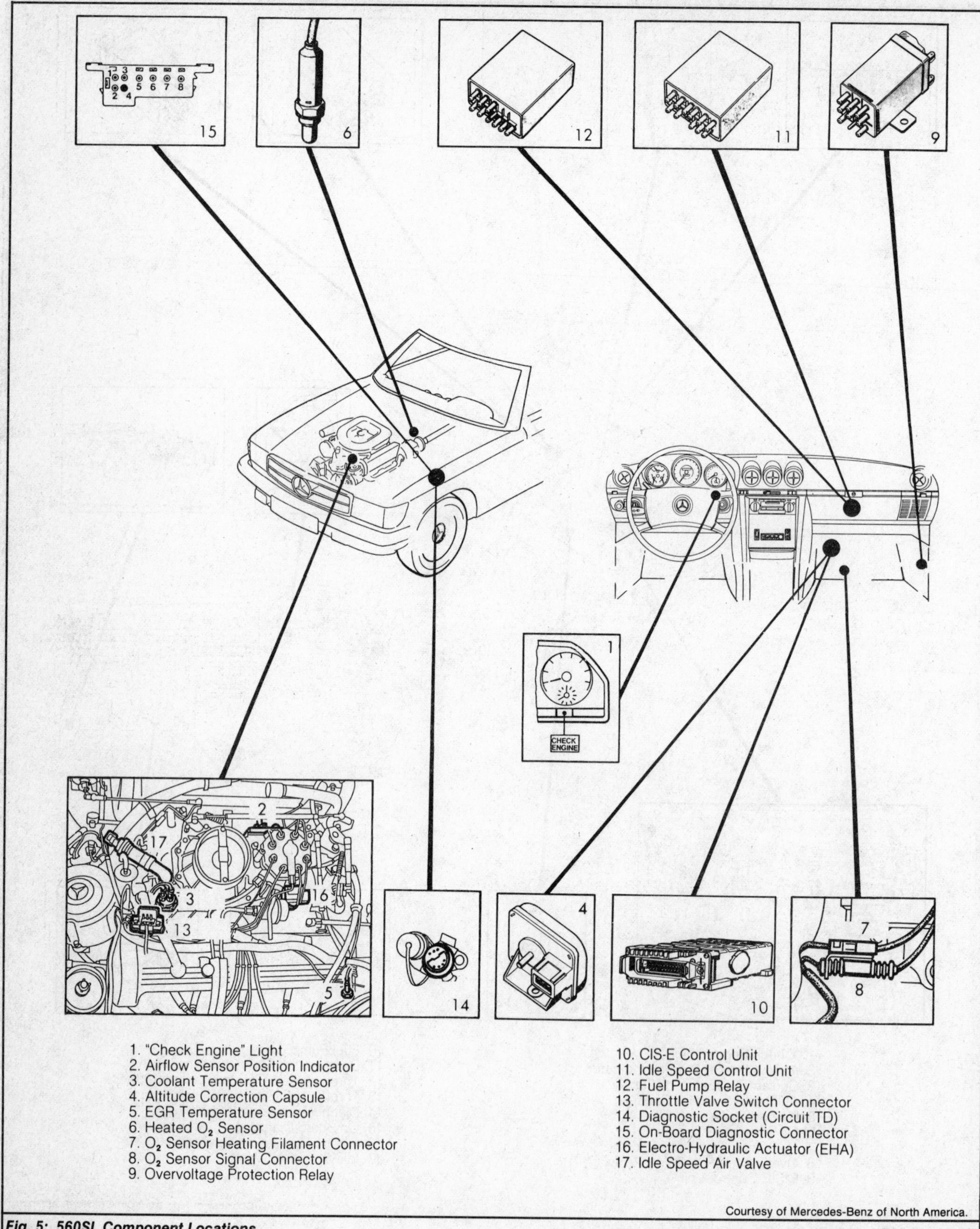
CHECK ENGINE

1. "Check Engine" Light
2. Airflow Sensor Position Indicator
3. Coolant Temperature Sensor
4. Altitude Correction Capsule
5. EGR Temperature Sensor
6. Heated $O_2$ Sensor
7. $O_2$ Sensor Heating Filament Connector
8. $O_2$ Sensor Signal Connector
9. Overvoltage Protection Relay
10. CIS-E Control Unit
11. Idle Speed Control Unit
12. Fuel Pump Relay
13. Throttle Valve Switch Connector
14. Diagnostic Socket (Circuit TD)
15. On-Board Diagnostic Connector
16. Electro-Hydraulic Actuator (EHA)
17. Idle Speed Air Valve

Courtesy of Mercedes-Benz of North America.

***Fig. 5: 560SL Component Locations***

# 1988 COMPUTERIZED ENGINE CONTROLS
## Mercedes-Benz CIS-E System (Cont.)

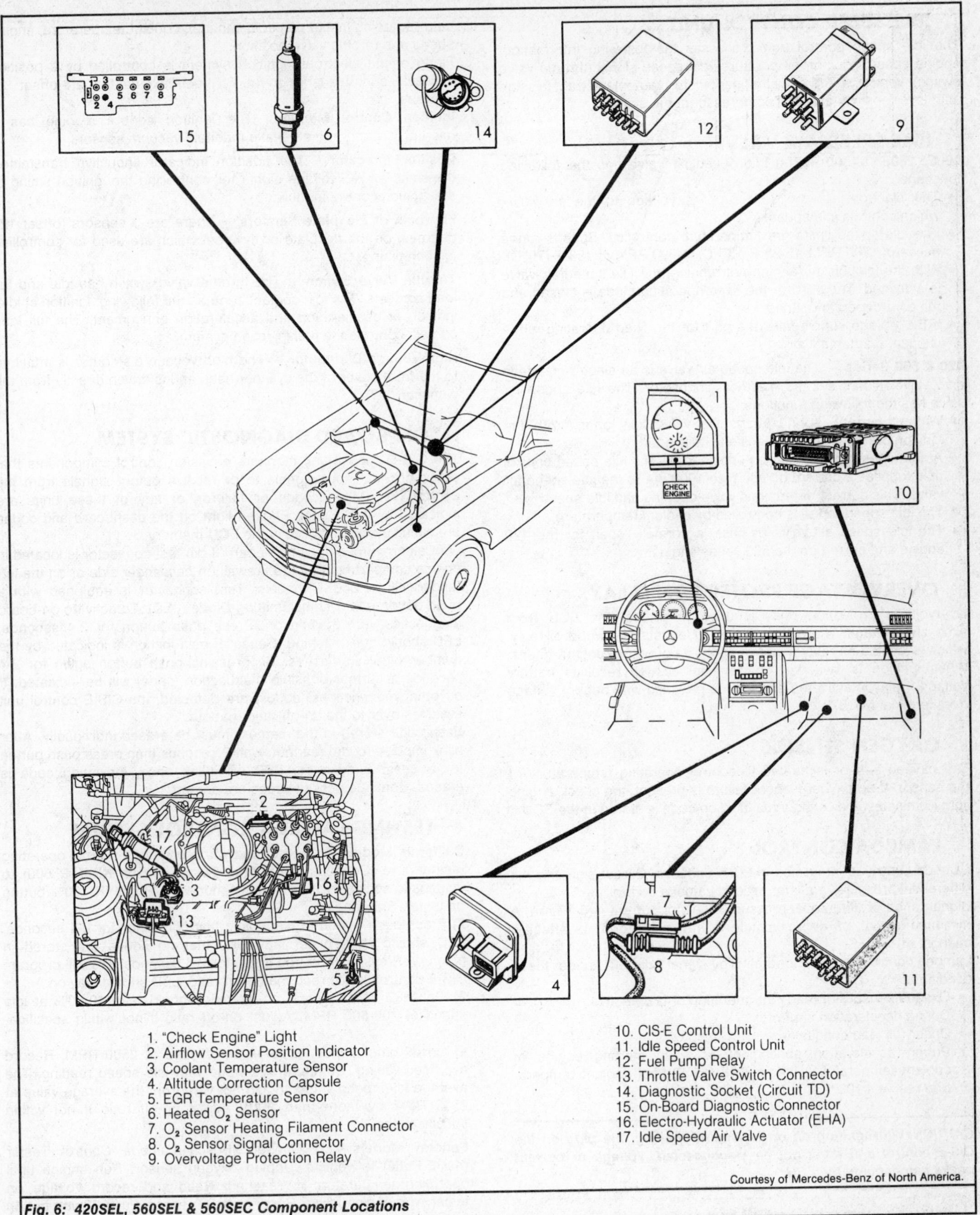

15
6
14
12
9
1
CHECK ENGINE
10
2
17
3
13
16
5
4
7
8
11


1. "Check Engine" Light
2. Airflow Sensor Position Indicator
3. Coolant Temperature Sensor
4. Altitude Correction Capsule
5. EGR Temperature Sensor
6. Heated $O_2$ Sensor
7. $O_2$ Sensor Heating Filament Connector
8. $O_2$ Sensor Signal Connector
9. Overvoltage Protection Relay
10. CIS-E Control Unit
11. Idle Speed Control Unit
12. Fuel Pump Relay
13. Throttle Valve Switch Connector
14. Diagnostic Socket (Circuit TD)
15. On-Board Diagnostic Connector
16. Electro-Hydraulic Actuator (EHA)
17. Idle Speed Air Valve

Courtesy of Mercedes-Benz of North America.

**Fig. 6: 420SEL, 560SEL & 560SEC Component Locations**

## IDLE SPEED CONTROL UNIT

The idle speed control unit processes the following information: engine speed, coolant temperature, idle speed signal (throttle valve switch), vehicle speed signal (speedometer), automatic transmission shift lever position and A/C compressor cut-in signal.

## IDLE SPEED AIR VALVE

**190E, 260E & 300** – The idle speed air valve has the following functions:

- The electronic control unit supplies voltage to the air valve, which controls idle speed.
- The idle speed limits are temperature controlled. Speeds range between 1200 RPM at -23°F (-30°C) to 900 RPM at 158°F (70°C).
- With the ignition on (engine not running) the idle speed air valve is activated. The port for the fixed operating mode is closed and the control port is opened.
- If the voltage supply fails, the port for the fixed operating mode is opened automatically.

**420 & 560 Series** – The idle speed air valve is an electro-magnetic disc valve. It has a 2-pin electrical connector. The idle speed air valve has the following functions:

- Without current, spring keeps the valve fully open. With the ignition turned on, the valve is also fully open.
- At idle speed (depending on engine load), the idle speed control unit supplies a current of less than 1000 mA to the idle speed air valve. This current determines valve opening and idle speed.
- The idle speed range is controlled by coolant temperature.
- The idle speed air valve by-pass is normally open for the 420 engine and closed on the 560 series engine.

## OVERVOLTAGE PROTECTION RELAY

Overvoltage protection relay is used to protect the ECU from excessive voltage. There is a 10-amp fuse installed on top of relay, which is located on relay board at right side of engine compartment. When ignition is switched on, terminal No. 15 receives battery voltage. Relay is activated and ECU is provided with battery voltage from terminal No. 87.

## OXYGEN SENSOR

The oxygen sensor is heated to control operating temperature of the sensor. If an oxygen sensor failure is present, the check engine light illuminates, indicating a malfunction code is stored in the ECU.

## LAMBDA CONTROL

Lambda control is integrated in ECU functions. Output signal to the differential pressure regulator used in Lambda control.

Signal range of differential pressure regulator current is 0-16 mA. A minimum signal of approximately 8 mA is needed to affect a change.

Lambda control is made inoperative by signal from ECU under these conditions:

- Oxygen sensor not ready for operation or is defective.
- During deceleration shut-off.
- Under full load conditions.
- During acceleration enrichment or when starting engine at coolant temperatures below 60°F (15°C) until coolant temperature reaches 105°F (40°C).

---

***CAUTION: With ignition on or the engine running, the plug on the CIS-E control unit must not be disconnected. Voltage or current peaks can damage the ECU.***

---

## EZL IGNITION OPERATION

The ignition control module stores ignition specifications for typical engine operating conditions and outputs signals based on input data regarding intake manifold vacuum, coolant temperature, engine speed and throttle valve position.

Firing of the electronic ignition system is controlled by a position indicator, and 3 sensors on the flywheel/flexplate that are offset 120 degrees.

**Ignition Control Module** – The ignition control module has a microprocessor, and an intake manifold vacuum sensor.

**Position Indicator** – The position indicator (inductive transmitter) transmits an AC voltage signal for controlling the ignition timing to the ignition control module.

**Flywheel or Flexplate Sensors** – There are 3 sensors (offset 120 degrees) on the flexplate or flywheel which are used for controlling ignition timing.

**Throttle Valve Switch** – The throttle valve switch has idle and full load contacts. The idle contact controls the following: ignition at idle, ignition at deceleration and acceleration enrichment. The full load contact controls the fuel injection system.

**High Voltage Distributor** – The high voltage distributor is attached to the front cover of the cylinder head and is driven directly from the camshaft.

## ON-BOARD DIAGNOSTIC SYSTEM

The CIS-E control unit monitors emission control components that either provide input signals to or receive output signals from the control unit. Malfunctions or failures of any of these units are indicated by the "Check Engine" light on the dashboard and codes are simultaneously stored in the ECU memory.

On California models, an on-board 8-pin test connector is located in engine compartment by the firewall on passenger side or on the left fenderwell on 560SL models. Test connector is equipped with a push button and a Light Emitting Diode (LED). To activate on-board diagnostics, turn ignition on. Press push button for 2-4 seconds, LED should start flashing. Cause of malfunction is indicated by the number of blinks/flashes. By pressing push button again for 2-4 seconds, a further possible malfunction (code) will be indicated. If no other malfunctions (codes) are detected, the CIS-E control unit switches over to the on-off ratio readout.

Each code stored in the memory must be erased individually. After blink impulse (code) readout, wait 2 seconds then press push button for at least 6 seconds. LED will blink once, indicating code is erased. Continue until all codes are erased.

## TESTING LAMBDA CONTROL SYSTEM

**California Models – 1)** Start and warm engine to normal operating temperature. Connect on-off ratio Tester (Bosch KDJE-P 600) to diagnostic socket located on left fenderwell. Press IR 100% button on tester. Start engine.

**2)** Press push button in diagnostic test connector for 2-4 seconds. LED should blink once, indicating that no codes are stored in memory. Press push button again for 2-4 seconds, this will program CIS-E control unit to read the on-off ratio. LED should stay on.

**3)** On 190E (2.3L) series, on-off ratio should read 40-60% at idle speed of 700-800 RPM. Adjust on-off ratio if not within specifications.

**4)** On all other series, observe on-off ratio at 2500 RPM. Record average reading. Compare this value with idle speed reading. The average idle speed value should not vary from the average value at 2500 RPM by more than ±10. Adjust on-off ratio if not within specifications.

**Federal Models – 1)** Connect Bosch Lambda Control Tester (KDJE-P600) to vehicle. Unplug oxygen sensor. Run engine until operating temperature is reached. Read and record voltage on tester with engine idling. Reconnect $O_2$ sensor. Push 12-volt button on tester.

**2)** Set engine speed to 2000 RPM. If engine is at operating temperature, voltage reading should not vary from previously recorded voltage by more than 0.8 volts. If reading is correct, lambda control is working and test is complete

## TROUBLE SHOOTING

### MALFUNCTION DIAGNOSTIC CODES

| Trouble Code/No. of Flashes | Malfunctioning Component |
|---|---|
| 1 | No system malfunction |
| 2 | Throttle valve switch |
| 3 | Coolant temperature sensor |
| 4 | Airflow sensor position indicator |
| 5 | Oxygen sensor |
| 6 | Not used |
| 7 | TD signal |
| 8 | Altitude correction capsule |
| 9 | Electro-Hydraulic Actuator (EHA) |
| 10 | Throttle valve switch<br>Idle speed contact |
| 11 | Not used |
| 12 [1] | EGR temperature sensor |

[1] - California 420 & 560 series only.

## TESTING WITH IMPULSE COUNTER

***NOTE:** All testing made with Socket Box (124 589 33 63 00) connected to CIS-E control unit connector and multimeter/impulse counter connected to socket box. On California models, codes retrieved from on-board diagnostic are the same as indicated here, including testing procedures.*

**CODE 1** - Indicates no system malfunction.

**CODE 2 - Throttle Valve Switch - 1)** Turn ignition "OFF". Unplug CIS-E control unit connector. Connect ohmmeter lead between sockets No. 2 and No. 5 of socket box. *See Fig. 7*. With throttle at wide open position, ohmmeter should read less than 1 ohm resistance. If not, check wire harness.

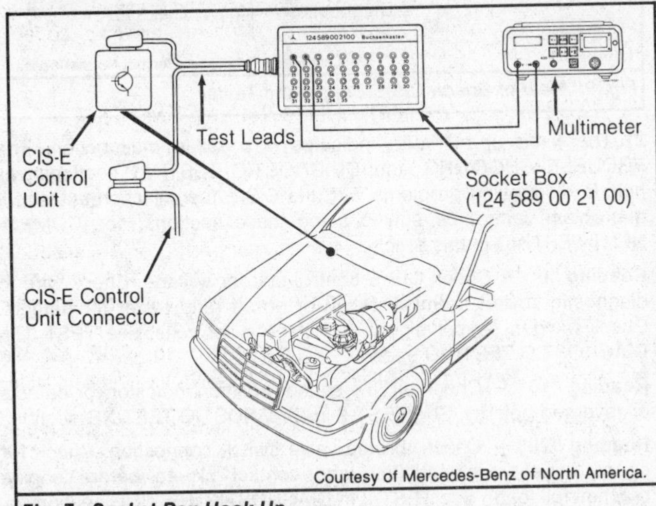
CIS-E Control Unit
Test Leads
Socket Box (124 589 00 21 00)
Multimeter
CIS-E Control Unit Connector
Courtesy of Mercedes-Benz of North America.

***Fig. 7: Socket Box Hook-Up***

**2)** Unplug throttle valve switch connector. With ohmmeter leads between sockets No. 5 and No. 3 of socket box, ohmmeter reading should be less than one ohm. With ohmmeter leads between ground and socket No. 2, ohmmeter reading should be less than one ohm. If not, repair open circuit.

**3)** With ohmmeter leads between pins No. 2 and 3 of throttle switch connector, ohmmeter should read infinite resistance. With throttle valve at wide open position, ohmmeter should read less than one ohm. Adjust or replace throttle valve switch if reading is out of range.

**CODE 3 - Coolant Temperature Sensor - 1)** Turn ignition to "OFF" position. Unplug CIS-E control unit connector. Check resistance between sockets No. 7 and No. 21. Resistance reading should be as indicated in table. *See Fig. 8*. If not okay, check wiring.

**2)** Unplug coolant temperature sensor connector. Measure resistance between any 2 of the diagonally opposed terminals and compare resistance values from each internal sensor. Resistance reading should be as indicated in table. *See Fig. 8*. If not okay, replace sensor.

**3)** Check wiring harness continuity to CIS-E control unit. Resistance should be less than one ohm. If not okay, check for open circuit.

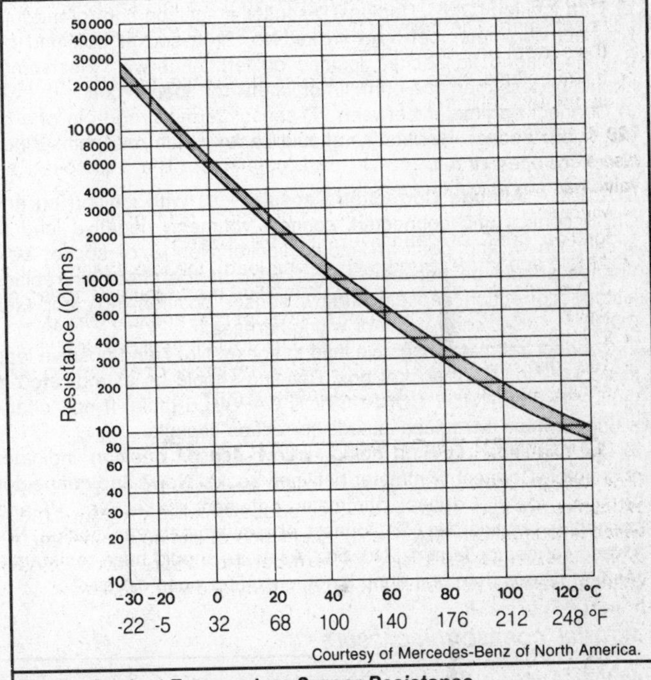
Resistance (Ohms)
50000
40000
30000
20000
10000
8000
6000
4000
3000
2000
1000
800
600
400
300
200
100
80
60
40
30
20
10
-30 -20 0 20 40 60 80 100 120 °C
-22 -5 32 68 100 140 176 212 248 °F
Courtesy of Mercedes-Benz of North America.

***Fig. 8: Coolant Temperature Sensor Resistance***

**CODE 4 - Airflow Sensor Position Indicator - 1)** CIS-E control unit connected, engine at idle and at operating temperature. Connect voltmeter negative lead to socket No. 7 and positive lead to socket No. 18 of socket box. Voltmeter should read 4.6-5.1 volts. If not within range, proceed to **CODE 8** testing procedures.

**2)** Connect negative voltmeter lead to socket No. 7 and positive lead to socket No. 17. Voltmeter should read 0.55 to 0.95 volt. If not, check or replace airflow sensor position indicator or CIS-E control unit.

**3)** Turn ignition "OFF". Unplug connector on airflow position indicator. Check resistance between pins one and 3 of connector. Ohmmeter should read 3600-4400 ohms. Move ohmmeter lead from pin 3 to pin 2 of connector and slowly deflect airflow sensor plate by hand. Resistance reading should increase continuously up to half of travel, then decrease again. If not, replace airflow sensor.

**4)** Measure airflow sensor position indicator wiring harness resistance. Connect ohmmeter between socket No. 7 and wiring harness connector terminal No. one. Connect ohmmeter to socket No. 18 and wiring harness connector terminal No. 3. Connect ohmmeter between socket No. 17 and wiring harness connector terminal No. 2. All these should have a resistance of less than one ohm. If not, check for open circuit.

**CODE 5 - Oxygen Sensor - 1)** With engine at operating temperature and at idle, CIS-E control unit connected. Connect voltmeter negative lead socket No. 7 and postive lead to No. 8 of socket box. Voltage should fluctuate between 0.1-0.9 volts. If not, check $O_2$ sensor wiring circuit.

**2)** Disconnect $O_2$ sensor signal connector and ground terminal. Connect voltmeter negative lead to socket No. 7 and $O_2$ sensor signal connector socket. With engine at idle, voltmeter reading should be greater than 450 millivolt. If not, replace $O_2$ sensor.
**3)** Turn ignition "OFF". Unplug CIS-E control unit connector. Connect ohmmeter between socket No. 7 and 8 of socket box. Ohmmeter should read infinity. Connect ohmmeter to socket No. 8 and $O_2$ wiring harness pin. Resistance should be less than one ohm. If not, check for open circuit.

**CODE 7 - TD-Signal - 1)** With engine at operating temperature and at idle, CIS-E control unit connected, connect voltmeter negative lead to socket No. 2 and positive lead to No. 25 of socket box. Voltmeter reading should be between 6-12 volts. If not, check wiring or replace ignition control module.
**2)** Turn ignition "OFF". Unplug TD-sensor at ignition control module. Connect ohmmeter between socket No. 2 on socket box and pin one on diagnostic socket, located on left fenderwell. Resistance should be less than one ohm. If not, check for open circuit.
**3)** Connect ohmmeter between TD-sensor terminal and pin one on diagnostic socket. Resistance should be less than one ohm. If not, check for open circuit.

**CODE 8 - Altitude Correction Capsule - 1)** With ignition on and CIS-E control unit connected, connect voltmeter negative lead to socket No. 7 and positive lead to socket No. 18 of socket box. Voltage should be between 4.6-5.1 volts. If not check or replace altitude correction capsule, airflow sensor position indicator (see **CODE 4**), CIS-E control unit or wiring harness.
**2)** Connect voltmeter negative lead to socket No. 7 and positive lead to socket No. 11 of socket box. Reading should be as indicated in table. See ALTITUDE CORRECTION CAPSULE table. If not, check wiring harness or replace altitude correction capsule.
**3)** Turn ignition "OFF". Unplug airflow sensor position indicator connector. Connect ohmmeter between socket No. 7 and connector terminal No. 3. Connect ohmmeter between socket No. 18 and connector terminal No. 2. Connect ohmmeter between socket No. 11 and connector terminal No. one. All these should have resistance reading of less than one ohm. If not, check for open circuit.

***ALTITUDE CORRECTION CAPSULE***

| Altitude Above Sea Level Ft. (M) | Barometric Pressure psi (kg/cm²) | Control Current Voltage |
|---|---|---|
| 0 (0) | 14.408 (1.0) | 3-5 |
| 3281 (1000) | 13.039 (.92) | 2-4 |
| 6562 (2000) | 11.531 (.81) | 1-3 |

**CODE 9 - Electro-Hydraulic Actuator (EHA) - 1)** Turn ignition "OFF". Unplug CIS-E control unit connector. Connect ohmmeter between sockets No. 10 and 12 on socket box. Resistance should be between 18.5-20.5 ohms. If not, check EHA.
**2)** Unplug EHA connector. Connect ohmmeter between pins No. one and 2 of EHA terminal. Resistance should be between 18.5-20.5 ohms. If not, replace EHA.
**3)** Check wiring harness circuit. Connect ohmmeter between socket No. 10 and wiring harness terminal No. 2. Connect ohmmeter between socket No. 12 and wiring harness terminal No. one. Both should have less than one ohm resistance. If not, check for open circuit.

**CODE 10 - Idle Speed Contact - 1)** Turn ignition "OFF". Unplug CIS-E control unit connector and EZL ignition control module connector (terminals marked 1-4). Connect ohmmeter between sockets No. 2 and 13 on socket box. Resistance should be less than one ohm. Depress accelerator pedal, resistance reading should show infinity. If not, check idle speed contact or wiring circuit.
**2)** Unplug throttle valve switch. Connect ohmmeter between terminals No. one and 2 of throttle switch. Resistance should be less than one ohm. Open throttle valve, resistance reading should show infinity. If not, adjust or replace throttle valve switch.
**3)** Check wiring harness. Connect ohmmeter between socket No. 13 on socket box and terminal No. one of wiring harness terminal. Connect ohmmeter between wiring harness terminal No. 2 and ground. Both should have a resistance of less than one ohm. If not, check for open circuit.

**CODE 12 - EGR Temperature Sensor, 420 & 560 (California Only) - 1)** Connect voltmeter negative lead to socket No. 7 and positive lead to socket No. 19 of socket box. With engine at operating temperature, raise engine speed to 4000 RPM for about one minute. Voltmeter should read less than 4.7 volts. If not, check EGR temperature sensor, EGR valve or wiring circuit.
**2)** Disconnect EGR temperature sensor connector. Connect ohmmeter between socket No. 19 and Green/Violet harness connector wire. Connect ohmmeter between socket No. 7 and Brown/White wire of sensor ground. Both should have a resistance of less than one ohm. If not, check for open circuit. If okay, replace EGR temperature sensor.

## TESTING WITH ON-OFF RATIO TESTER

***NOTE: On California models, the CIS-E control unit must first be programmed to read the On-Off ratio if On-Off Ratio Tester (KDJE-P 600) is to be used.***

**1)** Connect Bosch Tester (KDJE-P600) to CIS-E diagnostic socket. All on-off ratio values are to be checked with engine running at idle speed and at operating temperature. *See Fig. 9.*

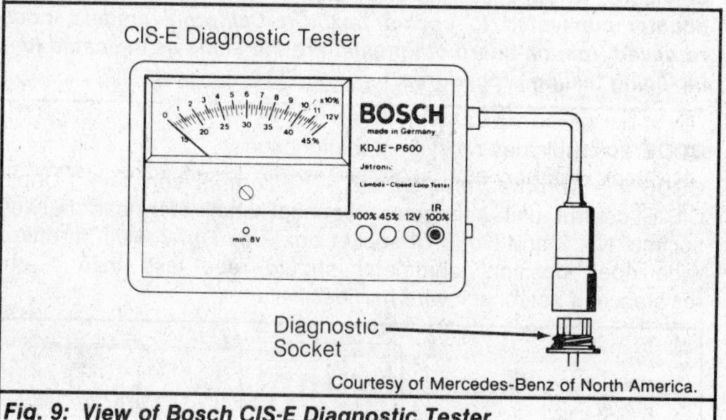
CIS-E Diagnostic Tester
BOSCH
made in Germany
KDJE-P600
Lambda-Closed Loop Tester
100% 45% 12V IR 100%
min. 8V
Diagnostic Socket
Courtesy of Mercedes-Benz of North America.

***Fig. 9: View of Bosch CIS-E Diagnostic Tester***

**2)** The fixed on-off ratio indicates a possible malfunction. The TROUBLE SHOOTING and DIAGNOSTIC TESTING sections will help in diagnosing problems with the CIS-E fuel injection system. If a problem cannot be solved using these sections, see COMPONENT TESTING in this article.

**Reading "0"** - Check CIS-E control unit for voltage. Check wire to diagnostic socket, terminal No. 3 or on-off ratio tester for defects. Check oxygen sensor signal. If voltage is 12 volts, see TEST 1 in DIAGNOSTIC TESTING section.

**Reading "10"** - Check airflow sensor position indicator for defects or reversed polarity. See TEST 2 in DIAGNOSTIC TESTING section.

**Reading "20"** - Check throttle valve switch connection. Check for opens or short circuit (full load contact closed before engine reaches full load). See TEST 3 in DIAGNOSTIC TESTING section.

**Reading "30"** - Check for short or open connection between CIS-E control unit and coolant temperature senor. If idle speed is too high, check for defective coolant temperature sensor. See TEST 4 in DIAGNOSTIC TESTING section.

**Reading "40"** - Check for short or open connection to airflow sensor position indicator. Check for defective airflow sensor position indicator. See TEST 2 in DIAGNOSTIC TESTING section.

**Reading "50"** – Check oxygen sensor operating temperature. Check for open in circuit. See TEST 5 in DIAGNOSTIC TESTING section.

**Reading "60"** – Not used.

**Reading "70"** – Check for interruption of TD signal. Check for defective wiring. See TEST 6 in DIAGNOSTIC TESTING section.

**Reading "80"** – Check for wiring interruption to altitude sensor or defective sensor. See TEST 7 in DIAGNOSTIC TESTING section.

**Reading "90"** – Not used.

**Reading "100"** – Check for defective overvoltage protection relay (idle speed too high, about 1800 RPM). Check air/fuel mixture for being too lean. Check oxygen sensor for short circuit to ground. Check wiring between CIS-E control unit and Electro-Hydraulic Actuator (EHA). Check EHA current (about 75 mA). See TEST 8 in DIAGNOSTIC TESTING section.

## DIAGNOSTIC TESTING

### TEST 1

**Voltage Supply to CIS-E Control Unit – 1)** Unplug CIS-E control unit. Turn ignition on and check voltage between terminals No. one (+) and terminal 2 (-). Battery voltage should be indicated. If voltage is okay, check on-off ratio and oxygen sensor signal and adjust if necessary. If voltage is not okay, go to next step.
**2)** Check voltage between terminal No. 1 (+) and ground (battery). Voltage should be about 12 volts. If voltage is not okay, check fuse on overvoltage protection relay. Check wire connections and wire routing according to wiring diagram. If voltage is okay, go to next step.
**3)** Check wire from terminal No. 2 to ground for continuity. Resistance should be zero ohms (Ω). If not okay, repair circuit. If okay, go to next step.
**4)** Check wire between diagnostic socket terminal No. 3 and CIS-E control unit plug (terminal No. 23) for continuity. Resistance should be zero ohms (Ω). If okay, go to next step. If not okay, repair open.
**5)** Disconnect oxygen sensor connector and ground male terminal. Start engine. Measure voltage between female terminal and ground. Voltage should be above 450 mV. If not, replace oxygen sensor. If okay, test is complete.

### TEST 2

**Airflow Sensor Position Indicator – 1)** Loosen plug of airflow sensor position indicator so that voltage can be measured at the pins (do not disconnect plug). Start engine. Voltage at terminals No. 1-3 should be 4.5-5.5 volts. Voltage at terminals No. 1-2 should be .5-1.5 volts. If okay, go to next step. If not okay, go to step **3)**.
**2)** Stop engine and turn on ignition. Slowly deflect airflow sensor plate. Measure voltage between terminals No. one and 2. Voltage should increase steadily to 4.5-5.5 volts. If not okay, replace airflow sensor. If okay, test is complete.
**3)** Stop engine. Check wires between airflow sensor position indicator and CIS-E control unit plug for continuity. Check wire routing according to wiring diagram. Resistance should be zero ohms (Ω). If okay, go to next step. If not okay, repair circuit opens.
**4)** Start engine and run at idle speed (engine at operating temperature). Check on-off ratio at diagnostic socket, tester needle should oscillate. If not okay, check diagnostic socket. If okay, test is complete.

### TEST 3

**Full Load Contact & Airflow Sensor Position Indicator – 1)** Disconnect plug of throttle valve switch. Measure resistance between terminals No. 3 and 2 (full load contact) at idle position. Measurement should be infinity (∞). At full load, (full load contact) should measure about zero ohms (Ω). At partial load, the full load contact should read infinity (∞). If not okay, adjust or replace throttle valve switch. If okay, go to next step.
**2)** Check continuity of wires from throttle valve switch to CIS-E control unit and to engine ground. Resistance should be about zero ohms (Ω). If not okay, repair interruption. If okay, check airflow sensor position indicator.

### TEST 4

**Coolant Temperature Sensor – 1)** Unplug coolant temperature sensor. Test resistance from sensor terminal to ground (idle speed okay with connection to ground or too high with interruption). If not okay, replace coolant temperature sensor. If okay, go to next step. *See Fig. 9.*
**2)** Check wire (Green/Red) between terminal No. 21 of CIS-E control unit plug to coolant sensor connector for continuity. Resistance should be about zero ohms (Ω). If not okay, repair interruption. If okay, test is complete.

### TEST 5

**Oxygen Sensor – 1)** Disconnect oxygen sensor plug and connect male terminal to ground. Start engine. Test sensor voltage between female terminal and ground. Sensor voltage should be around 450 mV. If not, replace oxygen sensor. If okay, go to next step.
**2)** Stop engine. Check wire from oxygen sensor plug to CIS-E control unit (terminal No. 8) for continuity. Resistance should be about zero ohms (Ω). If not, repair circuit. If okay, test is complete.

### TEST 6

**TD Signal – 1)** Disconnect CIS-E control unit plug. Start engine. Check voltage between terminal No. 25 (control unit plug) and ground. Voltage should be 6-12 volts. If incorrect, go to next step. If okay, test is complete.
**2)** Unplug fuel pump relay. Check wire between terminal No. 10 (relay plug) and terminal No. 25 on CIS-E control unit plug for continuity. Resistance should be zero ohms (Ω). If not, repair interruption. If okay, check wires to ignition control module for continuity.

### TEST 7

**Altitude Correction Capsule – 1)** Disconnect plug on altitude correction capsule. Turn ignition on. Check voltage between terminals No. 2 and 3. Voltage should be about 5 volts. If not okay, check power supply and ground according to wiring diagram. If okay, go to next step.
**2)** Turn ignition off. Check wire between altitude correction capsule plug (terminal No. one) to CIS-E control unit plug (terminal No. 11) for continuity. Resistance should be about zero ohms (Ω). If not, repair interruption. If okay, go to next step.
**3)** Start engine and run at idle speed and at operating temperature. The on-off ratio needle should oscillate. If not, replace altitude correction capsule. If okay, test is complete.

### TEST 8

***NOTE: If on-off ratio is 100% and idle speed is too high, check fuse on overvoltage protection relay and/or power supply and engine ground connection.***

**On-Off Ratio – 1)** On-off ratio cannot be adjusted. If on-off ratio tester needle oscillates, go to next step. If okay, test is complete.
**2)** Disconnect oxygen sensor plug and connect male part of plug to ground. Start engine and test sensor voltage between female part of plug and ground. Sensor voltage should be above 450 mV. If not, replace oxygen sensor. If okay, go to next step.

**3)** Stop engine. Check wire from oxygen sensor plug to CIS-E control unit (terminal No. 8) for continuity. Resistance should be about zero ohms (Ω). If not, repair circuit. If okay, go to next step.
**4)** Loosen plug of oxygen sensor heater so that voltage can be measured at the pins (DO NOT disconnect plug). Pull off fuel pump relay and bridge terminals No. 7 and 8. Reading should be about 12 volts. If not okay, repair interruption. If okay, go to next step.
**5)** Unplug oxygen sensor heater plug. Connect Test Cable (102 589 04 63 00) with Adapter Plug (903 589 03 63 00). Measure current draw, which should be above .5 amps. If not, replace oxygen sensor. If okay, test is complete.

## COMPONENT TESTING

### EZL IGNITION

**Engine Not Running – 1)** Connect multimeter and Engine Tester (MCM-2110). Crank engine and check dwell angle. Measurement should be 1-50% or 1-30 degrees of dwell. If not, go to next step. If okay, check ignition timing at cranking RPM. Timing should be about one degree BTDC. If not okay, go to step **4)**.
**2)** With ignition on, test voltage between terminal No. 5 of diagnostic socket (coil terminal No. 15) and ground. Nominal value should be 12 volts. If okay, go to next step. If not okay, test voltage supply from ignition switch. Test voltage difference between terminals No. 5 and 4 of diagnostic socket (coil terminals No. one and 15). Should read zero volts. If not, proceed to next step.
**3)** Unplug ignition position indicator (Green wire) from ignition control module. Test resistance of sensor between connector terminals No. 7 and 31 with ohmmeter. Specification is 730-910 ohms (Ω). If not, replace position indicator. If okay, go to next step.
**4)** Measure dwell angle. If no dwell angle is indicated, replace ignition control module.

**Engine Running – 1)** Run engine at idle (operating temperature). Check ignition timing. Specification is 7-11 degrees. If not, go to next step. If okay, go to step **4)**.
**2)** Pull plug from throttle valve switch connector. Test resistance of throttle valve switch on connector. Between terminals No. one and 2, (idle speed position) about zero ohms (Ω). Between terminals No. 2 and 3, (full load position) about zero ohms (Ω). Between terminals No. 1-2 and 2-3, (partial load) infinity (∞). If not, adjust or replace throttle valve switch. If okay, replace ignition control module.
**3)** Run engine at 3200 RPM. Check ignition timing (vacuum line connected). Specification is 40-44 degrees ATDC at 3200 RPM. If not, go to next step. If okay, go to step **6)**.
**4)** Check vacuum line from intake manifold to ignition control module for leaks. If no leaks are present check resistance of reference resistor (EZL). Pull sensor signal input plug on ignition control module and check resistance with ohmmeter between connector terminal No. 3 and ground. Go to next step.
**5)** Specification is 750 ohms (Ω). If okay, replace ignition control module. If not okay, check wire for interruptions or replace connector. Go to next step.
**6)** Pull vacuum line from ignition control module and run engine at 3200 RPM. Check ignition timing. Specification is 27-31 degrees at 3200 RPM. If okay, go to step **8)**. If not okay, go to next step.
**7)** Unplug coolant temperature sensor. Test resistance from sensor terminal to ground. Test resistance at 2 different temperatures. If not within specifications, replace sensor. *See Fig. 8*. If values are okay, go to next step.
**8)** Run engine at 3200 RPM (vacuum line connected). Check dwell angle. Specification is 24-53 degrees. If not okay, replace ignition control module. If okay, test is complete.

### ELECTRONIC IDLE SPEED CONTROL

**190E, 260E & 300 Series – 1)** Connect Test Cable (103 589 00 63 00) to idle speed air valve and on-off ratio tester. Push IR 100% button. With engine at idle and at normal operating temperature, tester should read a minimum value of 36-50% at 650-750 RPM. If okay, test is complete. If not okay, proceed to next step.
**2)** If readout was between 50 and 100%, check for air leak or air restriction. If readout was between zero or 100%, turn engine off. Disconnect plug from idle speed air valve. Briefly apply battery voltage to idle speed air valve. Idle speed air valve should switch audibly or can be felt with hand. If not okay, replace idle speed air valve. If valve clicks or switching could be felt, proceed to next step.
**3)** Test voltage supply. Turn ignition on. Voltage on terminal No. 2 of idle speed air valve plug should be around 12 volts. Test Red/White wire for continuity between terminal No. one if idle speed air valve plug and terminal No. 3 of CIS-E control unit plug. If not okay, repair open circuit. If okay, proceed to next step.
**4)** Test input signals at coolant temperature sensor, airflow sensor position indicator, idle speed contact on throttle valve switch or CIS-E control unit.

**420SEL & 560 Series –** Idle speed is controlled by idle speed control unit. Control unit is located behind the glove box on 560SL models. On 420SEL and other 560 series, control unit is located on firewall inside the passenger compartment.
Idle adjustments can only be obtained by connecting terminal "C" (terminal No. 5 on control unit connector) to ground. This will raise idle speed by 50 RPM. This procedure can also be used on 1986-87 models, except on 420SEL where the idle speed control unit must first be replaced with the 1988 version, as the previuos control units do not have connecting terminal "C".

### COLD START VALVE

**190E, 260E & 300 Series (Auxiliary Air Valve) – 1)** Check switch-off point of auxiliary air valve. With coolant temperature below 70°F (20°C), engine should idle at 900-1200 RPM. Idle RPM should drop to normal when operating temperature reaches 160°F (70°C).
**2)** If cold start idle is too low, compress connecting hose between idle speed air distributor and auxiliary air valve. If no RPM change occurs, auxiliary air valve is defective.
**3)** If idle RPM is too high at operating temperature, pinch connecting hose between idle speed air distributor and auxiliary air valve. If idle speed changes, auxiliary air valve is sticking or heating element is not functioning.
**4)** Check voltage and resistance of auxiliary air valve. Voltage should be 12 volts and resistance should be 40 ohms (Ω).

**190E, 260E & 300 Series (Cold Start Injector) – 1)** Disconnect cold start injector. Connect multimeter to cold start injector connector. Remove ignition distributor transmitter plug from switching unit (Green cable) or install Protective Plug (102 589 02 21 00) on diagnostic socket.
**2)** Check voltage while cranking starter motor. Reading should be at least 10 volts. Disconnect fuel line on cold start injector. Remove injector and reconnect fuel line. Hold cold start valve into container.
**3)** Disconnect electrical plug at thermo time switch. Connect terminal "W" on plug to ground with jumper wire. Below 45°F (5°C), it is not necessary to ground thermo time switch connector. Start engine. Fuel spray from cold start injector should be cone shaped. Disconnect ground test lead if used.
**4)** Dry any gasoline from nozzle of cold start valve. No droplets should form. Remove jumper wire. Install injector with new gasket. Reconnect wiring. Install relay and reconnect fuel line.

---

***NOTE: During warm-up and at operating temperature, current to differential pressure regulator is determined by coolant temperature sensor, $O_2$ sensor and ECU.***

---

**420 & 560 Series – 1)** With ignition off, disconnect coolant temperature sensor. Unplug Green cable on ignition control module. Crank engine and check voltage at plug of cold start valve. Voltage should be 10 volts for about 9 seconds. If okay, test is complete. If not okay, go to next step.

# 1988 COMPUTERIZED ENGINE CONTROLS
# Mercedes-Benz CIS-E System (Cont.)

**2)** Check wire from cold start valve to fuel pump relay and ground wire to engine for continuity. Resistance should be zero ohms (Ω). If not, repair open circuit. Go to next step. If okay, test is complete.
**3)** With coolant temperature sensor disconnected, check voltage between fuel pump relay connector terminal and engine ground (-). Check terminal No. 2 and engine ground (-). Crank engine (do not start). Voltage at fuel pump relay connector should be 10 volts. Voltage at terminal No. 2 should be 3.5-5.0 volts. If not to specification, repair wiring circuits. If okay, replace fuel pump relay.

## DECELERATION SHUTOFF

**190E, 260E & 300 Series – 1)** On California models, program CIS-E control unit to provide on-off ratio output. Connect on-off ratio tester to diagnostic socket. With engine at idle and operating temperature and tester needle oscillating, go to next step. If it does not oscilliate, perform on-off ratio trouble shooting. Refer to TESTING WITH ON-OFF RATIO TESTER.
**2)** Disconnect throttle valve switch and install jumper between terminals No. one and 2 of connector. Increase engine speed to 2500 RPM. Keep engine speed constant and manually operate deceleration shutoff microswitch. Engine should start surging. If on-off ratio is constant at 50%, check adjustment of slotted lever and throttle valve switch. If on-off ratio is not constant at 50%, proceed to next step.
**3)** Test resistance of microswitch. Resistance should read zero ohm at idle position and infinity with free travel on lever cancelled. If okay, proceed to next step. If not okay, replace microswitch.
**4)** With engine at idle, test RPM signal (TD) between CIS-E control unit terminal No. 25 and Green/Yellow wire of control unit plug. If voltage is between 6-12 volts, replace control unit. If not, repair open circuit.

**420 & 560 Series – 1)** On California models, program CIS-E control unit to provide on-off ratio output. Connect on-off ratio tester to diagnostic socket. With engine at idle and operating temperature and tester needle oscillating, go to next step. If needle does not oscilliate, perform on-off ratio trouble shooting. Refer to TESTING WITH ON-OFF RATIO TESTER.
**2)** Drive vehicle. With engine speed at 2500 RPM, shift transmission selector lever in position "2". When vehicle is decelerated (throttle valve closed), on-off ratio should jump to about 95% when engine RPM drops below 1100 RPM and then falls momentarily to 50% and then the control range is ended. If okay, test is complete. If not okay proceed to next step.
**3)** Check idle speed contact on throttle valve switch and TD-signal. Refer to Codes 7 and 10. Test speed signal. Check circuit between CIS-E control unit connector through the idle speed control unit and electronic speedometer for continuity. Resistance should read zero ohm. If not, check for open circuit. If okay, test is complete.

## IDLE & FULL LOAD CONTACT

**1)** Connect on-off ratio tester to diagnostic socket and turn on ignition. On-off ratio should be about 70%. Move airflow sensor plate about .80" (20 mm). On-off ratio should be about 10%. Go to next step.
**2)** If reading is 70%, throttle valve contact does not close or there's an interruption in wire to idle speed contact. Close airflow sensor plate. On-off ratio should be 40%. Go to next step.
**3)** Open throttle valve fully. On-off ratio should be 20%. If not okay, replace full load contact. If okay, test is complete.

## OVERVOLTAGE PROTECTION RELAY

**1)** Check fuse on overvoltage protection relay. If not okay, replace fuse. If fuse is okay, go to next step.
**2)** Disconnect overvoltage protection relay. Bridge terminals No. 1 and 2. Check voltage between terminal No. 1 of CIS-E control unit plug and ground. Voltage should be about 12 volts. If not okay, check power supply. If okay, go to next step.
**3)** Turn ignition on. Check voltage between terminal No. 5 (-) and terminal No. 6 (+) of overvoltage protection relay connector. Voltage should be about 12 volts. If not okay, repair interruption. If okay, replace overvoltage protection relay.

## AIR INJECTION

**1)** With engine at operating temperature, disconnect coolant temperature sensor. Connect 2.5 k/ohm test resistor to simulate 68°F (20°C). Disconnect vacuum line from side connection of switchover valve and connect vacuum tester with "Y" fitting. Go to next step.
**2)** Start engine. Disconnect suction hose at air pump filter and close with finger. Air pump should be running and vacuum should be about 20 in. Hg. Suction should be felt at end of hose to air pump. If not okay, go to step **4)**. If okay, go to next step.
**3)** The air pump must disengage after about one minute and the vacuum drop to zero. If not okay, unplug air injection relay. If vacuum drops, replace air injection relay. If vacuum doesn't drop, check routing of vacuum lines and switchover valve. Repair or replace components as necessary.
**4)** Unplug air injection relay. Check voltage between terminals No. one and 3 at plug. Voltage should be about 12 volts. If not okay, check power supply and ground wiring. Check air shutoff valve function and air hoses for proper routing. If okay, go to next step.
**5)** Check voltage between terminal No. one and terminal No. 2 at plug. Voltage should be 12 volts. If not okay, check power supply. If okay, replace air injection relay.

## EGR SYSTEM (420 & 560 SERIES ONLY)

**1)** Apply about 12 in. Hg to EGR valve. Disconnect vacuum line. The EGR valve should close. If not okay, replace EGR valve. If okay, go to next step.
**2)** Run engine at idle speed. Apply about 12 in. Hg to EGR valve. Engine should run rough at idle. If not okay, replace EGR valve. If okay, go to next step.
**3)** Connect vacuum tester to EGR vacuum line using a "Y" fitting. Increase engine speed slowly to about 4000 RPM. Tester should indicate vacuum. If okay, test is complete. If not okay, go to next step.
**4)** Disconnect vacuum line from thermo valve and connect vacuum tester with "Y" fitting to vacuum line and thermo valve and apply vacuum. Thermo valve should be open with coolant temperature above 122°F (50°C) and closed with coolant temperature below that. If okay, proceed to next step. If not okay, replace thermo valve.
**5)** Test thermo valve for leaks. Seal straight connection of thermo valve. Check and ensure vacuum is held at angular connection to thermo valve. If okay, test is complete. If not okay, replace thermo valve.

## AIRFLOW SENSOR PLATE

**1)** Remove fuel pump relay. Bridge relay connector terminals No. 7 and 8 to build up fuel pressure. Center airflow sensor plate using feeler gauges of .002" (.05 mm) thickness between edge of sensor plate and housing. Airflow sensor plate should not bind even with slight lateral pressure eliminating any bearing play.
**2)** Tighten screw holding plate to lever. Push sensor plate down manually to check for smooth operation. Plate should not bind in housing bore. Release plate and allow it to return to rest position. Plate should not bind and should audibly knock against resilient stop. Check and recenter plate, if necessary.
**3)** Check rest position of sensor plate. Upper edge of plate should be flush with upper edge of cylindrical portion of housing. Upper edge of plate may be higher than edge in housing by maximum of .008" (.2 mm). *See Fig. 10.*
**4)** Free play of .04-.08" (1-2 mm) should exist between rest position and point at which adjusting lever touches control piston. Gently drive guide pin down into housing if plate is high. If plate is low, remove mixture control unit. Gently drive guide pin out from below.

***NOTE: Avoid repeated adjustments of press fitted guide pin as pin will become loose in housing.***

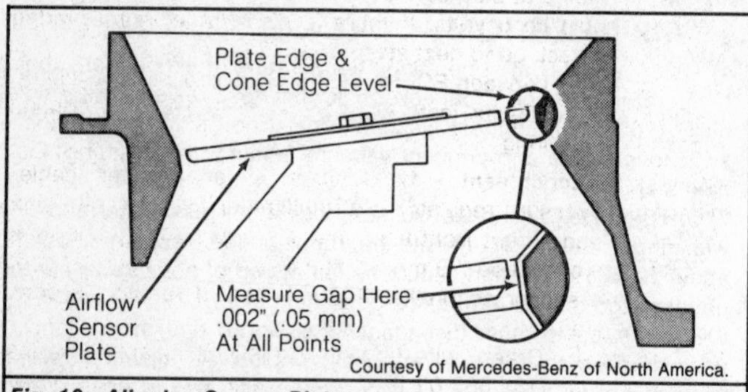
Plate Edge &
Cone Edge Level
Airflow
Sensor
Plate
Measure Gap Here
.002" (.05 mm)
At All Points
Courtesy of Mercedes-Benz of North America.

*Fig. 10: Aligning Sensor Plate*

## FUEL DELIVERY & SYSTEM PRESSURES

**Visual Check (Fuel Leak) – 1)** Remove air cleaner and check for any visible fuel leaks. Remove fuel pump relay from relay board. Bridge terminals No. 7 and 8 long enough to establish fuel pressure. Push airflow sensor plate down manually.

**2)** Uniform resistance should be felt throughout travel after slight amount of free travel. No binding should be felt if sensor plate is released quickly. If upward movement of sensor plate is slow, resistance from control piston closely following adjusting lever should be felt. No binding should be evident.

**3)** Push airflow sensor plate completely down and hold there briefly. Slight fuel seepage past control piston is acceptable. If no fuel leaks have been found, go to next test.

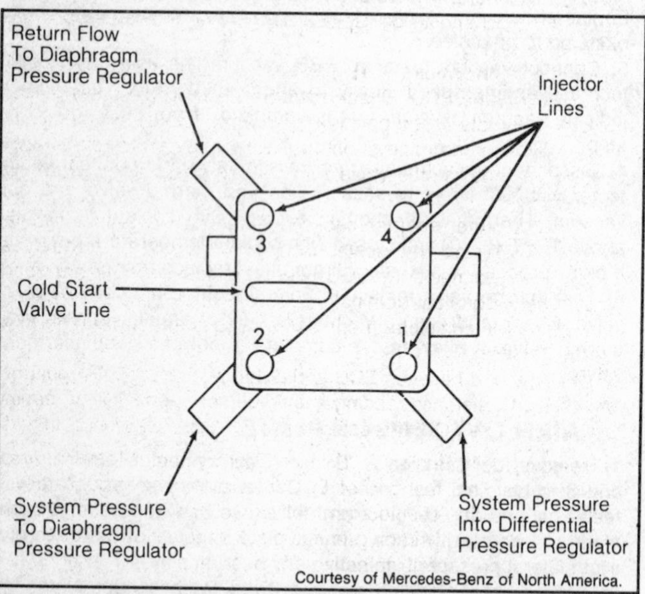
Return Flow
To Diaphragm
Pressure Regulator
Injector
Lines
3
4
Cold Start
Valve Line
2
1
System Pressure
To Diaphragm
Pressure Regulator
System Pressure
Into Differential
Pressure Regulator
Courtesy of Mercedes-Benz of North America.

*Fig. 11: Testing 190E Fuel Distributor*

**System Pressure – 1)** There are 2 versions of Fuel Pressure Gauge (100 589 00 21 00) available. One version has junction block with 2 valve handles on it, which are numbered "1" or "3" in following procedure. Hose exiting side of junction block by "1" valve handle is hose "1".

**2)** Second version has single valve handle on junction block. Hose leaving junction block 180 degrees from valve handle is "B" and hose leaving junction block 180 degrees from line to gauge is "A". When testing system pressure, close valve "1" and open valve "3" on first version or open valve on second version.

**3)** Remove plug from test port in lower chamber of fuel distributor. Connect fuel pressure gauge line "1" or "A" to test port in lower chamber of fuel distributor. Use M12 X 1.5/M8 X 1 Reducing Bushing (102 589 06 63 00) to connect hose to chamber port.

**4)** Remove fuel supply line for cold start valve from top of fuel distributor. Attach pressure gauge line "3" or "B" to cold start fitting on fuel distributor upper chamber. System pressure is checked with engine off. Engine temperature has no effect upon system pressure test. Remove fuel pump relay. Bridge terminals No. 7 and 8.

**5)** System pressure should be 76.9-79.8 psi (5.4-5.6 kg/cm²). If pressure is incorrect, check for defective fuel pump, restricted fuel return line or defective differential pressure regulator. Open pressure gauge valve "1". Remove fuel pump relay bridge.

**Lower Chamber (Differential) Pressure – 1)** Connect Meter Adapter Cable (102 589 04 63 00) between differential pressure regulator and multimeter. Disconnect $O_2$ sensor lead at connector located under right front floor mat. Turn ignition on. Meter reading for lower chamber pressure should be constant 7-9 mA. If reading is incorrect, check lambda control.

***NOTE: During warm-up and at operating temperature, current to differential pressure regulator is determined by coolant temperature sensor, $O_2$ sensor and ECU.***

**2)** Bridge fuel pump relay socket, terminals No. 7 and 8. Lower chamber pressure should be about 5.8 psi (.4 kg/cm²) less than system pressure reading determined earlier. Unplug coolant temperature sensor.

**3)** Note lower chamber pressure and differential pressure regulator current. If coolant temperature sensor plug is disconnected, temperature sensor resistance should be zero ohms (Ω), differential pressure regulator current should be about 114-132 mA, and lower chamber pressure should be about 15.95-18.85 psi (1.1-1.3 kg/cm²) less than system pressure. Reconnect coolant temperature sensor.

**4)** Check pressure and current values at coolant temperature of 64°F (20°C). Sensor resistance should be 2200-2800 ohms (Ω). Differential pressure regulator current 9-14 mA and lower chamber pressure should be about 5.8 psi (.4 kg/cm²) less than system pressure.

**5)** Check pressure and current values at coolant temperature of 176°F (80°C). Sensor resistance should be 290-370 ohms (Ω), differential pressure regulator current 7-9 mA and lower chamber pressure should be about 5.8 psi (.4 kg/cm²) less than system pressure.

**6)** Check pressure and current values at coolant temperature of 212°F (100°C). Sensor resistance should be 140-220 ohms (Ω), differential pressure regulator current 7-9 mA and lower chamber pressure should be about 5.8 psi (.4 kg/cm²) less than system pressure.

**7)** If not to specification, check coolant temperature sensor for malfunction. Coolant temperature sensor should also be checked if there are warm-up problems with vehicle. Test lambda control. If lower chamber pressure is too high, check orifice in fuel distributor for restriction. Install fuel pump relay. Reconnect $O_2$ sensor.

**Residual Pressure & Internal Leak Testing – 1)** Run engine and check fuel pressures as described previously. Turn engine off and check residual pressure. Pressure should slowly drop below 41 psi (2.9 kg/cm²), which is pressure required to open fuel injectors. If pressure drops rapidly to zero psi, replace check valve on fuel pump.

**2)** If pressure drops slowly to zero psi, disconnect fuel return line at diaphragm pressure regulator. There should be no flow of fuel, although slight seepage is acceptable. Plug return line IMMEDIATELY if fuel flows heavily.

**3)** Pinch leak line at fuel accumulator. If pressure holds with line pinched, replace fuel accumulator. If no leaks have been found, remove cold start valve from manifold and check it for leaks under pressure. Replace valve if it leaks.

**4)** Disconnect pressure gauge and clean up any spilled fuel. Reconnect all fuel lines and run engine. Visually check all connections and lines for leaks.

**Fuel Pump Delivery Volume – 1)** Remove fuel pump relay. Check current draw between socket No. 7 (terminal No. 87) and socket No. 8 (terminal No. 30). Draw of 6 amps indicates good fuel pump. Replace fuel pump if draw is more than 7 amps. Disconnect return line at diaphragm pressure regulator.
**2)** Attach a hose to fitting on regulator. Place other end of hose in measuring glass or beaker. Bridge sockets No. 7 and 8 with jumper wire and run fuel pump for 50 seconds. Delivery volume should be .95 qt. (.90L) in 50 seconds with 11.5 volts supplied to fuel pump.
**3)** If delivery volume is low, ensure pump is receiving 11.5 volts. Check if dirty strainer in feed connection of fuel distributor is causing restriction. Check for pinched fuel lines.
**4)** Pinch by-pass line of fuel accumulator and repeat delivery volume test. If volume is correct, replace fuel accumulator. If volume is low, replace fuel filter and repeat test. Replace fuel pump if volume remains low. Reconnect fuel return line and install fuel pump relay.

**Fuel Distributor Delivery Volume – 1)** Unplug oxygen sensor lead under right front floor mat. Disconnect small fuel return line running between fuel distributor and diaphragm pressure regulator at fuel distributor end. Plug line. Connect hose to open fuel distributor port.
**2)** Place other end of hose in measuring glass or beaker. Remove fuel pump relay. Bridge sockets No. 7 and 8 with jumper wire to run fuel pump for one minute. Fuel delivery volume should be 4.4-5.0 ozs. (.13-.15L) per minute with 11.5 volts to fuel pump. If delivery volume is too low, replace either fuel distributor or differential pressure regulator.

## ELECTRICAL COMPONENTS

**Fuel Pump Relay – 1)** Remove fuel pump relay from board. Connect positive lead of multimeter to socket No. 8 (terminal No. 30) and negative lead to socket No. 11 (terminal No. 31) of connector. Measure voltage. If reading is 12 volts, go to step **3)**. If reading is zero volts, go to next step.
**2)** Remove negative lead of multimeter from socket No. 11 (terminal No. 31) and connect to vehicle ground. If reading is 12 volts, check Brown wire from terminal No. 31 for short. If voltage is zero, check Red wire from terminal No. 30 for short. Repair wiring if necessary.
**3)** Switch on ignition and check voltage at socket No. 9 (terminal No. 15) of connector. If reading is zero volts, check Black/Red wire from terminal No. 15 to fuse box for short. Repair wiring if necessary. If reading is 12 volts, go to next step.
**4)** Using dwell meter, connect positive lead to socket No. 10 (terminal TD). Dwell angle should be 7-34 degrees. If dwell is incorrect, check Green/Yellow wire from jack 10 (terminal TD) to TZL (transistor ignition) switching unit for short. If wiring is good, replace switching unit. If dwell reading is good, go to next step.
**5)** Bridge socket No. 7 (terminal No. 87) and socket No. 8 (terminal No. 30) with jumper wire. If fuel pump is running, test is completed. If fuel pump is not running, go to next step.
**6)** Check Black/Red/White wire from terminal No. 87 to fuel pump for short. If wiring is good, replace fuel pump relay. If fuel pump still does not run, replace fuel pump.

**Coolant Temperature Sensor – 1)** Disconnect plug from coolant temperature sensor. Using ohmmeter, check resistance between sensor terminal and ground. Measure resistance at 2 different temperatures. If readings are not correct, replace coolant temperature sensor. If coolant temperature sensor is good, go to next step.
**2)** Connect meter adapter cable between differential pressure regulator and multimeter. Set meter to mA scale. Disconnect wire to $O_2$ sensor. Turn ignition on and check current reading. At operating temperature, reading should be 7-9 mA.
**3)** At coolant temperature of 60°F (20°C), reading should be 9-14 mA. If wiring to temperature sensor is disconnected, reading should be 114-132 mA. If readings are correct, unit is okay and test is completed. If readings are not correct, go to next step.
**4)** Disconnect plug to differential pressure regulator. Resistance reading of regulator should be 18-21 ohms (Ω). If reading is not in range, replace differential pressure regulator. If reading is good, go to next step.
**5)** Check voltage at plug connector for coolant temperature sensor. Voltage should be 5 volts. If there is no voltage, repair wiring. If voltage is correct, go to next step.
**6)** Check wiring between ECU and differential pressure regulator for continuity. If continuity tests good, replace ECU. If no continuity, repair short in wiring.

**After-Start Enrichment – 1)** Connect meter adapter cable to differential pressure regulator. Set multimeter to mA scale. Unplug $O_2$ sensor under right front floor mat. Current reading at operating temperature should be 7-9 mA. If reading is not correct, test coolant temperature sensor as previously described. If reading is correct, go to next step.
**2)** Disconnect Green wire of ignition switching unit or install Protective Plug (102 589 02 21 00) into diagnostic socket. Simulate coolant temperature of 60°F (20°C) by connecting 2500-ohm (Ω) resistor wire between coolant temperature sensor lead and ground. Crank engine for about 3 seconds and let key return to "ON" position. DO NOT turn ignition off.
**3)** After 4 seconds (including 3 seconds of cranking), current reading should increase to 24 mA. After 20 seconds, current reading should drop to 9-14 mA, which is basic warm-up current value. If readings are correct, test is complete. If readings are not correct, go to next step.
**4)** Connect voltmeter between ECU connector terminal No. 24 and ground. Crank starter motor. Cranking voltage signal (terminal No. 50 voltage) should be 10 volts. If not, check and repair wiring. If voltage is correct, go to next step.
**5)** Check wiring between ECU connector and differential pressure regulator connector. See WIRING DIAGRAM for wiring color and terminal numbers. If resistance reading is zero ohms (Ω), circuit is good and ECU should be replaced. If reading indicates open circuit (∞), repair wiring.

**Full-Load Enrichment – 1)** Disconnect wiring between throttle valve switch and ECU. Check resistance of throttle valve switch at male plug. In idle speed position, resistance should be infinity. In full load position, resistance should be zero ohms. If readings are not correct, replace throttle valve switch. If readings are correct, go to next step.
**2)** Connect meter adapter cable to differential pressure regulator. Set multimeter to mA scale. Bridge connector of throttle valve switch that connects to ECU. Turn ignition on. Current reading should have constant nominal value of 7-9 mA. If current reading is correct, test is complete. If current reading is not correct, go to next step.
**3)** Check wiring between ECU and differential pressure regulator for continuity. Resistance reading should be zero ohms (Ω). If reading is correct, replace ECU. If reading is not correct, repair short in wiring.

**Overvoltage Protection – 1)** Turn ignition on. Measure voltage between terminal No. one of ECU connector and ground. *See Fig. 12 or 13.* Reading should show battery voltage. If reading is correct, test is complete. If reading is incorrect, check fuse on overvoltage relay. Replace fuse if defective. Turn ignition on. If fuse does not blow, go to next step. If fuse blows, repair short in wiring.
**2)** Remove overvoltage protection relay. Bridge sockets No. one and 2 with jumper wire. Battery voltage should be present at terminal No. one of ECU. If not, repair wiring circuit. If battery voltage is present, go to next step.
**3)** Test voltage at sockets No. 6 and 5 on connector for relay. If battery voltage is present, replace overvoltage protection relay. If battery voltage is not present, repair wiring. Test is complete.

**Altitude Correction – 1)** Connect meter adapter cable to differential pressure regulator. Set multimeter to mA scale. Disconnect $O_2$ sensor and turn ignition on. Disconnect wiring from altitude sensor to simulate sea level operation. Current reading should be 7-9 mA.

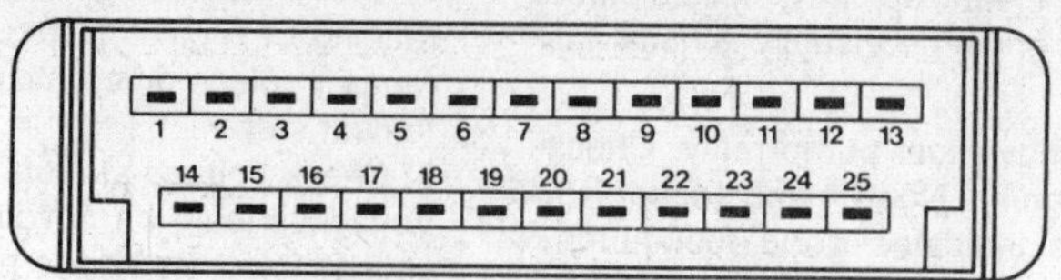
1 2 3 4 5 6 7 8 9 10 11 12 13
14 15 16 17 18 19 20 21 22 23 24 25

1. Battery Voltage
2. Ground (Engine)
3. Idle Speed Air Valve
4. Not Used
5. Full Load Contact
6. Hall Effect Full Load Sensor
7. Wire Ground Connection
8. $O_2$ Sensor Signal
9. TF-Signal To Fuel Pump Relay
10. Electro-Hydraulic Actuator
11. Altitude Correction
12. Electro-Hydraulic Actuator
13. Idle Speed Contact
14. Not Used
15. Circuit 30a From Overvoltage Relay (Calif.) Check Engine Light (Federal)
16. Selector Lever Position
17. Airflow Sensor Position Indicator Signal
18. Voltage Supply: Altitude Correction Capsule Airflow Sensor Position Indicator
19. A/C Compressor Engagement Signal
20. Ground (Battery)
21. Coolant Temperature Sensor
22. Not Used
23. Lambda Signal: Check Engine Light (Calif.)
24. Deceleration Shut-Off Microswitch
25. TD-Signal

*Fig. 12: 190, 260 & 300 Series CIS-E Control Unit Terminal*

**2)** Reconnect altitude sensor wiring. Check current reading. See ALTITUDE CORRECTION FACTOR table for correct current readings at different barometric pressures and different elevations above sea level. If current readings are correct, test is complete.

**3)** If readings are incorrect, disconnect altitude sensor. Check that voltage between socket No. one and ground is 6 volts. Voltage between sockets No. 2 and 3 should be 8 volts. If readings are correct, replace altitude sensor. If readings are incorrect, repair wiring.

**Electronic Idle Speed Control – 1)** Connect test cable to Bosch Lambda Control Tester (KDJE-P 600) and to idle speed air valve. Push IR 100% button. Engine should be at idle speed and operating temperature. Nominal value reading should be 27-29% at 670-770 RPM. If reading is correct, test is complete. If reading is not correct, go to next step.

**2)** If reading is higher or lower, adjust valve to nominal value or test microswitch. If reading is 0%, test voltage at plug of idle speed air valve. Connect multimeter between socket No. 2 and ground. If reading is not correct, repair wiring circuit. Reading should be 12 volts. If reading is correct, go to next step.

**3)** Measure resistances of idle speed air valve. Between terminals No. 2 and 3 or 2 and 1, reading should be 12 ohms. If not correct, replace idle speed air valve. If correct, test is complete.

***NOTE: If voltage at sockets No. 1 and 3 (tested individually to ground) is 12 volts, check Brown ground wire from terminal No. 20 to ECU for continuity. Repair wiring or replace ECU as necessary.***

**Idle Speed Stabilization (Automatic Transmission Engaged) – 1)** Set parking brake. Run engine at idle and warm up to operating temperature. Engine should idle between 570-670 RPM. If correct, test is complete. If not correct, go to next step.

**2)** Using multimeter, test input at ECU (terminal No. 16 to battery positive). With shifter in position "P" or "N", reading should be 12 volts. With shifter in "D", reading should drop below battery voltage. If reading is incorrect on either test, repair short in circuit. If reading is correct, test is complete.

**Idle Speed Stabilization (A/C Compressor Engaged) – 1)** Set parking brake. Run engine at idle and warm up to operating temperature. Engine should idle between 670-770 RPM. If correct, test is complete. If not correct, go to next step.

**2)** Using multimeter, test input voltage at ECU between terminal No. 19 and ground. Readings should be 12 volts with A/C compressor on and zero volts with A/C compressor off. If reading is incorrect on either test, repair short in circuit. If reading is correct, test is complete.

**Throttle Valve Switch –** Set multimeter to read highest ohm scale. Check full throttle speed stop by pushing throttle valve against full throttle stop. Reading should be zero ohms. As throttle valve is turned slightly toward idle, reading should move to infinity. If readings are not correct, replace throttle valve switch.

1 2 3 4 5 6 7 8 9 10 11 12 13
14 15 16 17 18 19 20 21 22 23 24 25

1. Battery Voltage
2. Ground (Engine)
3. Not Used
4. Not Used
5. Full Load Contact
6. Not Used
7. Wire Ground Connection
8. $O_2$ Sensor Signal
9. TF-Signal To Fuel Pump Relay & Idle Speed Control Unit
10. Electro-Hydraulic Actuator
11. Altitude Correction Signal
12. Electro-Hydraulic Actuator
13. Idle Speed Contact
14. Air Injection Relay
15. Circuit 30a From Overvoltage Relay (Calif.) Check Engine Light (Federal)
16. Selector Lever Position
17. Airflow Sensor Position Indicator Signal
18. Voltage Supply: Altitude Correction Capsule Airflow Sensor Position Indicator
19. EGR Temperature Sensor
20. Ground (Battery)
21. Coolant Temperature Sensor
22. Not Used
23. Lambda Signal: Check Engine Light (Calif.)
24. Speed Signal (Electronic Speedometer)
25. TD-Signal

*Fig. 13: 420 & 560 Series CIS-E Control Unit Terminal*

# 1988 COMPUTERIZED ENGINE CONTROLS
## Mercedes-Benz CIS-E System (Cont.)

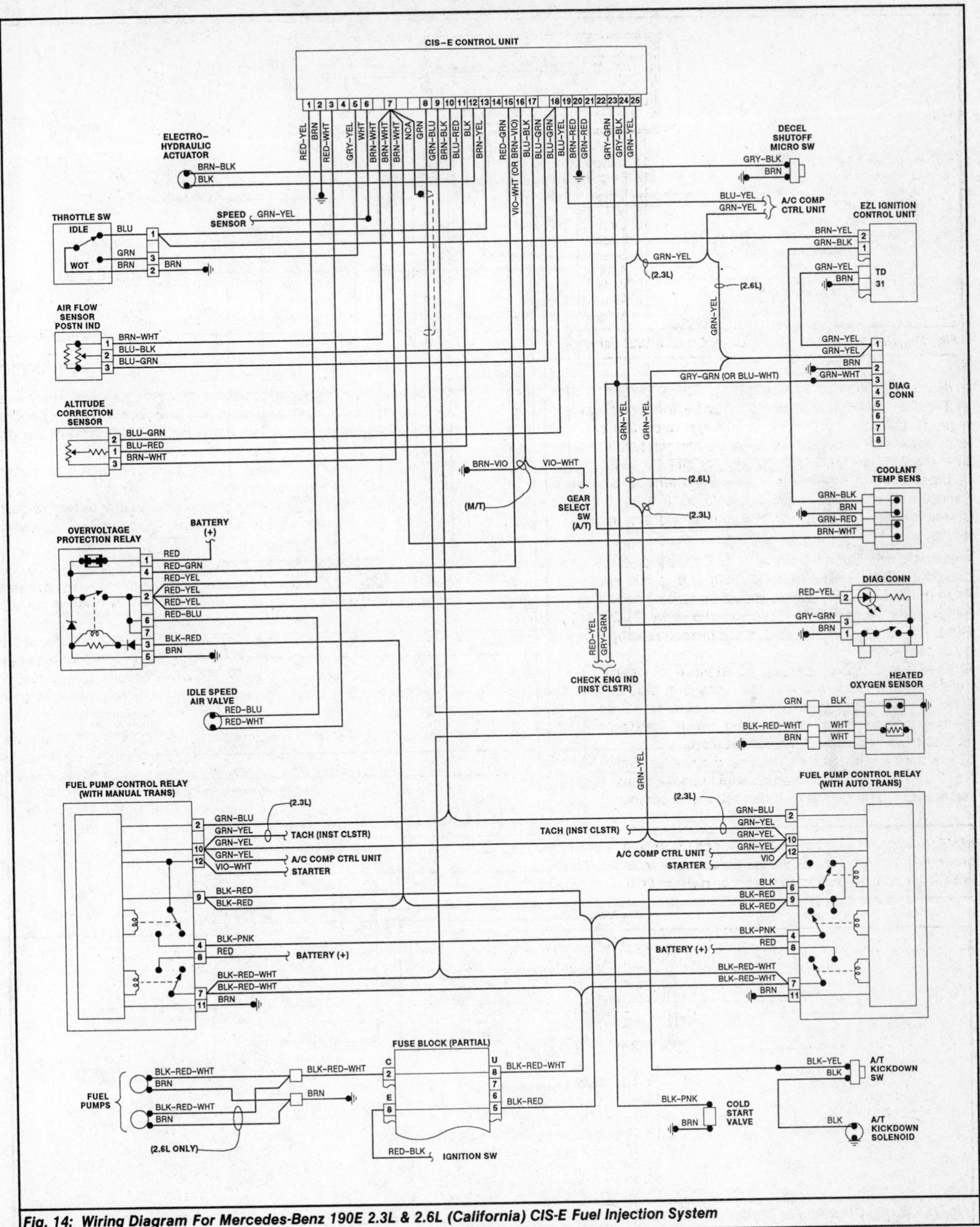
CIS-E CONTROL UNIT
ELECTRO-HYDRAULIC ACTUATOR
THROTTLE SW
IDLE
WOT
SPEED SENSOR
AIR FLOW SENSOR POSTN IND
ALTITUDE CORRECTION SENSOR
OVERVOLTAGE PROTECTION RELAY
BATTERY (+)
IDLE SPEED AIR VALVE
DECEL SHUTOFF MICRO SW
A/C COMP CTRL UNIT
EZL IGNITION CONTROL UNIT
DIAG CONN
COOLANT TEMP SENS
GEAR SELECT SW (A/T)
CHECK ENG IND (INST CLSTR)
HEATED OXYGEN SENSOR
FUEL PUMP CONTROL RELAY (WITH MANUAL TRANS)
FUEL PUMP CONTROL RELAY (WITH AUTO TRANS)
TACH (INST CLSTR)
A/C COMP CTRL UNIT
STARTER
BATTERY (+)
FUSE BLOCK (PARTIAL)
FUEL PUMPS
(2.6L ONLY)
IGNITION SW
COLD START VALVE
A/T KICKDOWN SW
A/T KICKDOWN SOLENOID

*Fig. 14: Wiring Diagram For Mercedes-Benz 190E 2.3L & 2.6L (California) CIS-E Fuel Injection System*

# 1988 COMPUTERIZED ENGINE CONTROLS
## Mercedes-Benz CIS-E System (Cont.)

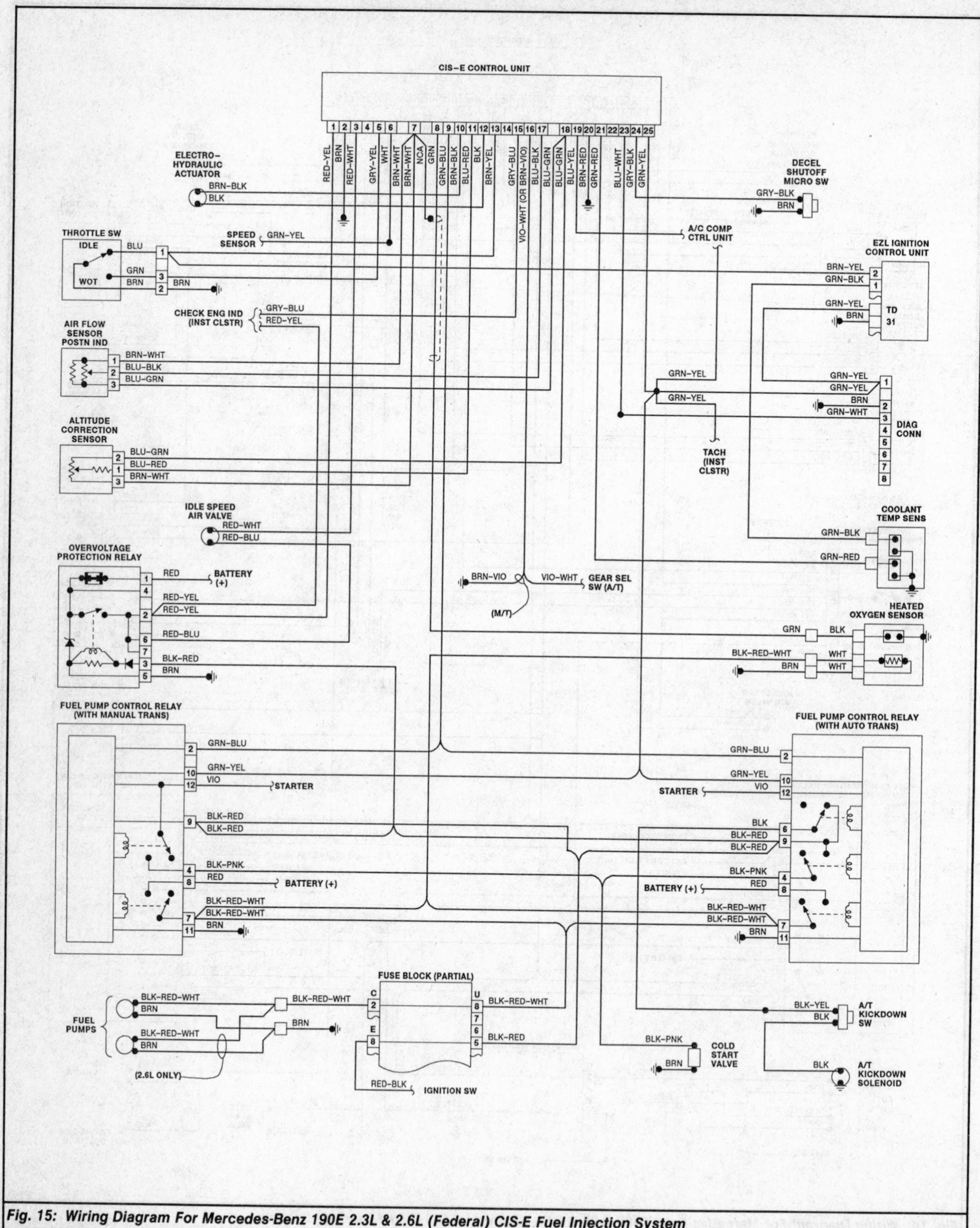

CIS–E CONTROL UNIT
ELECTRO-HYDRAULIC ACTUATOR
BRN–BLK
BLK
THROTTLE SW
IDLE
WOT
SPEED SENSOR
GRN–YEL
CHECK ENG IND (INST CLSTR)
GRY–BLU
RED–YEL
AIR FLOW SENSOR POSTN IND
BRN–WHT
BLU–BLK
BLU–GRN
ALTITUDE CORRECTION SENSOR
BLU–RED
IDLE SPEED AIR VALVE
RED–WHT
RED–BLU
OVERVOLTAGE PROTECTION RELAY
BATTERY (+)
BLK–RED
BRN
DECEL SHUTOFF MICRO SW
GRY–BLK
A/C COMP CTRL UNIT
EZL IGNITION CONTROL UNIT
BRN–YEL
GRN–BLK
TD
31
GRN–WHT
DIAG CONN
TACH (INST CLSTR)
COOLANT TEMP SENS
GRN–RED
BRN–VIO
VIO–WHT
GEAR SEL SW (A/T)
(M/T)
HEATED OXYGEN SENSOR
GRN
BLK–RED–WHT
WHT
FUEL PUMP CONTROL RELAY (WITH MANUAL TRANS)
FUEL PUMP CONTROL RELAY (WITH AUTO TRANS)
GRN–BLU
VIO
STARTER
BLK–PNK
RED
FUSE BLOCK (PARTIAL)
FUEL PUMPS
(2.6L ONLY)
RED–BLK
IGNITION SW
COLD START VALVE
BLK–YEL
A/T KICKDOWN SW
A/T KICKDOWN SOLENOID


*Fig. 15: Wiring Diagram For Mercedes-Benz 190E 2.3L & 2.6L (Federal) CIS-E Fuel Injection System*

# 1988 COMPUTERIZED ENGINE CONTROLS
## Mercedes-Benz CIS-E System (Cont.)

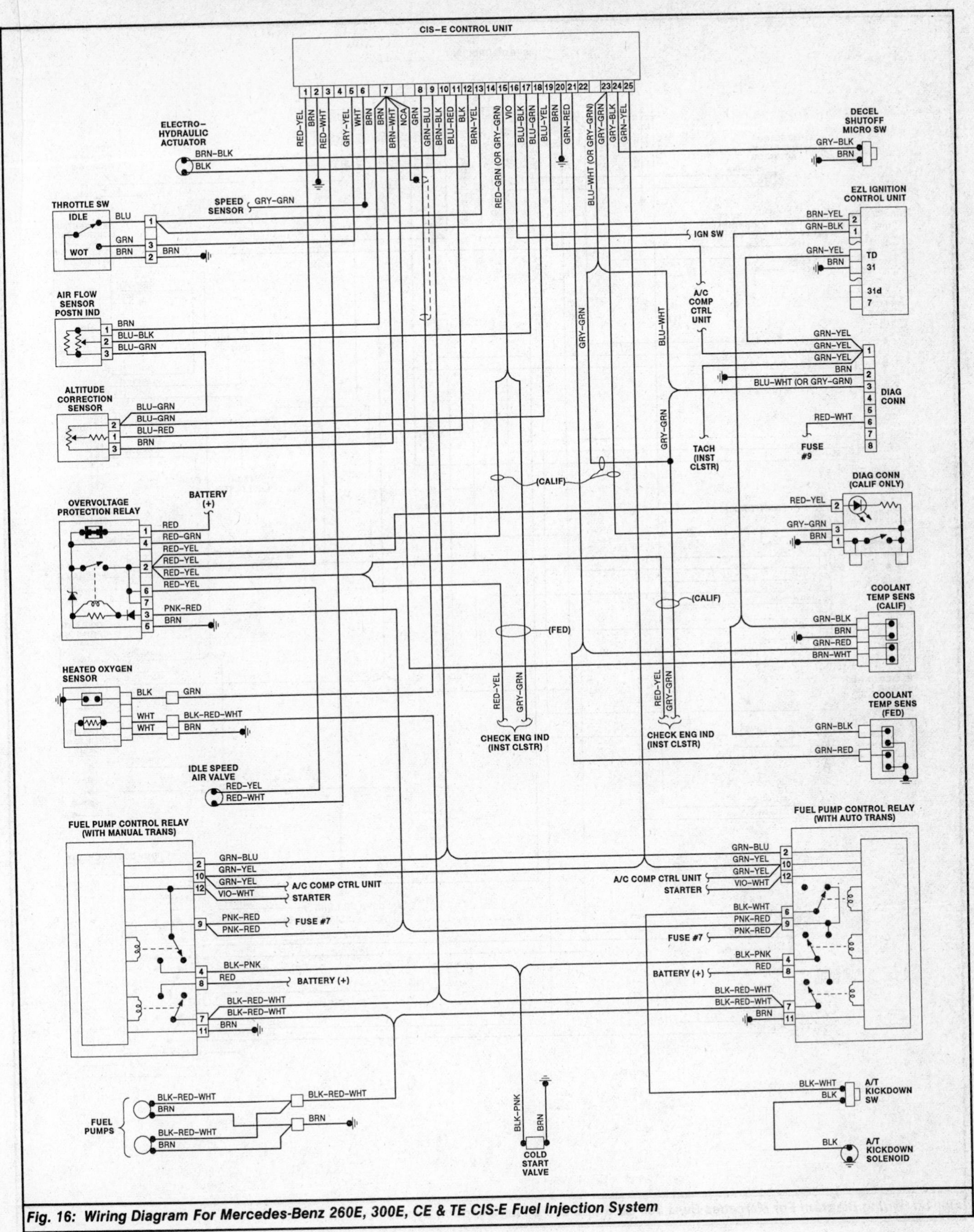

CIS-E CONTROL UNIT
ELECTRO-HYDRAULIC ACTUATOR
THROTTLE SW
IDLE
WOT
SPEED SENSOR
AIR FLOW SENSOR POSTN IND
ALTITUDE CORRECTION SENSOR
OVERVOLTAGE PROTECTION RELAY
BATTERY (+)
HEATED OXYGEN SENSOR
IDLE SPEED AIR VALVE
FUEL PUMP CONTROL RELAY (WITH MANUAL TRANS)
A/C COMP CTRL UNIT
STARTER
FUSE #7
BATTERY (+)
FUEL PUMPS
COLD START VALVE
CHECK ENG IND (INST CLSTR)
(CALIF)
(FED)
IGN SW
A/C COMP CTRL UNIT
TACH (INST CLSTR)
DECEL SHUTOFF MICRO SW
EZL IGNITION CONTROL UNIT
TD
31
31d
7
DIAG CONN
FUSE #9
DIAG CONN (CALIF ONLY)
COOLANT TEMP SENS (CALIF)
COOLANT TEMP SENS (FED)
FUEL PUMP CONTROL RELAY (WITH AUTO TRANS)
A/T KICKDOWN SW
A/T KICKDOWN SOLENOID


*Fig. 16: Wiring Diagram For Mercedes-Benz 260E, 300E, CE & TE CIS-E Fuel Injection System*

# 1988 COMPUTERIZED ENGINE CONTROLS
## Mercedes-Benz CIS-E System (Cont.)

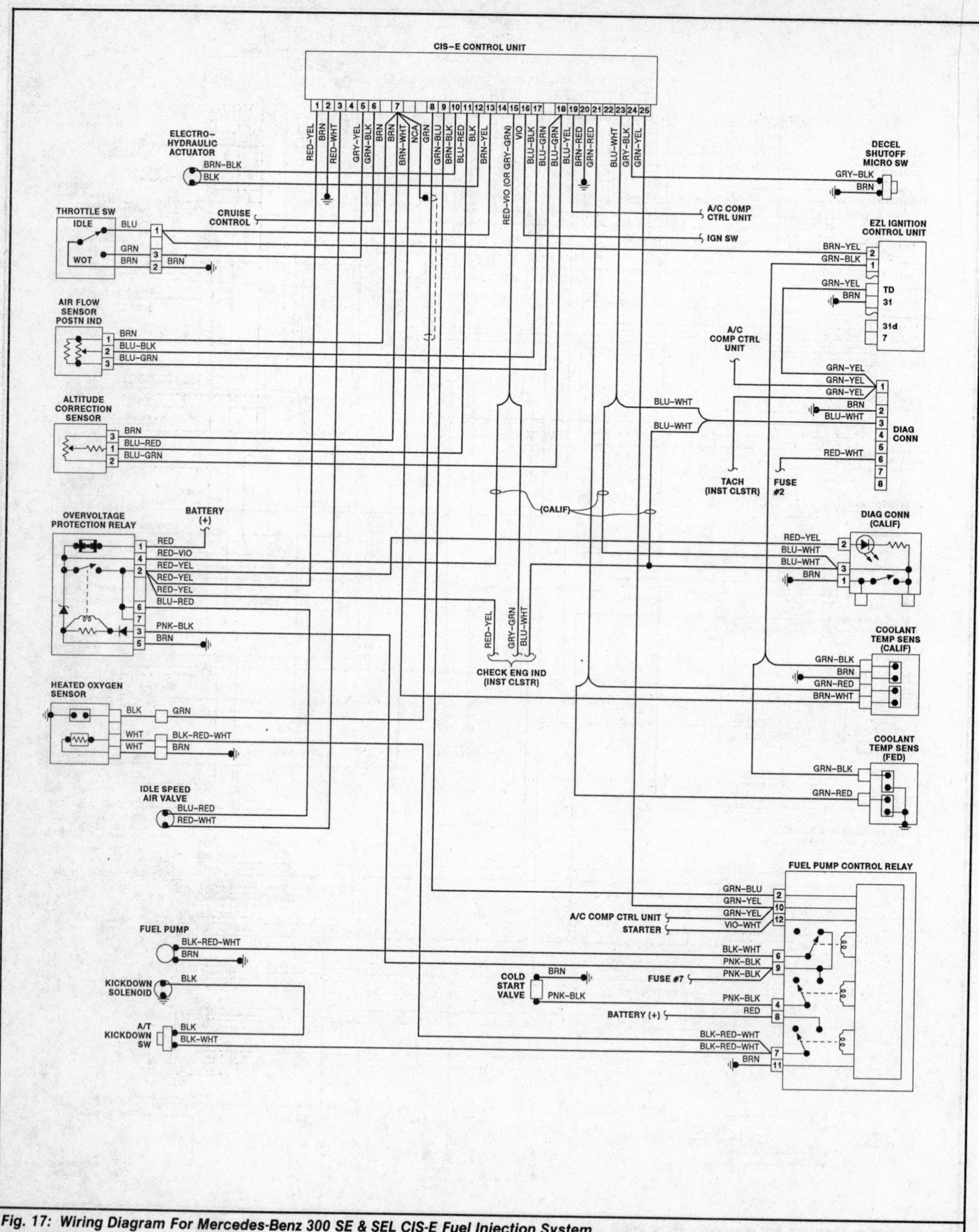
CIS-E CONTROL UNIT
ELECTRO-HYDRAULIC ACTUATOR
THROTTLE SW
IDLE
WOT
CRUISE CONTROL
AIR FLOW SENSOR POSTN IND
ALTITUDE CORRECTION SENSOR
OVERVOLTAGE PROTECTION RELAY
BATTERY (+)
HEATED OXYGEN SENSOR
IDLE SPEED AIR VALVE
FUEL PUMP
KICKDOWN SOLENOID
A/T KICKDOWN SW
COLD START VALVE
CHECK ENG IND (INST CLSTR)
(CALIF)
A/C COMP CTRL UNIT
IGN SW
TACH (INST CLSTR)
FUSE #2
DECEL SHUTOFF MICRO SW
EZL IGNITION CONTROL UNIT
TD
31
31d
DIAG CONN
DIAG CONN (CALIF)
COOLANT TEMP SENS (CALIF)
COOLANT TEMP SENS (FED)
FUEL PUMP CONTROL RELAY
STARTER
FUSE #7
BATTERY (+)

Fig. 17: Wiring Diagram For Mercedes-Benz 300 SE & SEL CIS-E Fuel Injection System

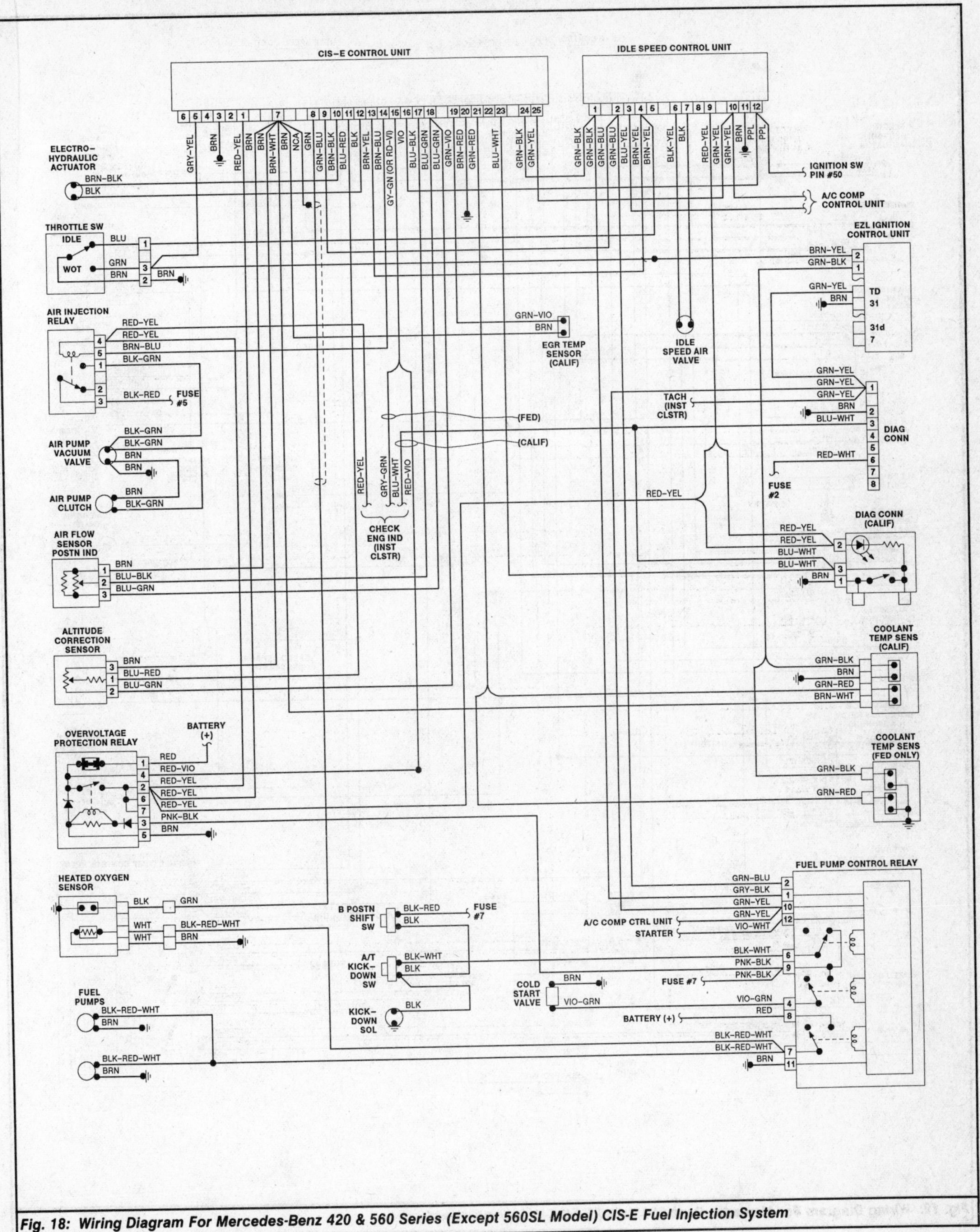
CIS-E CONTROL UNIT
IDLE SPEED CONTROL UNIT
ELECTRO-HYDRAULIC ACTUATOR
THROTTLE SW
IDLE
WOT
AIR INJECTION RELAY
FUSE #5
AIR PUMP VACUUM VALVE
AIR PUMP CLUTCH
AIR FLOW SENSOR POSTN IND
ALTITUDE CORRECTION SENSOR
OVERVOLTAGE PROTECTION RELAY
BATTERY (+)
HEATED OXYGEN SENSOR
FUEL PUMPS
IGNITION SW PIN #50
A/C COMP CONTROL UNIT
EZL IGNITION CONTROL UNIT
EGR TEMP SENSOR (CALIF)
IDLE SPEED AIR VALVE
TACH (INST CLSTR)
DIAG CONN
FUSE #2
(FED)
(CALIF)
CHECK ENG IND (INST CLSTR)
DIAG CONN (CALIF)
COOLANT TEMP SENS (CALIF)
COOLANT TEMP SENS (FED ONLY)
FUEL PUMP CONTROL RELAY
B POSTN SHIFT SW
FUSE #7
A/T KICK-DOWN SW
KICK-DOWN SOL
COLD START VALVE
A/C COMP CTRL UNIT
STARTER
BATTERY (+)

Fig. 18: Wiring Diagram For Mercedes-Benz 420 & 560 Series (Except 560SL Model) CIS-E Fuel Injection System

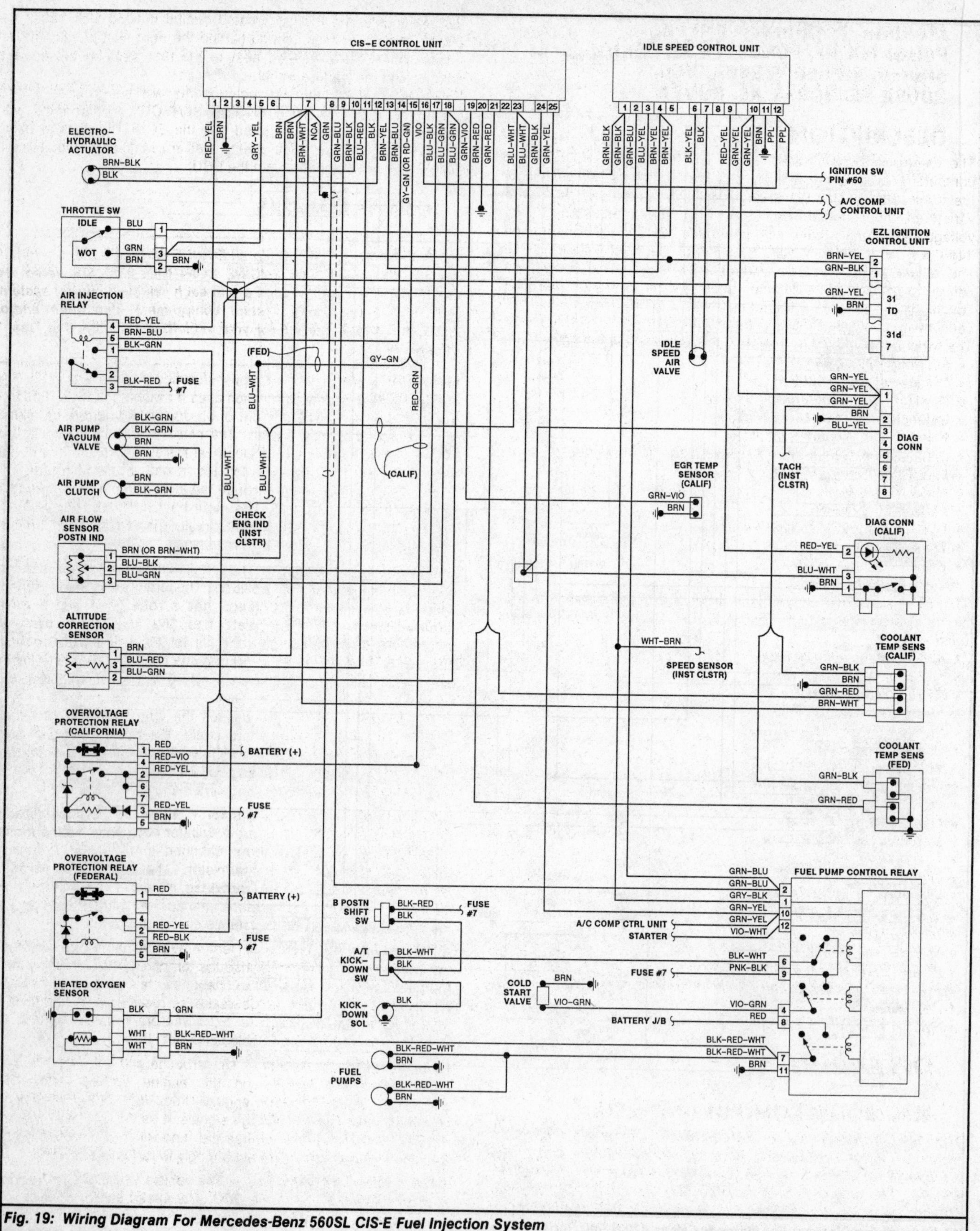
CIS-E CONTROL UNIT
IDLE SPEED CONTROL UNIT
ELECTRO-HYDRAULIC ACTUATOR
THROTTLE SW
IDLE
WOT
AIR INJECTION RELAY
FUSE #7
AIR PUMP VACUUM VALVE
AIR PUMP CLUTCH
AIR FLOW SENSOR POSTN IND
BRN (OR BRN-WHT)
ALTITUDE CORRECTION SENSOR
OVERVOLTAGE PROTECTION RELAY (CALIFORNIA)
BATTERY (+)
OVERVOLTAGE PROTECTION RELAY (FEDERAL)
HEATED OXYGEN SENSOR
(FED)
(CALIF)
CHECK ENG IND (INST CLSTR)
GY-GN (OR RD-GN)
IGNITION SW PIN #50
A/C COMP CONTROL UNIT
EZL IGNITION CONTROL UNIT
31
TD
31d
7
IDLE SPEED AIR VALVE
DIAG CONN
EGR TEMP SENSOR (CALIF)
TACH (INST CLSTR)
DIAG CONN (CALIF)
SPEED SENSOR (INST CLSTR)
COOLANT TEMP SENS (CALIF)
COOLANT TEMP SENS (FED)
FUEL PUMP CONTROL RELAY
A/C COMP CTRL UNIT
STARTER
B POSTN SHIFT SW
A/T KICK-DOWN SW
KICK-DOWN SOL
COLD START VALVE
FUSE #7
BATTERY J/B
FUEL PUMPS

Fig. 19: Wiring Diagram For Mercedes-Benz 560SL CIS-E Fuel Injection System

# 1988 COMPUTERIZED ENGINE CONTROLS
# Nissan Electronic Concentrated Control System

**Maxima, Pathfinder, Pickup, Pulsar NX XE, Pulsar NX SE, Sentra, Stanza, Stanza Wagon, Van, 200SX SE, 200SX XE, 300ZX**

## DESCRIPTION

The Electronic Concentrated Engine Control System (ECCS) is a computerized emission, ignition, and fuel control system. A single Electronic Control Unit (ECU) accepts input voltage signals from a variety of input components. The ECU compares each of the voltage input signals to a preset parameter which is preprogrammed into the ECU. It instantly analyzes each of the input voltage values and adjusts output voltage signals accordingly. This allows the vehicle to perform at its optimum under a wide variety of operating conditions. All vehicles are equipped with different combinations of sensors and engine control components. *See Figs. 1 through 12.*

The sensors inputting information to the ECU include the following:

- Air Temperature Sensor
- Crankshaft Angle Sensor
- Cylinder Head Temperature Sensor
- Detonation Sensor (Turbo Models)
- Exhaust Gas Oxygen Sensor
- Exhaust Gas Temperature Sensor (California Models)
- Fuel Temperature Sensor
- Mass Airflow Meter
- Park/Neutral Switch
- Power Steering Oil Pressure Switch
- Throttle Position Switch
- Vacuum Control Valve
- Vehicle Speed Sensor

The ECU processes information from these input sensors and sends appropriate voltage control signals to the following engine controls:

- Airflow Meter Self-Cleaning
- Air Induction Control Valve
- Air Regulator Control
- Auxilary Air Control Valve
- Canister Purge Valve
- Denotation Sensor
- EGR Control Solenoid Valve
- Exhaust Gas Sensor Heater Control
- Fail-Safe System
- Fuel Injectors
- Fuel Pressure Regulator
- Fuel Pump Control
- Idle Air Adjusting Unit
- Idle Speed Control Valve
- Idle-Up Solenoid
- Mixture Heater
- Mixture Ratio Feedback Control
- Power Transistor(s) & Ignition Coil(s)
- Pressure Regulator Control Solenoid Valve
- Self-Diagnostics
- Spark Plug Switching Control

## OPERATION

### ELECTRONIC CONTROL UNIT (ECU)

The ECU consists of a microcomputer, inspection lights, a diagnostic mode selector (or on/off switch), connectors and wiring for voltage signal input, voltage signal output and power supply. *See Fig. 13.* The unit is not serviceable and should not be opened. Monitor lights are provided on side of unit so system operation can be checked. The control unit contains memory and logic circuits that enable it to interpret sensor inputs and control various engine systems. On Maxima, Pathfinder/Pickup, Pulsar, Sentra and Stanza models, the ECU is located under the passenger seat. On Stanza Wagon models, the ECU is located under the driver's seat. On 200SX models, the ECU is located behind the left kick panel. On 300ZX models, ECU is located behind the right kick panel. On Van models, the ECU is located next to the rear seat on the driver's side, behind the left kick panel.

For ease of understanding, components will be grouped into 2 categories. The first being ENGINE SENSORS, components with voltage signals that are inputted into the ECU. The second being ENGINE CONTROLS, components that are controlled with voltage signals that are outputted from the ECU.

### ENGINE SENSORS

***NOTE: Vehicles do not contain all ENGINE SENSORS that are listed, nor do they control all ENGINE CONTROLS that are listed. To determine which components are in each vehicle's control system, refer to the applicable system components illustration and/or applicable wiring diagram for your vehicle application. See Figs. 1 through 12.***

**Mass Airflow Meter** – Two types of airflow meters are used. The first is a potentiometer type which uses a swinging door to measure the rate of air flow. The amount of air door movement is translated to the ECU via voltage signals. The second type measures airflow by monitoring the change of electrical resistance in the circuit that dissipates heat from the wire located in path of incoming air. The more incoming air entering through the airflow meter, the more heat removed from the hot wire. The more heat removed from hot wire the less resistance present in that circuit. The ECU evaluates the air flow rate through this change in resistance.

**Crankshaft Angle Sensor** – The crankshaft angle sensor monitors engine speed and piston position. The crankshaft angle sensor, which is built into the distributor, has a rotor plate and a wave-forming circuit. The rotor plate has 360 small slits, each slit determines crankshaft angle (one slit for each degree of rotation) and 4 or 6 large slits at 90 or 60 degrees each, to determine engine speed (4 slits at 90 degrees on 4 cyl., 6 slits at 60 degrees on 6 cyl.).

When the signal rotor plate passes the space between the Light Emitting Diode (LED) and photo diode, the slit in the signal rotor plate alternately cuts the light which is sent to the photo diode from the LED. This causes a pulsating voltage, which is converted into an on-off pulse by the wave-forming circuit and sent to the ECU.

**Cylinder Head Temperature Sensor** – A cylinder head temperature sensor is installed or built into the cylinder head near the thermostat housing. The sensor monitors changes in temperature through resistance readings of a thermistor. The thermistor, which is incorporated in the sensor, provides a varying resistance measurement as engine temperature changes. As temperature around the sensor increases, the resistance decreases.

**Air Temperature Sensor** – Air temperature sensors are installed in the intake air passage and sense the temperature of incoming air. A thermistor, which is sensitive to changes in temperature of incoming air, is used to increase or decrease its resistance in response to temperature rise or fall. The ECU interprets these signals and adjusts its output control signals accordingly.

**Detonation (Knock) Sensor** – On turbocharged vehicles, the detonation sensor is located on the engine cylinder block. The detonation sensor detects engine "knocking" and converts the "knocking" intensity into voltage signals. It sends a voltage signal to the ECU identifying how intense the "knocking" is. The control unit then modifies ignition timing accordingly to reduce detonation.

**Vehicle Speed Sensor (VSS)** – The vehicle speed sensor provides a vehicle speed signal to the ECU. The speed sensor consists of a reed switch, which is installed in the speedometer unit and transforms vehicle speed into a pulse signal. On digital type speedometer models, the sensor consists of an LED, photo diode, shutter and wave forming circuit. Its operating principle is the same as the crank angle sensor.

Pressure Regulator Control Solenoid Valve
Idle-Up Solenoid
FICD Solenoid
Air Regulator
EGR Control Valve
Fuel Filter
EGR Control Solenoid Valve
Fuel Temperature Sensor
AIV Control Solenoid Valve
Pressure Regulator
AIV Unit
Airflow Meter
Cylinder Head Temperature Sensor
Idle Switch
Throttle Chamber
BCDD
ECCS Relay
Ignition Coil & Power Transistor
Crank Angle Sensor
Injector
Exhaust Gas Sensor

Courtesy of Nissan Motor Co., U.S.A.

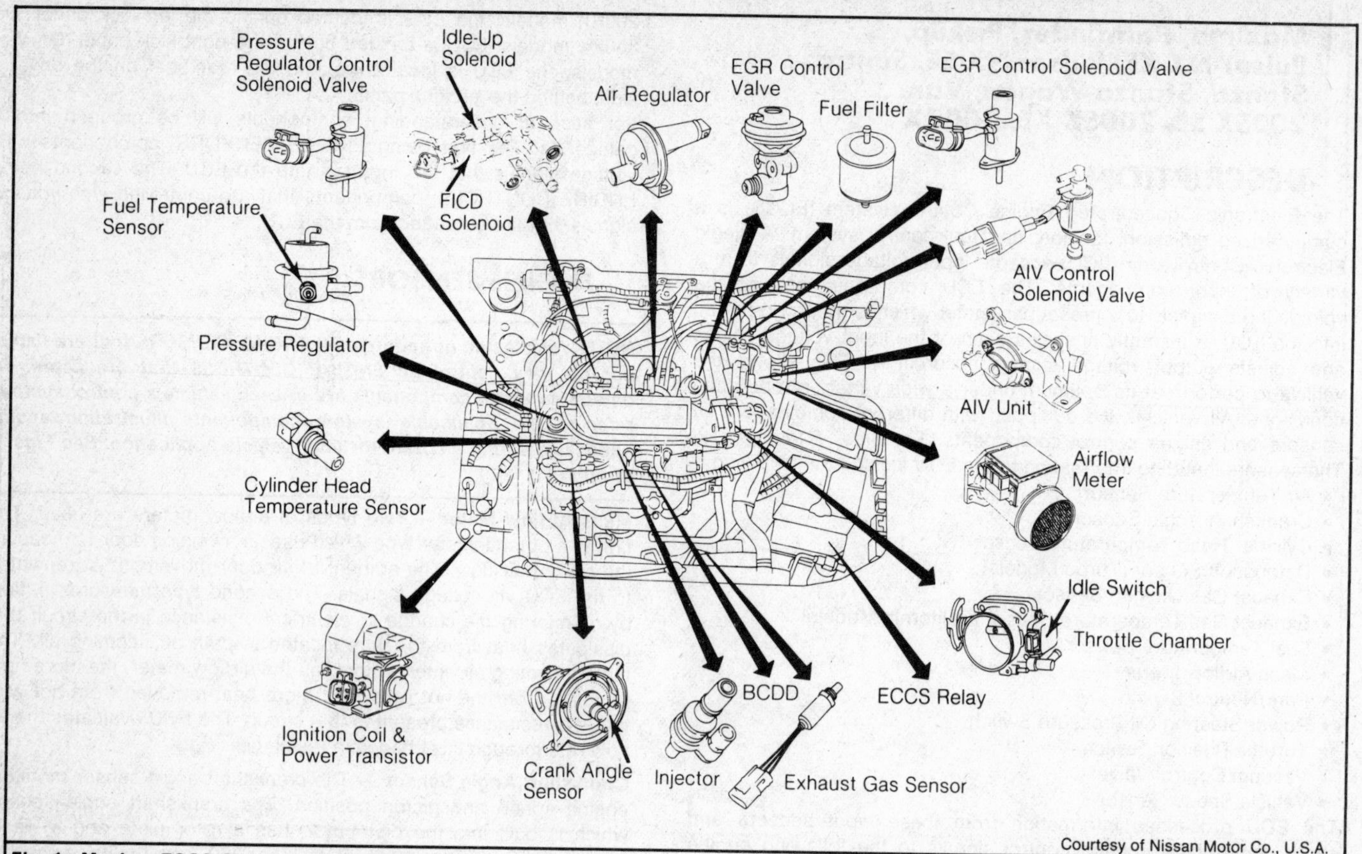

***Fig. 1: Maxima ECCS Component Locations***

EGR Control Valve
BPT Valve
AB Valve
Air Temperature Sensor
Exhaust Gas Sensor
Fuel Filter
AIV Vacuum Cut Solenoid Valve
Exhaust Gas Temperature Sensor
AIV Box
(4WD)
(2WD)
(Cap Color -Red)
AIV Case (For Cold AIV)
Mixture Heater
INTAKE SIDE
EGR Vacuum Cut Solenoid Valve
Ignition Coil & Power Transistor
Coolant Temperature Sensor
Crank Angle Sensor
EXHAUST SIDE
(Cap Color-Black)

Courtesy of Nissan Motor Co., U.S.A.

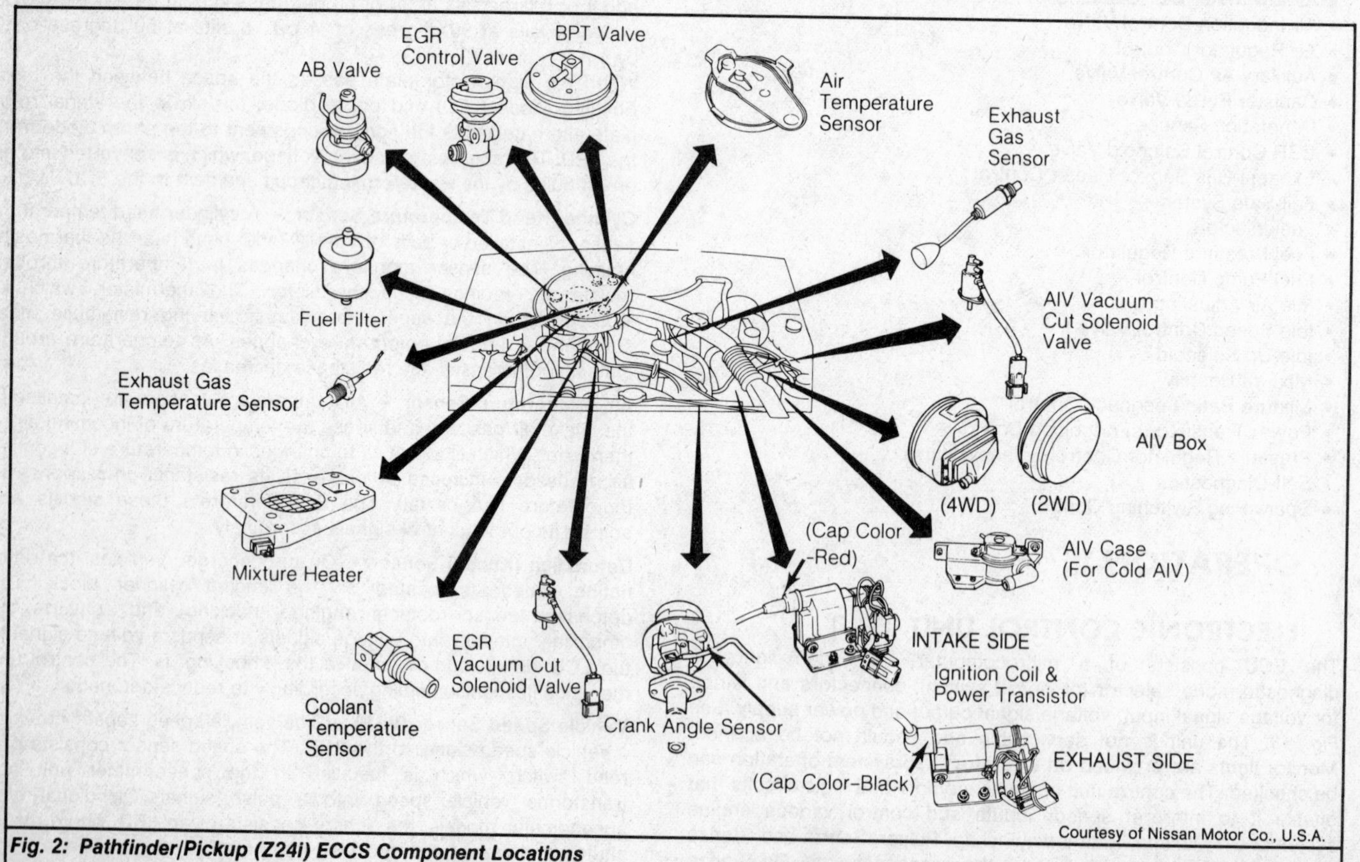

***Fig. 2: Pathfinder/Pickup (Z24i) ECCS Component Locations***

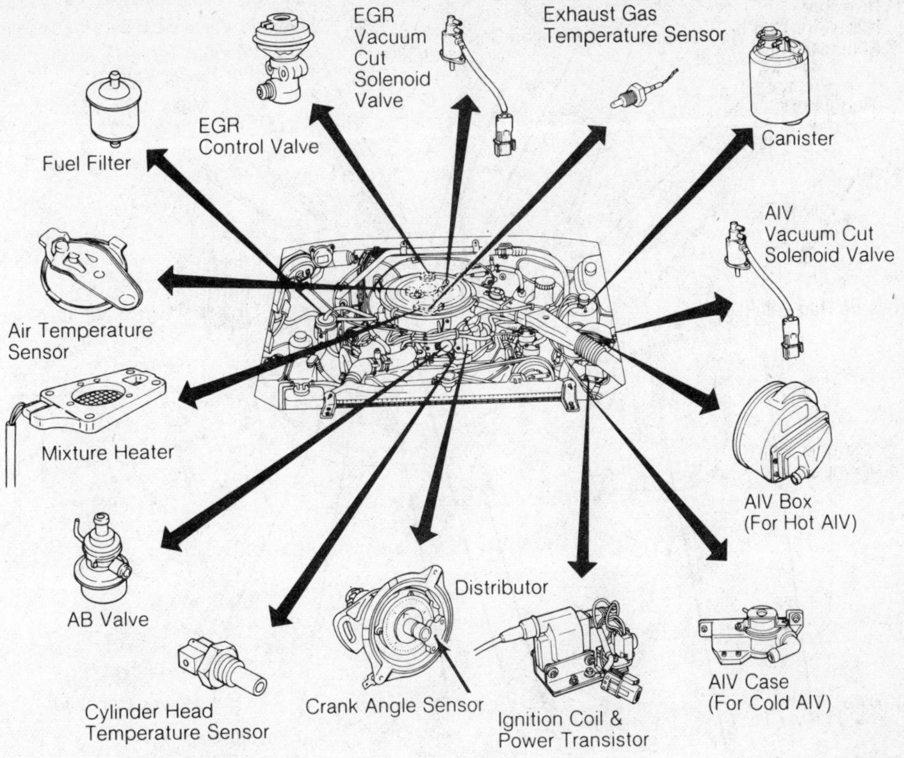

EGR Vacuum Cut Solenoid Valve
Exhaust Gas Temperature Sensor
Fuel Filter
EGR Control Valve
Canister
AIV Vacuum Cut Solenoid Valve
Air Temperature Sensor
Mixture Heater
AIV Box (For Hot AIV)
AB Valve
Distributor
Cylinder Head Temperature Sensor
Crank Angle Sensor
Ignition Coil & Power Transistor
AIV Case (For Cold AIV)

Courtesy of Nissan Motor Co., U.S.A.

***Fig. 3: Pathfinder/Pickup (VG30i) ECCS Component Locations***

Throttle Body Assembly
Fuel Filter
Mixture Heater
Carbon Canister
AIV Control Valve
Coolant Temperature Sensor
Ignition Coil & Power Transistor
AIV Control Solenoid Valve
EGR & Canister Control Solenoid Valve
Exhaust Gas Sensor
BPT Valve
Crank Angle Sensor
EGR Control Valve

Courtesy of Nissan Motor Co., U.S.A.

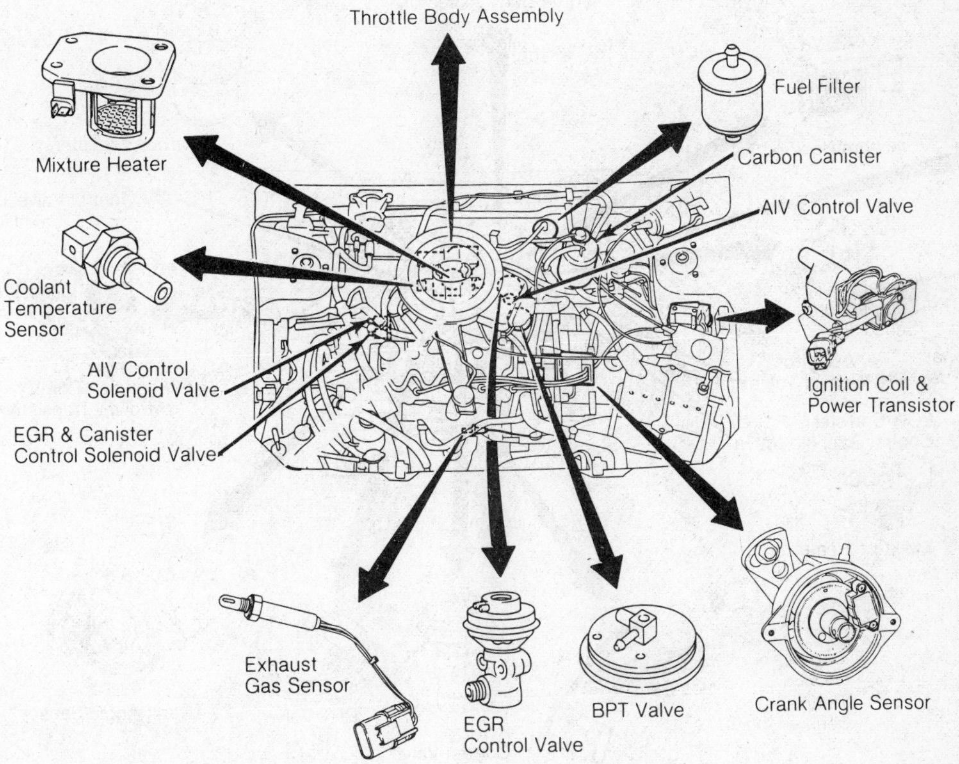

***Fig. 4: Pulsar NX SE ECCS Component Locations***

# Nissan Electronic Concentrated Control System (Cont.)

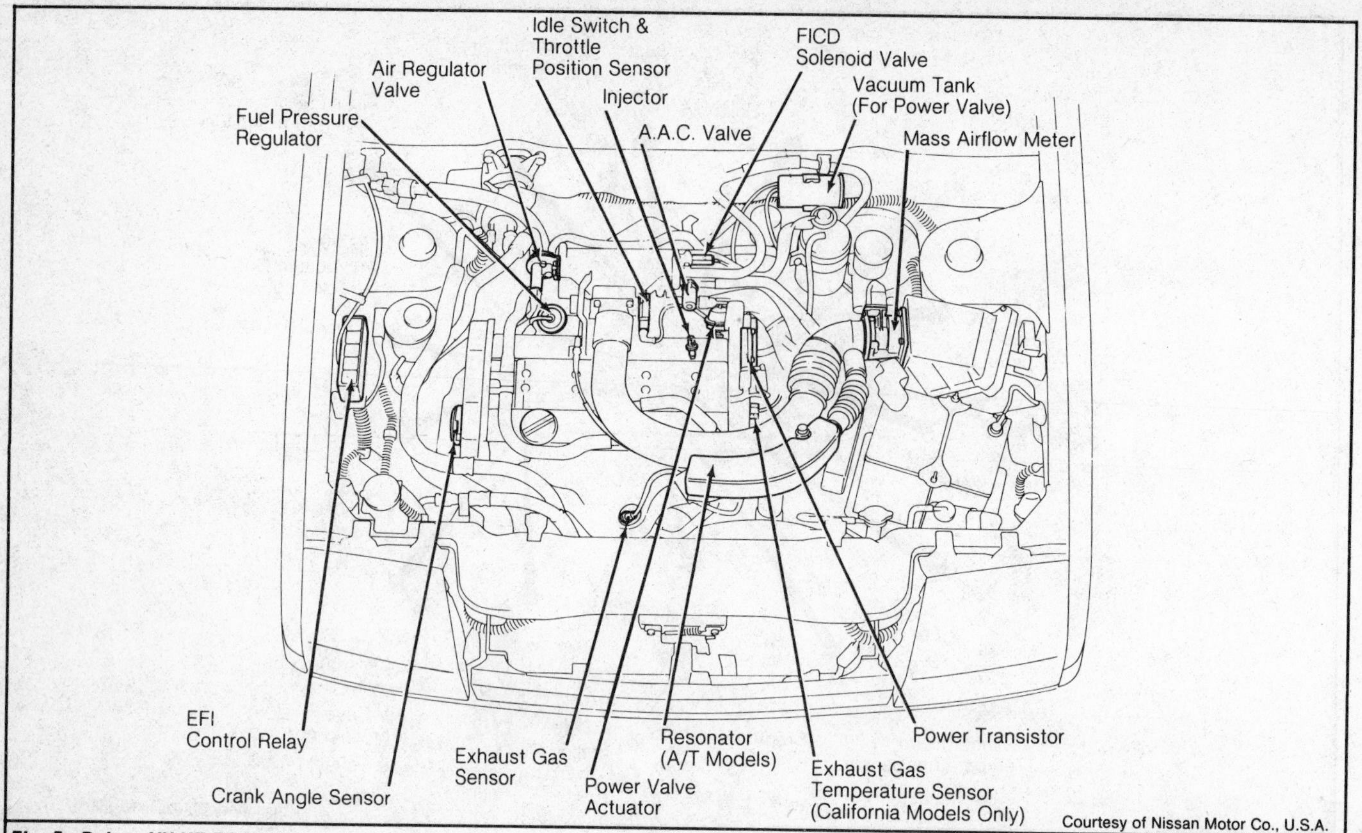

Idle Switch &
Throttle
Position Sensor
Air Regulator
Valve
FICD
Solenoid Valve
Vacuum Tank
(For Power Valve)
Injector
Fuel Pressure
Regulator
A.A.C. Valve
Mass Airflow Meter
EFI
Control Relay
Crank Angle Sensor
Exhaust Gas
Sensor
Power Valve
Actuator
Resonator
(A/T Models)
Exhaust Gas
Temperature Sensor
(California Models Only)
Power Transistor
Courtesy of Nissan Motor Co., U.S.A.

***Fig. 5:* Pulsar NX XE ECCS Component Locations**

Throttle Body Assembly
AIV For Catalyst
(4WD)
Mixture Heater
Fuel Filter
Carbon Canister
AIV Control Valve
Coolant
Temperature
Sensor
AIV Control
Solenoid Valve
EGR/Canister
Control Solenoid Valve
Ignition Coil &
Power Transistor
Exhaust
Gas Sensor
EGR
Control Valve
BPT Valve
Crank Angle Sensor
Courtesy of Nissan Motor Co., U.S.A.

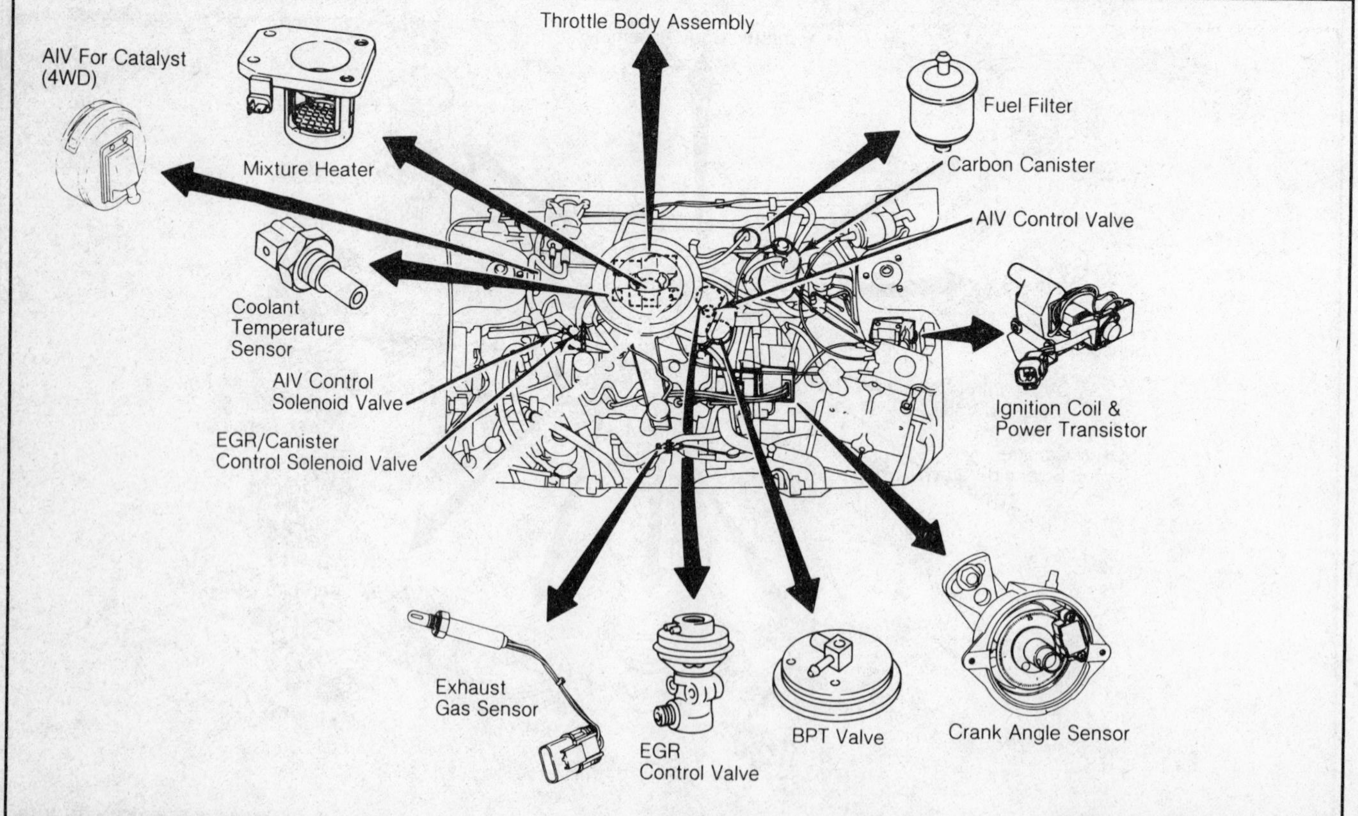

***Fig. 6:* Sentra ECCS Component Locations**

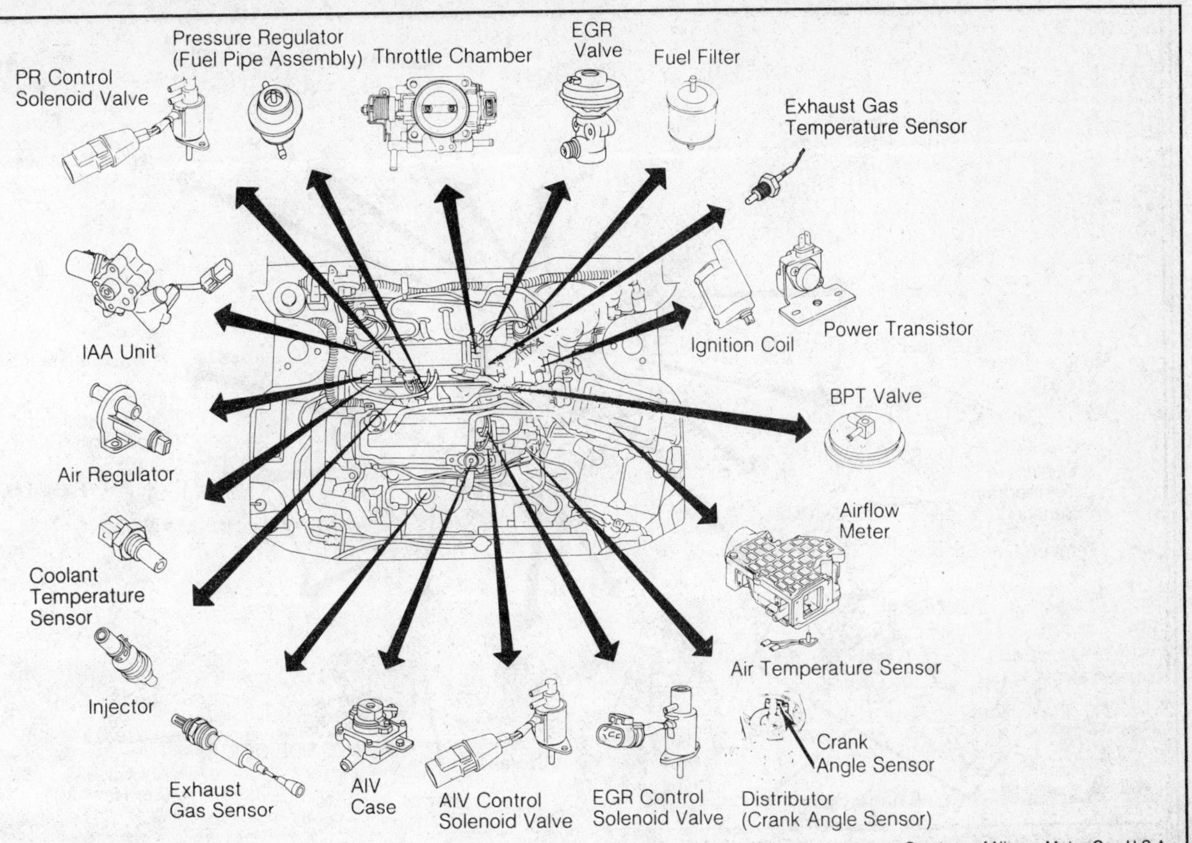

PR Control Solenoid Valve
Pressure Regulator (Fuel Pipe Assembly)
Throttle Chamber
EGR Valve
Fuel Filter
Exhaust Gas Temperature Sensor
IAA Unit
Ignition Coil
Power Transistor
BPT Valve
Air Regulator
Airflow Meter
Coolant Temperature Sensor
Injector
Air Temperature Sensor
Crank Angle Sensor
Exhaust Gas Sensor
AIV Case
AIV Control Solenoid Valve
EGR Control Solenoid Valve
Distributor (Crank Angle Sensor)

Courtesy of Nissan Motor Co., U.S.A.

***Fig. 7: Stanza ECCS Component Locations***

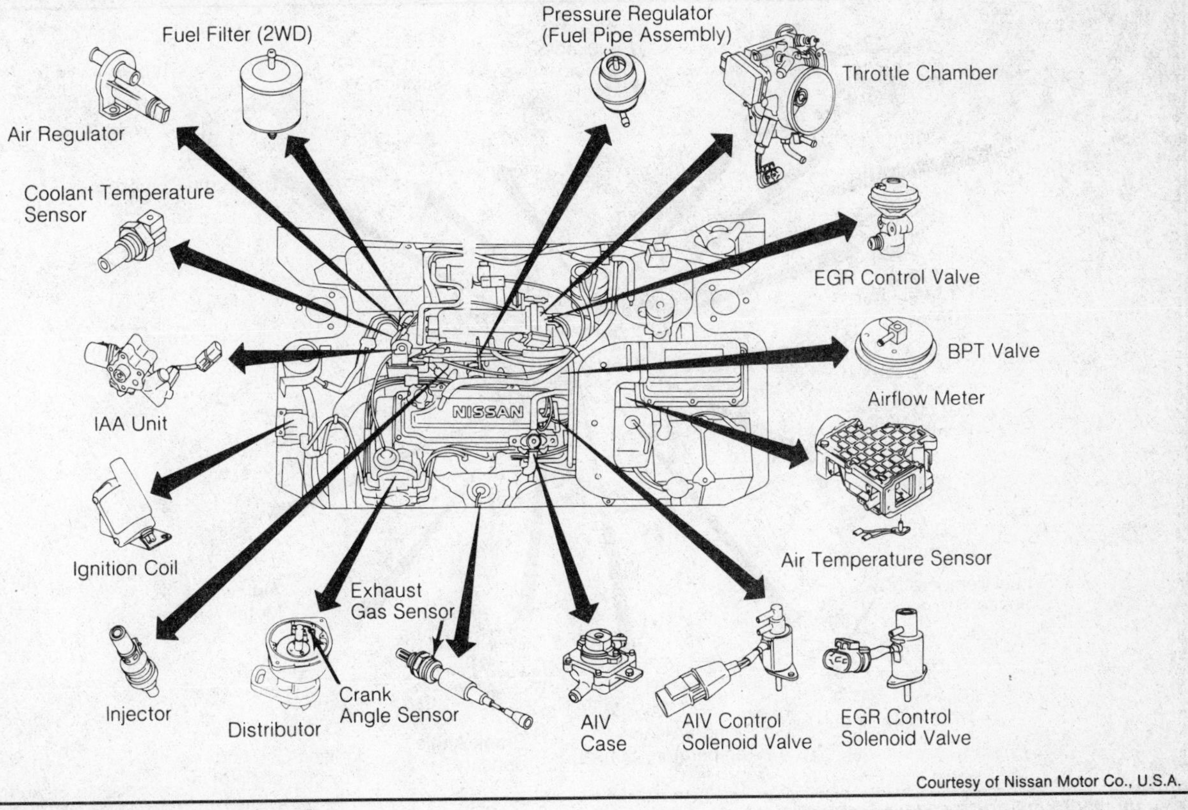

Fuel Filter (2WD)
Pressure Regulator (Fuel Pipe Assembly)
Throttle Chamber
Air Regulator
Coolant Temperature Sensor
EGR Control Valve
BPT Valve
IAA Unit
Airflow Meter
Ignition Coil
Air Temperature Sensor
Exhaust Gas Sensor
Injector
Distributor
Crank Angle Sensor
AIV Case
AIV Control Solenoid Valve
EGR Control Solenoid Valve

Courtesy of Nissan Motor Co., U.S.A.

***Fig. 8: Stanza Wagon ECCS Component Locations***

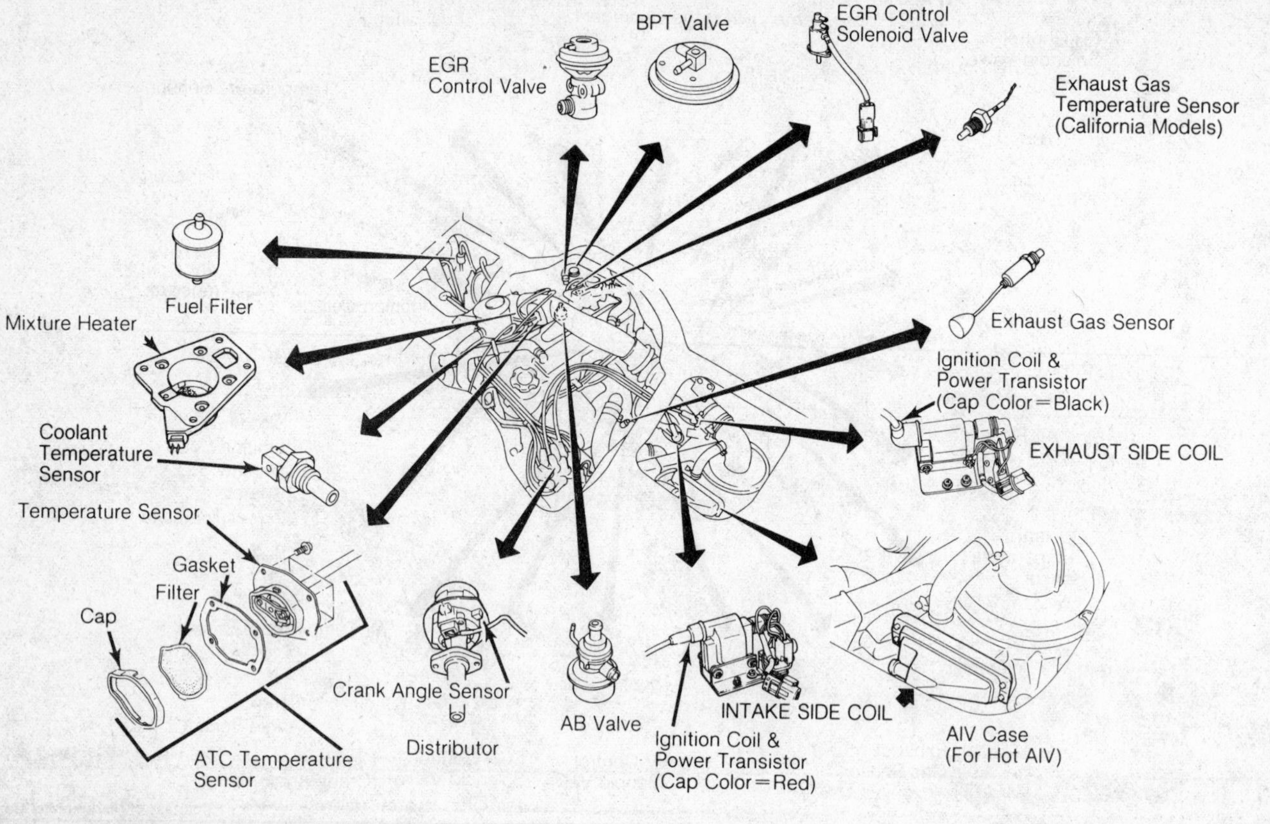

BPT Valve
EGR Control Solenoid Valve
EGR Control Valve
Exhaust Gas Temperature Sensor (California Models)
Fuel Filter
Mixture Heater
Exhaust Gas Sensor
Ignition Coil & Power Transistor (Cap Color = Black)
EXHAUST SIDE COIL
Coolant Temperature Sensor
Temperature Sensor
Gasket
Filter
Cap
Crank Angle Sensor
AB Valve
INTAKE SIDE COIL
Distributor
ATC Temperature Sensor
Ignition Coil & Power Transistor (Cap Color = Red)
AIV Case (For Hot AIV)

Courtesy of Nissan Motor Co., U.S.A.

**Fig. 9: Van ECCS Component Locations**

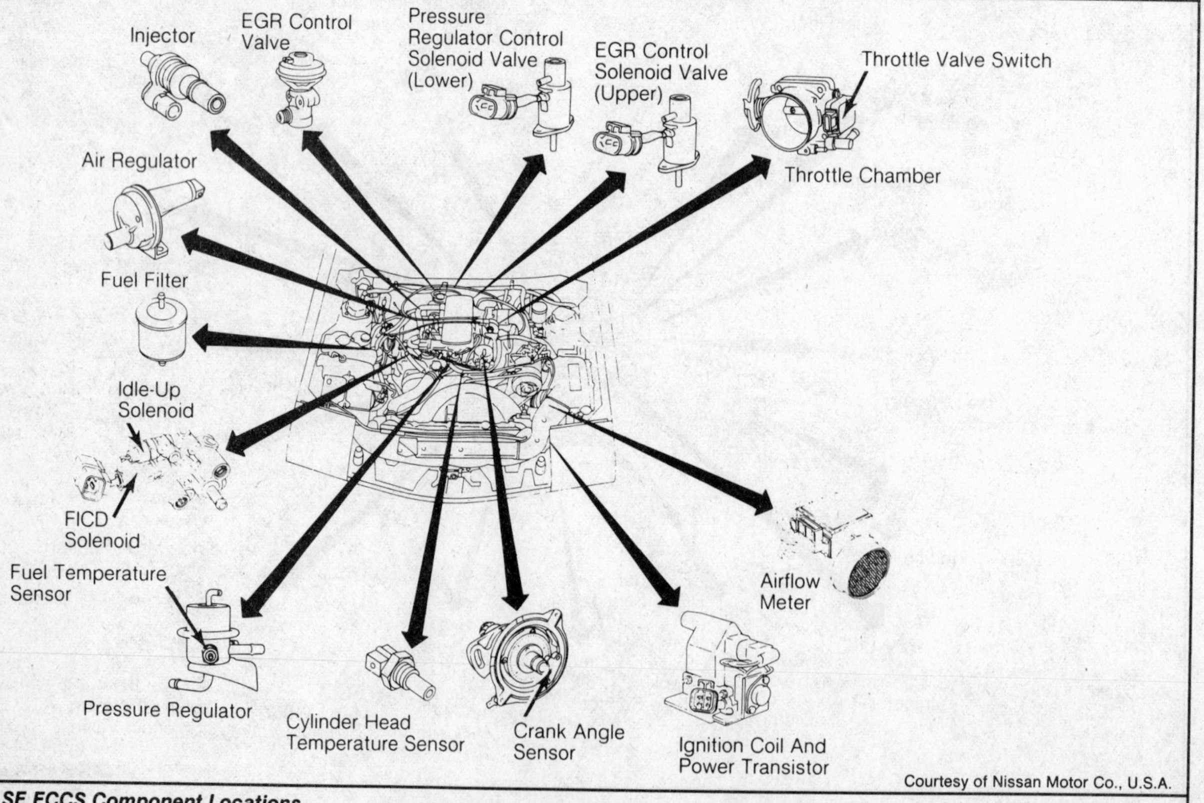

Injector
EGR Control Valve
Pressure Regulator Control Solenoid Valve (Lower)
EGR Control Solenoid Valve (Upper)
Throttle Valve Switch
Air Regulator
Throttle Chamber
Fuel Filter
Idle-Up Solenoid
FICD Solenoid
Fuel Temperature Sensor
Airflow Meter
Pressure Regulator
Cylinder Head Temperature Sensor
Crank Angle Sensor
Ignition Coil And Power Transistor

Courtesy of Nissan Motor Co., U.S.A.

**Fig. 10: 200SX SE ECCS Component Locations**

# 1988 COMPUTERIZED ENGINE CONTROLS
## Nissan Electronic Concentrated Control System (Cont.)

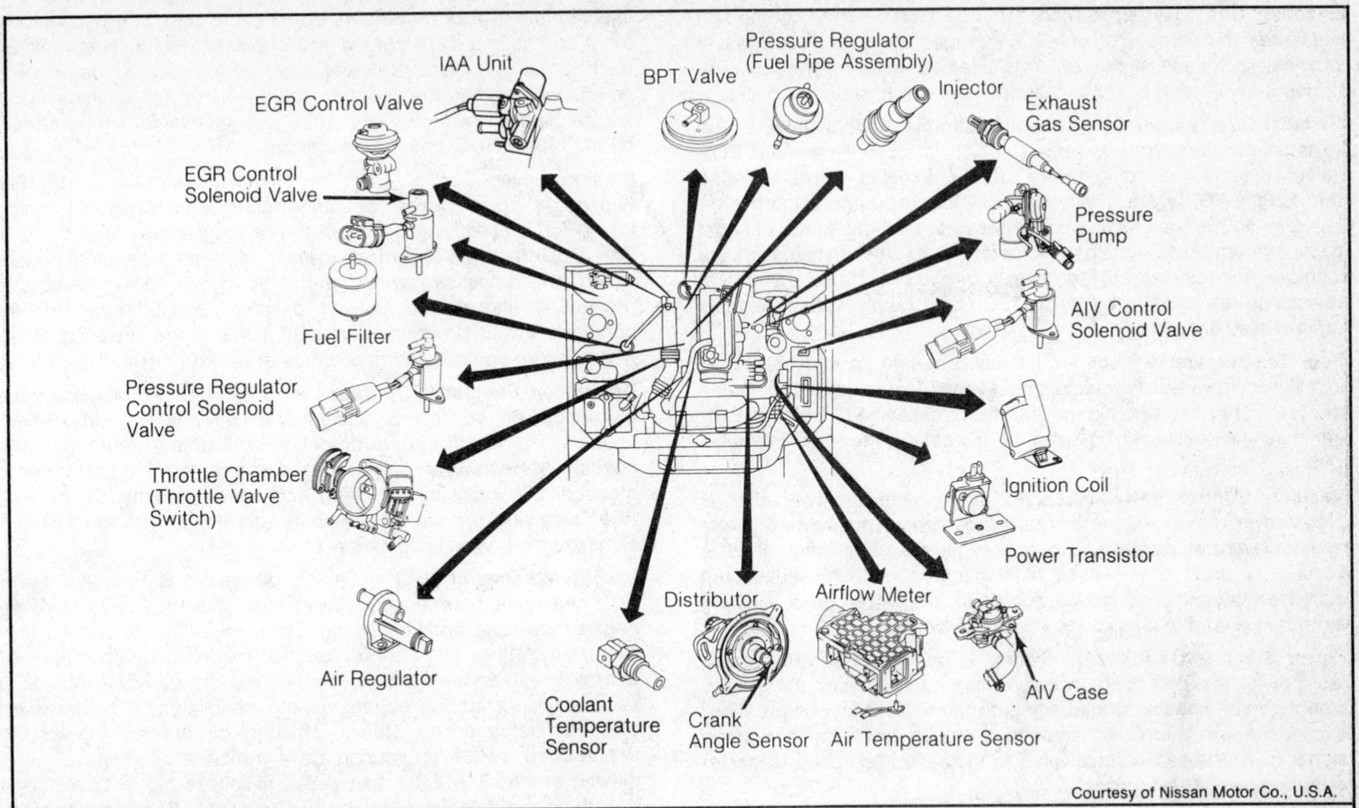

IAA Unit
EGR Control Valve
BPT Valve
Pressure Regulator (Fuel Pipe Assembly)
Injector
Exhaust Gas Sensor
EGR Control Solenoid Valve
Pressure Pump
AIV Control Solenoid Valve
Fuel Filter
Pressure Regulator Control Solenoid Valve
Throttle Chamber (Throttle Valve Switch)
Ignition Coil
Power Transistor
Distributor
Airflow Meter
Air Regulator
AIV Case
Coolant Temperature Sensor
Crank Angle Sensor
Air Temperature Sensor

Courtesy of Nissan Motor Co., U.S.A.

***Fig. 11: 200SX XE ECCS Component Locations***

EGR Control Solenoid Valve
EGR Control Valve
Throttle Valve Switch
Exhaust Gas Sensor
Exhaust Gas Temperature Sensor
Throttle Chamber
Turbocharger
Air Regulator
Ignition Coil
Power Transistor
Fuel Filter
Pressure Regulator Control Soleniod Valve
Detonation Sensor (VG30E) Engine)
Idle-Up Solenoid Valve (VG30E Engine)
Injector
FICD
FICD
Airflow Meter
Auxiliary Air Control (AAC) Valve (VG30ET Engine)
Pressure Regulator (With Fuel Temperature Sensor)
Cylinder Head Temperature Sensor
AIV Unit
Distributor
Crank Angle Sensor
AIV Control Solenoid Valve

Courtesy of Nissan Motor Co., U.S.A.

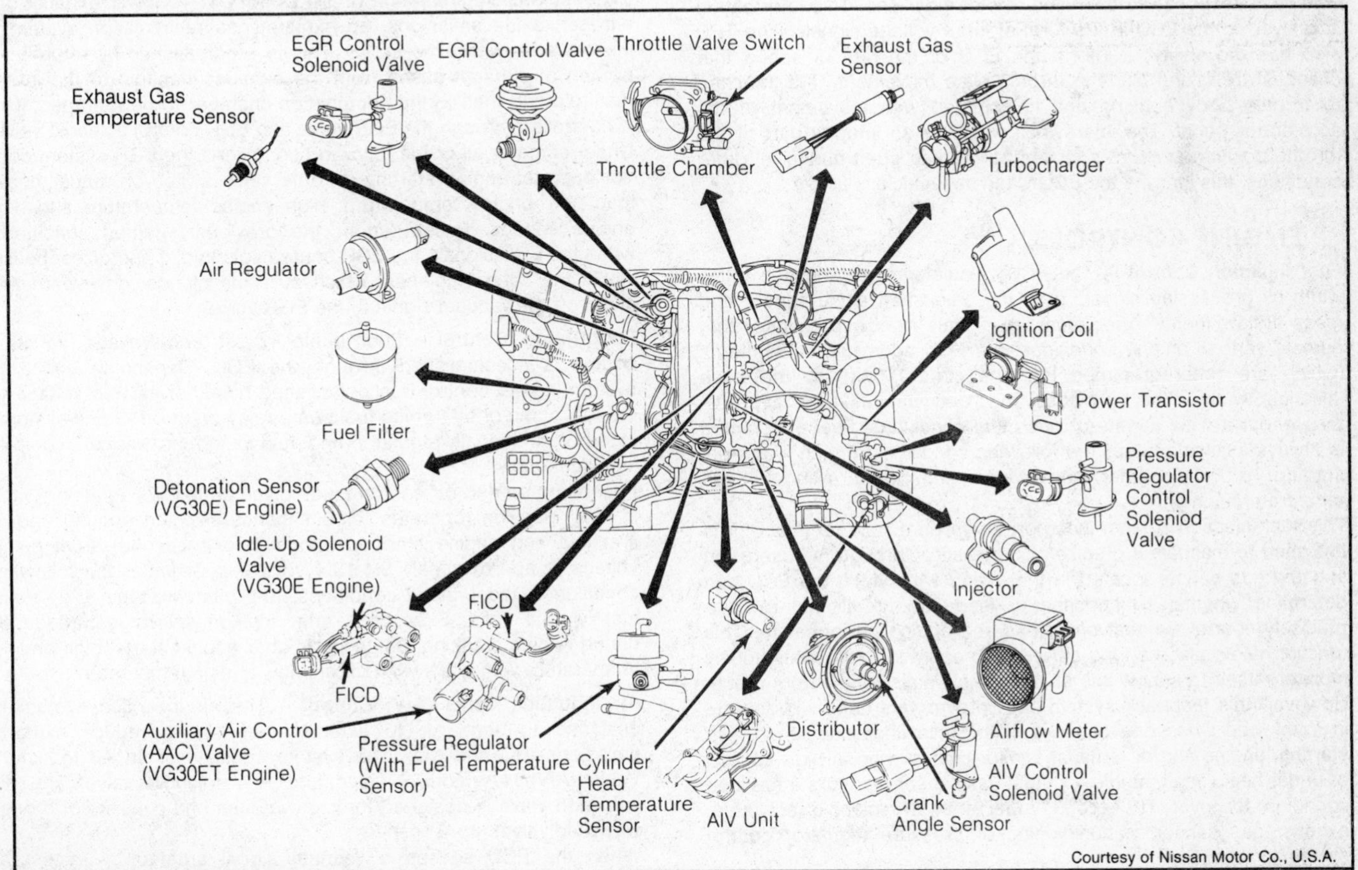

***Fig. 12: 300ZX ECCS Component Locations***

**Exhaust Gas Oxygen Sensor ($O_2$ Sensor)** – This component measures the amount of unburned oxygen in the exhaust gas. It provides a voltage signal which is used to adjust air/fuel mixture (amount of injection time), so that optimum combustion can occur.

**Exhaust Gas Temperature Sensor (California Models Only)** – The exhaust gas temperature sensor, which is located near the EGR valve, detects the temperature of the exhaust gases passing through the EGR valve. The sensor which incorporates a thermistor, changes its resistance value in response to changes in the exhaust gas temperatures. As the temperature of the exhaust gases increase, the resistance of the sensor decreases. These changes of resistance are interpreted by the ECU and output voltage signals are modified accordingly.

**Fuel Temperature Sensor** – The fuel temperature sensor is built into the fuel pressure regulator and senses fuel temperature. When the fuel temperature is higher than the prespecified level, the ECU enriches the fuel being injected by increasing the injection pulse width.

**Vacuum Control Valve (VCV)** – The vacuum control valve is provided to reduce engine lubricating oil consumption when intake manifold vacuum increases due to very high level deceleration. The vacuum control valve senses high manifold vacuum, as vacuum increases beyond a predetermined point, the valve opens allowing air to be pulled directly into the intake manifold.

**Power Steering Oil Pressure Switch** – This switch is attached to the power steering high pressure line and detects the power steering load, sending a load signal to the ECU. When oil pressure exceeds a predetermined amount, the ECU will send a voltage signal to idle speed control valve to increase idle speed to assist with the power steering load.

**Throttle Position Sensor (TPS) & Idle Switch** – The throttle position sensor incorporates a potentiometer which varies output voltage in response to changing throttle positions. This information is relayed to the ECU in the form of input voltage signals. The TPS also has the ability to inform the ECU of the rate of speed that changes are taking place in throttle plate movement. It is attached to throttle body housing and is actuated with movement of the accelerator pedal. The idle switch, which is an integral part of the throttle position sensor, is closed at idle and open during all other conditions, this informs the ECU when the vehicle is at idle.

## ENGINE CONTROLS

**Fuel Injection Control** – The ECU calculates base injection pulse width by processing signals from the crankshaft angle sensor and mass airflow meter. After receiving signals from each sensor that detects various engine conditions, the ECU adds fuel enrichments (which are preprogrammed into the control unit), to the base injection width. This provides the optimum mixture available throughout a wide variety of operating conditions. Fuel enrichment is always available under the following conditions: during warm-up, starting, off idle, under heavy load and when cylinder head temperature is high.

This fuel injection system incorporates mixture ratio feedback. It is designed to maintain a precise mixture ratio. Through the use of an exhaust gas sensor located in the exhaust manifold, the ECU can determine whether to enrichen or lean out the air/fuel ratio to precisely control exhaust emissions and engine performance. This function takes place during closed loop operation and continuously monitors itself to stay within an acceptable emissions output range. However, this feedback system can be overridden and will operate in open loop when one or more of the following conditions exist: starting, engine and/or exhaust sensor cold, driving at high speeds or under heavy load, at idle, exhaust gas sensor monitors a too lean condition for over 10 seconds, fuel shut-off solenoid activated, exhaust gas sensor malfunctioning or pressure regulator control system in operation.

Two methods of multi-port fuel injection are used. They are simultaneous and group injection. In simultaneous injection, fuel is injected into all 4 or 6 cylinders at the same time. In group injection, the 4 or 6 injectors are divided into 2 groups and fuel is injected into each group of injectors separately. When any of the following conditions are met, fuel injection shifts from group to simultaneous: engine speed exceeds 300 RPM, cylinder head temperature is below 140°F (60°C) and during starting.

**Ignition Timing Control** – Ignition timing is controlled by the ECU depending upon engine operating conditions. Optimum ignition timing for each driving condition is pre-programmed into the ECU. The ECU receives electrical signals from its operating sensors which are processed within the logic circuit. After determining present driving conditions and optimum timing signal for that condition, the ECU outputs a voltage signal to the power transistor, which in turn controls timing advance or retard.

**Detonation Feedback Operation** – The retard system, controlled by denotation sensor, is designed exclusively for turbocharged engines. The retard system does not work under normal operating conditions. However, if engine knock occurs, the detonation sensor monitors the knocking condition and sends a signal to the ECU. After receiving the signal, the ECU retards the ignition timing to eliminate the knocking condition.

**Idle Speed Control (ISC)** – Engine idle speed is controlled by the ECU depending upon engine operating conditions. The ECU senses engine operating conditions and determines the best idle speed. Under any (depending upon system) of the following conditions the ECU will send an on signal to compensate idle speed: starting to 20 seconds after start, low battery voltage, headlights on, heater switch on, rear defogger on, power steering oil pressure switch on, radiator fan switch on, during deceleration and when vehicle is moving at idle. The ECU then sends a voltage signal to either the idle-up solenoid or the Auxiliary Air Control (AAC) valve (depending upon system) to either reduce or increase idle speed.

**Exhaust Gas Recirculation (EGR) Control** – To lower exhaust gas nitrogen oxide emissions, an exhaust gas recirculation system is incorporated within the ECCS. This is accomplished by returning a portion of exhaust gases from the exhaust manifold to the intake manifold and then to the combustion chamber to be reburned. This is controlled through the EGR valve and EGR control solenoid valve. Under some or all of the following conditions the EGR system does not operate: engine starting, throttle valve switch on, under heavy load, low engine temperature, high engine temperature and high engine speeds. Except under the previously named conditions, when the ECU signals the EGR control solenoid, it energizes the coil within the control solenoid which pulls the plunger downward and shuts off the vacuum signal to the EGR valve.

**Fuel Pump Control** – Fuel pump on/off and voltage variation control is accomplished through the ECU. Depending upon the system in use, control is accomplished by either varying voltage to the fuel pump or by turning fuel pump relay on or off. Some systems incorporate the air regulator and fuel pump on and off controls simultaneously.

Fuel pump on and off control takes place as follows: ignition switch in "ON" position (operates for 5 seconds), engine running and/or cranking and engine stopped (stops in one second). Fuel pump voltage is approximately 9.4-13.4 volts except under the following conditions. Under these conditions, fuel pump voltage is approximately 13.4 volts: 5 seconds after ignition switch is turned off, during engine cranking, 30 seconds after engine starts, high engine temperature with idle switch off and low engine temperature.

**Air Induction Valve (AIV) Control** – The air induction system is designed to send air to exhaust manifold to reduce exhaust emissions (HC and CO). The system consists of an Air Induction Valve (AIV), AIV control valve and AIV solenoid valve. The air induction valve is designed for one-way use and consists of a one-way reed valve.

When the ECU senses a vacuum signal created by excessive exhaust pressure pulsations in the exhaust manifold, it sends a voltage signal to the AIV solenoid valve to activate the AIV control valve. The control valve opens up and allows air to enter the exhaust system upstream of the 3-way catalytic converter. This system also operates during deceleration for the purpose of blowing water off around the air injection valve.

**Fuel Pressure Regulator Control** – This system is designed to improve hot engine startability by cutting off intake manifold vacuum and increasing fuel pressure. When coolant temperature is above a preset limit and engine speed is lower than 2500 RPM or with a light load, the ECU sends a voltage signal to pressure regulator control solenoid valve. The electronic signal from the ECU energizes the coil inside of the pressure regulator control valve and pulls the plunger downward. This cuts off intake manifold vacuum and the positive pressure produced by pump is sent to the pressure regulator, therefore increasing fuel pressure. On some models, the fuel line is supplied with high pressure which is stored in a surge tank.

**Air Regulator Control** – The air regulator provides an air by-pass when engine is cold for purposes of fast idle during warm-up. A bi-metallic heater and rotary shutter valve control the rate of by-passing air. When the bi-metallic heater and shutter are cold, air by-pass port is open. As engine starts and an electrical current is permitted to flow through the bi-metallic heater, it warms up and closes the air by-pass port.

Some systems incorporate air regulator and fuel pump on and off controls simultaneously. Fuel pump and air regulator on and off control takes place as follows: ignition switch in "ON" position (operates for 5 seconds), engine running or cranking and engine stopped (stops in one second).

**Auxiliary Air Control Valve (AAC)** – The ECU processes signals from monitoring sensors to determine the optimum idle speed under varying engine conditions. The ECU senses engine condition and determines the best idle speed from the cylinder head temperature sensor and the transaxle gear position. It then sends an electrical on-off signal that corresponds to the difference between actual idle speed and optimum idle speed. The AAC valve then regulates the amount of by-passing air by monitoring the length of time that the electrical on signal is presented.

**Airflow Meter Self-Cleaning Control** – This system is designed to heat the "hot wire" of the airflow meter after ignition switch is turned to the "OFF" position. This is to clean any foreign matter that may have adhered to it during operation. After the engine has stopped, the ECU sends a signal to heat the "hot wire" to 1832°F (1000°C) to burn off any foreign material under the following conditions: if engine reached a certain predetermined RPM, vehicle speed reached a mimimum MPH, coolant temperature was between 2 preset standards and only when engine is stopped by ignition key (not stalled).

**Spark Plug Switching Control** – The spark plug switching system is designed to change ignition system firing from 2 spark plugs to one spark plug. Normally, depending upon the system, the switching of 2 spark plugs to one takes place during heavy load driving conditions in order to reduce engine noise. Under all other conditions, a 2 spark plug ignition system is in effect.

**Mixture Heater Control** – The mixture heater is located between the throttle valve and the intake manifold. It is designed to atomize fuel during cold engine starts. The ECU controls the on and off cycles of the mixture heater. When the coolant temperature is less than a preset mimimum and the engine is running the ECU will send an on signal to the mixture heater. The mixture heater will remain on several minutes after coolant temperature has reached the mimimum temperature preset requirement.

**Idle Air Adjusting (IAA) Unit** – The idle air adjusting unit is a combination of the Auxiliary Air Control (AAC) valve, Fast Idle Control Device (FICD), Vacuum Control Valve (VCV) and incorporates an idle speed adjusting screw. It receives its voltage signals from the ECU to control the idle speed at predetermined amounts depending on existing operating conditions.

## FAIL-SAFE SYSTEM CONTROL

**Mass Airflow Meter** – If airflow meter output voltage is less than or greater than the preprogrammed valve, the ECU senses an airflow meter malfunction signal. The ECU then temporarily takes its driving condition information from the throttle position sensor. During this period of time, the ECU limits the RPM of the vehicle to a preset amount. This serves to alert the vehicle driver that the vehicle is driving under fail-safe conditions and needs attention.

**Cylinder Head Temperature Sensor** – If the cylinder head temperature sensor circuit is open, the ECU will hold the injector pulse width to a preset amount. This preset amount is equivalent to when the cylinder head temperature is between 68°F (20°C) and 176°F (80°C), therefore allowing the vehicle to reach its destination.

**Fuel Pump** – Depending upon the system, if the ECU senses that the fuel pump circuit is malfunctioning, it will energize the fuel pump relay until the engine is stopped. Permitting the vehicle to reach its destination before repairing the problem.

**Injector Malfunctioning** – When the ECU senses that engine speed is less than a predetermined amount in the alternating injection mode (except during acceleration) and that injection pulse angle (crank angle) is less than a preset amount and at least one injector does not inject fuel 4 times in a row due to electrical problems, it determines there is an injector failure. If only one injector fails, the ECU will permit the vehicle to start and drive, but only to a predetermined maximum RPM. When the engine reaches this maximum RPM it will not go faster, indicating the fail-safe system is in effect and informing the driver that attention to the vehicle is needed.

## CHECK ENGINE LIGHT

**California Models Only** – All California vehicles are equipped with a "Check Engine" light located on the instrument panel. The light will illuminate when the ignition switch is turned to the "ON" position (bulb check) and when systems related to the emission controls are malfunctioning during normal operation (Mode 1) with the engine running.

***NOTE: Under normal operation, the vehicle operates in Mode 1 of self diagnostics. If an emission control problem is detected the "Check Engine" light will illuminate. Then the ECU automatically enters Mode 2 and the "Check Engine" light will flash simultaneously with the Red LED inspection light on the ECU. The trouble codes for each malfunction can be identified by entering Mode 3 and obtaining the identification trouble code for that fault.***

Depending on the vehicles control system, some or all of the following components are monitored by the "Check Engine" light function: Code 12-Mass Airflow Meter, Code 14-Vehicle Speed Sensor, Code 23-Idle Switch Circuit, Code 24-Full Throttle Switch Circuit, Code 31-Engine Control Unit (ECU), Code 32-EGR Function, Code 33-Exhaust Gas Sensor Circuit and Code 45-Injector Leakage.

# TESTING & DIAGNOSIS

## DESCRIPTION

The self-diagnostic system is used for diagnosing malfunctions of major sensors and actuators of the Electronic Concentrated Engine Control System (ECCS). There are 5 modes of diagnosis within the system. Before selecting any mode of self-diagnosis, always perform the PRELIMINARY CHECKS first or diagnostic results and/or diagnostic time may be invalid.

***CAUTION: When performing PRELIMINARY CHECKS, be careful not to erase any diagnostic information stored in the ECU memory. See MEMORY ERASE for procedures to avoid.***

Modes 1 and 2 are used for monitoring LED inspection lights which flash in accordance to the air/fuel mixture ratio. Mode 3 is used for obtaining trouble codes for component or circuit failures. Mode 4 is used to determine if malfunction(s) are present in the on/off controlled switches of the system. Mode 5 is used for monitoring the system and its components during actual driving conditions, usually to simulate an intermittent condition.

**Mode 1: Mixture Ratio Feedback Control Monitor "A"** – During normal vehicle operation the ECU is always in Mode 1. After warm-up and during closed loop operation, the Green LED inspection light turns on when a lean condition is detected and goes off when a rich condition is detected. During open loop operation, the Green LED light stays either on or off, which ever the light condition was just prior to switching to open loop. During open or closed loop operation, the Red inspection light stays off, with the exception of California models that have a "Check Engine" light that is illuminated on the instrument panel. See CHECK ENGINE LIGHT and MODES 1 & 2 MIXTURE RATIO MONITORS A & B CHART.

**Mode 2: Mixture Ratio Feedback Control Monitor "B"** – The Green inspection light functions the same as in Mode 1. During closed loop operation, Red inspection light turns on and off simultaneously with Green inspection light when mixture ratio is being controlled correctly within the specified range. If a rich condition is detected, the Red light will remain illuminated. If a lean condition is detected, the Red light will remain off. During open loop operation, the Red inspection light is simultaneous with the Green inspection light, with the exception of California models that have a "Check Engine" light that is illuminated on the instrument panel. See CHECK ENGINE LIGHT and MODES 1 & 2 MIXTURE RATIO MONITORS A & B CHART.

**Mode 3: Self-Diagnosis** – The ECU constantly monitors the operation of sensors and actuators, regardless of ignition key position. When a malfunction is suspected, the information can be retrieved from system memory by turning the diagnostic mode selector (or on/off switch Pathfinder/Pickup and Van models to "ON" position) on the side of ECU to Mode 3. *See Fig. 13.*

When properly activated, the Red and Green LED lights will flash appropriately to signal the code number of the malfunctioning part(s). First the Red light will flash and then the Green light will follow. Red light flashes refer to number of tens in the code number. Green light flashes refer to number of ones in the code number. All codes are classified in 2 digit numbers. For example, if Red light flashes once and Green light flashes twice, code 12 is detected. All codes are stored for 50 ignition starts from the time the malfunction is last detected. A code of 55 indicates no problem in components monitored by the ECU.

When diagnostic code(s) are obtained, refer to the SYSTEM INSPECTION TABLE that applies to the application of vehicle and perform the test that it refers to. If no diagnostic codes are obtained, define the driveability symptom and refer to the DRIVEABILITY INSPECTION TABLE that applies to that vehicle (perform Mode 4 first). There you will find a list of common driveability symptoms, find the symptom that your vehicle is exhibiting and check all the components in that column as well as any tests listed.

If engine cranks, but fails to start, crank engine more than 2 seconds prior to starting self-diagnosis in Mode 3. Do not erase stored memory codes prior to self-diagnosis (Mode 3) or intermittent malfunctions will be lost. Stored memory is lost if battery is disconnected or if Mode 4 is selected after Mode 3.

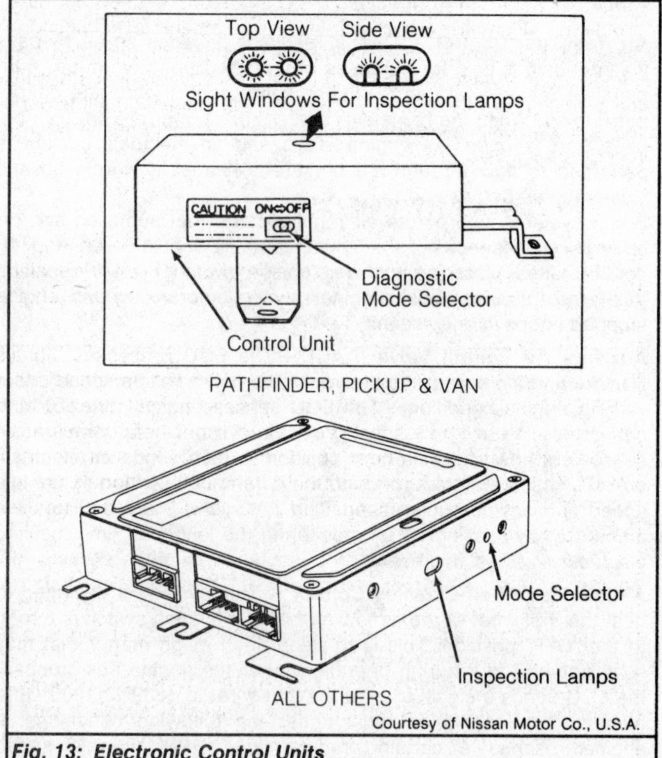
Top View
Side View
Sight Windows For Inspection Lamps
CAUTION
ON⇔OFF
Diagnostic Mode Selector
Control Unit
PATHFINDER, PICKUP & VAN
Mode Selector
Inspection Lamps
ALL OTHERS
Courtesy of Nissan Motor Co., U.S.A.

*Fig. 13: Electronic Control Units*

| Mode | LED | Engine stopped | Engine running: Open loop condition | Engine running: Closed loop condition | | |
|---|---|---|---|---|---|---|
| Mode I (Monitor A) | Green | ON | OFF | • OFF: rich condition<br>• ON: lean condition<br>• Maintains conditions before changing between open and closed loop | | |
| | Red | ON | OFF | OFF | | |
| Mode II (Monitor B) | Green | ON | OFF | • OFF: rich condition<br>• ON: lean condition<br>• Maintains conditions before changing between open and closed loop | | |
| | Red | OFF | OFF | Compensating mixture ratio | | |
| | | | | More than 5% rich | Between 5% lean and 5% rich | More than 5% lean |
| | | | | OFF | Synchronized with green LED | ON |

**MODES 1 & 2 MIXTURE RATIO FEEDBACK CONTROL MONITORS A & B CHART**

**Mode 4: Switches On-Off Diagnosis** - During this mode the ECU monitors the performance of the components that are controlled by on/off voltage signals. The ECU will monitor switch on-off conditions and store any malfunction information in ECU memory. The switches being monitored are the throttle switch, starter switch and the vehicle speed sensor.

To test operation of the throttle switch and/or starter switch while in Mode 4 of diagnosis, observe the Red LED light on the ECU. Each time ignition switch is turned from "ON" to "OFF" position or "OFF" to "ON" position, Red LED light should blink on or off each time switching is detected.

To test the vehicle speed sensor while in Mode 4 of diagnosis, observe Green LED light of ECU. When vehicle speed is less than 12 MPH, the Green light should be off. When vehicle speed exceeds 12 MPH, Green light on ECU should illuminate.

**Mode 5: Real Time Diagnosis** - This mode is used to detect problems within the active system. The moment a malfunction is detected the display lights will present the malfunctioning code immediately. Making this mode of inspection advantageous because the condition can be found by observing the inspection lights during the actual driving conditions under which the malfunction intermittent or otherwise takes place.

## PRELIMINARY CHECKS

***NOTE:* Prior to performing any diagnostics or engine related testing, perform all preliminary tests first. Set all adjustments to specifications listed on vehicle emissions decal.**

**1)** On all vehicles, check idle speed with automatic transmissions in "DRIVE" position (if equipped) and ensure correct idle RPM is obtained. Ensure ignition timing is set to proper specification. On Stanza, Stanza Wagon, PulsarNX SE and 200SX XE models, check idle CO to insure that it is less than 5% and 300ZX models are less than 8%. Follow procedures outlined in steps **2)** through **7)** to check CO output.

**2)** Disconnect throttle switch harness connector, exhaust gas sensor connector and install a 2500 ohm resistor into the temperature sensor circuit with sensor disconnected. On 300ZX models, acceptable CO level can be confirmed by ensuring that the Red LED light flashes in Mode 2.

**3)** On Maxima and 200SX SE ensure that CO levels are acceptable by confirming that the Red LED light flashes in Mode 2 with all systems in tact. On Sentra and PulsarNX XE models, race engine with all systems intact and immediately after engine returns to idle, confirm that both LED lights flash simultaneously in Mode 2.

**4)** On Van models, disconnect Air Induction Valve (AIV) and install a 2500 ohm resistor into the temperature sensor circuit with sensor disconnected. To confirm acceptable Co level, ensure that Red LED light flashes in Mode 2. On Pathfinder/Pickup models, confirm acceptable CO level by ensuring that Red LED light flashes in Mode 2.

**5)** On all models, maintain idle speed at middle engine speed (approximately 2000 RPM). On Maxima, 200SX XE, and 300ZX models, Green inspection light should flash 5 or more times in 10 seconds in Mode 1.

**6)** On PulsarNX XE and Sentra models, while in Mode 2 of diagnostics, confirm simultaneous flashes from Red and Green inspection lights. On PulsarNX SE, Stanza, Stanza Wagon and 200SX XE models, Red and Green inspection lights should flash simultaneously 9 or more times in 10 seconds while in Mode 2.

**7)** On Pathfinder/Pickup (VG30i), while in Mode 2 of diagnostics, Red and Green inspection lights should flash simultaneously 5 or more times in 10 seconds. On Pathfinder/Pickup (Z24i) and Van models, Red and Green inspection lights should flash simultaneously 7 or more times in 10 seconds while in Mode 2.

**8)** Perform an idle speed switch test. Idle speed should increase to the amount specified in the IDLE SWITCH SPEED INCREASES chart when idle speed switch is turned from "OFF" to "ON" position. If idle is not as specified, adjust accordingly.

***IDLE SWITCH SPEED INCREASES***

| Model | Automatic "N" Position | Manual | RPM + or - |
|---|---|---|---|
| Maxima | 250 | 250 | 150 |
| Pathfinder/Pickup | | | |
| VG30i | 250 | 250 | 150 |
| Z24i | [1] | [1] | [1] |
| PulsarNX SE | 250 | 250 | 150 |
| PulsarNX XE | [2] | [2] | [2] |
| Sentra | [2] | [2] | [2] |
| Stanza | 250 | 250 | 150 |
| Stanza Wagon | 250 | 250 | 150 |
| Van | [1] | [1] | [1] |
| 200SX SE & XE | 250 | 250 | 150 |
| 300ZX | 250 | 250 | 150 |

[1] - At 1600 RPM, when idle switch is activated from off to on, speed should increase up to 2150 RPM. When turned from on to off, speed should decrease as low as 1350 RPM.

[2] - Should be in "ON" position at idle and "OFF" position when accelerator pedal is depressed.

**9)** On all models, perform a test drive to evaluate the effectiveness of any adjustments that may have been made. On all models, if any driveability problems still exist, see SYSTEM INSPECTION CHART or DRIVEABILITY INSPECTION CHART.
CHART.

**10)** On Pathfinder/Pickup, PulsarNX XE, Sentra and 200SX SE models, perform the Mode 3 Self-Diagnosis, then the Mode 4 Switch On/Off Test Diagnosis and a test drive to determine if intermittent problems exist. Write down any diagnostic codes may which appear.

**11)** On PulsarNX SE, Stanza, Stanza Wagon and 200SX XE models, perform a Mode 3 Self-Diagnosis test. Write down any diagnostic codes which appear during the Mode 3 test. On Van models, perform the Mode 3 Self-Diagnosis, Mode 4 Switch On/Off Diagnosis and Mode 5 Real Time Diagnosis. On all models, a test drive to determine if any remaining problems exist.

**12)** If the results of the test drive are unsatisfactory (codes are presented), refer to the applicable SYSTEM INSPECTION CHART. For driveability problems, see applicable DRIVEABILITY INSPECTION CHART.

**13)** After all replacements and/or repairs are completed, test drive the vehicle to evaluate the vehicles performance after the diagnosis and repair procedure is completed.

## STARTING & CHANGING MODES OF SELF-DIAGNOSIS

**1)** On all models except Pathfinder/Pickup and Van, turn ignition switch to "ON" position. Turn diagnostic mode selector of ECU fully clockwise and wait for inspection lights to begin flashing. Inspection lights will flash once indicating Mode 1, twice indicating Mode 2, etc. Count the number of flashes. Right after the number of flashes which corresponds to the diagnostic mode you wish to enter appears, immediately turn the mode selector fully counterclockwise *See Fig. 13*.

**2)** On Pathfinder/Pickup and Van models, turn ignition switch to the "ON" position. Turn diagnostic mode selector to the "ON" position and wait for inspection lights to begin flashing. Inspection lights will flash once indicating Mode 1, twice indicating Mode 2, etc. Count the number of flashes. Right after the number of flashes which corresponds to the diagnostic mode you wish to enter appears, immediately turn the mode on-off switch to "OFF" position. *See Fig. 13*.

**3)** On all models, if the mode selector or mode on/off switch ("ON" position) is kept in the full clockwise position, the mode selections will continuously change. From Mode 1 to Mode 2 up to Mode 5, then it turns to Mode 1 again and the process continues. This will not erase the memory.

## MEMORY ERASE

***CAUTION: Be sure all needed diagnostic codes are extracted from the ECU memory before disconnecting battery or switching from Mode 3 into Mode 4.***

***NOTE: If ignition switch is turned to "OFF" position in any mode of diagnosis, then turned to "ON" position after ECU has completely lost power, the diagnosis mode will automatically return to Mode 1 and begin cycling through modes again, but memory will not be erased.***

Stored memory will be erased if battery is disconnected or Mode 4 is selected after Mode 3. Only if mode select switch is turned counterclockwise (Mode on-off switch to "OFF" position for Pathfinder/Pickup and Van models) after Mode 3 and then after Mode 4 is selected, will stored memory be erased. However, if mode selector switch is turned fully clockwise (on-off switch turned to "ON" position for Pathfinder/Pickup and Van models), diagnosis modes will continue to change in order until a certain mode is selected, this does not erase the stored memory.

## KEYS TO SYMBOLS

DISCONNECT
: Make check after disconnecting the connector to be measured.

CONNECT
: Make check after connecting the connector to be measured.

**NOTE:** **When measuring voltage or resistance at a connector with tester probes, there 2 methods of measurement. One is done from the terminal side and the other is done from the harness side. Before taking any measurments, confirm the symbol mark.**

H.S.
: Testing to be done from harness side.

T.S.
: Testing to be done from the terminal side.

N.G. - Not Good

O.K. - Okay

## CAUTIONS

Before connecting or disconnecting ECU harness connector to or from the ECU, be sure that ignition switch is in the "OFF" position and negative battery cable is disconnected or damage to the ECU may result. This is important because battery voltage is applied to the ECU even when the ignition switch is in the "OFF" position.

When performing an ECU input/output signal inspection, remove pin terminal retainer from connectors. This will make probing of the connector pins easier and safer.

When connecting or disconnecting pin connectors from the ECU, take care not to bend or break any pin terminals. Before replacing ECU, perform the ECU input/output signal inspection to be sure ECU is malfunctioning.

When measuring voltage supply to ECU controlled components, be sure not to touch probe testers together. Separating test probes is helpful. This will prevent accidentally making contact between the 2 probes, causing a shorted circuit and damaging the ECU.

***TROUBLE CODE IDENTIFICATION CHART***

| Code Number | Test Letter | Malfunctioning Component |
|---|---|---|
| 11 | A | Crank Angle Sensor |
| 12 | B | Mass Airflow Sensor |
| 13 | C | Coolant Temp. Sensor |
| 14 | D | Vehicle Speed Sensor |
| 21 | E | Ignition Signal/Knock Sensor |
| 22 | F | [3]Fuel Pump |
| 23 & 24 [2] | G | Idle Switch |
| 25 | I | Idle Speed Control Valve |
| 31 | H | ECU Malfunction |
| 32 | J | EGR Function |
| 33 | K | Exhaust Gas Sensor |
| 35 | L | Exhaust Gas Temp. Sensor |
| 42 | N | Fuel Temp. Sensor |
| 43 | O | Throttle Position Sensor |
| 45 | P | Injector Leakage |
| 51 | Q | Injector Malfunction |
| [1] | Q | Injector Malfunction |
| [2] | R | Start Signal |
| [1] | S | Air Regulator |
| [1] | T | Auxiliary Air Control Valve |
| [1] | U | Spark Plug Switching |
| [1] | V | Power & Ground Circuits |
| [1] | W | EGR Control |
| [1] | X | Idle-Up Control |
| [1] | Y | Air Injection Valve |
| [1] | Z | Clutch/Neutral/Inhibitor Switches |
| [1] | AA | IAA or FICD Control |
| [1] | BB | Main Relay |
| [1] | CC | Pressure Regulator Control |
| [1] | DD | Fuel Pump Relay |
| [1] | EE | Load Signal |
| [1] | FF | Power Valve Control |
| [1] | GG | A/C & P/S Switches |
| [1] | HH | Mixture Heater |
| [1] | II | Mixture Heater Relay |
| [1] | JJ | Fuel Pump |

[1] - Does not set a trouble (non-self diagnostic item).
[2] - Does not set a trouble (switch on/off diagnosis).
[3] - All models do not set a code 22 for fuel pump malfunctions. Use test JJ for vehicles with fuel pumps that are non self-diagnostic items.
[4] - All models do not set a code 23 for idle switch malfunctions. Only Stanza, Stanza Wagon and 200SX XE models set a code 24 for idle switch malfunctions.

PREPARATION

1. Make certain that the following components are in good working order: battery, ignition system, engine oil & coolant levels, fuses, E.C.C.S. harness connectors, vacuum hoses, air intake system (oil filter cap, oil level gauge, etc.) fuel pressure, A.I.V. hose, engine compression, E.G.R. valve operation and throttle valve operation.
2. On models with A/C, make all checks with A/C off.
3. On models equipped with automatic transmissions, make the following checks in "D" position: idle RPM, ignition timing and mixture ratio adjusment.
4. When measuring "CO" percentage, insert probe at least 16" into the tail pipe.

WARNING
a. When selector lever is shifted to "D" position, apply parking brake and block both front and rear wheels with chocks.
b. Depress brake pedal while racing engine to prevent forward surge.
c. After adjustments are made, shift transmission into "P" or "N" position to remove wheels chocks.

Overall Inspection Sequence

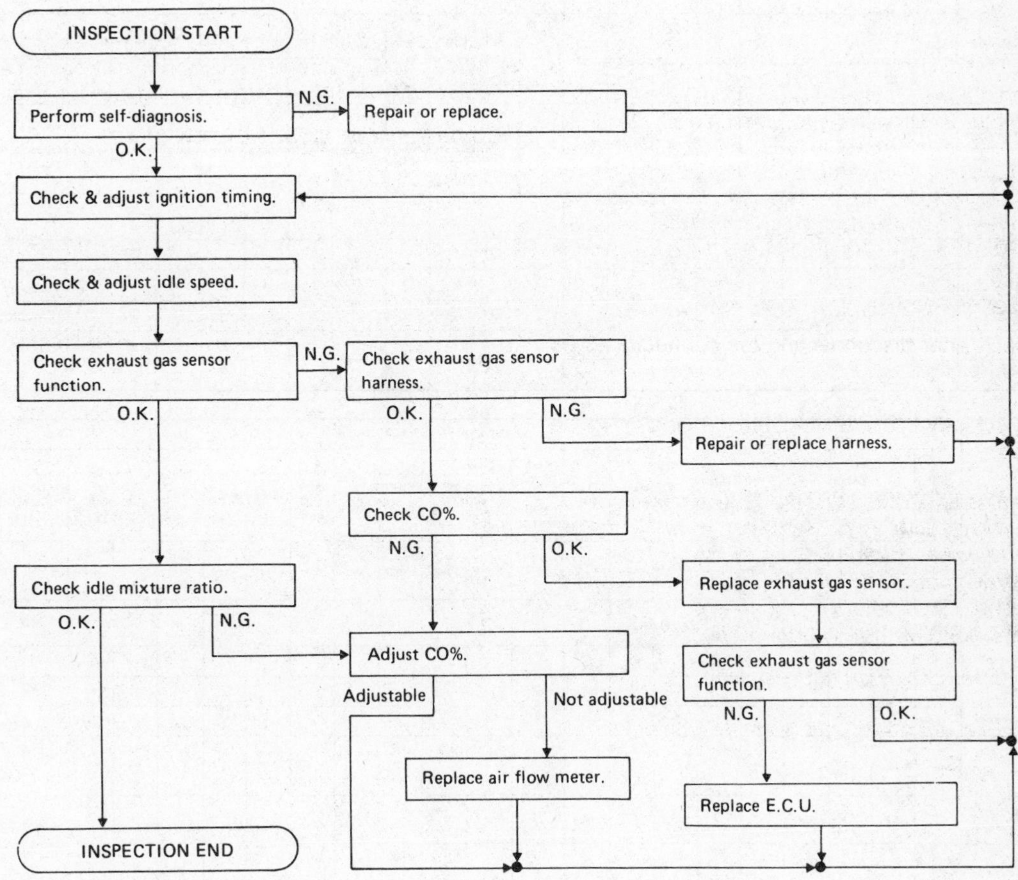
INSPECTION START
Perform self-diagnosis.
N.G.
Repair or replace.
O.K.
Check & adjust ignition timing.
Check & adjust idle speed.
Check exhaust gas sensor function.
N.G.
Check exhaust gas sensor harness.
O.K.
O.K.
N.G.
Repair or replace harness.
Check CO%.
N.G.
O.K.
Replace exhaust gas sensor.
Check idle mixture ratio.
O.K.
N.G.
Adjust CO%.
Check exhaust gas sensor function.
Adjustable
Not adjustable
N.G.
O.K.
Replace air flow meter.
Replace E.C.U.
INSPECTION END

MEASURING VOLTAGE OR RESISTANCE OF E.C.U.

1. Disconnect battery ground cable.
2. Disconnect 20 and 16-pin connectors.
3. Remove pin terminal retainer from 20 and 16 pin connectors for easiest access.
4. Carefully, connect 20 and 16 pin connectors to E.CU.
5. Connect battery ground cable.
6. Measure voltage at each terminal by following E.C.U. INSPECTION TABLE.

CAUTION
a. Perform all voltage measurements with connectors connected.
b. Perform all resistance tests with connectors disconnected.
c. Ensure that there are no bent or broken pins at the E.C.U. connectors.
d. Do not touch tester probes between terminals No. 27 and No. 28 or between No. 35 and No. 36.

Courtesy of Nissan Motor Co., U.S.A.

***Preparation For Testing***

# Nissan Electronic Concentrated Control System (Cont.)

| Inspection Item / Trouble Items Concerned With Driveability (Proceed to Test) | General Inspection – Fuel Flow System: Fuel level | Fuel Flow System: Fuel pump | Fuel Flow System: Fuel filter | Fuel Flow System: Fuel line | Electric System: Battery | Electric System: Spark plug | Electric System: Ignition wire | Electric System: Alternator | Electric System: Starter | Air Flow System: Air cleaner | Air Flow System: Air flow line | Air Flow System: E.G.R. B.P.T. valve | Air Flow System: A.I.V. control valve | Air Flow System: F.I.C.D. solenoid valve | Air Flow System: Air regulator | Air Flow System: P.C.V. | A.A.C. Valve: Short | A.A.C. Valve: Open | E.C.C.S. System Inspection – Crank Angle Sensor: 180° signal noise | Crank Angle Sensor: 180° signal faults | Crank Angle Sensor: 1° signal faults | Vehicle Speed Sensor: Short | Vehicle Speed Sensor: Open | Vehicle Speed Sensor: Poor connection |
|---|---|---|---|---|---|---|---|---|---|---|---|---|---|---|---|---|---|---|---|---|---|---|---|---|
| Proceed to Test | – | F | – | – | V | U | – | | R | – | B | J | Y | AA | S | – | T | | | A | | | D | |
| Surge – Road/Load Driving – Heavy load | | | O | O | | ◎ | O | | | O | O | O | | I | | O | | | O | O | O | | | |
| Surge – Road/Load Driving – Middle load | | | O | O | | ◎ | O | | | O | O | ◎ | | | | O | | | O | O | O | | | |
| Surge – Road/Load Driving – Light load | | | O | O | | ◎ | O | | | O | O | ◎ | | | | O | | | O | O | O | | | |
| Surge – Accelerating Driving – Slow acceleration | | | O | O | | ◎ | O | | | O | O | ◎ | | | | O | | | O | O | O | | | |
| Surge – Decelerating Driving – Rapid deceleration | | | | | | ◎ | O | | | O | O | O | | | | O | O | O | O | O | O | O | O | O |
| Surge – Decelerating Driving – Slow deceleration | | | | | | ◎ | O | | | O | O | O | | | | O | O | O | O | O | O | O | O | O |
| Hesitation – Rapid acceleration | | | O | O | | ◎ | O | | | O | O | O | | | | O | | | O | O | O | | | |
| Hesitation – Slow acceleration | | | O | O | | ◎ | O | | | O | O | O | | | | O | | | O | O | O | | | |
| Stumble – Rapid acceleration | | | O | O | | ◎ | O | | | O | O | O | | | | O | | | O | O | O | | | |
| Stumble – Slow acceleration | | | O | O | | ◎ | O | | | O | O | O | | | | O | | | O | O | O | | | |
| Backfire | | | O | O | | | O | | | | O | | | | | O | | | O | O | O | | | |
| After Fire | | | | | | ◎ | O | | | O | | | O | | | O | O | O | O | O | O | | | |
| Idle Stability | | | | | | ◎ | O | O | | O | O | ◎ | | O | O | O | ◎ | ◎ | O | O | O | O | O | O |
| Engine Stall | O | O | O | O | O | ◎ | O | O | | O | O | O | | O | O | O | ◎ | ◎ | ◎ | ◎ | ◎ | | | |
| Startability | O | O | | | O | ◎ | O | O | O | O | O | | | | O | O | O | O | ◎ | ◎ | ◎ | | | |

| Inspection Item / Trouble Items Concerned With Driveability (Proceed to Test) | E.C.C.S. System Inspection – Air Flow Meter: Poor connection | Water Temperature Sensor: Short | Water Temperature Sensor: Open | Water Temperature Sensor: Poor connection | Throttle Valve Switch: Short | Throttle Valve Switch: Open | Exhaust Gas Sensor: Short | Exhaust Gas Sensor: Open | Injector: Clogging | Neutral/Inhibitor Switch: Short | Start Signal: Short | Start Signal: Open | Ignition Signal: Short | Ignition Signal: Open | Battery Voltage: Low voltage | Fuel Pump Circuit: Short | Fuel Pump Circuit: Open | Fuel Pump Circuit: Poor connection | E.G.R. Control Solenoid Valve: Short | E.G.R. Control Solenoid Valve: Open | A.I.V. Control Solenoid Valve: Short | A.I.V. Control Solenoid Valve: Open | P.R. Control Solenoid Valve: Short | P.R. Control Solenoid Valve: Open |
|---|---|---|---|---|---|---|---|---|---|---|---|---|---|---|---|---|---|---|---|---|---|---|---|---|
| Proceed to Test | A | | C | | G & O | | K & L | | Q | Z | R | | E | | V | | F | | W | | Y | | CC | |
| Surge – Road/Load Driving – Heavy load | ◎ | O | O | O | | | O | O | Q | | | | | | | | | O | ◎ | ◎ | | | | |
| Surge – Road/Load Driving – Middle load | ◎ | O | O | O | | | O | O | ◎ | | | | | | | | | O | ◎ | ◎ | | | | |
| Surge – Road/Load Driving – Light load | ◎ | O | O | O | | | O | O | ◎ | | | | | | | | | O | ◎ | ◎ | | | | |
| Surge – Accelerating Driving – Slow acceleration | ◎ | O | O | O | O | O | O | O | ◎ | | | | | | | | | O | ◎ | ◎ | | | | |
| Surge – Decelerating Driving – Rapid deceleration | ◎ | O | O | O | O | O | O | O | ◎ | | | | | | | | | O | O | O | | | | |
| Surge – Decelerating Driving – Slow deceleration | ◎ | O | O | O | O | O | O | O | ◎ | | | | | | | | | O | O | O | | | | |
| Hesitation – Rapid acceleration | ◎ | O | O | O | O | O | O | O | ◎ | O | | | | | | | | O | O | O | | | | |
| Hesitation – Slow acceleration | ◎ | O | O | O | O | O | O | O | ◎ | O | | | | | | | | O | O | O | | | | |
| Stumble – Rapid acceleration | ◎ | O | O | O | O | O | | | ◎ | O | | | | | | | | O | O | O | | | O | O |
| Stumble – Slow acceleration | ◎ | O | O | O | O | O | | | ◎ | O | | | | | | | | O | O | O | | | O | O |
| Backfire | ◎ | O | | O | O | O | O | O | ◎ | O | | | | | | | | O | | | | | | |
| After Fire | ◎ | | O | O | O | O | O | O | ◎ | O | | | | | | | | | ◎ | ◎ | O | O | | O |
| Idle Stability | O | O | O | O | O | O | O | O | ◎ | O | | | | | | | | O | O | O | | | | |
| Engine Stall | ◎ | O | O | O | O | O | O | O | ◎ | O | | | O | O | O | O | O | O | | | | | O | O |
| Startability | O | O | O | O | | | | | ◎ | O | O | O | O | O | O | O | O | O | | | | | O | O |

**This table indicates the inspection items for each type of symptom. It is necessary for each symptom to check sensors or actuators marked "◎" or "O".**
**Items marked "◎" have a significant influence on driveability. Prior to items marked "O", check items marked "◎".**
**Improper mixture ratio, improper ignition condition, and an excess of E.G.R. volume can cause any symptom.**

Courtesy of Nissan Motor Co., U.S.A.

***All Models – Driveability Inspection Tables***

# Nissan Electronic Concentrated Control System (Cont.)

| Sensor & actuator / Proceed to Test: / System | Crank angle sensor | Air flow meter | Water temperature sensor | Ignition switch | Injector | Throttle valve switch | Neutral/ inhibitor switch | Exhaust gas sensor |
|---|---|---|---|---|---|---|---|---|
| | A | B | C | E | P & Q | G & O | Z | K & L |
| Fuel injection & mixture ratio feedback control | O | O | O | O | O | O | O | O |
| Ignition timing control | O | O | O | O | | O | | |
| A.I.V. control | O | | O | | | O | | O |
| Fuel pump control | O | | | O | | | | |
| Fuel pressure control | O | | O | O | O | | | |
| Idle speed control | O | | O | O | | O | O | |
| E.G.R. control | O | | O | O | | O | | |

| Sensor & actuator / Proceed to Test: / System | A.I.V. control solenoid valve | E.G.R. control solenoid valve | P.R. control solenoid valve/ Fuel pump relay | A.A.C. valve | Air regulator | Vehicle speed sensor | E.F.I. main relay |
|---|---|---|---|---|---|---|---|
| | Y | J & W | CC & DD | T | S | D | BB |
| Fuel injection & mixture ratio feedback control | | | | | | O | O |
| Ignition timing control | | | | | | | O |
| A.I.V. control | O | | | | | | O |
| Fuel pump control | | | | | | | O |
| Fuel pressure control | | | O | | | | O |
| Idle speed control | | | | O | O | O | O |
| E.G.R. control | | O | | | | | O |

**This table indicates the inspection items for the E.C.C.S. control system. For each system, it is necessary to check sensors or actuators marked "O".**

***TEST LETTER REFERENCE CHART***

| Component/Circuit | Test Letter(s) |
|---|---|
| Crank Angle Sensor | A |
| Mass Airflow Sensor | B |
| Cylinder Head Temperature Sensor | C |
| Vehicle Speed Sensor | D |
| Ignition Signal | E |
| Fuel Pump | F |
| Idle Switch | G |
| Electronic Control Unit Check | H |
| Idle Speed Control Valve | I |
| EGR Function | J |
| Exhaust Gas Sensor | K |
| Exhaust Gas Temperature Sensor | L |
| Detonation Sensor | E & M |
| Fuel Temperature Sensor | N |
| Throttle Position Sensor | O |
| Injector Leak Check | P |
| Injector Malfunction | Q |
| Start Signal | R |

***TEST LETTER REFERENCE CHART (Cont.)***

| Component/Circuit | Test Letter(s) |
|---|---|
| Air Regulator | S |
| Auxiliary Air Control | T |
| Spark Plug Switching | U |
| Power & Ground Source | V |
| EGR Control | W |
| Idle Up Control | X |
| Air Injection Valve | Y |
| Clutch/Neutral/Inhibitor Switches | Z |
| Fast Idle Control Device (F.I.C.D.) | AA |
| Main Relay/Main EFI Relay/E.C.C.S. Relay | BB |
| Pressure Regulator Control | CC |
| Fuel Pump Relay | DD |
| Load Signal | EE |
| Idle Air Adjusting (I.A.A.) Signal | AA |
| Power Valve Control | FF |
| Air Conditioning/Power Steering Switches | GG |
| Mixture Heater | HH |
| Mixture Heater Relay | II |

Courtesy of Nissan Motor Co., U.S.A.

***All Models – Systems Inspection Tables & Test Letter Reference Charts***

# Nissan Electronic Concentrated Control System (Cont.)

| TERMINAL NO. | ITEM | CONDITION | *DATA |
|---|---|---|---|
| 2 | Idle-up solenoid valve (VG30E) | **Engine is running and gear position is in P or N (A/T).**<br>— For about 20 seconds after starting engine<br>— Steering wheel is turned.<br>— Blower and air conditioner switches are "ON".<br>— Lighting switch is "ON". | 0.1 - 0.4V |
| | | **Engine is running.**<br>— Except the conditions shown above | BATTERY VOLTAGE (11 - 14V) |
| | A.A.C. valve (VG30ET) 300ZX Only | **Engine is running.**<br>— Idle speed (after warm-up) | 6.0 - 8.0V |
| 3 | Ignition check | Ignition Switch "ON" (200SX SE)<br>Engine Running (Maxima and 300ZX) | 11-14V (200SX SE)<br>9-12V (Maxima and 300ZX, decreases as engine is revved up) |
| 4 | E.G.R. control solenoid valve | **Engine is running after being warmed up.**<br>— High engine revolution<br>— Idle speed (Throttle valve switch "ON".) | Approximately 1.0V |
| | | **Engine is running.**<br>— Low engine revolution | BATTERY VOLTAGE (11 - 14V) |
| 5 | Ignition signal | **Engine is running.**<br>— Idle speed | 0.5-2.0V (200SX SE only)<br>0.4-0.6V (Maxima and 300ZX) |
| | | **Engine is running.**<br>— Engine speed is 2,000 rpm. | 1.2-1.5V (Maxima and 300ZX) |
| 6 | E.F.I. main relay | Ignition Switch "On" (200SX SE only) | |
| 6 | E.C.C.S. relay-1 (Main relay) | **Engine is running.**<br>↓<br>**Ignition switch "OFF"**<br>— For approximately 8 seconds after turning ignition switch "OFF" | 0.7 - 0.9V |
| | | **Ignition switch "OFF"**<br>— Within approximately 8 seconds after turning ignition switch "OFF". | BATTERY VOLTAGE (11 - 14V) |

Courtesy of Nissan Motor Co., U.S.A.

*Maxima, 200SX SE & 300ZX – ECU Input/Output Voltage Signal Inspection Table*

| TERMINAL NO. | ITEM | CONDITION | *DATA |
|---|---|---|---|
| 8 | Crank angle sensor (Position signal) | Engine is running. **Do not run engine at high speed under no-load.** | 2.3-2.7V |
| 9 | Start signal | Cranking | 8-14V |
| 10 | Neutral switch (M/T) Inhibitor switch (A/T) | Ignition switch "ON" — Gear position is in Neutral or Parking. | 0V |
| | | Ignition switch "ON" — Any gear position except Neutral or Parking | BATTERY VOLTAGE (11 - 14V) |
| 12 | Airflow Meter | Engine revolution is above 1,500 rpm and vehicle speed is more than 20 km/h (12MPH). ↓ Ignition switch "OFF" — For 6 seconds after turning ignition switch "OFF" | 0V |
| | | Engine revolution is above 1,500 rpm and vehicle speed is more than 20 km/h (12 MPH). ↓ Ignition switch "OFF" — For 1 second after the above 6 seconds have passed. | 9.0 - 10.0V |
| 14 | A.I.V. control solenoid valve (Maxima and 300ZX only) | Ignition Switch "OFF" (Maxima) Ignition Switch "ON" (300ZX) | 0.7 - 0.9V |
| | | Ignition switch "ON" — Depress accelerator pedal. (Throttle valve switch "OFF") | BATTERY VOLTAGE (11 - 14V) |
| 15 | Fuel temperature sensor | Engine is running. — Idle speed | 0.5V Output voltage varies with engine temperature. |
| 16 | Air regulator | Engine is running. | 0.6 - 0.9V |
| 17 | Crank angle sensor (Reference signal) | Engine is running. **Do not run engine at high speed under no-load.** | 0.2 - 0.4V |

Courtesy of Nissan Motor Co., U.S.A.

***Maxima, 200SX SE & 300ZX – ECU Input/Output Voltage Signal Inspection Table***

# Nissan Electronic Concentrated Control System (Cont.)

| TERMINAL NO. | ITEM | CONDITION | *DATA |
|---|---|---|---|
| 18 | Throttle valve switch (⊖ side) | Ignition switch "ON"<br>— Release accelerator pedal. (Throttle valve switch "OFF") | 9.0 - 10.0V |
| | | Ignition switch "ON"<br>— Depress accelerator pedal. (Throttle valve switch "ON") | 0V |
| 19 | Pressure regulator control solenoid valve | Stop and restart engine after warming it up.<br>— For 30 seconds | 0.8 - 1.0V |
| | | Stop and restart engine after warming it up.<br>— After 3 minutes | BATTERY VOLTAGE (11 - 14V) |
| 20 | Fuel pump relay | Engine is running. | BATTERY VOLTAGE (11 - 14V) |
| 22 | Load signal | Engine is running and gear position is in P or N (A/T).<br>— Steering wheel is turned.<br>— Blower and air conditioner switchs are "ON".<br>— Lighting switch is "ON". | BATTERY VOLTAGE (11 - 14V) |
| | | Engine is running.<br>— Except conditions shown above | 0V |
| 23 | Cylinder head temperature sensor | Engine is running. | 0 - 5.0V<br>Output voltage varies with engine temperature. |
| 24 | Exhaust gas sensor | Engine is running.<br>— After warming up sufficiently | 0 - Approximately 1.0V |
| 25 | Idle switch (⊕side) | Ignition switch "ON" | 9.0 - 10.0V |
| 27<br>35 | Power source for E.C.U. | Ignition switch "ON" | BATTERY VOLTAGE (11 - 14V) |
| 29 | Vehicle speed sensor | Ignition switch "ON"<br>— While rotating rear wheel slowly | 0 or 7.4V |

Courtesy of Nissan Motor Co., U.S.A.

*Maxima, 200SX SE & 300ZX – ECU Input/Output Voltage Signal Inspection Table*

| TERMINAL NO. | ITEM | CONDITION | *DATA |
|---|---|---|---|
| 30 | Exhaust gas temperature sensor (Only for California model) (300ZX Only) | Engine is running. — Idle speed | 1.0 - 2.0V |
| | | Engine is running. — E.G.R. system is operating. | 0 - 1.0V |
| 30 & 31<br>31 | Air flow meter | Engine is running.<br>**Do not run engine at high speed under no-load.** | 2.0 - 4.0V<br>Output voltage varies with engine revolution and throttle valve movement. |
| 34 | Ignition switch signal | Ignition switch "ON" | BATTERY VOLTAGE (11 - 14V) |
| 101<br>102<br>103<br>104<br>105<br>106<br>114 | Injector | Engine is running. | BATTERY VOLTAGE (11 - 14V) |
| 108 | Fuel pump<br>Ignition Switch "OFF" (200SX SE) | Ignition switch "ON" — For 5 seconds after turning ignition switch "ON" | 0.1 - 0.3V |
| | | Ignition switch "ON" — After 5 seconds have passed | 9 - 14V |
| 110<br>300ZX only | Throttle sensor (Only for California model) | Ignition switch "ON" | 0.4 - 4.0V |
| 115<br>300ZX only | Exhaust gas sensor heater | Ignition switch "ON" | BATTERY VOLTAGE (11 - 14V) |

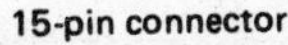
15-pin connector

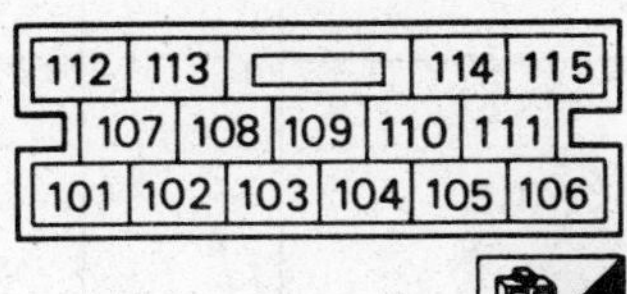
112 113 114 115
107 108 109 110 111
101 102 103 104 105 106
H.S

20-pin connector

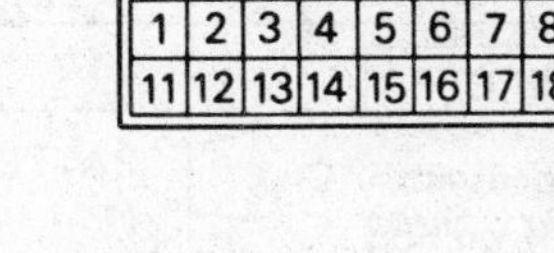
1 2 3 4 5 6 7 8 9 10
11 12 13 14 15 16 17 18 19 20

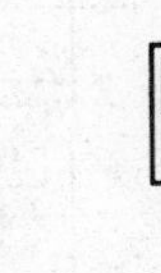
H.S.

16-pin connector

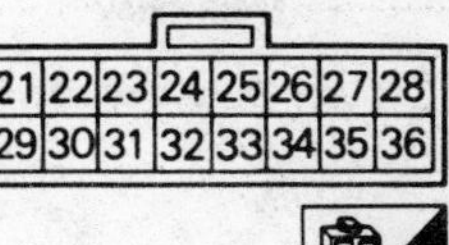
21 22 23 24 25 26 27 28
29 30 31 32 33 34 35 36

H.S.

Courtesy of Nissan Motor Co., U.S.A.

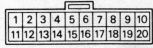

***Maxima, 200SX SE & 300ZX – ECU Input/Output Voltage Signal Inspection Table***

| TERMINAL NO. | ITEM | CONDITION | *DATA | ENGINE | |
|---|---|---|---|---|---|
| | | | | VG30i | Z24i |
| 2 | Idle-up solenoid | Engine is running.<br>— For about 20 seconds after starting engine.<br>— Steering wheel is turned.<br>— Blower switch is "ON".<br>— Headlamps are in high beam position. | Approximately 1.0V | ○ | ○ |
| | | Engine is running.<br>— Except the conditions shown above | BATTERY VOLTAGE (11 - 14V) | | |
| 3 | Ignition check | Engine is running.<br>— Idle speed | 9 - 12V (Decreases as engine revs up.) | ○ | ○ |
| 4 | E.G.R. cut solenoid | Engine is running.<br>— High engine revolution<br>— Idle speed | 0.8 - 1.0V | ○ | ○ |
| | | Engine is running.<br>— Except the above | BATTERY VOLTAGE (11 - 14V) | | |
| 5 | Ignition signal | Engine is running.<br>— Idle speed | 0.4 - 0.6V | ○ | |
| | | | 0.2-0.4V (Z24i)<br>Approximately 0.8V (Van) | | ○ (Intake) |
| | | Engine is running.<br>— Engine speed is 2,000 rpm. | Approximately 1.0V | ○ | |
| | | | Approximately 0.8V (Z24i & Van) | | ○ (Intake) |
| 6 | Main relay | Engine is running.<br>↓<br>Ignition switch "OFF"<br>— For 15 seconds after turning off ignition switch. | 0.8 - 1.0V | ○ | ○ |
| | | Ignition switch "OFF"<br>— In 15 seconds after turning off ignition switch. | BATTERY VOLTAGE (11 - 14V) | | |

20-pin connector

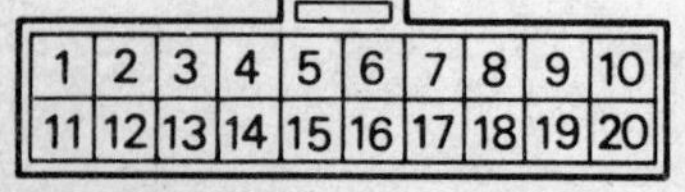
1 2 3 4 5 6 7 8 9 10
11 12 13 14 15 16 17 18 19 20

H.S.

16-pin connector

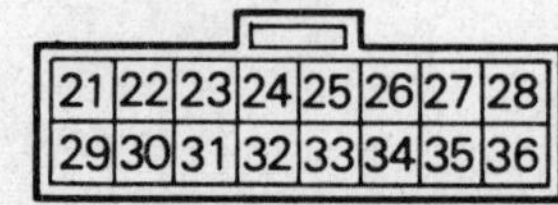
21 22 23 24 25 26 27 28
29 30 31 32 33 34 35 36

H.S.

15-pin connector

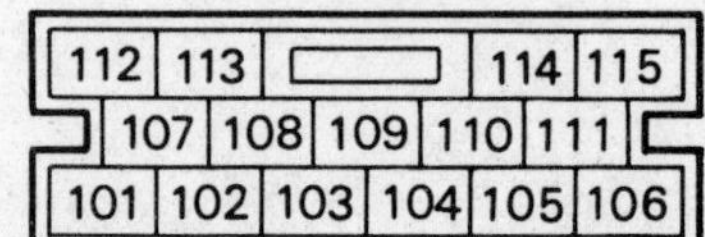
112 113 114 115
107 108 109 110 111
101 102 103 104 105 106

H.S.

Courtesy of Nissan Motor Co., U.S.A.

*Pathfinder/Pickup (Z24i & VG30i) & Van – ECU Input/Output Voltage Signal Inspection Table*

| TERMINAL NO. | ITEM | CONDITION | *DATA | ENGINE VG30i | ENGINE Z24i |
|---|---|---|---|---|---|
| 8 | Crank angle sensor (Position signal) | Engine is running. Do not run engine at high speed under no load. | 2.5 - 2.7V | ○ | ○ |
| 9 | Start signal | Cranking | 8 - 12V | ○ | ○ |
| 10 | Neutral/clutch switch or Inhibitor switch | Ignition switch "ON" — Neutral/Parking | 0V | ○ | ○ |
| | | Ignition switch "ON" — Except the above gear position | Approximately 5V (0V: with clutch disengaged) | | |
| 12 | Mixture heater relay | Engine is running. — Engine is cold or during warm up. [Water temperature is below 70°C (158°F).] | 0.7 - 0.9V | ○ | ○ |
| | | Engine is running. — After warming up. [Water temperature is above 70°C (158°F).] | BATTERY VOLTAGE (11 - 14V) | | |
| 14 | Ignition signal | Engine is running. — Idle speed | 0.2 - 0.4V | | ○ (Ex-haust) |
| | | Engine is running. — Engine speed is 2,000 rpm | Approximately 0.8V | | |
| 15 | Air conditioner relay Van Only | Engine is running. — Air conditioner magnet clutch switch is "OFF". | 0V | | |
| | | Engine is running. — Air conditioner magnet clutch switch is "ON". | BATTERY VOLTAGE (11 - 14V) | | |
| 16 | F.I.C.D. solenoid valve Van Only | Engine is running. — Air conditioner magnet clutch switch is "OFF". | BATTERY VOLTAGE (11 - 14V) | | |
| | | Engine is running. — Air conditioner magnet clutch switch is "ON". | 0.7 - 0.9V | | |

Courtesy of Nissan Motor Co., U.S.A.

*Pathfinder/Pickup (Z24i & VG30i) & Van – ECU Input/Output Voltage Signal Inspection Table*

# Nissan Electronic Concentrated Control System (Cont.)

| TERMINAL NO. | ITEM | CONDITION | *DATA | ENGINE | |
|---|---|---|---|---|---|
| | | | | VG30i | Z24i |
| 17 | Crank angle sensor (Reference signal) | Engine is running. **Do not run engine at high speed under no load.** | 0.2 - 0.4V | O | O |
| 18 | Idle switch (⊖ side) | Ignition switch "ON" — Throttle valve: idle position **Inspection should be done after warming up engine sufficiently.** | Approximately 5-10V | O | O |
| | | Ignition switch "ON" — Throttle valve: except idle position | Approximately 0V | | |
| 19 | Throttle sensor | Ignition switch "ON" **Inspection should be done after warming up engine sufficiently.** | 0.4 - 4.0V Output voltage varies with the throttle valve opening angle. | O | O |
| 20 | A.I.V. cut solenoid Pathfinder/Pickup VG30i Only | Engine is running. — Engine is cold. [Water temperature is below 15°C (59°F).] | 0.8 - 0.9V | O | O (Only 2WD) |
| | | Engine is running. — During warming up [Water temperature is between 15°C (59°F) and 40°C (104°F).] | BATTERY VOLTAGE (11 - 14V) | | |
| | | Engine is running. — After warming up. [Water temperature is above 40°C (104°F).] Idle condition after 3,000 rpm no load driving for 10 seconds | 0.8 - 0.9V | | |
| | | When depressing accelerator pedal at the above condition. | BATTERY VOLTAGE (11 - 14V) | | |
| 22 | Load signal | Engine is running. — Steering wheel is turned. — Blower switch is "ON". — Headlamps are in high beam. | BATTERY VOLTAGE (11 - 14V) | O | |
| | | Engine is running. — Except the conditions shown above | Approximately 0V | | |

Courtesy of Nissan Motor Co., U.S.A.

***Pathfinder/Pickup (Z24i & VG30i) & Van – ECU Input/Output Voltage Signal Inspection Table***

# Nissan Electronic Concentrated Control System (Cont.)

| TERMINAL NO. | ITEM | CONDITION | *DATA | ENGINE VG30i | ENGINE Z24i |
|---|---|---|---|---|---|
| 23 | Water or cylinder head temperature sensor | Engine is running. | 1.0 - 5.0V<br>Output voltage varies with engine water temperature. | ○ | ○ |
| 24 | Exhaust gas sensor | Engine is running.<br>After warming up sufficiently. | 0 - Approximately 1.0V | ○ | ○ |
| 25 | Throttle sensor (⊕ side) Van Only | Engine is running. | Approximately 5.0V | | |
| 33 | Idle switch (⊕ side) | Engine is running.<br>Ignition Switch "ON" (Van only) | 9 - 11V<br>5.0V (Van only) | ○ | ○ |
| | | Engine is running.<br>Engine speed is 2,000 rpm. | BATTERY VOLTAGE (11 - 14V) | | |
| 27<br>35 | Power source for E.C.U. | Ignition switch "ON" | BATTERY VOLTAGE (11 - 14V) | ○ | ○ |
| 31 | Airflow Meter | Engine is running.<br>**Do not run engine at high speed under no load.** | 1.0 - 3.0V<br>Output voltage varies with engine revolution and throttle valve movement. | ○ | ○ |
| 101<br>102<br>103<br>104<br>114 | Injector | Engine is running. | BATTERY VOLTAGE (11 - 14V) | ○ | ○ |
| 108 | Fuel pump relay | Ignition switch "ON"<br>For 5 seconds after turning ignition switch "ON".<br>Engine is running. | 0.7 - 0.9V | ○ | ○ |
| | | Ignition switch "ON"<br>In 5 seconds after turning ignition switch "ON". | BATTERY VOLTAGE (11 - 14V) | | |
| 111 | Exhaust gas temperature sensor | Engine is running.<br>Idle speed | 1.0 - 2.0V | ○ (Only California model) | ○ (Only California model) |
| | | Engine is running.<br>E.G.R. system is operating. | 0 - 1.0V | | |

Courtesy of Nissan Motor Co., U.S.A.

***Pathfinder/Pickup (Z24i & VG30i) & Van – ECU Input/Output Voltage Signal Inspection Table***

# Nissan Electronic Concentrated Control System (Cont.)

| TERMINAL NO. | ITEM | CONDITION | *DATA |
|---|---|---|---|
| 2 | A.A.C. valve | Engine is running. — At idle (after warming up) | 6.0-10.0V |
| 3 | Ignition signal (from resistor) | Ignition switch "ON" | BATTERY VOLTAGE (11 - 14V) |
| 4 | E.G.R. control solenoid valve | Engine is running. — Engine is cold. [Water temperature is below 60°C (140°F).] | 0.7 - 0.9V |
| | | Engine is running. — After warming up [Water temperature is between 60°C (140°F) and 105°C (221°F).] | BATTERY VOLTAGE (11 - 14V) |
| 5 | Ignition signal (from intake side power transistor) | Engine is running. | 0.4 - 2.2V Output voltage varies with engine speed. |
| 6 | E.F.I. relay (Stanza and 200SX XE) E.C.C.S. relay (Stanza Wagon) | Ignition switch "ON" | 0.8 - 1.0V |
| 8 | Crank angle sensor (position signal) | Engine is running. **Do not turn engine at high speed under no-load.** | 2.2 - 2.8V |
| 9 | Start signal | Ignition switch "START" | BATTERY VOLTAGE (11 - 14V) |
| 10 | Neutral signal | Ignition switch "ON" — Gear position: Neutral (M/T) : N or P range (A/T) | 0V |
| | | Ignition switch "ON" — Gear position: [Except neutral (M/T) Except N or P range (A/T)] | BATTERY VOLTAGE (11 - 14V) |
| 14 | Ignition signal (from exhaust side power transistor) | Engine is running. **Do not turn engine at high speed under no-load.** | 0.4 - 2.2V (Output voltage varies with engine revolution.) |
| 15 | A.I.V. control solenoid valve | Engine is running. — At idle | 0.7 - 0.9V |
| | | Engine is running. — When depressing accelerator pedal [Water temperature is above 50°C (122°F).] | BATTERY VOLTAGE (11 - 14V) |
| 16 | Air regulator | Ignition switch "ON" — For 5 seconds after turning ignition switch "ON" | 0.7 - 0.9V |
| | | Ignition switch "ON" — 5 seconds after turning ignition switch "ON" | BATTERY VOLTAGE (11 - 14V) |

Courtesy of Nissan Motor Co., U.S.A.

*Stanza, Stanza Wagon & 200SX XE – ECU Input/Output Voltage Signal Inspection Table*

| TERMINAL NO. | ITEM | CONDITION | *DATA |
|---|---|---|---|
| 17 | Crank angle sensor (Reference signal) | Engine is running. **Do not turn engine at high speed under no-load.** | 0.2 - 0.4V |
| 18 | Idle switch (⊖ side) | Ignition switch "ON" — Throttle valve: idle position | 9 - 10V |
| | | Ignition switch "ON" — Throttle valve: except idle position | 0V |
| 19 | Pressure regulator control solenoid valve<br>Stanza and 200SX SE Only | Ignition switch "ON" — For approximately 3 minutes after turning ignition switch to "START". [Water temperature is above 60°C (140°F).] | 0.7-0.9V Stanza<br>0.8-1.0V 200SX XE Only |
| | | Ignition switch "ON" — Approximately 3 minutes after turning ignition switch to "START". [Water temperature is above 60°C (140°F).] | BATTERY VOLTAGE (11 - 14V) |
| | | Ignition switch "ON" or "START". [Water temperature is below 60°C (140°F).] | |
| 21 | Full throttle switch (⊖ side) | Ignition switch "ON" — Throttle valve: fully open | 9 - 10V |
| | | Ignition switch "ON" — Throttle valve: Any position except full throttle | 0V |
| 22 | Air conditioner signal (Air conditioner equipped model) | Ignition switch "ON" — Air conditioner switch and heater fan switch "ON" | BATTERY VOLTAGE (11 - 14V) |
| | | Ignition switch "ON" — Air conditioner switch "OFF" | 0V |
| 23 | Water temperature sensor | Engine is running. | 1.0 - 5.0V<br>Output voltage varies with engine water temperature. |
| 24 | Exhaust gas sensor | Engine is running. — After warming up sufficiently. | 0 - Approximately 1.0V |
| 25 | Idle switch and full throttle switch (⊕ side) | Ignition switch "ON" | 9 - 10V |
| 27<br>35 | Power source for E.C.U. | Ignition switch "ON" | BATTERY VOLTAGE (11 - 14V) |

Courtesy of Nissan Motor Co., U.S.A.

***Stanza, Stanza Wagon & 200SX XE – ECU Input/Output Voltage Signal Inspection Table***

# Nissan Electronic Concentrated Control System (Cont.)

| TERMINAL NO. | ITEM | CONDITION | *DATA |
|---|---|---|---|
| 29 | Vehicle speed sensor | Ignition switch "ON"<br>When rotating front wheel slowly | Voltage varies between 0V and approximately 5V. |
| 30 | Air temperature sensor | Ignition switch "ON" | Approximately 3V<br>[Air temperature is 20°C (68°F).]<br>Output voltage varies with air temperature. |
| 31 | Air flow meter | Engine is running.<br>**Do not turn engine at high speed under no-load.** | 0-5.0V<br>Output voltage varies with engine revolution. |
| 33 | Power source for air flow meter | Ignition switch "ON" | 8V |
| 34 | Ignition switch signal | Ignition switch "ON" | BATTERY VOLTAGE<br>(11 - 14V) |
| 101<br>102<br>104<br>105<br>114 | Injector | Ignition switch "OFF" | BATTERY VOLTAGE<br>(11 - 14V) |
| 108 | Fuel pump | Ignition switch "ON"<br>For 5 seconds after turning ignition switch "ON". | 0.5-0.9V |
| | | Ignition switch "ON"<br>Within 5 seconds after turning ignition switch "ON". | BATTERY VOLTAGE<br>(9-14V) |

PIN CONNECTOR TERMINAL LAYOUT

15-pin connector

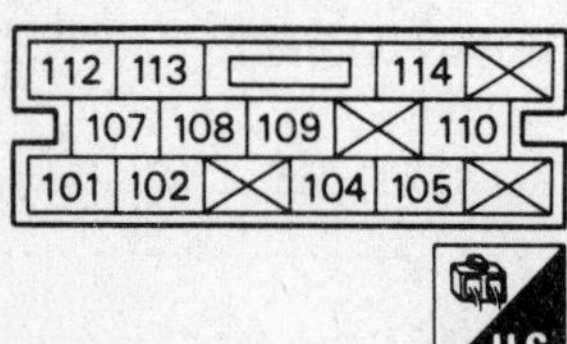
112 113 114
107 108 109 110
101 102 104 105
H.S.

20-pin connector

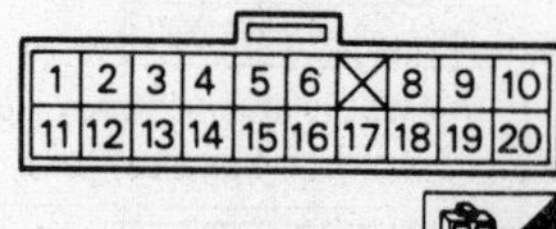
1 2 3 4 5 6 8 9 10
11 12 13 14 15 16 17 18 19 20
H.S.

16-pin connector

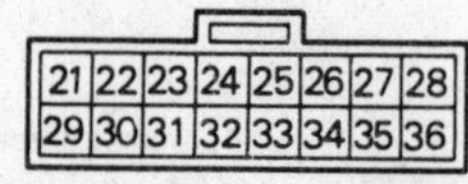
21 22 23 24 25 26 27 28
29 30 31 32 33 34 35 36

H.S.

Courtesy of Nissan Motor Co., U.S.A.

*Stanza, Stanza Wagon & 200SX XE – ECU Input/Output Voltage Signal Inspection Table*

**E16i PIN CONNECTOR TERMINAL LAYOUT**

20-pin connector

| 1 | 2 | 3 | X | 5 | 6 | 7 | 8 | 9 | 10 |
|---|---|---|---|---|---|---|---|---|---|
| 11 | 12 | X | X | 15 | 16 | 17 | 18 | 19 | X |

H.S.

16-pin connector

| 21 | 22 | 23 | 24 | 25 | 26 | 27 | 28 |
|---|---|---|---|---|---|---|---|
| 29 | 30 | 31 | X | 33 | 34 | 35 | 36 |

H.S.

15-pin connector

| 112 | 113 | | 114 | X |
|---|---|---|---|---|
| 107 | 108 | 109 | 110 | 111 |
| 101 | 102 | X | X | X | X |

H.S.

**E.C.U. INSPECTION TABLE**

| TERMINAL NO. | ITEM | CONDITION | DATA (Reference values) |
|---|---|---|---|
| 2 | Power steering oil pressure switch | Engine is idling. — When turning steering wheel. | Approximately 0V |
| | | Engine is idling. — With wheels straight ahead. | 8 - 9V |
| 3 | Ignition signal (from resistor) | Ignition switch "ON" | 11 - 12V |
| 5 | Ignition signal (from power transistor) | Ignition switch "ON" | Approximately 0.1V |
| | | Engine is running. — Rev up engine speed to 2,000 - 3,000 rpm. | 0.5 - 2.0V |
| 6 | Main relay | Ignition switch "ON" | 0.8 - 1.0V |
| 7 | E.G.R. & canister control solenoid valve | Vehicle speed is below 10 km/h (6 MPH). | 0.7 - 1.0V |
| | | Vehicle speed is above 10 km/h (6 MPH) and load is applied. — Engine is cold or during warm-up. [Water temperature is below 60°C (140°F).] | 0.7 - 1.0V |
| | | Vehicle speed is above 10 km/h (6 MPH) and load is applied. — After warming up. [Water temperature is above 80°C (176°F)] | BATTERY VOLTAGE |
| 8 | Crank angle sensor (1° signal) | Engine is running. — Rev up engine speed to 2,000 - 3,000 rpm. | 2.3 - 2.7V |
| 9 | Start signal | Cranking (Starter motor "S" terminal disconnected) | BATTERY VOLTAGE |

| TERMINAL NO. | ITEM | CONDITION | DATA (Reference values) |
|---|---|---|---|
| 10 | Neutral/Clutch/Inhibitor switch | Ignition switch "ON" — • M/T model Clutch pedal depressed or transaxle in "N" position • A/T model Transaxle in "N" or "P" position | 0V |
| | | Ignition switch "ON" — • M/T model Clutch pedal released and transaxle except "N" position • A/T model Transaxle except "N" and "P" position | BATTERY VOLTAGE |

Courtesy of Nissan Motor Co., U.S.A.

***Stanza, Stanza Wagon & 200SX XE – ECU Input/Output Voltage Signal Inspection Table***

# Nissan Electronic Concentrated Control System (Cont.)

| TERMINAL NO. | ITEM | CONDITION | DATA (Reference values) |
|---|---|---|---|
| 12 | Airflow Meter | Drive vehicle<br>• Rev up engine speed to more than 2,000 rpm and return to idle.<br>• Drive vehicle at more than 20 km/h (12 MPH).<br>• Water temperature is between 60°C (140°F) and 95°C (203°F).<br>Stop engine. | Voltage should appear.<br>Key "OFF"<br>Approximately 0V<br>Several sec. |
| 15 | A.I.V. control solenoid valve | After warm-up<br>After idling has continued for several seconds. | 0.7 - 0.9V |
| | | Except above | BATTERY VOLTAGE |
| 16 | Mixture heater | Start engine when engine is cold [Water temperature is below 50°C (122°F)].<br>Until several minutes pass after water temperature exceeds 50°C (122°F). | 0.7 - 0.9V |
| | | After warm-up | BATTERY VOLTAGE |
| 17 | Crank angle sensor (180° signal) | Engine is running.<br>Rev up engine speed to 2,000 - 3,000 rpm. | 0.1 - 0.4V |
| 22 | Air conditioner switch | Engine is running.<br>Air conditioner "ON". | BATTERY VOLTAGE |
| | | Air conditioner "OFF". | 0V |
| 23 | Water temperature sensor | Engine is running.<br>Engine cold → After warm-up. | 0.5 - 5.0V<br>Output voltage varies with engine water temperature. |
| 24 | Exhaust gas sensor | Engine is running.<br>After warming up sufficiently. | 0-1.0V |
| 25 | Throttle Position Sensor (⊕ side) | Ignition switch "ON" | Approximately 5.0V |
| 27<br>35 | Power source for E.C.U. | Ignition switch "ON" | BATTERY VOLTAGE |
| 29 | Vehicle speed sensor | Drive vehicle slowly. | 0V or 4.8V<br>Output voltage changes, one to another, repeatedly. |
| 18 | Idle switch | Ignition switch "ON"<br>Accelerator pedal released. | 9 - 10V |
| | | Accelerator pedal depressed. | Approximately 0V |
| 19 | Throttle sensor | Ignition switch "ON"<br>Depress throttle valve slowly. | 0.5 - 5.0V<br>Output voltage varies with the throttle valve opening angle. |

Courtesy of Nissan Motor Co., U.S.A.

***Pulsar NX XE & Sentra – ECU Input/Output Voltage Signal Inspection Table***

| TERMINAL NO. | ITEM | CONDITION | DATA (Reference values) |
|---|---|---|---|
| 31 | Airflow Meter | Engine is running. — Rev up engine speed to 2,000 - 3,000 rpm. | 2.4 - 4.0V |
| 33 | Idle switch (⊕ side) | Ignition switch "ON" — Accelerator pedal released. | Approximately 10V |
| | | Ignition switch "ON" — Accelerator pedal depressed. | BATTERY VOLTAGE |
| 34 | Ignition switch ("ON" signal) | Ignition switch "ON" | BATTERY VOLTAGE |
| 101<br>102 | Injector | Ignition switch "OFF" | BATTERY VOLTAGE |
| 108 | Fuel pump | Ignition switch "ON" — Engine stopped. | BATTERY VOLTAGE |
| | | Ignition switch "ON" — Engine is running. | 0.7 - 0.9V |
| 110 | I.S.C. valve (Opening side) | Engine is idling (After warm-up). — Throttle sensor harness connector disconnected. | 11 - 12V |
| | | Engine is idling (After warm-up). — With air conditioner "ON" | 8 - 10V |
| 111 | I.S.C. valve (Closing side) | Engine is idling (After warm-up). — Throttle sensor harness connector disconnected. | 2 - 3V |
| | | Engine is idling (After warm-up). — With air conditioner "ON" | 4 - 6V |

Courtesy of Nissan Motor Co., U.S.A.

***Pulsar NX XE & Sentra – ECU Input/Output Voltage Signal Inspection Table***

# Nissan Electronic Concentrated Control System (Cont.)

| TERMINAL NO. | ITEM | CONDITION | *DATA |
|---|---|---|---|
| 1 | Ignition signal for No. 1 cylinder | Engine is running. | 0 - 1.0V |
| 2 | Ignition signal for No. 2 cylinder | | |
| 8 | Ignition signal for No. 3 cylinder | | |
| 9 | Ignition signal for No. 4 cylinder | | |
| 7 | Exhaust gas temperature sensor | Engine is running. — Idle speed | 1.0 - 2.0V |
| | | Engine is running. — E.G.R. system is operating. | 0 - 1.0V |
| 10 | Air conditioner cut signal | Engine is running. — Idle speed | 0 - 1.0V |
| | | Engine is running. — Sudden racing | BATTERY VOLTAGE (11 - 14V) |
| 11 | Power valve control solenoid valve | Engine is running. — Engine speed is less than approximately 4,000 rpm. | Approximately 1V |
| | | Engine is running. — Engine speed is more than approximately 4,000 rpm. | BATTERY VOLTAGE (11 - 14V) |
| 15 | Airflow Meter | Engine is running. **Do not run engine at high speed under no-load.** | 1.0 - 3.0V Output voltage varies with engine revolution. |
| 17 | Water temperature sensor | Engine is running. | 1.0 - 5.0V Output voltage varies with engine water temperature. |

Courtesy of Nissan Motor Co., U.S.A.

***Pulsar NX XE & Sentra – ECU Input/Output Voltage Signal Inspection Table***

# 1988 COMPUTERIZED ENGINE CONTROLS
## Nissan Electronic Concentrated Control System (Cont.)

| TERMINAL NO. | ITEM | CONDITION | *DATA |
|---|---|---|---|
| 18 | Exhaust gas sensor | Engine is running. — After warming up sufficiently | 0 - Approximately 1.0V |
| 19 | Throttle Position Sensor | Ignition switch "ON" | 0.4 - 4.0V<br>Output voltage varies with the throttle valve opening angle. |
| 21<br>31 | Crank angle sensor (Reference signal) | Engine is running.<br>**Do not run engine at high speed under no-load.** | 0.6 - 0.7V |
| 22<br>32 | Crank angle sensor (Position signal) | Engine is running.<br>**Do not run engine at high speed under no-load.** | 2.0 - 2.5V |
| 34 | Idle switch ( ⊖ side) | Ignition switch "ON" — Throttle valve: idle position | Approximately 9 - 10V |
| | | Ignition switch "ON" — Throttle valve: Any position except idle position | 0V |
| 35 | Start signal | Cranking | 8 - 12V |
| 36 | Neutral switch & Inhibitor switch | Ignition switch "ON" — Neutral/Parking | 0V |
| | | Ignition switch "ON" — Except the above gear position | BATTERY VOLTAGE (11 - 14V) |
| 37 | Ignition switch | Ignition switch "OFF" | 0V |
| | | Ignition switch "ON" | BATTERY VOLTAGE (11 - 14V) |
| 41 | Air conditioner | Engine is running. — Both air conditioner switch and blower switch are "ON". | BATTERY VOLTAGE (11 - 14V) |

Courtesy of Nissan Motor Co., U.S.A.

***Pulsar NX XE & Sentra – ECU Input/Output Voltage Signal Inspection Table***

| TERMINAL NO. | ITEM | CONDITION | *DATA |
|---|---|---|---|
| 44 | Idle switch (⊕ side) | Ignition switch "ON" — Throttle valve: idle position | Approximately 9 - 11V |
| | | Ignition switch "ON" — Throttle valve: Except idle position | BATTERY VOLTAGE (11 - 14V) |
| 46 | Power source (Back-up) | Ignition switch "OFF" | BATTERY VOLTAGE (11 - 14V) |
| 39<br>47 | Power source for E.C.U. | Ignition switch "ON" | BATTERY VOLTAGE (11 - 14V) |
| 101 | Injector No. 1 | Engine is running. | BATTERY VOLTAGE (11 - 14V) |
| 103 | Injector No. 3 | | |
| 110 | Injector No. 2 | | |
| 112 | Injector No. 4 | | |
| 102 | A.I.V. control solenoid | Engine is running. — Idle speed | 0 - 1.0V |
| | | Engine is running. — Accelerator pedal is depressed. — After warming up | BATTERY VOLTAGE (11 - 14V) |
| 104 | Fuel pump relay | Ignition switch "ON" — For 5 seconds after turning ignition switch "ON"<br>Engine is running. | 0.7 - 0.9V |
| | | Ignition switch "ON" — In 5 seconds after turning ignition switch "ON" | BATTERY VOLTAGE (11 - 14V) |

Courtesy of Nissan Motor Co., U.S.A.

***Pulsar NX SE Only – ECU Input/Output Voltage Signal Inspection Table***

| TERMINAL NO. | ITEM | CONDITION | *DATA |
|---|---|---|---|
| 105 | E.G.R. control solenoid valve | Engine is running. – Engine is cold. [Water temperature is below 60°C (140°F).] | 0.7 - 0.9V |
| | | Engine is running. – After warming up [Water temperature is between 65°C (149°F) and 105°C (221°F).] | BATTERY VOLTAGE (11 - 14V) |
| 113 | A.A.C. valve | Engine is running. – Idle speed | 8 - 10V |
| | | Engine is running. – Steering wheel is turned. – Air conditioner is operating. – Rear defogger is "ON". – Head lights are in high position. | 7 - 8V |

E.C.U. PIN CONNECTOR TERMINAL LAYOUT

101 102 103 104 105 107 108
109 110 112 113 115 116

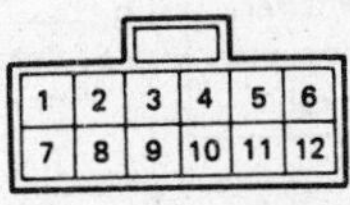
1 2 3 4 5 6
7 8 9 10 11 12

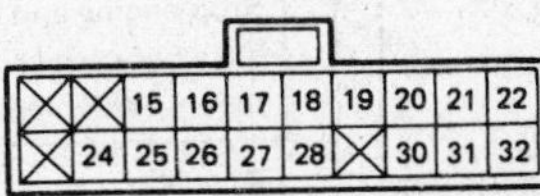
15 16 17 18 19 20 21 22
24 25 26 27 28 30 31 32

33 34 35 36 37 38 39 40
41 44 46 47 48

H.S.

H.S.

H.S.

H.S.

Courtesy of Nissan Motor Co., U.S.A.

***Pulsar NX SE Only – ECU Input/Output Voltage Signal Inspection Table***

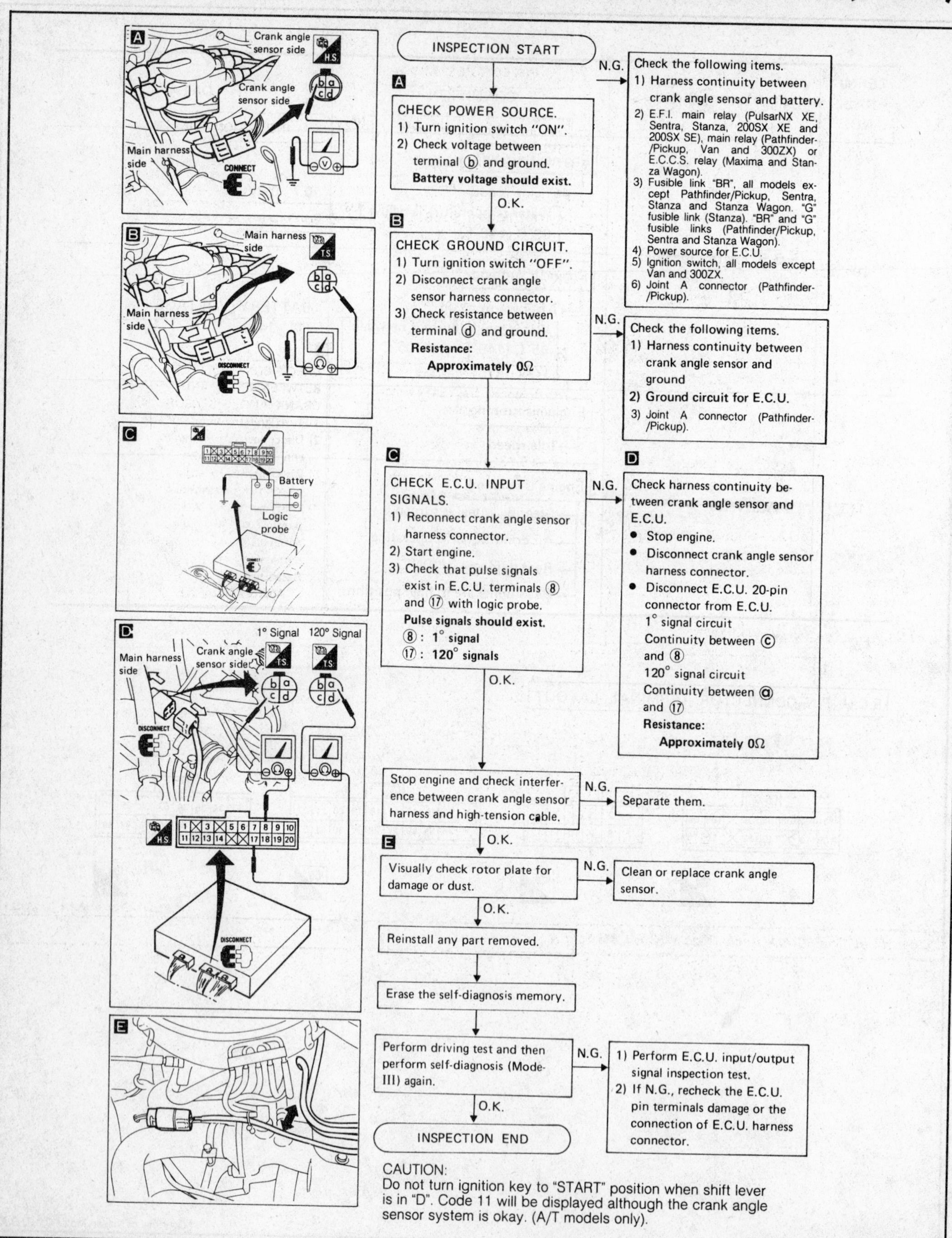
A
Crank angle sensor side
H.S.
Crank angle sensor side
Main harness side
CONNECT
B
Main harness side
T.S.
Main harness side
DISCONNECT
C
Battery
Logic probe
D
1° Signal
120° Signal
Main harness side
Crank angle sensor side
T.S.
DISCONNECT
H.S.
DISCONNECT
E
INSPECTION START
A
CHECK POWER SOURCE.
1) Turn ignition switch "ON".
2) Check voltage between terminal ⓑ and ground.
Battery voltage should exist.
N.G.
Check the following items.
1) Harness continuity between crank angle sensor and battery.
2) E.F.I. main relay (PulsarNX XE, Sentra, Stanza, 200SX XE and 200SX SE), main relay (Pathfinder-/Pickup, Van and 300ZX) or E.C.C.S. relay (Maxima and Stanza Wagon).
3) Fusible link "BR", all models except Pathfinder/Pickup, Sentra, Stanza and Stanza Wagon. "G" fusible link (Stanza). "BR" and "G" fusible links (Pathfinder/Pickup, Sentra and Stanza Wagon).
4) Power source for E.C.U.
5) Ignition switch, all models except Van and 300ZX.
6) Joint A connector (Pathfinder-/Pickup).
O.K.
B
CHECK GROUND CIRCUIT.
1) Turn ignition switch "OFF".
2) Disconnect crank angle sensor harness connector.
3) Check resistance between terminal ⓓ and ground.
Resistance:
Approximately 0Ω
N.G.
Check the following items.
1) Harness continuity between crank angle sensor and ground
2) Ground circuit for E.C.U.
3) Joint A connector (Pathfinder-/Pickup).
C
CHECK E.C.U. INPUT SIGNALS.
1) Reconnect crank angle sensor harness connector.
2) Start engine.
3) Check that pulse signals exist in E.C.U. terminals ⑧ and ⑰ with logic probe.
Pulse signals should exist.
⑧ : 1° signal
⑰ : 120° signals
N.G.
D
Check harness continuity between crank angle sensor and E.C.U.
• Stop engine.
• Disconnect crank angle sensor harness connector.
• Disconnect E.C.U. 20-pin connector from E.C.U.
1° signal circuit
Continuity between ⓒ and ⑧
120° signal circuit
Continuity between ⓐ and ⑰
Resistance:
Approximately 0Ω
O.K.
Stop engine and check interference between crank angle sensor harness and high-tension cable.
N.G.
Separate them.
O.K.
E
Visually check rotor plate for damage or dust.
N.G.
Clean or replace crank angle sensor.
O.K.
Reinstall any part removed.
Erase the self-diagnosis memory.
Perform driving test and then perform self-diagnosis (Mode-III) again.
N.G.
1) Perform E.C.U. input/output signal inspection test.
2) If N.G., recheck the E.C.U. pin terminals damage or the connection of E.C.U. harness connector.
O.K.
INSPECTION END
CAUTION:
Do not turn ignition key to "START" position when shift lever is in "D". Code 11 will be displayed although the crank angle sensor system is okay. (A/T models only).
Courtesy of Nissan Motor Co., U.S.A.

*All Models Except Pulsar NX SE. Crank Angle Sensor (Code 11) Test A*

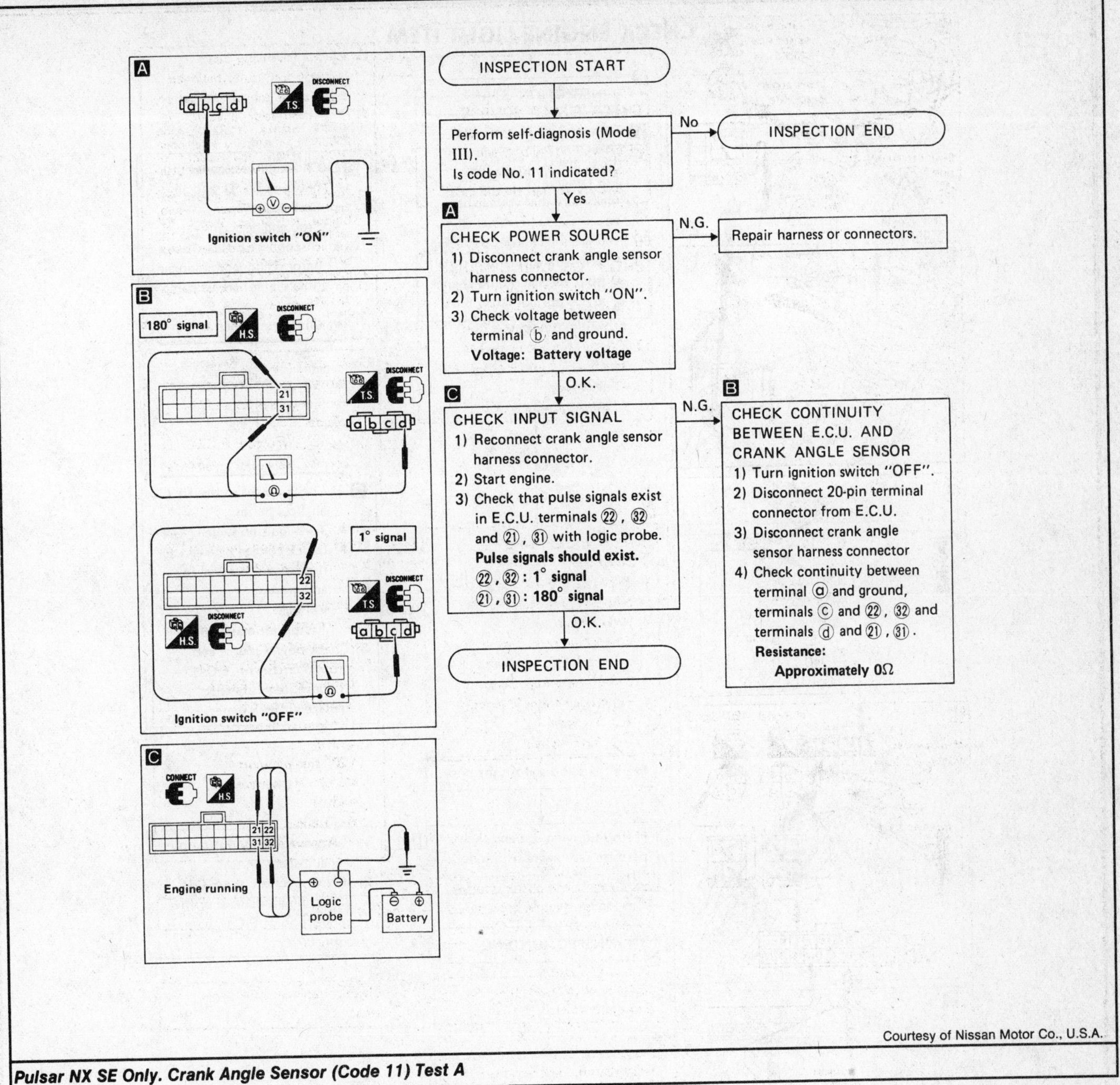
A
DISCONNECT
a b c d
T.S.
Ignition switch "ON"
B
180° signal
H.S.
DISCONNECT
21
31
T.S.
a b c d
1° signal
22
32
Ignition switch "OFF"
C
CONNECT
H.S.
21 22
31 32
Engine running
Logic probe
Battery
INSPECTION START
Perform self-diagnosis (Mode III).
Is code No. 11 indicated?
No
INSPECTION END
Yes
A
CHECK POWER SOURCE
1) Disconnect crank angle sensor harness connector.
2) Turn ignition switch "ON".
3) Check voltage between terminal ⓑ and ground.
Voltage: Battery voltage
N.G.
Repair harness or connectors.
O.K.
C
CHECK INPUT SIGNAL
1) Reconnect crank angle sensor harness connector.
2) Start engine.
3) Check that pulse signals exist in E.C.U. terminals ㉒, ㉜ and ㉑, ㉛ with logic probe.
Pulse signals should exist.
㉒, ㉜ : 1° signal
㉑, ㉛ : 180° signal
N.G.
B
CHECK CONTINUITY BETWEEN E.C.U. AND CRANK ANGLE SENSOR
1) Turn ignition switch "OFF".
2) Disconnect 20-pin terminal connector from E.C.U.
3) Disconnect crank angle sensor harness connector
4) Check continuity between terminal ⓐ and ground, terminals ⓒ and ㉒, ㉜ and terminals ⓓ and ㉑, ㉛.
Resistance:
Approximately 0Ω
O.K.
INSPECTION END
Courtesy of Nissan Motor Co., U.S.A.

*Pulsar NX SE Only. Crank Angle Sensor (Code 11) Test A*

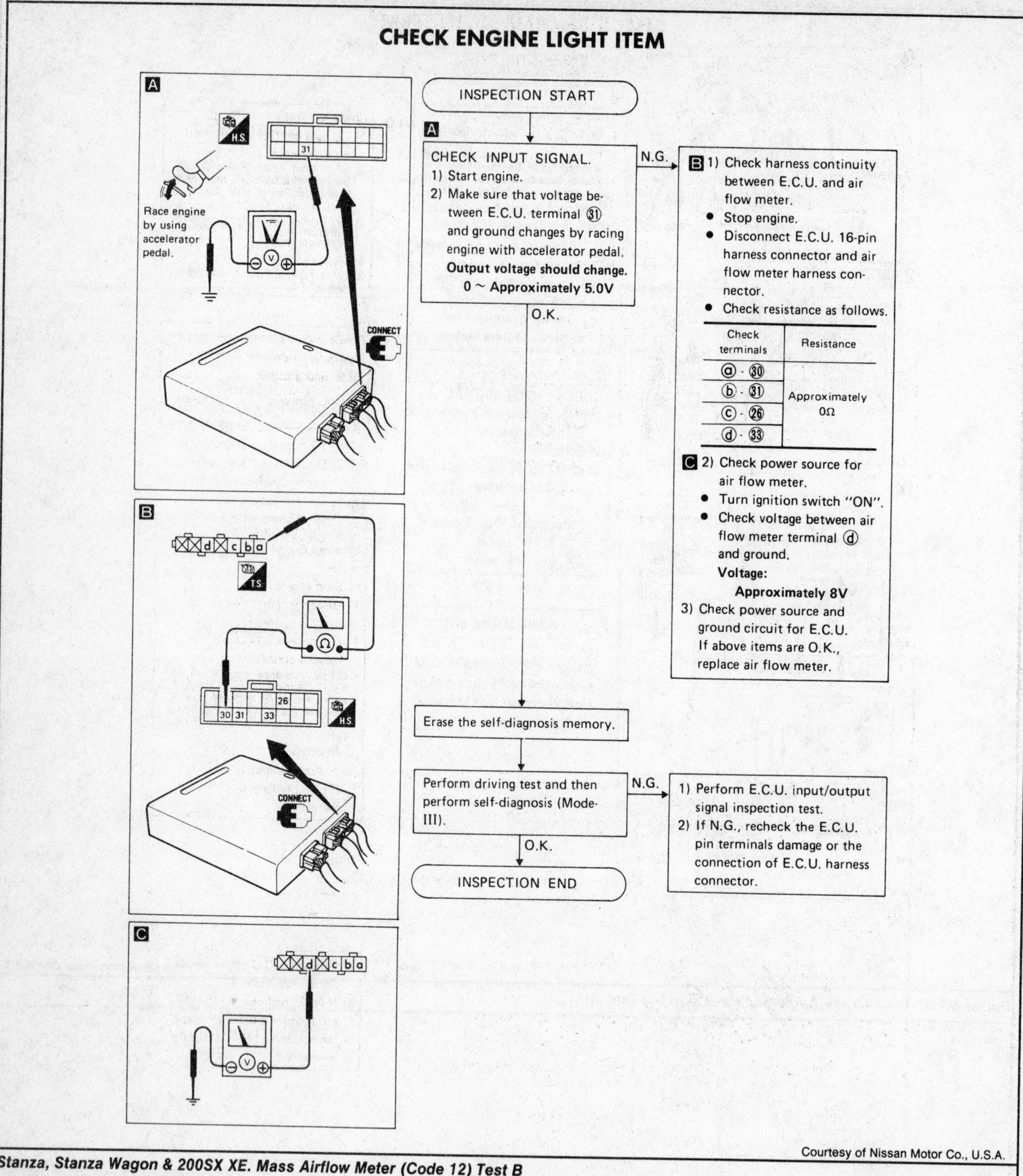
CHECK ENGINE LIGHT ITEM
A
H.S.
31
Race engine by using accelerator pedal.
V
CONNECT
B
d c b a
T.S.
Ω
26
30 31 33
H.S.
CONNECT
C
d c b a
V
INSPECTION START
A
CHECK INPUT SIGNAL.
1) Start engine.
2) Make sure that voltage between E.C.U. terminal ㉛ and ground changes by racing engine with accelerator pedal.
Output voltage should change.
0 ~ Approximately 5.0V
N.G.
B 1) Check harness continuity between E.C.U. and air flow meter.
• Stop engine.
• Disconnect E.C.U. 16-pin harness connector and air flow meter harness connector.
• Check resistance as follows.
Check terminals | Resistance
ⓐ - ㉚ | Approximately 0Ω
ⓑ - ㉛
ⓒ - ㉖
ⓓ - ㉝
C 2) Check power source for air flow meter.
• Turn ignition switch "ON".
• Check voltage between air flow meter terminal ⓓ and ground.
Voltage:
Approximately 8V
3) Check power source and ground circuit for E.C.U.
If above items are O.K., replace air flow meter.
O.K.
Erase the self-diagnosis memory.
Perform driving test and then perform self-diagnosis (Mode-III).
N.G.
1) Perform E.C.U. input/output signal inspection test.
2) If N.G., recheck the E.C.U. pin terminals damage or the connection of E.C.U. harness connector.
O.K.
INSPECTION END
Courtesy of Nissan Motor Co., U.S.A.

*Stanza, Stanza Wagon & 200SX XE. Mass Airflow Meter (Code 12) Test B*

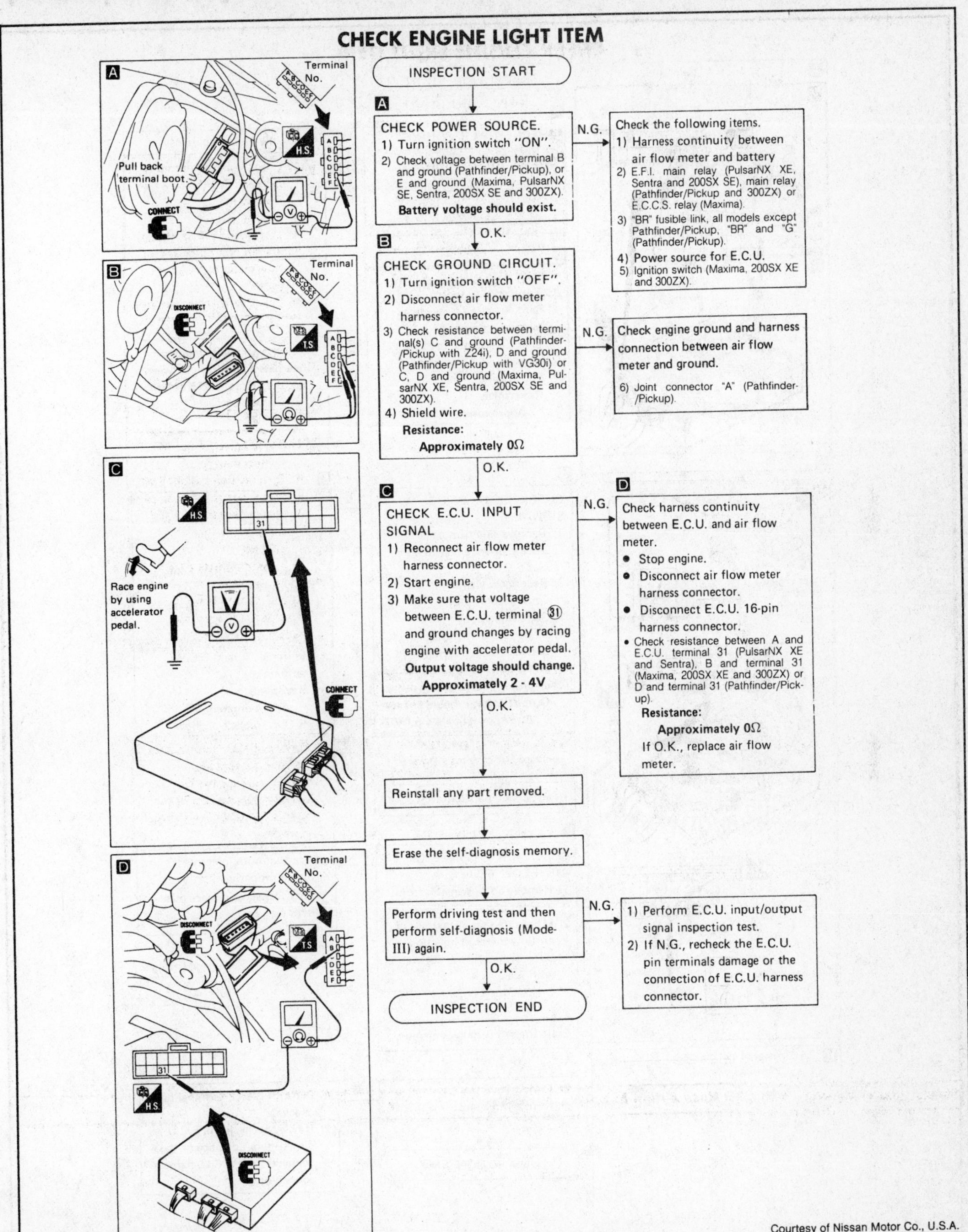
CHECK ENGINE LIGHT ITEM
A
Terminal No.
H.S.
Pull back terminal boot.
CONNECT
B
Terminal No.
DISCONNECT
T.S.
C
H.S.
31
Race engine by using accelerator pedal.
CONNECT
D
Terminal No.
DISCONNECT
T.S.
31
H.S.
DISCONNECT
INSPECTION START
A
CHECK POWER SOURCE.
1) Turn ignition switch "ON".
2) Check voltage between terminal B and ground (Pathfinder/Pickup), or E and ground (Maxima, PulsarNX SE, Sentra, 200SX SE and 300ZX).
Battery voltage should exist.
N.G.
Check the following items.
1) Harness continuity between air flow meter and battery
2) E.F.I. main relay (PulsarNX XE, Sentra and 200SX SE), main relay (Pathfinder/Pickup and 300ZX) or E.C.C.S. relay (Maxima).
3) "BR" fusible link, all models except Pathfinder/Pickup, "BR" and "G" (Pathfinder/Pickup).
4) Power source for E.C.U.
5) Ignition switch (Maxima, 200SX XE and 300ZX).
O.K.
B
CHECK GROUND CIRCUIT.
1) Turn ignition switch "OFF".
2) Disconnect air flow meter harness connector.
3) Check resistance between terminal(s) C and ground (Pathfinder-/Pickup with Z24i), D and ground (Pathfinder/Pickup with VG30i) or C, D and ground (Maxima, PulsarNX XE, Sentra, 200SX SE and 300ZX).
4) Shield wire.
Resistance:
Approximately 0Ω
N.G.
Check engine ground and harness connection between air flow meter and ground.
6) Joint connector "A" (Pathfinder-/Pickup).
O.K.
C
CHECK E.C.U. INPUT SIGNAL
1) Reconnect air flow meter harness connector.
2) Start engine.
3) Make sure that voltage between E.C.U. terminal 31 and ground changes by racing engine with accelerator pedal.
Output voltage should change.
Approximately 2 - 4V
N.G.
D
Check harness continuity between E.C.U. and air flow meter.
• Stop engine.
• Disconnect air flow meter harness connector.
• Disconnect E.C.U. 16-pin harness connector.
• Check resistance between A and E.C.U. terminal 31 (PulsarNX XE and Sentra), B and terminal 31 (Maxima, 200SX XE and 300ZX) or D and terminal 31 (Pathfinder/Pickup).
Resistance:
Approximately 0Ω
If O.K., replace air flow meter.
O.K.
Reinstall any part removed.
Erase the self-diagnosis memory.
Perform driving test and then perform self-diagnosis (Mode-III) again.
N.G.
1) Perform E.C.U. input/output signal inspection test.
2) If N.G., recheck the E.C.U. pin terminals damage or the connection of E.C.U. harness connector.
O.K.
INSPECTION END

Courtesy of Nissan Motor Co., U.S.A.

*Maxima, Pathfinder/Pickup (Z24i & VG30i), Pulsar NX XE, Sentra, 200SX SE & 300ZX. Mass Airflow Meter (Code 12) Test B*

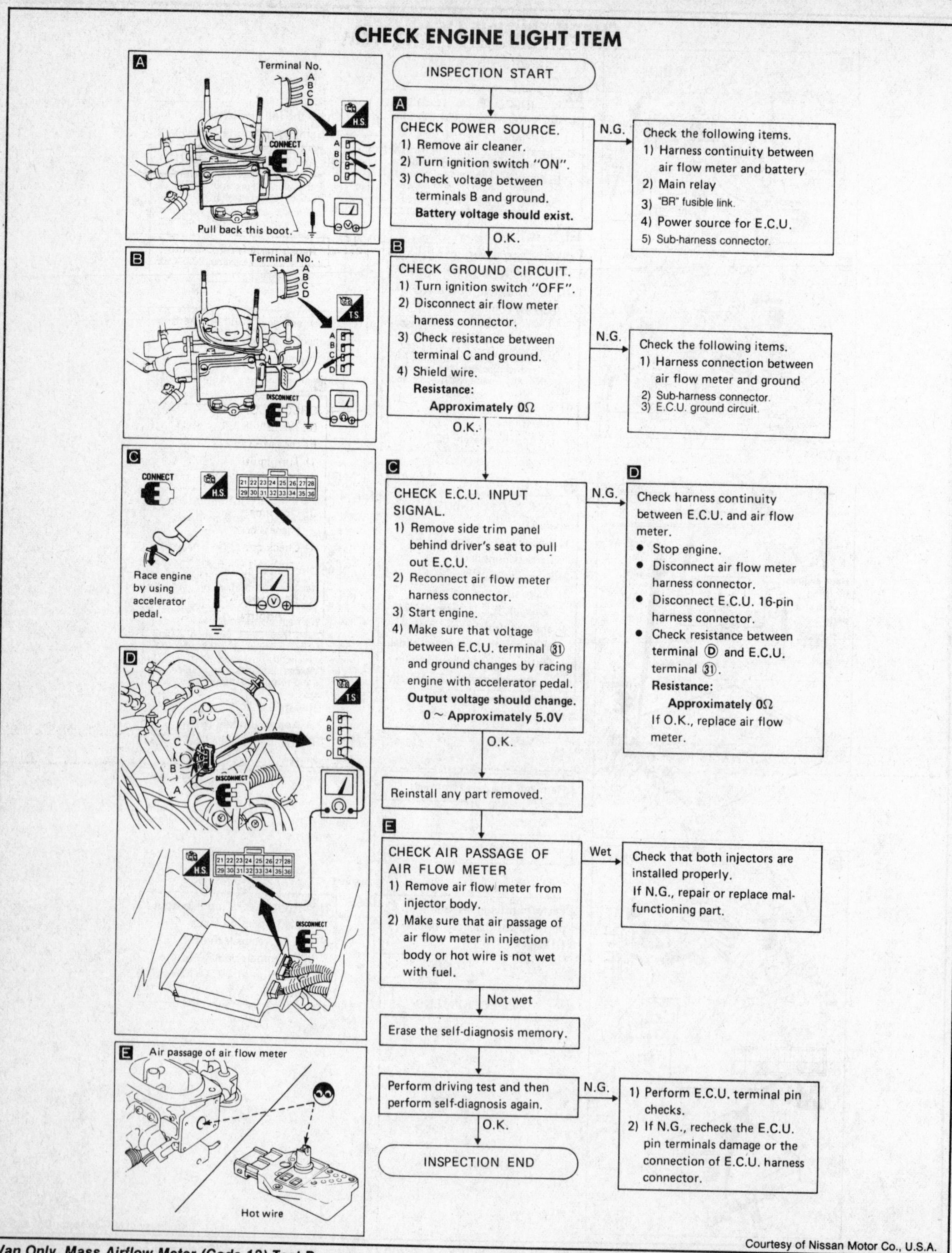
CHECK ENGINE LIGHT ITEM
A
Terminal No.
A
B
C
D
H.S.
CONNECT
Pull back this boot.
B
Terminal No.
T.S.
DISCONNECT
C
CONNECT
H.S.
21 22 23 24 25 26 27 28
29 30 31 32 33 34 35 36
Race engine by using accelerator pedal.
D
T.S.
DISCONNECT
H.S.
E
Air passage of air flow meter
Hot wire
INSPECTION START
A
CHECK POWER SOURCE.
1) Remove air cleaner.
2) Turn ignition switch "ON".
3) Check voltage between terminals B and ground.
Battery voltage should exist.
N.G.
Check the following items.
1) Harness continuity between air flow meter and battery
2) Main relay
3) "BR" fusible link.
4) Power source for E.C.U.
5) Sub-harness connector.
O.K.
B
CHECK GROUND CIRCUIT.
1) Turn ignition switch "OFF".
2) Disconnect air flow meter harness connector.
3) Check resistance between terminal C and ground.
4) Shield wire.
Resistance:
Approximately 0Ω
N.G.
Check the following items.
1) Harness connection between air flow meter and ground
2) Sub-harness connector.
3) E.C.U. ground circuit.
O.K.
C
CHECK E.C.U. INPUT SIGNAL.
1) Remove side trim panel behind driver's seat to pull out E.C.U.
2) Reconnect air flow meter harness connector.
3) Start engine.
4) Make sure that voltage between E.C.U. terminal ㉛ and ground changes by racing engine with accelerator pedal.
Output voltage should change.
0 ~ Approximately 5.0V
N.G.
D
Check harness continuity between E.C.U. and air flow meter.
• Stop engine.
• Disconnect air flow meter harness connector.
• Disconnect E.C.U. 16-pin harness connector.
• Check resistance between terminal Ⓓ and E.C.U. terminal ㉛.
Resistance:
Approximately 0Ω
If O.K., replace air flow meter.
O.K.
Reinstall any part removed.
E
CHECK AIR PASSAGE OF AIR FLOW METER
1) Remove air flow meter from injector body.
2) Make sure that air passage of air flow meter in injection body or hot wire is not wet with fuel.
Wet
Check that both injectors are installed properly.
If N.G., repair or replace malfunctioning part.
Not wet
Erase the self-diagnosis memory.
Perform driving test and then perform self-diagnosis again.
N.G.
1) Perform E.C.U. terminal pin checks.
2) If N.G., recheck the E.C.U. pin terminals damage or the connection of E.C.U. harness connector.
O.K.
INSPECTION END

Courtesy of Nissan Motor Co., U.S.A.

*Van Only. Mass Airflow Meter (Code 12) Test B*

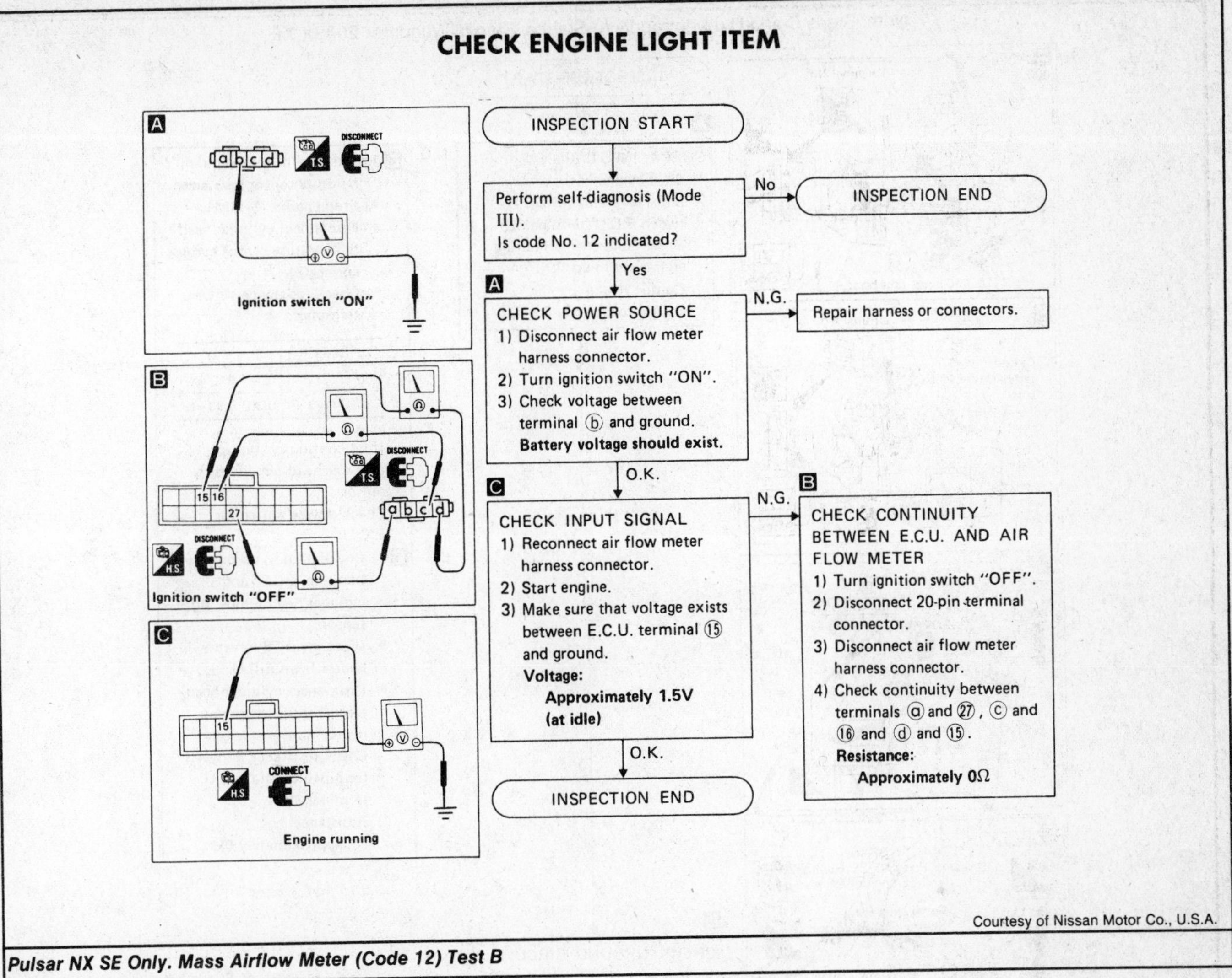
CHECK ENGINE LIGHT ITEM
A
DISCONNECT
T.S.
Ignition switch "ON"
B
15 16
27
DISCONNECT
H.S.
Ignition switch "OFF"
C
15
CONNECT
Engine running
INSPECTION START
Perform self-diagnosis (Mode III).
Is code No. 12 indicated?
No
INSPECTION END
Yes
A
CHECK POWER SOURCE
1) Disconnect air flow meter harness connector.
2) Turn ignition switch "ON".
3) Check voltage between terminal ⓑ and ground.
Battery voltage should exist.
N.G.
Repair harness or connectors.
O.K.
C
CHECK INPUT SIGNAL
1) Reconnect air flow meter harness connector.
2) Start engine.
3) Make sure that voltage exists between E.C.U. terminal ⑮ and ground.
Voltage:
Approximately 1.5V (at idle)
N.G.
B
CHECK CONTINUITY BETWEEN E.C.U. AND AIR FLOW METER
1) Turn ignition switch "OFF".
2) Disconnect 20-pin terminal connector.
3) Disconnect air flow meter harness connector.
4) Check continuity between terminals ⓐ and ㉗, ⓒ and ⑯ and ⓓ and ⑮.
Resistance:
Approximately 0Ω
O.K.
INSPECTION END
Courtesy of Nissan Motor Co., U.S.A.

*Pulsar NX SE Only. Mass Airflow Meter (Code 12) Test B*

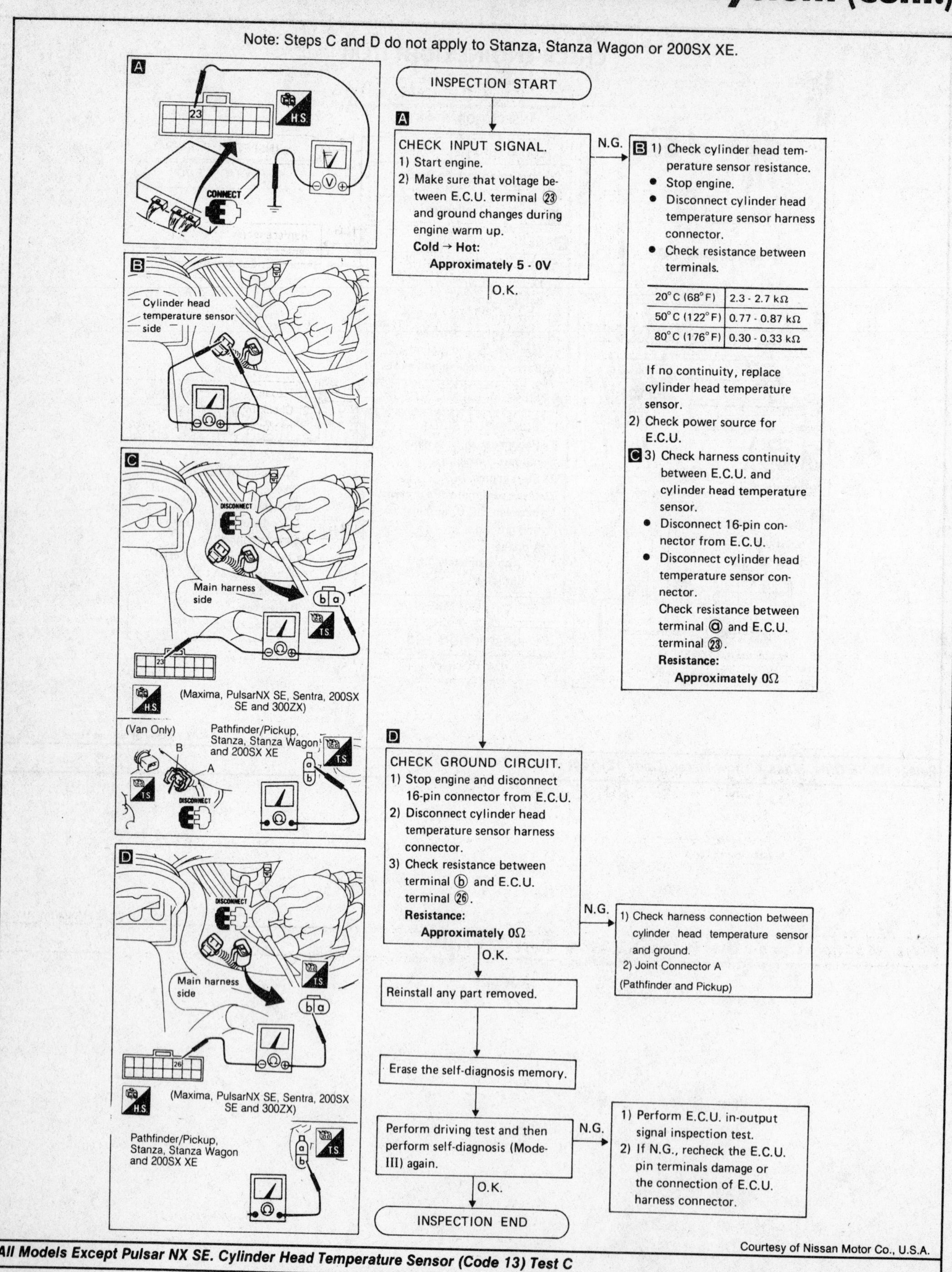
Note: Steps C and D do not apply to Stanza, Stanza Wagon or 200SX XE.
A
23
H.S.
CONNECT
Cylinder head temperature sensor side
B
C
DISCONNECT
Main harness side
b a
T.S.
23
H.S.
(Maxima, PulsarNX SE, Sentra, 200SX SE and 300ZX)
(Van Only)
B
A
Pathfinder/Pickup, Stanza, Stanza Wagon and 200SX XE
a
b
D
DISCONNECT
Main harness side
b a
T.S.
26
H.S.
(Maxima, PulsarNX SE, Sentra, 200SX SE and 300ZX)
Pathfinder/Pickup, Stanza, Stanza Wagon and 200SX XE
INSPECTION START
A
CHECK INPUT SIGNAL.
1) Start engine.
2) Make sure that voltage between E.C.U. terminal (23) and ground changes during engine warm up.
Cold → Hot:
Approximately 5 - 0V
N.G.
B 1) Check cylinder head temperature sensor resistance.
• Stop engine.
• Disconnect cylinder head temperature sensor harness connector.
• Check resistance between terminals.
20°C (68°F) | 2.3 - 2.7 kΩ
50°C (122°F) | 0.77 - 0.87 kΩ
80°C (176°F) | 0.30 - 0.33 kΩ
If no continuity, replace cylinder head temperature sensor.
2) Check power source for E.C.U.
C 3) Check harness continuity between E.C.U. and cylinder head temperature sensor.
• Disconnect 16-pin connector from E.C.U.
• Disconnect cylinder head temperature sensor connector.
Check resistance between terminal (a) and E.C.U. terminal (23).
Resistance:
Approximately 0Ω
O.K.
D
CHECK GROUND CIRCUIT.
1) Stop engine and disconnect 16-pin connector from E.C.U.
2) Disconnect cylinder head temperature sensor harness connector.
3) Check resistance between terminal (b) and E.C.U. terminal (26).
Resistance:
Approximately 0Ω
N.G.
1) Check harness connection between cylinder head temperature sensor and ground.
2) Joint Connector A (Pathfinder and Pickup)
O.K.
Reinstall any part removed.
Erase the self-diagnosis memory.
Perform driving test and then perform self-diagnosis (Mode-III) again.
N.G.
1) Perform E.C.U. in-output signal inspection test.
2) If N.G., recheck the E.C.U. pin terminals damage or the connection of E.C.U. harness connector.
O.K.
INSPECTION END
Courtesy of Nissan Motor Co., U.S.A.

***All Models Except Pulsar NX SE. Cylinder Head Temperature Sensor (Code 13) Test C***

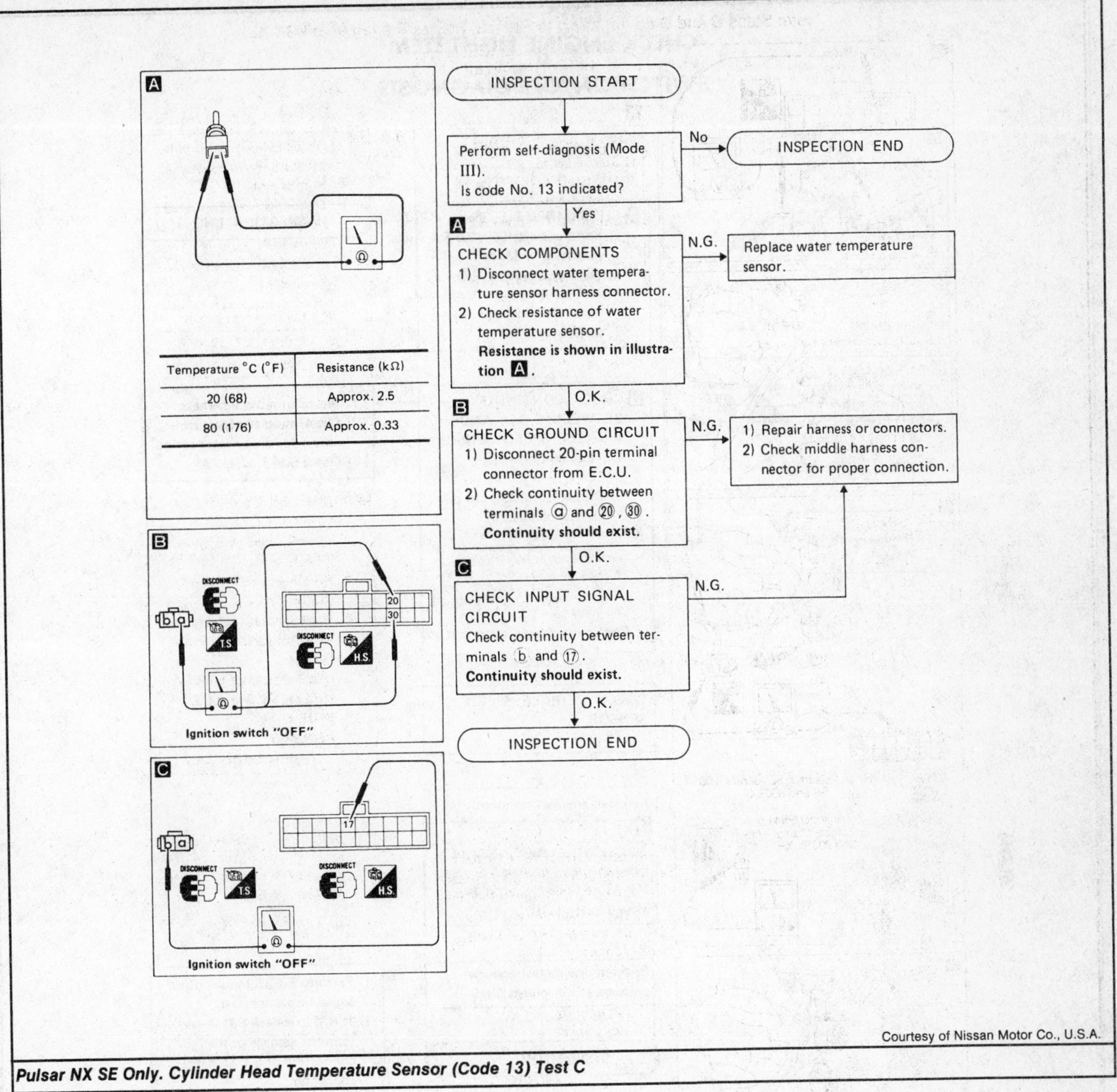
A
Temperature °C (°F) | Resistance (kΩ)
20 (68) | Approx. 2.5
80 (176) | Approx. 0.33
B
DISCONNECT
T.S.
H.S.
20
30
Ignition switch "OFF"
C
17
DISCONNECT
T.S.
H.S.
Ignition switch "OFF"
INSPECTION START
Perform self-diagnosis (Mode III).
Is code No. 13 indicated?
No
INSPECTION END
Yes
A
CHECK COMPONENTS
1) Disconnect water temperature sensor harness connector.
2) Check resistance of water temperature sensor.
Resistance is shown in illustration A.
N.G.
Replace water temperature sensor.
O.K.
B
CHECK GROUND CIRCUIT
1) Disconnect 20-pin terminal connector from E.C.U.
2) Check continuity between terminals ⓐ and ⑳, ㉚.
Continuity should exist.
N.G.
1) Repair harness or connectors.
2) Check middle harness connector for proper connection.
O.K.
C
CHECK INPUT SIGNAL CIRCUIT
Check continuity between terminals ⓑ and ⑰.
Continuity should exist.
N.G.
O.K.
INSPECTION END

Courtesy of Nissan Motor Co., U.S.A.

*Pulsar NX SE Only. Cylinder Head Temperature Sensor (Code 13) Test C*

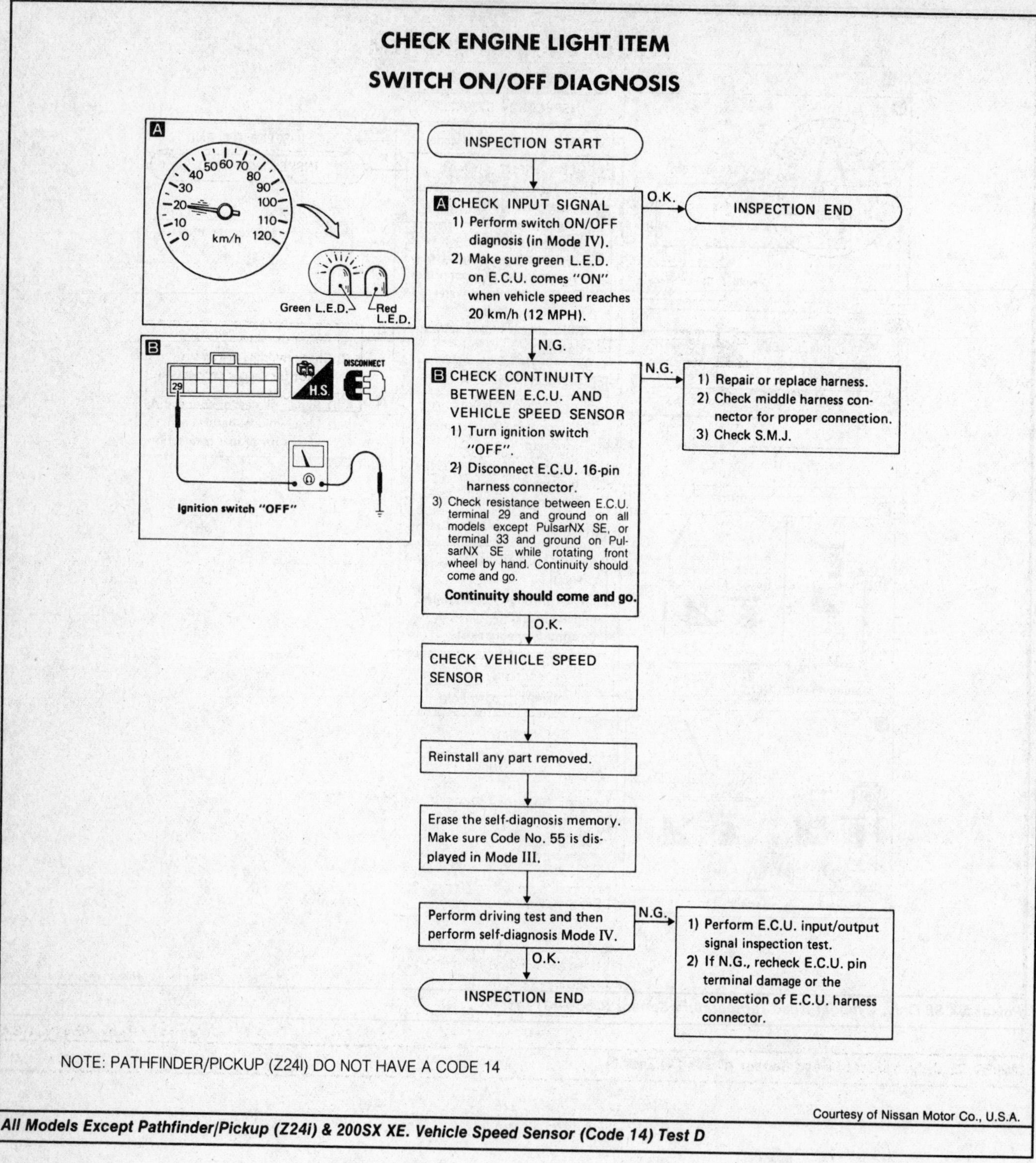
CHECK ENGINE LIGHT ITEM
SWITCH ON/OFF DIAGNOSIS
A
km/h
Green L.E.D.
Red L.E.D.
B
29
DISCONNECT
H.S.
Ignition switch "OFF"
INSPECTION START
A CHECK INPUT SIGNAL
1) Perform switch ON/OFF diagnosis (in Mode IV).
2) Make sure green L.E.D. on E.C.U. comes "ON" when vehicle speed reaches 20 km/h (12 MPH).
O.K.
INSPECTION END
N.G.
B CHECK CONTINUITY BETWEEN E.C.U. AND VEHICLE SPEED SENSOR
1) Turn ignition switch "OFF".
2) Disconnect E.C.U. 16-pin harness connector.
3) Check resistance between E.C.U. terminal 29 and ground on all models except PulsarNX SE, or terminal 33 and ground on PulsarNX SE while rotating front wheel by hand. Continuity should come and go.
Continuity should come and go.
N.G.
1) Repair or replace harness.
2) Check middle harness connector for proper connection.
3) Check S.M.J.
O.K.
CHECK VEHICLE SPEED SENSOR
Reinstall any part removed.
Erase the self-diagnosis memory. Make sure Code No. 55 is displayed in Mode III.
Perform driving test and then perform self-diagnosis Mode IV.
N.G.
1) Perform E.C.U. input/output signal inspection test.
2) If N.G., recheck E.C.U. pin terminal damage or the connection of E.C.U. harness connector.
O.K.
INSPECTION END
NOTE: PATHFINDER/PICKUP (Z24I) DO NOT HAVE A CODE 14
Courtesy of Nissan Motor Co., U.S.A.

*All Models Except Pathfinder/Pickup (Z24i) & 200SX XE. Vehicle Speed Sensor (Code 14) Test D*

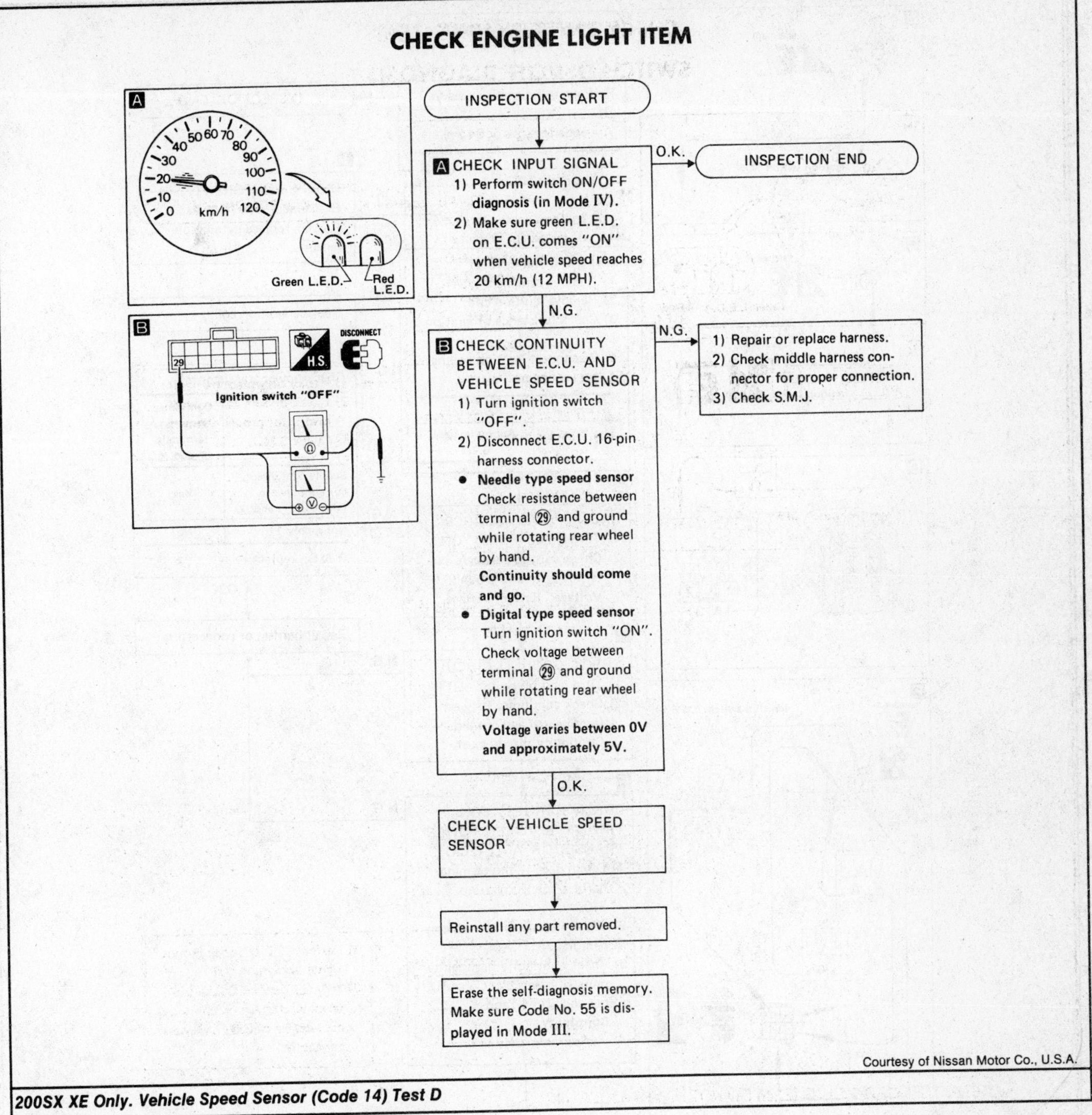
CHECK ENGINE LIGHT ITEM
A
0
10
20
30
40
50
60
70
80
90
100
110
120
km/h
Green L.E.D.
Red L.E.D.
B
29
DISCONNECT
H.S.
Ignition switch "OFF"
INSPECTION START
A CHECK INPUT SIGNAL
1) Perform switch ON/OFF diagnosis (in Mode IV).
2) Make sure green L.E.D. on E.C.U. comes "ON" when vehicle speed reaches 20 km/h (12 MPH).
O.K.
INSPECTION END
N.G.
B CHECK CONTINUITY BETWEEN E.C.U. AND VEHICLE SPEED SENSOR
1) Turn ignition switch "OFF".
2) Disconnect E.C.U. 16-pin harness connector.
● Needle type speed sensor
Check resistance between terminal ㉙ and ground while rotating rear wheel by hand.
Continuity should come and go.
● Digital type speed sensor
Turn ignition switch "ON".
Check voltage between terminal ㉙ and ground while rotating rear wheel by hand.
Voltage varies between 0V and approximately 5V.
N.G.
1) Repair or replace harness.
2) Check middle harness connector for proper connection.
3) Check S.M.J.
O.K.
CHECK VEHICLE SPEED SENSOR
Reinstall any part removed.
Erase the self-diagnosis memory. Make sure Code No. 55 is displayed in Mode III.
Courtesy of Nissan Motor Co., U.S.A.

***200SX XE Only. Vehicle Speed Sensor (Code 14) Test D***

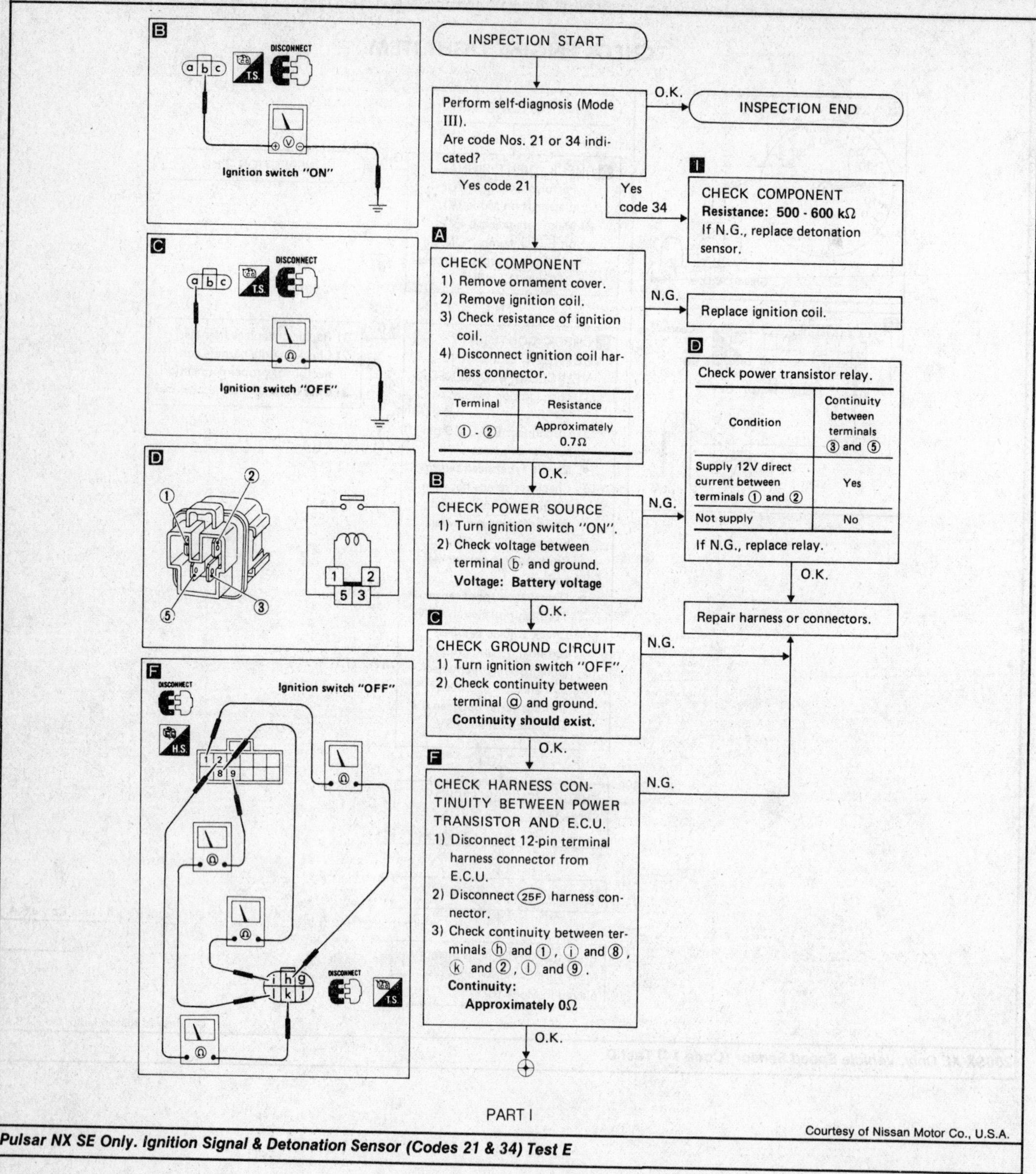
B
DISCONNECT
a b c
T.S.
Ignition switch "ON"
C
DISCONNECT
a b c
T.S.
Ignition switch "OFF"
D
1
2
3
5
1 2
5 3
F
DISCONNECT
H.S.
Ignition switch "OFF"
1 2
8 9
i h g
j k l
DISCONNECT
T.S.
INSPECTION START
Perform self-diagnosis (Mode III).
Are code Nos. 21 or 34 indicated?
O.K.
INSPECTION END
Yes code 21
Yes code 34
I
CHECK COMPONENT
Resistance: 500 - 600 kΩ
If N.G., replace detonation sensor.
A
CHECK COMPONENT
1) Remove ornament cover.
2) Remove ignition coil.
3) Check resistance of ignition coil.
4) Disconnect ignition coil harness connector.
Terminal
Resistance
① - ②
Approximately 0.7Ω
N.G.
Replace ignition coil.
D
Check power transistor relay.
Condition
Continuity between terminals ③ and ⑤
Supply 12V direct current between terminals ① and ②
Yes
Not supply
No
If N.G., replace relay.
O.K.
B
CHECK POWER SOURCE
1) Turn ignition switch "ON".
2) Check voltage between terminal ⓑ and ground.
Voltage: Battery voltage
N.G.
O.K.
Repair harness or connectors.
C
CHECK GROUND CIRCUIT
1) Turn ignition switch "OFF".
2) Check continuity between terminal ⓐ and ground.
Continuity should exist.
N.G.
O.K.
F
CHECK HARNESS CONTINUITY BETWEEN POWER TRANSISTOR AND E.C.U.
1) Disconnect 12-pin terminal harness connector from E.C.U.
2) Disconnect 25F harness connector.
3) Check continuity between terminals ⓗ and ①, ⓘ and ⑧, ⓚ and ②, ⓛ and ⑨.
Continuity:
Approximately 0Ω
N.G.
O.K.
PART I



*Pulsar NX SE Only. Ignition Signal & Detonation Sensor (Codes 21 & 34) Test E*

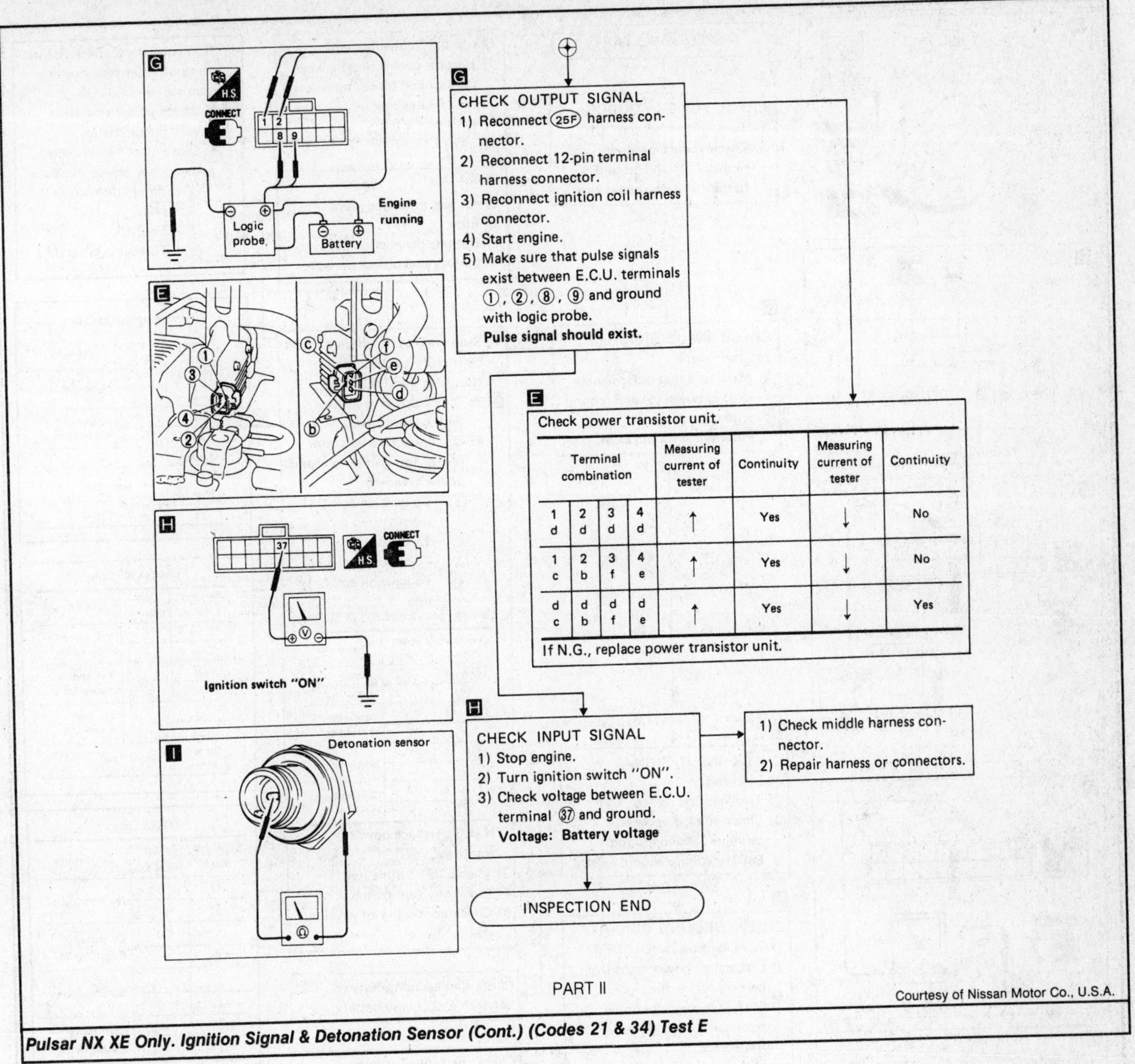
G
H.S.
CONNECT
1 2
8 9
Engine running
Logic probe
Battery
G
CHECK OUTPUT SIGNAL
1) Reconnect 25F harness connector.
2) Reconnect 12-pin terminal harness connector.
3) Reconnect ignition coil harness connector.
4) Start engine.
5) Make sure that pulse signals exist between E.C.U. terminals ①, ②, ⑧, ⑨ and ground with logic probe.
Pulse signal should exist.
E
E
Check power transistor unit.
If N.G., replace power transistor unit.
H
CONNECT
H.S.
37
Ignition switch "ON"
H
CHECK INPUT SIGNAL
1) Stop engine.
2) Turn ignition switch "ON".
3) Check voltage between E.C.U. terminal ㊲ and ground.
Voltage: Battery voltage
1) Check middle harness connector.
2) Repair harness or connectors.
I
Detonation sensor
INSPECTION END
PART II
Courtesy of Nissan Motor Co., U.S.A.

Check power transistor unit.

| Terminal combination | | | | Measuring current of tester | Continuity | Measuring current of tester | Continuity |
|---|---|---|---|---|---|---|---|
| 1 d | 2 d | 3 d | 4 d | ↑ | Yes | ↓ | No |
| 1 c | 2 b | 3 f | 4 e | ↑ | Yes | ↓ | No |
| d c | d b | d f | d e | ↑ | Yes | ↓ | Yes |

If N.G., replace power transistor unit.

*Pulsar NX XE Only. Ignition Signal & Detonation Sensor (Cont.) (Codes 21 & 34) Test E*

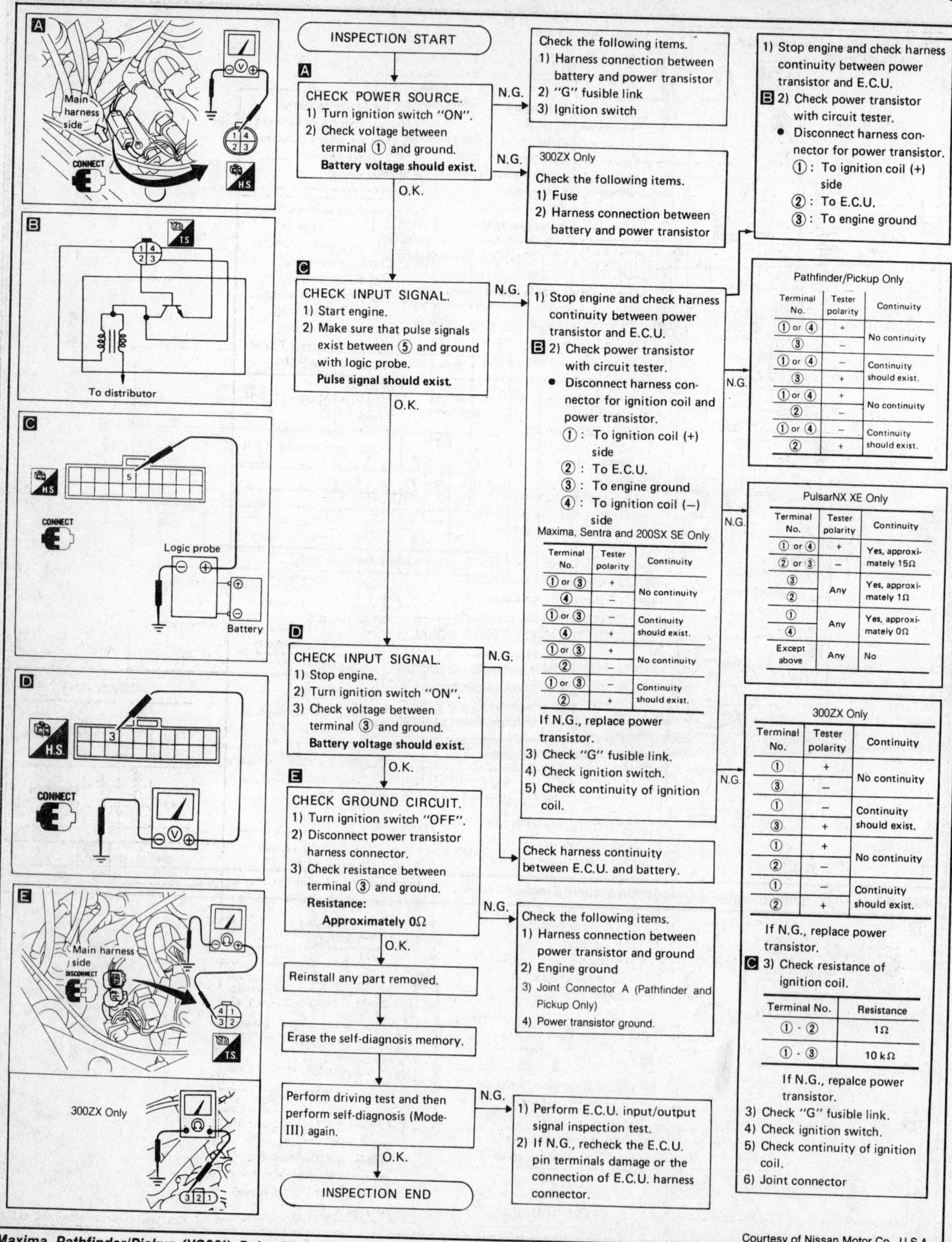
A
Main harness side
CONNECT
H.S.
B
T.S.
To distributor
C
H.S.
CONNECT
Logic probe
Battery
D
H.S.
CONNECT
E
Main harness side
DISCONNECT
T.S.
300ZX Only
INSPECTION START
A
CHECK POWER SOURCE.
1) Turn ignition switch "ON".
2) Check voltage between terminal ① and ground.
Battery voltage should exist.
N.G.
Check the following items.
1) Harness connection between battery and power transistor
2) "G" fusible link
3) Ignition switch
N.G.
300ZX Only
Check the following items.
1) Fuse
2) Harness connection between battery and power transistor
O.K.
1) Stop engine and check harness continuity between power transistor and E.C.U.
B 2) Check power transistor with circuit tester.
• Disconnect harness connector for power transistor.
①: To ignition coil (+) side
②: To E.C.U.
③: To engine ground
C
CHECK INPUT SIGNAL.
1) Start engine.
2) Make sure that pulse signals exist between ⑤ and ground with logic probe.
Pulse signal should exist.
N.G.
1) Stop engine and check harness continuity between power transistor and E.C.U.
B 2) Check power transistor with circuit tester.
• Disconnect harness connector for ignition coil and power transistor.
①: To ignition coil (+) side
②: To E.C.U.
③: To engine ground
④: To ignition coil (−) side
Maxima, Sentra and 200SX SE Only
Terminal No. | Tester polarity | Continuity
① or ③ | + | No continuity
④ | − |
① or ③ | − | Continuity should exist.
④ | + |
① or ③ | + | No continuity
② | − |
① or ③ | − | Continuity should exist.
② | + |
If N.G., replace power transistor.
3) Check "G" fusible link.
4) Check ignition switch.
5) Check continuity of ignition coil.
N.G.
Pathfinder/Pickup Only
Terminal No. | Tester polarity | Continuity
① or ④ | + | No continuity
③ | − |
① or ④ | − | Continuity should exist.
③ | + |
① or ④ | + | No continuity
② | − |
① or ④ | − | Continuity should exist.
② | + |
N.G.
PulsarNX XE Only
Terminal No. | Tester polarity | Continuity
① or ④ | + | Yes, approximately 15Ω
② or ③ | − |
③ | Any | Yes, approximately 1Ω
② | |
① | Any | Yes, approximately 0Ω
④ | |
Except above | Any | No
N.G.
300ZX Only
Terminal No. | Tester polarity | Continuity
① | + | No continuity
③ | − |
① | − | Continuity should exist.
③ | + |
① | + | No continuity
② | − |
① | − | Continuity should exist.
② | + |
If N.G., replace power transistor.
C 3) Check resistance of ignition coil.
Terminal No. | Resistance
① - ② | 1Ω
① - ③ | 10 kΩ
If N.G., repalce power transistor.
3) Check "G" fusible link.
4) Check ignition switch.
5) Check continuity of ignition coil.
6) Joint connector
O.K.
D
CHECK INPUT SIGNAL.
1) Stop engine.
2) Turn ignition switch "ON".
3) Check voltage between terminal ③ and ground.
Battery voltage should exist.
N.G.
Check harness continuity between E.C.U. and battery.
O.K.
E
CHECK GROUND CIRCUIT.
1) Turn ignition switch "OFF".
2) Disconnect power transistor harness connector.
3) Check resistance between terminal ③ and ground.
Resistance:
Approximately 0Ω
N.G.
Check the following items.
1) Harness connection between power transistor and ground
2) Engine ground
3) Joint Connector A (Pathfinder and Pickup Only)
4) Power transistor ground.
O.K.
Reinstall any part removed.
Erase the self-diagnosis memory.
Perform driving test and then perform self-diagnosis (Mode-III) again.
N.G.
1) Perform E.C.U. input/output signal inspection test.
2) If N.G., recheck the E.C.U. pin terminals damage or the connection of E.C.U. harness connector.
O.K.
INSPECTION END

Courtesy of Nissan Motor Co., U.S.A.

*Maxima, Pathfinder/Pickup (VG30i), PulsarNX XE, Sentra, 200SX SE & 300ZX. Ignition Signal (Code 21) Test E*

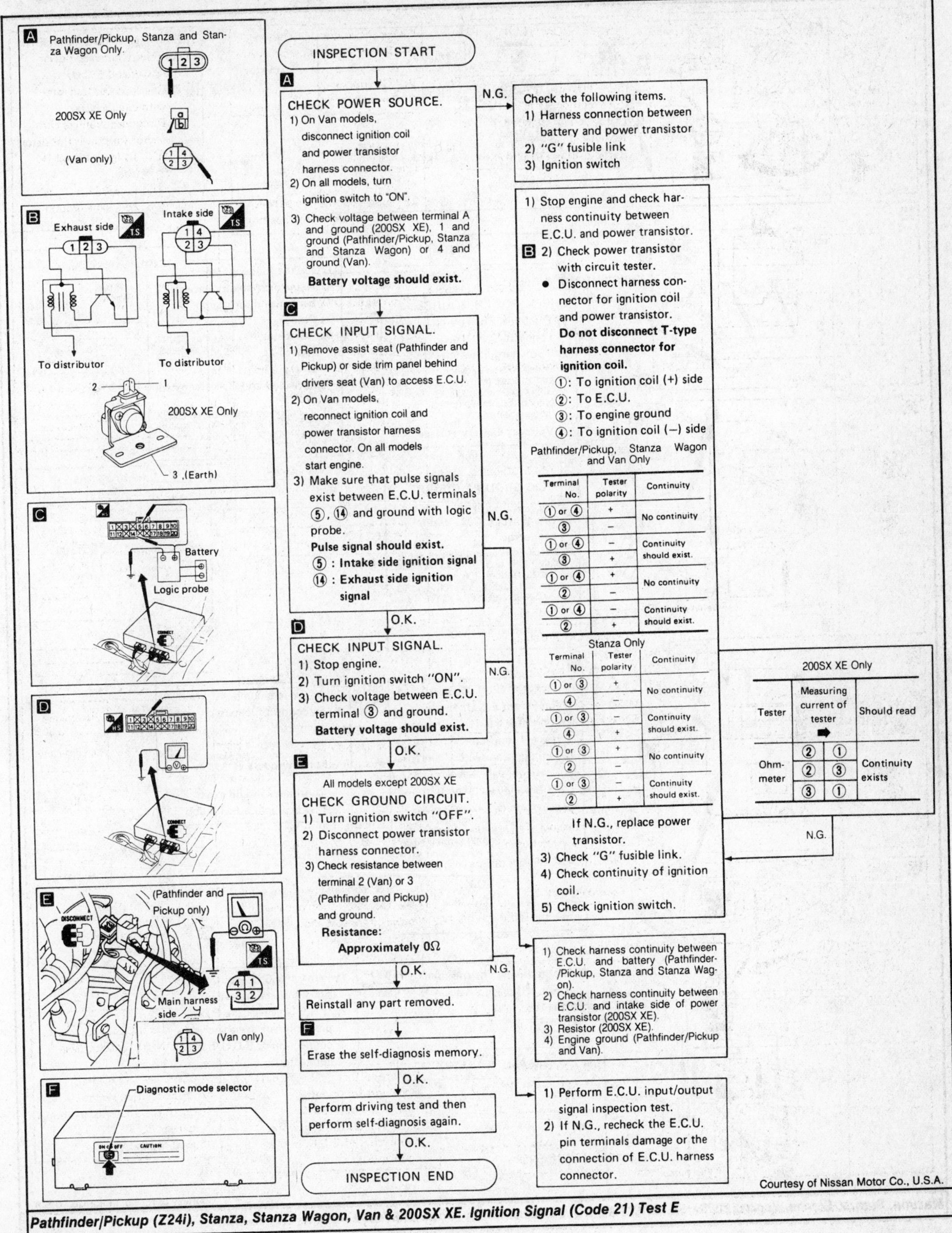
A Pathfinder/Pickup, Stanza and Stanza Wagon Only.
1 2 3
200SX XE Only
a b
(Van only)
1 4 2 3
B Exhaust side
T.S
1 2 3
Intake side
T.S
1 4 2 3
To distributor
To distributor
2
1
200SX XE Only
3 ,(Earth)
C
Battery
Logic probe
CONNECT
D
H.S
CONNECT
E
DISCONNECT
(Pathfinder and Pickup only)
T.S
4 1 3 2
Main harness side
1 4 2 3
(Van only)
F
Diagnostic mode selector
ON OFF
CAUTION
INSPECTION START
A
CHECK POWER SOURCE.
1) On Van models, disconnect ignition coil and power transistor harness connector.
2) On all models, turn ignition switch to "ON".
3) Check voltage between terminal A and ground (200SX XE), 1 and ground (Pathfinder/Pickup, Stanza and Stanza Wagon) or 4 and ground (Van).
Battery voltage should exist.
N.G.
Check the following items.
1) Harness connection between battery and power transistor
2) "G" fusible link
3) Ignition switch
C
CHECK INPUT SIGNAL.
1) Remove assist seat (Pathfinder and Pickup) or side trim panel behind drivers seat (Van) to access E.C.U.
2) On Van models, reconnect ignition coil and power transistor harness connector. On all models start engine.
3) Make sure that pulse signals exist between E.C.U. terminals ⑤, ⑭ and ground with logic probe.
Pulse signal should exist.
⑤ : Intake side ignition signal
⑭ : Exhaust side ignition signal
N.G.
1) Stop engine and check harness continuity between E.C.U. and power transistor.
B 2) Check power transistor with circuit tester.
● Disconnect harness connector for ignition coil and power transistor.
Do not disconnect T-type harness connector for ignition coil.
①: To ignition coil (+) side
②: To E.C.U.
③: To engine ground
④: To ignition coil (−) side
Pathfinder/Pickup, Stanza Wagon and Van Only
Terminal No. | Tester polarity | Continuity
① or ④ | + | No continuity
③ | − |
① or ④ | − | Continuity should exist.
③ | + |
① or ④ | + | No continuity
② | − |
① or ④ | − | Continuity should exist.
② | + |
Stanza Only
Terminal No. | Tester polarity | Continuity
① or ③ | + | No continuity
④ | − |
① or ③ | − | Continuity should exist.
④ | + |
① or ③ | + | No continuity
② | − |
① or ③ | − | Continuity should exist.
② | + |
If N.G., replace power transistor.
3) Check "G" fusible link.
4) Check continuity of ignition coil.
5) Check ignition switch.
200SX XE Only
Tester | Measuring current of tester | | Should read
Ohm-meter | ② | ① | Continuity exists
| ② | ③ |
| ③ | ① |
N.G.
O.K.
D
CHECK INPUT SIGNAL.
1) Stop engine.
2) Turn ignition switch "ON".
3) Check voltage between E.C.U. terminal ③ and ground.
Battery voltage should exist.
N.G.
O.K.
E
All models except 200SX XE
CHECK GROUND CIRCUIT.
1) Turn ignition switch "OFF".
2) Disconnect power transistor harness connector.
3) Check resistance between terminal 2 (Van) or 3 (Pathfinder and Pickup) and ground.
Resistance:
Approximately 0Ω
N.G.
1) Check harness continuity between E.C.U. and battery (Pathfinder-/Pickup, Stanza and Stanza Wagon).
2) Check harness continuity between E.C.U. and intake side of power transistor (200SX XE).
3) Resistor (200SX XE).
4) Engine ground (Pathfinder/Pickup and Van).
O.K.
Reinstall any part removed.
F
Erase the self-diagnosis memory.
O.K.
Perform driving test and then perform self-diagnosis again.
O.K.
INSPECTION END
1) Perform E.C.U. input/output signal inspection test.
2) If N.G., recheck the E.C.U. pin terminals damage or the connection of E.C.U. harness connector.
Courtesy of Nissan Motor Co., U.S.A.

Pathfinder/Pickup (Z24i), Stanza, Stanza Wagon, Van & 200SX XE. Ignition Signal (Code 21) Test E

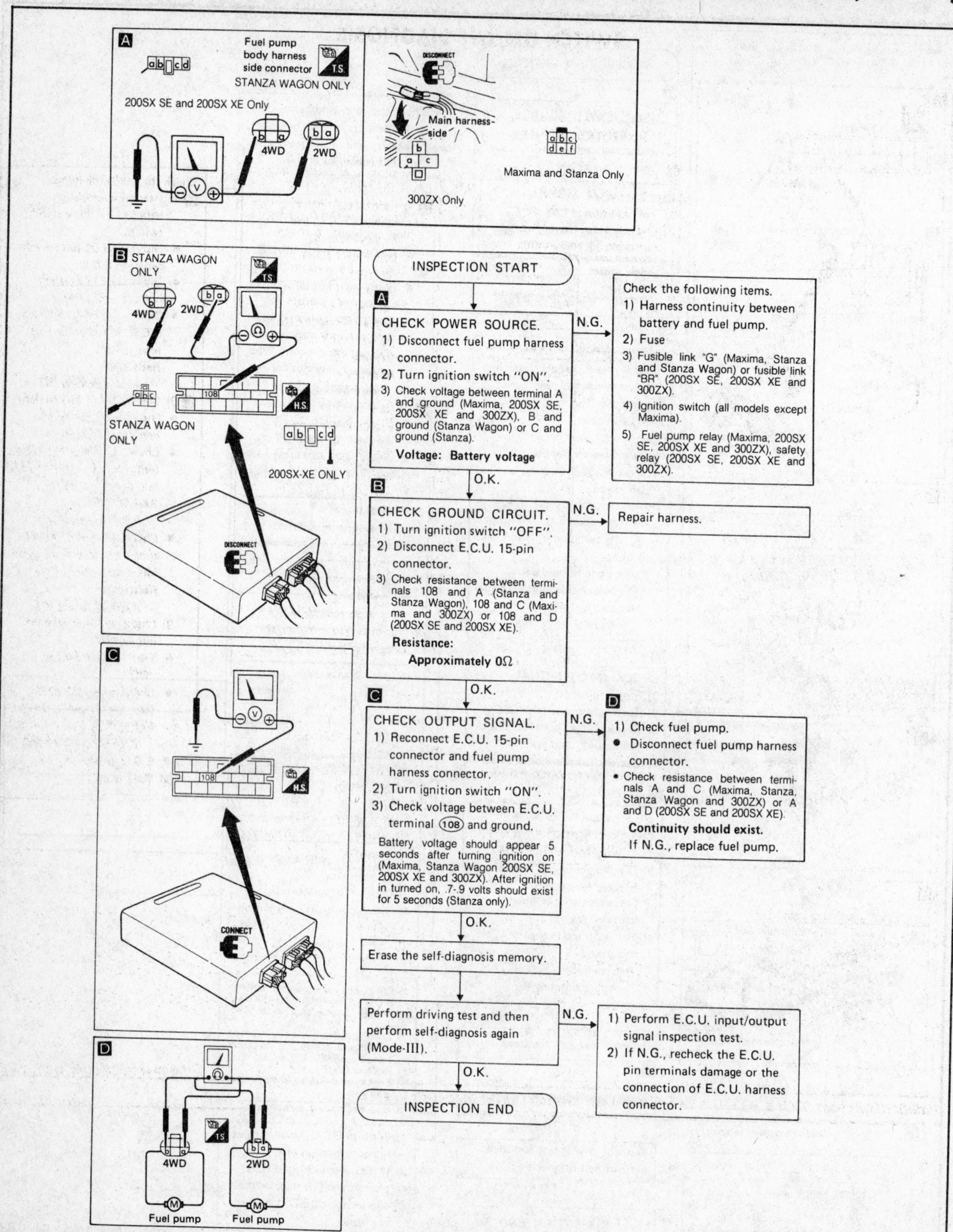
A
Fuel pump body harness side connector
STANZA WAGON ONLY
200SX SE and 200SX XE Only
4WD
2WD
DISCONNECT
Main harness-side
300ZX Only
Maxima and Stanza Only
B STANZA WAGON ONLY
4WD
2WD
STANZA WAGON ONLY
200SX-XE ONLY
DISCONNECT
C
CONNECT
D
4WD
2WD
Fuel pump
Fuel pump
INSPECTION START
A
CHECK POWER SOURCE.
1) Disconnect fuel pump harness connector.
2) Turn ignition switch "ON".
3) Check voltage between terminal A and ground (Maxima, 200SX SE, 200SX XE and 300ZX), B and ground (Stanza Wagon) or C and ground (Stanza).
Voltage: Battery voltage
N.G.
Check the following items.
1) Harness continuity between battery and fuel pump.
2) Fuse
3) Fusible link "G" (Maxima, Stanza and Stanza Wagon) or fusible link "BR" (200SX SE, 200SX XE and 300ZX).
4) Ignition switch (all models except Maxima).
5) Fuel pump relay (Maxima, 200SX SE, 200SX XE and 300ZX), safety relay (200SX SE, 200SX XE and 300ZX).
O.K.
B
CHECK GROUND CIRCUIT.
1) Turn ignition switch "OFF".
2) Disconnect E.C.U. 15-pin connector.
3) Check resistance between terminals 108 and A (Stanza and Stanza Wagon), 108 and C (Maxima and 300ZX) or 108 and D (200SX SE and 200SX XE).
Resistance:
Approximately 0Ω
N.G.
Repair harness.
O.K.
C
CHECK OUTPUT SIGNAL.
1) Reconnect E.C.U. 15-pin connector and fuel pump harness connector.
2) Turn ignition switch "ON".
3) Check voltage between E.C.U. terminal (108) and ground.
Battery voltage should appear 5 seconds after turning ignition on (Maxima, Stanza Wagon 200SX SE, 200SX XE and 300ZX). After ignition in turned on, .7-.9 volts should exist for 5 seconds (Stanza only).
N.G.
D
1) Check fuel pump.
• Disconnect fuel pump harness connector.
• Check resistance between terminals A and C (Maxima, Stanza, Stanza Wagon and 300ZX) or A and D (200SX SE and 200SX XE).
Continuity should exist.
If N.G., replace fuel pump.
O.K.
Erase the self-diagnosis memory.
Perform driving test and then perform self-diagnosis again (Mode-III).
N.G.
1) Perform E.C.U. input/output signal inspection test.
2) If N.G., recheck the E.C.U. pin terminals damage or the connection of E.C.U. harness connector.
O.K.
INSPECTION END

Courtesy of Nissan Motor Co., U.S.A.

*Maxima, Stanza, Stanza Wagon, 200SX SE, 200SX XE & 300ZX Fuel Pump (Code 22) Test F*

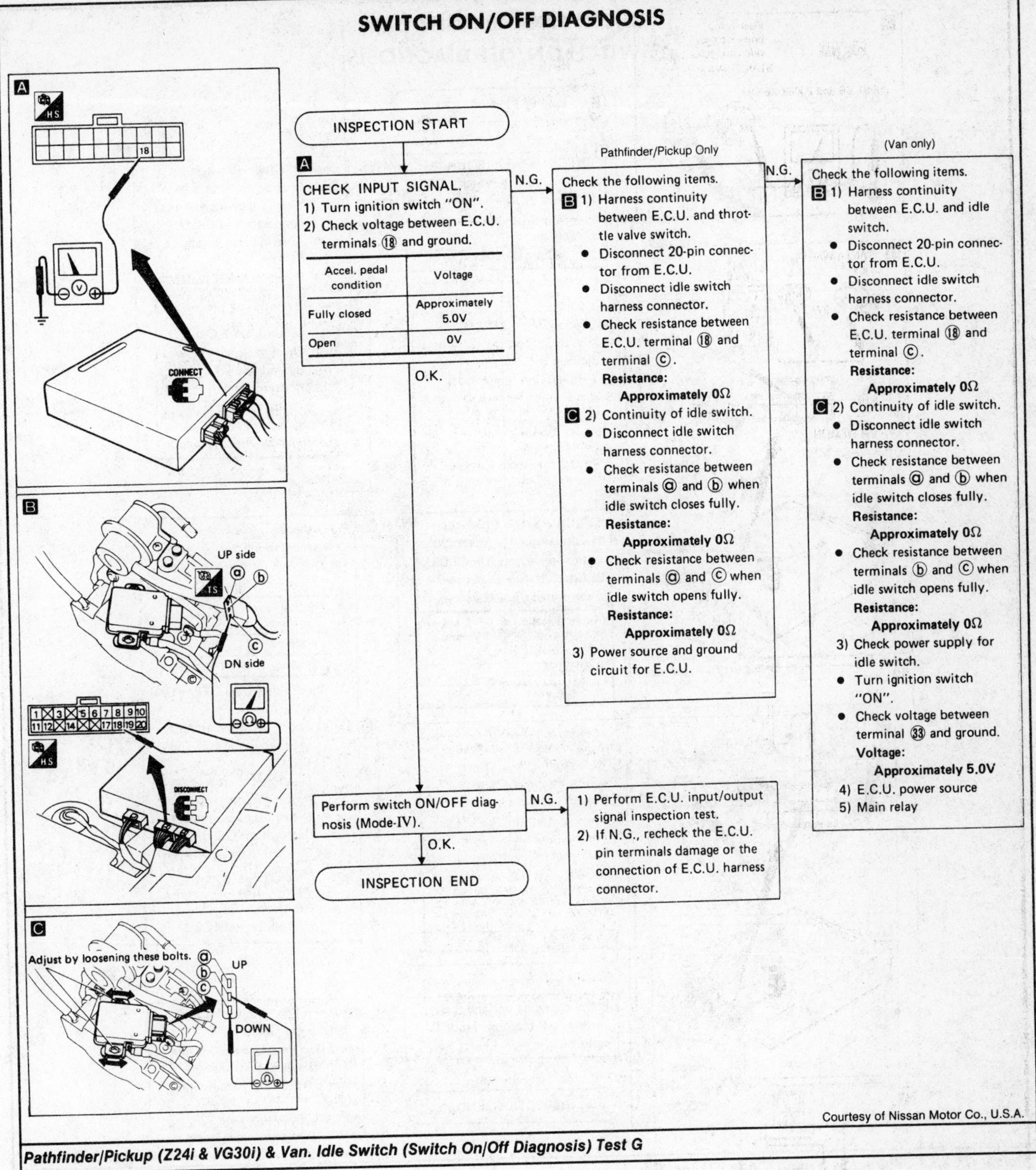
SWITCH ON/OFF DIAGNOSIS
A
18
CONNECT
B
UP side
ⓐ
ⓑ
ⓒ
DN side
1 3 5 6 7 8 9 10
11 12 14 17 18 19 20
DISCONNECT
C
Adjust by loosening these bolts.
ⓐ
ⓑ
ⓒ
UP
DOWN
INSPECTION START
A CHECK INPUT SIGNAL.
1) Turn ignition switch "ON".
2) Check voltage between E.C.U. terminals ⑱ and ground.
Accel. pedal condition | Voltage
Fully closed | Approximately 5.0V
Open | 0V
N.G.
Pathfinder/Pickup Only
Check the following items.
B 1) Harness continuity between E.C.U. and throttle valve switch.
• Disconnect 20-pin connector from E.C.U.
• Disconnect idle switch harness connector.
• Check resistance between E.C.U. terminal ⑱ and terminal ⓒ.
Resistance: Approximately 0Ω
C 2) Continuity of idle switch.
• Disconnect idle switch harness connector.
• Check resistance between terminals ⓐ and ⓑ when idle switch closes fully.
Resistance: Approximately 0Ω
• Check resistance between terminals ⓐ and ⓒ when idle switch opens fully.
Resistance: Approximately 0Ω
3) Power source and ground circuit for E.C.U.
N.G.
(Van only)
Check the following items.
B 1) Harness continuity between E.C.U. and idle switch.
• Disconnect 20-pin connector from E.C.U.
• Disconnect idle switch harness connector.
• Check resistance between E.C.U. terminal ⑱ and terminal ⓒ.
Resistance: Approximately 0Ω
C 2) Continuity of idle switch.
• Disconnect idle switch harness connector.
• Check resistance between terminals ⓐ and ⓑ when idle switch closes fully.
Resistance: Approximately 0Ω
• Check resistance between terminals ⓑ and ⓒ when idle switch opens fully.
Resistance: Approximately 0Ω
3) Check power supply for idle switch.
• Turn ignition switch "ON".
• Check voltage between terminal ㉝ and ground.
Voltage: Approximately 5.0V
4) E.C.U. power source
5) Main relay
O.K.
Perform switch ON/OFF diagnosis (Mode-IV).
N.G.
1) Perform E.C.U. input/output signal inspection test.
2) If N.G., recheck the E.C.U. pin terminals damage or the connection of E.C.U. harness connector.
O.K.
INSPECTION END
Courtesy of Nissan Motor Co., U.S.A.

*Pathfinder/Pickup (Z24i & VG30i) & Van. Idle Switch (Switch On/Off Diagnosis) Test G*

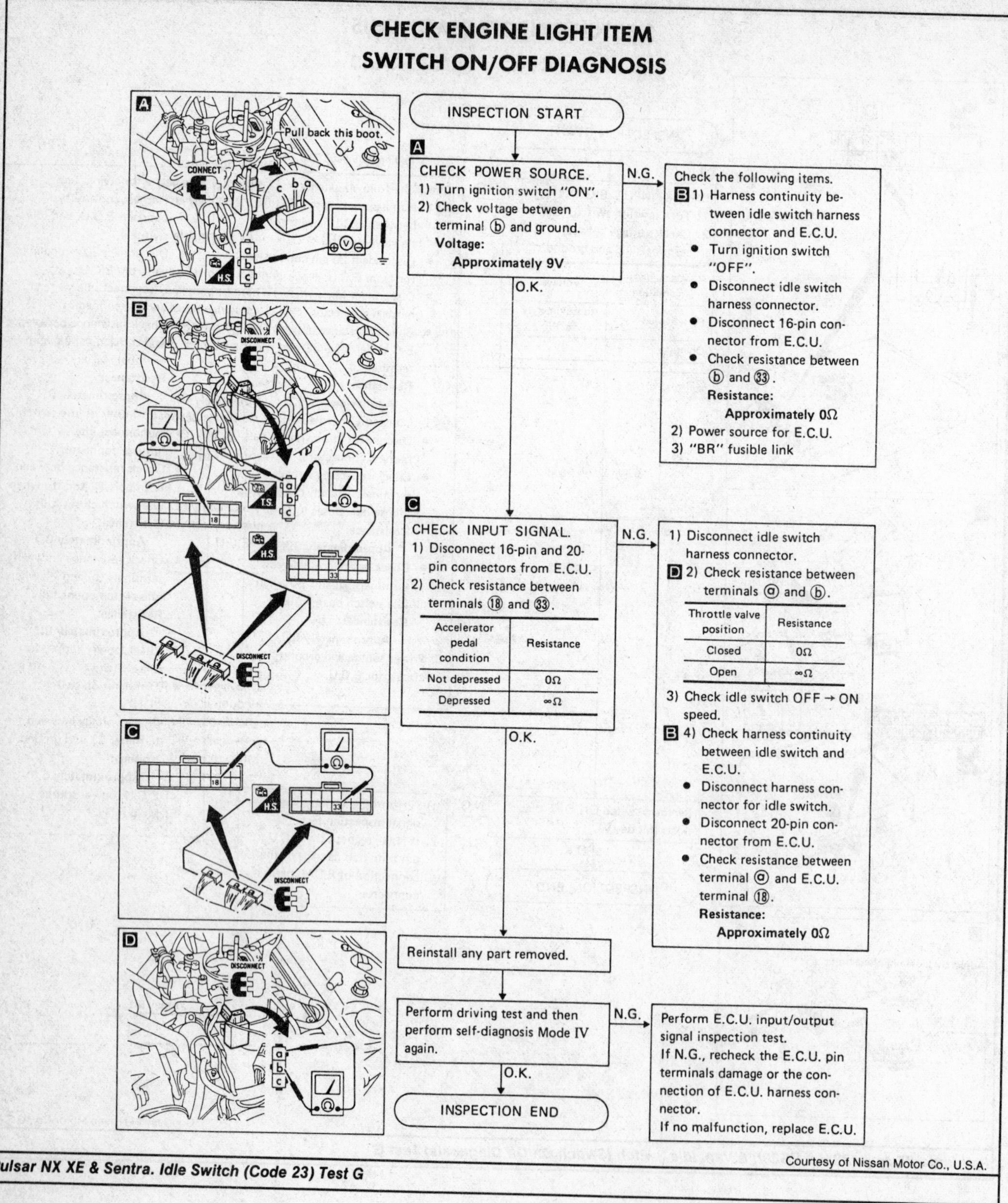
CHECK ENGINE LIGHT ITEM
SWITCH ON/OFF DIAGNOSIS
A
Pull back this boot.
CONNECT
c b a
a
b
c
H.S.
B
DISCONNECT
a
b
c
T.S.
18
H.S.
33
DISCONNECT
C
18
H.S.
33
DISCONNECT
D
DISCONNECT
a
b
c
INSPECTION START
A
CHECK POWER SOURCE.
1) Turn ignition switch "ON".
2) Check voltage between terminal ⓑ and ground.
Voltage:
Approximately 9V
N.G.
Check the following items.
B 1) Harness continuity between idle switch harness connector and E.C.U.
• Turn ignition switch "OFF".
• Disconnect idle switch harness connector.
• Disconnect 16-pin connector from E.C.U.
• Check resistance between ⓑ and ㉝.
Resistance:
Approximately 0Ω
2) Power source for E.C.U.
3) "BR" fusible link
O.K.
C
CHECK INPUT SIGNAL.
1) Disconnect 16-pin and 20-pin connectors from E.C.U.
2) Check resistance between terminals ⑱ and ㉝.
Accelerator pedal condition | Resistance
Not depressed | 0Ω
Depressed | ∞Ω
N.G.
1) Disconnect idle switch harness connector.
D 2) Check resistance between terminals ⓐ and ⓑ.
Throttle valve position | Resistance
Closed | 0Ω
Open | ∞Ω
3) Check idle switch OFF → ON speed.
B 4) Check harness continuity between idle switch and E.C.U.
• Disconnect harness connector for idle switch.
• Disconnect 20-pin connector from E.C.U.
• Check resistance between terminal ⓐ and E.C.U. terminal ⑱.
Resistance:
Approximately 0Ω
O.K.
Reinstall any part removed.
Perform driving test and then perform self-diagnosis Mode IV again.
N.G.
Perform E.C.U. input/output signal inspection test.
If N.G., recheck the E.C.U. pin terminals damage or the connection of E.C.U. harness connector.
If no malfunction, replace E.C.U.
O.K.
INSPECTION END

*Pulsar NX XE & Sentra. Idle Switch (Code 23) Test G*

Courtesy of Nissan Motor Co., U.S.A.

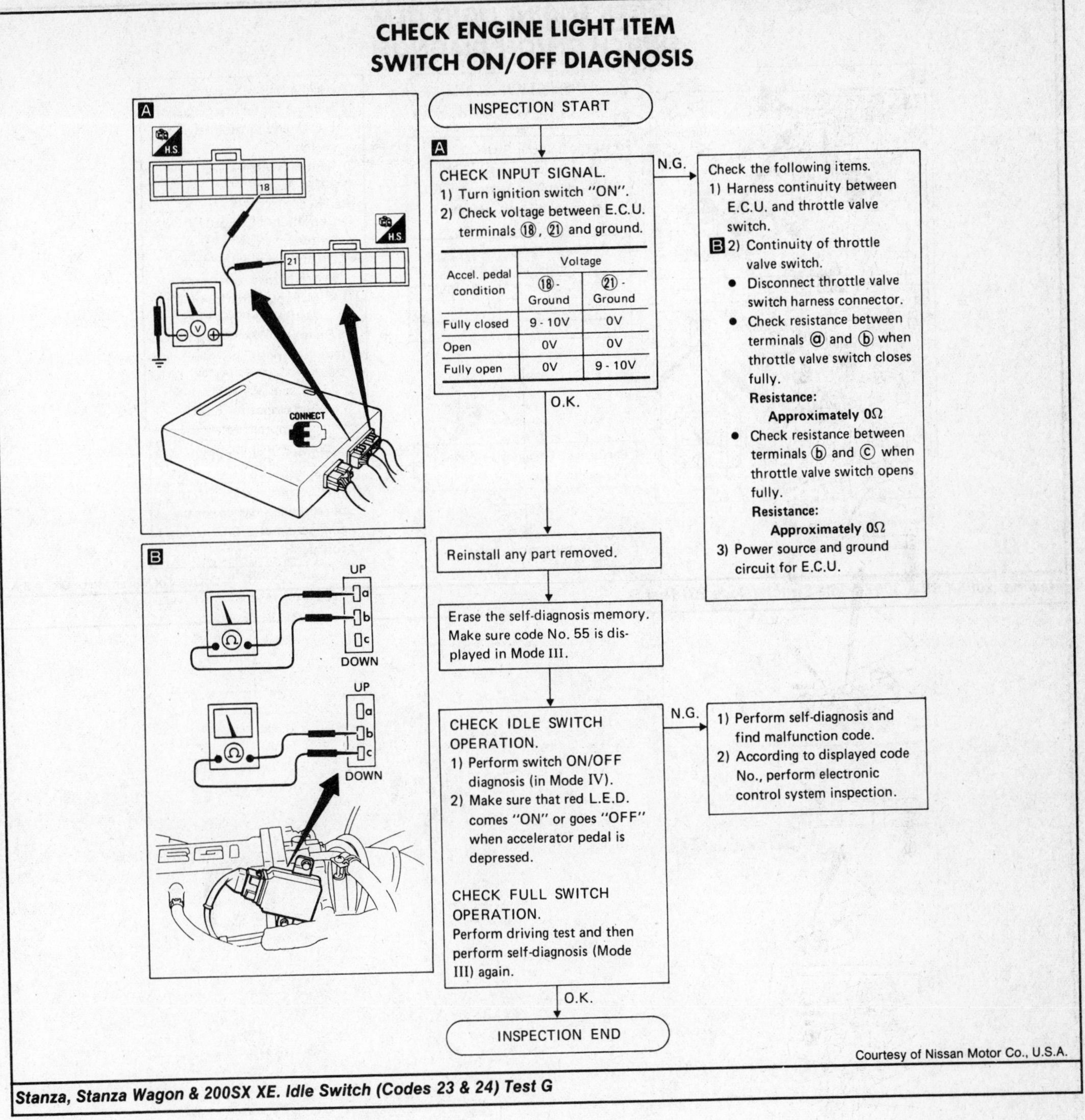
CHECK ENGINE LIGHT ITEM
SWITCH ON/OFF DIAGNOSIS
A
H.S.
18
21
CONNECT
B
UP
a
b
c
DOWN
INSPECTION START
A
CHECK INPUT SIGNAL.
1) Turn ignition switch "ON".
2) Check voltage between E.C.U. terminals ⑱, ㉑ and ground.
Accel. pedal condition | Voltage ⑱ - Ground | ㉑ - Ground
Fully closed | 9 - 10V | 0V
Open | 0V | 0V
Fully open | 0V | 9 - 10V
N.G.
Check the following items.
1) Harness continuity between E.C.U. and throttle valve switch.
B 2) Continuity of throttle valve switch.
• Disconnect throttle valve switch harness connector.
• Check resistance between terminals ⓐ and ⓑ when throttle valve switch closes fully.
Resistance:
Approximately 0Ω
• Check resistance between terminals ⓑ and ⓒ when throttle valve switch opens fully.
Resistance:
Approximately 0Ω
3) Power source and ground circuit for E.C.U.
O.K.
Reinstall any part removed.
Erase the self-diagnosis memory. Make sure code No. 55 is displayed in Mode III.
CHECK IDLE SWITCH OPERATION.
1) Perform switch ON/OFF diagnosis (in Mode IV).
2) Make sure that red L.E.D. comes "ON" or goes "OFF" when accelerator pedal is depressed.
CHECK FULL SWITCH OPERATION.
Perform driving test and then perform self-diagnosis (Mode III) again.
N.G.
1) Perform self-diagnosis and find malfunction code.
2) According to displayed code No., perform electronic control system inspection.
O.K.
INSPECTION END
Courtesy of Nissan Motor Co., U.S.A.

*Stanza, Stanza Wagon & 200SX XE. Idle Switch (Codes 23 & 24) Test G*

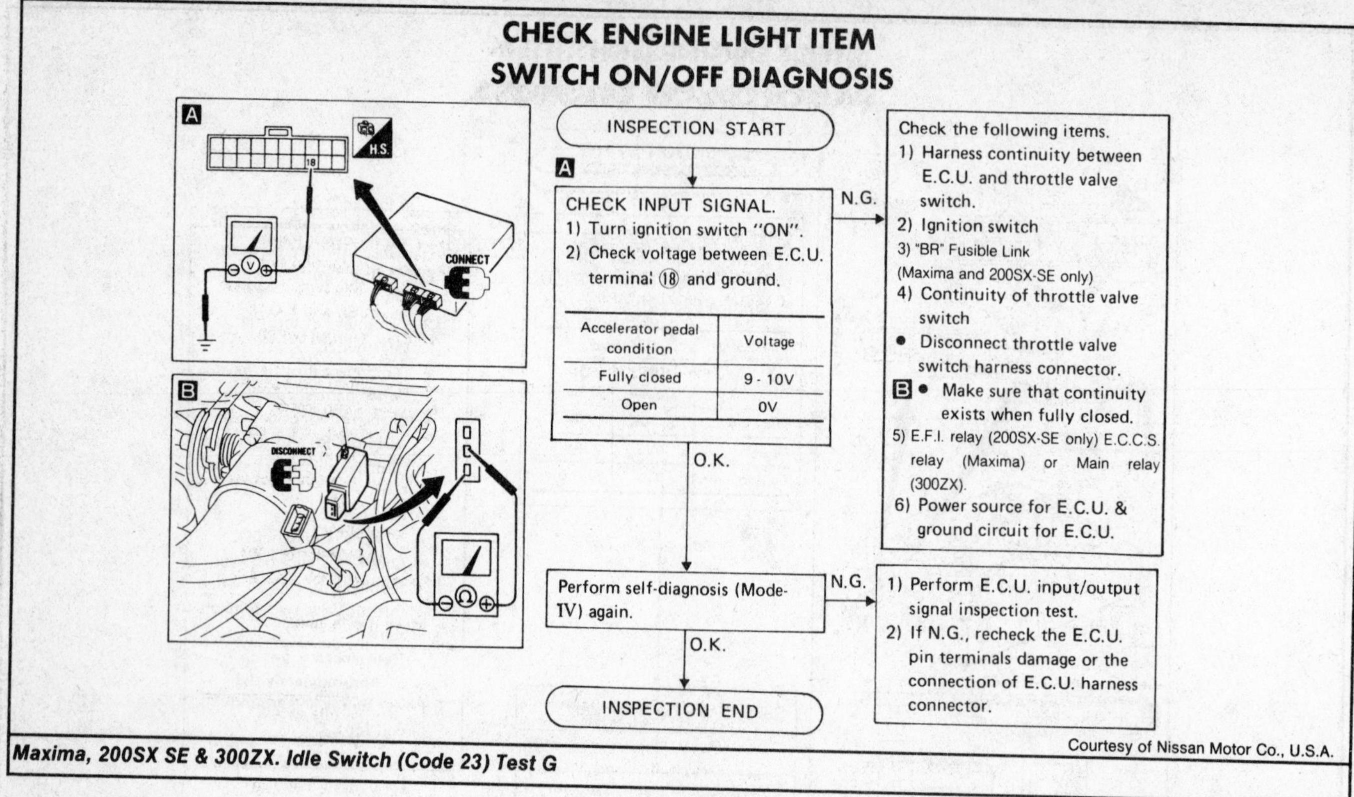
CHECK ENGINE LIGHT ITEM
SWITCH ON/OFF DIAGNOSIS
A
H.S.
18
CONNECT
B
DISCONNECT
INSPECTION START
A
CHECK INPUT SIGNAL.
1) Turn ignition switch "ON".
2) Check voltage between E.C.U. terminal ⑱ and ground.
Accelerator pedal condition | Voltage
Fully closed | 9 - 10V
Open | 0V
N.G.
Check the following items.
1) Harness continuity between E.C.U. and throttle valve switch.
2) Ignition switch
3) "BR" Fusible Link (Maxima and 200SX-SE only)
4) Continuity of throttle valve switch
• Disconnect throttle valve switch harness connector.
B • Make sure that continuity exists when fully closed.
5) E.F.I. relay (200SX-SE only) E.C.C.S. relay (Maxima) or Main relay (300ZX).
6) Power source for E.C.U. & ground circuit for E.C.U.
O.K.
Perform self-diagnosis (Mode-IV) again.
N.G.
1) Perform E.C.U. input/output signal inspection test.
2) If N.G., recheck the E.C.U. pin terminals damage or the connection of E.C.U. harness connector.
O.K.
INSPECTION END
Courtesy of Nissan Motor Co., U.S.A.

*Maxima, 200SX SE & 300ZX. Idle Switch (Code 23) Test G*

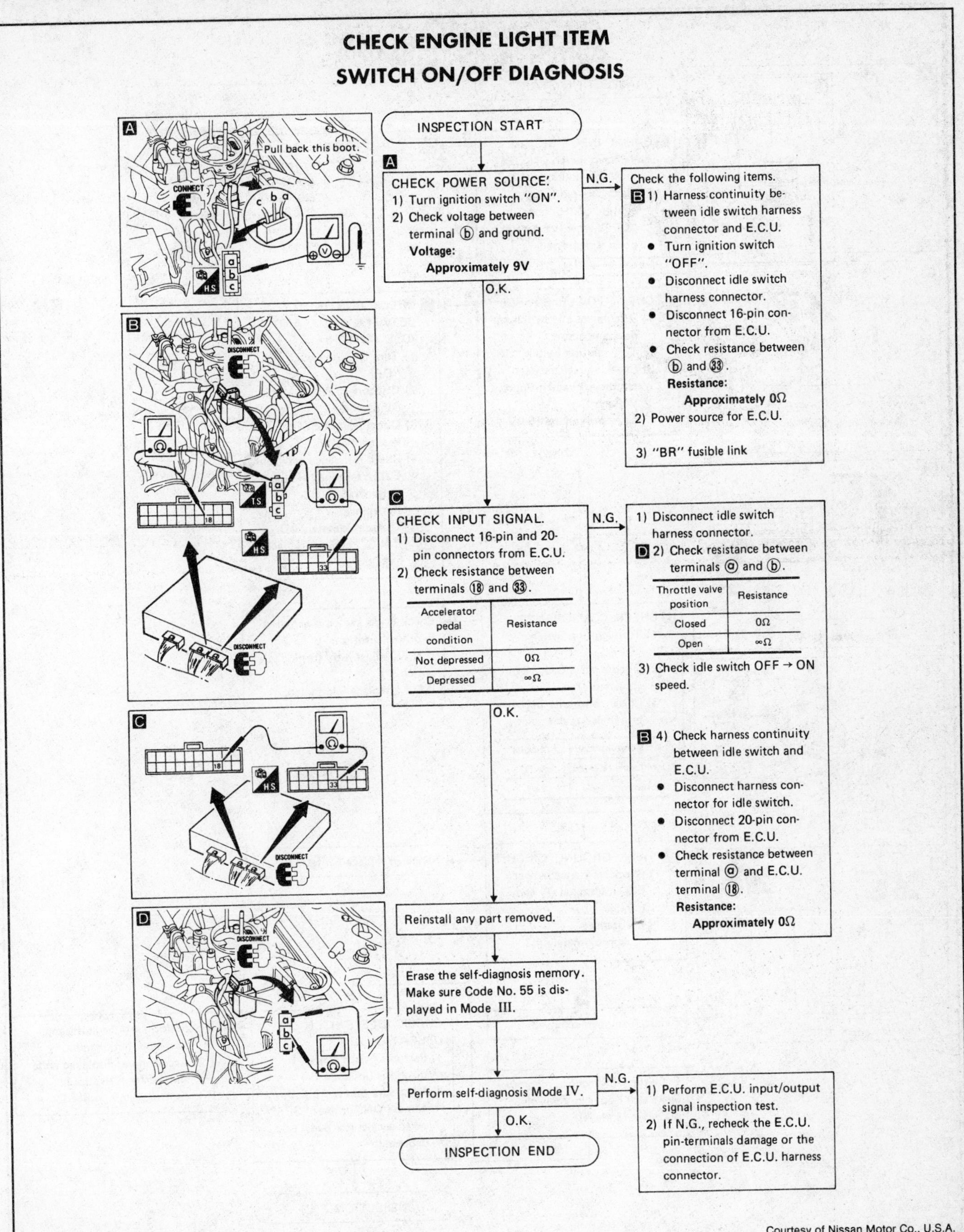
CHECK ENGINE LIGHT ITEM
SWITCH ON/OFF DIAGNOSIS
A
Pull back this boot.
CONNECT
c b a
a
b
c
H.S
B
DISCONNECT
T.S
18
H.S
33
DISCONNECT
C
18
H.S
33
DISCONNECT
D
DISCONNECT
a
b
c
INSPECTION START
A
CHECK POWER SOURCE:
1) Turn ignition switch "ON".
2) Check voltage between terminal ⓑ and ground.
Voltage:
Approximately 9V
N.G.
Check the following items.
B 1) Harness continuity between idle switch harness connector and E.C.U.
• Turn ignition switch "OFF".
• Disconnect idle switch harness connector.
• Disconnect 16-pin connector from E.C.U.
• Check resistance between ⓑ and ㉝.
Resistance:
Approximately 0Ω
2) Power source for E.C.U.
3) "BR" fusible link
O.K.
C
CHECK INPUT SIGNAL.
1) Disconnect 16-pin and 20-pin connectors from E.C.U.
2) Check resistance between terminals ⑱ and ㉝.
Accelerator pedal condition | Resistance
Not depressed | 0Ω
Depressed | ∞Ω
N.G.
1) Disconnect idle switch harness connector.
D 2) Check resistance between terminals ⓐ and ⓑ.
Throttle valve position | Resistance
Closed | 0Ω
Open | ∞Ω
3) Check idle switch OFF → ON speed.
B 4) Check harness continuity between idle switch and E.C.U.
• Disconnect harness connector for idle switch.
• Disconnect 20-pin connector from E.C.U.
• Check resistance between terminal ⓐ and E.C.U. terminal ⑱.
Resistance:
Approximately 0Ω
O.K.
Reinstall any part removed.
Erase the self-diagnosis memory. Make sure Code No. 55 is displayed in Mode III.
Perform self-diagnosis Mode IV.
N.G.
1) Perform E.C.U. input/output signal inspection test.
2) If N.G., recheck the E.C.U. pin-terminals damage or the connection of E.C.U. harness connector.
O.K.
INSPECTION END



*Sentra Only. Idle Switch (Switch On/Off Diagnosis) (Code 23) Test G*

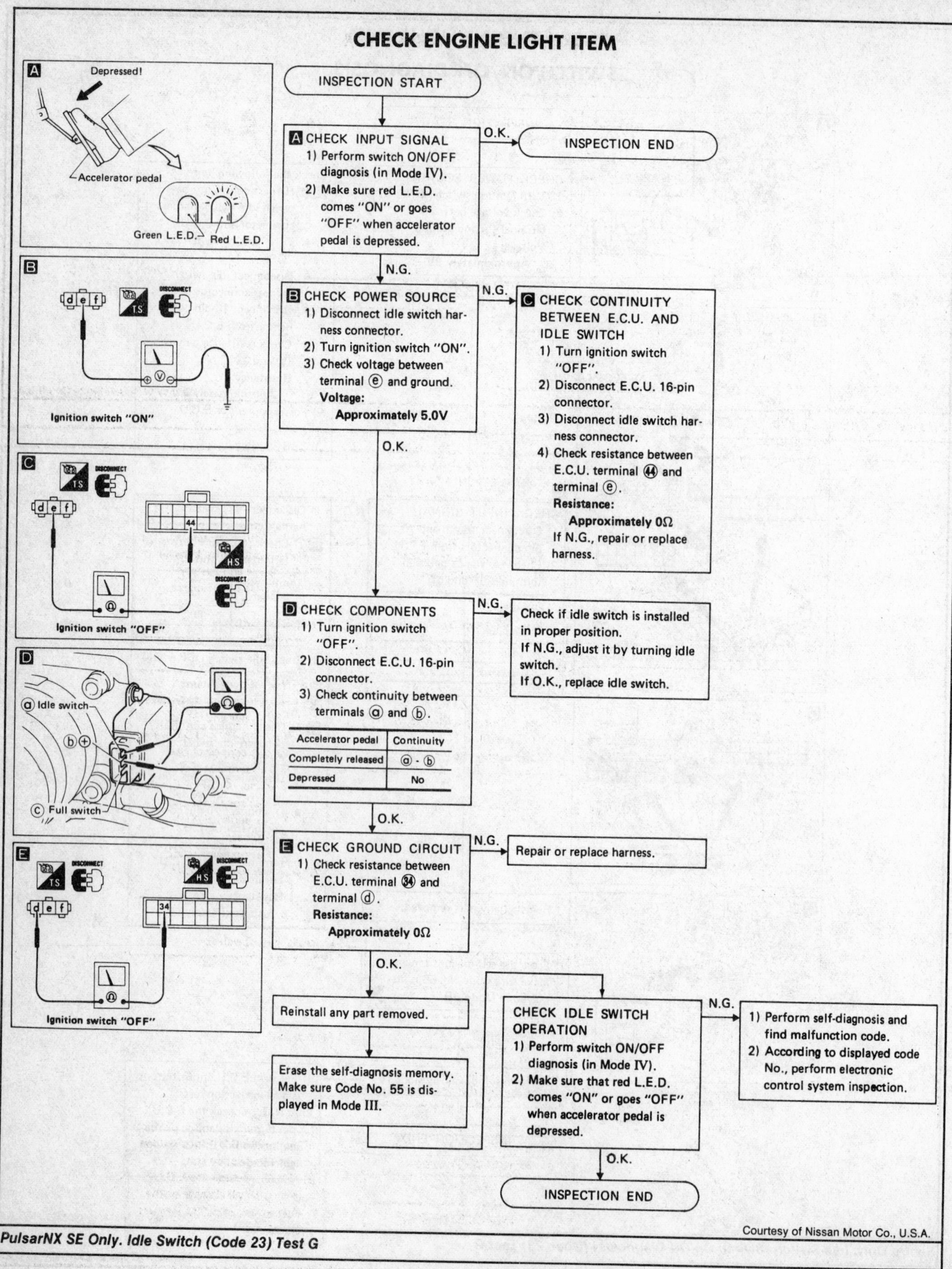
CHECK ENGINE LIGHT ITEM
A
Depressed!
Accelerator pedal
Green L.E.D.
Red L.E.D.
B
d e f
T.S
DISCONNECT
Ignition switch "ON"
C
44
H.S
Ignition switch "OFF"
D
ⓐ Idle switch
ⓑ ⊕
ⓒ Full switch
E
34
Ignition switch "OFF"
INSPECTION START
A CHECK INPUT SIGNAL
1) Perform switch ON/OFF diagnosis (in Mode IV).
2) Make sure red L.E.D. comes "ON" or goes "OFF" when accelerator pedal is depressed.
O.K.
INSPECTION END
N.G.
B CHECK POWER SOURCE
1) Disconnect idle switch harness connector.
2) Turn ignition switch "ON".
3) Check voltage between terminal ⓔ and ground.
Voltage:
Approximately 5.0V
N.G.
C CHECK CONTINUITY BETWEEN E.C.U. AND IDLE SWITCH
1) Turn ignition switch "OFF".
2) Disconnect E.C.U. 16-pin connector.
3) Disconnect idle switch harness connector.
4) Check resistance between E.C.U. terminal ㊹ and terminal ⓔ.
Resistance:
Approximately 0Ω
If N.G., repair or replace harness.
O.K.
D CHECK COMPONENTS
1) Turn ignition switch "OFF".
2) Disconnect E.C.U. 16-pin connector.
3) Check continuity between terminals ⓐ and ⓑ.
Accelerator pedal | Continuity
Completely released | ⓐ - ⓑ
Depressed | No
N.G.
Check if idle switch is installed in proper position.
If N.G., adjust it by turning idle switch.
If O.K., replace idle switch.
O.K.
E CHECK GROUND CIRCUIT
1) Check resistance between E.C.U. terminal ㉞ and terminal ⓓ.
Resistance:
Approximately 0Ω
N.G.
Repair or replace harness.
O.K.
Reinstall any part removed.
Erase the self-diagnosis memory. Make sure Code No. 55 is displayed in Mode III.
CHECK IDLE SWITCH OPERATION
1) Perform switch ON/OFF diagnosis (in Mode IV).
2) Make sure that red L.E.D. comes "ON" or goes "OFF" when accelerator pedal is depressed.
N.G.
1) Perform self-diagnosis and find malfunction code.
2) According to displayed code No., perform electronic control system inspection.
O.K.
INSPECTION END
Courtesy of Nissan Motor Co., U.S.A.

*PulsarNX SE Only. Idle Switch (Code 23) Test G*

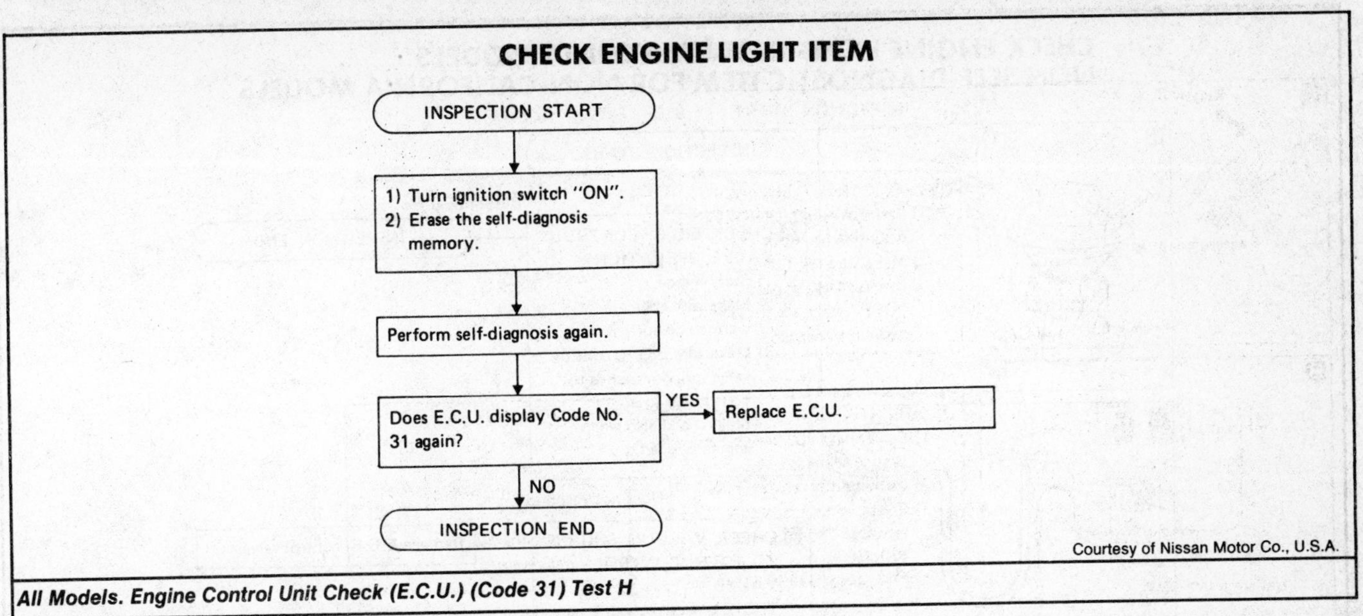

CHECK ENGINE LIGHT ITEM
INSPECTION START
1) Turn ignition switch "ON".
2) Erase the self-diagnosis memory.
Perform self-diagnosis again.
Does E.C.U. display Code No. 31 again?
YES
Replace E.C.U.
NO
INSPECTION END
Courtesy of Nissan Motor Co., U.S.A.


*All Models. Engine Control Unit Check (E.C.U.) (Code 31) Test H*

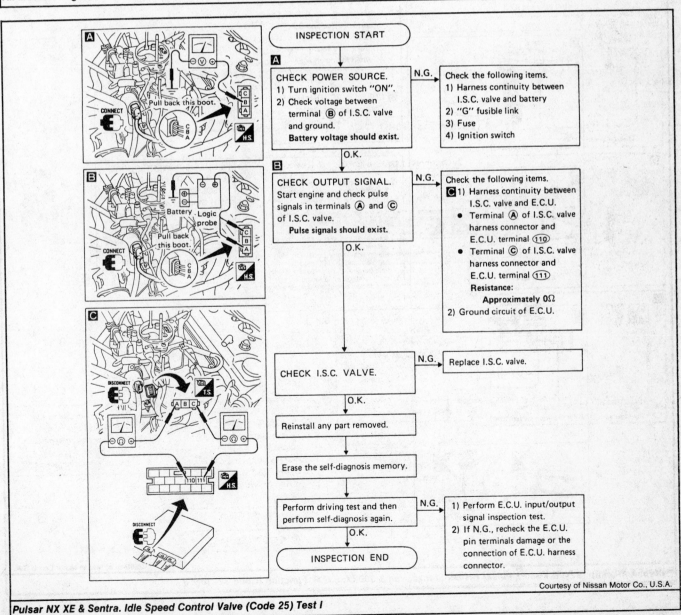

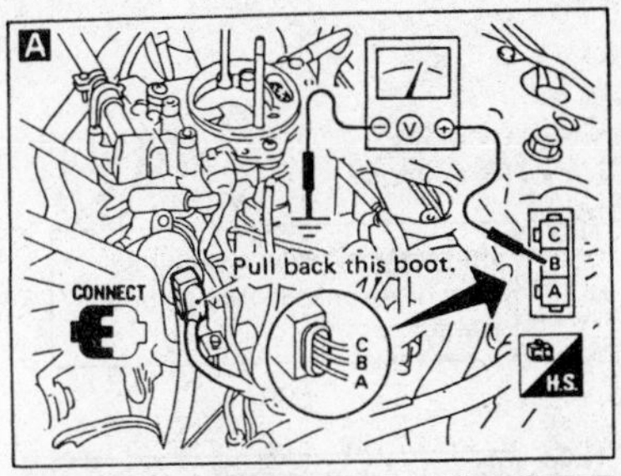

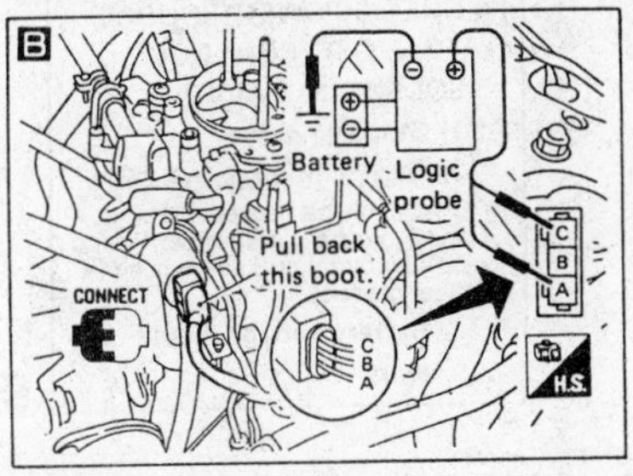

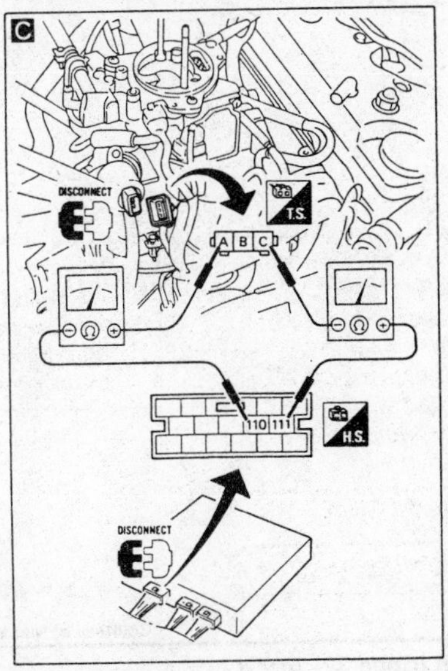

**A** Pull back this boot. CONNECT. H.S.

**B** Battery. Logic probe. Pull back this boot. CONNECT. H.S.

**C** DISCONNECT. T.S. 110 111. H.S. DISCONNECT.

INSPECTION START

**A** CHECK POWER SOURCE.
1) Turn ignition switch "ON".
2) Check voltage between terminal Ⓑ of I.S.C. valve and ground.
**Battery voltage should exist.**

N.G. → Check the following items.
1) Harness continuity between I.S.C. valve and battery
2) "G" fusible link
3) Fuse
4) Ignition switch

O.K.

**B** CHECK OUTPUT SIGNAL.
Start engine and check pulse signals in terminals Ⓐ and Ⓒ of I.S.C. valve.
**Pulse signals should exist.**

N.G. → Check the following items.
**C** 1) Harness continuity between I.S.C. valve and E.C.U.
- Terminal Ⓐ of I.S.C. valve harness connector and E.C.U. terminal (110)
- Terminal Ⓒ of I.S.C. valve harness connector and E.C.U. terminal (111)

**Resistance:**
**Approximately 0Ω**

2) Ground circuit of E.C.U.

O.K.

CHECK I.S.C. VALVE.

N.G. → Replace I.S.C. valve.

O.K.

Reinstall any part removed.

Erase the self-diagnosis memory.

Perform driving test and then perform self-diagnosis again.

N.G. →
1) Perform E.C.U. input/output signal inspection test.
2) If N.G., recheck the E.C.U. pin terminals damage or the connection of E.C.U. harness connector.

O.K.

INSPECTION END

Courtesy of Nissan Motor Co., U.S.A.

*Pulsar NX XE & Sentra. Idle Speed Control Valve (Code 25) Test I*

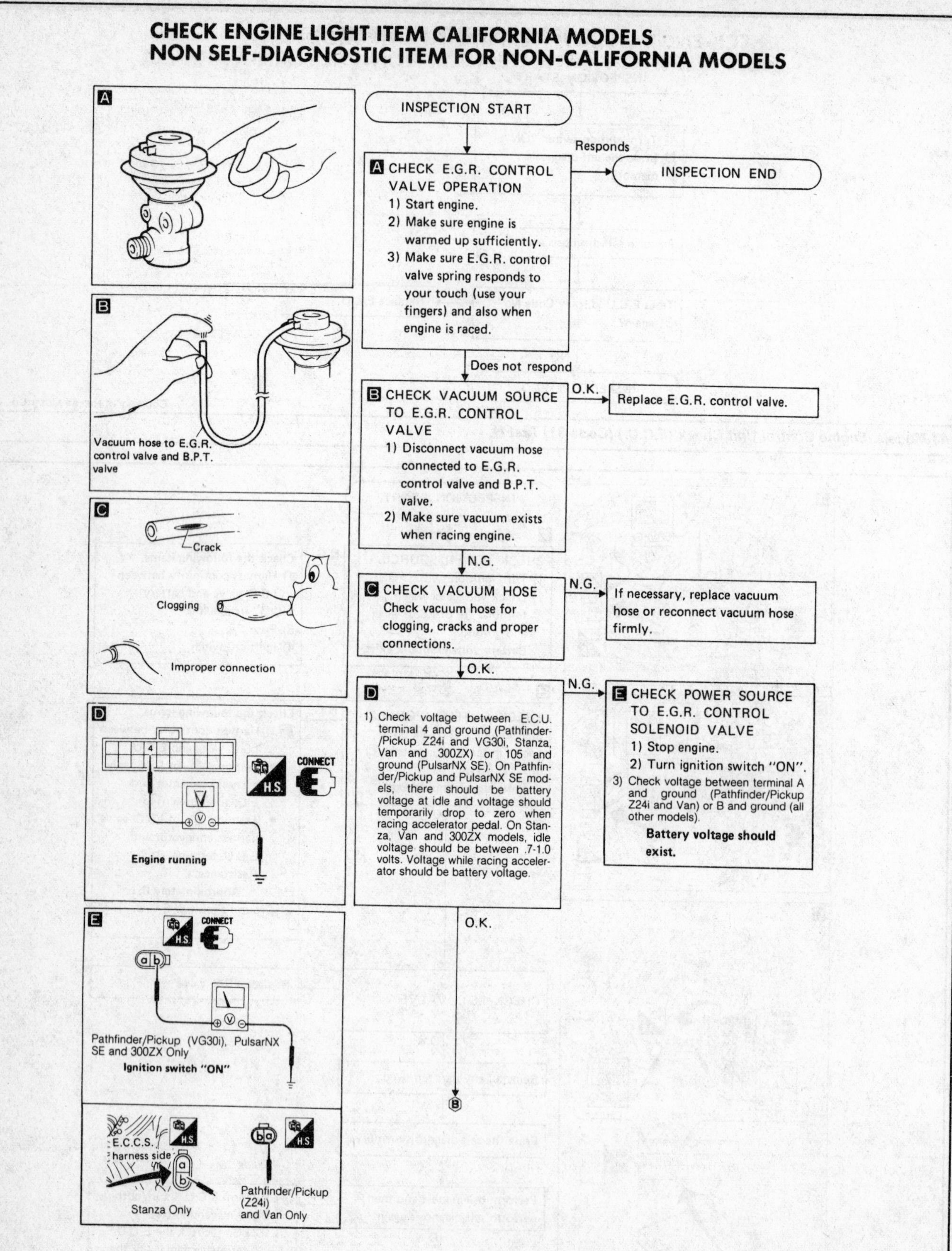
CHECK ENGINE LIGHT ITEM CALIFORNIA MODELS
NON SELF-DIAGNOSTIC ITEM FOR NON-CALIFORNIA MODELS
A
B
Vacuum hose to E.G.R. control valve and B.P.T. valve
C
Crack
Clogging
Improper connection
D
CONNECT
H.S.
Engine running
E
CONNECT
H.S.
Pathfinder/Pickup (VG30i), PulsarNX SE and 300ZX Only
Ignition switch "ON"
E.C.C.S. harness side
Stanza Only
Pathfinder/Pickup (Z24i) and Van Only
INSPECTION START
A CHECK E.G.R. CONTROL VALVE OPERATION
1) Start engine.
2) Make sure engine is warmed up sufficiently.
3) Make sure E.G.R. control valve spring responds to your touch (use your fingers) and also when engine is raced.
Responds
INSPECTION END
Does not respond
B CHECK VACUUM SOURCE TO E.G.R. CONTROL VALVE
1) Disconnect vacuum hose connected to E.G.R. control valve and B.P.T. valve.
2) Make sure vacuum exists when racing engine.
O.K.
Replace E.G.R. control valve.
N.G.
C CHECK VACUUM HOSE
Check vacuum hose for clogging, cracks and proper connections.
N.G.
If necessary, replace vacuum hose or reconnect vacuum hose firmly.
O.K.
D
1) Check voltage between E.C.U. terminal 4 and ground (Pathfinder-/Pickup Z24i and VG30i, Stanza, Van and 300ZX) or 105 and ground (PulsarNX SE). On Pathfinder/Pickup and PulsarNX SE models, there should be battery voltage at idle and voltage should temporarily drop to zero when racing accelerator pedal. On Stanza, Van and 300ZX models, idle voltage should be between .7-1.0 volts. Voltage while racing accelerator should be battery voltage.
N.G.
E CHECK POWER SOURCE TO E.G.R. CONTROL SOLENOID VALVE
1) Stop engine.
2) Turn ignition switch "ON".
3) Check voltage between terminal A and ground (Pathfinder/Pickup Z24i and Van) or B and ground (all other models).
Battery voltage should exist.
O.K.
B

Courtesy of Nissan Motor Co., U.S.A.

*Pathfinder/Pickup (Z24i & VG30i), Pulsar NX SE, Stanza, Van & 300ZX. E.G.R. Function (Code 32) Test J*

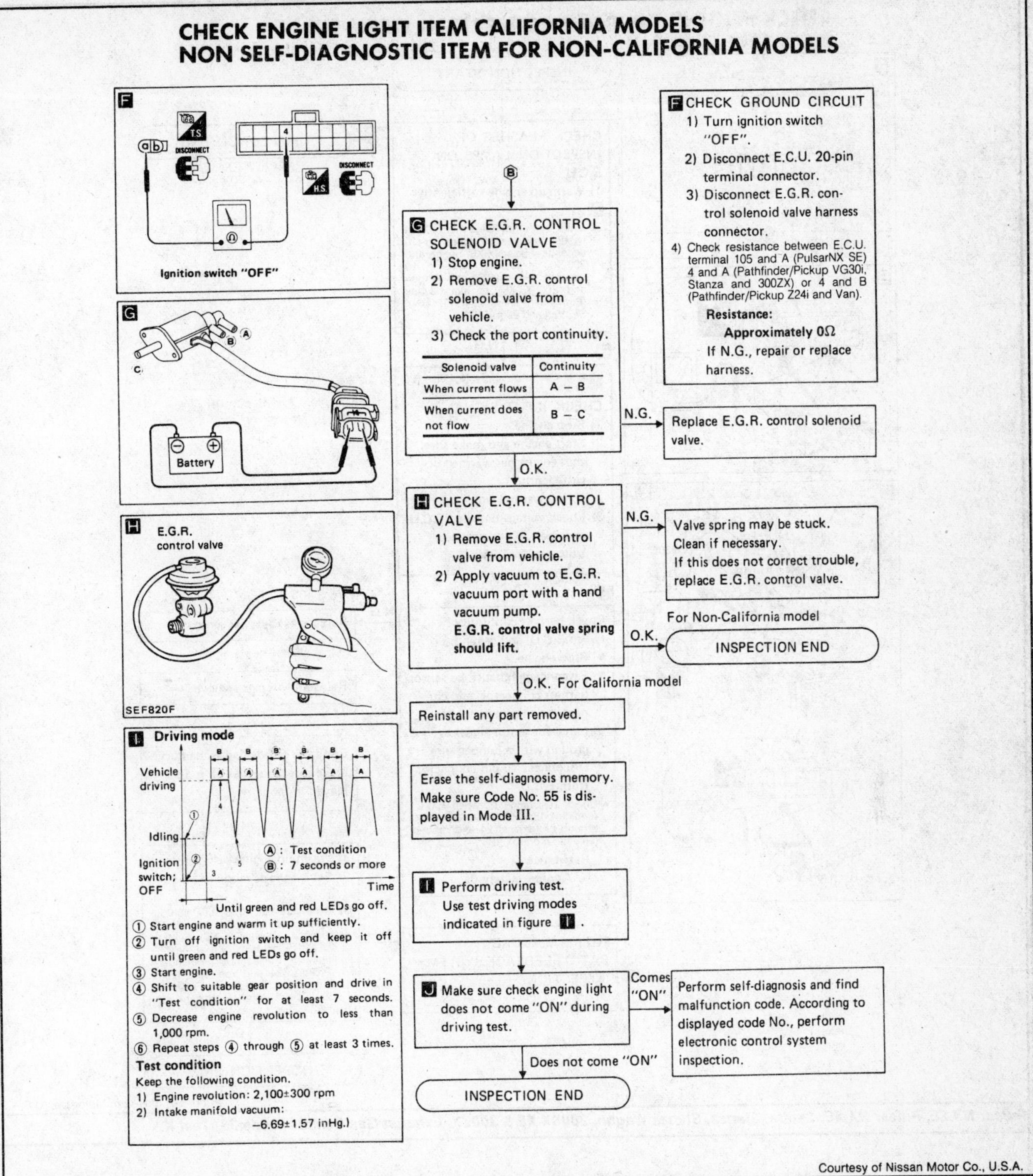

CHECK ENGINE LIGHT ITEM CALIFORNIA MODELS
NON SELF-DIAGNOSTIC ITEM FOR NON-CALIFORNIA MODELS
F
T.S.
DISCONNECT
H.S.
DISCONNECT
Ignition switch "OFF"
G
A
B
C
Battery
H
E.G.R.
control valve
SEF820F
I Driving mode
Vehicle driving
Idling
Ignition switch; OFF
Time
Ⓐ: Test condition
Ⓑ: 7 seconds or more
Until green and red LEDs go off.
① Start engine and warm it up sufficiently.
② Turn off ignition switch and keep it off until green and red LEDs go off.
③ Start engine.
④ Shift to suitable gear position and drive in "Test condition" for at least 7 seconds.
⑤ Decrease engine revolution to less than 1,000 rpm.
⑥ Repeat steps ④ through ⑤ at least 3 times.
Test condition
Keep the following condition.
1) Engine revolution: 2,100±300 rpm
2) Intake manifold vacuum: –6.69±1.57 inHg.)
B
G CHECK E.G.R. CONTROL SOLENOID VALVE
1) Stop engine.
2) Remove E.G.R. control solenoid valve from vehicle.
3) Check the port continuity.
Solenoid valve | Continuity
When current flows | A – B
When current does not flow | B – C
N.G.
Replace E.G.R. control solenoid valve.
O.K.
H CHECK E.G.R. CONTROL VALVE
1) Remove E.G.R. control valve from vehicle.
2) Apply vacuum to E.G.R. vacuum port with a hand vacuum pump.
E.G.R. control valve spring should lift.
N.G.
Valve spring may be stuck. Clean if necessary. If this does not correct trouble, replace E.G.R. control valve.
For Non-California model
O.K.
INSPECTION END
O.K. For California model
Reinstall any part removed.
Erase the self-diagnosis memory. Make sure Code No. 55 is displayed in Mode III.
I Perform driving test. Use test driving modes indicated in figure I.
J Make sure check engine light does not come "ON" during driving test.
Comes "ON"
Perform self-diagnosis and find malfunction code. According to displayed code No., perform electronic control system inspection.
Does not come "ON"
INSPECTION END
F CHECK GROUND CIRCUIT
1) Turn ignition switch "OFF".
2) Disconnect E.C.U. 20-pin terminal connector.
3) Disconnect E.G.R. control solenoid valve harness connector.
4) Check resistance between E.C.U. terminal 105 and A (PulsarNX SE) 4 and A (Pathfinder/Pickup VG30i, Stanza and 300ZX) or 4 and B (Pathfinder/Pickup Z24i and Van).
Resistance:
Approximately 0Ω
If N.G., repair or replace harness.


Courtesy of Nissan Motor Co., U.S.A.

*Pathfinder/Pickup (Z24i & VG30i), Pulsar NX SE, Stanza, Van & 300ZX. E.G.R. Function (Cont.) (Code 32) Test J*

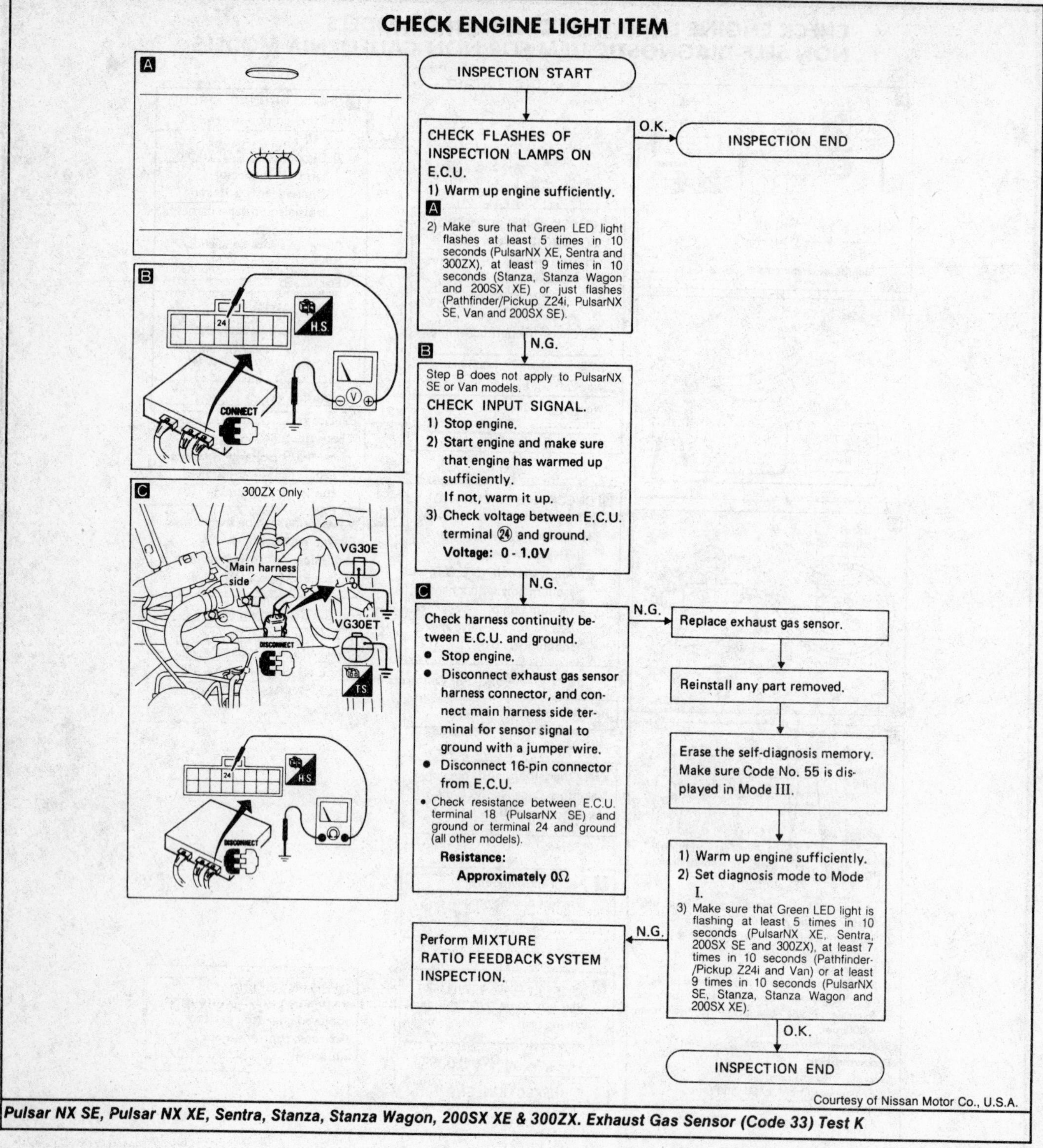
CHECK ENGINE LIGHT ITEM
A
B
24
H.S.
CONNECT
C
300ZX Only
VG30E
Main harness side
VG30ET
DISCONNECT
T.S.
24
H.S.
DISCONNECT
INSPECTION START
CHECK FLASHES OF INSPECTION LAMPS ON E.C.U.
1) Warm up engine sufficiently.
A
2) Make sure that Green LED light flashes at least 5 times in 10 seconds (PulsarNX XE, Sentra and 300ZX), at least 9 times in 10 seconds (Stanza, Stanza Wagon and 200SX XE) or just flashes (Pathfinder/Pickup Z24i, PulsarNX SE, Van and 200SX SE).
O.K.
INSPECTION END
N.G.
B
Step B does not apply to PulsarNX SE or Van models.
CHECK INPUT SIGNAL.
1) Stop engine.
2) Start engine and make sure that engine has warmed up sufficiently.
If not, warm it up.
3) Check voltage between E.C.U. terminal ㉔ and ground.
Voltage: 0 - 1.0V
N.G.
C
Check harness continuity between E.C.U. and ground.
● Stop engine.
● Disconnect exhaust gas sensor harness connector, and connect main harness side terminal for sensor signal to ground with a jumper wire.
● Disconnect 16-pin connector from E.C.U.
• Check resistance between E.C.U. terminal 18 (PulsarNX SE) and ground or terminal 24 and ground (all other models).
Resistance:
Approximately 0Ω
N.G.
Replace exhaust gas sensor.
Reinstall any part removed.
Erase the self-diagnosis memory. Make sure Code No. 55 is displayed in Mode III.
1) Warm up engine sufficiently.
2) Set diagnosis mode to Mode I.
3) Make sure that Green LED light is flashing at least 5 times in 10 seconds (PulsarNX XE, Sentra, 200SX SE and 300ZX), at least 7 times in 10 seconds (Pathfinder-/Pickup Z24i and Van) or at least 9 times in 10 seconds (PulsarNX SE, Stanza, Stanza Wagon and 200SX XE).
N.G.
Perform MIXTURE RATIO FEEDBACK SYSTEM INSPECTION.
O.K.
INSPECTION END
Courtesy of Nissan Motor Co., U.S.A.

***Pulsar NX SE, Pulsar NX XE, Sentra, Stanza, Stanza Wagon, 200SX XE & 300ZX. Exhaust Gas Sensor (Code 33) Test K***

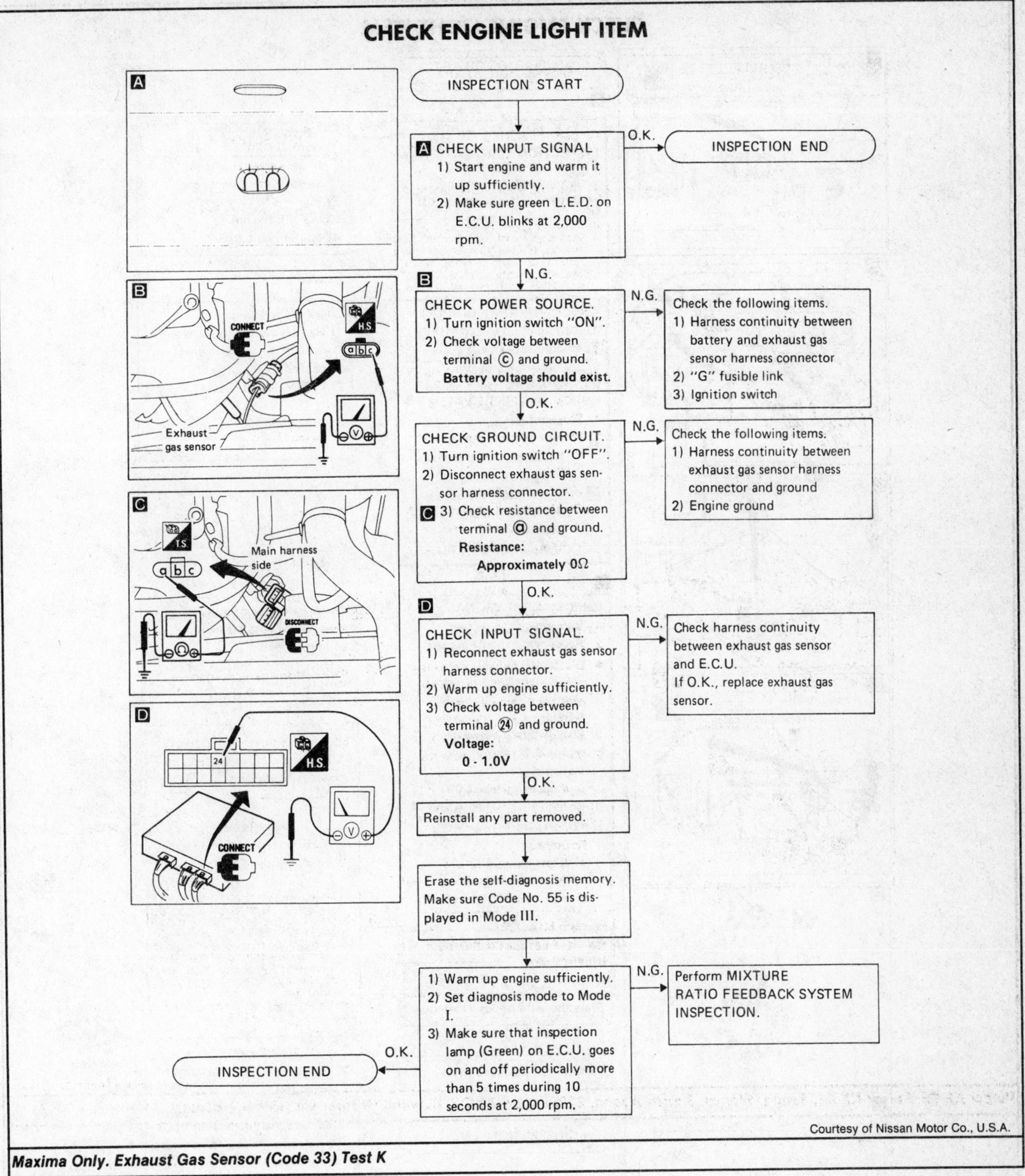
CHECK ENGINE LIGHT ITEM
A
B
CONNECT
H.S.
a b c
Exhaust gas sensor
C
T.S.
Main harness side
a b c
DISCONNECT
D
24
H.S.
CONNECT
INSPECTION START
A CHECK INPUT SIGNAL
1) Start engine and warm it up sufficiently.
2) Make sure green L.E.D. on E.C.U. blinks at 2,000 rpm.
O.K.
INSPECTION END
N.G.
B
CHECK POWER SOURCE.
1) Turn ignition switch "ON".
2) Check voltage between terminal ⓒ and ground.
Battery voltage should exist.
N.G.
Check the following items.
1) Harness continuity between battery and exhaust gas sensor harness connector
2) "G" fusible link
3) Ignition switch
O.K.
CHECK GROUND CIRCUIT.
1) Turn ignition switch "OFF".
2) Disconnect exhaust gas sensor harness connector.
C 3) Check resistance between terminal ⓐ and ground.
Resistance:
Approximately 0Ω
N.G.
Check the following items.
1) Harness continuity between exhaust gas sensor harness connector and ground
2) Engine ground
O.K.
D
CHECK INPUT SIGNAL.
1) Reconnect exhaust gas sensor harness connector.
2) Warm up engine sufficiently.
3) Check voltage between terminal ㉔ and ground.
Voltage:
0 - 1.0V
N.G.
Check harness continuity between exhaust gas sensor and E.C.U.
If O.K., replace exhaust gas sensor.
O.K.
Reinstall any part removed.
Erase the self-diagnosis memory. Make sure Code No. 55 is displayed in Mode III.
1) Warm up engine sufficiently.
2) Set diagnosis mode to Mode I.
3) Make sure that inspection lamp (Green) on E.C.U. goes on and off periodically more than 5 times during 10 seconds at 2,000 rpm.
N.G.
Perform MIXTURE RATIO FEEDBACK SYSTEM INSPECTION.
O.K.
INSPECTION END
Courtesy of Nissan Motor Co., U.S.A.

*Maxima Only. Exhaust Gas Sensor (Code 33) Test K*

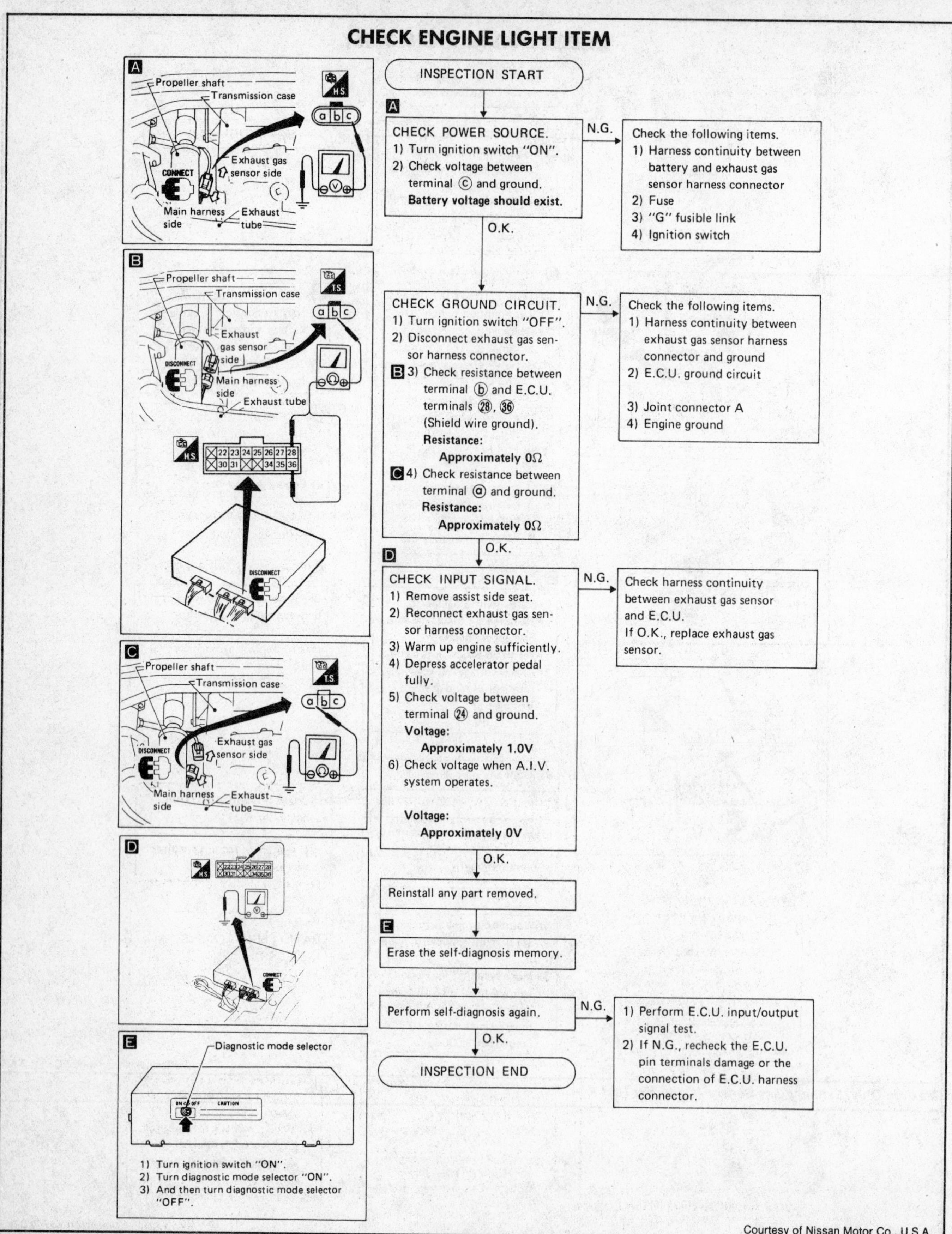
CHECK ENGINE LIGHT ITEM
A
Propeller shaft
Transmission case
H.S.
a b c
CONNECT
Exhaust gas sensor side
Main harness side
Exhaust tube
B
Propeller shaft
Transmission case
T.S.
a b c
Exhaust gas sensor side
DISCONNECT
Main harness side
Exhaust tube
H.S.
22 23 24 25 26 27 28
30 31 34 35 36
DISCONNECT
C
Propeller shaft
Transmission case
T.S.
a b c
DISCONNECT
Exhaust gas sensor side
Main harness side
Exhaust tube
D
H.S.
CONNECT
E
Diagnostic mode selector
ON OFF
CAUTION
1) Turn ignition switch "ON".
2) Turn diagnostic mode selector "ON".
3) And then turn diagnostic mode selector "OFF".
INSPECTION START
A
CHECK POWER SOURCE.
1) Turn ignition switch "ON".
2) Check voltage between terminal ⓒ and ground.
Battery voltage should exist.
N.G.
Check the following items.
1) Harness continuity between battery and exhaust gas sensor harness connector
2) Fuse
3) "G" fusible link
4) Ignition switch
O.K.
CHECK GROUND CIRCUIT.
1) Turn ignition switch "OFF".
2) Disconnect exhaust gas sensor harness connector.
B 3) Check resistance between terminal ⓑ and E.C.U. terminals ㉘, ㊱ (Shield wire ground).
Resistance:
Approximately 0Ω
C 4) Check resistance between terminal ⓐ and ground.
Resistance:
Approximately 0Ω
N.G.
Check the following items.
1) Harness continuity between exhaust gas sensor harness connector and ground
2) E.C.U. ground circuit
3) Joint connector A
4) Engine ground
O.K.
D
CHECK INPUT SIGNAL.
1) Remove assist side seat.
2) Reconnect exhaust gas sensor harness connector.
3) Warm up engine sufficiently.
4) Depress accelerator pedal fully.
5) Check voltage between terminal ㉔ and ground.
Voltage:
Approximately 1.0V
6) Check voltage when A.I.V. system operates.
Voltage:
Approximately 0V
N.G.
Check harness continuity between exhaust gas sensor and E.C.U.
If O.K., replace exhaust gas sensor.
O.K.
Reinstall any part removed.
E
Erase the self-diagnosis memory.
Perform self-diagnosis again.
N.G.
1) Perform E.C.U. input/output signal test.
2) If N.G., recheck the E.C.U. pin terminals damage or the connection of E.C.U. harness connector.
O.K.
INSPECTION END

Courtesy of Nissan Motor Co., U.S.A.

***Pathfinder/Pickup (VG30i) Only. Exhaust Gas Sensor (Code 33) Test K***

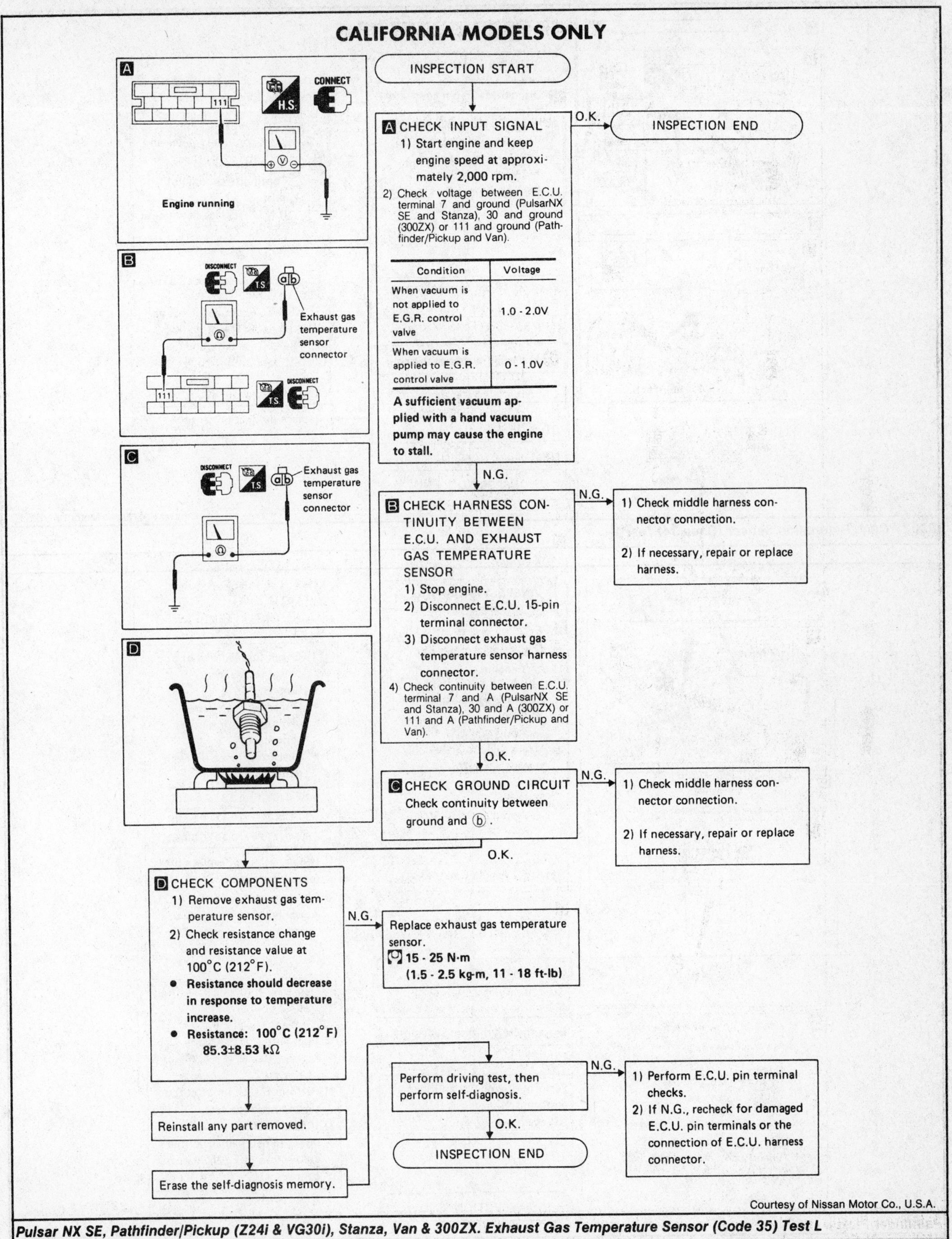
CALIFORNIA MODELS ONLY
A
CONNECT
H.S.
111
Engine running
B
DISCONNECT
T.S.
Exhaust gas temperature sensor connector
111
DISCONNECT
T.S.
C
DISCONNECT
T.S.
Exhaust gas temperature sensor connector
D
INSPECTION START
A CHECK INPUT SIGNAL
1) Start engine and keep engine speed at approximately 2,000 rpm.
2) Check voltage between E.C.U. terminal 7 and ground (PulsarNX SE and Stanza), 30 and ground (300ZX) or 111 and ground (Pathfinder/Pickup and Van).
Condition | Voltage
When vacuum is not applied to E.G.R. control valve | 1.0 - 2.0V
When vacuum is applied to E.G.R. control valve | 0 - 1.0V
A sufficient vacuum applied with a hand vacuum pump may cause the engine to stall.
O.K.
INSPECTION END
N.G.
B CHECK HARNESS CONTINUITY BETWEEN E.C.U. AND EXHAUST GAS TEMPERATURE SENSOR
1) Stop engine.
2) Disconnect E.C.U. 15-pin terminal connector.
3) Disconnect exhaust gas temperature sensor harness connector.
4) Check continuity between E.C.U. terminal 7 and A (PulsarNX SE and Stanza), 30 and A (300ZX) or 111 and A (Pathfinder/Pickup and Van).
N.G.
1) Check middle harness connector connection.
2) If necessary, repair or replace harness.
O.K.
C CHECK GROUND CIRCUIT
Check continuity between ground and ⓑ.
N.G.
1) Check middle harness connector connection.
2) If necessary, repair or replace harness.
O.K.
D CHECK COMPONENTS
1) Remove exhaust gas temperature sensor.
2) Check resistance change and resistance value at 100°C (212°F).
• Resistance should decrease in response to temperature increase.
• Resistance: 100°C (212°F) 85.3±8.53 kΩ
N.G.
Replace exhaust gas temperature sensor.
15 - 25 N·m
(1.5 - 2.5 kg-m, 11 - 18 ft-lb)
Reinstall any part removed.
Erase the self-diagnosis memory.
Perform driving test, then perform self-diagnosis.
N.G.
1) Perform E.C.U. pin terminal checks.
2) If N.G., recheck for damaged E.C.U. pin terminals or the connection of E.C.U. harness connector.
O.K.
INSPECTION END
Courtesy of Nissan Motor Co., U.S.A.

***Pulsar NX SE, Pathfinder/Pickup (Z24i & VG30i), Stanza, Van & 300ZX. Exhaust Gas Temperature Sensor (Code 35) Test L***

# 1988 COMPUTERIZED ENGINE CONTROLS
## Nissan Electronic Concentrated Control System (Cont.)

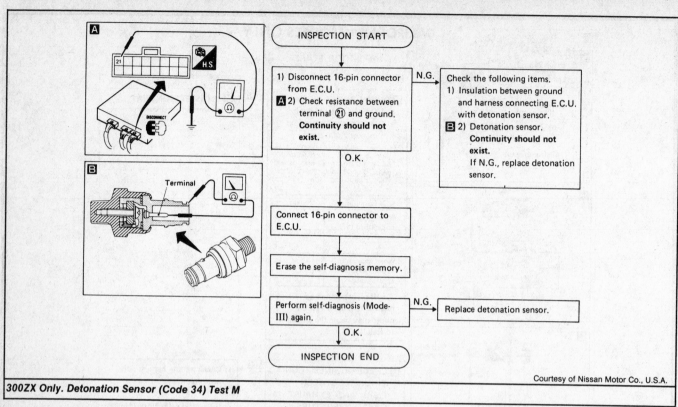

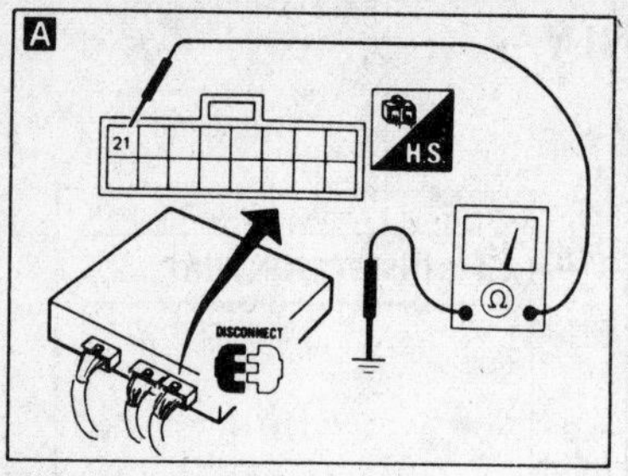

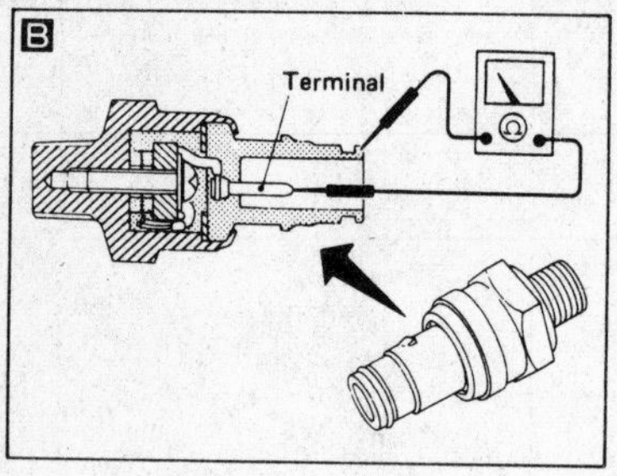

INSPECTION START

1) Disconnect 16-pin connector from E.C.U.
A 2) Check resistance between terminal ㉑ and ground. **Continuity should not exist.**

N.G. → Check the following items.
1) Insulation between ground and harness connecting E.C.U. with detonation sensor.
B 2) Detonation sensor. **Continuity should not exist.** If N.G., replace detonation sensor.

O.K. ↓

Connect 16-pin connector to E.C.U.

Erase the self-diagnosis memory.

Perform self-diagnosis (Mode-III) again.

N.G. → Replace detonation sensor.

O.K. ↓

INSPECTION END

Courtesy of Nissan Motor Co., U.S.A.

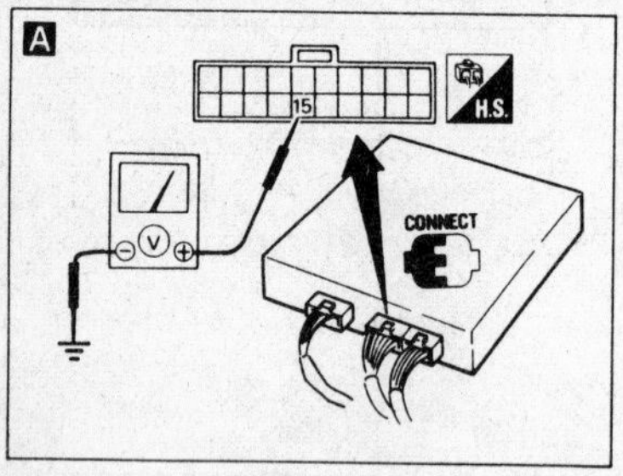

***300ZX Only. Detonation Sensor (Code 34) Test M***

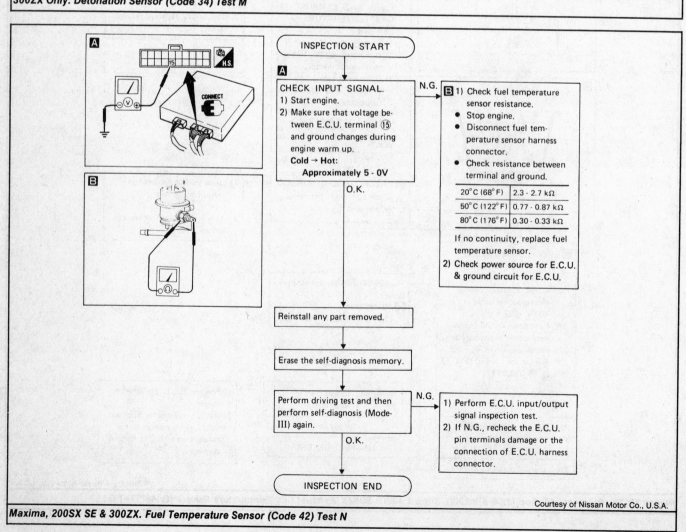

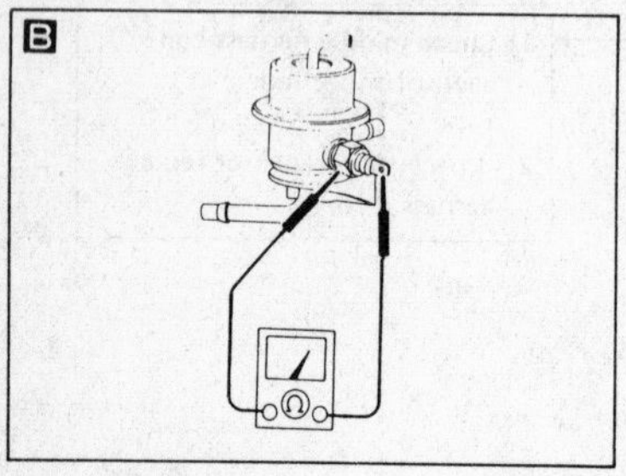

INSPECTION START

A

CHECK INPUT SIGNAL.
1) Start engine.
2) Make sure that voltage between E.C.U. terminal ⑮ and ground changes during engine warm up.
**Cold → Hot:**
**Approximately 5 - 0V**

N.G. → B 1) Check fuel temperature sensor resistance.
- Stop engine.
- Disconnect fuel temperature sensor harness connector.
- Check resistance between terminal and ground.

| | |
|---|---|
| 20°C (68°F) | 2.3 - 2.7 kΩ |
| 50°C (122°F) | 0.77 - 0.87 kΩ |
| 80°C (176°F) | 0.30 - 0.33 kΩ |

If no continuity, replace fuel temperature sensor.
2) Check power source for E.C.U. & ground circuit for E.C.U.

O.K. ↓

Reinstall any part removed.

Erase the self-diagnosis memory.

Perform driving test and then perform self-diagnosis (Mode-III) again.

N.G. → 1) Perform E.C.U. input/output signal inspection test.
2) If N.G., recheck the E.C.U. pin terminals damage or the connection of E.C.U. harness connector.

O.K. ↓

INSPECTION END

Courtesy of Nissan Motor Co., U.S.A.

***Maxima, 200SX SE & 300ZX. Fuel Temperature Sensor (Code 42) Test N***

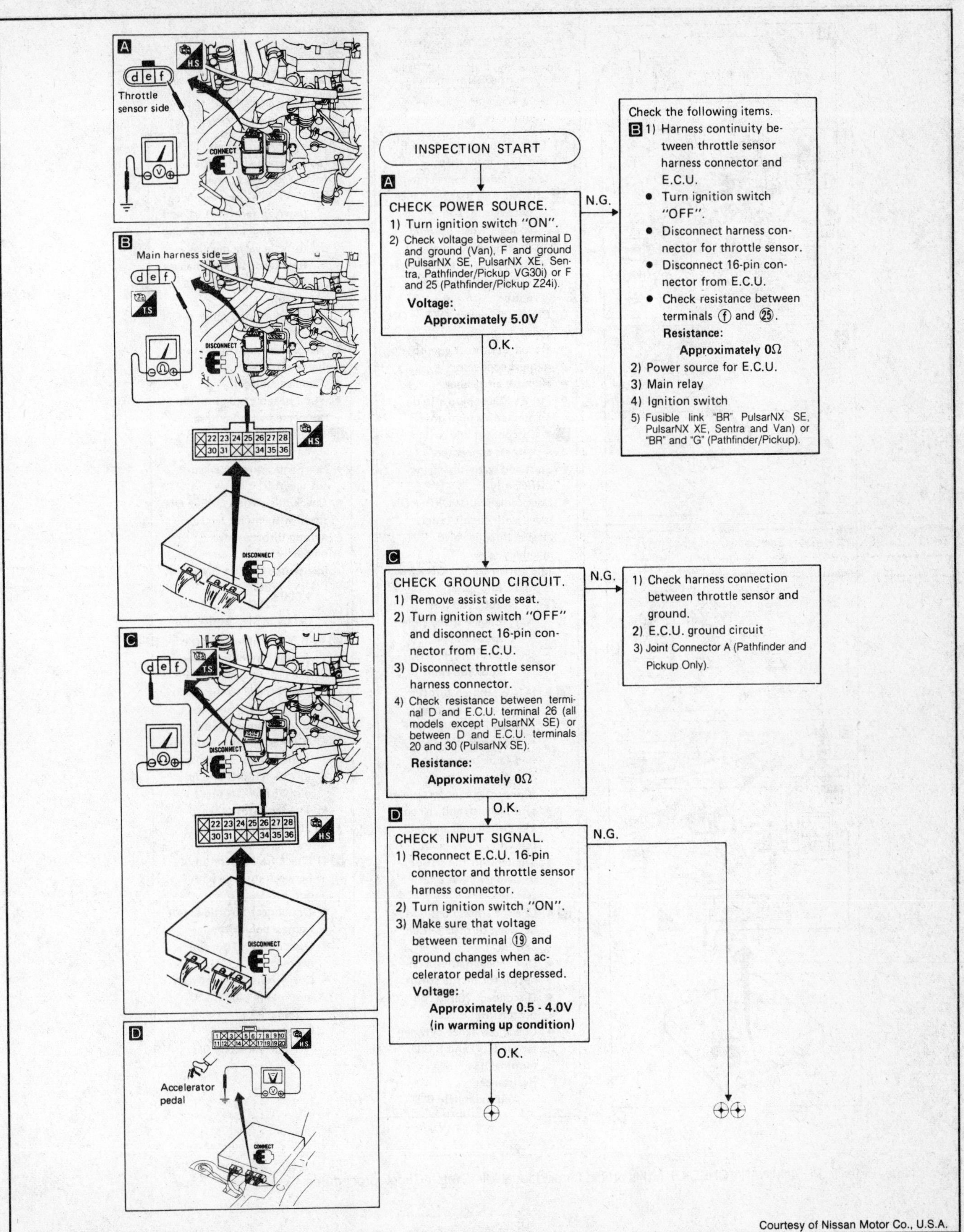
A
d e f
Throttle sensor side
H.S.
CONNECT
B
Main harness side
d e f
T.S.
DISCONNECT
22 23 24 25 26 27 28
30 31 34 35 36
H.S.
DISCONNECT
C
d e f
T.S.
DISCONNECT
22 23 24 25 26 27 28
30 31 34 35 36
H.S.
DISCONNECT
D
Accelerator pedal
H.S.
CONNECT
INSPECTION START
A
CHECK POWER SOURCE.
1) Turn ignition switch "ON".
2) Check voltage between terminal D and ground (Van), F and ground (PulsarNX SE, PulsarNX XE, Sentra, Pathfinder/Pickup VG30i) or F and 25 (Pathfinder/Pickup Z24i).
Voltage:
Approximately 5.0V
N.G.
Check the following items.
B 1) Harness continuity between throttle sensor harness connector and E.C.U.
• Turn ignition switch "OFF".
• Disconnect harness connector for throttle sensor.
• Disconnect 16-pin connector from E.C.U.
• Check resistance between terminals (f) and (25).
Resistance:
Approximately 0Ω
2) Power source for E.C.U.
3) Main relay
4) Ignition switch
5) Fusible link "BR" PulsarNX SE, PulsarNX XE, Sentra and Van) or "BR" and "G" (Pathfinder/Pickup).
O.K.
C
CHECK GROUND CIRCUIT.
1) Remove assist side seat.
2) Turn ignition switch "OFF" and disconnect 16-pin connector from E.C.U.
3) Disconnect throttle sensor harness connector.
4) Check resistance between terminal D and E.C.U. terminal 26 (all models except PulsarNX SE) or between D and E.C.U. terminals 20 and 30 (PulsarNX SE).
Resistance:
Approximately 0Ω
N.G.
1) Check harness connection between throttle sensor and ground.
2) E.C.U. ground circuit
3) Joint Connector A (Pathfinder and Pickup Only).
O.K.
D
CHECK INPUT SIGNAL.
1) Reconnect E.C.U. 16-pin connector and throttle sensor harness connector.
2) Turn ignition switch "ON".
3) Make sure that voltage between terminal (19) and ground changes when accelerator pedal is depressed.
Voltage:
Approximately 0.5 - 4.0V
(in warming up condition)
N.G.
O.K.

Courtesy of Nissan Motor Co., U.S.A.

*Pulsar NX SE, Pulsar NX XE, Pathfinder/Pickup (Z24i & VG30i), Sentra & Van. Throttle Position Sensor (Code 43) Test O*

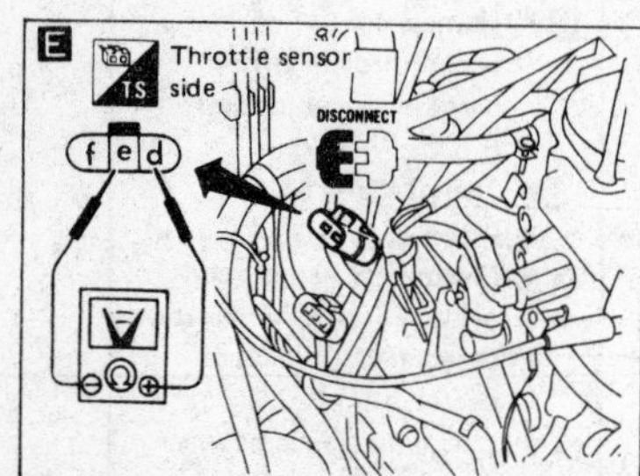
E
Throttle sensor side
f e d
DISCONNECT

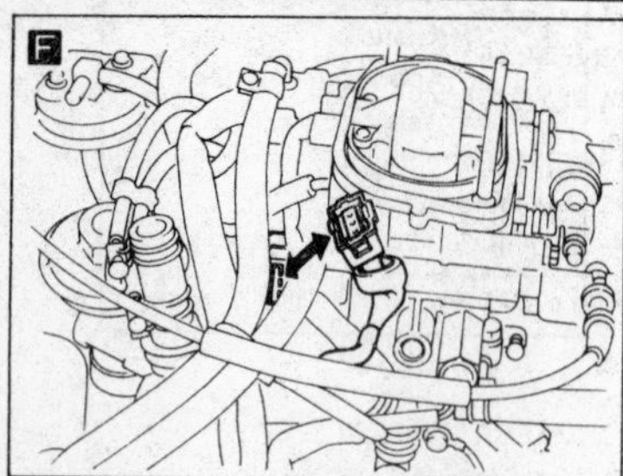
F

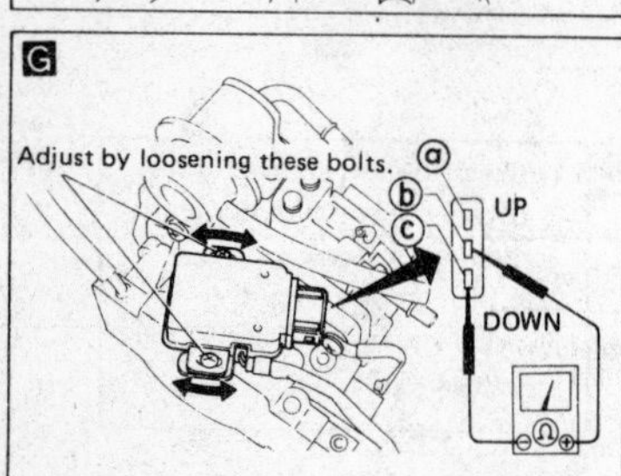
G
Adjust by loosening these bolts.
UP
DOWN

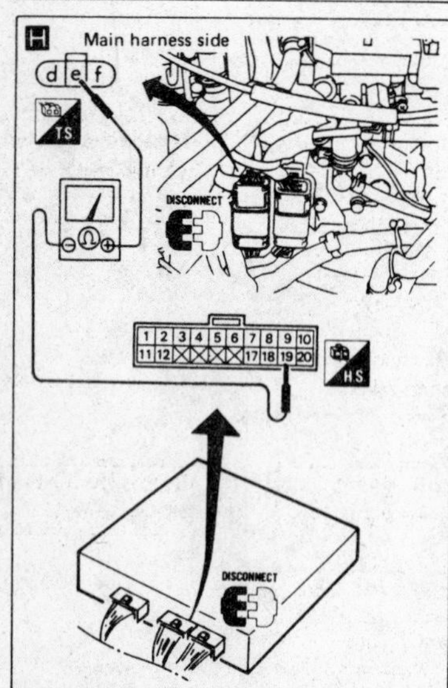
H
Main harness side
d e f
DISCONNECT

PulsarNX SE, PulsarNX XE, Pathfinder/Pickup (VG30i) and Sentra

1) Turn ignition switch "OFF" and disconnect throttle sensor harness connector.

E 2) Make sure that resistance between ⓓ and ⓔ changes when opening throttle valve manually.
**Resistance should changes.**
If not, replace throttle sensor.

3) Check idle switch OFF → ON speed.

- Reconnect throttle sensor harness connector.
- Remove air cleaner.
- Put a suitable plug into disconnected vacuum hose.
- F Disconnect idle switch harness connector.
- Start and warm up engine sufficiently.
- Check idle switch OFF → ON speed with circuit tester, closing throttle valve manually.

**Idle switch OFF → ON speed:**
**M/T: Idle speed + 250±150 rpm**
**A/T: Engine speed (Idle speed in "N" position) + 250±150 rpm**

- G If N.G., loosen throttle sensor installing screws, then set idle switch OFF → ON speed to the specified value by turning throttle sensor body. (Connect circuit tester with terminals ⓐ and ⓑ on idle switch side and find out OFF → ON point.)
- Tighten throttle sensor installing screws after setting.

H 4) Check harness continuity between throttle sensor and E.C.U.

- Disconnect harness connector for thrttle sensor.
- Disconnect 20-pin connector from E.C.U.
- Check resistance between terminal ⓔ and E.C.U. terminal ⑲.

**Resistance:**
**Approximately 0Ω**

Pathfinder/Pickup (Z24i) and Van

1) Turn ignition switch "OFF" and disconnect throttle sensor harness connector.

E 2) Make sure that resistance between terminals ⓓ and ⓔ changes when opening throttle valve manually.
**Resistance should changes.**
If not, replace throttle sensor.

3) Check idle switch OFF → ON speed.

- Reconnect throttle sensor harness connector.
- Remove air duct.
- Put a suitable plug into disconnected vacuum hose.
- F Disconnect idle switch harness connector.
- Start and warm up engine sufficiently.
- Check idle switch OFF → ON speed with circuit tester, closing throttle valve manually.

**Idle switch OFF → ON speed:**
**$1,600^{+550}_{-250}$ rpm**
**(A/T: in "N" position)**

- G If N.G., loosen throttle sensor installing screws, then set idle switch OFF → ON speed to the specified value by turning throttle sensor body. (Connect circuit tester with terminals ⓑ and ⓒ on idle switch side and find out OFF → ON point.)
- Tighten throttle sensor installing screws after setting.

H 4) Check harness continuity between throttle sensor and E.C.U.

- Disconnect throttle sensor harness connector.
- Disconnect 20-pin connector from E.C.U.
- Check resistance between terminal ⓔ and E.C.U. terminal ⑲.

**Resistance:**
**Approximately 0Ω**

Note: Refer to PRELIMINARY CHECKS in this article for addtional Idle Switch Check procedures.

Courtesy of Nissan Motor Co., U.S.A.

***Pulsar NX SE, Pulsar NX XE, Pathfinder/Pickup (Z24i & VG30i), Sentra & Van. Throttle Position Sensor (Cont.) (Code 43) Test O***

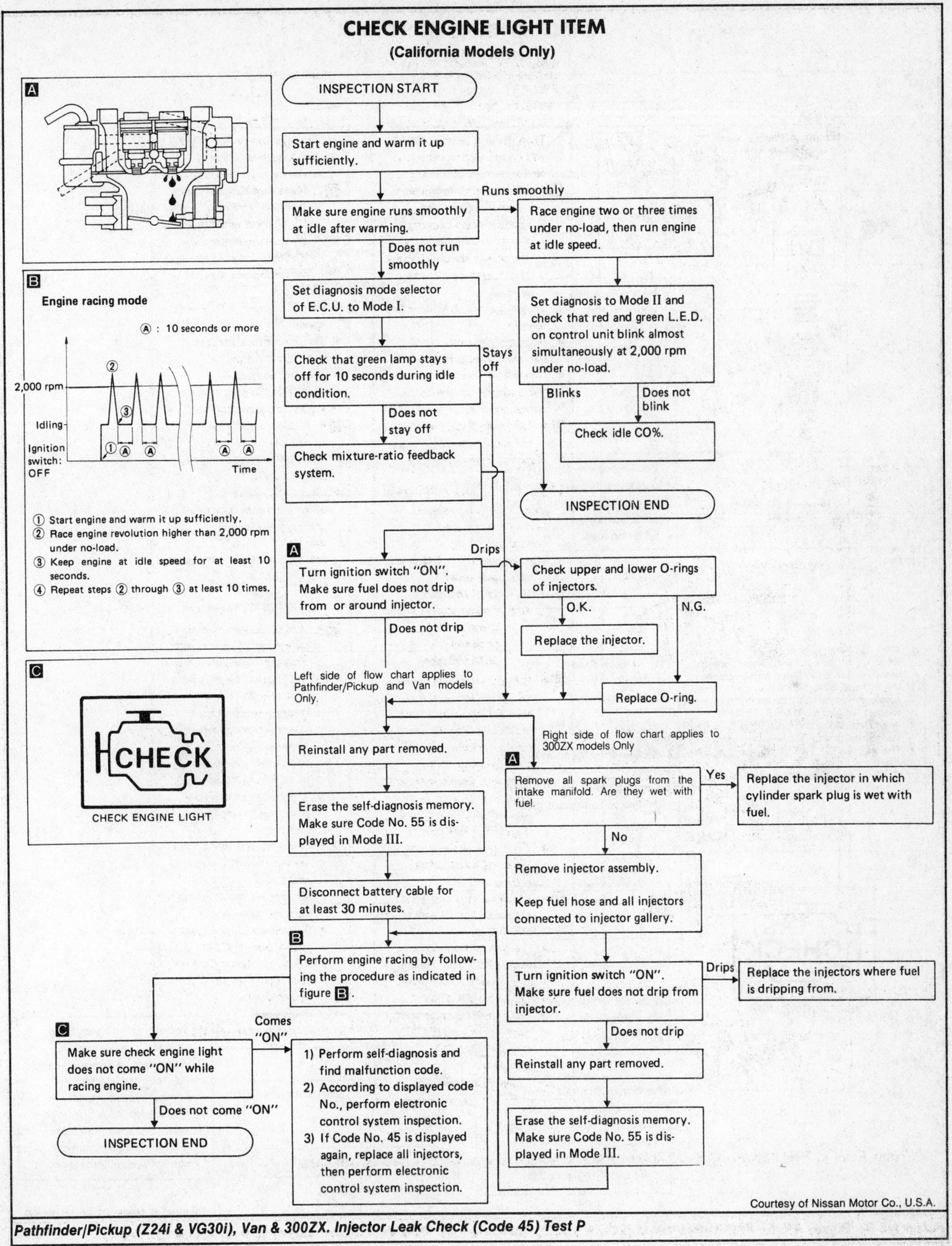
CHECK ENGINE LIGHT ITEM
(California Models Only)
A
B
Engine racing mode
Ⓐ : 10 seconds or more
2,000 rpm
Idling
Ignition switch: OFF
Time
① Start engine and warm it up sufficiently.
② Race engine revolution higher than 2,000 rpm under no-load.
③ Keep engine at idle speed for at least 10 seconds.
④ Repeat steps ② through ③ at least 10 times.
C
CHECK
CHECK ENGINE LIGHT
INSPECTION START
Start engine and warm it up sufficiently.
Make sure engine runs smoothly at idle after warming.
Runs smoothly
Race engine two or three times under no-load, then run engine at idle speed.
Does not run smoothly
Set diagnosis mode selector of E.C.U. to Mode I.
Set diagnosis to Mode II and check that red and green L.E.D. on control unit blink almost simultaneously at 2,000 rpm under no-load.
Check that green lamp stays off for 10 seconds during idle condition.
Stays off
Blinks
Does not blink
Check idle CO%.
Does not stay off
Check mixture-ratio feedback system.
INSPECTION END
A
Turn ignition switch "ON". Make sure fuel does not drip from or around injector.
Drips
Check upper and lower O-rings of injectors.
O.K.
N.G.
Replace the injector.
Does not drip
Left side of flow chart applies to Pathfinder/Pickup and Van models Only.
Replace O-ring.
Reinstall any part removed.
Right side of flow chart applies to 300ZX models Only
A
Remove all spark plugs from the intake manifold. Are they wet with fuel.
Yes
Replace the injector in which cylinder spark plug is wet with fuel.
Erase the self-diagnosis memory. Make sure Code No. 55 is displayed in Mode III.
No
Remove injector assembly.
Keep fuel hose and all injectors connected to injector gallery.
Disconnect battery cable for at least 30 minutes.
B
Perform engine racing by following the procedure as indicated in figure B.
Turn ignition switch "ON". Make sure fuel does not drip from injector.
Drips
Replace the injectors where fuel is dripping from.
C
Make sure check engine light does not come "ON" while racing engine.
Comes "ON"
1) Perform self-diagnosis and find malfunction code.
2) According to displayed code No., perform electronic control system inspection.
3) If Code No. 45 is displayed again, replace all injectors, then perform electronic control system inspection.
Does not drip
Reinstall any part removed.
Does not come "ON"
INSPECTION END
Erase the self-diagnosis memory. Make sure Code No. 55 is displayed in Mode III.
Courtesy of Nissan Motor Co., U.S.A.

*Pathfinder/Pickup (Z24i & VG30i), Van & 300ZX. Injector Leak Check (Code 45) Test P*

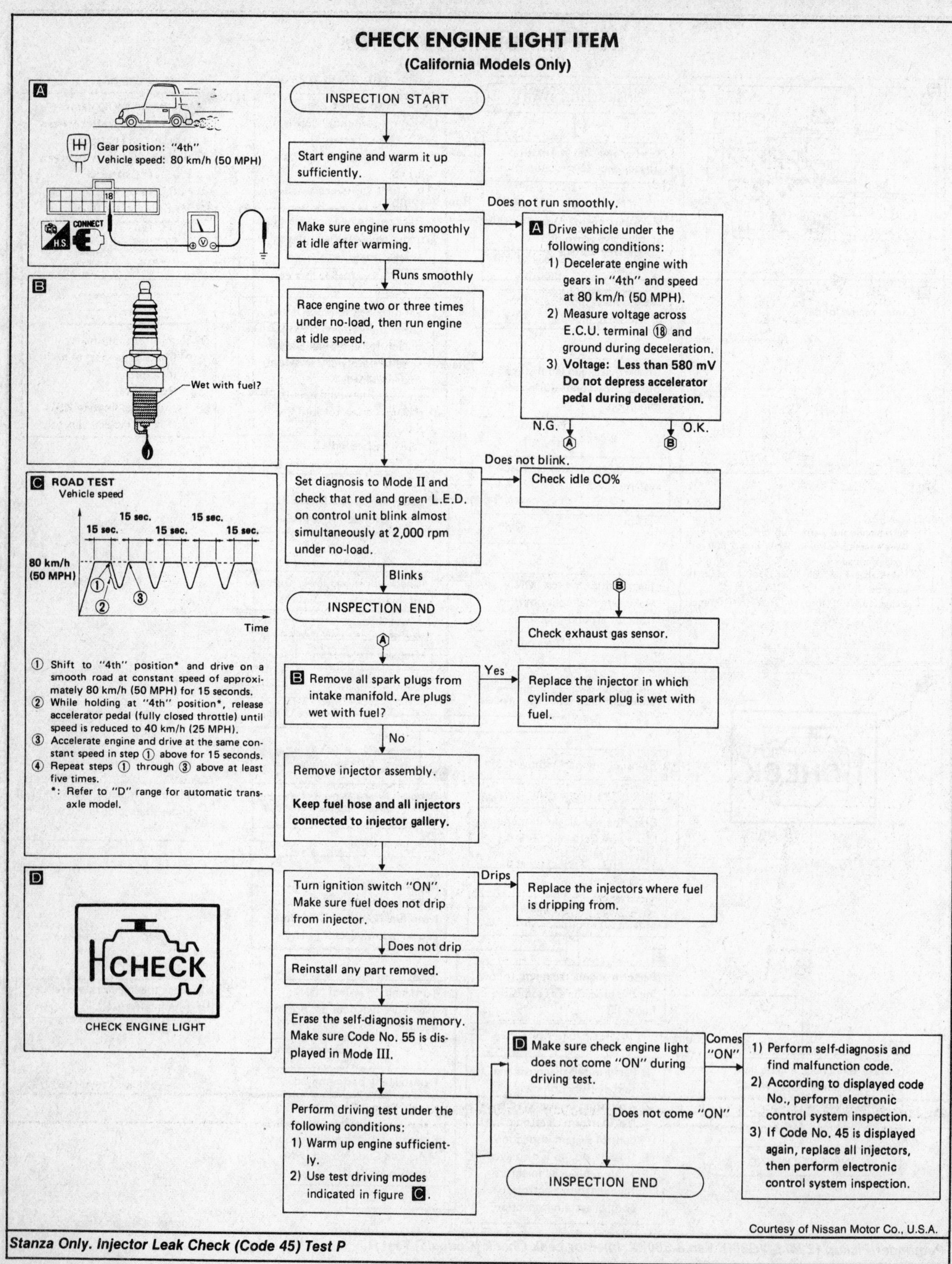
CHECK ENGINE LIGHT ITEM
(California Models Only)
A
Gear position: "4th"
Vehicle speed: 80 km/h (50 MPH)
18
CONNECT
H.S.
B
Wet with fuel?
C ROAD TEST
Vehicle speed
15 sec.
15 sec.
15 sec.
15 sec.
15 sec.
80 km/h
(50 MPH)
Time
① Shift to "4th" position* and drive on a smooth road at constant speed of approximately 80 km/h (50 MPH) for 15 seconds.
② While holding at "4th" position*, release accelerator pedal (fully closed throttle) until speed is reduced to 40 km/h (25 MPH).
③ Accelerate engine and drive at the same constant speed in step ① above for 15 seconds.
④ Repeat steps ① through ③ above at least five times.
*: Refer to "D" range for automatic transaxle model.
D
CHECK
CHECK ENGINE LIGHT
INSPECTION START
Start engine and warm it up sufficiently.
Make sure engine runs smoothly at idle after warming.
Does not run smoothly.
A Drive vehicle under the following conditions:
1) Decelerate engine with gears in "4th" and speed at 80 km/h (50 MPH).
2) Measure voltage across E.C.U. terminal ⑱ and ground during deceleration.
3) Voltage: Less than 580 mV Do not depress accelerator pedal during deceleration.
N.G.
A
O.K.
B
Runs smoothly
Race engine two or three times under no-load, then run engine at idle speed.
Does not blink.
Check idle CO%
Set diagnosis to Mode II and check that red and green L.E.D. on control unit blink almost simultaneously at 2,000 rpm under no-load.
Blinks
INSPECTION END
B
Check exhaust gas sensor.
A
B Remove all spark plugs from intake manifold. Are plugs wet with fuel?
Yes
Replace the injector in which cylinder spark plug is wet with fuel.
No
Remove injector assembly.
Keep fuel hose and all injectors connected to injector gallery.
Turn ignition switch "ON". Make sure fuel does not drip from injector.
Drips
Replace the injectors where fuel is dripping from.
Does not drip
Reinstall any part removed.
Erase the self-diagnosis memory. Make sure Code No. 55 is displayed in Mode III.
Perform driving test under the following conditions:
1) Warm up engine sufficiently.
2) Use test driving modes indicated in figure C.
D Make sure check engine light does not come "ON" during driving test.
Comes "ON"
1) Perform self-diagnosis and find malfunction code.
2) According to displayed code No., perform electronic control system inspection.
3) If Code No. 45 is displayed again, replace all injectors, then perform electronic control system inspection.
Does not come "ON"
INSPECTION END

Courtesy of Nissan Motor Co., U.S.A.

*Stanza Only. Injector Leak Check (Code 45) Test P*

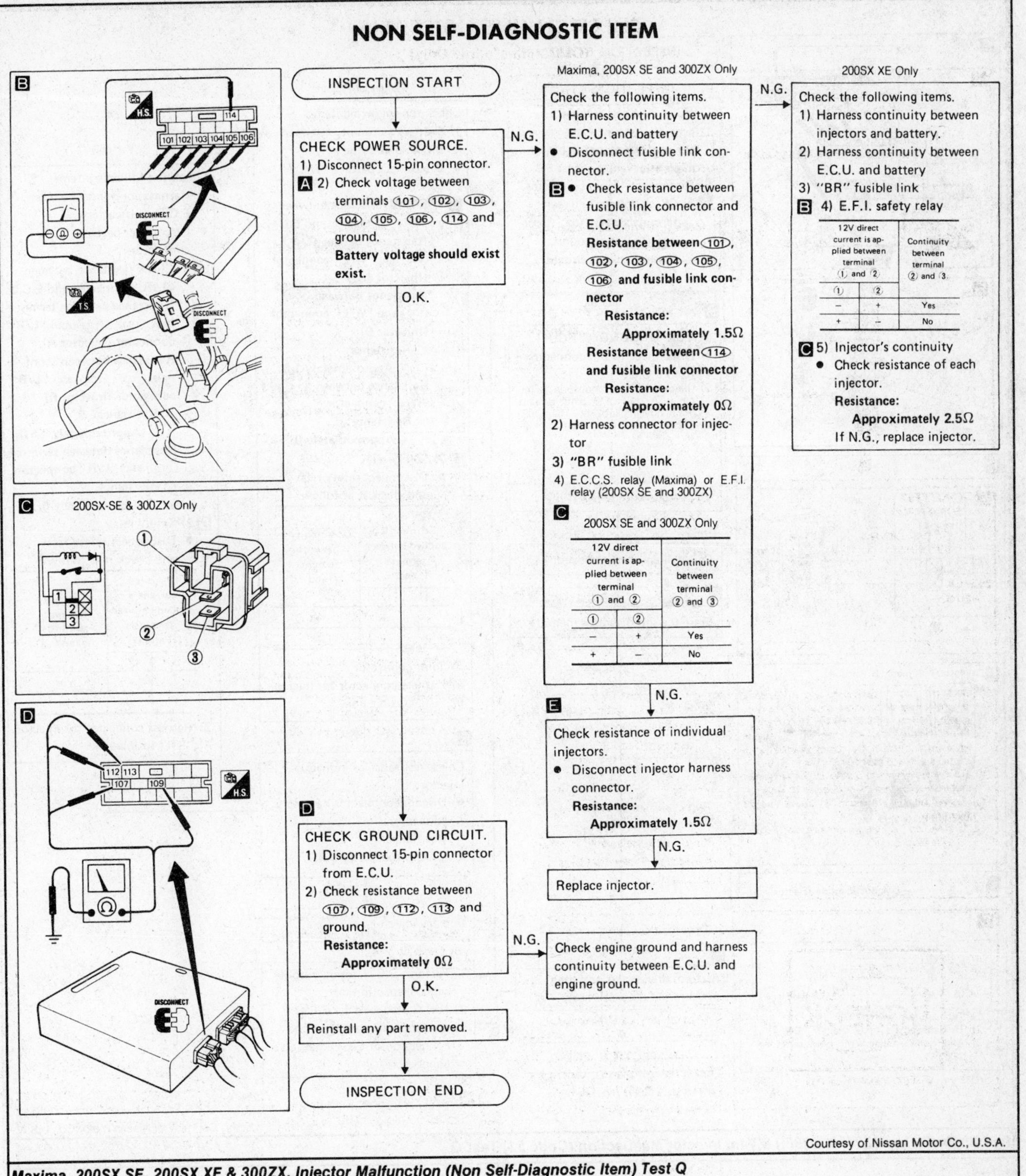
NON SELF-DIAGNOSTIC ITEM
B
H.S.
114
101 102 103 104 105 106
DISCONNECT
T.S.
DISCONNECT
C
200SX-SE & 300ZX Only
1
2
3
D
112 113
107 109
H.S.
DISCONNECT
INSPECTION START
CHECK POWER SOURCE.
1) Disconnect 15-pin connector.
A 2) Check voltage between terminals 101, 102, 103, 104, 105, 106, 114 and ground.
Battery voltage should exist.
N.G.
O.K.
Maxima, 200SX SE and 300ZX Only
Check the following items.
1) Harness continuity between E.C.U. and battery
● Disconnect fusible link connector.
B ● Check resistance between fusible link connector and E.C.U.
Resistance between 101, 102, 103, 104, 105, 106 and fusible link connector
Resistance: Approximately 1.5Ω
Resistance between 114 and fusible link connector
Resistance: Approximately 0Ω
2) Harness connector for injector
3) "BR" fusible link
4) E.C.C.S. relay (Maxima) or E.F.I. relay (200SX SE and 300ZX)
C
200SX SE and 300ZX Only
12V direct current is applied between terminal 1 and 2
Continuity between terminal 2 and 3
1 2
– + Yes
+ – No
N.G.
200SX XE Only
Check the following items.
1) Harness continuity between injectors and battery.
2) Harness continuity between E.C.U. and battery
3) "BR" fusible link
B 4) E.F.I. safety relay
12V direct current is applied between terminal 1 and 2
Continuity between terminal 2 and 3
1 2
– + Yes
+ – No
C 5) Injector's continuity
● Check resistance of each injector.
Resistance: Approximately 2.5Ω
If N.G., replace injector.
N.G.
E
Check resistance of individual injectors.
● Disconnect injector harness connector.
Resistance: Approximately 1.5Ω
N.G.
Replace injector.
D
CHECK GROUND CIRCUIT.
1) Disconnect 15-pin connector from E.C.U.
2) Check resistance between 107, 109, 112, 113 and ground.
Resistance: Approximately 0Ω
N.G.
Check engine ground and harness continuity between E.C.U. and engine ground.
O.K.
Reinstall any part removed.
INSPECTION END
Courtesy of Nissan Motor Co., U.S.A.

*Maxima, 200SX SE, 200SX XE & 300ZX. Injector Malfunction (Non Self-Diagnostic Item) Test Q*

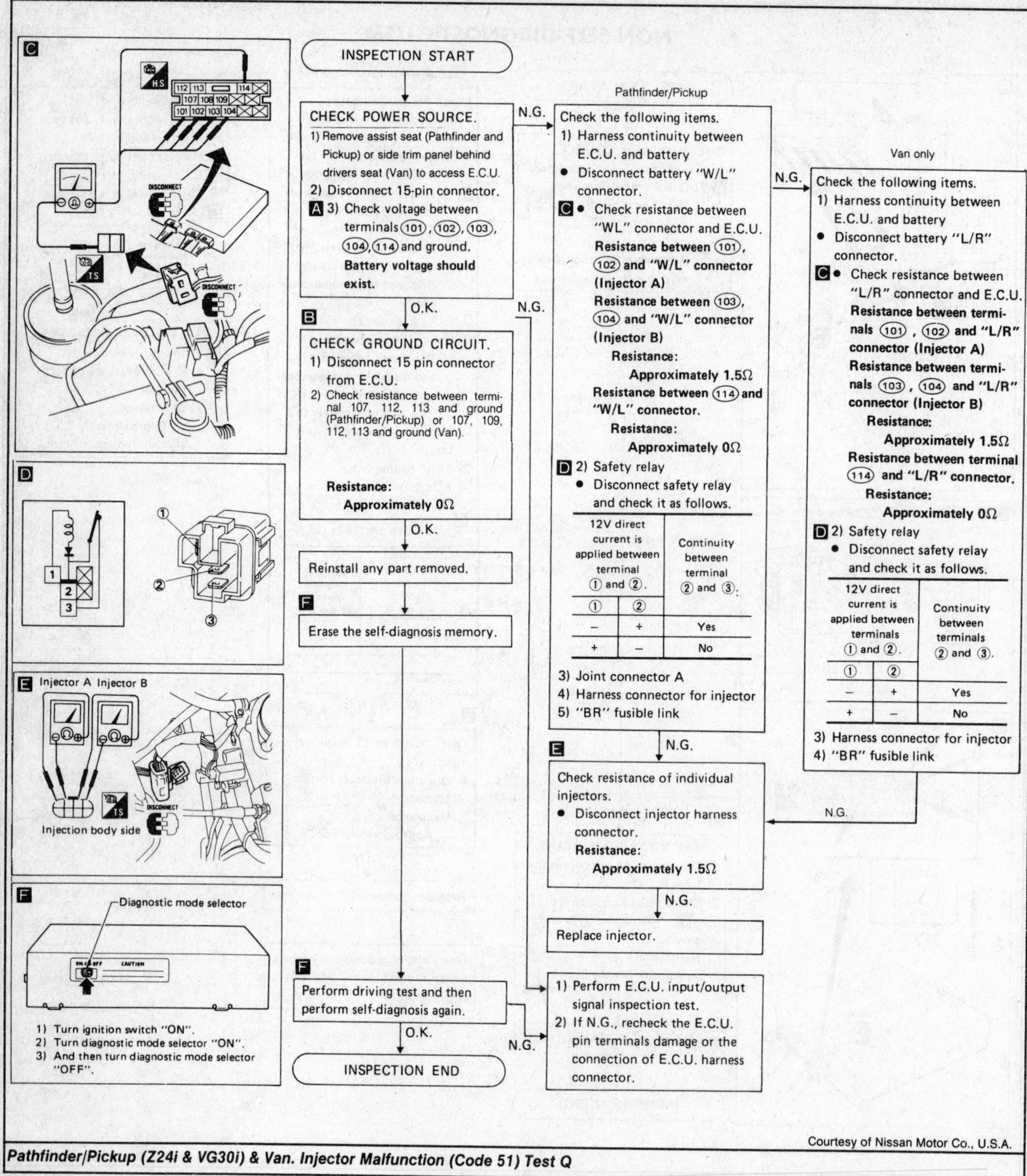
C
H.S
112 113 114
107 108 109
101 102 103 104
DISCONNECT
TS
DISCONNECT
D
①
1
2
3
②
③
E Injector A Injector B
TS
DISCONNECT
Injection body side
F
Diagnostic mode selector
ON OFF
CAUTION
1) Turn ignition switch "ON".
2) Turn diagnostic mode selector "ON".
3) And then turn diagnostic mode selector "OFF".
INSPECTION START
CHECK POWER SOURCE.
1) Remove assist seat (Pathfinder and Pickup) or side trim panel behind drivers seat (Van) to access E.C.U.
2) Disconnect 15-pin connector.
A 3) Check voltage between terminals (101), (102), (103), (104), (114) and ground.
Battery voltage should exist.
O.K.
B
CHECK GROUND CIRCUIT.
1) Disconnect 15 pin connector from E.C.U.
2) Check resistance between terminal 107, 112, 113 and ground (Pathfinder/Pickup) or 107, 109, 112, 113 and ground (Van).
Resistance: Approximately 0Ω
O.K.
Reinstall any part removed.
F
Erase the self-diagnosis memory.
F
Perform driving test and then perform self-diagnosis again.
O.K.
INSPECTION END
N.G.
Pathfinder/Pickup
Check the following items.
1) Harness continuity between E.C.U. and battery
• Disconnect battery "W/L" connector.
C • Check resistance between "WL" connector and E.C.U.
Resistance between (101), (102) and "W/L" connector (Injector A)
Resistance between (103), (104) and "W/L" connector (Injector B)
Resistance: Approximately 1.5Ω
Resistance between (114) and "W/L" connector.
Resistance: Approximately 0Ω
D 2) Safety relay
• Disconnect safety relay and check it as follows.
12V direct current is applied between terminal ① and ②. | Continuity between terminal ② and ③.
① | ② |
– | + | Yes
+ | – | No
3) Joint connector A
4) Harness connector for injector
5) "BR" fusible link
N.G.
Van only
Check the following items.
1) Harness continuity between E.C.U. and battery
• Disconnect battery "L/R" connector.
C • Check resistance between "L/R" connector and E.C.U.
Resistance between terminals (101), (102) and "L/R" connector (Injector A)
Resistance between terminals (103), (104) and "L/R" connector (Injector B)
Resistance: Approximately 1.5Ω
Resistance between terminal (114) and "L/R" connector.
Resistance: Approximately 0Ω
D 2) Safety relay
• Disconnect safety relay and check it as follows.
12V direct current is applied between terminals ① and ②. | Continuity between terminals ② and ③.
① | ② |
– | + | Yes
+ | – | No
3) Harness connector for injector
4) "BR" fusible link
N.G.
E
Check resistance of individual injectors.
• Disconnect injector harness connector.
Resistance: Approximately 1.5Ω
N.G.
Replace injector.
1) Perform E.C.U. input/output signal inspection test.
2) If N.G., recheck the E.C.U. pin terminals damage or the connection of E.C.U. harness connector.
Courtesy of Nissan Motor Co., U.S.A.

Pathfinder/Pickup (Z24i & VG30i) & Van. Injector Malfunction (Code 51) Test Q

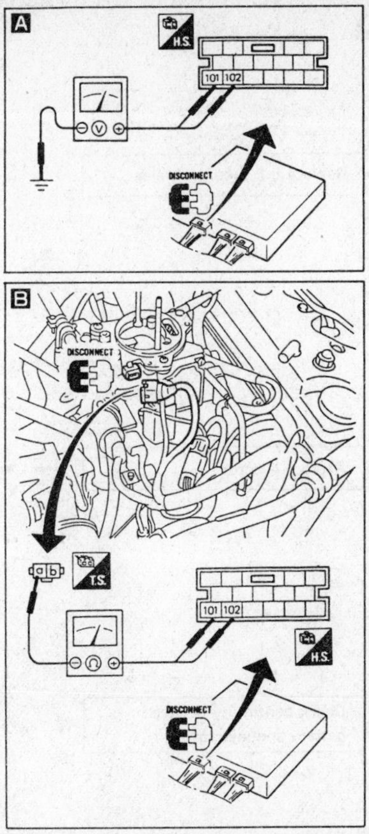

A
H.S.
101 102
DISCONNECT

B
DISCONNECT
a b
T.S.
101 102
H.S.
DISCONNECT

## NON SELF-DIAGNOSTIC ITEM

INSPECTION START

A

CHECK POWER SOURCE.
1) Disconnect E.C.U. 15-pin connector.
2) Check voltage between terminals (101), (102) and ground.
**Battery voltage should exist.**

N.G. → Check the following items.
B 1) Harness continuity between terminal (a) of injector harness connector and terminals (101), (102) of E.C.U.
C 2) Injector cover continuity
3) Injector
Remove injector and check continuity between injector terminals.
4) Harness continuity between injector harness connector and battery.
5) Joint connector A
6) Fusible link "BR"

O.K. ↓

CHECK GROUND CIRCUIT.

↓

Perform driving test and then perform E.C.U. input/output signal inspection test.

N.G. → Recheck the E.C.U. pin terminals or the connection of E.C.U. harness connector for damage.

O.K. ↓

INSPECTION END

Courtesy of Nissan Motor Co., U.S.A.

***Pulsar NX XE & Sentra. Injector Malfunction (Non Self-Diagnostic Item) Test Q***

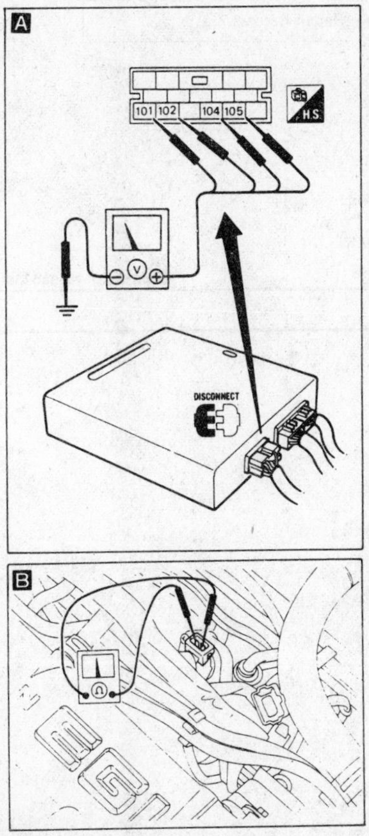

A
101 102 104 105
H.S.
DISCONNECT

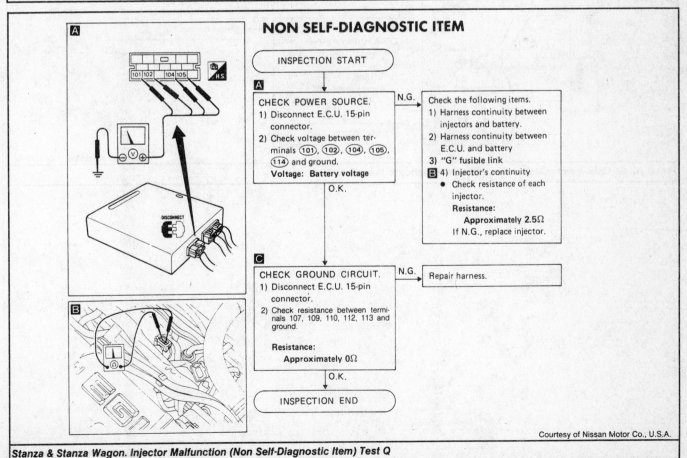

B

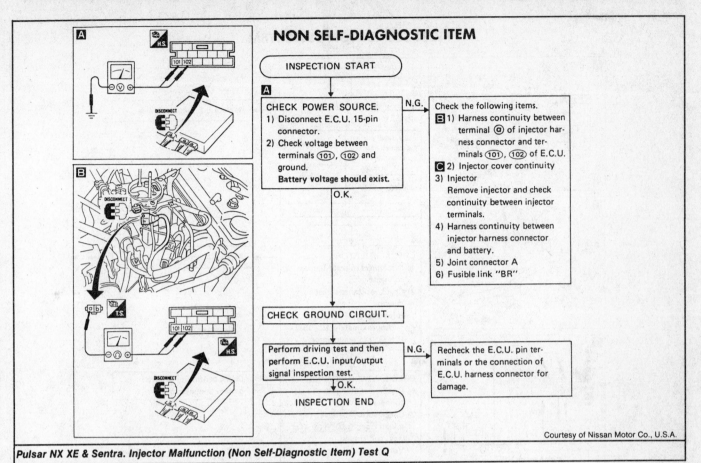

## NON SELF-DIAGNOSTIC ITEM

INSPECTION START

A

CHECK POWER SOURCE.
1) Disconnect E.C.U. 15-pin connector.
2) Check voltage between terminals (101), (102), (104), (105), (114) and ground.
**Voltage: Battery voltage**

N.G. → Check the following items.
1) Harness continuity between injectors and battery.
2) Harness continuity between E.C.U. and battery
3) "G" fusible link
B 4) Injector's continuity
- Check resistance of each injector.
**Resistance:**
**Approximately 2.5Ω**
If N.G., replace injector.

O.K. ↓

C

CHECK GROUND CIRCUIT.
1) Disconnect E.C.U. 15-pin connector.
2) Check resistance between terminals 107, 109, 110, 112, 113 and ground.

**Resistance:**
**Approximately 0Ω**

N.G. → Repair harness.

O.K. ↓

INSPECTION END

Courtesy of Nissan Motor Co., U.S.A.

***Stanza & Stanza Wagon. Injector Malfunction (Non Self-Diagnostic Item) Test Q***

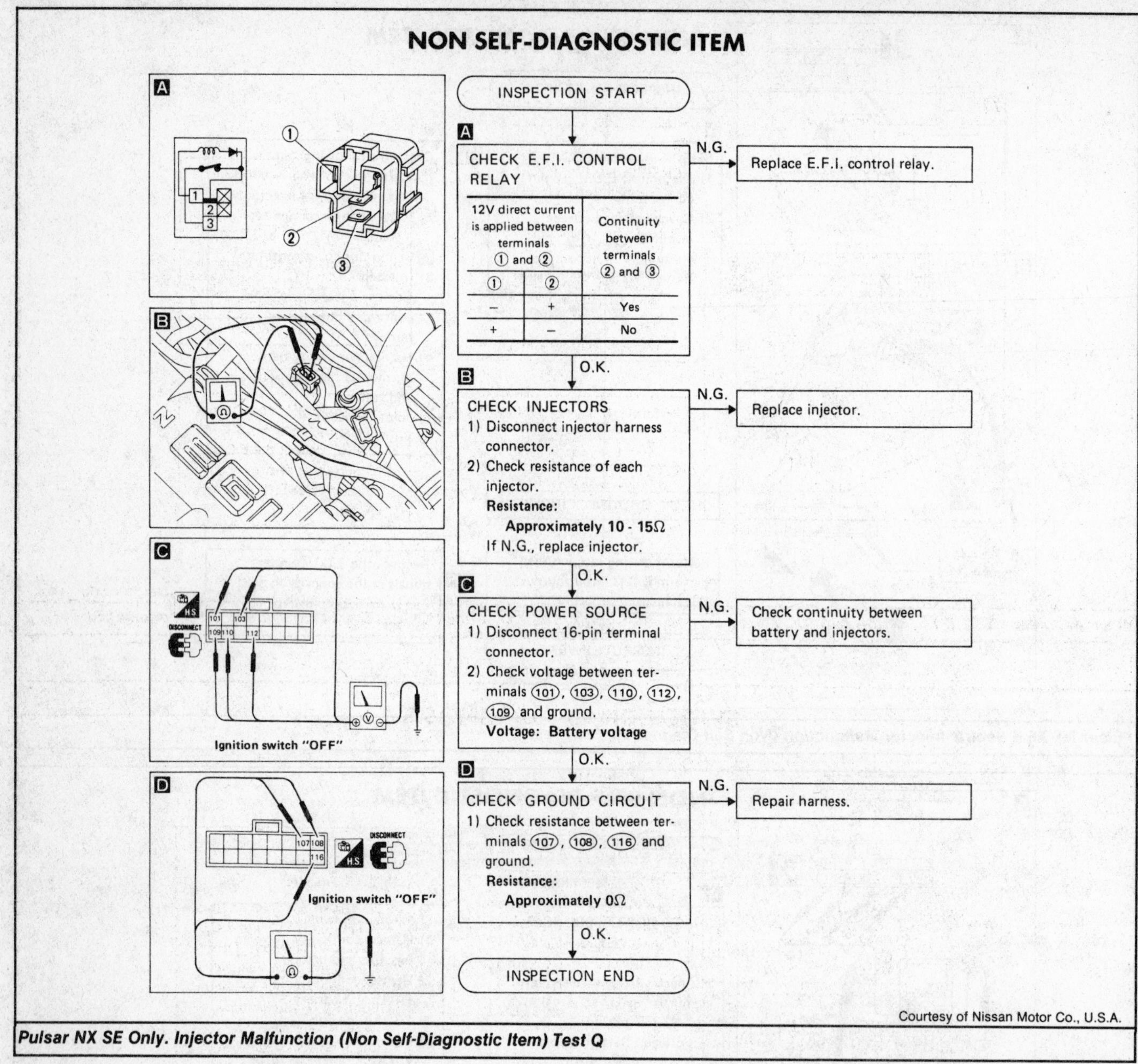
NON SELF-DIAGNOSTIC ITEM
INSPECTION START
A
CHECK E.F.I. CONTROL RELAY
12V direct current is applied between terminals ① and ②
Continuity between terminals ② and ③
① ②
– + Yes
+ – No
N.G.
Replace E.F.I. control relay.
O.K.
B
CHECK INJECTORS
1) Disconnect injector harness connector.
2) Check resistance of each injector.
Resistance:
Approximately 10 - 15Ω
If N.G., replace injector.
N.G.
Replace injector.
O.K.
C
CHECK POWER SOURCE
1) Disconnect 16-pin terminal connector.
2) Check voltage between terminals 101, 103, 110, 112, 109 and ground.
Voltage: Battery voltage
N.G.
Check continuity between battery and injectors.
O.K.
D
CHECK GROUND CIRCUIT
1) Check resistance between terminals 107, 108, 116 and ground.
Resistance:
Approximately 0Ω
N.G.
Repair harness.
O.K.
INSPECTION END
101
103
109
110
112
DISCONNECT
H.S.
Ignition switch "OFF"
107
108
116
Ignition switch "OFF"
Courtesy of Nissan Motor Co., U.S.A.

**Pulsar NX SE Only. Injector Malfunction (Non Self-Diagnostic Item) Test Q**

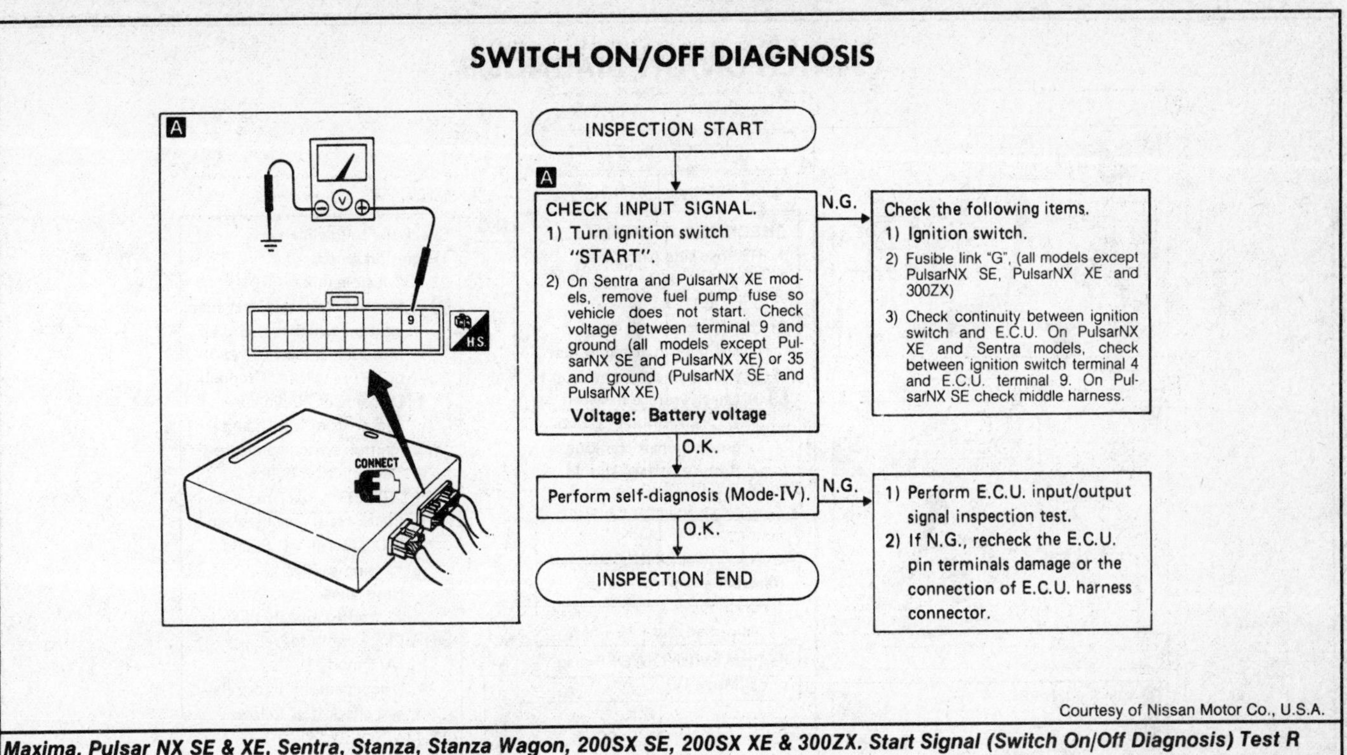
SWITCH ON/OFF DIAGNOSIS
A
9
HS
CONNECT
INSPECTION START
A
CHECK INPUT SIGNAL.
1) Turn ignition switch "START".
2) On Sentra and PulsarNX XE models, remove fuel pump fuse so vehicle does not start. Check voltage between terminal 9 and ground (all models except PulsarNX SE and PulsarNX XE) or 35 and ground (PulsarNX SE and PulsarNX XE)
Voltage: Battery voltage
N.G.
Check the following items.
1) Ignition switch.
2) Fusible link "G", (all models except PulsarNX SE, PulsarNX XE and 300ZX)
3) Check continuity between ignition switch and E.C.U. On PulsarNX XE and Sentra models, check between ignition switch terminal 4 and E.C.U. terminal 9. On PulsarNX SE check middle harness.
O.K.
Perform self-diagnosis (Mode-IV).
N.G.
1) Perform E.C.U. input/output signal inspection test.
2) If N.G., recheck the E.C.U. pin terminals damage or the connection of E.C.U. harness connector.
O.K.
INSPECTION END

Courtesy of Nissan Motor Co., U.S.A.

***Maxima, Pulsar NX SE & XE, Sentra, Stanza, Stanza Wagon, 200SX SE, 200SX XE & 300ZX. Start Signal (Switch On/Off Diagnosis) Test R***

## SWITCH ON/OFF DIAGNOSIS

A

HS

CONNECT

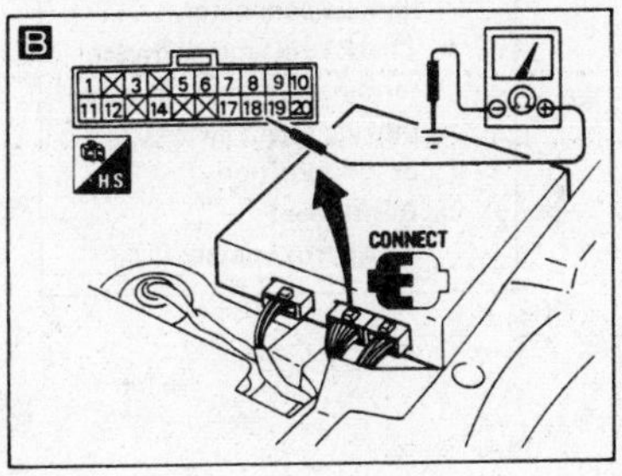

B

HS

CONNECT

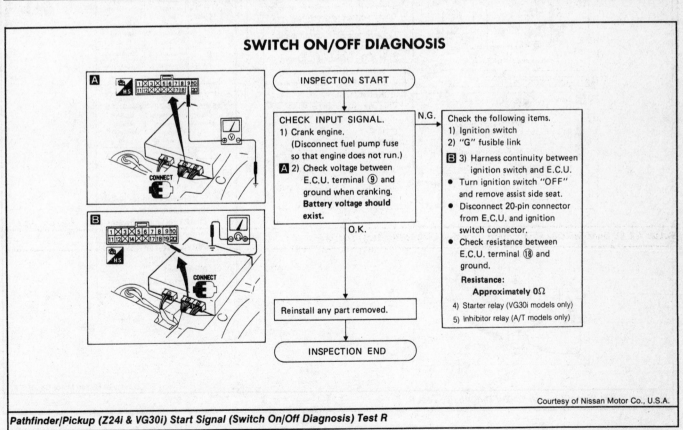

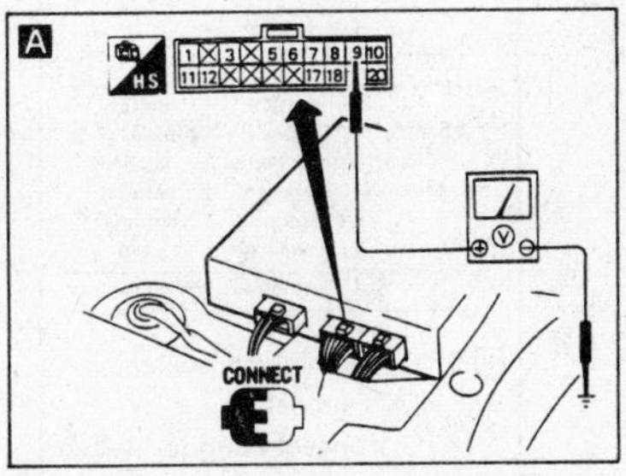

INSPECTION START

CHECK INPUT SIGNAL.

1) Crank engine.
(Disconnect fuel pump fuse so that engine does not run.)

A 2) Check voltage between E.C.U. terminal ⑨ and ground when cranking.
**Battery voltage should exist.**

N.G.

Check the following items.

1) Ignition switch
2) "G" fusible link

B 3) Harness continuity between ignition switch and E.C.U.

- Turn ignition switch "OFF" and remove assist side seat.
- Disconnect 20-pin connector from E.C.U. and ignition switch connector.
- Check resistance between E.C.U. terminal ⑱ and ground.

**Resistance:**
**Approximately 0Ω**

4) Starter relay (VG30i models only)
5) Inhibitor relay (A/T models only)

O.K.

Reinstall any part removed.

INSPECTION END

Courtesy of Nissan Motor Co., U.S.A.

***Pathfinder/Pickup (Z24i & VG30i) Start Signal (Switch On/Off Diagnosis) Test R***

# Nissan Electronic Concentrated Control System (Cont.)

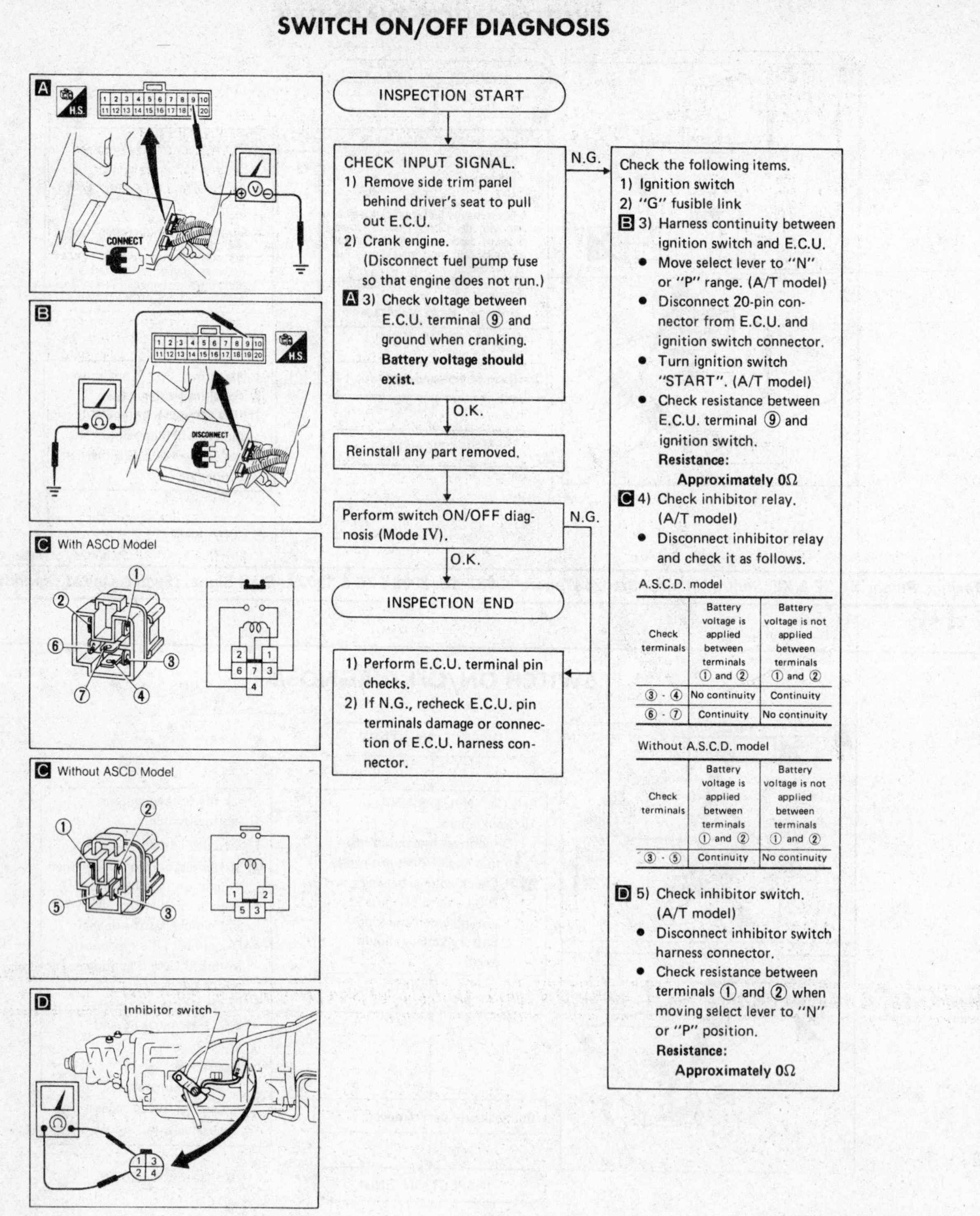
SWITCH ON/OFF DIAGNOSIS
A
H.S.
CONNECT
B
H.S.
DISCONNECT
C With ASCD Model
C Without ASCD Model
D
Inhibitor switch
INSPECTION START
CHECK INPUT SIGNAL.
1) Remove side trim panel behind driver's seat to pull out E.C.U.
2) Crank engine. (Disconnect fuel pump fuse so that engine does not run.)
A 3) Check voltage between E.C.U. terminal ⑨ and ground when cranking. Battery voltage should exist.
N.G.
O.K.
Reinstall any part removed.
Perform switch ON/OFF diagnosis (Mode IV).
N.G.
O.K.
INSPECTION END
1) Perform E.C.U. terminal pin checks.
2) If N.G., recheck E.C.U. pin terminals damage or connection of E.C.U. harness connector.
Check the following items.
1) Ignition switch
2) "G" fusible link
B 3) Harness continuity between ignition switch and E.C.U.
• Move select lever to "N" or "P" range. (A/T model)
• Disconnect 20-pin connector from E.C.U. and ignition switch connector.
• Turn ignition switch "START". (A/T model)
• Check resistance between E.C.U. terminal ⑨ and ignition switch.
Resistance:
Approximately 0Ω
C 4) Check inhibitor relay. (A/T model)
• Disconnect inhibitor relay and check it as follows.
A.S.C.D. model

| Check terminals | Battery voltage is applied between terminals ① and ② | Battery voltage is not applied between terminals ① and ② |
|---|---|---|
| ③ - ④ | No continuity | Continuity |
| ⑥ - ⑦ | Continuity | No continuity |

Without A.S.C.D. model

| Check terminals | Battery voltage is applied between terminals ① and ② | Battery voltage is not applied between terminals ① and ② |
|---|---|---|
| ③ - ⑤ | Continuity | No continuity |

D 5) Check inhibitor switch. (A/T model)
• Disconnect inhibitor switch harness connector.
• Check resistance between terminals ① and ② when moving select lever to "N" or "P" position.
Resistance:
Approximately 0Ω

Courtesy of Nissan Motor Co., U.S.A.

*Van Only. Start Signal (Switch On/Off Diagnosis) Test R*

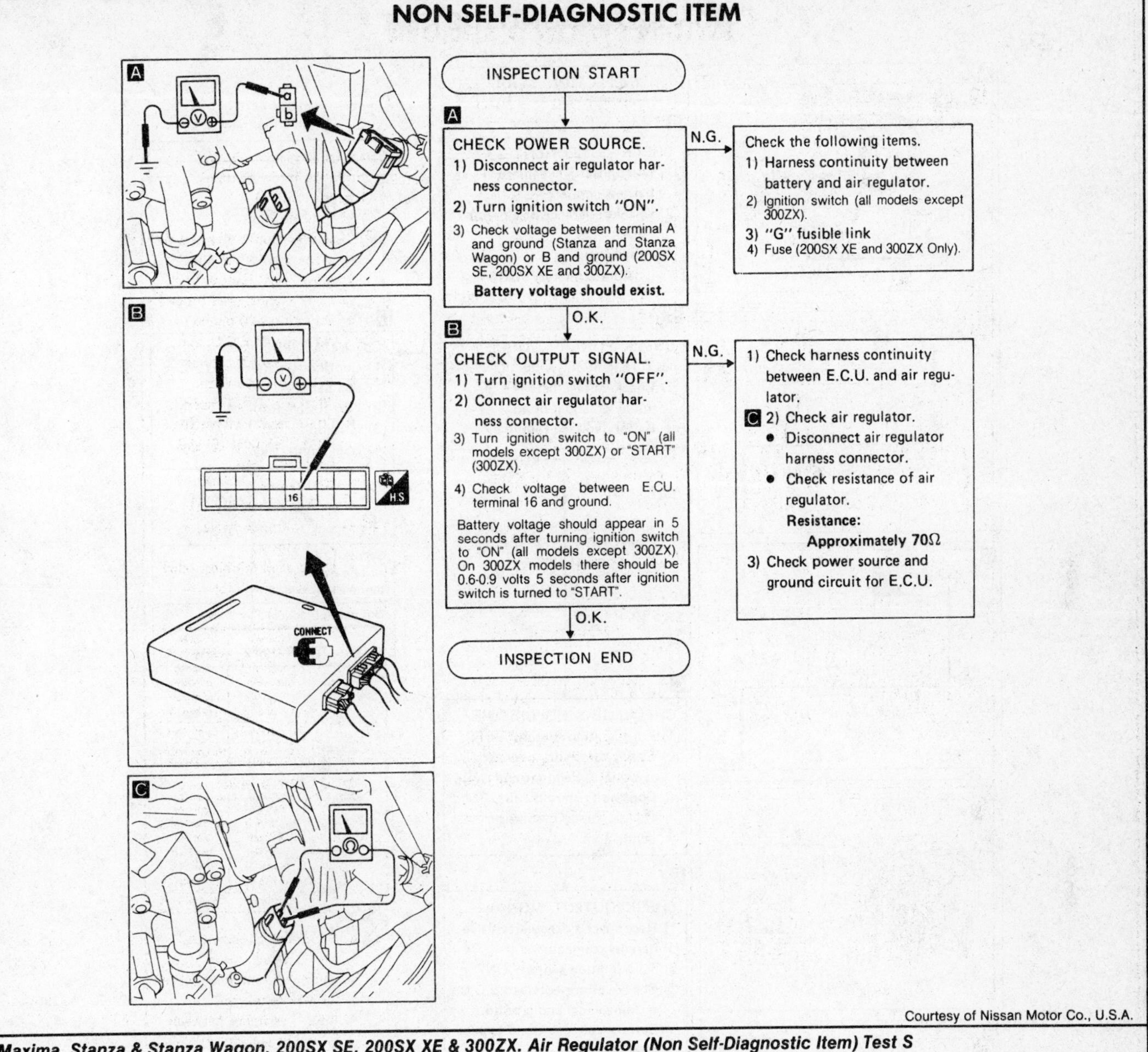
NON SELF-DIAGNOSTIC ITEM
INSPECTION START
A
CHECK POWER SOURCE.
1) Disconnect air regulator harness connector.
2) Turn ignition switch "ON".
3) Check voltage between terminal A and ground (Stanza and Stanza Wagon) or B and ground (200SX SE, 200SX XE and 300ZX).
Battery voltage should exist.
N.G.
Check the following items.
1) Harness continuity between battery and air regulator.
2) Ignition switch (all models except 300ZX).
3) "G" fusible link
4) Fuse (200SX XE and 300ZX Only).
O.K.
B
CHECK OUTPUT SIGNAL.
1) Turn ignition switch "OFF".
2) Connect air regulator harness connector.
3) Turn ignition switch to "ON" (all models except 300ZX) or "START" (300ZX).
4) Check voltage between E.CU. terminal 16 and ground.
Battery voltage should appear in 5 seconds after turning ignition switch to "ON" (all models except 300ZX). On 300ZX models there should be 0.6-0.9 volts 5 seconds after ignition switch is turned to "START".
N.G.
1) Check harness continuity between E.C.U. and air regulator.
C 2) Check air regulator.
• Disconnect air regulator harness connector.
• Check resistance of air regulator.
Resistance:
Approximately 70Ω
3) Check power source and ground circuit for E.C.U.
O.K.
INSPECTION END
A
a
b
B
16
HS
CONNECT
C
Courtesy of Nissan Motor Co., U.S.A.

***Maxima, Stanza & Stanza Wagon, 200SX SE, 200SX XE & 300ZX. Air Regulator (Non Self-Diagnostic Item) Test S***

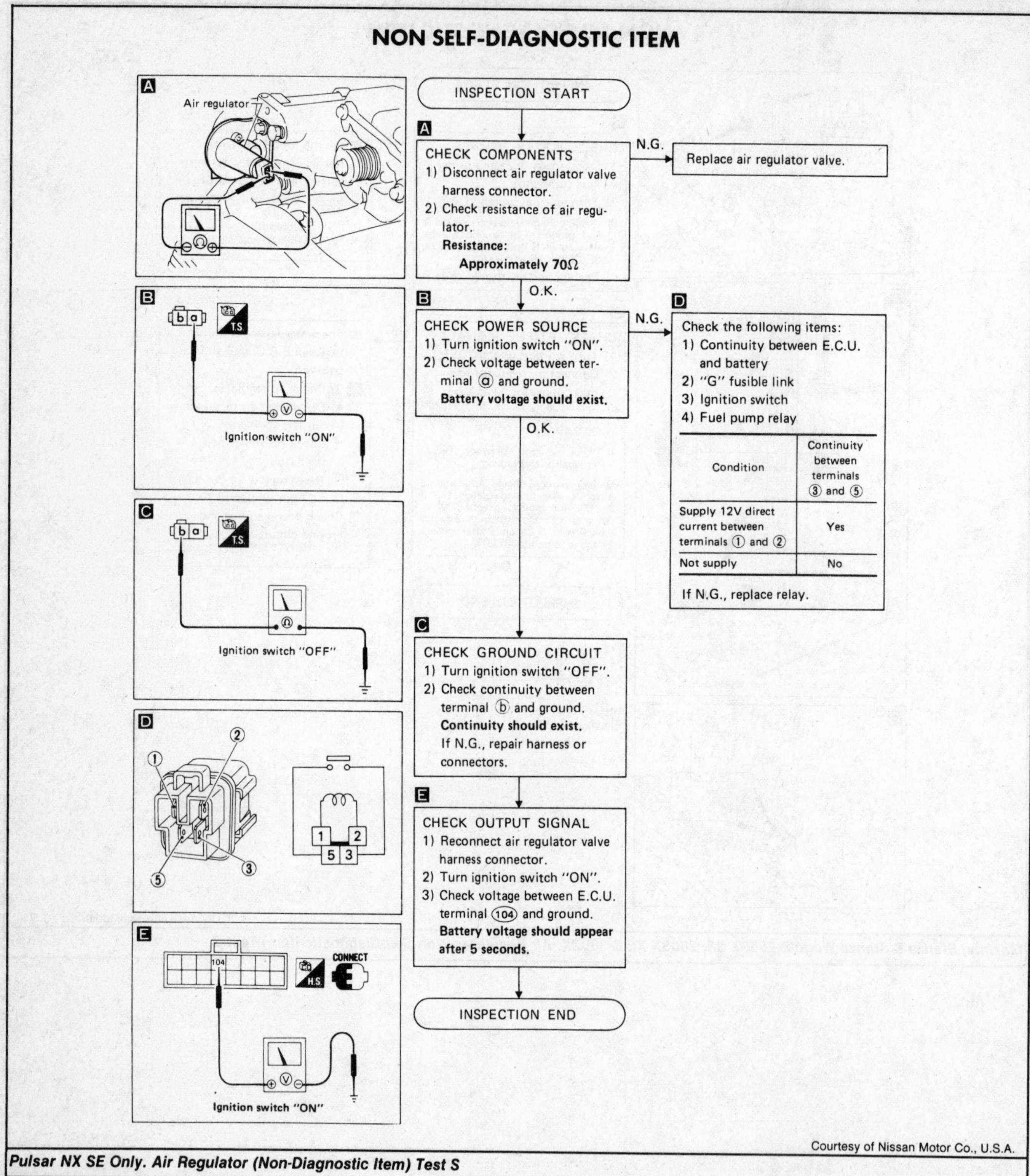
NON SELF-DIAGNOSTIC ITEM
A
Air regulator
B
b a
T.S.
Ignition switch "ON"
C
b a
T.S.
Ignition switch "OFF"
D
1
2
3
5
1 2
5 3
E
104
H.S.
CONNECT
Ignition switch "ON"
INSPECTION START
A
CHECK COMPONENTS
1) Disconnect air regulator valve harness connector.
2) Check resistance of air regulator.
Resistance:
Approximately 70Ω
N.G.
Replace air regulator valve.
O.K.
B
CHECK POWER SOURCE
1) Turn ignition switch "ON".
2) Check voltage between terminal ⓐ and ground.
Battery voltage should exist.
N.G.
D
Check the following items:
1) Continuity between E.C.U. and battery
2) "G" fusible link
3) Ignition switch
4) Fuel pump relay
Condition
Continuity between terminals ③ and ⑤
Supply 12V direct current between terminals ① and ②
Yes
Not supply
No
If N.G., replace relay.
O.K.
C
CHECK GROUND CIRCUIT
1) Turn ignition switch "OFF".
2) Check continuity between terminal ⓑ and ground.
Continuity should exist.
If N.G., repair harness or connectors.
E
CHECK OUTPUT SIGNAL
1) Reconnect air regulator valve harness connector.
2) Turn ignition switch "ON".
3) Check voltage between E.C.U. terminal (104) and ground.
Battery voltage should appear after 5 seconds.
INSPECTION END
Courtesy of Nissan Motor Co., U.S.A.

*Pulsar NX SE Only. Air Regulator (Non-Diagnostic Item) Test S*

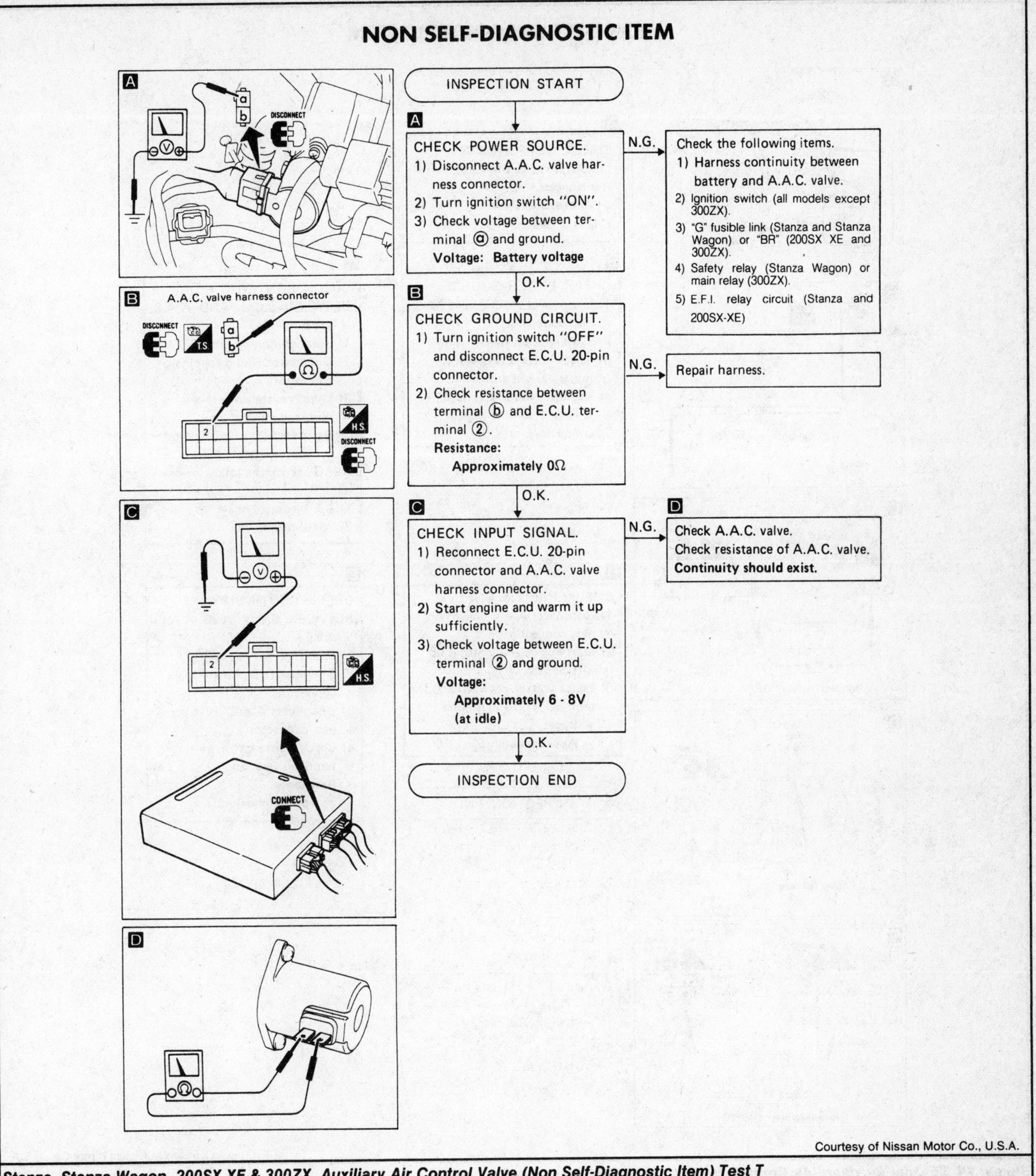
NON SELF-DIAGNOSTIC ITEM
A
DISCONNECT
a
b
B
A.A.C. valve harness connector
DISCONNECT
T.S.
H.S.
2
C
H.S.
CONNECT
D
INSPECTION START
A
CHECK POWER SOURCE.
1) Disconnect A.A.C. valve harness connector.
2) Turn ignition switch "ON".
3) Check voltage between terminal ⓐ and ground.
Voltage: Battery voltage
N.G.
Check the following items.
1) Harness continuity between battery and A.A.C. valve.
2) Ignition switch (all models except 300ZX).
3) "G" fusible link (Stanza and Stanza Wagon) or "BR" (200SX XE and 300ZX).
4) Safety relay (Stanza Wagon) or main relay (300ZX).
5) E.F.I. relay circuit (Stanza and 200SX-XE)
O.K.
B
CHECK GROUND CIRCUIT.
1) Turn ignition switch "OFF" and disconnect E.C.U. 20-pin connector.
2) Check resistance between terminal ⓑ and E.C.U. terminal ②.
Resistance:
Approximately 0Ω
N.G.
Repair harness.
O.K.
C
CHECK INPUT SIGNAL.
1) Reconnect E.C.U. 20-pin connector and A.A.C. valve harness connector.
2) Start engine and warm it up sufficiently.
3) Check voltage between E.C.U. terminal ② and ground.
Voltage:
Approximately 6 - 8V
(at idle)
N.G.
D
Check A.A.C. valve.
Check resistance of A.A.C. valve.
Continuity should exist.
O.K.
INSPECTION END

Courtesy of Nissan Motor Co., U.S.A.

***Stanza, Stanza Wagon, 200SX XE & 300ZX. Auxiliary Air Control Valve (Non Self-Diagnostic Item) Test T***

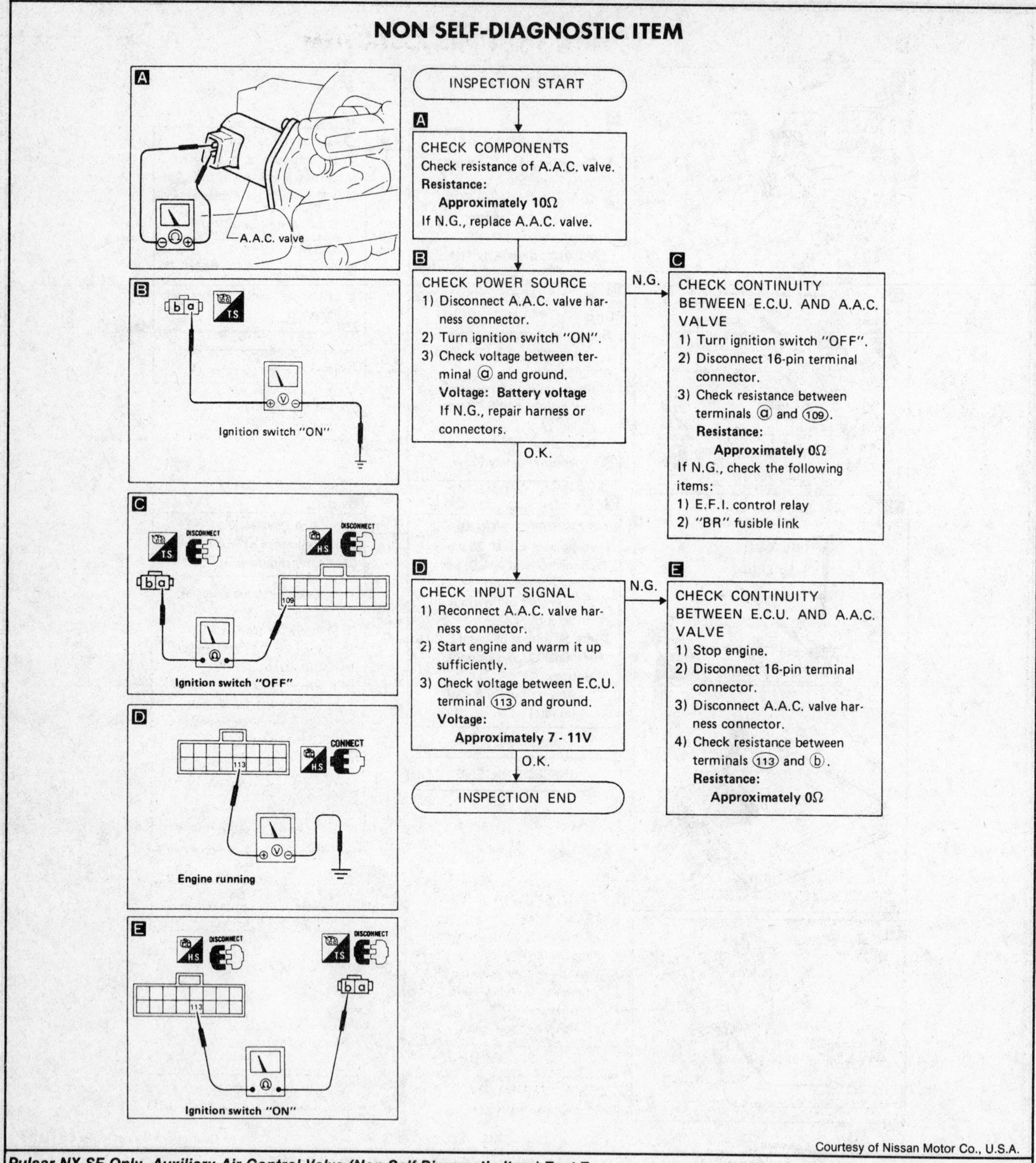
NON SELF-DIAGNOSTIC ITEM
A
A.A.C. valve
B
Ignition switch "ON"
C
DISCONNECT
DISCONNECT
109
Ignition switch "OFF"
D
CONNECT
113
Engine running
E
DISCONNECT
DISCONNECT
113
Ignition switch "ON"
INSPECTION START
A
CHECK COMPONENTS
Check resistance of A.A.C. valve.
Resistance:
Approximately 10Ω
If N.G., replace A.A.C. valve.
B
CHECK POWER SOURCE
1) Disconnect A.A.C. valve harness connector.
2) Turn ignition switch "ON".
3) Check voltage between terminal ⓐ and ground.
Voltage: Battery voltage
If N.G., repair harness or connectors.
N.G.
C
CHECK CONTINUITY BETWEEN E.C.U. AND A.A.C. VALVE
1) Turn ignition switch "OFF".
2) Disconnect 16-pin terminal connector.
3) Check resistance between terminals ⓐ and (109).
Resistance:
Approximately 0Ω
If N.G., check the following items:
1) E.F.I. control relay
2) "BR" fusible link
O.K.
D
CHECK INPUT SIGNAL
1) Reconnect A.A.C. valve harness connector.
2) Start engine and warm it up sufficiently.
3) Check voltage between E.C.U. terminal (113) and ground.
Voltage:
Approximately 7 - 11V
N.G.
E
CHECK CONTINUITY BETWEEN E.C.U. AND A.A.C. VALVE
1) Stop engine.
2) Disconnect 16-pin terminal connector.
3) Disconnect A.A.C. valve harness connector.
4) Check resistance between terminals (113) and ⓑ.
Resistance:
Approximately 0Ω
O.K.
INSPECTION END
Courtesy of Nissan Motor Co., U.S.A.

***Pulsar NX SE Only. Auxiliary Air Control Valve (Non Self-Diagnostic Item) Test T***

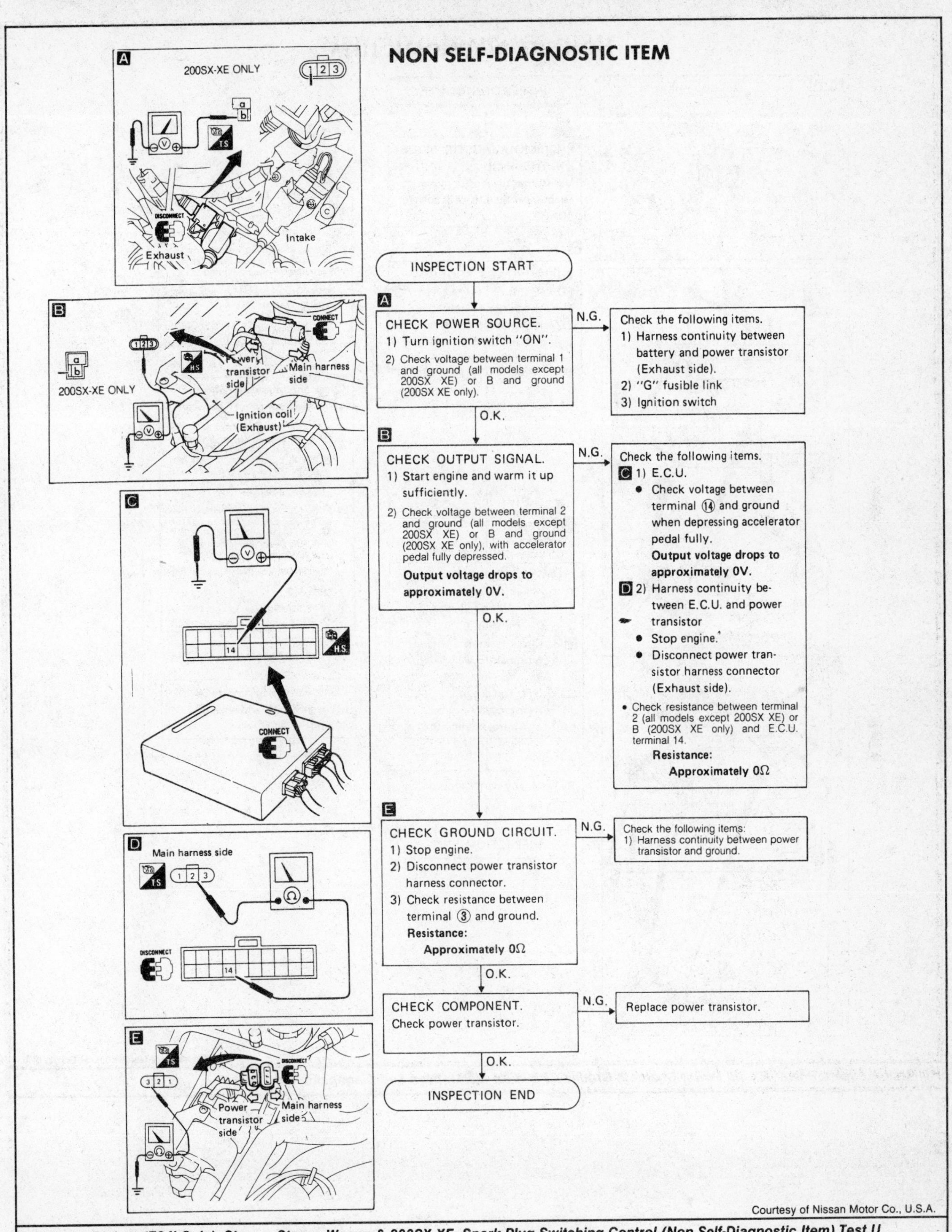
NON SELF-DIAGNOSTIC ITEM
A
200SX-XE ONLY
a
b
TS
DISCONNECT
Exhaust
Intake
B
200SX-XE ONLY
CONNECT
HS
Power transistor side
Main harness side
Ignition coil (Exhaust)
C
14
H.S.
CONNECT
D
Main harness side
TS
1 2 3
DISCONNECT
14
E
TS
DISCONNECT
3 2 1
Power transistor side
Main harness side
INSPECTION START
A
CHECK POWER SOURCE.
1) Turn ignition switch "ON".
2) Check voltage between terminal 1 and ground (all models except 200SX XE) or B and ground (200SX XE only).
N.G.
Check the following items.
1) Harness continuity between battery and power transistor (Exhaust side).
2) "G" fusible link
3) Ignition switch
O.K.
B
CHECK OUTPUT SIGNAL.
1) Start engine and warm it up sufficiently.
2) Check voltage between terminal 2 and ground (all models except 200SX XE) or B and ground (200SX XE only), with accelerator pedal fully depressed.
Output voltage drops to approximately 0V.
N.G.
Check the following items.
C 1) E.C.U.
• Check voltage between terminal ⑭ and ground when depressing accelerator pedal fully.
Output voltage drops to approximately 0V.
D 2) Harness continuity between E.C.U. and power transistor
• Stop engine.
• Disconnect power transistor harness connector (Exhaust side).
• Check resistance between terminal 2 (all models except 200SX XE) or B (200SX XE only) and E.C.U. terminal 14.
Resistance:
Approximately 0Ω
O.K.
E
CHECK GROUND CIRCUIT.
1) Stop engine.
2) Disconnect power transistor harness connector.
3) Check resistance between terminal ③ and ground.
Resistance:
Approximately 0Ω
N.G.
Check the following items:
1) Harness continuity between power transistor and ground.
O.K.
CHECK COMPONENT.
Check power transistor.
N.G.
Replace power transistor.
O.K.
INSPECTION END
Courtesy of Nissan Motor Co., U.S.A.

*Pathfinder/Pickup (Z24i Only), Stanza, Stanza Wagon & 200SX XE. Spark Plug Switching Control (Non Self-Diagnostic Item) Test U*

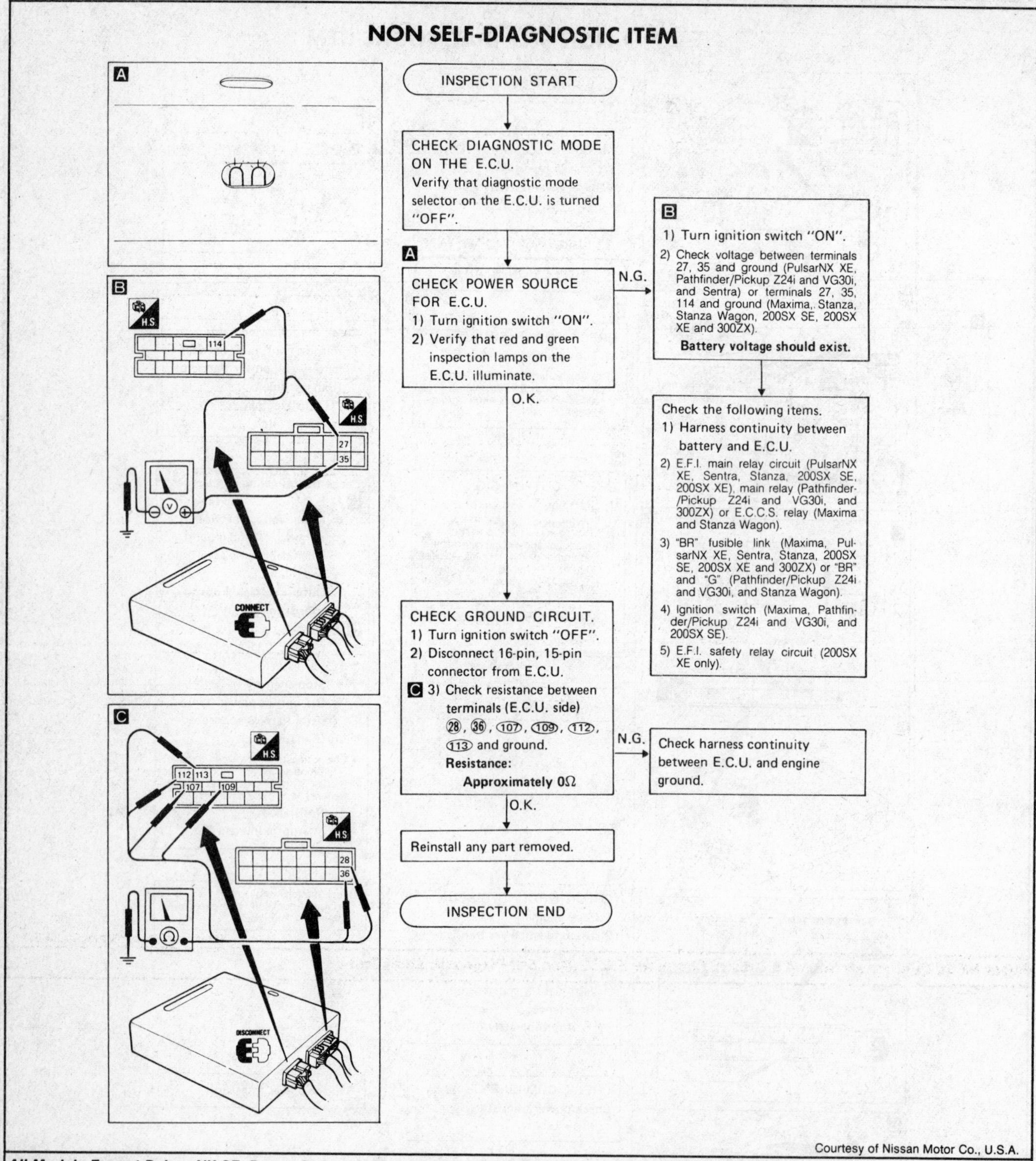
NON SELF-DIAGNOSTIC ITEM
A
B
H.S.
114
H.S.
27
35
CONNECT
C
H.S.
112
113
107
109
H.S.
28
36
DISCONNECT
INSPECTION START
CHECK DIAGNOSTIC MODE ON THE E.C.U.
Verify that diagnostic mode selector on the E.C.U. is turned "OFF".
A
CHECK POWER SOURCE FOR E.C.U.
1) Turn ignition switch "ON".
2) Verify that red and green inspection lamps on the E.C.U. illuminate.
N.G.
B
1) Turn ignition switch "ON".
2) Check voltage between terminals 27, 35 and ground (PulsarNX XE, Pathfinder/Pickup Z24i and VG30i, and Sentra) or terminals 27, 35, 114 and ground (Maxima, Stanza, Stanza Wagon, 200SX SE, 200SX XE and 300ZX).
Battery voltage should exist.
Check the following items.
1) Harness continuity between battery and E.C.U.
2) E.F.I. main relay circuit (PulsarNX XE, Sentra, Stanza, 200SX SE, 200SX XE), main relay (Pathfinder-/Pickup Z24i and VG30i, and 300ZX) or E.C.C.S. relay (Maxima and Stanza Wagon).
3) "BR" fusible link (Maxima, PulsarNX XE, Sentra, Stanza, 200SX SE, 200SX XE and 300ZX) or "BR" and "G" (Pathfinder/Pickup Z24i and VG30i, and Stanza Wagon).
4) Ignition switch (Maxima, Pathfinder/Pickup Z24i and VG30i, and 200SX SE).
5) E.F.I. safety relay circuit (200SX XE only).
O.K.
CHECK GROUND CIRCUIT.
1) Turn ignition switch "OFF".
2) Disconnect 16-pin, 15-pin connector from E.C.U.
C 3) Check resistance between terminals (E.C.U. side) 28, 36, 107, 109, 112, 113 and ground.
Resistance:
Approximately 0Ω
N.G.
Check harness continuity between E.C.U. and engine ground.
O.K.
Reinstall any part removed.
INSPECTION END
Courtesy of Nissan Motor Co., U.S.A.

*All Models Except Pulsar NX SE. Power Source & Ground Circuit for E.C.U. (Non Self-Diagnostic Item) Test V*

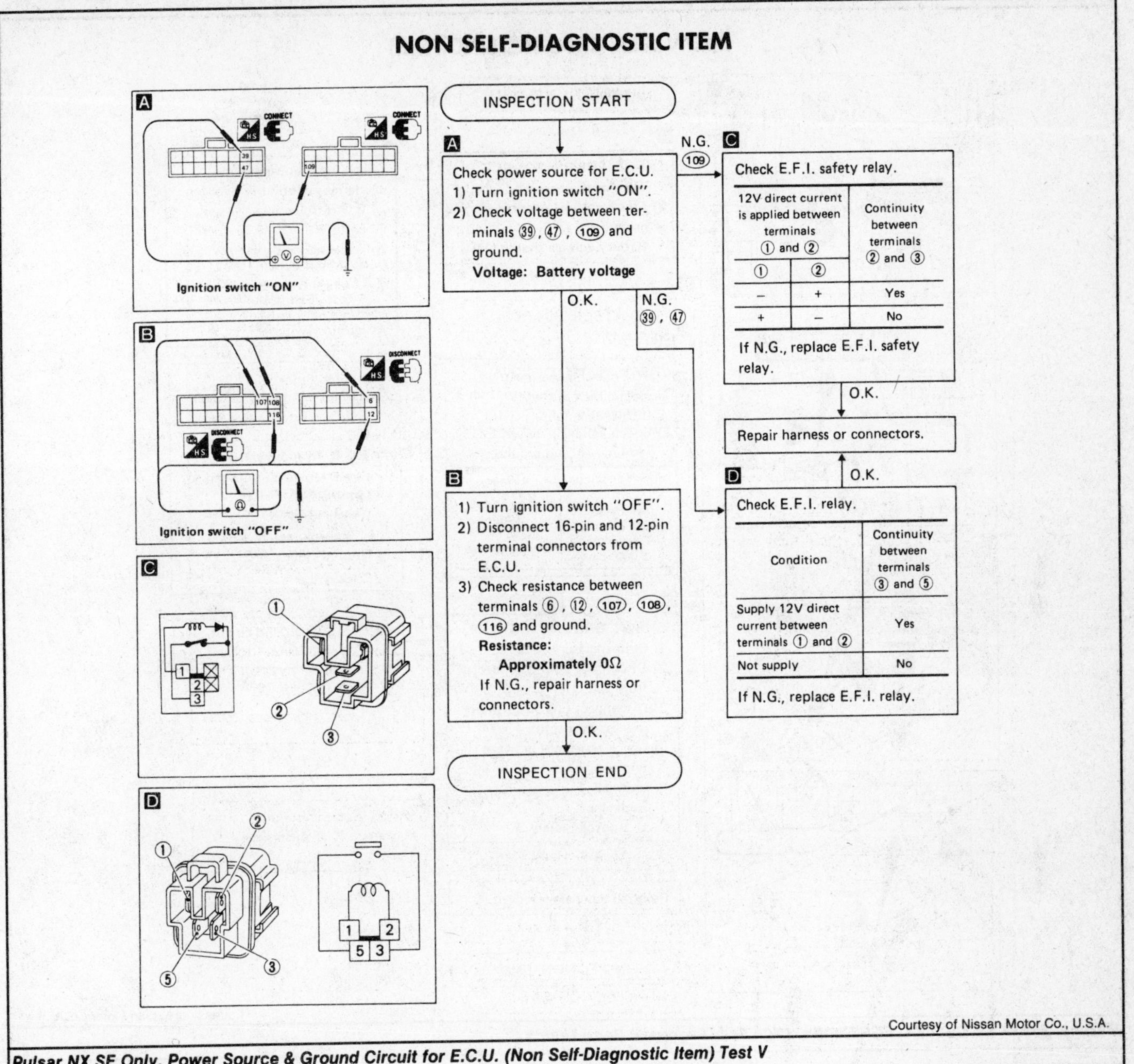
NON SELF-DIAGNOSTIC ITEM
A
CONNECT
39
47
109
Ignition switch "ON"
B
DISCONNECT
107 108
116
6
12
Ignition switch "OFF"
C
1
2
3
D
1
2
3
5
INSPECTION START
A
Check power source for E.C.U.
1) Turn ignition switch "ON".
2) Check voltage between terminals 39, 47, 109 and ground.
Voltage: Battery voltage
N.G. 109
C
Check E.F.I. safety relay.
12V direct current is applied between terminals 1 and 2
Continuity between terminals 2 and 3
– + Yes
+ – No
If N.G., replace E.F.I. safety relay.
O.K.
Repair harness or connectors.
O.K.
N.G. 39, 47
D
Check E.F.I. relay.
Condition
Continuity between terminals 3 and 5
Supply 12V direct current between terminals 1 and 2 Yes
Not supply No
If N.G., replace E.F.I. relay.
O.K.
B
1) Turn ignition switch "OFF".
2) Disconnect 16-pin and 12-pin terminal connectors from E.C.U.
3) Check resistance between terminals 6, 12, 107, 108, 116 and ground.
Resistance:
Approximately 0Ω
If N.G., repair harness or connectors.
O.K.
INSPECTION END
Courtesy of Nissan Motor Co., U.S.A.

***Pulsar NX SE Only. Power Source & Ground Circuit for E.C.U. (Non Self-Diagnostic Item) Test V***

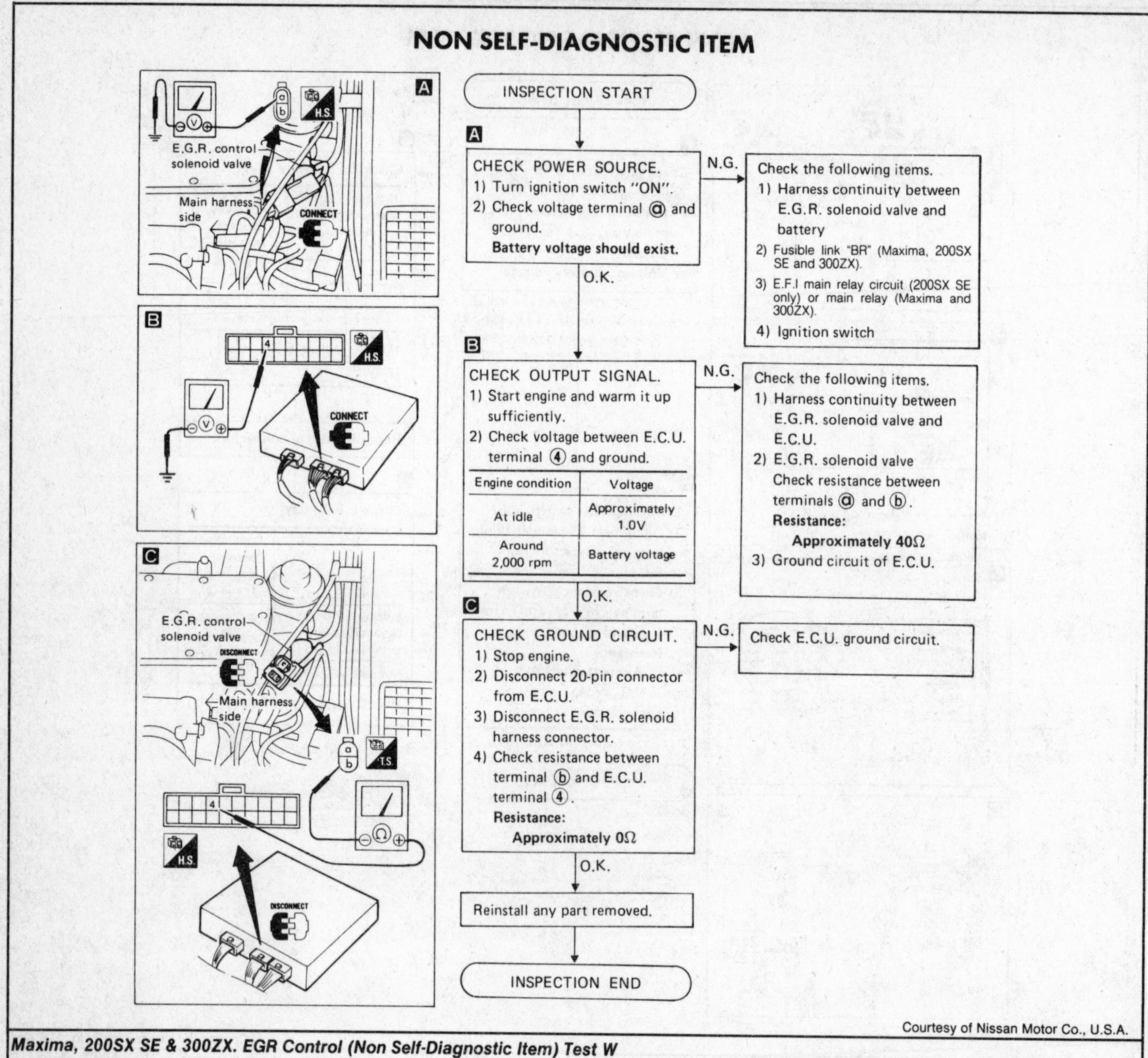
NON SELF-DIAGNOSTIC ITEM
A
E.G.R. control solenoid valve
Main harness side
CONNECT
H.S.
B
4
CONNECT
H.S.
C
E.G.R. control solenoid valve
DISCONNECT
Main harness side
T.S.
4
H.S.
DISCONNECT
INSPECTION START
A
CHECK POWER SOURCE.
1) Turn ignition switch "ON".
2) Check voltage terminal ⓐ and ground.
Battery voltage should exist.
N.G.
Check the following items.
1) Harness continuity between E.G.R. solenoid valve and battery
2) Fusible link "BR" (Maxima, 200SX SE and 300ZX).
3) E.F.I main relay circuit (200SX SE only) or main relay (Maxima and 300ZX).
4) Ignition switch
O.K.
B
CHECK OUTPUT SIGNAL.
1) Start engine and warm it up sufficiently.
2) Check voltage between E.C.U. terminal ④ and ground.
Engine condition
Voltage
At idle
Approximately 1.0V
Around 2,000 rpm
Battery voltage
N.G.
Check the following items.
1) Harness continuity between E.G.R. solenoid valve and E.C.U.
2) E.G.R. solenoid valve Check resistance between terminals ⓐ and ⓑ.
Resistance:
Approximately 40Ω
3) Ground circuit of E.C.U.
O.K.
C
CHECK GROUND CIRCUIT.
1) Stop engine.
2) Disconnect 20-pin connector from E.C.U.
3) Disconnect E.G.R. solenoid harness connector.
4) Check resistance between terminal ⓑ and E.C.U. terminal ④.
Resistance:
Approximately 0Ω
N.G.
Check E.C.U. ground circuit.
O.K.
Reinstall any part removed.
INSPECTION END
Courtesy of Nissan Motor Co., U.S.A.

*Maxima, 200SX SE & 300ZX. EGR Control (Non Self-Diagnostic Item) Test W*

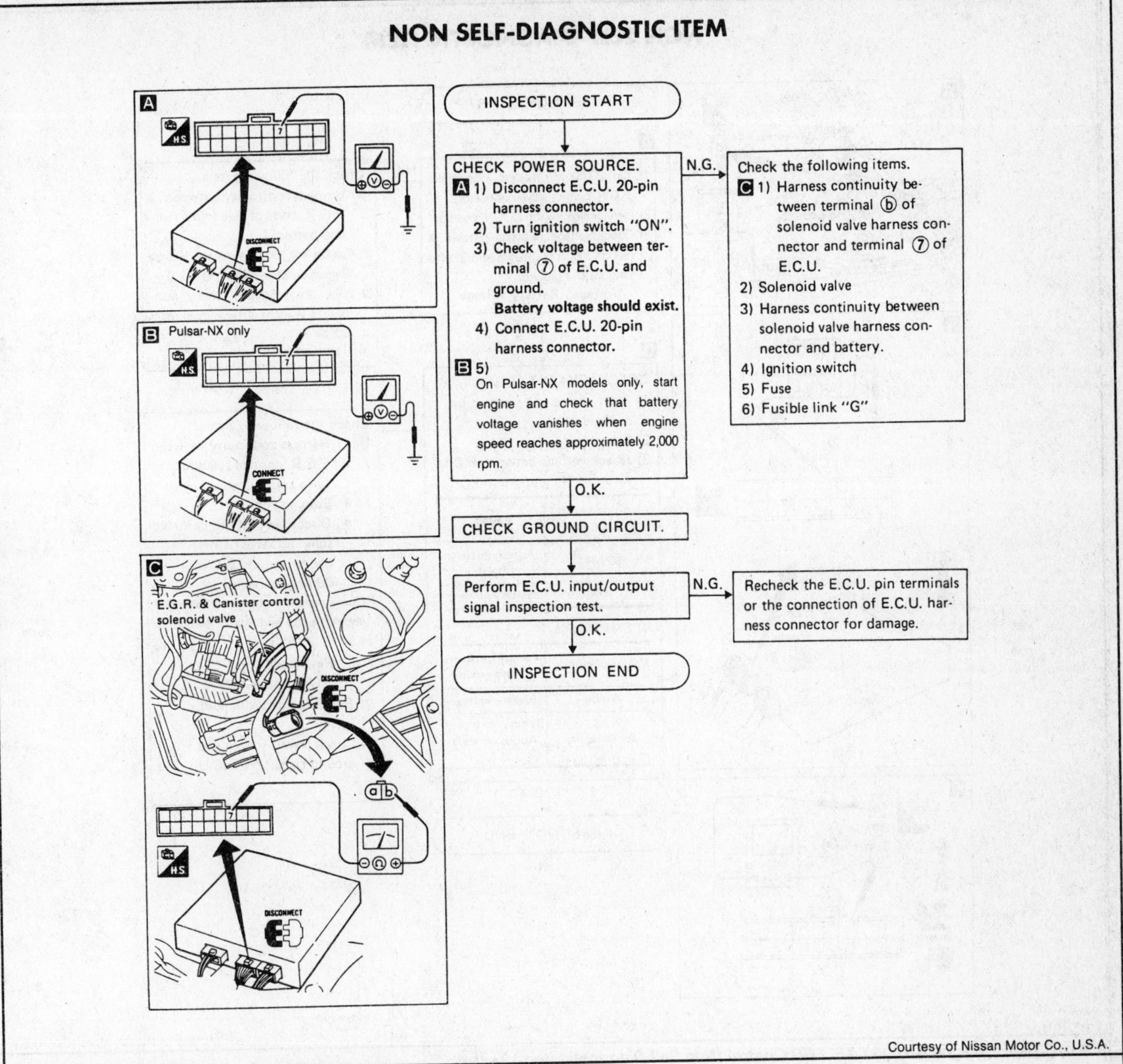
NON SELF-DIAGNOSTIC ITEM
A
DISCONNECT
B Pulsar-NX only
CONNECT
C
E.G.R. & Canister control solenoid valve
DISCONNECT
INSPECTION START
CHECK POWER SOURCE.
A 1) Disconnect E.C.U. 20-pin harness connector.
2) Turn ignition switch "ON".
3) Check voltage between terminal ⑦ of E.C.U. and ground.
Battery voltage should exist.
4) Connect E.C.U. 20-pin harness connector.
B 5) On Pulsar-NX models only, start engine and check that battery voltage vanishes when engine speed reaches approximately 2,000 rpm.
N.G.
Check the following items.
C 1) Harness continuity between terminal ⓑ of solenoid valve harness connector and terminal ⑦ of E.C.U.
2) Solenoid valve
3) Harness continuity between solenoid valve harness connector and battery.
4) Ignition switch
5) Fuse
6) Fusible link "G"
O.K.
CHECK GROUND CIRCUIT.
Perform E.C.U. input/output signal inspection test.
N.G.
Recheck the E.C.U. pin terminals or the connection of E.C.U. harness connector for damage.
O.K.
INSPECTION END
Courtesy of Nissan Motor Co., U.S.A.

*Pulsar NX XE & Sentra. EGR Control & Canister Purge Solenoid Control Valve (Non Self-Diagnostic Item) Test W*

# Nissan Electronic Concentrated Control System (Cont.)

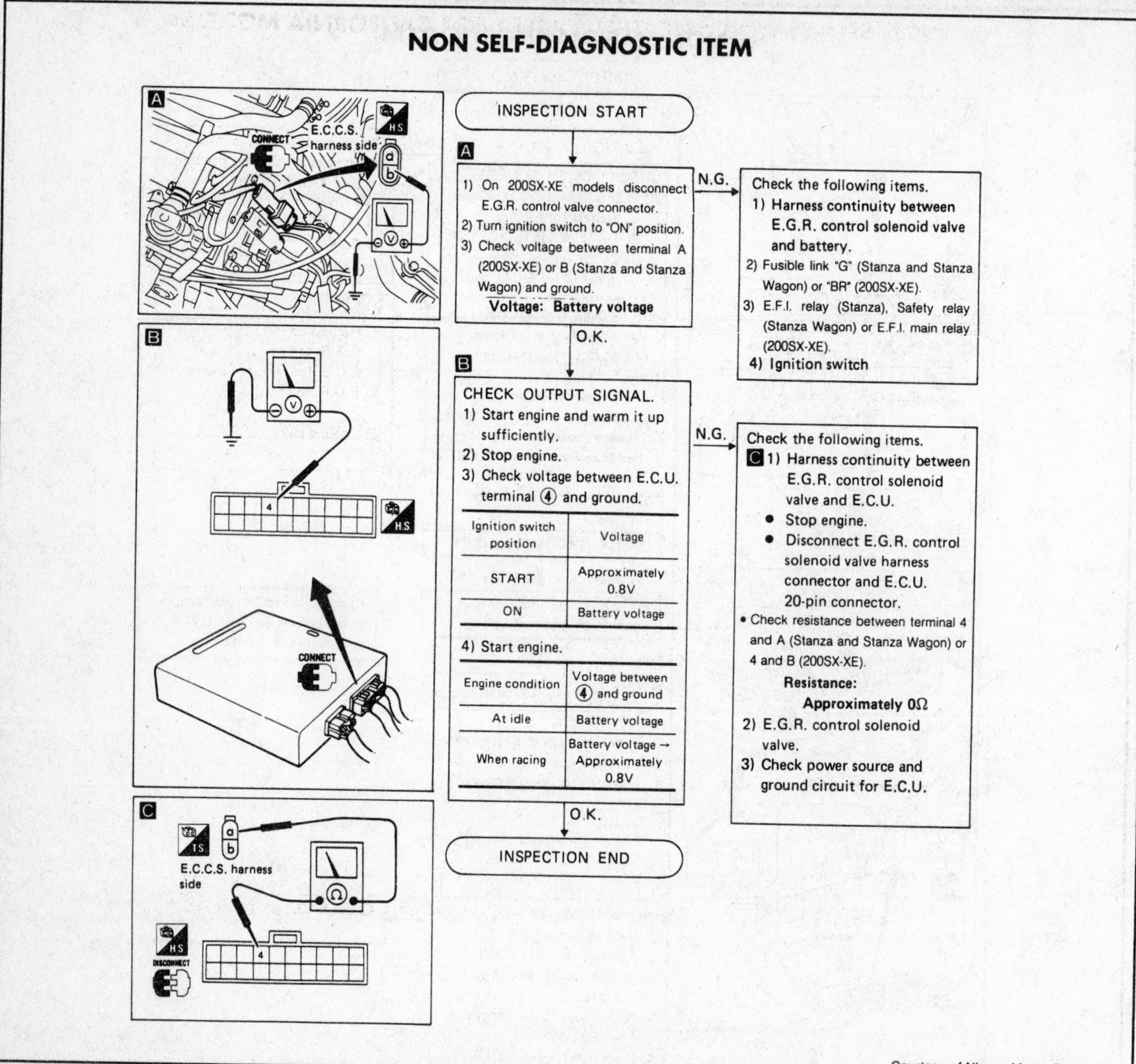
NON SELF-DIAGNOSTIC ITEM
A
CONNECT
E.C.C.S. harness side
HS
INSPECTION START
A
1) On 200SX-XE models disconnect E.G.R. control valve connector.
2) Turn ignition switch to "ON" position.
3) Check voltage between terminal A (200SX-XE) or B (Stanza and Stanza Wagon) and ground.
Voltage: Battery voltage
N.G.
Check the following items.
1) Harness continuity between E.G.R. control solenoid valve and battery.
2) Fusible link "G" (Stanza and Stanza Wagon) or "BR" (200SX-XE).
3) E.F.I. relay (Stanza), Safety relay (Stanza Wagon) or E.F.I. main relay (200SX-XE).
4) Ignition switch
O.K.
B
CHECK OUTPUT SIGNAL.
1) Start engine and warm it up sufficiently.
2) Stop engine.
3) Check voltage between E.C.U. terminal ④ and ground.
Ignition switch position | Voltage
START | Approximately 0.8V
ON | Battery voltage
4) Start engine.
Engine condition | Voltage between ④ and ground
At idle | Battery voltage
When racing | Battery voltage → Approximately 0.8V
N.G.
Check the following items.
C 1) Harness continuity between E.G.R. control solenoid valve and E.C.U.
• Stop engine.
• Disconnect E.G.R. control solenoid valve harness connector and E.C.U. 20-pin connector.
• Check resistance between terminal 4 and A (Stanza and Stanza Wagon) or 4 and B (200SX-XE).
Resistance: Approximately 0Ω
2) E.G.R. control solenoid valve.
3) Check power source and ground circuit for E.C.U.
O.K.
INSPECTION END
B
4
HS
CONNECT
C
TS
a
b
E.C.C.S. harness side
HS
DISCONNECT
4

Courtesy of Nissan Motor Co., U.S.A.

*Stanza, Stanza Wagon & 200SX XE. EGR Control (Non Self-Diagnostic Item) Test W*

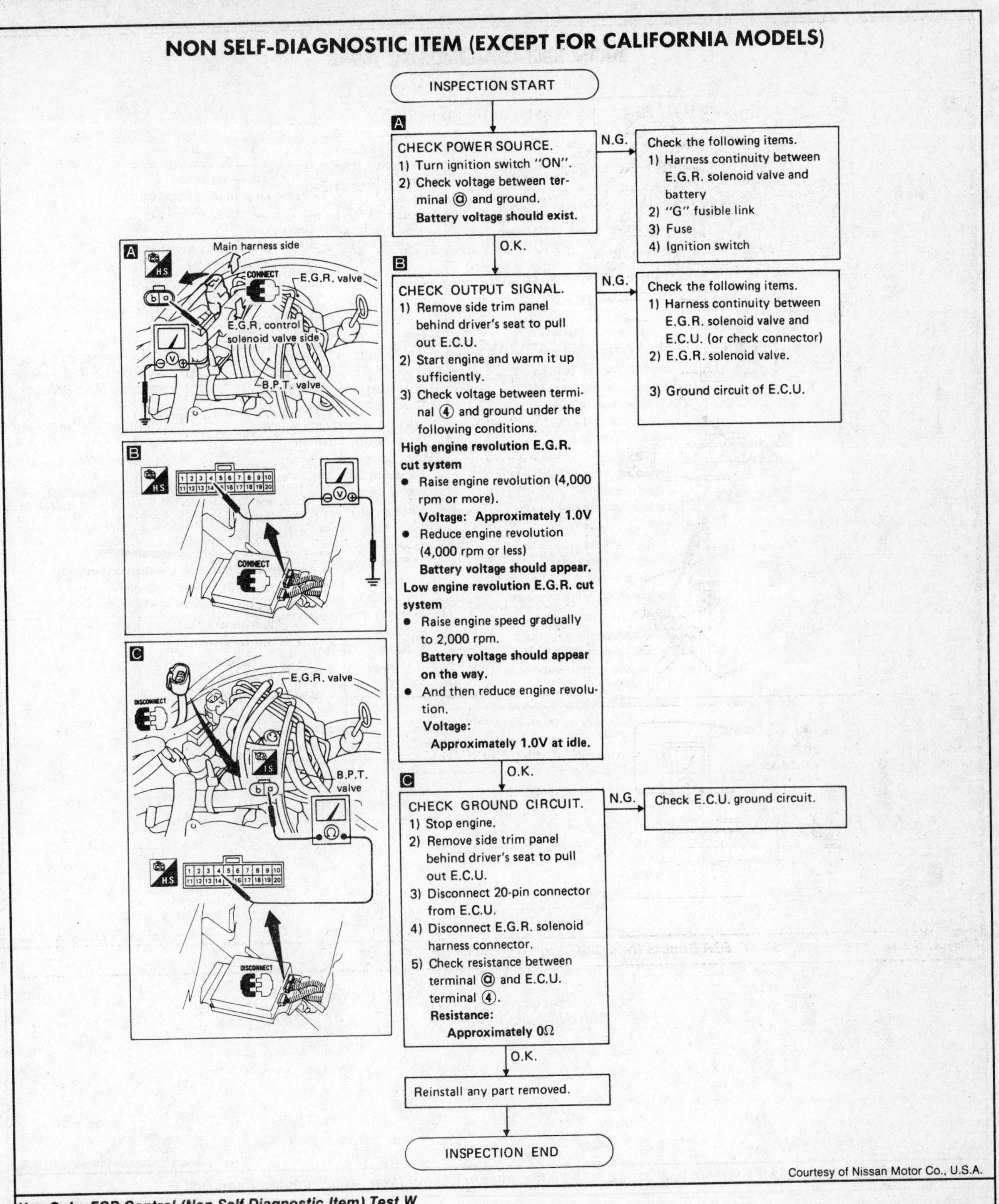
NON SELF-DIAGNOSTIC ITEM (EXCEPT FOR CALIFORNIA MODELS)
INSPECTION START
A
CHECK POWER SOURCE.
1) Turn ignition switch "ON".
2) Check voltage between terminal ⓐ and ground.
Battery voltage should exist.
N.G.
Check the following items.
1) Harness continuity between E.G.R. solenoid valve and battery
2) "G" fusible link
3) Fuse
4) Ignition switch
O.K.
B
CHECK OUTPUT SIGNAL.
1) Remove side trim panel behind driver's seat to pull out E.C.U.
2) Start engine and warm it up sufficiently.
3) Check voltage between terminal ④ and ground under the following conditions.
High engine revolution E.G.R. cut system
● Raise engine revolution (4,000 rpm or more).
Voltage: Approximately 1.0V
● Reduce engine revolution (4,000 rpm or less)
Battery voltage should appear.
Low engine revolution E.G.R. cut system
● Raise engine speed gradually to 2,000 rpm.
Battery voltage should appear on the way.
● And then reduce engine revolution.
Voltage:
Approximately 1.0V at idle.
N.G.
Check the following items.
1) Harness continuity between E.G.R. solenoid valve and E.C.U. (or check connector)
2) E.G.R. solenoid valve.
3) Ground circuit of E.C.U.
O.K.
C
CHECK GROUND CIRCUIT.
1) Stop engine.
2) Remove side trim panel behind driver's seat to pull out E.C.U.
3) Disconnect 20-pin connector from E.C.U.
4) Disconnect E.G.R. solenoid harness connector.
5) Check resistance between terminal ⓐ and E.C.U. terminal ④.
Resistance:
Approximately 0Ω
N.G.
Check E.C.U. ground circuit.
O.K.
Reinstall any part removed.
INSPECTION END
A
Main harness side
CONNECT
E.G.R. valve
E.G.R. control solenoid valve side
B.P.T. valve
B
CONNECT
C
E.G.R. valve
DISCONNECT
B.P.T. valve
DISCONNECT

Courtesy of Nissan Motor Co., U.S.A.

*Van Only. EGR Control (Non Self-Diagnostic Item) Test W*

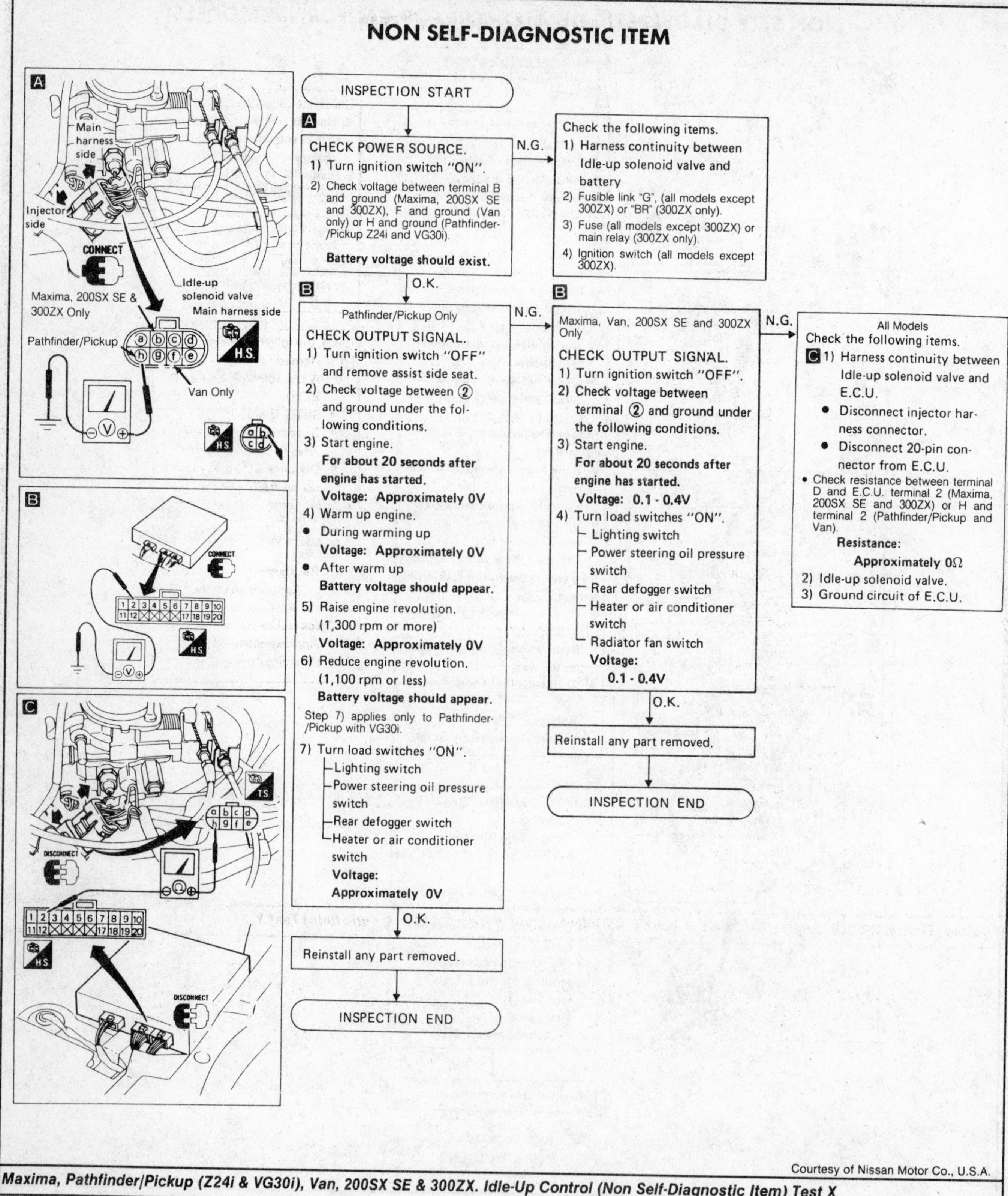
NON SELF-DIAGNOSTIC ITEM
A
Main harness side
Injector side
CONNECT
Idle-up solenoid valve
Maxima, 200SX SE & 300ZX Only
Main harness side
Pathfinder/Pickup
a b c d
h g f e
H.S.
Van Only
B
CONNECT
1 2 3 4 5 6 7 8 9 10
11 12 17 18 19 20
H.S
C
T.S
DISCONNECT
1 2 3 4 5 6 7 8 9 10
11 12 17 18 19 20
H.S
DISCONNECT
INSPECTION START
A
CHECK POWER SOURCE.
1) Turn ignition switch "ON".
2) Check voltage between terminal B and ground (Maxima, 200SX SE and 300ZX), F and ground (Van only) or H and ground (Pathfinder-/Pickup Z24i and VG30i).
Battery voltage should exist.
N.G.
Check the following items.
1) Harness continuity between Idle-up solenoid valve and battery
2) Fusible link "G", (all models except 300ZX) or "BR" (300ZX only).
3) Fuse (all models except 300ZX) or main relay (300ZX only).
4) Ignition switch (all models except 300ZX).
O.K.
B
Pathfinder/Pickup Only
CHECK OUTPUT SIGNAL.
1) Turn ignition switch "OFF" and remove assist side seat.
2) Check voltage between ② and ground under the following conditions.
3) Start engine.
For about 20 seconds after engine has started.
Voltage: Approximately 0V
4) Warm up engine.
• During warming up
Voltage: Approximately 0V
• After warm up
Battery voltage should appear.
5) Raise engine revolution. (1,300 rpm or more)
Voltage: Approximately 0V
6) Reduce engine revolution. (1,100 rpm or less)
Battery voltage should appear.
Step 7) applies only to Pathfinder-/Pickup with VG30i.
7) Turn load switches "ON".
Lighting switch
Power steering oil pressure switch
Rear defogger switch
Heater or air conditioner switch
Voltage:
Approximately 0V
O.K.
Reinstall any part removed.
INSPECTION END
N.G.
B
Maxima, Van, 200SX SE and 300ZX Only
CHECK OUTPUT SIGNAL.
1) Turn ignition switch "OFF".
2) Check voltage between terminal ② and ground under the following conditions.
3) Start engine.
For about 20 seconds after engine has started.
Voltage: 0.1 - 0.4V
4) Turn load switches "ON".
Lighting switch
Power steering oil pressure switch
Rear defogger switch
Heater or air conditioner switch
Radiator fan switch
Voltage:
0.1 - 0.4V
O.K.
Reinstall any part removed.
INSPECTION END
N.G.
All Models
Check the following items.
C 1) Harness continuity between Idle-up solenoid valve and E.C.U.
• Disconnect injector harness connector.
• Disconnect 20-pin connector from E.C.U.
• Check resistance between terminal D and E.C.U. terminal 2 (Maxima, 200SX SE and 300ZX) or H and terminal 2 (Pathfinder/Pickup and Van).
Resistance:
Approximately 0Ω
2) Idle-up solenoid valve.
3) Ground circuit of E.C.U.

Courtesy of Nissan Motor Co., U.S.A.

*Maxima, Pathfinder/Pickup (Z24i & VG30i), Van, 200SX SE & 300ZX. Idle-Up Control (Non Self-Diagnostic Item) Test X*

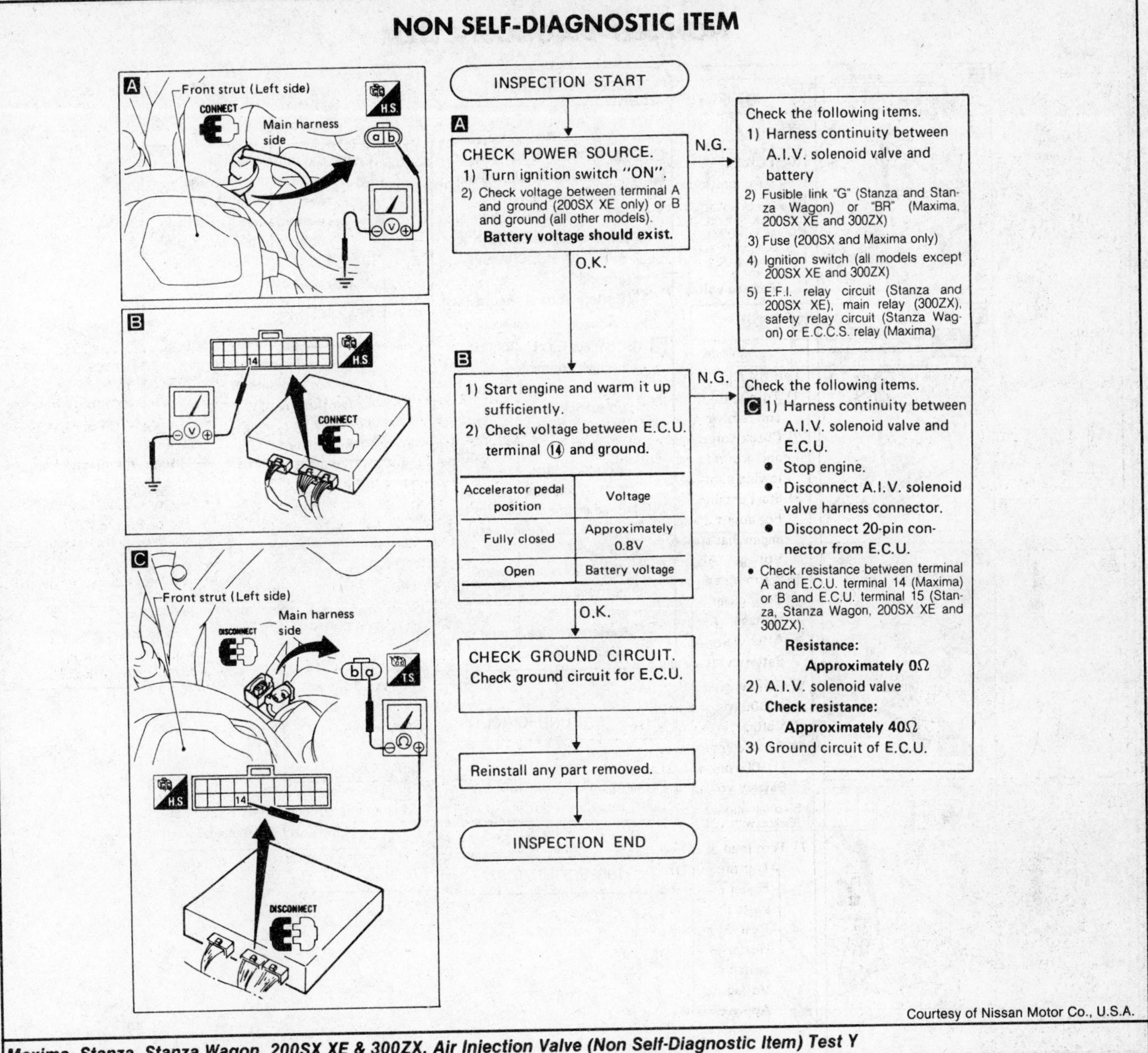
NON SELF-DIAGNOSTIC ITEM
A
Front strut (Left side)
CONNECT
Main harness side
H.S.
a b
B
14
H.S.
CONNECT
C
Front strut (Left side)
DISCONNECT
Main harness side
b a
T.S.
H.S.
14
DISCONNECT
INSPECTION START
A
CHECK POWER SOURCE.
1) Turn ignition switch "ON".
2) Check voltage between terminal A and ground (200SX XE only) or B and ground (all other models).
Battery voltage should exist.
N.G.
O.K.
Check the following items.
1) Harness continuity between A.I.V. solenoid valve and battery
2) Fusible link "G" (Stanza and Stanza Wagon) or "BR" (Maxima, 200SX XE and 300ZX)
3) Fuse (200SX and Maxima only)
4) Ignition switch (all models except 200SX XE and 300ZX)
5) E.F.I. relay circuit (Stanza and 200SX XE), main relay (300ZX), safety relay circuit (Stanza Wagon) or E.C.C.S. relay (Maxima)
B
1) Start engine and warm it up sufficiently.
2) Check voltage between E.C.U. terminal ⑭ and ground.
Accelerator pedal position
Voltage
Fully closed
Approximately 0.8V
Open
Battery voltage
N.G.
Check the following items.
C 1) Harness continuity between A.I.V. solenoid valve and E.C.U.
● Stop engine.
● Disconnect A.I.V. solenoid valve harness connector.
● Disconnect 20-pin connector from E.C.U.
• Check resistance between terminal A and E.C.U. terminal 14 (Maxima) or B and E.C.U. terminal 15 (Stanza, Stanza Wagon, 200SX XE and 300ZX).
Resistance:
Approximately 0Ω
2) A.I.V. solenoid valve
Check resistance:
Approximately 40Ω
3) Ground circuit of E.C.U.
O.K.
CHECK GROUND CIRCUIT.
Check ground circuit for E.C.U.
Reinstall any part removed.
INSPECTION END
Courtesy of Nissan Motor Co., U.S.A.

*Maxima, Stanza, Stanza Wagon, 200SX XE & 300ZX. Air Injection Valve (Non Self-Diagnostic Item) Test Y*

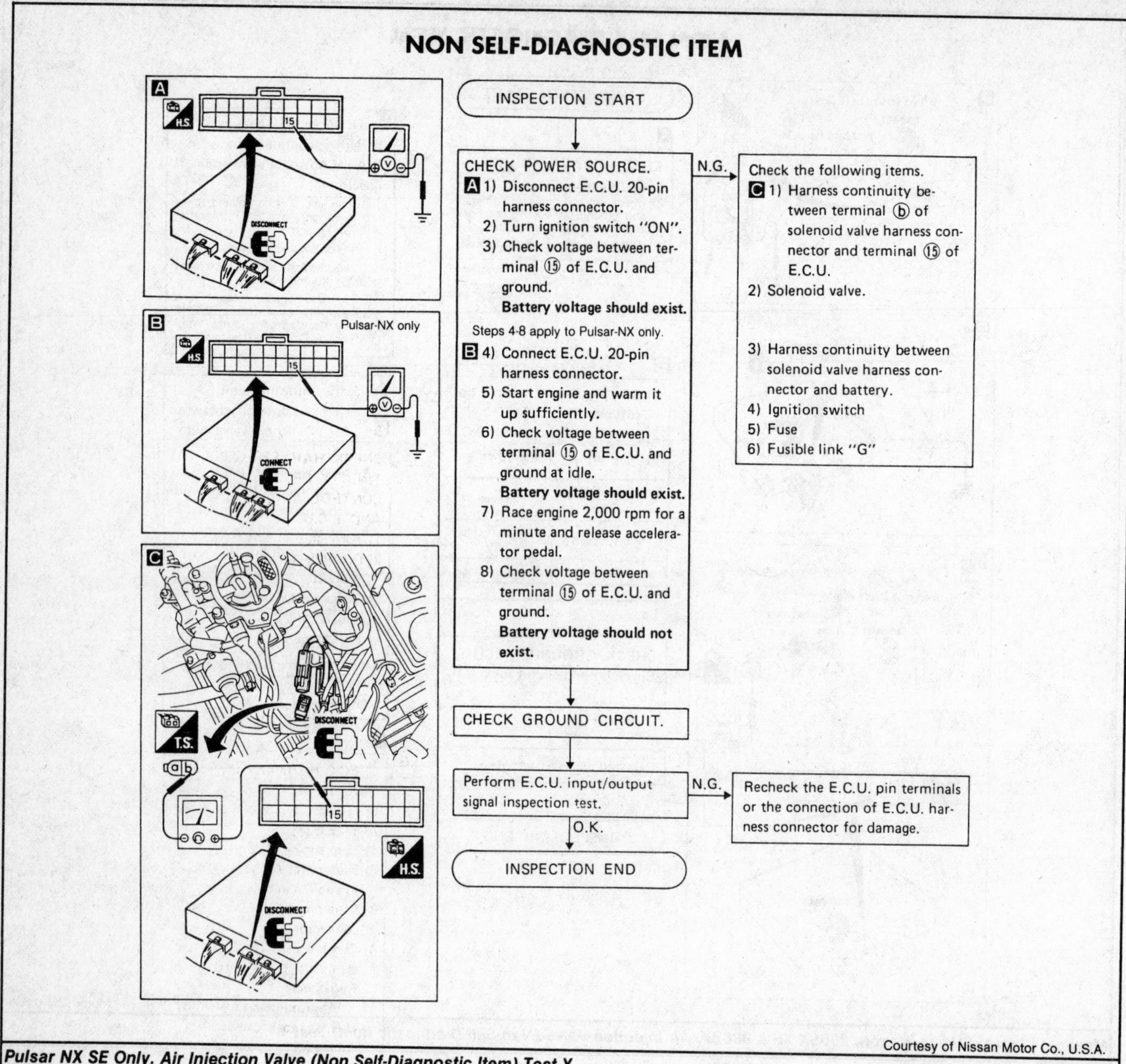
NON SELF-DIAGNOSTIC ITEM
A
H.S.
15
DISCONNECT
B
Pulsar-NX only
H.S.
15
CONNECT
C
T.S.
DISCONNECT
a b
15
H.S.
DISCONNECT
INSPECTION START
CHECK POWER SOURCE.
A 1) Disconnect E.C.U. 20-pin harness connector.
2) Turn ignition switch "ON".
3) Check voltage between terminal ⑮ of E.C.U. and ground.
Battery voltage should exist.
Steps 4-8 apply to Pulsar-NX only.
B 4) Connect E.C.U. 20-pin harness connector.
5) Start engine and warm it up sufficiently.
6) Check voltage between terminal ⑮ of E.C.U. and ground at idle.
Battery voltage should exist.
7) Race engine 2,000 rpm for a minute and release accelerator pedal.
8) Check voltage between terminal ⑮ of E.C.U. and ground.
Battery voltage should not exist.
N.G.
Check the following items.
C 1) Harness continuity between terminal ⓑ of solenoid valve harness connector and terminal ⑮ of E.C.U.
2) Solenoid valve.
3) Harness continuity between solenoid valve harness connector and battery.
4) Ignition switch
5) Fuse
6) Fusible link "G"
CHECK GROUND CIRCUIT.
Perform E.C.U. input/output signal inspection test.
N.G.
Recheck the E.C.U. pin terminals or the connection of E.C.U. harness connector for damage.
O.K.
INSPECTION END
Courtesy of Nissan Motor Co., U.S.A.

*Pulsar NX SE Only. Air Injection Valve (Non Self-Diagnostic Item) Test Y*

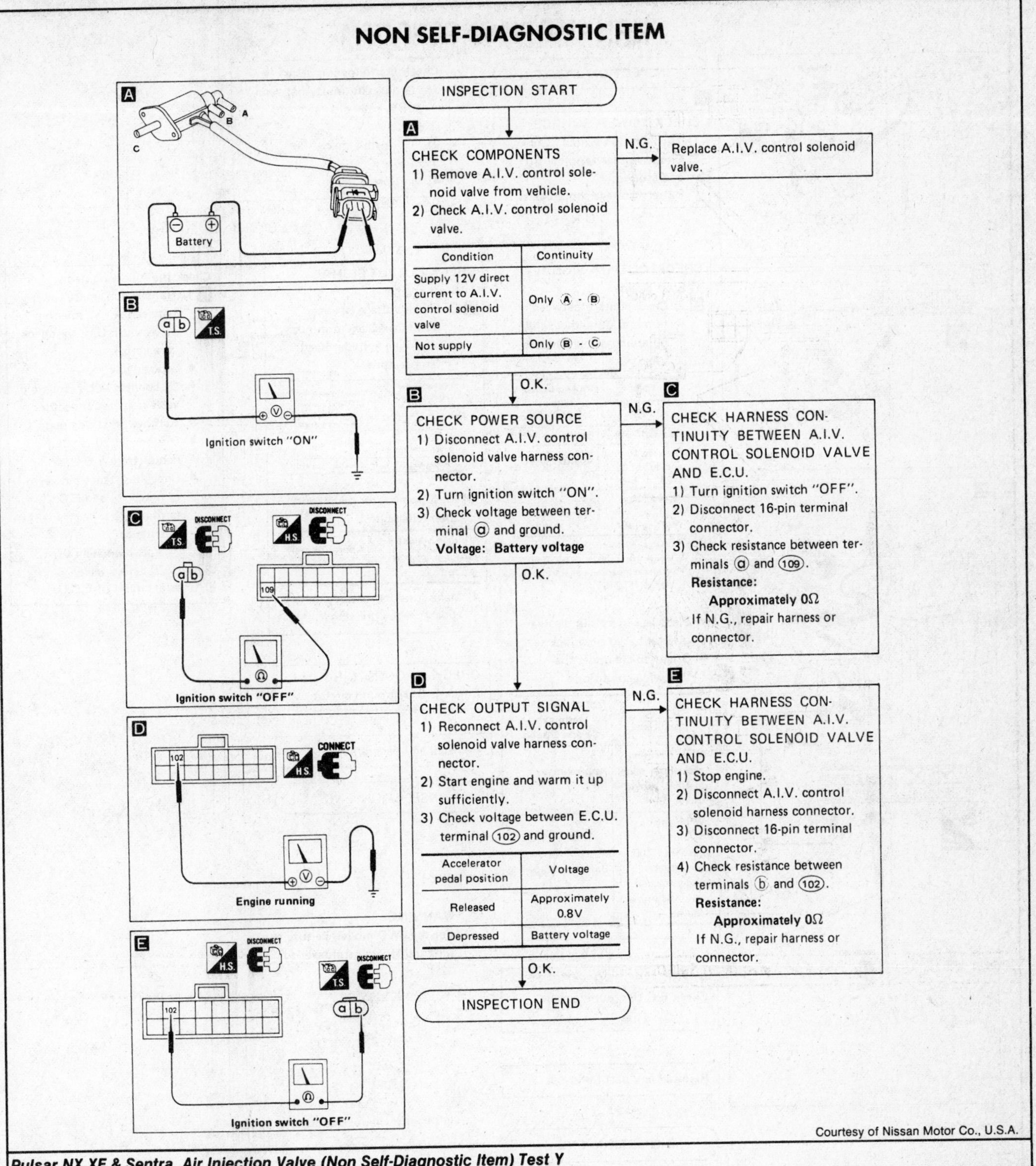
NON SELF-DIAGNOSTIC ITEM
A
C
B
A
Battery
B
a b
T.S.
Ignition switch "ON"
C
T.S.
DISCONNECT
H.S.
DISCONNECT
a b
109
Ignition switch "OFF"
D
102
H.S.
CONNECT
Engine running
E
H.S.
DISCONNECT
T.S.
DISCONNECT
102
a b
Ignition switch "OFF"
INSPECTION START
A
CHECK COMPONENTS
1) Remove A.I.V. control solenoid valve from vehicle.
2) Check A.I.V. control solenoid valve.
Condition | Continuity
Supply 12V direct current to A.I.V. control solenoid valve | Only A - B
Not supply | Only B - C
N.G.
Replace A.I.V. control solenoid valve.
O.K.
B
CHECK POWER SOURCE
1) Disconnect A.I.V. control solenoid valve harness connector.
2) Turn ignition switch "ON".
3) Check voltage between terminal a and ground.
Voltage: Battery voltage
N.G.
C
CHECK HARNESS CONTINUITY BETWEEN A.I.V. CONTROL SOLENOID VALVE AND E.C.U.
1) Turn ignition switch "OFF".
2) Disconnect 16-pin terminal connector.
3) Check resistance between terminals a and 109.
Resistance:
Approximately 0Ω
If N.G., repair harness or connector.
O.K.
D
CHECK OUTPUT SIGNAL
1) Reconnect A.I.V. control solenoid valve harness connector.
2) Start engine and warm it up sufficiently.
3) Check voltage between E.C.U. terminal 102 and ground.
Accelerator pedal position | Voltage
Released | Approximately 0.8V
Depressed | Battery voltage
N.G.
E
CHECK HARNESS CONTINUITY BETWEEN A.I.V. CONTROL SOLENOID VALVE AND E.C.U.
1) Stop engine.
2) Disconnect A.I.V. control solenoid harness connector.
3) Disconnect 16-pin terminal connector.
4) Check resistance between terminals b and 102.
Resistance:
Approximately 0Ω
If N.G., repair harness or connector.
O.K.
INSPECTION END
Courtesy of Nissan Motor Co., U.S.A.

***Pulsar NX XE & Sentra. Air Injection Valve (Non Self-Diagnostic Item) Test Y***

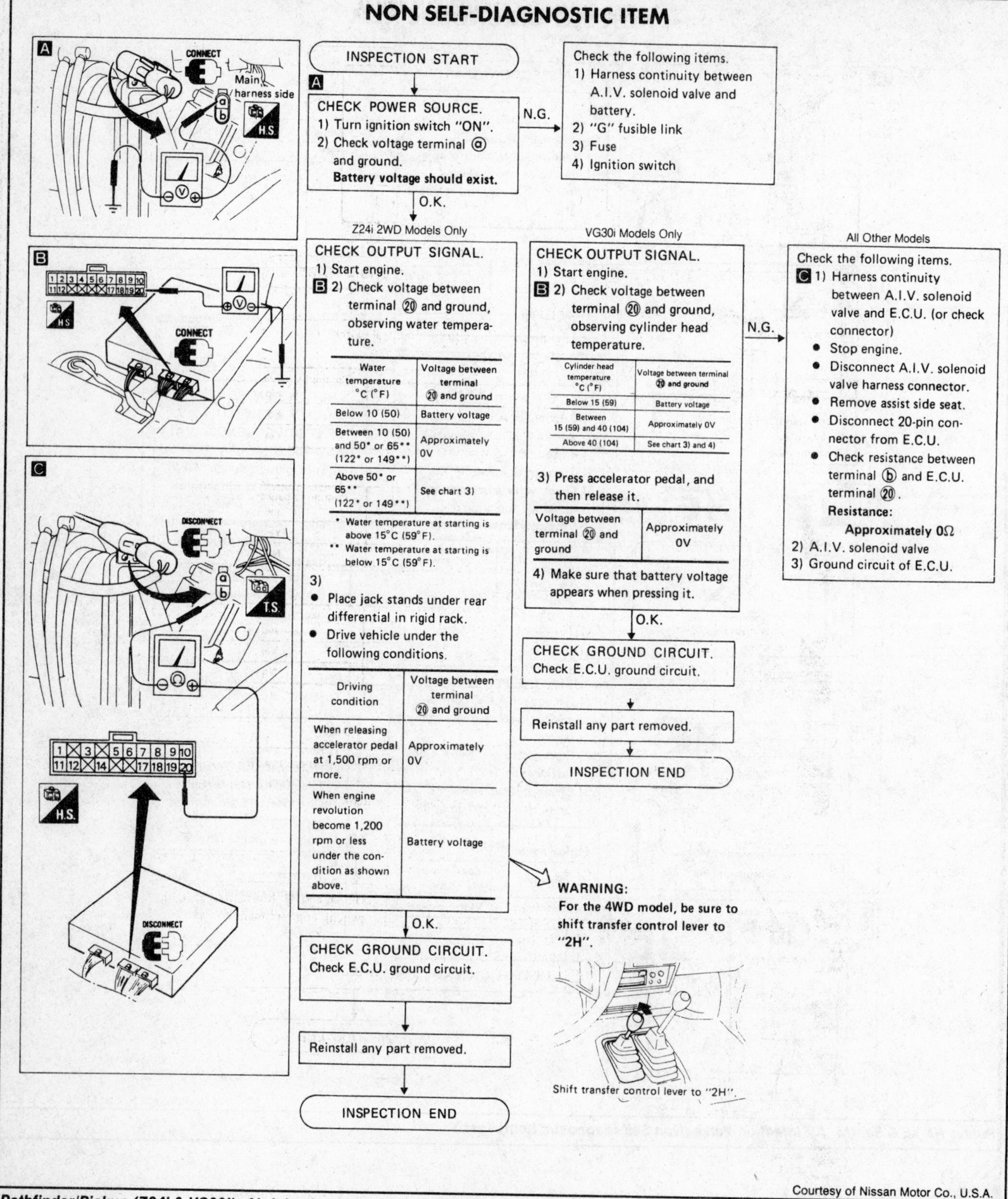
NON SELF-DIAGNOSTIC ITEM
A
CONNECT
Main harness side
a
b
H.S.
B
CONNECT
H.S.
C
DISCONNECT
T.S.
H.S.
DISCONNECT
INSPECTION START
A
CHECK POWER SOURCE.
1) Turn ignition switch "ON".
2) Check voltage terminal ⓐ and ground.
Battery voltage should exist.
N.G.
Check the following items.
1) Harness continuity between A.I.V. solenoid valve and battery.
2) "G" fusible link
3) Fuse
4) Ignition switch
O.K.
Z24i 2WD Models Only
CHECK OUTPUT SIGNAL.
1) Start engine.
B 2) Check voltage between terminal ⑳ and ground, observing water temperature.

| Water temperature °C (°F) | Voltage between terminal ⑳ and ground |
|---|---|
| Below 10 (50) | Battery voltage |
| Between 10 (50) and 50* or 65** (122* or 149**) | Approximately 0V |
| Above 50* or 65** (122* or 149**) | See chart 3) |

* Water temperature at starting is above 15°C (59°F).
** Water temperature at starting is below 15°C (59°F).
3)
• Place jack stands under rear differential in rigid rack.
• Drive vehicle under the following conditions.

| Driving condition | Voltage between terminal ⑳ and ground |
|---|---|
| When releasing accelerator pedal at 1,500 rpm or more. | Approximately 0V |
| When engine revolution become 1,200 rpm or less under the condition as shown above. | Battery voltage |

O.K.
CHECK GROUND CIRCUIT.
Check E.C.U. ground circuit.
Reinstall any part removed.
INSPECTION END
VG30i Models Only
CHECK OUTPUT SIGNAL.
1) Start engine.
B 2) Check voltage between terminal ⑳ and ground, observing cylinder head temperature.

| Cylinder head temperature °C (°F) | Voltage between terminal ⑳ and ground |
|---|---|
| Below 15 (59) | Battery voltage |
| Between 15 (59) and 40 (104) | Approximately 0V |
| Above 40 (104) | See chart 3) and 4) |

3) Press accelerator pedal, and then release it.

| Voltage between terminal ⑳ and ground | Approximately 0V |
|---|---|

4) Make sure that battery voltage appears when pressing it.
O.K.
CHECK GROUND CIRCUIT.
Check E.C.U. ground circuit.
Reinstall any part removed.
INSPECTION END
N.G.
All Other Models
Check the following items.
C 1) Harness continuity between A.I.V. solenoid valve and E.C.U. (or check connector)
• Stop engine.
• Disconnect A.I.V. solenoid valve harness connector.
• Remove assist side seat.
• Disconnect 20-pin connector from E.C.U.
• Check resistance between terminal ⓑ and E.C.U. terminal ⑳.
Resistance:
Approximately 0Ω
2) A.I.V. solenoid valve
3) Ground circuit of E.C.U.
WARNING:
For the 4WD model, be sure to shift transfer control lever to "2H".
Shift transfer control lever to "2H".
Courtesy of Nissan Motor Co., U.S.A.

**Pathfinder/Pickup (Z24i & VG30i). Air Injection Valve (Non Self-Diagnostic Item) Test Y**

# Nissan Electronic Concentrated Control System (Cont.)

## NON SELF-DIAGNOSTIC ITEM

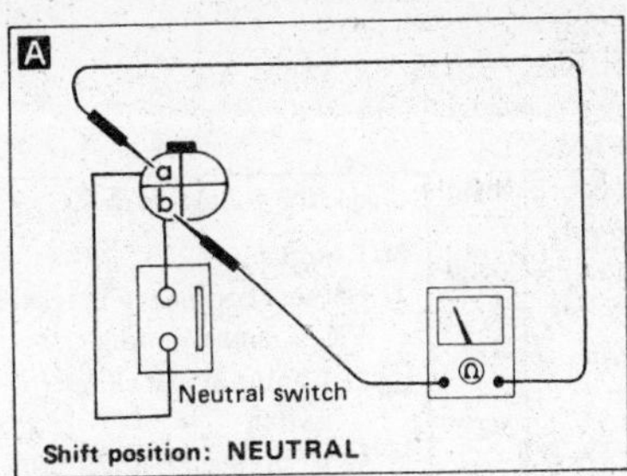
A
a
b
Neutral switch
Shift position: NEUTRAL

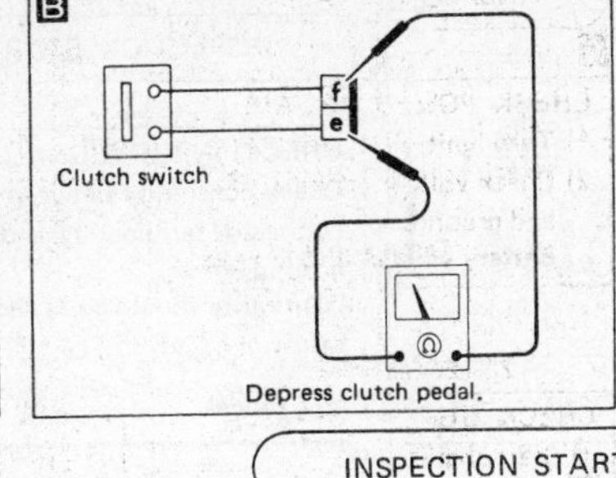
B
Clutch switch
f
e
Depress clutch pedal.

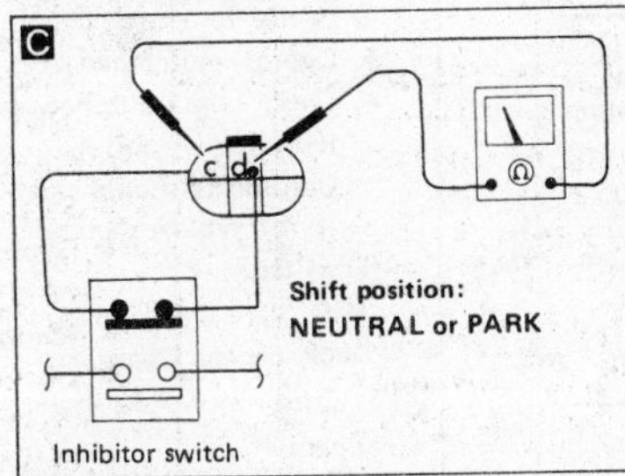
C
c
d
Shift position:
NEUTRAL or PARK
Inhibitor switch

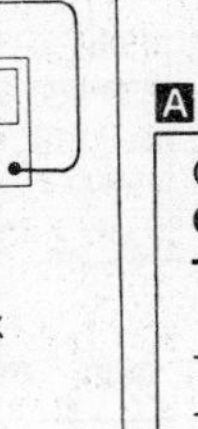

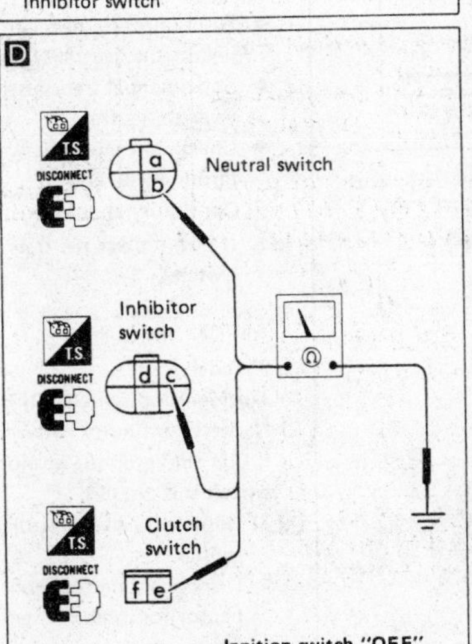
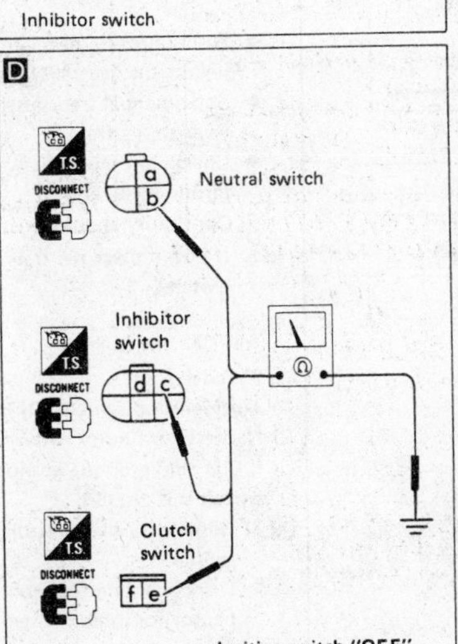
D
T.S.
DISCONNECT
Neutral switch
a
b
Inhibitor switch
d
c
Clutch switch
f
e
Ignition switch "OFF"

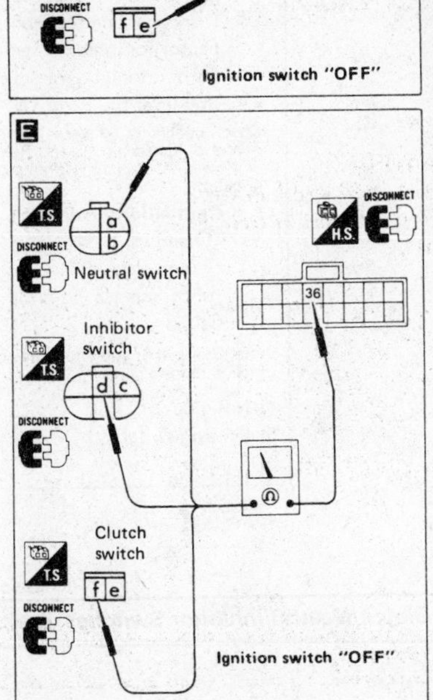
E
T.S.
DISCONNECT
a
b
Neutral switch
H.S.
36
Inhibitor switch
d
c
Clutch switch
f
e
Ignition switch "OFF"

INSPECTION START

**A B C**

Check clutch switch and neutral switch.

**Clutch switch**

| Conditions | Continuity between terminals ⓔ and ⓕ |
|---|---|
| Release clutch pedal | No |
| Depress clutch pedal | Yes |

**Neutral switch**

| Conditions | Continuity between terminals ⓐ and ⓑ |
|---|---|
| Shift to "Neutral" | Yes |
| Shift to other positions | No |

**Inhibitor switch**

| Conditions | Continuity between terminals ⓒ and ⓓ |
|---|---|
| Shift to "Neutral" or "Park" | Yes |
| Except above | No |

If N.G., replace faulty switches.

O.K.

**D**

Check continuity between terminal ⓑ and ground (for neutral switch), terminal ⓔ and ground (for clutch switch), and terminal ⓒ and ground (for inhibitor switch).
**Continuity should exist.**
If N.G., repair harness or connectors.

O.K.

**E**

Check continuity between terminals ⓐ and ㊱ (for neutral switch), terminals ⓕ and ㊱ (for clutch switch), and terminals ⓓ and ㊱ (for inhibitor switch).
**Continuity should exist.**
If N.G., repair harness or connectors.

INSPECTION END

Courtesy of Nissan Motor Co., U.S.A.

***Pulsar NX SE Only. Clutch/Neutral/Inhibitor Switches (Non Self-Diagnostic Items) Test Z***

# Nissan Electronic Concentrated Control System (Cont.)

## NON SELF-DIAGNOSTIC ITEM

A

1 2 3 4 5 6 7 8 9 10
11 12 17 18 19 20

H.S.

CONNECT

B

PulsarNX XE, Pathfinder/Pickup and Sentra only

T.S.

DISCONNECT

Clutch switch side

B

Stanza and Stanza Wagon Only

T.S.

DISCONNECT

4WD (M/T model)

2WD (M/T model)

Neutral (inhibitor) switch side

A/T model

C

T.S.

DISCONNECT

Neutral switch side

D

T.S.

DISCONNECT

a b c d
h g f e

Inhibitor switch side

INSPECTION START

**A**

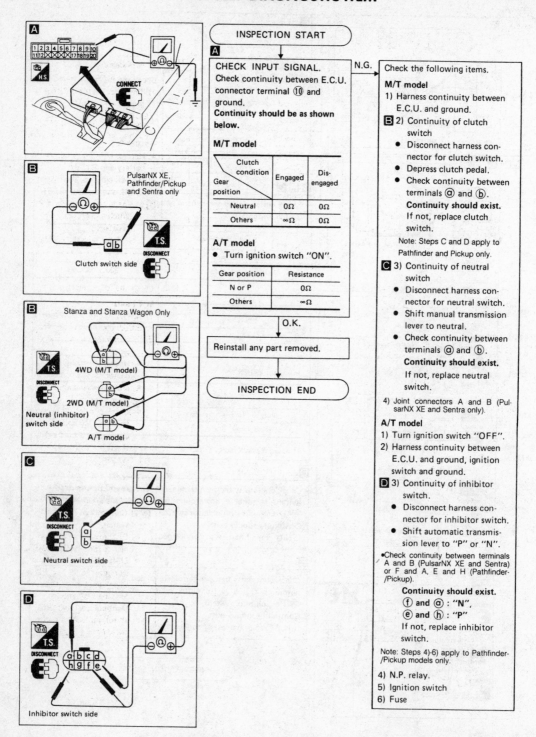

CHECK INPUT SIGNAL.
Check continuity between E.C.U. connector terminal ⑩ and ground.
**Continuity should be as shown below.**

**M/T model**

| Gear position \ Clutch condition | Engaged | Dis-engaged |
|---|---|---|
| Neutral | 0Ω | 0Ω |
| Others | ∞Ω | 0Ω |

**A/T model**

- Turn ignition switch "ON".

| Gear position | Resistance |
|---|---|
| N or P | 0Ω |
| Others | ∞Ω |

O.K. → Reinstall any part removed. → INSPECTION END

N.G. →

Check the following items.

**M/T model**

1) Harness continuity between E.C.U. and ground.

**B** 2) Continuity of clutch switch
- Disconnect harness connector for clutch switch.
- Depress clutch pedal.
- Check continuity between terminals ⓐ and ⓑ.

**Continuity should exist.**
If not, replace clutch switch.

Note: Steps C and D apply to Pathfinder and Pickup only.

**C** 3) Continuity of neutral switch
- Disconnect harness connector for neutral switch.
- Shift manual transmission lever to neutral.
- Check continuity between terminals ⓐ and ⓑ.

**Continuity should exist.**
If not, replace neutral switch.

4) Joint connectors A and B (PulsarNX XE and Sentra only).

**A/T model**

1) Turn ignition switch "OFF".
2) Harness continuity between E.C.U. and ground, ignition switch and ground.

**D** 3) Continuity of inhibitor switch.
- Disconnect harness connector for inhibitor switch.
- Shift automatic transmission lever to "P" or "N".
- Check continuity between terminals A and B (PulsarNX XE and Sentra) or F and A, E and H (Pathfinder/Pickup).

**Continuity should exist.**
**ⓕ and ⓐ : "N".**
**ⓔ and ⓗ : "P"**
If not, replace inhibitor switch.

Note: Steps 4)-6) apply to Pathfinder/Pickup models only.

4) N.P. relay.
5) Ignition switch
6) Fuse

Courtesy of Nissan Motor Co., U.S.A.

*Pulsar NX XE, Pathfinder/Pickup (Z24i & VG30i), Sentra, Stanza, Stanza Wagon. Clutch/Neutral/Inhibitor Switches Test Z*

## NON SELF-DIAGNOSTIC ITEM

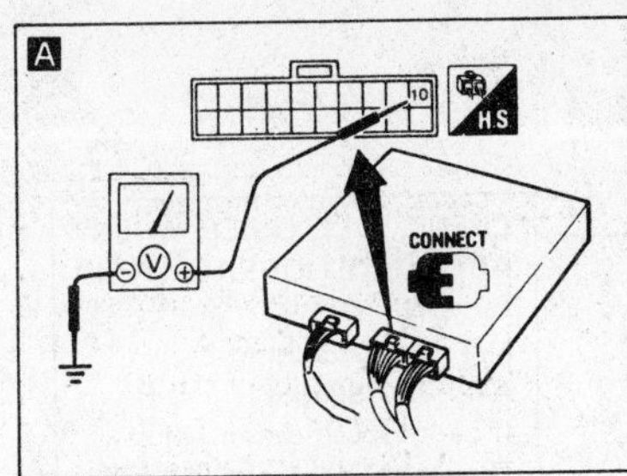
A
10
H.S
CONNECT

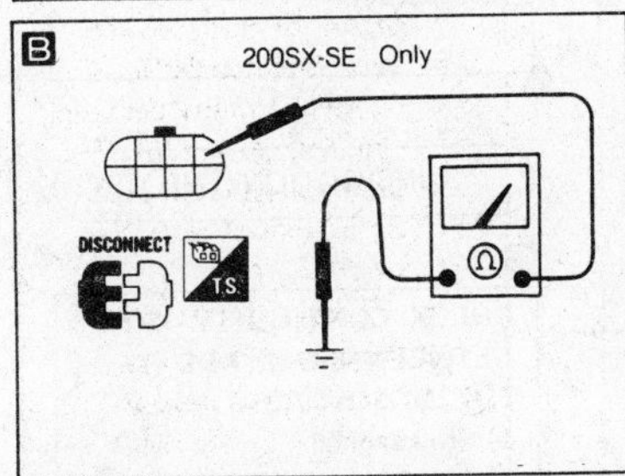
B
200SX-SE Only
DISCONNECT
T.S.

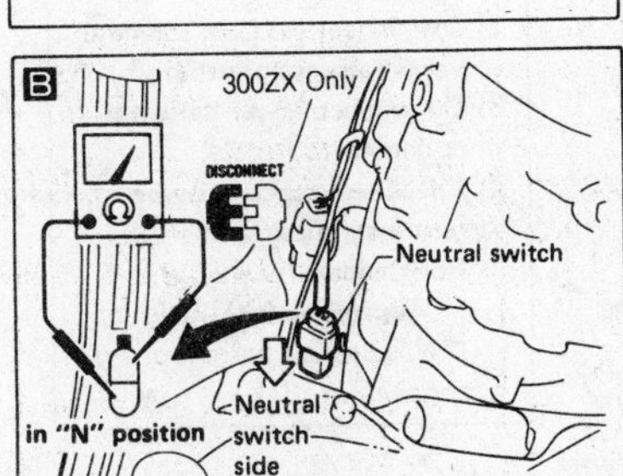
B
300ZX Only
DISCONNECT
Neutral switch
in "N" position
Neutral switch side

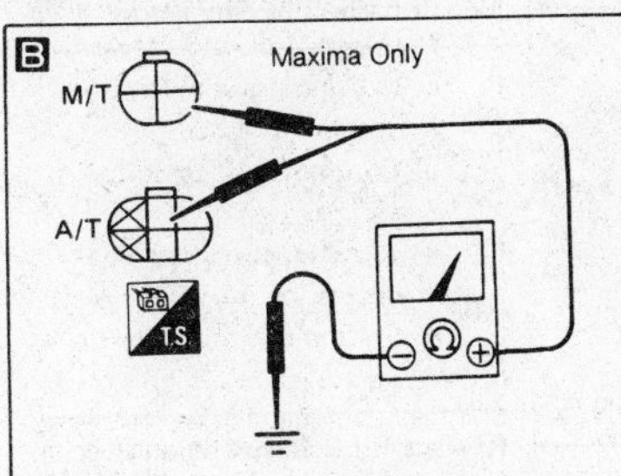
B
Maxima Only
M/T
A/T
T.S.

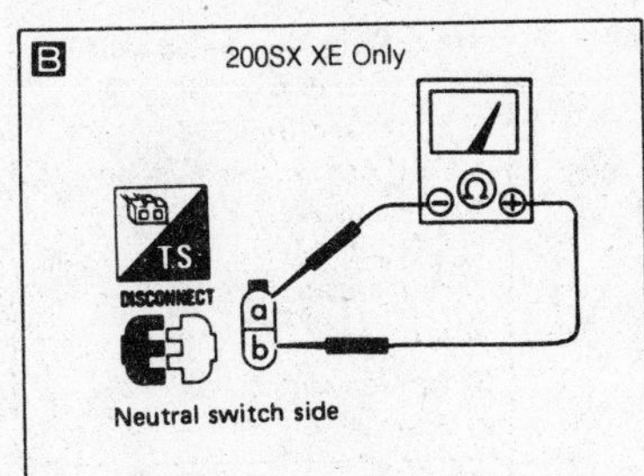
B
200SX XE Only
T.S.
DISCONNECT
a
b
Neutral switch side

INSPECTION START

A

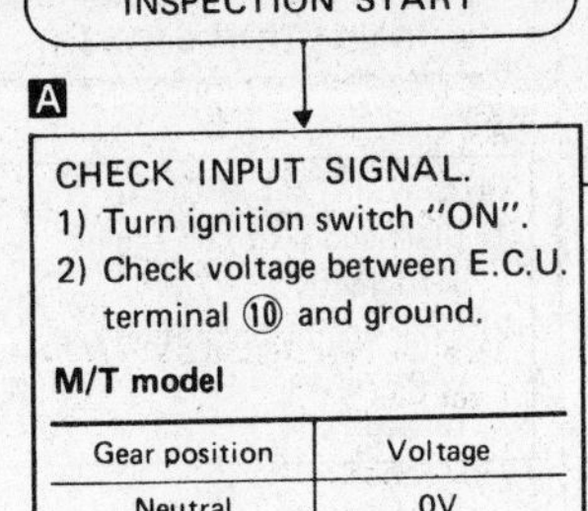

CHECK INPUT SIGNAL.
1) Turn ignition switch "ON".
2) Check voltage between E.C.U. terminal ⑩ and ground.

**M/T model**

| Gear position | Voltage |
|---|---|
| Neutral | 0V |
| Others | Battery voltage |

Maxima and 200SX XE Only

**A/T model**

| Gear position | Resistance |
|---|---|
| N or P | 0V |
| Others | Battery voltage (11 - 14V) |

N.G.

All models except 200SX XE.

Check the following items.
1) Power source for E.C.U & ground circuit for E.C.U.
2) E.C.C.S. relay-1 (Maxima) or E.F.I. main relay (200SX SE and 300ZX)
3) Fusible link "G" (Maxima and 200SX SE)
4) Harness continuity between battery and E.C.U.
5) Harness continuity between E.C.U. and Neutral switch.
B 6) Check resistance Neutral switch and ground.
**Resistance:**
**Approximately 0Ω**

N.G.

200SX XE Only

Check the following items.

**M/T model**
1) Harness continuity between E.C.U. and neutral switch.
B 2) Continuity of neutral switch
- Disconnect harness connector for neutral switch.
- Shift manual transmission lever to neutral.
- Check continuity between terminals ⓐ and ⓑ.
**Continuity should exist.**
If not, replace neutral switch.

**A/T model**
1) Harness continuity between E.C.U. and inhibitor switch.
C 2) Continuity of inhibitor switch.
- Disconnect harness connector for inhibitor switch.
- Shift automatic transmission lever to "P" or "N".
- Check continuity between terminals ⓐ and ⓑ.
**Continuity should exist.**
If not, replace inhibitor switch.

Courtesy of Nissan Motor Co., U.S.A.

***Maxima, 200SX SE, 200SX XE & 300ZX. Clutch/Neutral/Inhibitor Switches (Non Self-Diagnostic Items) Test Z***

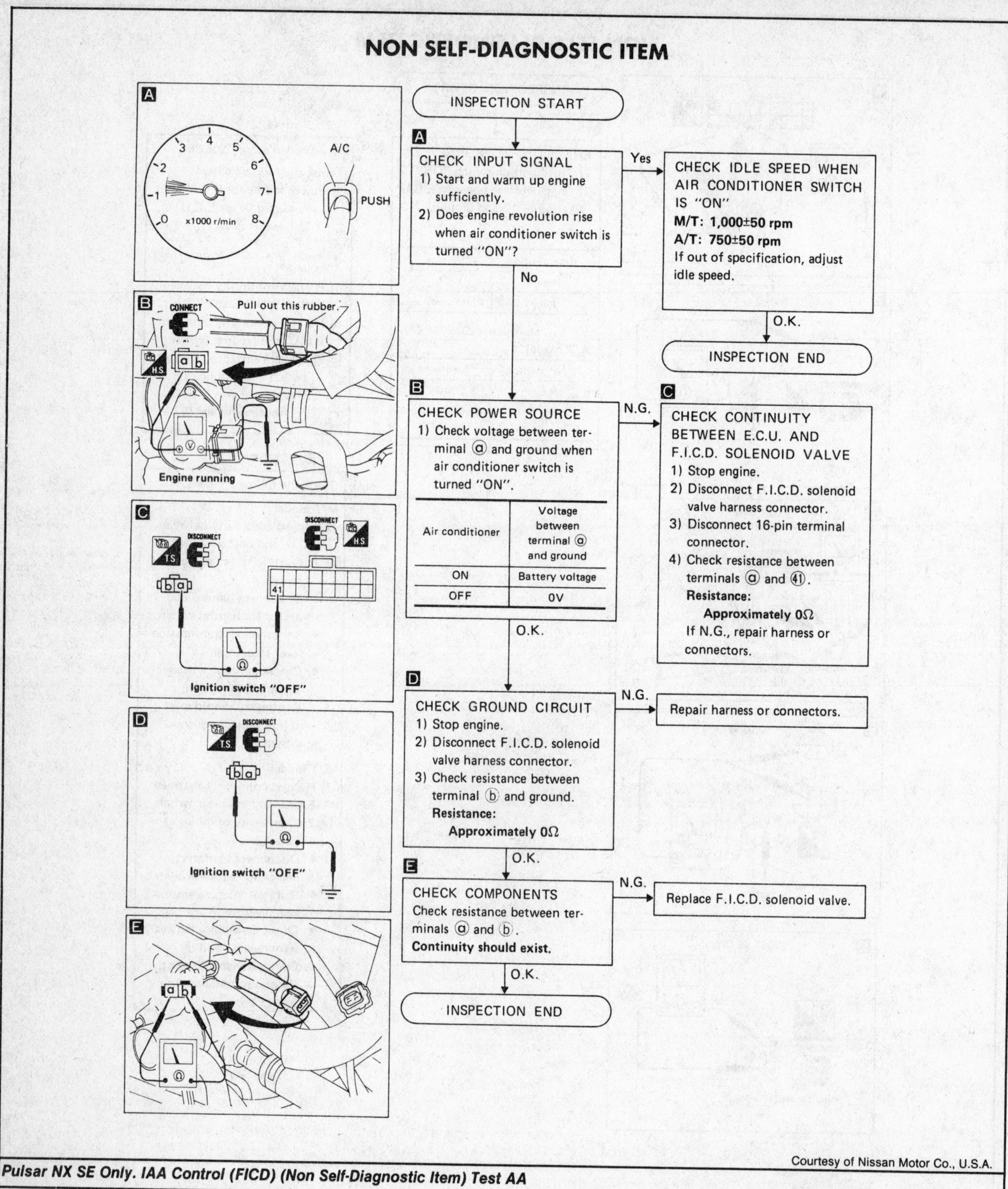
NON SELF-DIAGNOSTIC ITEM
A
3
4
5
2
6
1
7
0
8
x1000 r/min
A/C
PUSH
B
CONNECT
Pull out this rubber.
H.S.
a b
Engine running
C
DISCONNECT
T.S.
H.S.
b a
41
Ignition switch "OFF"
D
DISCONNECT
T.S.
b a
Ignition switch "OFF"
E
a b
INSPECTION START
A
CHECK INPUT SIGNAL
1) Start and warm up engine sufficiently.
2) Does engine revolution rise when air conditioner switch is turned "ON"?
Yes
CHECK IDLE SPEED WHEN AIR CONDITIONER SWITCH IS "ON"
M/T: 1,000±50 rpm
A/T: 750±50 rpm
If out of specification, adjust idle speed.
O.K.
INSPECTION END
No
B
CHECK POWER SOURCE
1) Check voltage between terminal ⓐ and ground when air conditioner switch is turned "ON".
Air conditioner | Voltage between terminal ⓐ and ground
ON | Battery voltage
OFF | 0V
N.G.
C
CHECK CONTINUITY BETWEEN E.C.U. AND F.I.C.D. SOLENOID VALVE
1) Stop engine.
2) Disconnect F.I.C.D. solenoid valve harness connector.
3) Disconnect 16-pin terminal connector.
4) Check resistance between terminals ⓐ and ㊶.
Resistance:
Approximately 0Ω
If N.G., repair harness or connectors.
O.K.
D
CHECK GROUND CIRCUIT
1) Stop engine.
2) Disconnect F.I.C.D. solenoid valve harness connector.
3) Check resistance between terminal ⓑ and ground.
Resistance:
Approximately 0Ω
N.G.
Repair harness or connectors.
O.K.
E
CHECK COMPONENTS
Check resistance between terminals ⓐ and ⓑ.
Continuity should exist.
N.G.
Replace F.I.C.D. solenoid valve.
O.K.
INSPECTION END
Courtesy of Nissan Motor Co., U.S.A.

*Pulsar NX SE Only. IAA Control (FICD) (Non Self-Diagnostic Item) Test AA*

# 1988 COMPUTERIZED ENGINE CONTROLS
## Nissan Electronic Concentrated Control System (Cont.)

### NON SELF-DIAGNOSTIC ITEM

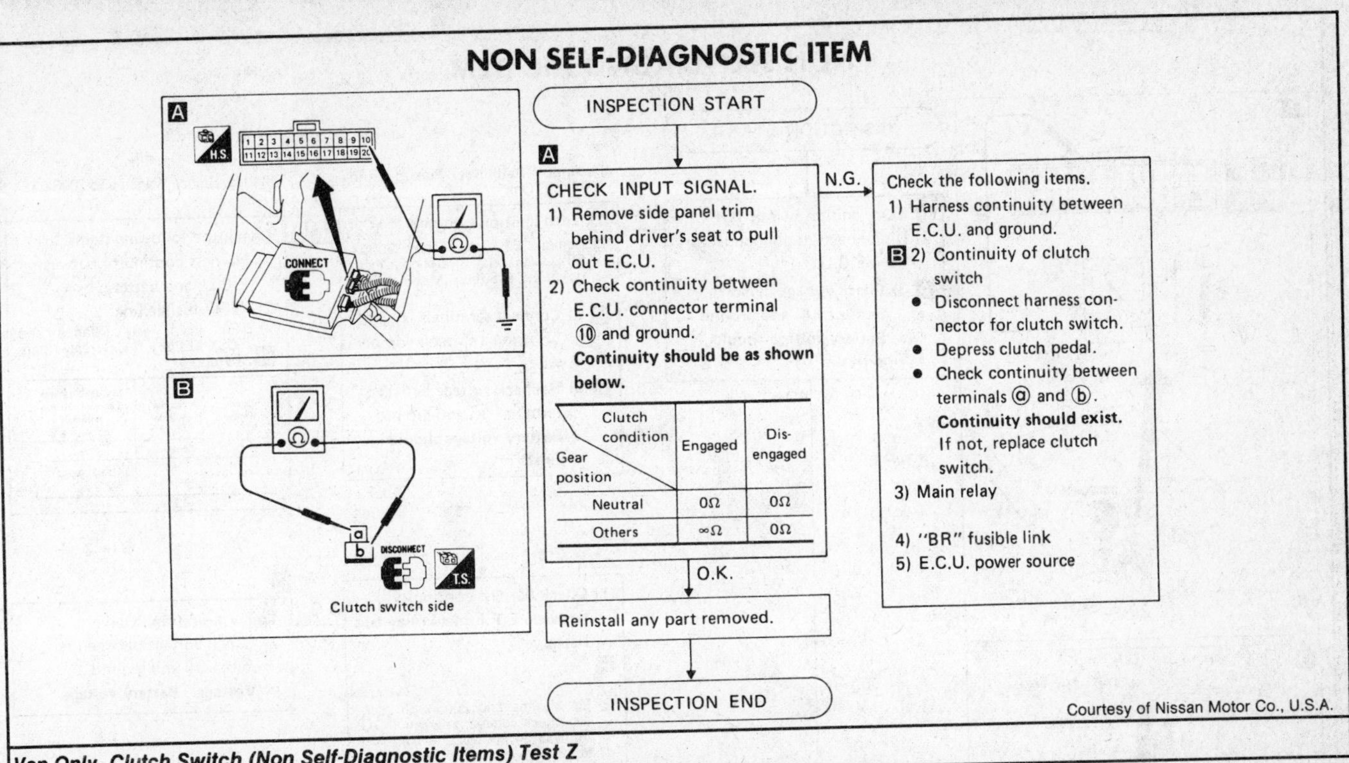
A
H.S.
CONNECT
B
a
b
DISCONNECT
T.S.
Clutch switch side

INSPECTION START

A **CHECK INPUT SIGNAL.**
1) Remove side panel trim behind driver's seat to pull out E.C.U.
2) Check continuity between E.C.U. connector terminal ⑩ and ground.
**Continuity should be as shown below.**

| Gear position \ Clutch condition | Engaged | Dis-engaged |
|---|---|---|
| Neutral | 0Ω | 0Ω |
| Others | ∞Ω | 0Ω |

N.G. → Check the following items.
1) Harness continuity between E.C.U. and ground.
B 2) Continuity of clutch switch
- Disconnect harness connector for clutch switch.
- Depress clutch pedal.
- Check continuity between terminals ⓐ and ⓑ. **Continuity should exist.** If not, replace clutch switch.

3) Main relay
4) "BR" fusible link
5) E.C.U. power source

O.K. → Reinstall any part removed.

INSPECTION END

Courtesy of Nissan Motor Co., U.S.A.

***Van Only. Clutch Switch (Non Self-Diagnostic Items) Test Z***

### NON SELF-DIAGNOSTIC ITEM

B
H.S.
Battery voltage
CONNECT

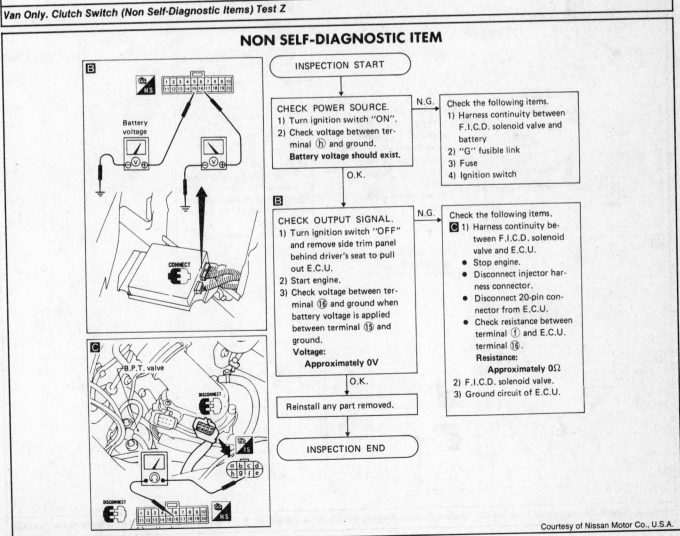

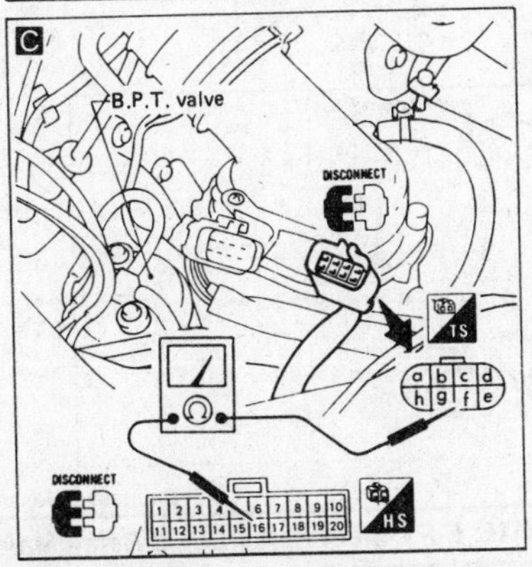

C
B.P.T. valve
DISCONNECT
T.S.
DISCONNECT
H.S.

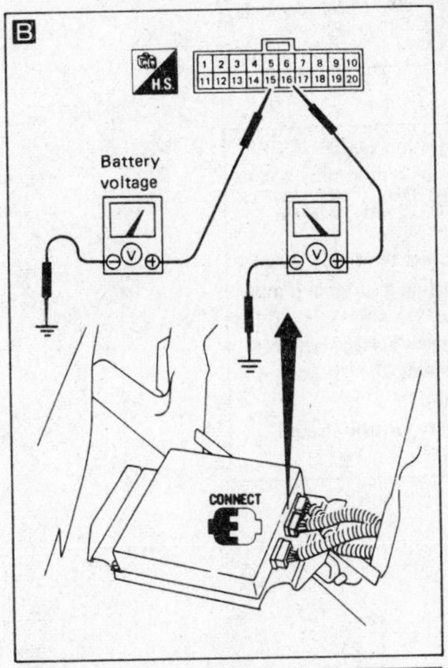

INSPECTION START

**CHECK POWER SOURCE.**
1) Turn ignition switch "ON".
2) Check voltage between terminal ⓗ and ground.
**Battery voltage should exist.**

N.G. → Check the following items.
1) Harness continuity between F.I.C.D. solenoid valve and battery
2) "G" fusible link
3) Fuse
4) Ignition switch

O.K.

B **CHECK OUTPUT SIGNAL.**
1) Turn ignition switch "OFF" and remove side trim panel behind driver's seat to pull out E.C.U.
2) Start engine.
3) Check voltage between terminal ⑯ and ground when battery voltage is applied between terminal ⑮ and ground.
**Voltage:**
**Approximately 0V**

N.G. → Check the following items.
C 1) Harness continuity between F.I.C.D. solenoid valve and E.C.U.
- Stop engine.
- Disconnect injector harness connector.
- Disconnect 20-pin connector from E.C.U.
- Check resistance between terminal ⓕ and E.C.U. terminal ⑯.
**Resistance:**
**Approximately 0Ω**

2) F.I.C.D. solenoid valve.
3) Ground circuit of E.C.U.

O.K. → Reinstall any part removed.

INSPECTION END

Courtesy of Nissan Motor Co., U.S.A.

***Van Only. FICD (Non Self-Diagnostic Item) Test AA***

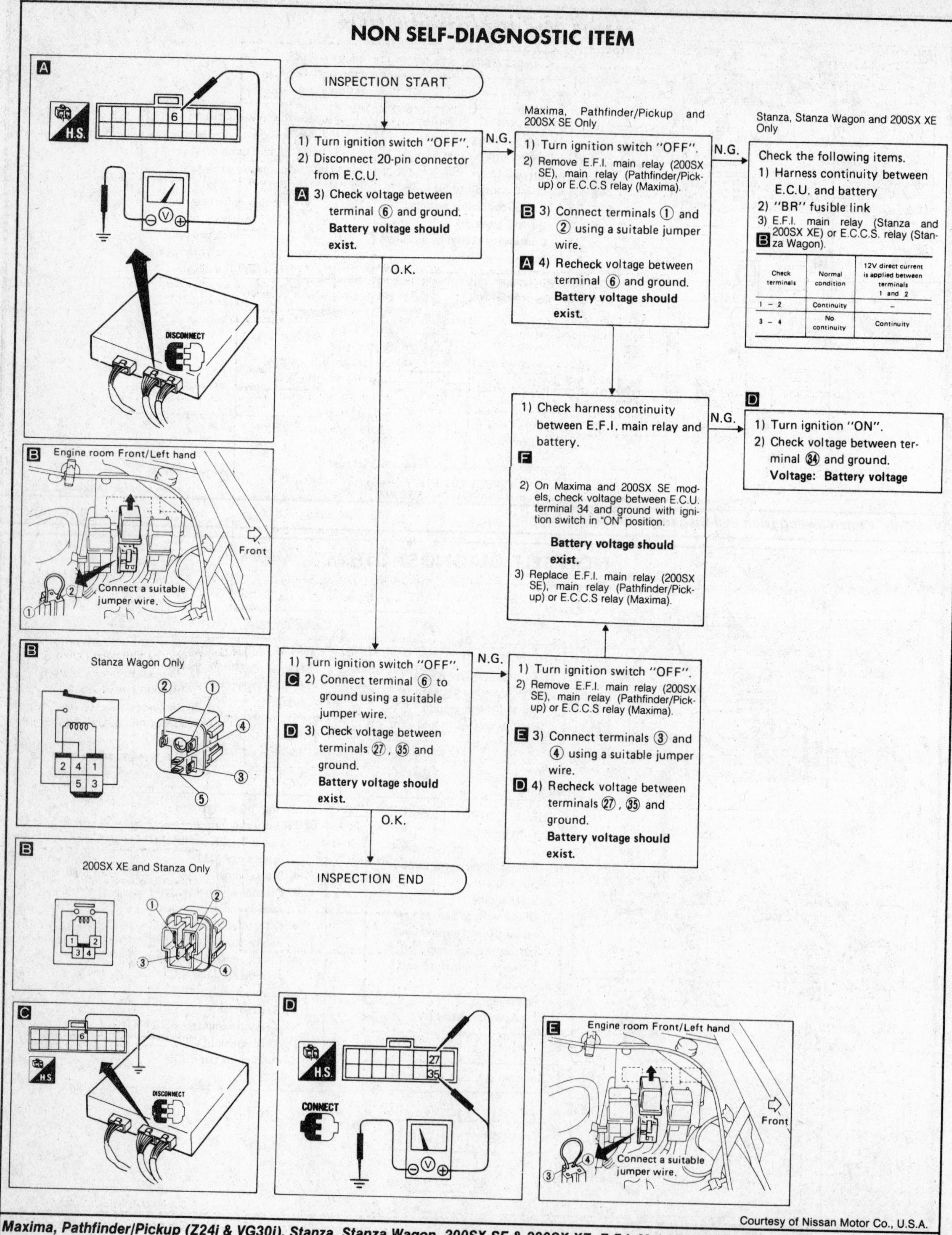
NON SELF-DIAGNOSTIC ITEM
INSPECTION START
1) Turn ignition switch "OFF".
2) Disconnect 20-pin connector from E.C.U.
A 3) Check voltage between terminal ⑥ and ground.
Battery voltage should exist.
N.G.
O.K.
Maxima, Pathfinder/Pickup and 200SX SE Only
1) Turn ignition switch "OFF".
2) Remove E.F.I. main relay (200SX SE), main relay (Pathfinder/Pickup) or E.C.C.S relay (Maxima).
B 3) Connect terminals ① and ② using a suitable jumper wire.
A 4) Recheck voltage between terminal ⑥ and ground.
Battery voltage should exist.
N.G.
Stanza, Stanza Wagon and 200SX XE Only
Check the following items.
1) Harness continuity between E.C.U. and battery
2) "BR" fusible link
3) E.F.I. main relay (Stanza and 200SX XE) or E.C.C.S. relay (Stanza Wagon).
B
Check terminals
Normal condition
12V direct current is applied between terminals 1 and 2
1 – 2
Continuity
–
3 – 4
No continuity
Continuity
1) Check harness continuity between E.F.I. main relay and battery.
F
2) On Maxima and 200SX SE models, check voltage between E.C.U. terminal 34 and ground with ignition switch in "ON" position.
Battery voltage should exist.
3) Replace E.F.I. main relay (200SX SE), main relay (Pathfinder/Pickup) or E.C.C.S relay (Maxima).
N.G.
D
1) Turn ignition "ON".
2) Check voltage between terminal ㉞ and ground.
Voltage: Battery voltage
1) Turn ignition switch "OFF".
C 2) Connect terminal ⑥ to ground using a suitable jumper wire.
D 3) Check voltage between terminals ㉗, ㉟ and ground.
Battery voltage should exist.
N.G.
O.K.
1) Turn ignition switch "OFF".
2) Remove E.F.I. main relay (200SX SE), main relay (Pathfinder/Pickup) or E.C.C.S relay (Maxima).
E 3) Connect terminals ③ and ④ using a suitable jumper wire.
D 4) Recheck voltage between terminals ㉗, ㉟ and ground.
Battery voltage should exist.
INSPECTION END
A
6
H.S.
DISCONNECT
B
Engine room Front/Left hand
Front
Connect a suitable jumper wire.
B
Stanza Wagon Only
B
200SX XE and Stanza Only
C
6
H.S.
DISCONNECT
D
H.S.
27
35
CONNECT
E
Engine room Front/Left hand
Front
Connect a suitable jumper wire.

Courtesy of Nissan Motor Co., U.S.A.

***Maxima, Pathfinder/Pickup (Z24i & VG30i), Stanza, Stanza Wagon, 200SX SE & 200SX XE. E F I Main Relay/ECCS Relay/Main Relay Test BB***

# 1988 COMPUTERIZED ENGINE CONTROLS
## Nissan Electronic Concentrated Control System (Cont.)

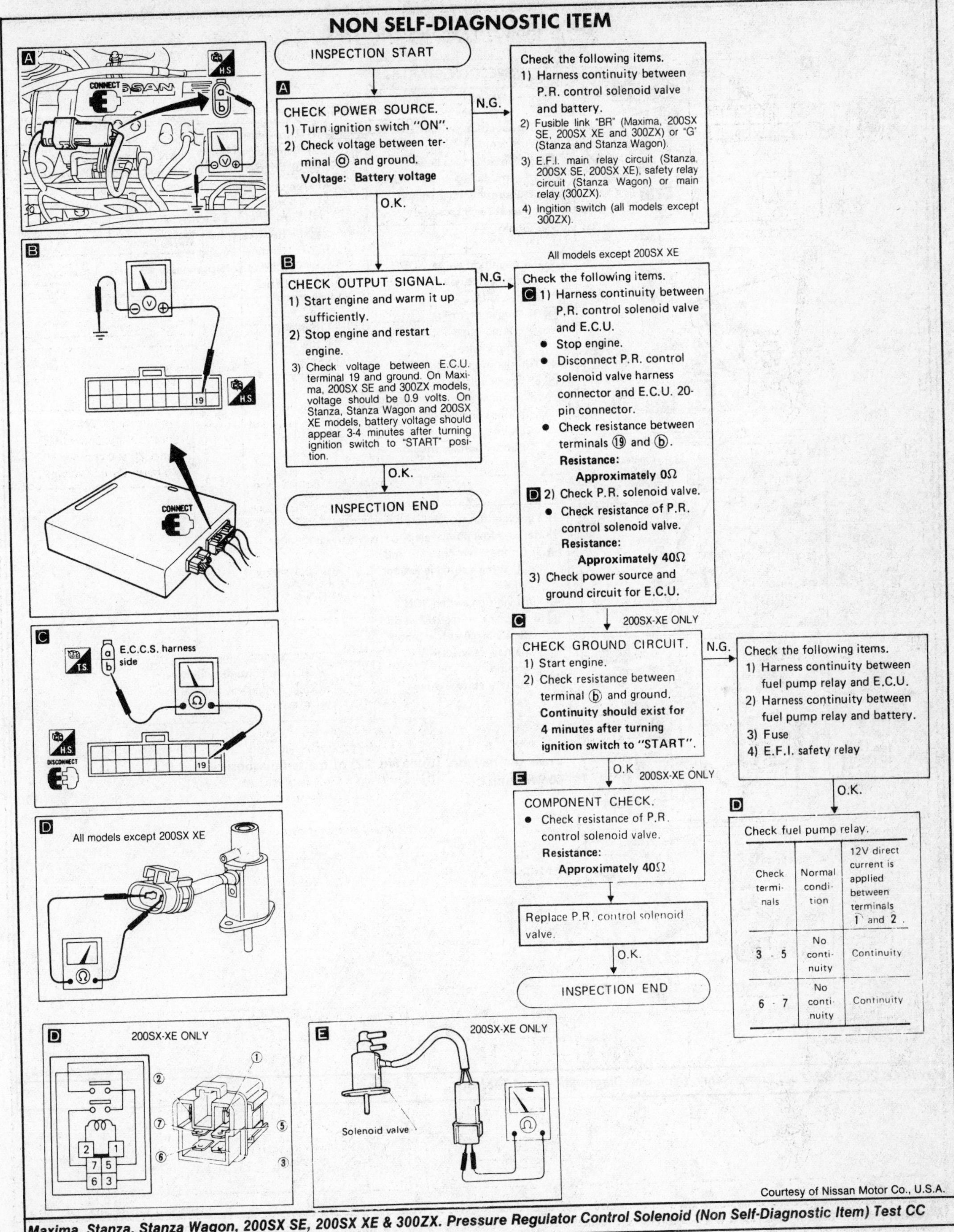
NON SELF-DIAGNOSTIC ITEM
INSPECTION START
A
CHECK POWER SOURCE.
1) Turn ignition switch "ON".
2) Check voltage between terminal ⓐ and ground.
Voltage: Battery voltage
N.G.
Check the following items.
1) Harness continuity between P.R. control solenoid valve and battery.
2) Fusible link "BR" (Maxima, 200SX SE, 200SX XE and 300ZX) or "G" (Stanza and Stanza Wagon).
3) E.F.I. main relay circuit (Stanza, 200SX SE, 200SX XE), safety relay circuit (Stanza Wagon) or main relay (300ZX).
4) Ingition switch (all models except 300ZX).
O.K.
B
CHECK OUTPUT SIGNAL.
1) Start engine and warm it up sufficiently.
2) Stop engine and restart engine.
3) Check voltage between E.C.U. terminal 19 and ground. On Maxima, 200SX SE and 300ZX models, voltage should be 0.9 volts. On Stanza, Stanza Wagon and 200SX XE models, battery voltage should appear 3-4 minutes after turning ignition switch to "START" position.
N.G.
All models except 200SX XE
Check the following items.
C 1) Harness continuity between P.R. control solenoid valve and E.C.U.
• Stop engine.
• Disconnect P.R. control solenoid valve harness connector and E.C.U. 20-pin connector.
• Check resistance between terminals ⑲ and ⓑ.
Resistance: Approximately 0Ω
D 2) Check P.R. solenoid valve.
• Check resistance of P.R. control solenoid valve.
Resistance: Approximately 40Ω
3) Check power source and ground circuit for E.C.U.
O.K.
INSPECTION END
200SX-XE ONLY
C
CHECK GROUND CIRCUIT.
1) Start engine.
2) Check resistance between terminal ⓑ and ground.
Continuity should exist for 4 minutes after turning ignition switch to "START".
N.G.
Check the following items.
1) Harness continuity between fuel pump relay and E.C.U.
2) Harness continuity between fuel pump relay and battery.
3) Fuse
4) E.F.I. safety relay
O.K.
D
Check fuel pump relay.
O.K
200SX-XE ONLY
E
COMPONENT CHECK.
• Check resistance of P.R. control solenoid valve.
Resistance: Approximately 40Ω
Replace P.R. control solenoid valve.
O.K.
INSPECTION END
A
CONNECT
HS
a
b
B
19
HS
CONNECT
C
E.C.C.S. harness side
a
b
TS
HS
DISCONNECT
19
D
All models except 200SX XE
D
200SX-XE ONLY
1
2
7
5
6
3
E
200SX-XE ONLY
Solenoid valve

| Check terminals | Normal condition | 12V direct current is applied between terminals 1 and 2. |
|---|---|---|
| 3 - 5 | No continuity | Continuity |
| 6 - 7 | No continuity | Continuity |

Courtesy of Nissan Motor Co., U.S.A.

**Maxima, Stanza, Stanza Wagon, 200SX SE, 200SX XE & 300ZX. Pressure Regulator Control Solenoid (Non Self-Diagnostic Item) Test CC**

# Nissan Electronic Concentrated Control System (Cont.)

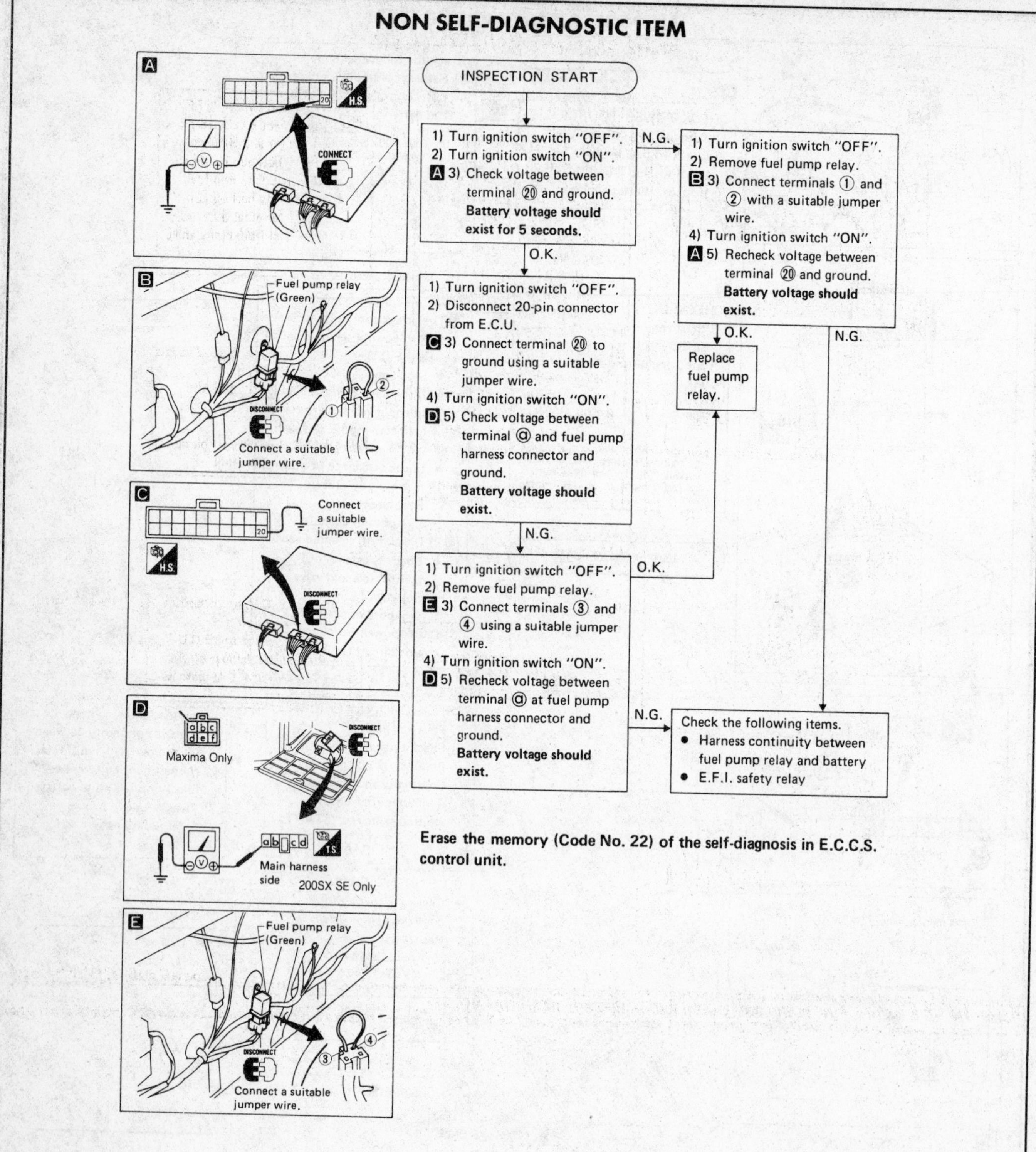
NON SELF-DIAGNOSTIC ITEM
A
CONNECT
H.S.
20
B
Fuel pump relay
(Green)
DISCONNECT
Connect a suitable
jumper wire.
C
Connect
a suitable
jumper wire.
DISCONNECT
D
Maxima Only
DISCONNECT
Main harness
side
200SX SE Only
T.S.
E
Fuel pump relay
(Green)
DISCONNECT
Connect a suitable
jumper wire.
INSPECTION START
1) Turn ignition switch "OFF".
2) Turn ignition switch "ON".
A 3) Check voltage between terminal ⑳ and ground.
Battery voltage should exist for 5 seconds.
N.G.
1) Turn ignition switch "OFF".
2) Remove fuel pump relay.
B 3) Connect terminals ① and ② with a suitable jumper wire.
4) Turn ignition switch "ON".
A 5) Recheck voltage between terminal ⑳ and ground.
Battery voltage should exist.
O.K.
1) Turn ignition switch "OFF".
2) Disconnect 20-pin connector from E.C.U.
C 3) Connect terminal ⑳ to ground using a suitable jumper wire.
4) Turn ignition switch "ON".
D 5) Check voltage between terminal ⓐ and fuel pump harness connector and ground.
Battery voltage should exist.
O.K.
Replace fuel pump relay.
N.G.
N.G.
1) Turn ignition switch "OFF".
2) Remove fuel pump relay.
E 3) Connect terminals ③ and ④ using a suitable jumper wire.
4) Turn ignition switch "ON".
D 5) Recheck voltage between terminal ⓐ at fuel pump harness connector and ground.
Battery voltage should exist.
O.K.
N.G.
Check the following items.
• Harness continuity between fuel pump relay and battery
• E.F.I. safety relay
Erase the memory (Code No. 22) of the self-diagnosis in E.C.C.S. control unit.

Courtesy of Nissan Motor Co., U.S.A.

*Maxima & 200SX SE. Fuel Pump Relay. (Non Self-Diagnostic Item) Test DD*

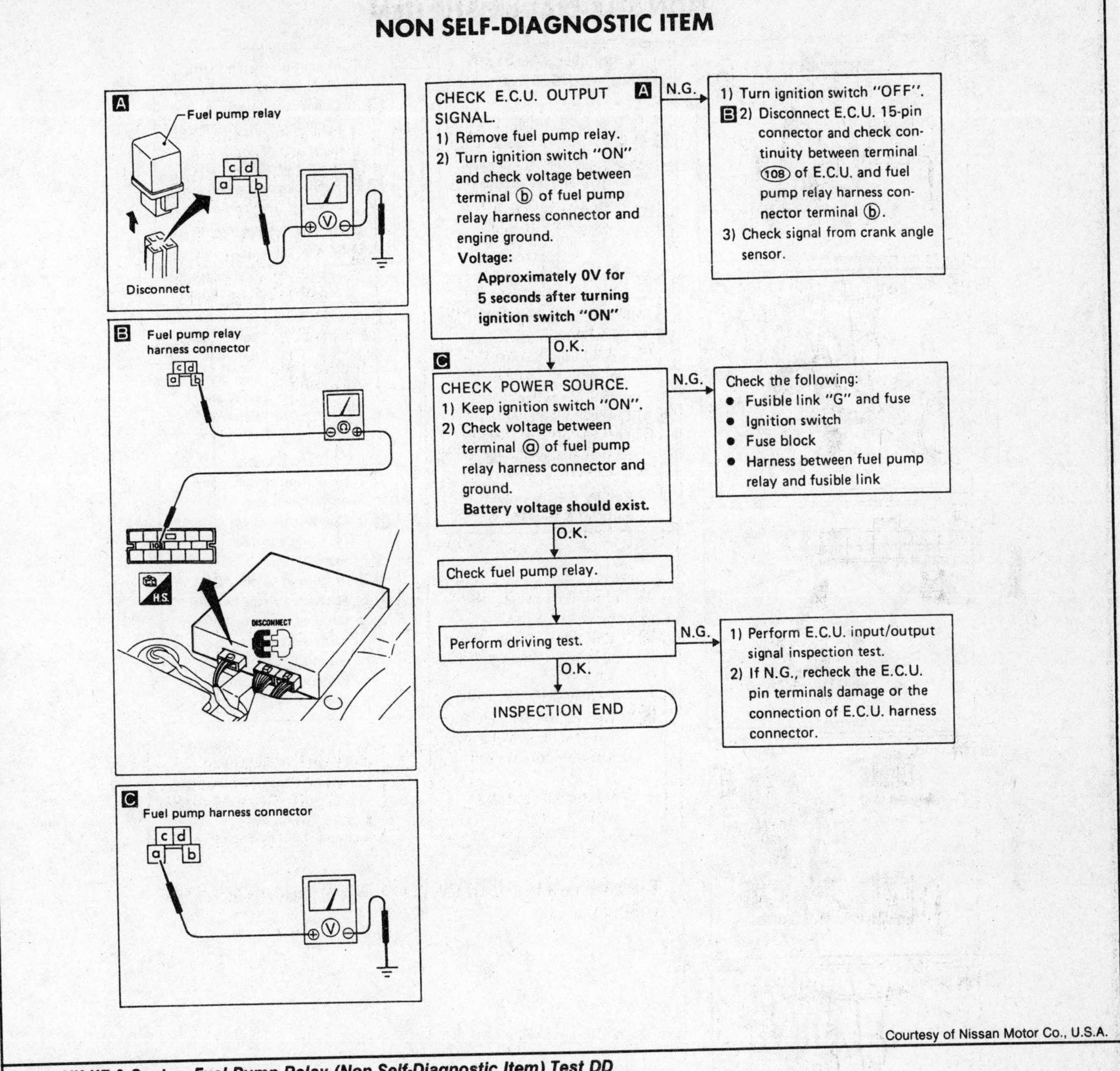
NON SELF-DIAGNOSTIC ITEM
A
Fuel pump relay
c d
a b
Disconnect
B
Fuel pump relay harness connector
108
H.S.
DISCONNECT
C
Fuel pump harness connector
CHECK E.C.U. OUTPUT SIGNAL. A
1) Remove fuel pump relay.
2) Turn ignition switch "ON" and check voltage between terminal ⓑ of fuel pump relay harness connector and engine ground.
Voltage:
Approximately 0V for 5 seconds after turning ignition switch "ON"
N.G.
1) Turn ignition switch "OFF".
B 2) Disconnect E.C.U. 15-pin connector and check continuity between terminal (108) of E.C.U. and fuel pump relay harness connector terminal ⓑ.
3) Check signal from crank angle sensor.
O.K.
C
CHECK POWER SOURCE.
1) Keep ignition switch "ON".
2) Check voltage between terminal ⓐ of fuel pump relay harness connector and ground.
Battery voltage should exist.
N.G.
Check the following:
• Fusible link "G" and fuse
• Ignition switch
• Fuse block
• Harness between fuel pump relay and fusible link
O.K.
Check fuel pump relay.
Perform driving test.
N.G.
1) Perform E.C.U. input/output signal inspection test.
2) If N.G., recheck the E.C.U. pin terminals damage or the connection of E.C.U. harness connector.
O.K.
INSPECTION END

Courtesy of Nissan Motor Co., U.S.A.

*Pulsar NX XE & Sentra. Fuel Pump Relay (Non Self-Diagnostic Item) Test DD*

## NON SELF-DIAGNOSTIC ITEM

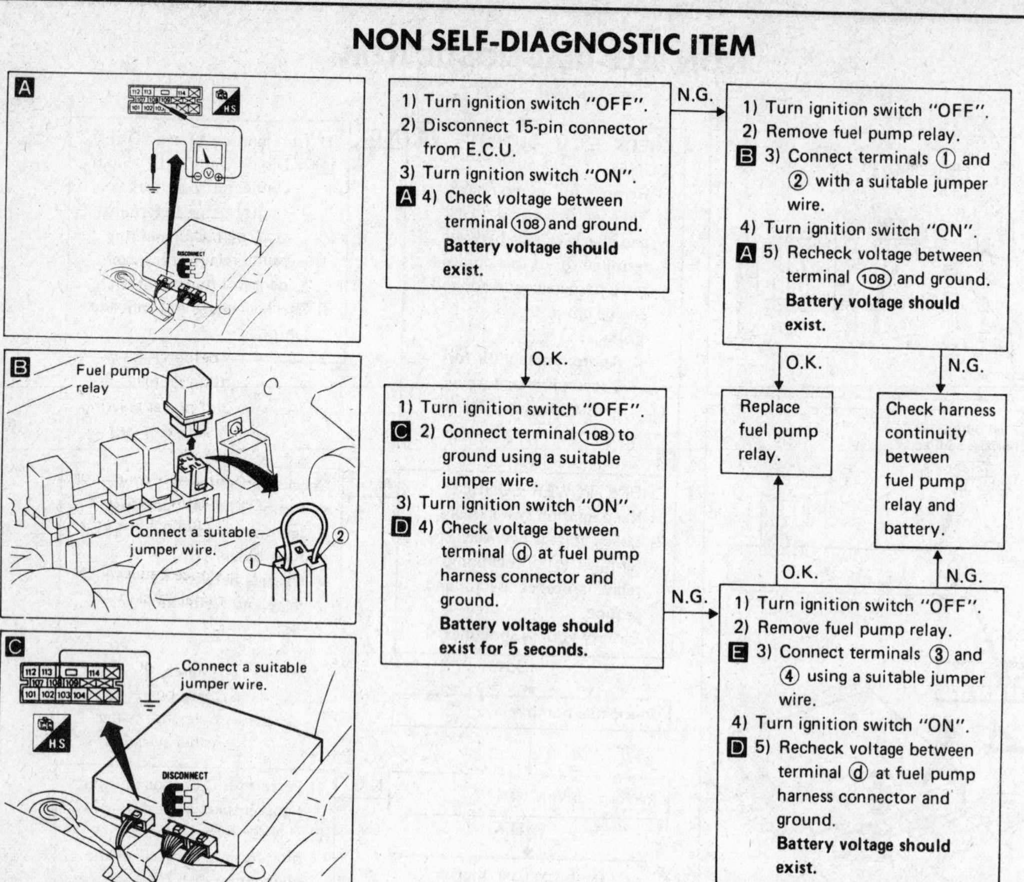
1) Turn ignition switch "OFF".
2) Disconnect 15-pin connector from E.C.U.
3) Turn ignition switch "ON".
A 4) Check voltage between terminal (108) and ground.
Battery voltage should exist.
N.G.
1) Turn ignition switch "OFF".
2) Remove fuel pump relay.
B 3) Connect terminals ① and ② with a suitable jumper wire.
4) Turn ignition switch "ON".
A 5) Recheck voltage between terminal (108) and ground.
Battery voltage should exist.
O.K.
Replace fuel pump relay.
N.G.
Check harness continuity between fuel pump relay and battery.
O.K.
1) Turn ignition switch "OFF".
C 2) Connect terminal (108) to ground using a suitable jumper wire.
3) Turn ignition switch "ON".
D 4) Check voltage between terminal ⓓ at fuel pump harness connector and ground.
Battery voltage should exist for 5 seconds.
N.G.
1) Turn ignition switch "OFF".
2) Remove fuel pump relay.
E 3) Connect terminals ③ and ④ using a suitable jumper wire.
4) Turn ignition switch "ON".
D 5) Recheck voltage between terminal ⓓ at fuel pump harness connector and ground.
Battery voltage should exist.
O.K.
N.G.
A
DISCONNECT
B
Fuel pump relay
Connect a suitable jumper wire.
C
Connect a suitable jumper wire.
HS
DISCONNECT

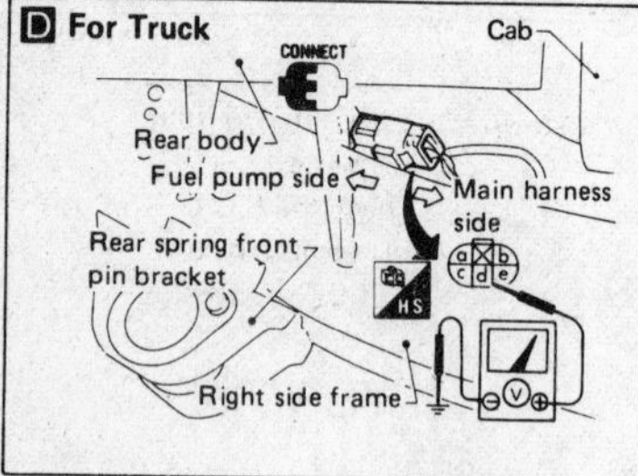
D For Truck
CONNECT
Cab
Rear body
Fuel pump side
Main harness side
Rear spring front pin bracket
HS
Right side frame

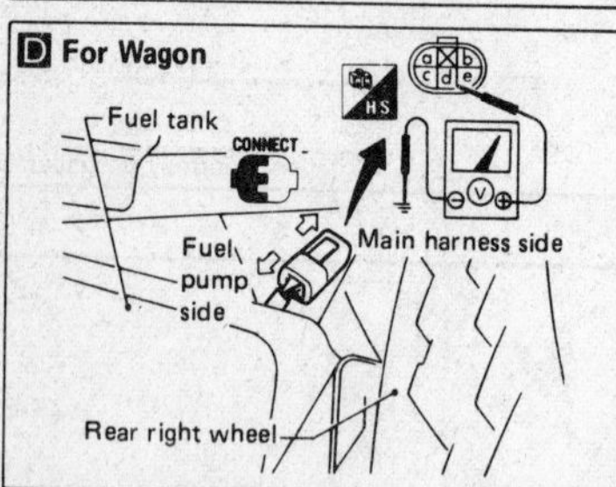
D For Wagon
Fuel tank
CONNECT
HS
Fuel pump side
Main harness side
Rear right wheel

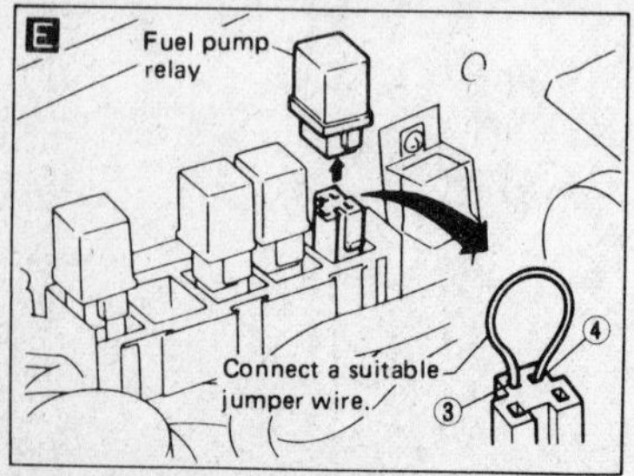
E
Fuel pump relay
Connect a suitable jumper wire.

Courtesy of Nissan Motor Co., U.S.A.

*Pathfinder/Pickup (Z24i & VG30i). Fuel Pump Relay (Non Self-Diagnostic Item) Test DD*

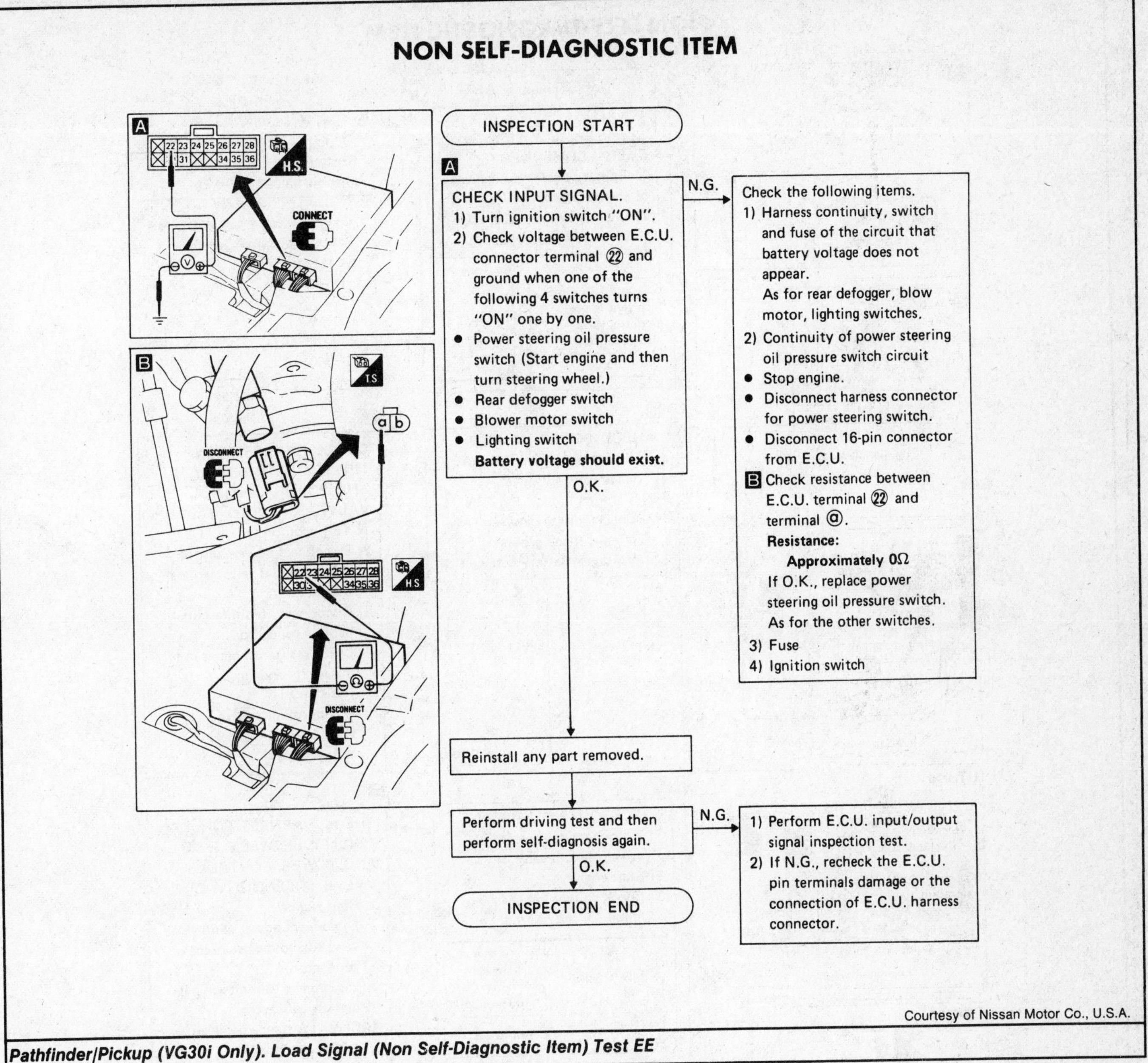
NON SELF-DIAGNOSTIC ITEM
A
22 23 24 25 26 27 28
31 34 35 36
H.S.
CONNECT
B
T.S.
a b
DISCONNECT
22 23 24 25 26 27 28
30 34 35 36
H.S.
DISCONNECT
INSPECTION START
A
CHECK INPUT SIGNAL.
1) Turn ignition switch "ON".
2) Check voltage between E.C.U. connector terminal ㉒ and ground when one of the following 4 switches turns "ON" one by one.
• Power steering oil pressure switch (Start engine and then turn steering wheel.)
• Rear defogger switch
• Blower motor switch
• Lighting switch
Battery voltage should exist.
N.G.
Check the following items.
1) Harness continuity, switch and fuse of the circuit that battery voltage does not appear.
As for rear defogger, blow motor, lighting switches.
2) Continuity of power steering oil pressure switch circuit
• Stop engine.
• Disconnect harness connector for power steering switch.
• Disconnect 16-pin connector from E.C.U.
B Check resistance between E.C.U. terminal ㉒ and terminal ⓐ.
Resistance:
Approximately 0Ω
If O.K., replace power steering oil pressure switch.
As for the other switches.
3) Fuse
4) Ignition switch
O.K.
Reinstall any part removed.
Perform driving test and then perform self-diagnosis again.
N.G.
1) Perform E.C.U. input/output signal inspection test.
2) If N.G., recheck the E.C.U. pin terminals damage or the connection of E.C.U. harness connector.
O.K.
INSPECTION END
Courtesy of Nissan Motor Co., U.S.A.

***Pathfinder/Pickup (VG30i Only). Load Signal (Non Self-Diagnostic Item) Test EE***

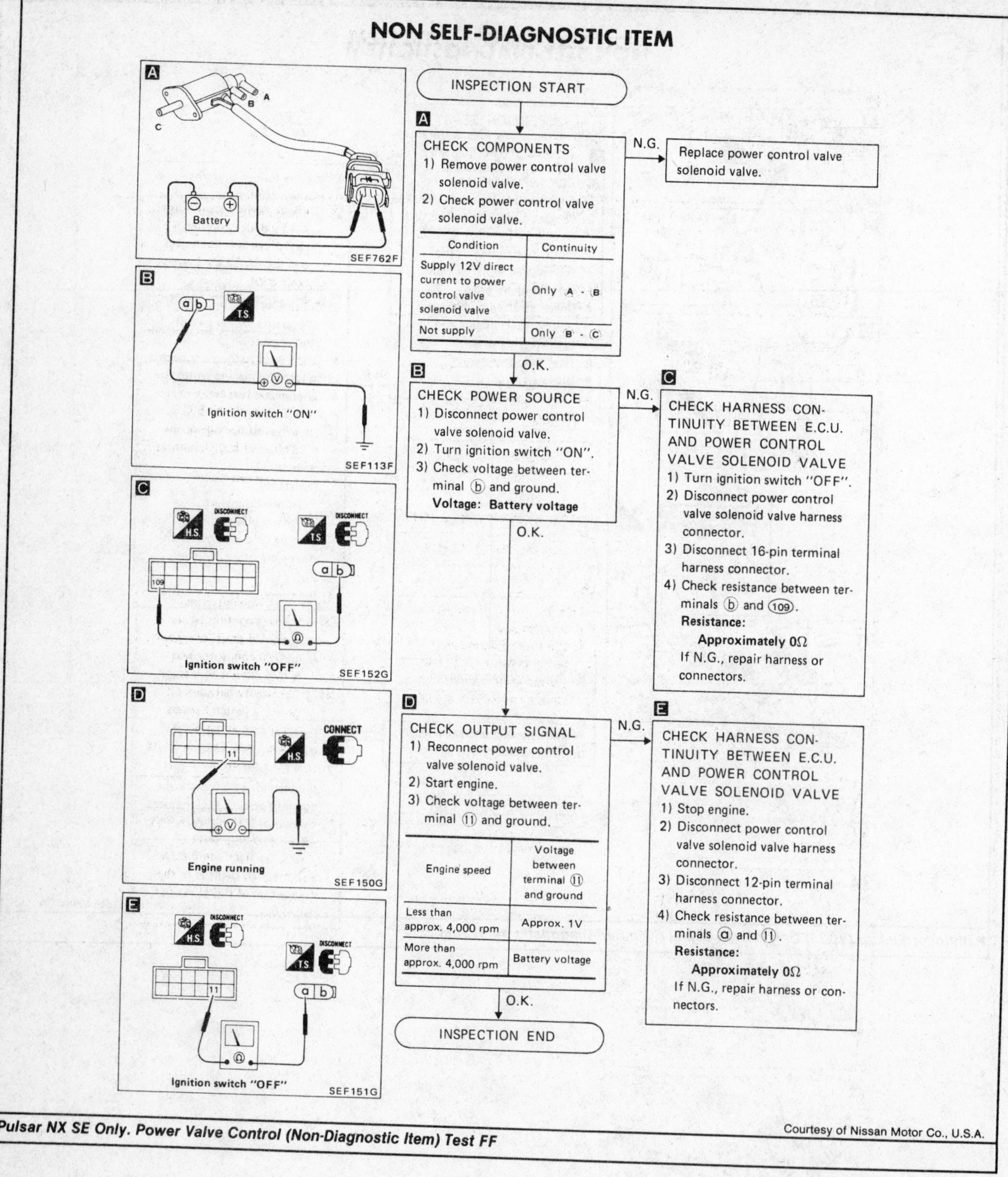
NON SELF-DIAGNOSTIC ITEM
A
C
B
A
Battery
SEF762F
B
a b
T.S.
Ignition switch "ON"
SEF113F
C
H.S.
DISCONNECT
T.S.
DISCONNECT
109
a b
Ignition switch "OFF"
SEF152G
D
11
H.S.
CONNECT
Engine running
SEF150G
E
H.S.
DISCONNECT
T.S.
DISCONNECT
11
a b
Ignition switch "OFF"
SEF151G
INSPECTION START
A
CHECK COMPONENTS
1) Remove power control valve solenoid valve.
2) Check power control valve solenoid valve.
Condition
Continuity
Supply 12V direct current to power control valve solenoid valve
Only A - B
Not supply
Only B - C
N.G.
Replace power control valve solenoid valve.
O.K.
B
CHECK POWER SOURCE
1) Disconnect power control valve solenoid valve.
2) Turn ignition switch "ON".
3) Check voltage between terminal ⓑ and ground.
Voltage: Battery voltage
N.G.
C
CHECK HARNESS CONTINUITY BETWEEN E.C.U. AND POWER CONTROL VALVE SOLENOID VALVE
1) Turn ignition switch "OFF".
2) Disconnect power control valve solenoid valve harness connector.
3) Disconnect 16-pin terminal harness connector.
4) Check resistance between terminals ⓑ and (109).
Resistance:
Approximately 0Ω
If N.G., repair harness or connectors.
O.K.
D
CHECK OUTPUT SIGNAL
1) Reconnect power control valve solenoid valve.
2) Start engine.
3) Check voltage between terminal ⑪ and ground.
Engine speed
Voltage between terminal ⑪ and ground
Less than approx. 4,000 rpm
Approx. 1V
More than approx. 4,000 rpm
Battery voltage
N.G.
E
CHECK HARNESS CONTINUITY BETWEEN E.C.U. AND POWER CONTROL VALVE SOLENOID VALVE
1) Stop engine.
2) Disconnect power control valve solenoid valve harness connector.
3) Disconnect 12-pin terminal harness connector.
4) Check resistance between terminals ⓐ and ⑪.
Resistance:
Approximately 0Ω
If N.G., repair harness or connectors.
O.K.
INSPECTION END

*Pulsar NX SE Only. Power Valve Control (Non-Diagnostic Item) Test FF*

Courtesy of Nissan Motor Co., U.S.A.

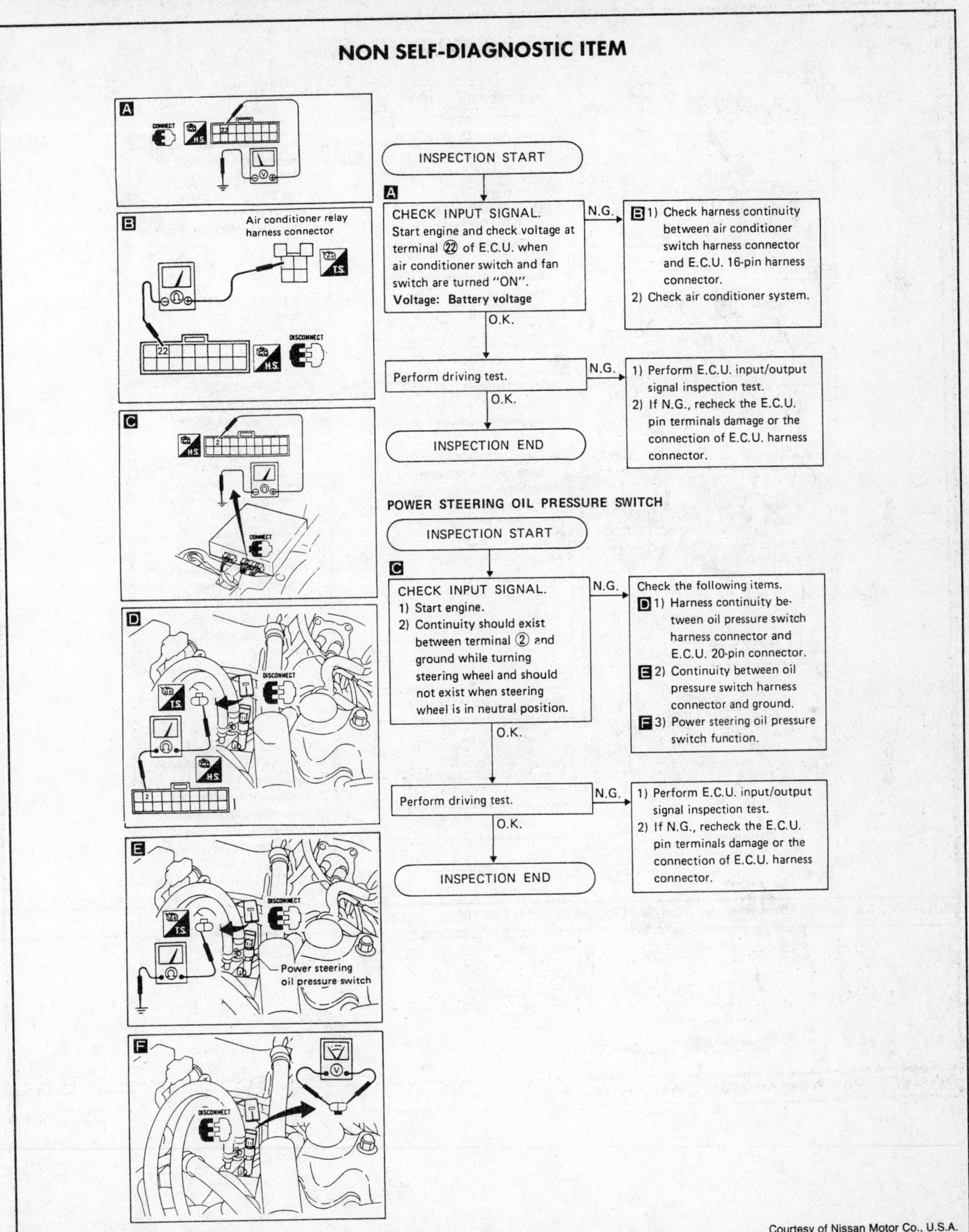
NON SELF-DIAGNOSTIC ITEM
INSPECTION START
A
CHECK INPUT SIGNAL.
Start engine and check voltage at terminal ㉒ of E.C.U. when air conditioner switch and fan switch are turned "ON".
Voltage: Battery voltage
N.G.
B 1) Check harness continuity between air conditioner switch harness connector and E.C.U. 16-pin harness connector.
2) Check air conditioner system.
O.K.
Perform driving test.
N.G.
1) Perform E.C.U. input/output signal inspection test.
2) If N.G., recheck the E.C.U. pin terminals damage or the connection of E.C.U. harness connector.
O.K.
INSPECTION END
POWER STEERING OIL PRESSURE SWITCH
INSPECTION START
C
CHECK INPUT SIGNAL.
1) Start engine.
2) Continuity should exist between terminal ② and ground while turning steering wheel and should not exist when steering wheel is in neutral position.
N.G.
Check the following items.
D 1) Harness continuity between oil pressure switch harness connector and E.C.U. 20-pin connector.
E 2) Continuity between oil pressure switch harness connector and ground.
F 3) Power steering oil pressure switch function.
O.K.
Perform driving test.
N.G.
1) Perform E.C.U. input/output signal inspection test.
2) If N.G., recheck the E.C.U. pin terminals damage or the connection of E.C.U. harness connector.
O.K.
INSPECTION END
A
CONNECT
H.S.
22
B
Air conditioner relay harness connector
T.S.
22
DISCONNECT
H.S.
C
H.S.
2
CONNECT
D
DISCONNECT
T.S.
H.S.
2
E
DISCONNECT
T.S.
Power steering oil pressure switch
F
DISCONNECT

Courtesy of Nissan Motor Co., U.S.A.

*Pulsar NX XE & Sentra. Air Conditioning Switch & Power Steering Oil Pressure Switch (Non Self-Diagnostic Item) Test GG*

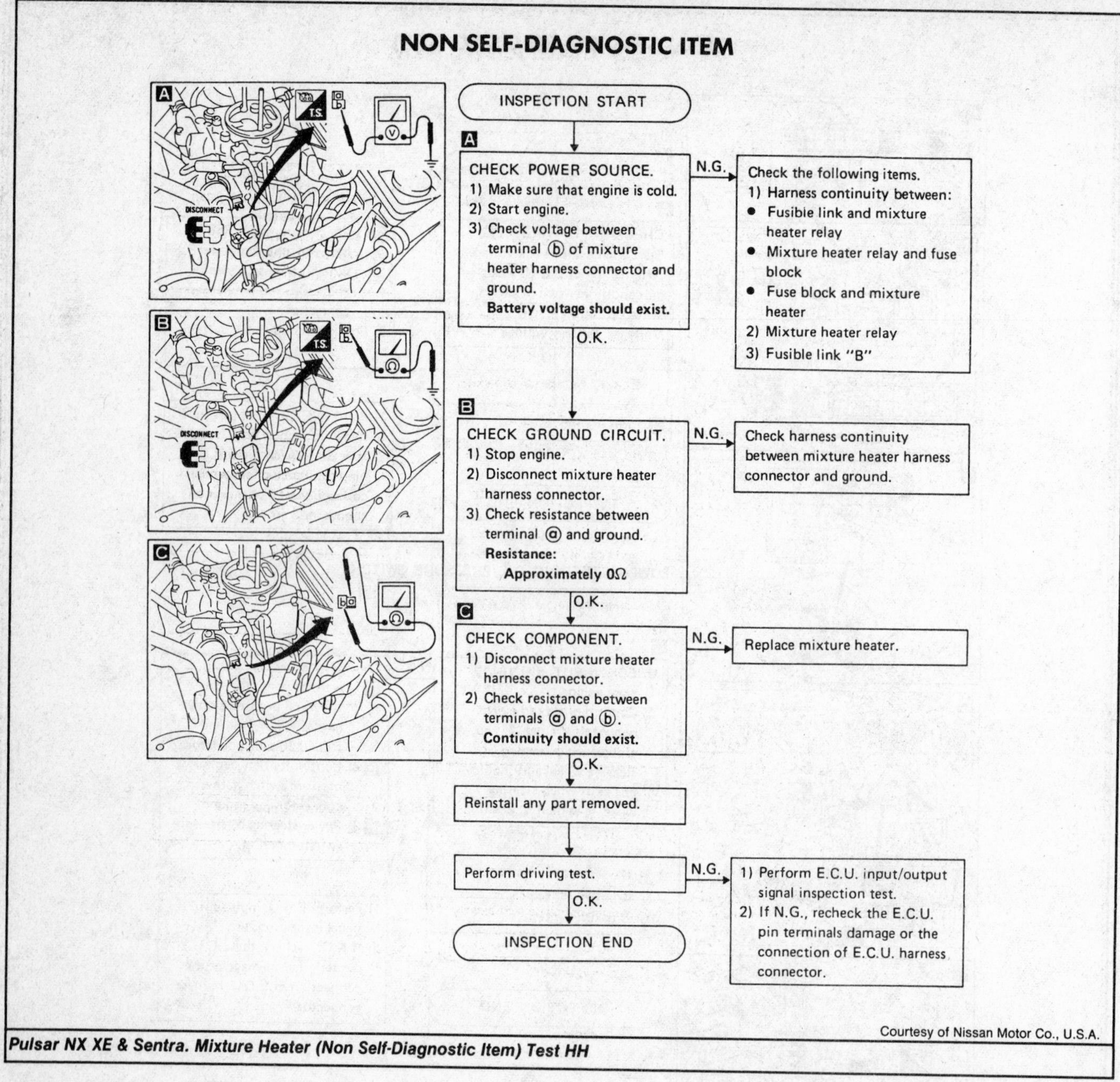
NON SELF-DIAGNOSTIC ITEM
A
B
C
DISCONNECT
T.S.
INSPECTION START
CHECK POWER SOURCE.
1) Make sure that engine is cold.
2) Start engine.
3) Check voltage between terminal ⓑ of mixture heater harness connector and ground.
Battery voltage should exist.
N.G.
Check the following items.
1) Harness continuity between:
• Fusible link and mixture heater relay
• Mixture heater relay and fuse block
• Fuse block and mixture heater
2) Mixture heater relay
3) Fusible link "B"
O.K.
CHECK GROUND CIRCUIT.
1) Stop engine.
2) Disconnect mixture heater harness connector.
3) Check resistance between terminal ⓐ and ground.
Resistance:
Approximately 0Ω
N.G.
Check harness continuity between mixture heater harness connector and ground.
O.K.
CHECK COMPONENT.
1) Disconnect mixture heater harness connector.
2) Check resistance between terminals ⓐ and ⓑ.
Continuity should exist.
N.G.
Replace mixture heater.
O.K.
Reinstall any part removed.
Perform driving test.
N.G.
1) Perform E.C.U. input/output signal inspection test.
2) If N.G., recheck the E.C.U. pin terminals damage or the connection of E.C.U. harness connector.
O.K.
INSPECTION END
Courtesy of Nissan Motor Co., U.S.A.

*Pulsar NX XE & Sentra. Mixture Heater (Non Self-Diagnostic Item) Test HH*

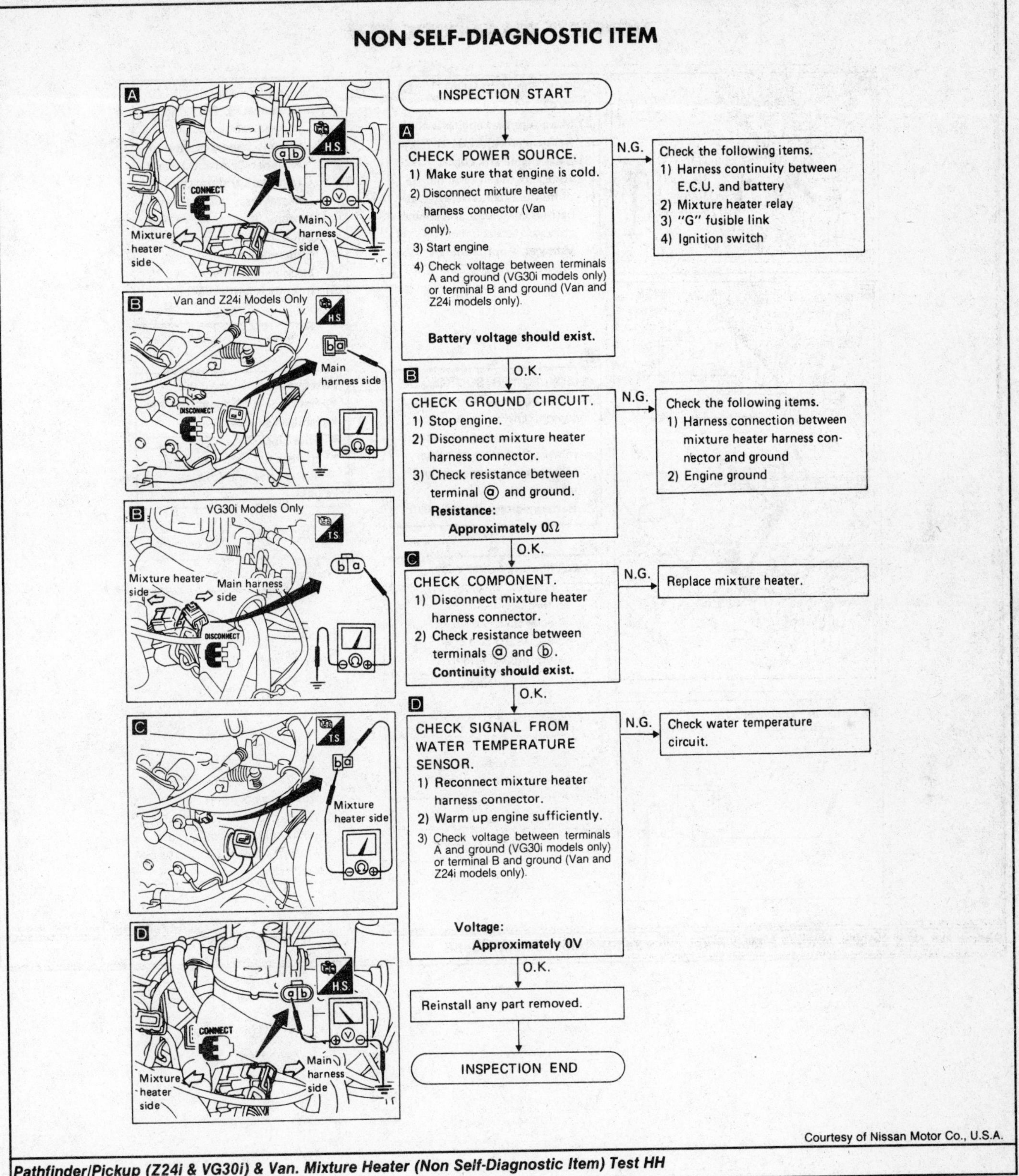
NON SELF-DIAGNOSTIC ITEM
A
H.S.
CONNECT
Mixture heater side
Main harness side
B Van and Z24i Models Only
H.S.
Main harness side
DISCONNECT
B VG30i Models Only
T.S.
Mixture heater side
Main harness side
DISCONNECT
C
T.S.
Mixture heater side
D
H.S.
CONNECT
Mixture heater side
Main harness side
INSPECTION START
A
CHECK POWER SOURCE.
1) Make sure that engine is cold.
2) Disconnect mixture heater harness connector (Van only).
3) Start engine
4) Check voltage between terminals A and ground (VG30i models only) or terminal B and ground (Van and Z24i models only).
Battery voltage should exist.
N.G.
Check the following items.
1) Harness continuity between E.C.U. and battery
2) Mixture heater relay
3) "G" fusible link
4) Ignition switch
O.K.
B
CHECK GROUND CIRCUIT.
1) Stop engine.
2) Disconnect mixture heater harness connector.
3) Check resistance between terminal ⓐ and ground.
Resistance:
Approximately 0Ω
N.G.
Check the following items.
1) Harness connection between mixture heater harness connector and ground
2) Engine ground
O.K.
C
CHECK COMPONENT.
1) Disconnect mixture heater harness connector.
2) Check resistance between terminals ⓐ and ⓑ.
Continuity should exist.
N.G.
Replace mixture heater.
O.K.
D
CHECK SIGNAL FROM WATER TEMPERATURE SENSOR.
1) Reconnect mixture heater harness connector.
2) Warm up engine sufficiently.
3) Check voltage between terminals A and ground (VG30i models only) or terminal B and ground (Van and Z24i models only).
Voltage:
Approximately 0V
N.G.
Check water temperature circuit.
O.K.
Reinstall any part removed.
INSPECTION END
Courtesy of Nissan Motor Co., U.S.A.

*Pathfinder/Pickup (Z24i & VG30i) & Van. Mixture Heater (Non Self-Diagnostic Item) Test HH*

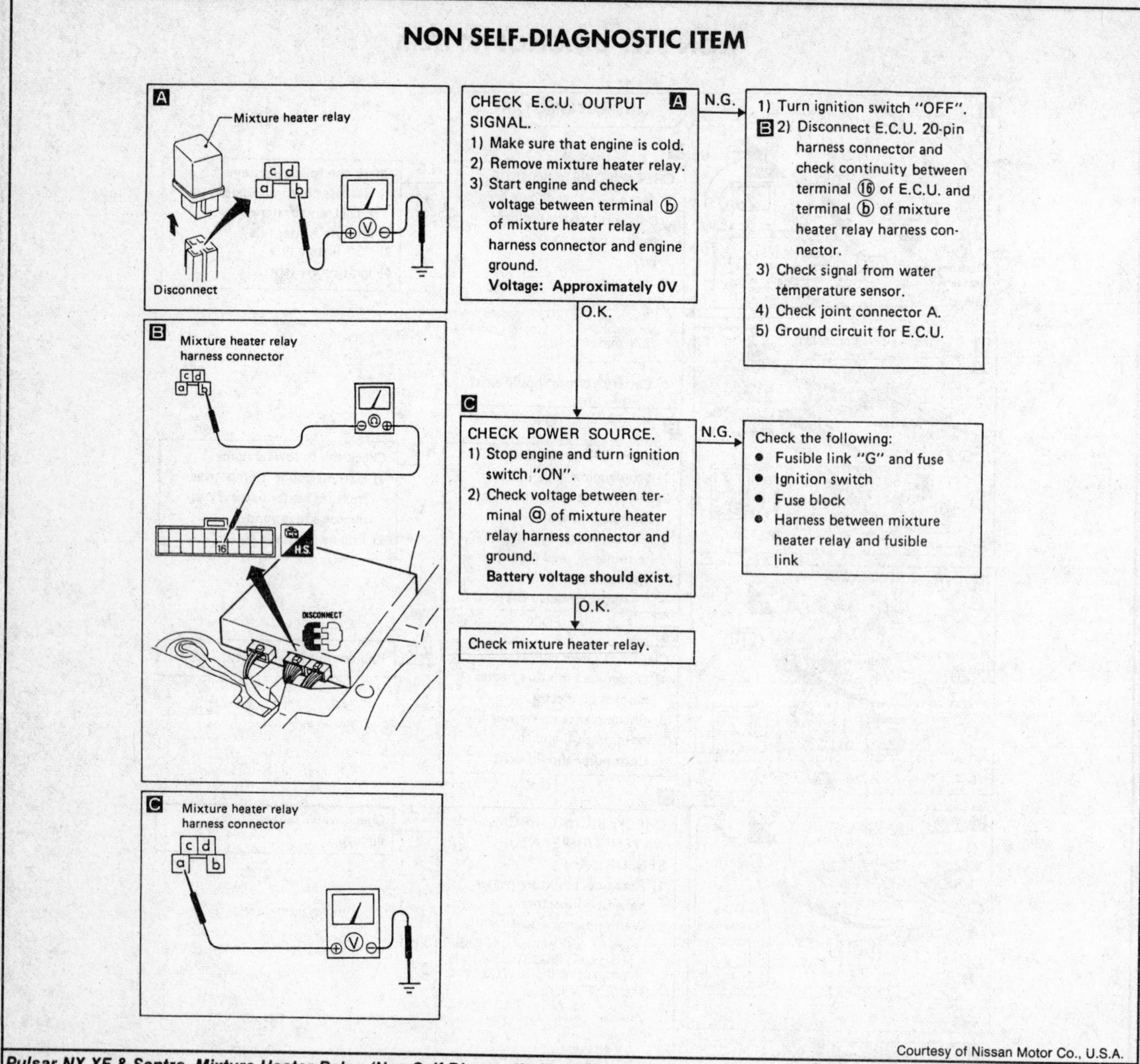
NON SELF-DIAGNOSTIC ITEM
A
Mixture heater relay
c d
a b
Disconnect
B
Mixture heater relay
harness connector
16
H.S.
DISCONNECT
C
Mixture heater relay
harness connector
CHECK E.C.U. OUTPUT SIGNAL. A
1) Make sure that engine is cold.
2) Remove mixture heater relay.
3) Start engine and check voltage between terminal ⓑ of mixture heater relay harness connector and engine ground.
Voltage: Approximately 0V
N.G.
1) Turn ignition switch "OFF".
B 2) Disconnect E.C.U. 20-pin harness connector and check continuity between terminal ⑯ of E.C.U. and terminal ⓑ of mixture heater relay harness connector.
3) Check signal from water temperature sensor.
4) Check joint connector A.
5) Ground circuit for E.C.U.
O.K.
C
CHECK POWER SOURCE.
1) Stop engine and turn ignition switch "ON".
2) Check voltage between terminal ⓐ of mixture heater relay harness connector and ground.
Battery voltage should exist.
N.G.
Check the following:
• Fusible link "G" and fuse
• Ignition switch
• Fuse block
• Harness between mixture heater relay and fusible link
O.K.
Check mixture heater relay.
Courtesy of Nissan Motor Co., U.S.A.

***Pulsar NX XE & Sentra. Mixture Heater Relay (Non Self-Diagnostic Item) Test II***

# 1988 COMPUTERIZED ENGINE CONTROLS
## Nissan Electronic Concentrated Control System (Cont.)

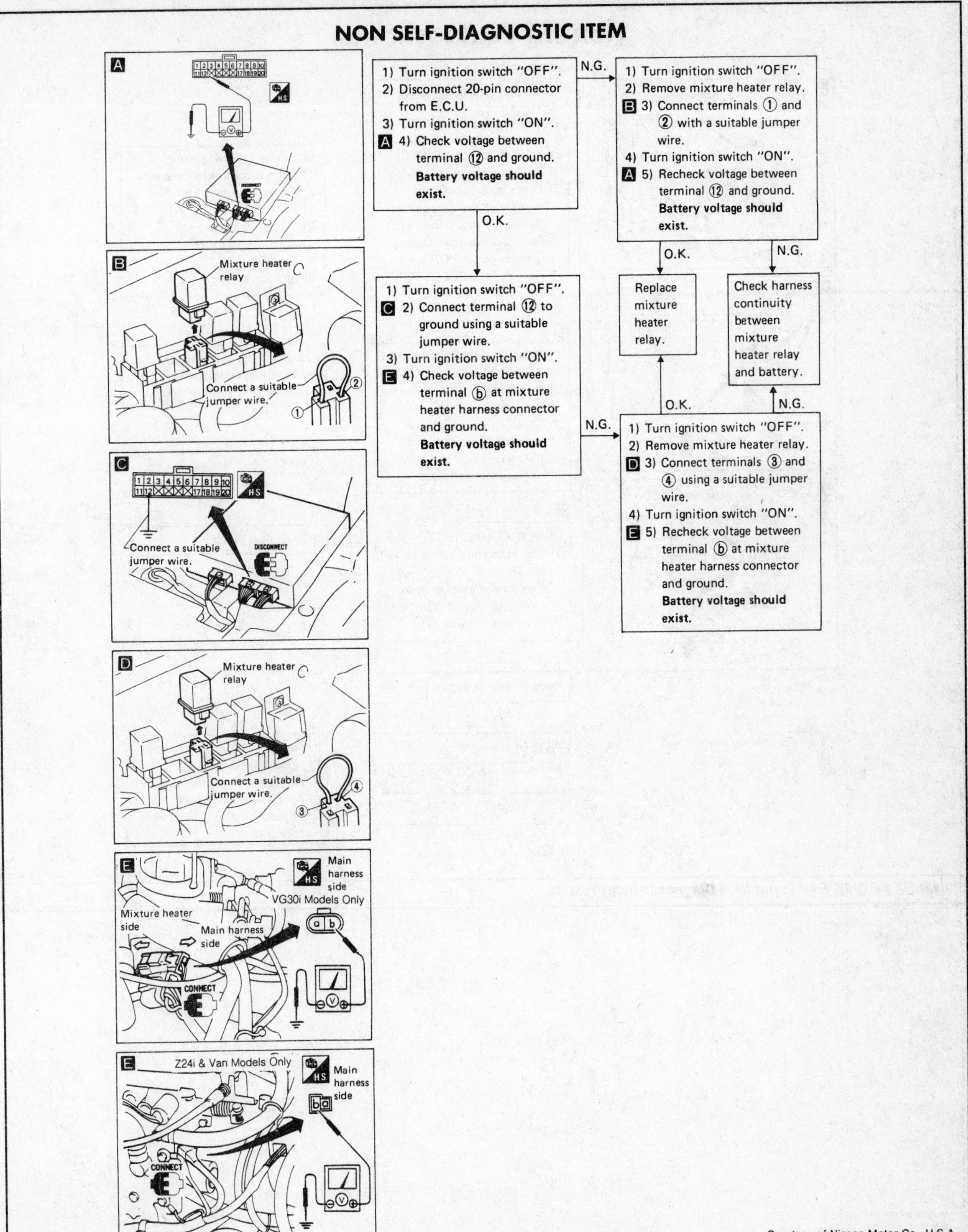
NON SELF-DIAGNOSTIC ITEM
1) Turn ignition switch "OFF".
2) Disconnect 20-pin connector from E.C.U.
3) Turn ignition switch "ON".
A 4) Check voltage between terminal ⑫ and ground.
Battery voltage should exist.
N.G.
1) Turn ignition switch "OFF".
2) Remove mixture heater relay.
B 3) Connect terminals ① and ② with a suitable jumper wire.
4) Turn ignition switch "ON".
A 5) Recheck voltage between terminal ⑫ and ground.
Battery voltage should exist.
O.K.
Replace mixture heater relay.
N.G.
Check harness continuity between mixture heater relay and battery.
O.K.
1) Turn ignition switch "OFF".
C 2) Connect terminal ⑫ to ground using a suitable jumper wire.
3) Turn ignition switch "ON".
E 4) Check voltage between terminal ⓑ at mixture heater harness connector and ground.
Battery voltage should exist.
N.G.
1) Turn ignition switch "OFF".
2) Remove mixture heater relay.
D 3) Connect terminals ③ and ④ using a suitable jumper wire.
4) Turn ignition switch "ON".
E 5) Recheck voltage between terminal ⓑ at mixture heater harness connector and ground.
Battery voltage should exist.
O.K.
N.G.
A
HS
DISCONNECT
B
Mixture heater relay
Connect a suitable jumper wire.
① ②
C
HS
Connect a suitable jumper wire.
DISCONNECT
D
Mixture heater relay
Connect a suitable jumper wire.
③ ④
E
HS
Main harness side
VG30i Models Only
Mixture heater side
Main harness side
CONNECT
a b
E
Z24i & Van Models Only
HS
Main harness side
CONNECT
b a

Courtesy of Nissan Motor Co., U.S.A.

*Pathfinder/Pickup (Z24i & VG30i) & Van. Mixture Heater Relay (Non Self-Diagnostic Item) Test II*

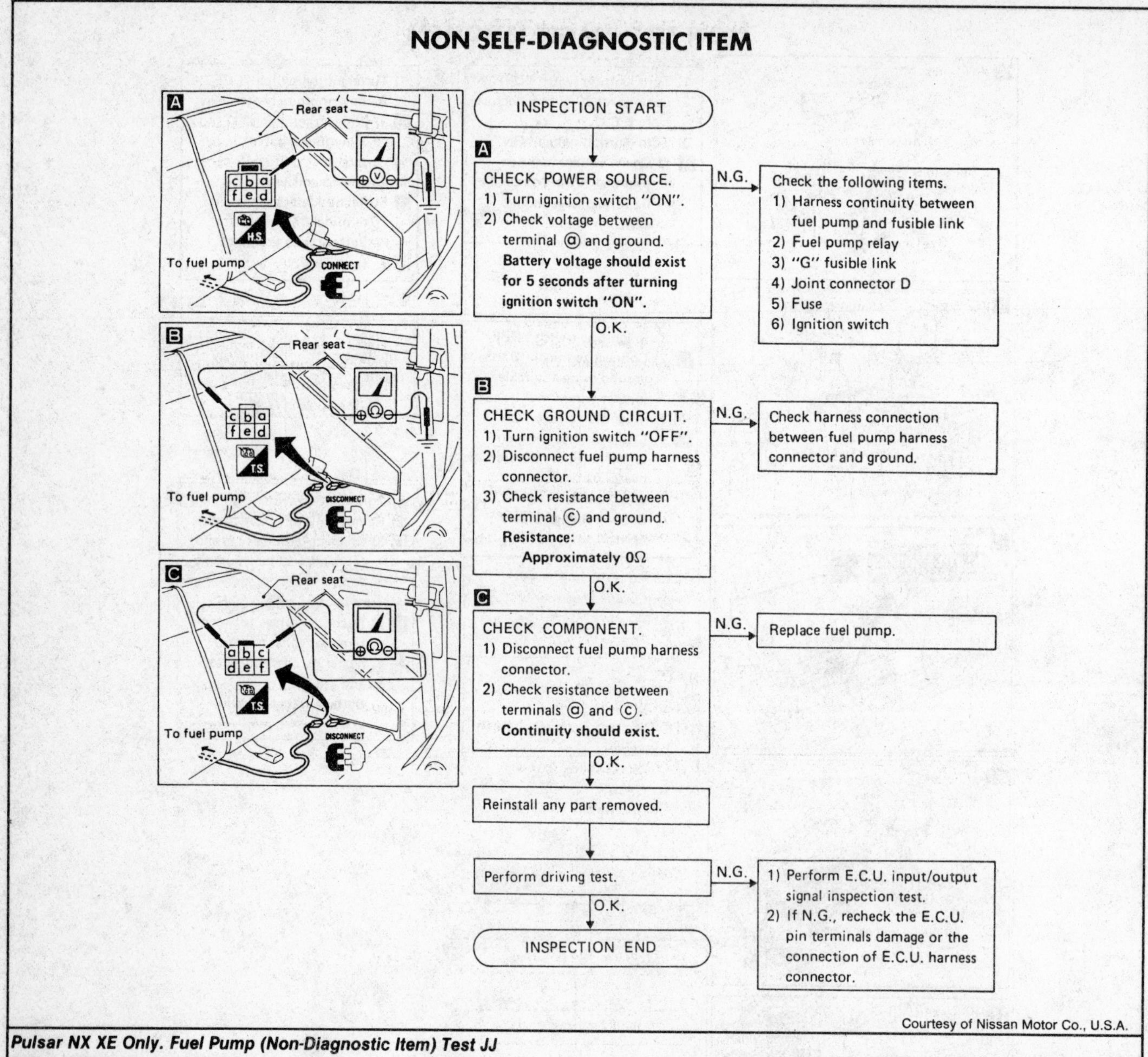
NON SELF-DIAGNOSTIC ITEM
A
Rear seat
c b a
f e d
H.S.
To fuel pump
CONNECT
B
Rear seat
c b a
f e d
T.S.
To fuel pump
DISCONNECT
C
Rear seat
a b c
d e f
T.S.
To fuel pump
DISCONNECT
INSPECTION START
A
CHECK POWER SOURCE.
1) Turn ignition switch "ON".
2) Check voltage between terminal ⓐ and ground.
Battery voltage should exist for 5 seconds after turning ignition switch "ON".
N.G.
Check the following items.
1) Harness continuity between fuel pump and fusible link
2) Fuel pump relay
3) "G" fusible link
4) Joint connector D
5) Fuse
6) Ignition switch
O.K.
B
CHECK GROUND CIRCUIT.
1) Turn ignition switch "OFF".
2) Disconnect fuel pump harness connector.
3) Check resistance between terminal ⓒ and ground.
Resistance:
Approximately 0Ω
N.G.
Check harness connection between fuel pump harness connector and ground.
O.K.
C
CHECK COMPONENT.
1) Disconnect fuel pump harness connector.
2) Check resistance between terminals ⓐ and ⓒ.
Continuity should exist.
N.G.
Replace fuel pump.
O.K.
Reinstall any part removed.
Perform driving test.
N.G.
1) Perform E.C.U. input/output signal inspection test.
2) If N.G., recheck the E.C.U. pin terminals damage or the connection of E.C.U. harness connector.
O.K.
INSPECTION END
Courtesy of Nissan Motor Co., U.S.A.

*Pulsar NX XE Only. Fuel Pump (Non-Diagnostic Item) Test JJ*

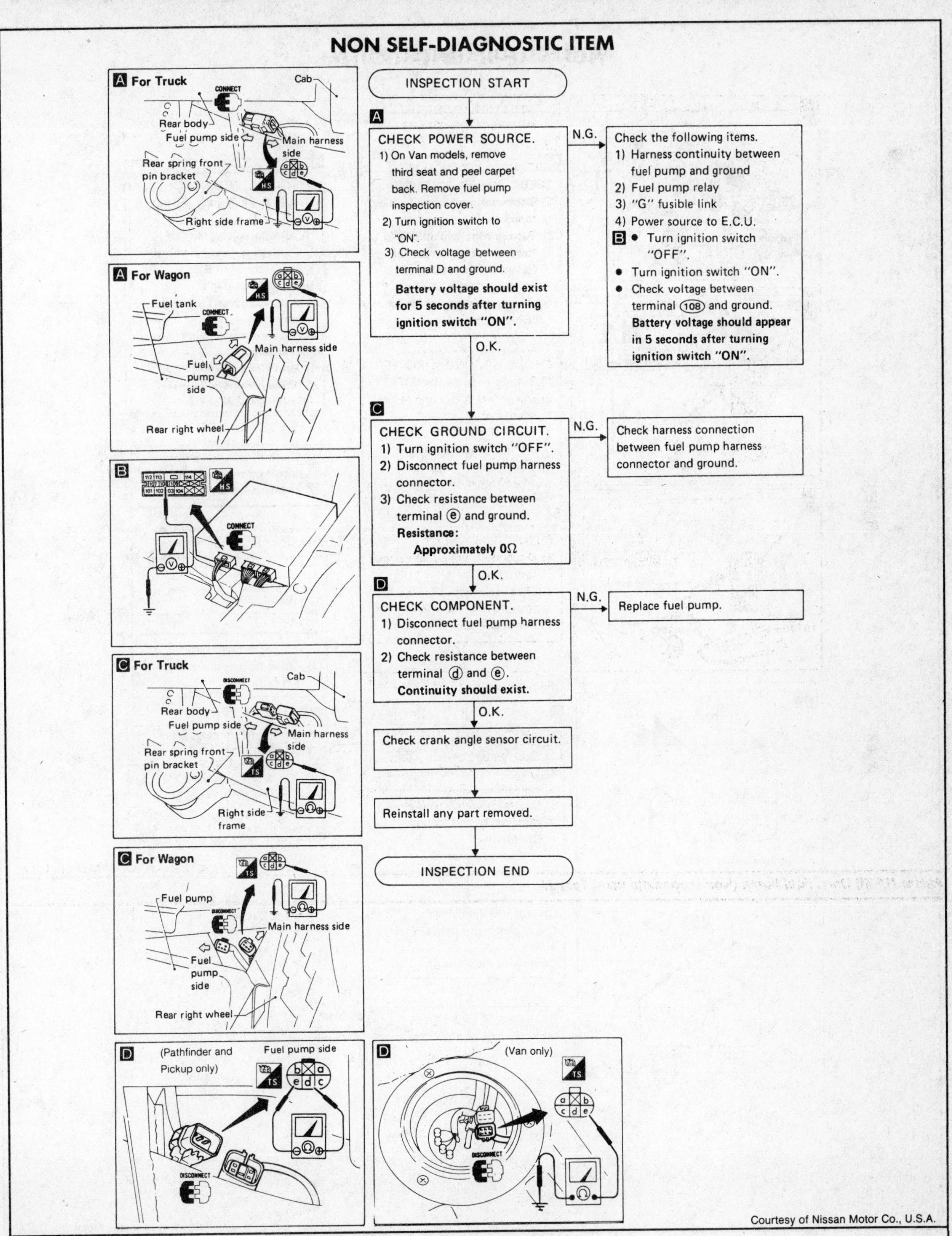
NON SELF-DIAGNOSTIC ITEM
A For Truck
Cab
CONNECT
Rear body
Fuel pump side
Main harness side
Rear spring front pin bracket
Right side frame
A For Wagon
Fuel tank
CONNECT
Main harness side
Fuel pump side
Rear right wheel
B
CONNECT
C For Truck
DISCONNECT
Cab
Rear body
Fuel pump side
Main harness side
Rear spring front pin bracket
Right side frame
C For Wagon
Fuel pump
DISCONNECT
Main harness side
Fuel pump side
Rear right wheel
D
(Pathfinder and Pickup only)
Fuel pump side
DISCONNECT
D
(Van only)
DISCONNECT
INSPECTION START
A
CHECK POWER SOURCE.
1) On Van models, remove third seat and peel carpet back. Remove fuel pump inspection cover.
2) Turn ignition switch to "ON".
3) Check voltage between terminal D and ground.
Battery voltage should exist for 5 seconds after turning ignition switch "ON".
N.G.
Check the following items.
1) Harness continuity between fuel pump and ground
2) Fuel pump relay
3) "G" fusible link
4) Power source to E.C.U.
B • Turn ignition switch "OFF".
• Turn ignition switch "ON".
• Check voltage between terminal (108) and ground.
Battery voltage should appear in 5 seconds after turning ignition switch "ON".
O.K.
C
CHECK GROUND CIRCUIT.
1) Turn ignition switch "OFF".
2) Disconnect fuel pump harness connector.
3) Check resistance between terminal (e) and ground.
Resistance:
Approximately 0Ω
N.G.
Check harness connection between fuel pump harness connector and ground.
O.K.
D
CHECK COMPONENT.
1) Disconnect fuel pump harness connector.
2) Check resistance between terminal (d) and (e).
Continuity should exist.
N.G.
Replace fuel pump.
O.K.
Check crank angle sensor circuit.
Reinstall any part removed.
INSPECTION END

Courtesy of Nissan Motor Co., U.S.A.

***Pathfinder/Pickup (Z24i & VG30i) & Van. Fuel Pump (Non-Diagnostic Item) Test JJ***

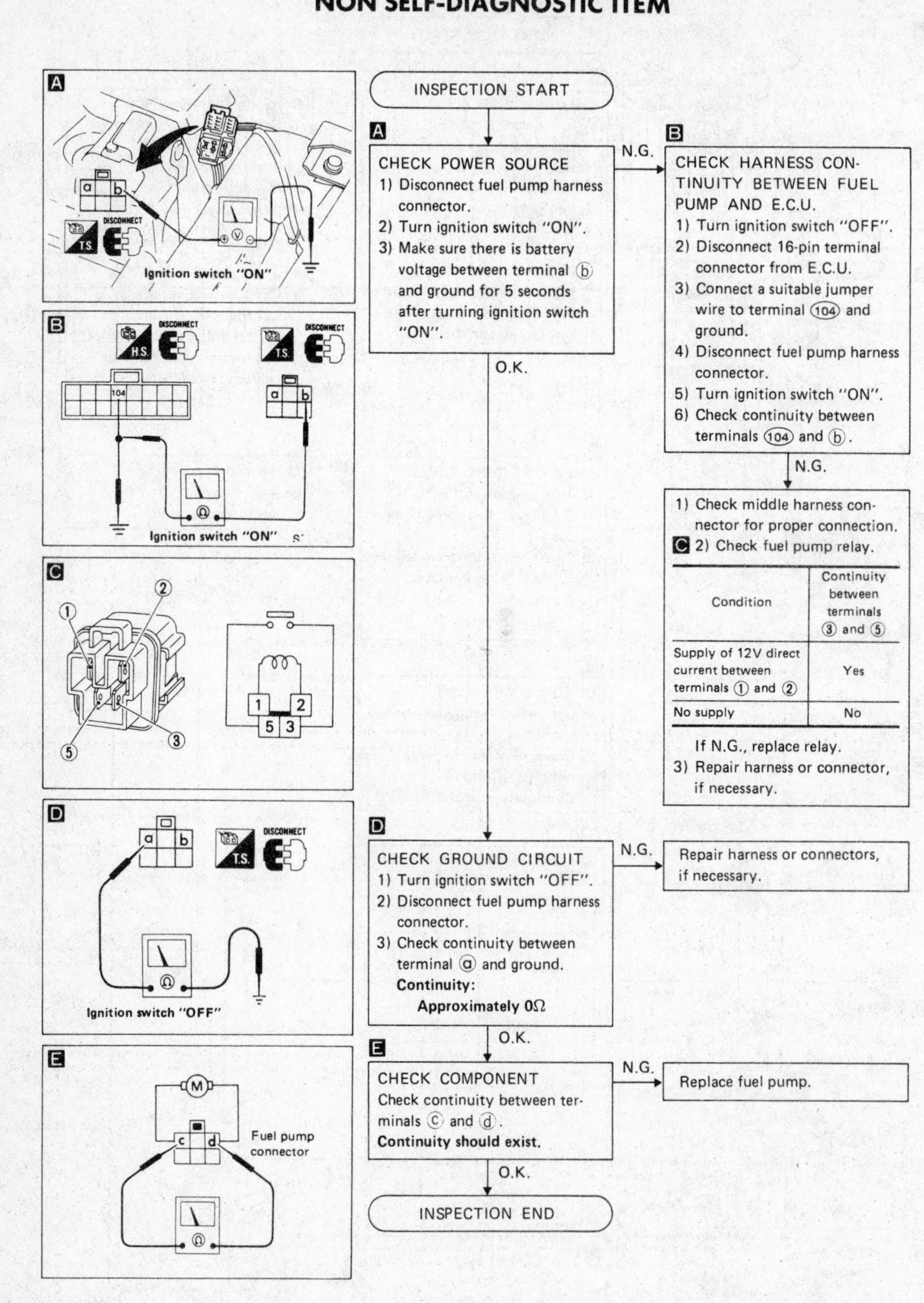
NON SELF-DIAGNOSTIC ITEM
A
Ignition switch "ON"
DISCONNECT
T.S.
B
DISCONNECT
H.S.
T.S.
104
Ignition switch "ON"
C
1 2
5 3
D
DISCONNECT
T.S.
Ignition switch "OFF"
E
M
c d
Fuel pump connector
INSPECTION START
A
CHECK POWER SOURCE
1) Disconnect fuel pump harness connector.
2) Turn ignition switch "ON".
3) Make sure there is battery voltage between terminal ⓑ and ground for 5 seconds after turning ignition switch "ON".
N.G.
B
CHECK HARNESS CONTINUITY BETWEEN FUEL PUMP AND E.C.U.
1) Turn ignition switch "OFF".
2) Disconnect 16-pin terminal connector from E.C.U.
3) Connect a suitable jumper wire to terminal (104) and ground.
4) Disconnect fuel pump harness connector.
5) Turn ignition switch "ON".
6) Check continuity between terminals (104) and ⓑ.
N.G.
1) Check middle harness connector for proper connection.
C 2) Check fuel pump relay.
Condition | Continuity between terminals ③ and ⑤
Supply of 12V direct current between terminals ① and ② | Yes
No supply | No
If N.G., replace relay.
3) Repair harness or connector, if necessary.
O.K.
D
CHECK GROUND CIRCUIT
1) Turn ignition switch "OFF".
2) Disconnect fuel pump harness connector.
3) Check continuity between terminal ⓐ and ground.
Continuity:
Approximately 0Ω
N.G.
Repair harness or connectors, if necessary.
O.K.
E
CHECK COMPONENT
Check continuity between terminals ⓒ and ⓓ.
Continuity should exist.
N.G.
Replace fuel pump.
O.K.
INSPECTION END

Courtesy of Nissan Motor Co., U.S.A.

*Pulsar NX SE Only. Fuel Pump (Non-Diagnostic Item) Test JJ*

# Nissan Electronic Concentrated Control System (Cont.)

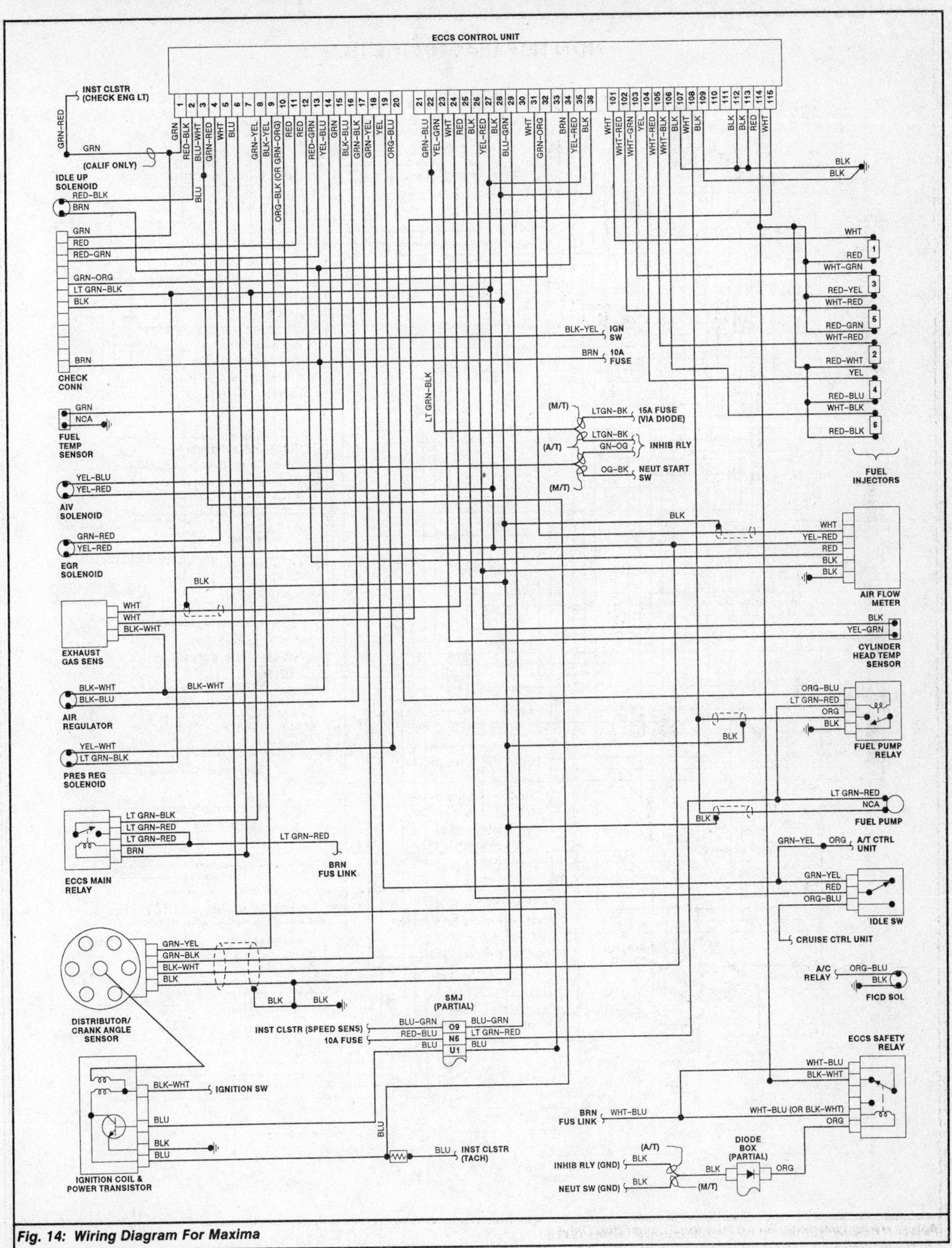
ECCS CONTROL UNIT
INST CLSTR (CHECK ENG LT)
(CALIF ONLY)
IDLE UP SOLENOID
CHECK CONN
FUEL TEMP SENSOR
AIV SOLENOID
EGR SOLENOID
EXHAUST GAS SENS
AIR REGULATOR
PRES REG SOLENOID
ECCS MAIN RELAY
BRN FUS LINK
DISTRIBUTOR/ CRANK ANGLE SENSOR
SMJ (PARTIAL)
INST CLSTR (SPEED SENS)
10A FUSE
IGNITION SW
INST CLSTR (TACH)
IGNITION COIL & POWER TRANSISTOR
IGN SW
10A FUSE
15A FUSE (VIA DIODE)
INHIB RLY
NEUT START SW
FUEL INJECTORS
AIR FLOW METER
CYLINDER HEAD TEMP SENSOR
FUEL PUMP RELAY
FUEL PUMP
A/T CTRL UNIT
IDLE SW
CRUISE CTRL UNIT
A/C RELAY
FICD SOL
ECCS SAFETY RELAY
BRN FUS LINK
INHIB RLY (GND)
NEUT SW (GND)
DIODE BOX (PARTIAL)

Fig. 14: Wiring Diagram For Maxima

# 1988 COMPUTERIZED ENGINE CONTROLS
## Nissan Electronic Concentrated Control System (Cont.)

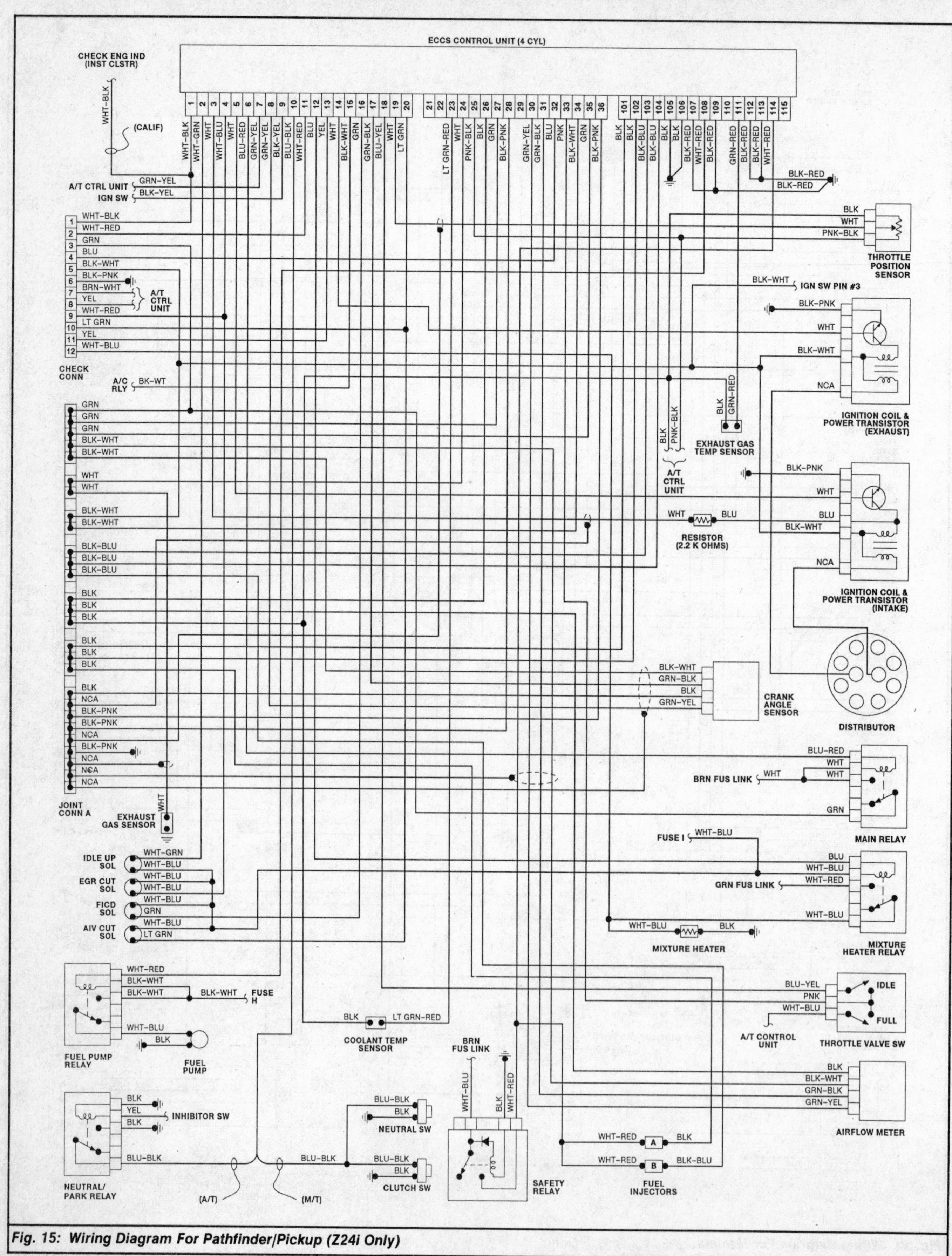

*Fig. 15: Wiring Diagram For Pathfinder/Pickup (Z24i Only)*

# 1988 COMPUTERIZED ENGINE CONTROLS
## Nissan Electronic Concentrated Control System (Cont.)

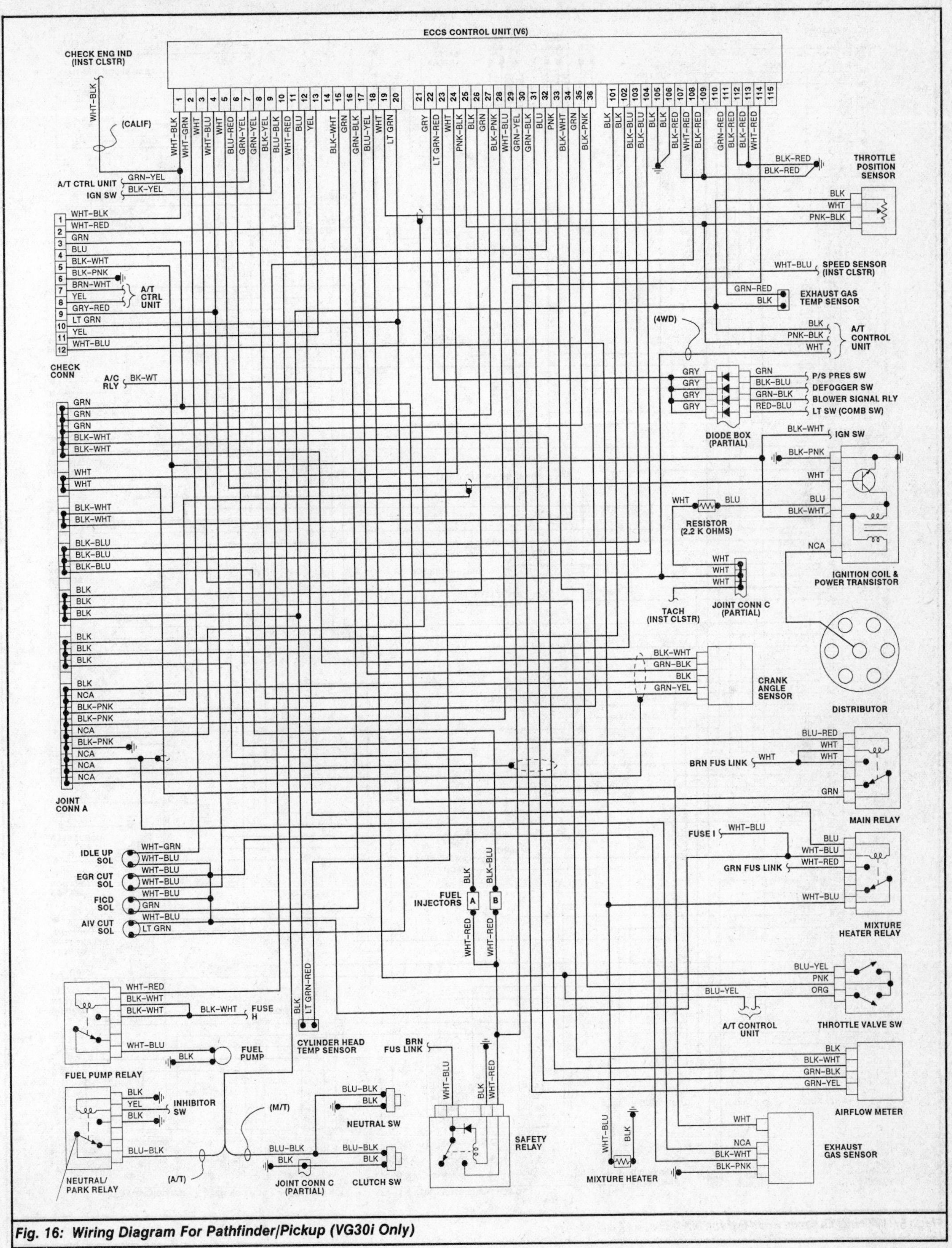

*Fig. 16: Wiring Diagram For Pathfinder/Pickup (VG30i Only)*

# 1988 COMPUTERIZED ENGINE CONTROLS
## Nissan Electronic Concentrated Control System (Cont.)

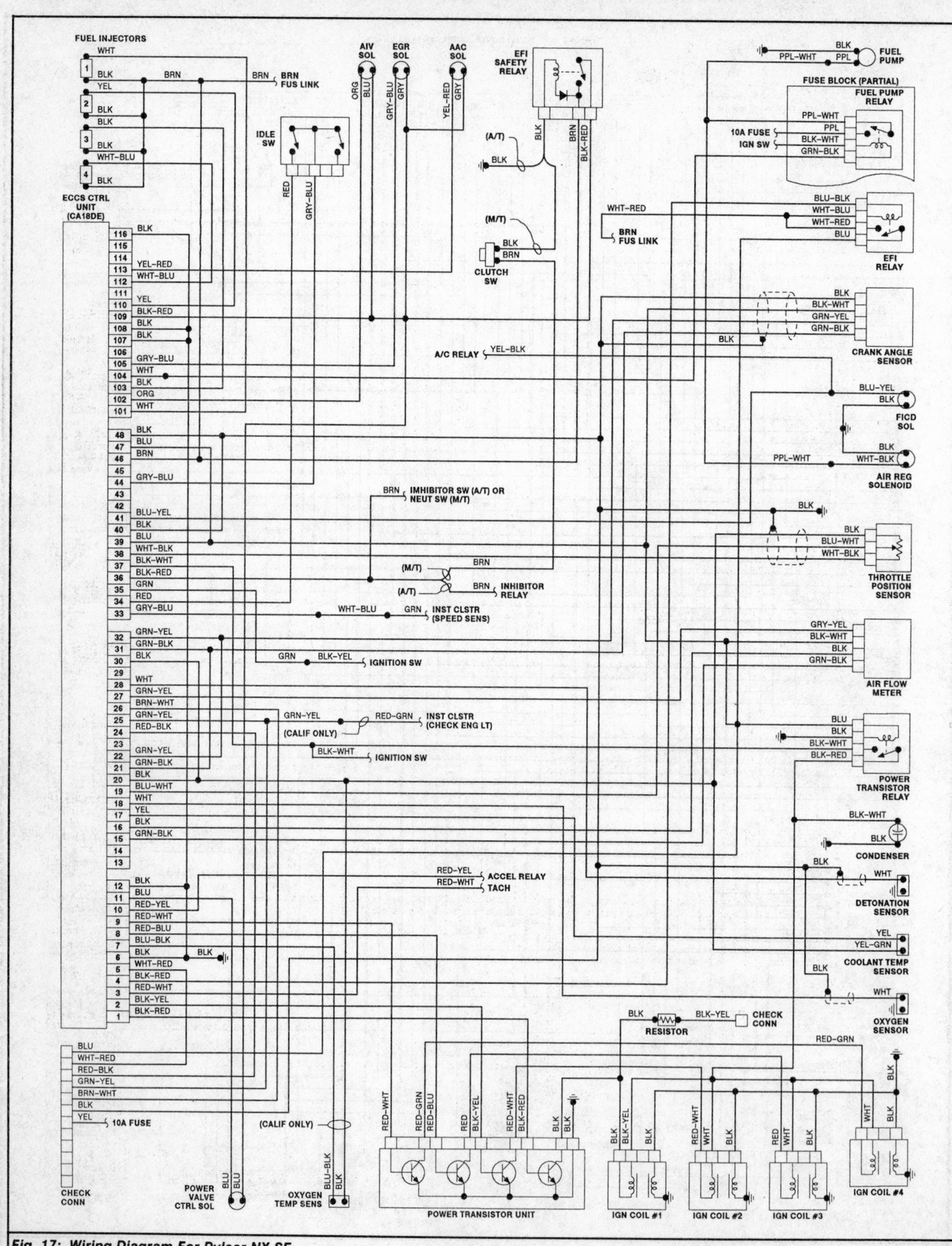

FUEL INJECTORS
WHT
BLK
YEL
BRN
BRN FUS LINK
WHT-BLU
ECCS CTRL UNIT (CA18DE)
AIV SOL
EGR SOL
AAC SOL
ORG
BLU
GRY-BLU
GRY
YEL-RED
IDLE SW
RED
EFI SAFETY RELAY
(A/T)
(M/T)
BLK
BRN
BLK-RED
CLUTCH SW
WHT-RED
A/C RELAY
YEL-BLK
IMHIBITOR SW (A/T) OR NEUT SW (M/T)
INHIBITOR RELAY
WHT-BLU
GRN
INST CLSTR (SPEED SENS)
BLK-YEL
IGNITION SW
GRN-YEL
RED-GRN
INST CLSTR (CHECK ENG LT)
(CALIF ONLY)
BLK-WHT
RED-YEL
ACCEL RELAY
RED-WHT
TACH
FUEL PUMP
PPL-WHT
PPL
FUSE BLOCK (PARTIAL)
FUEL PUMP RELAY
10A FUSE
IGN SW
BLK-WHT
GRN-BLK
BLU-BLK
WHT-BLU
BLU
EFI RELAY
CRANK ANGLE SENSOR
BLU-YEL
FICD SOL
AIR REG SOLENOID
BLU-WHT
THROTTLE POSITION SENSOR
GRY-YEL
AIR FLOW METER
POWER TRANSISTOR RELAY
CONDENSER
DETONATION SENSOR
YEL
YEL-GRN
COOLANT TEMP SENSOR
OXYGEN SENSOR
RESISTOR
CHECK CONN
10A FUSE
CHECK CONN
POWER VALVE CTRL SOL
BLU-BLK
OXYGEN TEMP SENS
RED-BLU
POWER TRANSISTOR UNIT
IGN COIL #1
IGN COIL #2
IGN COIL #3
IGN COIL #4


*Fig. 17: Wiring Diagram For Pulsar NX SE*

## Nissan Electronic Concentrated Control System (Cont.)

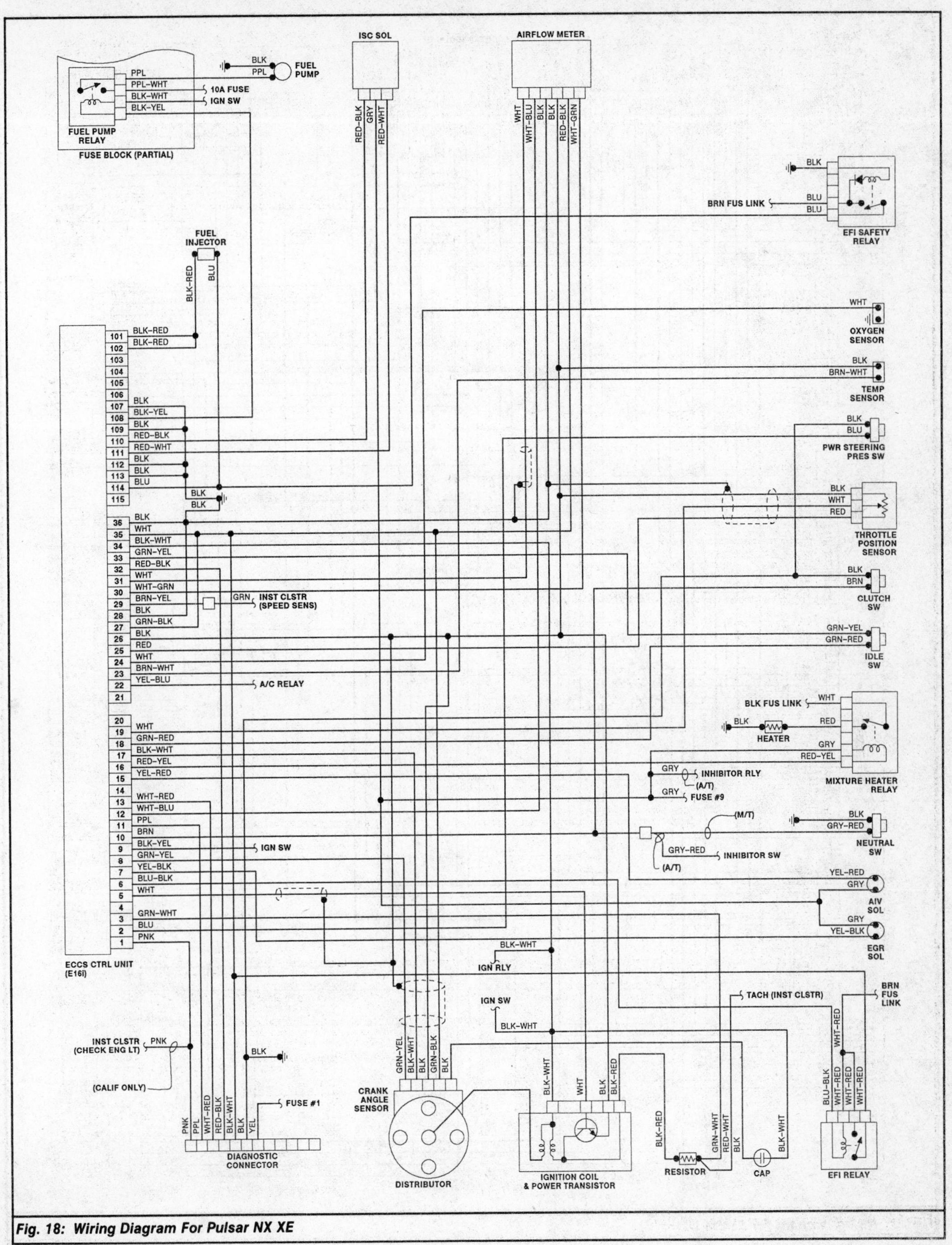
ISC SOL
AIRFLOW METER
FUEL PUMP
10A FUSE
IGN SW
FUEL PUMP RELAY
FUSE BLOCK (PARTIAL)
BRN FUS LINK
EFI SAFETY RELAY
FUEL INJECTOR
OXYGEN SENSOR
TEMP SENSOR
PWR STEERING PRES SW
THROTTLE POSITION SENSOR
INST CLSTR (SPEED SENS)
CLUTCH SW
IDLE SW
A/C RELAY
BLK FUS LINK
HEATER
MIXTURE HEATER RELAY
INHIBITOR RLY
FUSE #9
NEUTRAL SW
INHIBITOR SW
AIV SOL
EGR SOL
ECCS CTRL UNIT (E16i)
IGN RLY
TACH (INST CLSTR)
BRN FUS LINK
INST CLSTR (CHECK ENG LT)
(CALIF ONLY)
FUSE #1
CRANK ANGLE SENSOR
DIAGNOSTIC CONNECTOR
DISTRIBUTOR
IGNITION COIL & POWER TRANSISTOR
RESISTOR
CAP
EFI RELAY

*Fig. 18: Wiring Diagram For Pulsar NX XE*

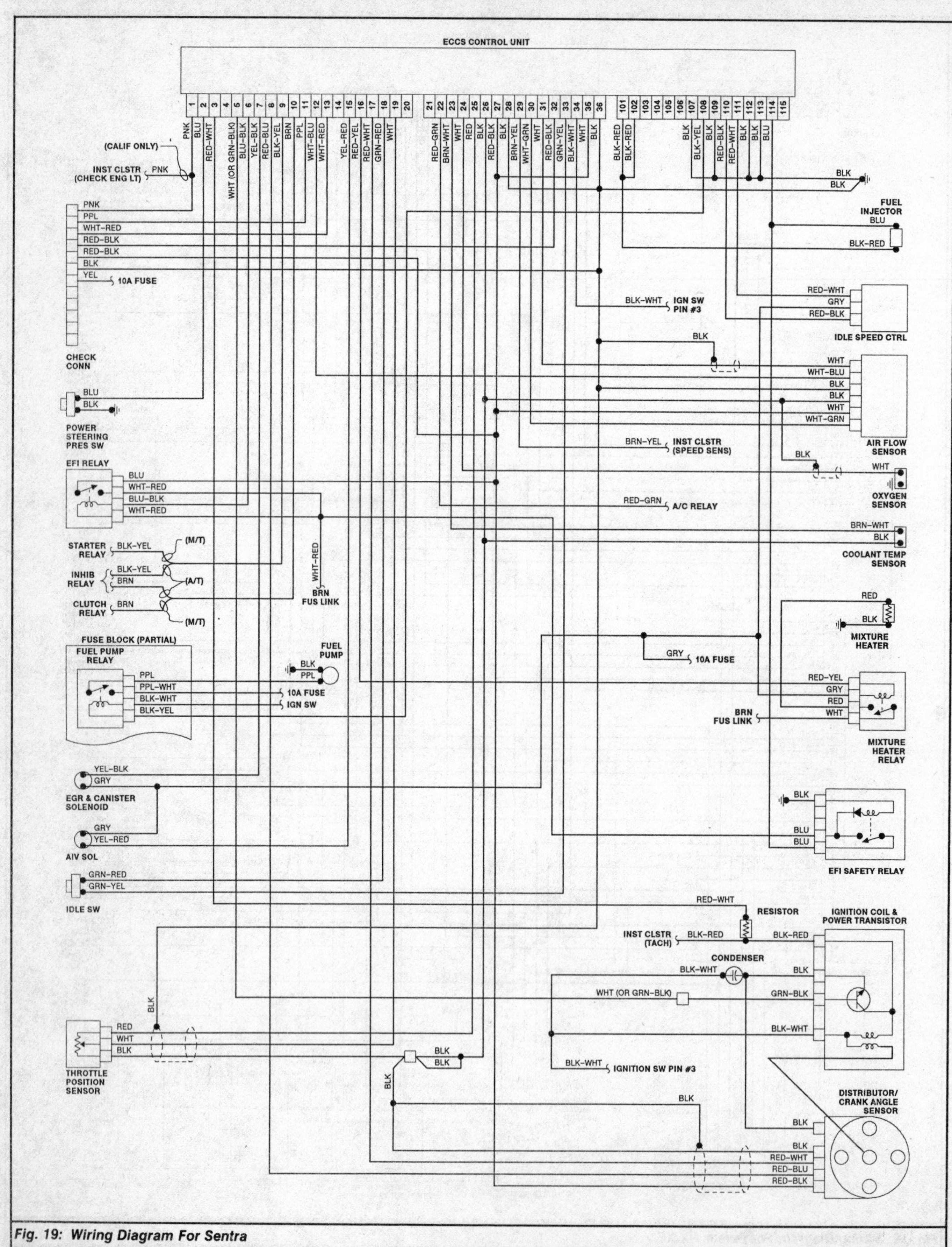
ECCS CONTROL UNIT
(CALIF ONLY)
INST CLSTR (CHECK ENG LT)
CHECK CONN
10A FUSE
POWER STEERING PRES SW
EFI RELAY
STARTER RELAY
INHIB RELAY
CLUTCH RELAY
(M/T)
(A/T)
BRN FUS LINK
FUSE BLOCK (PARTIAL)
FUEL PUMP RELAY
FUEL PUMP
IGN SW
EGR & CANISTER SOLENOID
AIV SOL
IDLE SW
THROTTLE POSITION SENSOR
FUEL INJECTOR
IGN SW PIN #3
IDLE SPEED CTRL
AIR FLOW SENSOR
INST CLSTR (SPEED SENS)
OXYGEN SENSOR
A/C RELAY
COOLANT TEMP SENSOR
MIXTURE HEATER
MIXTURE HEATER RELAY
EFI SAFETY RELAY
RESISTOR
INST CLSTR (TACH)
CONDENSER
IGNITION COIL & POWER TRANSISTOR
IGNITION SW PIN #3
DISTRIBUTOR/ CRANK ANGLE SENSOR

*Fig. 19: Wiring Diagram For Sentra*

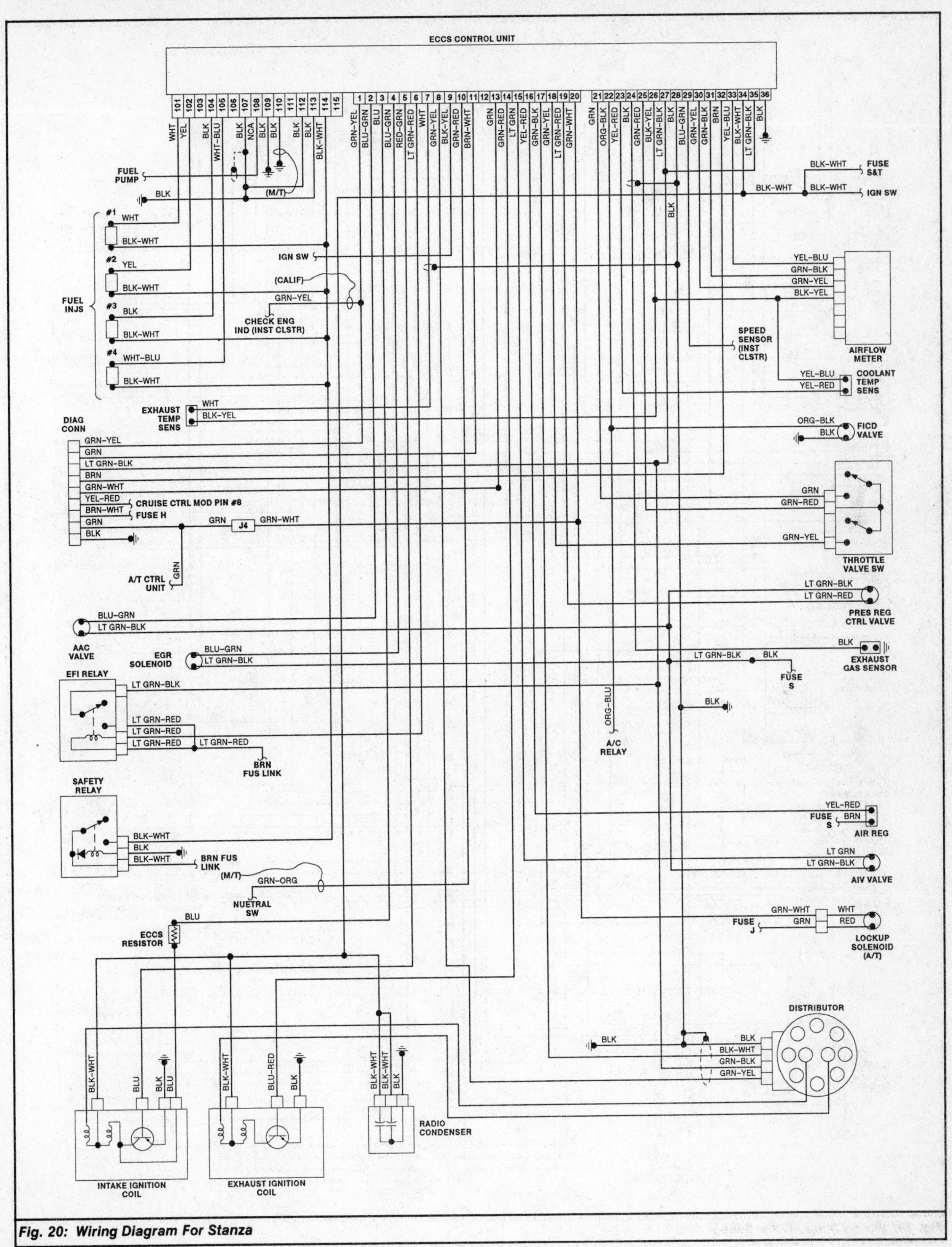
ECCS CONTROL UNIT
FUEL PUMP
FUEL INJS
IGN SW
CHECK ENG IND (INST CLSTR)
EXHAUST TEMP SENS
DIAG CONN
CRUISE CTRL MOD PIN #8
FUSE H
A/T CTRL UNIT
AAC VALVE
EGR SOLENOID
EFI RELAY
BRN FUS LINK
SAFETY RELAY
NUETRAL SW
ECCS RESISTOR
INTAKE IGNITION COIL
EXHAUST IGNITION COIL
RADIO CONDENSER
DISTRIBUTOR
FUSE S&T
AIRFLOW METER
SPEED SENSOR (INST CLSTR)
COOLANT TEMP SENS
FICD VALVE
THROTTLE VALVE SW
PRES REG CTRL VALVE
EXHAUST GAS SENSOR
A/C RELAY
AIR REG
AIV VALVE
LOCKUP SOLENOID (A/T)

*Fig. 20: Wiring Diagram For Stanza*

# 1988 COMPUTERIZED ENGINE CONTROLS
## Nissan Electronic Concentrated Control System (Cont.)

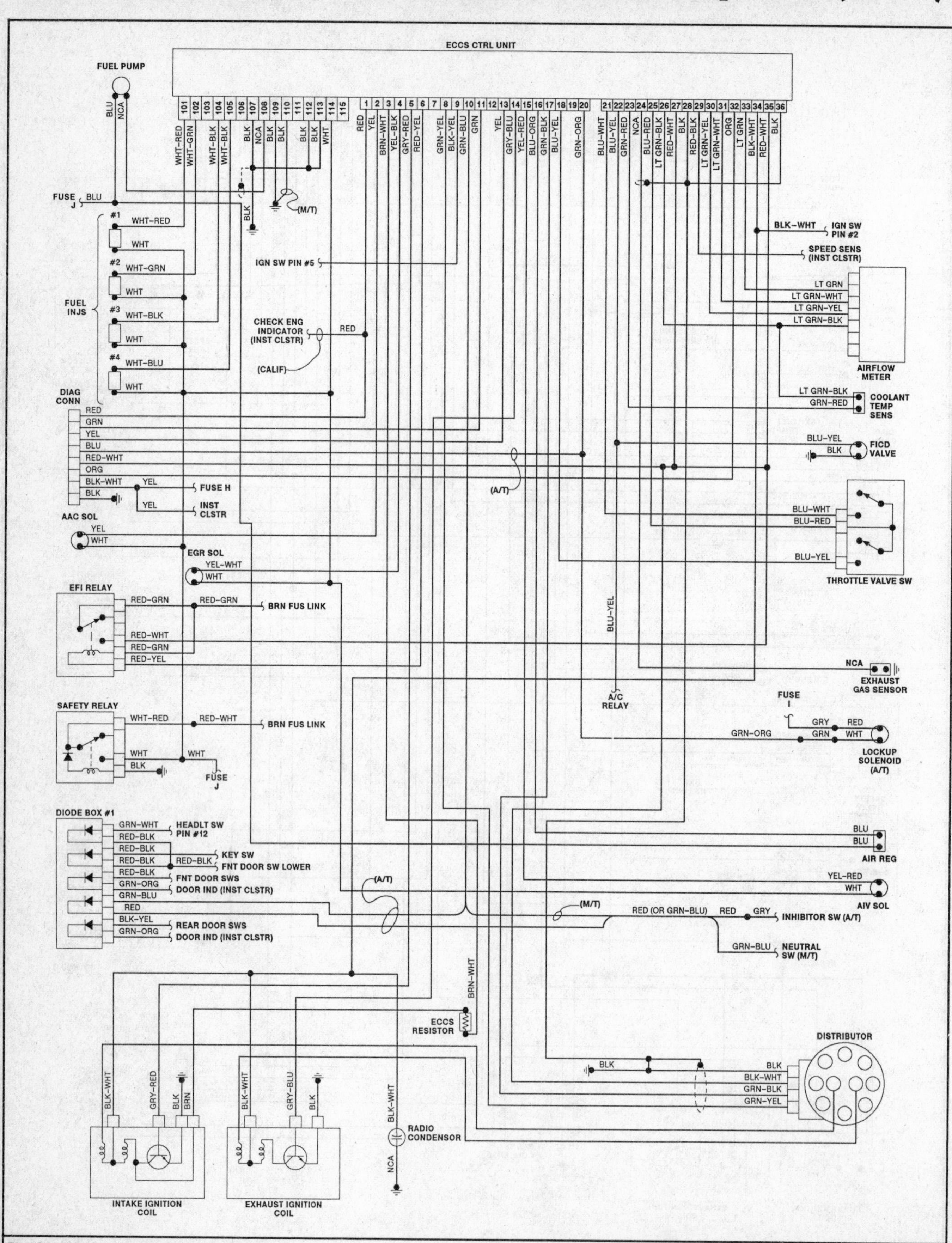
ECCS CTRL UNIT
FUEL PUMP
FUSE J
FUEL INJS
DIAG CONN
FUSE H
INST CLSTR
AAC SOL
EGR SOL
EFI RELAY
BRN FUS LINK
SAFETY RELAY
DIODE BOX #1
HEADLT SW PIN #12
KEY SW
FNT DOOR SW LOWER
FNT DOOR SWS
DOOR IND (INST CLSTR)
REAR DOOR SWS
IGN SW PIN #5
CHECK ENG INDICATOR (INST CLSTR)
(CALIF)
IGN SW PIN #2
SPEED SENS (INST CLSTR)
AIRFLOW METER
COOLANT TEMP SENS
FICD VALVE
THROTTLE VALVE SW
A/C RELAY
EXHAUST GAS SENSOR
LOCKUP SOLENOID (A/T)
AIR REG
AIV SOL
INHIBITOR SW (A/T)
NEUTRAL SW (M/T)
ECCS RESISTOR
RADIO CONDENSOR
DISTRIBUTOR
INTAKE IGNITION COIL
EXHAUST IGNITION COIL

*Fig. 21: Wiring Diagram For Stanza Wagon*

# Nissan Electronic Concentrated Control System (Cont.)

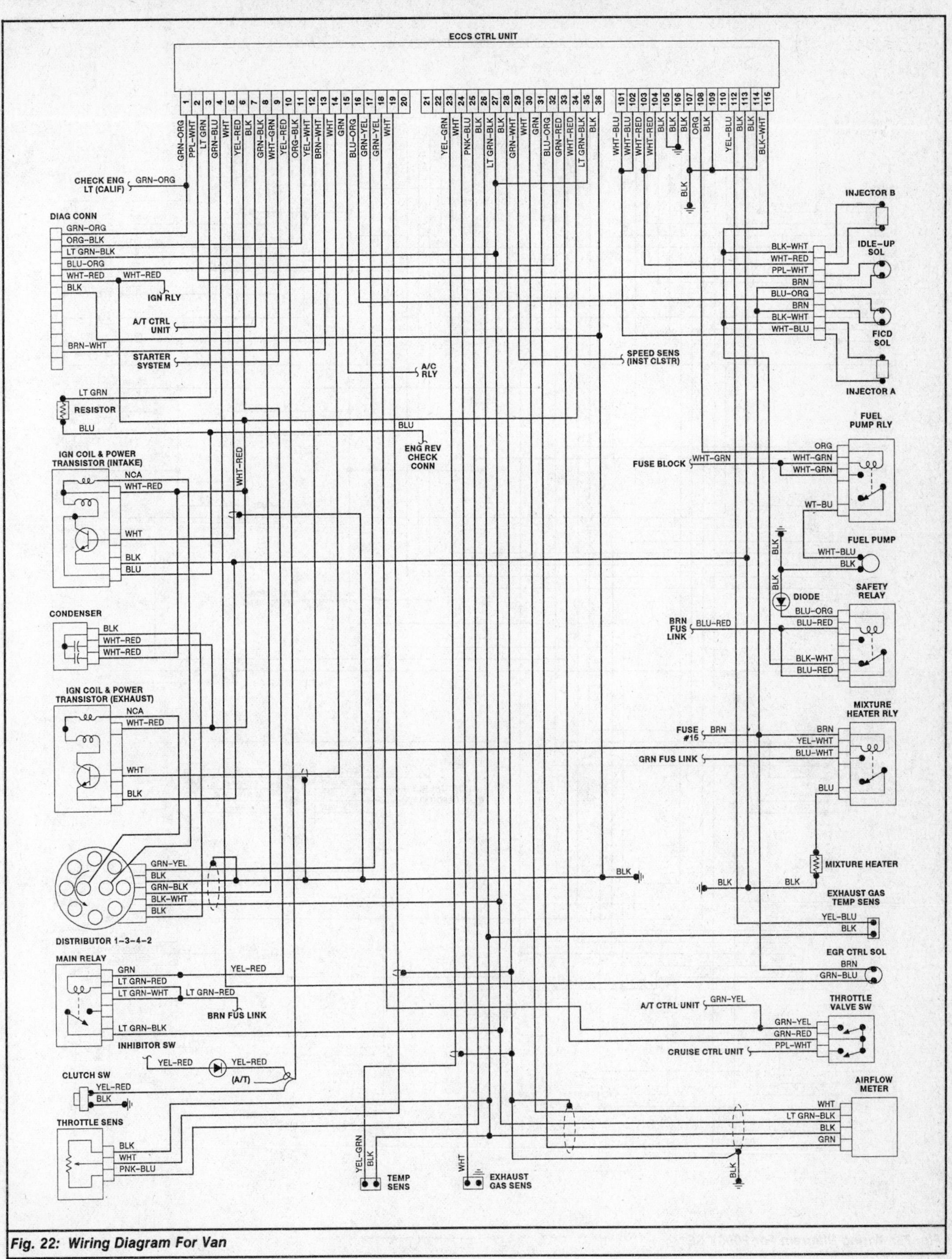
ECCS CTRL UNIT
CHECK ENG LT (CALIF)
DIAG CONN
IGN RLY
A/T CTRL UNIT
STARTER SYSTEM
RESISTOR
IGN COIL & POWER TRANSISTOR (INTAKE)
CONDENSER
IGN COIL & POWER TRANSISTOR (EXHAUST)
DISTRIBUTOR 1-3-4-2
MAIN RELAY
BRN FUS LINK
INHIBITOR SW
CLUTCH SW
THROTTLE SENS
TEMP SENS
EXHAUST GAS SENS
A/C RLY
ENG REV CHECK CONN
SPEED SENS (INST CLSTR)
INJECTOR B
IDLE-UP SOL
FICD SOL
INJECTOR A
FUEL PUMP RLY
FUSE BLOCK
FUEL PUMP
DIODE
SAFETY RELAY
BRN FUS LINK
MIXTURE HEATER RLY
FUSE #15
GRN FUS LINK
MIXTURE HEATER
EXHAUST GAS TEMP SENS
EGR CTRL SOL
A/T CTRL UNIT
THROTTLE VALVE SW
CRUISE CTRL UNIT
AIRFLOW METER

*Fig. 22: Wiring Diagram For Van*

# Nissan Electronic Concentrated Control System (Cont.)

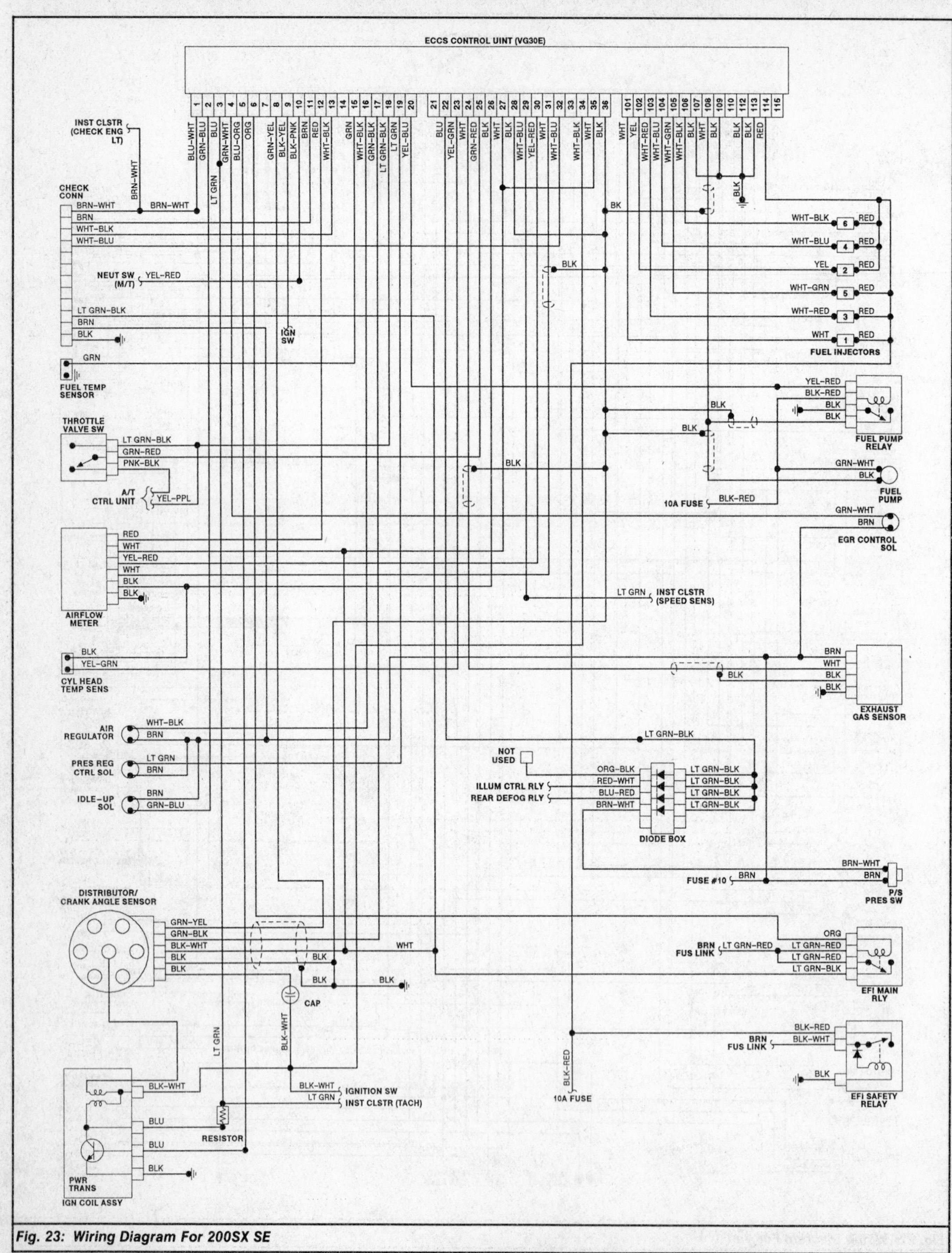
ECCS CONTROL UINT (VG30E)
INST CLSTR (CHECK ENG LT)
CHECK CONN
NEUT SW (M/T)
IGN SW
FUEL TEMP SENSOR
THROTTLE VALVE SW
A/T CTRL UNIT
AIRFLOW METER
CYL HEAD TEMP SENS
AIR REGULATOR
PRES REG CTRL SOL
IDLE-UP SOL
DISTRIBUTOR/ CRANK ANGLE SENSOR
CAP
IGNITION SW
INST CLSTR (TACH)
RESISTOR
PWR TRANS
IGN COIL ASSY
FUEL INJECTORS
FUEL PUMP RELAY
FUEL PUMP
10A FUSE
EGR CONTROL SOL
INST CLSTR (SPEED SENS)
EXHAUST GAS SENSOR
NOT USED
ILLUM CTRL RLY
REAR DEFOG RLY
DIODE BOX
FUSE #10
P/S PRES SW
BRN FUS LINK
EFI MAIN RLY
EFI SAFETY RELAY

Fig. 23: Wiring Diagram For 200SX SE

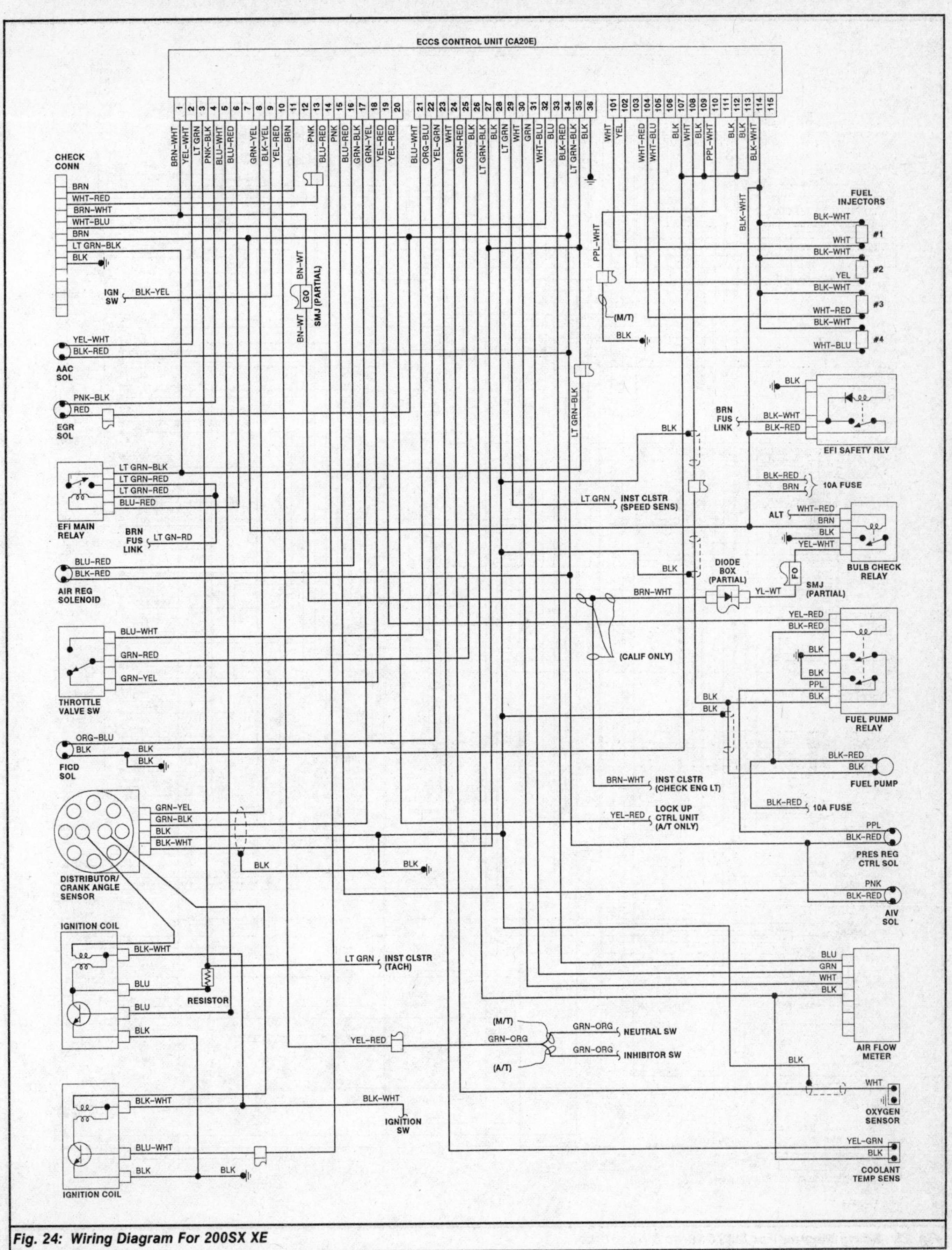
ECCS CONTROL UNIT (CA20E)
CHECK CONN
IGN SW
BLK-YEL
SMJ (PARTIAL)
AAC SOL
EGR SOL
EFI MAIN RELAY
BRN FUS LINK
AIR REG SOLENOID
THROTTLE VALVE SW
FICD SOL
DISTRIBUTOR/ CRANK ANGLE SENSOR
IGNITION COIL
RESISTOR
INST CLSTR (TACH)
IGNITION SW
FUEL INJECTORS
#1
#2
#3
#4
(M/T)
EFI SAFETY RLY
BRN FUS LINK
10A FUSE
INST CLSTR (SPEED SENS)
ALT
BULB CHECK RELAY
DIODE BOX (PARTIAL)
SMJ (PARTIAL)
(CALIF ONLY)
FUEL PUMP RELAY
FUEL PUMP
INST CLSTR (CHECK ENG LT)
LOCK UP CTRL UNIT (A/T ONLY)
PRES REG CTRL SOL
AIV SOL
AIR FLOW METER
NEUTRAL SW
INHIBITOR SW
(A/T)
OXYGEN SENSOR
COOLANT TEMP SENS

Fig. 24: Wiring Diagram For 200SX XE

# Nissan Electronic Concentrated Control System (Cont.)

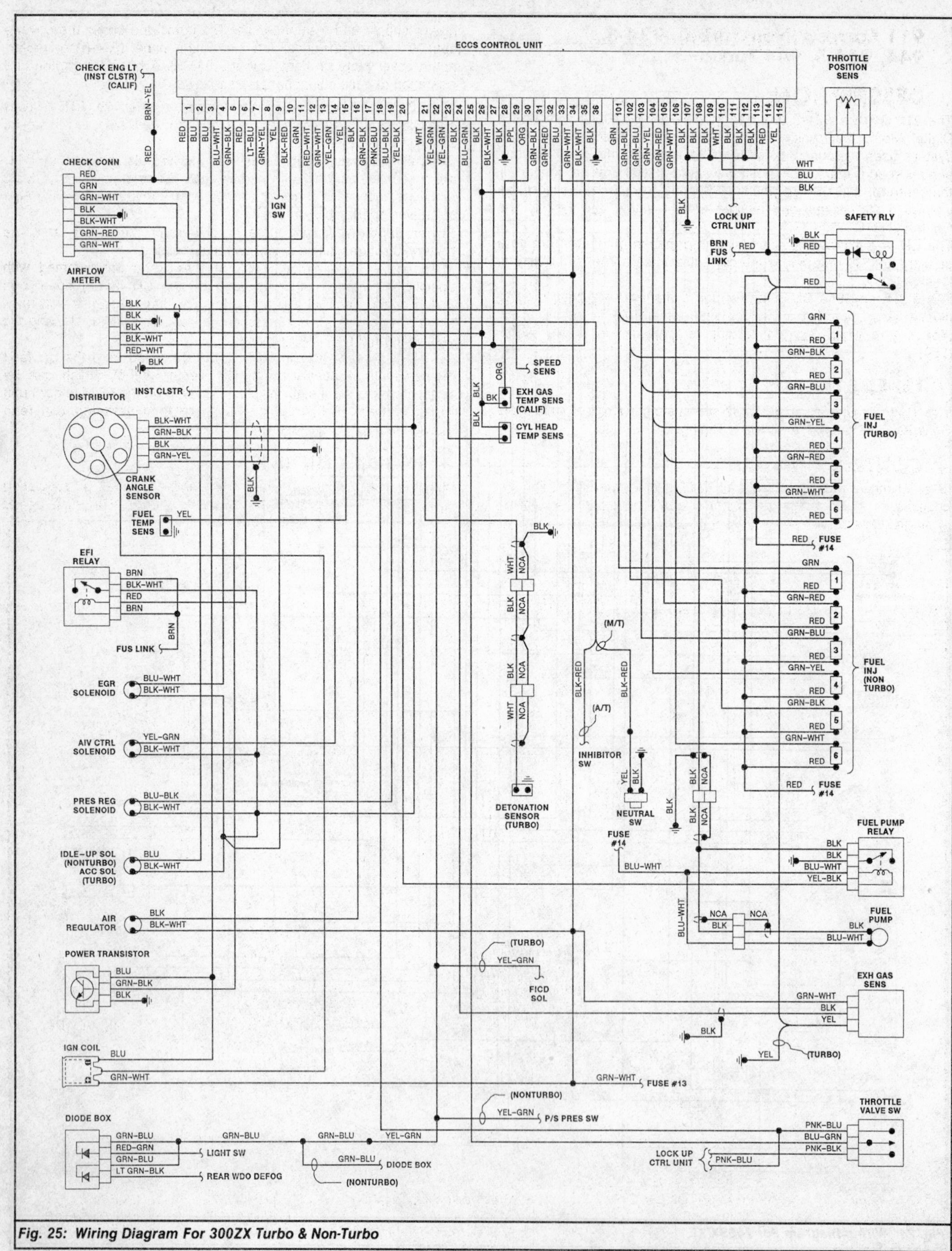
ECCS CONTROL UNIT
CHECK ENG LT (INST CLSTR) (CALIF)
CHECK CONN
IGN SW
AIRFLOW METER
INST CLSTR
DISTRIBUTOR
CRANK ANGLE SENSOR
FUEL TEMP SENS
EFI RELAY
FUS LINK
EGR SOLENOID
AIV CTRL SOLENOID
PRES REG SOLENOID
IDLE-UP SOL (NONTURBO) ACC SOL (TURBO)
AIR REGULATOR
POWER TRANSISTOR
IGN COIL
DIODE BOX
LIGHT SW
REAR WDO DEFOG
(NONTURBO)
THROTTLE POSITION SENS
LOCK UP CTRL UNIT
SAFETY RLY
BRN FUS LINK
SPEED SENS
EXH GAS TEMP SENS (CALIF)
CYL HEAD TEMP SENS
FUEL INJ (TURBO)
FUSE #14
FUEL INJ (NON TURBO)
(M/T)
(A/T)
INHIBITOR SW
NEUTRAL SW
DETONATION SENSOR (TURBO)
FUEL PUMP RELAY
FUEL PUMP
(TURBO)
FICD SOL
EXH GAS SENS
FUSE #13
P/S PRES SW
THROTTLE VALVE SW
LOCK UP CTRL UNIT

*Fig. 25: Wiring Diagram For 300ZX Turbo & Non-Turbo*

# Porsche DME Digital Engine Control

## 911 Carrera (Non-Turbo), 924-S, 944, 944-S, 944 Turbo

## DESCRIPTION

The 911 Carrera, 924-S and 944 models are equipped with Bosch Digital Motor Electronic (DME) engine control system. The DME system uses various data sensors to monitor intake air volume, engine speed, crankshaft position, coolant temperature, intake air temperature, and throttle position. Signals from these sensors, as well as a start signal and oxygen sensor signal, are sent to the Control Unit (CU).

The CU is a microcomputer. Using information obtained from data sensors, the CU determines the correct amount of fuel and optimum ignition timing.

The 924-S and 944 DME control unit switches from open loop to closed loop operation when coolant temperature is above 113°F (45°C), and when oxygen sensor temperature is above 480°F (250°C).

## OPERATION

The DME system consists of 4 sub-systems: Control Unit, Data Sensors, Fuel Control, and Spark Timing.

## CONTROL UNIT (CU)

The CU monitors and controls all DME system functions. The CU consists of input/output devices, Central Processing Unit (CPU), power supply and memories. The CU is located under the driver's seat (911 Carrera), under left instrument panel (924-S) or underneath cover plate on right footwell (944-S). A brief description and operation of each component is as follows:

**Input/Output Devices** – These integral devices of CU convert electrical signals received by data sensors and switches to digital signals for use by CPU.

**Central Processing Unit (CPU)** – Digital signals received by CPU are used to perform all mathematical computations and logic functions necessary to deliver proper air/fuel mixture. The CPU also calculates spark timing information.

**Power Supply** – Main source of power for the CU is from the battery, through ignition circuit and main relay.

**Memories** – The memory bank of the CU is programmed with specific information which is used by the CU during open loop (spark timing and fuel injection rate). This information is also used when a sensor or other component fails in the system, allowing the vehicle to be driven in for repairs.

On 944-S models, trouble code(s) can be called from the CU fault memory with a special diagnostic Tester (9268), which can be connected to a diagnostic terminal provided on the DME control unit wiring harness. Fault/trouble codes are then activated and read through the diagnostic tester.

## ENGINE CONTROLS

**Idle Speed Stabilization** – The 911 Carrera uses an air regulating valve to provide both auxiliary air valve operation and idle speed

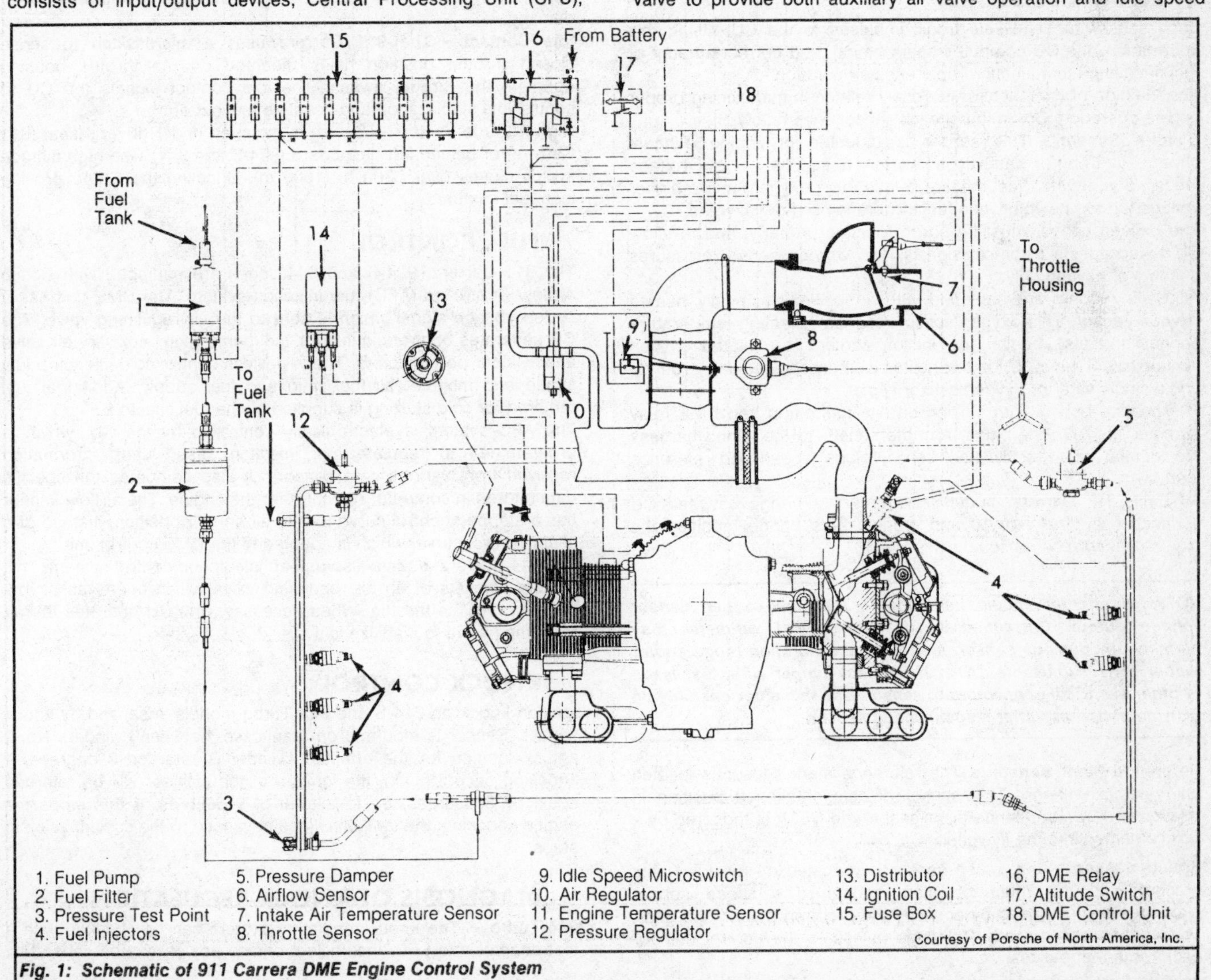
From Battery
From Fuel Tank
To Fuel Tank
To Throttle Housing
1. Fuel Pump
2. Fuel Filter
3. Pressure Test Point
4. Fuel Injectors
5. Pressure Damper
6. Airflow Sensor
7. Intake Air Temperature Sensor
8. Throttle Sensor
9. Idle Speed Microswitch
10. Air Regulator
11. Engine Temperature Sensor
12. Pressure Regulator
13. Distributor
14. Ignition Coil
15. Fuse Box
16. DME Relay
17. Altitude Switch
18. DME Control Unit
Courtesy of Porsche of North America, Inc.

*Fig. 1: Schematic of 911 Carrera DME Engine Control System*

stabilization. It is located near the throttle body. The air regulating valve is controlled by the CU. When necessary, the air regulating valve will adjust the air by-pass opening to maintain both cold and warm engine idle speeds.

**Auxiliary Air Valve** – The 924-S and 944 (except 944-S) use an auxiliary air valve to provide additional air during cold engine starts and warm-up. It is located next to throttle body. The valve consists of an electrically heated bi-metallic strip, movable disc and air by-pass channel. The heater coil on the bi-metallic strip is energized by the fuel pump relay.

Control of the valve is based upon engine temperature. The air by-pass channel is open when engine is cold and gradually closes as temperature rises. At predetermined temperatures, air by-pass channel is blocked and additional airflow stops.

**Idle Positioner** – It is not possible to adjust idle speed. The idle speed positioner automatically adjusts idle speed. The idle positioner is a single coil, rotary air control valve that is mounted on the lower intake induction manifold.

**Fuel Pressure Regulator** – The pressure regulator is located at the end of the injection collection line. Pressure regulator maintains constant fuel pressure to the fuel injectors.

**Pressure Damper** – The pressure damper is located at the end of right fuel collector (911 Carrera) or between fuel tank and injection collector tube (924-S and 944). The damper absorbs the pressure oscillation caused by the injection cycle.

## ENGINE SENSORS

Each sensor furnishes electronic impulses to the CU. Using this information, the CU computes spark timing, and correct amount of fuel necessary to maintain proper engine operation.

The function of each sensor is closely related in maintaining proper engine operation. Operation of each sensor is as follows:

**Oxygen Sensor** – This sensor is mounted in engine exhaust stream, in front of catalytic converter. It supplies a low voltage (under .5 volt) when fuel mixture is lean (high oxygen) and a higher voltage (up to one volt) when fuel mixture is rich (low oxygen).

The oxygen sensor must be hot to function properly, and to allow CU to accept its electrical signals. The oxygen sensor measures quantity of oxygen only.

All Calif. models are equipped with a special electrically heated oxygen sensor. This oxygen sensor reaches operating temperature sooner and also begins to function earlier. The heated oxygen sensor has 3 wires, 2 for the heater element (power and ground), and a single wire for oxygen sensor signal.

The heating begins with ignition on (via fuel pump and DME relay terminal No. 87). The plugs from the sensor to the wiring harness are located near the flywheel sensor plugs (speed and reference mark).

All Calif. 911 Carrera models also mount a bridge between CU connector terminal No. 10 and ground. This bridge modifies the oxygen sensor control setting.

***NOTE:** No attempt should be made to measure oxygen sensor voltage output. Current drain of conventional voltmeter may permanently damage sensor, shift sensor calibration range and/or render sensor unusable. DO NOT connect jumper wire, test leads or other electrical connectors to sensor. Use these devices only on CU side of harness after disconnecting sensor.*

**Reference Mark Sensor** – The reference mark sensor is located on crankcase flange. This sensor detects crankshaft position in relation to TDC, and sends this signal to the CU. It is triggered by a bolt cemented into the flywheel.

**Speed Sensor** – The speed sensor is mounted on an adjustable bracket with the reference mark sensor. The speed sensor measures engine speed by counting the teeth on starter ring gear. The speed sensor sends 2 voltage pulses to the control unit for each tooth that passes.

**Engine Temperature Sensor** – This sensor is located in cylinder head (911 Carrera) or in the coolant stream of the intake manifold (924-S and 944). This sensor supplies engine temperature (911 Carrera) or coolant temperature (924-S and 944) information to the CU. This information affects the air/fuel ratio (as engine temperature varies with time during a cold start) and spark timing.

**Intake Air Temperature Sensor** – This sensor is located in the air stream of the airflow meter, and supplies incoming air temperature information to the CU. The CU uses this along with other information in regulating the fuel injection rate.

**Airflow Sensor** – This sensor is located in the air stream of the airflow meter, and supplies air volume information to the CU. The CU uses this and other information in regulating the fuel injection rate.

The airflow meter incorporates an airflow measuring plate. The airflow plate opens when the engine draws in air. The plate is connected to a potentiometer. The potentiometer transmits an electrical signal determined by position of the measuring flap, to inform the CU of engine load.

The potentiometer within the airflow meter prevents loss of engine power during sudden acceleration or deceleration by signaling the CU of necessary fuel enrichment requirements.

**Throttle Switch** – A contact-type throttle switch is located on the throttle body. The 911 Carrera has one contact for wide open throttle position. The 924-S and 944 has 2 switch contacts. The idle contact signals the CU to control idle stabilization and coasting fuel cut-off. The full throttle contact signals the CU for optimum power demand.

**Idle Contact** – The 911 Carrera uses a microswitch to sense closed throttle position. It is mounted on the throttle housing opposite the throttle switch. The idle contact signals the CU to control idle stabilization and coasting fuel cut-off.

**High Altitude Switch** – Switch is mounted under driver's seat (911 Carrera) or behind left dashboard (924-S and 944). The high altitude switch closes over 3300 ft. (1000 m), signaling the CU to provide lean fuel mixture.

## FUEL CONTROL

The 911 Carrera, 924-S and 944 series are equipped with Bosch Airflow Controlled (AFC) fuel injection system. The DME unit has a cycled voltage signal which is sent to the air regulating valve. The CU generates control signals for fuel pump relay, auxiliary air valve and cylinder port injectors. These devices control cold idle, curb idle speed and mixture, air/fuel ratio and fuel supply. Additional fuel required for cold starting is supplied by the fuel injectors.

The AFC system is electronically controlled by the CU, which is programmed to regulate fuel injection based upon information received from various data sensors. It also compares the specific data (stored in computer memory) for the engine. The airflow sensor has a stepped control curve for the air sensor position, instead of a linear control curve, which is adapted to the DME control unit.

The 911 Carrera models also use an idle speed control system. This system consists of an air regulating valve which opens an air by-pass around the throttle. When necessary, the CU operates the air regulating valve to stabilize idle speed.

## KNOCK CONTROL

Ignition knock on 944-S and 944 Turbo models is sensed by knock sensor. Sensor is mounted on crankcase, between cylinders No. 2 and 3. Ignition for the affected cylinder is retarded 3 degrees. If knocking occurs again, the ignition of the cylinder will be retarded again by 3 degrees, up to a total of 9 degrees. If this stops the engine knocking, the ignition will be advanced to the correct value in steps.

## DIAGNOSIS OF KNOCK REGULATION

**944 Turbo** – The knock regulation system can be checked with a test adapter and LED. Insufficient engine power may be caused by low charging air pressure, engine knock or ignition timing not conforming with the test values.

When the test adapter is connected to the diagnosis plug, the engine speed will increase to more than 1500 RPM. If the LED remains dark, there is no fault in the knock regulation system. If the LED is on continuously, there is a problem. The problem can be found by dropping engine speed to below 1500 RPM. The LED will start flashing trouble codes.

## SELF-DIAGNOSIS (944-S ONLY)

***NOTE: List of fault codes are not available from manufacturer.***

The self-diagnosis with fault memory is integrated into the DME control unit. It detects and stores certain faults in the fuel injection, ignition and knock control systems in the memory.

Fault codes can be retrieved from the memory with the use of a special Tester (9268), which can be connected to a plug or diagnostic connector provided on the DME wiring harness. Codes are displayed in 4 digits on the tester. The tester can also be used to check or operate input and output functions.

**Input Diagnosis** – It is also possible to check the function of certain input signals such as, idle speed and full load contacts, A/C switch, and A/C compressor clutch.

**Output Diagnosis** – It is possible to check or operate a number of output functions with the diagnostic tester, in addition to reading fault memory codes. Components that can be tested by special Tester (9268) are, idle speed control, fuel injectors, tank venting valve and resonance flap on cars with catalytic converter.

## SPARK CONTROL

Spark control allows the CU to determine the exact instant that ignition is required, based upon information received from data sensors.

At the optimum time, the CU breaks the primary circuit of the ignition coil, producing a high voltage at coil center tower. This voltage surge fires the spark plug at the proper time for most efficient combustion, eliminating the need for vacuum and/or centrifugal advance.

# ADJUSTMENTS

## SPEED SENSOR CLEARANCE

***NOTE: Adjusting speed sensor automatically adjusts reference mark sensor. Sensors cannot be adjusted separately.***

**1)** The speed sensor bracket is mounted on the crankcase flange with 2 bolts. To adjust clearance, loosen bolts and turn sensor holder. Clearance should be .030-034" (.75-.85 mm).

**2)** To adjust clearance with engine installed in vehicle, remove speed sensor. Using a depth gauge, measure distance from sensor holder's upper surface to tooth head on starter ring gear.

**3)** Measure length of speed sensor. Subtract speed sensor length from holder-to-flywheel tooth distance. Difference should be .030-.034" (.75-.85 mm).

**4)** If not to specification, loosen screws and turn holder until holder-to-flywheel tooth distance is equal to the length of the sensor plus the specified clearance. Tighten screws, and install speed sensor in holder.

## IDLE SPEED & MIXTURE

**911 Carrera Model** – On 911 Carrera, idle stabilizer must be by-passed. See IDLE SPEED & MIXTURE in PORSCHE TUNE-UP PROCEDURES. Idle speed is adjusted by turning adjusting screw, located at by-pass port of throttle housing.

## THROTTLE SWITCH

**924-S & 944** – Position throttle against idle stop. Loosen throttle switch and turn until idle contacts are closed. Tighten throttle switch. Ensure throttle switch opens at a 1 degree throttle opening.

# DIAGNOSIS & TESTING

***NOTE: The DME system tests are limited. Complete testing of the DME system requires an oscilloscope, voltmeter, ohmmeter and special test leads to insert in multiple pin CU connector.***

***On 944-S a self-diagnosis with fault memory is integrated in the DME control unit. Faults can be called from memory with a special diagnostic Tester (9268), which can be connected to diagnostic connector on DME control unit wiring harness.***

## AIRFLOW SENSOR

**Power Supply (Except 944 Turbo)** – Pull back plug seal of airflow sensor plug (plug remains connected). Connect voltmeter on terminal No. 3 and ground through back of plug. Reading should be approximately 5.5 to 6.5 volts.

**Intake Air Temperature Sensor (All Except 944 Turbo)** – Pull off airflow sensor plug. Connect an ohmmeter to terminals No. 1 and 4 of airflow sensor (on control unit terminal No. 6 and 22). Readings should be as shown in INTAKE AIR TEMPERATURE SENSOR RESISTANCE table. If temperature sensor has an open circuit, it should cause a richer mixture. If temperature sensor has a grounded circuit, it should cause a leaner mixture.

***INTAKE AIR TEMPERATURE SENSOR RESISTANCE***

| Temperature | Ohms |
|---|---|
| 32°F (0°C) | 4400-6800 |
| 60-85°F (15-30°C) | 1400-3600 |
| 105°F (40°C) | 1000-1300 |

**Intake Air Temperature Sensor (944 Turbo)** – **1)** Loosen and fold down control unit bracket in passenger side kick panel. Pull out and remove plug connector on DME control unit. Remove upper section of plug connector, cutting cable band and removing fastening screw. Pull plug upper section away lengthwise.

**2)** Check supply voltage of airflow sensor. Connect voltmeter to terminals No. 9 and 5 (ground) on reverse side of control unit. Nominal value should be about 5 volts.

**3)** Remove air filter and connect voltmeter to terminals No. 7 and 5 (ground) on control unit plug. Check voltage drop on airflow sensor. Nominal voltage should be about 250-260 mV.

**4)** Push air flap to full load through air intake opening. Nominal value should be about 4.6 volts. Check temperature sensor (NTC 1 intake air temperature). Jumper terminals No. 22 and 6 on the pulled control unit plug. Using ohmmeter, measure resistance. Nominal value should be 1.4-3.6 ohms at 59-86°F (15-30°C) and 1-1.3 ohms at about 104°F (40°C).

***NOTE: Break on temperature sensor causes rich mixture. Short circuit on temperature sensor causes lean mixture.***

## COOLANT TEMPERATURE SENSOR

Remove CU connector plug. On 944-S models, connect ohmmeter between CU terminal No. 45 and ground. On all other models, connect ohmmeter between CU terminal No. 13 and ground. Compare ohmmeter readings to COOLANT TEMPERATURE SENSOR RESISTANCE table.

# Porsche DME Digital Engine Control (Cont.)

*COOLANT TEMPERATURE SENSOR RESISTANCE*

| Temperature | [1] Ohms |
|---|---|
| 50°F (10°C) | 3300-4100 |
| 68°F (20°C) | 2200-2800 |
| 104°F (40°C) | 1000-1300 |
| 176°F (80°C) | 290-350 |
| 212°F (100°C) | 160-210 |

[1] - All specifications are ±10%.

## CU POWER SUPPLY

**1)** Disconnect CU connector. Connect positive voltmeter lead to terminal No. 35 of CU harness connector. Connect negative test lead to terminal No. 5 of CU harness connector. Turn ignition on. Voltmeter should read battery voltage.
**2)** Connect voltmeter positive test lead to terminal No. 18 of CU harness connector. Connect negative test lead to terminal No. 5 of CU harness connector. Turn ignition on. Voltmeter should read battery voltage.
**3)** If no voltage is available, remove DME power relay. Using a jumper wire, connect terminals No. 30 and 87. Repeat voltage checks in steps **1)** and **2)**. On 944 series, connect voltmeter between terminals No. 3 of 9-pin connector and ground. If no voltage is present, check battery and related circuits.

## DME CONTROL

**1)** Reconnect the fuel pressure regulator vacuum hose. Disconnect oxygen sensor. Connect oxygen sensor harness connector terminal to ground.
**2)** Check if the CO% level increases. If not, check wire from CU connector terminal No. 24 to oxygen sensor plug. If no problem is found, replace oxygen sensor.

## ELECTRICAL CONNECTIONS

***CAUTION: DME ignition system voltage is extremely high. Always turn ignition switch to "OFF" position or remove battery ground cable when connecting testers or replacing system components. High voltage is also present at terminal No. 1 of CU.***

**1)** On 911 Carrera models, ensure all electrical connections are free of corrosion and securely attached. Check DME ground wires on cylinder No. 1 intake pipe and fuel filter mount. Check ground strap between body and transmission/engine.
**2)** Check electrical plug connections on No. 14 pin plug on control plate in engine compartment and No. 6 pin plug for DME on left front crossmember (below heater blower).
**3)** Check connections as follows:

- Engine temperature sensor.
- Speed sensor.
- Reference mark sensor.
- No. 3 pin on air regulating valve.
- No. 2 pin on idle microswitch plug.
- No. 3 pin on throttle switch.
- No. 5 pin on airflow sensor plug.
- No. 2 pin plugs on all injectors.
- No. 35 pin on DME control unit.
- No. 6 pin of DME relay plug.
- No. 2 pin of high altitude switch plug.

**4)** On 924-S and 944 models, also check as follows:

- 9-pin connector above brake pedal.
- 4-pin airflow connector.
- 3-pin throttle switch connector.
- 35-pin CU connector.
- 2-pin temperature sensor connector.
- $O_2$ sensor connector.
- Flywheel sensor connectors.

***NOTE: CU connector is held in place by a catch. Push catch to the right and pull off plug with a downward motion.***

## FUEL PRESSURE

**1)** Locate fuel pipe cap nut at end of fuel rail (left side on 911 Carrera). Remove cap, being careful that sealing ball does not fall out. Connect a Test Pressure Gauge (P 378).
**2)** Start engine and maintain idle speed. Pressure gauge should show 29.4 psi (2.06 kg/cm²). Disconnect vacuum line at pressure regulator. Pressure gauge should show 33.8-39.7 psi (2.37-2.78 kg/cm²).
**3)** Pinch fuel return line of pressure regulator. Pressure gauge should show a minimum of 59.0 psi (4.13 kg/cm²). If fuel pump does not meet specifications, check fuel filter or replace fuel pump and retest.
**4)** If engine will not start, check fuse No. 2. If good, remove DME relay (911 Carrera), or fuel pump relay "U" (924S and 944) and bridge terminals No. 30 and 87b. Pressure gauge should show 33.8-39.7 psi (2.37-2.78 kg/cm²).

## HIGH ALTITUDE SWITCH

**1)** Locate the high altitude switch under driver's seat (911 Carrera), or left instrument panel (944). Disconnect the altitude switch plug. Connect an ohmmeter to switch terminals. The altitude switch should be open under 3300 ft. (1000 m).
**2)** Warm engine to operating temperature. Disconnect oxygen sensor. Disconnect high altitude switch. Remove vacuum hose from fuel pressure regulator and plug.
**3)** Connect an exhaust gas analyzer to exhaust pipe. Operate engine at 2000 RPM and note CO% level.
**4)** Bridge the high altitude switch harness terminals. At 2000 RPM, CO% level should be leaner. If not, check high altitude connectors. Ensure continuity of one wire to ground. The other wire should have continuity to CU terminal No. 28.

## IDLE ACTUATOR/ AIR REGULATING VALVE

**911 Carrera & 944 Turbo - 1)** Remove plug connection on idle actuator. Turn ignition on. Connect voltmeter to middle contact of plug connector and ground. Nominal value should be 12 volts.
**2)** Reconnect plug connector on idle actuator and connect tachometer. During stable idle, screw in throttle by-pass screw. After a short time, idle speed should re-adjust itself.
**3)** To check the activation of idle actuator by the control unit, connect a new or proper functioning idle actuator to plug connector. Turn ignition on. The idle actuator should vibrate.

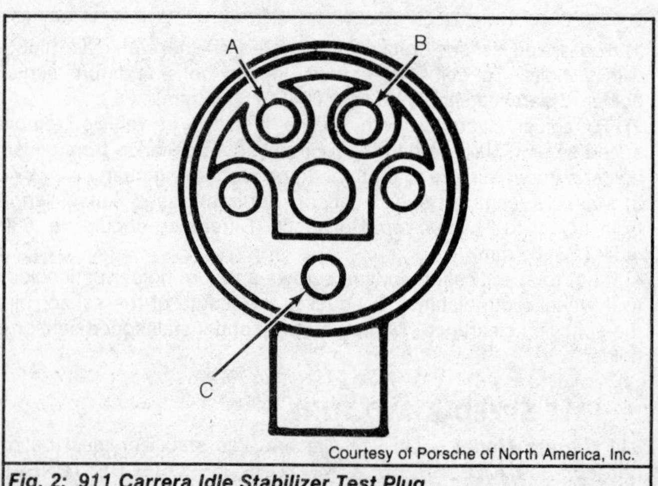
A
B
C
Courtesy of Porsche of North America, Inc.

*Fig. 2: 911 Carrera Idle Stabilizer Test Plug*

**4)** Start engine and increase idle speed by screwing out air circulation screw. The idle actuator should turn in the direction of closing. After lowering idle speed, the idle actuator should turn in the direction of opening.

## IGNITION CIRCUIT POWER CHECK

Connect positive voltmeter lead to terminal No. 1 of CU harness connector. Connect negative lead to ground. Turn ignition on, but do not start engine. Voltmeter should register battery voltage. If not, check wiring back to battery.

## IGNITION COIL RESISTANCE CHECK

**Primary Resistance – 1)** With ignition switch in the "OFF" position, disconnect wires from primary terminals of ignition coil to isolate it from the system. Set ohmmeter at x1 scale.
**2)** Connect ohmmeter leads to 2 primary terminals. Reading should be .4-.6 ohm. If not, replace ignition coil.

**Secondary Resistance – 1)** With ignition switch in the "OFF" position, remove wire from coil tower. Set ohmmeter at x1000 scale. Connect ohmmeter leads to ignition coil positive terminal and coil tower.
**2)** Reading should be 5000-7200 ohms. If not within specifications, replace ignition coil.

## IGNITION RESISTANCE CHECKS

Shielded resistance of spark plug connectors should be 3000 ohms. Shielded resistance of distributor rotor, and of all distributor cap connections should be 1000 ohms.

## KNOCK/CHARGING PRESSURE CONTROL

The knock/charging pressure control includes a self-monitoring system. If a defect has been found, the engine will operate on a safety system (basic turbo boost pressure up to about 4 psi overpressure and 6° retarded on timing).
Defect will read out only after a test drive without switching off the ignition. A defect stored in memory is erased when ignition is switched off.

## OXYGEN SENSOR

***NOTE:** It is important that intake air temperature be 60-95°F (15-35°C) for CO level adjustments.*

**1)** Connect an exhaust gas analyzer to test point. Warm engine to operating temperature. Disconnect oxygen sensor wire. Note CO% level.
**2)** Disconnect and plug vacuum hose from fuel pressure regulator. The CO% level should increase. Reconnect oxygen sensor wire. The CO level should decrease to 0.6-1.0% (911 Carrera), or 0.4-0.8% (944). If not, test the DME control.

## REFERENCE MARK SENSOR CHECK

**1)** Using same LED tester as used for testing speed sensor, connect positive lead to CU harness connector terminal No. 25 and negative lead to terminal No. 26.
**2)** Disconnect and ground coil wire. Crank engine over. If sensor is sending a signal, LED should flicker dimly.

## SPEED SENSOR CHECK

**1)** Obtain a Fresnel lens front LED from an electronics store or use Special Test Unit (171 919 061B). Connect a 220 ohm-1/4 watt resistor in series with one of the LED terminals.
**2)** Connect positive LED test lead to terminal No. 8 of CU harness connector. Connect negative LED test lead to terminal No. 27 of same connector. Disconnect and ground coil wire. Crank engine. LED will flicker dimly if speed sensor is sending a signal.

## THROTTLE SWITCH

**Checking Idle Switch Function –** Operate accelerator linkage carefully approximately .039" (1 mm). The microswitch should open without the throttle opening and there must be a definite increase in idle speed. Speed should increase 500 RPM. Ignition timing advance should be 12 degrees BTDC. If nothing happens, check microswitch and its adjustment.

**Checking Activation of Control Unit – 1)** With engine at idle speed, pull off plug on idle switch. Engine speed should increase 500 RPM. Ignition timing should advance 12 degrees BTDC.
**2)** If nothing happens, check wire between idle switch plug and control unit plug for breaks according to wiring diagram. If necessary, replace control unit.

**Checking Coasting Fuel Shutoff – 1)** With engine at idle speed, bridge disconnected plug of idle switch with a jumper wire. Accelerate engine to approximately 1300 RPM. Engine should begin to surge (this is coasting fuel shutoff).
**2)** If engine does not surge, check wire between idle switch plug and control unit plug for breaks according to wiring diagram. If necessary, replace control unit.

**Full Load Enrichment – 1)** With engine at idle speed, pull off plug on idle switch. Engine RPM should go up to 1300 RPM and ignition timing should be 12 degrees BTDC. Pull off plug on throttle switch (full load contact).
**2)** Bridge connections on plug with a jumper wire. Engine speed should drop by approximately 100 to 200 RPM and ignition timing will be retarded approximately 4 to 8 degrees. If nothing happens, check wire between throttle switch plug and control unit plug for breaks.

# REMOVAL & INSTALLATION

***NOTE:** The removal and installation procedures are for 944-S model only.*

## DISTRIBUTOR CAP

**Removal – 1)** Make a tool from a 4 1/2 to 6" long screwdriver. The screwdriver tip must be approximately 5/16" wide. Heat screwdriver and bend to a 90 degree angle about 3 1/2" from the end of tip.
**2)** Push in lower clamping hook with a screwdriver, and turn to the right (clockwise). Push in on upper clamping hook. Turn it to the right and remove cap.

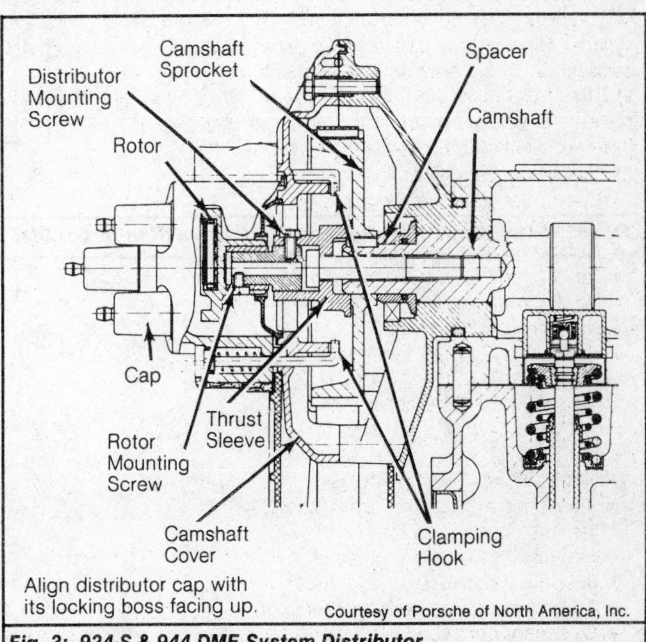
Camshaft Sprocket
Spacer
Distributor Mounting Screw
Camshaft
Rotor
Cap
Thrust Sleeve
Rotor Mounting Screw
Camshaft Cover
Clamping Hook
Align distributor cap with its locking boss facing up.
Courtesy of Porsche of North America, Inc.

*Fig. 3: 924-S & 944 DME System Distributor*

**Installation** – **1)** Before installing cap, remove spark plug wire for No. 3 cylinder to provide access to clamping hook. Align distributor cap with its locking boss facing up.

**2)** Align clamping hooks in distributor cap so they are positioned horizontally and facing toward left side when viewed from front. Guide hooks into both slots, and engage distributor cap by turning back and forth slightly. Watch position of dust cap.

**3)** Turn both clamping hooks against left stop. Press in on hooks far enough so that they can be turned counterclockwise approximately 1/4 turn and engage when released.

**4)** Ensure distributor cap fits tightly. Ensure hooks are firmly engaged. Reinstall spark plug wire for No. 3 cylinder on distributor cap.

## IDLE ACTUATOR

**Removal** – **1)** Disconnect battery ground lead. Disconnect cable on cruise control motor. Pull off vacuum hoses on pressure regulator and pressure damper. Remove spark plug connectors.

**2)** Remove distributor cap. Unscrew fuel distribution pipe with fuel injectors and ignition leads on intake air distributor and camshaft housing. Carefully remove fuel distribution pipe with fuel injectors and ignition leads from intake air distributor and set aside.

**3)** Disconnect throttle operating cable. Loosen and remove vacuum hoses from intake air distributor. Remove intake air distributor with throttle housing, and cover intake ports leading to intake valves.

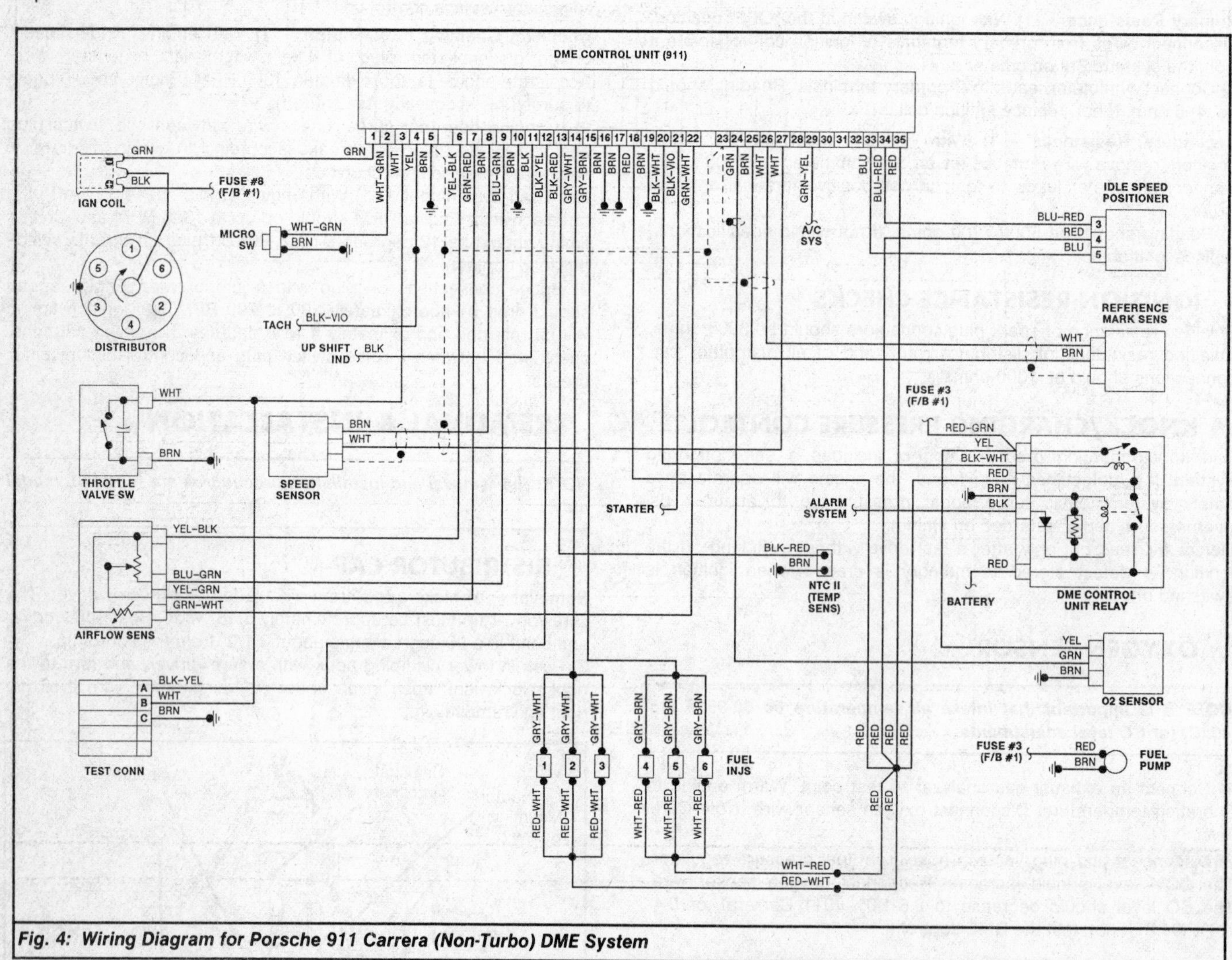
DME CONTROL UNIT (911)
1 2 3 4 5 6 7 8 9 10 11 12 13 14 15 16 17 18 19 20 21 22 23 24 25 26 27 28 29 30 31 32 33 34 35
WHT-GRN
GRN
WHT
YEL
BRN
YEL-BLK
GRN-RED
BRN
BLU-GRN
BRN
BLK
BLK-YEL
BLK-RED
GRY-WHT
GRY-BRN
BRN
BRN
RED
BRN
BLK-WHT
BLK-VIO
GRN-WHT
GRN
BRN
WHT
WHT
GRN-YEL
BLU
BLU-RED
RED
GRN
BLK
FUSE #8 (F/B #1)
IGN COIL
MICRO SW
WHT-GRN
BRN
DISTRIBUTOR
TACH
BLK-VIO
UP SHIFT IND
BLK
A/C SYS
IDLE SPEED POSITIONER
BLU-RED
RED
BLU
REFERENCE MARK SENS
WHT
BRN
THROTTLE VALVE SW
WHT
BRN
SPEED SENSOR
BRN
WHT
FUSE #3 (F/B #1)
RED-GRN
YEL
BLK-WHT
RED
BRN
BLK
STARTER
ALARM SYSTEM
RED
BATTERY
DME CONTROL UNIT RELAY
BLK-RED
BRN
NTC II (TEMP SENS)
AIRFLOW SENS
YEL-BLK
BLU-GRN
YEL-GRN
GRN-WHT
O2 SENSOR
YEL
GRN
BRN
TEST CONN
BLK-YEL
WHT
BRN
A
B
C
GRY-WHT
GRY-WHT
GRY-WHT
GRY-BRN
GRY-BRN
GRY-BRN
1 2 3 4 5 6
FUEL INJS
RED-WHT
RED-WHT
RED-WHT
WHT-RED
WHT-RED
WHT-RED
RED
RED
RED
RED
RED
FUSE #3 (F/B #1)
RED
BRN
FUEL PUMP
WHT-RED
RED-WHT

*Fig. 4: Wiring Diagram for Porsche 911 Carrera (Non-Turbo) DME System*

**4)** Disconnect electric plug connection on idle actuator. Unscrew Allen head bolt on crankcase and take out idle actuator with bracket. Loosen hose connections from charging air guide pipe and remove.

**Installation** - To install, reverse removal procedure. When installing idle actuator, note airflow direction. Make sure to position vacuum hoses and hose clamps correctly. Always replace seals for intake air distributor and hollow-core bolt.

## ROTOR

**1)** With distributor cap removed, split the dust shield at base of rotor. Remove dust shield. Remove hex head bolt from rotor assembly. Pull rotor assembly from shaft.

**2)** To reinstall, push rotor assembly onto shaft. Ensure rotor assembly bottoms on shaft. Install a new mounting screw and tighten to 35 INCH lbs. (4 N.m).

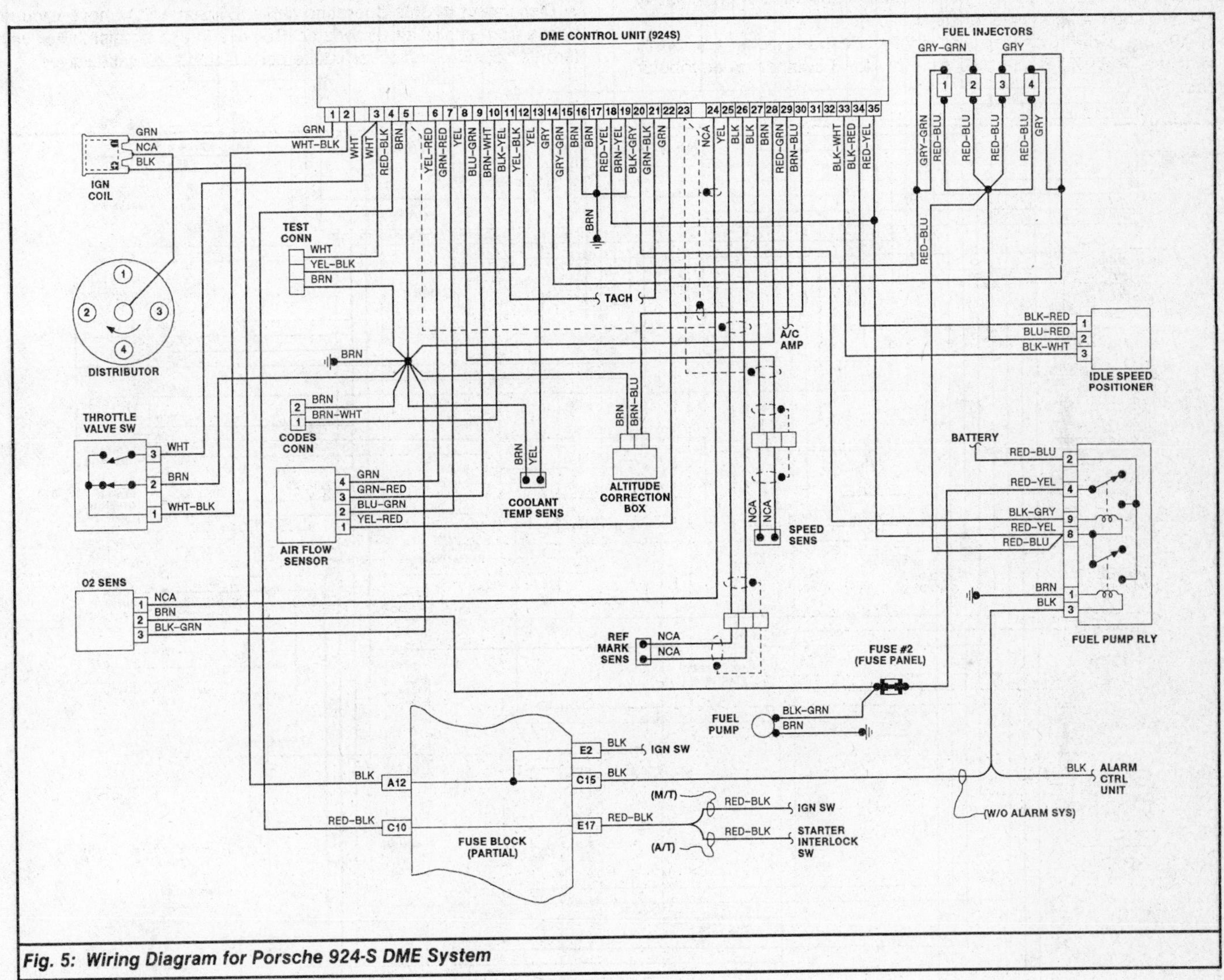
DME CONTROL UNIT (924S)
FUEL INJECTORS
IGN COIL
DISTRIBUTOR
TEST CONN
THROTTLE VALVE SW
CODES CONN
AIR FLOW SENSOR
COOLANT TEMP SENS
ALTITUDE CORRECTION BOX
TACH
A/C AMP
IDLE SPEED POSITIONER
BATTERY
SPEED SENS
FUEL PUMP RLY
O2 SENS
REF MARK SENS
FUSE #2 (FUSE PANEL)
FUEL PUMP
IGN SW
ALARM CTRL UNIT
(W/O ALARM SYS)
(M/T)
(A/T)
STARTER INTERLOCK SW
FUSE BLOCK (PARTIAL)

*Fig. 5: Wiring Diagram for Porsche 924-S DME System*

# 1988 COMPUTERIZED ENGINE CONTROLS
## Porsche DME Digital Engine Control (Cont.)

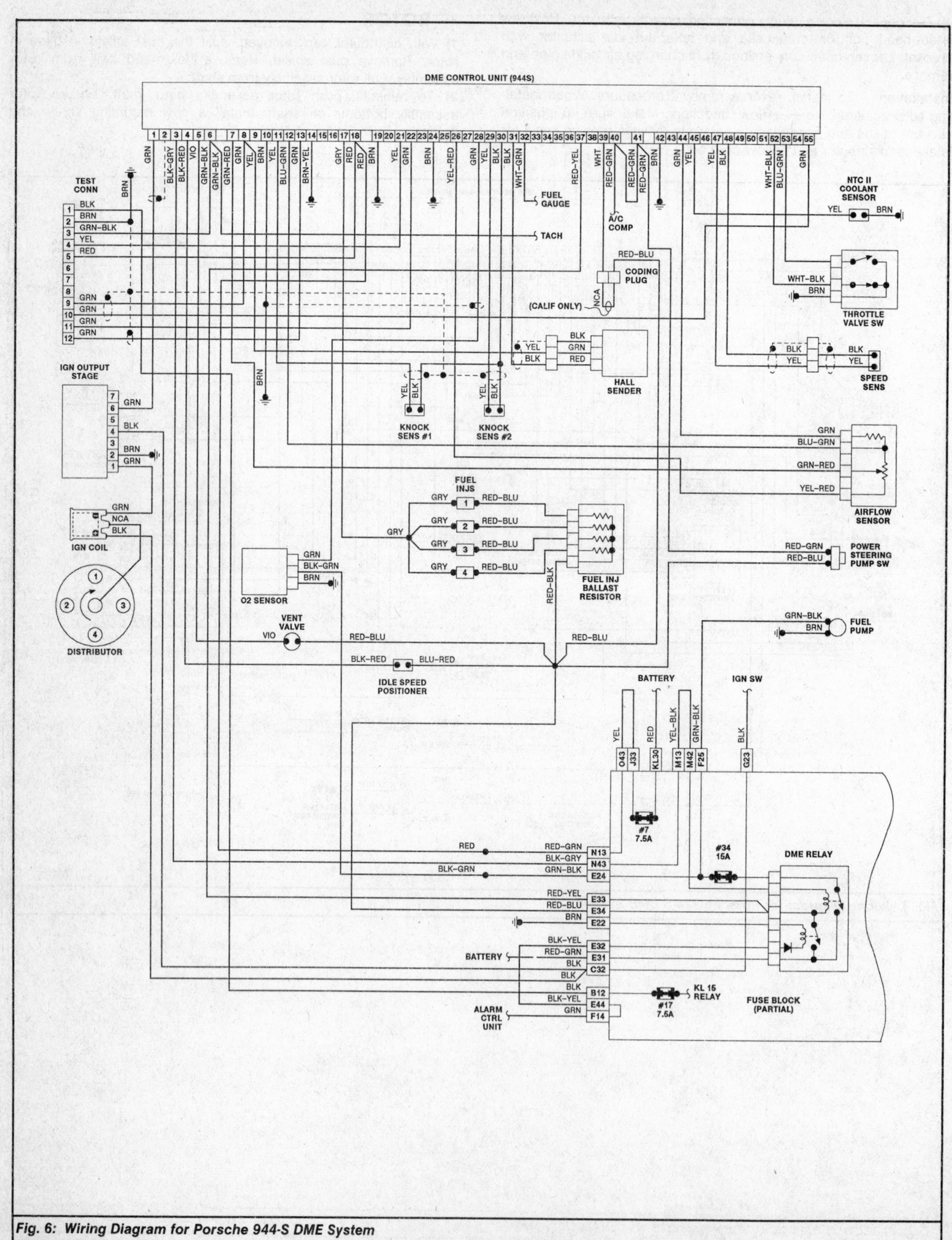

*Fig. 6: Wiring Diagram for Porsche 944-S DME System*

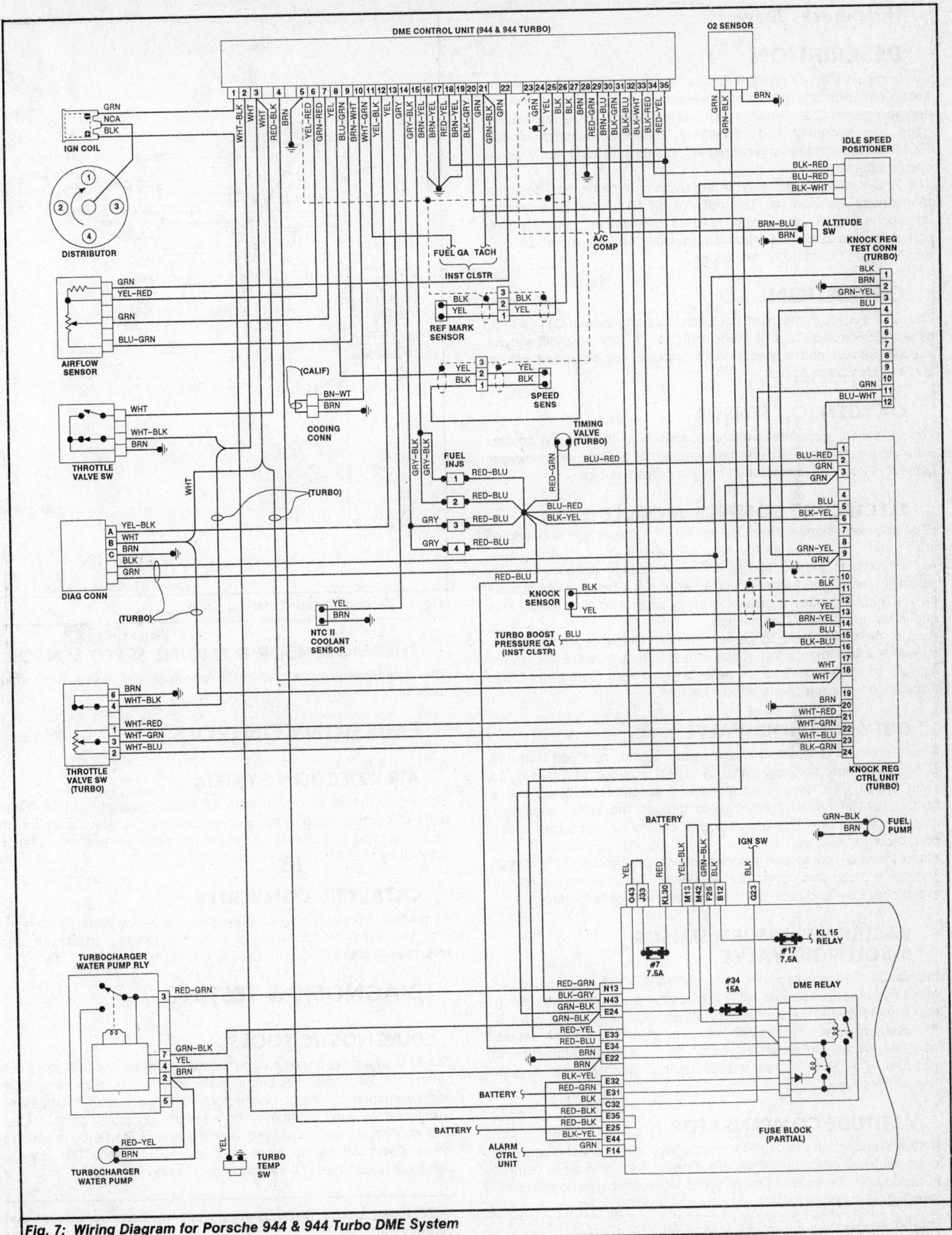
DME CONTROL UNIT (944 & 944 TURBO)
O2 SENSOR
IGN COIL
GRN
NCA
BLK
DISTRIBUTOR
IDLE SPEED POSITIONER
BLK-RED
BLU-RED
BLK-WHT
FUEL GA
TACH
INST CLSTR
A/C COMP
BRN-BLU
BRN
ALTITUDE SW
KNOCK REG TEST CONN (TURBO)
AIRFLOW SENSOR
YEL-RED
BLU-GRN
REF MARK SENSOR
(CALIF)
BN-WT
CODING CONN
SPEED SENS
THROTTLE VALVE SW
WHT
WHT-BLK
TIMING VALVE (TURBO)
FUEL INJS
RED-BLU
BLU-RED
BLK-YEL
(TURBO)
DIAG CONN
YEL-BLK
GRY
KNOCK SENSOR
NTC II COOLANT SENSOR
TURBO BOOST PRESSURE GA (INST CLSTR)
THROTTLE VALVE SW (TURBO)
WHT-RED
WHT-GRN
WHT-BLU
KNOCK REG CTRL UNIT (TURBO)
BATTERY
IGN SW
FUEL PUMP
GRN-BLK
KL 15 RELAY
#17 7.5A
#7 7.5A
#34 15A
DME RELAY
TURBOCHARGER WATER PUMP RLY
RED-GRN
BLK-GRY
GRN-BLK
TURBO TEMP SW
ALARM CTRL UNIT
FUSE BLOCK (PARTIAL)
TURBOCHARGER WATER PUMP
RED-YEL

Fig. 7: Wiring Diagram for Porsche 944 & 944 Turbo DME System

# 1988 COMPUTERIZED ENGINE CONTROLS
## Subaru EFC Carburetor

**Hatchback, Justy**

## DESCRIPTION

Electronically Fuel Controlled (EFC) carburetor system is a computerized emission and fuel control system. The EFC system controls engine operation and lowers exhaust emissions while maintaining good fuel economy and driveability. Electronic Control Module (ECM) controls many engine related systems to constantly adjust engine operation.

The EFC system is primarily an emission control system, designed to maintain an ideal air/fuel ratio of 14.7:1 under all operating conditions. When the ideal ratio is maintained, the catalytic converter can control Carbon Monoxide (CO), Hydrocarbon (HC) and Nitrogen Oxide (NOx) emissions.

## OPERATION

The EFC system consists of the following components: Oxygen ($O_2$) sensor, Electronic Control Module (ECM), 2 duty solenoid valves, vacuum sensor and solenoid, thermosensor, engine speed sensor and altitude compensator.

### OXYGEN ($O_2$) SENSOR

The $O_2$ sensor generates voltage according to the oxygen content within exhaust gases. The voltage created is greater when oxygen content is low, and lesser when oxygen content is high.

### ELECTRONIC CONTROL MODULE (ECM)

ECM receives signals from $O_2$ sensor, thermosensor and engine speed sensor to adjust air/fuel ratio to proper level.

Air/fuel ratio is judged to be rich when voltage produced by $O_2$ sensor is higher than a set specified level. As a result, ECM signals duty solenoid to pass a greater quantity of air into carburetor. This additional air leans air/fuel mixture.

Air/fuel ratio is judged to be lean when voltage produced by $O_2$ sensor is lower than a set specified level. As a result, ECM issues signals to duty soleniod to pass less air into carburetor. The elimination of air enrichens air/fuel mixture.

### DUTY SOLENOID VALVE

A duty solenoid is installed in carburetor. Signals received from the ECM cause duty solenoid valve to repeat opening and closing in short cycles. The valve is equipped with a control air bleed and a control fuel jet. When current flows through the valve, a plunger inside moves down. This opens port to control air bleed and closes port to control fuel jet.

When there is no current a spring moves plunger up. This closes port to air bleed and opens port to fuel jet. These ports are routed to both the slow and main ports on primary side of carburetor.

### VACUUM (PRESSURE) SENSOR & SOLENOID VALVE

The vacuum sensor provides accurate sensing of changes within intake manifold. A solenoid valve is placed in pressure line between intake manifold and vacuum sensor. When vacuum solenoid valve is off, vacuum sensor measures vacuum (pressure) in the intake manifold. When solenoid valve is on, it senses atmospheric pressure. The ECM is fed this information and corrects air/fuel mixture. *See Fig. 1.*

### ALTITUDE COMPENSATOR

Altitude compensator is used for compensation of air/fuel mixture in response to elevation by means of supplying additional air to control air passages. The solenoid valve opens when atmospheric pressure detected by pressure sensor is 12 psi (.84 kg/cm²) or less.

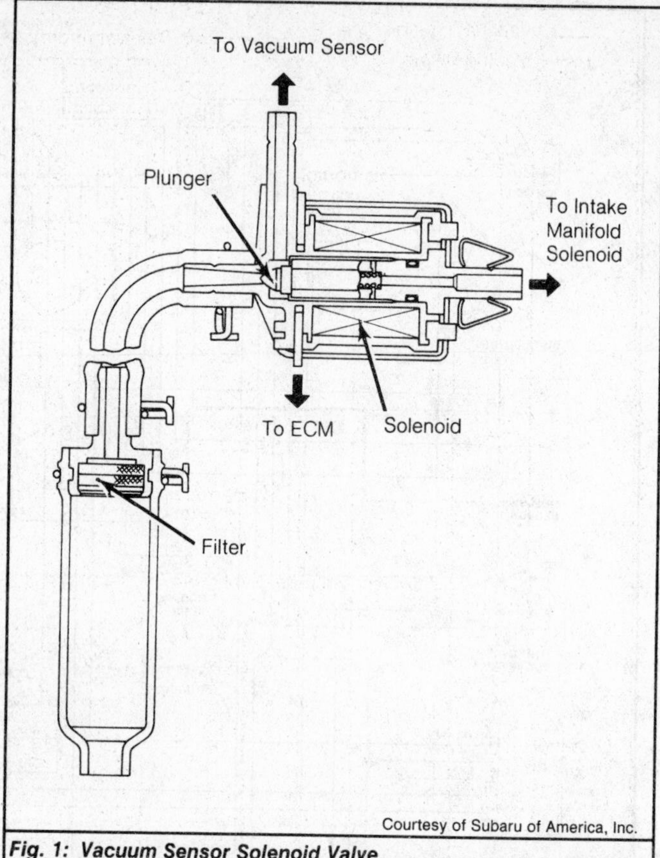
To Vacuum Sensor
Plunger
To Intake
Manifold
Solenoid
To ECM
Solenoid
Filter
Courtesy of Subaru of America, Inc.

*Fig. 1: Vacuum Sensor Solenoid Valve*

### THERMOSENSOR & ENGINE SPEED SENSOR

These sensors provide coolant temperature and engine RPM input to ECM.

## EMISSION CONTROLS

### AIR INJECTION SYSTEM

Secondary (fresh) air drawn from air cleaner is supplied to exhaust ports of cylinder head. Also, a constant supply of secondary (fresh) air is supplied to exhaust port near upstream portion of oxidation catalyst by rear Air Suction Valve (ASV).

### CATALYTIC CONVERTER

All models equipped with EFC system use 3-way catalytic converters. This type of converter permits simultaneous oxidation and reduction to reduce CO, HC and NOx emissions.

## DIAGNOSIS & TESTING

### DIAGNOSTIC TOOLS

The EFC system requires a circuit tester, stethoscope and a dry-cell battery for diagnosis. The circuit tester is used to measure voltage and resistance of check connectors. It is also used to measure resistance of duty solenoids and vacuum (pressure) sensor after lead connectors are unplugged. Stethoscope or vinyl tube is used to check operating sound from duty solenoid valves. The dry-cell battery is used to test $O_2$ sensor and its wiring for defects.

***NOTE:** Insert circuit tester probes from the harness side of test connectors.*

# 1988 COMPUTERIZED ENGINE CONTROLS
## Subaru EFC Carburetor (Cont.)

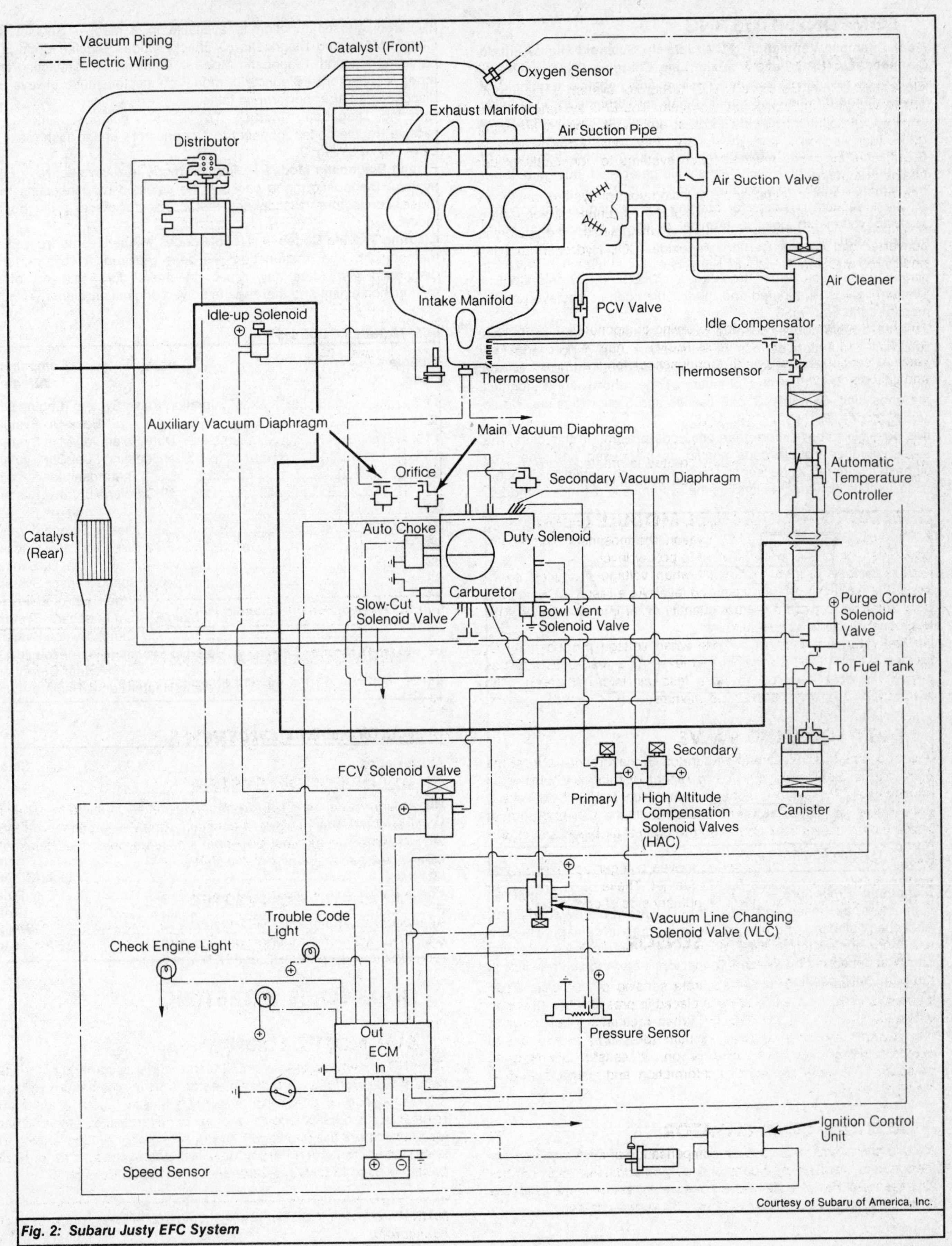

Vacuum Piping
Electric Wiring
Catalyst (Front)
Oxygen Sensor
Exhaust Manifold
Air Suction Pipe
Distributor
Air Suction Valve
Air Cleaner
Intake Manifold
PCV Valve
Idle-up Solenoid
Idle Compensator
Thermosensor
Thermosensor
Auxiliary Vacuum Diaphragm
Main Vacuum Diaphragm
Orifice
Secondary Vacuum Diaphragm
Automatic Temperature Controller
Catalyst (Rear)
Auto Choke
Duty Solenoid
Carburetor
Slow-Cut Solenoid Valve
Bowl Vent Solenoid Valve
Purge Control Solenoid Valve
To Fuel Tank
FCV Solenoid Valve
Secondary
Primary
High Altitude Compensation Solenoid Valves (HAC)
Canister
Vacuum Line Changing Solenoid Valve (VLC)
Trouble Code Light
Check Engine Light
Pressure Sensor
Out
ECM
In
Ignition Control Unit
Speed Sensor




*Fig. 2: Subaru Justy EFC System*

## COMPONENT TESTING

**Float Chamber Ventilation (FCV), Idle-Up Solenoid High Altitude Compensator (HAC), and Vacuum Line Charging (VLC) Valves –** 1) Check resistance between positive and negative terminals of valve. Standard resistance should be 16.2-19.8 ohms for FCV valve and 32.7-39.9 ohms for all others. If not within specifications replace valve(s).

**2)** Check resistance between positive and negative terminals of valve and valve body. Resistance should be at least .001 ohm. If not within specification replace valve.

**3)** Check vacuum passage for opening and closing operation while applying voltage to positive terminal of valve. Repeat test using negative terminal.

**Diagnostic System –** ECM of EFC system is equipped with a self-diagnostic function. When trouble occurs, ECS (Electronic Control System) light is illuminated and the trouble code is displayed on $O_2$ monitor light. *See Fig. 3*.

To read trouble codes, observe oxygen sensor monitor light. This light has 2 duration periods of illumination, one period long (1.2 seconds) and one period short (.3 seconds). The long period signifies the tens digit in a numbered code. Short period signifies the ones digit. Example: 3 long flashes and 5 short flashes, would signify a code 35.

It is possible to have more than one code present. In this case, the lowest number trouble code should be diagnosed first, the next highest numbered code second and so on (sequentially). Trouble codes will be repeated as long as the system is in diagnostic mode.

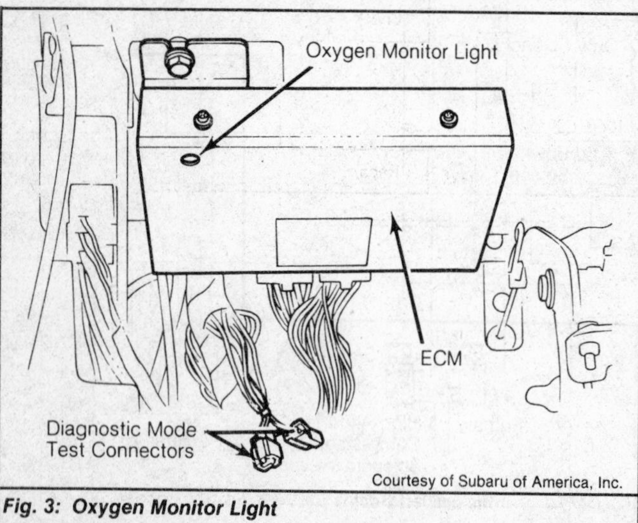
Oxygen Monitor Light
ECM
Diagnostic Mode
Test Connectors
Courtesy of Subaru of America, Inc.

*Fig. 3: Oxygen Monitor Light*

**Diagnostic Procedure – 1)** Prior to diagnosis, ensure that all connectors, air hoses and vacuum hoses are properly connected. Also check all parts and electric wiring for cuts or damage. Be sure to turn ignition switch to "OFF" position before replacing a defective part. Reconnect all hoses and connectors before ignition switch is turned to "ON" position.

**2)** Self-diagnostic function is available in 2 modes: Regular (U-Check) Mode and Diagnostic (D-Check) Mode. Regular Mode is a continual function. Diagnostic Mode is obtained by connecting test mode connectors. Diagnostic mode connector must always be disconnected after performing tests.

**Entering Diagnostic Mode –** To activate diagnostic mode to receive trouble codes, connect test connectors under dash (next to ECM box). *See Fig. 3*.

**Exiting Diagnostic Modes –** Regular mode is always active in EFC system. Diagnostic mode can only be selected by connecting test mode connectors. Disconnect test connector to exit diagnostic mode.

**Clearing Trouble Codes –** Trouble codes will be cleared from ECM memory only after malfunction has been repaired. Always perform diagnostic test after any repair to make sure that no other malfunction exists and that repairs solved original problem.

***ECM TROUBLE CODE LIST***

| Trouble Code | Component Affected |
|---|---|
| 11 | Ignition Pulse System (Engine Off) |
| 12 | Back-Up System |
| 14 | Duty Solenoid Valve System |
| 15 | Coasting Fuel-Cut System |
| 21 | Thermosensor System |
| 22 | VLC Solenoid Valve System |
| 23 | Pressure Sensor |
| 24 | Idle-Up Solenoid Valve |
| 25 | FCV Solenoid Valve Control |
| 32 | $O_2$ Sensor |
| 33 | Car Speed Sensor System |
| 35 | Purge Control Solenoid |
| 41 | Main System Feedback System |
| 52 | Clutch Switch System |
| 62 | Idle-Up System (Clearance Light & Rear Defogger) |
| 63 | Idle-Up System (Heater Fan & Radiator Fan) |

***WIRE COLOR ABBREVIATION CHART***

| Abbreviation | Color |
|---|---|
| B | Black |
| Br | Brown |
| G | Green |
| Gr | Gray |
| L | Blue |
| Lg | Light Green |
| P | Pink |
| R | Red |
| W | White |
| Y | Yellow |

# 1988 COMPUTERIZED ENGINE CONTROLS
## Subaru EFC Carburetor (Cont.)

### BASIC TROUBLE SHOOTING PROCEDURES

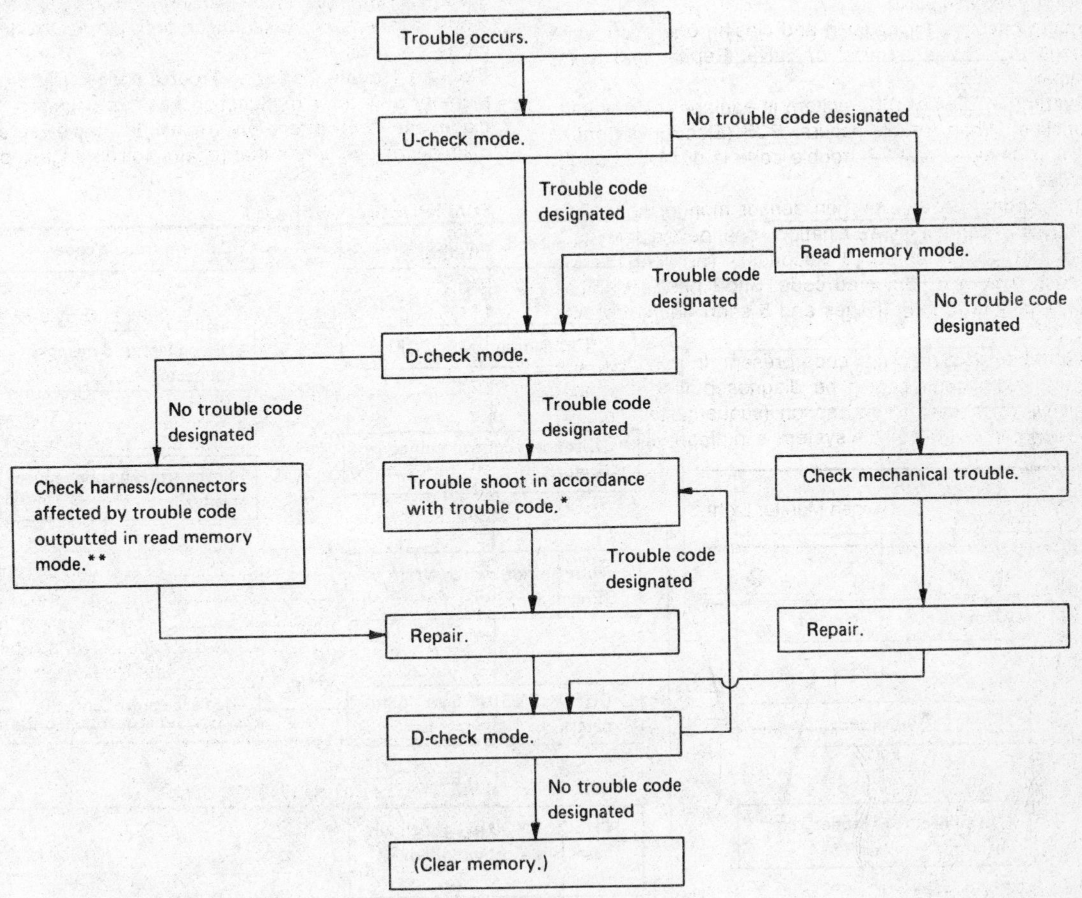

Trouble occurs.
U-check mode.
No trouble code designated
Trouble code designated
Read memory mode.
Trouble code designated
No trouble code designated
D-check mode.
No trouble code designated
Trouble code designated
Check harness/connectors affected by trouble code outputted in read memory mode.**
Trouble shoot in accordance with trouble code.*
Check mechanical trouble.
Trouble code designated
Repair.
Repair.
D-check mode.
No trouble code designated
(Clear memory.)


* **When more than one trouble code is outputted, begin trouble shooting with the smallest trouble code number and proceed to the next higher code.**
**After correcting each problem, conduct the D-check and ensure that the corresponding trouble code no longer appears.**

** **When more than one trouble code is outputted, check all related harness connectors, starting with that corresponding to the smallest trouble code number and proceeding to the next higher code.**

# 1988 COMPUTERIZED ENGINE CONTROLS
## Subaru EFC Carburetor (Cont.)

## READ MEMORY MODE

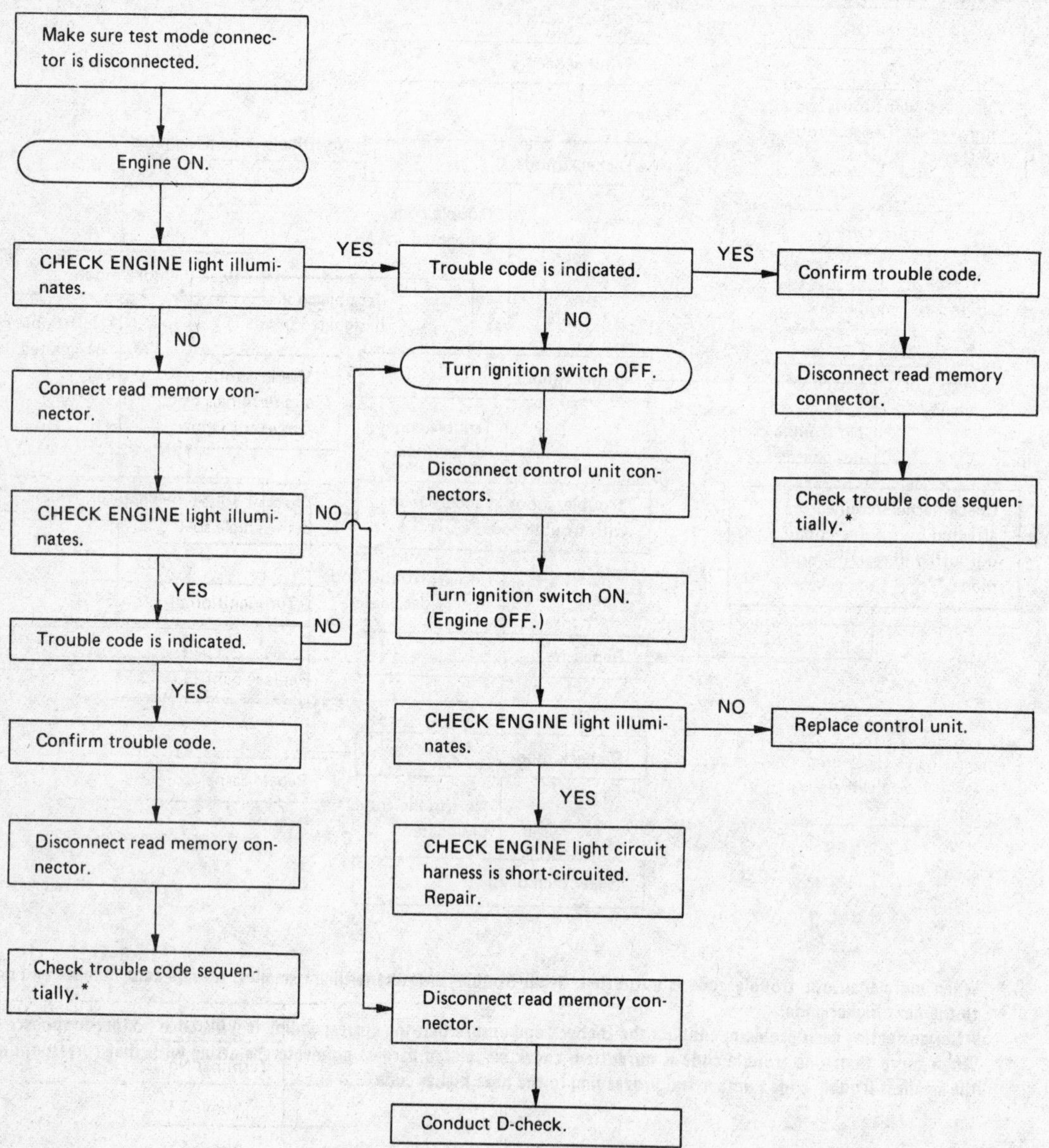

Make sure test mode connector is disconnected.
Engine ON.
CHECK ENGINE light illuminates.
YES
NO
Trouble code is indicated.
YES
NO
Confirm trouble code.
Disconnect read memory connector.
Check trouble code sequentially.*
Connect read memory connector.
CHECK ENGINE light illuminates.
NO
YES
Trouble code is indicated.
NO
YES
Confirm trouble code.
Disconnect read memory connector.
Check trouble code sequentially.*
Turn ignition switch OFF.
Disconnect control unit connectors.
Turn ignition switch ON. (Engine OFF.)
CHECK ENGINE light illuminates.
NO
Replace control unit.
YES
CHECK ENGINE light circuit harness is short-circuited. Repair.
Disconnect read memory connector.
Conduct D-check.


* **When more than one trouble code is outputted, begin trouble shooting with the smallest trouble code number and proceed to the next higher code.**
**After correcting each problem, conduct the D-check and ensure that the corresponding trouble code no longer appears.**

Courtesy of Subaru of America, Inc.

## D-CHECK MODE

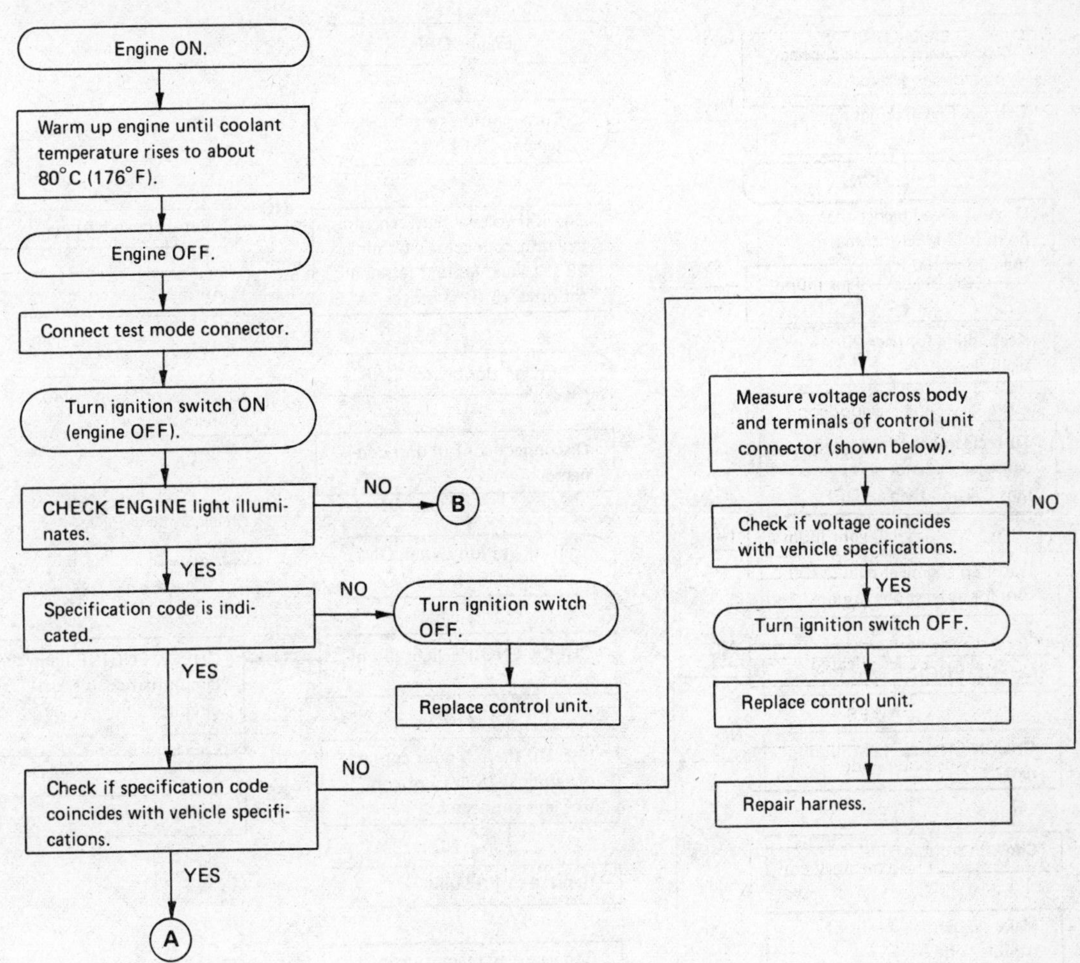
Engine ON.
Warm up engine until coolant temperature rises to about 80°C (176°F).
Engine OFF.
Connect test mode connector.
Turn ignition switch ON (engine OFF).
CHECK ENGINE light illuminates.
NO
B
YES
Specification code is indicated.
NO
Turn ignition switch OFF.
Replace control unit.
YES
Check if specification code coincides with vehicle specifications.
NO
YES
A
Measure voltage across body and terminals of control unit connector (shown below).
Check if voltage coincides with vehicle specifications.
NO
YES
Turn ignition switch OFF.
Replace control unit.
Repair harness.

**Specification codes and voltage**

| Specification | | Specification code | Voltage (connector – body) | |
|---|---|---|---|---|
| | | | Terminal No. 33 | Terminal No. 35 |
| 49-state and Canada | FWD | 01 | Above 7 V | Above 7 V |
| | 4WD | 05 | Above 2 V | Below 7 V |
| California | FWD | 02 | Below 7 V | Above 2 V |
| | 4WD | 06 | Below 2 V | Below 2 V |

## D-CHECK MODE (Cont.)

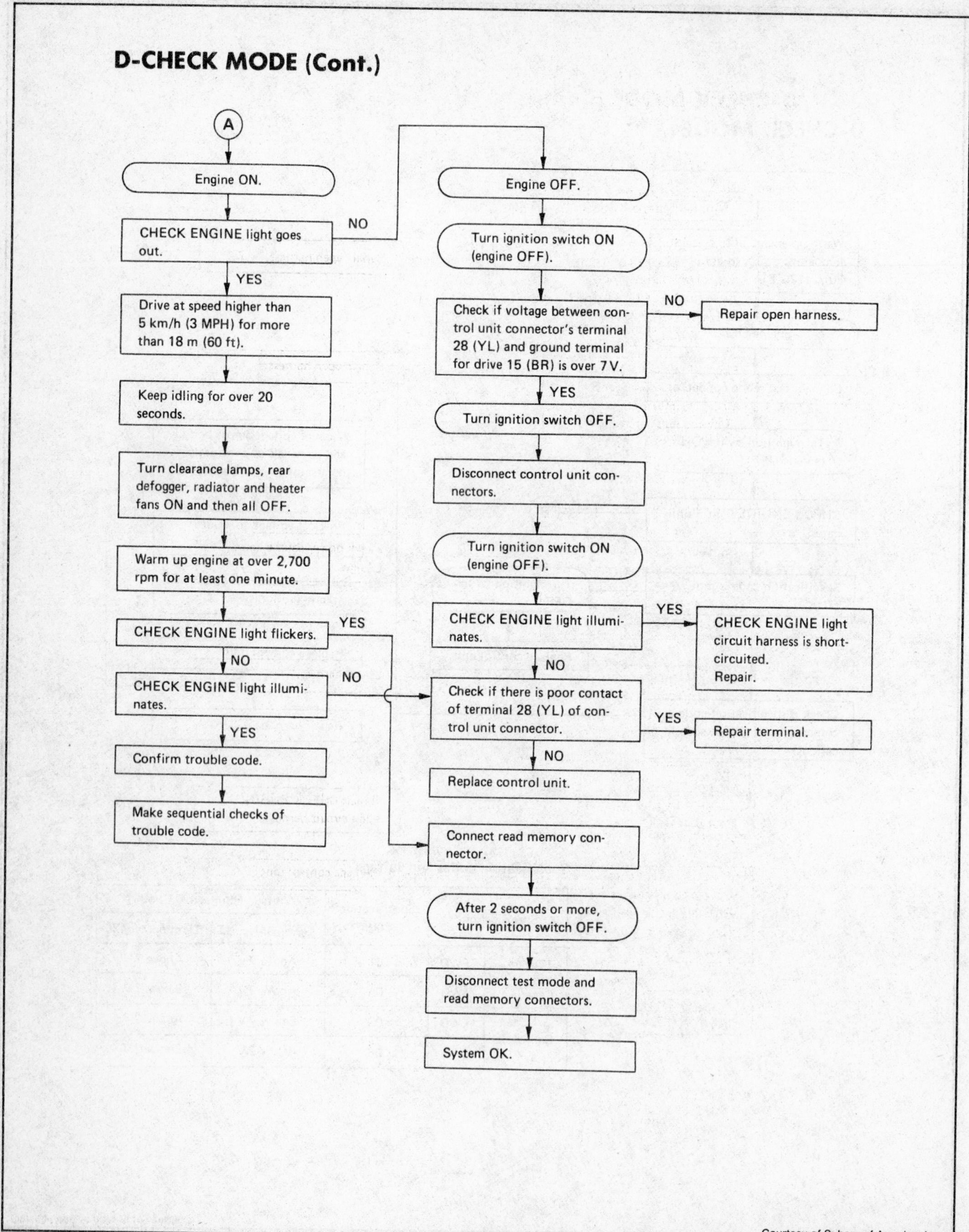
A
Engine ON.
CHECK ENGINE light goes out.
NO
YES
Drive at speed higher than 5 km/h (3 MPH) for more than 18 m (60 ft).
Keep idling for over 20 seconds.
Turn clearance lamps, rear defogger, radiator and heater fans ON and then all OFF.
Warm up engine at over 2,700 rpm for at least one minute.
CHECK ENGINE light flickers.
YES
NO
CHECK ENGINE light illuminates.
NO
YES
Confirm trouble code.
Make sequential checks of trouble code.
Engine OFF.
Turn ignition switch ON (engine OFF).
Check if voltage between control unit connector's terminal 28 (YL) and ground terminal for drive 15 (BR) is over 7V.
NO
Repair open harness.
YES
Turn ignition switch OFF.
Disconnect control unit connectors.
Turn ignition switch ON (engine OFF).
CHECK ENGINE light illuminates.
YES
CHECK ENGINE light circuit harness is short-circuited. Repair.
NO
Check if there is poor contact of terminal 28 (YL) of control unit connector.
YES
Repair terminal.
NO
Replace control unit.
Connect read memory connector.
After 2 seconds or more, turn ignition switch OFF.
Disconnect test mode and read memory connectors.
System OK.

Courtesy of Subaru of America, Inc.

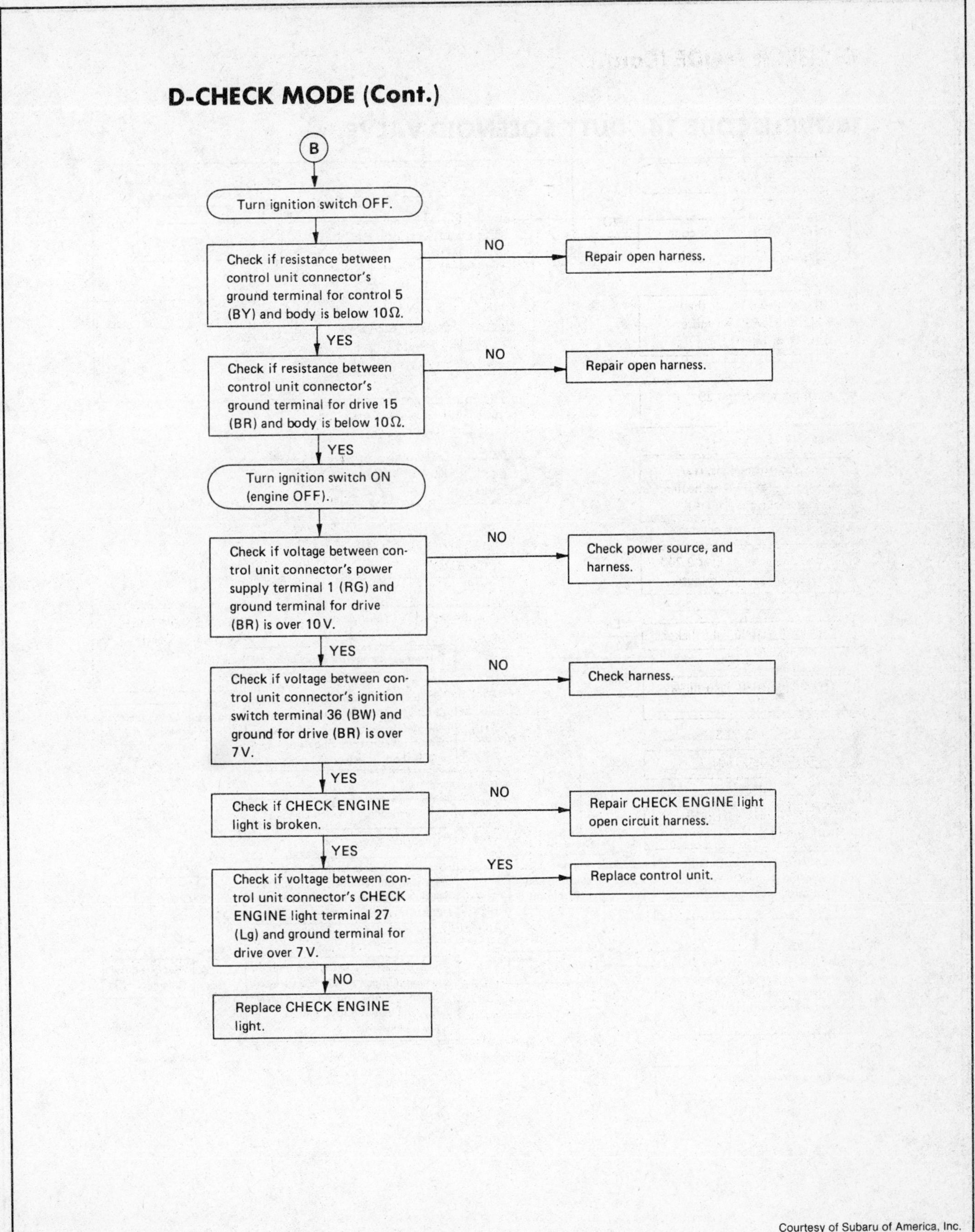
D-CHECK MODE (Cont.)
B
Turn ignition switch OFF.
Check if resistance between control unit connector's ground terminal for control 5 (BY) and body is below 10Ω.
NO
Repair open harness.
YES
Check if resistance between control unit connector's ground terminal for drive 15 (BR) and body is below 10Ω.
NO
Repair open harness.
YES
Turn ignition switch ON (engine OFF).
Check if voltage between control unit connector's power supply terminal 1 (RG) and ground terminal for drive (BR) is over 10 V.
NO
Check power source, and harness.
YES
Check if voltage between control unit connector's ignition switch terminal 36 (BW) and ground for drive (BR) is over 7 V.
NO
Check harness.
YES
Check if CHECK ENGINE light is broken.
NO
Repair CHECK ENGINE light open circuit harness.
YES
Check if voltage between control unit connector's CHECK ENGINE light terminal 27 (Lg) and ground terminal for drive over 7 V.
YES
Replace control unit.
NO
Replace CHECK ENGINE light.
Courtesy of Subaru of America, Inc.

## TROUBLE CODE 14: DUTY SOLENOID VALVE

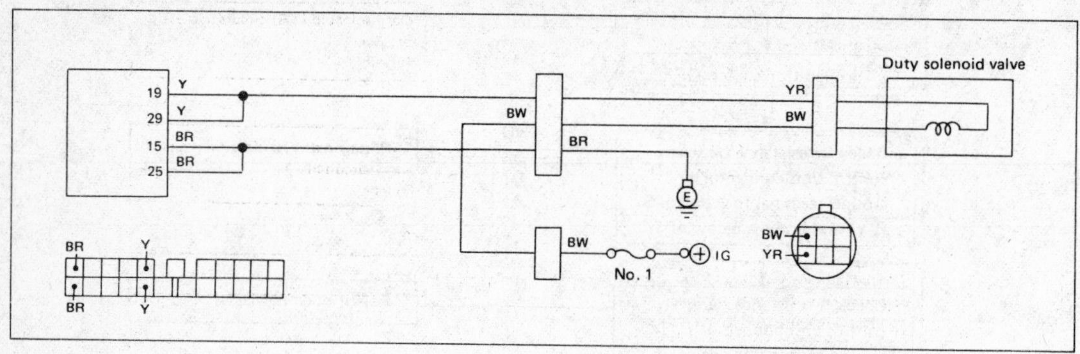
Duty solenoid valve
19
29
15
25
Y
Y
BR
BR
YR
BW
BW
BR
E
BW
No. 1
IG
BW
YR
BR
Y
BR
Y

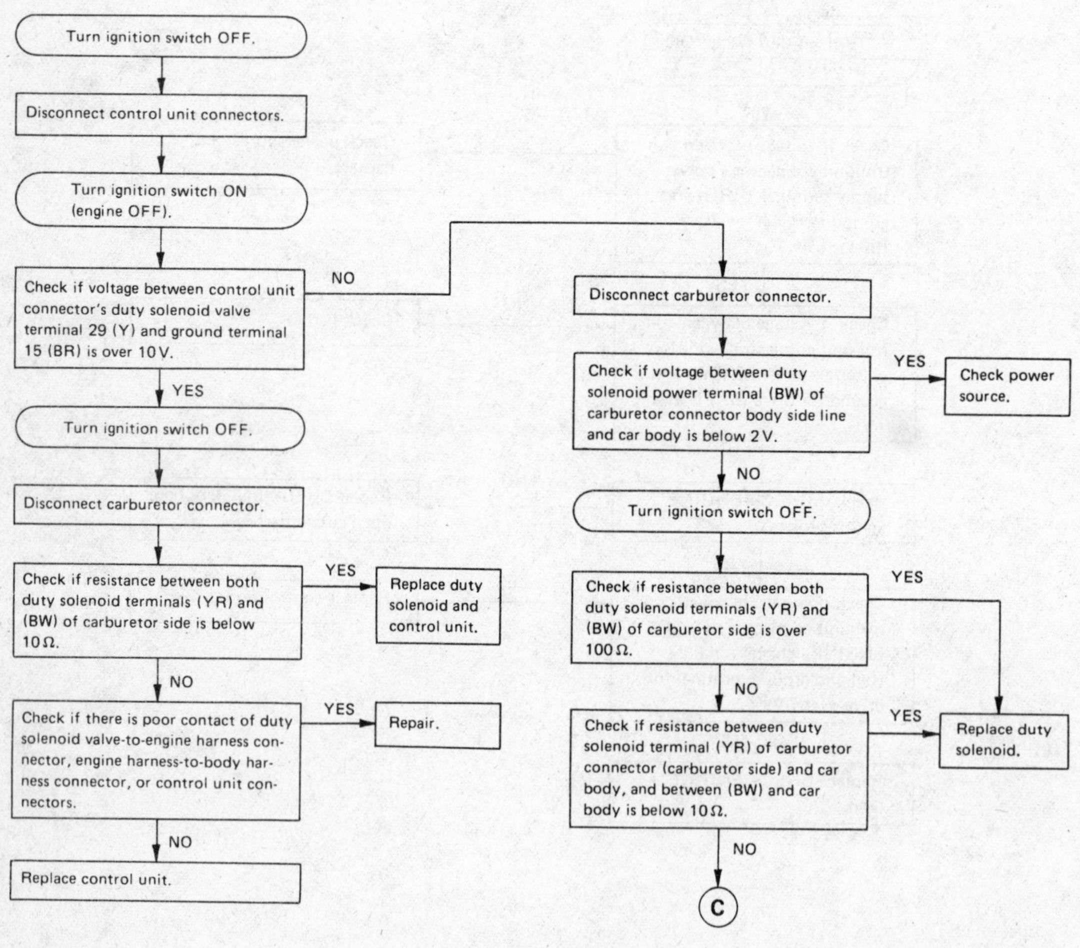
Turn ignition switch OFF.
Disconnect control unit connectors.
Turn ignition switch ON (engine OFF).
Check if voltage between control unit connector's duty solenoid valve terminal 29 (Y) and ground terminal 15 (BR) is over 10V.
NO
YES
Turn ignition switch OFF.
Disconnect carburetor connector.
Check if resistance between both duty solenoid terminals (YR) and (BW) of carburetor side is below 10Ω.
YES
Replace duty solenoid and control unit.
NO
Check if there is poor contact of duty solenoid valve-to-engine harness connector, engine harness-to-body harness connector, or control unit connectors.
YES
Repair.
NO
Replace control unit.
Disconnect carburetor connector.
Check if voltage between duty solenoid power terminal (BW) of carburetor connector body side line and car body is below 2V.
YES
Check power source.
NO
Turn ignition switch OFF.
Check if resistance between both duty solenoid terminals (YR) and (BW) of carburetor side is over 100Ω.
YES
NO
Check if resistance between duty solenoid terminal (YR) of carburetor connector (carburetor side) and car body, and between (BW) and car body is below 10Ω.
YES
Replace duty solenoid.
NO
C

Courtesy of Subaru of America, Inc.

## TROUBLE CODE 14: DUTY SOLENOID VALVE (Cont.)

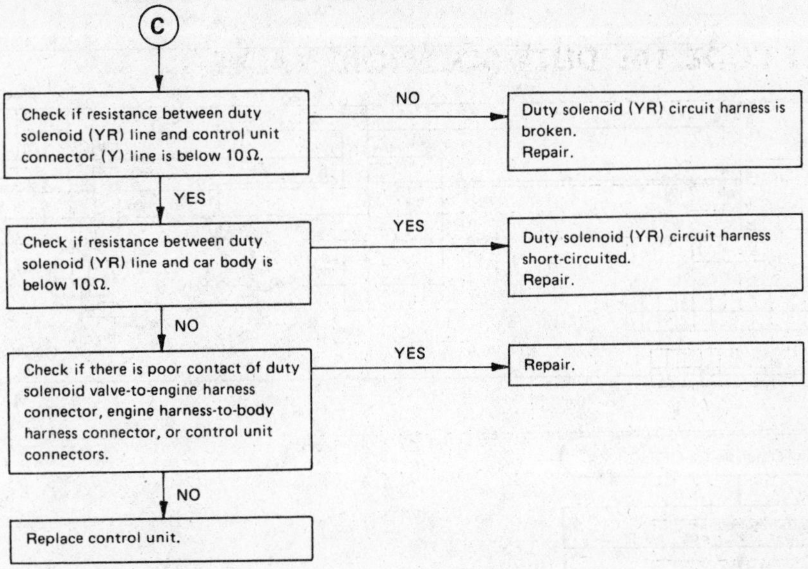

(C)

Check if resistance between duty solenoid (YR) line and control unit connector (Y) line is below 10 Ω.

- NO → Duty solenoid (YR) circuit harness is broken. Repair.
- YES ↓

Check if resistance between duty solenoid (YR) line and car body is below 10 Ω.

- YES → Duty solenoid (YR) circuit harness short-circuited. Repair.
- NO ↓

Check if there is poor contact of duty solenoid valve-to-engine harness connector, engine harness-to-body harness connector, or control unit connectors.

- YES → Repair.
- NO ↓

Replace control unit.

Courtesy of Subaru of America, Inc.

## TROUBLE CODE 15: COASTING FUEL-CUT SYSTEM

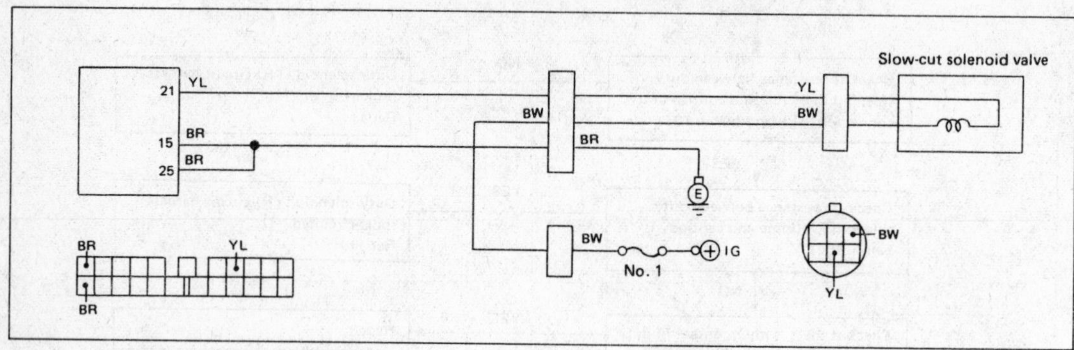
Slow-cut solenoid valve
21
YL
15
BR
25
BR
BW
BR
YL
BW
E
BR
YL
BR
BW
No. 1
IG
BW
YL

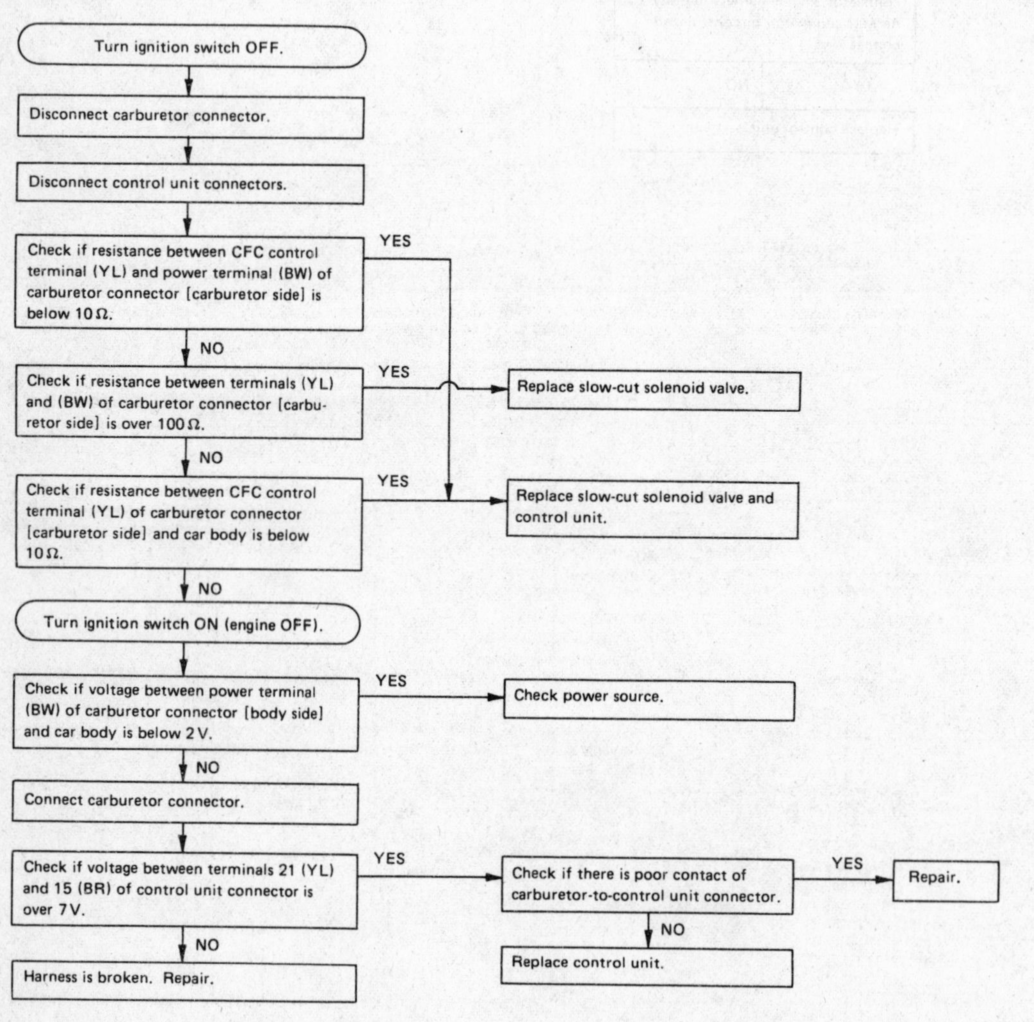
Turn ignition switch OFF.
Disconnect carburetor connector.
Disconnect control unit connectors.
Check if resistance between CFC control terminal (YL) and power terminal (BW) of carburetor connector [carburetor side] is below 10 Ω.
YES
NO
Check if resistance between terminals (YL) and (BW) of carburetor connector [carbu-retor side] is over 100 Ω.
YES
Replace slow-cut solenoid valve.
NO
Check if resistance between CFC control terminal (YL) of carburetor connector [carburetor side] and car body is below 10 Ω.
YES
Replace slow-cut solenoid valve and control unit.
NO
Turn ignition switch ON (engine OFF).
Check if voltage between power terminal (BW) of carburetor connector [body side] and car body is below 2 V.
YES
Check power source.
NO
Connect carburetor connector.
Check if voltage between terminals 21 (YL) and 15 (BR) of control unit connector is over 7 V.
YES
Check if there is poor contact of carburetor-to-control unit connector.
YES
Repair.
NO
Replace control unit.
NO
Harness is broken. Repair.

Courtesy of Subaru of America, Inc.

## TROUBLE CODE 21: WATER TEMPERATURE SENSOR

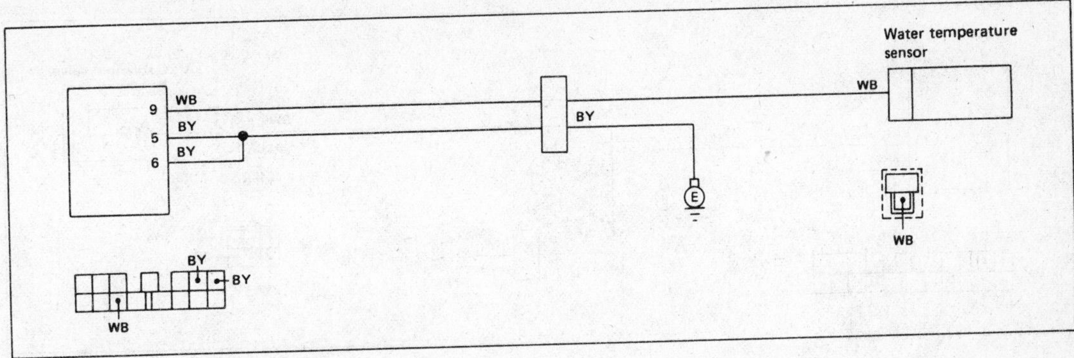
Water temperature sensor
WB
9
WB
5
BY
6
BY
BY
E
WB
BY
BY
WB

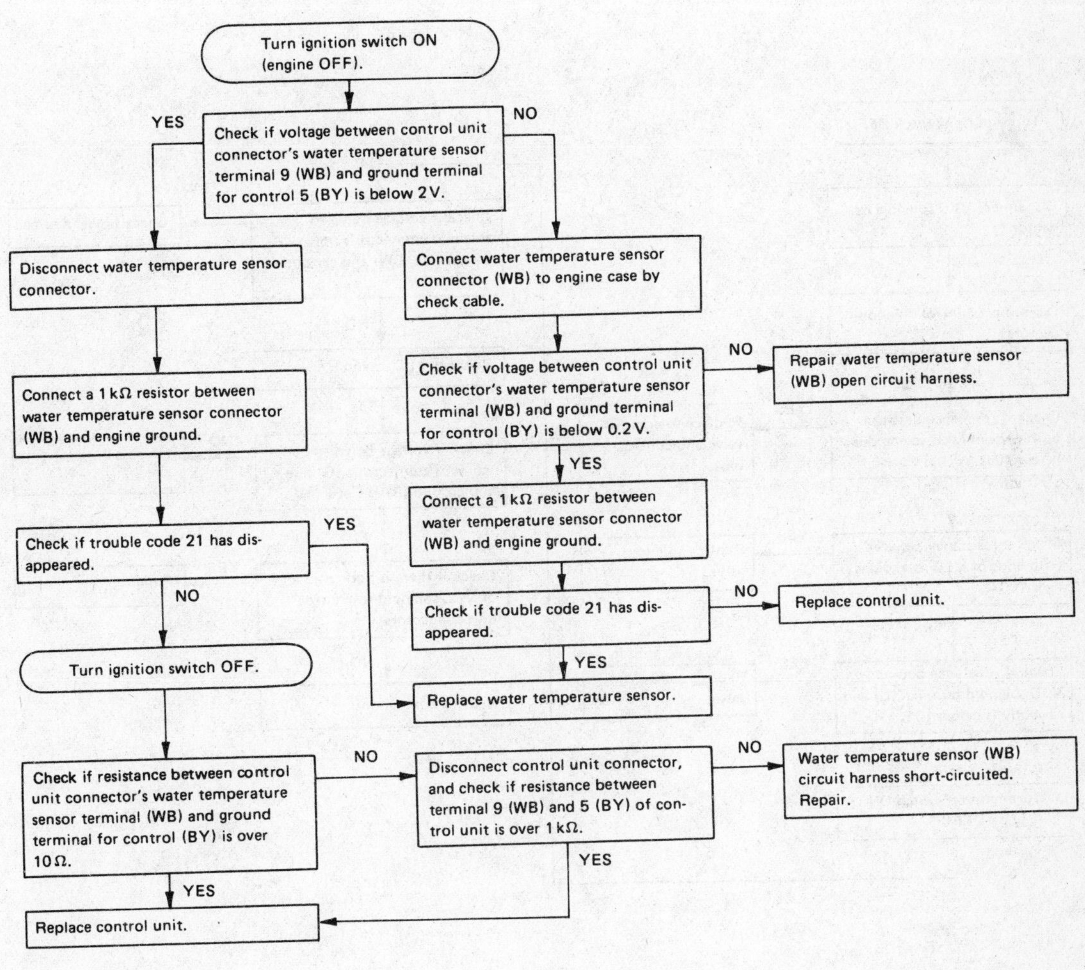
Turn ignition switch ON (engine OFF).
Check if voltage between control unit connector's water temperature sensor terminal 9 (WB) and ground terminal for control 5 (BY) is below 2 V.
YES
NO
Disconnect water temperature sensor connector.
Connect a 1 kΩ resistor between water temperature sensor connector (WB) and engine ground.
Check if trouble code 21 has disappeared.
YES
NO
Turn ignition switch OFF.
Check if resistance between control unit connector's water temperature sensor terminal (WB) and ground terminal for control (BY) is over 10 Ω.
YES
Replace control unit.
NO
Disconnect control unit connector, and check if resistance between terminal 9 (WB) and 5 (BY) of control unit is over 1 kΩ.
NO
Water temperature sensor (WB) circuit harness short-circuited. Repair.
YES
Connect water temperature sensor connector (WB) to engine case by check cable.
Check if voltage between control unit connector's water temperature sensor terminal (WB) and ground terminal for control (BY) is below 0.2 V.
NO
Repair water temperature sensor (WB) open circuit harness.
YES
Connect a 1 kΩ resistor between water temperature sensor connector (WB) and engine ground.
Check if trouble code 21 has disappeared.
NO
Replace control unit.
YES
Replace water temperature sensor.

## TROUBLE CODE 22: VLC SOLENOID VALVE

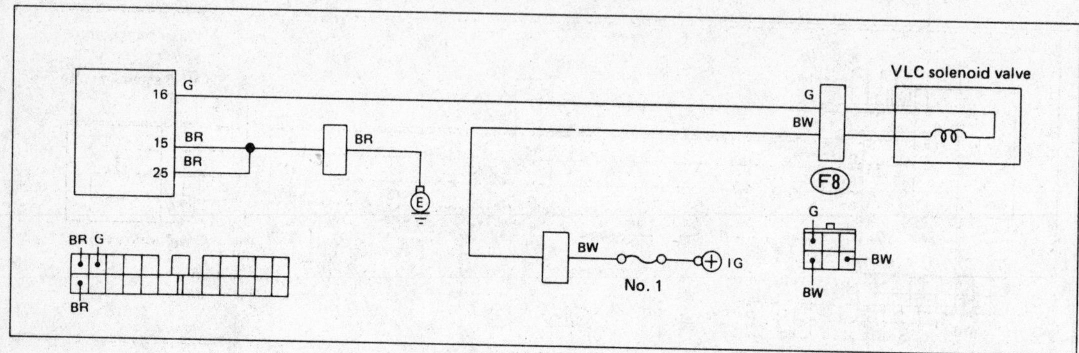
VLC solenoid valve
16
G
15
BR
25
BR
BR
E
G
BW
F8
BR G
BR
BW
No. 1
IG
G
BW
BW

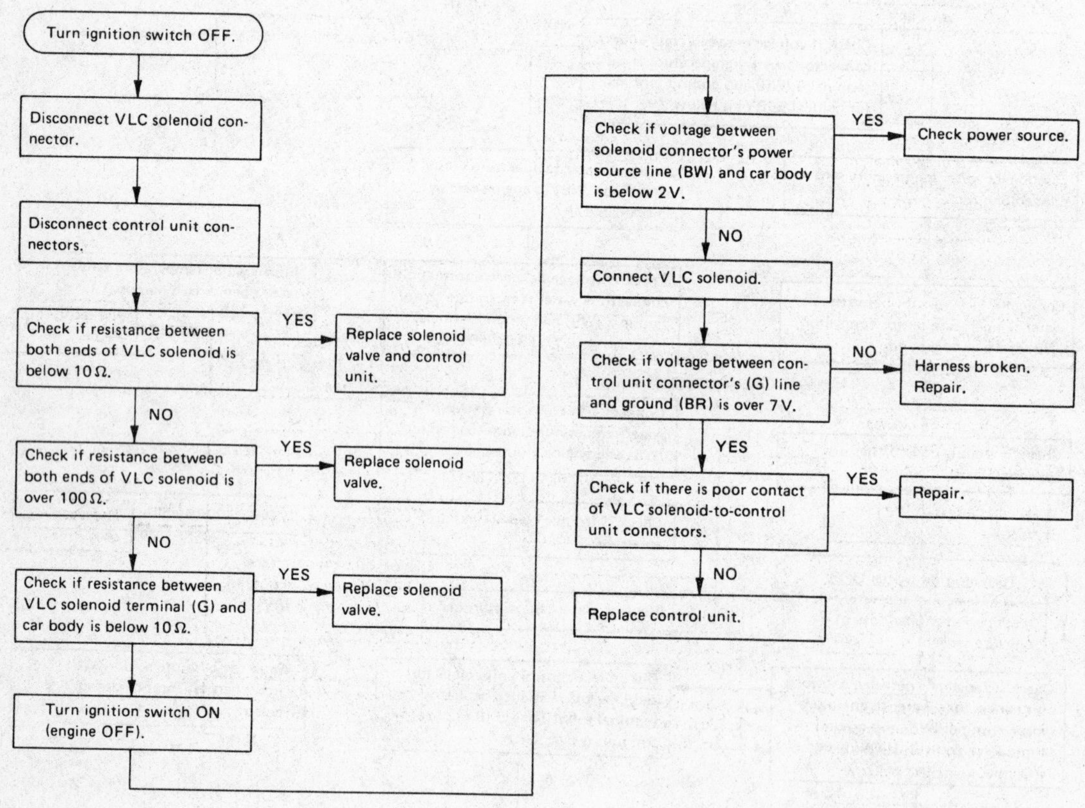
Turn ignition switch OFF.
Disconnect VLC solenoid connector.
Disconnect control unit connectors.
Check if resistance between both ends of VLC solenoid is below 10 Ω.
YES
Replace solenoid valve and control unit.
NO
Check if resistance between both ends of VLC solenoid is over 100 Ω.
YES
Replace solenoid valve.
NO
Check if resistance between VLC solenoid terminal (G) and car body is below 10 Ω.
YES
Replace solenoid valve.
Turn ignition switch ON (engine OFF).
Check if voltage between solenoid connector's power source line (BW) and car body is below 2V.
YES
Check power source.
NO
Connect VLC solenoid.
Check if voltage between control unit connector's (G) line and ground (BR) is over 7V.
NO
Harness broken. Repair.
YES
Check if there is poor contact of VLC solenoid-to-control unit connectors.
YES
Repair.
NO
Replace control unit.

Courtesy of Subaru of America, Inc.

## TROUBLE CODE 23: PRESSURE SENSOR

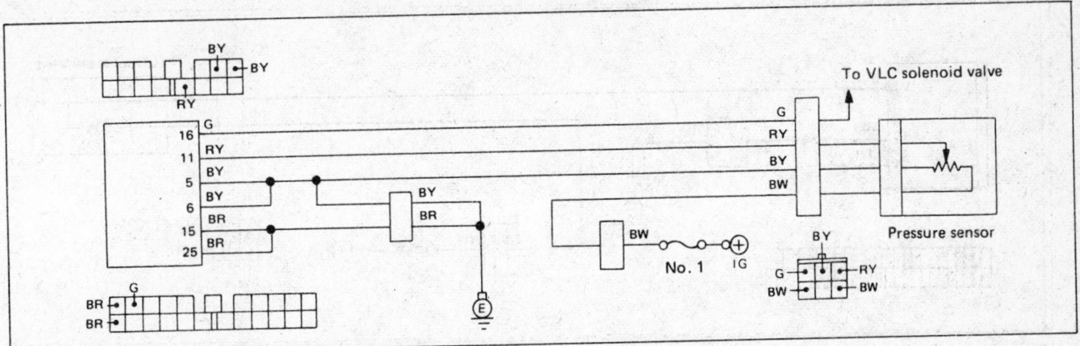
BY
BY
RY
To VLC solenoid valve
G
16
RY
11
BY
5
BY
6
BR
15
BR
25
BY
BR
G
RY
BY
BW
Pressure sensor
BW
No. 1
IG
BY
G
RY
BW
BW
E
G
BR
BR

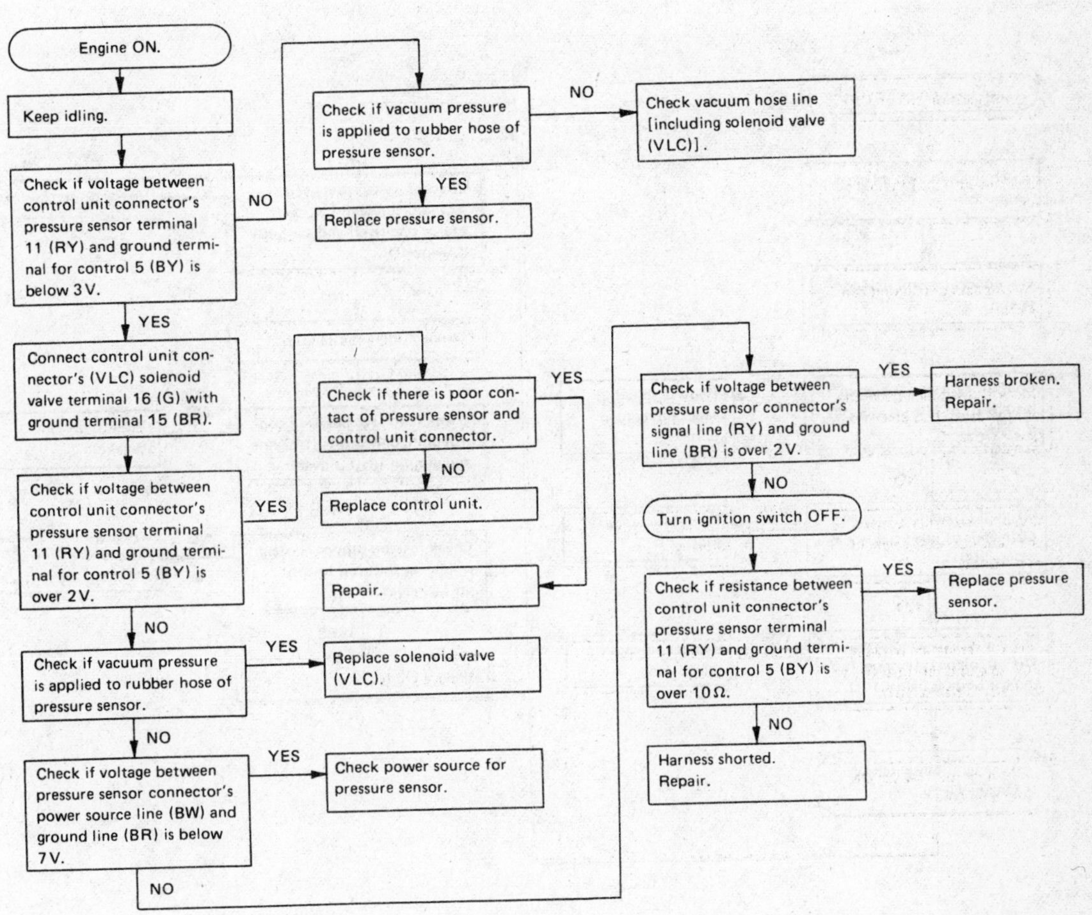
Engine ON.
Keep idling.
Check if voltage between control unit connector's pressure sensor terminal 11 (RY) and ground terminal for control 5 (BY) is below 3V.
NO
Check if vacuum pressure is applied to rubber hose of pressure sensor.
NO
Check vacuum hose line [including solenoid valve (VLC)].
YES
Replace pressure sensor.
YES
Connect control unit connector's (VLC) solenoid valve terminal 16 (G) with ground terminal 15 (BR).
Check if voltage between control unit connector's pressure sensor terminal 11 (RY) and ground terminal for control 5 (BY) is over 2V.
YES
Check if there is poor contact of pressure sensor and control unit connector.
YES
NO
Replace control unit.
Repair.
NO
Check if vacuum pressure is applied to rubber hose of pressure sensor.
YES
Replace solenoid valve (VLC).
NO
Check if voltage between pressure sensor connector's power source line (BW) and ground line (BR) is below 7V.
YES
Check power source for pressure sensor.
NO
Check if voltage between pressure sensor connector's signal line (RY) and ground line (BR) is over 2V.
YES
Harness broken. Repair.
NO
Turn ignition switch OFF.
Check if resistance between control unit connector's pressure sensor terminal 11 (RY) and ground terminal for control 5 (BY) is over 10 Ω.
YES
Replace pressure sensor.
NO
Harness shorted. Repair.

Courtesy of Subaru of America, Inc.

## TROUBLE CODE 24: IDLE-UP SOLENOID

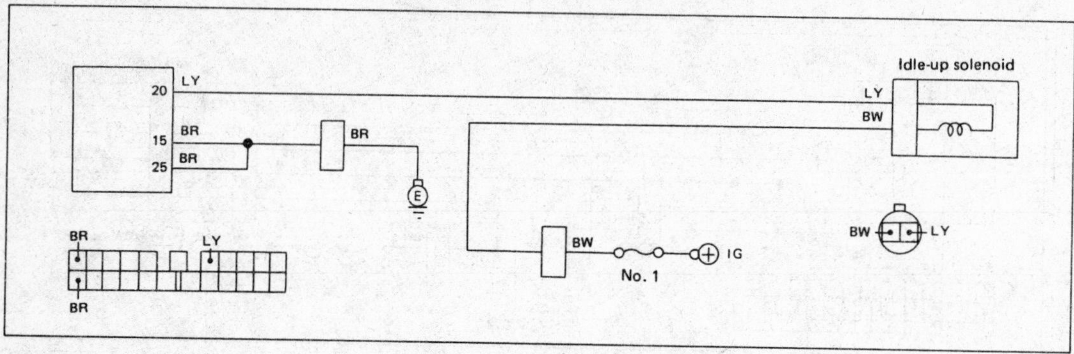
Idle-up solenoid
20
LY
15
BR
25
BR
BR
E
LY
BW
BR
LY
BR
BW
No. 1
IG
BW
LY

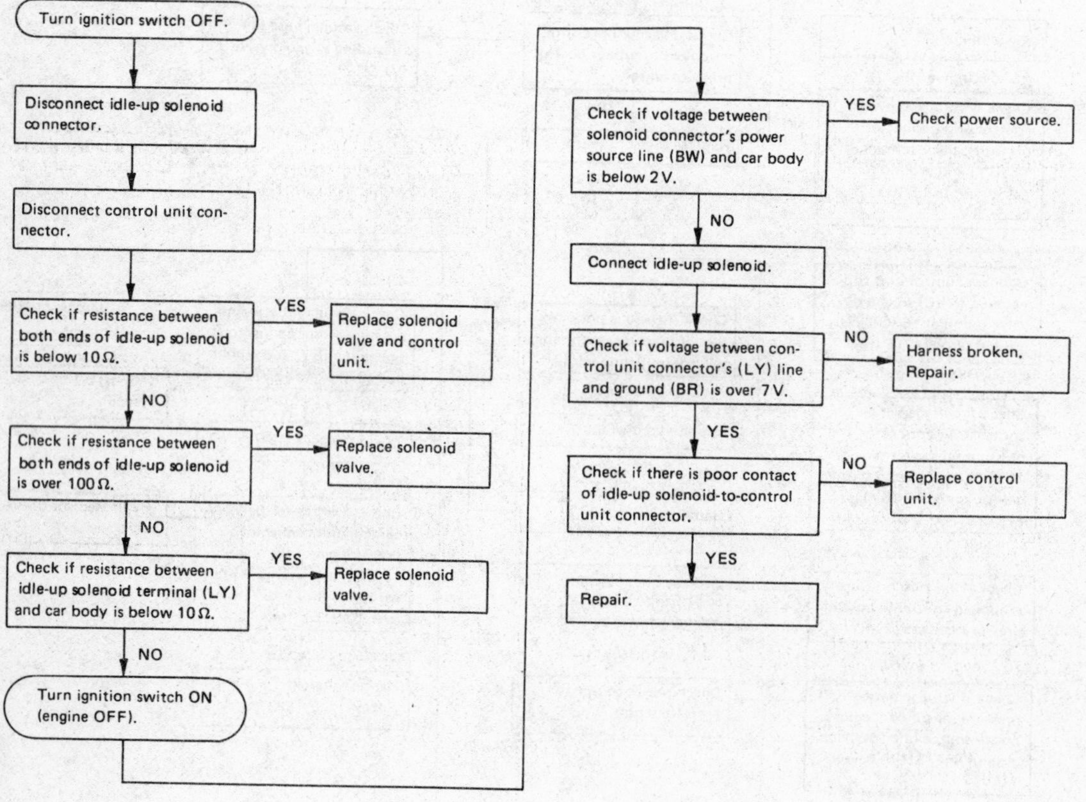
Turn ignition switch OFF.
Disconnect idle-up solenoid connector.
Disconnect control unit connector.
Check if resistance between both ends of idle-up solenoid is below 10 Ω.
YES
Replace solenoid valve and control unit.
NO
Check if resistance between both ends of idle-up solenoid is over 100 Ω.
YES
Replace solenoid valve.
NO
Check if resistance between idle-up solenoid terminal (LY) and car body is below 10 Ω.
YES
Replace solenoid valve.
NO
Turn ignition switch ON (engine OFF).
Check if voltage between solenoid connector's power source line (BW) and car body is below 2 V.
YES
Check power source.
NO
Connect idle-up solenoid.
Check if voltage between control unit connector's (LY) line and ground (BR) is over 7 V.
NO
Harness broken. Repair.
YES
Check if there is poor contact of idle-up solenoid-to-control unit connector.
NO
Replace control unit.
YES
Repair.

Courtesy of Subaru of America, Inc.

## TROUBLE CODE 25: FCV SOLENOID VALVE

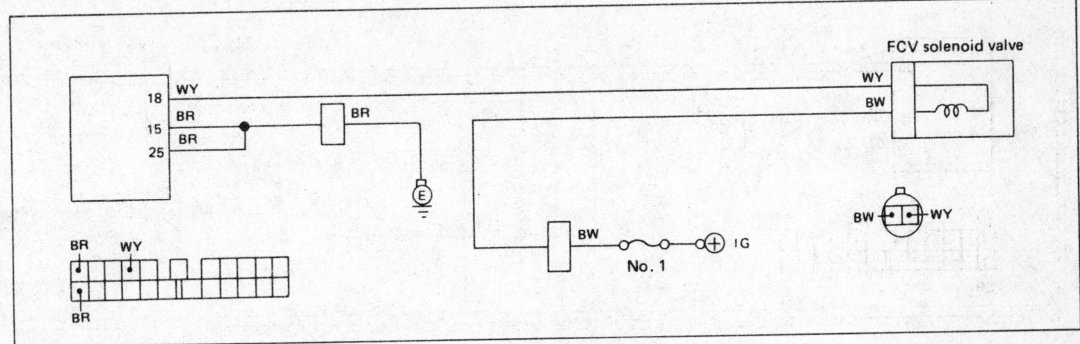
FCV solenoid valve
WY
BW
18
WY
BR
15
BR
25
BR
E
BW
No. 1
IG
BW
WY
BR
WY
BR

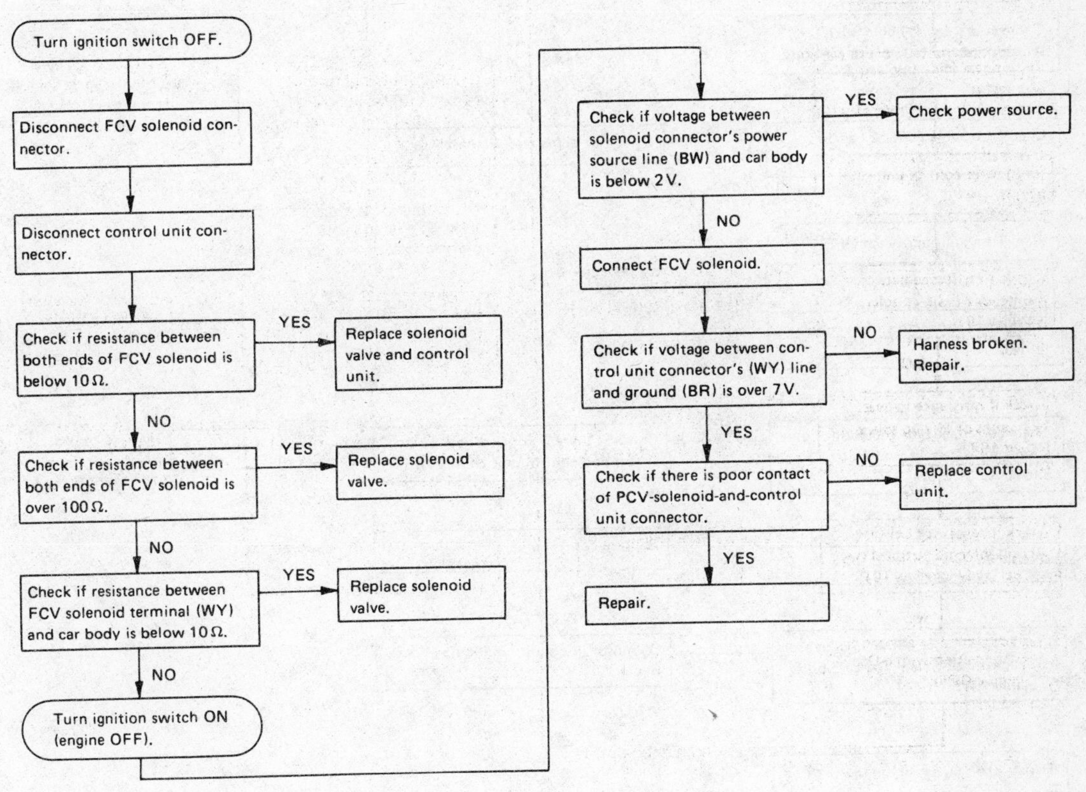
Turn ignition switch OFF.
Disconnect FCV solenoid connector.
Disconnect control unit connector.
Check if resistance between both ends of FCV solenoid is below 10 Ω.
YES
Replace solenoid valve and control unit.
NO
Check if resistance between both ends of FCV solenoid is over 100 Ω.
YES
Replace solenoid valve.
NO
Check if resistance between FCV solenoid terminal (WY) and car body is below 10 Ω.
YES
Replace solenoid valve.
NO
Turn ignition switch ON (engine OFF).
Check if voltage between solenoid connector's power source line (BW) and car body is below 2 V.
YES
Check power source.
NO
Connect FCV solenoid.
Check if voltage between control unit connector's (WY) line and ground (BR) is over 7 V.
NO
Harness broken. Repair.
YES
Check if there is poor contact of PCV-solenoid-and-control unit connector.
NO
Replace control unit.
YES
Repair.

Courtesy of Subaru of America, Inc.

## TROUBLE CODE 32: $O_2$ SENSOR

12
SB (W)
SB (W)
SB: Sealed wire
SB

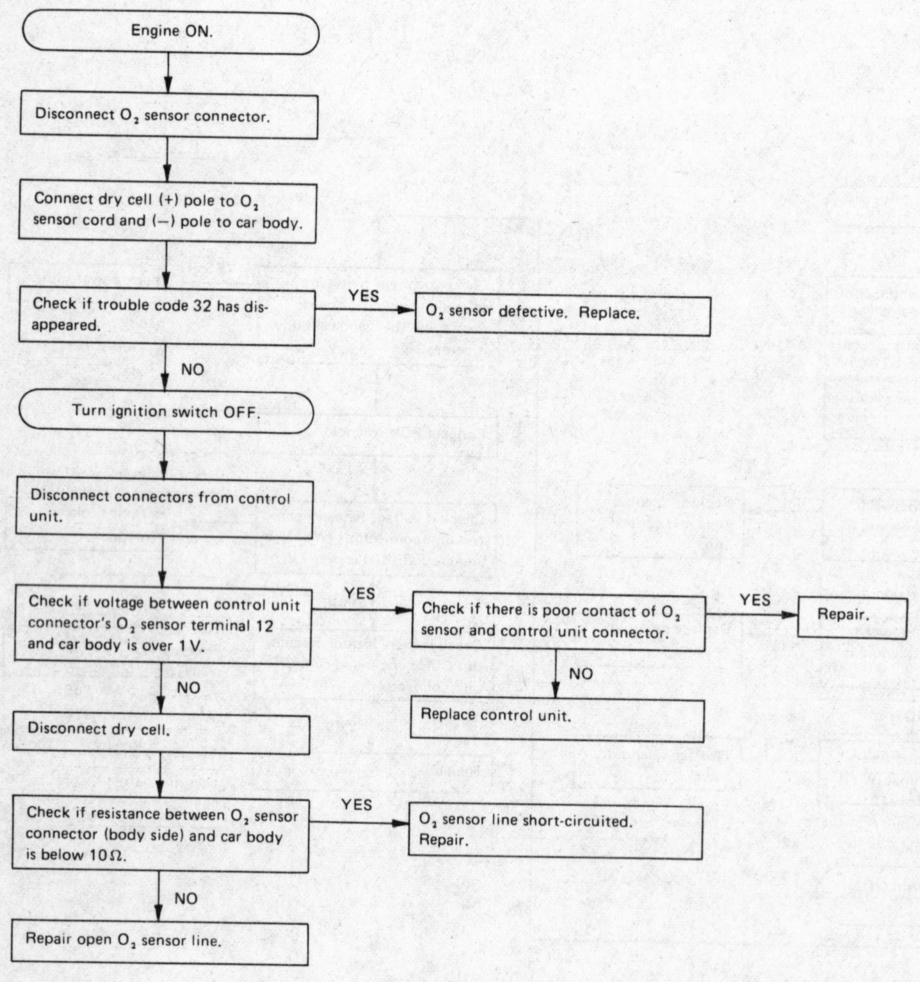
Engine ON.
Disconnect O2 sensor connector.
Connect dry cell (+) pole to O2 sensor cord and (–) pole to car body.
Check if trouble code 32 has disappeared.
YES
O2 sensor defective. Replace.
NO
Turn ignition switch OFF.
Disconnect connectors from control unit.
Check if voltage between control unit connector's O2 sensor terminal 12 and car body is over 1 V.
YES
Check if there is poor contact of O2 sensor and control unit connector.
YES
Repair.
NO
Replace control unit.
NO
Disconnect dry cell.
Check if resistance between O2 sensor connector (body side) and car body is below 10 Ω.
YES
O2 sensor line short-circuited. Repair.
NO
Repair open O2 sensor line.

Courtesy of Subaru of America, Inc.

## TROUBLE CODE 33: CAR SPEED SENSOR

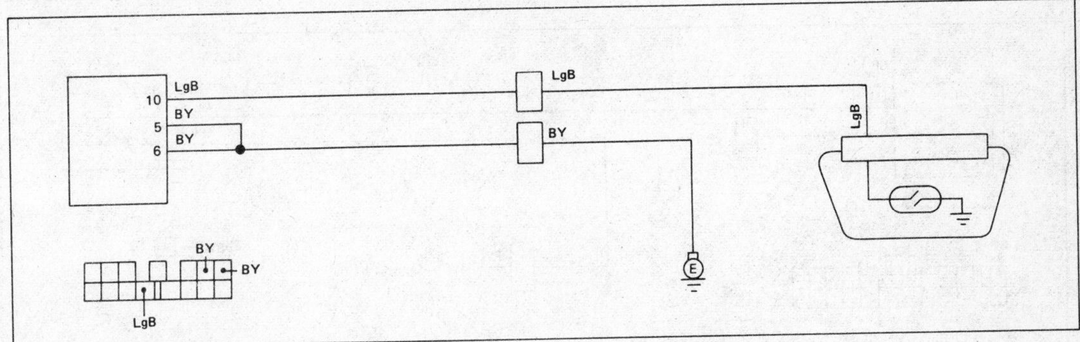
LgB
10
BY
5
BY
6
LgB
BY
LgB
BY
BY
LgB
E

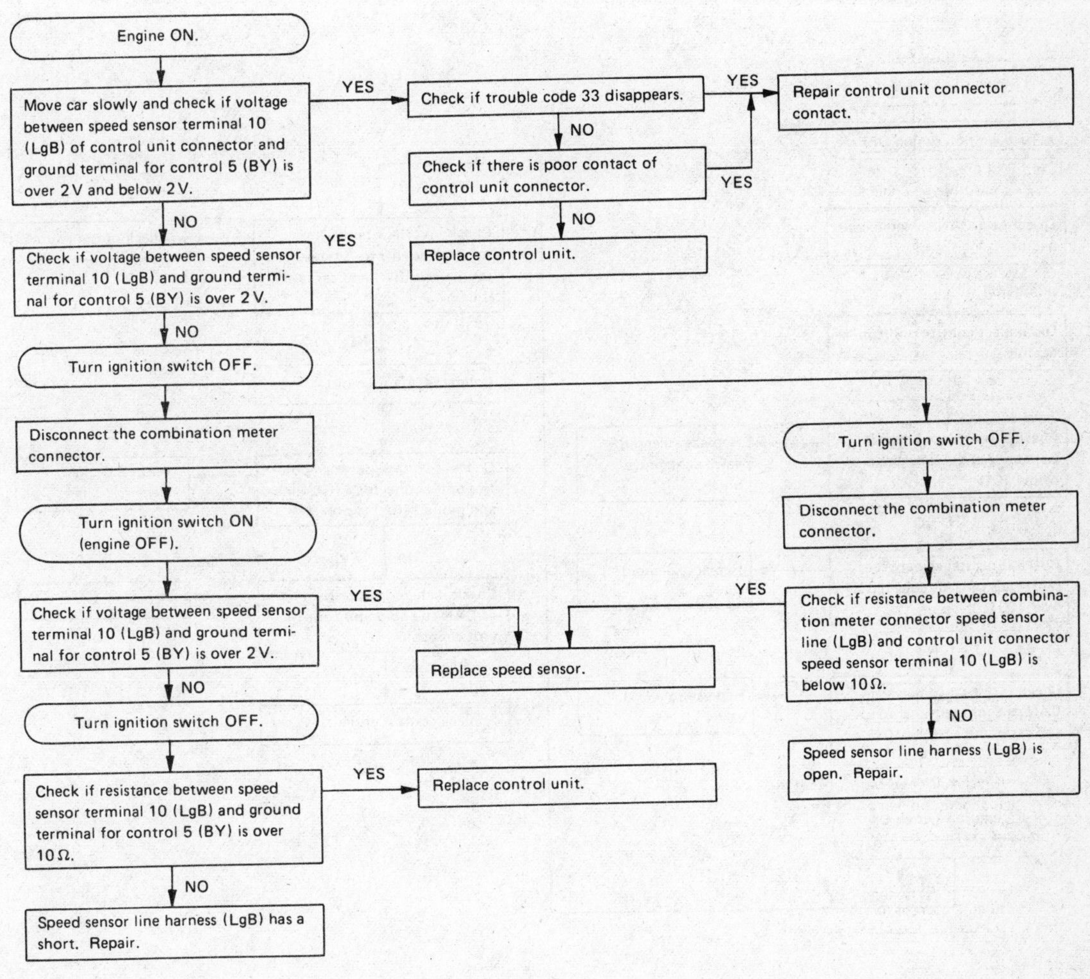
Engine ON.
Move car slowly and check if voltage between speed sensor terminal 10 (LgB) of control unit connector and ground terminal for control 5 (BY) is over 2 V and below 2 V.
YES
Check if trouble code 33 disappears.
YES
Repair control unit connector contact.
NO
Check if there is poor contact of control unit connector.
YES
NO
Replace control unit.
NO
Check if voltage between speed sensor terminal 10 (LgB) and ground terminal for control 5 (BY) is over 2 V.
YES
NO
Turn ignition switch OFF.
Disconnect the combination meter connector.
Turn ignition switch ON (engine OFF).
Check if voltage between speed sensor terminal 10 (LgB) and ground terminal for control 5 (BY) is over 2 V.
YES
Replace speed sensor.
NO
Turn ignition switch OFF.
Check if resistance between speed sensor terminal 10 (LgB) and ground terminal for control 5 (BY) is over 10 Ω.
YES
Replace control unit.
NO
Speed sensor line harness (LgB) has a short. Repair.
Turn ignition switch OFF.
Disconnect the combination meter connector.
Check if resistance between combination meter connector speed sensor line (LgB) and control unit connector speed sensor terminal 10 (LgB) is below 10 Ω.
YES
NO
Speed sensor line harness (LgB) is open. Repair.

Courtesy of Subaru of America, Inc.

## TROUBLE CODE 35: PURGE CONTROL SOLENOID

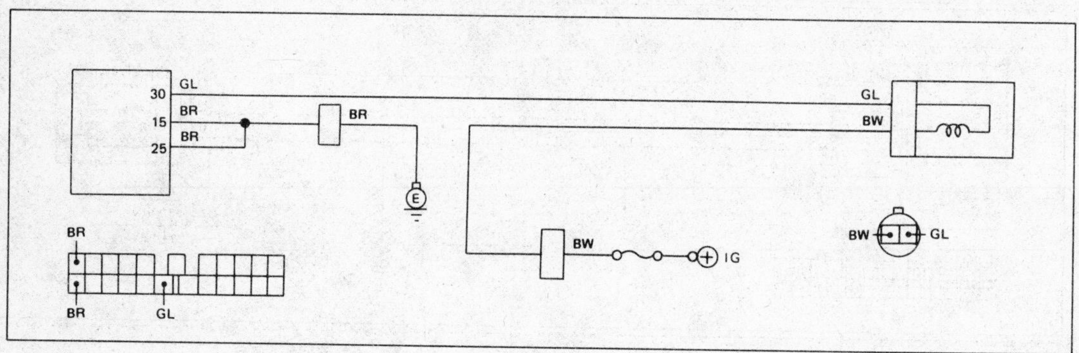
30
15
25
GL
BR
BR
BR
E
GL
BW
BW
IG
BW
GL
BR
BR
GL

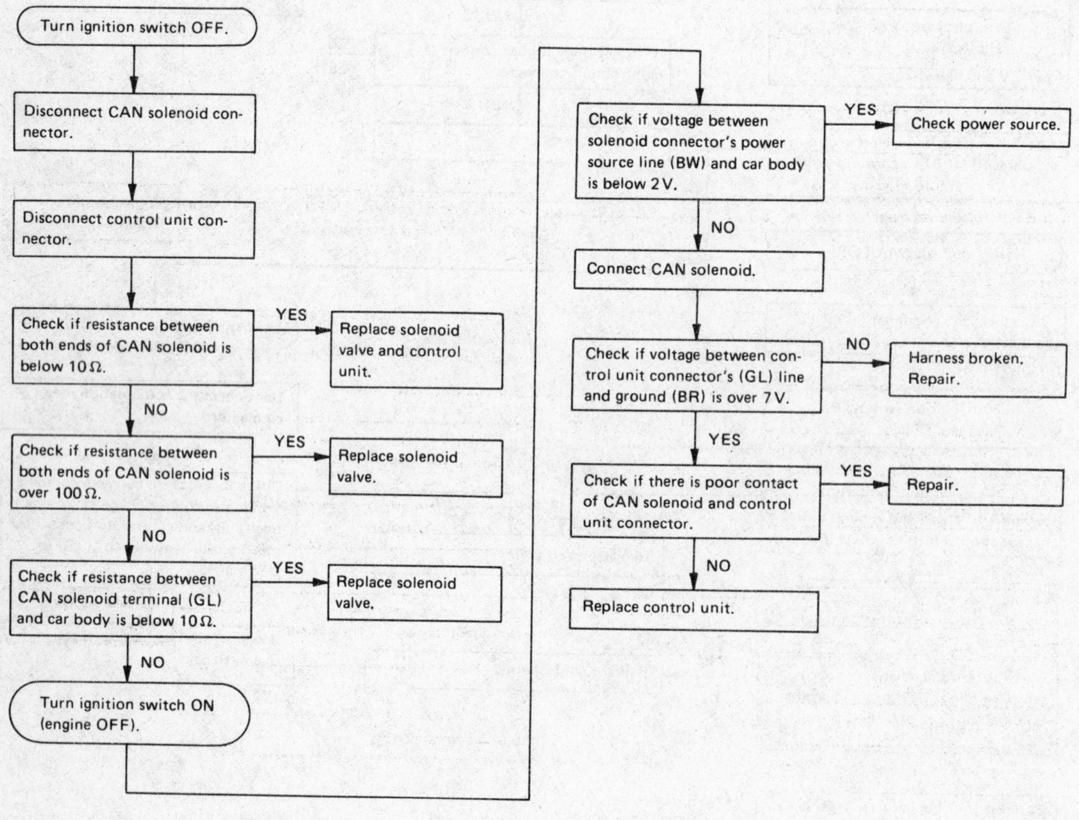
Turn ignition switch OFF.
Disconnect CAN solenoid connector.
Disconnect control unit connector.
Check if resistance between both ends of CAN solenoid is below 10Ω.
YES
Replace solenoid valve and control unit.
NO
Check if resistance between both ends of CAN solenoid is over 100Ω.
YES
Replace solenoid valve.
NO
Check if resistance between CAN solenoid terminal (GL) and car body is below 10Ω.
YES
Replace solenoid valve.
NO
Turn ignition switch ON (engine OFF).
Check if voltage between solenoid connector's power source line (BW) and car body is below 2V.
YES
Check power source.
NO
Connect CAN solenoid.
Check if voltage between control unit connector's (GL) line and ground (BR) is over 7V.
NO
Harness broken. Repair.
YES
Check if there is poor contact of CAN solenoid and control unit connector.
YES
Repair.
NO
Replace control unit.

## TROUBLE CODE 52: CLUTCH SWITCH

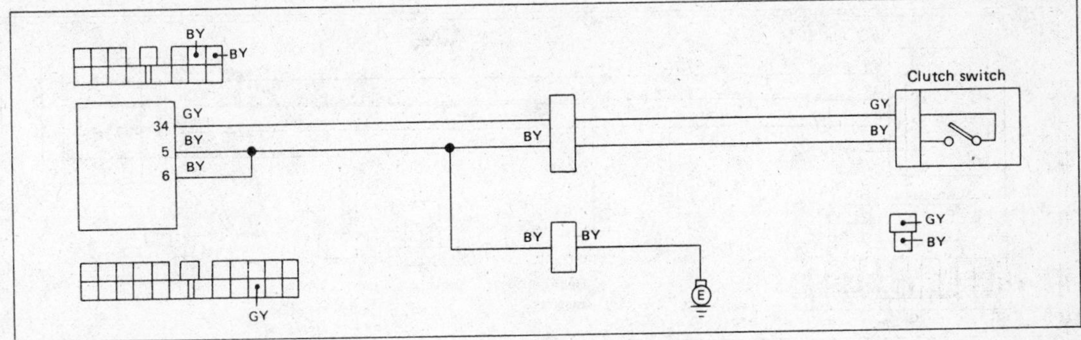
BY
BY
Clutch switch
34
GY
5
BY
6
BY
BY
GY
BY
BY
BY
GY
BY
E
GY

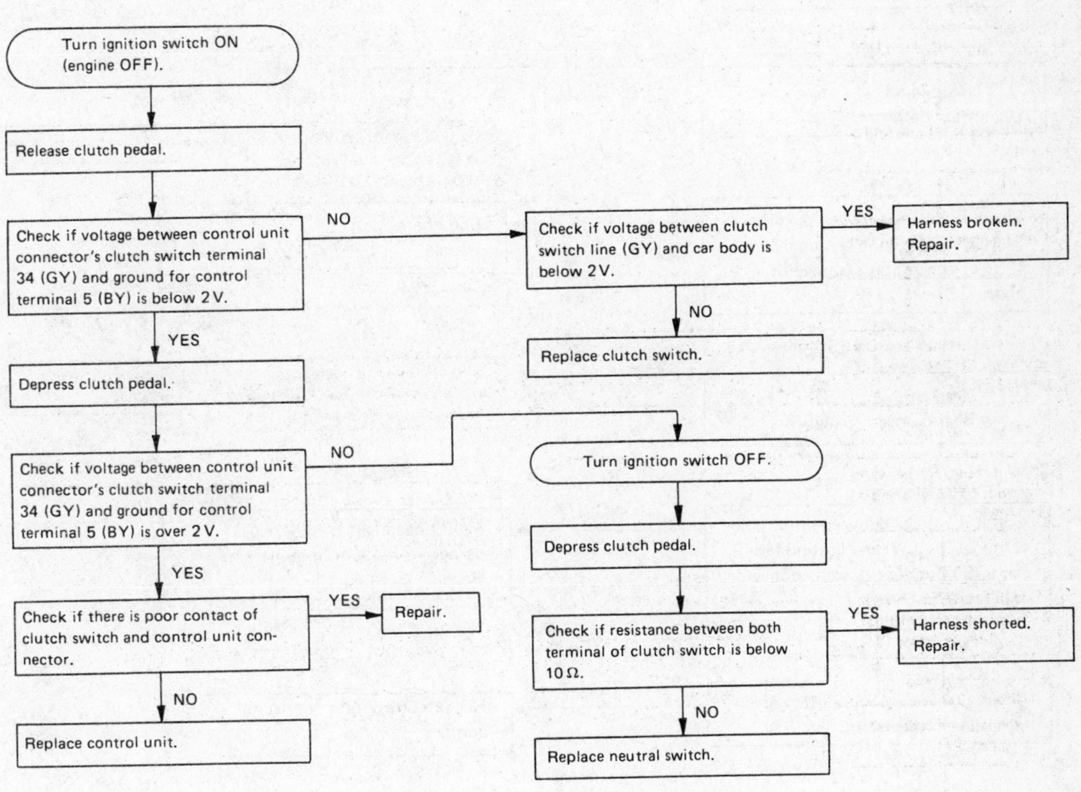
Turn ignition switch ON (engine OFF).
Release clutch pedal.
Check if voltage between control unit connector's clutch switch terminal 34 (GY) and ground for control terminal 5 (BY) is below 2 V.
NO
Check if voltage between clutch switch line (GY) and car body is below 2 V.
YES
Harness broken. Repair.
NO
Replace clutch switch.
YES
Depress clutch pedal.
Check if voltage between control unit connector's clutch switch terminal 34 (GY) and ground for control terminal 5 (BY) is over 2 V.
NO
Turn ignition switch OFF.
Depress clutch pedal.
Check if resistance between both terminal of clutch switch is below 10 Ω.
YES
Harness shorted. Repair.
NO
Replace neutral switch.
YES
Check if there is poor contact of clutch switch and control unit connector.
YES
Repair.
NO
Replace control unit.

Courtesy of Subaru of America, Inc.

## TROUBLE CODE 62: IDLE-UP SYSTEM

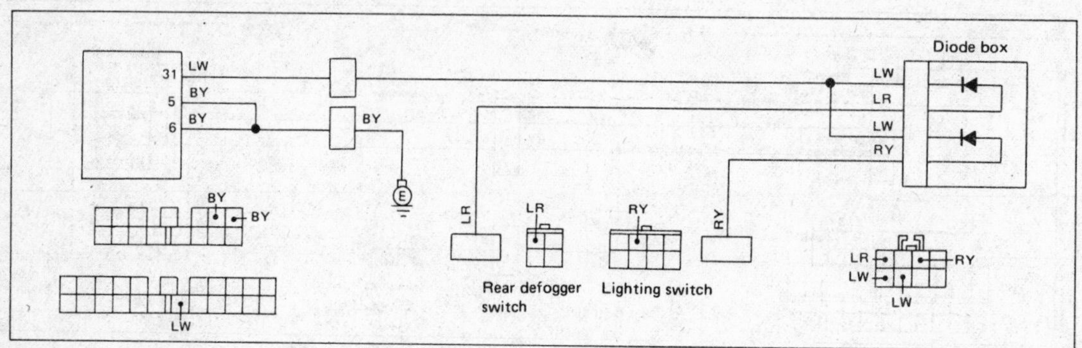
31
5
6
LW
BY
BY
BY
BY
BY
LW
LR
LR
Rear defogger switch
RY
Lighting switch
RY
Diode box
LW
LR
LW
RY
LR
LW
RY
LW

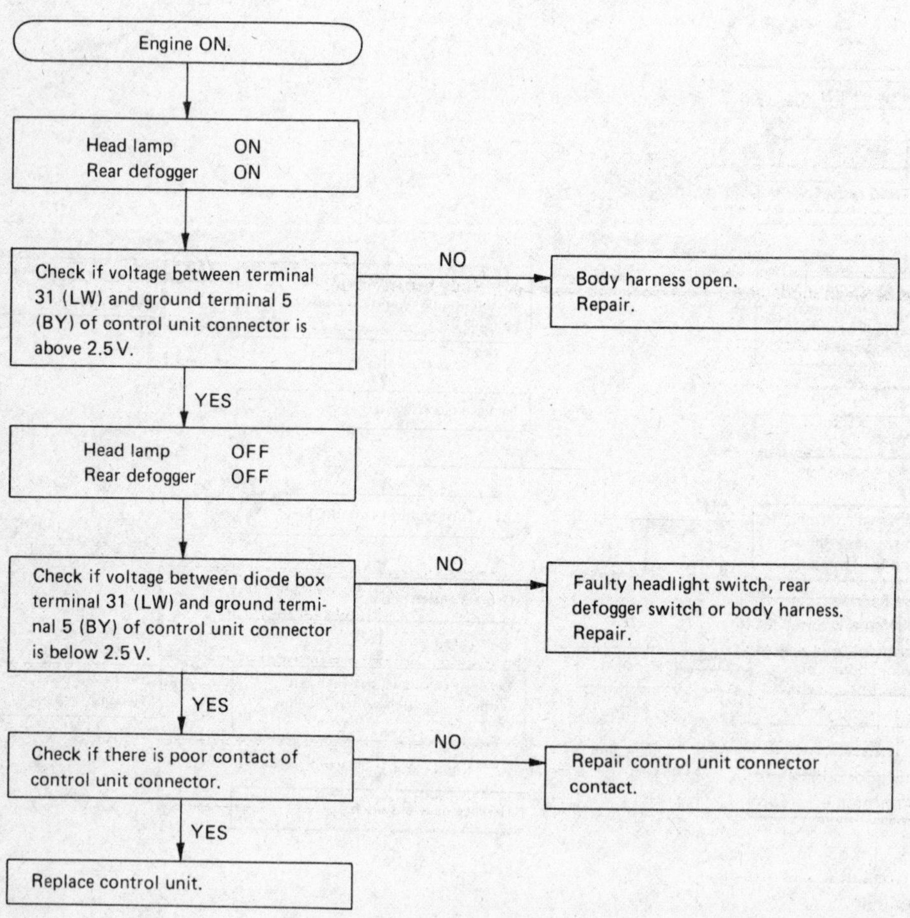
Engine ON.
Head lamp ON
Rear defogger ON
Check if voltage between terminal 31 (LW) and ground terminal 5 (BY) of control unit connector is above 2.5 V.
NO
Body harness open. Repair.
YES
Head lamp OFF
Rear defogger OFF
Check if voltage between diode box terminal 31 (LW) and ground terminal 5 (BY) of control unit connector is below 2.5 V.
NO
Faulty headlight switch, rear defogger switch or body harness. Repair.
YES
Check if there is poor contact of control unit connector.
NO
Repair control unit connector contact.
YES
Replace control unit.

Courtesy of Subaru of America, Inc.

## TROUBLE CODE 63: IDLE-UP SYSTEM

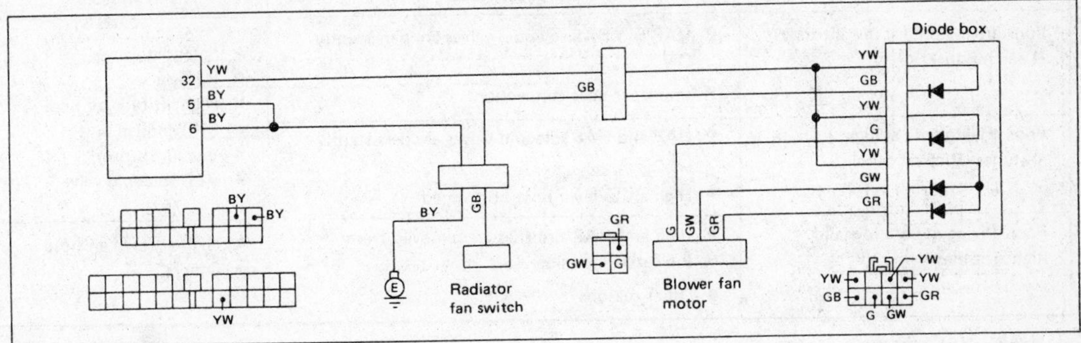
Diode box
YW
32
BY
5
BY
6
GB
YW
GB
YW
G
YW
GW
GR
BY
BY
BY
GB
GR
GW
G
G
GW
GR
YW
E
Radiator
fan switch
Blower fan
motor
YW
YW
YW
GB
GR
G
GW

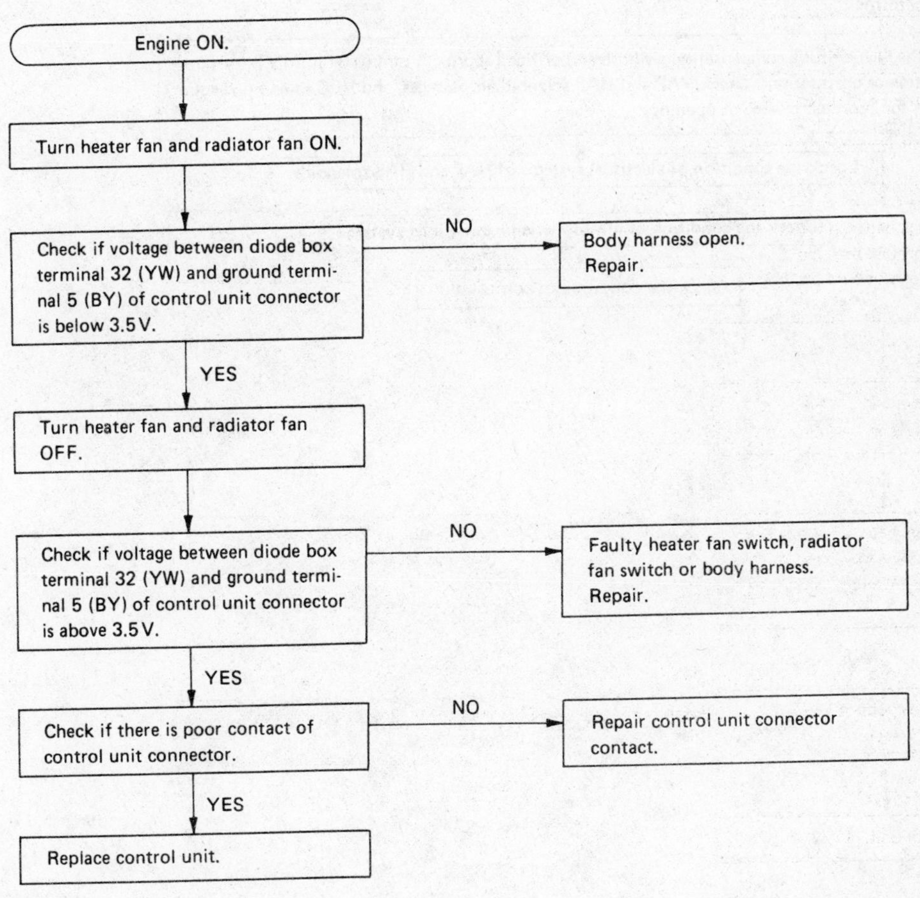
Engine ON.
Turn heater fan and radiator fan ON.
Check if voltage between diode box terminal 32 (YW) and ground terminal 5 (BY) of control unit connector is below 3.5 V.
NO
Body harness open. Repair.
YES
Turn heater fan and radiator fan OFF.
Check if voltage between diode box terminal 32 (YW) and ground terminal 5 (BY) of control unit connector is above 3.5 V.
NO
Faulty heater fan switch, radiator fan switch or body harness. Repair.
YES
Check if there is poor contact of control unit connector.
NO
Repair control unit connector contact.
YES
Replace control unit.

Courtesy of Subaru of America, Inc.

## TROUBLE SHOOTING FOR HIGH ALTITUDE COMPENSATOR SYSTEM (HAC)

| Symptom | Probable cause | Parts affected |
|---|---|---|
| Poor driving only at low altitudes (Lean mixture) | • HAP and HAS solenoid valves are persistently ON<br>• Improper hose connection | • Solenoid valve<br>• Harness<br>• High altitude air hose<br>• EFC control unit<br>• Vacuum sensor<br>• VLC solenoid valve |
| Poor driving only at high altitudes (Rich mixture) | • HAP and HAS solenoid valves are persistently OFF<br>• High altitude air hose obstructed | |
| Poor driving at both low and high altitudes | • HAP and HAS air hoses are removed from the carburetor side<br>• Other reasons* | • High altitude air hose<br>• Others* |

HAP HAC primary
HAS HAC secondary
* Poor driving at both high and low altitudes often occurs when the problem is in an area other than the HAC system. Refer to the Troubleshooting chart under "2-3. Engine".

**Inspection procedures**

Check the high altitude compensation air hose and orifice [approx. 1 mm (0.04 in) dia.] for poor connection or obstructions. Check HAP and HAS solenoid air passages, and VLC solenoid vacuum passages for improper closing or opening.

↓

Check the condition of electrical systems of HAP and HAS solenoids.

↓

Check the condition of atmospheric pressure inlet system.

↓

Check the condition of control unit.

Courtesy of Subaru of America, Inc.

## ELECTRICAL SYSTEM OF HIGH ALTITUDE PRIMARY (HAP) & HIGH ALTITUDE SECONDARY (HAS) SOLENOID VALVE

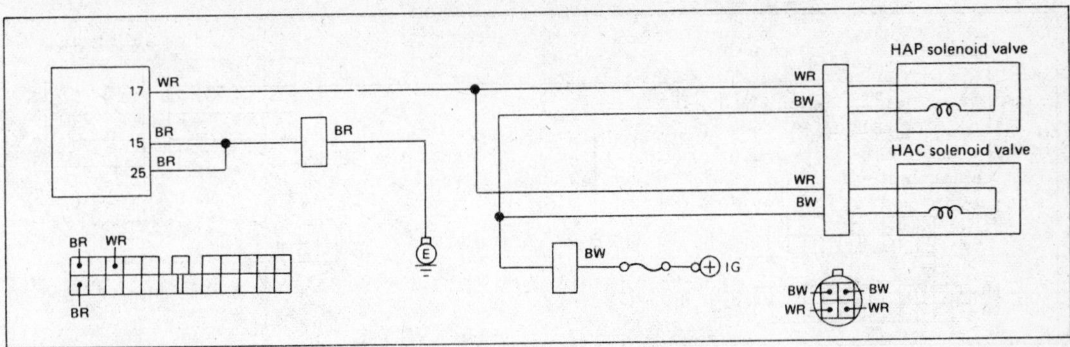
HAP solenoid valve
HAC solenoid valve
17
15
25
WR
BR
BW
E
IG

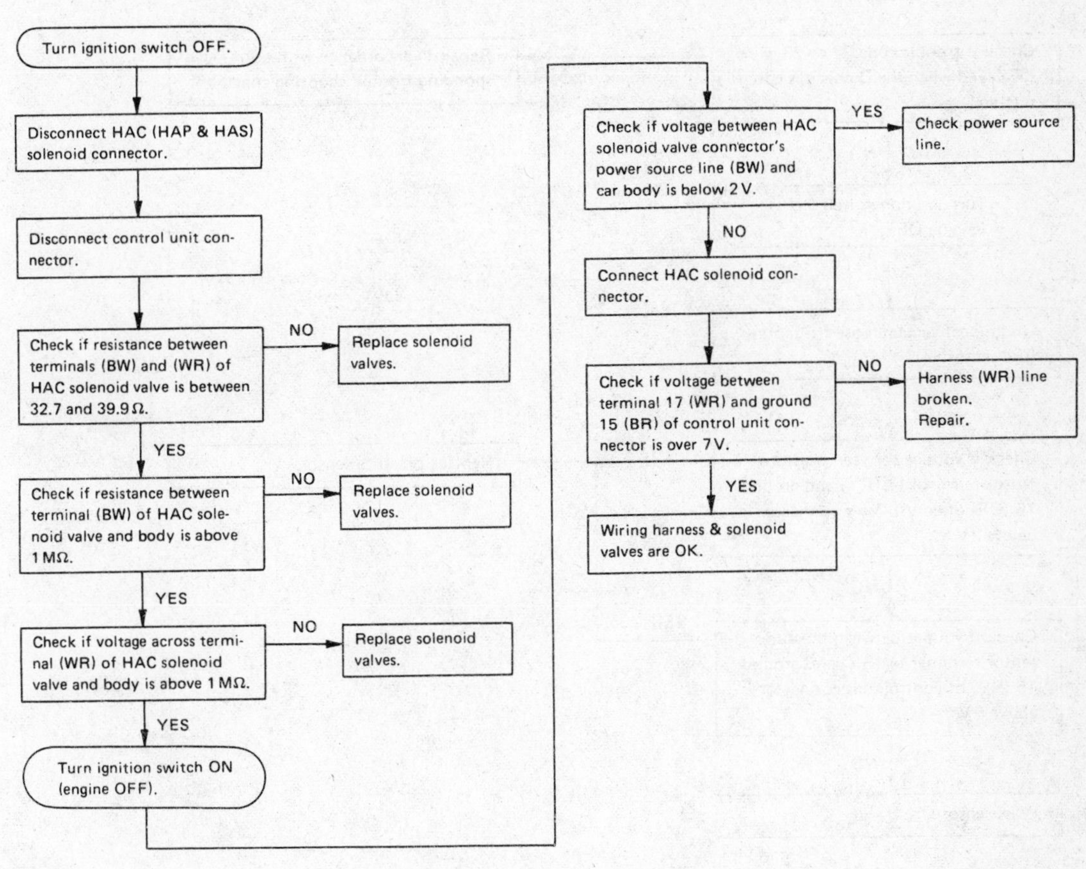
Turn ignition switch OFF.
Disconnect HAC (HAP & HAS) solenoid connector.
Disconnect control unit connector.
Check if resistance between terminals (BW) and (WR) of HAC solenoid valve is between 32.7 and 39.9 Ω.
NO
Replace solenoid valves.
YES
Check if resistance between terminal (BW) of HAC solenoid valve and body is above 1 MΩ.
NO
Replace solenoid valves.
YES
Check if voltage across terminal (WR) of HAC solenoid valve and body is above 1 MΩ.
NO
Replace solenoid valves.
YES
Turn ignition switch ON (engine OFF).
Check if voltage between HAC solenoid valve connector's power source line (BW) and car body is below 2 V.
YES
Check power source line.
NO
Connect HAC solenoid connector.
Check if voltage between terminal 17 (WR) and ground 15 (BR) of control unit connector is over 7 V.
NO
Harness (WR) line broken. Repair.
YES
Wiring harness & solenoid valves are OK.

## AIR (ATMOSPHERIC PRESSURE) INLET SYSTEM

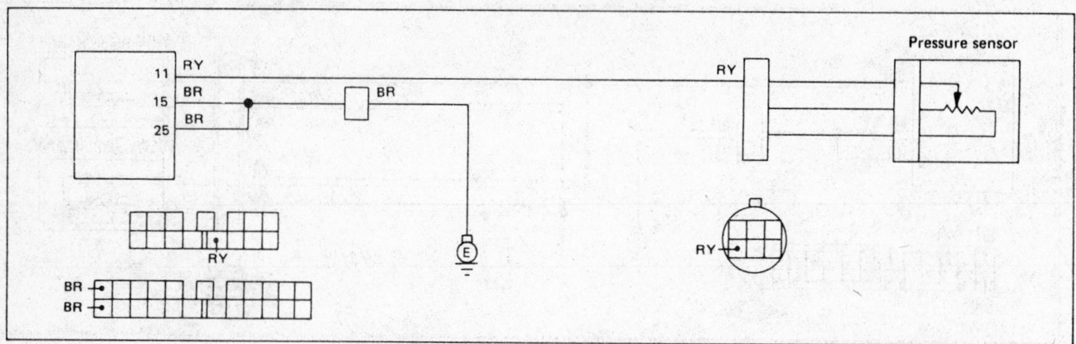
Pressure sensor
RY
11
BR
15
BR
25
BR
RY
E
RY
BR
BR
RY

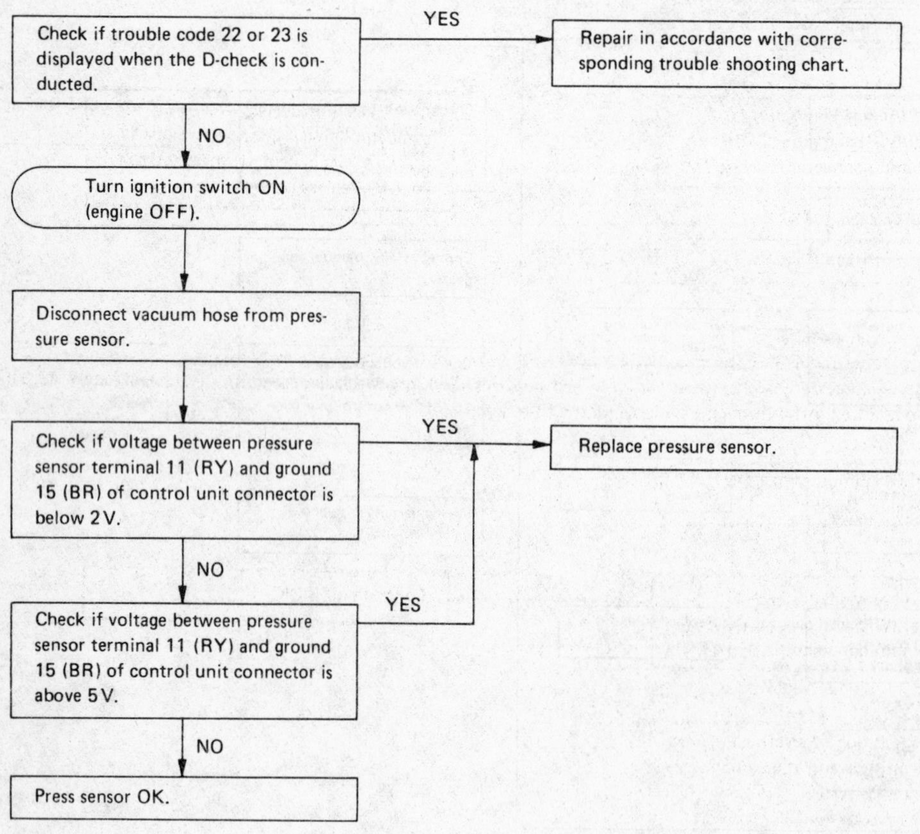
Check if trouble code 22 or 23 is displayed when the D-check is conducted.
YES
Repair in accordance with corresponding trouble shooting chart.
NO
Turn ignition switch ON (engine OFF).
Disconnect vacuum hose from pressure sensor.
Check if voltage between pressure sensor terminal 11 (RY) and ground 15 (BR) of control unit connector is below 2 V.
YES
Replace pressure sensor.
NO
Check if voltage between pressure sensor terminal 11 (RY) and ground 15 (BR) of control unit connector is above 5 V.
YES
NO
Press sensor OK.

Courtesy of Subaru of America, Inc.

## CONTROL UNIT INSPECTION

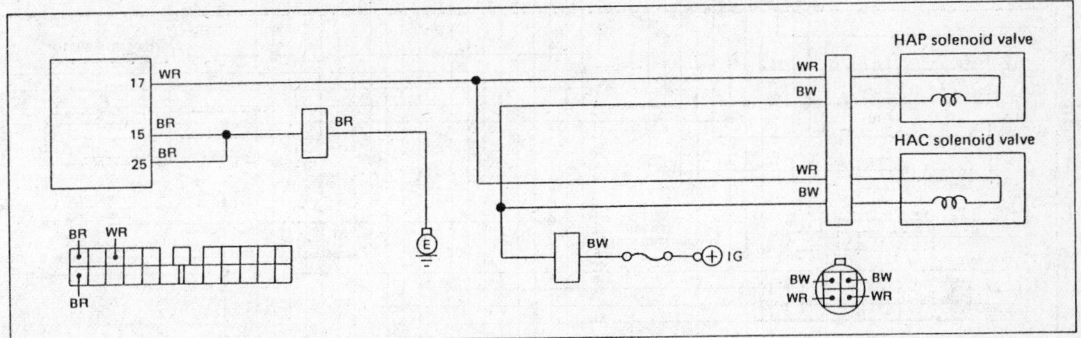
HAP solenoid valve
HAC solenoid valve
17
15
25
WR
BR
BR
BR
WR
BW
WR
BW
BR
WR
BR
E
BW
IG
BW
WR
BW
WR

(1) Poor driving at low altitudes
Connect a vacuum hose running between VLC solenoid and air intake manifold directly to the pressure sensor to maintain atmospheric pressure of at least 93.3 kPa (700 mmHg, 27.56 inHg).

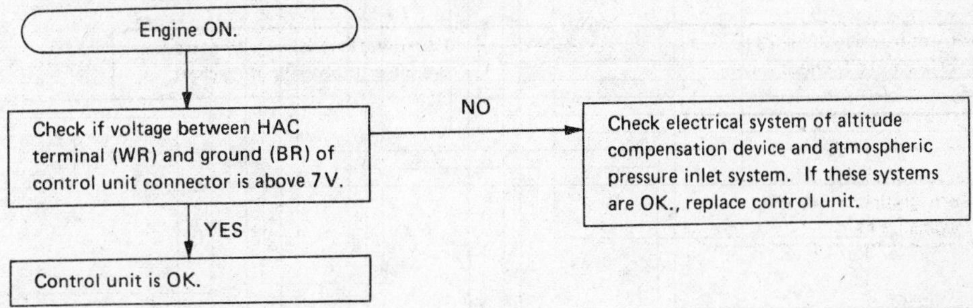
Engine ON.
Check if voltage between HAC terminal (WR) and ground (BR) of control unit connector is above 7 V.
NO
Check electrical system of altitude compensation device and atmospheric pressure inlet system. If these systems are OK., replace control unit.
YES
Control unit is OK.

(2) Poor driving at high altitudes
- Check that atmospheric pressure is below 84.0 kPa (630 mmHg, 24.80 inHg) during inspection.
- If atmospheric pressure higher than the specified above is used, apply vacuum pressure of approximately 40.0 kPa (300 mmHg, 11.81 inHg) through the nipple on the filter side.

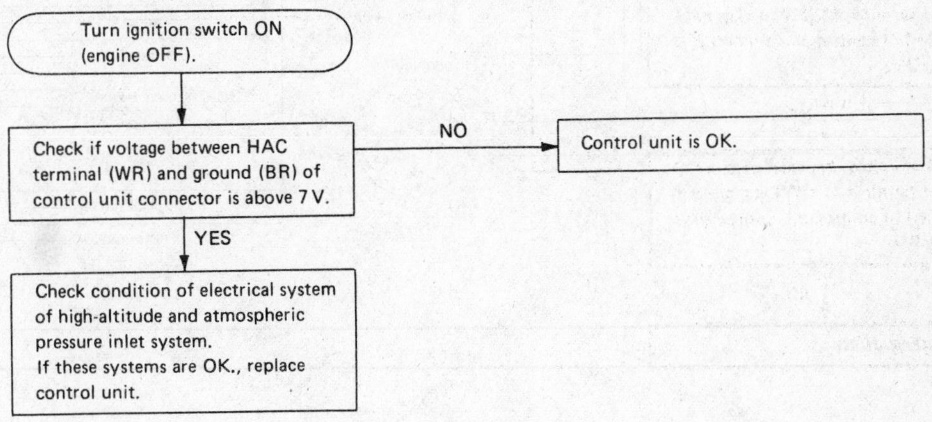
Turn ignition switch ON (engine OFF).
Check if voltage between HAC terminal (WR) and ground (BR) of control unit connector is above 7 V.
NO
Control unit is OK.
YES
Check condition of electrical system of high-altitude and atmospheric pressure inlet system.
If these systems are OK., replace control unit.

Courtesy of Subaru of America, Inc.

# 1988 COMPUTERIZED ENGINE CONTROLS
## Subaru EFC Carburetor (Cont.)

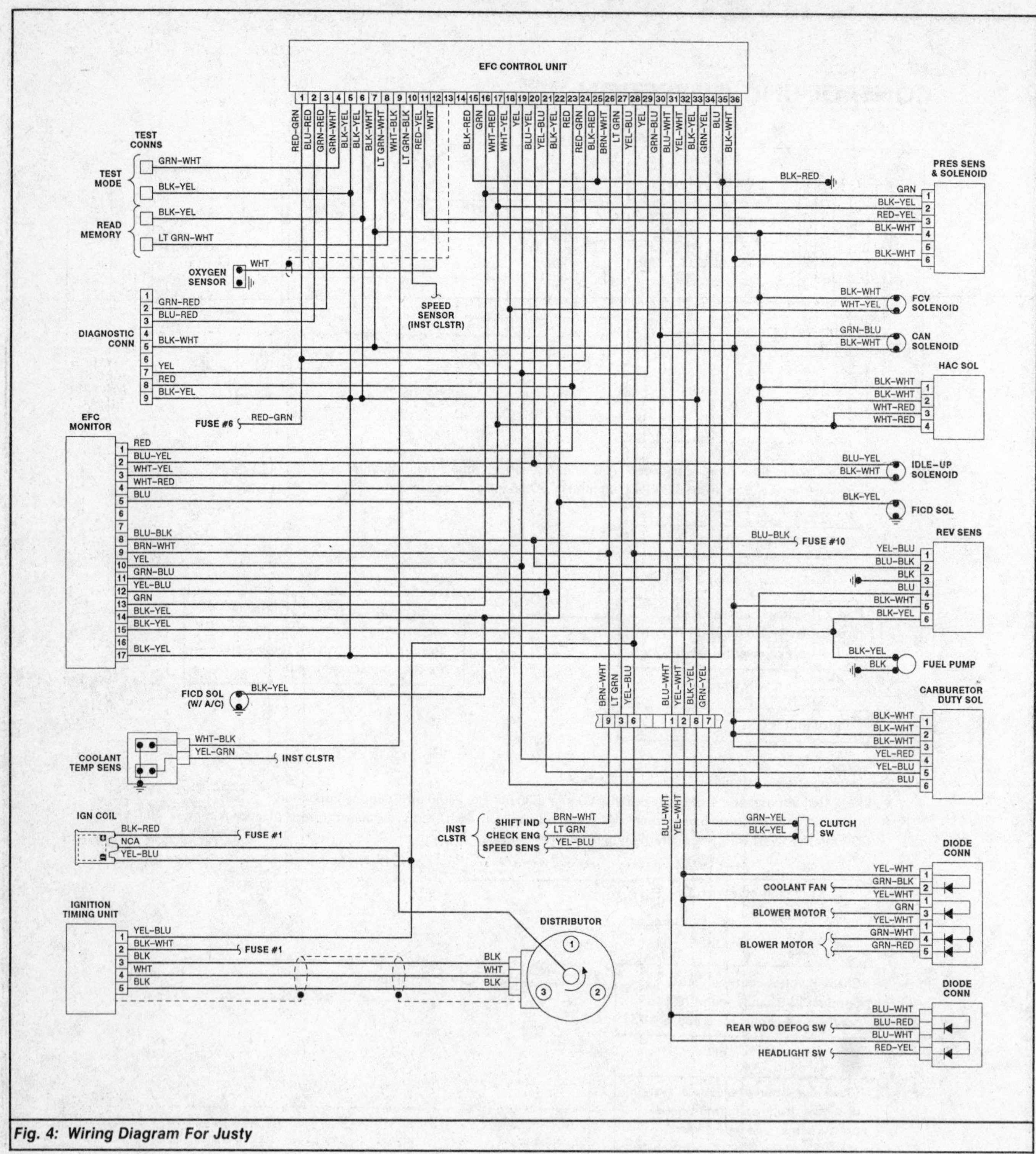
EFC CONTROL UNIT
TEST CONNS
TEST MODE
READ MEMORY
OXYGEN SENSOR
SPEED SENSOR (INST CLSTR)
DIAGNOSTIC CONN
EFC MONITOR
FUSE #6
FICD SOL (W/ A/C)
COOLANT TEMP SENS
INST CLSTR
IGN COIL
NCA
FUSE #1
IGNITION TIMING UNIT
DISTRIBUTOR
SHIFT IND
CHECK ENG
SPEED SENS
PRES SENS & SOLENOID
FCV SOLENOID
CAN SOLENOID
HAC SOL
IDLE-UP SOLENOID
FICD SOL
REV SENS
FUSE #10
FUEL PUMP
CARBURETOR DUTY SOL
CLUTCH SW
DIODE CONN
COOLANT FAN
BLOWER MOTOR
REAR WDO DEFOG SW
HEADLIGHT SW

*Fig. 4: Wiring Diagram For Justy*

# 1988 COMPUTERIZED ENGINE CONTROLS
## Subaru EFC Carburetor (Cont.)

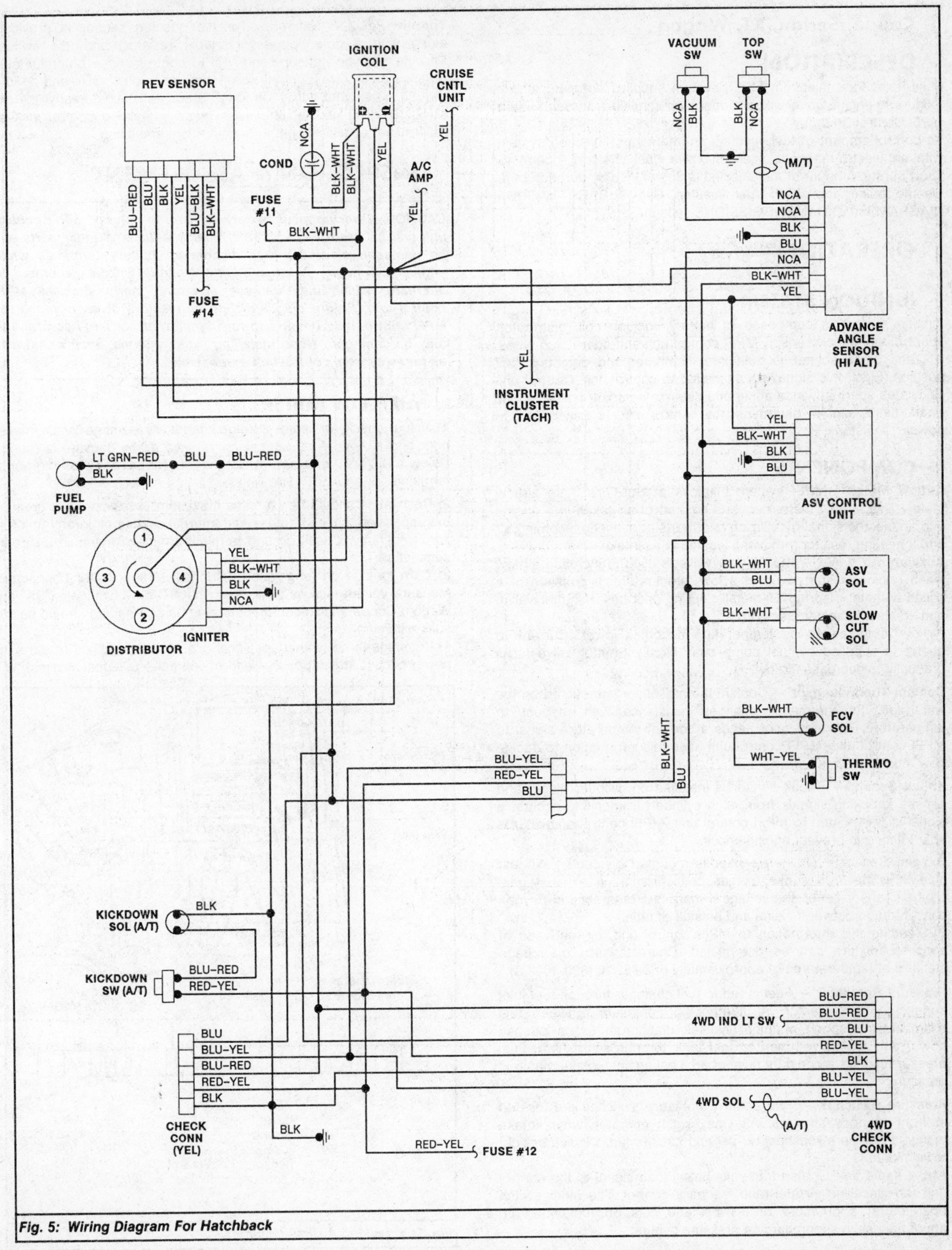

REV SENSOR
IGNITION COIL
CRUISE CNTL UNIT
COND
FUSE #11
A/C AMP
FUSE #14
VACUUM SW
TOP SW
(M/T)
ADVANCE ANGLE SENSOR (HI ALT)
INSTRUMENT CLUSTER (TACH)
ASV CONTROL UNIT
FUEL PUMP
DISTRIBUTOR
IGNITER
ASV SOL
SLOW CUT SOL
FCV SOL
THERMO SW
KICKDOWN SOL (A/T)
KICKDOWN SW (A/T)
4WD IND LT SW
4WD SOL
(A/T)
CHECK CONN (YEL)
FUSE #12
4WD CHECK CONN
BLU-RED
BLU
BLK
YEL
BLU-BLK
BLK-WHT
NCA
RED-YEL
BLU-YEL
LT GRN-RED
WHT-YEL


Fig. 5: Wiring Diagram For Hatchback

### Coupe, Sedan, XT, Wagon

## DESCRIPTION

Multi-Point Fuel Injection (MPFI) system supplies optimum air/fuel mixture to engine under various operating conditions through use of MPFI Control Unit.

To control amount of fuel injected, an intermittent injection system, with an electro-magnetic injection valve (fuel injector), opens for short bursts. Amount of fuel injected is determined by duration of an electric pulse applied to fuel injector. See SUBARU VACUUM DIAGRAMS in EXHAUST EMISSIONS section.

## OPERATION

### IGNITION SYSTEM

Ignition system is composed of battery, ignition coil, distributor, spark plugs, knock sensor, MPFI control unit and spark plug wires. A crank angle sensor is built into distributor and detects crank position. Electronic signal is transmitted to control unit. Control unit calculates spark advance angle and determines spark timing signal. Spark timing signal, determined by control unit, is transmitted to power transistor.

### COMPONENTS

**Airflow Meter** – MPFI system employs a "Hot-Wire" type airflow meter. This airflow meter converts amount of air taken into engine into an electric signal by utilizing heat transfer between incoming air and a heating resistor (hot wire), located in air intake.

**Auxiliary Air Valve** – Auxiliary air valve is used to increase airflow when engine is started up at a low temperature. It consists of a coiled bi-metallic spring. Bi-metallic spring operates a shutter valve, and an electric heater element.

Airflow is increased as temperature becomes lower. Current to heater is supplied by fuel pump relay circuit. Shutter valve turns gradually to decrease airflow.

**Coolant Thermosensor** – Coolant thermosensor is mounted on the waterpipe. Its thermistor changes resistance with respect to temperature. Thermosensor sends a coolant temperature signal to MPFI control unit. MPFI control unit uses this information to decide how much fuel to inject.

**Knock Sensor** – Knock sensor is installed on cylinder block, and senses knocking signals from each cylinder. If knocking occurs, a signal is transmitted to MPFI control unit. MPFI control unit retards spark timing to prevent engine knock.

**Oxygen Sensor** – Oxygen sensor is mounted on center exhaust pipe. It is used to sense oxygen concentration in exhaust gas. Oxygen sensor generates voltage if there is a difference in oxygen concentration between inside and outside of tube.

By sending this information to MPFI control unit, air/fuel ratio of supplied mixture can be determined. Characteristics of voltage stabilize at temperatures of approximately 572-752° F (300-400° C).

**Pressure Regulator** – Fuel is fed to fuel chamber through fuel inlet connected with injector. A difference in pressure between fuel chamber and spring chamber causes diaphragm to be pushed down, and fuel is returned to fuel tank through return line. Fuel pressure is kept a constant level of 36.3 psi against intake manifold pressure.

**Pressure Switches** – Two positive pressure switches are located in front of body strut mount. One switch operates when intake manifold pressure reaches 1.0 psi and causes turbo indicator light to illuminate.

At the same time, it also transmits heavy load signal to the control unit for cancelling air/fuel ratio feedback control. The other switch operates at a pressure of 9.1 psi and cuts off fuel when an abnormal rise in supercharging pressure occurs.

**Throttle Position Sensor** – Throttle position sensor is provided along with a potentiometer (variable resistor) and idle switch. Throttle position sensor sends MPFI control unit a potentiometer output signal corresponding to opening of throttle valve and an idle switch signal that turns on only when throttle is nearly to idle position. MPFI control unit uses these signals to control air/fuel ratio during acceleration and deceleration, and idling.

## INSPECTION & ADJUSTMENT

***CAUTION: Never connect battery in reverse polarity. MPFI control unit will be destroyed instantly. Fuel injector and other parts will be damaged also. DO NOT disconnect battery terminals while engine is running. A large counter voltage will be generated in alternator which may damage electronic parts such as MPFI control unit. Before disconnecting connectors of each sensor or MPFI control unit, be sure to turn ignition off, or MPFI control unit may be damaged. When installing radio antenna, ensure that it is as far away from control unit as possible.***

### AIRFLOW METER

**1)** Visual check for leaks, foreign matter, or damage in air intake boot and airflow meter. Repair or replace if any damage is found. Using a DVOM, measure resistance between body and ground terminals "B" and "BR". *See Fig. 1.*

**2)** Resistance should be 10 ohms maximum. If resistance is greater than specified, check harness and internal circuits of control unit for zero continuity. Check ground terminal on intake manifold for poor connection.

**3)** Turn ignition on (engine off). Connect airflow meter connector. Measure voltage across power terminal "R" on XT models ("SA" on Wagon, Coupe and Sedan models) and body. Reading should be 10 volts minimum.

**4)** If voltage is not within specifications, check condition of parts in power circuit. Attach positive lead of voltmeter to signal terminal "W"

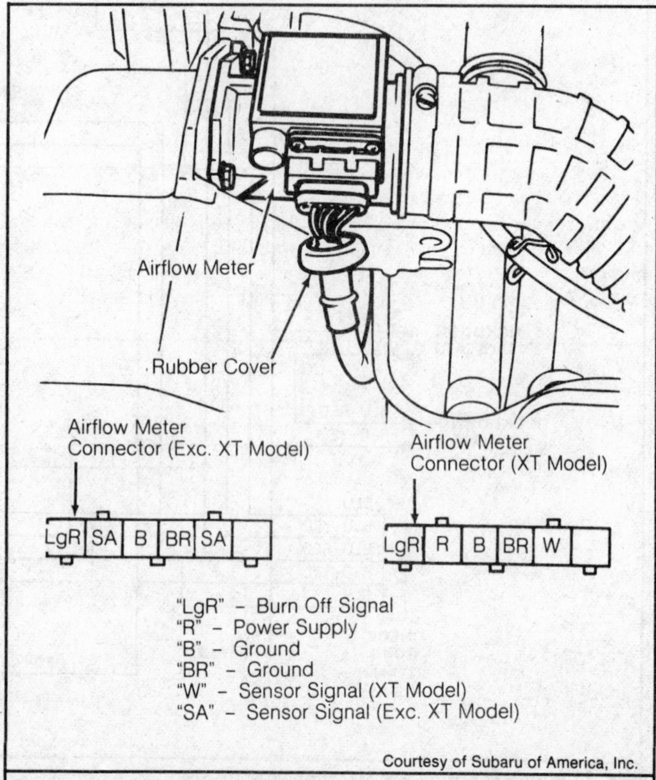
Airflow Meter
Rubber Cover
Airflow Meter Connector (Exc. XT Model)
Airflow Meter Connector (XT Model)
LgR
SA
B
BR
SA
LgR
R
B
BR
W
"LgR" - Burn Off Signal
"R" - Power Supply
"B" - Ground
"BR" - Ground
"W" - Sensor Signal (XT Model)
"SA" - Sensor Signal (Exc. XT Model)
Courtesy of Subaru of America, Inc.

***Fig. 1: Checking Airflow Meter***

on XT models ("SA" on Wagon, Coupe and Sedan models) and negative lead to ground terminal "BR". Voltage should be 1-2 volts.

**5)** If not within specificatons, replace airflow meter. If voltage is within specificatons, remove airflow meter from air cleaner. Blow air from air cleaner side to check if voltage across terminals "W" on XT models ("SA" on Wagon, Coupe and Sedan models) and "BR" on XT models ("B" on Wagon, Coupe and Sedan models) is greater than that measured in step **4)**.

**6)** If not, replace airflow meter. Install airflow meter on air cleaner. Start engine, and warm until coolant temperature reaches approximately 176°F (80°C). Drive at speed greater than 15 MPH for at least one minute.

**7)** Run engine at speeds greater than 2000 RPM. While idling engine, measure voltage across terminal "LgR" of airflow meter connector and body. Zero volts under normal operating conditions is okay.

**8)** Turn ignition off. If 12 volts are present, check across terminal "LgR" and body for one second shortly after ignition has been turned off.

**9)** If 12 volts is not present, check harness from control unit to airflow meter for discontinuity.

## THROTTLE SWITCH

**Idle Contact – 1)** Insert a thickness gauge between stopper screw of throttle body and stopper arm. Check for continuity between terminals No. 3 and No. 4 on XT models ("A" and "C" on Wagon, Coupe and Sedan models). *See Figs. 2 and 3.*

**2)** Make sure that terminals No. 3 and No. 4 on XT models ("A" and "C" on Wagon, Coupe and Sedan models) are conducting when throttle is closed fully. Make sure that terminals No. 3 and No. 4 on XT models ("A" and "C" on Wagon, Coupe and Sedan models) are conducting when thickness of gauge is .022" (.55 mm). This corresponds to a throttle opening of 1.5 degrees.

**3)** Make sure that terminals No. 3 and No. 4 on XT models ("A" and "C" on Wagon, Coupe and Sedan models) are not conducting when feeler gauge thickness is .362" (.92 mm). This corresponds to a throttle opening of 2.5 degrees. If specifications are not as specified, loosen 2 screws securing throttle switch to throttle body. Turn throttle switch main body until correct adjustment is obtained.

**Throttle Opening Signal –** Measure resistance between terminals No. 2 and No. 3 on XT models (No. 1 and No. 2 on Wagon, Coupe and Sedan models). *See Figs. 2 and 4.* Resistance should be 6000-18,000 ohms. If resistance is not within specifications, replace sensor. Measure resistance between terminals No. 1 and No. 3. Resistance should be 5800-17,800 ohms with throttle closed and 15,000-51,000 ohms with throttle open. Ensure that resistance changes smoothly between fully closed and fully opened throttle positions. If resistance is out of specifications, replace sensor.

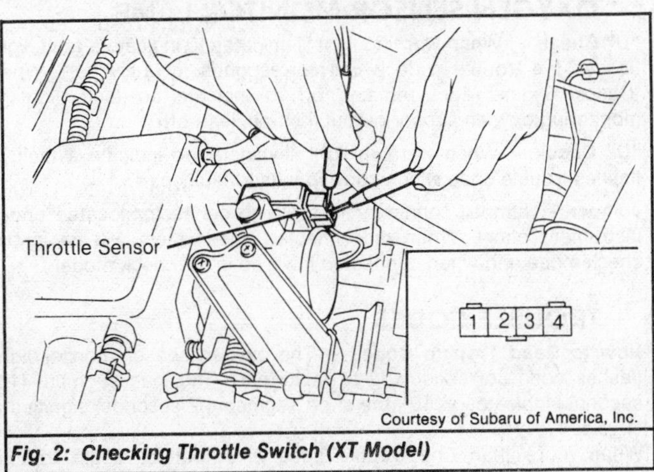
Throttle Sensor
1
2
3
4
Courtesy of Subaru of America, Inc.

*Fig. 2: Checking Throttle Switch (XT Model)*

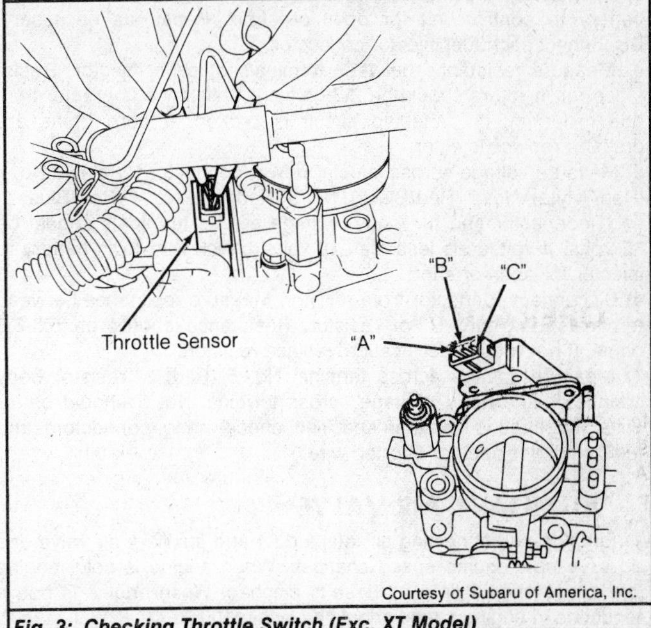
"B"
"C"
Throttle Sensor
"A"
Courtesy of Subaru of America, Inc.

*Fig. 3: Checking Throttle Switch (Exc. XT Model)*

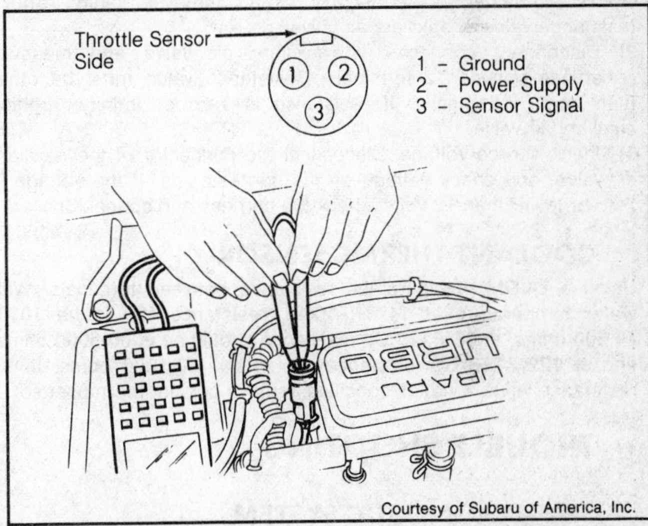
Throttle Sensor Side
1
2
3
1 – Ground
2 – Power Supply
3 – Sensor Signal
Courtesy of Subaru of America, Inc.

*Fig. 4: Checking Throttle Opening Signal (Exc. XT Model)*

## DASHPOT

Warm up engine to normal operating temperature and check that idle speed is correct. Under no load condition, turn the throttle lever by hand and increase engine speed until end of dashpot is off throttle cam. Gradually return throttle lever and read engine RPM when throttle cam contacts end of dash pot. If engine is not within 2800-3400 RPM, loosen lock nut of dashpot and turn dashpot until this specification is obtained. After adjustment, tighten lock nut securely. Race engine and make sure idle returns correctly to idle speed as throttle is released.

## FUEL INJECTOR & RESISTOR

**1)** Using a stethoscope or a long screwdriver, make sure fuel injectors are making a clicking sound. If this operating noise cannot be heard from any one injector, disconnect control unit connector.

**2)** Measure voltage across body and terminals No. 49, 50, 51, and 52 of control unit connector body side. See WIRING DIAGRAMS. Terminal voltage should be 12 volts.

**3)** If voltage is below 10 volts in any circuit, check affected wire from battery to control unit for open or short. Repair as necessary. Disconnect each fuel injector connector.

**4)** Measure resistance between terminals of each injector. Resistance for injectors should be 2-3 ohms. If resistance is greater than one milli-ohm, the affected circuit is broken. If zero ohms are present, replace injector.

**5)** Measure voltage across injector power connector terminals No. 1 (Red/White), No. 2 (Red/Black), No. 3 (Red) and No. 4 (Red/Blue) of each connector and the body. Voltage across terminals should be 12 volts. If voltage is less than 10 volts, check wire from battery to injector for open or short.

**6)** Disconnect connector from resistor. Measure resistance between terminals "W" and "B" of resistor. Resistance should be 5.8-6.5 ohms. If not within specification, replace resistor.

**7)** Measure voltage across terminal No. 5 (Red) of resistor body connector and body. Voltage across terminal No. 5 should be 12 volts. If voltage is less than specified, check wiring, connectors, and fusible link for open or shorted wire.

### AUXILIARY AIR VALVE

**1)** Pinch hose connecting air intake duct and auxiliary air valve and observe how engine speed changes. When engine is cold, engine idle speed should drop as hose is pinched. When engine is hot, a reduction in engine speed should be within 100 RPM.

**2)** If engine speed will not drop to idling RPM smoothly, heater circuit or heater power supply circuit may be faulty. Check resistance value of auxiliary air valve.

**3)** Disconnect connector of auxiliary air valve and measure resistance between 2 terminals. Resistance value must be other than zero and infinity. If resistance is zero or infinity, replace auxiliary air valve.

**4)** Check source voltage. Disconnect the connector of the auxiliary air valve, and check voltage on the harness side. If the voltage is zero or lower than 12 volts, check the harness and connector.

### COOLANT THERMOSENSOR

Using a DVOM, measure the resistance between terminals. With water temperature at 14°F (-10°C), resistance should be 7000-11,500 ohms, at 68°F (20°C), resistance should be 2000-3000 ohms, and at 122°F (50°C), resistance should be 700-1000 ohms. If the resistance value is not as specified, replace coolant thermosensor.

## TROUBLE SHOOTING

### SELF-DIAGNOSTIC SYSTEM

Self-diagnostic system detects and indicates a fault in various inputs and outputs of electronic control. Warning light ("Check Engine" light) on the instrument panel indicates occurrence of a fault or trouble. Light Emitting Diode (LED) in control unit also indicates a trouble code. *See Figs. 5 and 6*.

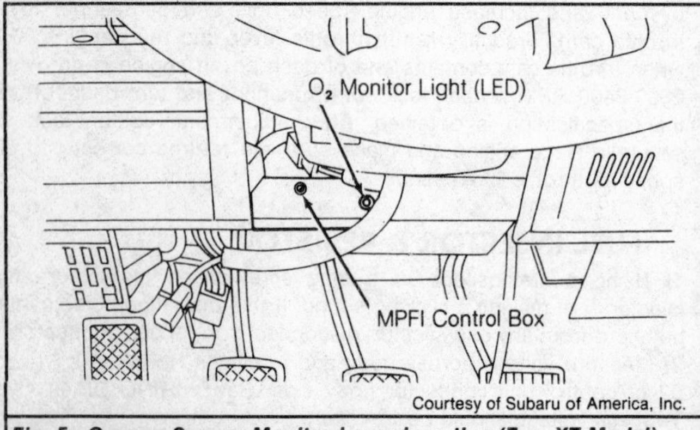
O₂ Monitor Light (LED)
MPFI Control Box
Courtesy of Subaru of America, Inc.

*Fig. 5: Oxygen Sensor Monitor Lamp Location (Exc. XT Model)*

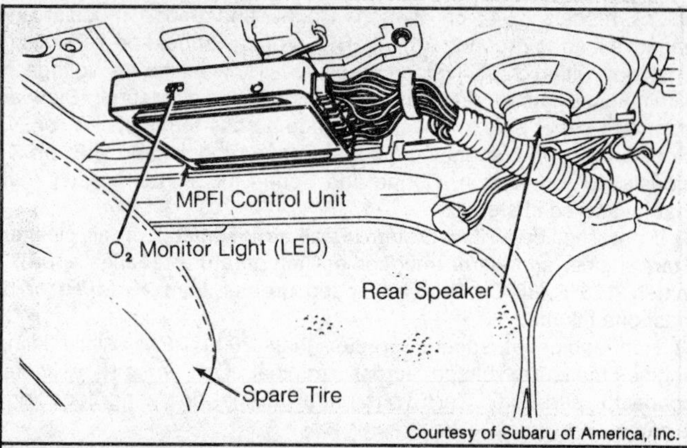
MPFI Control Unit
O₂ Monitor Light (LED)
Rear Speaker
Spare Tire
Courtesy of Subaru of America, Inc.

*Fig. 6: Oxygen Sensor Monitor Lamp Location (XT Model)*

**Self-Diagnostic Function** – The MPFI control unit receives information from various sensors and sends output information to fuel injectors, fuel pump, etc. It also examines the input/output information and matches it with predetermined levels. If a predetermined level is not satisfied, the warning light is signaled to driver.

**Fail-Safe Function** – When a part has been judged faulty by the self-diagnostic system, the MPFI control unit generates a signal called the associated pseudo signal. This signal is a fixed value, which allows the vehicle to run until the failed part can be repaired or replaced.

### SELF-DIAGNOSTIC MODES

**"U" Check Mode** – The "U" check is a user-oriented mode in which only the MPFI components necessary for start-up and drive are diagnosed. When a fault occurs, the warning light ("Check Engine" light), is illuminated to indicate to the driver that inspection is necessary. Diagnosis of other parts, which do not give significant adverse effect to start-up and driveability, are excluded from this mode.

**"D" Check Mode** – The "D" check is a special mode which can be performed by connecting a jumper. *See Fig. 8, 9 or 10*. (For the "U" check, no jumper connection is required). This mode is used in inspection by the technician at end of the assembly line. It diagnoses almost all MPFI component parts. If a fault is detected, warning light ("Check Engine" light) goes on. In either "U" or "D" check, if the warning light ("Check Engine" light) turns on due to a fault, oxygen monitor light of MPFI control unit flashes the code corresponding to the faulty part. Also, in both check modes, fail-safe function works on the same condition.

### OXYGEN SENSOR MONITOR LAMP

**"U" Check** – When warning light illuminates to indicate a fault, light flashes the trouble code which corresponds to faulty part. When "Check Engine" light remains off to indicate no fault, light is monitoring oxygen sensor output (rich-on, lean-off).

**"D" Check** – When warning light illuminates to indicate a fault, it flashes trouble code which corresponds to faulty part.

**Jumper** – Jumper connector is a Green connector located under instrument panel. When disconnected, the system will be in "U" check mode and when connected it will be in "D" check mode.

### TROUBLE CODES

**How to Read Trouble Codes** – The oxygen sensor monitor light flashes code corresponding to faulty part. The long segment (1.2 seconds) indicates a "10", the short segment (.2 seconds) signifies a "1". *See Fig. 10*.

When more than one trouble code is outputted, begin trouble shooting with the smallest trouble code number and proceed to next higher code

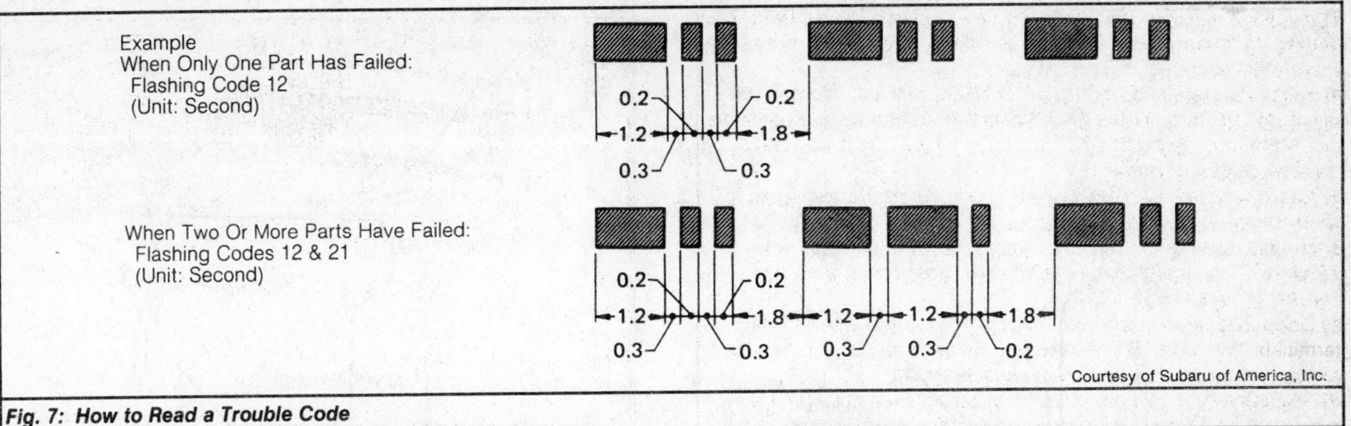
Example
When Only One Part Has Failed:
Flashing Code 12
(Unit: Second)
When Two Or More Parts Have Failed:
Flashing Codes 12 & 21
(Unit: Second)
0.2
1.2
1.8
0.3
Courtesy of Subaru of America, Inc.

*Fig. 7: How to Read a Trouble Code*

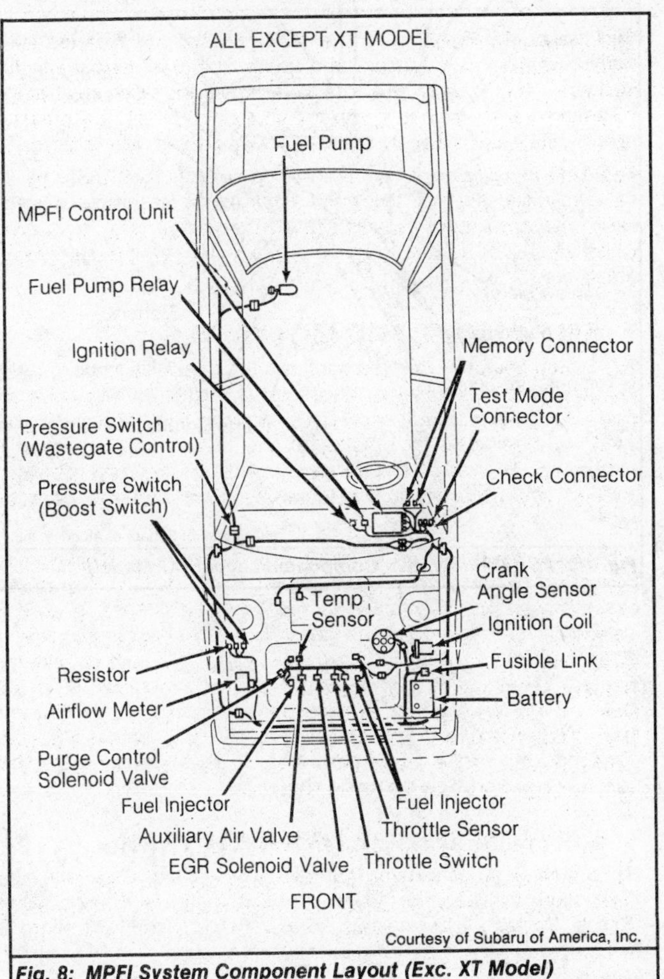
ALL EXCEPT XT MODEL
Fuel Pump
MPFI Control Unit
Fuel Pump Relay
Ignition Relay
Memory Connector
Test Mode Connector
Pressure Switch (Wastegate Control)
Check Connector
Pressure Switch (Boost Switch)
Crank Angle Sensor
Temp Sensor
Ignition Coil
Fusible Link
Resistor
Battery
Airflow Meter
Purge Control Solenoid Valve
Fuel Injector
Fuel Injector
Throttle Sensor
Auxiliary Air Valve
EGR Solenoid Valve
Throttle Switch
FRONT
Courtesy of Subaru of America, Inc.

*Fig. 8: MPFI System Component Layout (Exc. XT Model)*

***TROUBLE CODES***

| Code | Trouble |
|---|---|
| 11 | Crank Angle Sensor (No Reference Pulse) |
| 12 | Starter Switch |
| 13 | Crank Angle Sensor (No Position Pulse) |
| 14 | Fuel Injectors (No. 1 & 2) |
| 15 | Fuel Injectors (No. 3 & 4) |
| 21 | Coolant Temperature Sensor |
| 22 | Knock Sensor |
| 23 | Airflow Meter |
| 24 [1] | By-pass Air Control Valve |
| 25 [1] | Fuel Injectors (No. 3 & 4) |
| 31 | Throttle Sensor |
| 32 | Oxygen Sensor |
| 33 | Speed Sensor |
| 34 [2] | EGR Solenoid Valve |
| 35 | Purge Control Solenoid Valve |
| 41 | Lean Condition |
| 42 | Idle Switch |
| 51 | Neutral Switch |

[1] – 6-cylinder XT model only.
[2] – Exc. Calif. models.

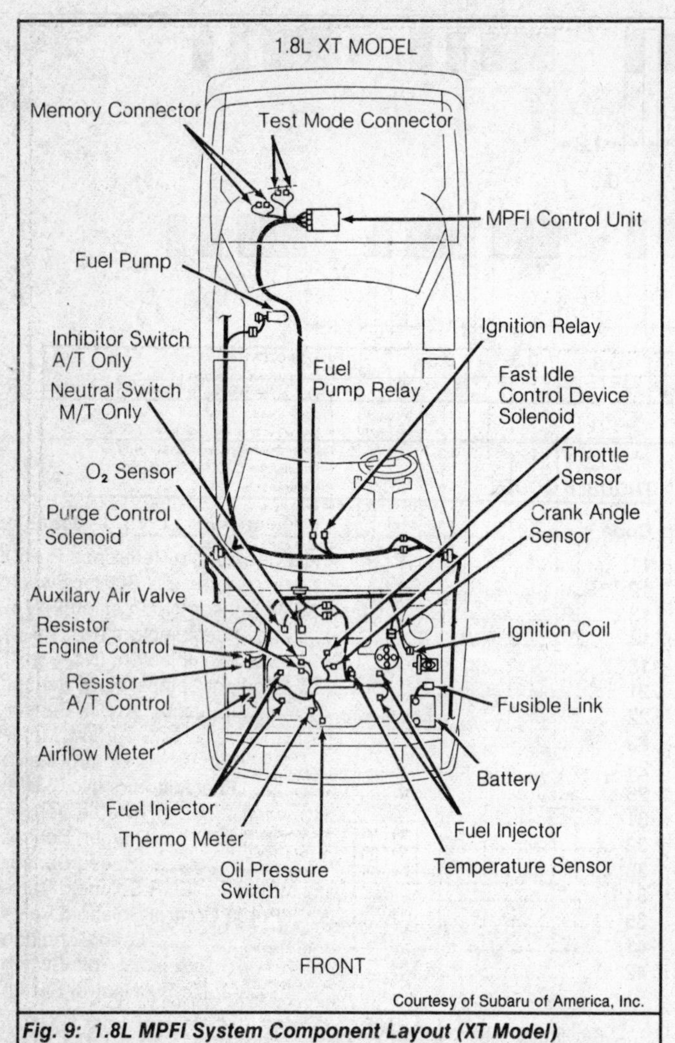
1.8L XT MODEL
Memory Connector
Test Mode Connector
MPFI Control Unit
Fuel Pump
Ignition Relay
Inhibitor Switch
A/T Only
Fuel
Pump Relay
Fast Idle
Control Device
Solenoid
Neutral Switch
M/T Only
Throttle
Sensor
$O_2$ Sensor
Crank Angle
Sensor
Purge Control
Solenoid
Auxilary Air Valve
Resistor
Engine Control
Ignition Coil
Resistor
A/T Control
Fusible Link
Airflow Meter
Battery
Fuel Injector
Thermo Meter
Fuel Injector
Oil Pressure
Switch
Temperature Sensor
FRONT
Courtesy of Subaru of America, Inc.

Fig. 9: 1.8L MPFI System Component Layout (XT Model)

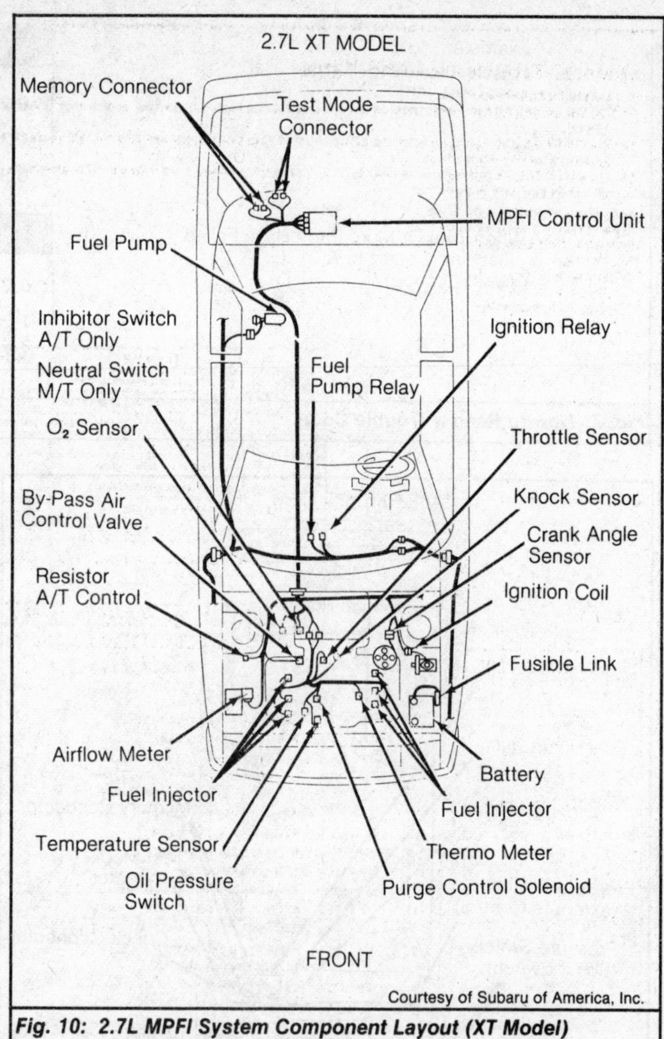
2.7L XT MODEL
Memory Connector
Test Mode
Connector
MPFI Control Unit
Fuel Pump
Inhibitor Switch
A/T Only
Ignition Relay
Neutral Switch
M/T Only
Fuel
Pump Relay
$O_2$ Sensor
Throttle Sensor
By-Pass Air
Control Valve
Knock Sensor
Crank Angle
Sensor
Resistor
A/T Control
Ignition Coil
Fusible Link
Airflow Meter
Battery
Fuel Injector
Fuel Injector
Temperature Sensor
Thermo Meter
Oil Pressure
Switch
Purge Control Solenoid
FRONT
Courtesy of Subaru of America, Inc.

Fig. 10: 2.7L MPFI System Component Layout (XT Model)

## General Troubleshooting Table

*: The CHECK ENGINE light blinks.
*1: The CHECK ENGINE light blinks when contact is resumed during inspection (although poor contact is present in the D-check).
*2: The CHECK ENGINE light lights when the mixture is leaner than that specified and does not light (U-check) or blink (D-check) when the mixture is richer.
*3: The CHECK ENGINE light lights when abnormality is detected in the D-check mode if the idle switch persistently remains off with the accelerator pedal released.

Symbols shown in the table refer to the degree of possibility of the reason for the trouble ("Very often" to "Rarely").
◎ : Very often
○ : Sometimes
△ : Rarely
☆ : Occurs only in extremely low temperatures

| TROUBLE | | |
|---|---|---|
| 1 | Engine will not start | No initial combustion |
| 2 | | Initial combustion occurs. |
| 3 | | Engine stalls after initial combustion. |
| 4 | Rough idle and engine stall | |
| 5 | Inability to drive at constant speed | |
| 6 | Inability to accelerate and decelerate | |
| 7 | Engine does not return to idle. | |
| 8 | Afterburning in exhaust system | |
| 9 | Knocking | |
| 10 | Excessive fuel consumption | |
| 11 | | |
| U | CHECK ENGINE light operation | U-check mode & read memory mode |
| D | | D-check mode |

| POSSIBLE CAUSE | 1 | 2 | 3 | 4 | 5 | 6 | 7 | 8 | 9 | 10 | 11 | CHECK ENGINE light U | CHECK ENGINE light D |
|---|---|---|---|---|---|---|---|---|---|---|---|---|---|
| **AIR FLOW METER** | | | | | | | | | | | | | |
| • Connector not connected | | | ☆ | ◎ | | | | △ | △ | ○ | | ON | ON |
| • Poor contact of terminal | | | △ | ◎ | ◎ | ◎ | | ◎ | ○ | △ | | ON | *1 |
| • Short circuit | | | ☆ | ◎ | | | | △ | ○ | △ | | ON | ON |
| • Discontinuity of wiring harness | | | ☆ | ◎ | | | | △ | △ | ○ | | ON | ON |
| • Performance characteristics unusual | | | ○ | ○ | ○ | ○ | | △ | ◎ | ○ | | *2 | *2 |
| **COOLANT THERMOSENSOR** | | | | | | | | | | | | | |
| • Connector not connected | | ☆ | ○ | ☆ | | ○ | | ○ | ○ | ○ | | ON | ON |
| • Poor contact of terminal | | △ | △ | ◎ | ○ | ○ | | ◎ | △ | ○ | | ON | *1 |
| • Short circuit | | ☆ | ○ | ☆ | | ○ | | ○ | ○ | ○ | | ON | ON |
| • Discontinuity of wiring harness | | ☆ | ○ | ☆ | | ○ | | ○ | ○ | ○ | | ON | ON |
| • Performance characteristics unusual | | ☆ | ○ | ☆ | | ○ | | ◎ | ◎ | ◎ | | *2 | *2 |
| **IDLE SWITCH OF THROTTLE SENSOR** | | | | | | | | | | | | | |
| • Connector not connected | | | | | ○ | ◎ | | ◎ | | | | OFF | ON |
| • Poor contact of terminal | | | | | ○ | | | ○ | | | | ON | *1 |
| • Short circuit | | | | | ○ | △ | | ○ | | | | ON | ON |
| • Discontinuity of wiring harness | | | | | | △ | | ○ | | | | OFF | ON |
| • Improper adjustment | | | | | | | | ○ | | | | OFF | *3 |
| **THROTTLE SENSOR** | | | | | | | | | | | | | |
| • Connector not connected | | | | | | ◎ | | ◎ | | | | ON | ON |
| • Poor contact of terminal | | | | | ◎ | ◎ | | ◎ | | | | ON | *1 |
| • Short circuit | △ | | | | | ◎ | | ◎ | | | | ON | ON |
| • Discontinuity of wiring harness | | | | | | ◎ | | ◎ | | | | ON | ON |
| • Performance characteristics unusual | | ○ | ○ | △ | ○ | ◎ | | ◎ | | | | OFF | * |
| **PRESSURE REGULATOR** | | | | | | | | | | | | | |
| • Sensing hose not connected | | ○ | ○ | ◎ | ◎ | ◎ | ○ | | △ | | | *2 | *2 |
| • Fuel pressure too high | | △ | | | | ○ | | ○ | | ◎ | | OFF | * |
| • Fuel pressure too low | ○ | ○ | ○ | ◎ | ◎ | ◎ | | ◎ | | | | *2 | *2 |
| **FUEL INJECTOR** | | | | | | | | | | | | | |
| • Connector not connected | | ◎ | ◎ | ○ | ○ | ○ | | ○ | ○ | | | ON | *1 |
| • Poor contact of terminal | | ○ | ○ | ○ | ◎ | ◎ | | ○ | | | | ON | ON |
| • Short circuit | | ◎ | ◎ | ○ | ○ | ○ | | ○ | | | | ON | ON |
| • Discontinuity of wiring harness | | ◎ | ◎ | ○ | ○ | ○ | | ○ | ○ | | | ON | ON |
| • Performance characteristics unusual | | △ | ○ | ○ | △ | ○ | | ○ | △ | ○ | | *2 | *2 |
| • Clogged filter | | △ | ○ | △ | △ | ○ | | ○ | △ | | | *2 | *2 |
| • Clogged nozzle | | △ | ○ | ○ | ○ | ○ | | ○ | △ | | | *2 | *2 |
| • Stuck open | ○ | | | | | | | | | | | OFF | * |
| • Slight leakage from seat | | | | ○ | | | | ○ | | ○ | | OFF | * |
| **CRANK ANGLE SENSOR** | | | | | | | | | | | | | |
| • Connector disconnected | ◎ | | | | | | | | | | | ON | ON |
| • Poor contact of terminal | | ○ | ○ | ◎ | ◎ | ◎ | | ○ | ○ | | | ON | *1 |
| • Short circuit | ◎ | | | | | | | | | | | ON | ON |
| • Discontinuity of wiring harness | ◎ | | | | | | | | | | | ON | ON |
| **POWER TRANSISTOR OF IGNITION COIL** | | | | | | | | | | | | | |
| • Connector not connected | ◎ | | | | | | | | | | | OFF | * |
| • Poor contact of terminal | | ○ | ○ | ◎ | ◎ | ◎ | | ○ | | | | OFF | * |
| • Short circuit | ◎ | | | | | | | | | | | OFF | * |
| • Discontinuity of wiring harness | ◎ | | | | | | | | | | | OFF | * |
| **AIR REGULATOR** | | | | | | | | | | | | | |
| • Connector not connected | | | | | | | ◎ | | | | | OFF | * |
| • Short circuit | | ○ | ◎ | ○ | | | | | | | | OFF | * |
| • Discontinuity of wiring harness | | | | | | | ◎ | | | | | OFF | * |
| **KNOCK SENSOR** | | | | | | | | | | | | | |
| • Connector not connected | | | | | | | | | ◎ | | | ON | ON |
| • Short circuit | | | | | ○ | ○ | | | | | | ON | ON |
| • Discontinuity of wiring harness | | | | | | | | | ◎ | | | ON | ON |
| **DUTY SOLENOID** | | | | | | | | | | | | | |
| • Connector disconnected | | | | | | △ | | | | | | OFF | * |
| • Poor contact of terminal | | | | | | | | | | | | OFF | * |
| • Short circuit | | | | | | | | | ○ | | | OFF | * |
| • Discontinuity of wiring harness | | | | | | △ | | | | | | OFF | * |
| • Disconnected or cracked hose | | | | ○ | ○ | ○ | ○ | ○ | ○ | | | OFF | * |
| **AIR CONTROL VALVE [2700 cc model only]** | | | | | | | | | | | | | |
| • Connector not connected | | ○ | △ | ◎ | | | | | | | | ON | ON |
| • Poor contact of terminal | | △ | ○ | ◎ | | | | | | | | ON | *1 |
| • Short circuit | | | | ○ | | | | ○ | | | | ON | ON |
| • Discontinuity of wiring harness | | ○ | △ | ◎ | | | | | | | | ON | ON |
| • IAS improperly adjusted | | | | ◎ | | | ◎ | | | | | OFF | * |
| • Stuck open | | | | | | ◎ | ◎ | | | | | ON | * |
| • Stuck closed | | ○ | ○ | ◎ | | | | | | | | OFF | * |
| **ENGINE GROUNDING** | | | | | | | | | | | | | |
| • Disconnecting of engine grounding terminal at intake manifold | ○ | | | | | | | | | | | ON | |
| • Poor contact of engine grounding terminal | ◎ | ◎ | ○ | ◎ | ◎ | ◎ | | | | | | ON | *1 |
| • Discontinuity of wiring harness for engine grounding | ○ | | | | | | | | | | | ON | |

Courtesy of Subaru of America, Inc.

*Fig. 11: General Trouble Shooting Table*

## TROUBLE SHOOTING CHART FOR SELF-DIAGNOSIS

### Basic Trouble Shooting Procedures

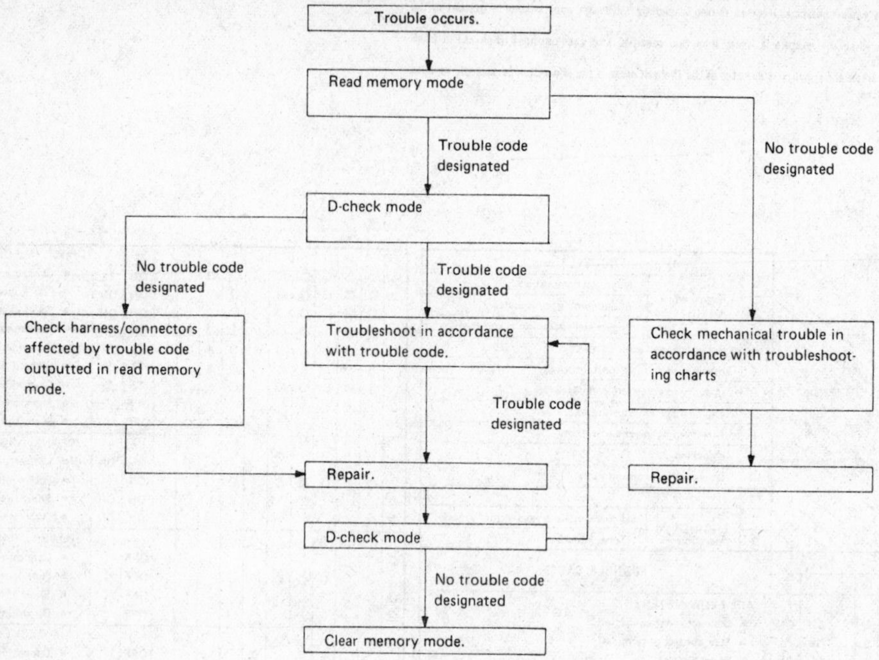

Trouble occurs.

Read memory mode

Trouble code designated

No trouble code designated

D-check mode

No trouble code designated

Trouble code designated

Check harness/connectors affected by trouble code outputted in read memory mode.

Troubleshoot in accordance with trouble code.

Check mechanical trouble in accordance with troubleshooting charts

Trouble code designated

Repair.

Repair.

D-check mode

No trouble code designated

Clear memory mode.

## MEMORY MODE

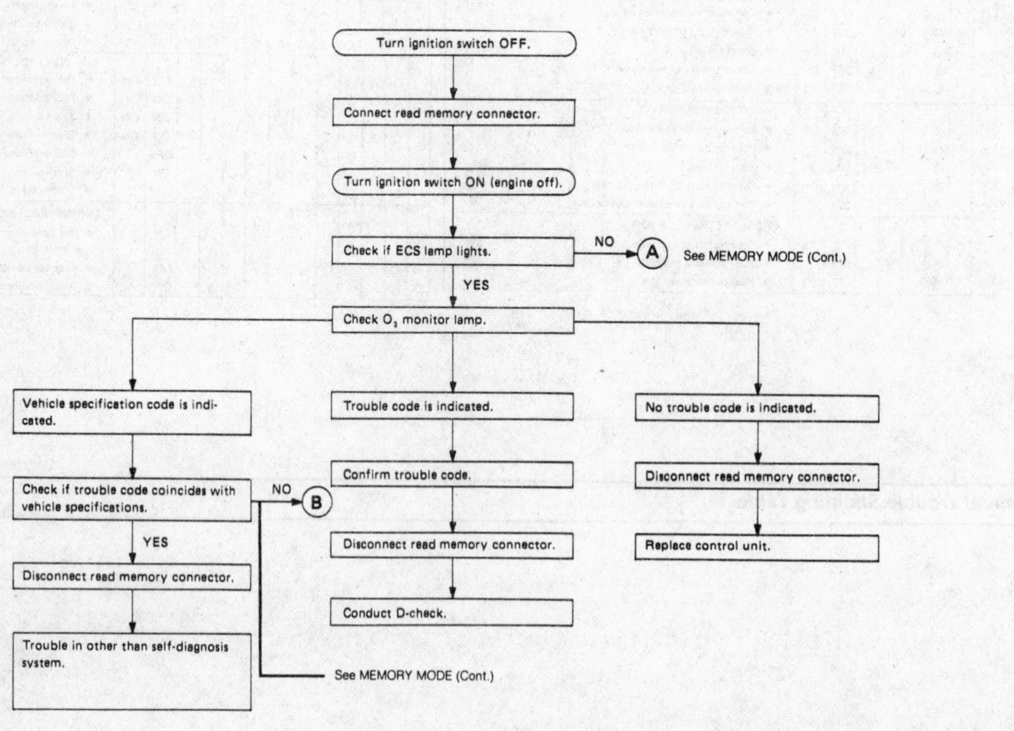
Turn ignition switch OFF.
Connect read memory connector.
Turn ignition switch ON (engine off).
Check if ECS lamp lights.
NO
A
See MEMORY MODE (Cont.)
YES
Check $O_2$ monitor lamp.
Vehicle specification code is indicated.
Trouble code is indicated.
No trouble code is indicated.
Check if trouble code coincides with vehicle specifications.
NO
B
YES
Confirm trouble code.
Disconnect read memory connector.
Disconnect read memory connector.
Replace control unit.
Disconnect read memory connector.
Conduct D-check.
Trouble in other than self-diagnosis system.
See MEMORY MODE (Cont.)

Courtesy of Subaru of America, Inc.

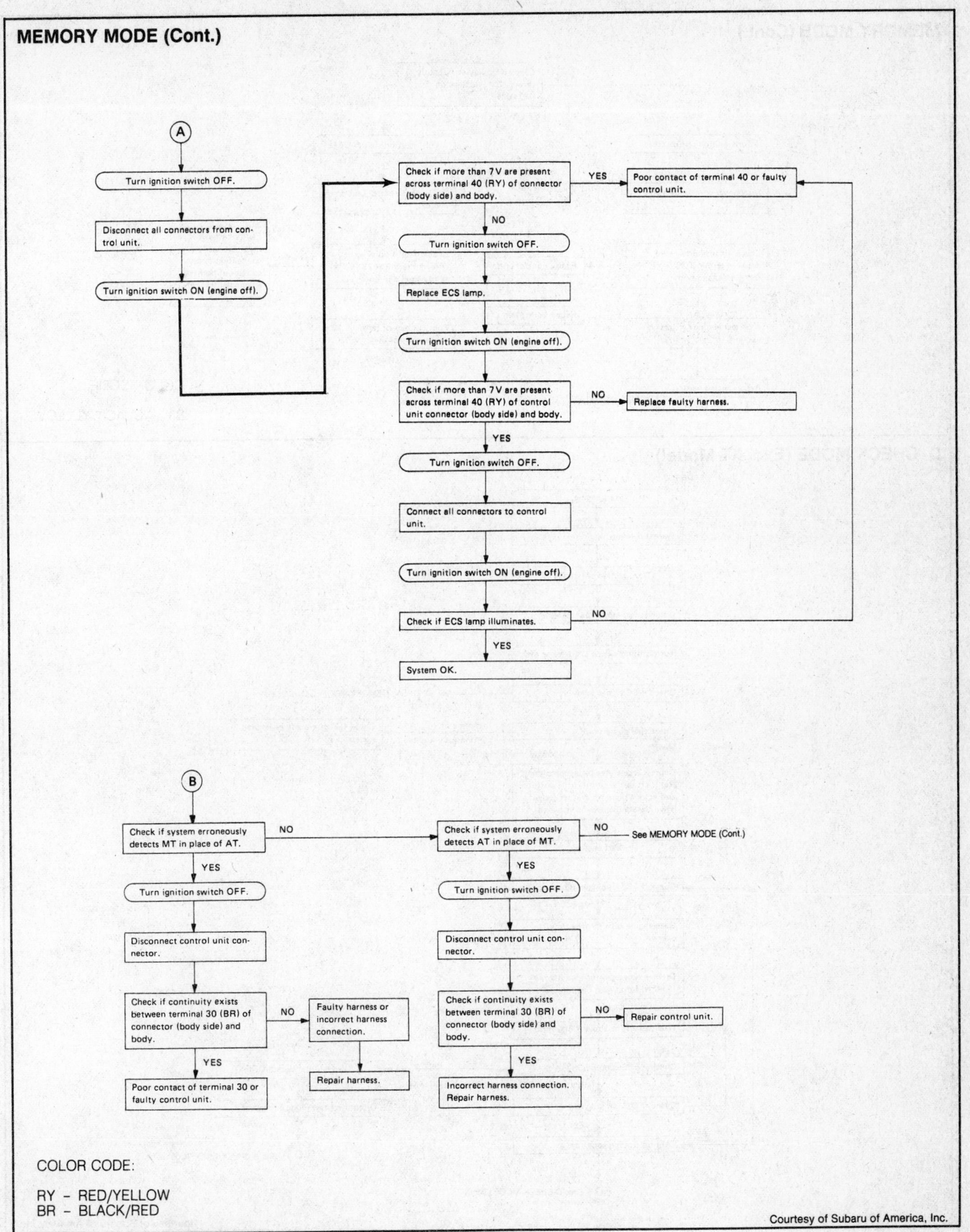
MEMORY MODE (Cont.)
A
Turn ignition switch OFF.
Disconnect all connectors from control unit.
Turn ignition switch ON (engine off).
Check if more than 7 V are present across terminal 40 (RY) of connector (body side) and body.
YES
Poor contact of terminal 40 or faulty control unit.
NO
Turn ignition switch OFF.
Replace ECS lamp.
Turn ignition switch ON (engine off).
Check if more than 7 V are present across terminal 40 (RY) of control unit connector (body side) and body.
NO
Replace faulty harness.
YES
Turn ignition switch OFF.
Connect all connectors to control unit.
Turn ignition switch ON (engine off).
Check if ECS lamp illuminates.
NO
YES
System OK.
B
Check if system erroneously detects MT in place of AT.
NO
Check if system erroneously detects AT in place of MT.
NO
See MEMORY MODE (Cont.)
YES
Turn ignition switch OFF.
Disconnect control unit connector.
Check if continuity exists between terminal 30 (BR) of connector (body side) and body.
NO
Faulty harness or incorrect harness connection.
Repair harness.
YES
Poor contact of terminal 30 or faulty control unit.
YES
Turn ignition switch OFF.
Disconnect control unit connector.
Check if continuity exists between terminal 30 (BR) of connector (body side) and body.
NO
Repair control unit.
YES
Incorrect harness connection. Repair harness.
COLOR CODE:
RY – RED/YELLOW
BR – BLACK/RED
Courtesy of Subaru of America, Inc.

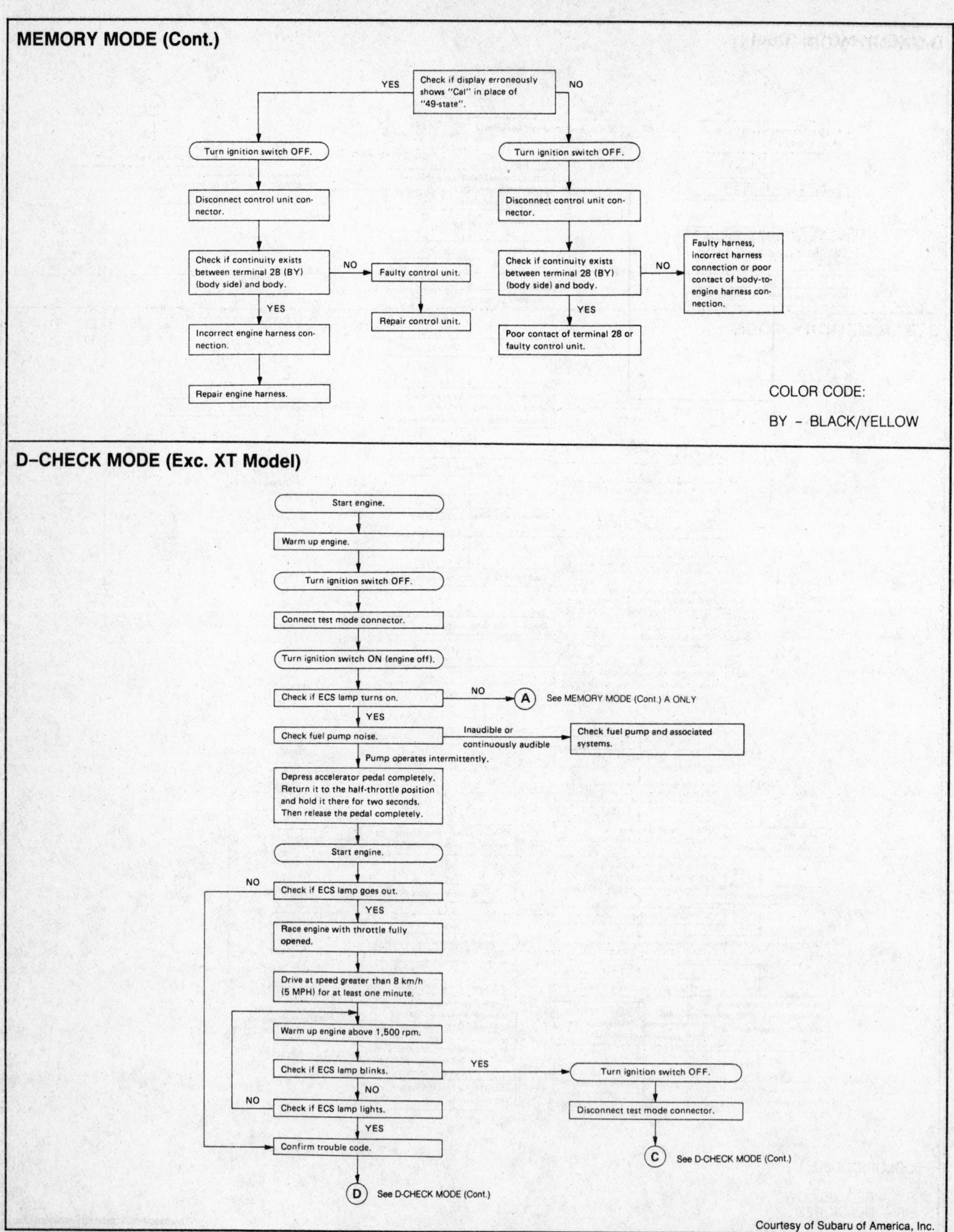
MEMORY MODE (Cont.)
Check if display erroneously shows "Cal" in place of "49-state".
YES
NO
Turn ignition switch OFF.
Disconnect control unit connector.
Check if continuity exists between terminal 28 (BY) (body side) and body.
NO
Faulty control unit.
Repair control unit.
YES
Incorrect engine harness connection.
Repair engine harness.
Turn ignition switch OFF.
Disconnect control unit connector.
Check if continuity exists between terminal 28 (BY) (body side) and body.
NO
Faulty harness, incorrect harness connection or poor contact of body-to-engine harness connection.
YES
Poor contact of terminal 28 or faulty control unit.
COLOR CODE:
BY - BLACK/YELLOW
D–CHECK MODE (Exc. XT Model)
Start engine.
Warm up engine.
Turn ignition switch OFF.
Connect test mode connector.
Turn ignition switch ON (engine off).
Check if ECS lamp turns on.
NO
A
See MEMORY MODE (Cont.) A ONLY
YES
Check fuel pump noise.
Inaudible or continuously audible
Check fuel pump and associated systems.
Pump operates intermittently.
Depress accelerator pedal completely. Return it to the half-throttle position and hold it there for two seconds. Then release the pedal completely.
Start engine.
Check if ECS lamp goes out.
NO
YES
Race engine with throttle fully opened.
Drive at speed greater than 8 km/h (5 MPH) for at least one minute.
Warm up engine above 1,500 rpm.
Check if ECS lamp blinks.
YES
Turn ignition switch OFF.
Disconnect test mode connector.
C
See D-CHECK MODE (Cont.)
NO
Check if ECS lamp lights.
NO
YES
Confirm trouble code.
D
See D-CHECK MODE (Cont.)
Courtesy of Subaru of America, Inc.

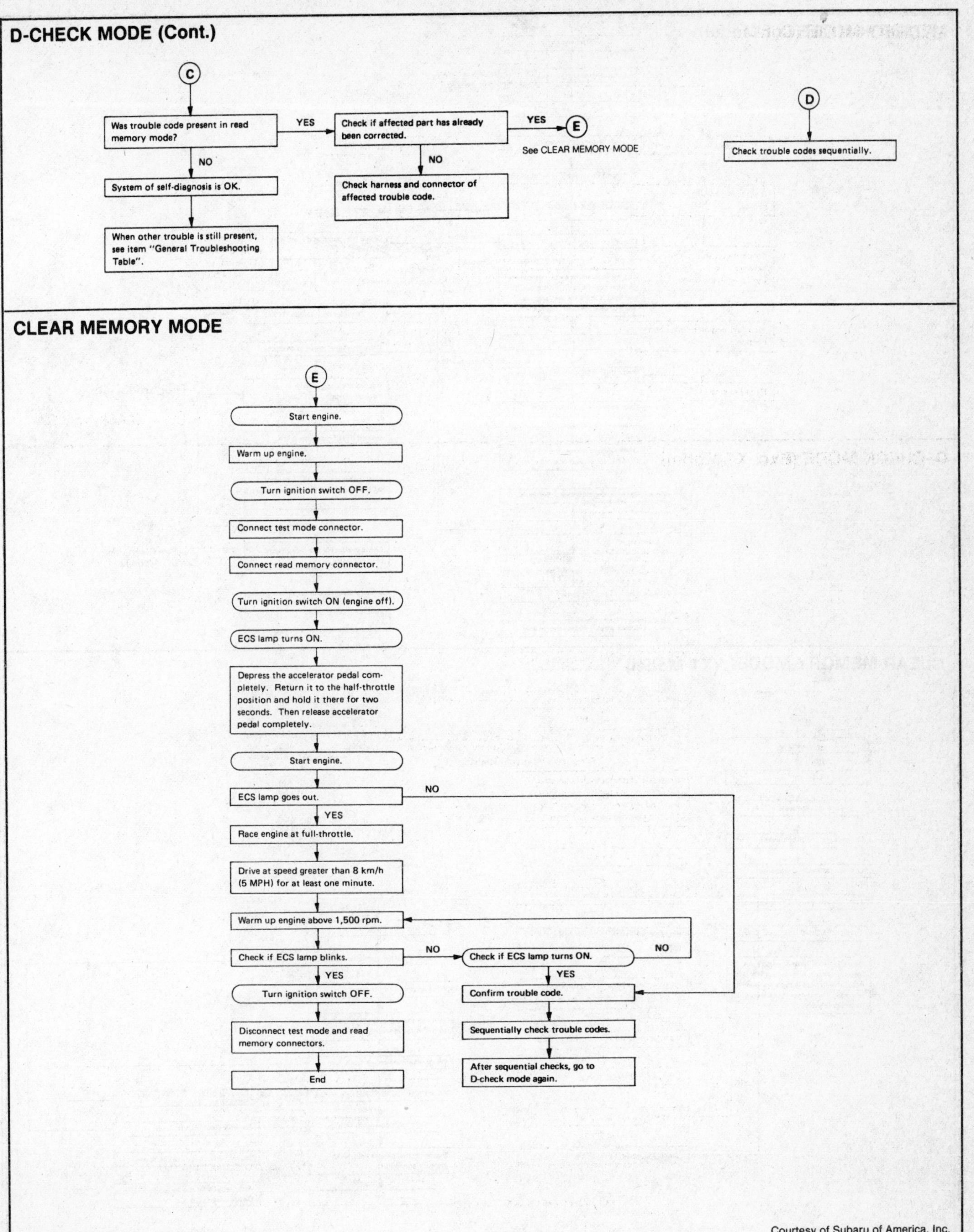
D-CHECK MODE (Cont.)
C
Was trouble code present in read memory mode?
YES
Check if affected part has already been corrected.
YES
E
See CLEAR MEMORY MODE
NO
System of self-diagnosis is OK.
When other trouble is still present, see item "General Troubleshooting Table".
NO
Check harness and connector of affected trouble code.
D
Check trouble codes sequentially.
CLEAR MEMORY MODE
E
Start engine.
Warm up engine.
Turn ignition switch OFF.
Connect test mode connector.
Connect read memory connector.
Turn ignition switch ON (engine off).
ECS lamp turns ON.
Depress the accelerator pedal completely. Return it to the half-throttle position and hold it there for two seconds. Then release accelerator pedal completely.
Start engine.
ECS lamp goes out.
NO
YES
Race engine at full-throttle.
Drive at speed greater than 8 km/h (5 MPH) for at least one minute.
Warm up engine above 1,500 rpm.
Check if ECS lamp blinks.
NO
Check if ECS lamp turns ON.
NO
YES
Turn ignition switch OFF.
YES
Confirm trouble code.
Disconnect test mode and read memory connectors.
Sequentially check trouble codes.
End
After sequential checks, go to D-check mode again.
Courtesy of Subaru of America, Inc.

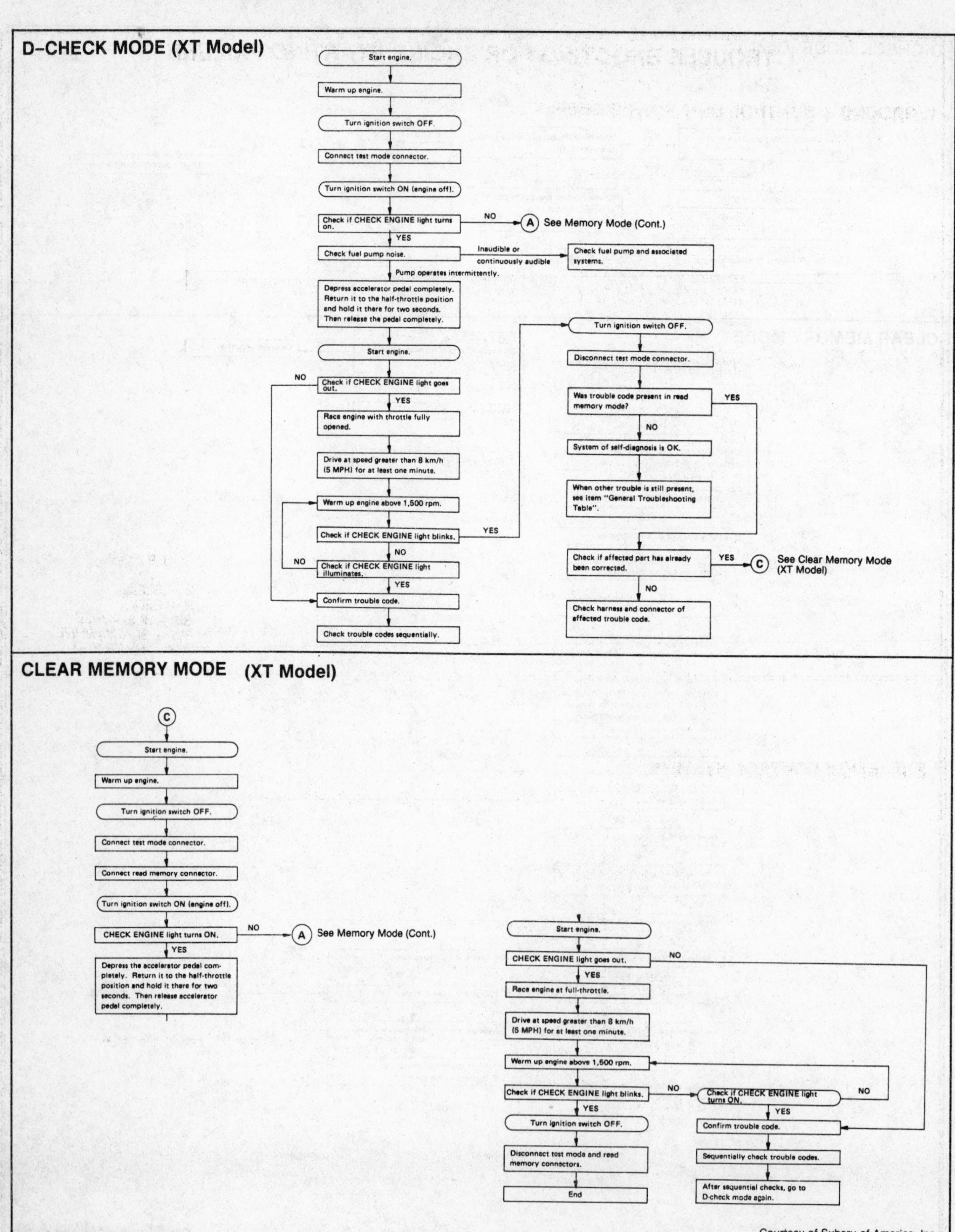
D–CHECK MODE (XT Model)
Start engine.
Warm up engine.
Turn ignition switch OFF.
Connect test mode connector.
Turn ignition switch ON (engine off).
Check if CHECK ENGINE light turns on.
NO
A See Memory Mode (Cont.)
YES
Check fuel pump noise.
Inaudible or continuously audible
Check fuel pump and associated systems.
Pump operates intermittently.
Depress accelerator pedal completely. Return it to the half-throttle position and hold it there for two seconds. Then release the pedal completely.
Start engine.
NO
Check if CHECK ENGINE light goes out.
YES
Race engine with throttle fully opened.
Drive at speed greater than 8 km/h (5 MPH) for at least one minute.
Warm up engine above 1,500 rpm.
Check if CHECK ENGINE light blinks.
YES
NO
NO
Check if CHECK ENGINE light illuminates.
YES
Confirm trouble code.
Check trouble codes sequentially.
Turn ignition switch OFF.
Disconnect test mode connector.
Was trouble code present in read memory mode?
YES
NO
System of self-diagnosis is OK.
When other trouble is still present, see item "General Troubleshooting Table".
Check if affected part has already been corrected.
YES
C See Clear Memory Mode (XT Model)
NO
Check harness and connector of affected trouble code.
CLEAR MEMORY MODE (XT Model)
C
Start engine.
Warm up engine.
Turn ignition switch OFF.
Connect test mode connector.
Connect read memory connector.
Turn ignition switch ON (engine off).
CHECK ENGINE light turns ON.
NO
A See Memory Mode (Cont.)
YES
Depress the accelerator pedal completely. Return it to the half-throttle position and hold it there for two seconds. Then release accelerator pedal completely.
Start engine.
CHECK ENGINE light goes out.
NO
YES
Race engine at full-throttle.
Drive at speed greater than 8 km/h (5 MPH) for at least one minute.
Warm up engine above 1,500 rpm.
Check if CHECK ENGINE light blinks.
NO
Check if CHECK ENGINE light turns ON.
NO
YES
YES
Turn ignition switch OFF.
Confirm trouble code.
Disconnect test mode and read memory connectors.
Sequentially check trouble codes.
End
After sequential checks, go to D-check mode again.
Courtesy of Subaru of America, Inc.

# TROUBLE SHOOTING FOR ENGINE STARTING FAILURE

## 1. GROUND & CONTROL UNIT POWER SUPPLY

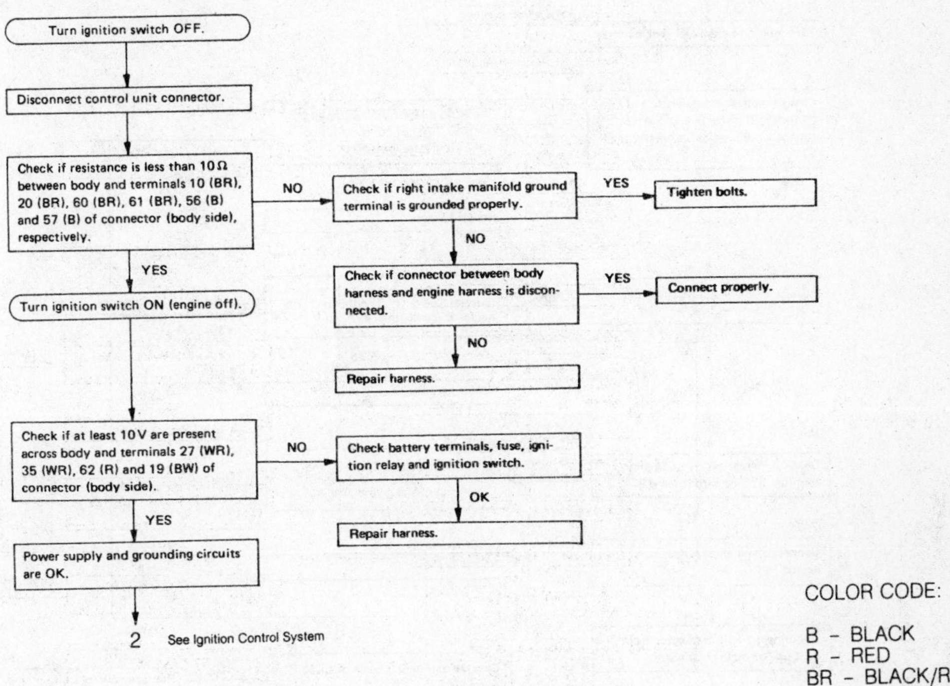

Turn ignition switch OFF.
Disconnect control unit connector.
Check if resistance is less than 10 Ω between body and terminals 10 (BR), 20 (BR), 60 (BR), 61 (BR), 56 (B) and 57 (B) of connector (body side), respectively.
NO
Check if right intake manifold ground terminal is grounded properly.
YES
Tighten bolts.
NO
Check if connector between body harness and engine harness is disconnected.
YES
Connect properly.
NO
Repair harness.
YES
Turn ignition switch ON (engine off).
Check if at least 10 V are present across body and terminals 27 (WR), 35 (WR), 62 (R) and 19 (BW) of connector (body side).
NO
Check battery terminals, fuse, ignition relay and ignition switch.
OK
Repair harness.
YES
Power supply and grounding circuits are OK.
2 See Ignition Control System


COLOR CODE:

B – BLACK
R – RED
BR – BLACK/RED
BW – BLACK/WHITE
WR – WHITE/RED

## 2. IGNITION CONTROL SYSTEM

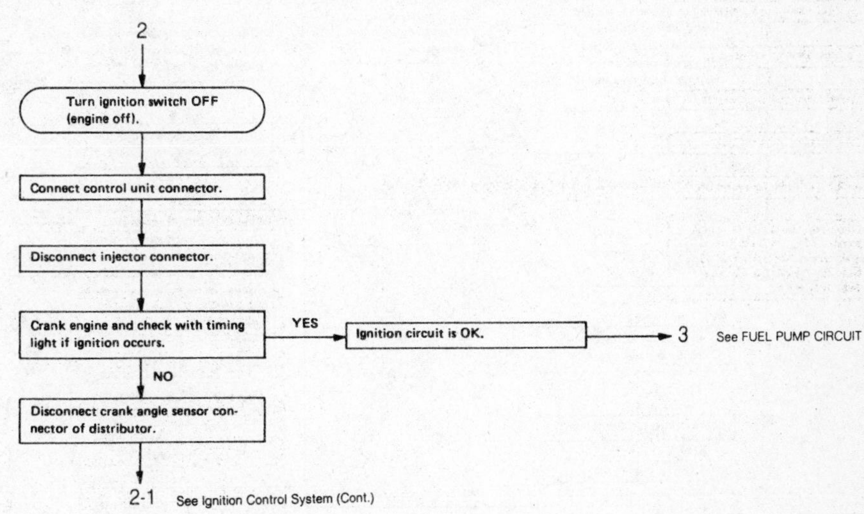

2
Turn ignition switch OFF (engine off).
Connect control unit connector.
Disconnect injector connector.
Crank engine and check with timing light if ignition occurs.
YES
Ignition circuit is OK.
3 See FUEL PUMP CIRCUIT
NO
Disconnect crank angle sensor connector of distributor.
2-1 See Ignition Control System (Cont.)


Courtesy of Subaru of America, Inc.

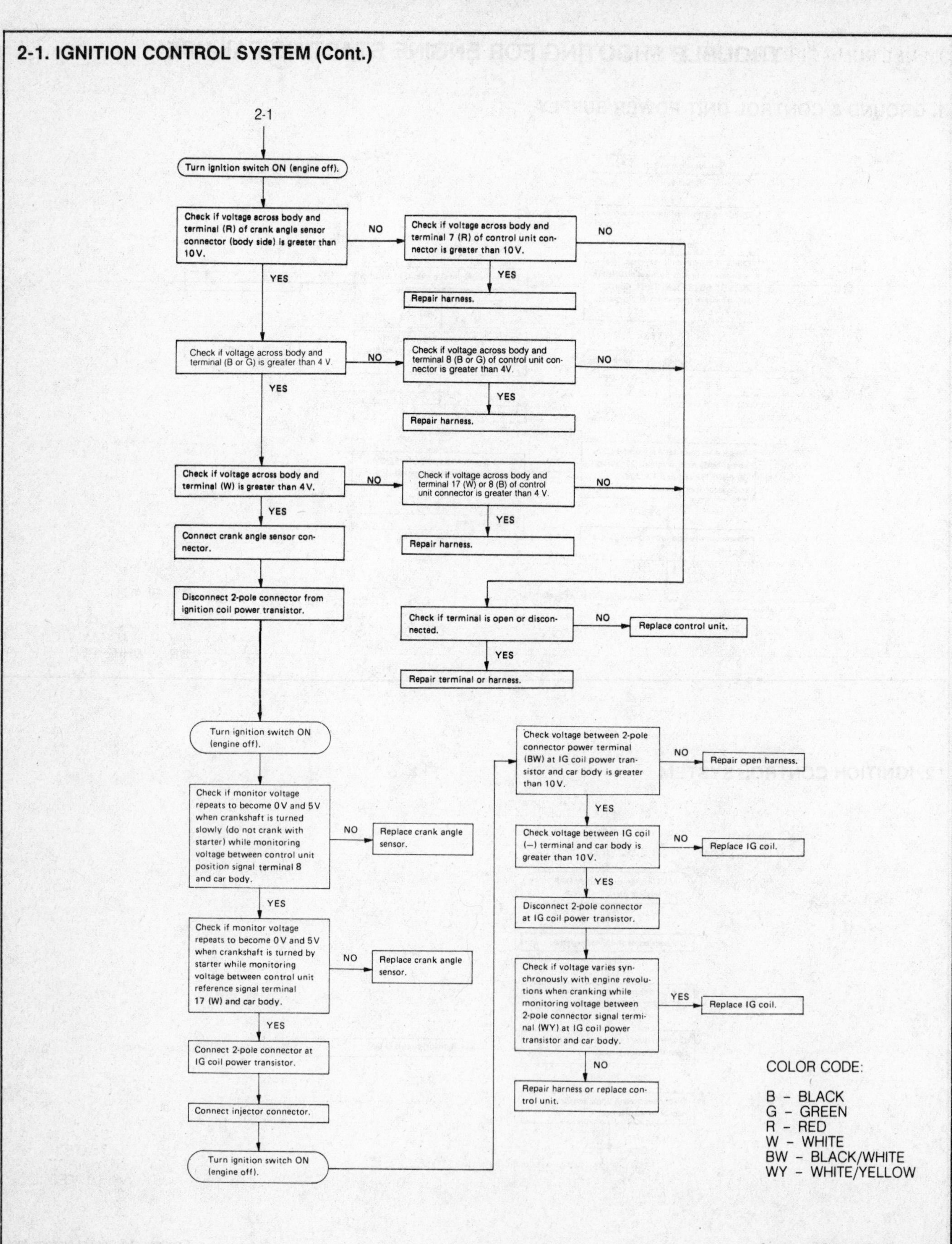
2-1. IGNITION CONTROL SYSTEM (Cont.)
2-1
Turn ignition switch ON (engine off).
Check if voltage across body and terminal (R) of crank angle sensor connector (body side) is greater than 10 V.
NO
Check if voltage across body and terminal 7 (R) of control unit connector is greater than 10 V.
NO
YES
Repair harness.
YES
Check if voltage across body and terminal (B or G) is greater than 4 V.
NO
Check if voltage across body and terminal 8 (B or G) of control unit connector is greater than 4V.
NO
YES
Repair harness.
YES
Check if voltage across body and terminal (W) is greater than 4 V.
NO
Check if voltage across body and terminal 17 (W) or 8 (B) of control unit connector is greater than 4 V.
NO
YES
Repair harness.
YES
Connect crank angle sensor connector.
Disconnect 2-pole connector from ignition coil power transistor.
Check if terminal is open or disconnected.
NO
Replace control unit.
YES
Repair terminal or harness.
Turn ignition switch ON (engine off).
Check if monitor voltage repeats to become 0 V and 5 V when crankshaft is turned slowly (do not crank with starter) while monitoring voltage between control unit position signal terminal 8 and car body.
NO
Replace crank angle sensor.
YES
Check if monitor voltage repeats to become 0 V and 5 V when crankshaft is turned by starter while monitoring voltage between control unit reference signal terminal 17 (W) and car body.
NO
Replace crank angle sensor.
YES
Connect 2-pole connector at IG coil power transistor.
Connect injector connector.
Turn ignition switch ON (engine off).
Check voltage between 2-pole connector power terminal (BW) at IG coil power transistor and car body is greater than 10 V.
NO
Repair open harness.
YES
Check voltage between IG coil (–) terminal and car body is greater than 10 V.
NO
Replace IG coil.
YES
Disconnect 2-pole connector at IG coil power transistor.
Check if voltage varies synchronously with engine revolutions when cranking while monitoring voltage between 2-pole connector signal terminal (WY) at IG coil power transistor and car body.
YES
Replace IG coil.
NO
Repair harness or replace control unit.
COLOR CODE:
B – BLACK
G – GREEN
R – RED
W – WHITE
BW – BLACK/WHITE
WY – WHITE/YELLOW
Courtesy of Subaru of America, Inc.

### 3. FUEL PUMP CIRCUIT (Exc. XT Model)

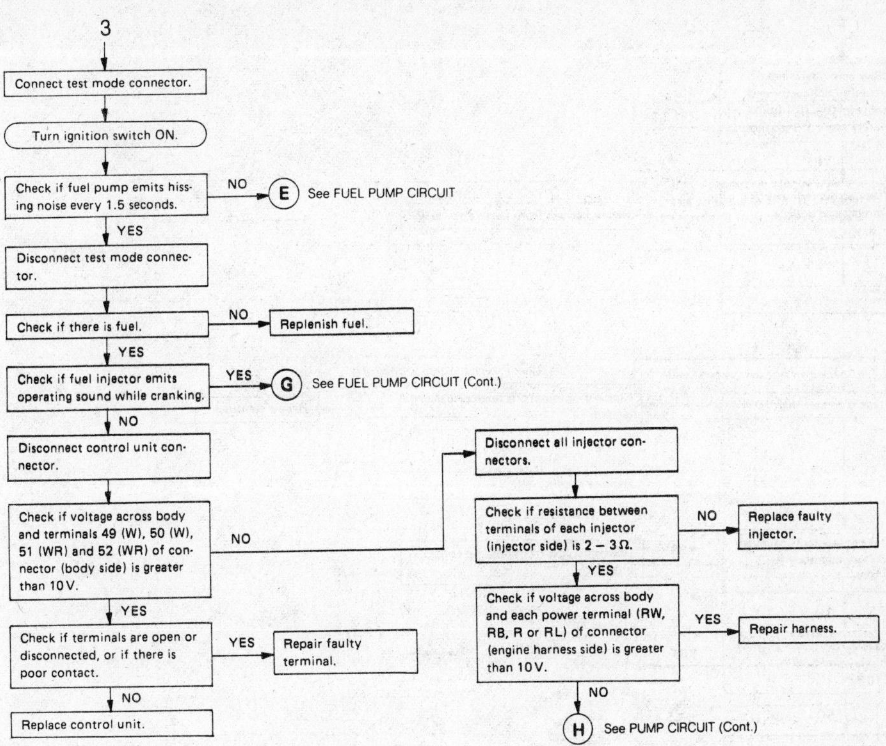
3
Connect test mode connector.
Turn ignition switch ON.
Check if fuel pump emits hissing noise every 1.5 seconds.
NO
E
See FUEL PUMP CIRCUIT
YES
Disconnect test mode connector.
Check if there is fuel.
NO
Replenish fuel.
YES
Check if fuel injector emits operating sound while cranking.
YES
G
See FUEL PUMP CIRCUIT (Cont.)
NO
Disconnect control unit connector.
Check if voltage across body and terminals 49 (W), 50 (W), 51 (WR) and 52 (WR) of connector (body side) is greater than 10V.
NO
Disconnect all injector connectors.
Check if resistance between terminals of each injector (injector side) is 2 – 3 Ω.
NO
Replace faulty injector.
YES
Check if voltage across body and each power terminal (RW, RB, R or RL) of connector (engine harness side) is greater than 10V.
YES
Repair harness.
NO
H
See PUMP CIRCUIT (Cont.)
YES
Check if terminals are open or disconnected, or if there is poor contact.
YES
Repair faulty terminal.
NO
Replace control unit.

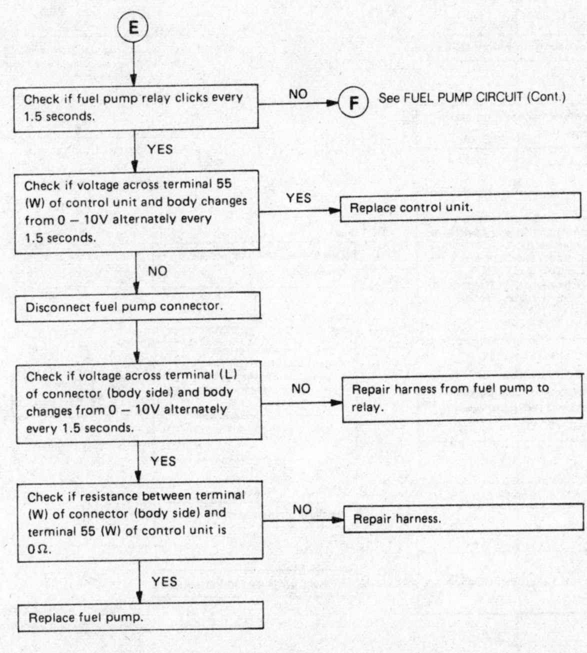
E
Check if fuel pump relay clicks every 1.5 seconds.
NO
F
See FUEL PUMP CIRCUIT (Cont.)
YES
Check if voltage across terminal 55 (W) of control unit and body changes from 0 – 10V alternately every 1.5 seconds.
YES
Replace control unit.
NO
Disconnect fuel pump connector.
Check if voltage across terminal (L) of connector (body side) and body changes from 0 – 10V alternately every 1.5 seconds.
NO
Repair harness from fuel pump to relay.
YES
Check if resistance between terminal (W) of connector (body side) and terminal 55 (W) of control unit is 0 Ω.
NO
Repair harness.
YES
Replace fuel pump.

COLOR CODE:

L – BLUE
R – RED
W – WHITE
RB – RED/BLACK
RL – RED/BLUE
RW – RED/WHITE
WR – WHITE/RED

Courtesy of Subaru of America, Inc.

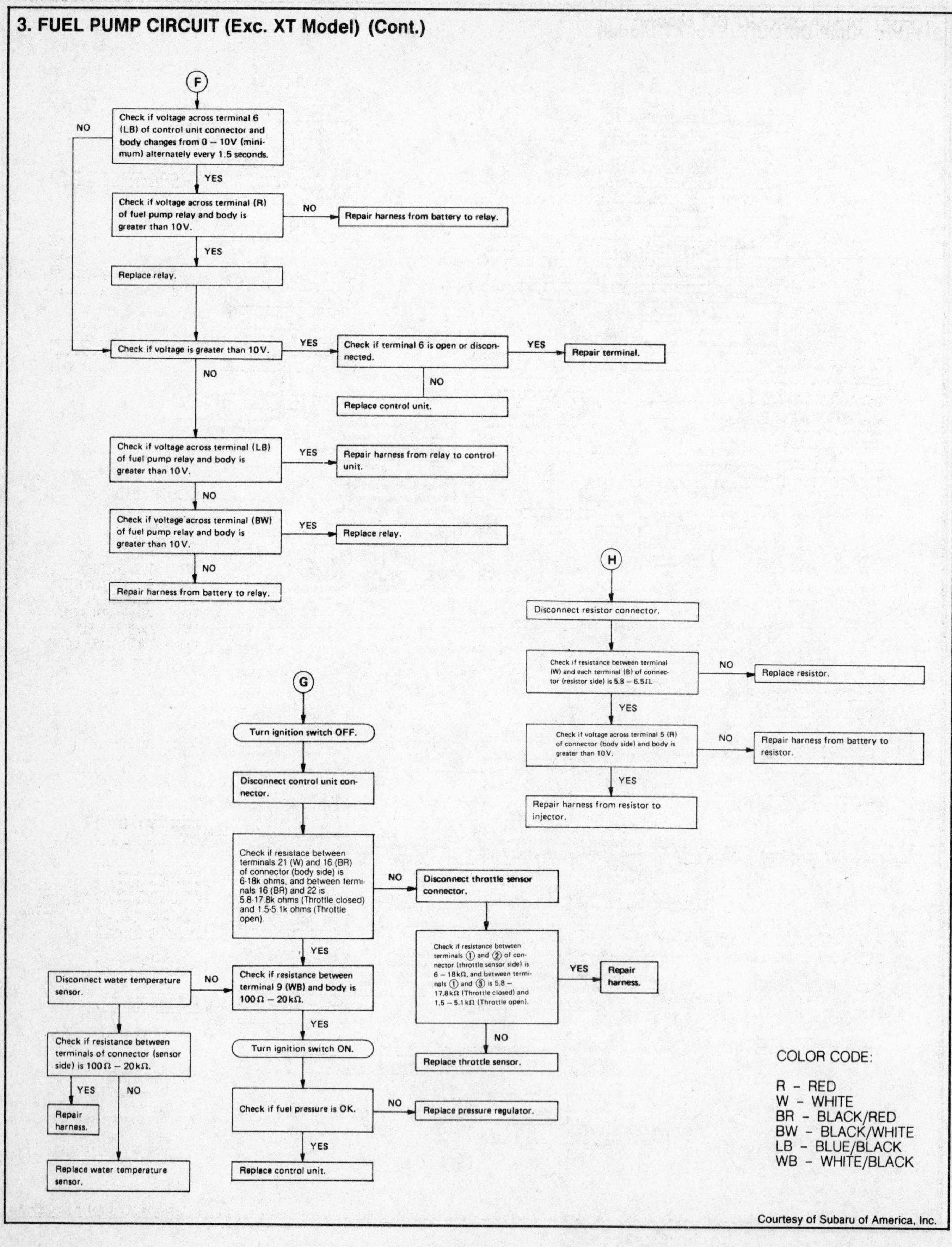
3. FUEL PUMP CIRCUIT (Exc. XT Model) (Cont.)
F
Check if voltage across terminal 6 (LB) of control unit connector and body changes from 0 – 10V (minimum) alternately every 1.5 seconds.
NO
YES
Check if voltage across terminal (R) of fuel pump relay and body is greater than 10V.
NO
Repair harness from battery to relay.
YES
Replace relay.
Check if voltage is greater than 10V.
YES
Check if terminal 6 is open or disconnected.
YES
Repair terminal.
NO
Replace control unit.
NO
Check if voltage across terminal (LB) of fuel pump relay and body is greater than 10V.
YES
Repair harness from relay to control unit.
NO
Check if voltage across terminal (BW) of fuel pump relay and body is greater than 10V.
YES
Replace relay.
NO
Repair harness from battery to relay.
H
Disconnect resistor connector.
Check if resistance between terminal (W) and each terminal (B) of connector (resistor side) is 5.8 – 6.5Ω.
NO
Replace resistor.
YES
Check if voltage across terminal 5 (R) of connector (body side) and body is greater than 10V.
NO
Repair harness from battery to resistor.
YES
Repair harness from resistor to injector.
G
Turn ignition switch OFF.
Disconnect control unit connector.
Check if resistace between terminals 21 (W) and 16 (BR) of connector (body side) is 6-18k ohms, and between terminals 16 (BR) and 22 is 5.8-17.8k ohms (Throttle closed) and 1.5-5.1k ohms (Throttle open).
NO
Disconnect throttle sensor connector.
Check if resistance between terminals ① and ② of connector (throttle sensor side) is 6 – 18kΩ, and between terminals ① and ③ is 5.8 – 17.8kΩ (Throttle closed) and 1.5 – 5.1kΩ (Throttle open).
YES
Repair harness.
NO
Replace throttle sensor.
YES
Check if resistance between terminal 9 (WB) and body is 100Ω – 20kΩ.
NO
Disconnect water temperature sensor.
Check if resistance between terminals of connector (sensor side) is 100Ω – 20kΩ.
YES
Repair harness.
NO
Replace water temperature sensor.
YES
Turn ignition switch ON.
Check if fuel pressure is OK.
NO
Replace pressure regulator.
YES
Replace control unit.
COLOR CODE:
R – RED
W – WHITE
BR – BLACK/RED
BW – BLACK/WHITE
LB – BLUE/BLACK
WB – WHITE/BLACK

Courtesy of Subaru of America, Inc.

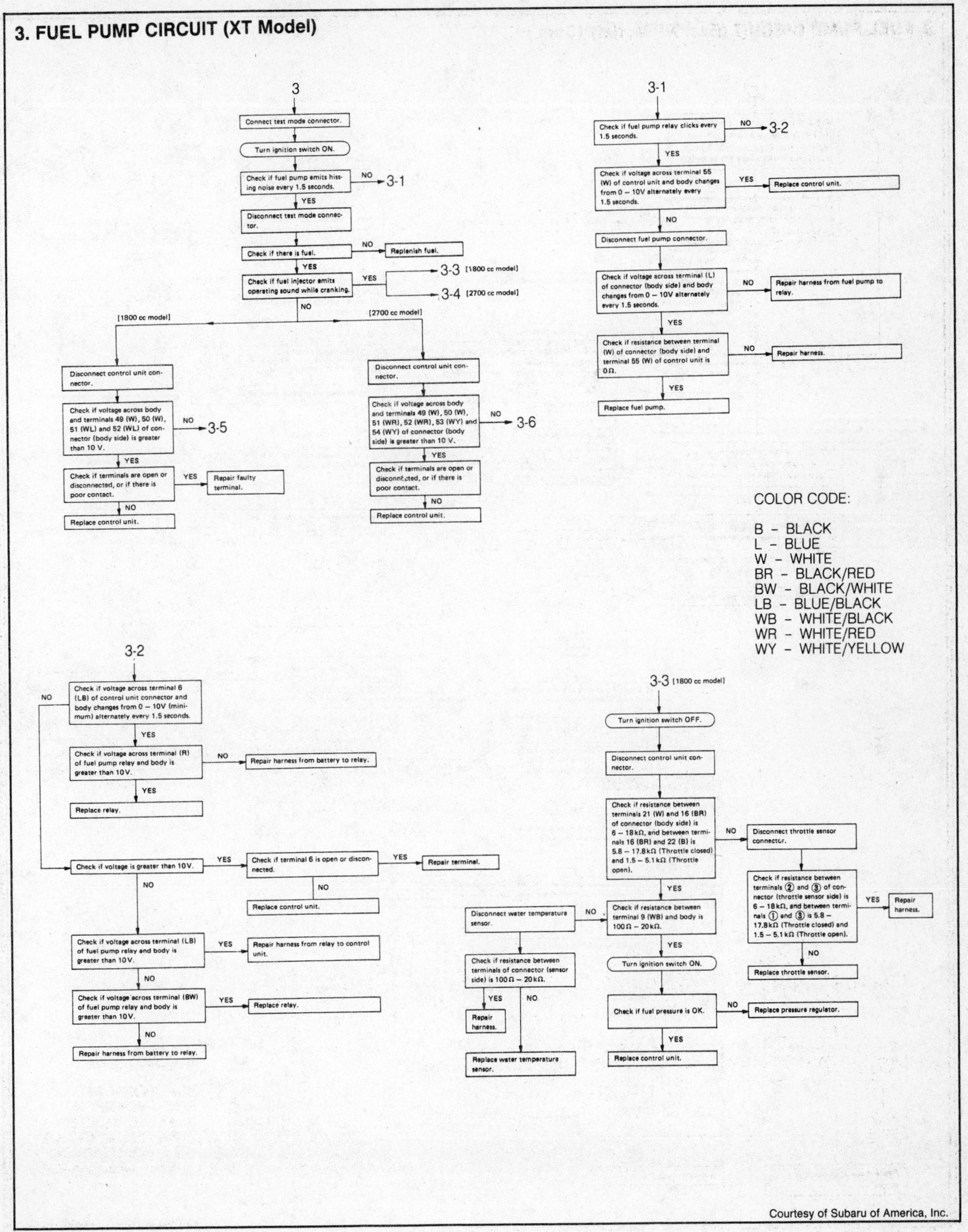
3. FUEL PUMP CIRCUIT (XT Model)
3
Connect test mode connector.
Turn ignition switch ON.
Check if fuel pump emits hissing noise every 1.5 seconds.
NO
3-1
YES
Disconnect test mode connector.
Check if there is fuel.
NO
Replenish fuel.
YES
Check if fuel injector emits operating sound while cranking.
YES
3-3 [1800 cc model]
3-4 [2700 cc model]
NO
[1800 cc model]
[2700 cc model]
Disconnect control unit connector.
Check if voltage across body and terminals 49 (W), 50 (W), 51 (WL) and 52 (WL) of connector (body side) is greater than 10 V.
NO
3-5
YES
Check if terminals are open or disconnected, or if there is poor contact.
YES
Repair faulty terminal.
NO
Replace control unit.
Disconnect control unit connector.
Check if voltage across body and terminals 49 (W), 50 (W), 51 (WR), 52 (WR), 53 (WY) and 54 (WY) of connector (body side) is greater than 10 V.
NO
3-6
YES
Check if terminals are open or disconnected, or if there is poor contact.
NO
Replace control unit.
3-1
Check if fuel pump relay clicks every 1.5 seconds.
NO
3-2
YES
Check if voltage across terminal 55 (W) of control unit and body changes from 0 – 10V alternately every 1.5 seconds.
YES
Replace control unit.
NO
Disconnect fuel pump connector.
Check if voltage across terminal (L) of connector (body side) and body changes from 0 – 10V alternately every 1.5 seconds.
NO
Repair harness from fuel pump to relay.
YES
Check if resistance between terminal (W) of connector (body side) and terminal 55 (W) of control unit is 0 Ω.
NO
Repair harness.
YES
Replace fuel pump.
COLOR CODE:
B – BLACK
L – BLUE
W – WHITE
BR – BLACK/RED
BW – BLACK/WHITE
LB – BLUE/BLACK
WB – WHITE/BLACK
WR – WHITE/RED
WY – WHITE/YELLOW
3-2
Check if voltage across terminal 6 (LB) of control unit connector and body changes from 0 – 10V (minimum) alternately every 1.5 seconds.
NO
YES
Check if voltage across terminal (R) of fuel pump relay and body is greater than 10V.
NO
Repair harness from battery to relay.
YES
Replace relay.
Check if voltage is greater than 10V.
YES
Check if terminal 6 is open or disconnected.
YES
Repair terminal.
NO
Replace control unit.
NO
Check if voltage across terminal (LB) of fuel pump relay and body is greater than 10V.
YES
Repair harness from relay to control unit.
NO
Check if voltage across terminal (BW) of fuel pump relay and body is greater than 10V.
YES
Replace relay.
NO
Repair harness from battery to relay.
3-3 [1800 cc model]
Turn ignition switch OFF.
Disconnect control unit connector.
Check if resistance between terminals 21 (W) and 16 (BR) of connector (body side) is 6 – 18kΩ, and between terminals 16 (BR) and 22 (B) is 5.8 – 17.8kΩ (Throttle closed) and 1.5 – 5.1kΩ (Throttle open).
NO
Disconnect throttle sensor connector.
Check if resistance between terminals ② and ③ of connector (throttle sensor side) is 6 – 18kΩ, and between terminals ① and ③ is 5.8 – 17.8kΩ (Throttle closed) and 1.5 – 5.1kΩ (Throttle open).
YES
Repair harness.
NO
Replace throttle sensor.
YES
Check if resistance between terminal 9 (WB) and body is 100Ω – 20kΩ.
NO
Disconnect water temperature sensor.
Check if resistance between terminals of connector (sensor side) is 100Ω – 20kΩ.
YES
Repair harness.
NO
Replace water temperature sensor.
YES
Turn ignition switch ON.
Check if fuel pressure is OK.
NO
Replace pressure regulator.
YES
Replace control unit.

Courtesy of Subaru of America, Inc.

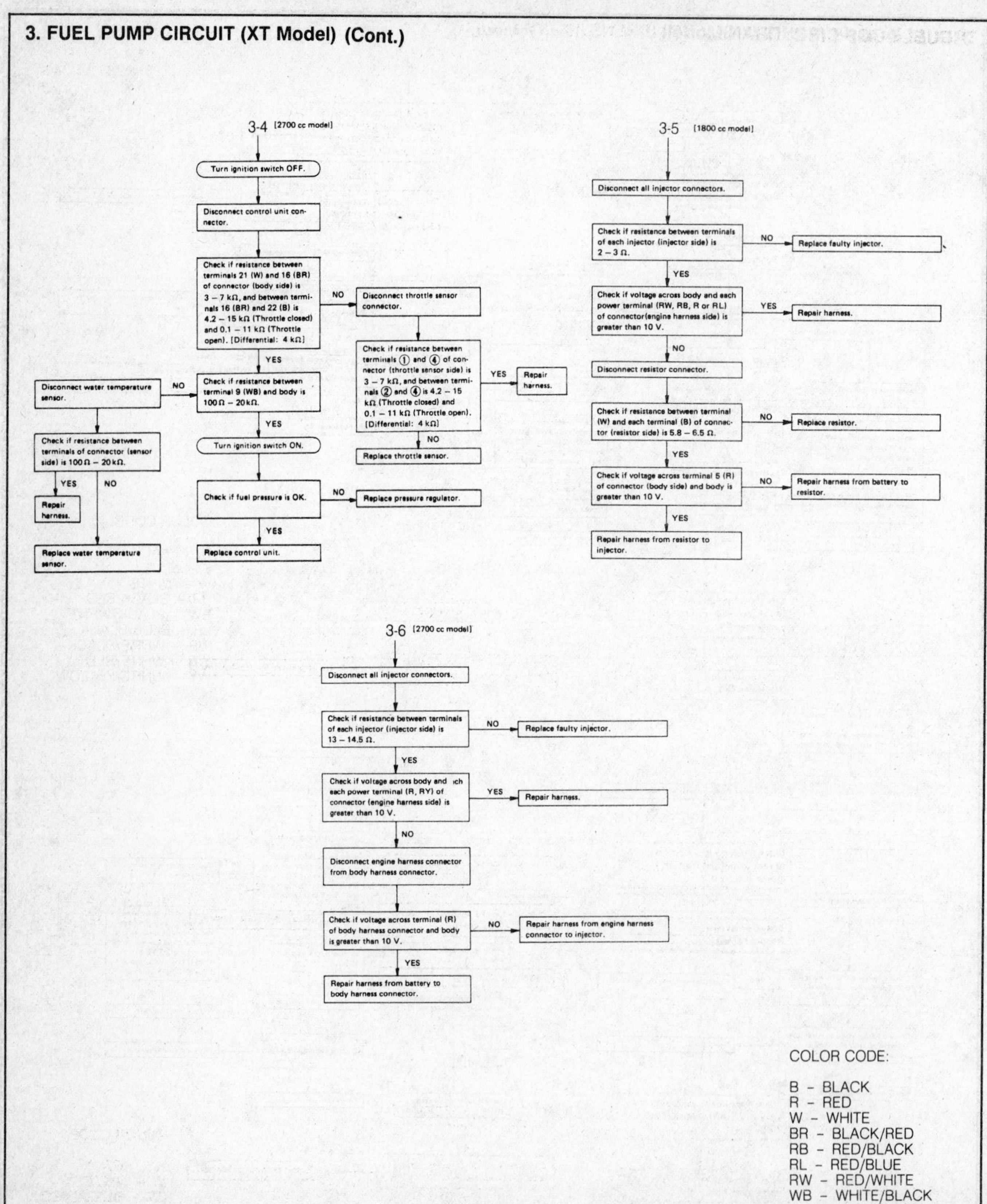
3. FUEL PUMP CIRCUIT (XT Model) (Cont.)
3-4 [2700 cc model]
Turn ignition switch OFF.
Disconnect control unit connector.
Check if resistance between terminals 21 (W) and 16 (BR) of connector (body side) is 3 – 7 kΩ, and between terminals 16 (BR) and 22 (B) is 4.2 – 15 kΩ (Throttle closed) and 0.1 – 11 kΩ (Throttle open). [Differential: 4 kΩ]
NO
Disconnect throttle sensor connector.
Check if resistance between terminals ① and ④ of connector (throttle sensor side) is 3 – 7 kΩ, and between terminals ② and ④ is 4.2 – 15 kΩ (Throttle closed) and 0.1 – 11 kΩ (Throttle open). [Differential: 4 kΩ]
YES
Repair harness.
NO
Replace throttle sensor.
YES
Check if resistance between terminal 9 (WB) and body is 100Ω – 20kΩ.
NO
Disconnect water temperature sensor.
Check if resistance between terminals of connector (sensor side) is 100Ω – 20kΩ.
YES
Repair harness.
NO
Replace water temperature sensor.
YES
Turn ignition switch ON.
Check if fuel pressure is OK.
NO
Replace pressure regulator.
YES
Replace control unit.
3-5 [1800 cc model]
Disconnect all injector connectors.
Check if resistance between terminals of each injector (injector side) is 2 – 3 Ω.
NO
Replace faulty injector.
YES
Check if voltage across body and each power terminal (RW, RB, R or RL) of connector(engine harness side) is greater than 10 V.
YES
Repair harness.
NO
Disconnect resistor connector.
Check if resistance between terminal (W) and each terminal (B) of connector (resistor side) is 5.8 – 6.5 Ω.
NO
Replace resistor.
YES
Check if voltage across terminal 5 (R) of connector (body side) and body is greater than 10 V.
NO
Repair harness from battery to resistor.
YES
Repair harness from resistor to injector.
3-6 [2700 cc model]
Disconnect all injector connectors.
Check if resistance between terminals of each injector (injector side) is 13 – 14.5 Ω.
NO
Replace faulty injector.
YES
Check if voltage across body and each power terminal (R, RY) of connector (engine harness side) is greater than 10 V.
YES
Repair harness.
NO
Disconnect engine harness connector from body harness connector.
Check if voltage across terminal (R) of body harness connector and body is greater than 10 V.
NO
Repair harness from engine harness connector to injector.
YES
Repair harness from battery to body harness connector.
COLOR CODE:
B - BLACK
R - RED
W - WHITE
BR - BLACK/RED
RB - RED/BLACK
RL - RED/BLUE
RW - RED/WHITE
WB - WHITE/BLACK

Courtesy of Subaru of America, Inc.

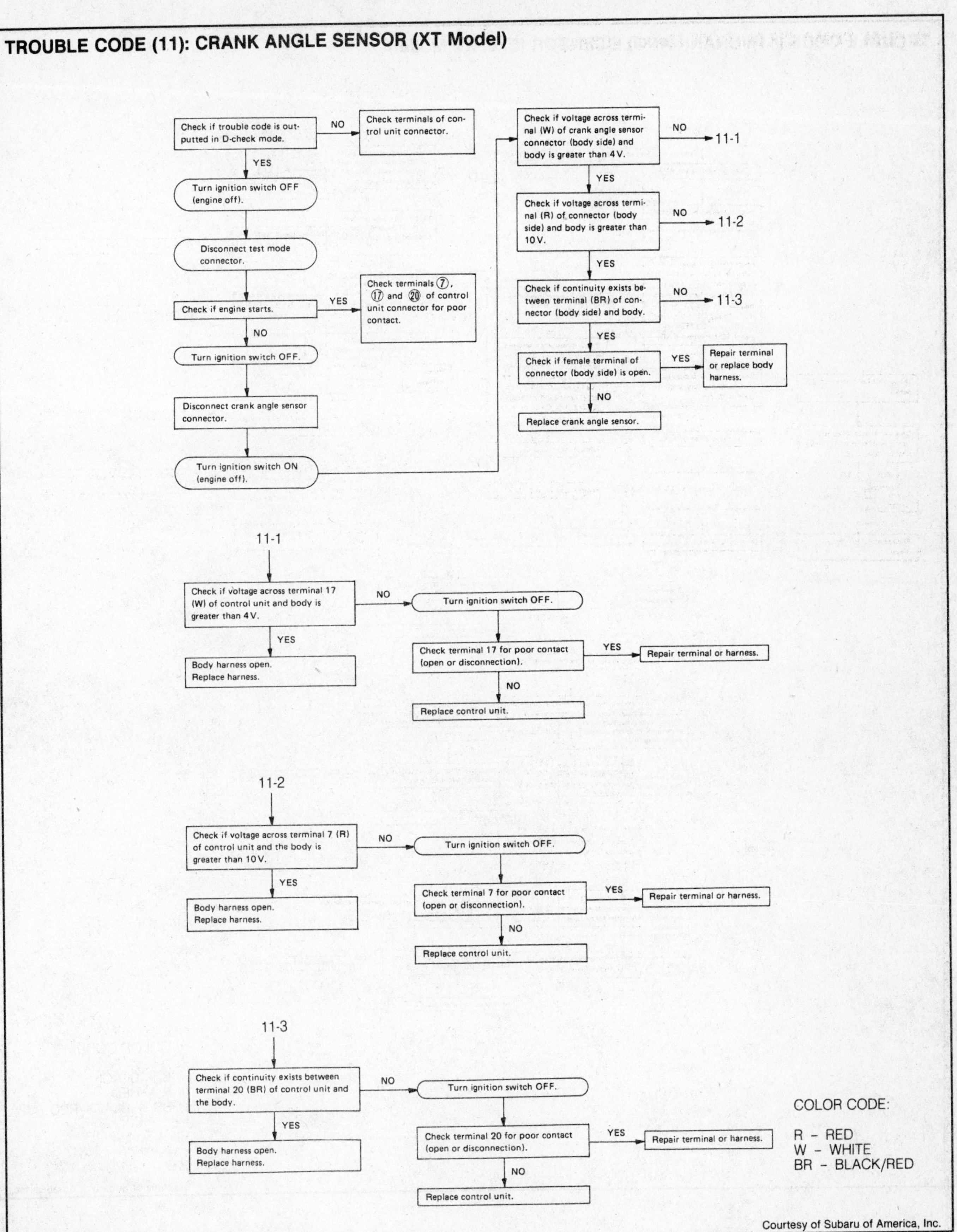
TROUBLE CODE (11): CRANK ANGLE SENSOR (XT Model)
Check if trouble code is outputted in D-check mode.
NO
Check terminals of control unit connector.
YES
Turn ignition switch OFF (engine off).
Disconnect test mode connector.
Check if engine starts.
YES
Check terminals ⑦, ⑰ and ⑳ of control unit connector for poor contact.
NO
Turn ignition switch OFF.
Disconnect crank angle sensor connector.
Turn ignition switch ON (engine off).
Check if voltage across terminal (W) of crank angle sensor connector (body side) and body is greater than 4 V.
NO
11-1
YES
Check if voltage across terminal (R) of connector (body side) and body is greater than 10 V.
NO
11-2
YES
Check if continuity exists between terminal (BR) of connector (body side) and body.
NO
11-3
YES
Check if female terminal of connector (body side) is open.
YES
Repair terminal or replace body harness.
NO
Replace crank angle sensor.
11-1
Check if voltage across terminal 17 (W) of control unit and body is greater than 4 V.
NO
Turn ignition switch OFF.
YES
Body harness open. Replace harness.
Check terminal 17 for poor contact (open or disconnection).
YES
Repair terminal or harness.
NO
Replace control unit.
11-2
Check if voltage across terminal 7 (R) of control unit and the body is greater than 10 V.
NO
Turn ignition switch OFF.
YES
Body harness open. Replace harness.
Check terminal 7 for poor contact (open or disconnection).
YES
Repair terminal or harness.
NO
Replace control unit.
11-3
Check if continuity exists between terminal 20 (BR) of control unit and the body.
NO
Turn ignition switch OFF.
YES
Body harness open. Replace harness.
Check terminal 20 for poor contact (open or disconnection).
YES
Repair terminal or harness.
NO
Replace control unit.
COLOR CODE:
R - RED
W - WHITE
BR - BLACK/RED
Courtesy of Subaru of America, Inc.

## TROUBLE CODE (11): CRANK ANGLE SENSOR (Exc. XT Model)

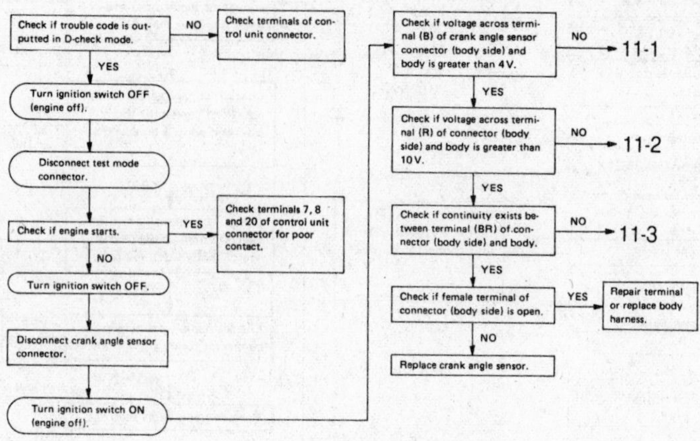
Check if trouble code is outputted in D-check mode.
NO
Check terminals of control unit connector.
YES
Turn ignition switch OFF (engine off).
Disconnect test mode connector.
Check if engine starts.
YES
Check terminals 7, 8 and 20 of control unit connector for poor contact.
NO
Turn ignition switch OFF.
Disconnect crank angle sensor connector.
Turn ignition switch ON (engine off).
Check if voltage across terminal (B) of crank angle sensor connector (body side) and body is greater than 4 V.
NO
11-1
YES
Check if voltage across terminal (R) of connector (body side) and body is greater than 10 V.
NO
11-2
YES
Check if continuity exists between terminal (BR) of connector (body side) and body.
NO
11-3
YES
Check if female terminal of connector (body side) is open.
YES
Repair terminal or replace body harness.
NO
Replace crank angle sensor.

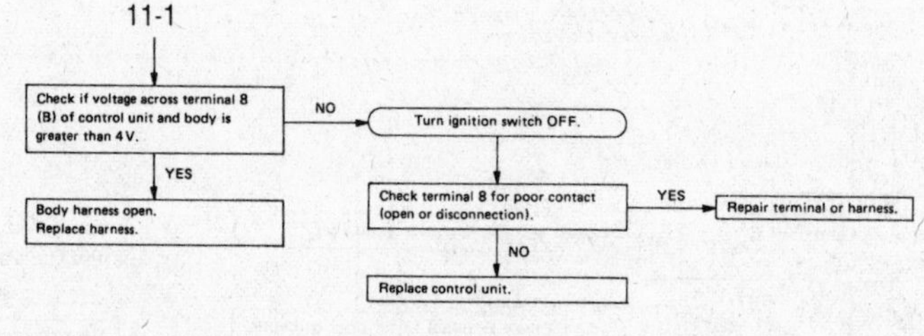
11-1
Check if voltage across terminal 8 (B) of control unit and body is greater than 4 V.
NO
Turn ignition switch OFF.
YES
Body harness open. Replace harness.
Check terminal 8 for poor contact (open or disconnection).
YES
Repair terminal or harness.
NO
Replace control unit.

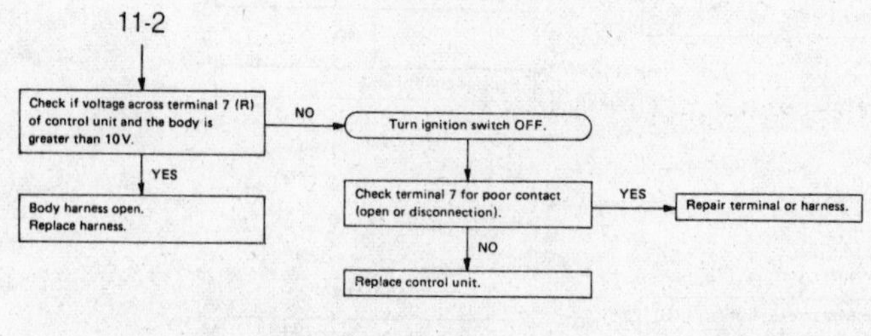
11-2
Check if voltage across terminal 7 (R) of control unit and the body is greater than 10 V.
NO
Turn ignition switch OFF.
YES
Body harness open. Replace harness.
Check terminal 7 for poor contact (open or disconnection).
YES
Repair terminal or harness.
NO
Replace control unit.

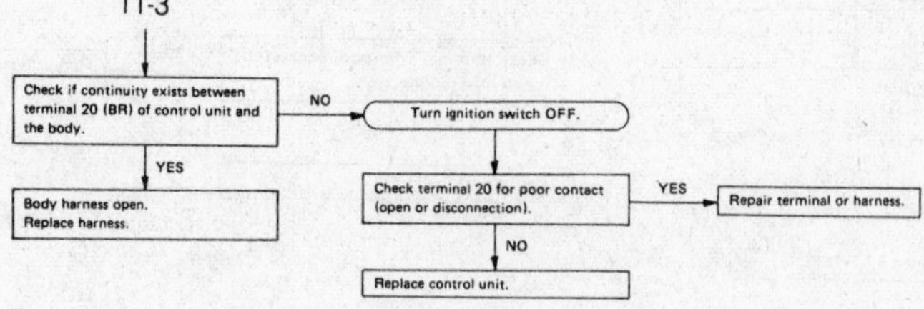
11-3
Check if continuity exists between terminal 20 (BR) of control unit and the body.
NO
Turn ignition switch OFF.
YES
Body harness open. Replace harness.
Check terminal 20 for poor contact (open or disconnection).
YES
Repair terminal or harness.
NO
Replace control unit.

COLOR CODE:

B – BLACK
R – RED
BR – BLACK/RED

Courtesy of Subaru of America, Inc.

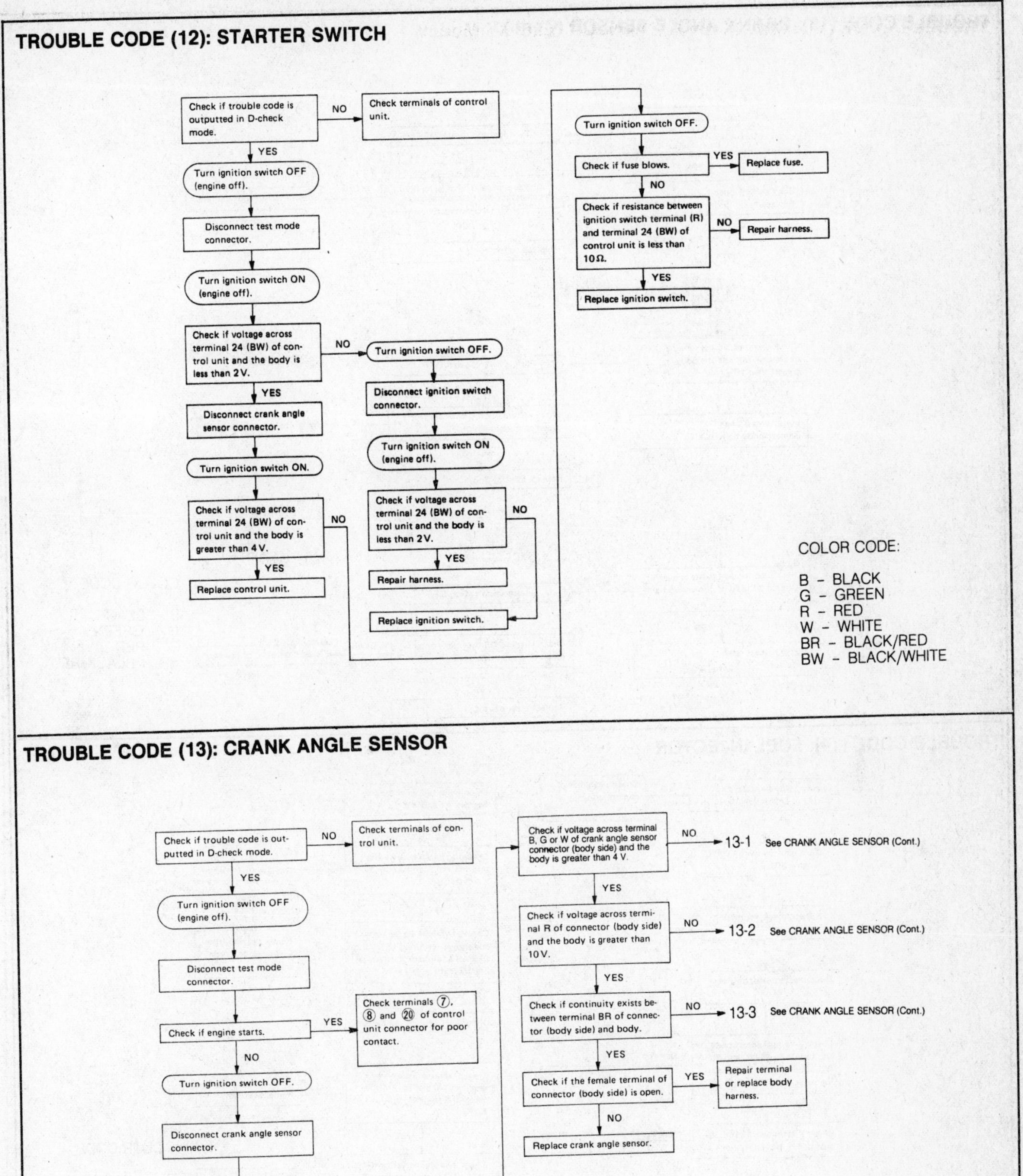
TROUBLE CODE (12): STARTER SWITCH
Check if trouble code is outputted in D-check mode.
NO
Check terminals of control unit.
YES
Turn ignition switch OFF (engine off).
Disconnect test mode connector.
Turn ignition switch ON (engine off).
Check if voltage across terminal 24 (BW) of control unit and the body is less than 2 V.
NO
Turn ignition switch OFF.
Disconnect ignition switch connector.
Turn ignition switch ON (engine off).
Check if voltage across terminal 24 (BW) of control unit and the body is less than 2 V.
NO
YES
Repair harness.
Replace ignition switch.
YES
Disconnect crank angle sensor connector.
Turn ignition switch ON.
Check if voltage across terminal 24 (BW) of control unit and the body is greater than 4 V.
NO
YES
Replace control unit.
Turn ignition switch OFF.
Check if fuse blows.
YES
Replace fuse.
NO
Check if resistance between ignition switch terminal (R) and terminal 24 (BW) of control unit is less than 10 Ω.
NO
Repair harness.
YES
Replace ignition switch.
COLOR CODE:
B – BLACK
G – GREEN
R – RED
W – WHITE
BR – BLACK/RED
BW – BLACK/WHITE
TROUBLE CODE (13): CRANK ANGLE SENSOR
Check if trouble code is outputted in D-check mode.
NO
Check terminals of control unit.
YES
Turn ignition switch OFF (engine off).
Disconnect test mode connector.
Check if engine starts.
YES
Check terminals ⑦, ⑧ and ⑳ of control unit connector for poor contact.
NO
Turn ignition switch OFF.
Disconnect crank angle sensor connector.
Turn ignition switch ON (engine off).
Check if voltage across terminal B, G or W of crank angle sensor connector (body side) and the body is greater than 4 V.
NO
13-1
See CRANK ANGLE SENSOR (Cont.)
YES
Check if voltage across terminal R of connector (body side) and the body is greater than 10 V.
NO
13-2
See CRANK ANGLE SENSOR (Cont.)
YES
Check if continuity exists between terminal BR of connector (body side) and body.
NO
13-3
See CRANK ANGLE SENSOR (Cont.)
YES
Check if the female terminal of connector (body side) is open.
YES
Repair terminal or replace body harness.
NO
Replace crank angle sensor.

Courtesy of Subaru of America, Inc.

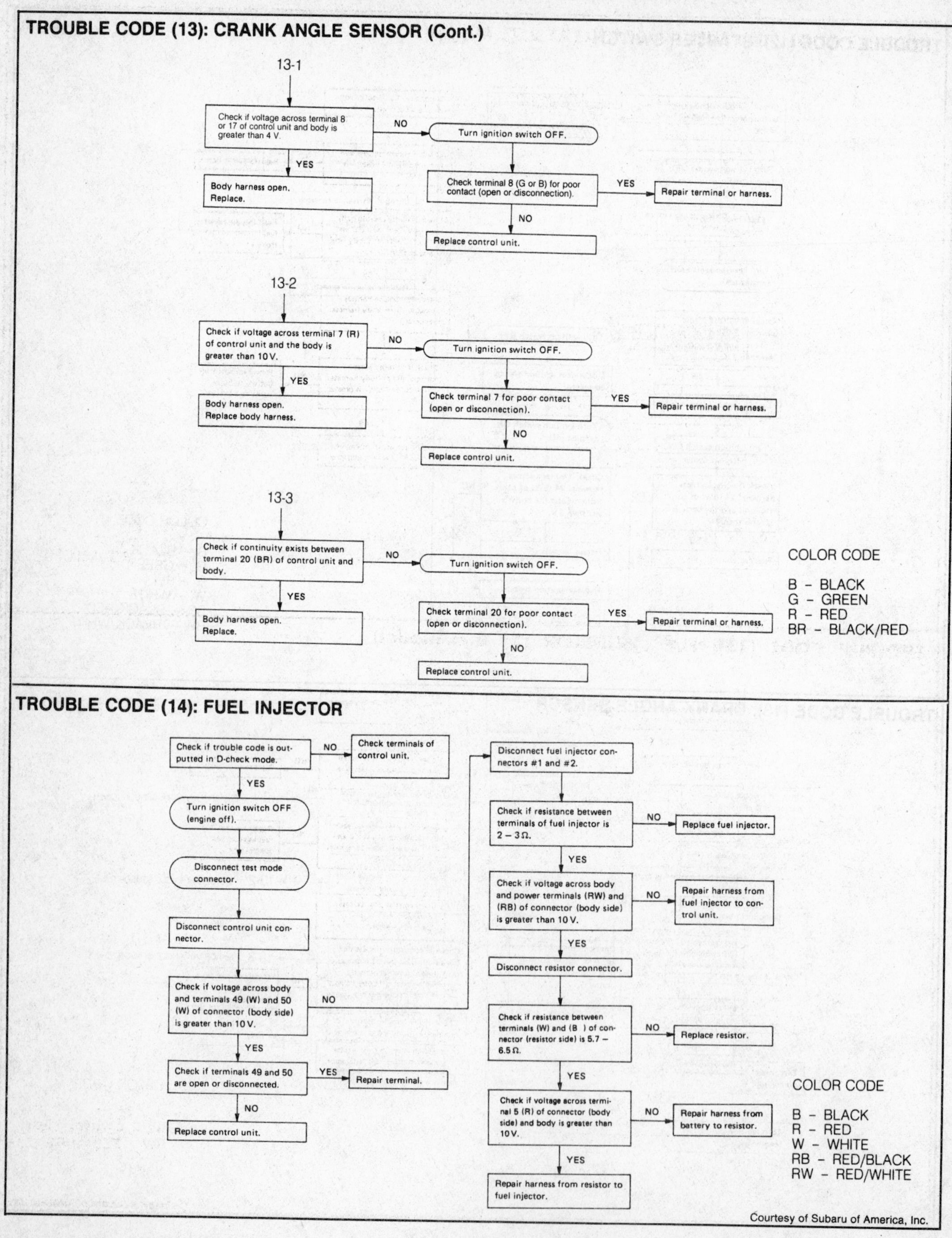
TROUBLE CODE (13): CRANK ANGLE SENSOR (Cont.)
13-1
Check if voltage across terminal 8 or 17 of control unit and body is greater than 4 V.
NO
Turn ignition switch OFF.
YES
Body harness open. Replace.
Check terminal 8 (G or B) for poor contact (open or disconnection).
YES
Repair terminal or harness.
NO
Replace control unit.
13-2
Check if voltage across terminal 7 (R) of control unit and the body is greater than 10 V.
NO
Turn ignition switch OFF.
YES
Body harness open. Replace body harness.
Check terminal 7 for poor contact (open or disconnection).
YES
Repair terminal or harness.
NO
Replace control unit.
13-3
Check if continuity exists between terminal 20 (BR) of control unit and body.
NO
Turn ignition switch OFF.
YES
Body harness open. Replace.
Check terminal 20 for poor contact (open or disconnection).
YES
Repair terminal or harness.
NO
Replace control unit.
COLOR CODE
B – BLACK
G – GREEN
R – RED
BR – BLACK/RED
TROUBLE CODE (14): FUEL INJECTOR
Check if trouble code is outputted in D-check mode.
NO
Check terminals of control unit.
YES
Turn ignition switch OFF (engine off).
Disconnect test mode connector.
Disconnect control unit connector.
Check if voltage across body and terminals 49 (W) and 50 (W) of connector (body side) is greater than 10 V.
NO
YES
Check if terminals 49 and 50 are open or disconnected.
YES
Repair terminal.
NO
Replace control unit.
Disconnect fuel injector connectors #1 and #2.
Check if resistance between terminals of fuel injector is 2 – 3 Ω.
NO
Replace fuel injector.
YES
Check if voltage across body and power terminals (RW) and (RB) of connector (body side) is greater than 10 V.
NO
Repair harness from fuel injector to control unit.
YES
Disconnect resistor connector.
Check if resistance between terminals (W) and (B ) of connector (resistor side) is 5.7 – 6.5 Ω.
NO
Replace resistor.
YES
Check if voltage across terminal 5 (R) of connector (body side) and body is greater than 10 V.
NO
Repair harness from battery to resistor.
YES
Repair harness from resistor to fuel injector.
COLOR CODE
B – BLACK
R – RED
W – WHITE
RB – RED/BLACK
RW – RED/WHITE
Courtesy of Subaru of America, Inc.

## TROUBLE CODE (14): FUEL INJECTOR (XT 2.7L Model)

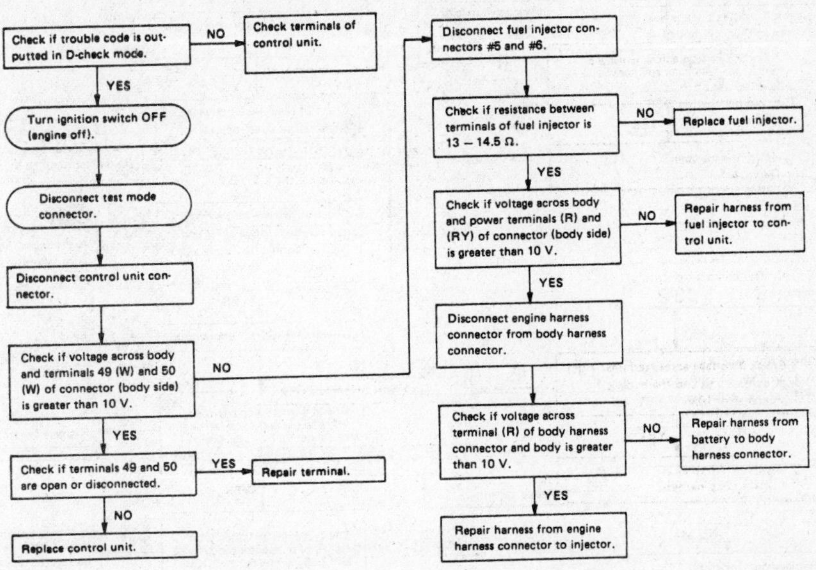
Check if trouble code is outputted in D-check mode.
NO
Check terminals of control unit.
YES
Turn ignition switch OFF (engine off).
Disconnect test mode connector.
Disconnect control unit connector.
Check if voltage across body and terminals 49 (W) and 50 (W) of connector (body side) is greater than 10 V.
NO
YES
Check if terminals 49 and 50 are open or disconnected.
YES
Repair terminal.
NO
Replace control unit.
Disconnect fuel injector connectors #5 and #6.
Check if resistance between terminals of fuel injector is 13 – 14.5 Ω.
NO
Replace fuel injector.
YES
Check if voltage across body and power terminals (R) and (RY) of connector (body side) is greater than 10 V.
NO
Repair harness from fuel injector to control unit.
YES
Disconnect engine harness connector from body harness connector.
Check if voltage across terminal (R) of body harness connector and body is greater than 10 V.
NO
Repair harness from battery to body harness connector.
YES
Repair harness from engine harness connector to injector.

COLOR CODE:

R - RED
W - WHITE
RY - RED/YELLOW

## TROUBLE CODE (15): FUEL INJECTOR (XT 2.7L Model)

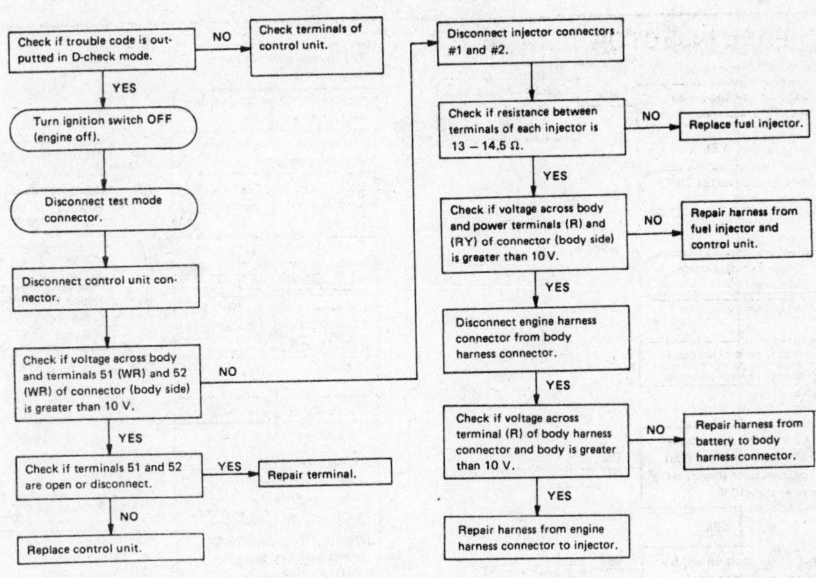
Check if trouble code is outputted in D-check mode.
NO
Check terminals of control unit.
YES
Turn ignition switch OFF (engine off).
Disconnect test mode connector.
Disconnect control unit connector.
Check if voltage across body and terminals 51 (WR) and 52 (WR) of connector (body side) is greater than 10 V.
NO
YES
Check if terminals 51 and 52 are open or disconnect.
YES
Repair terminal.
NO
Replace control unit.
Disconnect injector connectors #1 and #2.
Check if resistance between terminals of each injector is 13 – 14.5 Ω.
NO
Replace fuel injector.
YES
Check if voltage across body and power terminals (R) and (RY) of connector (body side) is greater than 10 V.
NO
Repair harness from fuel injector and control unit.
YES
Disconnect engine harness connector from body harness connector.
YES
Check if voltage across terminal (R) of body harness connector and body is greater than 10 V.
NO
Repair harness from battery to body harness connector.
YES
Repair harness from engine harness connector to injector.

COLOR CODE:

R - RED
RY - RED/YELLOW
RW - RED/WHITE

Courtesy of Subaru of America, Inc.

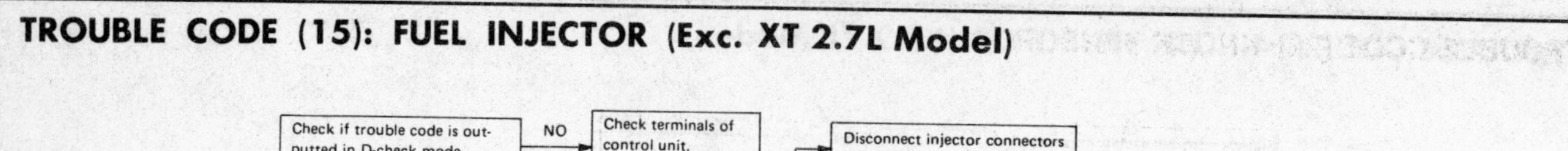

## TROUBLE CODE (15): FUEL INJECTOR (Exc. XT 2.7L Model)

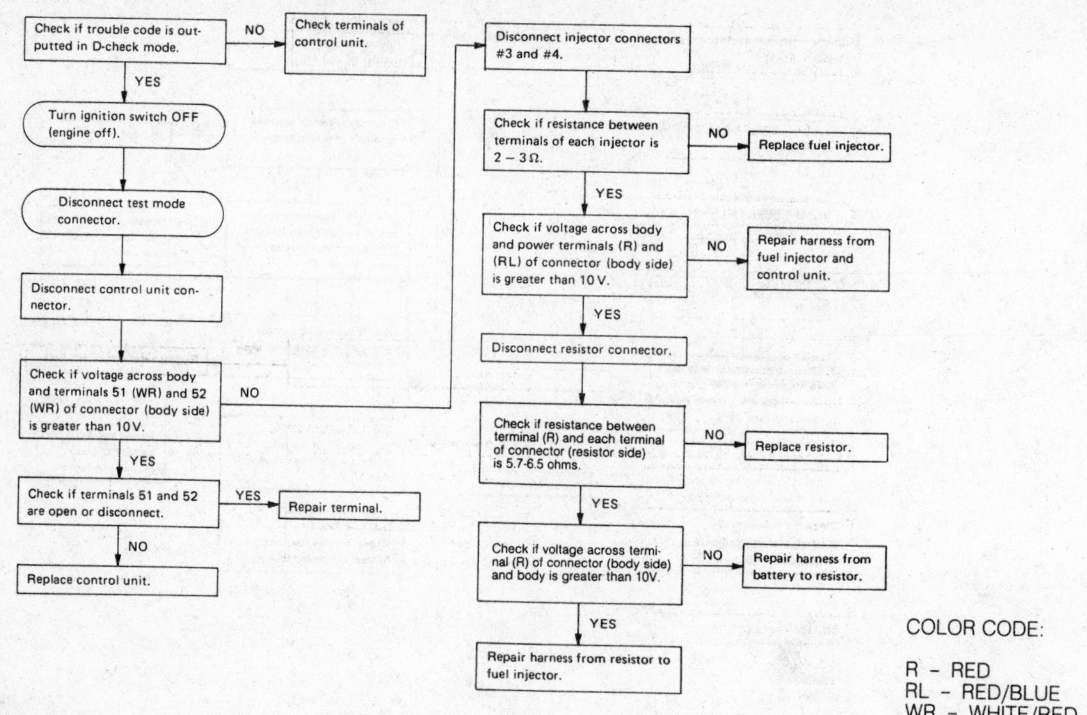
Check if trouble code is outputted in D-check mode.
NO
Check terminals of control unit.
YES
Turn ignition switch OFF (engine off).
Disconnect test mode connector.
Disconnect control unit connector.
Check if voltage across body and terminals 51 (WR) and 52 (WR) of connector (body side) is greater than 10V.
NO
YES
Check if terminals 51 and 52 are open or disconnect.
YES
Repair terminal.
NO
Replace control unit.
Disconnect injector connectors #3 and #4.
Check if resistance between terminals of each injector is 2 – 3Ω.
NO
Replace fuel injector.
YES
Check if voltage across body and power terminals (R) and (RL) of connector (body side) is greater than 10V.
NO
Repair harness from fuel injector and control unit.
YES
Disconnect resistor connector.
Check if resistance between terminal (R) and each terminal of connector (resistor side) is 5.7-6.5 ohms.
NO
Replace resistor.
YES
Check if voltage across terminal (R) of connector (body side) and body is greater than 10V.
NO
Repair harness from battery to resistor.
YES
Repair harness from resistor to fuel injector.
COLOR CODE:
R - RED
RL - RED/BLUE
WR - WHITE/RED

## TROUBLE CODE (21): COOLANT THERMOSENSOR

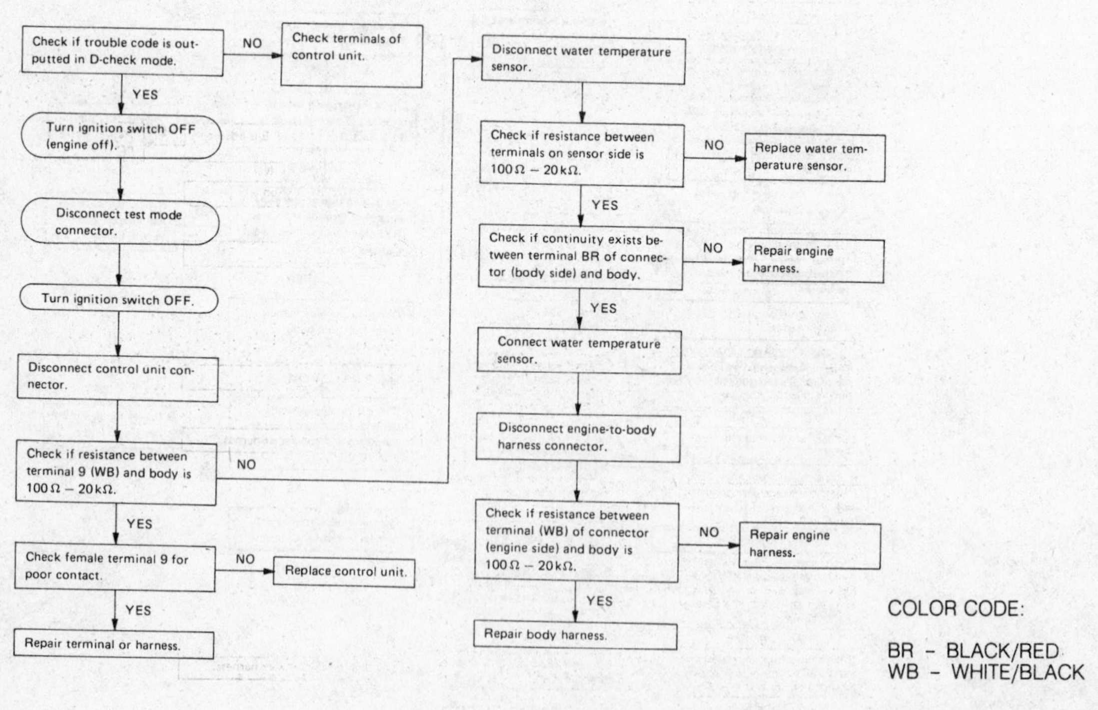
Check if trouble code is outputted in D-check mode.
NO
Check terminals of control unit.
YES
Turn ignition switch OFF (engine off).
Disconnect test mode connector.
Turn ignition switch OFF.
Disconnect control unit connector.
Check if resistance between terminal 9 (WB) and body is 100Ω – 20kΩ.
NO
YES
Check female terminal 9 for poor contact.
NO
Replace control unit.
YES
Repair terminal or harness.
Disconnect water temperature sensor.
Check if resistance between terminals on sensor side is 100Ω – 20kΩ.
NO
Replace water temperature sensor.
YES
Check if continuity exists between terminal BR of connector (body side) and body.
NO
Repair engine harness.
YES
Connect water temperature sensor.
Disconnect engine-to-body harness connector.
Check if resistance between terminal (WB) of connector (engine side) and body is 100Ω – 20kΩ.
NO
Repair engine harness.
YES
Repair body harness.
COLOR CODE:
BR - BLACK/RED
WB - WHITE/BLACK

Courtesy of Subaru of America, Inc.

# 1988 COMPUTERIZED ENGINE CONTROLS
## Subaru – MPFI (Cont.)

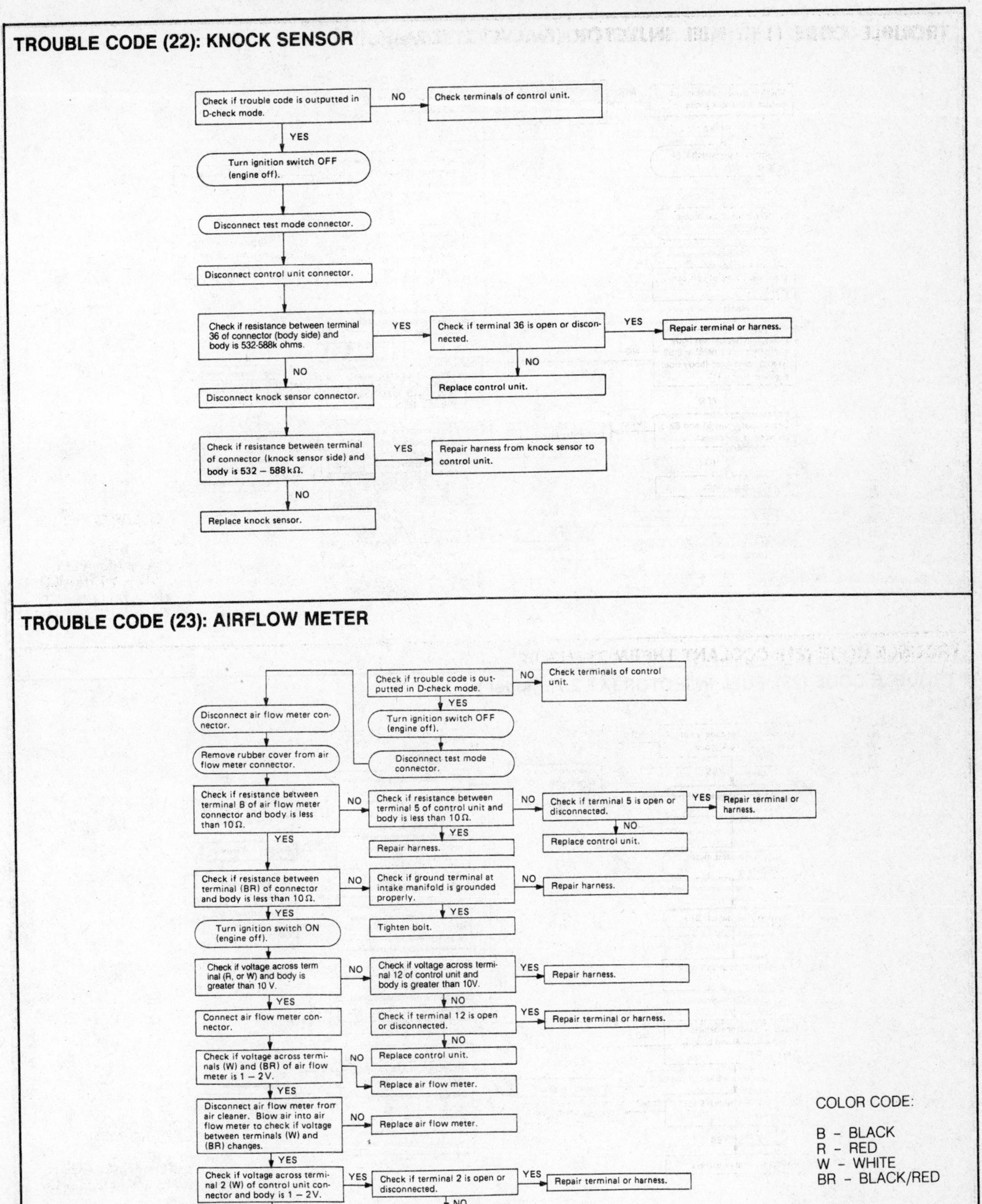
TROUBLE CODE (22): KNOCK SENSOR
Check if trouble code is outputted in D-check mode.
NO
Check terminals of control unit.
YES
Turn ignition switch OFF (engine off).
Disconnect test mode connector.
Disconnect control unit connector.
Check if resistance between terminal 36 of connector (body side) and body is 532-588k ohms.
YES
Check if terminal 36 is open or disconnected.
YES
Repair terminal or harness.
NO
Replace control unit.
NO
Disconnect knock sensor connector.
Check if resistance between terminal of connector (knock sensor side) and body is 532 – 588 kΩ.
YES
Repair harness from knock sensor to control unit.
NO
Replace knock sensor.
TROUBLE CODE (23): AIRFLOW METER
Check if trouble code is outputted in D-check mode.
NO
Check terminals of control unit.
YES
Turn ignition switch OFF (engine off).
Disconnect test mode connector.
Disconnect air flow meter connector.
Remove rubber cover from air flow meter connector.
Check if resistance between terminal B of air flow meter connector and body is less than 10 Ω.
NO
Check if resistance between terminal 5 of control unit and body is less than 10 Ω.
NO
Check if terminal 5 is open or disconnected.
YES
Repair terminal or harness.
NO
Replace control unit.
YES
Repair harness.
YES
Check if resistance between terminal (BR) of connector and body is less than 10 Ω.
NO
Check if ground terminal at intake manifold is grounded properly.
NO
Repair harness.
YES
Tighten bolt.
YES
Turn ignition switch ON (engine off).
Check if voltage across terminal (R, or W) and body is greater than 10 V.
NO
Check if voltage across terminal 12 of control unit and body is greater than 10V.
YES
Repair harness.
NO
Check if terminal 12 is open or disconnected.
YES
Repair terminal or harness.
NO
Replace control unit.
YES
Connect air flow meter connector.
Check if voltage across terminals (W) and (BR) of air flow meter is 1 – 2 V.
NO
Replace air flow meter.
YES
Disconnect air flow meter from air cleaner. Blow air into air flow meter to check if voltage between terminals (W) and (BR) changes.
NO
Replace air flow meter.
YES
Check if voltage across terminal 2 (W) of control unit connector and body is 1 – 2 V.
YES
Check if terminal 2 is open or disconnected.
YES
Repair terminal or harness.
NO
Replace control unit.
NO
Repair harness.
COLOR CODE:
B – BLACK
R – RED
W – WHITE
BR – BLACK/RED
Courtesy of Subaru of America, Inc.

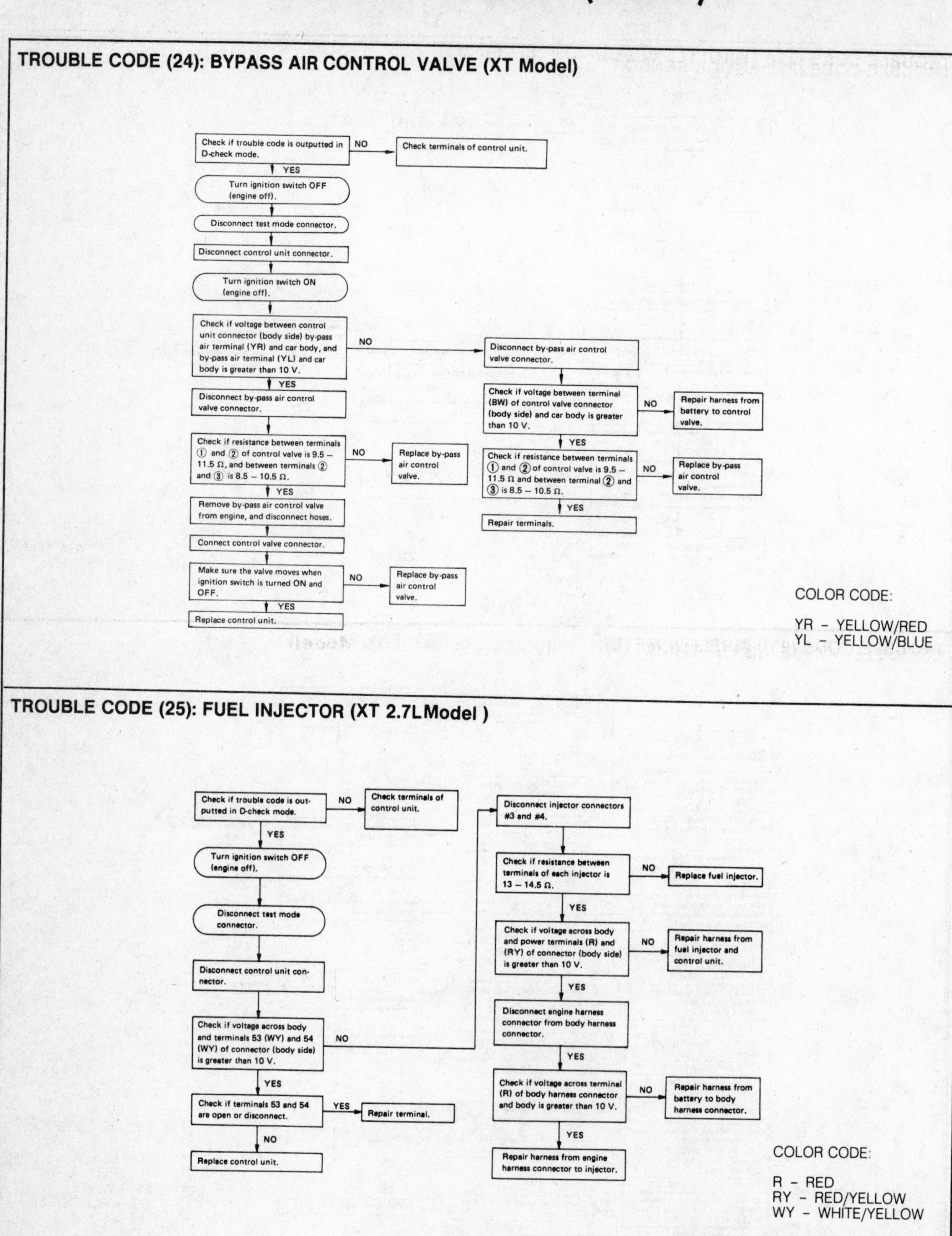
TROUBLE CODE (24): BYPASS AIR CONTROL VALVE (XT Model)
Check if trouble code is outputted in D-check mode.
NO
Check terminals of control unit.
YES
Turn ignition switch OFF (engine off).
Disconnect test mode connector.
Disconnect control unit connector.
Turn ignition switch ON (engine off).
Check if voltage between control unit connector (body side) by-pass air terminal (YR) and car body, and by-pass air terminal (YL) and car body is greater than 10 V.
NO
Disconnect by-pass air control valve connector.
Check if voltage between terminal (BW) of control valve connector (body side) and car body is greater than 10 V.
NO
Repair harness from battery to control valve.
YES
Check if resistance between terminals ① and ② of control valve is 9.5 – 11.5 Ω and between terminal ② and ③ is 8.5 – 10.5 Ω.
NO
Replace by-pass air control valve.
YES
Repair terminals.
YES
Disconnect by-pass air control valve connector.
Check if resistance between terminals ① and ② of control valve is 9.5 – 11.5 Ω, and between terminals ② and ③ is 8.5 – 10.5 Ω.
NO
Replace by-pass air control valve.
YES
Remove by-pass air control valve from engine, and disconnect hoses.
Connect control valve connector.
Make sure the valve moves when ignition switch is turned ON and OFF.
NO
Replace by-pass air control valve.
YES
Replace control unit.
COLOR CODE:
YR – YELLOW/RED
YL – YELLOW/BLUE
TROUBLE CODE (25): FUEL INJECTOR (XT 2.7L Model)
Check if trouble code is outputted in D-check mode.
NO
Check terminals of control unit.
YES
Turn ignition switch OFF (engine off).
Disconnect test mode connector.
Disconnect control unit connector.
Check if voltage across body and terminals 53 (WY) and 54 (WY) of connector (body side) is greater than 10 V.
NO
Disconnect injector connectors #3 and #4.
Check if resistance between terminals of each injector is 13 – 14.5 Ω.
NO
Replace fuel injector.
YES
Check if voltage across body and power terminals (R) and (RY) of connector (body side) is greater than 10 V.
NO
Repair harness from fuel injector and control unit.
YES
Disconnect engine harness connector from body harness connector.
YES
Check if voltage across terminal (R) of body harness connector and body is greater than 10 V.
NO
Repair harness from battery to body harness connector.
YES
Repair harness from engine harness connector to injector.
YES
Check if terminals 53 and 54 are open or disconnect.
YES
Repair terminal.
NO
Replace control unit.
COLOR CODE:
R – RED
RY – RED/YELLOW
WY – WHITE/YELLOW

Courtesy of Subaru of America, Inc.

## TROUBLE CODE (31): THROTTLE SENSOR (XT 2.7L Model)

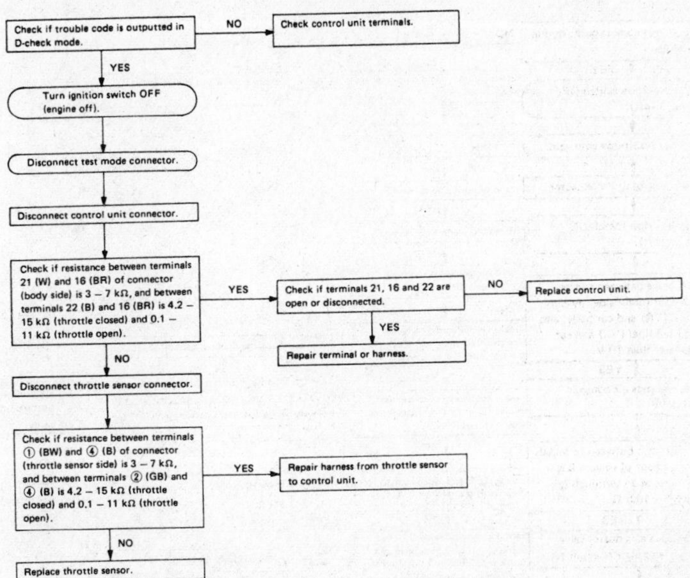
Check if trouble code is outputted in D-check mode.
NO
Check control unit terminals.
YES
Turn ignition switch OFF (engine off).
Disconnect test mode connector.
Disconnect control unit connector.
Check if resistance between terminals 21 (W) and 16 (BR) of connector (body side) is 3 – 7 kΩ, and between terminals 22 (B) and 16 (BR) is 4.2 – 15 kΩ (throttle closed) and 0.1 – 11 kΩ (throttle open).
YES
Check if terminals 21, 16 and 22 are open or disconnected.
NO
Replace control unit.
YES
Repair terminal or harness.
NO
Disconnect throttle sensor connector.
Check if resistance between terminals ① (BW) and ④ (B) of connector (throttle sensor side) is 3 – 7 kΩ, and between terminals ② (GB) and ④ (B) is 4.2 – 15 kΩ (throttle closed) and 0.1 – 11 kΩ (throttle open).
YES
Repair harness from throttle sensor to control unit.
NO
Replace throttle sensor.

COLOR CODE:

B - BLACK
BR - BLACK/RED
BW - BLACK/WHITE
GB - GREEN/BLACK

## TROUBLE CODE (31): THROTTLE SENSOR (Exc. XT 2.7L Model)

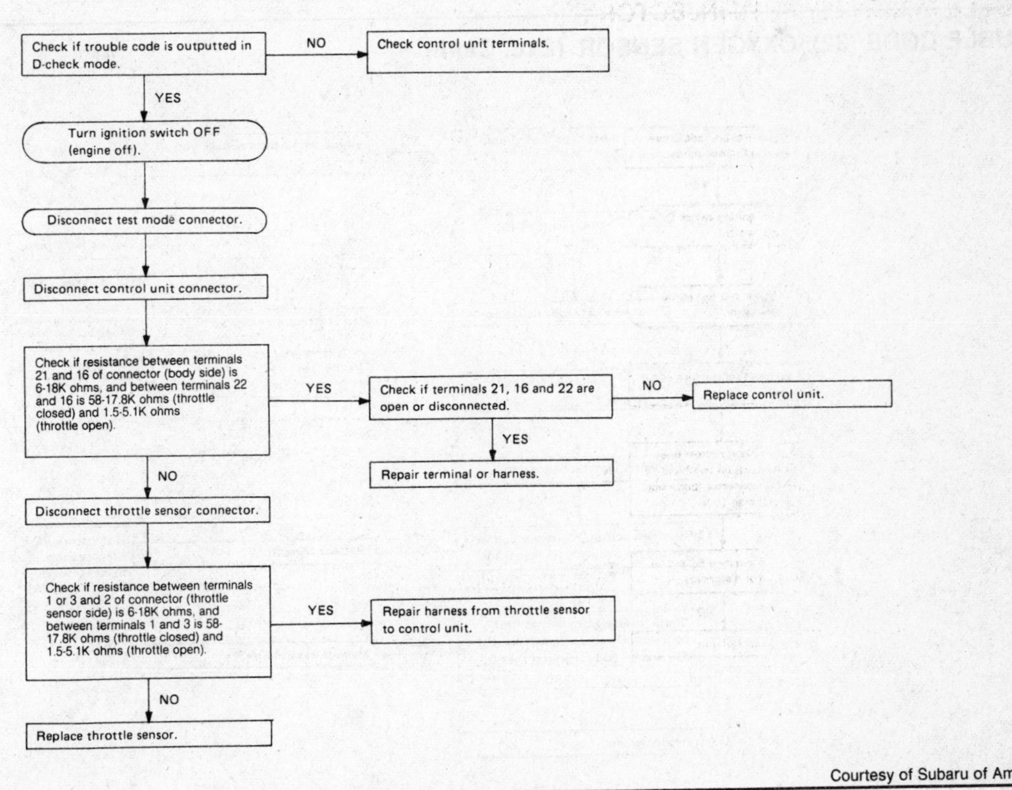
Check if trouble code is outputted in D-check mode.
NO
Check control unit terminals.
YES
Turn ignition switch OFF (engine off).
Disconnect test mode connector.
Disconnect control unit connector.
Check if resistance between terminals 21 and 16 of connector (body side) is 6-18K ohms, and between terminals 22 and 16 is 58-17.8K ohms (throttle closed) and 1.5-5.1K ohms (throttle open).
YES
Check if terminals 21, 16 and 22 are open or disconnected.
NO
Replace control unit.
YES
Repair terminal or harness.
NO
Disconnect throttle sensor connector.
Check if resistance between terminals 1 or 3 and 2 of connector (throttle sensor side) is 6-18K ohms, and between terminals 1 and 3 is 58-17.8K ohms (throttle closed) and 1.5-5.1K ohms (throttle open).
YES
Repair harness from throttle sensor to control unit.
NO
Replace throttle sensor.

Courtesy of Subaru of America, Inc.

## TROUBLE CODE (32): OXYGEN SENSOR (Calif.)

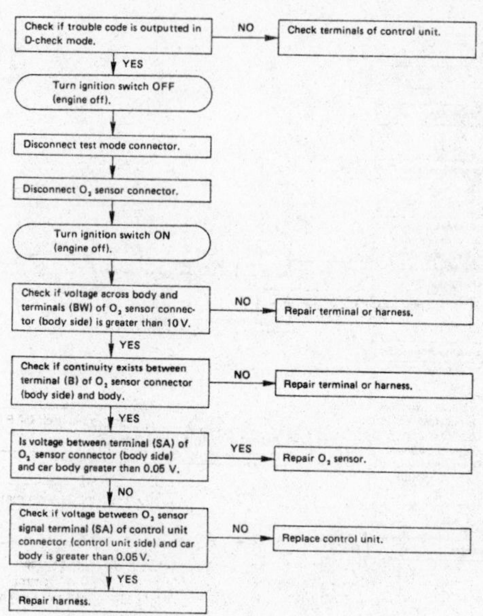
Check if trouble code is outputted in D-check mode.
NO
Check terminals of control unit.
YES
Turn ignition switch OFF (engine off).
Disconnect test mode connector.
Disconnect $O_2$ sensor connector.
Turn ignition switch ON (engine off).
Check if voltage across body and terminals (BW) of $O_2$ sensor connector (body side) is greater than 10 V.
NO
Repair terminal or harness.
YES
Check if continuity exists between terminal (B) of $O_2$ sensor connector (body side) and body.
NO
Repair terminal or harness.
YES
Is voltage between terminal (SA) of $O_2$ sensor connector (body side) and car body greater than 0.05 V.
YES
Repair $O_2$ sensor.
NO
Check if voltage between $O_2$ sensor signal terminal (SA) of control unit connector (control unit side) and car body is greater than 0.05 V.
NO
Replace control unit.
YES
Repair harness.

COLOR CODE:

B - BLACK
BW - BLACK/WHITE

## TROUBLE CODE (32): OXYGEN SENSOR (Exc. Calif.)

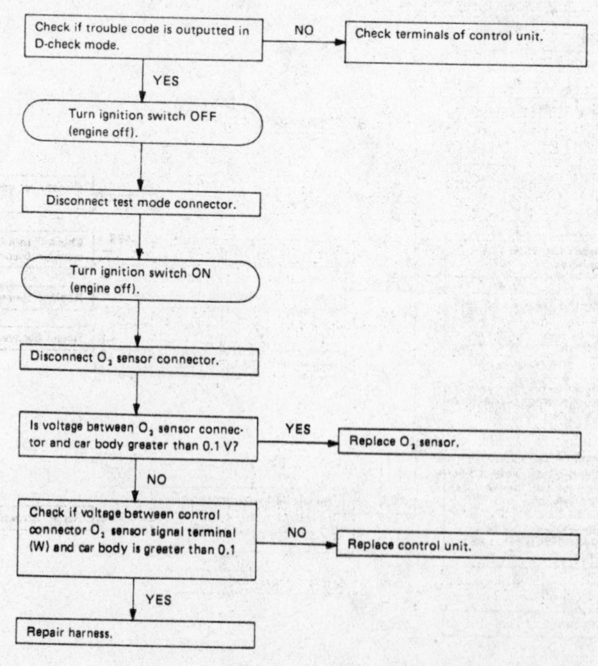
Check if trouble code is outputted in D-check mode.
NO
Check terminals of control unit.
YES
Turn ignition switch OFF (engine off).
Disconnect test mode connector.
Turn ignition switch ON (engine off).
Disconnect $O_2$ sensor connector.
Is voltage between $O_2$ sensor connector and car body greater than 0.1 V?
YES
Replace $O_2$ sensor.
NO
Check if voltage between control connector $O_2$ sensor signal terminal (W) and car body is greater than 0.1
NO
Replace control unit.
YES
Repair harness.

Courtesy of Subaru of America, Inc.

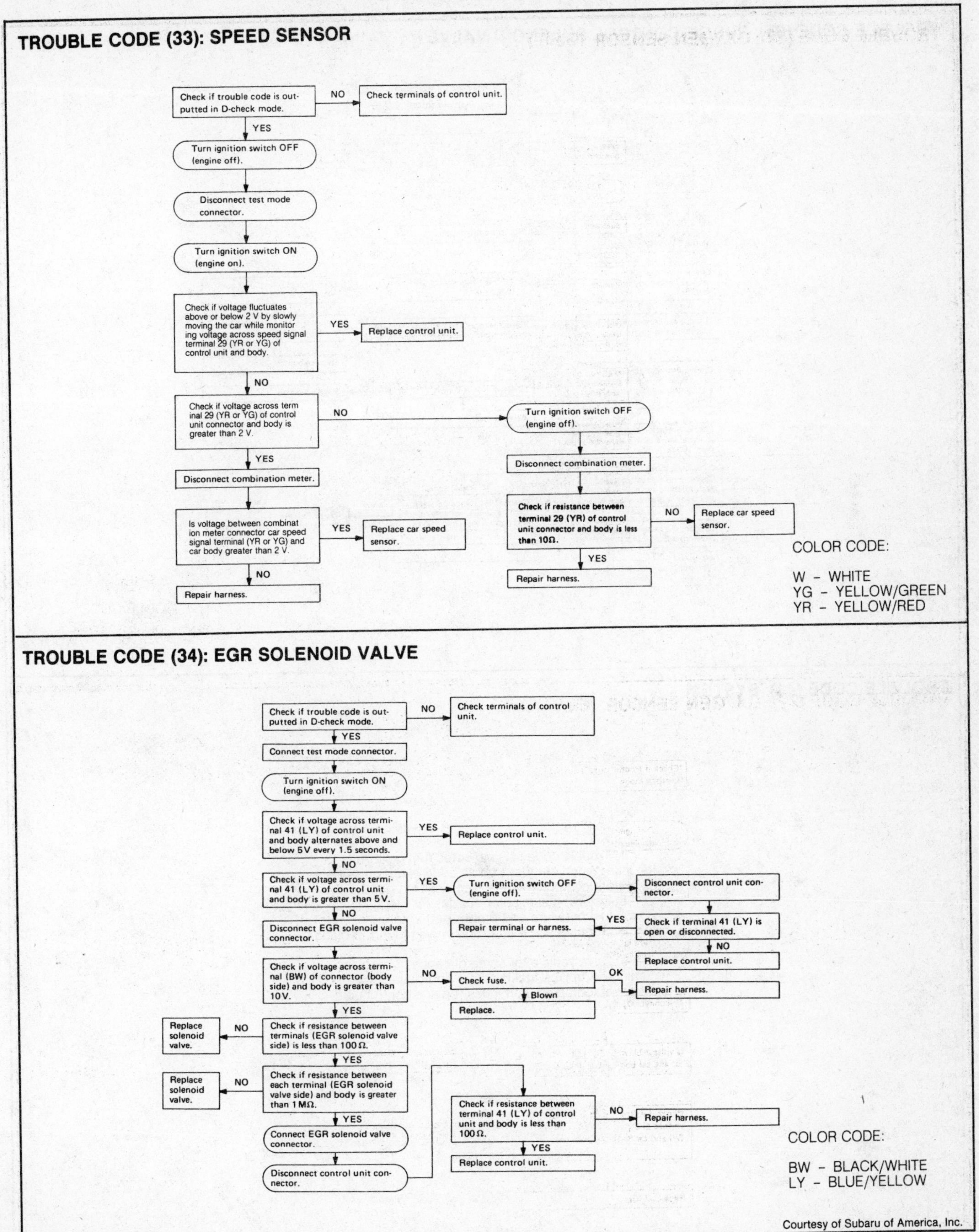
TROUBLE CODE (33): SPEED SENSOR
Check if trouble code is outputted in D-check mode.
NO
Check terminals of control unit.
YES
Turn ignition switch OFF (engine off).
Disconnect test mode connector.
Turn ignition switch ON (engine on).
Check if voltage fluctuates above or below 2 V by slowly moving the car while monitoring voltage across speed signal terminal 29 (YR or YG) of control unit and body.
YES
Replace control unit.
NO
Check if voltage across terminal 29 (YR or YG) of control unit connector and body is greater than 2 V.
NO
Turn ignition switch OFF (engine off).
Disconnect combination meter.
Check if resistance between terminal 29 (YR) of control unit connector and body is less than 10Ω.
NO
Replace car speed sensor.
YES
Repair harness.
YES
Disconnect combination meter.
Is voltage between combination meter connector car speed signal terminal (YR or YG) and car body greater than 2 V.
YES
Replace car speed sensor.
NO
Repair harness.
COLOR CODE:
W - WHITE
YG - YELLOW/GREEN
YR - YELLOW/RED
TROUBLE CODE (34): EGR SOLENOID VALVE
Check if trouble code is outputted in D-check mode.
NO
Check terminals of control unit.
YES
Connect test mode connector.
Turn ignition switch ON (engine off).
Check if voltage across terminal 41 (LY) of control unit and body alternates above and below 5V every 1.5 seconds.
YES
Replace control unit.
NO
Check if voltage across terminal 41 (LY) of control unit and body is greater than 5V.
YES
Turn ignition switch OFF (engine off).
Disconnect control unit connector.
Check if terminal 41 (LY) is open or disconnected.
YES
Repair terminal or harness.
NO
Replace control unit.
NO
Disconnect EGR solenoid valve connector.
Check if voltage across terminal (BW) of connector (body side) and body is greater than 10V.
NO
Check fuse.
OK
Repair harness.
Blown
Replace.
YES
Check if resistance between terminals (EGR solenoid valve side) is less than 100 Ω.
NO
Replace solenoid valve.
YES
Check if resistance between each terminal (EGR solenoid valve side) and body is greater than 1 MΩ.
NO
Replace solenoid valve.
YES
Connect EGR solenoid valve connector.
Disconnect control unit connector.
Check if resistance between terminal 41 (LY) of control unit and body is less than 100 Ω.
NO
Repair harness.
YES
Replace control unit.
COLOR CODE:
BW - BLACK/WHITE
LY - BLUE/YELLOW
Courtesy of Subaru of America, Inc.

## TROUBLE CODE (35): PURGE CONTROL SOLENOID VALVE

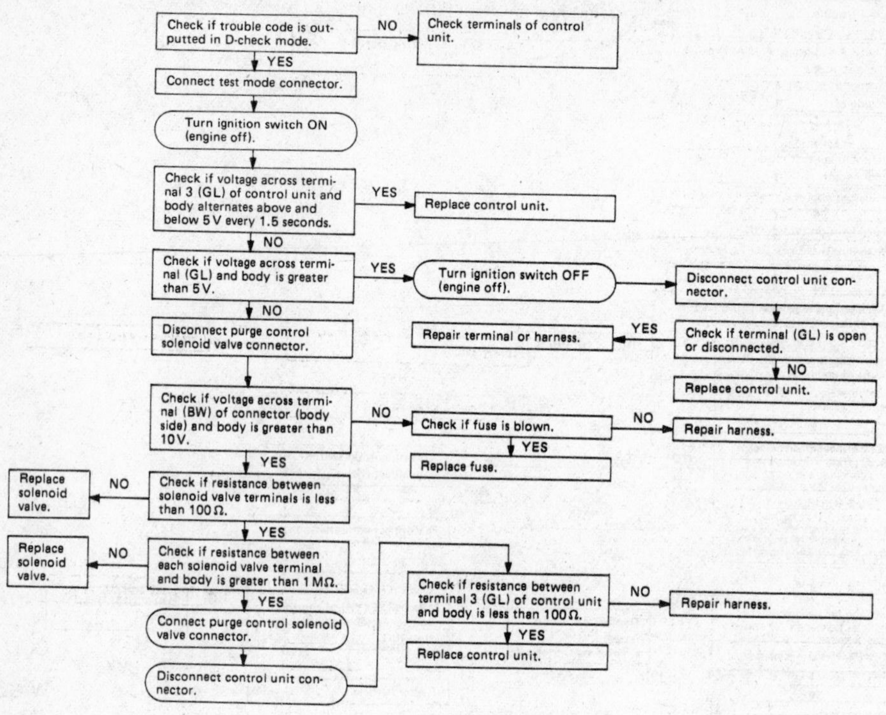
Check if trouble code is outputted in D-check mode.
NO
Check terminals of control unit.
YES
Connect test mode connector.
Turn ignition switch ON (engine off).
Check if voltage across terminal 3 (GL) of control unit and body alternates above and below 5 V every 1.5 seconds.
YES
Replace control unit.
NO
Check if voltage across terminal (GL) and body is greater than 5 V.
YES
Turn ignition switch OFF (engine off).
Disconnect control unit connector.
Check if terminal (GL) is open or disconnected.
YES
Repair terminal or harness.
NO
Replace control unit.
NO
Disconnect purge control solenoid valve connector.
Check if voltage across terminal (BW) of connector (body side) and body is greater than 10V.
NO
Check if fuse is blown.
NO
Repair harness.
YES
Replace fuse.
YES
Check if resistance between solenoid valve terminals is less than 100 Ω.
NO
Replace solenoid valve.
YES
Check if resistance between each solenoid valve terminal and body is greater than 1 MΩ.
NO
Replace solenoid valve.
YES
Connect purge control solenoid valve connector.
Disconnect control unit connector.
Check if resistance between terminal 3 (GL) of control unit and body is less than 100 Ω.
NO
Repair harness.
YES
Replace control unit.

COLOR CODE:

BW – BLACK/WHITE
GL – GREEN/BLUE

## TROUBLE CODE (41): SYSTEM

1) Trouble code (41) indicates fuel mixture is too lean. When another trouble code is not outputted, all system components are electrically in good order.

2) Inspect fuel injector nozzles for clogging. Check fuel pressure and proper performance of water temperature sensor. If no problem was found, replace air flow meter.

3) Drive vehicle for some distance. If problem continues, replace fuel injectors and drive some distance. If problem continues replace control unit.

Courtesy of Subaru of America, Inc.

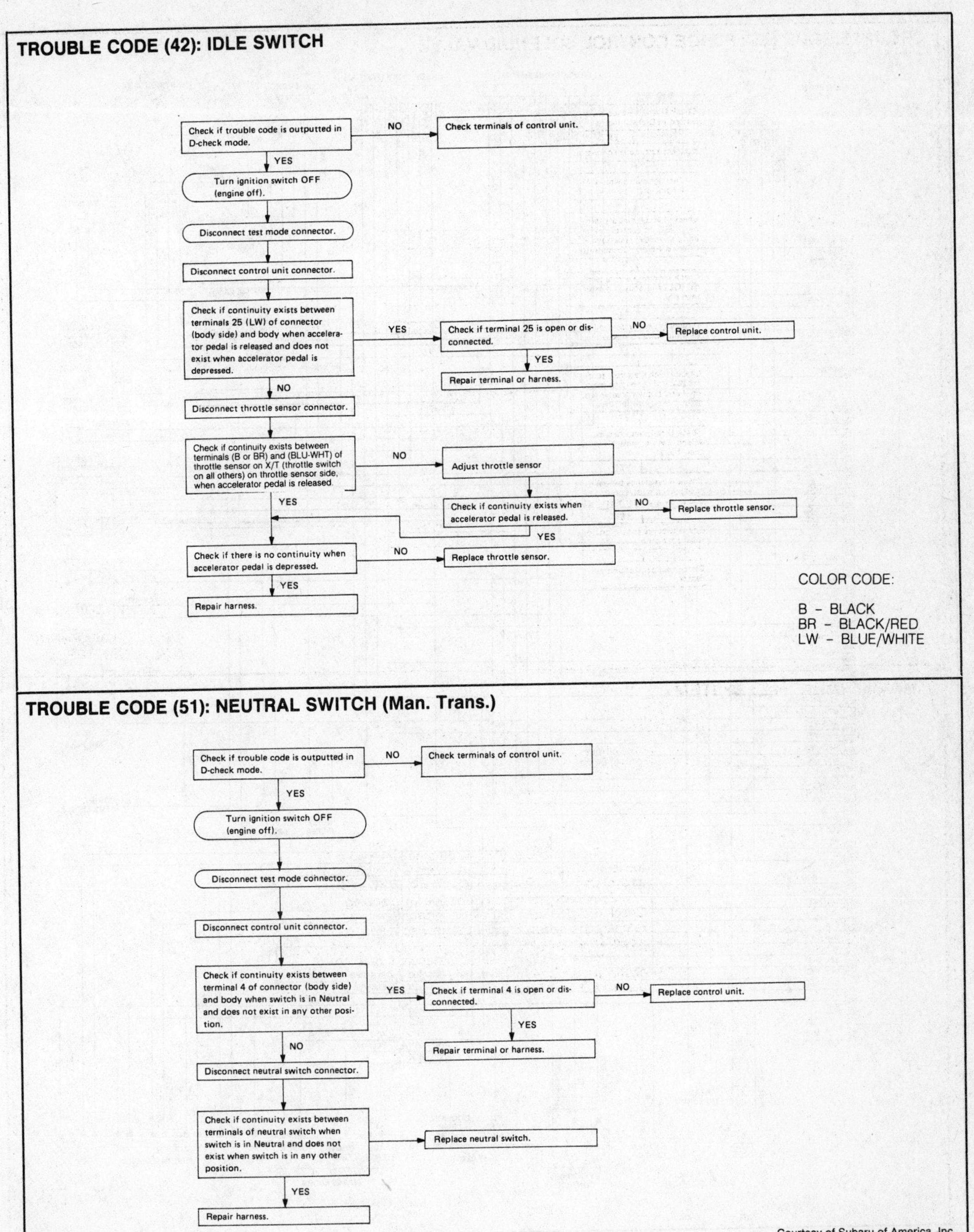
TROUBLE CODE (42): IDLE SWITCH
Check if trouble code is outputted in D-check mode.
NO
Check terminals of control unit.
YES
Turn ignition switch OFF (engine off).
Disconnect test mode connector.
Disconnect control unit connector.
Check if continuity exists between terminals 25 (LW) of connector (body side) and body when accelerator pedal is released and does not exist when accelerator pedal is depressed.
YES
Check if terminal 25 is open or disconnected.
NO
Replace control unit.
YES
Repair terminal or harness.
NO
Disconnect throttle sensor connector.
Check if continuity exists between terminals (B or BR) and (BLU-WHT) of throttle sensor on X/T (throttle switch on all others) on throttle sensor side, when accelerator pedal is released.
NO
Adjust throttle sensor
Check if continuity exists when accelerator pedal is released.
NO
Replace throttle sensor.
YES
YES
Check if there is no continuity when accelerator pedal is depressed.
NO
Replace throttle sensor.
YES
Repair harness.
COLOR CODE:
B - BLACK
BR - BLACK/RED
LW - BLUE/WHITE
TROUBLE CODE (51): NEUTRAL SWITCH (Man. Trans.)
Check if trouble code is outputted in D-check mode.
NO
Check terminals of control unit.
YES
Turn ignition switch OFF (engine off).
Disconnect test mode connector.
Disconnect control unit connector.
Check if continuity exists between terminal 4 of connector (body side) and body when switch is in Neutral and does not exist in any other position.
YES
Check if terminal 4 is open or disconnected.
NO
Replace control unit.
YES
Repair terminal or harness.
NO
Disconnect neutral switch connector.
Check if continuity exists between terminals of neutral switch when switch is in Neutral and does not exist when switch is in any other position.
Replace neutral switch.
YES
Repair harness.
Courtesy of Subaru of America, Inc.

# 1988 COMPUTERIZED ENGINE CONTROLS
## Subaru – MPFI (Cont.)

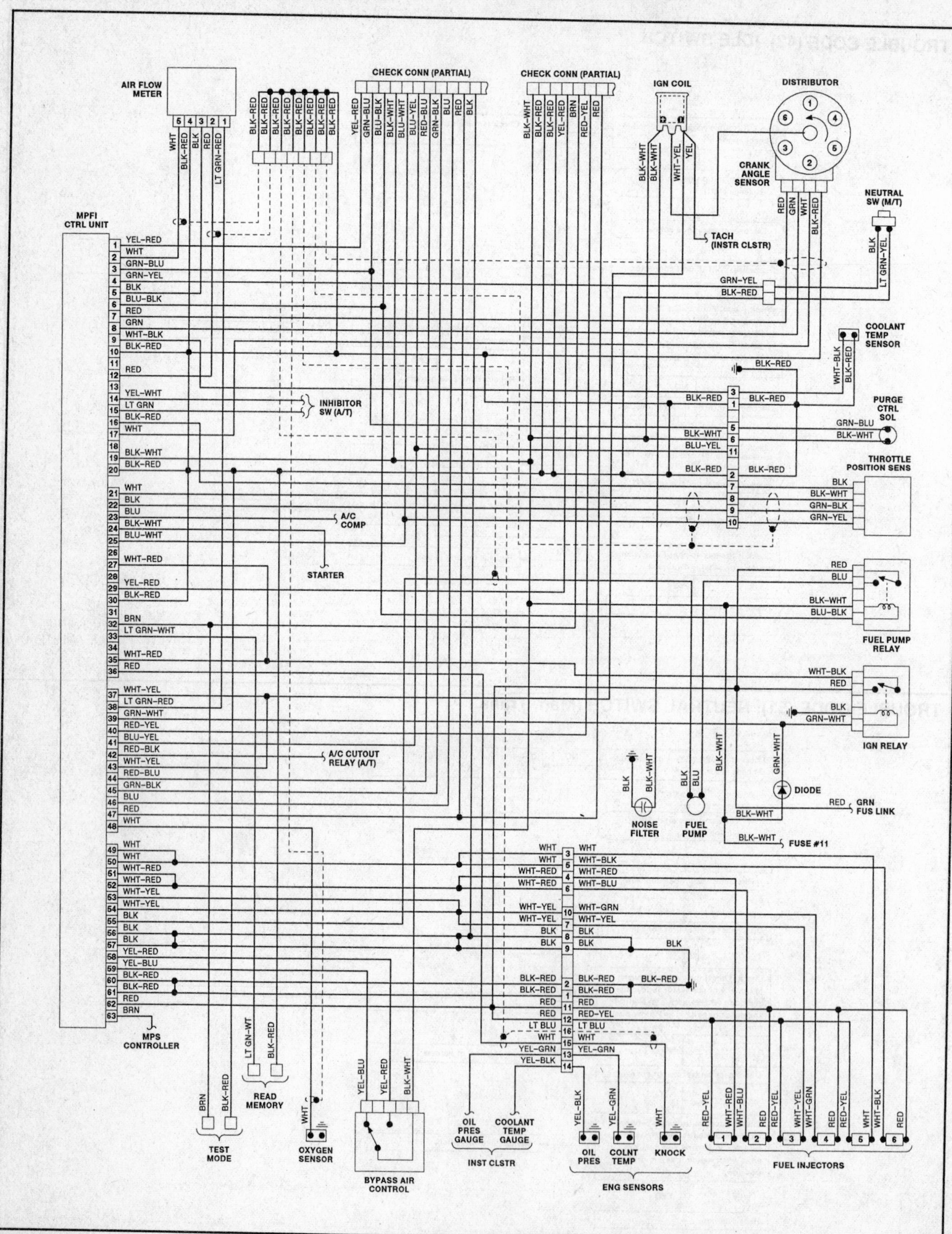
AIR FLOW METER
CHECK CONN (PARTIAL)
CHECK CONN (PARTIAL)
IGN COIL
DISTRIBUTOR
CRANK ANGLE SENSOR
NEUTRAL SW (M/T)
MPFI CTRL UNIT
TACH (INSTR CLSTR)
COOLANT TEMP SENSOR
INHIBITOR SW (A/T)
PURGE CTRL SOL
THROTTLE POSITION SENS
A/C COMP
STARTER
FUEL PUMP RELAY
IGN RELAY
A/C CUTOUT RELAY (A/T)
DIODE
RED GRN FUS LINK
NOISE FILTER
FUEL PUMP
FUSE #11
MPS CONTROLLER
READ MEMORY
TEST MODE
OXYGEN SENSOR
BYPASS AIR CONTROL
OIL PRES GAUGE
COOLANT TEMP GAUGE
INST CLSTR
OIL PRES
COLNT TEMP
KNOCK
ENG SENSORS
FUEL INJECTORS

*Fig. 12: Subaru XT Wiring Diagram*

# 1988 COMPUTERIZED ENGINE CONTROLS
## Subaru – MPFI (Cont.)

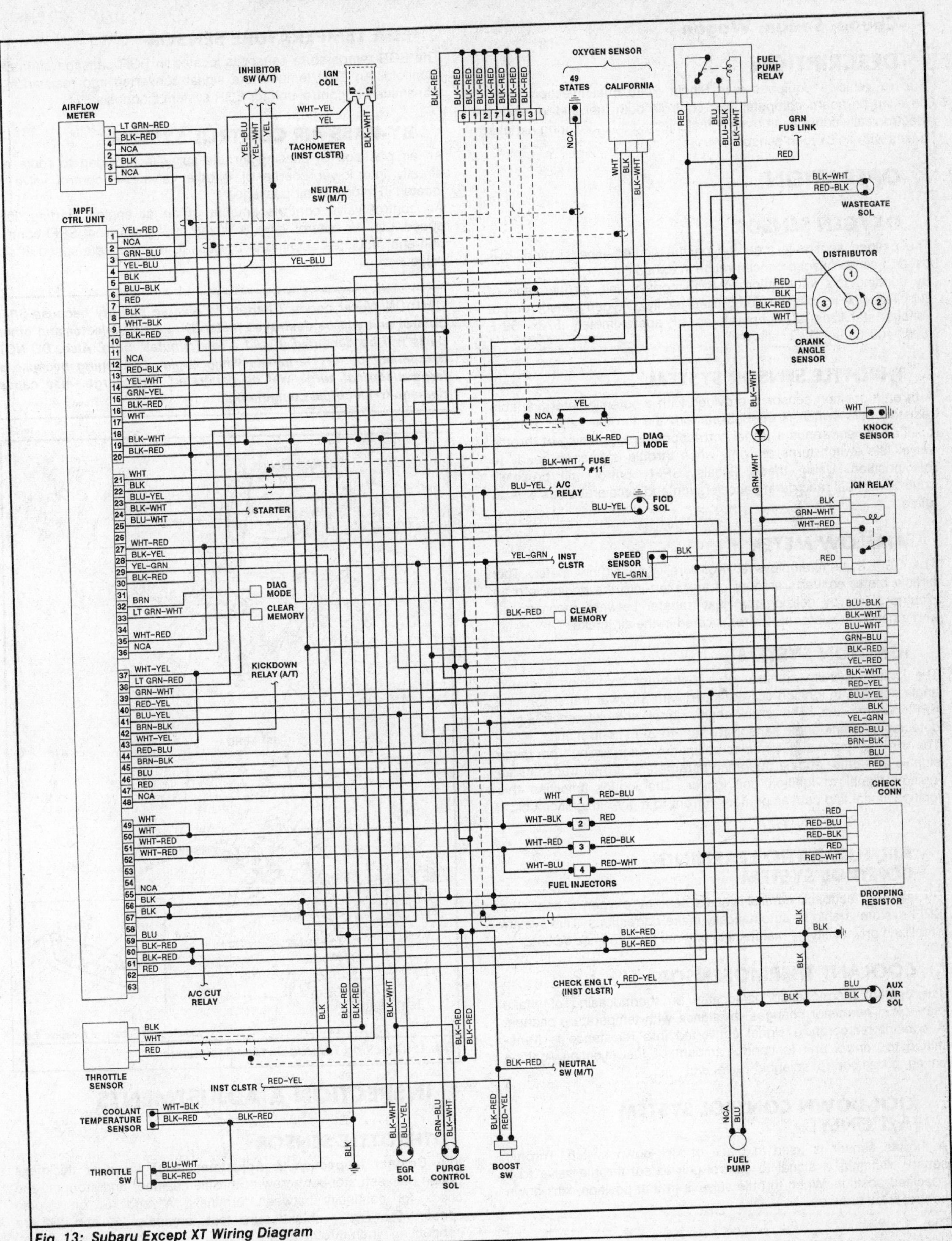

AIRFLOW METER
INHIBITOR SW (A/T)
IGN COIL
TACHOMETER (INST CLSTR)
NEUTRAL SW (M/T)
OXYGEN SENSOR
49 STATES
CALIFORNIA
FUEL PUMP RELAY
GRN FUS LINK
WASTEGATE SOL
MPFI CTRL UNIT
DISTRIBUTOR
CRANK ANGLE SENSOR
KNOCK SENSOR
DIAG MODE
FUSE #11
A/C RELAY
FICD SOL
IGN RELAY
STARTER
INST CLSTR
SPEED SENSOR
DIAG MODE
CLEAR MEMORY
CLEAR MEMORY
KICKDOWN RELAY (A/T)
CHECK CONN
FUEL INJECTORS
DROPPING RESISTOR
A/C CUT RELAY
CHECK ENG LT (INST CLSTR)
AUX AIR SOL
THROTTLE SENSOR
NEUTRAL SW (M/T)
INST CLSTR
COOLANT TEMPERATURE SENSOR
THROTTLE SW
EGR SOL
PURGE CONTROL SOL
BOOST SW
FUEL PUMP


Fig. 13: Subaru Except XT Wiring Diagram

## Coupe, Sedan, Wagon

# DESCRIPTION

Subaru vehicles equipped with Single Point Fuel Injection (SPFI) have an on-board computer that controls both fuel and ignition. It electronically controls amount of fuel injected by monitoring exhaust gases with an oxygen sensor.

# OPERATION

## OXYGEN SENSOR

The oxygen sensor is mounted on the center exhaust pipe. It is used to sense oxygen concentration in exhaust gas.

By sending this information to SPFI control unit, air/fuel ratio of supplied mixture can be determined easily. Oxygen sensor output voltage stabilizes at temperatures of approximately 572°-752°F (300°-400°C).

## THROTTLE SENSOR SYSTEM

A throttle position sensor is provided with a potentiometer (variable resistor). Idle switch is interlocked with the throttle valve. Throttle position sensor sends a signal corresponding to opening of throttle valve. Idle switch turns on, only when throttle is opened nearly to idle position. Using these signals, SPFI control unit precisely controls air-fuel ratio during acceleration and deceleration as well as idling.

## AIRFLOW METER

The SPFI system employs a "Hot-Wire" type airflow meter. This airflow meter converts amount of air taken into the engine into an electric signal by utilizing the heat transfer between incoming air and a heating resistor (hot wire), located in the air intake.

## IGNITION SYSTEM

The ignition system consists of a distributor containing a crank-angle sensor, an ignition coil equipped with a power transistor, and SPFI control unit. The crank-angle signal and reference signal detected by crank-angle sensor are sent to SPFI control unit.

The SPFI control unit determines optimum ignition timing from these signals and other engine operating parameters. It then transmits an ignition signal to ignition coil ignitor. The ignitor amplifies this ignition signal and causes primary current to trigger in ignition coil.

## AIR/FUEL RATIO LEARNING CONTROL SYSTEM

By learning feedback control signals sent by oxygen sensor, the SPFI system is able to automatically make corrections. This system stabilizes driveability by maintaining original performance values.

## COOLANT THERMOSENSOR

The coolant thermosensor is located on thermocasing of intake manifold. Thermistor changes resistance with temperature change. A coolant temperature signal converted into resistance is transmitted to control unit to control amount of fuel injection, ignition timing, purge control solenoid valve, etc.

## KICK-DOWN CONTROL SYSTEM (A/T ONLY)

A throttle sensor is used in place of kick-down switch. Throttle sensor transmits a signal to control unit to set throttle valve to a specified position. When throttle valve is in that position, kick-down control relay turns on.

## EGR TEMPERATURE SENSOR

The EGR temperature sensor is located in EGR passage on intake manifold. An EGR temperature signal converted into resistance is transmitted to control unit for EGR system diagnosis.

## BY-PASS AIR CONTROL SYSTEM

An air passage by-passing throttle valve is provided to route air directly into lower course of throttle valve. Air control valve is located in middle of air passage.

Air control valve controls amount of air at engine starting, idle speed, etc. Air control valve is driven by signals from SPFI control unit and regulates opening of by-pass to maintain idle speed at set value.

***CAUTION: Never connect battery in reverse polarity because SPFI control unit will be destroyed instantly and fuel injector and other parts will be damaged in just a few minutes more. Also, DO NOT disconnect battery terminals while engine is running because a large electrical surge will be generated. This surge, may cause damage to electrical components.***

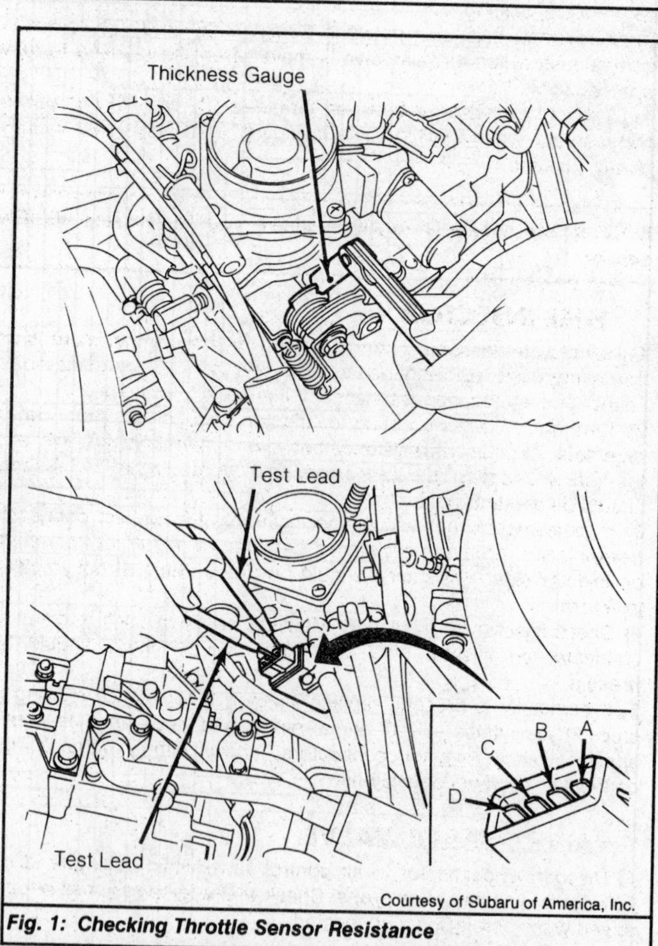
Thickness Gauge
Test Lead
C
B
A
D
Test Lead
Courtesy of Subaru of America, Inc.

***Fig. 1: Checking Throttle Sensor Resistance***

# INSPECTION & ADJUSTMENTS

## THROTTLE SENSOR

**Idle Contact Inspection & Adjustment – 1)** Insert a thickness gauge between stopper screw of throttle chamber and stopper, and check for continuity between terminals "A" and "B" on throttle sensor. *See Fig. 1.* Make sure that terminals "A" and "B" are conducting when throttle is fully closed.

# 1988 COMPUTERIZED ENGINE CONTROLS
# Subaru – SPFI (Cont.)

**2)** Make sure that terminals "A" and "B" are not conducting when throttle is fully open. Make sure that terminals "A" and "B" are conducting when thickness gauge is .012" (.31 mm). This corresponds to a throttle opening of one degree. Make sure that terminals "A" and "B" are not conducting when thickness gauge is .031" (.79 mm). This corresponds to a throttle opening of 2.5 degrees.
**3)** If standard is not as specified, loosen (2) screws securing throttle sensor to throttle chamber, and turn throttle sensor main body until correct adjustment is obtained.

***NOTE: If correct adjustment cannot be obtained, replace throttle sensor.***

**Throttle Opening Signal Inspection – 1)** Check that a resistance of 3500 to 6500 ohms exists between terminals "B" and "D". Check resistance between "B" and "D" and between "B" and "C" changes with opening of throttle valve.
**2)** Check that resistance between terminals "B" and "C" is less than 1000 ohms with throttle valve fully closed, and greater than 2400 ohms with valve fully opened (80% of resistance between terminals "B" and "D"). *See Fig. 1.*
**3)** Check that resistance between terminals "B" and "C" increases continuously when throttle valve is moved from fully closed to fully open position.
**4)** Check that resistance between terminals "B" and "C" decreases continuously when throttle valve is moved from fully open to fully closed position.

***NOTE: If any defect is found in above checks, replace throttle sensor.***

## FUEL INJECTOR

**1)** Using a stethoscope or long screwdriver, ensure that there is an operating noise (clicking noise) from injector. If operating noise cannot be heard, check resistance of injector on control side.
**2)** Turn ignition off. Disconnect connector from control unit. Use an ohmmeter to measure resistance between terminal No. 43 (RW) and terminal No. 48 (RB) of harness connector. A reading of .5-2.0 ohms should be present.
**3)** If resistance is not within specifications. Disconnect connector from injector. Measure resistance between terminals of connector on injector side. Resistance should be .5-2.0 ohms. If not, replace injector.
**4)** Check injector for insulation. Measure between each terminal of connector on injector side and body. No continuity should be present.
**5)** If continuity is present, replace injector. If resistance reading in step **2)** is outside .5-2.0 ohms range and resistance is within specification at injector connectors, check wiring harness and connector for poor connections.

## AIR CONTROL VALVE

**1)** Disconnect connector to air control valve while engine is idling. Check that engine speed drops. Check that engine resumes original speed when connector is connected.

***NOTE: Disconnecting connector causes a big change in RPM when engine is cold. When the engine is warm, a small change or almost no change in RPM is noticed.***

**2)** When the engine shows no change in speed, stop engine and disconnect connector from air control valve. Turn ignition on (engine off). Measure voltage across body and power terminal (BW) of air control valve connector (body side).
**3)** Voltage should be 10 volts minimum. If voltage is less than specified value, check the harness. Turn ignition off. Measure resistace between each terminal for connector on air control valve side.
**4)** Resistance should be 7.3-13.0 ohms. If resistance is not within specifications, replace air control valve.
**5)** Measure resistance between body and each terminal of connector on air control valve side. Resistance should be one milliohm (minimum). If not, replace air control valve.
**6)** Connect air control valve connector. Disconnect connnector from control unit. Turn ignition on. Measure voltage across body and terminal No. 45 (GR) of control unit connector.
**7)** Voltage should be a minimum of 10 volts. If voltage is less than specified value, check harness between air control valve and control unit.
**8)** Turn ignition off. Connect connnector to control unit. Monitor voltage across body and terminal No. 45 (GR) of control unit connnector. Turn ignition on.
**9)** Voltage should be one volt (maximum) for approximately one minute after ignition switch is turned on, 10 volts (minimum) one minute after ignition switch is turned on. If voltage is not within specification, problem is either poor contact of terminal or faulty control unit.
**10)** Turn ignition off. Disconnect air control valve hose. Turn ignition on (engine off). Look through open end of pipe. Ensure that valve moves from fully closed position to fully open position one minute after ignition switch is turned on. If valve does not operate properly, replace air control valve.

## PRESSURE REGULATOR

Disconnect fuel hose at fuel delivery pipe of throttle chamber and install a fuel pressure gauge. Measure fuel pressure when engine is at idle speed. With intake vacuum hose on, pressure should be 20-24 psi. (1.4-1.7 kg/cm²).

## AIRFLOW METER

**1)** Check for leaks or damage in connection between intake boot and airflow meter. Repair any defect found. Remove connectors from airflow meter, air intake boot, and airflow meter for air cleaner case.
**2)** Check exterior of airflow meter for damage. Check for foreign matter, water, oil in air passages, especially in by-pass. If any foreign matter is found, replace airflow sensor.

***NOTE: Be careful not to short circuit power source.***

**3)** Turn ignition off. Install airflow meter on air cleaner. Disconnect a connector from airflow meter and remove rubber cover from connector. Using a DVOM, measure resistance between airflow meter body and ground terminal (B). *See Fig. 2.*
**4)** Resistance reading should be 10 ohms (maximum). If resistance is greater than 10 ohms, check harness and internal circuits of control unit. Turn ignition on (engine off). Measure voltage across power terminal (R) and body.
**5)** Voltage reading should be 10 volts (minimum). If voltage is not as specified, check power supply (battery, fuses, control unit, harness connector, etc.).
**6)** Reconnect airflow meter connector. Attach positive (+) DVOM lead to signal terminal (W) and negative (-) lead to ground terminal (B). Measure voltage across terminal (W) and (B).
**7)** Voltage reading should be .1-.5 volt. If not, replace airflow meter. If voltage is present, remove upper section of air cleaner. Blow air from air cleaner side to check if voltage across terminals (W) and (B) is greater than .1-.5 volt. If voltage reading is not greater than .1-.5, replace airflow meter.

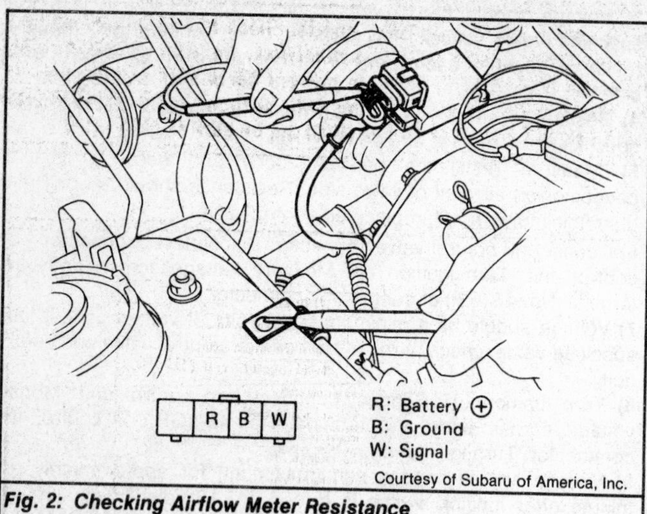
R B W
R: Battery ⊕
B: Ground
W: Signal
Courtesy of Subaru of America, Inc.

*Fig. 2: Checking Airflow Meter Resistance*

## COOLANT THERMOSENSOR

Place thermosensor in water of various temperatures and measure resistance between terminals using a DVOM. See COOLANT THERMOSENSOR TEMPERATURE table.

**COOLANT THERMOSENSOR TEMPERATURE**

| Temperature °F (°C) | Ohms |
|---|---|
| 14 (-10) | 7000-11,500 |
| 68 (20) | 2000-3000 |
| 122 (50) | 700-1000 |

# TROUBLE SHOOTING

## GENERAL INFORMATION

The self-diagnosis system detects and indicates faults in various inputs and outputs of electronic control. The warning light (ECS light) on the instrument panel, indicates that a fault has occured in the system. The Light Emitting Diode (LED) in the control unit indicates a trouble code has been set. *See Fig. 3*. If such a failure of sensors should occcur, the fail-safe function is provided to ensure minimal driveability.

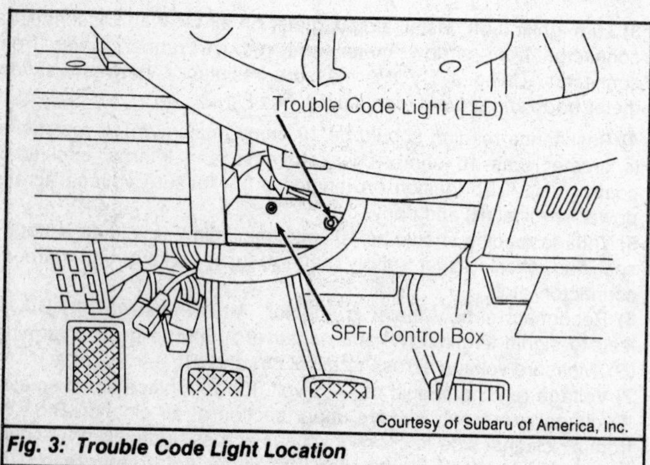
Trouble Code Light (LED)
SPFI Control Box
Courtesy of Subaru of America, Inc.

*Fig. 3: Trouble Code Light Location*

**RELATION BETWEEN MODES & CONNECTORS**

| Mode [1] | Read Memory Connector | Test Mode Connector |
|---|---|---|
| U-Check | Disconnect | Disconnect |
| Read Memory | Connect | Disconnect |
| D-Check | Disconnect | Connect |
| Clear Memory | Connect | Connect |

[1] – With ignition on, and engine running in clear memory mode. With ignition on, engine off on all other modes.

## SELF-DIAGNOSIS FUNCTION

The SPFI control unit receives input information from various sensors and produces output information for driving the fuel injector, fuel pump, etc. Also, it examines all input and output information and compares it to predetermined values or ranges. If a predetermined level is not satisfied or a fault is found, the warning light is illuminated.

The self-diagnosis function has four modes. U-check mode, read memory mode, D-check mode and clear memory mode. See TROUBLE SHOOTING CHARTS in this article. Two connectors (read memory and test mode), two lights (ESC and oxygen monitor) are used. The connectors are for mode selection and lamps monitor type of problem.

## FAIL-SAFE FUNCTION

When a part fails, the control unit generates a signal that compensates for the failed part.

## TROUBLE CODES

To read trouble codes, observe oxygen sensor monitor light. This light has two duration periods of illumination, one period long (1.2

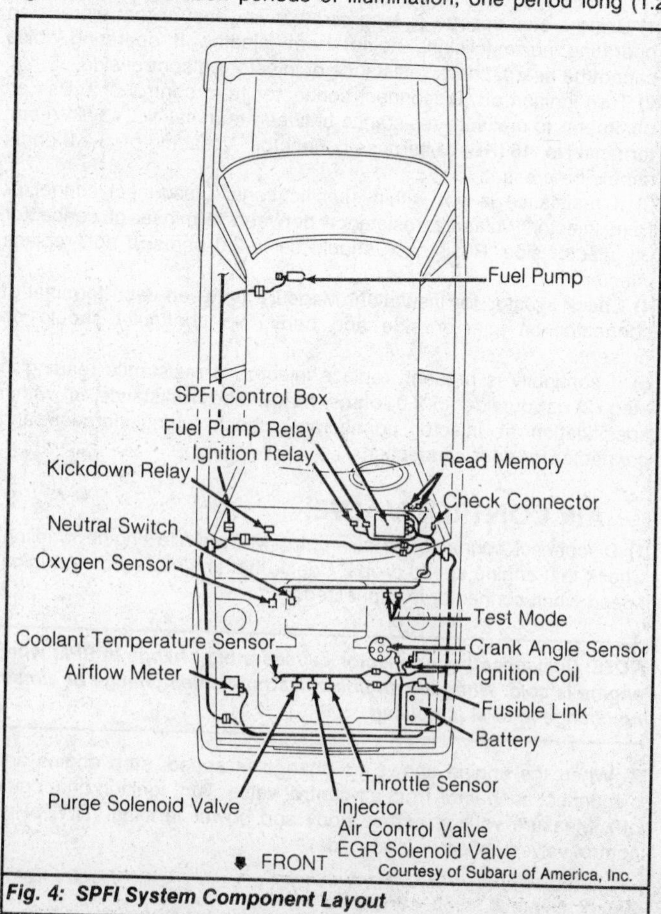
Fuel Pump
SPFI Control Box
Fuel Pump Relay
Ignition Relay
Kickdown Relay
Read Memory
Check Connector
Neutral Switch
Oxygen Sensor
Test Mode
Coolant Temperature Sensor
Crank Angle Sensor
Airflow Meter
Ignition Coil
Fusible Link
Battery
Throttle Sensor
Purge Solenoid Valve
Injector
Air Control Valve
EGR Solenoid Valve
FRONT
Courtesy of Subaru of America, Inc.

*Fig. 4: SPFI System Component Layout*

# 1988 COMPUTERIZED ENGINE CONTROLS
## Subaru – SPFI (Cont.)

seconds) and one period short (.3 seconds). The long period signifies the tens digit in a numbered code. Short period signifies the ones digit. So for example: 3 long flashes and 5 short flashes, that would signify a code 35.

It is possible to have more than one code present. In this case, the lowest number trouble code should be diagnosed first, the next highest numbered code second and so on. Trouble codes will be repeated as long as the system is in that particular diagnostic mode.

***NOTE:*** ***When using diagnostic charts, check the connector while it is connected unless specified otherwise. Be sure to check again from the beginning in order to prevent secondary trouble caused by repair work. When checking with vacuum hose disconnected from vacuum switch at Engine (E/G) on, be sure to plug hose.***

### GENERAL TROUBLE SHOOTING TABLE

: ECS lamp blinks.
∗1: ECS lamp blinks when contact is resumed during inspection (although poor contact is present in D-check).
∗2: ECS lamp lights when abnormality is detected in D-check mode, if idle switch persistently remains off with accelerator pedal released.
∗3: ECS lamp lights when specified preformance characteristics are unusual with throttle valve in slightly opened position.

Symbols shown in table refer to degree of possibility of the reason for trouble ("Very often" to "Rarely").
◎: Very often
○: Sometimes
△: Rarely
☆: Occurs only in extremly low temperatures.

| | TROUBLE | |
|---|---|---|
| 1 | Engine will not start. | No initial combustion |
| 2 | | Initial combustion occur. |
| 3 | | Engine stalls after initial combustion. |
| 4 | Rough idle and engine stall. | |
| 5 | Inability to drive at constant speed | |
| 6 | Inability to accelerate and decelerate | |
| 7 | Engine does not return to idle. | |
| 8 | Afterburning in exhaust system | |
| 9 | Knocking | |
| 10 | Excessive fuel consumption | |
| 11 | Inability to "kick-down" and upshift | |
| U | ECS lamp operation | U-check mode & read memory mode |
| D | | D-check mode |

| 1 | 2 | 3 | 4 | 5 | 6 | 7 | 8 | 9 | 10 | 11 | ECS lamp U | ECS lamp D | POSSIBLE CAUSE |
|---|---|---|---|---|---|---|---|---|---|---|---|---|---|
| | | | | | | | | | | | | | AIR FLOW METER |
| | | ☆ | ◎ | | | | △ | △ | ○ | | ON | ON | • Connector not connected |
| | | △ | ◎ | ◎ | ◎ | | ◎ | ○ | △ | | ON | ∗1 | • Poor contact of terminal |
| | | ☆ | ◎ | | | | △ | ○ | △ | | ON | ON | • Short circuit |
| | | ☆ | ◎ | | | | △ | △ | ○ | | ON | ON | • Discontinuity of wiring harness |
| | | ○ | ○ | ○ | ○ | | △ | ◎ | ○ | | OFF | | • Performance characteristics unusual |
| | | | | | | | | | | | | | COOLANT THERMOSENSOR |
| | ☆ | ○ | ☆ | | ○ | | ○ | ○ | ○ | | ON | ON | • Connector not connected |
| | △ | △ | ◎ | ○ | ○ | △ | ◎ | ◎ | ○ | | ON | ∗1 | • Poor contact of terminal |
| | ☆ | ○ | ☆ | | ○ | | ○ | ○ | ○ | | ON | ON | • Short circuit |
| | ☆ | ○ | ☆ | | ○ | | ○ | ◎ | ○ | | ON | ON | • Discontinuity of wiring harness |
| | ☆ | ○ | ○ | △ | ○ | ○ | ◎ | ◎ | ◎ | △ | OFF | | • Performance characteristics unusual |
| | | | | | | | | | | | | | IDLE SWITCH OF THROTTLE SENSOR |
| | | | ◎ | ○ | ◎ | ◎ | ◎ | | | | ON | ON | • Connector not connected |
| | | | ◎ | ○ | | ◎ | ◎ | | | | ON | ∗1 | • Poor contact of terminal |
| | | | ◎ | ◎ | △ | | ◎ | | | | ON | ON | • Short circuit |
| | | | ◎ | | △ | ◎ | ◎ | | | | ON | ON | • Discontinuity of wiring harness |
| | | | ◎ | | | ◎ | ◎ | | | | OFF | ∗2 | • Improper adjustment |
| | | | | | | | | | | | | | THROTTLE SENSOR |
| | | | | ◎ | ◎ | | ◎ | | | ○ | ON | ∗1 | • Poor contact of terminal |
| △ | | | ◎ | | ◎ | | ◎ | | | ◎ | ON | ON | • Short circuit |
| | | | △ | | ◎ | | ◎ | | | ◎ | ON | ON | • Discontinuity of wiring harness |
| | ○ | ○ | △ | ○ | ◎ | | ◎ | | | ◎ | OFF | ∗3 | • Performance characteristics unusual |
| | | | | | | | | | | | | | PRESSURE REGULATOR |
| | | | | | | | | △ | | | OFF | | • Sensing hose cracked or disconnected |
| | △ | | | | ○ | | ○ | | ◎ | | OFF | | • Fuel pressure too high |
| ○ | ○ | ○ | ◎ | ◎ | ◎ | | ◎ | | | | OFF | | • Fuel pressure too low |
| | | | | | | | | | | | | | FUEL INJECTOR |
| ○ | | | | | | | | | | | ON | ON | • Connector not connected |
| | ○ | ○ | ◎ | ◎ | ◎ | | ○ | | | | ON | ∗1 | • Poor contact of terminal |
| ○ | | | | | | | | | | | ON | ON | • Short circuit |
| ○ | | | | | | | | | | | ON | ON | • Discontinuity of wiring harness |
| | ○ | ○ | ◎ | ◎ | ◎ | | ◎ | | ◎ | | OFF | | • Performance characteristics unusual |
| | ○ | ○ | ○ | ○ | ○ | | | | | | OFF | | • Clogged filter |
| ○ | △ | | | | | | | | | | OFF | | • Stuck open |
| | | | ○ | | | | ○ | | ○ | | OFF | | • Slight leakage from seat |
| | | | | | | | | | | | | | AIR CONTROL VALVE |
| | ○ | △ | ◎ | | | | | | | | ON | ON | • Connector not connected |
| | △ | ○ | ◎ | | | | | | | | ON | ∗1 | • Poor contact of terminal |
| | | | ○ | | | | ○ | | | | ON | ON | • Short circuit |
| | ○ | △ | ◎ | | | | | | | | ON | ON | • Discontinuity of wiring harness |
| | | | ◎ | | | ◎ | | | | | OFF | | • IAS improperly adjusted |
| | | | | | | ◎ | | | | | OFF | | • Stuck open |
| | ○ | ○ | ◎ | | | | | | | | OFF | | • Stuck closed |
| | | | | | | | | | | | | | CRANK ANGLE SENSOR |
| ◎ | | | | | | | | | | | ON | ON | • Connector not connected |
| | ○ | ○ | ◎ | ◎ | ◎ | | ○ | ○ | | | ON | ∗1 | • Poor contact of terminal |
| ◎ | | | | | | | | | | | ON | ON | • Short circuit |
| ◎ | | | | | | | | | | | ON | ON | • Discontinuity of wiring harness |
| | | | | | | | | | | | | | POWER TRANSISTOR OF IGNITION COIL |
| ◎ | | | | | | | | | | | OFF | | • Connector not connected |
| | ○ | ○ | ◎ | ◎ | ◎ | | ○ | △ | | | OFF | | • Poor contact of terminal |
| ◎ | | | | | | | | | | | OFF | | • Short circuit |
| ◎ | | | | | | | | | | | OFF | | • Discontinuity of wiring harness |
| 1 | 2 | 3 | 4 | 5 | 6 | 7 | 8 | 9 | 10 | 11 | U | D | |

Courtesy of Subaru of America, Inc.

***Fig. 5: General Trouble Shooting Chart***

## TROUBLE SHOOTING CHARTS

### TROUBLE SHOOTING CHART FOR SELF- DIAGNOSIS SYSTEM

#### Basic Trouble Shooting Procedures

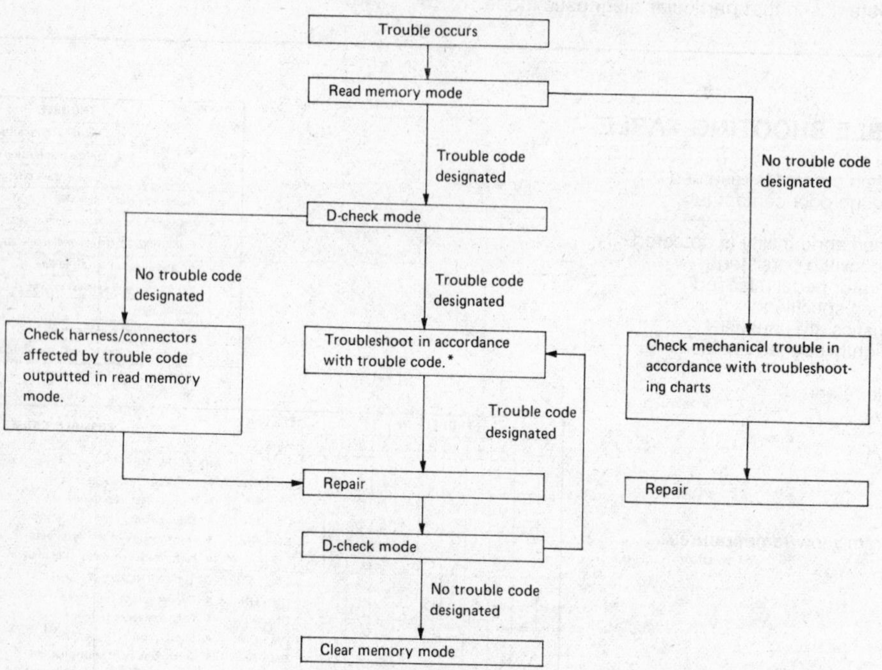
Trouble occurs
Read memory mode
Trouble code designated
No trouble code designated
D-check mode
No trouble code designated
Trouble code designated
Check harness/connectors affected by trouble code outputted in read memory mode.
Troubleshoot in accordance with trouble code.*
Check mechanical trouble in accordance with troubleshooting charts
Trouble code designated
Repair
Repair
D-check mode
No trouble code designated
Clear memory mode

#### MEMORY MODE

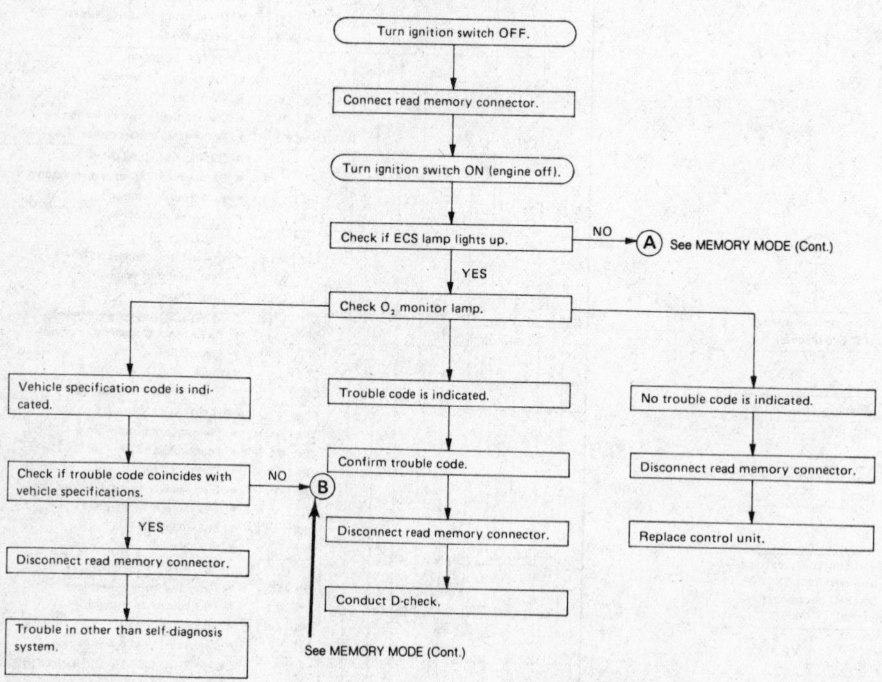
Turn ignition switch OFF.
Connect read memory connector.
Turn ignition switch ON (engine off).
Check if ECS lamp lights up.
NO
A See MEMORY MODE (Cont.)
YES
Check $O_2$ monitor lamp.
Vehicle specification code is indicated.
Trouble code is indicated.
No trouble code is indicated.
Check if trouble code coincides with vehicle specifications.
NO
B
Confirm trouble code.
Disconnect read memory connector.
YES
Disconnect read memory connector.
Replace control unit.
Disconnect read memory connector.
Conduct D-check.
Trouble in other than self-diagnosis system.
See MEMORY MODE (Cont.)

Courtesy of Subaru of America, Inc.

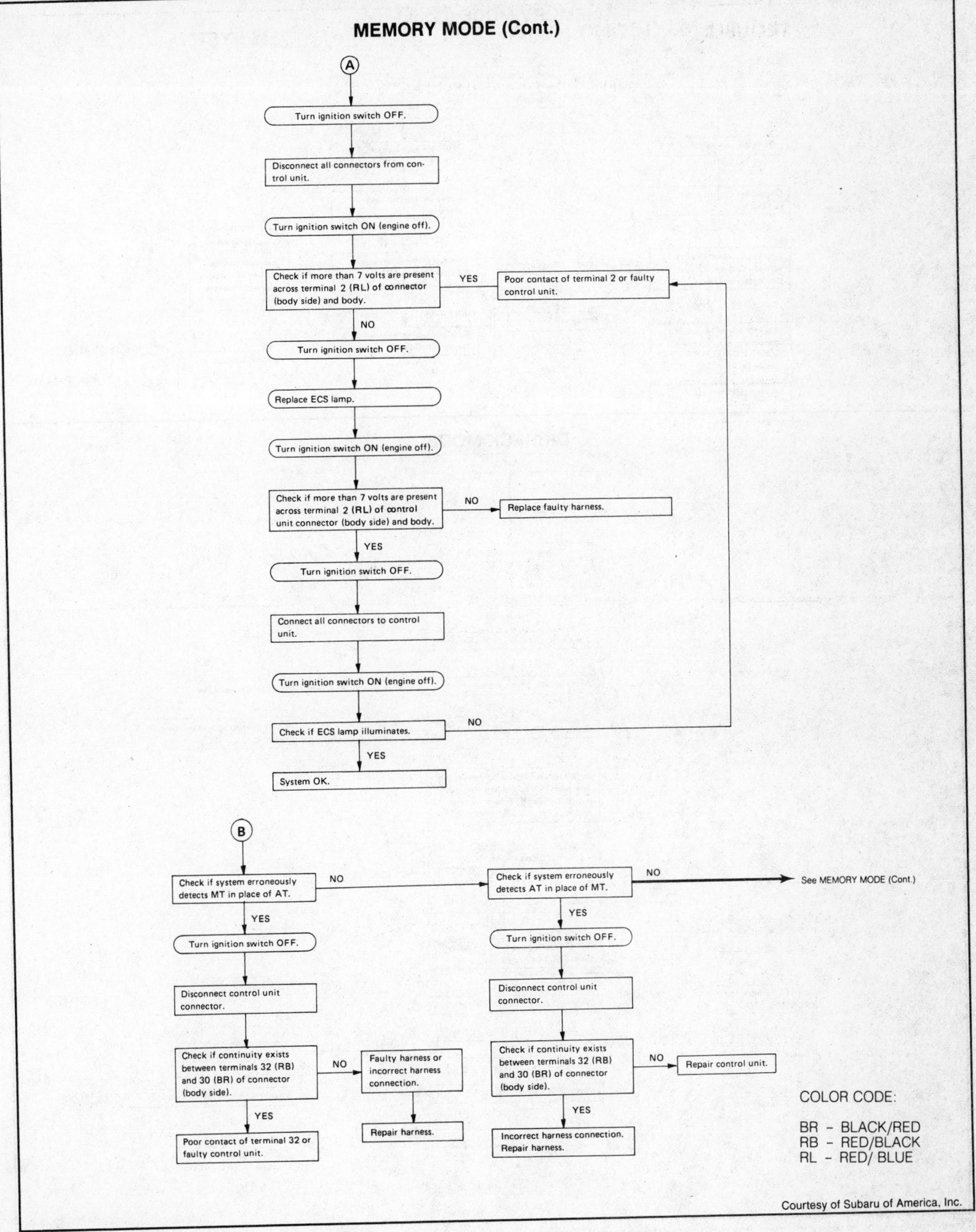
MEMORY MODE (Cont.)
A
Turn ignition switch OFF.
Disconnect all connectors from control unit.
Turn ignition switch ON (engine off).
Check if more than 7 volts are present across terminal 2 (RL) of connector (body side) and body.
YES
Poor contact of terminal 2 or faulty control unit.
NO
Turn ignition switch OFF.
Replace ECS lamp.
Turn ignition switch ON (engine off).
Check if more than 7 volts are present across terminal 2 (RL) of control unit connector (body side) and body.
NO
Replace faulty harness.
YES
Turn ignition switch OFF.
Connect all connectors to control unit.
Turn ignition switch ON (engine off).
Check if ECS lamp illuminates.
NO
YES
System OK.
B
Check if system erroneously detects MT in place of AT.
NO
Check if system erroneously detects AT in place of MT.
NO
See MEMORY MODE (Cont.)
YES
Turn ignition switch OFF.
Disconnect control unit connector.
Check if continuity exists between terminals 32 (RB) and 30 (BR) of connector (body side).
NO
Faulty harness or incorrect harness connection.
Repair harness.
YES
Poor contact of terminal 32 or faulty control unit.
YES
Turn ignition switch OFF.
Disconnect control unit connector.
Check if continuity exists between terminals 32 (RB) and 30 (BR) of connector (body side).
NO
Repair control unit.
YES
Incorrect harness connection. Repair harness.
COLOR CODE:
BR - BLACK/RED
RB - RED/BLACK
RL - RED/ BLUE
Courtesy of Subaru of America, Inc.

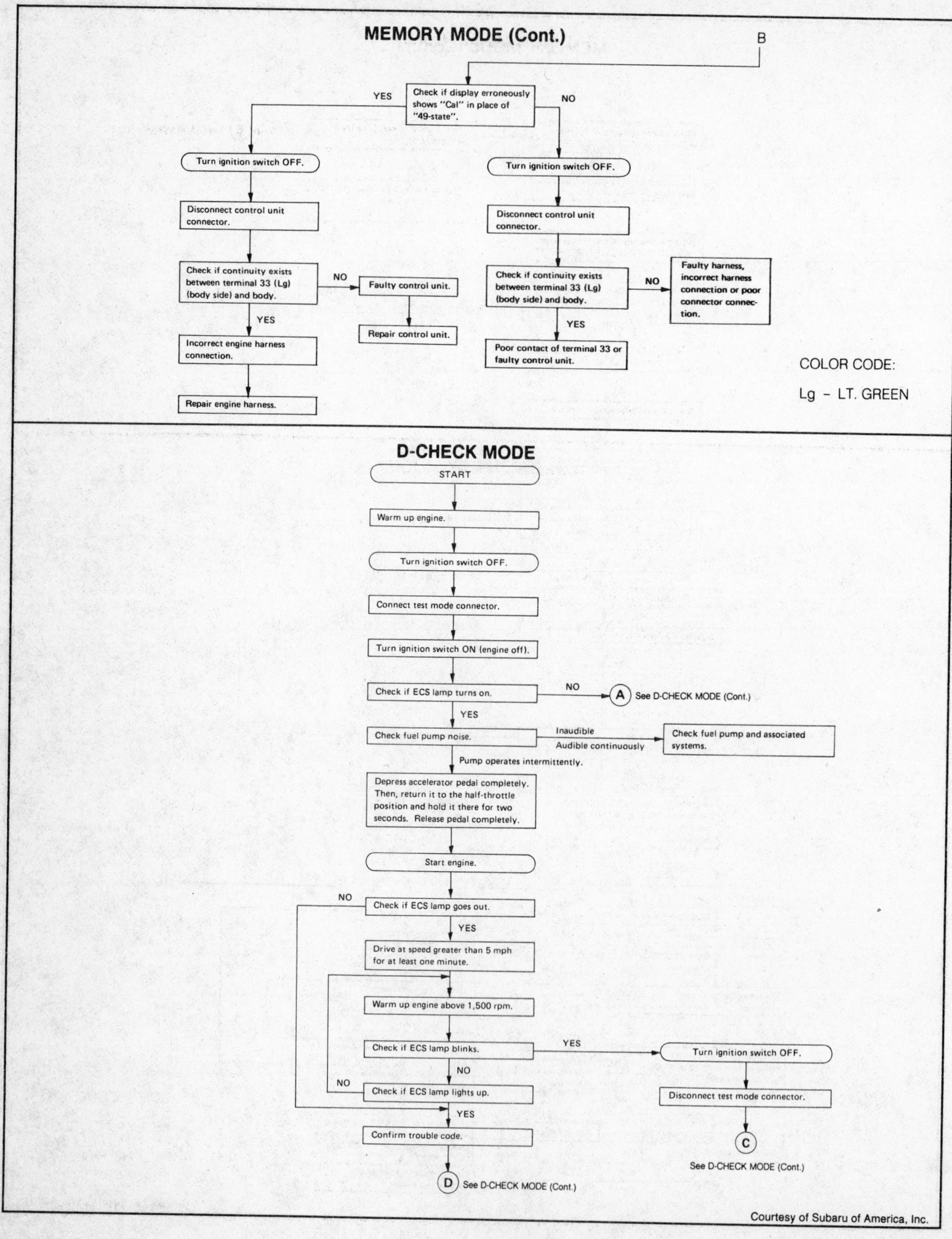
MEMORY MODE (Cont.)
B
Check if display erroneously shows "Cal" in place of "49-state".
YES
NO
Turn ignition switch OFF.
Disconnect control unit connector.
Check if continuity exists between terminal 33 (Lg) (body side) and body.
NO
Faulty control unit.
Repair control unit.
YES
Incorrect engine harness connection.
Repair engine harness.
Turn ignition switch OFF.
Disconnect control unit connector.
Check if continuity exists between terminal 33 (Lg) (body side) and body.
NO
Faulty harness, incorrect harness connection or poor connector connection.
YES
Poor contact of terminal 33 or faulty control unit.
COLOR CODE:
Lg - LT. GREEN
D-CHECK MODE
START
Warm up engine.
Turn ignition switch OFF.
Connect test mode connector.
Turn ignition switch ON (engine off).
Check if ECS lamp turns on.
NO
A
See D-CHECK MODE (Cont.)
YES
Check fuel pump noise.
Inaudible
Audible continuously
Check fuel pump and associated systems.
Pump operates intermittently.
Depress accelerator pedal completely. Then, return it to the half-throttle position and hold it there for two seconds. Release pedal completely.
Start engine.
NO
Check if ECS lamp goes out.
YES
Drive at speed greater than 5 mph for at least one minute.
Warm up engine above 1,500 rpm.
Check if ECS lamp blinks.
YES
Turn ignition switch OFF.
NO
Disconnect test mode connector.
NO
Check if ECS lamp lights up.
YES
Confirm trouble code.
C
See D-CHECK MODE (Cont.)
D
See D-CHECK MODE (Cont.)

Courtesy of Subaru of America, Inc.

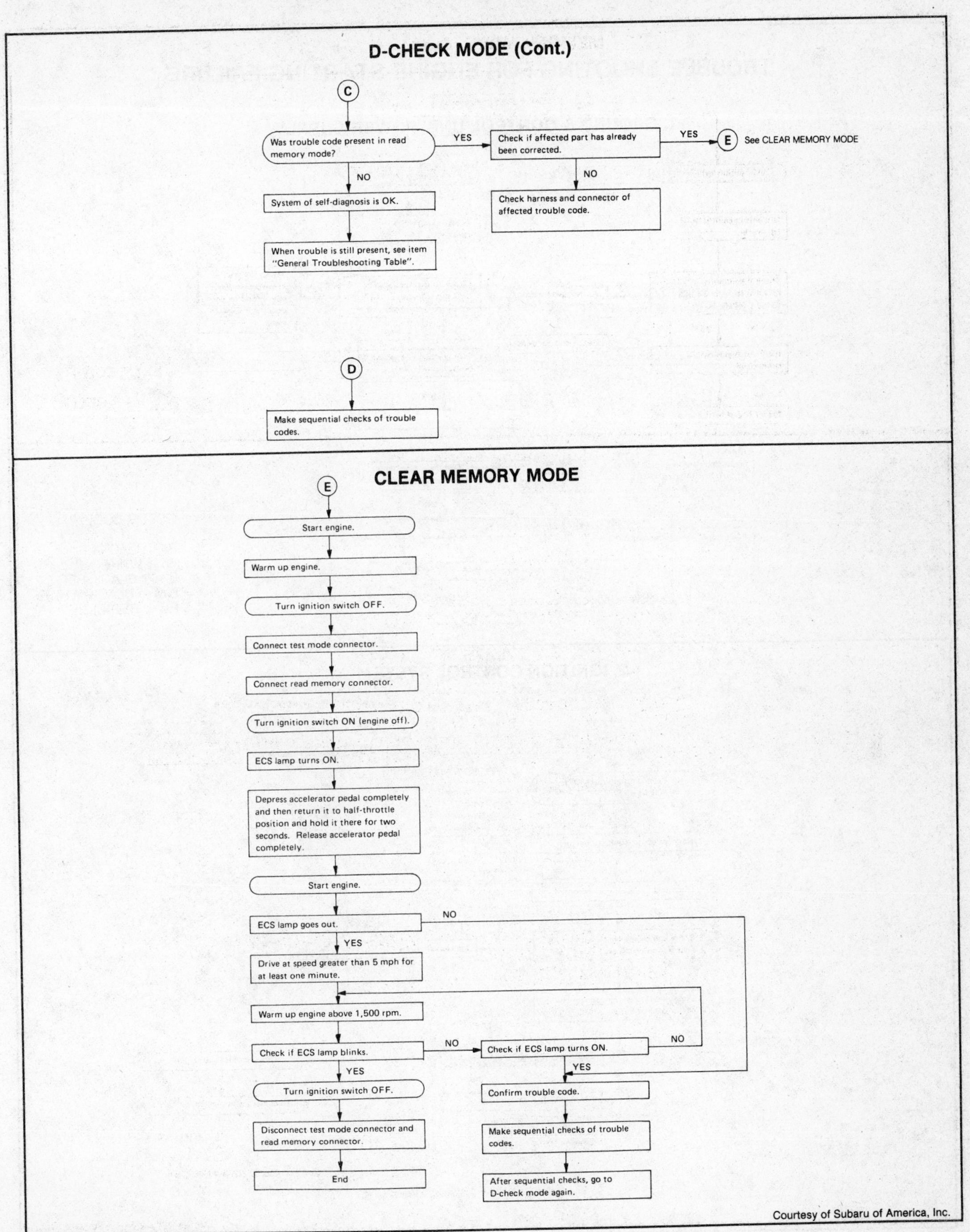
D-CHECK MODE (Cont.)
C
Was trouble code present in read memory mode?
YES
Check if affected part has already been corrected.
YES
E
See CLEAR MEMORY MODE
NO
Check harness and connector of affected trouble code.
NO
System of self-diagnosis is OK.
When trouble is still present, see item "General Troubleshooting Table".
D
Make sequential checks of trouble codes.
CLEAR MEMORY MODE
E
Start engine.
Warm up engine.
Turn ignition switch OFF.
Connect test mode connector.
Connect read memory connector.
Turn ignition switch ON (engine off).
ECS lamp turns ON.
Depress accelerator pedal completely and then return it to half-throttle position and hold it there for two seconds. Release accelerator pedal completely.
Start engine.
ECS lamp goes out.
NO
YES
Drive at speed greater than 5 mph for at least one minute.
Warm up engine above 1,500 rpm.
Check if ECS lamp blinks.
NO
Check if ECS lamp turns ON.
NO
YES
YES
Turn ignition switch OFF.
Confirm trouble code.
Disconnect test mode connector and read memory connector.
Make sequential checks of trouble codes.
End
After sequential checks, go to D-check mode again.

Courtesy of Subaru of America, Inc.

# TROUBLE SHOOTING FOR ENGINE STARTING FAILURE

## 1. GROUND & CONTROL UNIT POWER SUPPLY

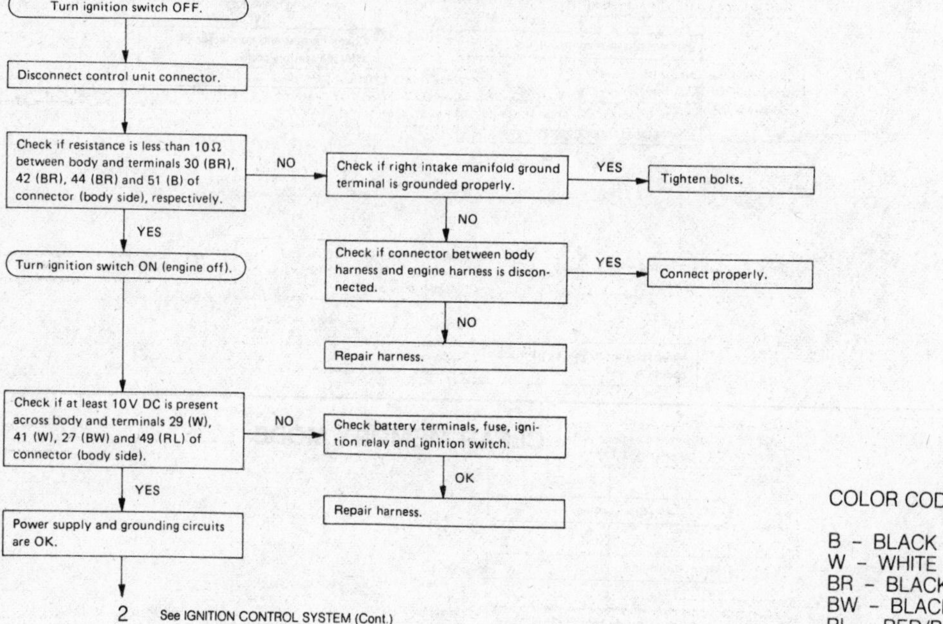
Turn ignition switch OFF.
Disconnect control unit connector.
Check if resistance is less than 10 Ω between body and terminals 30 (BR), 42 (BR), 44 (BR) and 51 (B) of connector (body side), respectively.
NO
Check if right intake manifold ground terminal is grounded properly.
YES
Tighten bolts.
NO
Check if connector between body harness and engine harness is disconnected.
YES
Connect properly.
NO
Repair harness.
YES
Turn ignition switch ON (engine off).
Check if at least 10 V DC is present across body and terminals 29 (W), 41 (W), 27 (BW) and 49 (RL) of connector (body side).
NO
Check battery terminals, fuse, ignition relay and ignition switch.
OK
Repair harness.
YES
Power supply and grounding circuits are OK.
2 See IGNITION CONTROL SYSTEM (Cont.)

COLOR CODE:

B – BLACK
W – WHITE
BR – BLACK/RED
BW – BLACK/WHITE
RL – RED/BLUE

## 2. IGNITION CONTROL SYSTEM

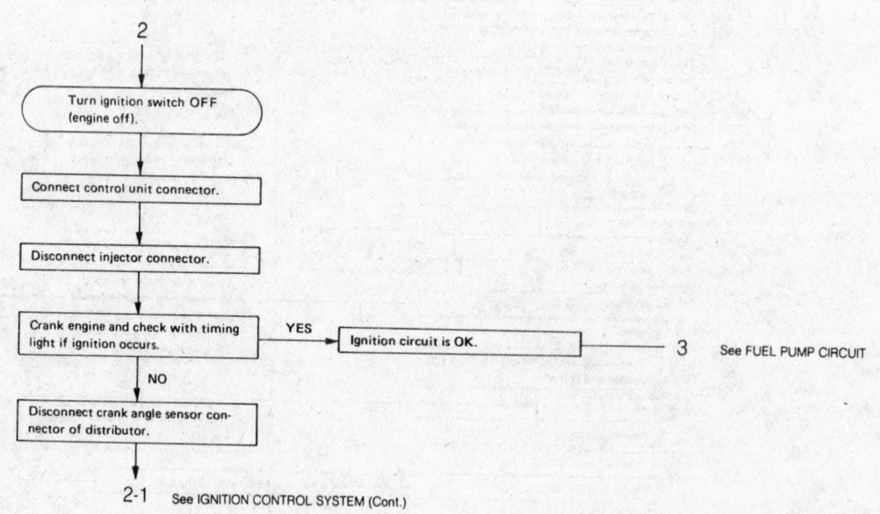
2
Turn ignition switch OFF (engine off).
Connect control unit connector.
Disconnect injector connector.
Crank engine and check with timing light if ignition occurs.
YES
Ignition circuit is OK.
3 See FUEL PUMP CIRCUIT
NO
Disconnect crank angle sensor connector of distributor.
2-1 See IGNITION CONTROL SYSTEM (Cont.)

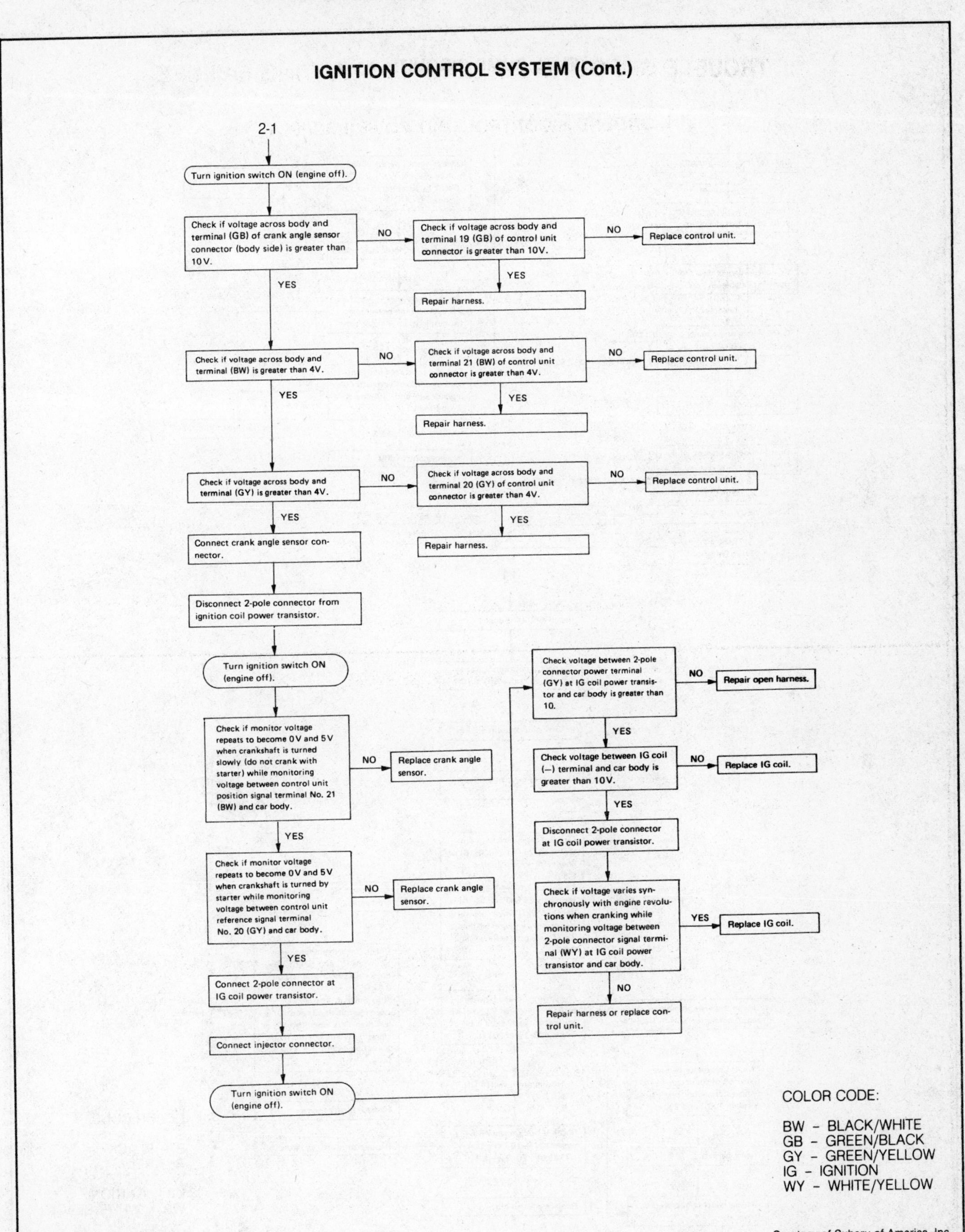
IGNITION CONTROL SYSTEM (Cont.)
2-1
Turn ignition switch ON (engine off).
Check if voltage across body and terminal (GB) of crank angle sensor connector (body side) is greater than 10V.
NO
Check if voltage across body and terminal 19 (GB) of control unit connector is greater than 10V.
NO
Replace control unit.
YES
Repair harness.
YES
Check if voltage across body and terminal (BW) is greater than 4V.
NO
Check if voltage across body and terminal 21 (BW) of control unit connector is greater than 4V.
NO
Replace control unit.
YES
Repair harness.
YES
Check if voltage across body and terminal (GY) is greater than 4V.
NO
Check if voltage across body and terminal 20 (GY) of control unit connector is greater than 4V.
NO
Replace control unit.
YES
Repair harness.
YES
Connect crank angle sensor connector.
Disconnect 2-pole connector from ignition coil power transistor.
Turn ignition switch ON (engine off).
Check if monitor voltage repeats to become 0V and 5V when crankshaft is turned slowly (do not crank with starter) while monitoring voltage between control unit position signal terminal No. 21 (BW) and car body.
NO
Replace crank angle sensor.
YES
Check if monitor voltage repeats to become 0V and 5V when crankshaft is turned by starter while monitoring voltage between control unit reference signal terminal No. 20 (GY) and car body.
NO
Replace crank angle sensor.
YES
Connect 2-pole connector at IG coil power transistor.
Connect injector connector.
Turn ignition switch ON (engine off).
Check voltage between 2-pole connector power terminal (GY) at IG coil power transistor and car body is greater than 10.
NO
Repair open harness.
YES
Check voltage between IG coil (–) terminal and car body is greater than 10V.
NO
Replace IG coil.
YES
Disconnect 2-pole connector at IG coil power transistor.
Check if voltage varies synchronously with engine revolutions when cranking while monitoring voltage between 2-pole connector signal terminal (WY) at IG coil power transistor and car body.
YES
Replace IG coil.
NO
Repair harness or replace control unit.
COLOR CODE:
BW – BLACK/WHITE
GB – GREEN/BLACK
GY – GREEN/YELLOW
IG – IGNITION
WY – WHITE/YELLOW
Courtesy of Subaru of America, Inc.

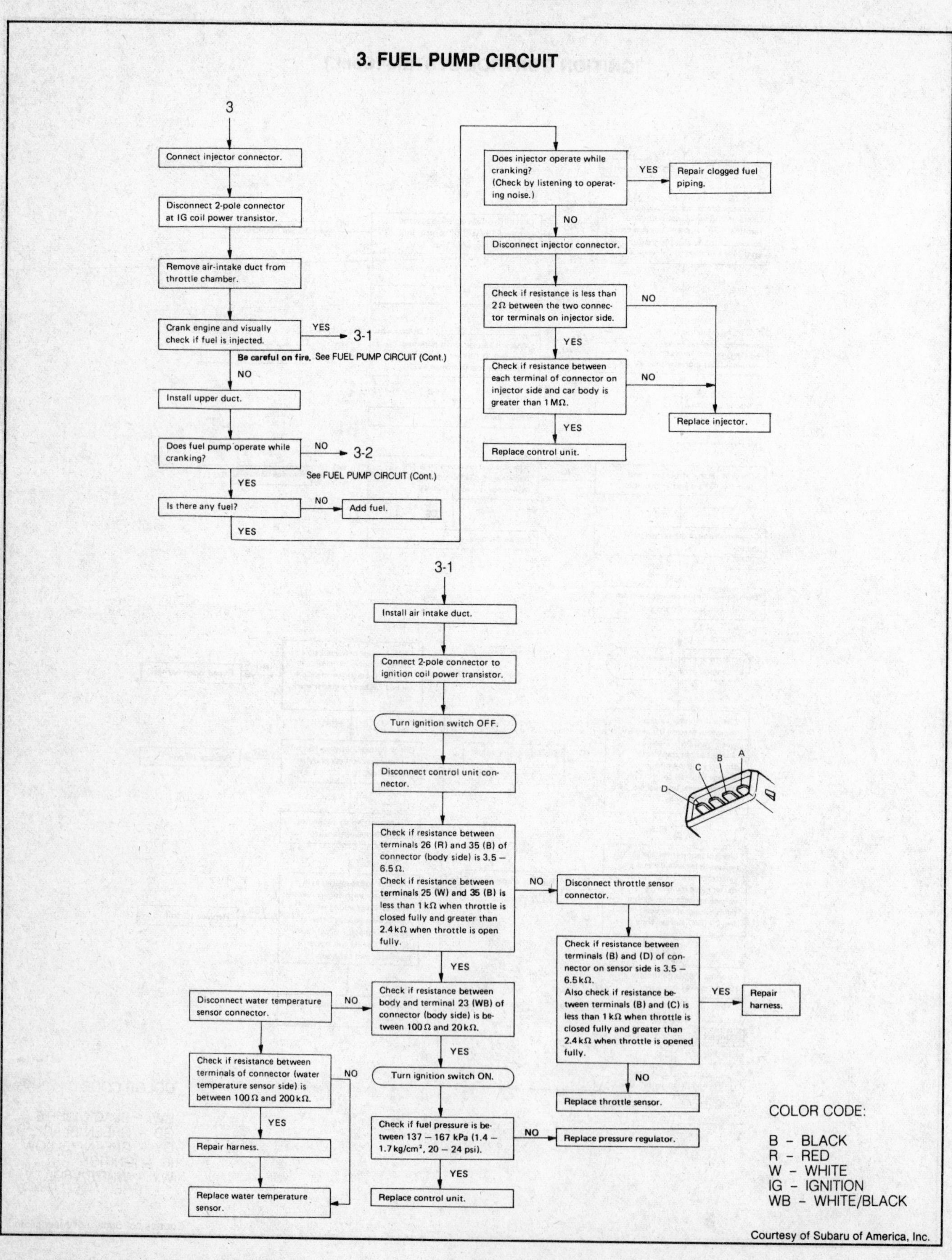
3. FUEL PUMP CIRCUIT
3
Connect injector connector.
Disconnect 2-pole connector at IG coil power transistor.
Remove air-intake duct from throttle chamber.
Crank engine and visually check if fuel is injected.
YES
3-1
Be careful on fire. See FUEL PUMP CIRCUIT (Cont.)
NO
Install upper duct.
Does fuel pump operate while cranking?
NO
3-2
See FUEL PUMP CIRCUIT (Cont.)
YES
Is there any fuel?
NO
Add fuel.
YES
Does injector operate while cranking? (Check by listening to operating noise.)
YES
Repair clogged fuel piping.
NO
Disconnect injector connector.
Check if resistance is less than 2 Ω between the two connector terminals on injector side.
NO
YES
Check if resistance between each terminal of connector on injector side and car body is greater than 1 MΩ.
NO
Replace injector.
YES
Replace control unit.
3-1
Install air intake duct.
Connect 2-pole connector to ignition coil power transistor.
Turn ignition switch OFF.
Disconnect control unit connector.
A
B
C
D
Check if resistance between terminals 26 (R) and 35 (B) of connector (body side) is 3.5 – 6.5 Ω. Check if resistance between terminals 25 (W) and 35 (B) is less than 1 kΩ when throttle is closed fully and greater than 2.4 kΩ when throttle is open fully.
NO
Disconnect throttle sensor connector.
Check if resistance between terminals (B) and (D) of connector on sensor side is 3.5 – 6.5 kΩ. Also check if resistance between terminals (B) and (C) is less than 1 kΩ when throttle is closed fully and greater than 2.4 kΩ when throttle is opened fully.
YES
Repair harness.
NO
Replace throttle sensor.
YES
Check if resistance between body and terminal 23 (WB) of connector (body side) is between 100 Ω and 20 kΩ.
NO
Disconnect water temperature sensor connector.
Check if resistance between terminals of connector (water temperature sensor side) is between 100 Ω and 200 kΩ.
NO
YES
Repair harness.
Replace water temperature sensor.
YES
Turn ignition switch ON.
Check if fuel pressure is between 137 – 167 kPa (1.4 – 1.7 kg/cm², 20 – 24 psi).
NO
Replace pressure regulator.
YES
Replace control unit.
COLOR CODE:
B - BLACK
R - RED
W - WHITE
IG - IGNITION
WB - WHITE/BLACK
Courtesy of Subaru of America, Inc.

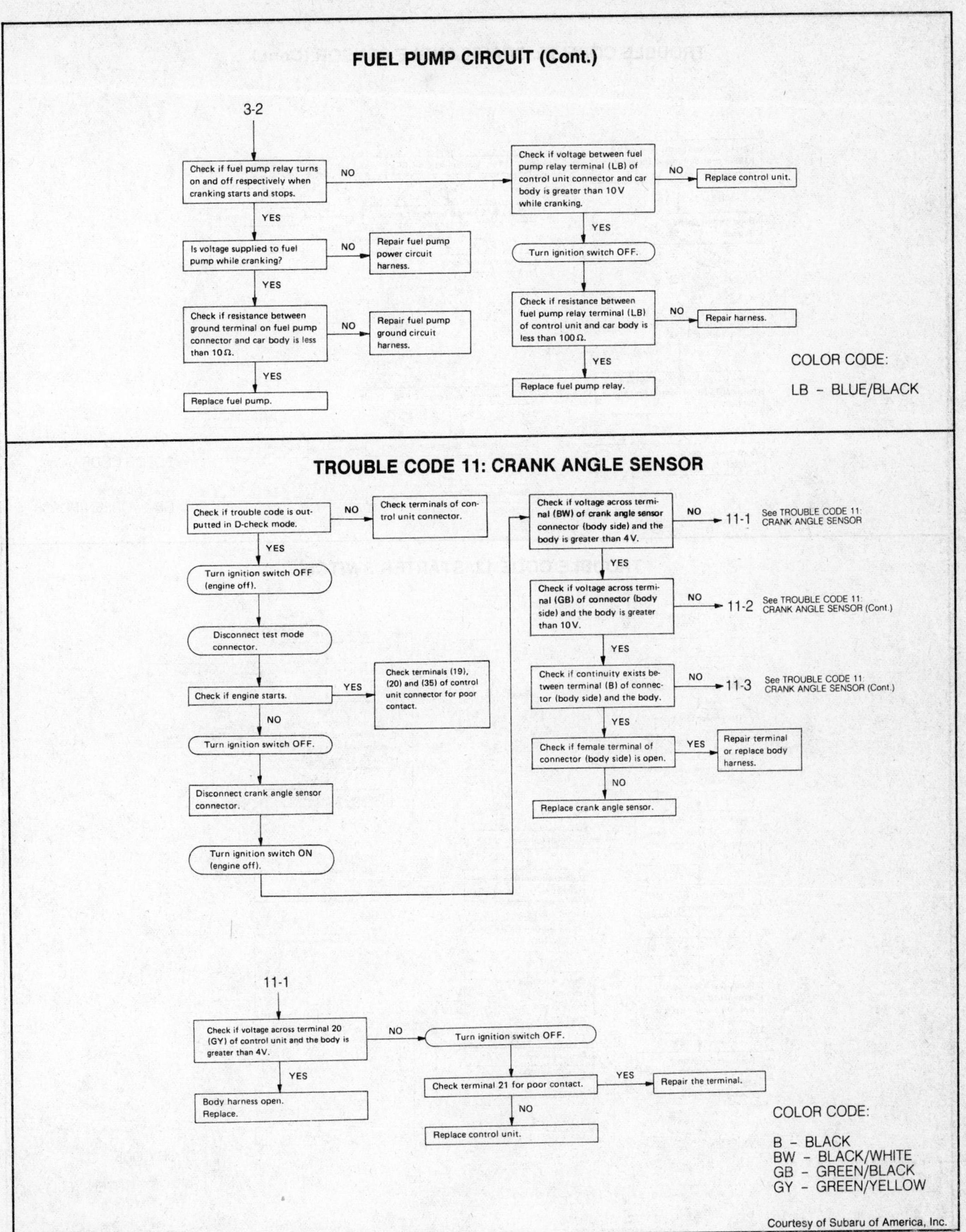
FUEL PUMP CIRCUIT (Cont.)
3-2
Check if fuel pump relay turns on and off respectively when cranking starts and stops.
NO
Check if voltage between fuel pump relay terminal (LB) of control unit connector and car body is greater than 10V while cranking.
NO
Replace control unit.
YES
Turn ignition switch OFF.
Check if resistance between fuel pump relay terminal (LB) of control unit and car body is less than 100Ω.
NO
Repair harness.
YES
Replace fuel pump relay.
YES
Is voltage supplied to fuel pump while cranking?
NO
Repair fuel pump power circuit harness.
YES
Check if resistance between ground terminal on fuel pump connector and car body is less than 10Ω.
NO
Repair fuel pump ground circuit harness.
YES
Replace fuel pump.
COLOR CODE:
LB – BLUE/BLACK
TROUBLE CODE 11: CRANK ANGLE SENSOR
Check if trouble code is outputted in D-check mode.
NO
Check terminals of control unit connector.
YES
Turn ignition switch OFF (engine off).
Disconnect test mode connector.
Check if engine starts.
YES
Check terminals (19), (20) and (35) of control unit connector for poor contact.
NO
Turn ignition switch OFF.
Disconnect crank angle sensor connector.
Turn ignition switch ON (engine off).
Check if voltage across terminal (BW) of crank angle sensor connector (body side) and the body is greater than 4V.
NO
11-1
See TROUBLE CODE 11: CRANK ANGLE SENSOR
YES
Check if voltage across terminal (GB) of connector (body side) and the body is greater than 10V.
NO
11-2
See TROUBLE CODE 11: CRANK ANGLE SENSOR (Cont.)
YES
Check if continuity exists between terminal (B) of connector (body side) and the body.
NO
11-3
See TROUBLE CODE 11: CRANK ANGLE SENSOR (Cont.)
YES
Check if female terminal of connector (body side) is open.
YES
Repair terminal or replace body harness.
NO
Replace crank angle sensor.
11-1
Check if voltage across terminal 20 (GY) of control unit and the body is greater than 4V.
NO
Turn ignition switch OFF.
Check terminal 21 for poor contact.
YES
Repair the terminal.
NO
Replace control unit.
YES
Body harness open. Replace.
COLOR CODE:
B – BLACK
BW – BLACK/WHITE
GB – GREEN/BLACK
GY – GREEN/YELLOW

Courtesy of Subaru of America, Inc.

## TROUBLE CODE 11: CRANK ANGLE SENSOR (Cont.)

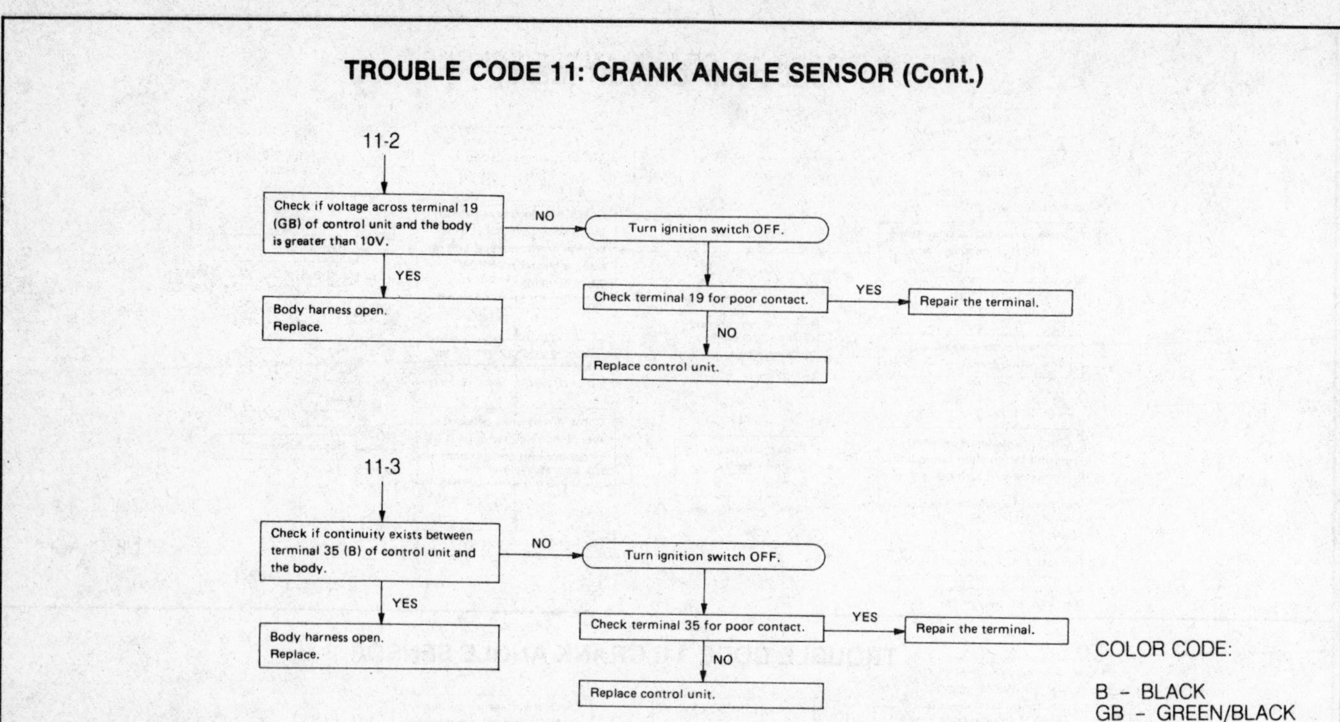
11-2
Check if voltage across terminal 19 (GB) of control unit and the body is greater than 10V.
NO
Turn ignition switch OFF.
YES
Body harness open. Replace.
Check terminal 19 for poor contact.
YES
Repair the terminal.
NO
Replace control unit.
11-3
Check if continuity exists between terminal 35 (B) of control unit and the body.
NO
Turn ignition switch OFF.
YES
Body harness open. Replace.
Check terminal 35 for poor contact.
YES
Repair the terminal.
NO
Replace control unit.

COLOR CODE:

B – BLACK
GB – GREEN/BLACK

## TROUBLE CODE 12: STARTER SWITCH

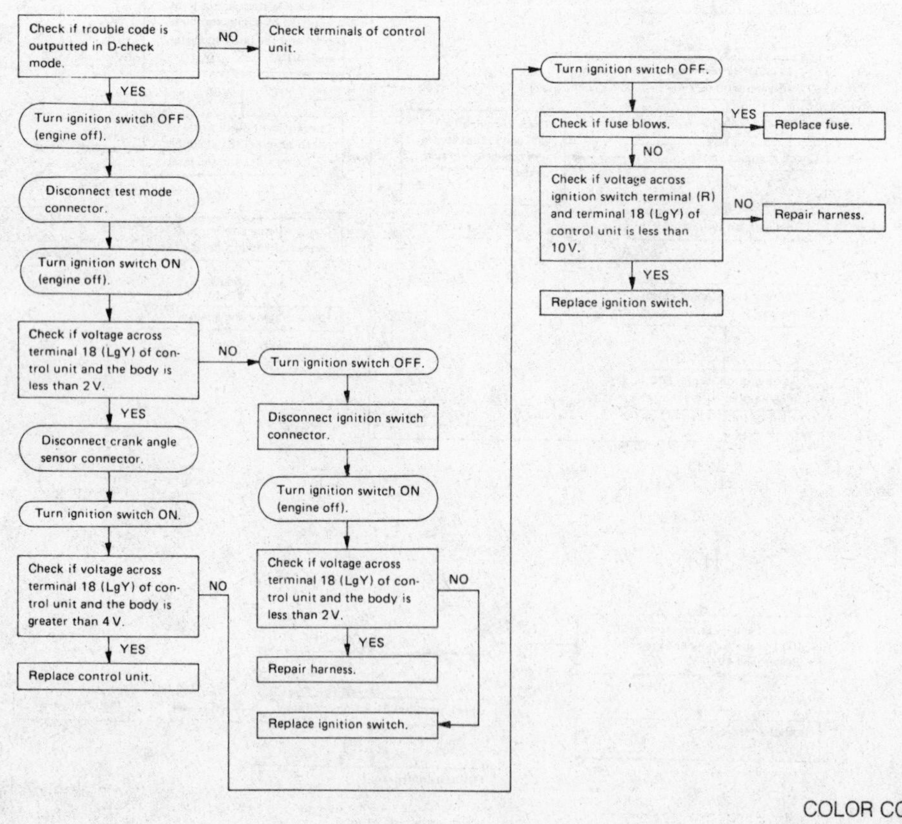
Check if trouble code is outputted in D-check mode.
NO
Check terminals of control unit.
YES
Turn ignition switch OFF (engine off).
Disconnect test mode connector.
Turn ignition switch ON (engine off).
Check if voltage across terminal 18 (LgY) of control unit and the body is less than 2 V.
NO
Turn ignition switch OFF.
YES
Disconnect crank angle sensor connector.
Disconnect ignition switch connector.
Turn ignition switch ON.
Turn ignition switch ON (engine off).
Check if voltage across terminal 18 (LgY) of control unit and the body is greater than 4 V.
NO
Check if voltage across terminal 18 (LgY) of control unit and the body is less than 2 V.
NO
YES
Replace control unit.
YES
Repair harness.
Replace ignition switch.
Turn ignition switch OFF.
Check if fuse blows.
YES
Replace fuse.
NO
Check if voltage across ignition switch terminal (R) and terminal 18 (LgY) of control unit is less than 10 V.
NO
Repair harness.
YES
Replace ignition switch.

COLOR CODE:

LgY – LT. GREEN/YELLOW

Courtesy of Subaru of America, Inc.

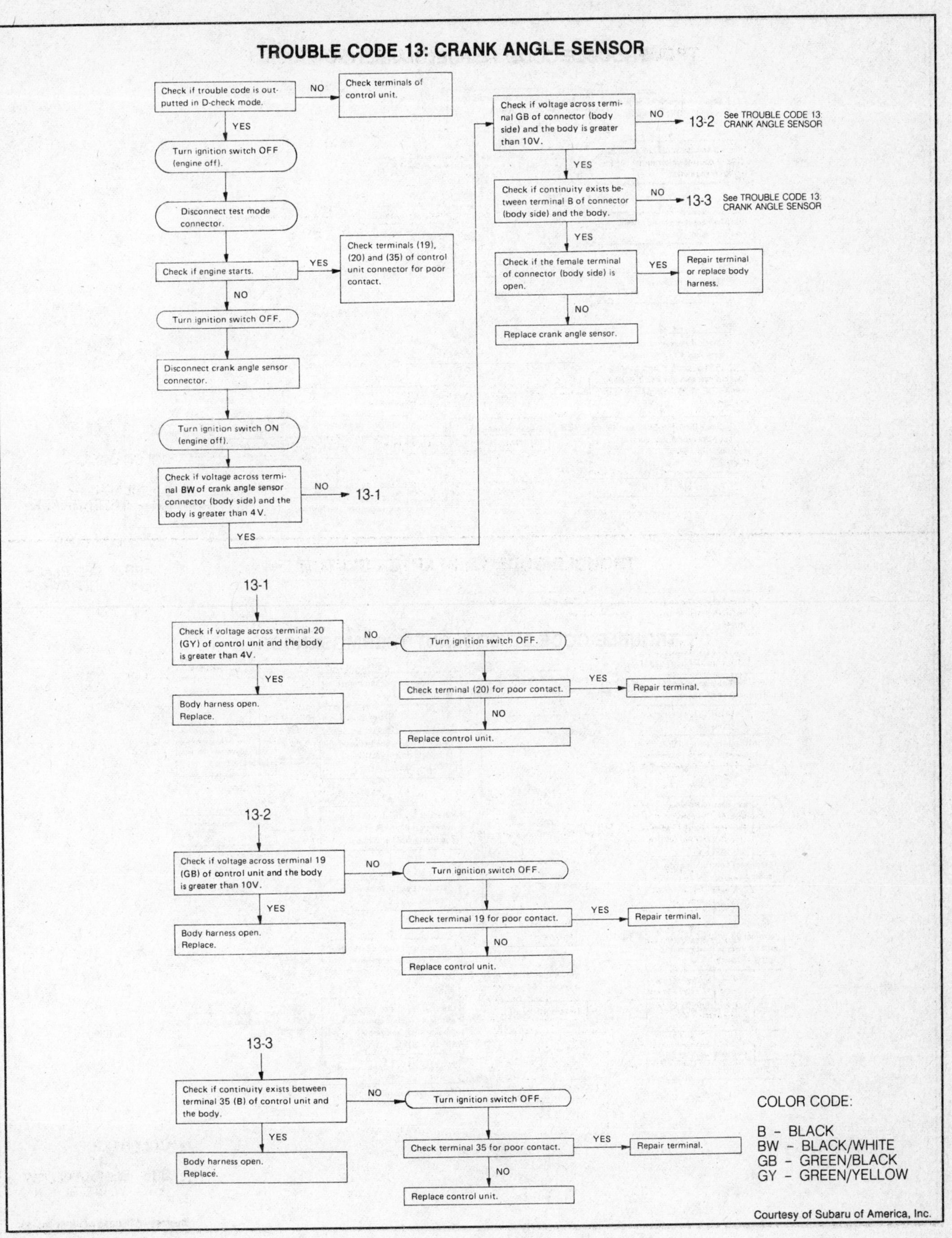
TROUBLE CODE 13: CRANK ANGLE SENSOR
Check if trouble code is outputted in D-check mode.
NO
Check terminals of control unit.
YES
Turn ignition switch OFF (engine off).
Disconnect test mode connector.
Check if engine starts.
YES
Check terminals (19), (20) and (35) of control unit connector for poor contact.
NO
Turn ignition switch OFF.
Disconnect crank angle sensor connector.
Turn ignition switch ON (engine off).
Check if voltage across terminal BW of crank angle sensor connector (body side) and the body is greater than 4V.
NO
13-1
YES
Check if voltage across terminal GB of connector (body side) and the body is greater than 10V.
NO
13-2
See TROUBLE CODE 13: CRANK ANGLE SENSOR
YES
Check if continuity exists between terminal B of connector (body side) and the body.
NO
13-3
See TROUBLE CODE 13: CRANK ANGLE SENSOR
YES
Check if the female terminal of connector (body side) is open.
YES
Repair terminal or replace body harness.
NO
Replace crank angle sensor.
13-1
Check if voltage across terminal 20 (GY) of control unit and the body is greater than 4V.
NO
Turn ignition switch OFF.
Check terminal (20) for poor contact.
YES
Repair terminal.
NO
Replace control unit.
YES
Body harness open. Replace.
13-2
Check if voltage across terminal 19 (GB) of control unit and the body is greater than 10V.
NO
Turn ignition switch OFF.
Check terminal 19 for poor contact.
YES
Repair terminal.
NO
Replace control unit.
YES
Body harness open. Replace.
13-3
Check if continuity exists between terminal 35 (B) of control unit and the body.
NO
Turn ignition switch OFF.
Check terminal 35 for poor contact.
YES
Repair terminal.
NO
Replace control unit.
YES
Body harness open. Replace.
COLOR CODE:
B - BLACK
BW - BLACK/WHITE
GB - GREEN/BLACK
GY - GREEN/YELLOW
Courtesy of Subaru of America, Inc.

## TROUBLE CODE 14: FUEL INJECTOR

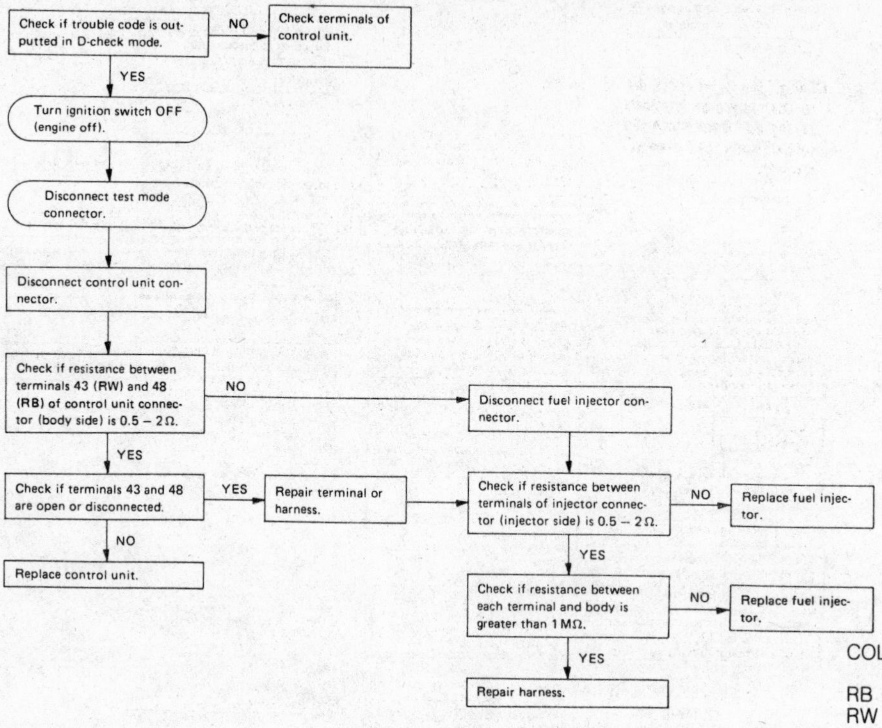

Check if trouble code is outputted in D-check mode.
NO
Check terminals of control unit.
YES
Turn ignition switch OFF (engine off).
Disconnect test mode connector.
Disconnect control unit connector.
Check if resistance between terminals 43 (RW) and 48 (RB) of control unit connector (body side) is 0.5 – 2 Ω.
NO
Disconnect fuel injector connector.
YES
Check if terminals 43 and 48 are open or disconnected.
YES
Repair terminal or harness.
NO
Replace control unit.
Check if resistance between terminals of injector connector (injector side) is 0.5 – 2 Ω.
NO
Replace fuel injector.
YES
Check if resistance between each terminal and body is greater than 1 MΩ.
NO
Replace fuel injector.
YES
Repair harness.

COLOR CODE:

RB – RED/BLACK
RW – RED/WHITE

## TROUBLE CODE 21: COOLANT THERMOSENSOR

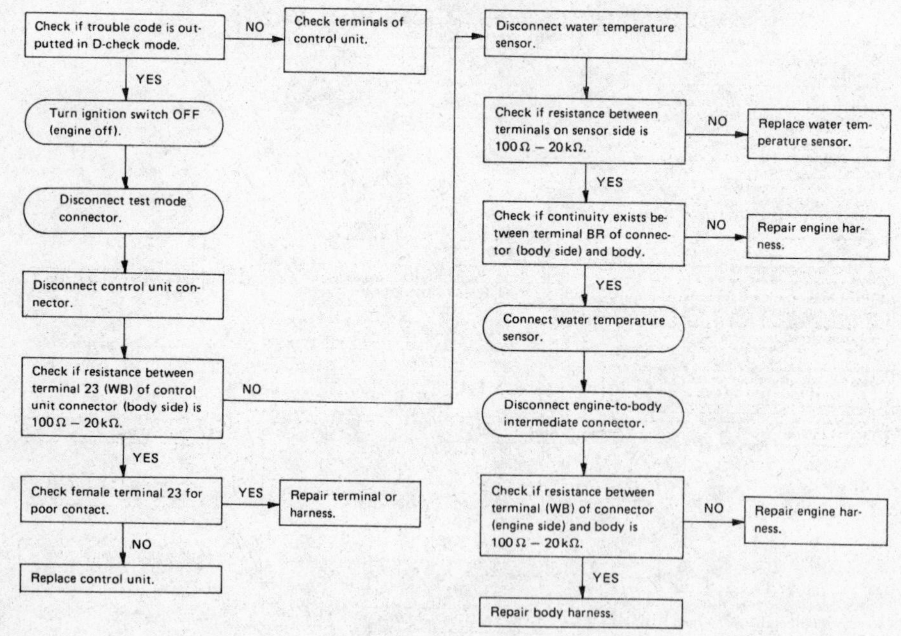
Check if trouble code is outputted in D-check mode.
NO
Check terminals of control unit.
YES
Turn ignition switch OFF (engine off).
Disconnect test mode connector.
Disconnect control unit connector.
Check if resistance between terminal 23 (WB) of control unit connector (body side) is 100 Ω – 20 kΩ.
NO
YES
Check female terminal 23 for poor contact.
YES
Repair terminal or harness.
NO
Replace control unit.
Disconnect water temperature sensor.
Check if resistance between terminals on sensor side is 100 Ω – 20 kΩ.
NO
Replace water temperature sensor.
YES
Check if continuity exists between terminal BR of connector (body side) and body.
NO
Repair engine harness.
YES
Connect water temperature sensor.
Disconnect engine-to-body intermediate connector.
Check if resistance between terminal (WB) of connector (engine side) and body is 100 Ω – 20 kΩ.
NO
Repair engine harness.
YES
Repair body harness.

COLOR CODE:

BR – BLACK/RED
WB – WHITE/BLACK

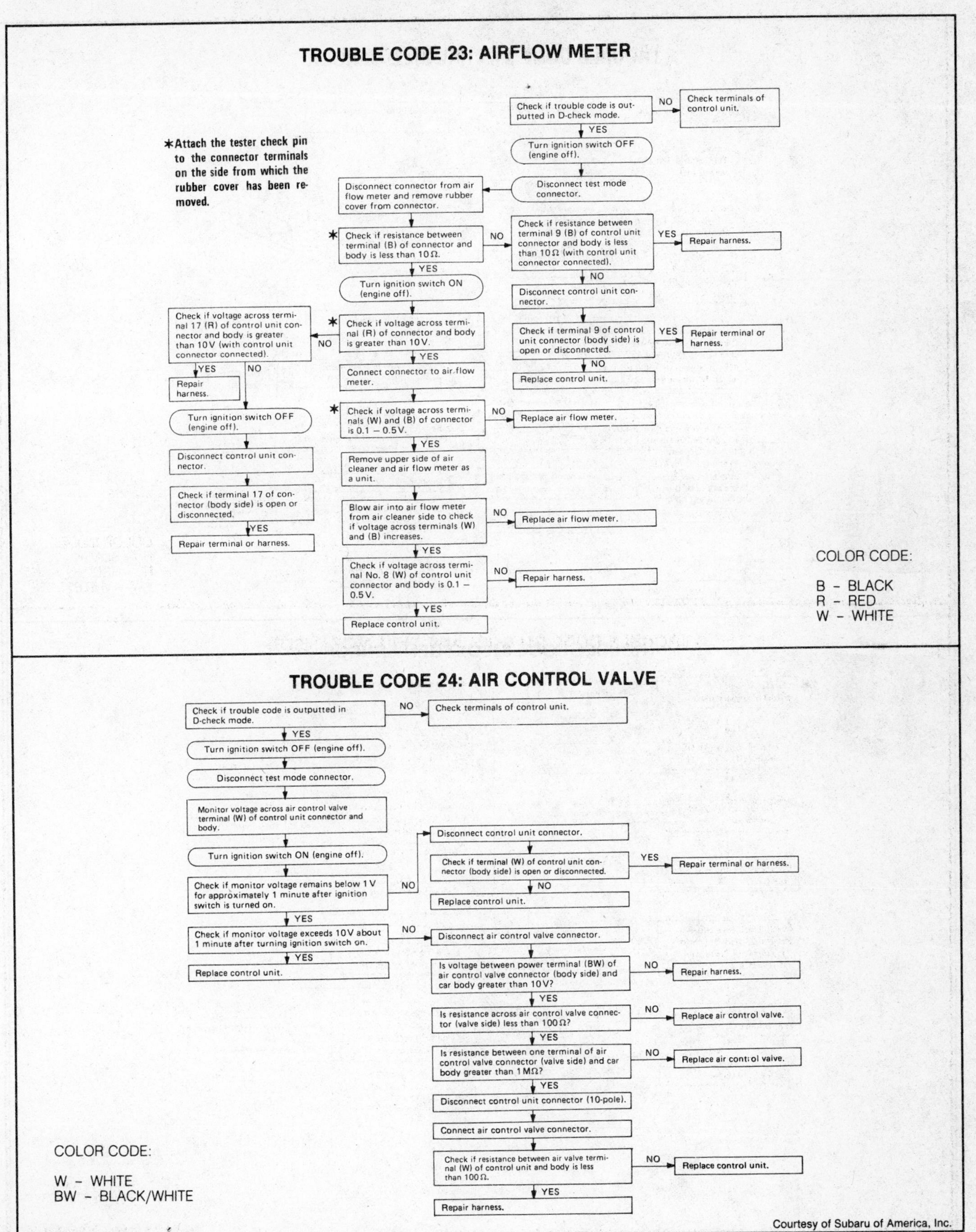
TROUBLE CODE 23: AIRFLOW METER
*Attach the tester check pin to the connector terminals on the side from which the rubber cover has been removed.
Check if trouble code is outputted in D-check mode.
NO
Check terminals of control unit.
YES
Turn ignition switch OFF (engine off).
Disconnect test mode connector.
Disconnect connector from air flow meter and remove rubber cover from connector.
* Check if resistance between terminal (B) of connector and body is less than 10 Ω.
NO
Check if resistance between terminal 9 (B) of control unit connector and body is less than 10 Ω (with control unit connector connected).
YES
Repair harness.
NO
Disconnect control unit connector.
Check if terminal 9 of control unit connector (body side) is open or disconnected.
YES
Repair terminal or harness.
NO
Replace control unit.
YES
Turn ignition switch ON (engine off).
* Check if voltage across terminal (R) of connector and body is greater than 10 V.
NO
Check if voltage across terminal 17 (R) of control unit connector and body is greater than 10 V (with control unit connector connected).
YES
Repair harness.
NO
Turn ignition switch OFF (engine off).
Disconnect control unit connector.
Check if terminal 17 of connector (body side) is open or disconnected.
YES
Repair terminal or harness.
YES
Connect connector to air flow meter.
* Check if voltage across terminals (W) and (B) of connector is 0.1 – 0.5 V.
NO
Replace air flow meter.
YES
Remove upper side of air cleaner and air flow meter as a unit.
Blow air into air flow meter from air cleaner side to check if voltage across terminals (W) and (B) increases.
NO
Replace air flow meter.
YES
Check if voltage across terminal No. 8 (W) of control unit connector and body is 0.1 – 0.5 V.
NO
Repair harness.
YES
Replace control unit.
COLOR CODE:
B – BLACK
R – RED
W – WHITE
TROUBLE CODE 24: AIR CONTROL VALVE
Check if trouble code is outputted in D-check mode.
NO
Check terminals of control unit.
YES
Turn ignition switch OFF (engine off).
Disconnect test mode connector.
Monitor voltage across air control valve terminal (W) of control unit connector and body.
Turn ignition switch ON (engine off).
Check if monitor voltage remains below 1 V for approximately 1 minute after ignition switch is turned on.
NO
Disconnect control unit connector.
Check if terminal (W) of control unit connector (body side) is open or disconnected.
YES
Repair terminal or harness.
NO
Replace control unit.
YES
Check if monitor voltage exceeds 10 V about 1 minute after turning ignition switch on.
NO
Disconnect air control valve connector.
Is voltage between power terminal (BW) of air control valve connector (body side) and car body greater than 10 V?
NO
Repair harness.
YES
Is resistance across air control valve connector (valve side) less than 100 Ω?
NO
Replace air control valve.
YES
Is resistance between one terminal of air control valve connector (valve side) and car body greater than 1 MΩ?
NO
Replace air control valve.
YES
Disconnect control unit connector (10-pole).
Connect air control valve connector.
Check if resistance between air valve terminal (W) of control unit and body is less than 100 Ω.
NO
Replace control unit.
YES
Repair harness.
YES
Replace control unit.
COLOR CODE:
W – WHITE
BW – BLACK/WHITE
Courtesy of Subaru of America, Inc.

## TROUBLE CODE 31: THROTTLE SENSOR

Check if trouble code is outputted in D-check mode.
- NO → Check control unit terminals.
- YES → Turn ignition switch OFF (engine off).

Disconnect test mode connector.

Disconnect control unit connector.

Check if resistance between terminals 26 (R) and 35 (B) of control unit connector is 3.5 – 6.5 kΩ.
- NO → Disconnect throttle sensor connector. → Check if resistance between terminals (B) and (D) is 3.5 – 6.5 kΩ.
  - YES → Replace throttle sensor.
  - NO → Repair harness.
- YES → Check if resistance between terminals 25 (W) and 35 (B) is less than 1 kΩ (when throttle is fully closed) and greater than 2.4 kΩ (when throttle is fully open).
  - NO → Disconnect throttle sensor connector. → Check if resistance between terminals (B) and (C) is less than 1 kΩ (when throttle is fully closed) and greater than 2.4 Ω (when throttle is fully open).
    - YES → Repair harness.
    - NO → Replace throttle sensor.
  - YES → Check if terminals 25, 26 and 35 are open or disconnected.
    - NO → Replace control unit.
    - YES → Repair terminal or harness.

A B C D

COLOR CODE:

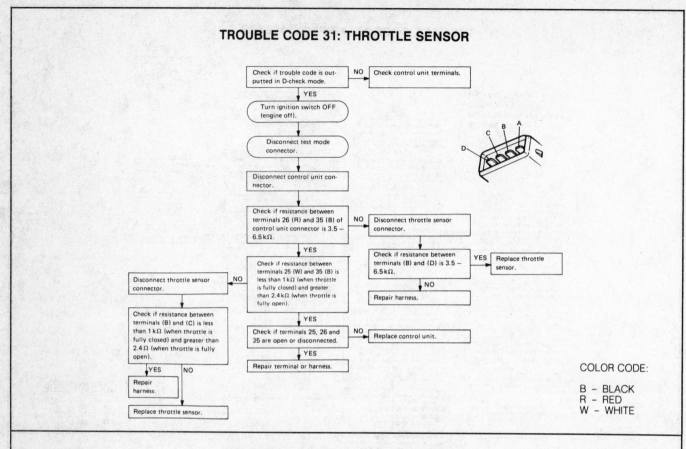

B – BLACK
R – RED
W – WHITE

## TROUBLE CODE 32: OXYGEN SENSOR

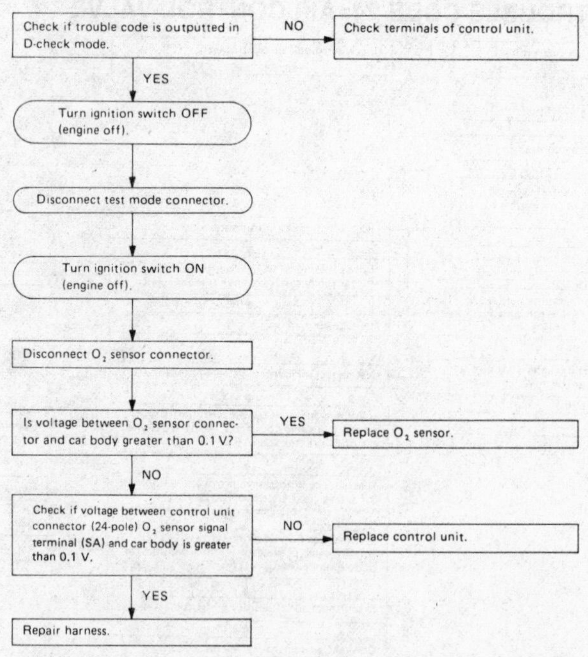
Check if trouble code is outputted in D-check mode.
NO
Check terminals of control unit.
YES
Turn ignition switch OFF (engine off).
Disconnect test mode connector.
Turn ignition switch ON (engine off).
Disconnect O₂ sensor connector.
Is voltage between O₂ sensor connector and car body greater than 0.1 V?
YES
Replace O₂ sensor.
NO
Check if voltage between control unit connector (24-pole) O₂ sensor signal terminal (SA) and car body is greater than 0.1 V.
NO
Replace control unit.
YES
Repair harness.

COLOR CODE:

SA – SEALED WIRE

Courtesy of Subaru of America, Inc.

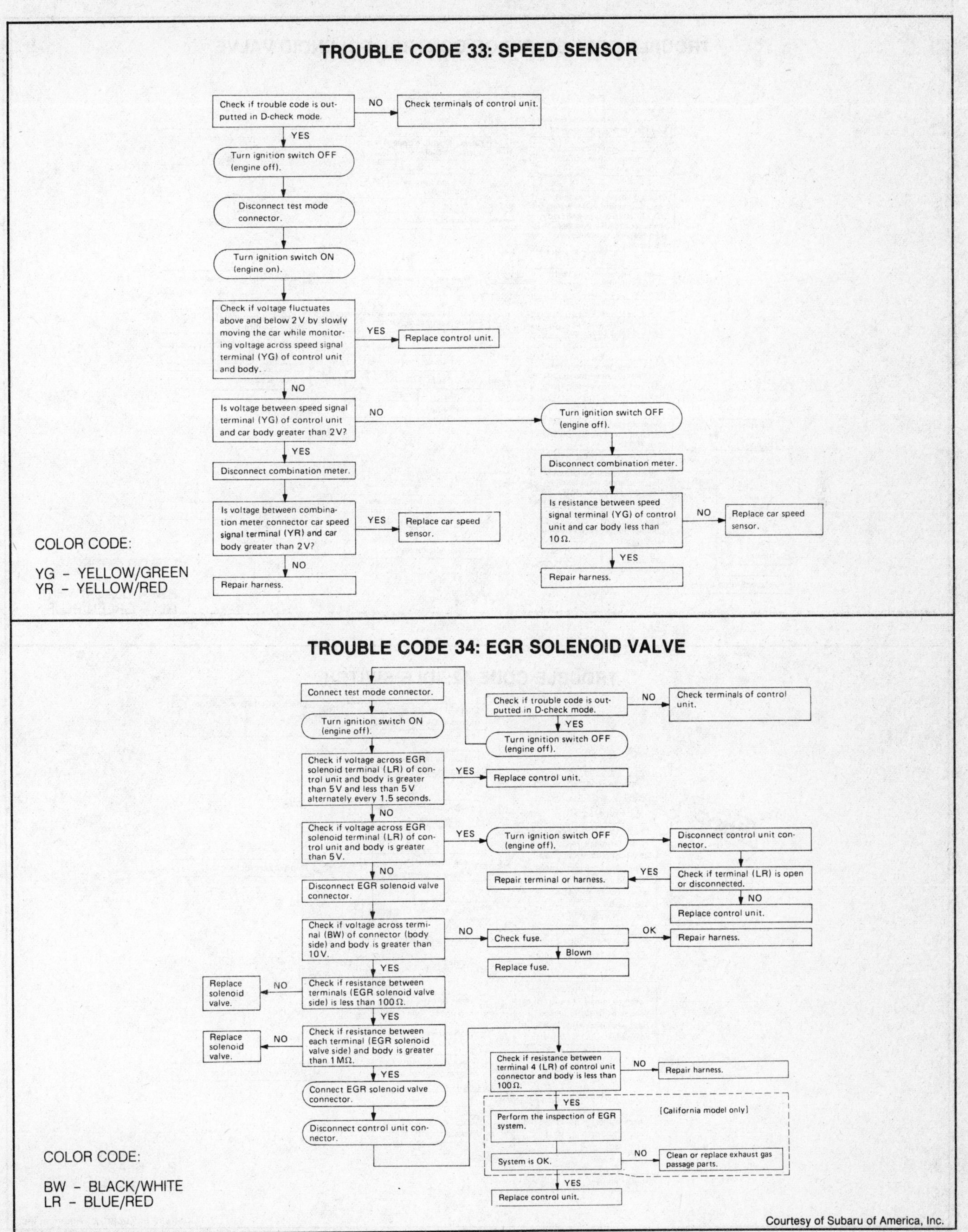
TROUBLE CODE 33: SPEED SENSOR
Check if trouble code is outputted in D-check mode.
NO
Check terminals of control unit.
YES
Turn ignition switch OFF (engine off).
Disconnect test mode connector.
Turn ignition switch ON (engine on).
Check if voltage fluctuates above and below 2 V by slowly moving the car while monitoring voltage across speed signal terminal (YG) of control unit and body.
YES
Replace control unit.
NO
Is voltage between speed signal terminal (YG) of control unit and car body greater than 2 V?
NO
Turn ignition switch OFF (engine off).
Disconnect combination meter.
Is resistance between speed signal terminal (YG) of control unit and car body less than 10 Ω.
NO
Replace car speed sensor.
YES
Repair harness.
YES
Disconnect combination meter.
Is voltage between combination meter connector car speed signal terminal (YR) and car body greater than 2 V?
YES
Replace car speed sensor.
NO
Repair harness.
COLOR CODE:
YG - YELLOW/GREEN
YR - YELLOW/RED
TROUBLE CODE 34: EGR SOLENOID VALVE
Check if trouble code is outputted in D-check mode.
NO
Check terminals of control unit.
YES
Turn ignition switch OFF (engine off).
Connect test mode connector.
Turn ignition switch ON (engine off).
Check if voltage across EGR solenoid terminal (LR) of control unit and body is greater than 5 V and less than 5 V alternately every 1.5 seconds.
YES
Replace control unit.
NO
Check if voltage across EGR solenoid terminal (LR) of control unit and body is greater than 5 V.
YES
Turn ignition switch OFF (engine off).
Disconnect control unit connector.
Check if terminal (LR) is open or disconnected.
YES
Repair terminal or harness.
NO
Replace control unit.
NO
Disconnect EGR solenoid valve connector.
Check if voltage across terminal (BW) of connector (body side) and body is greater than 10 V.
NO
Check fuse.
OK
Repair harness.
Blown
Replace fuse.
YES
Check if resistance between terminals (EGR solenoid valve side) is less than 100 Ω.
NO
Replace solenoid valve.
YES
Check if resistance between each terminal (EGR solenoid valve side) and body is greater than 1 MΩ.
NO
Replace solenoid valve.
YES
Connect EGR solenoid valve connector.
Disconnect control unit connector.
Check if resistance between terminal 4 (LR) of control unit connector and body is less than 100 Ω.
NO
Repair harness.
YES
[California model only]
Perform the inspection of EGR system.
System is OK.
NO
Clean or replace exhaust gas passage parts.
YES
Replace control unit.
COLOR CODE:
BW - BLACK/WHITE
LR - BLUE/RED

Courtesy of Subaru of America, Inc.

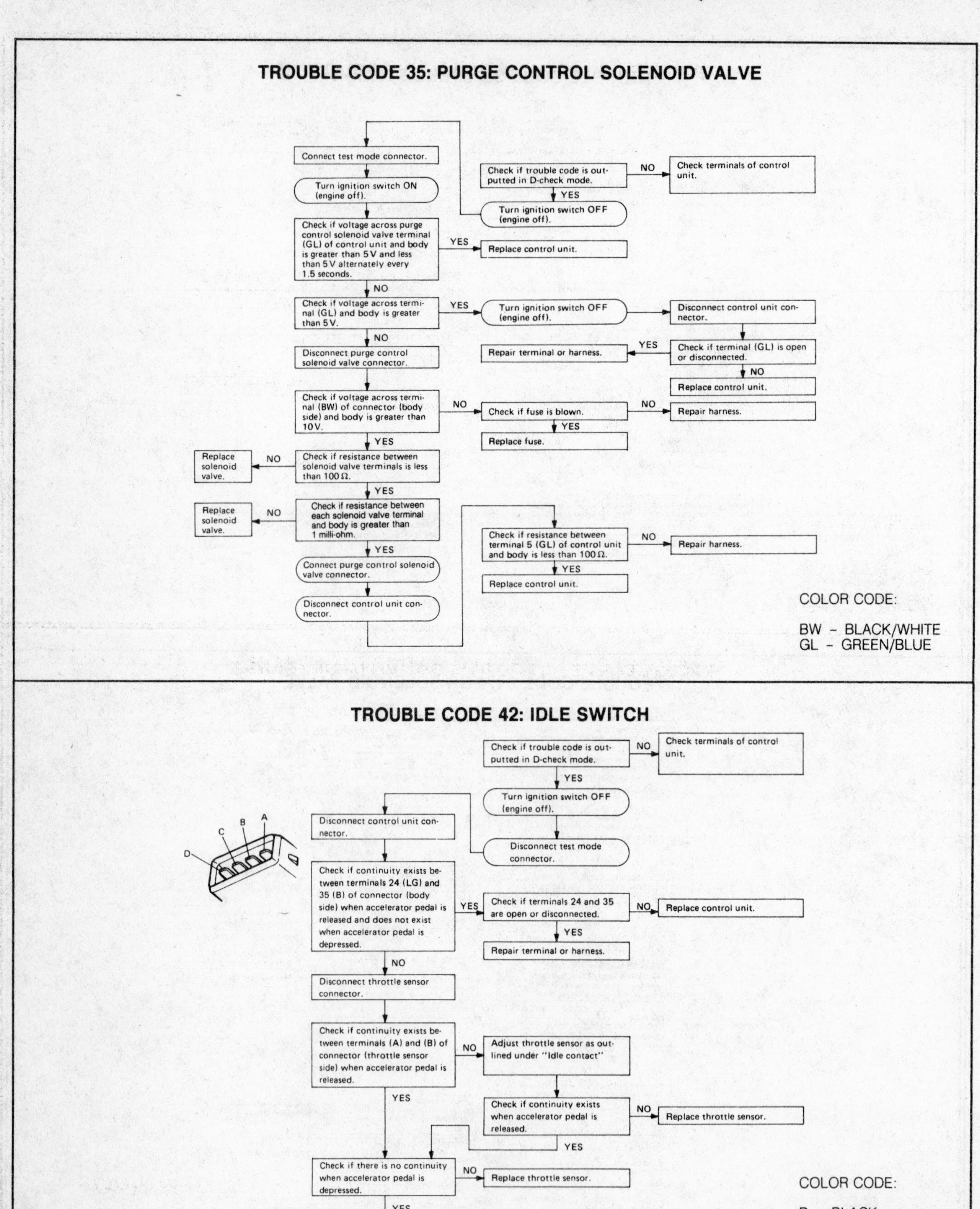
TROUBLE CODE 35: PURGE CONTROL SOLENOID VALVE
Connect test mode connector.
Turn ignition switch ON (engine off).
Check if voltage across purge control solenoid valve terminal (GL) of control unit and body is greater than 5 V and less than 5 V alternately every 1.5 seconds.
YES
Replace control unit.
NO
Check if voltage across terminal (GL) and body is greater than 5 V.
YES
Turn ignition switch OFF (engine off).
Disconnect control unit connector.
Check if terminal (GL) is open or disconnected.
YES
Repair terminal or harness.
NO
Replace control unit.
NO
Disconnect purge control solenoid valve connector.
Check if voltage across terminal (BW) of connector (body side) and body is greater than 10 V.
NO
Check if fuse is blown.
NO
Repair harness.
YES
Replace fuse.
YES
Check if resistance between solenoid valve terminals is less than 100 Ω.
NO
Replace solenoid valve.
YES
Check if resistance between each solenoid valve terminal and body is greater than 1 milli-ohm.
NO
Replace solenoid valve.
YES
Connect purge control solenoid valve connector.
Disconnect control unit connector.
Check if resistance between terminal 5 (GL) of control unit and body is less than 100 Ω.
NO
Repair harness.
YES
Replace control unit.
Check if trouble code is outputted in D-check mode.
NO
Check terminals of control unit.
YES
Turn ignition switch OFF (engine off).
COLOR CODE:
BW - BLACK/WHITE
GL - GREEN/BLUE
TROUBLE CODE 42: IDLE SWITCH
Check if trouble code is outputted in D-check mode.
NO
Check terminals of control unit.
YES
Turn ignition switch OFF (engine off).
Disconnect test mode connector.
Disconnect control unit connector.
A
B
C
D
Check if continuity exists between terminals 24 (LG) and 35 (B) of connector (body side) when accelerator pedal is released and does not exist when accelerator pedal is depressed.
YES
Check if terminals 24 and 35 are open or disconnected.
NO
Replace control unit.
YES
Repair terminal or harness.
NO
Disconnect throttle sensor connector.
Check if continuity exists between terminals (A) and (B) of connector (throttle sensor side) when accelerator pedal is released.
NO
Adjust throttle sensor as outlined under "Idle contact"
Check if continuity exists when accelerator pedal is released.
NO
Replace throttle sensor.
YES
YES
Check if there is no continuity when accelerator pedal is depressed.
NO
Replace throttle sensor.
YES
Repair harness.
COLOR CODE:
B - BLACK
LG - BLUE/GREEN

Courtesy of Subaru of America, Inc.

## TROUBLE CODE 45: KICKDOWN CONTROL RELAY

Check if trouble code is outputted in D-check mode.
NO
Check terminals of control unit.
YES
Turn ignition switch OFF (engine off).
Connect test mode connector.
Turn ignition switch ON (engine off).
Disconnect control unit connector.
Check if voltage across terminal 1 (LG) of connector (body side) and body is greater than 10 V.
NO
Disconnect kick-down relay connector.
Check if voltage across terminal (BW) of connector (body side) and body is greater than 10 V.
NO
Repair harness from ignition switch to relay.
YES
Check if continuity exists between terminals (BW) and (LG) of relay and their corresponding terminals.
NO
Replace relay.
YES
Repair harness from relay to control unit.
YES
Connect control unit connector.
Check if voltage across terminal 1 (LG) and body is less than 1 V.
NO
Disconnect control unit connector. Check if terminal 1 is open or disconnected.
NO
Replace control unit.
YES
Repair terminal or harness.
YES
Check if relay operates properly when ignition switch is repeatedly turned ON and OFF.
NO
Replace relay.
YES
Disconnect kick-down relay connector.
Check if continuity exists between terminal (L) of connector (body side) and body.
NO
Repair harness.
YES
Disconnect control unit connector.
Check if continuity exists between terminal 16 (LgR) of connector (body side) and body.
NO
Repair harness.
YES
Check if terminal 16 is open or disconnected.
YES
Repair terminal or harness.
NO
Replace control unit.

COLOR CODE:

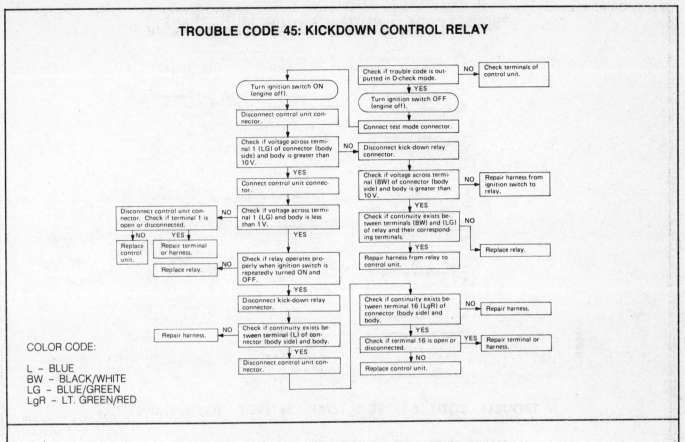

L – BLUE
BW – BLACK/WHITE
LG – BLUE/GREEN
LgR – LT. GREEN/RED

## TROUBLE CODE 51: NEUTRAL SWITCH (MAN. TRANS.)

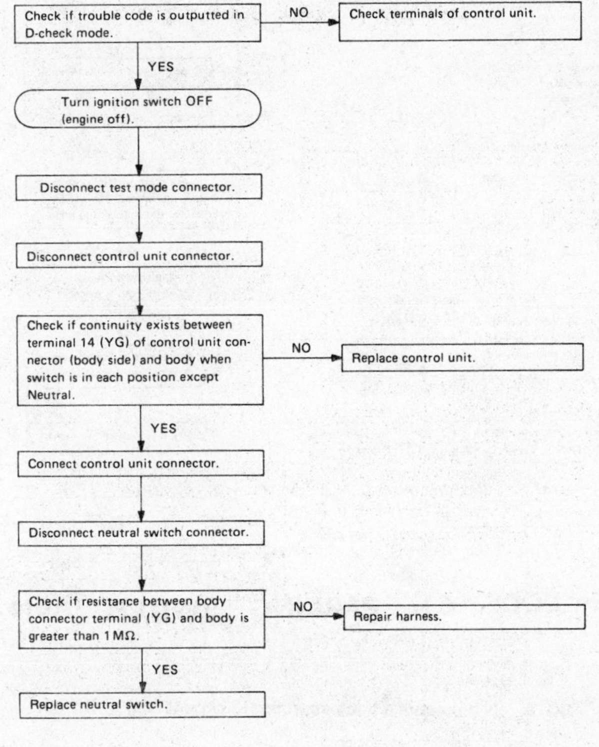

Check if trouble code is outputted in D-check mode.
NO
Check terminals of control unit.
YES
Turn ignition switch OFF (engine off).
Disconnect test mode connector.
Disconnect control unit connector.
Check if continuity exists between terminal 14 (YG) of control unit connector (body side) and body when switch is in each position except Neutral.
NO
Replace control unit.
YES
Connect control unit connector.
Disconnect neutral switch connector.
Check if resistance between body connector terminal (YG) and body is greater than 1 MΩ.
NO
Repair harness.
YES
Replace neutral switch.


COLOR CODE:

YG – YELLOW/GREEN

Courtesy of Subaru of America, Inc.

## TROUBLE CODE 51: NEUTRAL SWITCH (AUTO. TRANS.)

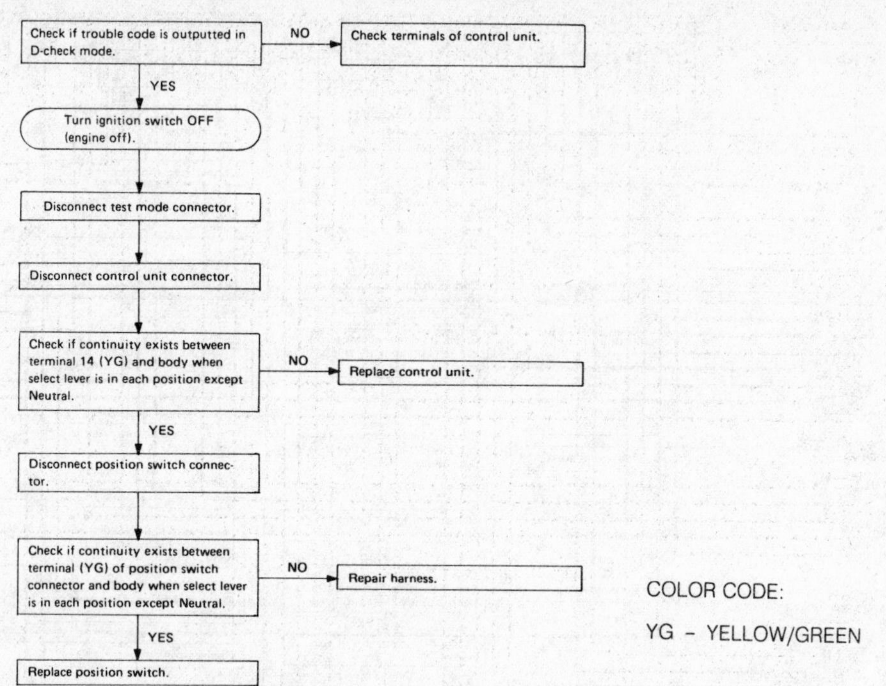
Check if trouble code is outputted in D-check mode.
NO
Check terminals of control unit.
YES
Turn ignition switch OFF (engine off).
Disconnect test mode connector.
Disconnect control unit connector.
Check if continuity exists between terminal 14 (YG) and body when select lever is in each position except Neutral.
NO
Replace control unit.
YES
Disconnect position switch connector.
Check if continuity exists between terminal (YG) of position switch connector and body when select lever is in each position except Neutral.
NO
Repair harness.
YES
Replace position switch.
COLOR CODE:
YG – YELLOW/GREEN

## TROUBLE CODE 55: EGR TEMP. SENSOR (Calif. Only)

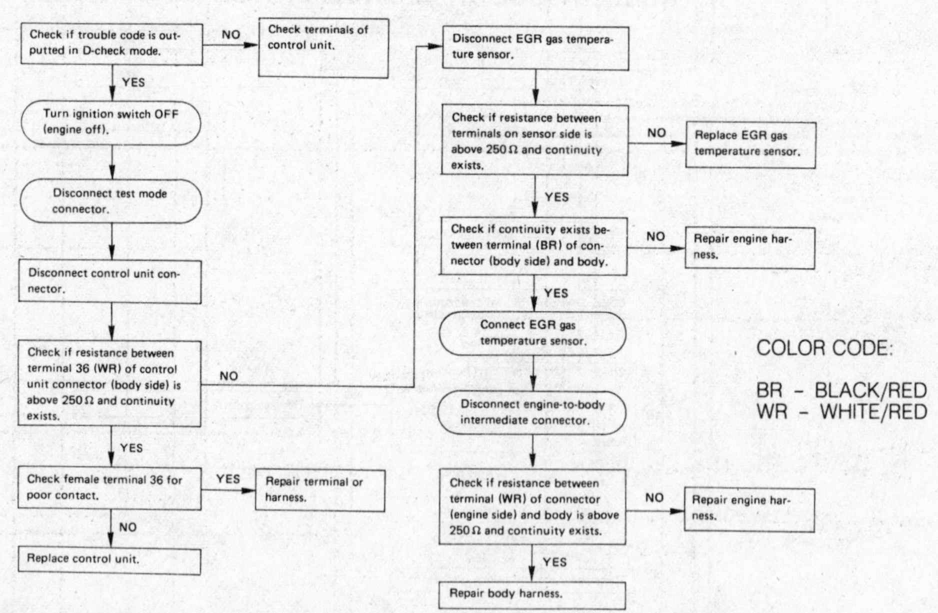
Check if trouble code is outputted in D-check mode.
NO
Check terminals of control unit.
YES
Turn ignition switch OFF (engine off).
Disconnect test mode connector.
Disconnect control unit connector.
Check if resistance between terminal 36 (WR) of control unit connector (body side) is above 250 Ω and continuity exists.
NO
YES
Check female terminal 36 for poor contact.
YES
Repair terminal or harness.
NO
Replace control unit.
Disconnect EGR gas temperature sensor.
Check if resistance between terminals on sensor side is above 250 Ω and continuity exists.
NO
Replace EGR gas temperature sensor.
YES
Check if continuity exists between terminal (BR) of connector (body side) and body.
NO
Repair engine harness.
YES
Connect EGR gas temperature sensor.
Disconnect engine-to-body intermediate connector.
Check if resistance between terminal (WR) of connector (engine side) and body is above 250 Ω and continuity exists.
NO
Repair engine harness.
YES
Repair body harness.
COLOR CODE:
BR – BLACK/RED
WR – WHITE/RED

## TROUBLE CODE 61: PARKING SWITCH (Auto. Trans.)

**NOTE:** If present, check appropriate circuits and switches.

Courtesy of Subaru of America, Inc.

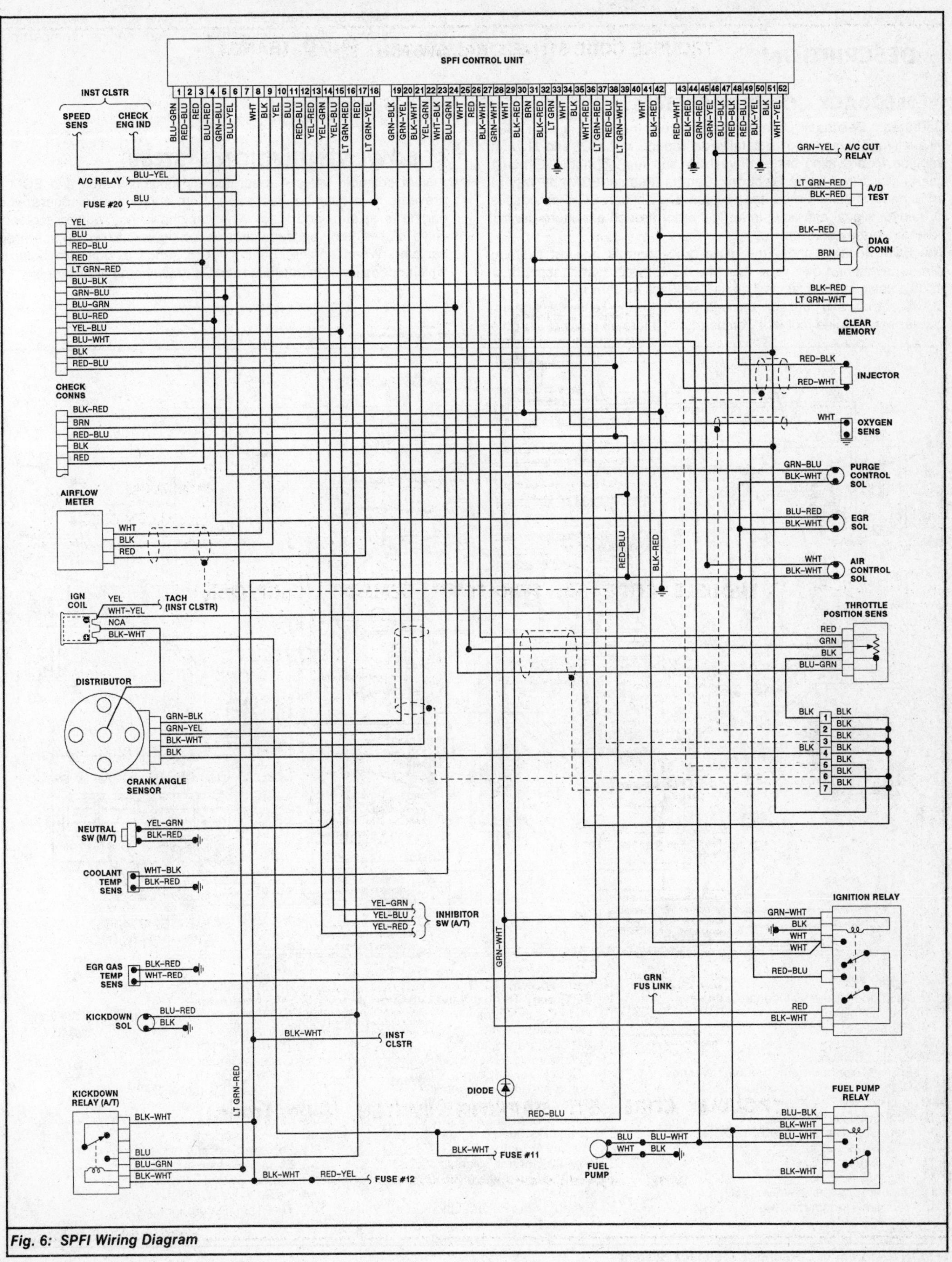
SPFI CONTROL UNIT
INST CLSTR
SPEED SENS
CHECK ENG IND
A/C RELAY
FUSE #20
CHECK CONNS
AIRFLOW METER
IGN COIL
TACH (INST CLSTR)
DISTRIBUTOR
CRANK ANGLE SENSOR
NEUTRAL SW (M/T)
COOLANT TEMP SENS
INHIBITOR SW (A/T)
EGR GAS TEMP SENS
KICKDOWN SOL
INST CLSTR
KICKDOWN RELAY (A/T)
FUSE #12
FUSE #11
DIODE
FUEL PUMP
GRN FUS LINK
A/C CUT RELAY
A/D TEST
DIAG CONN
CLEAR MEMORY
INJECTOR
OXYGEN SENS
PURGE CONTROL SOL
EGR SOL
AIR CONTROL SOL
THROTTLE POSITION SENS
IGNITION RELAY
FUEL PUMP RELAY

Fig. 6: SPFI Wiring Diagram

# Suzuki Carburetor FBC System

## Samurai

## DESCRIPTION

### FEEDBACK CONTROL SYSTEM

Carburetor Feedback Control (FBC) system maintains a controlled air/fuel ratio which allows catalyst to reduce HC, CO, and NOx in addition to providing better driveability and fuel economy. Exhaust gas is monitored by an Electronic Control Module (ECM) by way of an exhaust manifold mounted Oxygen ($O_2$) sensor. ECM processes $O_2$ sensor signal and adjusts air/fuel ratio through a mixture control solenoid in the carburetor.

The ECM, located under the glove box, controls fuel-cut system, idle-up system, bowl vent system, EGR system and secondary throttle valve system, as well as the feedback system.

ECM controls this function through the following received signals: $O_2$ sensor, engine coolant temperature (thermal) switch, throttle position (wide open and idle) switch, engine speed, electrical load, gear position, altitude compensation and engine compartment temperature. *See Fig. 1.*

## OPERATION

### BOWL VENTILATION SYSTEM

A vent solenoid valve is operated by ignition switch and ECM. It prevents float chamber fuel vapor from entering atmosphere when engine is at stop and load. When engine is not running, solenoid valve closes vent passage and vapor flows into a vapor storage canister. When engine running, ECM sends a signal to solenoid which opens inner vent tube. Vapor is drawn into carburetor.

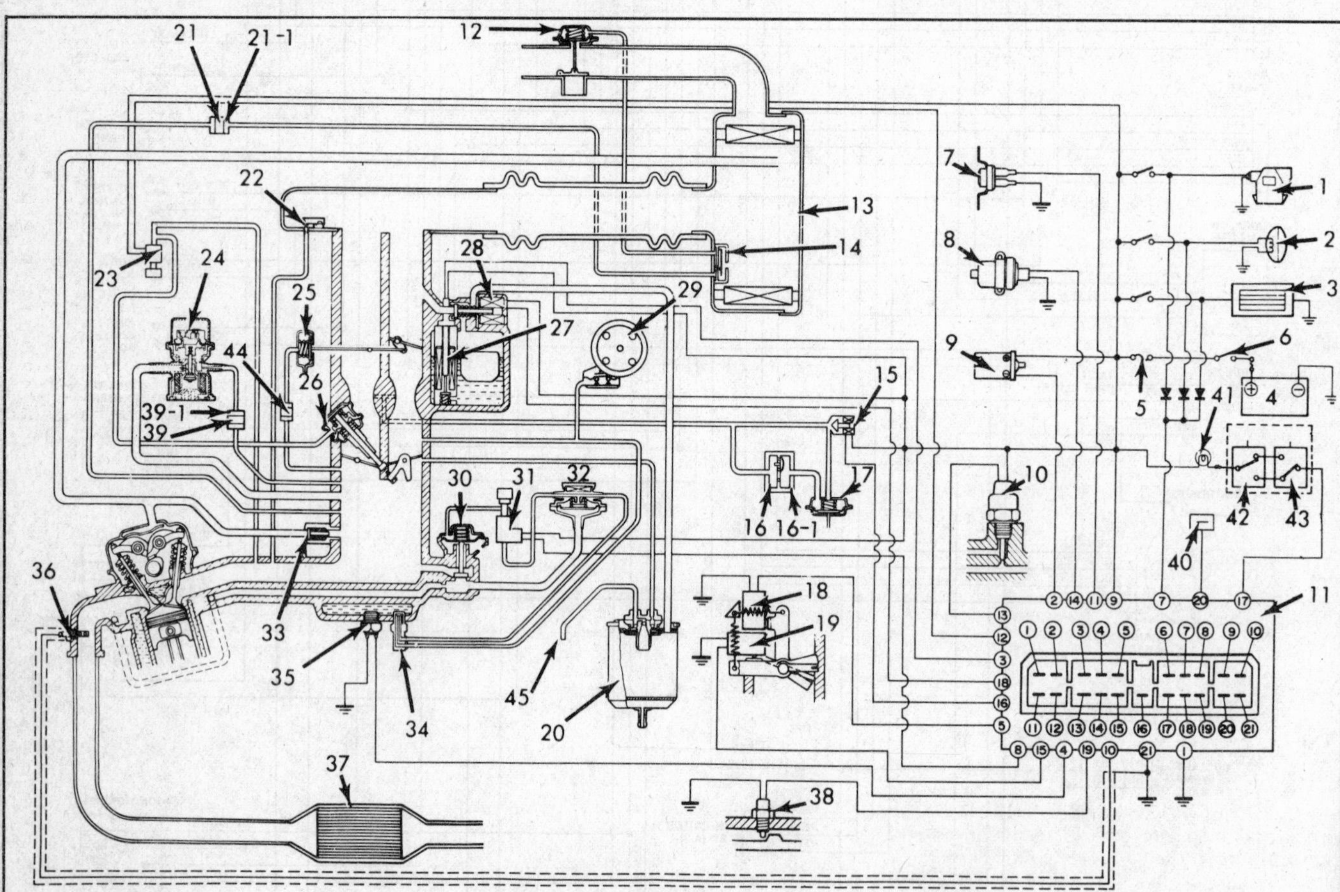

1. Heater Fan
2. Tail, Side Marker & License Lights
3. Rear Defogger
4. Battery
5. Circuit Fuse
6. Ignition Switch
7. Engine Compartment Thermal Switch
8. High Altitude Compensator (HAC)
9. Ignition Coil
10. Fuel-Cut Solenoid Valve
11. Electronic Control Module (ECM)
12. Air Control Actuator
13. Air Cleaner
14. Thermal Sensor
15. Vacuum Switching Valve (VSV)
16. Vacuum Transmitting Valve (VTV)

16-1. Brown Side (VTV)

17. Secondary Throttle Valve Actuator
18. Wide Open Microswitch
19. Idle Microswitch
20. Vapor Storage Canister
21. Check Valve (Black Side)

21-1. Check Valve (Orange Side)

22. Hot Idle Compensator (HIC)
23. 3-Way Solenoid Valve (TWSV)
24. Mixture Control Valve (MCV)
25. Choke Piston
26. Idle-Up Actuator
27. Mixture Control Solenoid Valve (MCSV)
28. Vent Solenoid Valve (VSV)
29. Distributor
30. Exhaust Gas Recirculation (EGR) Valve
31. 3-Way Solenoid Valve (TWSV)
32. EGR Modulator
33. Positive Crankcase Ventilation (PCV) Valve
34. Bi-Metallic Vacuum Switching Valve (BVSV)
35. Thermal Switch
36. Oxygen Sensor
37. 3-Way Catalyst
38. Fifth Gear Switch
39. Jet (Colorless Side)

39-1. Jet (Gray Side)

40. Check Connector
41. Oxygen Sensor Light
42. Mileage Sensor
43. Cancel Switch
44. Delay Valve (Orifice)
45. Fuel Tank Return Line

Courtesy of Suzuki of America Corp.

***Fig. 1: Diagram of Carburetor Feedback System***

## FUEL-CUT SYSTEM

Fuel-cut solenoid valve is operated by ignition switch. When ignition is turned off or during deceleration, electrical current to solenoid is cut off. The fuel-cut solenoid valve closes fuel passage and prevents fuel flow. During deceleration, fuel-cut solenoid eliminates fuel to engine temporarily. This occurs through signals from ECM, providing coolant temperature is normal, primary throttle valve is closed (idle micro switch is on) and engine speed exceeds 2400 RPM.

## HIGH ALTITUDE COMPENSATOR (HAC)

HAC senses barometric pressure and when air density is low, sends a signal to ECM. ECM adjusts the mixture control solenoid in carburetor to compensate for a rich air/fuel mixture condition.

## SECONDARY THROTTLE SYSTEM

When the primary throttle valve is almost completely open, the ECM signals the Vacuum Solenoid Valve (VSV) to open. Vacuum is then applied to secondary diaphragm, allowing the secondary throttle valve to respond to vacuum intensity.

# TESTING

## FEEDBACK SYSTEM CHECK

**1)** Turn cancel switch on. *See Fig. 2.* Turn ignition on, but do not start engine. "CHECK ENGINE" light should be on (not flashing). If light is not on, check and repair bulb and/or circuit.

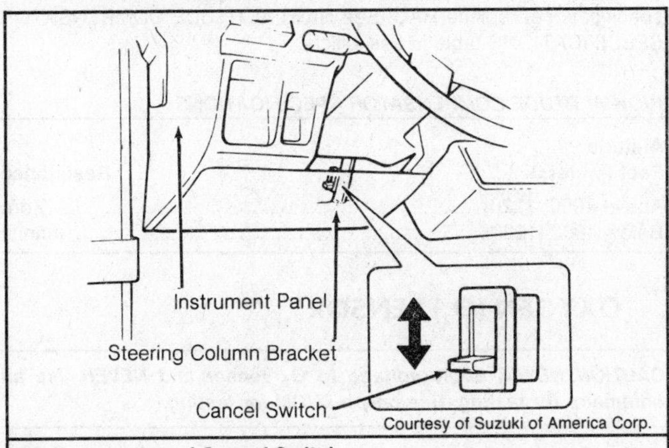
Instrument Panel
Steering Column Bracket
Cancel Switch
Courtesy of Suzuki of America Corp.

***Fig. 2: Location of Cancel Switch***

**2)** With "CHECK ENGINE" light operating, start engine and warm to normal operating temperature. Increase engine speed up to 1500-2000 RPM. "CHECK ENGINE" light will flash if system is operating properly. If light does not flash, check individual components. If system is operating properly, turn off cancel switch. Light should go out. Stop engine.

## THROTTLE POSITION SWITCH (WIDE OPEN & IDLE)

**1)** Warm engine to normal operating temperature. Turn off ignition. Using ohmmeter, connect negative probe to check terminal and connect positive probe to ground. *See Fig. 3.*

**2)** Turn ignition on and note ohmmeter indicator. See the MICROSWITCH TEST table in this article. If indicator does not deflect at all, reverse ohmmeter connection and retest. If test results are not as specified, check each microswitch and circuits.

**Idle Microswitch – 1)** Remove carburetor. Rotate fast idle cam counterclockwise and insert a pin through hole in cam and bracket, to lock cam in place. Connect ohmmeter to terminals of idle microswitch Green connector. *See Fig. 4.*

***MICROSWITCH TEST***

| Throttle Valve Position | Indicator Deflection |
|---|---|
| Idle Position | Swing |
| Half Open | Stay After Deflection |
| Wide Open | Swing |

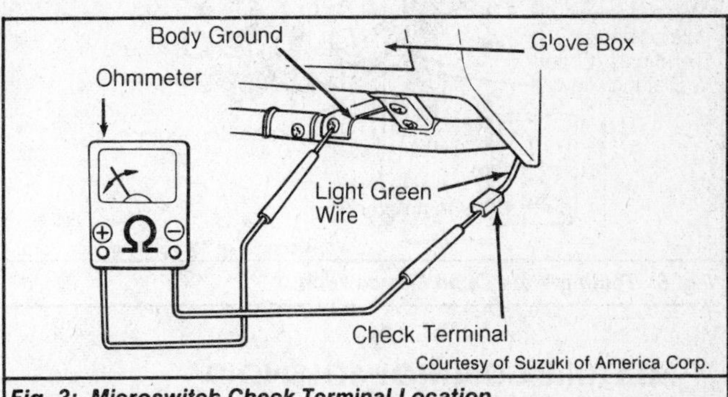
Body Ground
Glove Box
Ohmmeter
Light Green Wire
Check Terminal
Courtesy of Suzuki of America Corp.

***Fig. 3: Microswitch Check Terminal Location***

**2)** With throttle valve in idle position, ohmmeter should indicate zero ohm. With throttle valve opened 1/4 to 1/2, ohmmeter reading should be infinity. If not within the specifications, replace the idle microswitch.

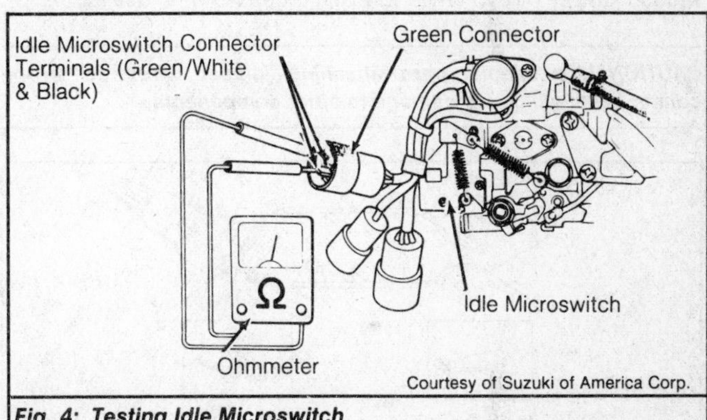
Idle Microswitch Connector Terminals (Green/White & Black)
Green Connector
Idle Microswitch
Ohmmeter
Courtesy of Suzuki of America Corp.

***Fig. 4: Testing Idle Microswitch***

**3)** Open throttle valve slowly until throttle valve-to-carburetor bore clearance is .014-.024" (.36-.62 mm). *See Fig. 5.* Ohmmeter reading should move from zero ohm to infinity. If not, adjust by bending lever. *See Fig. 5.* Bend lever down if clearance is less than specifications. Bend lever up if greater than specifications.

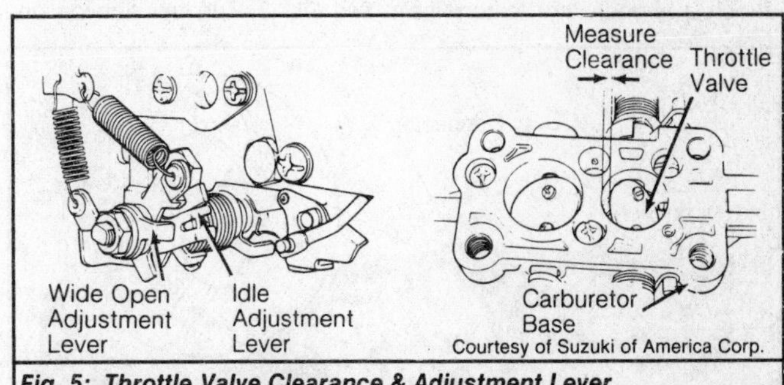
Measure Clearance
Throttle Valve
Wide Open Adjustment Lever
Idle Adjustment Lever
Carburetor Base
Courtesy of Suzuki of America Corp.

***Fig. 5: Throttle Valve Clearance & Adjustment Lever***

**Wide Open Microswitch – 1)** Connect ohmmeter to wide open microswitch connector. *See Fig. 6.* Ohmmeter should read zero ohm. With throttle valve fully opened, ohmmeter should read infinity. If not within specifications, replace microswitch.

**2)** Open throttle valve gradually until ohmmeter reads infinity. Measure throttle valve-to-carburetor clearance. Clearance should be .24-.28" (6.0-7.2 mm). *See Fig. 5.* If clearance is not within specifications, adjust by bending lever. *See Fig. 5.* With check completed, install carburetor.

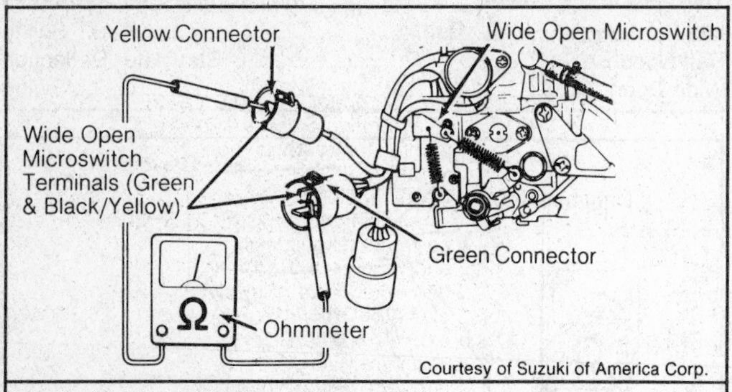
Yellow Connector
Wide Open Microswitch
Wide Open
Microswitch
Terminals (Green
& Black/Yellow)
Green Connector
Ohmmeter
Courtesy of Suzuki of America Corp.

***Fig. 6: Testing Wide Open Microswitch***

## MIXTURE CONTROL SOLENOID VALVE (MCSV) CHECK

**1)** Ensure ignition is off. Disconnect connectors from ECM, TWSV's and VSV. *See Fig. 1.* Disconnect mixture control solenoid valve connector at Green connector, located next to air duct. Attach a jumper wire to Yellow/Black wire and Black/White wire. Attach a second jumper wire to White wire and Blue/Red wire. *See Fig. 7.*

***CAUTION: Use special care attaching jumper wires as wrong connections will cause damage to other components.***

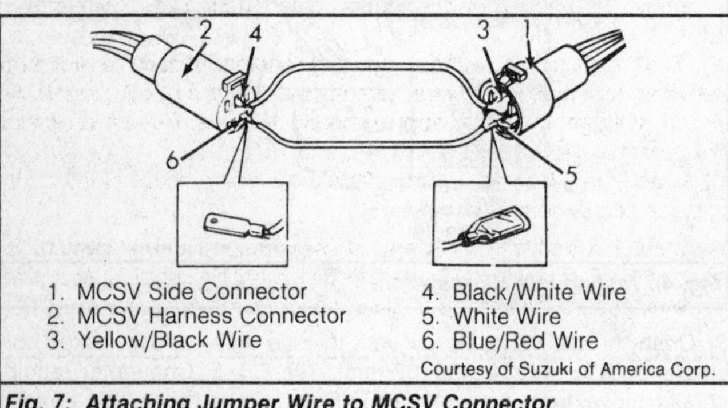
2
4
3
1
6
5
1. MCSV Side Connector
2. MCSV Harness Connector
3. Yellow/Black Wire
4. Black/White Wire
5. White Wire
6. Blue/Red Wire
Courtesy of Suzuki of America Corp.

***Fig. 7: Attaching Jumper Wire to MCSV Connector***

**2)** Remove cap from duty check connector, located on firewall and attach a jumper wire to terminals. *See Fig. 8.* Turn ignition on and off repeatedly (without starting engine). An operating sound should be heard from MCSV at carburetor. Check circuit and/or replace MCSV as necessary.

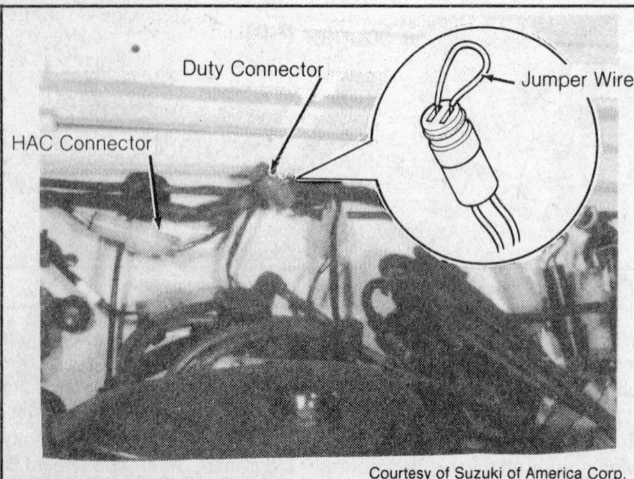
Duty Connector
Jumper Wire
HAC Connector
Courtesy of Suzuki of America Corp.

***Fig. 8: Duty Connector Locations & Identification***

## COOLANT TEMPERATURE (THERMAL) SWITCH

***NOTE: Thermal switch may be checked installed or removed. Procedure given is with switch installed. Specifications for both are the same.***

Disconnect thermal switch connector and attach ohmmeter between terminals. With coolant temperature BELOW 86°F (30°C), continuity should be present. With coolant temperature ABOVE 116°F (46.5°C), continuity should not be present. If not within specifications, replace switch.

## ENGINE COMPARTMENT THERMAL SWITCH

Disconnect engine compartment thermal switch electrical connector. *See Fig. 8.* Attach ohmmeter between terminals on switch side. With ambient temperature BELOW 44°F (7°C), zero ohm should be present. With ambient temperature ABOVE 67°F (19.5°C), ohmmeter should read infinity. If not within specifications, replace switch.

## HIGH ALTITUDE COMPENSATOR

Disconnect High Altitude Compensator (HAC) connector. *See Fig. 8.* Attach ohmmeter between terminals on HAC side. If not within specifications, replace HAC. See HIGH ALTITUDE COMPENSATOR SPECIFICATIONS table in this article.

***HIGH ALTITUDE COMPENSATOR SPECIFICATIONS***

| Altitude Feet (Meters) | Resistance |
|---|---|
| Above 4000 (1220) | Zero |
| Below 4000 (1220) | Infinite |

## OXYGEN ($O_2$) SENSOR

***CAUTION: NEVER apply voltage to $O_2$ sensor and NEVER use an ohmmeter for testing. Use only a DVOM for testing.***

**1)** Ensure engine is at normal operating temperature. Disconnect oxygen sensor. Attach DVOM to $O_2$ sensor connector terminal and ground. Increase and maintain engine speed at 1500-2000 RPM. Turn wide open microswitch off by moving carburetor lever downward. DVOM should show a reading of about .8 volts.
**2)** Decrease engine speed to 1000-1500 RPM. Disconnect mixture control valve vacuum hose at intake manifold. DVOM reading should drop below .2 volts. If not within specifications, replace $O_2$ sensor.

# CIRCUIT CHECKING

***NOTE: If feedback system does not seem to operate properly after components have been checked, perform these circuit checks.***

## ELECTRONIC CONTROL MODULE (ECM)

**Ground Circuits – 1)** ECM is grounded at both the dash and intake manifold. Feedback system will not function properly if either ground is not secure. Turn ignition off. Disconnect ECM connector.
**2)** Attach ohmmeter between terminal No. 1 (harness side) and ground. *See Fig. 10.* Note ohmmeter reading. Repeat procedure for terminal No. 21 and note ohmmeter reading. If ohmmeter readings at both terminals are zero, ground system is secure.

# Suzuki Carburetor FBC System (Cont.)

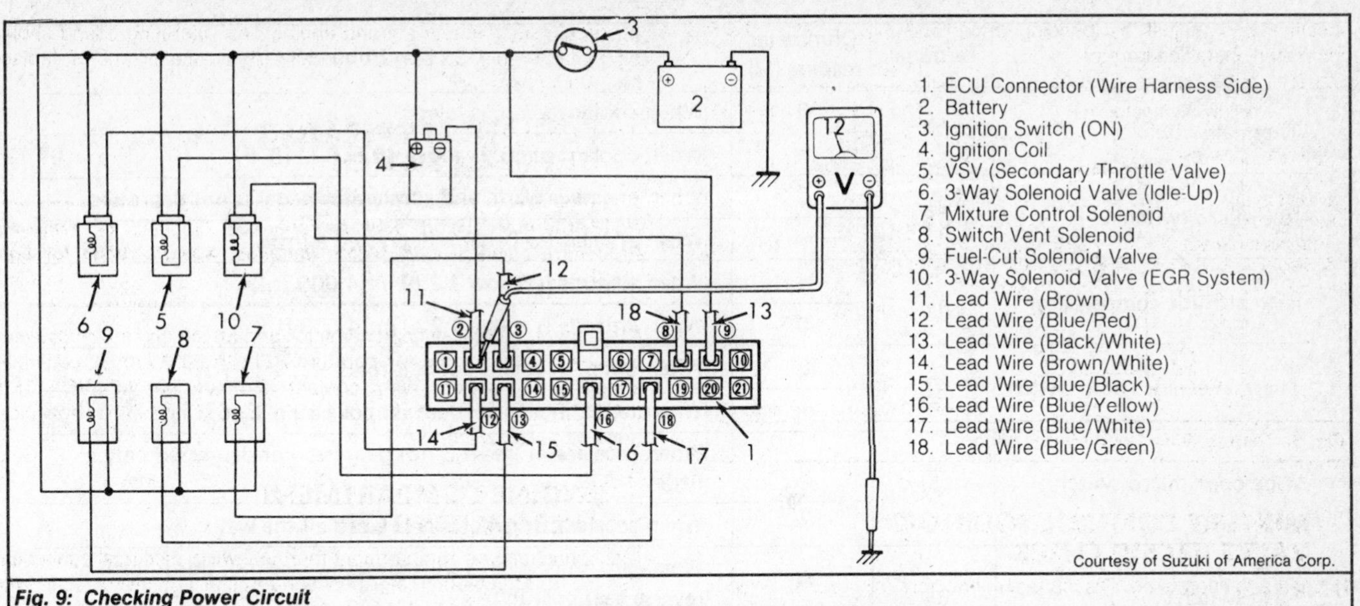
1. ECU Connector (Wire Harness Side)
2. Battery
3. Ignition Switch (ON)
4. Ignition Coil
5. VSV (Secondary Throttle Valve)
6. 3-Way Solenoid Valve (Idle-Up)
7. Mixture Control Solenoid
8. Switch Vent Solenoid
9. Fuel-Cut Solenoid Valve
10. 3-Way Solenoid Valve (EGR System)
11. Lead Wire (Brown)
12. Lead Wire (Blue/Red)
13. Lead Wire (Black/White)
14. Lead Wire (Brown/White)
15. Lead Wire (Blue/Black)
16. Lead Wire (Blue/Yellow)
17. Lead Wire (Blue/White)
18. Lead Wire (Blue/Green)
Courtesy of Suzuki of America Corp.

*Fig. 9: Checking Power Circuit*

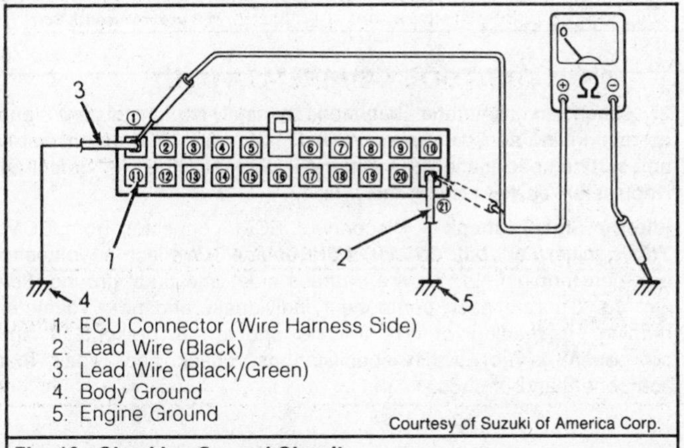
1. ECU Connector (Wire Harness Side)
2. Lead Wire (Black)
3. Lead Wire (Black/Green)
4. Body Ground
5. Engine Ground
Courtesy of Suzuki of America Corp.

*Fig. 10: Checking Ground Circuit*

**3)** If reading is not zero, repair ground as necessary. One ground wire is a Black/Green wire, mounted to firewall, near battery. Second ground wire is a Black wire, mounted to intake manifold, near thermostat housing.

**Power Circuits – 1)** Ignition coil, solenoids and/or solenoids valves are connected to ECM. If any component(s) is disconnected or fails, ECU detects an abnormalty. As a result, feedback will NOT operate properly. To check power circuits, disconnect ECM connector at ECM.

**2)** Turn ignition on without starting engine. Attach a voltmeter between terminal No. 2 (wire harness side) and a good ground. *See Fig. 9.* Voltage should be approximately 12 volts. Repeat procedure for terminals No. 3, 8, 9, 12, 13, 16, and 18.

**3)** If any circuit is not approximately 12 volts, repair wire and/or replace component as necessary.

**Sensors & Circuits – 1)** If any of the sensors and/or circuits fail, feedback system will NOT operate properly. To check sensors and circuits, ensure ignition is off. Disconnect ECM connector at ECM.

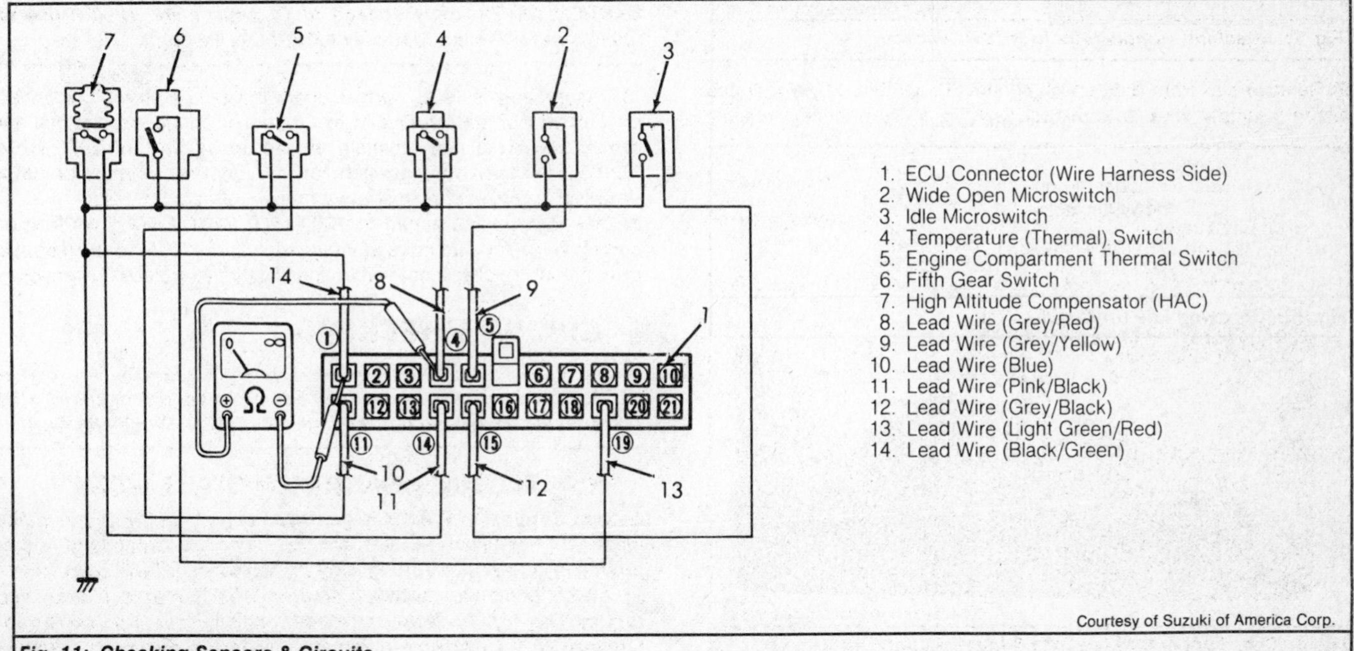
1. ECU Connector (Wire Harness Side)
2. Wide Open Microswitch
3. Idle Microswitch
4. Temperature (Thermal) Switch
5. Engine Compartment Thermal Switch
6. Fifth Gear Switch
7. High Altitude Compensator (HAC)
8. Lead Wire (Grey/Red)
9. Lead Wire (Grey/Yellow)
10. Lead Wire (Blue)
11. Lead Wire (Pink/Black)
12. Lead Wire (Grey/Black)
13. Lead Wire (Light Green/Red)
14. Lead Wire (Black/Green)
Courtesy of Suzuki of America Corp.

*Fig. 11: Checking Sensors & Circuits*

# Suzuki Carburetor FBC System (Cont.)

| Sensor | Terminal | Ohmmeter reading (Ω) | Condition |
|---|---|---|---|
| Thermal switch | ④ | 0 | When coolant temp. is low. |
| | | ∞ | When coolant temp. is above 46.5°C (116°F). |
| Idle micro switch | ⑮ | 0 | When engine is warm and accelerator pedal is not depressed. |
| | | ∞ | When accelerator pedal is depressed a little. |
| High altitude compensator | ⑭ | ∞ | When altitude is below 1,220 m (4,000 ft.). |
| | | 0 | When altitude is above 1,220 m (4,000 ft.). |
| Thermal engine room switch | ⑪ | 0 | When temp. in engine room is low. |
| | | ∞ | When temp. in engine room is above 19.5°C (67°F). |
| Wide open micro switch | ⑤ | 0 | When accelerator pedal is not depressed or depressed only a little. |
| | | ∞ | When accelerator pedal is depressed all the way. |
| Fifth switch | ⑲ | ∞ | When gear shift lever is shifted to low, second, third, forth or reverse gear position. |
| | | 0 | When gear shift lever is shifted to fifth gear position. |

Courtesy of Suzuki of America Corp.

*Fig. 12: Sensors & Circuits Specifications*

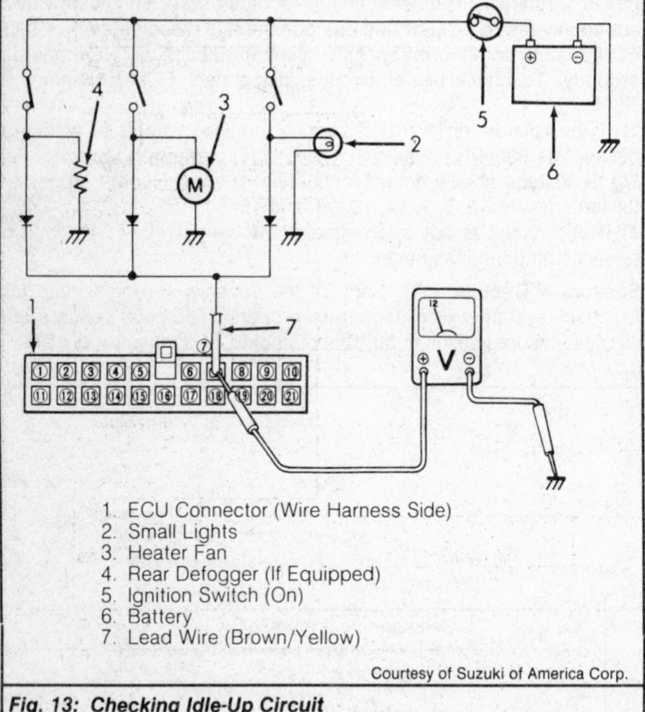

1
2
3
4
5
6
7
M
V
1. ECU Connector (Wire Harness Side)
2. Small Lights
3. Heater Fan
4. Rear Defogger (If Equipped)
5. Ignition Switch (On)
6. Battery
7. Lead Wire (Brown/Yellow)


Courtesy of Suzuki of America Corp.

*Fig. 13: Checking Idle-Up Circuit*

**2)** Attach an ohmmeter between terminal No. 1 (ground) and corresponding sensor terminal. *See Fig. 11 and 12.* If any circuit is not within specifications, component and/or circuit is defective. Replace or repair as necessary.

**Idle-Up Signal Check** – Disconnect ECM connector from ECM. Turn ignition on but do not start engine. Connect a voltmeter between terminal No. 7 (wire harness side) and body ground. *See Fig. 13.* Operate each component individually and note voltmeter reading. A reading of 11-14 volts should be present. If any component is not within specifications, check and repair that component and/or circuit.

# Suzuki Carburetor FBC System (Cont.)

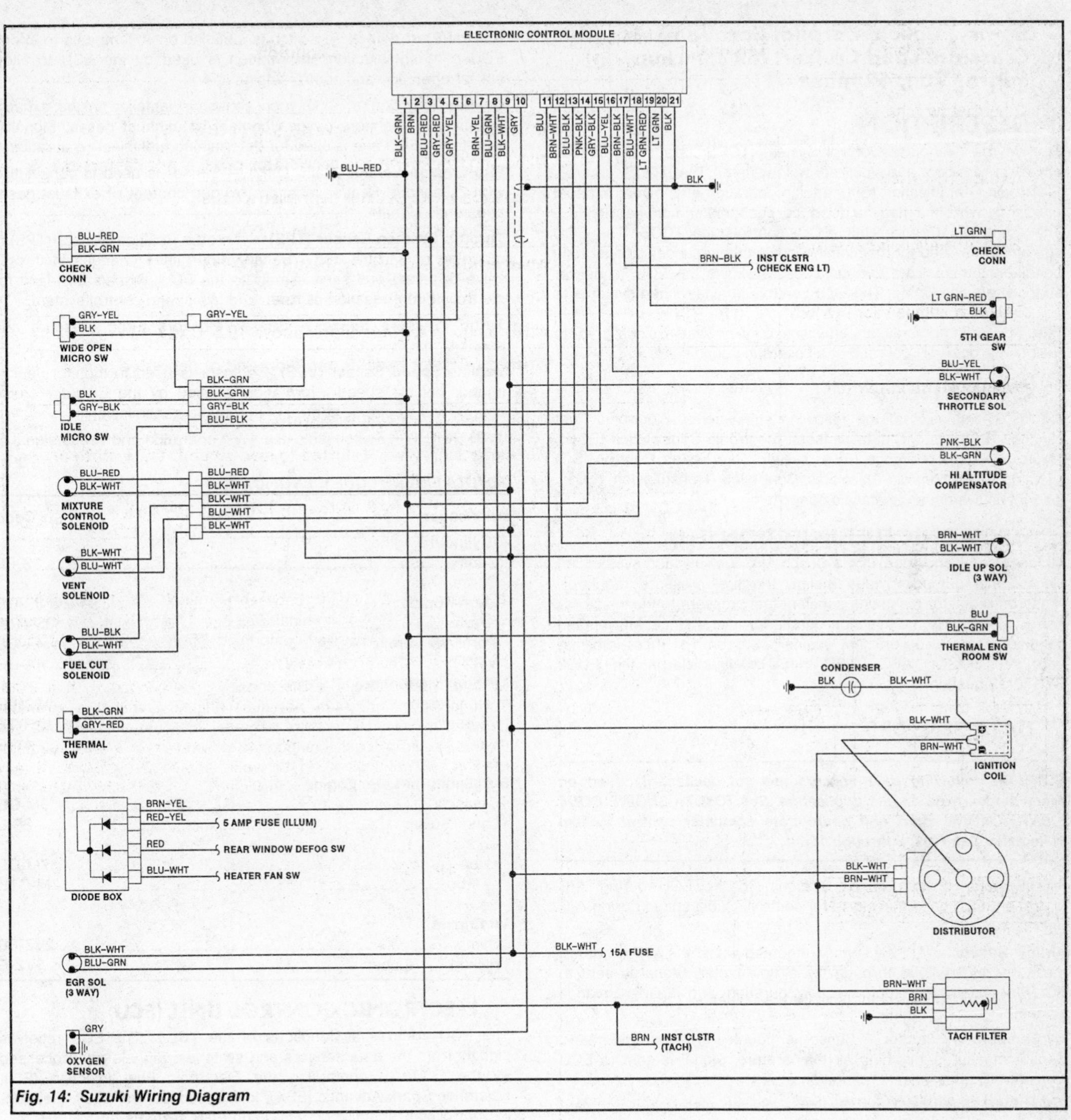
ELECTRONIC CONTROL MODULE
1 2 3 4 5 6 7 8 9 10 11 12 13 14 15 16 17 18 19 20 21
BLK-GRN
BRN
BLU-RED
GRY-RED
GRY-YEL
BRN-YEL
BLU-GRN
BLK-WHT
GRY
BLU
BRN-WHT
BLU-BLK
PNK-BLK
GRY-BLK
BLU-YEL
BRN-BLK
BLU-WHT
LT GRN-RED
LT GRN
BLK
CHECK CONN
WIDE OPEN MICRO SW
IDLE MICRO SW
MIXTURE CONTROL SOLENOID
VENT SOLENOID
FUEL CUT SOLENOID
THERMAL SW
5 AMP FUSE (ILLUM)
REAR WINDOW DEFOG SW
HEATER FAN SW
DIODE BOX
EGR SOL (3 WAY)
OXYGEN SENSOR
INST CLSTR (CHECK ENG LT)
5TH GEAR SW
SECONDARY THROTTLE SOL
HI ALTITUDE COMPENSATOR
IDLE UP SOL (3 WAY)
THERMAL ENG ROOM SW
CONDENSER
IGNITION COIL
DISTRIBUTOR
15A FUSE
INST CLSTR (TACH)
TACH FILTER

*Fig. 14: Suzuki Wiring Diagram*

# 1988 COMPUTERIZED ENGINE CONTROLS
# Toyota Computer Control System

## Camry, Celica, Corolla, Corolla FX-16, Cressida, Land Cruiser, MR2, Pickup, Supra, Van, 4Runner

## DESCRIPTION

The Toyota Computer Control System (TCCS) is a computerized emission, ignition and fuel control system. The TCCS controls Electronic Fuel Injection (EFI), engine operation and lowers exhaust emissions while maintaining good fuel economy and driveability.

The Electronic Control Unit (ECU) controls the TCCS. The ECU contains data used for maintaining ignition timing under all operating conditions. Input from various sensors allows the ECU to deliver spark at precise timing. The ECU controls engine related systems to adjust engine operation.

The TCCS is primarily an emission control system, designed to maintain proper air/fuel ratio at all operating conditions.

## OPERATION

The TCCS consists of the following subsystems: Electronic Fuel Injection (EFI) system, data sensors, Electronic Control Unit (ECU), Electronic Spark Advance (ESA) system, Idle Speed Control (ISC) system, EGR Control, Electronic Controlled Transmission (ECT), diagnostic system and catalytic converter.

### ELECTRONIC FUEL INJECTION (EFI)

All models are equipped with a Bosch AFC fuel injection system. An electric fuel pump provides fuel to the fuel pressure regulator. Pressure regulator maintains constant fuel pressure to the injectors. The ECU controls the injection duration in accordance with engine conditions to provide efficient engine operation. For more information, see BOSCH AFC FUEL INJECTION article in the FUEL SYSTEMS section.

### DATA SENSORS

***NOTE: The following data sensors are not necessarily used on every model. Note engine application. See TOYOTA ENGINE CODE IDENTIFICATION chart and appropriate computer control system schematic. See Figs. 5 through 16.***

**A/C Switch** – Switch sends a signal to the ECU during A/C operation. ECU uses this signal for controlling idle speed during A/C operation.

**Airflow Sensor** – Airflow sensor, mounted within the airflow meter, measures airflow rate through the airflow meter. Signal is sent to ECU for controlling fuel injection duration and spark advance system.

**Air Temperature Sensor** – Sensor is mounted in the airflow meter. Sensor measures incoming air temperature. Signal is sent to ECU for controlling fuel injection duration.

**Cold Start Injector Time Switch** – Switch determines coolant temperature and sends signal to ECU on some models for cold start injector control.

**Coolant Temperature Sensor** – Coolant temperature sensor sends signal to ECU in relation to coolant temperature. ECU uses sensor signal for controlling fuel injection duration, spark advance system, idle speed control system and EGR system.

**Coolant Temperature Switch** – Switch monitors coolant temperature and sends signal to ECU.

**EGR Gas Temperature Sensor** – Sensor determines EGR gas temperature and sends signal to ECU.

**Engine Speed** – Engine speed signal information is received from the ignition coil. The ECU uses these signals for fuel injection duration control and spark advance system operation.

**Knock Sensor** – Sensor monitiors ignition knock conditions and sends signal to ECU.

**Neutral/Start Switch** – Switch is installed on A/T models to inform ECU of gear selection. Information is used by the ECU to allow starter operation and control engine idle.

**Oxygen ($O_2$) Sensor** – Oxygen sensor is installed in the exhaust system and monitors oxygen content of exhaust gases. Signal is sent to the ECU and is used for determining fuel injection duration.

**Sub-Oxygen Sensor (Calif. Only)** – Sensor is used in conjunction with $O_2$ sensor. Sensor monitors oxygen content of exhaust gases and sends signal to the ECU.

**Throttle Position Sensor (TPS)** – Throttle Position Sensor (TPS) is mounted on throttle body. Sensor determines changes in throttle valve positions and send signals to the ECU. Signals are used for controlling fuel injection duration and idle speed control system.

**Turbo Pressure Sensor** – Sensor monitors turbo pressure and sends signal to ECU.

**Vehicle Speed Sensor (VSS)** – Sensor is used to monitor vehicle speed. Vehicle speed information is used by the ECU for cruise control and electronic control of automatic transmission.

**4WD Switch** – Switch indicates 4WD operation and sends signal to ECU.

***TOYOTA ENGINE CODE IDENTIFICATION***

| Application | Code |
|---|---|
| **4-Cylinder Engine** | |
| Camry | 3S-FE |
| Celica | |
| Non-Turbo | 3S-FE & 3S-GE |
| Turbo | 3S-GTE |
| Corolla & Corolla FX-16 | 4A-GE |
| MR2 | 4A-GE |
| Pickup & 4Runner | |
| Non-Turbo | 22R-E |
| Turbo | 22R-TE |
| Van | 4Y-E |
| **6-Cylinder (In-Line) Engine** | |
| Cressida | 5M-GE |
| Land Cruiser | 3F-E |
| Supra | |
| Non-Turbo | 7M-GE |
| Turbo | 7M-GTE |
| **V6 Engine** | |
| Camry | 2VZ-FE |
| Pickup & 4Runner | 3VZ-E |

### ELECTRONIC CONTROL UNIT (ECU)

The ECU controls all functions of the TCCS. The ECU receives signals from the data sensors and switches. Signals are processed by the ECU for controlling the Electronic Fuel Injection (EFI), Electronic Spark Advance (ESA), Idle Speed Control (ISC), Electronic Controlled Transmission (ECT) and EGR systems.

The ECU contains a fail-safe function used in case of a data sensor or switch failure. This function provides a back-up system to provide minimal driveability. The "CHECK ENGINE" light will also be activated during this function.

### DIAGNOSTIC SYSTEM

The ECU is equipped with a self-diagnostic system which detects system failures or abnormalities. When malfunction occurs, the "CHECK ENGINE" light on instrument panel is activated. On models with Super Monitor Display, trouble code may be obtained from the screen on the instrument panel.

By analyzing various signals, the ECU detects system malfunctions related to various operating parameter sensors. The ECU stores trouble codes associated with the detected failure until the diagnostic system is cleared. The "CHECK ENGINE" light will go out when trouble codes are cleared.

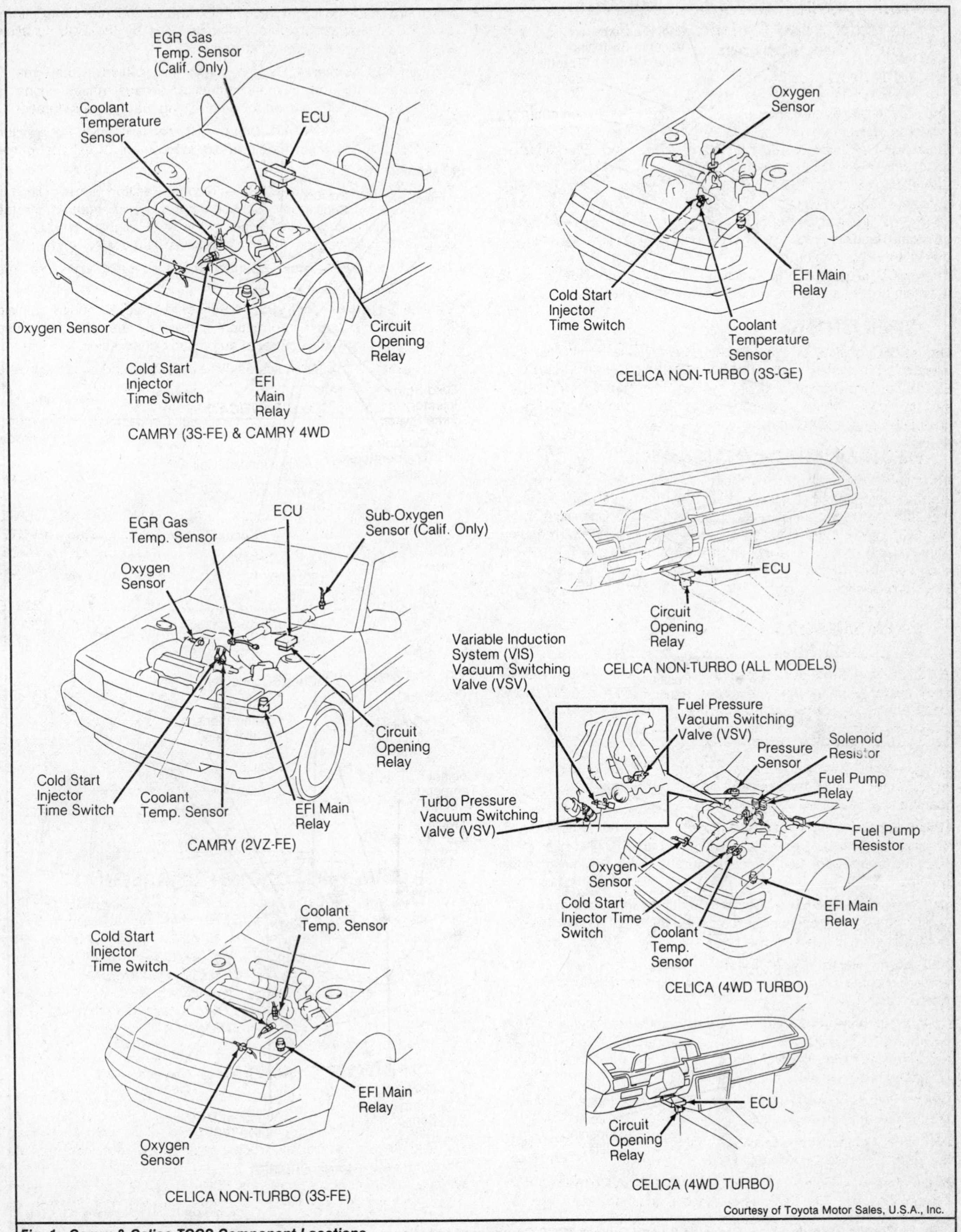
EGR Gas
Temp. Sensor
(Calif. Only)
Coolant
Temperature
Sensor
ECU
Oxygen Sensor
Circuit
Opening
Relay
Cold Start
Injector
Time Switch
EFI
Main
Relay
CAMRY (3S-FE) & CAMRY 4WD
Oxygen
Sensor
Cold Start
Injector
Time Switch
EFI Main
Relay
Coolant
Temperature
Sensor
CELICA NON-TURBO (3S-GE)
EGR Gas
Temp. Sensor
ECU
Sub-Oxygen
Sensor (Calif. Only)
Oxygen
Sensor
Circuit
Opening
Relay
Cold Start
Injector
Time Switch
Coolant
Temp. Sensor
EFI Main
Relay
CAMRY (2VZ-FE)
ECU
Circuit
Opening
Relay
CELICA NON-TURBO (ALL MODELS)
Variable Induction
System (VIS)
Vacuum Switching
Valve (VSV)
Fuel Pressure
Vacuum Switching
Valve (VSV)
Pressure
Sensor
Solenoid
Resistor
Fuel Pump
Relay
Turbo Pressure
Vacuum Switching
Valve (VSV)
Fuel Pump
Resistor
Oxygen
Sensor
Cold Start
Injector Time
Switch
Coolant
Temp.
Sensor
EFI Main
Relay
CELICA (4WD TURBO)
Coolant
Temp. Sensor
Cold Start
Injector
Time Switch
EFI Main
Relay
Oxygen
Sensor
CELICA NON-TURBO (3S-FE)
ECU
Circuit
Opening
Relay
CELICA (4WD TURBO)
Courtesy of Toyota Motor Sales, U.S.A., Inc.

*Fig. 1: Camry & Celica TCCS Component Locations*

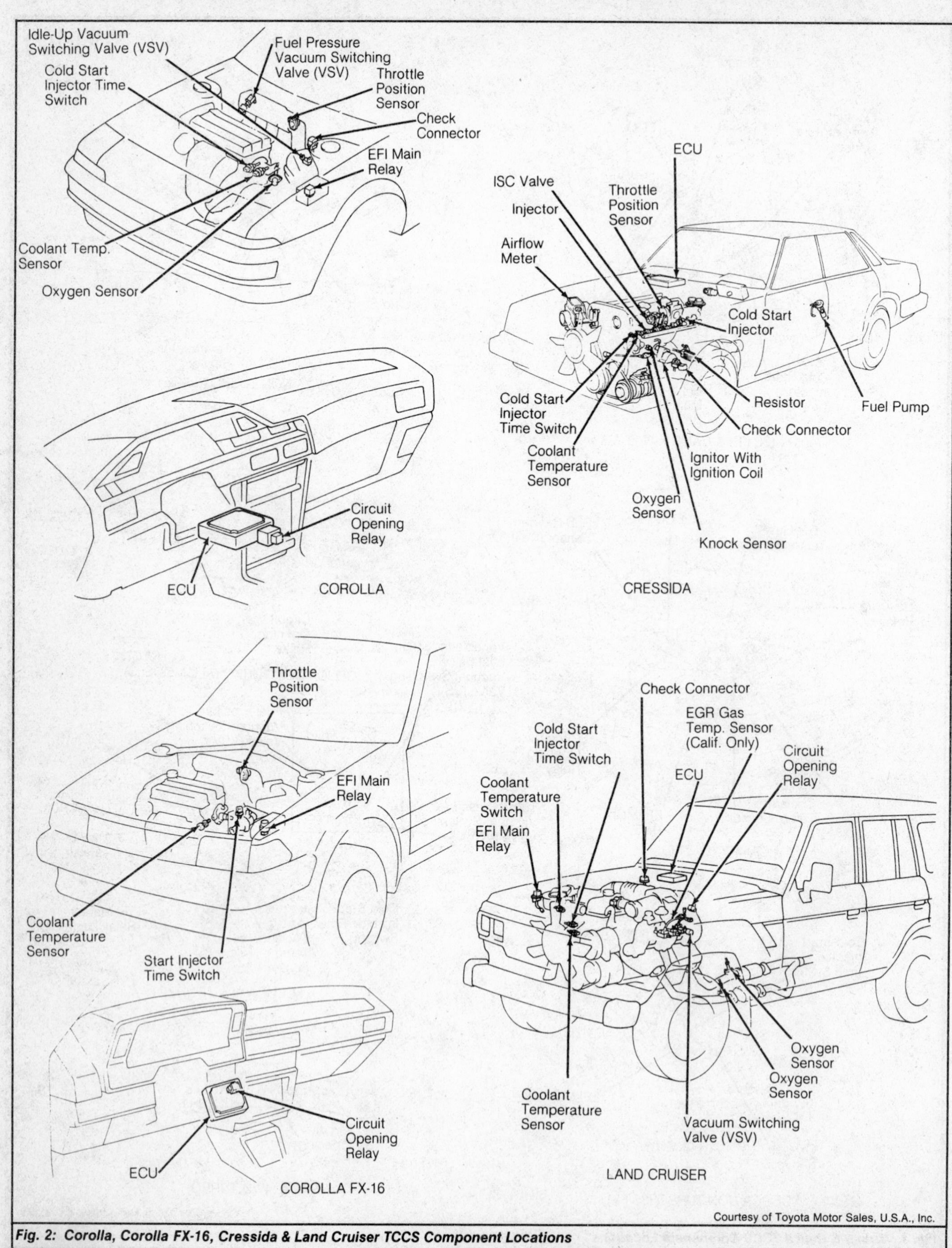
Idle-Up Vacuum
Switching Valve (VSV)
Fuel Pressure
Vacuum Switching
Valve (VSV)
Cold Start
Injector Time
Switch
Throttle
Position
Sensor
Check
Connector
EFI Main
Relay
Coolant Temp.
Sensor
Oxygen Sensor
Circuit
Opening
Relay
ECU
COROLLA
ECU
ISC Valve
Throttle
Position
Sensor
Injector
Airflow
Meter
Cold Start
Injector
Cold Start
Injector
Time Switch
Resistor
Fuel Pump
Check Connector
Coolant
Temperature
Sensor
Ignitor With
Ignition Coil
Oxygen
Sensor
Knock Sensor
CRESSIDA
Throttle
Position
Sensor
EFI Main
Relay
Coolant
Temperature
Sensor
Start Injector
Time Switch
Circuit
Opening
Relay
ECU
COROLLA FX-16
Check Connector
EGR Gas
Temp. Sensor
(Calif. Only)
Cold Start
Injector
Time Switch
ECU
Circuit
Opening
Relay
Coolant
Temperature
Switch
EFI Main
Relay
Oxygen
Sensor
Oxygen
Sensor
Coolant
Temperature
Sensor
Vacuum Switching
Valve (VSV)
LAND CRUISER
Courtesy of Toyota Motor Sales, U.S.A., Inc.

*Fig. 2: Corolla, Corolla FX-16, Cressida & Land Cruiser TCCS Component Locations*

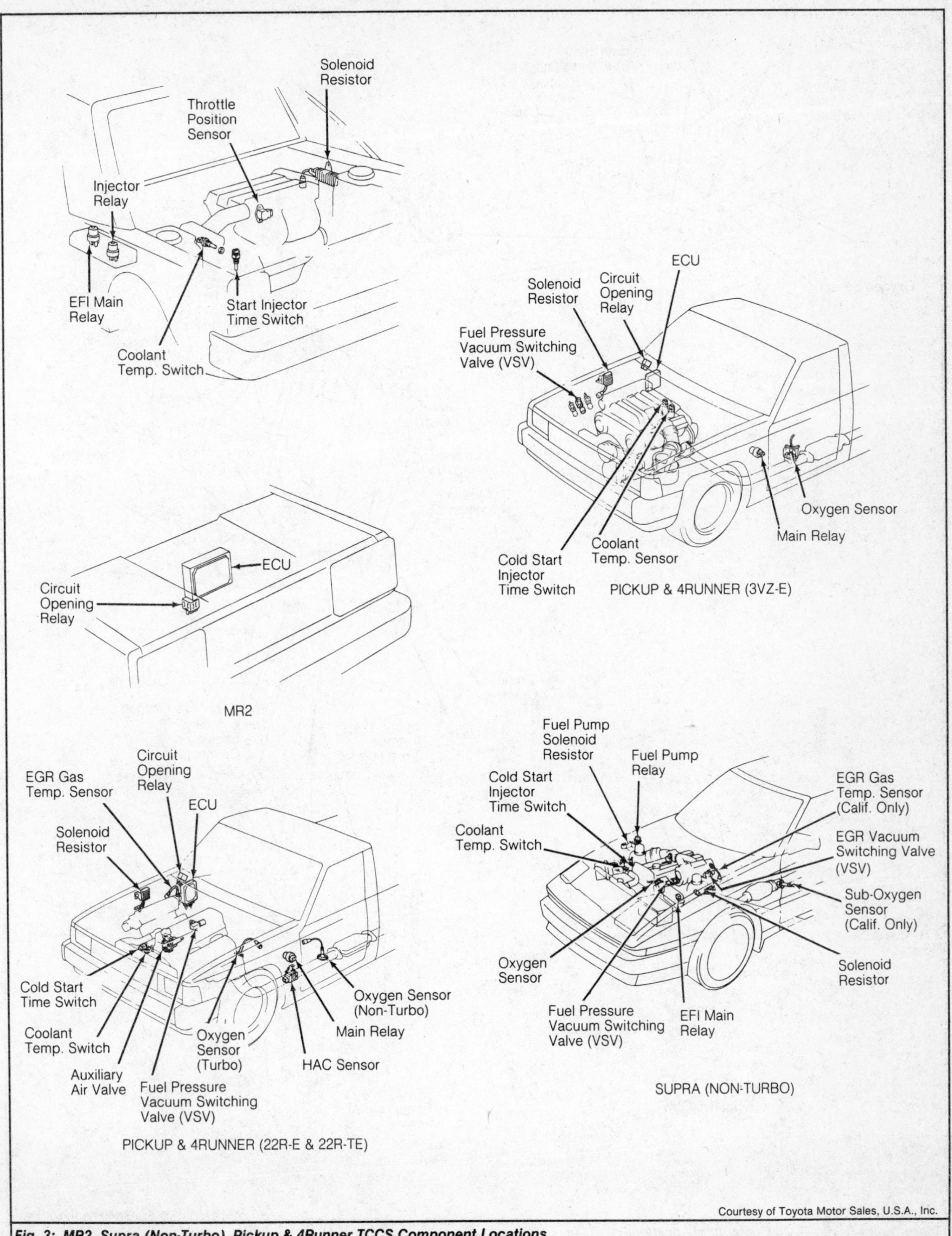
Solenoid Resistor
Throttle Position Sensor
Injector Relay
EFI Main Relay
Start Injector Time Switch
Coolant Temp. Switch
ECU
Circuit Opening Relay
MR2
ECU
Solenoid Resistor
Circuit Opening Relay
Fuel Pressure Vacuum Switching Valve (VSV)
Oxygen Sensor
Main Relay
Coolant Temp. Sensor
Cold Start Injector Time Switch
PICKUP & 4RUNNER (3VZ-E)
Circuit Opening Relay
EGR Gas Temp. Sensor
ECU
Solenoid Resistor
Cold Start Time Switch
Coolant Temp. Switch
Auxiliary Air Valve
Fuel Pressure Vacuum Switching Valve (VSV)
Oxygen Sensor (Turbo)
HAC Sensor
Main Relay
Oxygen Sensor (Non-Turbo)
PICKUP & 4RUNNER (22R-E & 22R-TE)
Fuel Pump Solenoid Resistor
Fuel Pump Relay
Cold Start Injector Time Switch
Coolant Temp. Switch
EGR Gas Temp. Sensor (Calif. Only)
EGR Vacuum Switching Valve (VSV)
Sub-Oxygen Sensor (Calif. Only)
Solenoid Resistor
Oxygen Sensor
Fuel Pressure Vacuum Switching Valve (VSV)
EFI Main Relay
SUPRA (NON-TURBO)

Courtesy of Toyota Motor Sales, U.S.A., Inc.

*Fig. 3: MR2, Supra (Non-Turbo), Pickup & 4Runner TCCS Component Locations*

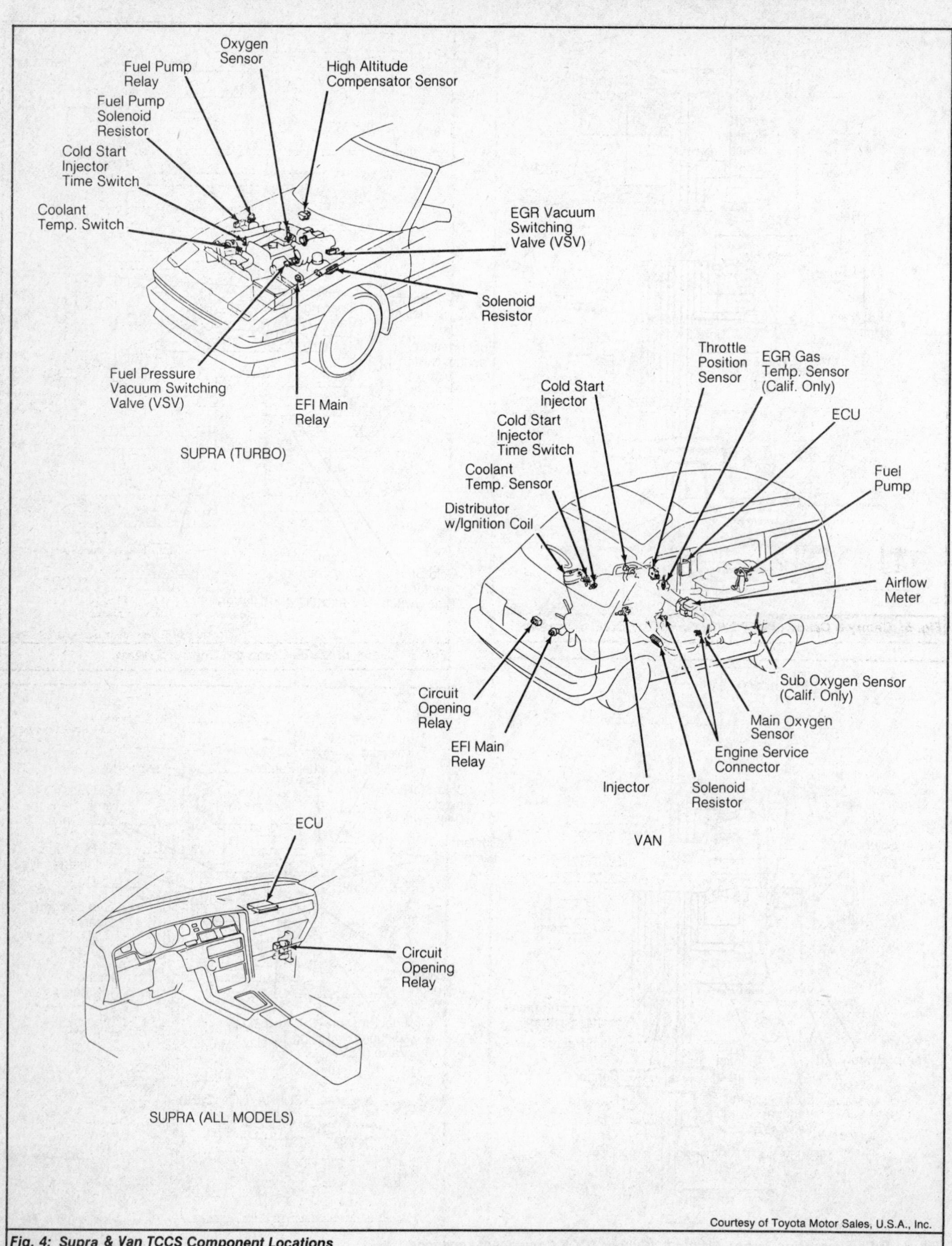
Oxygen Sensor
Fuel Pump Relay
High Altitude Compensator Sensor
Fuel Pump Solenoid Resistor
Cold Start Injector Time Switch
Coolant Temp. Switch
EGR Vacuum Switching Valve (VSV)
Solenoid Resistor
Fuel Pressure Vacuum Switching Valve (VSV)
EFI Main Relay
SUPRA (TURBO)
Throttle Position Sensor
EGR Gas Temp. Sensor (Calif. Only)
Cold Start Injector
ECU
Cold Start Injector Time Switch
Fuel Pump
Coolant Temp. Sensor
Distributor w/Ignition Coil
Airflow Meter
Sub Oxygen Sensor (Calif. Only)
Circuit Opening Relay
Main Oxygen Sensor
EFI Main Relay
Engine Service Connector
Injector
Solenoid Resistor
VAN
ECU
Circuit Opening Relay
SUPRA (ALL MODELS)
Courtesy of Toyota Motor Sales, U.S.A., Inc.

*Fig. 4: Supra & Van TCCS Component Locations*

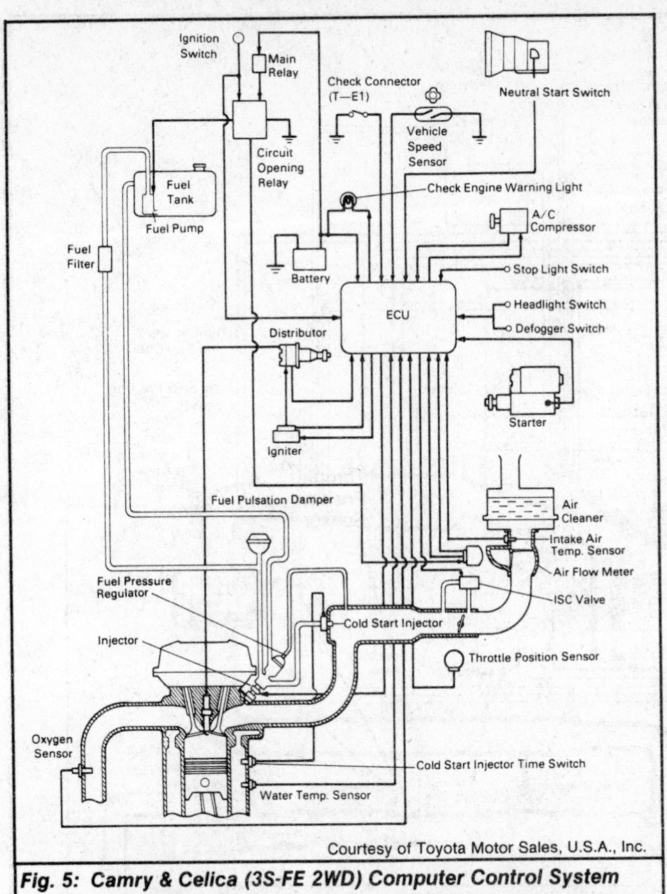
Ignition Switch
Main Relay
Check Connector (T—E1)
Neutral Start Switch
Vehicle Speed Sensor
Circuit Opening Relay
Fuel Tank
Fuel Pump
Check Engine Warning Light
A/C Compressor
Fuel Filter
Battery
Stop Light Switch
ECU
Headlight Switch
Distributor
Defogger Switch
Starter
Igniter
Fuel Pulsation Damper
Air Cleaner
Intake Air Temp. Sensor
Air Flow Meter
Fuel Pressure Regulator
ISC Valve
Cold Start Injector
Injector
Throttle Position Sensor
Oxygen Sensor
Cold Start Injector Time Switch
Water Temp. Sensor
Courtesy of Toyota Motor Sales, U.S.A., Inc.

*Fig. 5: Camry & Celica (3S-FE 2WD) Computer Control System*

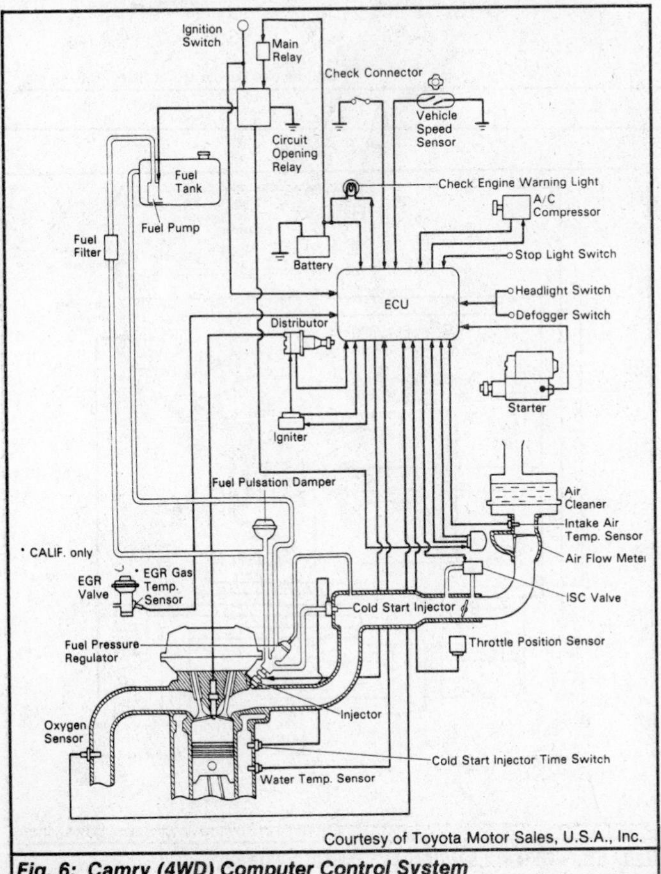
Ignition Switch
Main Relay
Check Connector
Vehicle Speed Sensor
Circuit Opening Relay
Fuel Tank
Check Engine Warning Light
A/C Compressor
Fuel Pump
Fuel Filter
Battery
Stop Light Switch
ECU
Headlight Switch
Distributor
Defogger Switch
Starter
Igniter
Fuel Pulsation Damper
Air Cleaner
Intake Air Temp. Sensor
* CALIF. only
Air Flow Meter
EGR Valve
* EGR Gas Temp. Sensor
ISC Valve
Cold Start Injector
Fuel Pressure Regulator
Throttle Position Sensor
Injector
Oxygen Sensor
Cold Start Injector Time Switch
Water Temp. Sensor
Courtesy of Toyota Motor Sales, U.S.A., Inc.

*Fig. 6: Camry (4WD) Computer Control System*

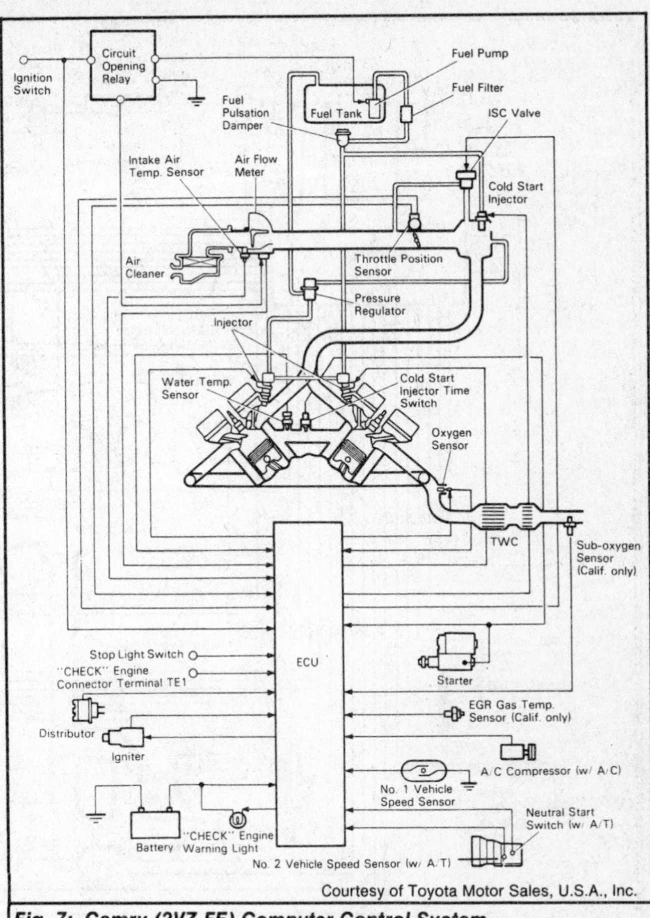
Circuit Opening Relay
Ignition Switch
Fuel Pump
Fuel Filter
Fuel Pulsation Damper
Fuel Tank
ISC Valve
Intake Air Temp. Sensor
Air Flow Meter
Cold Start Injector
Air Cleaner
Throttle Position Sensor
Pressure Regulator
Injector
Water Temp. Sensor
Cold Start Injector Time Switch
Oxygen Sensor
TWC
Sub-oxygen Sensor (Calif. only)
Stop Light Switch
"CHECK" Engine Connector Terminal TE1
ECU
Starter
EGR Gas Temp. Sensor (Calif. only)
Distributor
Igniter
A/C Compressor (w/ A/C)
No. 1 Vehicle Speed Sensor
Neutral Start Switch (w/ A/T)
Battery
"CHECK" Engine Warning Light
No. 2 Vehicle Speed Sensor (w/ A/T)
Courtesy of Toyota Motor Sales, U.S.A., Inc.

*Fig. 7: Camry (2VZ-FE) Computer Control System*

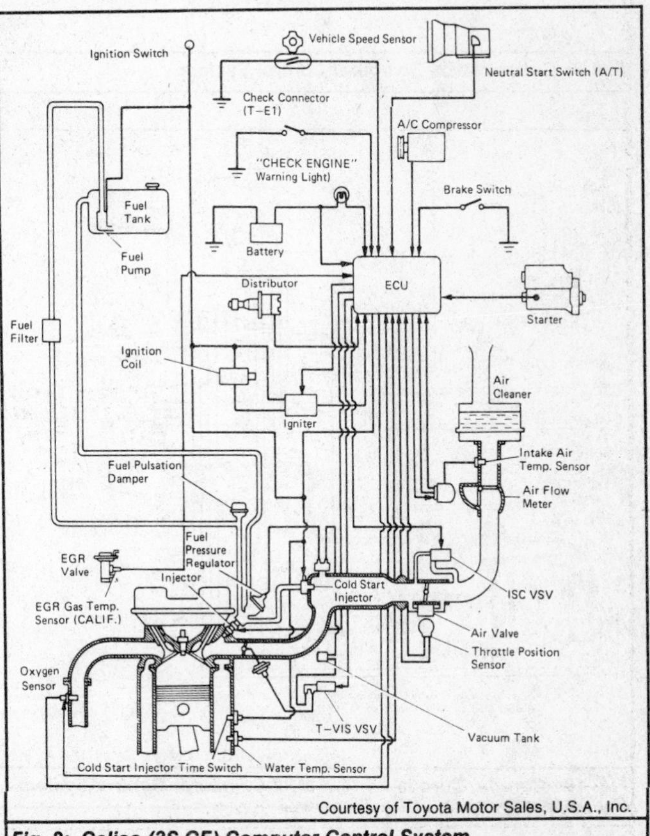
Vehicle Speed Sensor
Ignition Switch
Neutral Start Switch (A/T)
Check Connector (T—E1)
A/C Compressor
"CHECK ENGINE" Warning Light)
Brake Switch
Fuel Tank
Battery
Fuel Pump
ECU
Distributor
Starter
Fuel Filter
Ignition Coil
Air Cleaner
Igniter
Intake Air Temp. Sensor
Fuel Pulsation Damper
Air Flow Meter
Fuel Pressure Regulator
EGR Valve
Injector
Cold Start Injector
ISC VSV
EGR Gas Temp. Sensor (CALIF.)
Air Valve
Throttle Position Sensor
Oxygen Sensor
T—VIS VSV
Vacuum Tank
Cold Start Injector Time Switch
Water Temp. Sensor
Courtesy of Toyota Motor Sales, U.S.A., Inc.

*Fig. 8: Celica (3S-GE) Computer Control System*

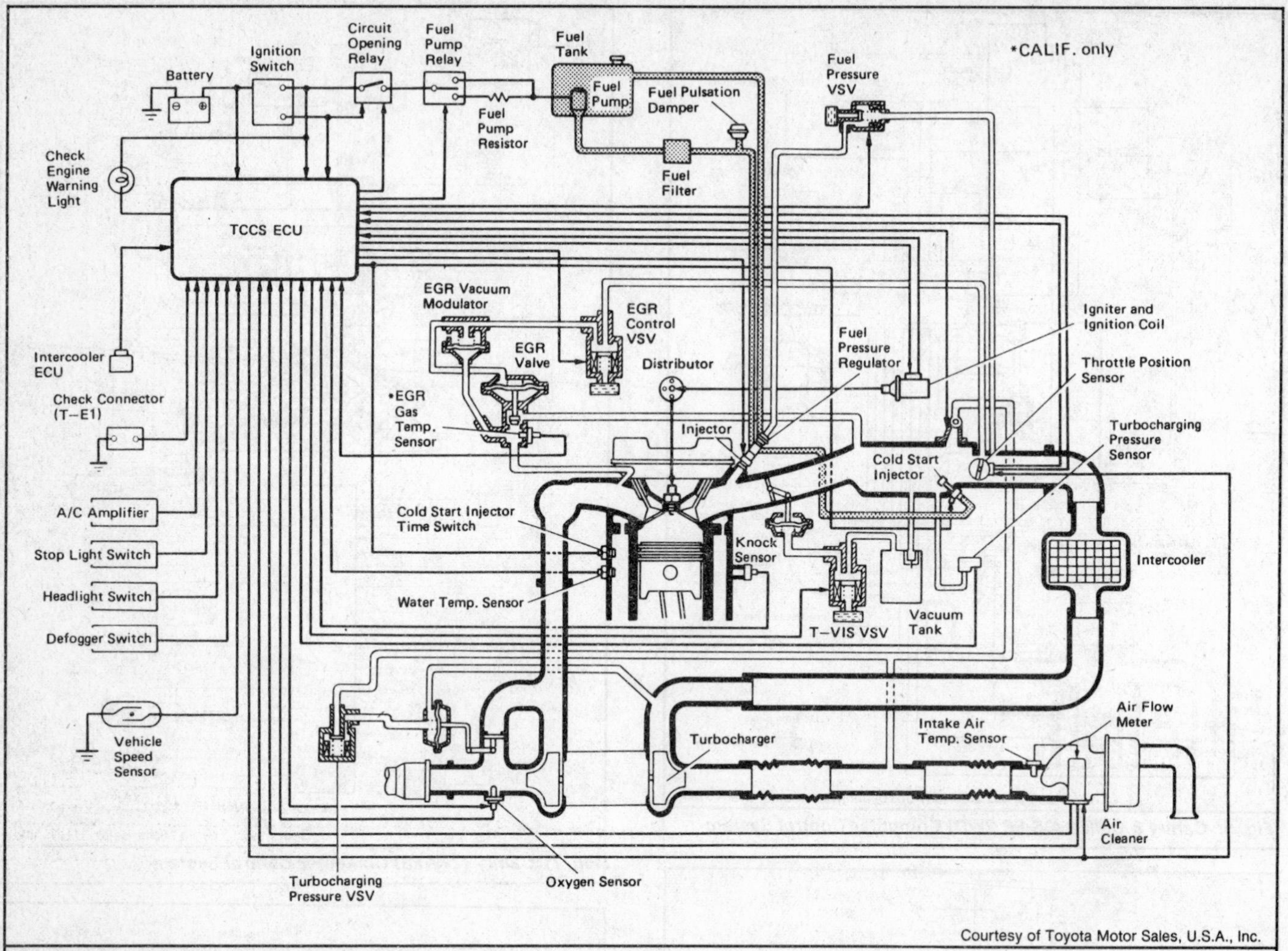

# 1988 COMPUTERIZED ENGINE CONTROLS
## Toyota Computer Control System (Cont.)

*CALIF. only

Battery
Ignition Switch
Circuit Opening Relay
Fuel Pump Relay
Fuel Tank
Fuel Pump
Fuel Pulsation Damper
Fuel Pump Resistor
Fuel Filter
Fuel Pressure VSV
Check Engine Warning Light
TCCS ECU
EGR Vacuum Modulator
EGR Control VSV
EGR Valve
*EGR Gas Temp. Sensor
Distributor
Fuel Pressure Regulator
Igniter and Ignition Coil
Throttle Position Sensor
Turbocharging Pressure Sensor
Intercooler ECU
Check Connector (T–E1)
Injector
Cold Start Injector
A/C Amplifier
Cold Start Injector Time Switch
Knock Sensor
Intercooler
Stop Light Switch
Headlight Switch
Water Temp. Sensor
Vacuum Tank
T–VIS VSV
Defogger Switch
Air Flow Meter
Vehicle Speed Sensor
Intake Air Temp. Sensor
Turbocharger
Air Cleaner
Turbocharging Pressure VSV
Oxygen Sensor

Courtesy of Toyota Motor Sales, U.S.A., Inc.

*Fig. 9: Celica (4WD) Computer Control System*

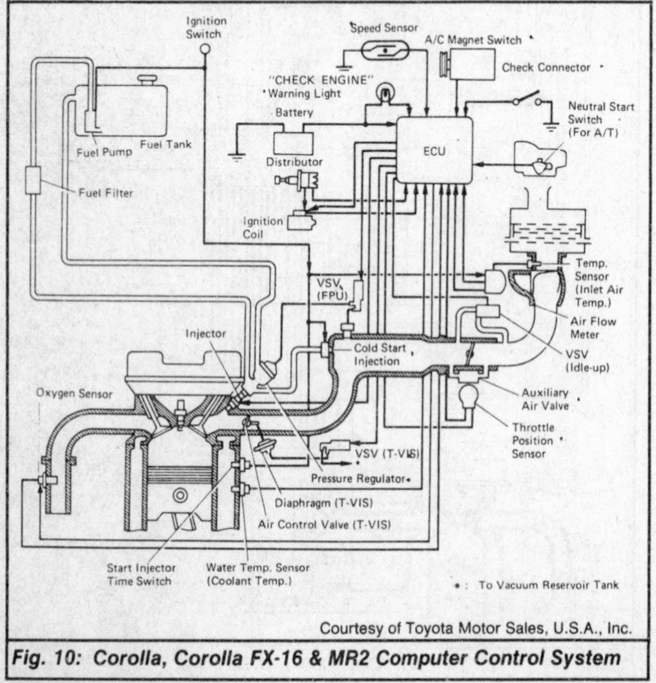
Ignition Switch
Speed Sensor
A/C Magnet Switch *
Check Connector *
"CHECK ENGINE" *Warning Light
Battery
Neutral Start Switch (For A/T)
Fuel Pump
Fuel Tank
Distributor
ECU
Fuel Filter
Ignition Coil
VSV (FPU)
Temp. Sensor (Inlet Air Temp.)
Air Flow Meter
Injector
Cold Start Injection
VSV (Idle-up)
Oxygen Sensor
Auxiliary Air Valve
Throttle Position * Sensor
VSV (T-VIS)
Pressure Regulator*
Diaphragm (T-VIS)
Air Control Valve (T-VIS)
Start Injector Time Switch
Water Temp. Sensor (Coolant Temp.)
* : To Vacuum Reservoir Tank

Courtesy of Toyota Motor Sales, U.S.A., Inc.

*Fig. 10: Corolla, Corolla FX-16 & MR2 Computer Control System*

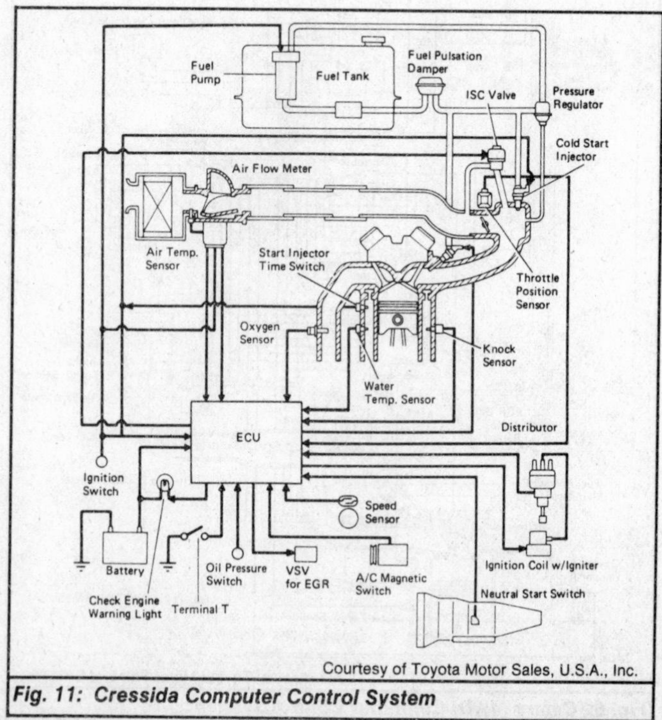
Fuel Pump
Fuel Tank
Fuel Pulsation Damper
ISC Valve
Pressure Regulator
Cold Start Injector
Air Flow Meter
Air Temp. Sensor
Start Injector Time Switch
Throttle Position Sensor
Oxygen Sensor
Knock Sensor
Water Temp. Sensor
Distributor
ECU
Ignition Switch
Speed Sensor
Battery
Oil Pressure Switch
VSV for EGR
A/C Magnetic Switch
Ignition Coil w/Igniter
Neutral Start Switch
Check Engine Warning Light
Terminal T

Courtesy of Toyota Motor Sales, U.S.A., Inc.

*Fig. 11: Cressida Computer Control System*

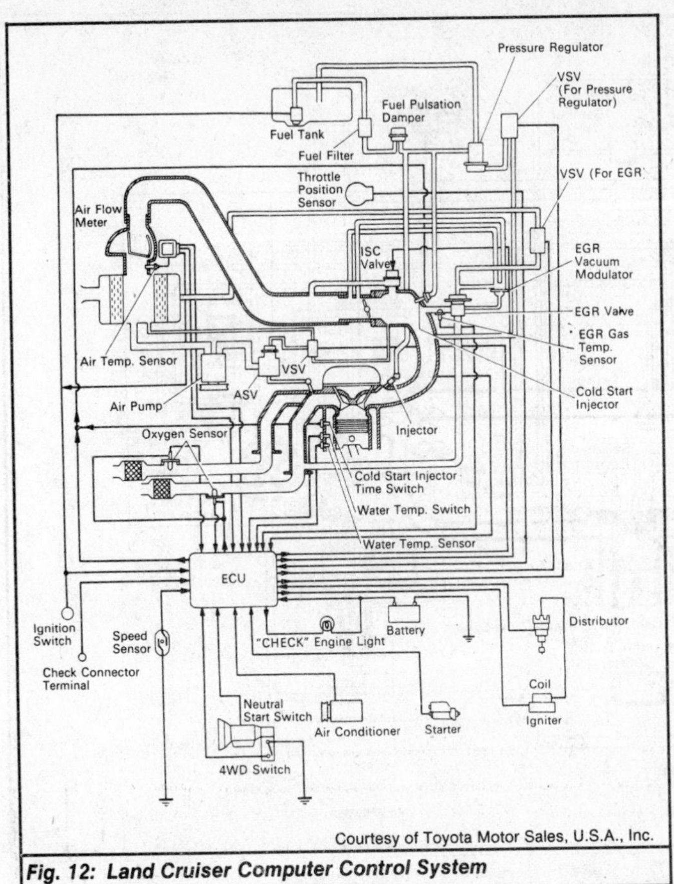
Pressure Regulator
VSV (For Pressure Regulator)
Fuel Pulsation Damper
Fuel Tank
Fuel Filter
Throttle Position Sensor
VSV (For EGR)
Air Flow Meter
ISC Valve
EGR Vacuum Modulator
EGR Valve
EGR Gas Temp. Sensor
Air Temp. Sensor
VSV
ASV
Cold Start Injector
Air Pump
Injector
Oxygen Sensor
Cold Start Injector Time Switch
Water Temp. Switch
Water Temp. Sensor
ECU
Ignition Switch
Speed Sensor
"CHECK" Engine Light
Battery
Distributor
Check Connector Terminal
Coil
Neutral Start Switch
Air Conditioner
Starter
Igniter
4WD Switch

Courtesy of Toyota Motor Sales, U.S.A., Inc.

**Fig. 12: Land Cruiser Computer Control System**

Fuel Tank
Fuel Pump
VSV (for FPU)
Pulsation Damper
Fuel Filter
Pressure Regulator
VSV (for A/C Idle-up)
Air Flow Meter
Throttle Position Sensor
Air Valve
Cold Start Injector
Intake Air Temp. Sensor
Water Temp. Sensor
Injector
Water Temp. Switch
Knock Sensor
Start Injector Time Switch
VSV (for AS)
Oxygen Sensor
VSV (for EGR)
ECU
Ignition Switch
Check Connector
Battery
Stop Light Switch
CHECK ENGINE Light
Distributor
Vehicle Speed Sensor
Igniter
4WD Switch
EGR Gas Temp. Sensor (California only)
Neutral Start Switch (A/T only)
A/C Compressure

Courtesy of Toyota Motor Sales, U.S.A., Inc.

**Fig. 14: Pickup & 4Runner (3VZ-E) Computer Control System**

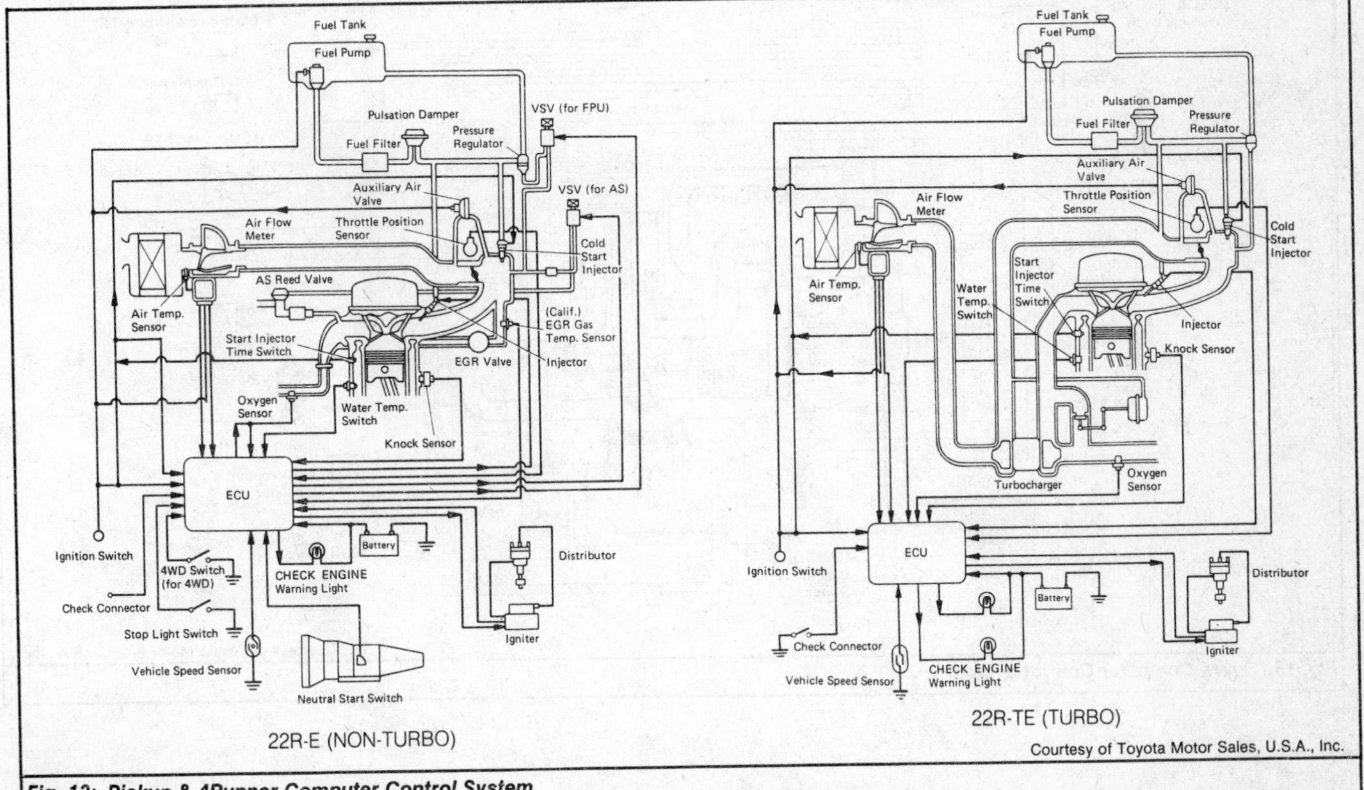
Fuel Tank
Fuel Pump
Pulsation Damper
VSV (for FPU)
Fuel Filter
Pressure Regulator
VSV (for AS)
Auxiliary Air Valve
Air Flow Meter
Throttle Position Sensor
Cold Start Injector
AS Reed Valve
Air Temp. Sensor
(Calif.) EGR Gas Temp. Sensor
Start Injector Time Switch
EGR Valve
Injector
Oxygen Sensor
Water Temp. Switch
Knock Sensor
ECU
Battery
Distributor
Ignition Switch
4WD Switch (for 4WD)
CHECK ENGINE Warning Light
Check Connector
Igniter
Stop Light Switch
Vehicle Speed Sensor
Neutral Start Switch
22R-E (NON-TURBO)
Fuel Tank
Fuel Pump
Pulsation Damper
Fuel Filter
Pressure Regulator
Auxiliary Air Valve
Air Flow Meter
Throttle Position Sensor
Cold Start Injector
Start Injector Time Switch
Air Temp. Sensor
Water Temp. Switch
Injector
Knock Sensor
Turbocharger
Oxygen Sensor
ECU
Ignition Switch
Distributor
Battery
Igniter
Check Connector
CHECK ENGINE Warning Light
Vehicle Speed Sensor
22R-TE (TURBO)

Courtesy of Toyota Motor Sales, U.S.A., Inc.

**Fig. 13: Pickup & 4Runner Computer Control System**

# 1988 COMPUTERIZED ENGINE CONTROLS
## Toyota Computer Control System (Cont.)

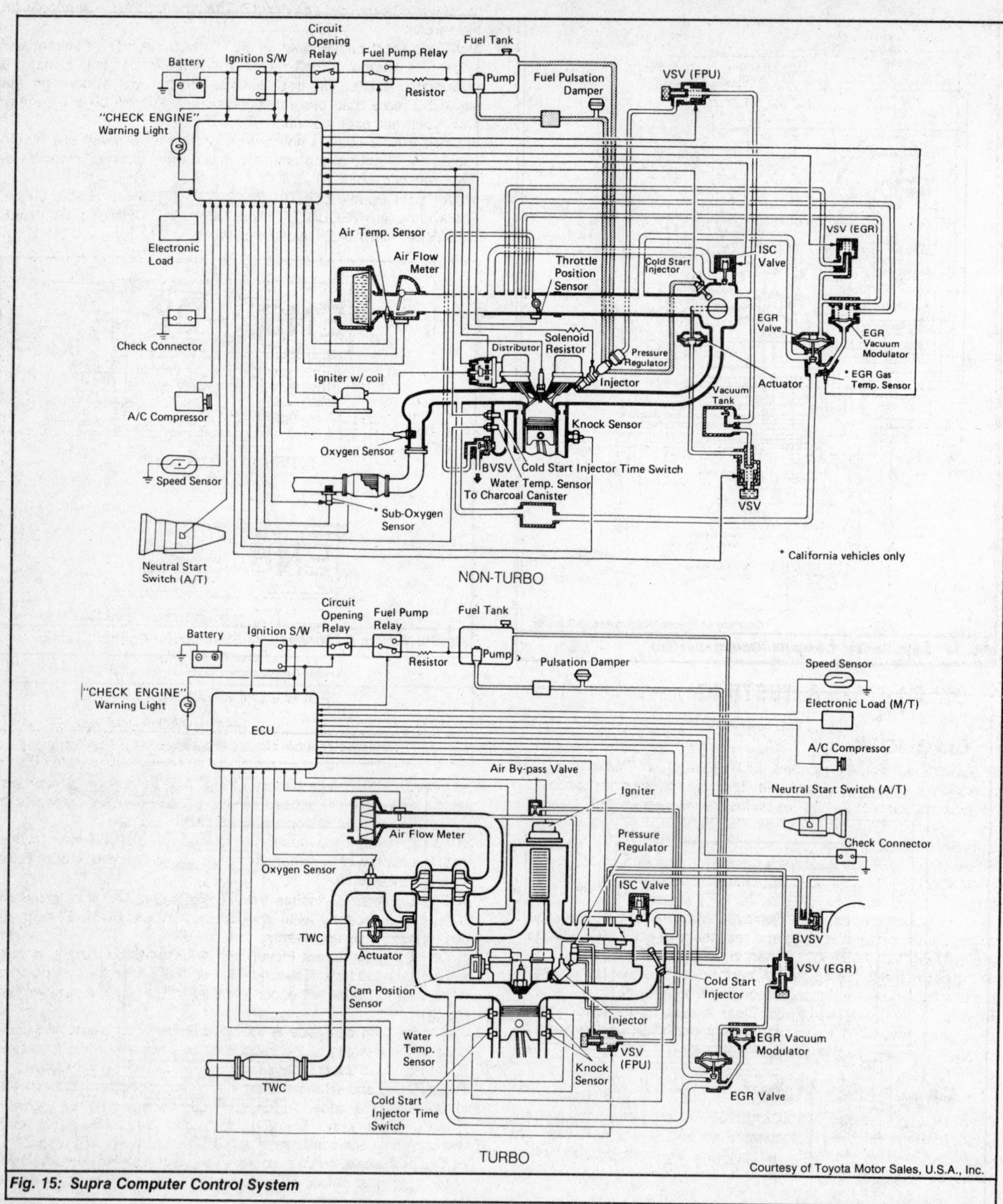

Battery
Ignition S/W
Circuit Opening Relay
Fuel Pump Relay
Fuel Tank
Pump
Resistor
Fuel Pulsation Damper
VSV (FPU)
"CHECK ENGINE" Warning Light
Electronic Load
Air Temp. Sensor
Air Flow Meter
Throttle Position Sensor
Cold Start Injector
ISC Valve
VSV (EGR)
EGR Valve
EGR Vacuum Modulator
Check Connector
Distributor
Solenoid Resistor
Pressure Regulator
Injector
Actuator
* EGR Gas Temp. Sensor
Igniter w/ coil
A/C Compressor
Vacuum Tank
Knock Sensor
Oxygen Sensor
Speed Sensor
BVSV
Cold Start Injector Time Switch
Water Temp. Sensor
To Charcoal Canister
VSV
* Sub-Oxygen Sensor
Neutral Start Switch (A/T)
* California vehicles only
NON-TURBO
Battery
Ignition S/W
Circuit Opening Relay
Fuel Pump Relay
Fuel Tank
Pump
Resistor
Pulsation Damper
Speed Sensor
"CHECK ENGINE" Warning Light
ECU
Electronic Load (M/T)
A/C Compressor
Air By-pass Valve
Igniter
Neutral Start Switch (A/T)
Air Flow Meter
Pressure Regulator
Check Connector
Oxygen Sensor
ISC Valve
TWC
Actuator
BVSV
VSV (EGR)
Cold Start Injector
Cam Position Sensor
Injector
EGR Vacuum Modulator
Water Temp. Sensor
VSV (FPU)
Knock Sensor
TWC
EGR Valve
Cold Start Injector Time Switch
TURBO


Courtesy of Toyota Motor Sales, U.S.A., Inc.

*Fig. 15: Supra Computer Control System*

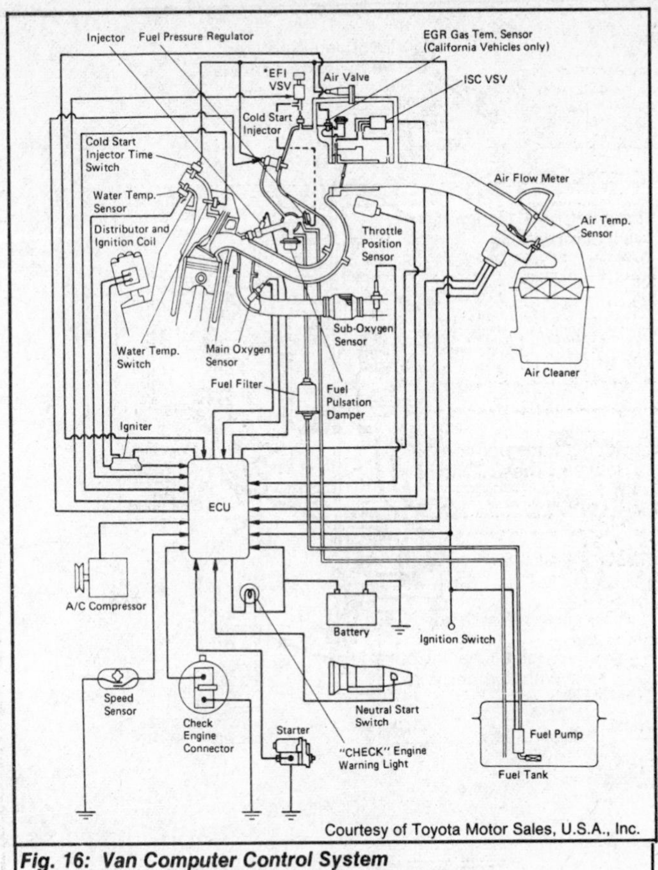
Injector
Fuel Pressure Regulator
EGR Gas Tem. Sensor (California Vehicles only)
*EFI VSV
Air Valve
ISC VSV
Cold Start Injector
Cold Start Injector Time Switch
Air Flow Meter
Water Temp. Sensor
Distributor and Ignition Coil
Throttle Position Sensor
Air Temp. Sensor
Sub-Oxygen Sensor
Water Temp. Switch
Main Oxygen Sensor
Air Cleaner
Fuel Filter
Fuel Pulsation Damper
Igniter
ECU
A/C Compressor
Battery
Ignition Switch
Speed Sensor
Check Engine Connector
Starter
Neutral Start Switch
"CHECK" Engine Warning Light
Fuel Pump
Fuel Tank
Courtesy of Toyota Motor Sales, U.S.A., Inc.

*Fig. 16: Van Computer Control System*

## DIAGNOSIS & TESTING

### DIAGNOSIS

**1)** Ensure all engine systems NOT related to TCCS are fully operational. Do not proceed with testing until all other problems have been repaired. Ensure fuses, fusible links and wire connectors are in good condition before diagnosing ECU.
**2)** Enter diagnostic mode and record trouble codes. Exit diagnostic mode. If no trouble codes were displayed, proceed to appropriate DIAGNOSTIC CIRCUIT CHECK charts. Follow instructions given there.
**3)** If no trouble codes were displayed after performing diagnostic circuit check, perform voltage and resistance checks. See appropriate ECU PIN VOLTAGE TEST chart in this article.
**4)** If trouble codes are displayed, perform tests to confirm cause of malfunction which set the corresponding trouble code.
**5)** After any repairs are made, clear trouble codes and perform diagnostic circuit check. Normal system operation code should be displayed if repair solved cause of malfunction.

### CHECK ENGINE LIGHT

Turn ignition on. The "CHECK ENGINE" light will activate with ignition on and engine not running. Start engine and note that light is not activated. If light remains activated, a system malfunction or abnormality exists.

### RETRIEVING TROUBLE CODES

**Cressida & Supra w/Super Monitor – 1)** Ensure battery voltage is greater than 11 volts and throttle valve is fully closed. Place transmission or transaxle in Neutral.
**2)** To enter diagnostic mode, turn ignition on. DO NOT start engine. Simultaneously push and hold in "SELECT" key and "INPUT M" keys for at least 3 seconds. *See Fig. 17.* The letters "DIAG" will appear on the screen.
**3)** After a short pause, hold in "SET" key for at least 3 seconds. If system is normal, "ENG -OK" will appear on the screen. If malfunction exists, the trouble code number will appear on the screen. If more than one number exists, there will be a 3 second pause between each number.
**4)** Once trouble code is noted, turn ignition off or push any button except "SET" so that the time appears on the screen. This will exit the diagnostic mode.
**5)** Compare trouble code to that listed to locate probable cause. See appropriate TROUBLE CODE IDENTIFICATION and TROUBLE CODES & PROBABLE CAUSE tables.

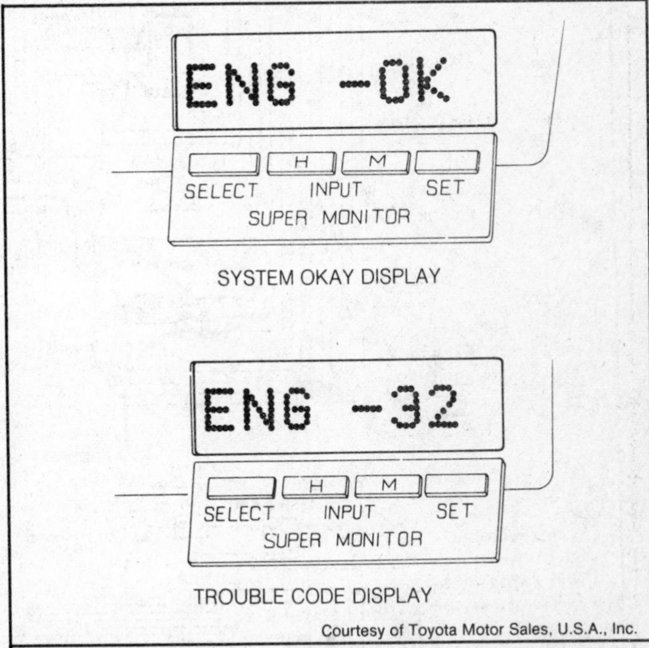
ENG -OK
H
M
SELECT
INPUT
SET
SUPER MONITOR
SYSTEM OKAY DISPLAY
ENG -32
H
M
SELECT
INPUT
SET
SUPER MONITOR
TROUBLE CODE DISPLAY
Courtesy of Toyota Motor Sales, U.S.A., Inc.

*Fig. 17: Retrieving Trouble Codes With Super Monitor Display*

**All Others – 1)** Ensure battery voltage is greater than 11 volts and throttle valve is fully closed. Place transmission or transaxle in Neutral and turn off all accessory switches.
**2)** To enter diagnostic mode, turn ignition on. DO NOT start engine. Install jumper wire between terminals of engine check connector. *See Figs. 18 and 19.*
**3)** Count number of flashes from "CHECK ENGINE" light. If system is operating properly (with no codes), "CHECK ENGINE" light will blink continuously and evenly.
**4)** On all models except Pickup and 4Runner turbo models, a code will be identified by a .5 second flash on and off for the first number. A 1.5 second pause will occur followed by the second number. *See Fig. 20.*
**5)** If more than one code is stored, a 2.5 second pause will occur prior to the flashing of the second code. Once all codes have been displayed, a 4.5 second pause will occur and code(s) will repeat.
**6)** On Pickup and 4Runner turbo models, count number of flashes to indicate trouble code. A 2.5 second pause will occur between trouble codes only. *See Fig. 21.* Once all codes have been displayed, a 4.5 second pause will occur and code(s) will repeat.
**7)** On all models, trouble codes are given from smallest value in order to largest value. After code(s) are retrieved, remove jumper wire to exit diagnostic mode.
**8)** Compare trouble code to that listed to locate probable cause. See appropriate TROUBLE CODE IDENTIFICATION and TROUBLE CODES & PROBABLE CAUSE tables.

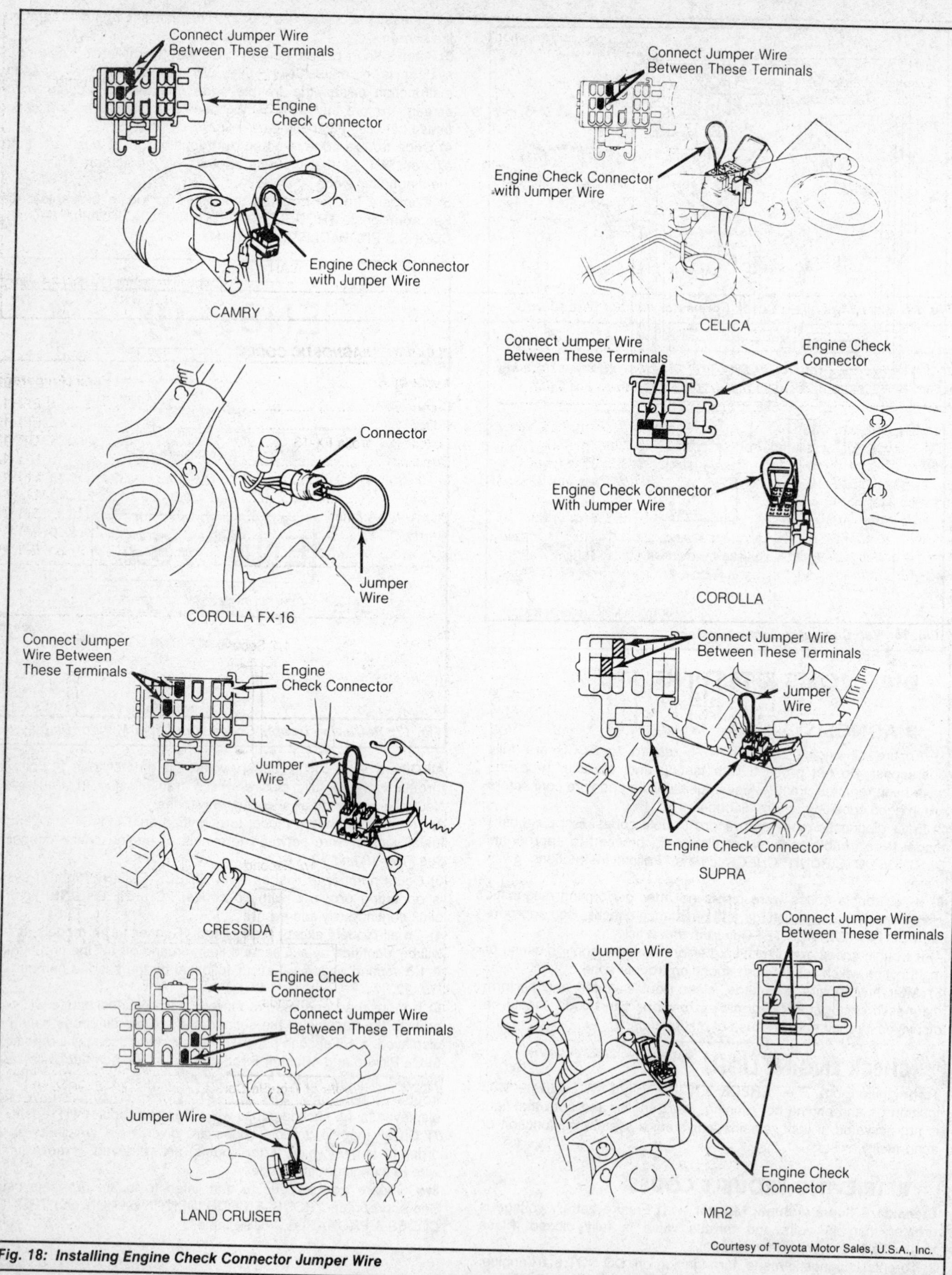
Connect Jumper Wire
Between These Terminals
Engine
Check Connector
Engine Check Connector
with Jumper Wire
CAMRY
Connect Jumper Wire
Between These Terminals
Engine Check Connector
with Jumper Wire
CELICA
Connector
Jumper
Wire
COROLLA FX-16
Connect Jumper Wire
Between These Terminals
Engine Check
Connector
Engine Check Connector
With Jumper Wire
COROLLA
Connect Jumper
Wire Between
These Terminals
Engine
Check Connector
Jumper
Wire
CRESSIDA
Connect Jumper Wire
Between These Terminals
Jumper
Wire
Engine Check Connector
SUPRA
Engine Check
Connector
Connect Jumper Wire
Between These Terminals
Jumper Wire
LAND CRUISER
Jumper Wire
Connect Jumper Wire
Between These Terminals
Engine Check
Connector
MR2
Courtesy of Toyota Motor Sales, U.S.A., Inc.

*Fig. 18: Installing Engine Check Connector Jumper Wire*

# 1988 COMPUTERIZED ENGINE CONTROLS
# Toyota Computer Control System (Cont.)

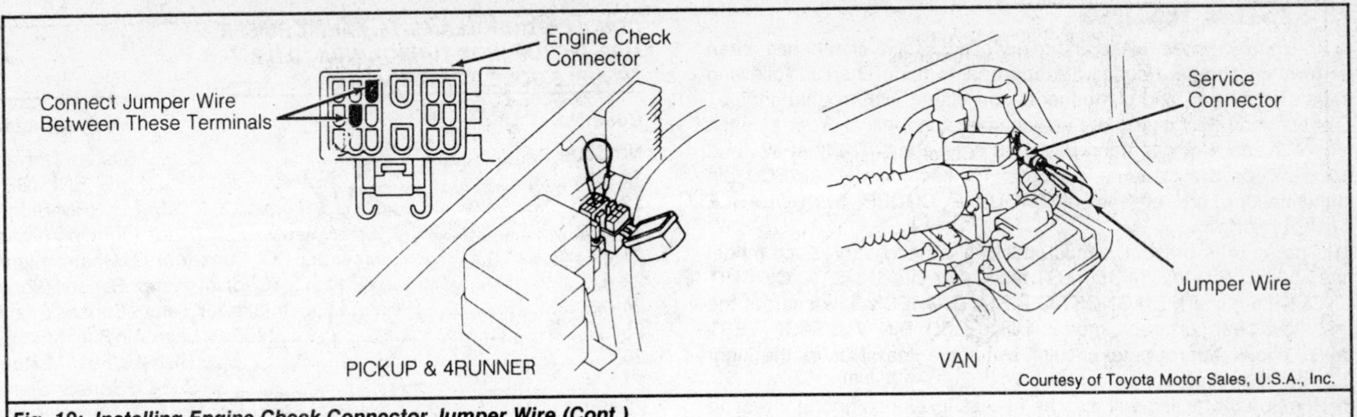
Engine Check
Connector
Connect Jumper Wire
Between These Terminals
PICKUP & 4RUNNER
Service
Connector
Jumper Wire
VAN
Courtesy of Toyota Motor Sales, U.S.A., Inc.

*Fig. 19: Installing Engine Check Connector Jumper Wire (Cont.)*

***CAUTION: Ensure trouble codes are cleared after performing repair. Road test and recheck that trouble code does not exist.***

**Clearing Trouble Codes – 1)** After repairs are performed, clear ECU memory of all stored trouble codes. To clear memory, turn ignition off and remove fuse from fuse block for 30 seconds or more. See CLEARING DIAGNOSTIC CODES table for appropriate fuse removal.

**2)** Fuse may require to be removed longer depending on the ambient temperature. Replace fuse and exit diagnostic mode. Trouble codes can also be cleared by disconnecting vehicle battery. However, other memory functions (clock, etc.), will need to be reset.

***CLEARING DIAGNOSTIC CODES***

| Application | Fuse (Amperage) |
|---|---|
| Camry | EFI (15) |
| Celica | EFI (15) |
| Corolla & Corolla FX-16 | STOP (15) |
| Cressida | EFI (15) |
| Land Cruiser | EFI (15) |
| MR2 | $AM_2$ (7.5) |
| Pickup & 4Runner | EFI (15) |
| Supra | EFI (15) |
| Van | EFI (15) |

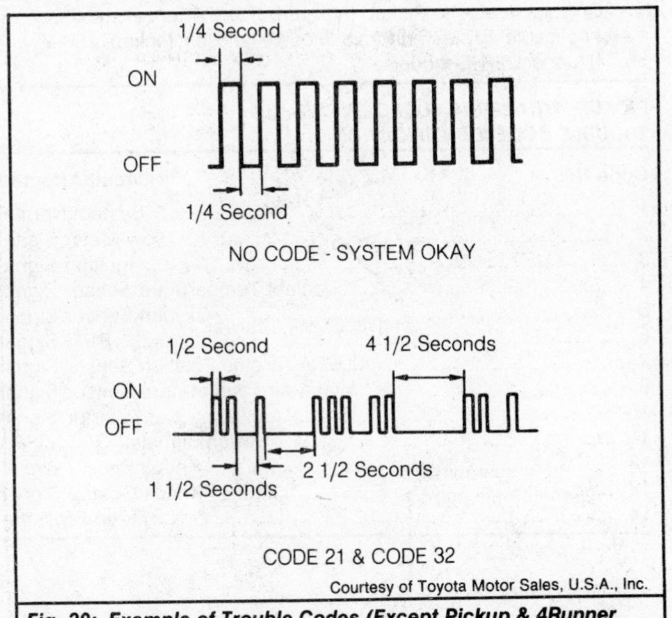
1/4 Second
ON
OFF
1/4 Second
NO CODE - SYSTEM OKAY
1/2 Second
4 1/2 Seconds
ON
OFF
2 1/2 Seconds
1 1/2 Seconds
CODE 21 & CODE 32
Courtesy of Toyota Motor Sales, U.S.A., Inc.

*Fig. 20: Example of Trouble Codes (Except Pickup & 4Runner Turbo)*

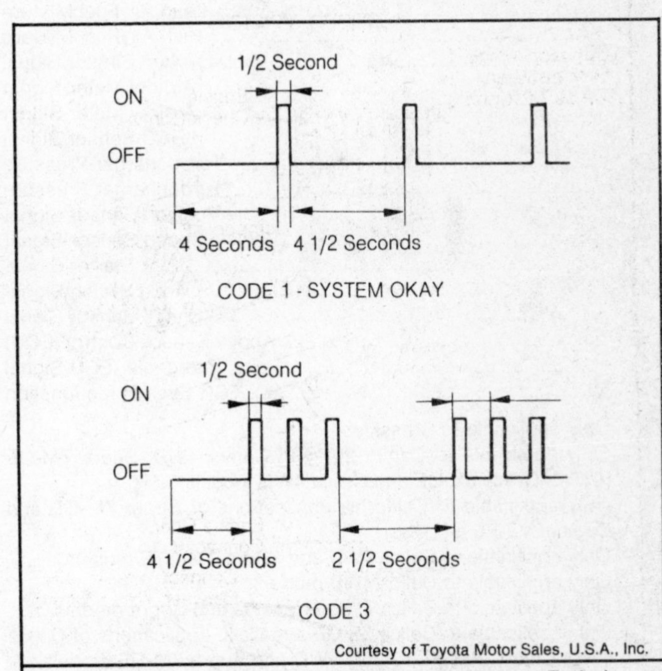
1/2 Second
ON
OFF
4 Seconds
4 1/2 Seconds
CODE 1 - SYSTEM OKAY
1/2 Second
ON
OFF
4 1/2 Seconds
2 1/2 Seconds
CODE 3
Courtesy of Toyota Motor Sales, U.S.A., Inc.

*Fig. 21: Example of Trouble Codes (Pickup & 4Runner Turbo)*

# 1988 COMPUTERIZED ENGINE CONTROLS
# Toyota Computer Control System (Cont.)

## SYSTEM TESTING

**1)** If trouble codes exist and diagnostic circuit check has been performed, compare code with appropriate code chart in following pages for circuits and components associated with trouble code(s). Trouble code flow charts are arranged in alphabetical order by each model. A test No. has been assigned each chart. The test No. and trouble code are in numerical order for each model. All ECU pin identifications are at end of TROUBLE CODES & PROBABLE CAUSE charts.

**2)** If no code is present, circuit checking is necessary. Each model has an ECU PIN VOLTAGE TEST table after DIAGNOSTIC CIRCUIT CHECK flow chart. DIAGNOSTIC CIRCUIT CHECK flow chart is the first flow chart on each model. Using ECU PIN VOLTAGE TEST table, check appropriate circuits using the test No. in the right column of the appropriate table.

**3)** Component testing will also be necessary. All component testing available from manufacturer and pretaining to CEC, follows the CEC flow charts. For components not covered, see appropriate article in FUEL or DISTRIBUTORS & IGNITION SYSTEMS.

***CAMRY, CELICA, CRESSIDA, SUPRA TROUBLE CODE IDENTIFICATION***

| Code No. | Circuit Affected |
|---|---|
| No Code | System Normal |
| 11 | ECU (B+) |
| 12 & 13 | RPM Signal |
| 14 | Ignition Signal |
| 21 | Oxygen Sensor Signal |
| 22 | Coolant Temp. Sensor Signal |
| 23 [1] | Intake Air Temp. Sensor Signal |
| 24 | Intake Air Temp. Sensor Signal |
| 25 [2] | Lean Air/Fuel Mixture |
| 26 [2] | Rich Air/Fuel Mixture |
| 27 [3] | Sub-Oxygen Sensor Signal |
| 31 | Airflow Meter Signal |
| 32 | Airflow Meter Signal<br>[4] HAC Sensor Signal |
| 34 [4] | Turbocharger Pressure |
| 35 [5] | Turbocharger Pressure |
| 41 | Throttle Position Sensor Signal |
| 42 | Vehicle Speed Sensor Signal |
| 43 | Starter Signal |
| 51 | Switch Signal |
| 52 [6] | Knock Sensor Signal |
| 53 [6] | Knock Sensor Control (ECU) |
| 54 [5] | Intercooler ECU Signal |
| 71 [7] | EGR System Malfunction |

[1] – Only applicable to Cressida.

[2] – Only applicable to Camry 2VZ-FE, Camry 4WD, Supra 7M-GE (Calif.), Celica 3S-GE and Celica 4WD models.

[3] – Only applicable to California applications of Supra 7M-GE and Camry 2VZ-FE models.

[4] – Only applicable to Celica 4WD and Supra 7M-GTE models.

[5] – Only applicable to Celica 4WD models.

[6] – Only applicable to Celica 4WD, Cressida and Supra models.

[7] – Only applicable to Celica 3S-GE and Calif. applications of Celica 4WD, Camry 2VZ-FE, Camry 4WD and Supra 7M-GE models.

***COROLLA, COROLLA FX-16, LAND CRUISER, MR2, PICKUP (NON-TURBO), 4RUNNER & VAN TROUBLE CODE IDENTIFICATION***

| Code No. | Circuit Affected |
|---|---|
| No Code | System Normal |
| 11 [1] | ECU (B+) |
| 12 & 13 | RPM Signal |
| 14 | Ignition Signal |
| 21 | $O_2$ Sensor or $O_2$ Heater Signal |
| 22 | Coolant Temp. Sensor Signal |
| 24 | Intake Air Temp. Sensor Signal |
| 25 | Lean Air/Fuel Mixture |
| 26 | Rich Air/Fuel Mixture |
| 27 [2] | Sub-$O_2$ Sensor Signal |
| 28 [3] | No. 2 $O_2$ Sensor or No. 2 $O_2$ Heater Signal |
| 31 | Airflow Meter Signal |
| 32 [1] | Airflow Meter Signal |
| 35 [4] | HAC Sensor Signal |
| 41 | Throttle Position Sensor Signal |
| 42 | Vehicle Speed Sensor Signal |
| 43 | Starter Signal |
| 51 | Switch Signal |
| 52 [5] | Knock Sensor Signal |
| 53 [5] | Knock Sensor Control (ECU) |
| 71 [6] | EGR System Malfunction |

[1] – Only applicable to Pickup 3VZ-E, 4Runner 3VZ-E and Land Cruiser models.

[2] – Only applicable to Van models.

[3] – Only applicable to Land Cruiser models.

[4] – Only applicable to Land Cruiser, Pickup 22R-E and 4Runner 22R-E models.

[5] – Only applicable to Pickup (non-turbo) and 4Runner models.

[6] – Applicable to all California models and all Pickup 22R-E and 4Runner 22R-E models.

***PICKUP WITH 22R-TE TURBO ENGINE TROUBLE CODE IDENTIFICATION***

| Code No. | Circuit Affected |
|---|---|
| 1 | System Normal |
| 2 | Airflow Meter Signal |
| 3 | Ignition Signal |
| 4 | Coolant Temperature Sensor Signal |
| 5 | Oxygen Sensor Signal |
| 6 | RPM Signal |
| 7 | Throttle Position Sensor Signal |
| 8 | Intake Air Temperature Sensor Signal |
| 10 | Starter Signal |
| 11 | Switch Signals ("ON", "OFF") |
| 12 | Knock Sensor Signal |
| 13 | Knock Control Signal |
| 14 | Turbo Pressure |

### CAMRY, CELICA, CRESSIDA, SUPRA TROUBLE CODES & PROBABLE CAUSE

| Code No. | Probable Cause |
|---|---|
| 11 | Main Relay and/or Circuit, Ignition Switch and/or Circuit, ECU |
| 12 | Distributor and/or Circuit, Starter Signal, ECU |
| 13 | Distributor and/or Circuit, ECU |
| 14 | Ignition Coil, Ignitor and/or Circuit, ECU |
| 21 | $O_2$ Sensor and/or $O_2$ Heater Signal and/or Circuit, ECU |
| 22 | Coolant Temp. Sensor and/or Circuit, ECU |
| 23 [1] | Intake Air Temp. Sensor and/or Circuit, ECU |
| 24 | Intake Air Temp. Sensor or Circuit, ECU |
| 25 [2] | Injector and/or Circuit, $O_2$ Sensor and/or, Circuit, Fuel Line Pressure, Airflow Meter, Coolant Temp. Sensor, Ignition System, ECU |
| 26 [2] | Injector and/or Circuit, Fuel Line Pressure, Cold Start Injector, Airflow Meter, Coolant Temp. Sensor, ECU |
| 27 [3] | Sub-$O_2$ Sensor/Heater and/or Circuit, ECU |
| 31 | Airflow Meter and/or Circuit, ECU |
| 32 [4] | Airflow Meter or Circuit, ECU |
| 34 [5] | Turbo, Turbo Pressure Sensor and/or Circuit, ECU |
| 35 [5] | Turbo Pressure Sensor and/or Circuit, Airflow Meter, ECU, Intercooler |
| 41 | Throttle Position Sensor and/or Circuit, ECU |
| 42 | Speed Sensor and/or Circuit, ECU |
| 43 | Ignition Switch and/or Circuit, ECU |
| 51 | Throttle Position Sensor and/or Circuit A/C Switch Circuit, A/C Amplifier, ECU Neutral/Start Switch and/or Circuit, Accelerator Pedal and/or Cable |
| 52 [6] | Knock Sensor or Circuit, ECU |
| 53 [6] | ECU |
| 54 [7] | Intercooler, Coolant Level Sensor and/or Circuit, Intercooler Water Pump and/or Circuit, Intercooler ECU, ECU |
| 71 [8] | EGR System, EGR Gas Temp. Sensor and/or Circuit, BVSV for EGR and/or Circuit, ECU |

[1] – Only applicable to Cressida.
[2] – Camry 4WD & V6, Celica 4WD & 3S-GE and Supra 7M-GE California models only.
[3] – Camry V6 and Supra 7M-GE California models only.
[4] – On Supra with 7M-GTE models, probable cause is HAC Sensor and/or circuit, or ECU.
[5] – On Celica 4WD models.
[6] – On Celica 4WD, Cressida and Supra.
[7] – On Celica 4WD models.
[8] – Camry 4WD & V6, Celica 4WD & 3S-GE and Supra California models only.

### COROLLA, COROLLA FX-16, LAND CRUISER, MR2, PICKUP (NON-TURBO), 4RUNNER & VAN TROUBLE CODES & PROBABLE CAUSE

| Code No. | Probable Cause |
|---|---|
| 11 [1] | Main Relay and/or Circuit, Ignition Switch and/or Circuit, ECU |
| 12 | Distributor and/or Circuit, Starter Signal, Ignitor, ECU |
| 13 | Distributor and/or Circuit, ECU |
| 14 | Ignition Coil, Ignitor and/or Circuit, ECU |
| 21 | $O_2$ Sensor and/or $O_2$ Heater Signal and/or Circuit, ECU |
| 22 | Coolant Temp. Sensor and/or Circuit, ECU |
| 24 | Intake Air Temp. Sensor or Circuit, ECU |
| 25 | Injector and/or Circuit, $O_2$ Sensor and/or Circuit Airflow Meter, ECU, Fuel Line Pressure Air Intake System, Ignition System |

### COROLLA, COROLLA FX-16, LAND CRUISER, MR2, PICKUP (NON-TURBO), 4RUNNER & VAN TROUBLE CODES & PROBABLE CAUSE (Cont.)

| Code No. | Probable Cause |
|---|---|
| 26 | Injector and/or Circuit, Fuel Line Pressure, Cold Start Injector, Airflow Meter, $O_2$ Sensor and/or Circuit, ECU |
| 27 [2] | Sub-$O_2$ Sensor/Heater and/or Circuit, ECU |
| 28 [3] | $O_2$ Sensor and/or $O_2$ Heater Signal and/or Circuit, ECU |
| 31 | Airflow Meter and/or Circuit, ECU |
| 32 [1] | Airflow Meter or Circuit, ECU |
| 35 [4] | HAC Sensor and/or Circuit, ECU |
| 41 | Throttle Position Sensor and/or Circuit, ECU |
| 42 | Vehicle Speed Sensor and/or Circuit, ECU |
| 43 | Ignition Switch and/or Circuit Starter Signal Circuit, ECU |
| 51 | Throttle Position Sensor and/or Circuit A/C Switch Circuit, A/C Amplifier, ECU Neutral/Start Switch and/or Circuit, Accelerator Pedal and/or Cable |
| 52 [5] | Knock Sensor or Circuit, ECU |
| 53 [5] | ECU |
| 71 [6] | EGR System, EGR Gas Temp. Sensor and/or Circuit, BVSV for EGR and/or Circuit, ECU |

[1] – Only applicable to Pickup 3VZ-E, 4Runner 3VZ-E and Land Cruiser models.
[2] – Only applicable to Van models.
[3] – Only applicable to Land Cruiser models.
[4] – Only applicable to Land Cruiser, Pickup 22R-E and 4Runner 22R-E models.
[5] – Only applicable to Pickup (non-turbo) and 4Runner models.
[6] – Applicable to all California models and all Pickup 22R-E and 4Runner 22R-E models.

### PICKUP WITH 22R-TE TURBO ENGINE TROUBLE CODES & PROBABLE CAUSE

| Code No. | Probable Cause |
|---|---|
| 1 | System Normal |
| 2 | Airflow Meter and/or Circuit |
| 3 | Ignitor, Coil and/or Circuit, ECU |
| 4 | Coolant Temp. Sensor and/or Circuit, ECU |
| 5 | Oxygen Sensor and/or Circuit, ECU |
| 6 | Distributor, Ignitor and/or Circuits |
| 7 | Throttle Position Sensor and/or Circuit |
| 8 | Intake Air Temp. Sensor and/or Circuit |
| 10 | Ignition Switch and/or Circuit, ECU |
| 11 | A/C Switch, Amplifier and/or Circuit, Neutral/Start Switch, Idle Switch, Throttle Position Sensor and/or Circuit, ECU |
| 12 | Knock Sensor and/or Circuit, ECU |
| 13 | ECU |
| 14 | Turbo, Airflow Meter, ECU |

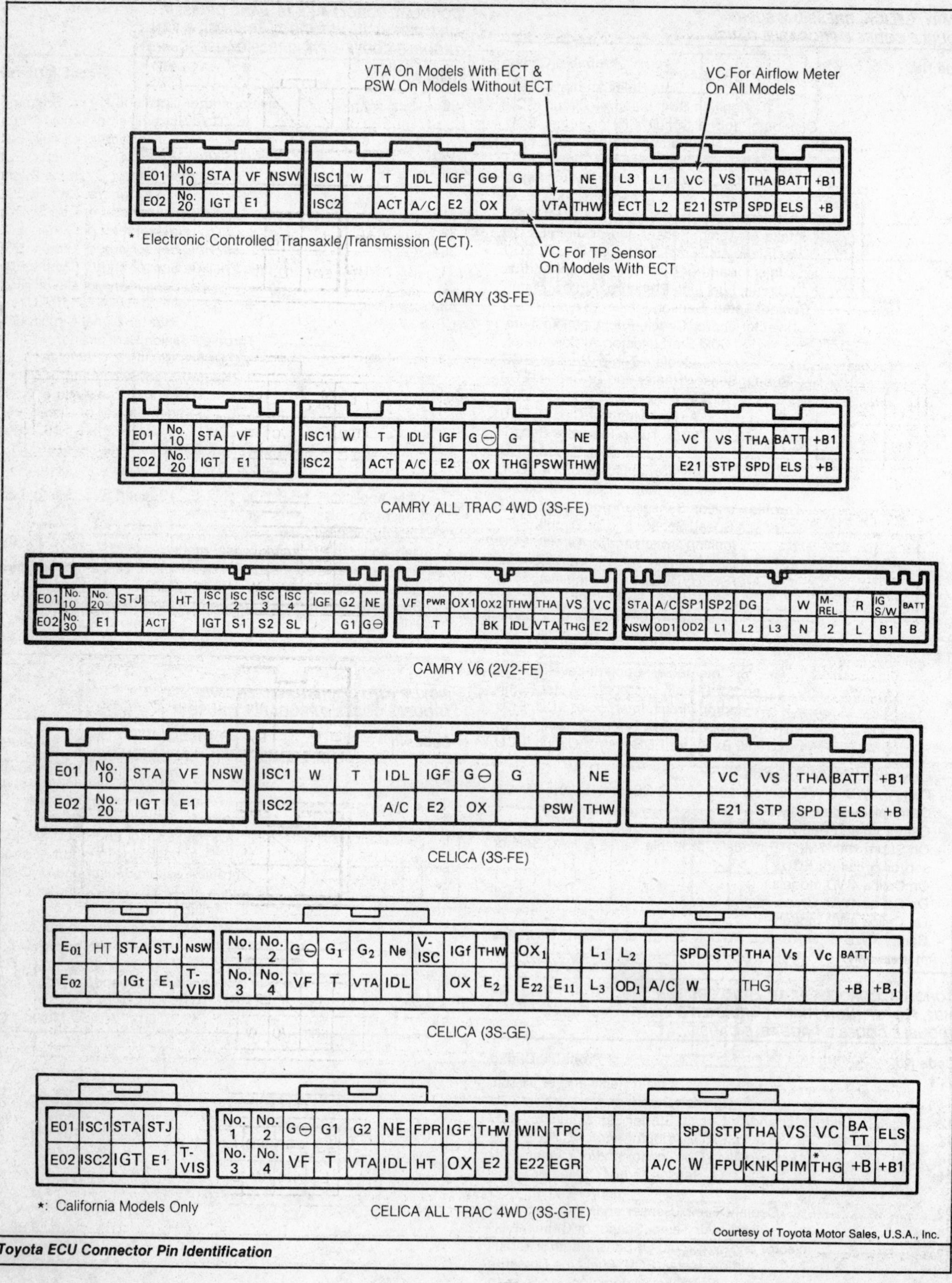
VTA On Models With ECT &
PSW On Models Without ECT
VC For Airflow Meter
On All Models
E01 No. 10 STA VF NSW ISC1 W T IDL IGF G⊖ G NE L3 L1 VC VS THA BATT +B1
E02 No. 20 IGT E1 ISC2 ACT A/C E2 OX VTA THW ECT L2 E21 STP SPD ELS +B
* Electronic Controlled Transaxle/Transmission (ECT).
VC For TP Sensor
On Models With ECT
CAMRY (3S-FE)
E01 No. 10 STA VF ISC1 W T IDL IGF G⊖ G NE VC VS THA BATT +B1
E02 No. 20 IGT E1 ISC2 ACT A/C E2 OX THG PSW THW E21 STP SPD ELS +B
CAMRY ALL TRAC 4WD (3S-FE)
E01 No. 10 No. 20 STJ HT ISC 1 ISC 2 ISC 3 ISC 4 IGF G2 NE VF PWR OX1 OX2 THW THA VS VC STA A/C SP1 SP2 DG W M-REL R IG S/W BATT
E02 No. 30 E1 ACT IGT S1 S2 SL G1 G⊖ T BK IDL VTA THG E2 NSW OD1 OD2 L1 L2 L3 N 2 L B1 B
CAMRY V6 (2V2-FE)
E01 No. 10 STA VF NSW ISC1 W T IDL IGF G⊖ G NE VC VS THA BATT +B1
E02 No. 20 IGT E1 ISC2 A/C E2 OX PSW THW E21 STP SPD ELS +B
CELICA (3S-FE)
E01 HT STA STJ NSW No. 1 No. 2 G⊖ G1 G2 Ne V-ISC IGf THW OX1 L1 L2 SPD STP THA Vs Vc BATT
E02 IGt E1 T-VIS No. 3 No. 4 VF T VTA IDL OX E2 E22 E11 L3 OD1 A/C W THG +B +B1
CELICA (3S-GE)
E01 ISC1 STA STJ No. 1 No. 2 G⊖ G1 G2 NE FPR IGF THW WIN TPC SPD STP THA VS VC BATT ELS
E02 ISC2 IGT E1 T-VIS No. 3 No. 4 VF T VTA IDL HT OX E2 E22 EGR A/C W FPU KNK PIM *THG +B +B1
*: California Models Only
CELICA ALL TRAC 4WD (3S-GTE)
Courtesy of Toyota Motor Sales, U.S.A., Inc.

*Toyota ECU Connector Pin Identification*

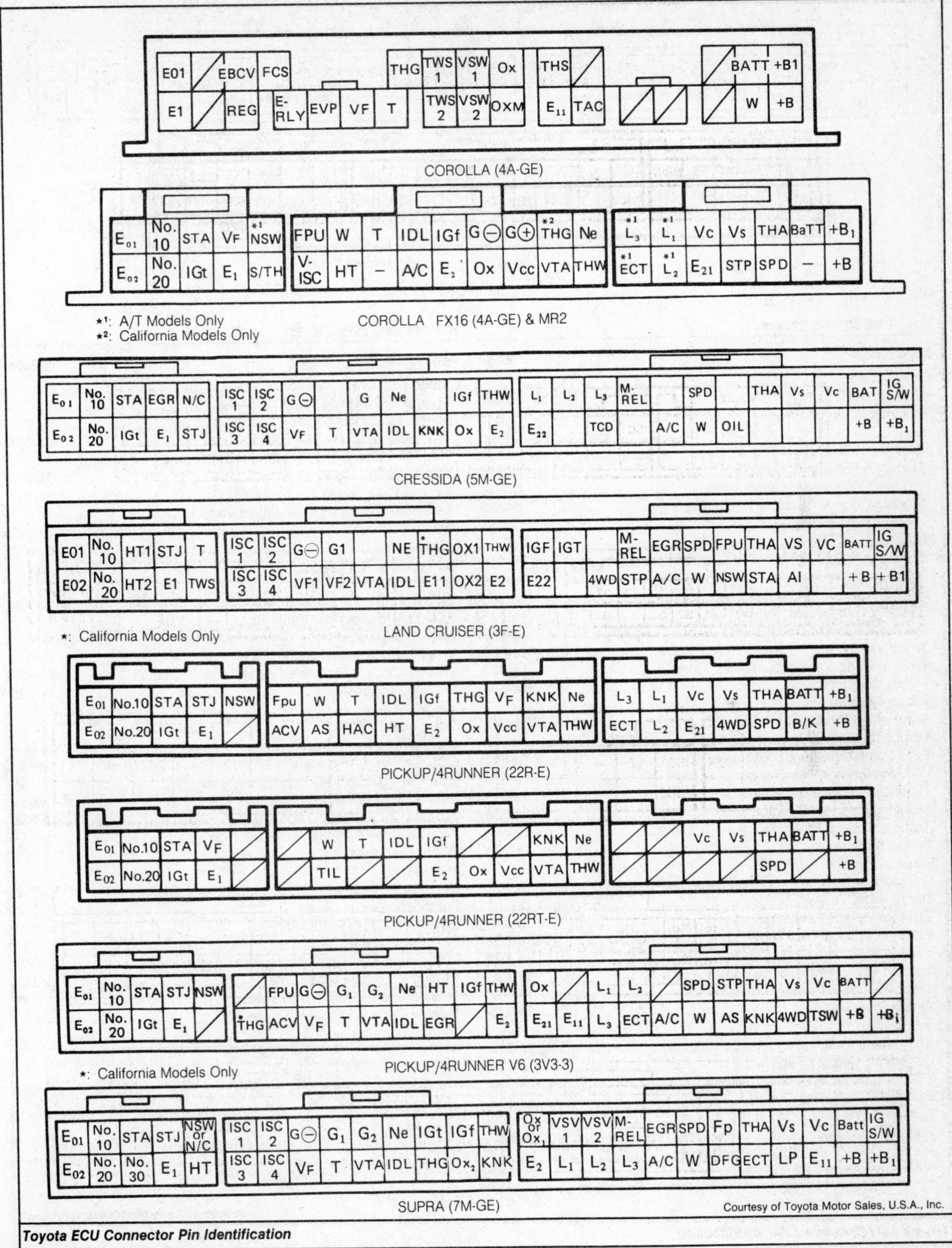
E01 EBCV FCS THG TWS 1 VSW 1 Ox THS BATT +B1
E1 REG E-RLY EVP VF T TWS 2 VSW 2 OXM E11 TAC W +B
COROLLA (4A-GE)
E01 No. 10 STA VF *1 NSW FPU W T IDL IGf G⊖ G⊕ *2 THG Ne *1 L3 *1 L1 Vc Vs THA BaTT +B1
E02 No. 20 IGt E1 S/TH V-ISC HT – A/C E2 Ox Vcc VTA THW *1 ECT *1 L2 E21 STP SPD – +B
*1: A/T Models Only
*2: California Models Only
COROLLA FX16 (4A-GE) & MR2
E01 No. 10 STA EGR N/C ISC 1 ISC 2 G⊖ G Ne IGf THW L1 L2 L3 M-REL SPD THA Vs Vc BAT IG S/W
E02 No. 20 IGt E1 STJ ISC 3 ISC 4 VF T VTA IDL KNK Ox E2 E22 TCD A/C W OIL +B +B1
CRESSIDA (5M-GE)
E01 No. 10 HT1 STJ T ISC 1 ISC 2 G⊖ G1 NE *THG OX1 THW IGF IGT M-REL EGR SPD FPU THA VS VC BATT IG S/W
E02 No. 20 HT2 E1 TWS ISC 3 ISC 4 VF1 VF2 VTA IDL E11 OX2 E2 E22 4WD STP A/C W NSW STA AI +B +B1
LAND CRUISER (3F-E)
*: California Models Only
E01 No.10 STA STJ NSW Fpu W T IDL IGf THG VF KNK Ne L3 L1 Vc Vs THA BATT +B1
E02 No.20 IGt E1 ACV AS HAC HT E2 Ox Vcc VTA THW ECT L2 E21 4WD SPD B/K +B
PICKUP/4RUNNER (22R-E)
E01 No.10 STA VF W T IDL IGf KNK Ne Vc Vs THA BATT +B1
E02 No.20 IGt E1 TIL E2 Ox Vcc VTA THW SPD +B
PICKUP/4RUNNER (22RT-E)
E01 No. 10 STA STJ NSW FPU G⊖ G1 G2 Ne HT IGf THW Ox L1 L2 SPD STP THA Vs Vc BATT
E02 No. 20 IGt E1 *THG ACV VF T VTA IDL EGR E2 E21 E11 L3 ECT A/C W AS KNK 4WD TSW +B +B1
*: California Models Only
PICKUP/4RUNNER V6 (3V3-3)
E01 No. 10 STA STJ NSW or N/C ISC 1 ISC 2 G⊖ G1 G2 Ne IGt IGf THW Ox or Ox1 VSV 1 VSV 2 M-REL EGR SPD Fp THA Vs Vc Batt IG S/W
E02 No. 20 No. 30 E1 HT ISC 3 ISC 4 VF T VTA IDL THG Ox2 KNK E2 L1 L2 L3 A/C W DFG ECT LP E11 +B +B1
SUPRA (7M-GE)
Courtesy of Toyota Motor Sales, U.S.A., Inc.
**Toyota ECU Connector Pin Identification**

# 1988 COMPUTERIZED ENGINE CONTROLS
## Toyota Computer Control System (Cont.)

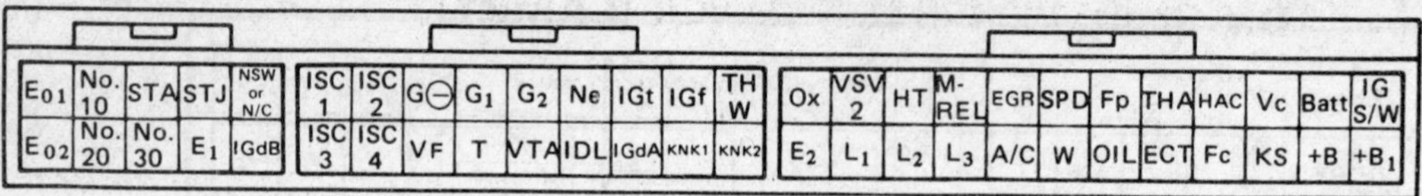
E01 No. 10 STA STJ NSW or N/C
E02 No. 20 No. 30 E1 IGdB
ISC 1 ISC 2 G⊖ G1 G2 Ne IGt IGf TH W
ISC 3 ISC 4 VF T VTA IDL IGdA KNK1 KNK2
Ox VSV 2 HT M-REL EGR SPD Fp THA HAC Vc Batt IG S/W
E2 L1 L2 L3 A/C W OIL ECT Fc KS +B +B1
DFG
TIL LP

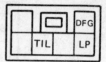

SUPRA (7M-GTE)

| E01 | No. 10 | STA | STJ | NSW | V-ISV | W | T | IDL | IGF | OX2 | | HT | NE | | | VC | VS | THA | BATT | +B1 |
|---|---|---|---|---|---|---|---|---|---|---|---|---|---|---|---|---|---|---|---|---|
| E02 | No. 20 | IGT | E1 | VF | ACV | TSW | *THG | A/C | E2 | OX1 | FPU | PSW | THW | | | E21 | | SPD | | +B |

*: California Models Only

VAN (4Y-E)

### TOYOTA CEC DIRECTORY



### TOYOTA CEC DIRECTORY



Courtesy of Toyota Motor Sales, U.S.A., Inc.

*Toyota ECU Connector Pin Identification*

# 1988 COMPUTERIZED ENGINE CONTROLS
## Toyota Computer Control System (Cont.)

### DIAGNOSTIC CIRCUIT CHECK (CAMRY)

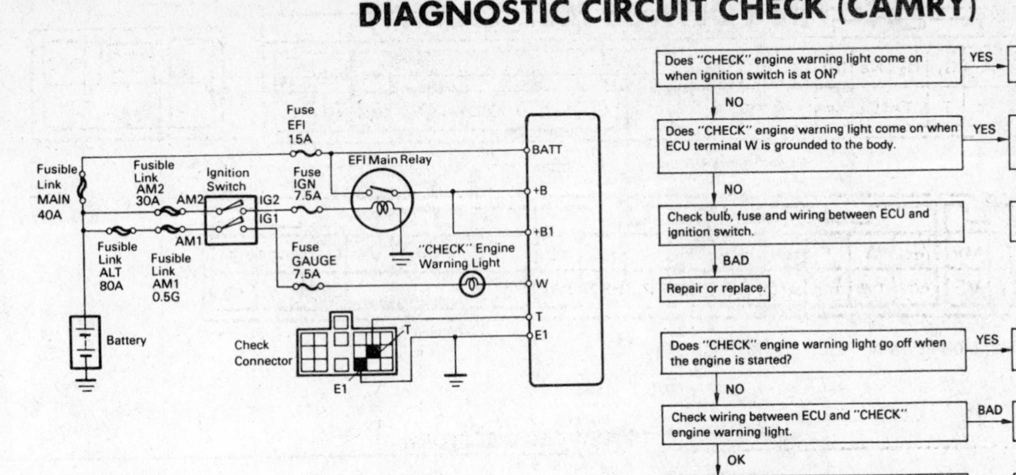

Fuse
EFI
15A
Fusible Link
MAIN
40A
Fusible Link
AM2
30A
Ignition Switch
AM2
IG2
IG1
AM1
Fuse
IGN
7.5A
EFI Main Relay
BATT
+B
+B1
Fusible Link
ALT
80A
Fusible Link
AM1
0.5G
Fuse
GAUGE
7.5A
"CHECK" Engine Warning Light
W
T
E1
Battery
Check Connector
E1


- Does "CHECK" engine warning light come on when ignition switch is at ON?
  - YES → System Normal
  - NO → Does "CHECK" engine warning light come on when ECU terminal W is grounded to the body?
    - YES → Check wiring between ECU terminal E1 and body ground.
      - OK → Try another ECU.
      - BAD → Repair or replace.
    - NO → Check bulb, fuse and wiring between ECU and ignition switch.
      - BAD → Repair or replace.

- Does "CHECK" engine warning light go off when the engine is started?
  - YES → System Normal
  - NO → Check wiring between ECU and "CHECK" engine warning light.
    - BAD → Repair.
    - OK → Is there diagnostic code output when check connector terminals T and E1 are short circuited?
      - NO → Try another ECU.
      - YES → Does "CHECK" engine warning light go out after repair according to malfunction code?
        - NO → Further repair required.
        - YES → System OK → Cancel out diagnostic code.

**4-CYLINDER**

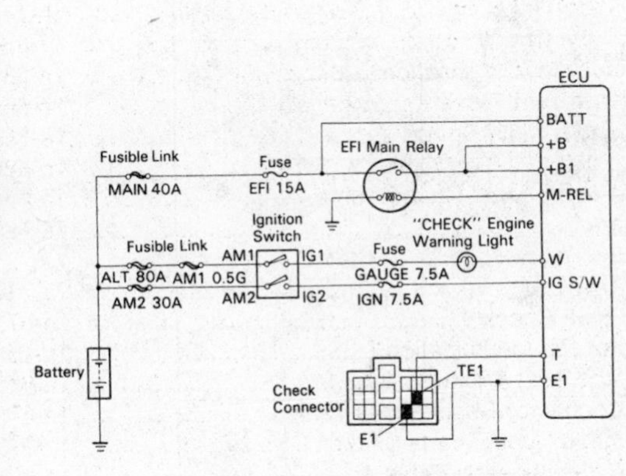

ECU
BATT
+B
+B1
M-REL
Fusible Link
MAIN 40A
Fuse
EFI 15A
EFI Main Relay
Ignition Switch
"CHECK" Engine Warning Light
Fusible Link
AM1
IG1
Fuse
W
ALT 80A
AM1 0.5G
GAUGE 7.5A
IG S/W
AM2 30A
AM2
IG2
IGN 7.5A
T
TE1
E1
Battery
Check Connector
E1


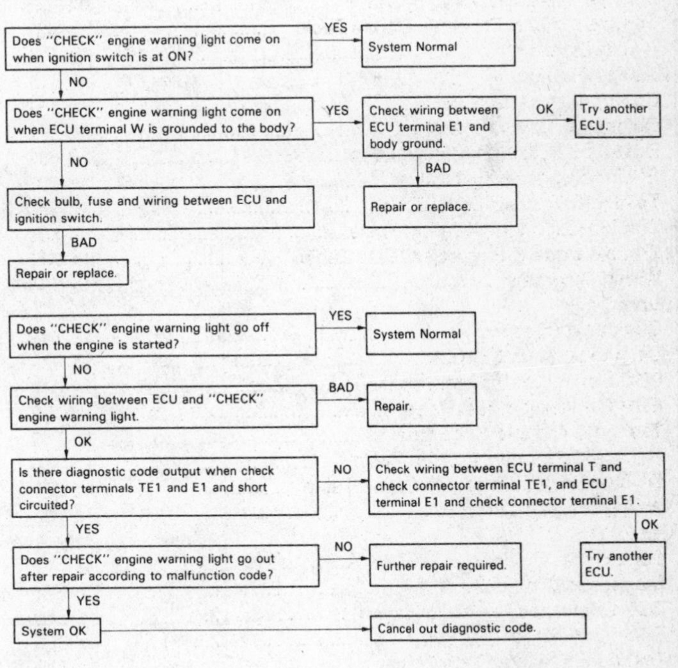

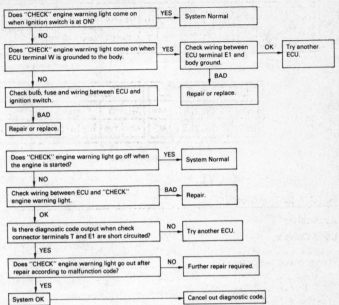

Does "CHECK" engine warning light come on when ignition switch is at ON?
YES
System Normal
NO
Does "CHECK" engine warning light come on when ECU terminal W is grounded to the body?
YES
Check wiring between ECU terminal E1 and body ground.
OK
Try another ECU.
BAD
Repair or replace.
NO
Check bulb, fuse and wiring between ECU and ignition switch.
BAD
Repair or replace.
Does "CHECK" engine warning light go off when the engine is started?
YES
System Normal
NO
Check wiring between ECU and "CHECK" engine warning light.
BAD
Repair.
OK
Is there diagnostic code output when check connector terminals TE1 and E1 and short circuited?
NO
Check wiring between ECU terminal T and check connector terminal TE1, and ECU terminal E1 and check connector terminal E1.
OK
Try another ECU.
YES
Does "CHECK" engine warning light go out after repair according to malfunction code?
NO
Further repair required.
YES
System OK
Cancel out diagnostic code.


**V6**

Courtesy of Toyota Motor Sales, U.S.A., Inc.

## ECU PIN VOLTAGE TEST (CAMRY)

### 4-CYL.

| Terminals | STD voltage (V) | Condition | | Test No. |
|---|---|---|---|---|
| +B / +B1 — E1 | 10 — 14 | Ignition S/W ON | | 1 |
| BATT — E1 | 10 — 14 | — | | 11 |
| IDL — E1 | 8 — 14 | Ignition S/W ON | Throttle valve open | 8 |
| PSW — E1 | 4 — 5 | | Throttle valve fully closed | |
| IDL — E2 | 4 — 6 | | Throttle valve open | |
| VTA — E2 | 0.1 — 1.0 | | Throttle valve fully closed | |
| | 4 — 5 | | Throttle valve open | |
| VC — E1 | 4 — 6 | | — | |
| IGT — E1 | 0.7 — 1.0 | Idling | | 2 |
| STA — E1 | 6 — 14 | Cranking | | 9 |
| No.10 — E01 / No.20 — E02 | 9 — 14 | Ignition S/W ON | | |
| W — E1 | 8 — 14 | No trouble (Check engine warning light off) and engine running | | 13 |
| VC — E2 | 4 — 6 | Ignition S/W ON | — | 7 |
| VS — E2 | 4 — 5 | | Measuring plate fully closed | |
| | 0.02 — 0.5 | | Measuring plate fully open | |
| | 2 — 4 | Idling | | |
| THA — E2 | 1 — 3 | Ignition S/W ON | Intake air temp. 20°C (68°F) | 5 |
| THW — E2 | 0.1 — 1.0 | | Coolant temp. 80°C (176°F) | 4 |
| ISC1 / ISC2 — E1 | 9 — 14 | | — | 14 |
| A/C — E1 | 8 — 14 | | Air conditioning ON | 15 |

### V6

| Terminals | Condition | | STD Voltage | Test No. |
|---|---|---|---|---|
| BATT - E1 | — | | 10 - 14 | 1 |
| IG S/W - E1 | Ignition S/W ON | | 10 - 14 | |
| M-REL - E1 | | | | |
| +B (+B1) - E1 | | | | |
| IDL - E2 | Ignition S/W ON | Throttle valve open | 4 - 6 | 8 |
| VC - E2 | | – | 4 - 6 | |
| VTA - E2 | | Throttle valve fully closed | 0.1 - 1.0 | |
| | | Throttle valve fully open | 4 - 5 | |
| VC - E2 | Ignition S/W ON | – | 4 - 6 | 7 |
| VS - E2 | | Measuring plate fully closed | 4 - 5 | |
| | | Measuring plate fully open | 0.02 - 0.08 | |
| | Idling | | 2 - 4 | |
| | 3,000 rpm | | 0.3 - 1.0 | |
| No. 10 / No. 20 / No. 30 - E01 / E02 | Ignition S/W ON | | 9 - 14 | 12 |
| THA - E2 | Ignition S/W ON | Intake air temperature 20°C (68°F) | 1 - 3 | 5 |
| THW - E2 | Ignition S/W ON | Coolant temperature 80°C (176°F) | 0.1 - 1.0 | 4 |
| STA - E1 | Cranking | | 6 - 14 | 9 |
| IGT - E1 | Idling | | 0.7 - 1.0 | 2 |
| ISC1 / ISC4 - E1 | Ignition S/W ON | | 9 - 14 | 14 |
| W - E1 | No trouble ("CHECK" engine warning light off) and engine running | | 8 - 14 | 13 |
| A/C - E1 | Ignition S/W ON | Air conditioning ON | 8 - 14 | |

Courtesy of Toyota Motor Sales, U.S.A., Inc.

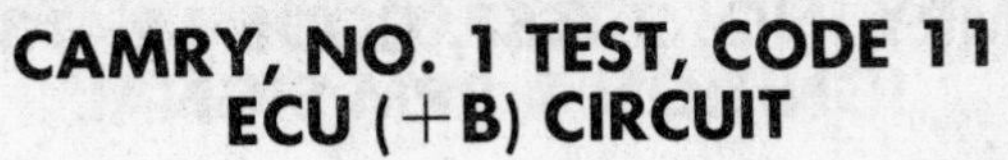

## CAMRY, NO. 1 TEST, CODE 11
## ECU (+B) CIRCUIT

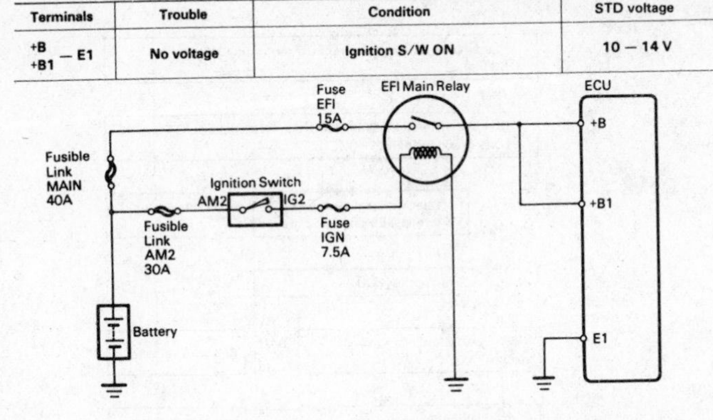

| Terminals | Trouble | Condition | STD voltage |
|---|---|---|---|
| +B<br>+B1 — E1 | No voltage | Ignition S/W ON | 10 — 14 V |

Fuse
EFI
15A
EFI Main Relay
ECU
+B
Fusible
Link
MAIN
40A
Ignition Switch
AM2
IG2
+B1
Fusible
Link
AM2
30A
Fuse
IGN
7.5A
Battery
E1

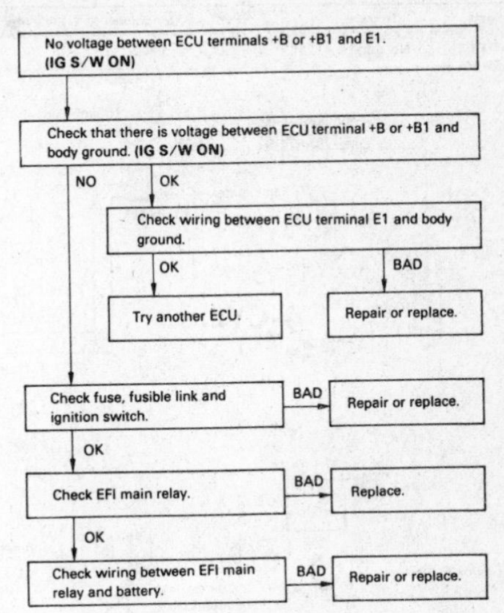

No voltage between ECU terminals +B or +B1 and E1. (IG S/W ON)
Check that there is voltage between ECU terminal +B or +B1 and body ground. (IG S/W ON)
NO
OK
Check wiring between ECU terminal E1 and body ground.
OK
BAD
Try another ECU.
Repair or replace.
Check fuse, fusible link and ignition switch.
BAD
Repair or replace.
OK
Check EFI main relay.
BAD
Replace.
OK
Check wiring between EFI main relay and battery.
BAD
Repair or replace.

### 4-CYL.

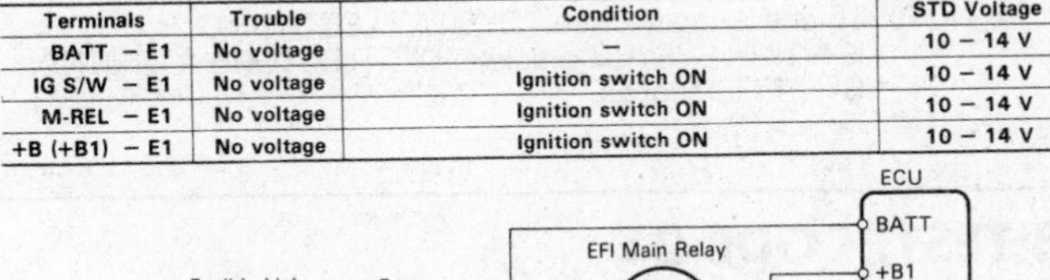

| Terminals | Trouble | Condition | STD Voltage |
|---|---|---|---|
| BATT — E1 | No voltage | — | 10 — 14 V |
| IG S/W — E1 | No voltage | Ignition switch ON | 10 — 14 V |
| M-REL — E1 | No voltage | Ignition switch ON | 10 — 14 V |
| +B (+B1) — E1 | No voltage | Ignition switch ON | 10 — 14 V |

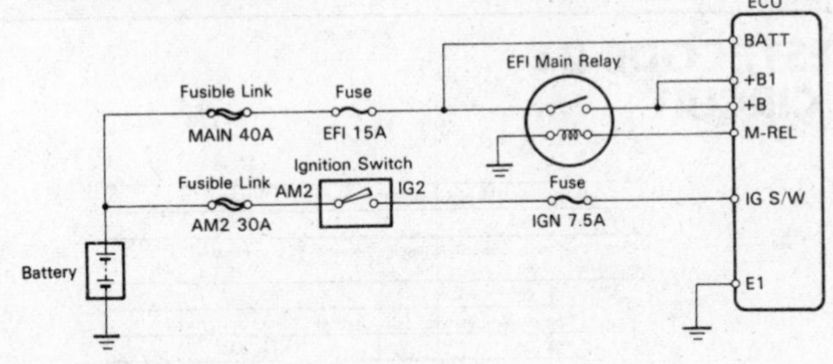

ECU
BATT
EFI Main Relay
+B1
+B
Fusible Link
Fuse
MAIN 40A
EFI 15A
M-REL
Ignition Switch
Fusible Link
AM2
IG2
Fuse
AM2 30A
IGN 7.5A
IG S/W
Battery
E1

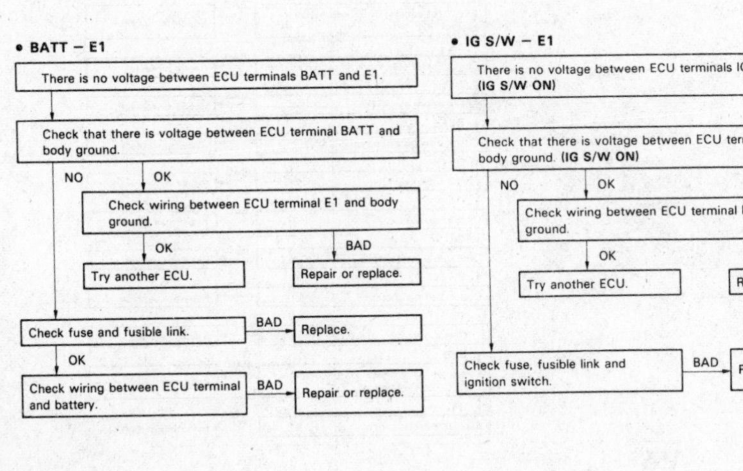

• BATT — E1
There is no voltage between ECU terminals BATT and E1.
Check that there is voltage between ECU terminal BATT and body ground.
NO
OK
Check wiring between ECU terminal E1 and body ground.
OK
BAD
Try another ECU.
Repair or replace.
Check fuse and fusible link.
BAD
Replace.
OK
Check wiring between ECU terminal and battery.
BAD
Repair or replace.
• IG S/W — E1
There is no voltage between ECU terminals IG S/W and E1. (IG S/W ON)
Check that there is voltage between ECU terminal IG S/W and body ground. (IG S/W ON)
NO
OK
Check wiring between ECU terminal E1 and body ground.
OK
BAD
Try another ECU.
Repair or replace.
Check fuse, fusible link and ignition switch.
BAD
Repair or replace.

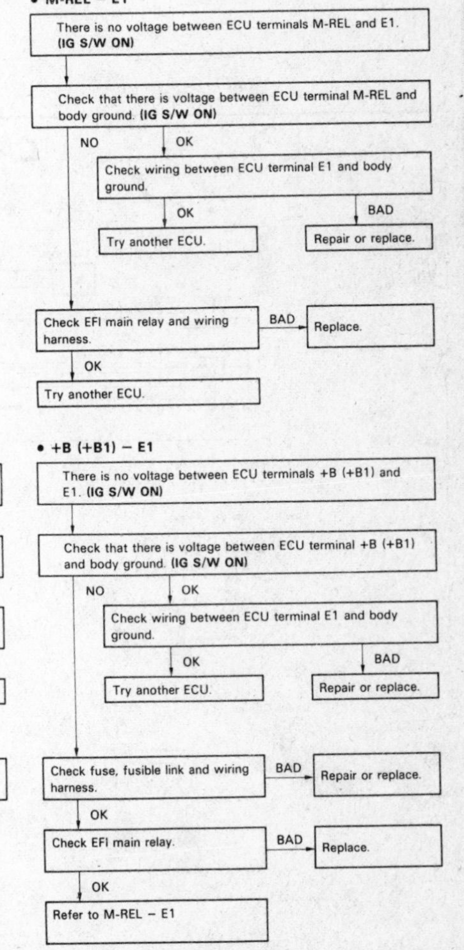

• M-REL — E1
There is no voltage between ECU terminals M-REL and E1. (IG S/W ON)
Check that there is voltage between ECU terminal M-REL and body ground. (IG S/W ON)
NO
OK
Check wiring between ECU terminal E1 and body ground.
OK
BAD
Try another ECU.
Repair or replace.
Check EFI main relay and wiring harness.
BAD
Replace.
OK
Try another ECU.
• +B (+B1) — E1
There is no voltage between ECU terminals +B (+B1) and E1. (IG S/W ON)
Check that there is voltage between ECU terminal +B (+B1) and body ground. (IG S/W ON)
NO
OK
Check wiring between ECU terminal E1 and body ground.
OK
BAD
Try another ECU.
Repair or replace.
Check fuse, fusible link and wiring harness.
BAD
Repair or replace.
OK
Check EFI main relay.
BAD
Replace.
OK
Refer to M-REL — E1

### V6

Courtesy of Toyota Motor Sales, U.S.A., Inc.

## CAMRY, NO. 2 TEST, CODE 12, 13, 14
## IGNITION & RPM SIGNAL

| Terminals | Trouble | Condition | STD voltage |
|---|---|---|---|
| IGT — E1 | No voltage | Idling | 0.7 — 1.0 V |

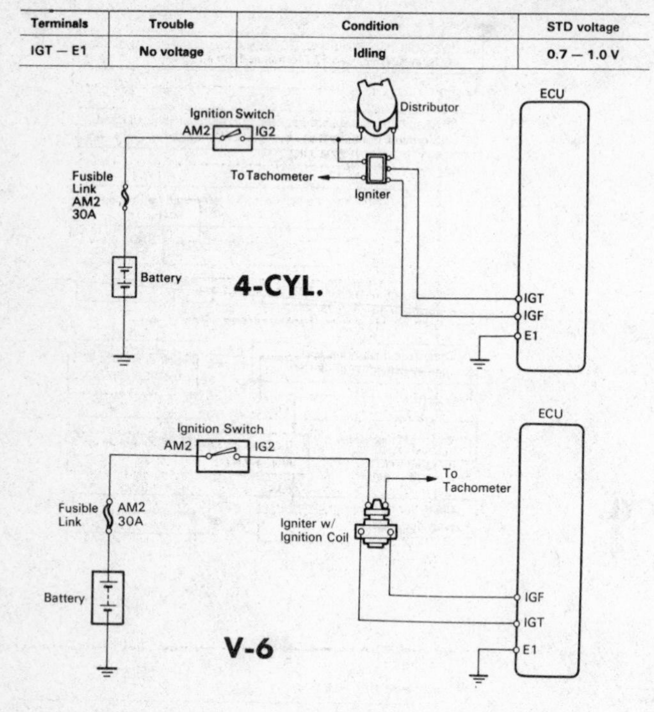
Ignition Switch
AM2
IG2
Distributor
ECU
Fusible Link AM2 30A
To Tachometer
Igniter
Battery
4-CYL.
IGT
IGF
E1
Ignition Switch
AM2
IG2
ECU
To Tachometer
Fusible Link
AM2 30A
Igniter w/ Ignition Coil
Battery
IGF
IGT
E1
V-6

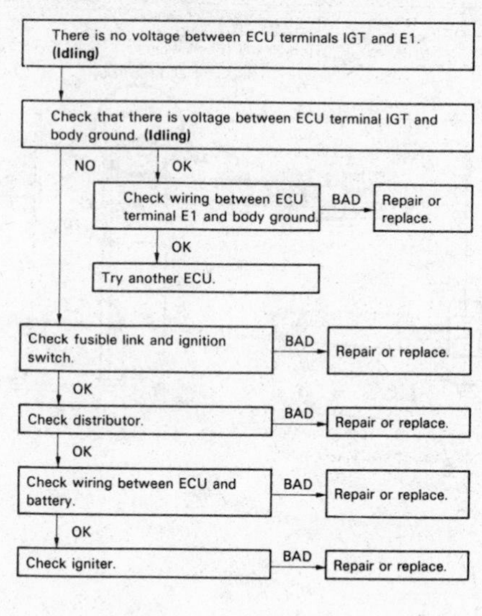
There is no voltage between ECU terminals IGT and E1. (Idling)
Check that there is voltage between ECU terminal IGT and body ground. (Idling)
NO
OK
Check wiring between ECU terminal E1 and body ground.
BAD
Repair or replace.
OK
Try another ECU.
Check fusible link and ignition switch.
BAD
Repair or replace.
OK
Check distributor.
BAD
Repair or replace.
OK
Check wiring between ECU and battery.
BAD
Repair or replace.
OK
Check igniter.
BAD
Repair or replace.

NOTE: To check ignitor, see TOYOTA ELECTRONIC IGNITION SYSTEM article in DISTRIBUTORS & IGNITION SYSTEMS section.

## CAMRY, NO. 3 TEST, CODE 21
## $O_2$ SENSOR CIRCUIT

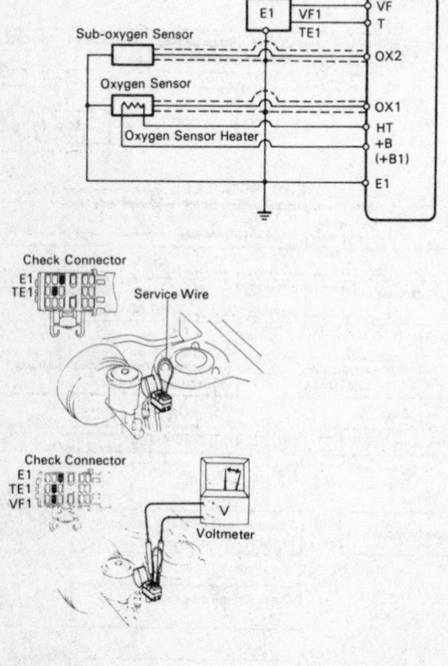
Check Connector
ECU
E1
VF1
TE1
VF
T
Sub-oxygen Sensor
OX2
Oxygen Sensor
OX1
HT
Oxygen Sensor Heater
+B (+B1)
E1
Check Connector
E1
TE1
Service Wire
Check Connector
E1
TE1
VF1
V
Voltmeter

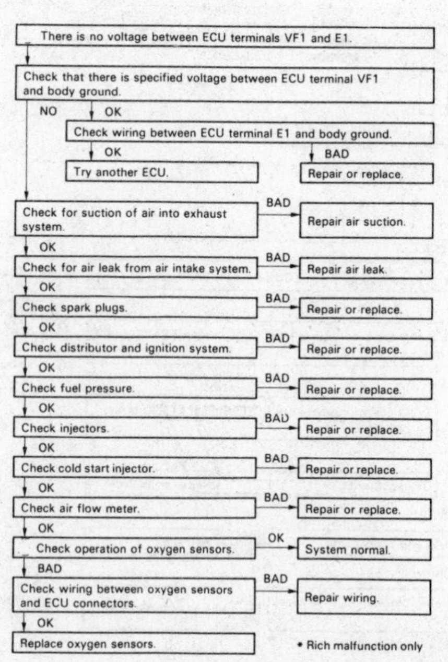
There is no voltage between ECU terminals VF1 and E1.
Check that there is specified voltage between ECU terminal VF1 and body ground.
NO
OK
Check wiring between ECU terminal E1 and body ground.
OK
BAD
Try another ECU.
Repair or replace.
Check for suction of air into exhaust system.
BAD
Repair air suction.
OK
Check for air leak from air intake system.
BAD
Repair air leak.
OK
Check spark plugs.
BAD
Repair or replace.
OK
Check distributor and ignition system.
BAD
Repair or replace.
OK
Check fuel pressure.
BAD
Repair or replace.
OK
Check injectors.
BAD
Repair or replace.
OK
Check cold start injector.
BAD
Repair or replace.
OK
Check air flow meter.
BAD
Repair or replace.
OK
* Check operation of oxygen sensors.
OK
System normal.
BAD
Check wiring between oxygen sensors and ECU connectors.
BAD
Repair wiring.
OK
Replace oxygen sensors.
* Rich malfunction only

V6

## CAMRY, NO. 4 TEST, CODE 22
## COOLANT TEMP. SENSOR CIRCUIT

| Terminals | Trouble | Condition | | STD voltage |
|---|---|---|---|---|
| THW — E2 | No voltage | IG S/W ON | Coolant temperature 80° (176°F) | 0.1 — 1.0 V |

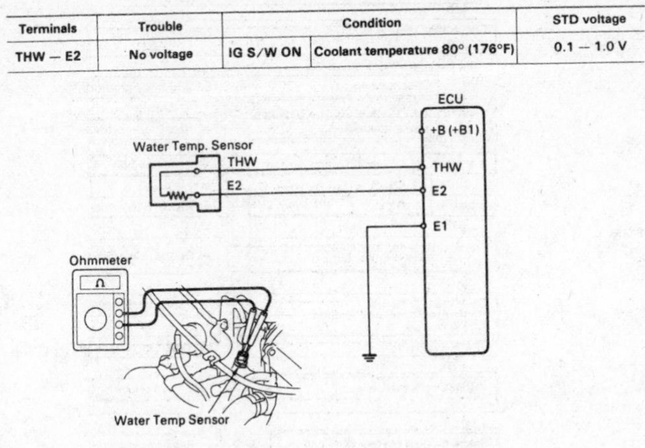
ECU
+B (+B1)
THW
E2
E1
Water Temp. Sensor
THW
E2
Ohmmeter
Ω
Water Temp Sensor

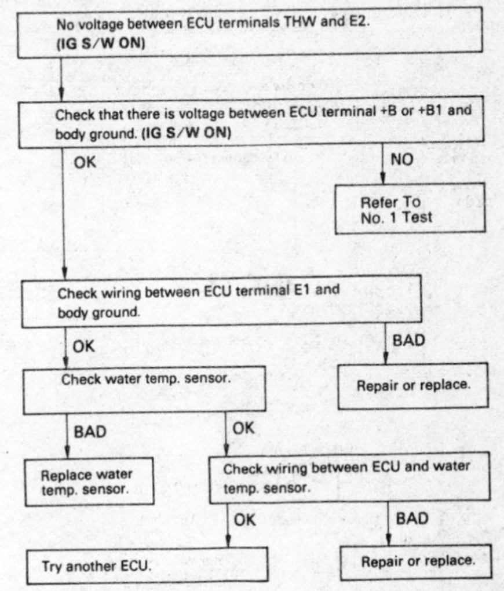
No voltage between ECU terminals THW and E2. (IG S/W ON)
Check that there is voltage between ECU terminal +B or +B1 and body ground. (IG S/W ON)
OK
NO
Refer To No. 1 Test
Check wiring between ECU terminal E1 and body ground.
OK
BAD
Check water temp. sensor.
Repair or replace.
BAD
OK
Replace water temp. sensor.
Check wiring between ECU and water temp. sensor.
OK
BAD
Try another ECU.
Repair or replace.

## CAMRY, NO. 5 TEST, CODE 24
## AIR TEMP. SENSOR CIRCUIT

| Terminals | Trouble | Condition | | STD voltage |
|---|---|---|---|---|
| THA — E2 | No voltage | IG S/W ON | Intake air temperature 20°C (68°F) | 1 — 3 V |

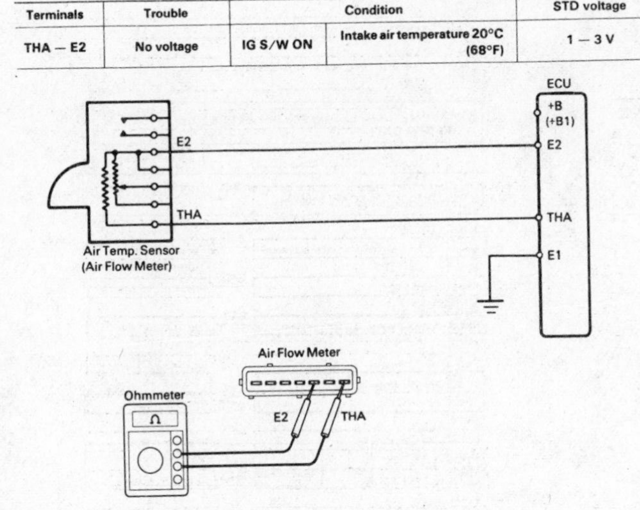
ECU
+B (+B1)
E2
THA
E1
E2
THA
Air Temp. Sensor (Air Flow Meter)
Air Flow Meter
Ohmmeter
Ω
E2
THA

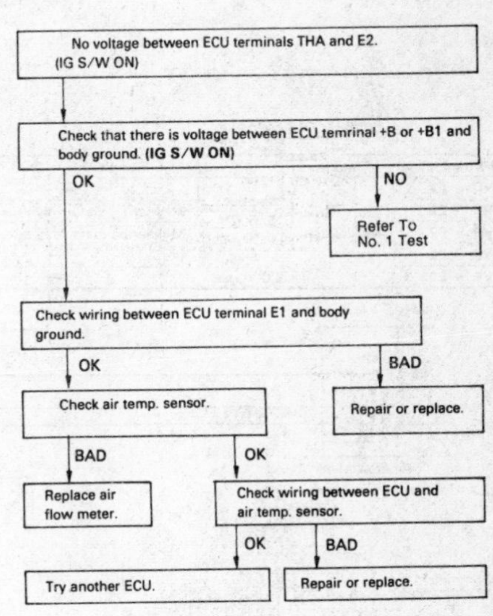
No voltage between ECU terminals THA and E2. (IG S/W ON)
Check that there is voltage between ECU temrinal +B or +B1 and body ground. (IG S/W ON)
OK
NO
Refer To No. 1 Test
Check wiring between ECU terminal E1 and body ground.
OK
BAD
Check air temp. sensor.
Repair or replace.
BAD
OK
Replace air flow meter.
Check wiring between ECU and air temp. sensor.
OK
BAD
Try another ECU.
Repair or replace.

Courtesy of Toyota Motor Sales, U.S.A., Inc.

## CAMRY, NO. 6 TEST, CODE 25, 26
## $O_2$ SENSOR CIRCUIT

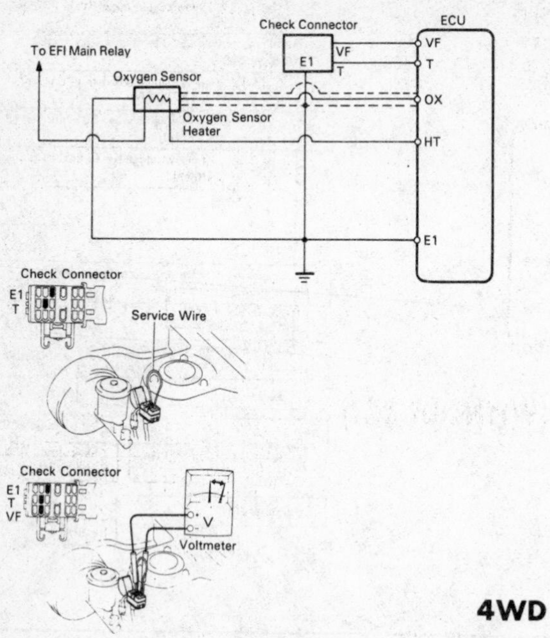
Check Connector
ECU
To EFI Main Relay
VF
E1
T
Oxygen Sensor
OX
Oxygen Sensor Heater
HT
E1
Check Connector
E1
T
Service Wire
Check Connector
E1
T
VF
V
Voltmeter

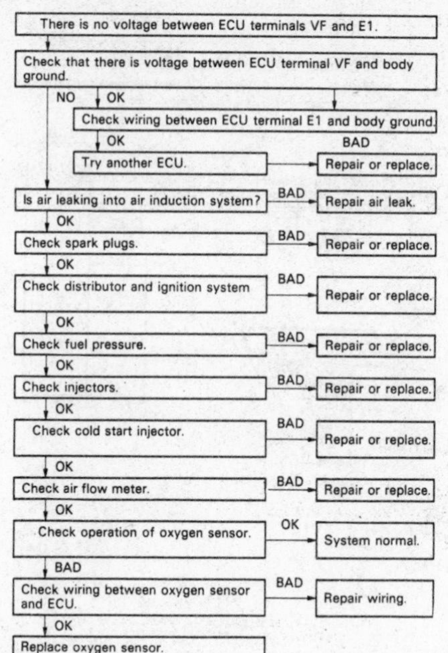
There is no voltage between ECU terminals VF and E1.
Check that there is voltage between ECU terminal VF and body ground.
NO
OK
Check wiring between ECU terminal E1 and body ground.
OK
BAD
Try another ECU.
Repair or replace.
Is air leaking into air induction system?
BAD
Repair air leak.
OK
Check spark plugs.
BAD
Repair or replace.
OK
Check distributor and ignition system
BAD
Repair or replace.
OK
Check fuel pressure.
BAD
Repair or replace.
OK
Check injectors.
BAD
Repair or replace.
OK
Check cold start injector.
BAD
Repair or replace.
OK
Check air flow meter.
BAD
Repair or replace.
OK
Check operation of oxygen sensor.
OK
System normal.
BAD
Check wiring between oxygen sensor and ECU.
BAD
Repair wiring.
OK
Replace oxygen sensor.

**4WD**

## CAMRY, NO. 7 TEST, CODE 31, 32
## AIRFLOW METER SIGNAL

| Terminals | Trouble | Condition | | STD Voltage |
|---|---|---|---|---|
| VC – E2 | No voltage | Ignition S/W ON | — | 4 – 6 V |
| VS – E2 | | | Measuring plate fully closed | 4 – 5 V |
| VS – E2 | | | Measuring plate fully open | 0.02 – 0.08 V |
| VS – E2 | | Idling | — | 2 – 4 V |
| VS – E2 | | 3,000 rpm | — | 0.3 – 1.0 V |

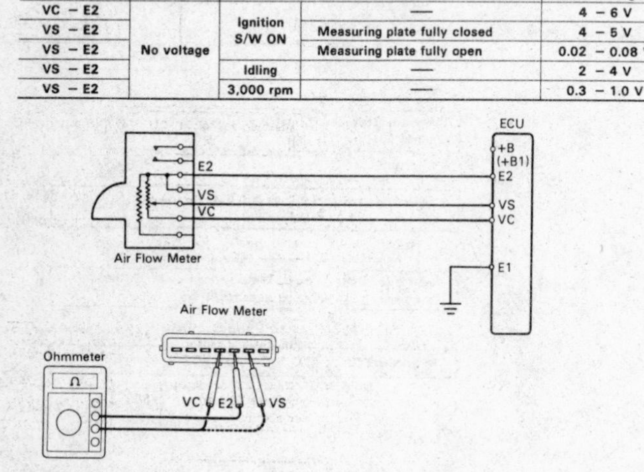
ECU
+B
(+B1)
E2
VS
VC
E1
E2
VS
VC
Air Flow Meter
Air Flow Meter
Ohmmeter
Ω
VC
E2
VS

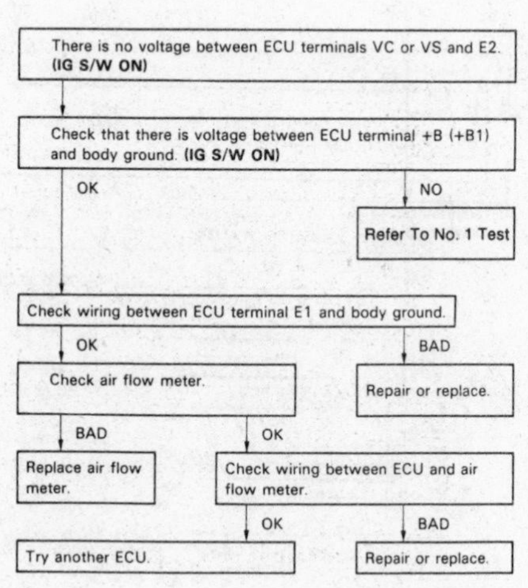
There is no voltage between ECU terminals VC or VS and E2. (IG S/W ON)
Check that there is voltage between ECU terminal +B (+B1) and body ground. (IG S/W ON)
OK
NO
Refer To No. 1 Test
Check wiring between ECU terminal E1 and body ground.
OK
BAD
Check air flow meter.
Repair or replace.
BAD
OK
Replace air flow meter.
Check wiring between ECU and air flow meter.
OK
BAD
Try another ECU.
Repair or replace.

Courtesy of Toyota Motor Sales, U.S.A., Inc.

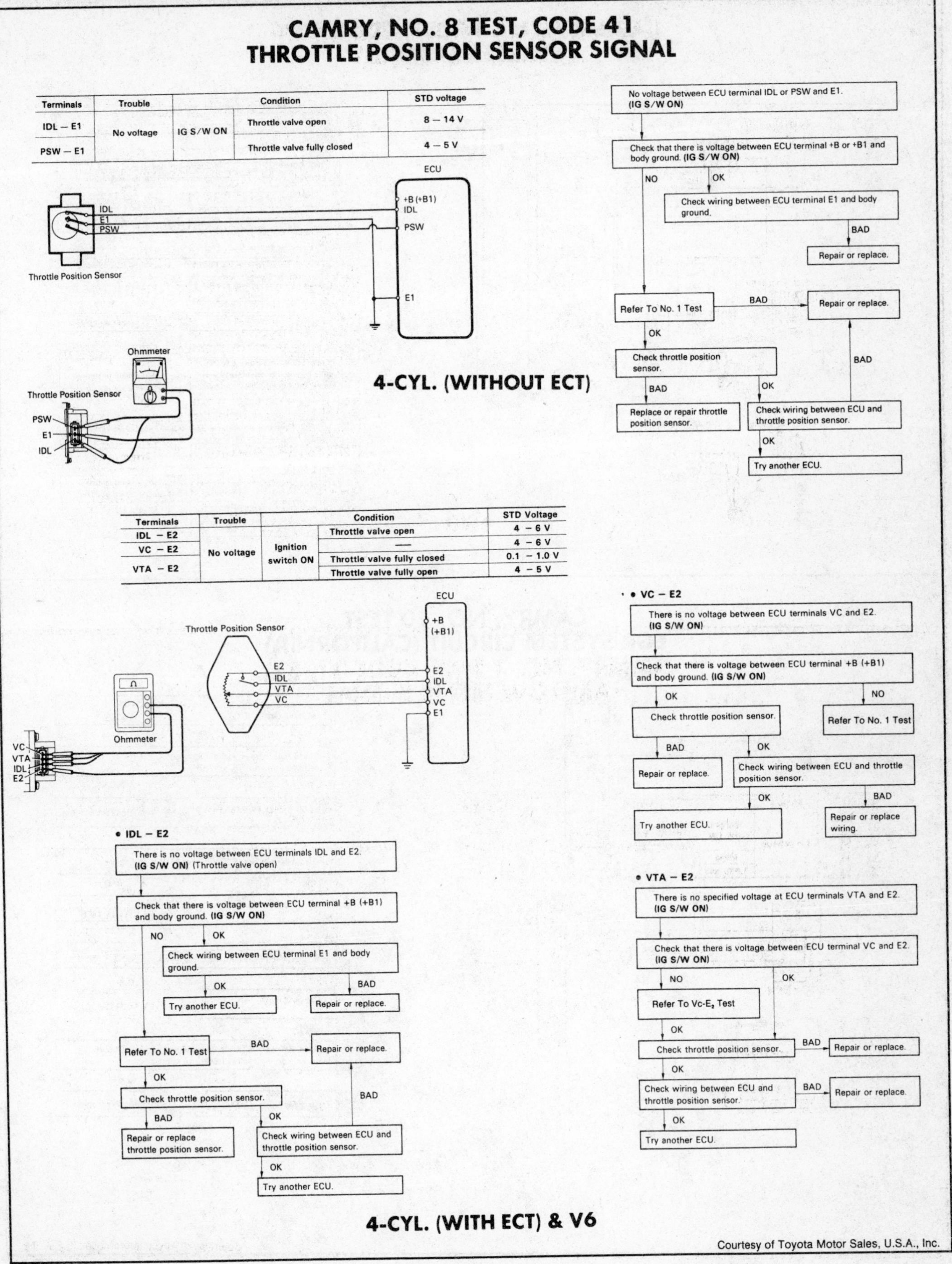

## CAMRY, NO. 8 TEST, CODE 41
## THROTTLE POSITION SENSOR SIGNAL

| Terminals | Trouble | Condition | | STD voltage |
|---|---|---|---|---|
| IDL – E1 | No voltage | IG S/W ON | Throttle valve open | 8 – 14 V |
| PSW – E1 | | | Throttle valve fully closed | 4 – 5 V |

ECU
+B (+B1)
IDL
PSW
E1
IDL
E1
PSW
Throttle Position Sensor
Ohmmeter
Throttle Position Sensor
PSW
E1
IDL
4-CYL. (WITHOUT ECT)
No voltage between ECU terminal IDL or PSW and E1. (IG S/W ON)
Check that there is voltage between ECU terminal +B or +B1 and body ground. (IG S/W ON)
NO
OK
Check wiring between ECU terminal E1 and body ground.
BAD
Repair or replace.
Refer To No. 1 Test
BAD
Repair or replace.
OK
Check throttle position sensor.
BAD
OK
BAD
Replace or repair throttle position sensor.
Check wiring between ECU and throttle position sensor.
OK
Try another ECU.

| Terminals | Trouble | Condition | | STD Voltage |
|---|---|---|---|---|
| IDL – E2 | No voltage | Ignition switch ON | Throttle valve open | 4 – 6 V |
| VC – E2 | | | — | 4 – 6 V |
| VTA – E2 | | | Throttle valve fully closed | 0.1 – 1.0 V |
| | | | Throttle valve fully open | 4 – 5 V |

ECU
+B
(+B1)
E2
IDL
VTA
VC
E1
Throttle Position Sensor
E2
IDL
VTA
VC
Ohmmeter
VC
VTA
IDL
E2
• IDL – E2
There is no voltage between ECU terminals IDL and E2. (IG S/W ON) (Throttle valve open)
Check that there is voltage between ECU terminal +B (+B1) and body ground. (IG S/W ON)
NO
OK
Check wiring between ECU terminal E1 and body ground.
OK
BAD
Try another ECU.
Repair or replace.
Refer To No. 1 Test
BAD
Repair or replace.
OK
Check throttle position sensor.
BAD
OK
BAD
Repair or replace throttle position sensor.
Check wiring between ECU and throttle position sensor.
OK
Try another ECU.
• VC – E2
There is no voltage between ECU terminals VC and E2. (IG S/W ON)
Check that there is voltage between ECU terminal +B (+B1) and body ground. (IG S/W ON)
OK
NO
Check throttle position sensor.
Refer To No. 1 Test
BAD
OK
Repair or replace.
Check wiring between ECU and throttle position sensor.
OK
BAD
Try another ECU.
Repair or replace wiring.
• VTA – E2
There is no specified voltage at ECU terminals VTA and E2. (IG S/W ON)
Check that there is voltage between ECU terminal VC and E2. (IG S/W ON)
NO
OK
Refer To Vc-E2 Test
OK
Check throttle position sensor.
BAD
Repair or replace.
OK
Check wiring between ECU and throttle position sensor.
BAD
Repair or replace.
OK
Try another ECU.
4-CYL. (WITH ECT) & V6
Courtesy of Toyota Motor Sales, U.S.A., Inc.

## CAMRY, NO. 9 TEST, CODE 43
## STARTER SIGNAL

| Terminals | Trouble | Condition | STD voltage |
|---|---|---|---|
| STA — E1 | No voltage | Cranking | 6 — 14 V |

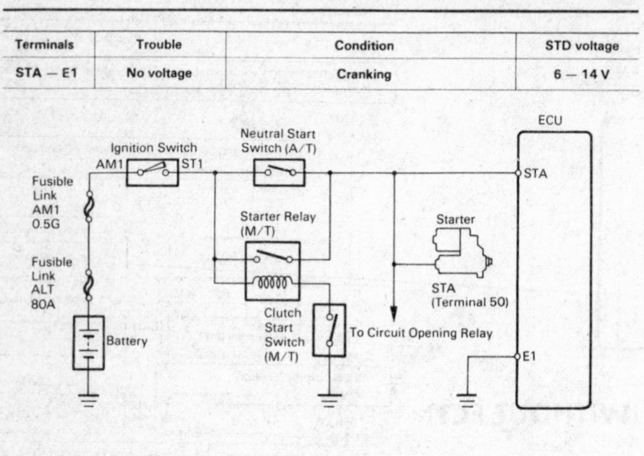
ECU
Ignition Switch
Neutral Start Switch (A/T)
AM1
ST1
STA
Fusible Link AM1 0.5G
Starter Relay (M/T)
Starter
Fusible Link ALT 80A
STA (Terminal 50)
Battery
Clutch Start Switch (M/T)
To Circuit Opening Relay
E1

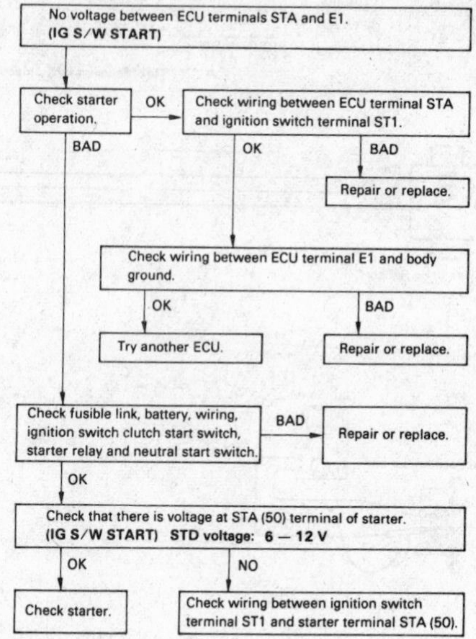
No voltage between ECU terminals STA and E1. (IG S/W START)
Check starter operation.
OK
Check wiring between ECU terminal STA and ignition switch terminal ST1.
BAD
OK
BAD
Repair or replace.
Check wiring between ECU terminal E1 and body ground.
OK
BAD
Try another ECU.
Repair or replace.
Check fusible link, battery, wiring, ignition switch clutch start switch, starter relay and neutral start switch.
BAD
Repair or replace.
OK
Check that there is voltage at STA (50) terminal of starter. (IG S/W START) STD voltage: 6 — 12 V
OK
NO
Check starter.
Check wiring between ignition switch terminal ST1 and starter terminal STA (50).

## CAMRY, NO. 10 TEST
## EGR SYSTEM CIRCUIT (CALIFORNIA)

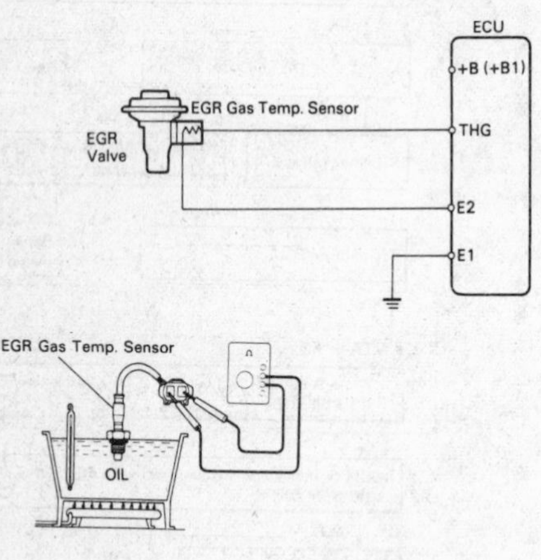
ECU
+B (+B1)
EGR Gas Temp. Sensor
THG
EGR Valve
E2
E1
EGR Gas Temp. Sensor
OIL

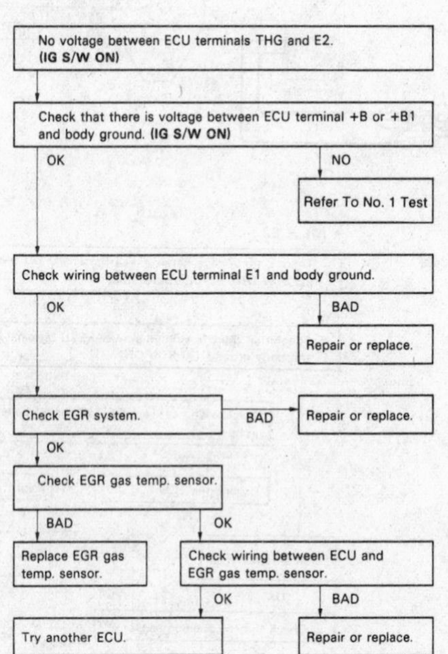
No voltage between ECU terminals THG and E2. (IG S/W ON)
Check that there is voltage between ECU terminal +B or +B1 and body ground. (IG S/W ON)
OK
NO
Refer To No. 1 Test
Check wiring between ECU terminal E1 and body ground.
OK
BAD
Repair or replace.
Check EGR system.
BAD
Repair or replace.
OK
Check EGR gas temp. sensor.
BAD
OK
Replace EGR gas temp. sensor.
Check wiring between ECU and EGR gas temp. sensor.
OK
BAD
Try another ECU.
Repair or replace.

Courtesy of Toyota Motor Sales, U.S.A., Inc.

## CAMRY, NO. 11 TEST
## ECU POWER SOURCE

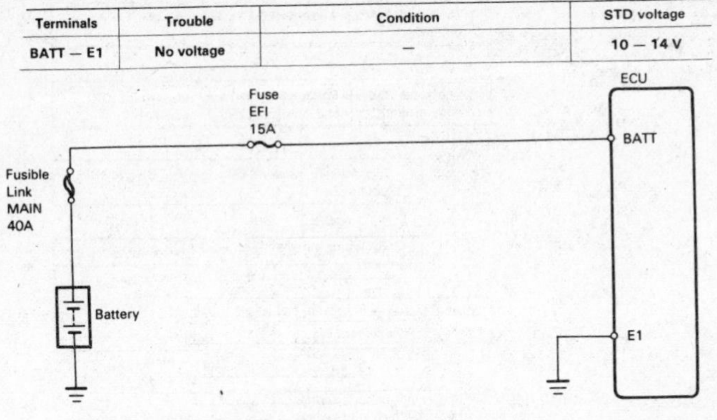

| Terminals | Trouble | Condition | STD voltage |
|---|---|---|---|
| BATT — E1 | No voltage | — | 10 — 14 V |

ECU
Fuse
EFI
15A
BATT
Fusible
Link
MAIN
40A
Battery
E1

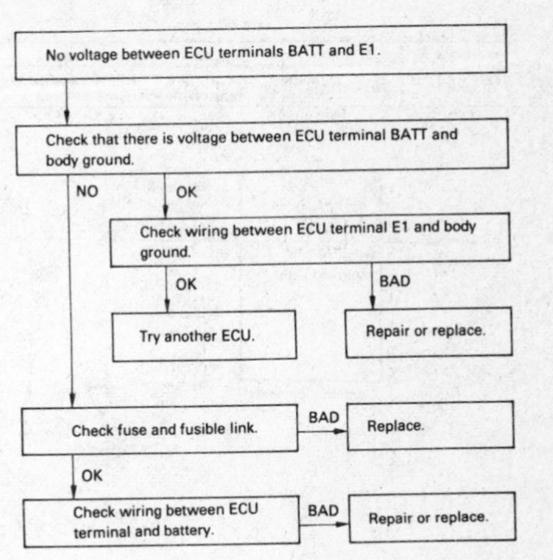
No voltage between ECU terminals BATT and E1.
Check that there is voltage between ECU terminal BATT and body ground.
NO
OK
Check wiring between ECU terminal E1 and body ground.
OK
BAD
Try another ECU.
Repair or replace.
Check fuse and fusible link.
BAD
Replace.
OK
Check wiring between ECU terminal and battery.
BAD
Repair or replace.

**4-CYL.**

## CAMRY, NO. 12 TEST
## INJECTOR CIRCUIT TEST

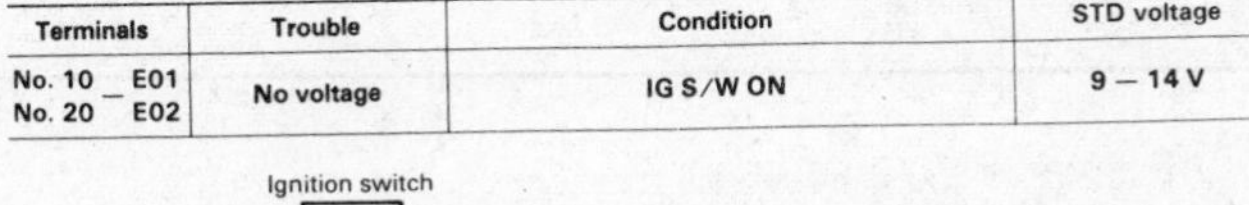

| Terminals | Trouble | Condition | STD voltage |
|---|---|---|---|
| No. 10 _ E01<br>No. 20 E02 | No voltage | IG S/W ON | 9 — 14 V |

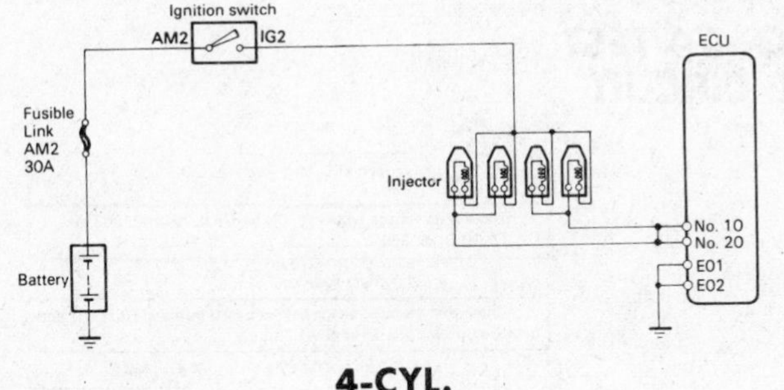
Ignition switch
AM2
IG2
ECU
Fusible
Link
AM2
30A
Injector
No. 10
No. 20
E01
E02
Battery

**4-CYL.**

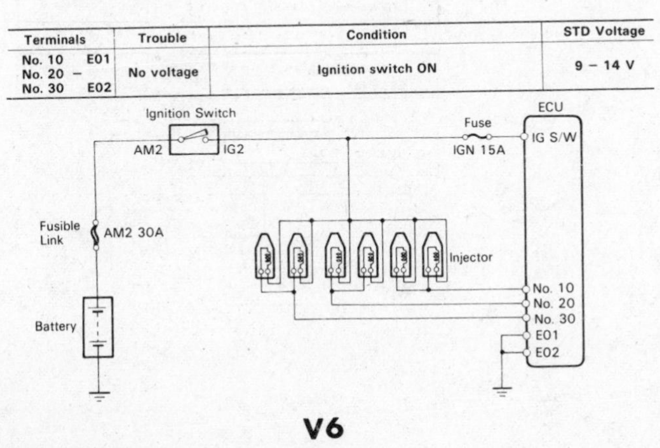

| Terminals | Trouble | Condition | STD Voltage |
|---|---|---|---|
| No. 10 E01<br>No. 20 –<br>No. 30 E02 | No voltage | Ignition switch ON | 9 – 14 V |

Ignition Switch
AM2
IG2
Fuse
IGN 15A
ECU
IG S/W
Fusible
Link
AM2 30A
Injector
No. 10
No. 20
No. 30
E01
E02
Battery

**V6**

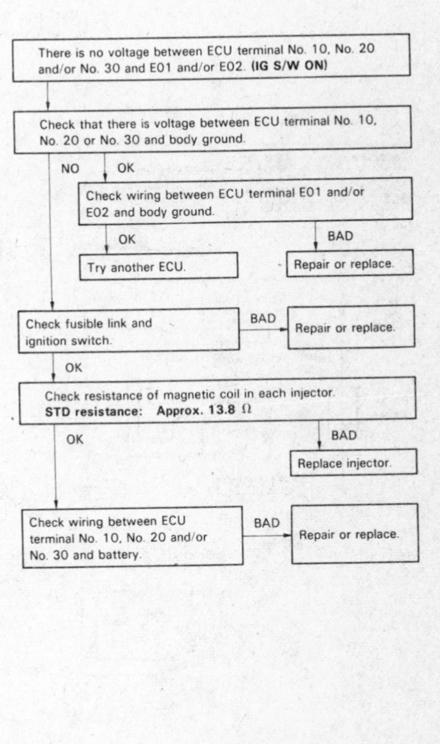
There is no voltage between ECU terminal No. 10, No. 20 and/or No. 30 and E01 and/or E02. (IG S/W ON)
Check that there is voltage between ECU terminal No. 10, No. 20 or No. 30 and body ground.
NO
OK
Check wiring between ECU terminal E01 and/or E02 and body ground.
OK
BAD
Try another ECU.
Repair or replace.
Check fusible link and ignition switch.
BAD
Repair or replace.
OK
Check resistance of magnetic coil in each injector.
STD resistance: Approx. 13.8 Ω
OK
BAD
Replace injector.
Check wiring between ECU terminal No. 10, No. 20 and/or No. 30 and battery.
BAD
Repair or replace.

Courtesy of Toyota Motor Sales, U.S.A., Inc.

## CAMRY, NO. 13 TEST
## "CHECK ENGINE" LIGHT CIRCUIT

| Terminals | Trouble | Condition | STD Voltage |
|---|---|---|---|
| W – E1 | No voltage | No trouble ("CHECK" engine warning light off) and engine running | 8 – 14 V |

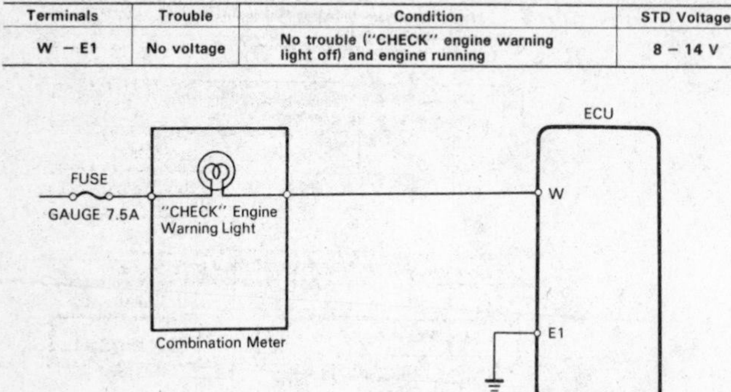
ECU
FUSE
GAUGE 7.5A
"CHECK" Engine Warning Light
W
E1
Combination Meter

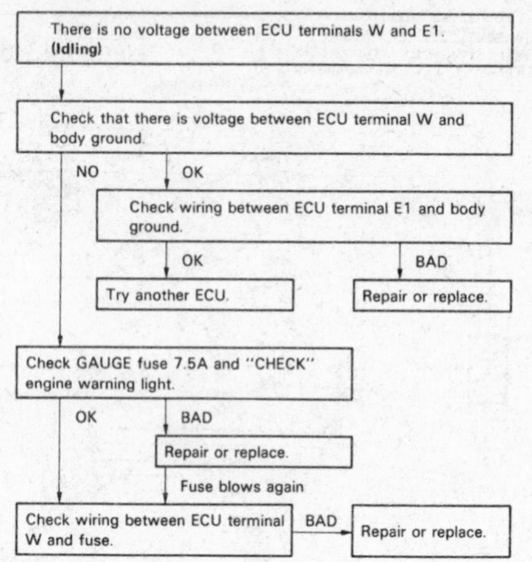
There is no voltage between ECU terminals W and E1. (Idling)
Check that there is voltage between ECU terminal W and body ground.
NO
OK
Check wiring between ECU terminal E1 and body ground.
OK
BAD
Try another ECU.
Repair or replace.
Check GAUGE fuse 7.5A and "CHECK" engine warning light.
OK
BAD
Repair or replace.
Fuse blows again
Check wiring between ECU terminal W and fuse.
BAD
Repair or replace.

## CAMRY, NO. 14 TEST
## ISC VALVE CIRCUIT

| Terminals | Trouble | Condition | STD voltage |
|---|---|---|---|
| ISC1 – E1<br>ISC2 | No voltage | IG S/W ON | 9 – 14 V |

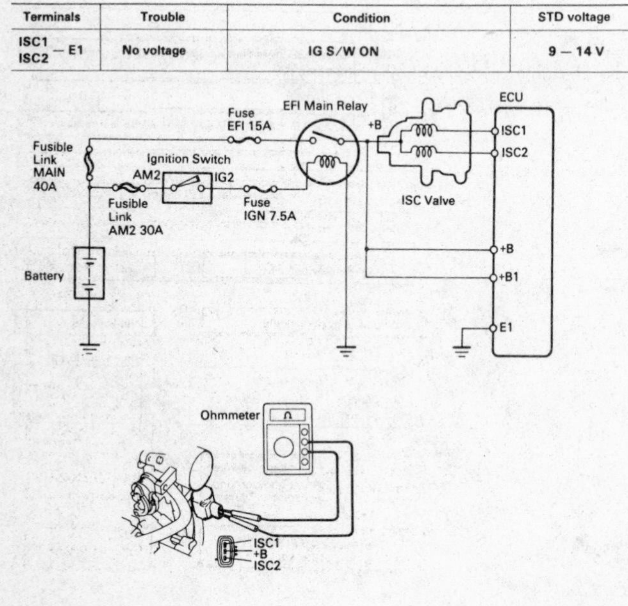
ECU
Fuse
EFI 15A
EFI Main Relay
+B
ISC1
ISC2
Fusible Link MAIN 40A
Ignition Switch
AM2
IG2
Fusible Link AM2 30A
Fuse IGN 7.5A
ISC Valve
+B
+B1
E1
Battery
Ohmmeter
ISC1
+B
ISC2

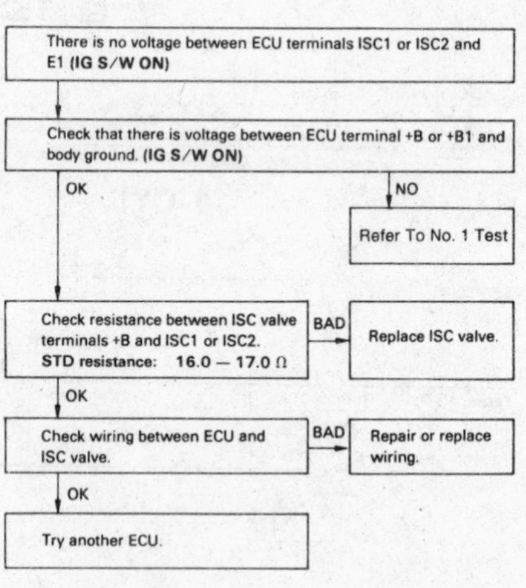
There is no voltage between ECU terminals ISC1 or ISC2 and E1 (IG S/W ON)
Check that there is voltage between ECU terminal +B or +B1 and body ground. (IG S/W ON)
OK
NO
Refer To No. 1 Test
Check resistance between ISC valve terminals +B and ISC1 or ISC2.
STD resistance: 16.0 – 17.0 Ω
BAD
Replace ISC valve.
OK
Check wiring between ECU and ISC valve.
BAD
Repair or replace wiring.
OK
Try another ECU.

4-CYL.

## CAMRY, NO. 14 TEST (Cont.)
## ISC VALVE CIRCUIT

| Terminals | Trouble | Condition | STD Voltage |
|---|---|---|---|
| ISC1 ~ ISC4 – E1 | No voltage | Ignition switch ON | 9 – 14 V |

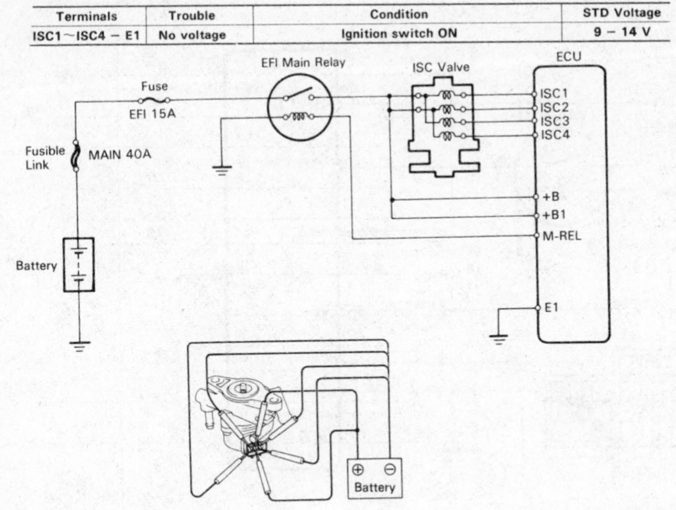

EFI Main Relay
ISC Valve
ECU
Fuse
EFI 15A
Fusible Link
MAIN 40A
Battery
ISC1
ISC2
ISC3
ISC4
+B
+B1
M-REL
E1
Battery


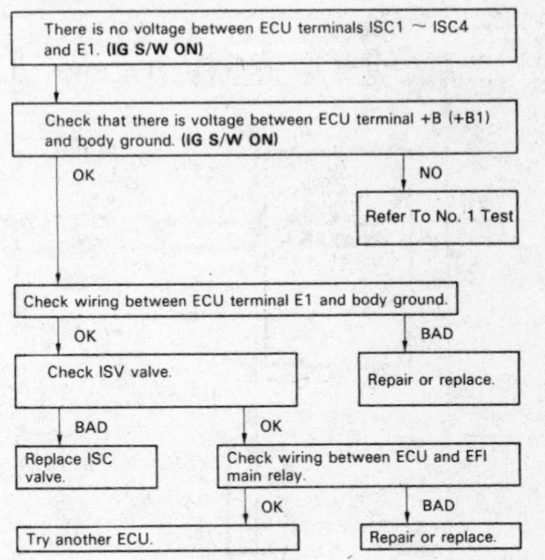

There is no voltage between ECU terminals ISC1 ~ ISC4 and E1. (IG S/W ON)
Check that there is voltage between ECU terminal +B (+B1) and body ground. (IG S/W ON)
OK
NO
Refer To No. 1 Test
Check wiring between ECU terminal E1 and body ground.
OK
BAD
Check ISV valve.
Repair or replace.
BAD
OK
Replace ISC valve.
Check wiring between ECU and EFI main relay.
OK
BAD
Try another ECU.
Repair or replace.


V6

## CAMRY, NO. 15 TEST
## A/C SWITCH CIRCUIT

| Terminals | Trouble | Condition | | STD Voltage |
|---|---|---|---|---|
| A/C – E1 | No voltage | Ignition switch ON | Air conditioning ON | 8 – 14 V |

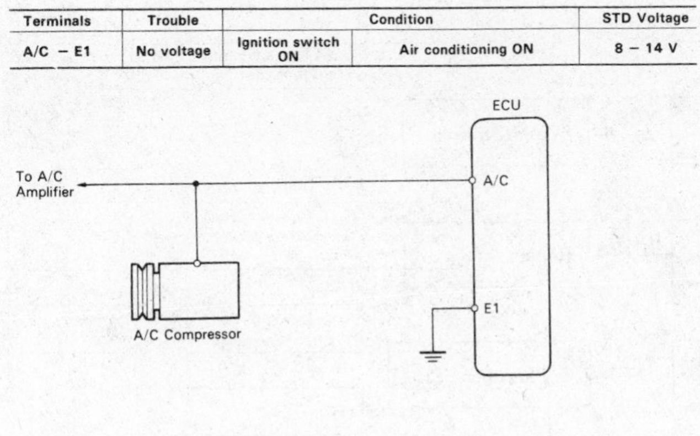

ECU
To A/C Amplifier
A/C
E1
A/C Compressor


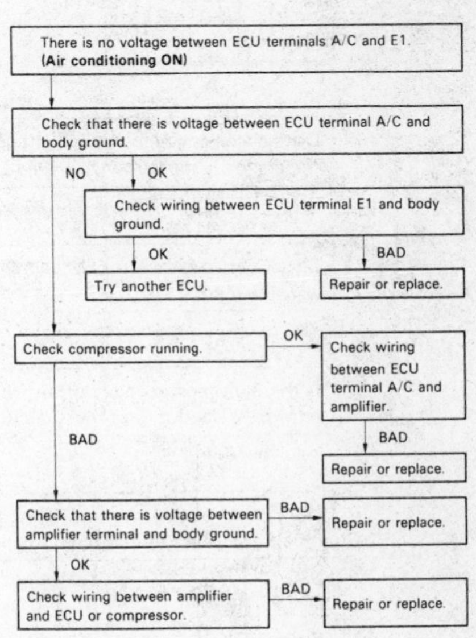

There is no voltage between ECU terminals A/C and E1. (Air conditioning ON)
Check that there is voltage between ECU terminal A/C and body ground.
NO
OK
Check wiring between ECU terminal E1 and body ground.
OK
BAD
Try another ECU.
Repair or replace.
Check compressor running.
OK
Check wiring between ECU terminal A/C and amplifier.
BAD
Repair or replace.
BAD
Check that there is voltage between amplifier terminal and body ground.
BAD
Repair or replace.
OK
Check wiring between amplifier and ECU or compressor.
BAD
Repair or replace.


Courtesy of Toyota Motor Sales, U.S.A., Inc.

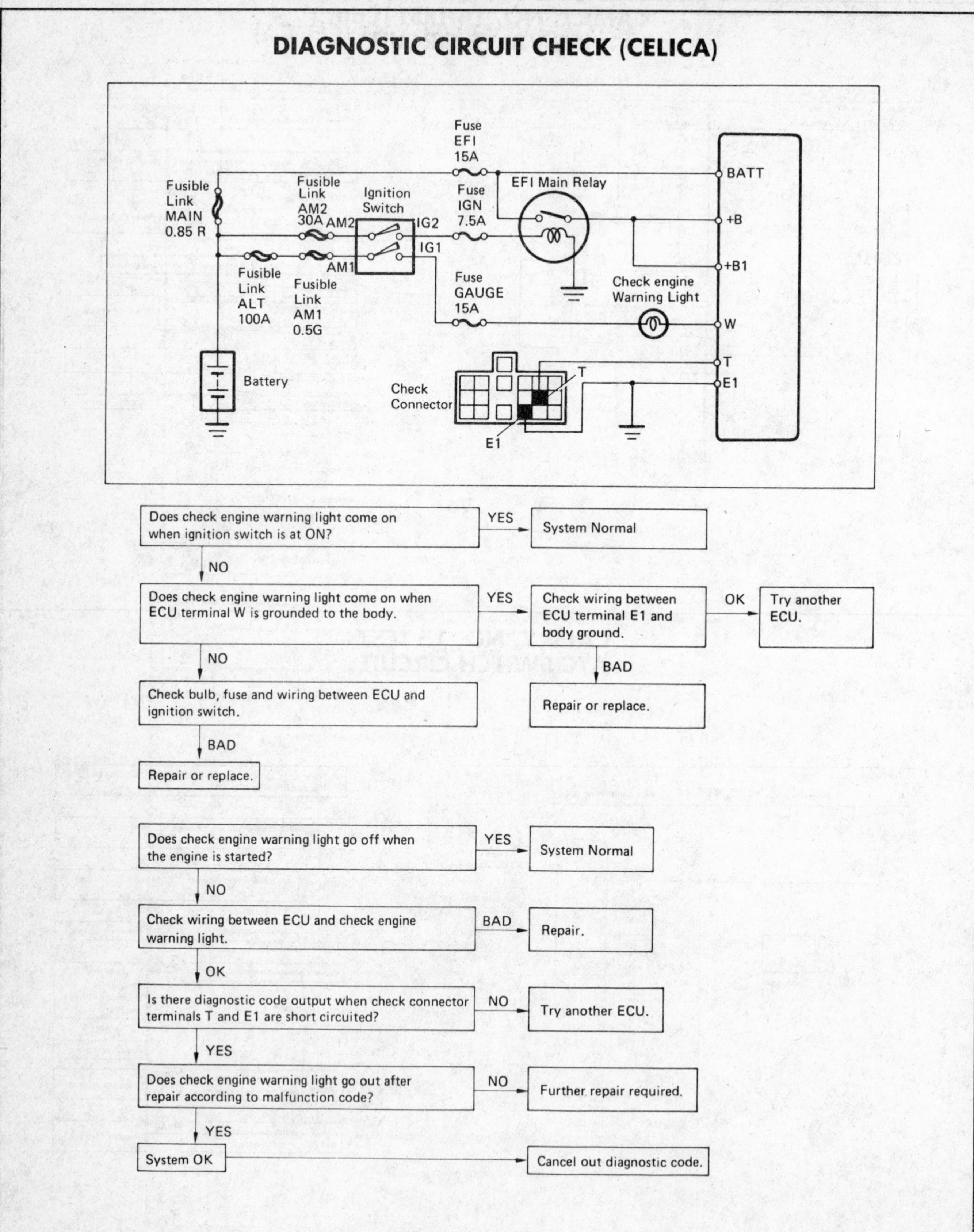
DIAGNOSTIC CIRCUIT CHECK (CELICA)
Fuse
EFI
15A
BATT
Fusible
Link
MAIN
0.85 R
Fusible
Link
AM2
30A
AM2
Ignition
Switch
IG2
Fuse
IGN
7.5A
EFI Main Relay
+B
IG1
AM1
+B1
Fusible
Link
ALT
100A
Fusible
Link
AM1
0.5G
Fuse
GAUGE
15A
Check engine
Warning Light
W
T
E1
Battery
Check
Connector
T
E1
Does check engine warning light come on when ignition switch is at ON?
YES
System Normal
NO
Does check engine warning light come on when ECU terminal W is grounded to the body.
YES
Check wiring between ECU terminal E1 and body ground.
OK
Try another ECU.
NO
BAD
Check bulb, fuse and wiring between ECU and ignition switch.
Repair or replace.
BAD
Repair or replace.
Does check engine warning light go off when the engine is started?
YES
System Normal
NO
Check wiring between ECU and check engine warning light.
BAD
Repair.
OK
Is there diagnostic code output when check connector terminals T and E1 are short circuited?
NO
Try another ECU.
YES
Does check engine warning light go out after repair according to malfunction code?
NO
Further repair required.
YES
System OK
Cancel out diagnostic code.

Courtesy of Toyota Motor Sales, U.S.A., Inc.

## ECU PIN VOLTAGE TEST (CELICA)

**2WD**

| Terminals | STD voltage (V) | Condition | | Test No. |
|---|---|---|---|---|
| +B +B1 – E1 | 10 – 14 | Ignition S/W ON | | 1 |
| BATT – E1 | 10 – 14 | – | | 11 |
| IDL – E1 | 8 – 14 | Ignition S/W ON | Throttle valve open | |
| PSW – E1 | 4 – 5 | | Throttle valve fully closed | 8 |
| IGT – E1 | 0.7 – 1.0 | Idling | | 2 |
| STA – E1 | 6 – 14 | Cranking | | 9 |
| No. 10 No. 20 – E01 E02 | 9 – 14 | Ignition S/W ON | | 12 |
| W – E1 | 8 – 14 | No trouble (check engine warning light off) and engine running | | 13 |
| VC – E2 | 4 – 6 | Ignition S/W ON | – | |
| VS – E2 | 4 – 5 | | Measuring plate fully closed | |
| | 0.02 – 0.5 | | Measuring plate fully open | |
| | 2 – 4 | Idling | | 6 |
| THA – E2 | 1 – 3 | Ignition S/W ON | Intake air temperature 20°C (68°F) | 5 |
| THW – E2 | 0.1 – 1.0 | | Coolant temperature 80°C (176°F) | 4 |
| ISC1 ISC2 – E1 | 9 – 14 | Ignition S/W ON | | 14 |
| A/C – E1 | 8 – 14 | Ignition S/W ON | Air conditioning ON | 15 |

**4WD**

| Terminals | STD voltage (V) | Condition | | Test No. |
|---|---|---|---|---|
| +B +B1 – E1 | 10 – 14 | Ignition S/W ON | | 1 |
| BATT – E1 | 10 – 14 | – | | 11 |
| IDL – E2 | 4 – 6 | Ignition S/W ON | Throttle valve open | |
| VTA – E2 | 0.1 – 1.0 | | Throttle valve fully closed | |
| | 3 – 4.5 | | Throttle valve open | |
| VC – E2 | 4 – 6 | | – | 8 |
| IGT – E1 | 0.7 – 1.0 | Cranking or idling | | 2 |
| STA – E1 | 6 – 14 | Cranking | | 9 |
| No. 1 No. 2 No. 3 No. 4 – E01 E02 | 10 – 14 | Ignition S/W ON | | 12 |
| W – E1 | 8 – 14 | No trouble (Check engine warning light off) and engine running | | 13 |
| VC – E2 | 4 – 6 | Ignition S/W ON | – | |
| VS – E2 | 4 – 6 | | Measuring plate fully closed | |
| | 1.0 or less | | Measuring plate fully open | |
| | 2 – 4 | Idling | | 6 |
| THA – E2 | 1 – 3 | Ignition S/W ON | Intake air temp. 20°C (68°F) | 5 |
| THW – E2 | 0.1 – 1.0 | | Coolant temp. 80°C (176°F) | 4 |
| ISC1 ISC2 – E1 | 9 – 14 | Ignition S/W ON | | 14 |
| PIM – E2 | 2.5 – 4.5 | | | |
| VC – E2 | 4 – 6 | | | 7 |
| A/C – E1 | 8 – 14 | Ignition S/W ON | Air conditioning ON | 15 |

Courtesy of Toyota Motor Sales, U.S.A., Inc.

## CELICA, NO. 1 TEST, CODE 11
## ECU (+B) CIRCUIT

| Terminals | Trouble | Condition | STD voltage |
|---|---|---|---|
| +B<br>+B1 – E1 | No voltage | Ignition S/W ON | 10 – 14 V |

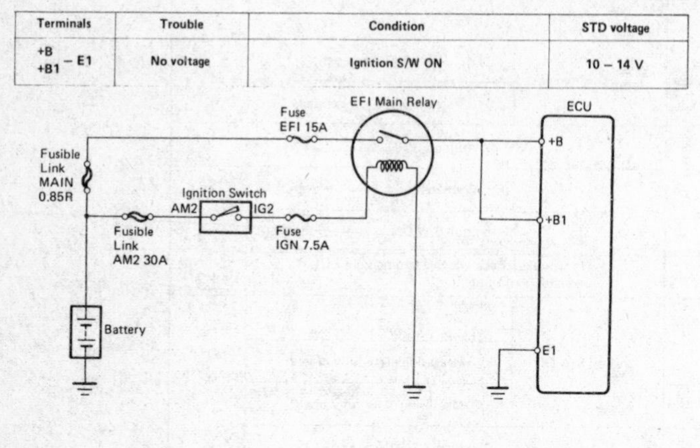
Fuse
EFI 15A
EFI Main Relay
ECU
+B
Fusible
Link
MAIN
0.85R
Ignition Switch
AM2
IG2
+B1
Fusible
Link
AM2 30A
Fuse
IGN 7.5A
Battery
E1

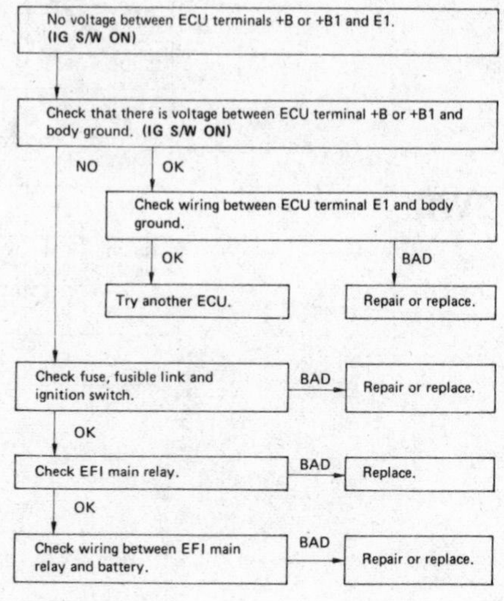
No voltage between ECU terminals +B or +B1 and E1.
(IG S/W ON)
Check that there is voltage between ECU terminal +B or +B1 and body ground. (IG S/W ON)
NO
OK
Check wiring between ECU terminal E1 and body ground.
OK
BAD
Try another ECU.
Repair or replace.
Check fuse, fusible link and ignition switch.
BAD
Repair or replace.
OK
Check EFI main relay.
BAD
Replace.
OK
Check wiring between EFI main relay and battery.
BAD
Repair or replace.

## CELICA, NO. 2 TEST, CODE 12, 13, 14
## RPM & IGNITION SIGNAL

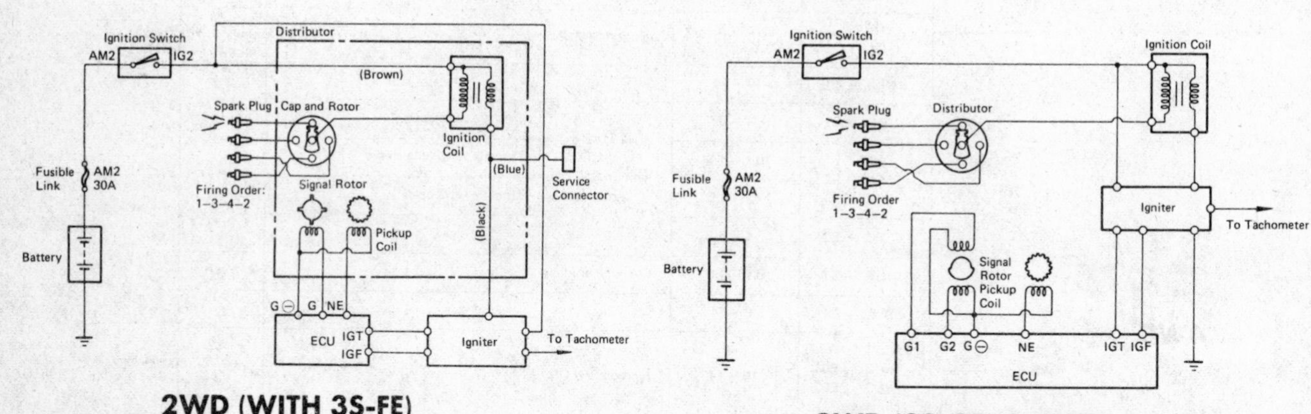
Ignition Switch
AM2
IG2
Distributor
(Brown)
Spark Plug
Cap and Rotor
Ignition
Coil
(Blue)
Service
Connector
Fusible
Link
AM2
30A
Firing Order:
1–3–4–2
Signal Rotor
Pickup
Coil
(Black)
Battery
G⊖
G
NE
ECU
IGT
IGF
Igniter
To Tachometer
2WD (WITH 3S-FE)
Ignition Switch
AM2
IG2
Ignition Coil
Spark Plug
Distributor
Fusible
Link
AM2
30A
Firing Order
1–3–4–2
Igniter
To Tachometer
Battery
Signal
Rotor
Pickup
Coil
G1
G2
G⊖
NE
IGT
IGF
ECU
2WD (3S-GE) & 4WD

No voltage between ECU terminals IGT and E1.
**(Cranking or Idling)**

Check that there is voltage between ECU terminal IGT and body ground. **(Idling)**

NO — OK

Check wiring between ECU terminal E1 and body ground. — BAD → Repair or replace.

OK

Try another ECU.

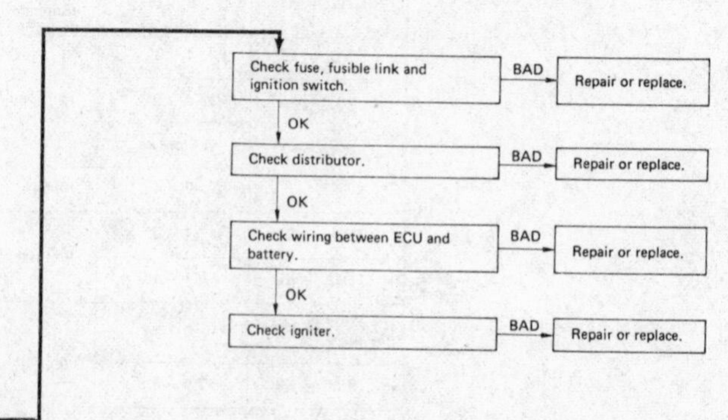
Check fuse, fusible link and ignition switch.
BAD
Repair or replace.
OK
Check distributor.
BAD
Repair or replace.
OK
Check wiring between ECU and battery.
BAD
Repair or replace.
OK
Check igniter.
BAD
Repair or replace.

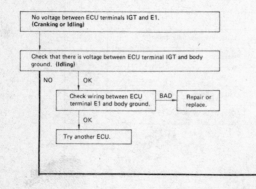

Courtesy of Toyota Motor Sales, U.S.A., Inc.

# CELICA, NO. 3 TEST, CODE 21, 25, 26
# $O_2$ SENSOR SIGNAL

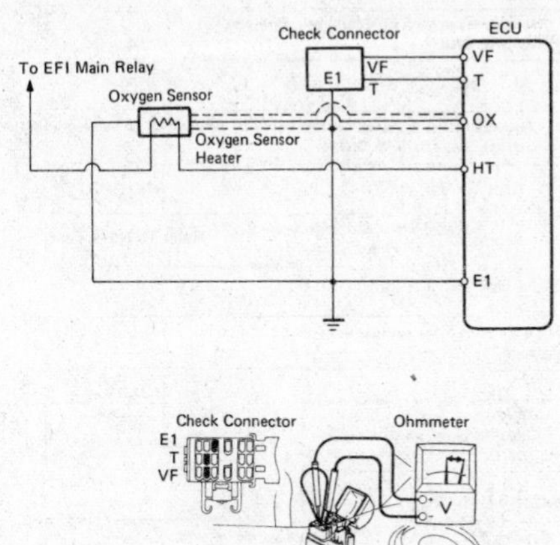
Check Connector
ECU
To EFI Main Relay
Oxygen Sensor
E1
VF
T
OX
Oxygen Sensor Heater
HT
E1
Check Connector
Ohmmeter
E1
T
VF
V

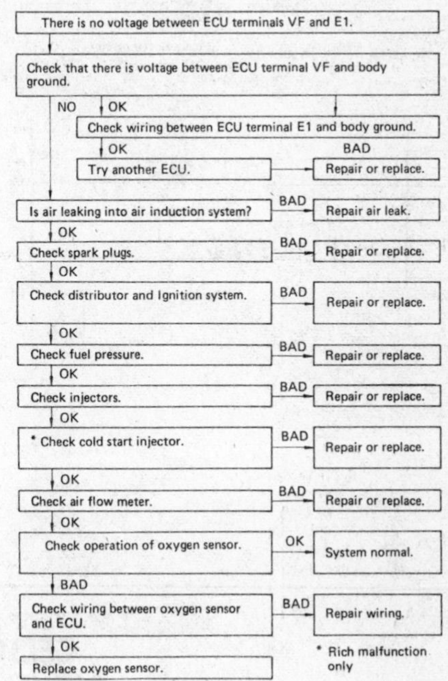
There is no voltage between ECU terminals VF and E1.
Check that there is voltage between ECU terminal VF and body ground.
NO
OK
Check wiring between ECU terminal E1 and body ground.
OK
BAD
Try another ECU.
Repair or replace.
Is air leaking into air induction system?
BAD
Repair air leak.
OK
Check spark plugs.
BAD
Repair or replace.
OK
Check distributor and Ignition system.
BAD
Repair or replace.
OK
Check fuel pressure.
BAD
Repair or replace.
OK
Check injectors.
BAD
Repair or replace.
OK
* Check cold start injector.
BAD
Repair or replace.
OK
Check air flow meter.
BAD
Repair or replace.
OK
Check operation of oxygen sensor.
OK
System normal.
BAD
Check wiring between oxygen sensor and ECU.
BAD
Repair wiring.
OK
Replace oxygen sensor.
* Rich malfunction only

# CELICA, NO. 4 TEST, CODE 22
# COOLANT TEMP. SENSOR SIGNAL

| Terminals | Trouble | Condition | | STD voltage |
|---|---|---|---|---|
| THW – E2 | No voltage | IG S/W ON | Coolant temperature 80°C (176°F) | 0.1 – 1.0 V |

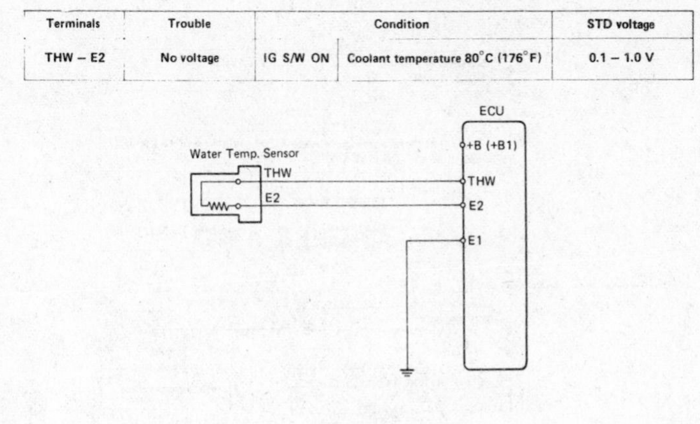
ECU
Water Temp. Sensor
+B (+B1)
THW
E2
THW
E2
E1

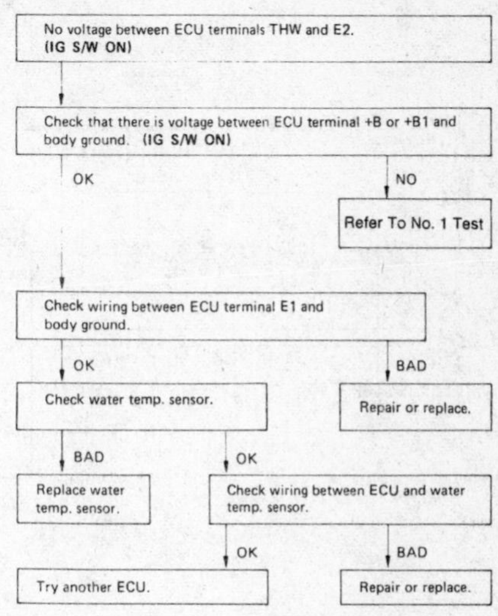
No voltage between ECU terminals THW and E2. (IG S/W ON)
Check that there is voltage between ECU terminal +B or +B1 and body ground. (IG S/W ON)
OK
NO
Refer To No. 1 Test
Check wiring between ECU terminal E1 and body ground.
OK
BAD
Check water temp. sensor.
Repair or replace.
BAD
OK
Replace water temp. sensor.
Check wiring between ECU and water temp. sensor.
OK
BAD
Try another ECU.
Repair or replace.

## CELICA, NO. 5 TEST, CODE 24
## INTAKE AIR TEMP. SENSOR SIGNAL

| Terminals | Trouble | Condition | | STD voltage |
|---|---|---|---|---|
| THA – E2 | No voltage | IG S/W ON | Intake air temperature 20°C (68°F) | 1 – 3 V |

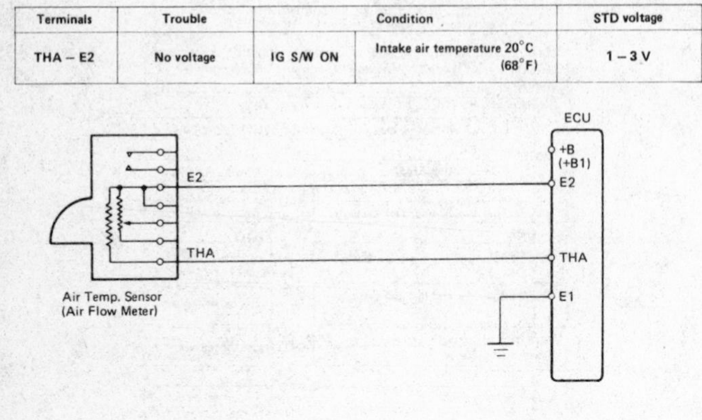
ECU
+B
(+B1)
E2
THA
E1
E2
THA
Air Temp. Sensor
(Air Flow Meter)

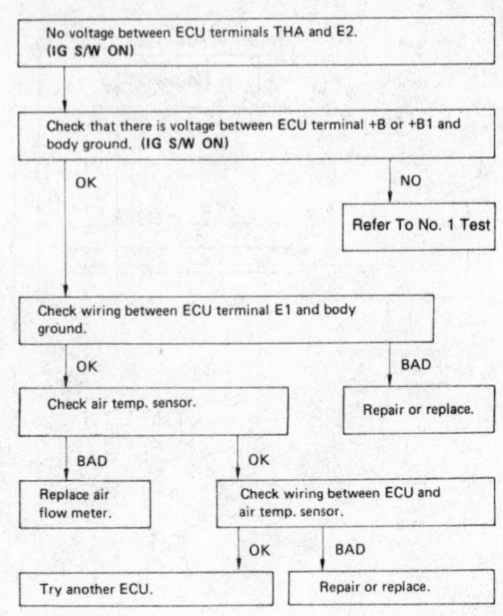
No voltage between ECU terminals THA and E2. (IG S/W ON)
Check that there is voltage between ECU terminal +B or +B1 and body ground. (IG S/W ON)
OK
NO
Refer To No. 1 Test
Check wiring between ECU terminal E1 and body ground.
OK
BAD
Check air temp. sensor.
Repair or replace.
BAD
OK
Replace air flow meter.
Check wiring between ECU and air temp. sensor.
OK
BAD
Try another ECU.
Repair or replace.

## CELICA, CODE 25, 26
## AIR/FUEL, LEAN OR RICH

**NOTE:** Use No. 3 test in this article.

## CELICA, NO. 6 TEST, CODE 31, 32
## AIRFLOW METER SIGNAL

| Terminals | Trouble | Condition | | STD voltage |
|---|---|---|---|---|
| VC – E2 | No voltage | IG S/W ON | – | 4 – 6 V |
| VS – E2 | | | Measuring plate fully closed | 4 – 5 V |
| | | | Measuring plate fully open | 0.02 – 0.5 V |
| | | | Idling | 2 – 4 V |

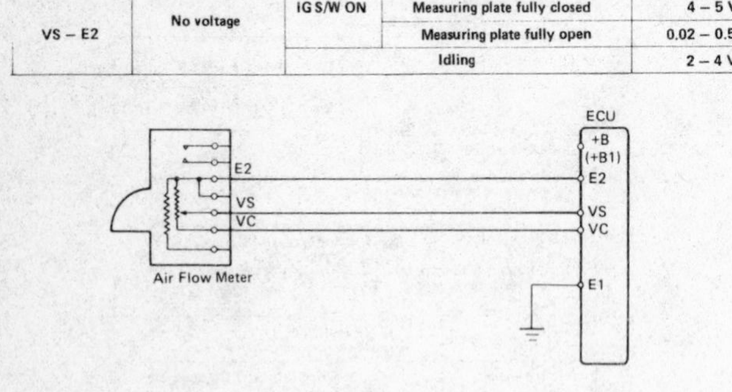
ECU
+B
(+B1)
E2
VS
VC
E1
E2
VS
VC
Air Flow Meter

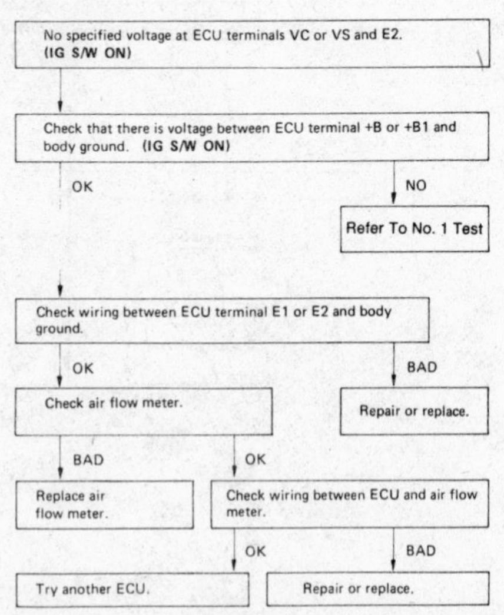
No specified voltage at ECU terminals VC or VS and E2. (IG S/W ON)
Check that there is voltage between ECU terminal +B or +B1 and body ground. (IG S/W ON)
OK
NO
Refer To No. 1 Test
Check wiring between ECU terminal E1 or E2 and body ground.
OK
BAD
Check air flow meter.
Repair or replace.
BAD
OK
Replace air flow meter.
Check wiring between ECU and air flow meter.
OK
BAD
Try another ECU.
Repair or replace.

## CELICA, NO. 7 TEST, CODE 34, 35
## TURBO PRESSURE SIGNAL

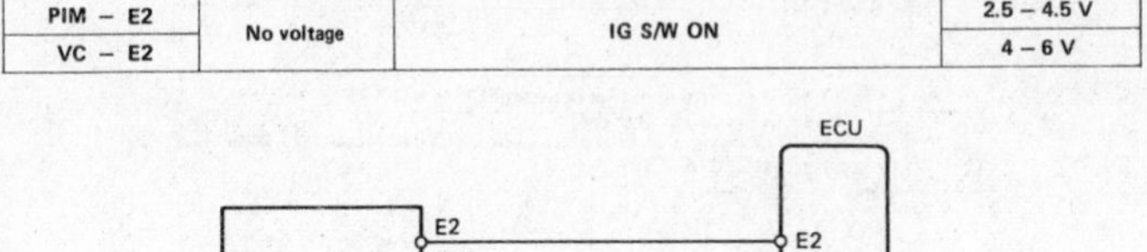

| Terminals | Trouble | Condition | STD voltage |
|---|---|---|---|
| PIM – E2 | No voltage | IG S/W ON | 2.5 – 4.5 V |
| VC – E2 | | | 4 – 6 V |

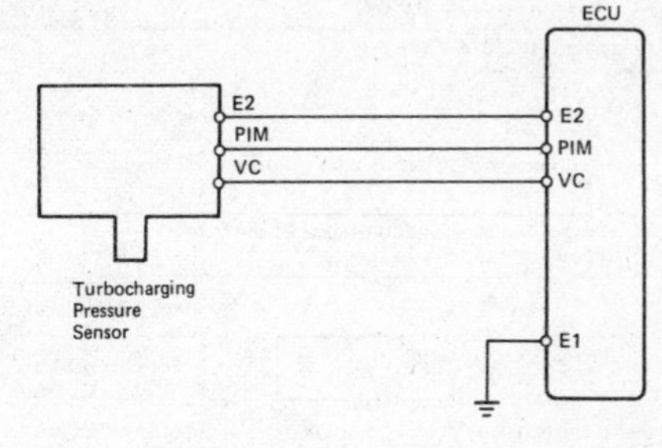
ECU
E2
PIM
VC
E2
PIM
VC
E1
Turbocharging
Pressure
Sensor

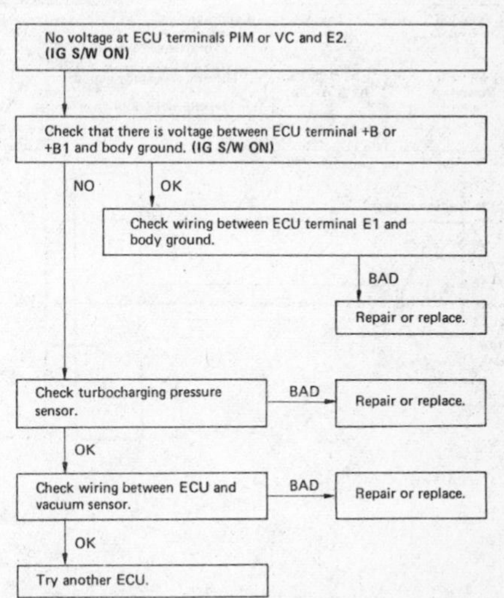
No voltage at ECU terminals PIM or VC and E2. (IG S/W ON)
Check that there is voltage between ECU terminal +B or +B1 and body ground. (IG S/W ON)
NO
OK
Check wiring between ECU terminal E1 and body ground.
BAD
Repair or replace.
Check turbocharging pressure sensor.
BAD
Repair or replace.
OK
Check wiring between ECU and vacuum sensor.
BAD
Repair or replace.
OK
Try another ECU.

## CELICA, NO. 8 TEST, CODE 41
## THROTTLE POSITION SENSOR SIGNAL

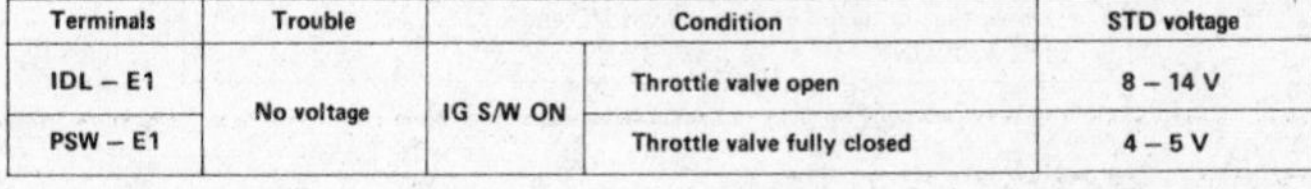

| Terminals | Trouble | Condition | | STD voltage |
|---|---|---|---|---|
| IDL – E1 | No voltage | IG S/W ON | Throttle valve open | 8 – 14 V |
| PSW – E1 | | | Throttle valve fully closed | 4 – 5 V |

ECU
IDL
E1
PSW
+B (+B1)
IDL
PSW
E1
Throttle Position Sensor

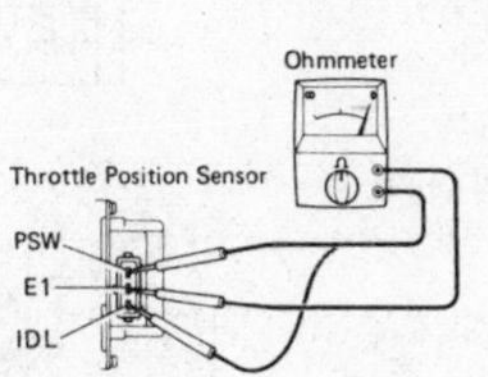
Ohmmeter
Throttle Position Sensor
PSW
E1
IDL

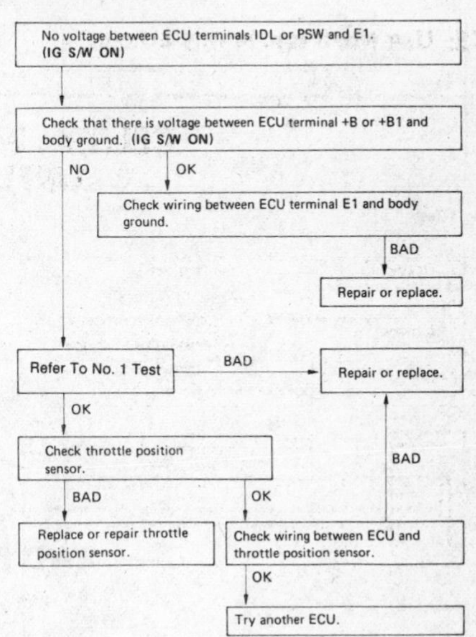
No voltage between ECU terminals IDL or PSW and E1. (IG S/W ON)
Check that there is voltage between ECU terminal +B or +B1 and body ground. (IG S/W ON)
NO
OK
Check wiring between ECU terminal E1 and body ground.
BAD
Repair or replace.
Refer To No. 1 Test
BAD
Repair or replace.
OK
Check throttle position sensor.
BAD
OK
BAD
Replace or repair throttle position sensor.
Check wiring between ECU and throttle position sensor.
OK
Try another ECU.

**2WD (WITH 3S-FE)**

Courtesy of Toyota Motor Sales, U.S.A., Inc.

## CELICA, NO. 8 TEST, CODE 41 (Cont.)
## THROTTLE POSITION SENSOR SIGNAL

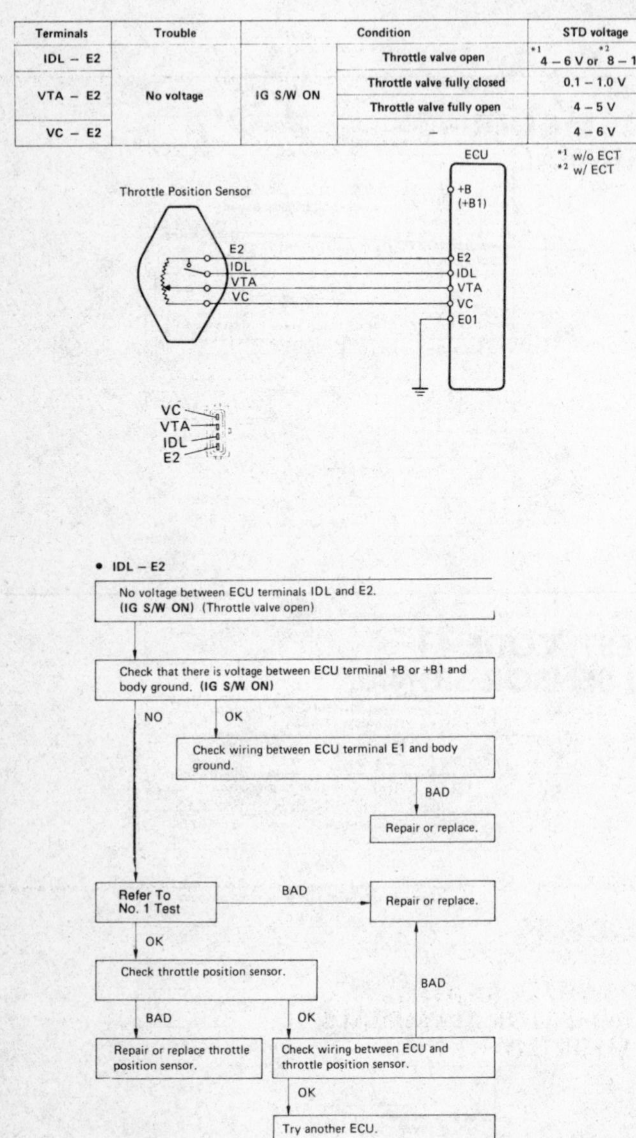

| Terminals | Trouble | Condition | | STD voltage |
|---|---|---|---|---|
| IDL – E2 | No voltage | IG S/W ON | Throttle valve open | 4 – 6 V[*1] or 8 – 14 V[*2] |
| VTA – E2 | | | Throttle valve fully closed | 0.1 – 1.0 V |
| | | | Throttle valve fully open | 4 – 5 V |
| VC – E2 | | | – | 4 – 6 V |

*1 w/o ECT
*2 w/ ECT

ECU
Throttle Position Sensor
E2
IDL
VTA
VC
+B
(+B1)
E2
IDL
VTA
VC
E01
VC
VTA
IDL
E2
• IDL – E2
No voltage between ECU terminals IDL and E2. (IG S/W ON) (Throttle valve open)
Check that there is voltage between ECU terminal +B or +B1 and body ground. (IG S/W ON)
NO
OK
Check wiring between ECU terminal E1 and body ground.
BAD
Repair or replace.
Refer To No. 1 Test
BAD
Repair or replace.
OK
Check throttle position sensor.
BAD
BAD
OK
Repair or replace throttle position sensor.
Check wiring between ECU and throttle position sensor.
OK
Try another ECU.

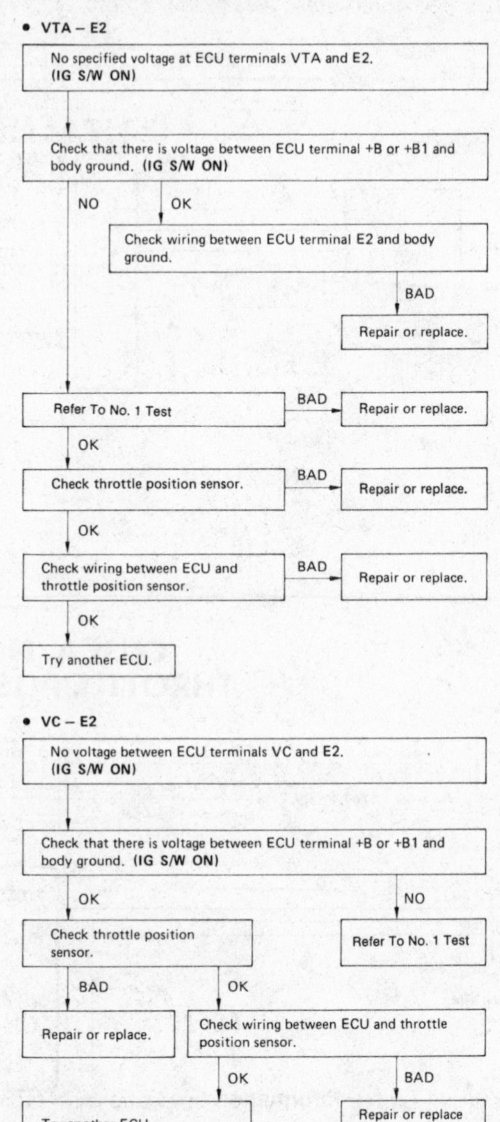

• VTA – E2
No specified voltage at ECU terminals VTA and E2. (IG S/W ON)
Check that there is voltage between ECU terminal +B or +B1 and body ground. (IG S/W ON)
NO
OK
Check wiring between ECU terminal E2 and body ground.
BAD
Repair or replace.
Refer To No. 1 Test
BAD
Repair or replace.
OK
Check throttle position sensor.
BAD
Repair or replace.
OK
Check wiring between ECU and throttle position sensor.
BAD
Repair or replace.
OK
Try another ECU.
• VC – E2
No voltage between ECU terminals VC and E2. (IG S/W ON)
Check that there is voltage between ECU terminal +B or +B1 and body ground. (IG S/W ON)
OK
NO
Check throttle position sensor.
Refer To No. 1 Test
BAD
OK
Repair or replace.
Check wiring between ECU and throttle position sensor.
OK
BAD
Try another ECU.
Repair or replace wiring.

**2WD (WITH 3S-GE) & 4WD**

Courtesy of Toyota Motor Sales, U.S.A., Inc.

## CELICA, CODE 42
## VEHICLE SPEED SENSOR

**NOTE: See component test in this article.**

## CELICA, NO. 9 TEST, CODE 43
## STARTER SIGNAL

| Terminals | Trouble | Condition | STD voltage |
|---|---|---|---|
| STA – E1 | No voltage | Cranking | 6 – 14 V |

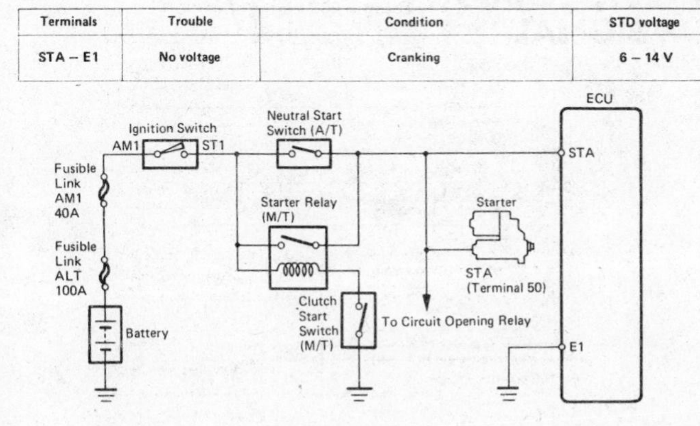
ECU
Ignition Switch
AM1
ST1
Neutral Start Switch (A/T)
STA
Fusible Link AM1 40A
Starter Relay (M/T)
Starter
Fusible Link ALT 100A
STA (Terminal 50)
Clutch Start Switch (M/T)
To Circuit Opening Relay
Battery
E1

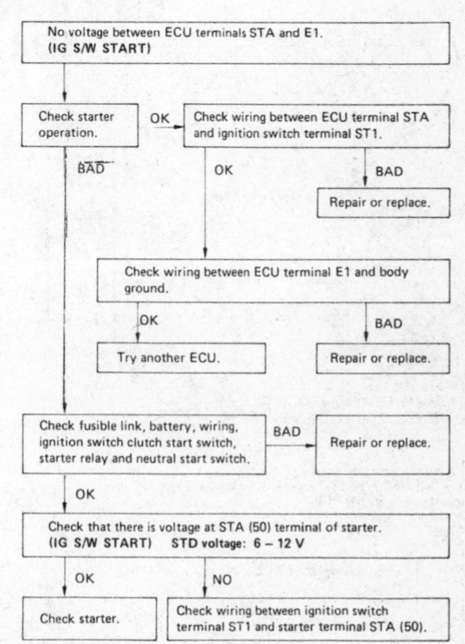
No voltage between ECU terminals STA and E1.
(IG S/W START)
Check starter operation.
OK
Check wiring between ECU terminal STA and ignition switch terminal ST1.
BAD
OK
BAD
Repair or replace.
Check wiring between ECU terminal E1 and body ground.
OK
BAD
Try another ECU.
Repair or replace.
Check fusible link, battery, wiring, ignition switch clutch start switch, starter relay and neutral start switch.
BAD
Repair or replace.
OK
Check that there is voltage at STA (50) terminal of starter.
(IG S/W START) STD voltage: 6 – 12 V
OK
NO
Check starter.
Check wiring between ignition switch terminal ST1 and starter terminal STA (50).

## CELICA, CODE 51

### NO "IDL", "NSW" OR "A/C" SIGNAL TO ECU, WITH CHECK CONNECTOR TERMINALS "E1" & "T" SHORTED

**NOTE: No further information available from manufacturer.**

## CELICA, CODE 52, 53
## KNOCK SENSOR SIGNAL

### OPEN OR SHORT IN KNOCK SENSOR SIGNAL (KNK) OR KNOCK CONTROL IN ECU FAULTY

**NOTE: No further information available from manufacturer.**

Courtesy of Toyota Motor Sales, U.S.A., Inc.

## CELICA, CODE 54
## INTERCOOLER ECU SIGNAL

### DUE TO LOW COOLANT LEVEL FOR INTERCOOLER AND/OR DEFECTIVE INTERCOOLER WATER PUMP MOTOR

**NOTE: No further information available from manufacturer.**

## CELICA, NO. 10 TEST, CODE 71
## EGR SYSTEM SIGNAL

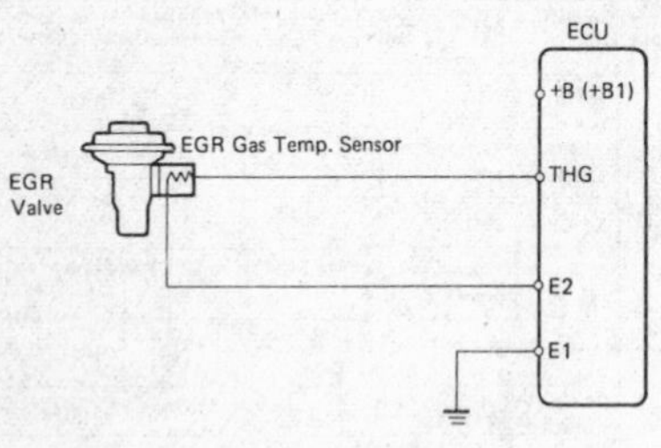
ECU
+B (+B1)
EGR Gas Temp. Sensor
THG
EGR
Valve
E2
E1

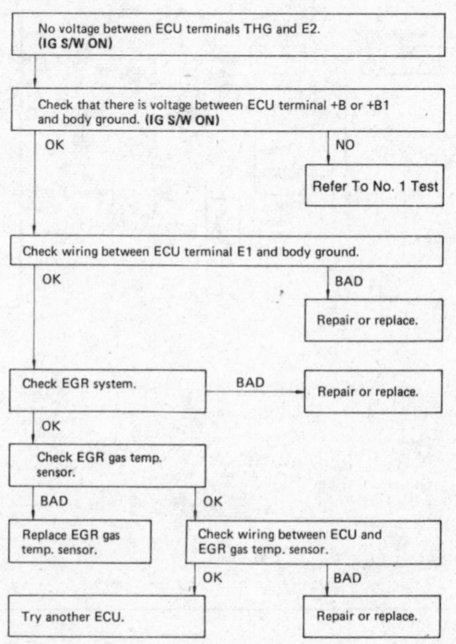
No voltage between ECU terminals THG and E2.
(IG S/W ON)
Check that there is voltage between ECU terminal +B or +B1 and body ground. (IG S/W ON)
OK
NO
Refer To No. 1 Test
Check wiring between ECU terminal E1 and body ground.
OK
BAD
Repair or replace.
Check EGR system.
BAD
Repair or replace.
OK
Check EGR gas temp. sensor.
BAD
OK
Replace EGR gas temp. sensor.
Check wiring between ECU and EGR gas temp. sensor.
OK
BAD
Try another ECU.
Repair or replace.

## CELICA, NO. 11 TEST
## ECU POWER SOURCE

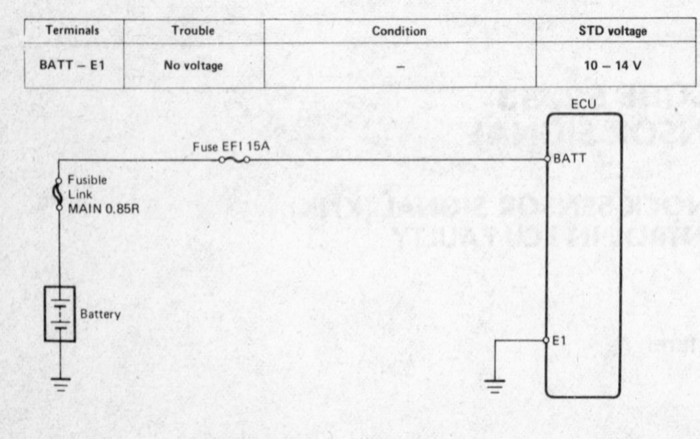

| Terminals | Trouble | Condition | STD voltage |
|---|---|---|---|
| BATT – E1 | No voltage | – | 10 – 14 V |

ECU
Fuse EFI 15A
BATT
Fusible
Link
MAIN 0.85R
Battery
E1

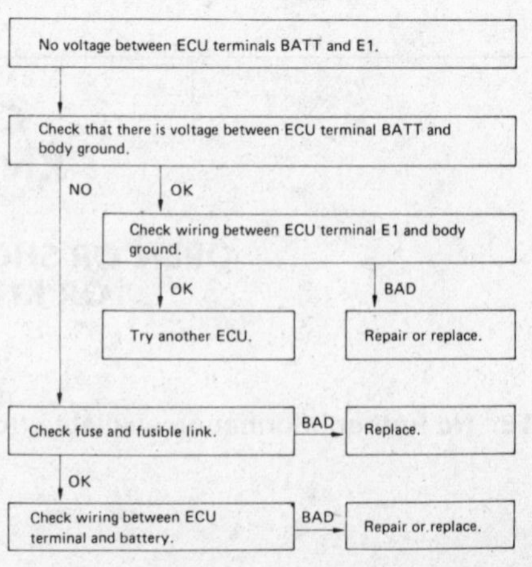
No voltage between ECU terminals BATT and E1.
Check that there is voltage between ECU terminal BATT and body ground.
NO
OK
Check wiring between ECU terminal E1 and body ground.
OK
BAD
Try another ECU.
Repair or replace.
Check fuse and fusible link.
BAD
Replace.
OK
Check wiring between ECU terminal and battery.
BAD
Repair or replace.

Courtesy of Toyota Motor Sales, U.S.A., Inc.

# CELICA, NO. 12 TEST
# INJECTOR CIRCUIT TEST

| Terminals | Trouble | Condition | STD voltage |
|---|---|---|---|
| No. 10 – E01<br>No. 20 – E02 | No voltage | IG S/W ON | 9 – 14 V |

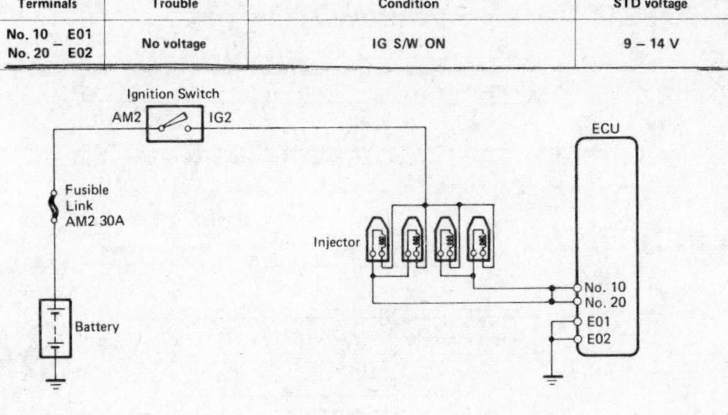
Ignition Switch
AM2
IG2
ECU
Fusible Link AM2 30A
Injector
No. 10
No. 20
E01
E02
Battery

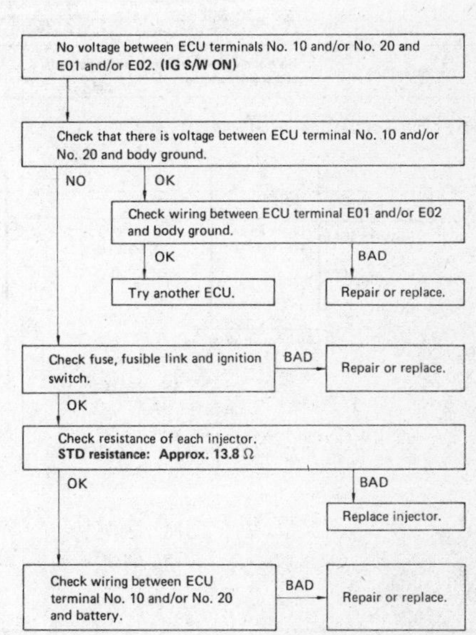
No voltage between ECU terminals No. 10 and/or No. 20 and E01 and/or E02. (IG S/W ON)
Check that there is voltage between ECU terminal No. 10 and/or No. 20 and body ground.
NO
OK
Check wiring between ECU terminal E01 and/or E02 and body ground.
OK
BAD
Try another ECU.
Repair or replace.
Check fuse, fusible link and ignition switch.
BAD
Repair or replace.
OK
Check resistance of each injector.
STD resistance: Approx. 13.8 Ω
OK
BAD
Replace injector.
Check wiring between ECU terminal No. 10 and/or No. 20 and battery.
BAD
Repair or replace.

## 2WD (WITH 3S-FE)

| Terminals | Trouble | Condition | STD voltage |
|---|---|---|---|
| No. 1<br>No. 2 – E01<br>No. 3 – E02<br>No. 4 | No voltage | IG S/W ON | 10 – 14 V |

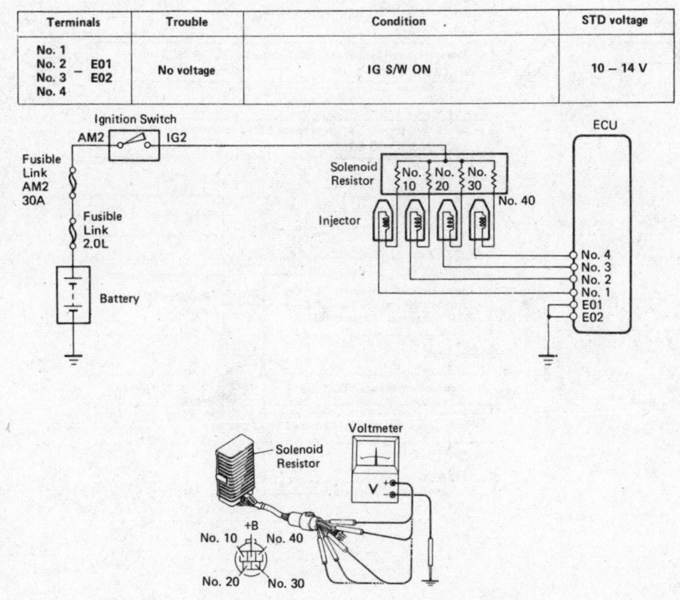
Ignition Switch
AM2
IG2
ECU
Fusible Link AM2 30A
Fusible Link 2.0L
Battery
Solenoid Resistor
No. 10
No. 20
No. 30
No. 40
Injector
No. 4
No. 3
No. 2
No. 1
E01
E02
Voltmeter
Solenoid Resistor
V
+B
No. 10
No. 40
No. 20
No. 30

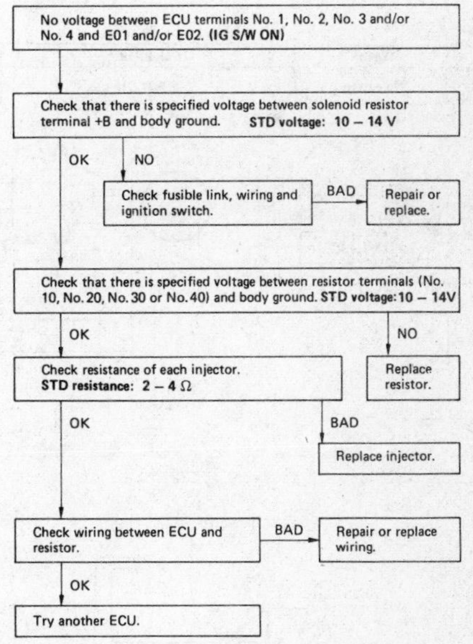
No voltage between ECU terminals No. 1, No. 2, No. 3 and/or No. 4 and E01 and/or E02. (IG S/W ON)
Check that there is specified voltage between solenoid resistor terminal +B and body ground. STD voltage: 10 – 14 V
OK
NO
Check fusible link, wiring and ignition switch.
BAD
Repair or replace.
Check that there is specified voltage between resistor terminals (No. 10, No. 20, No. 30 or No. 40) and body ground. STD voltage: 10 – 14V
OK
NO
Check resistance of each injector.
STD resistance: 2 – 4 Ω
Replace resistor.
OK
BAD
Replace injector.
Check wiring between ECU and resistor.
BAD
Repair or replace wiring.
OK
Try another ECU.

## 2WD (WITH 3S-GE) & 4WD

## CELICA, NO. 13 TEST
## "CHECK ENGINE" LIGHT CIRCUIT

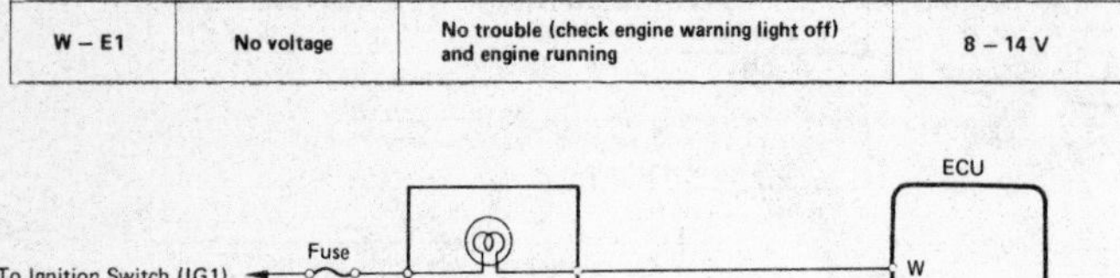

| Terminals | Trouble | Condition | STD voltage |
|---|---|---|---|
| W – E1 | No voltage | No trouble (check engine warning light off) and engine running | 8 – 14 V |

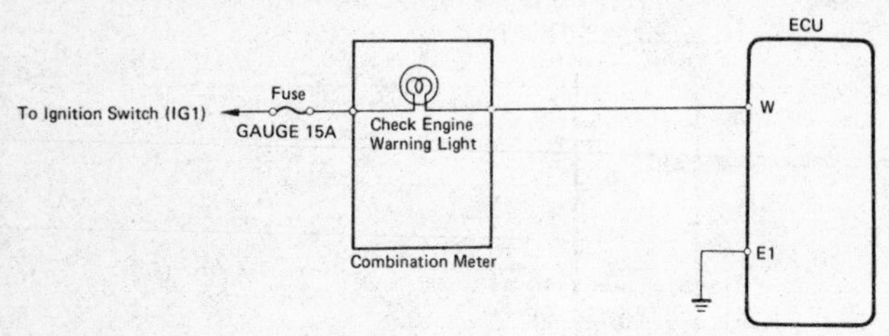
ECU
Fuse
To Ignition Switch (IG1)
GAUGE 15A
Check Engine
Warning Light
W
Combination Meter
E1

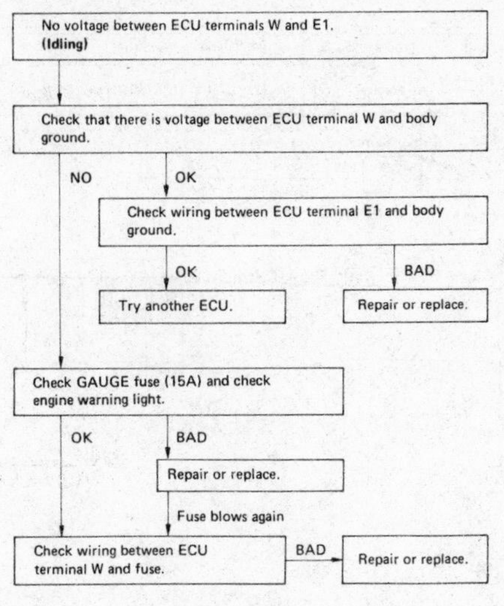
No voltage between ECU terminals W and E1. (Idling)
Check that there is voltage between ECU terminal W and body ground.
NO
OK
Check wiring between ECU terminal E1 and body ground.
OK
BAD
Try another ECU.
Repair or replace.
Check GAUGE fuse (15A) and check engine warning light.
OK
BAD
Repair or replace.
Fuse blows again
Check wiring between ECU terminal W and fuse.
BAD
Repair or replace.

## CELICA, NO. 14 TEST
## ISC VALVE CIRCUIT TEST

| Terminals | Trouble | Condition | STD voltage |
|---|---|---|---|
| ISC1 ISC2 – E1 | No voltage | IG S/W ON | 9 – 14 V |

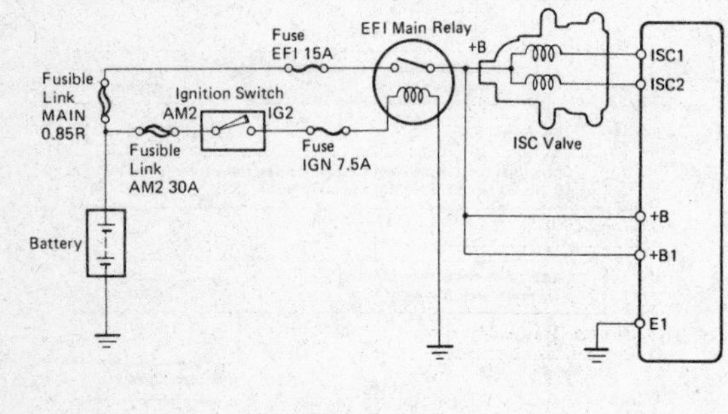
Fuse
EFI 15A
EFI Main Relay
+B
ISC1
ISC2
Fusible Link
MAIN 0.85R
Ignition Switch
AM2
IG2
Fusible Link
AM2 30A
Fuse
IGN 7.5A
ISC Valve
Battery
+B
+B1
E1

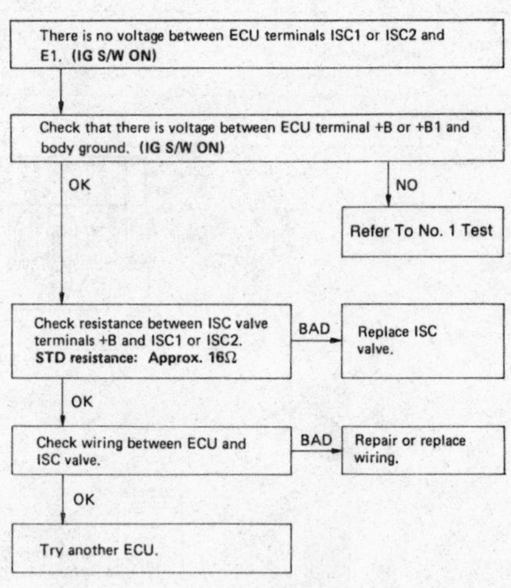
There is no voltage between ECU terminals ISC1 or ISC2 and E1. (IG S/W ON)
Check that there is voltage between ECU terminal +B or +B1 and body ground. (IG S/W ON)
OK
NO
Refer To No. 1 Test
Check resistance between ISC valve terminals +B and ISC1 or ISC2.
STD resistance: Approx. 16Ω
BAD
Replace ISC valve.
OK
Check wiring between ECU and ISC valve.
BAD
Repair or replace wiring.
OK
Try another ECU.

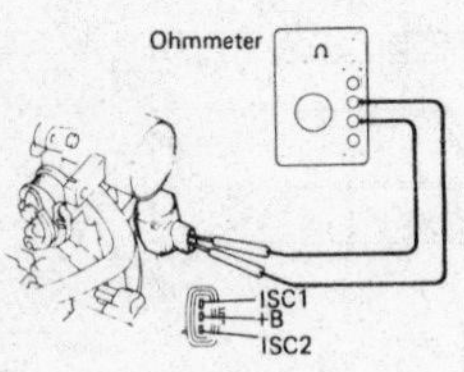
Ohmmeter
ISC1
+B
ISC2

**EXCEPT 2WD (WITH 3S-GE)**

## CELICA, NO. 15 TEST
## A/C SWITCH CIRCUIT

| Terminal | Trouble | Condition | STD voltage |
|---|---|---|---|
| A/C – E1 | No voltage | Air conditioning ON | 8 – 14 V |

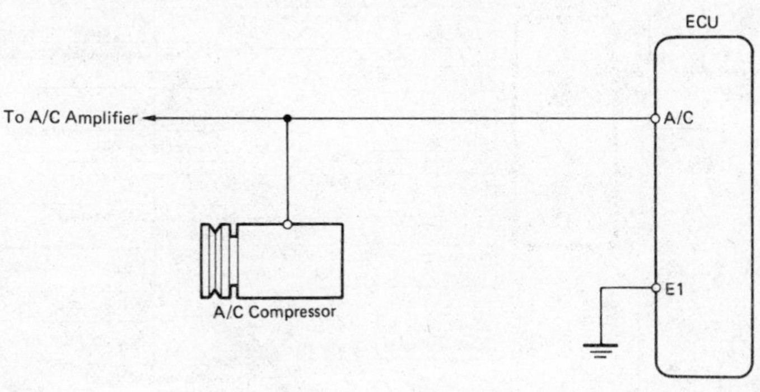
ECU
To A/C Amplifier
A/C
E1
A/C Compressor

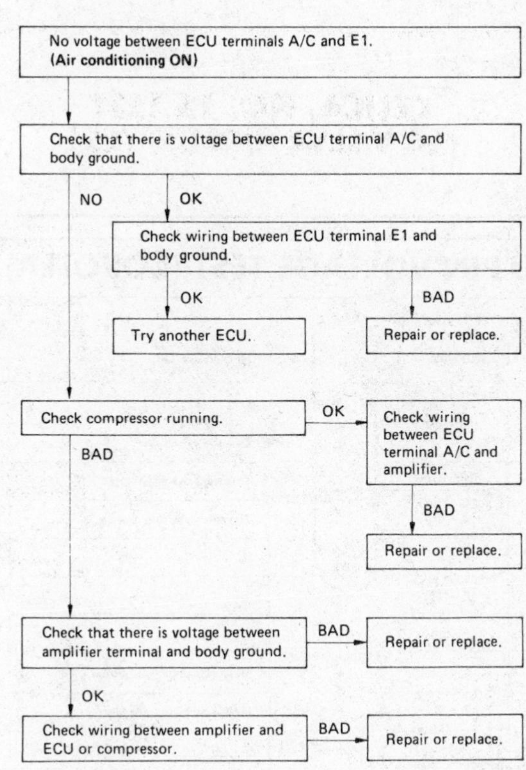
No voltage between ECU terminals A/C and E1.
(Air conditioning ON)
Check that there is voltage between ECU terminal A/C and body ground.
NO
OK
Check wiring between ECU terminal E1 and body ground.
OK
BAD
Try another ECU.
Repair or replace.
Check compressor running.
OK
Check wiring between ECU terminal A/C and amplifier.
BAD
BAD
Repair or replace.
Check that there is voltage between amplifier terminal and body ground.
BAD
Repair or replace.
OK
Check wiring between amplifier and ECU or compressor.
BAD
Repair or replace.

Courtesy of Toyota Motor Sales, U.S.A., Inc.

## DIAGNOSTIC CIRCUIT CHECK (COROLLA)

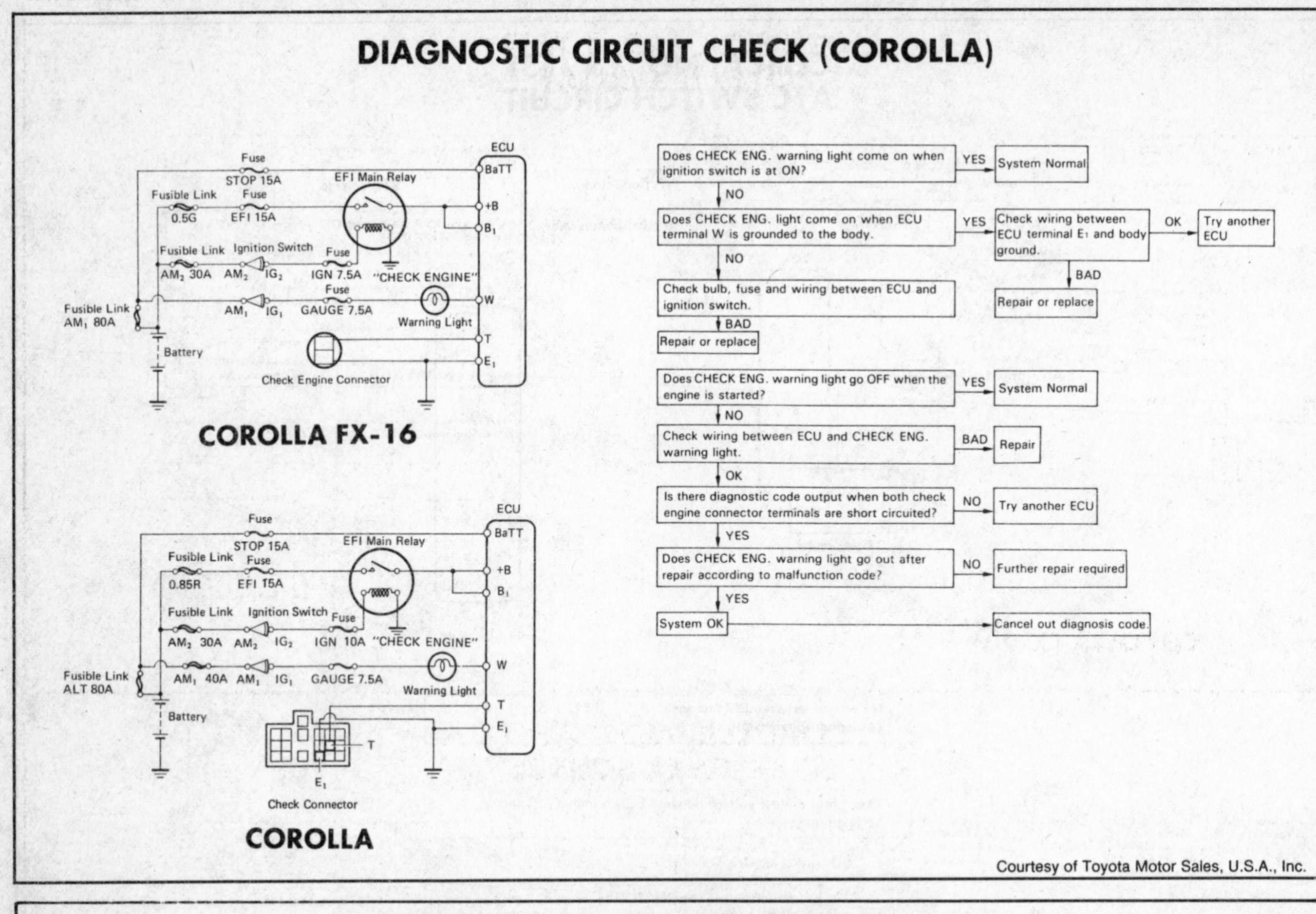
ECU
Fuse
STOP 15A
BaTT
EFI Main Relay
Fusible Link
Fuse
0.5G
EFI 15A
+B
B1
Fusible Link
Ignition Switch
Fuse
AM2 30A
AM2
IG2
IGN 7.5A
"CHECK ENGINE"
Fuse
Fusible Link
AM1 80A
AM1
IG1
GAUGE 7.5A
W
Warning Light
T
Battery
E1
Check Engine Connector
COROLLA FX-16
ECU
Fuse
BaTT
STOP 15A
EFI Main Relay
Fusible Link
Fuse
+B
0.85R
EFI 15A
B1
Fusible Link
Ignition Switch
Fuse
AM2 30A
AM2
IG2
IGN 10A
"CHECK ENGINE"
Fusible Link
ALT 80A
AM1 40A
AM1
IG1
GAUGE 7.5A
W
Warning Light
T
Battery
E1
T
E1
Check Connector
COROLLA
Does CHECK ENG. warning light come on when ignition switch is at ON?
YES
System Normal
NO
Does CHECK ENG. light come on when ECU terminal W is grounded to the body.
YES
Check wiring between ECU terminal E1 and body ground.
OK
Try another ECU
NO
BAD
Check bulb, fuse and wiring between ECU and ignition switch.
Repair or replace
BAD
Repair or replace
Does CHECK ENG. warning light go OFF when the engine is started?
YES
System Normal
NO
Check wiring between ECU and CHECK ENG. warning light.
BAD
Repair
OK
Is there diagnostic code output when both check engine connector terminals are short circuited?
NO
Try another ECU
YES
Does CHECK ENG. warning light go out after repair according to malfunction code?
NO
Further repair required
YES
System OK
Cancel out diagnosis code.

Courtesy of Toyota Motor Sales, U.S.A., Inc.

## ECU PIN VOLTAGE TEST (COROLLA)

| Terminals | STD voltage | Condition | | Test No. |
|---|---|---|---|---|
| +B – E1<br>+B1 – E1 | 10 – 14 | Ignition S/W ON | | 1 |
| BATT – E1 | 10 – 14 | — | | 2 |
| IDL – E2 | 10 – 14 | Ignition S/W ON | Throttle valve open | 8 |
| VTA – E2 | 0.1 – 1.0 | Ignition S/W ON | Throttle valve fully closed | |
| VTA – E2 | 4 – 5 | Ignition S/W ON | Throttle valve fully open | |
| Vcc – E2 | 4 – 6 | Ignition S/W ON | — | |
| +B1 – E2 | 10 – 14 | Ignition S/W ON | — | 7 |
| Vc – E2 | 6 – 10 | Ignition S/W ON | — | |
| Vs – E2 | 2 – 5.5 | Ignition S/W ON | Measuring plate fully closed | |
| Vs – E2 | 6 – 9 | Ignition S/W ON | Measuring plate fully open | |
| Vs – E2 | 2 – 8 | Idling | — | |
| No.10 – E01<br>No.20 – E02 | 9 – 14 | Ignition S/W ON | | 12 |
| W – E1 | 9 – 14 | No trouble (Check engine warning light off) and engine running | | 13 |
| THA – E2 | 1 – 3 | Ignition S/W ON | Intake air temperature 20°C (68°F) | 5 |
| THW – E2 | 0.1 – 1.0 | Ignition S/W ON | Coolant temperature 80°C (176°F) | 4 |
| STA – E1 | 6 – 14 | Ignition S/W ST position | | 9 |
| IGt – E1 | 0.7 – 1.0 | Idling | | 3 |
| A/C – E1 | 5 – 14 | Air conditioning ON | | 10 |

*: For Calif.

Courtesy of Toyota Motor Sales, U.S.A., Inc.

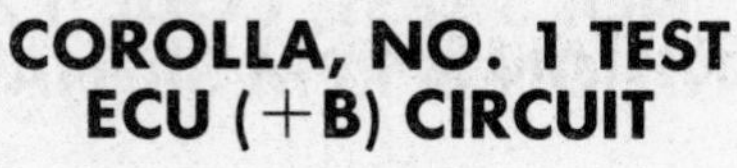

## COROLLA, NO. 1 TEST ECU (+B) CIRCUIT

| Terminals | Trouble | Condition | STD voltage |
|---|---|---|---|
| +B<br>+$B_1$ – $E_1$ | No voltage | IG S/W ON | 10 – 14 V |

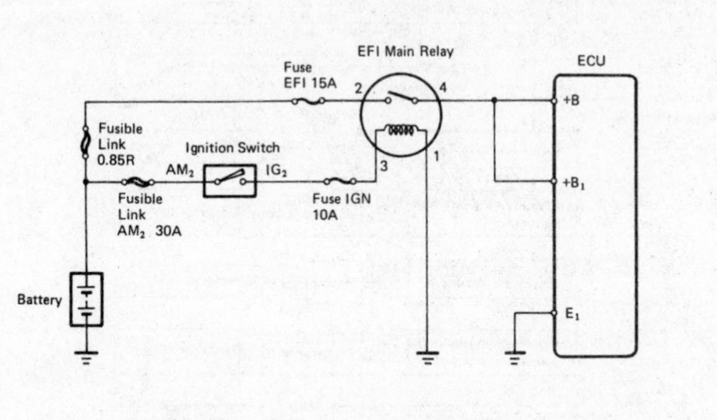
Fuse
EFI 15A
EFI Main Relay
ECU
+B
Fusible
Link
0.85R
Ignition Switch
$AM_2$
$IG_2$
Fusible
Link
$AM_2$ 30A
Fuse IGN
10A
+$B_1$
Battery
$E_1$

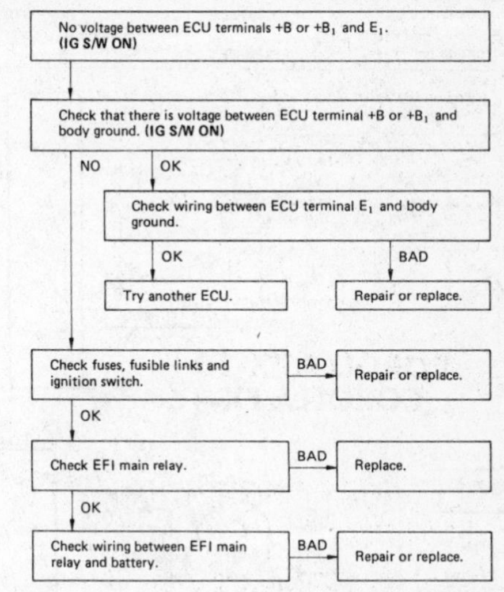
No voltage between ECU terminals +B or +$B_1$ and $E_1$. (IG S/W ON)
Check that there is voltage between ECU terminal +B or +$B_1$ and body ground. (IG S/W ON)
NO
OK
Check wiring between ECU terminal $E_1$ and body ground.
OK
BAD
Try another ECU.
Repair or replace.
Check fuses, fusible links and ignition switch.
BAD
Repair or replace.
OK
Check EFI main relay.
BAD
Replace.
OK
Check wiring between EFI main relay and battery.
BAD
Repair or replace.

**COROLLA FX-16**

## COROLLA, NO. 2 TEST ECU POWER SOURCE

| Terminals | Trouble | Condition | STD voltage |
|---|---|---|---|
| BATT – $E_1$ | No voltage | – | 10 – 14V |

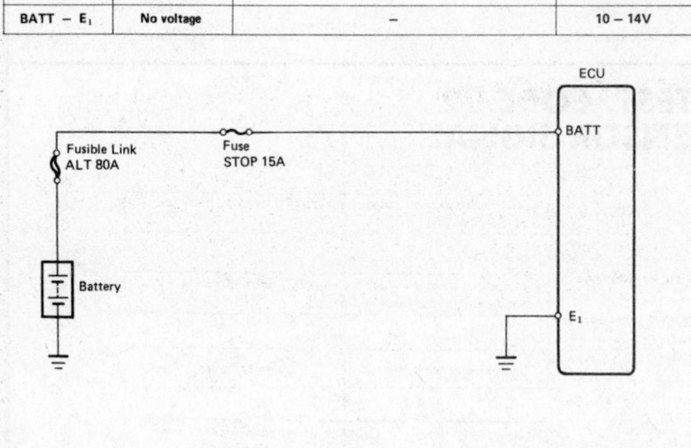
ECU
Fusible Link
ALT 80A
Fuse
STOP 15A
BATT
Battery
$E_1$

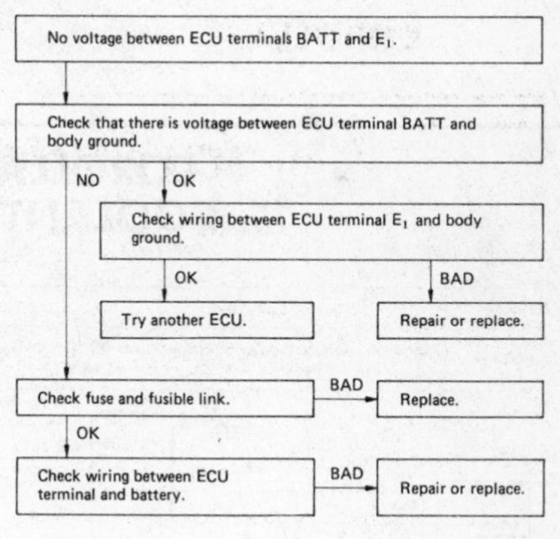
No voltage between ECU terminals BATT and $E_1$.
Check that there is voltage between ECU terminal BATT and body ground.
NO
OK
Check wiring between ECU terminal $E_1$ and body ground.
OK
BAD
Try another ECU.
Repair or replace.
Check fuse and fusible link.
BAD
Replace.
OK
Check wiring between ECU terminal and battery.
BAD
Repair or replace.

Courtesy of Toyota Motor Sales, U.S.A., Inc.

## COROLLA, NO. 3 TEST, CODE 12, 13, 14
## IGNITION & RPM SIGNAL

| Terminals | Trouble | Condition | STD voltage |
|---|---|---|---|
| IGt – E₁ | No voltage | Idling | 0.7 – 1.0 V |

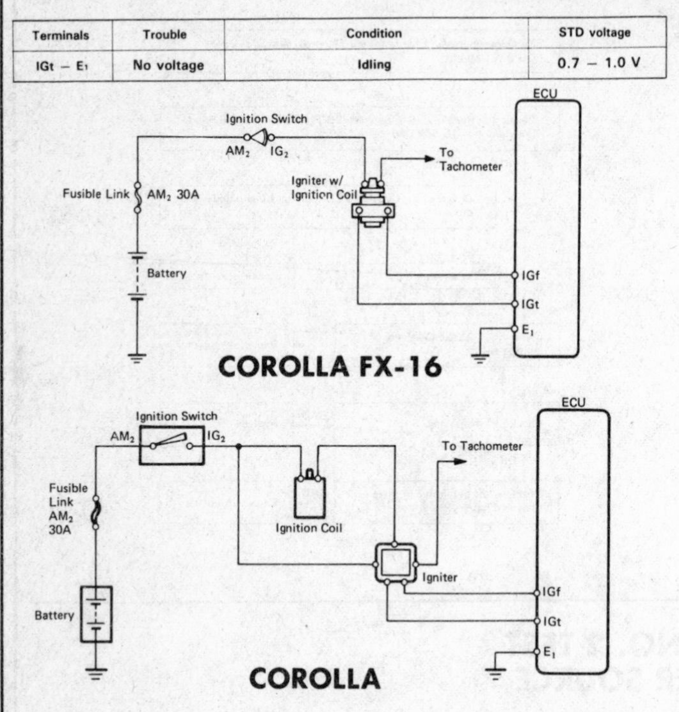
ECU
Ignition Switch
AM₂
IG₂
To Tachometer
Igniter w/ Ignition Coil
Fusible Link
AM₂ 30A
Battery
IGf
IGt
E₁
COROLLA FX-16
ECU
Ignition Switch
AM₂
IG₂
To Tachometer
Fusible Link AM₂ 30A
Ignition Coil
Igniter
Battery
IGf
IGt
E₁
COROLLA

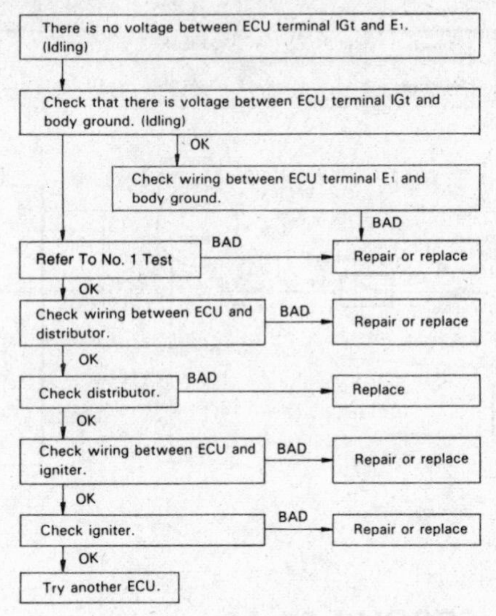
There is no voltage between ECU terminal IGt and E₁. (Idling)
Check that there is voltage between ECU terminal IGt and body ground. (Idling)
OK
Check wiring between ECU terminal E₁ and body ground.
BAD
Refer To No. 1 Test
BAD
Repair or replace
OK
Check wiring between ECU and distributor.
BAD
Repair or replace
OK
Check distributor.
BAD
Replace
OK
Check wiring between ECU and igniter.
BAD
Repair or replace
OK
Check igniter.
BAD
Repair or replace
OK
Try another ECU.

NOTE: To check ignitor, see TOYOTA ELECTRONIC IGNITION SYSTEM article in DISTRIBUTORS & IGNITION SYSTEMS section.

## COROLLA, NO. 4 TEST, CODE 22
## COOLANT TEMP. SENSOR SIGNAL

| Terminals | Trouble | Condition | | STD voltage |
|---|---|---|---|---|
| THW – E₂ | No voltage | Ignition switch ON | Coolant temperature 80°C (176°F) | 0.1 – 1.0 V |

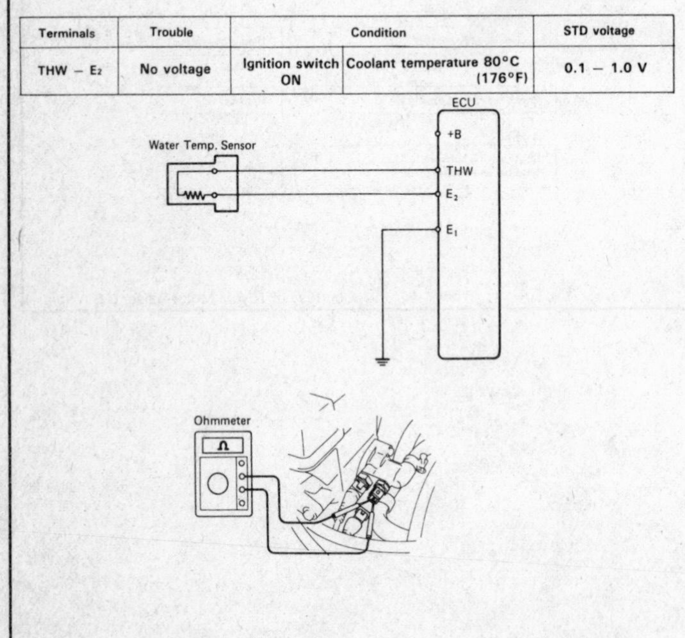
ECU
+B
Water Temp. Sensor
THW
E₂
E₁
Ohmmeter

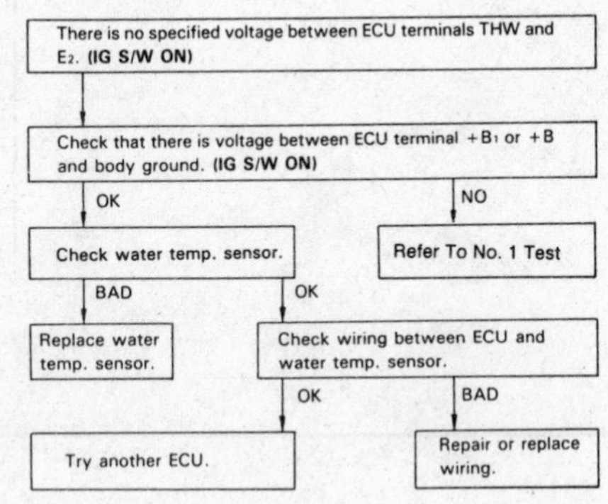
There is no specified voltage between ECU terminals THW and E₂. (IG S/W ON)
Check that there is voltage between ECU terminal +B₁ or +B and body ground. (IG S/W ON)
OK
NO
Check water temp. sensor.
Refer To No. 1 Test
BAD
OK
Replace water temp. sensor.
Check wiring between ECU and water temp. sensor.
OK
BAD
Try another ECU.
Repair or replace wiring.

Courtesy of Toyota Motor Sales, U.S.A., Inc.

## COROLLA, NO. 5 TEST, CODE 24
## INTAKE AIR TEMP. SENSOR SIGNAL

| Terminals | Trouble | Condition | | STD voltage |
|---|---|---|---|---|
| THA – E2 | No voltage | Ignition switch ON | Intake air temperature 20 °C (68 °F) | 1 – 3 V |

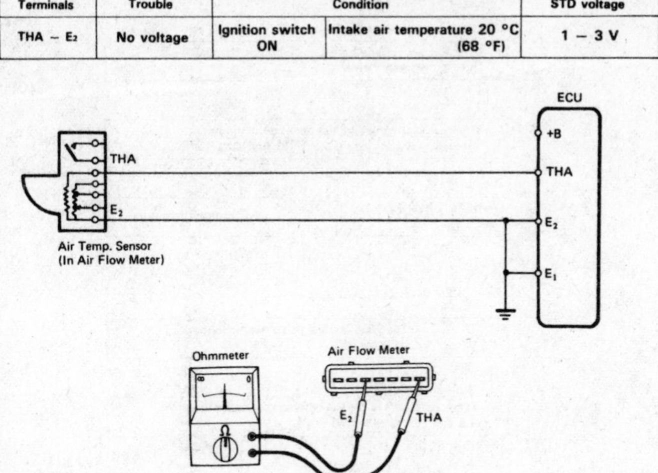
ECU
+B
THA
THA
E2
E2
E1
Air Temp. Sensor
(In Air Flow Meter)
Ohmmeter
Air Flow Meter
E2
THA

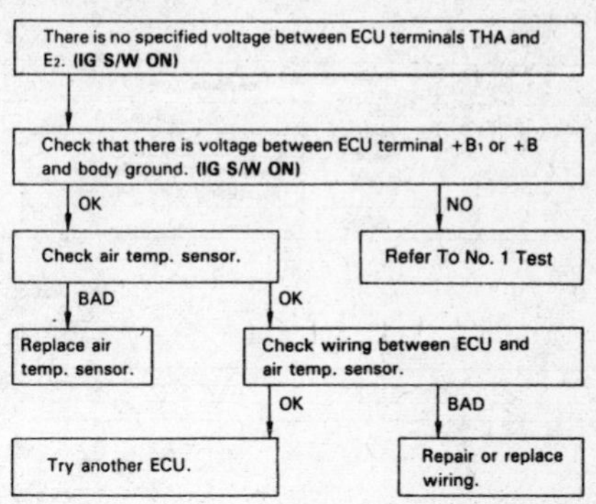
There is no specified voltage between ECU terminals THA and E2. (IG S/W ON)
Check that there is voltage between ECU terminal +B1 or +B and body ground. (IG S/W ON)
OK
NO
Check air temp. sensor.
Refer To No. 1 Test
BAD
OK
Replace air temp. sensor.
Check wiring between ECU and air temp. sensor.
OK
BAD
Try another ECU.
Repair or replace wiring.

## COROLLA, NO. 6 TEST, CODE 25, 26
## $O_2$ SENSOR SIGNAL

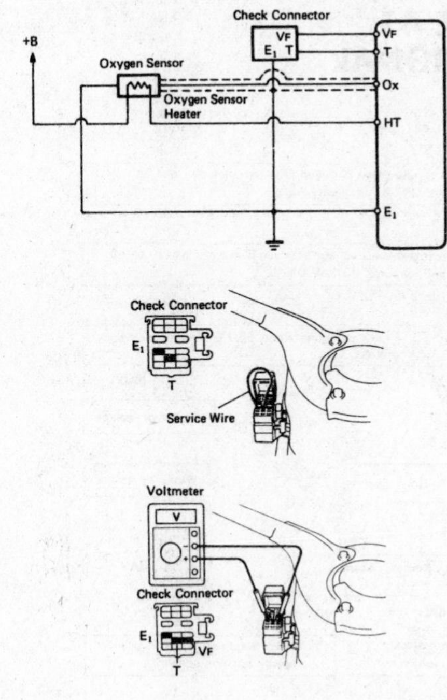
Check Connector
VF
E1 T
+B
Oxygen Sensor
Oxygen Sensor Heater
VF
T
Ox
HT
E1
Check Connector
E1
T
Service Wire
Voltmeter
V
Check Connector
E1
VF
T

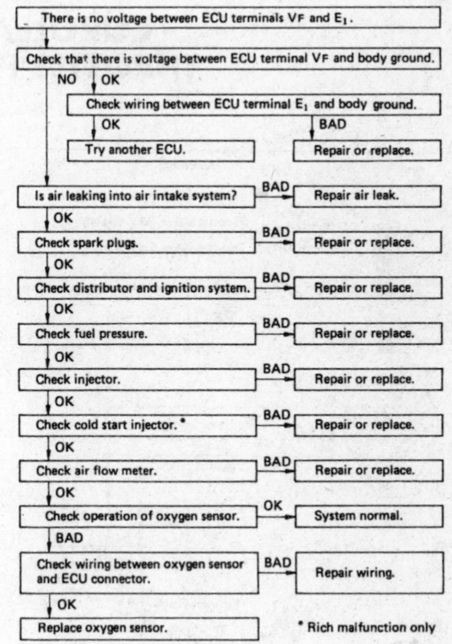
There is no voltage between ECU terminals VF and E1.
Check that there is voltage between ECU terminal VF and body ground.
NO
OK
Check wiring between ECU terminal E1 and body ground.
OK
BAD
Try another ECU.
Repair or replace.
Is air leaking into air intake system?
BAD
Repair air leak.
OK
Check spark plugs.
BAD
Repair or replace.
OK
Check distributor and ignition system.
BAD
Repair or replace.
OK
Check fuel pressure.
BAD
Repair or replace.
OK
Check injector.
BAD
Repair or replace.
OK
Check cold start injector.*
BAD
Repair or replace.
OK
Check air flow meter.
BAD
Repair or replace.
OK
Check operation of oxygen sensor.
OK
System normal.
BAD
Check wiring between oxygen sensor and ECU connector.
BAD
Repair wiring.
OK
Replace oxygen sensor.
* Rich malfunction only

## COROLLA, NO. 7 TEST, CODE 31
## AIRFLOW METER SIGNAL

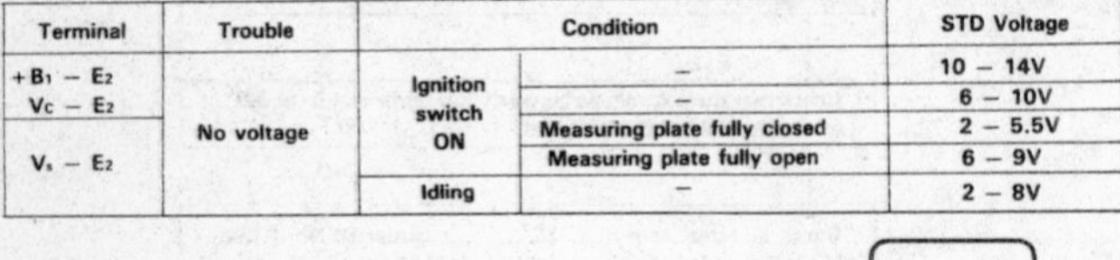

| Terminal | Trouble | Condition | | STD Voltage |
|---|---|---|---|---|
| +B1 – E2 | No voltage | Ignition switch ON | – | 10 – 14V |
| Vc – E2 | | | – | 6 – 10V |
| Vs – E2 | | | Measuring plate fully closed | 2 – 5.5V |
| | | | Measuring plate fully open | 6 – 9V |
| | | Idling | – | 2 – 8V |

+B
B1
Vc
Vs
E2
E1
ECU
VB
Vc
Vs
E2
Air Flow Meter

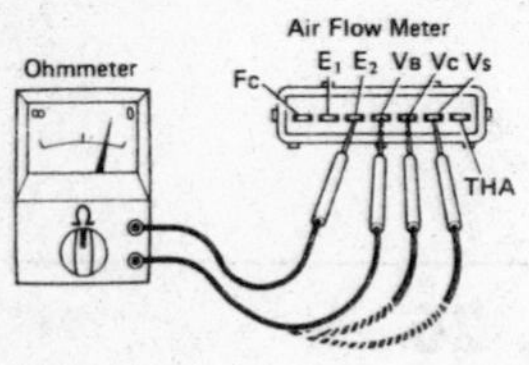
Air Flow Meter
Ohmmeter
Fc
E1 E2 VB Vc Vs
THA

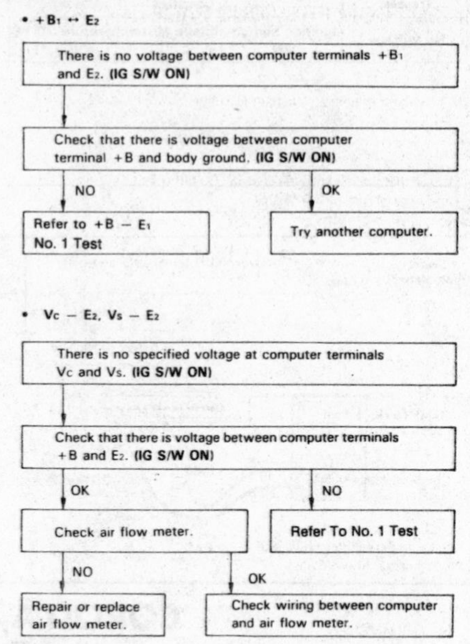
• +B1 ↔ E2
There is no voltage between computer terminals +B1 and E2. (IG S/W ON)
Check that there is voltage between computer terminal +B and body ground. (IG S/W ON)
NO
OK
Refer to +B – E1 No. 1 Test
Try another computer.
• Vc – E2, Vs – E2
There is no specified voltage at computer terminals Vc and Vs. (IG S/W ON)
Check that there is voltage between computer terminals +B and E2. (IG S/W ON)
OK
NO
Check air flow meter.
Refer To No. 1 Test
NO
OK
Repair or replace air flow meter.
Check wiring between computer and air flow meter.

## COROLLA, NO. 8 TEST, CODE 41
## THROTTLE POSITION SENSOR SIGNAL

| Terminals | Trouble | Condition | | STD voltage |
|---|---|---|---|---|
| IDL – E2 | No voltage | Ignition switch ON | Throttle valve open | 10 – 14 V |
| VTA – E2 | | | Throttle valve fully closed | 0.1 – 1.0 V |
| | | | Throttle valve fully open | 4 – 5 V |
| Vcc – E2 | | | – | 4 – 6 V |

ECU

Throttle Position Sensor

E2
IDL
VTA
Vcc

E2
E21
IDL
VTA
Vcc
E1

E2
IDL
VTA
Vcc

Thickness Gauge

Ohmmeter

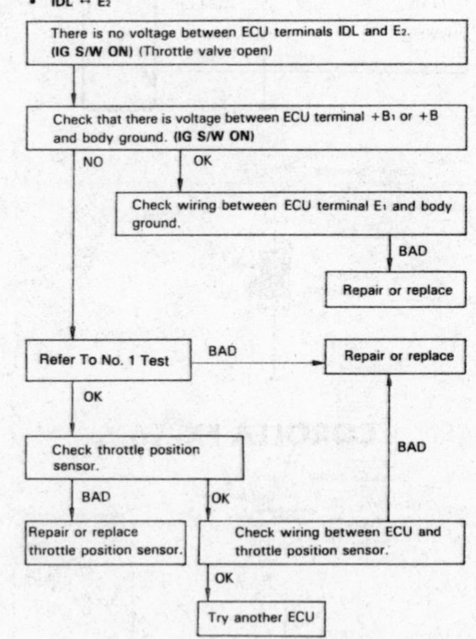
• IDL ↔ E2
There is no voltage between ECU terminals IDL and E2. (IG S/W ON) (Throttle valve open)
Check that there is voltage between ECU terminal +B1 or +B and body ground. (IG S/W ON)
NO
OK
Check wiring between ECU terminal E1 and body ground.
BAD
Repair or replace
Refer To No. 1 Test
BAD
Repair or replace
OK
BAD
Check throttle position sensor.
BAD
OK
Repair or replace throttle position sensor.
Check wiring between ECU and throttle position sensor.
OK
Try another ECU

CONTINUED ON NEXT PAGE.

Courtesy of Toyota Motor Sales, U.S.A., Inc.

# COROLLA, NO. 8 TEST, CODE 41 (Cont.)
## THROTTLE POSITION SENSOR SIGNAL

CONTINUED FROM PREVIOUS PAGE.

• VTA ↔ $E_2$

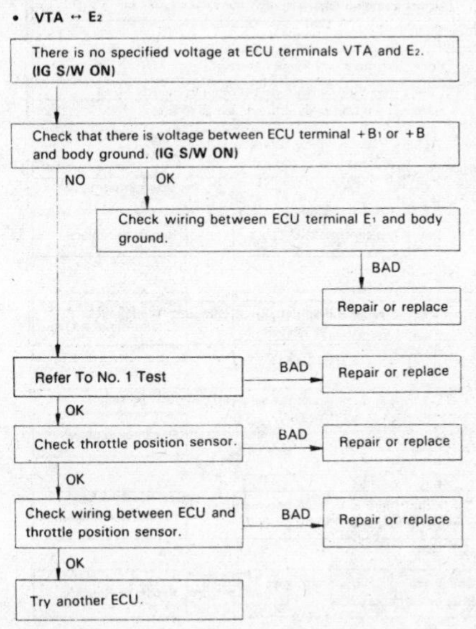
There is no specified voltage at ECU terminals VTA and E2. (IG S/W ON)
Check that there is voltage between ECU terminal +B1 or +B and body ground. (IG S/W ON)
NO
OK
Check wiring between ECU terminal E1 and body ground.
BAD
Repair or replace
Refer To No. 1 Test
BAD
Repair or replace
OK
Check throttle position sensor.
BAD
Repair or replace
OK
Check wiring between ECU and throttle position sensor.
BAD
Repair or replace
OK
Try another ECU.

• Vcc ↔ $E_2$

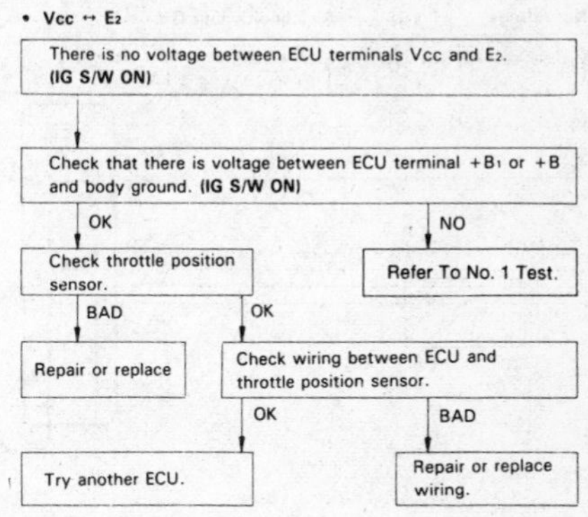
There is no voltage between ECU terminals Vcc and E2. (IG S/W ON)
Check that there is voltage between ECU terminal +B1 or +B and body ground. (IG S/W ON)
OK
NO
Check throttle position sensor.
Refer To No. 1 Test.
BAD
OK
Repair or replace
Check wiring between ECU and throttle position sensor.
OK
BAD
Try another ECU.
Repair or replace wiring.

# COROLLA, NO. 9 TEST, CODE 43
## STARTER SIGNAL

| Terminals | Trouble | Condition | STD voltage |
|---|---|---|---|
| STA – $E_1$ | No voltage | Ignition Switch ST position | 6 – 14V |

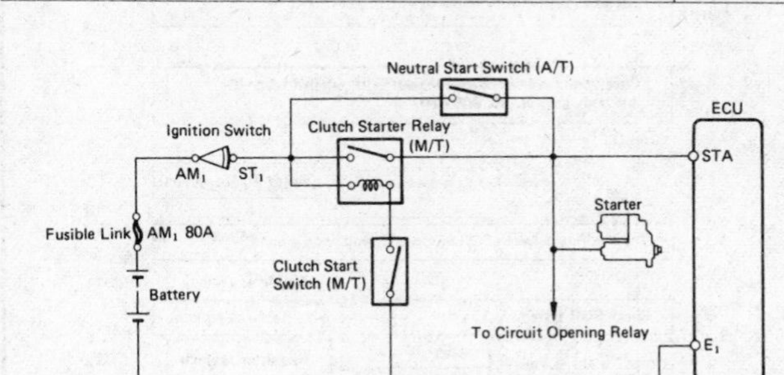
Neutral Start Switch (A/T)
Ignition Switch
Clutch Starter Relay
(M/T)
ECU
STA
AM1
ST1
Starter
Fusible Link
AM1 80A
Clutch Start Switch (M/T)
Battery
To Circuit Opening Relay
E1

COROLLA FX-16

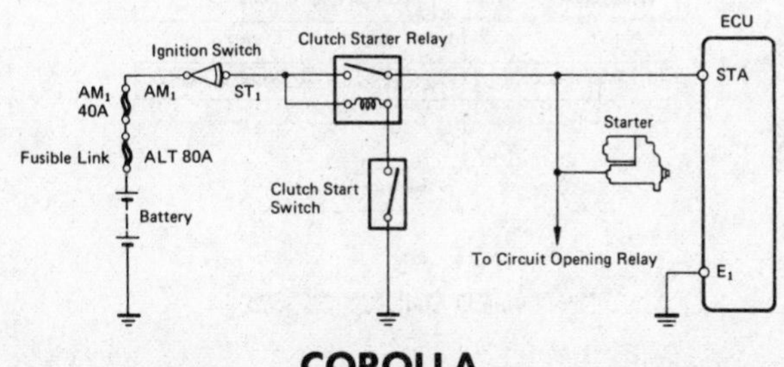
Ignition Switch
Clutch Starter Relay
ECU
AM1 40A
AM1
ST1
STA
Starter
Fusible Link
ALT 80A
Clutch Start Switch
Battery
To Circuit Opening Relay
E1

COROLLA

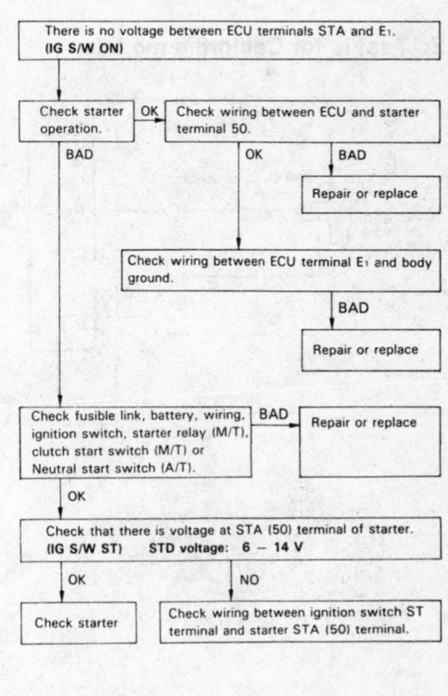
There is no voltage between ECU terminals STA and E1. (IG S/W ON)
Check starter operation.
OK
Check wiring between ECU and starter terminal 50.
BAD
OK
BAD
Repair or replace
Check wiring between ECU terminal E1 and body ground.
BAD
Repair or replace
Check fusible link, battery, wiring, ignition switch, starter relay (M/T), clutch start switch (M/T) or Neutral start switch (A/T).
BAD
Repair or replace
OK
Check that there is voltage at STA (50) terminal of starter. (IG S/W ST) STD voltage: 6 – 14 V
OK
NO
Check starter
Check wiring between ignition switch ST terminal and starter STA (50) terminal.

Courtesy of Toyota Motor Sales, U.S.A., Inc.

## COROLLA, NO. 10 TEST, CODE 51
## A/C SWITCH SIGNAL

| Terminals | Trouble | Condition | STD Voltage |
|---|---|---|---|
| A/C – $E_1$ | No voltage | Air conditioning ON | 5 – 14 V |

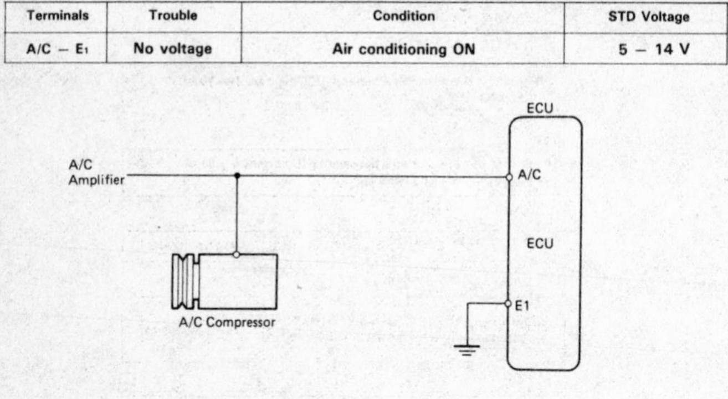
ECU
A/C
Amplifier
A/C
ECU
E1
A/C Compressor

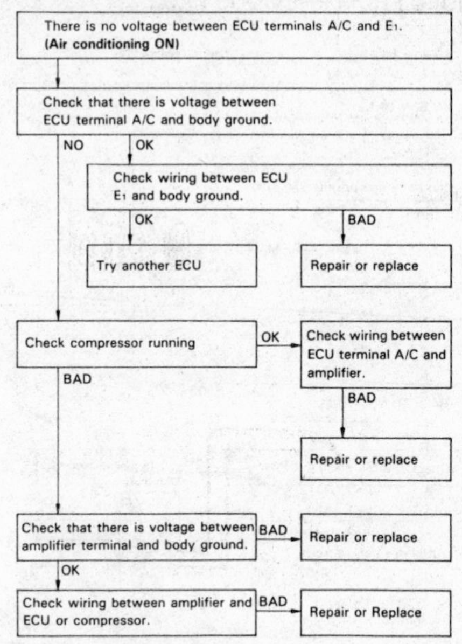
There is no voltage between ECU terminals A/C and E1. (Air conditioning ON)
Check that there is voltage between ECU terminal A/C and body ground.
NO
OK
Check wiring between ECU E1 and body ground.
OK
BAD
Try another ECU
Repair or replace
Check compressor running
OK
Check wiring between ECU terminal A/C and amplifier.
BAD
BAD
Repair or replace
Check that there is voltage between amplifier terminal and body ground.
BAD
Repair or replace
OK
Check wiring between amplifier and ECU or compressor.
BAD
Repair or Replace

## COROLLA, NO. 11 TEST, CODE 71
## EGR SYSTEM SIGNAL

**NOTE: Test is for California models.**

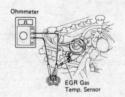

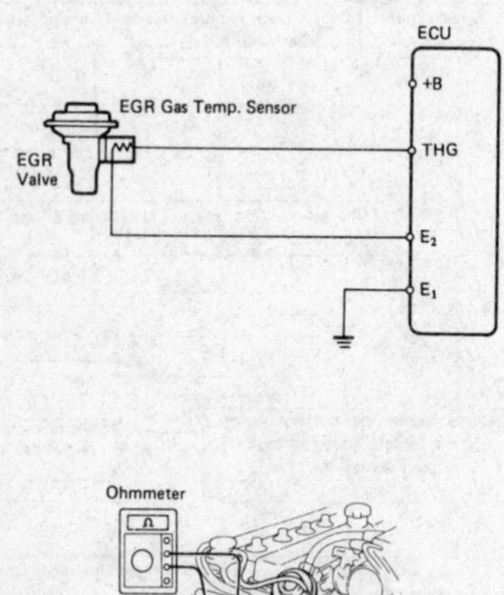
ECU
+B
EGR Gas Temp. Sensor
EGR
Valve
THG
E2
E1
Ohmmeter
EGR Gas
Temp. Sensor

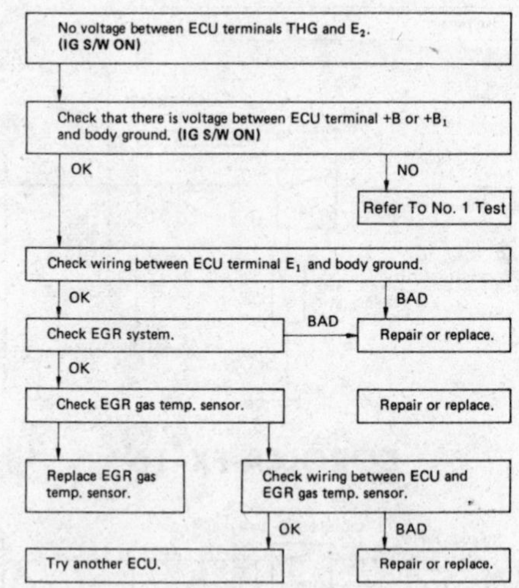
No voltage between ECU terminals THG and E2. (IG S/W ON)
Check that there is voltage between ECU terminal +B or +B1 and body ground. (IG S/W ON)
OK
NO
Refer To No. 1 Test
Check wiring between ECU terminal E1 and body ground.
OK
BAD
Check EGR system.
BAD
Repair or replace.
OK
Check EGR gas temp. sensor.
Repair or replace.
Replace EGR gas temp. sensor.
Check wiring between ECU and EGR gas temp. sensor.
OK
BAD
Try another ECU.
Repair or replace.

## COROLLA, NO. 12 TEST
## INJECTOR CIRCUIT TEST

| Terminals | Trouble | Condition | STD voltage |
|---|---|---|---|
| No. 10 – $E_{01}$<br>No. 20 – $E_{02}$ | No voltage | Ignition switch ON | 9 – 14V |

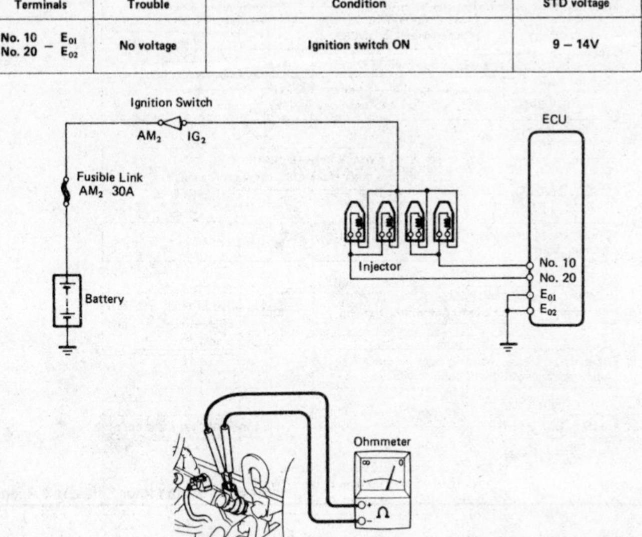
Ignition Switch
$AM_2$
$IG_2$
Fusible Link
$AM_2$ 30A
Battery
ECU
Injector
No. 10
No. 20
$E_{01}$
$E_{02}$
Ohmmeter

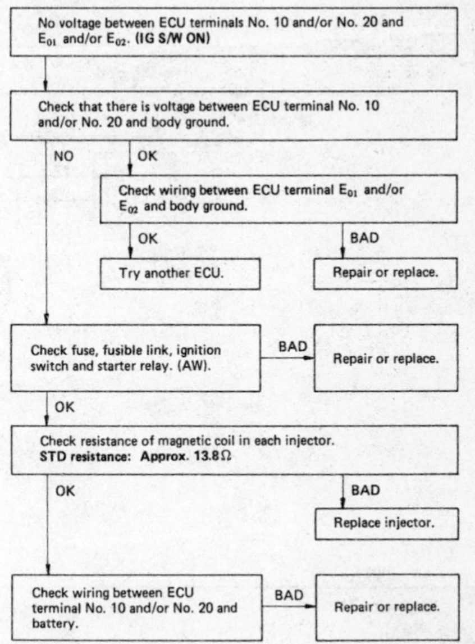
No voltage between ECU terminals No. 10 and/or No. 20 and $E_{01}$ and/or $E_{02}$. (IG S/W ON)
Check that there is voltage between ECU terminal No. 10 and/or No. 20 and body ground.
NO
OK
Check wiring between ECU terminal $E_{01}$ and/or $E_{02}$ and body ground.
OK
BAD
Try another ECU.
Repair or replace.
Check fuse, fusible link, ignition switch and starter relay. (AW).
BAD
Repair or replace.
OK
Check resistance of magnetic coil in each injector.
STD resistance: Approx. 13.8Ω
OK
BAD
Replace injector.
Check wiring between ECU terminal No. 10 and/or No. 20 and battery.
BAD
Repair or replace.

## COROLLA, NO. 13 TEST
## "CHECK ENGINE" CIRCUIT CHECK

| Terminals | Trouble | Condition | STD voltage |
|---|---|---|---|
| W – $E_1$ | No voltage | No trouble (check engine warning light off) and engine running. | 9 – 14V |

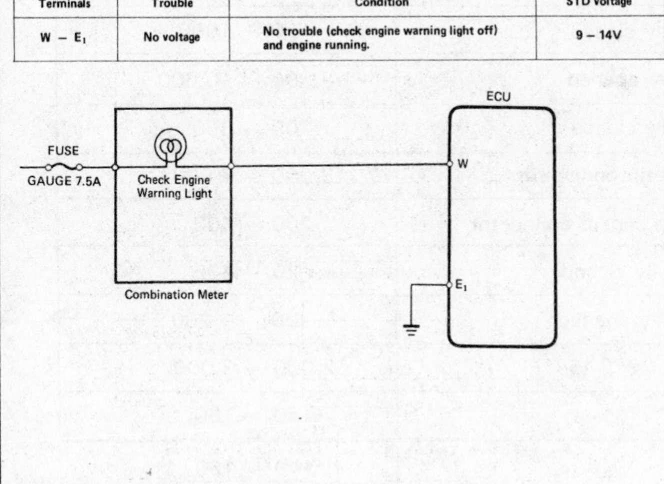
FUSE
GAUGE 7.5A
Check Engine
Warning Light
Combination Meter
ECU
W
$E_1$

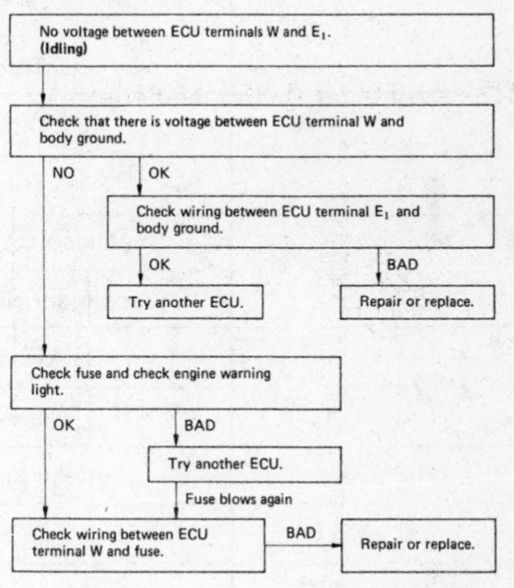
No voltage between ECU terminals W and $E_1$. (Idling)
Check that there is voltage between ECU terminal W and body ground.
NO
OK
Check wiring between ECU terminal $E_1$ and body ground.
OK
BAD
Try another ECU.
Repair or replace.
Check fuse and check engine warning light.
OK
BAD
Try another ECU.
Fuse blows again
Check wiring between ECU terminal W and fuse.
BAD
Repair or replace.

Courtesy of Toyota Motor Sales, U.S.A., Inc.

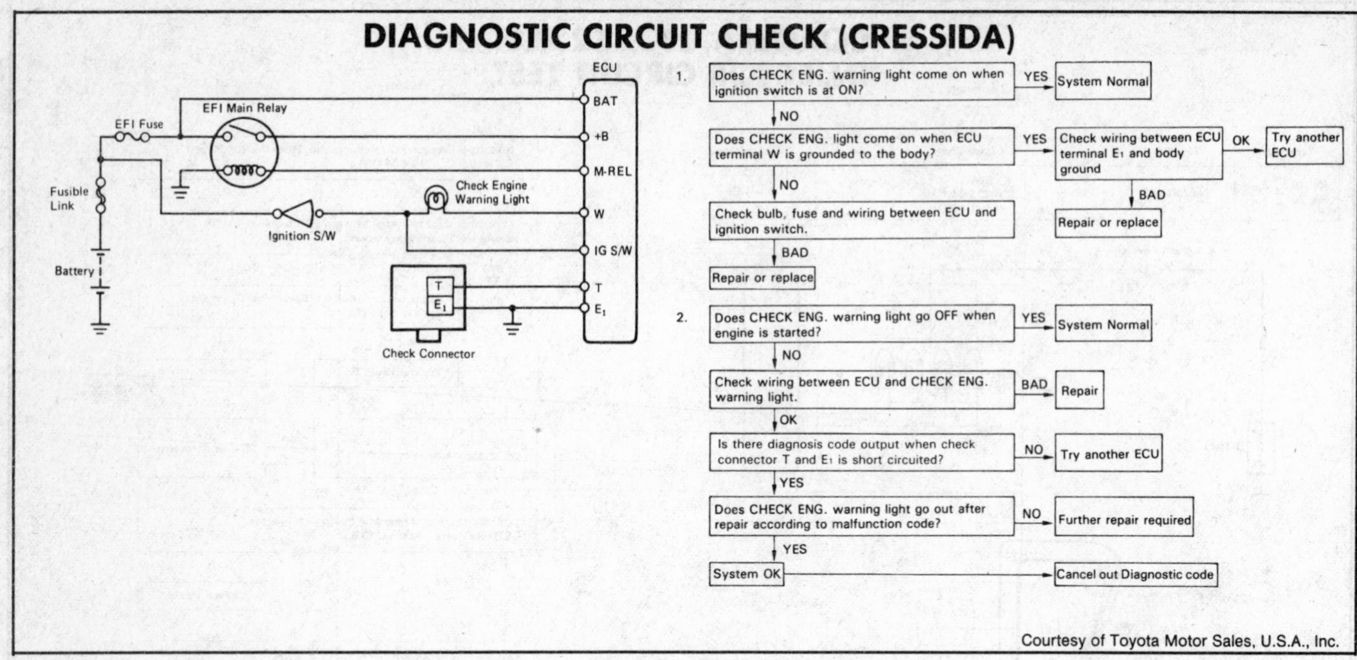
DIAGNOSTIC CIRCUIT CHECK (CRESSIDA)
ECU
BAT
+B
M-REL
W
IG S/W
T
E1
EFI Main Relay
EFI Fuse
Fusible Link
Battery
Ignition S/W
Check Engine Warning Light
Check Connector
1. Does CHECK ENG. warning light come on when ignition switch is at ON?
YES
System Normal
NO
Does CHECK ENG. light come on when ECU terminal W is grounded to the body?
YES
Check wiring between ECU terminal E1 and body ground
OK
Try another ECU
BAD
Repair or replace
NO
Check bulb, fuse and wiring between ECU and ignition switch.
BAD
Repair or replace
2. Does CHECK ENG. warning light go OFF when engine is started?
YES
System Normal
NO
Check wiring between ECU and CHECK ENG. warning light.
BAD
Repair
OK
Is there diagnosis code output when check connector T and E1 is short circuited?
NO
Try another ECU
YES
Does CHECK ENG. warning light go out after repair according to malfunction code?
NO
Further repair required
YES
System OK
Cancel out Diagnostic code
Courtesy of Toyota Motor Sales, U.S.A., Inc.

## ECU WIRING CONNECTOR RESISTANCES (CRESSIDA)

| Terminals | Condition | Resistance (Ω) |
|---|---|---|
| IDL — $E_{22}$ | Throttle valve open | ∞ |
| | Throttle valve fully closed | 0 — 100Ω |
| VTA — $E_{22}$ | Throttle valve fully opened | 3,300 — 10,000 |
| | Throttle valve fully closed | 200 — 800 |
| Vc — $E_{22}$ | Disconnect air flow meter connector | 3,000 — 7,000 |
| | Disconnect throttle position sensor connector | 200 — 400 |
| Vs — $E_2$ | Measuring plate fully closed | 20 — 400 |
| | Measuring plate fully opened | 200 — 1,200 |
| THA — $E_2$ | Intake air temperature 20°C (68°F) | 2,000 — 3,000 |
| G — G$\ominus$ | — | 140 — 180 |
| Ne — G$\ominus$ | — | 140 — 180 |
| $ISC_1$, $ISC_2$ $ISC_3$, $ISC_4$ — +B | — | 10 — 30 |

Courtesy of Toyota Motor Sales, U.S.A., Inc.

## ECU PIN VOLTAGE TEST (CRESSIDA)

| Terminals | Condition | | STD Voltage | Test No. |
|---|---|---|---|---|
| BAT – $E_1$ | — | | 10 – 14 | 1 |
| +B – $E_1$ | Ignition S/W ON | | | |
| IG S/W – $E_1$ | | | | |
| M-REL – $E_1$ | | | | |
| IDL – $E_{22}$ | Ignition S/W ON | Throttle valve open | 4 – 6 | 3 |
| $V_C$ – $E_{22}$ | | — | 4 – 6 | |
| VTA – $E_{22}$ | | Throttle valve fully closed | 0.1 – 1.0 | |
| | | Throttle valve fully opened | 4 – 5 | |
| $V_C$ – $E_2$ | Ignition S/W ON | — | 4 – 6 | 5 |
| $V_S$ – $E_2$ | | Measuring plate fully closed | 4 – 5 | |
| | | Measuring plate fully open | 0.02 – 0.08 | |
| | | Idling | 2 – 4 | |
| | | 3,000 rpm | 0.3 – 1.0 | |
| THA – $E_2$ | IG S/W ON | Intake air temperature 20°C (68°F) | 1 – 2 | |
| THW – $E_2$ | IG S/W ON | Coolant temperature 80°C (176°F) | 0.1 – 0.5 | 6 |
| STA – $E_1$ | Ignition S/W ST position | | 6 – 12 | 4 |
| No. 10 – $E_{01}$<br>No. 20 – $E_{02}$ | Ignition S/W ON | | 9 – 14 | 8 |
| IGt – $E_1$ | Cranking or idling | | 0.7 – 1.0 | 2 |
| $ISC_1$ ~ $ISC_4$ – $E_1$ | Ignition S/W ON | | 9 – 14 | 7 |
| | 2 – 3 secs, after engine off | | 9 – 14 | |

Courtesy of Toyota Motor Sales, U.S.A., Inc.

## CRESSIDA, NO. 1 TEST, CODE 11
## ECU (+B) CIRCUIT

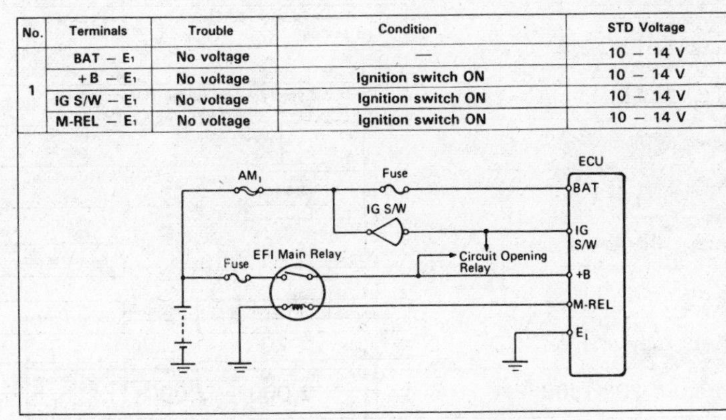

| No. | Terminals | Trouble | Condition | STD Voltage |
|---|---|---|---|---|
| 1 | BAT – $E_1$ | No voltage | — | 10 – 14 V |
| | +B – $E_1$ | No voltage | Ignition switch ON | 10 – 14 V |
| | IG S/W – $E_1$ | No voltage | Ignition switch ON | 10 – 14 V |
| | M-REL – $E_1$ | No voltage | Ignition switch ON | 10 – 14 V |

AM1
Fuse
IG S/W
ECU
BAT
IG S/W
Fuse
EFI Main Relay
Circuit Opening Relay
+B
M-REL
E1

• BAT – $E_1$

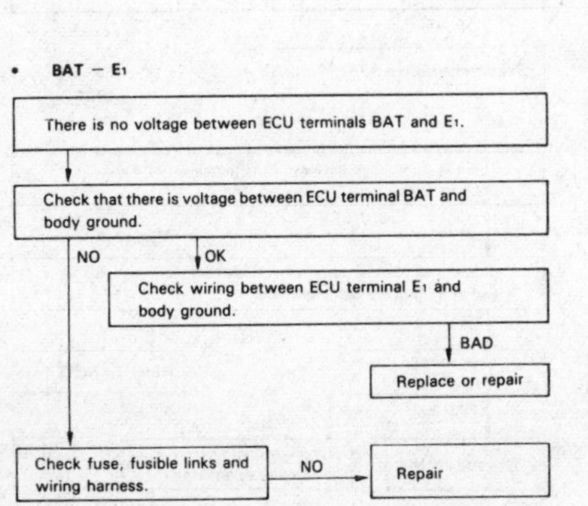
There is no voltage between ECU terminals BAT and E1.
Check that there is voltage between ECU terminal BAT and body ground.
NO
OK
Check wiring between ECU terminal E1 and body ground.
BAD
Replace or repair
Check fuse, fusible links and wiring harness.
NO
Repair

+B (+B1) – $E_1$

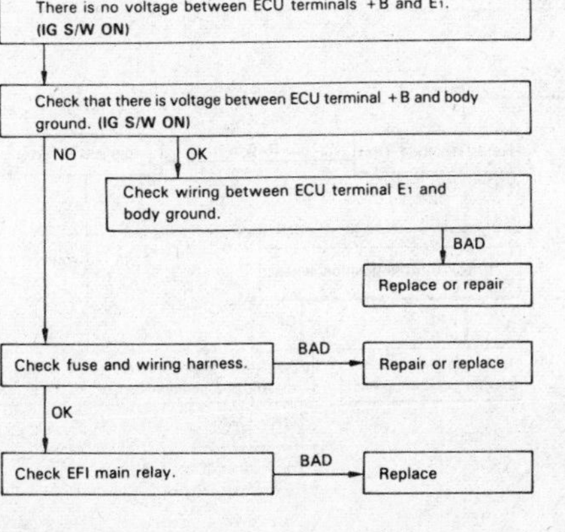
There is no voltage between ECU terminals +B and E1. (IG S/W ON)
Check that there is voltage between ECU terminal +B and body ground. (IG S/W ON)
NO
OK
Check wiring between ECU terminal E1 and body ground.
BAD
Replace or repair
Check fuse and wiring harness.
BAD
Repair or replace
OK
Check EFI main relay.
BAD
Replace

• IG S/W – $E_1$

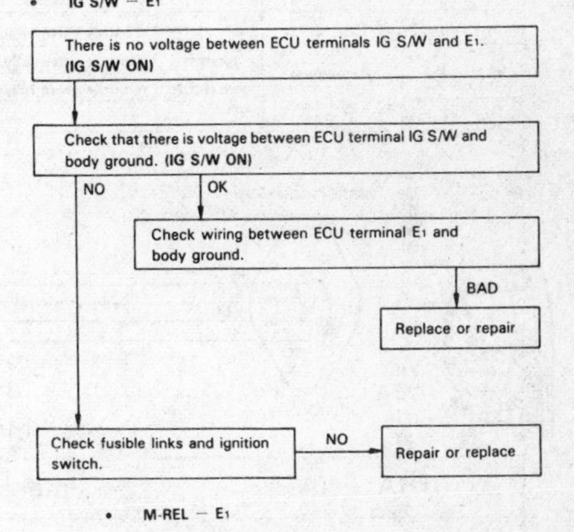
There is no voltage between ECU terminals IG S/W and E1. (IG S/W ON)
Check that there is voltage between ECU terminal IG S/W and body ground. (IG S/W ON)
NO
OK
Check wiring between ECU terminal E1 and body ground.
BAD
Replace or repair
Check fusible links and ignition switch.
NO
Repair or replace

• M-REL – $E_1$

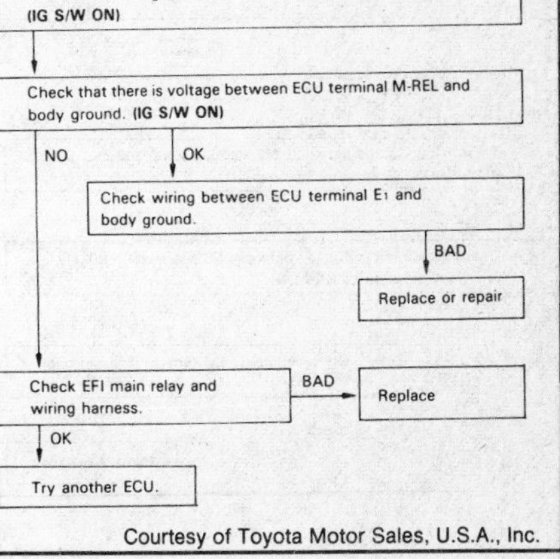
There is no voltage between ECU terminals M-REL and E1. (IG S/W ON)
Check that there is voltage between ECU terminal M-REL and body ground. (IG S/W ON)
NO
OK
Check wiring between ECU terminal E1 and body ground.
BAD
Replace or repair
Check EFI main relay and wiring harness.
BAD
Replace
OK
Try another ECU.

Courtesy of Toyota Motor Sales, U.S.A., Inc.

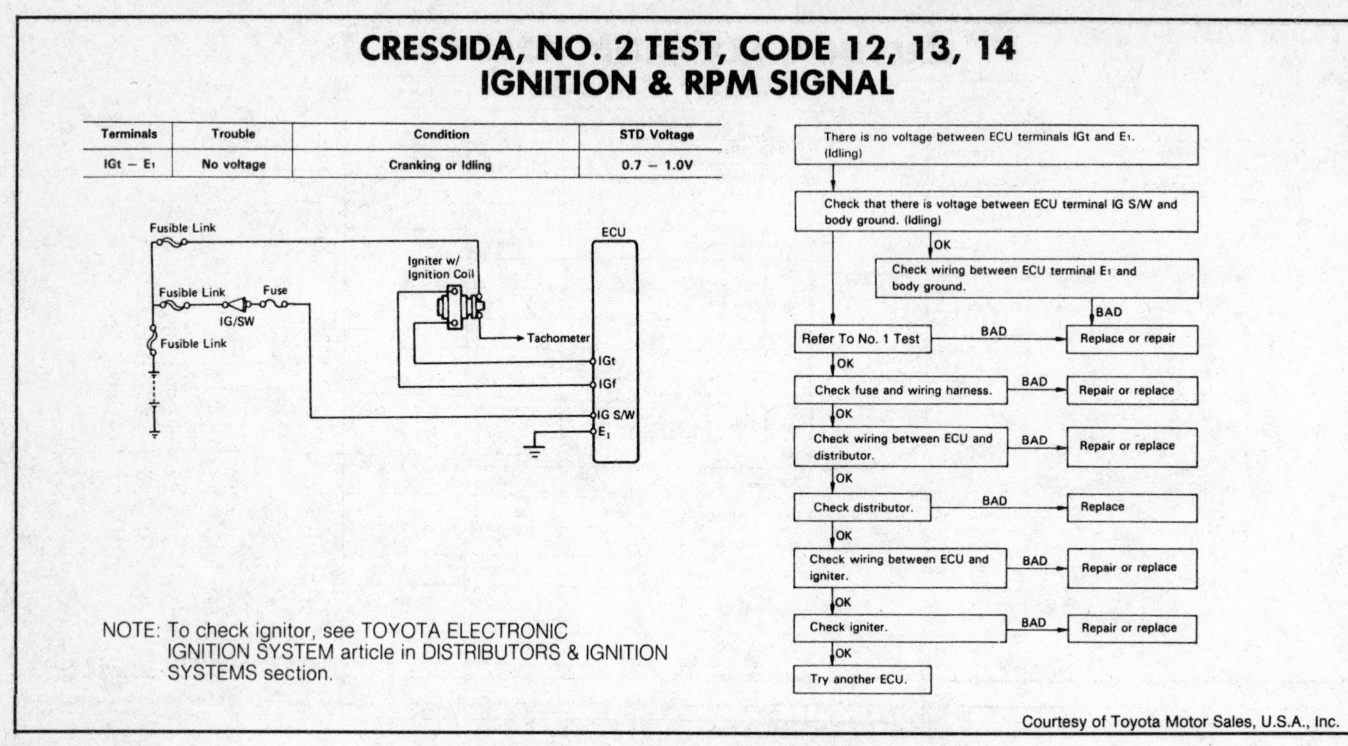

## CRESSIDA, NO. 2 TEST, CODE 12, 13, 14
## IGNITION & RPM SIGNAL

| Terminals | Trouble | Condition | STD Voltage |
|---|---|---|---|
| IGt – E1 | No voltage | Cranking or Idling | 0.7 – 1.0V |


Fusible Link
Fusible Link
Fuse
IG/SW
Fusible Link
Igniter w/ Ignition Coil
Tachometer
ECU
IGt
IGf
IG S/W
E1
There is no voltage between ECU terminals IGt and E1. (Idling)
Check that there is voltage between ECU terminal IG S/W and body ground. (Idling)
OK
Check wiring between ECU terminal E1 and body ground.
BAD
Refer To No. 1 Test
BAD
Replace or repair
OK
Check fuse and wiring harness.
BAD
Repair or replace
OK
Check wiring between ECU and distributor.
BAD
Repair or replace
OK
Check distributor.
BAD
Replace
OK
Check wiring between ECU and igniter.
BAD
Repair or replace
OK
Check igniter.
BAD
Repair or replace
OK
Try another ECU.


NOTE: To check ignitor, see TOYOTA ELECTRONIC IGNITION SYSTEM article in DISTRIBUTORS & IGNITION SYSTEMS section.

Courtesy of Toyota Motor Sales, U.S.A., Inc.

## CRESSIDA, NO. 3 TEST, CODE 23
## THROTTLE POSITION SENSOR SIGNAL

| Terminals | Trouble | Condition | | STD voltage |
|---|---|---|---|---|
| IDL – $E_{22}$ | No voltage | Ignition switch ON | Throttle valve open | 4 – 6 V |
| VTA – $E_{22}$ | | | Throttle valve fully closed | 0.1 – 1.0 V |
| | | | Throttle valve fully open | 4 – 5 V |
| Vc – $E_{22}$ | | | – | 4 – 6 V |

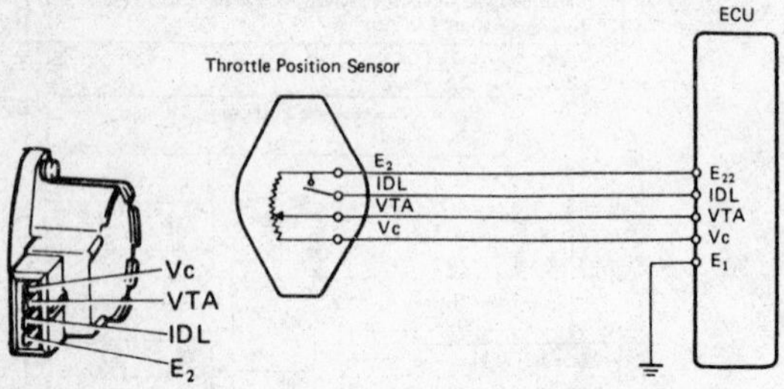

Throttle Position Sensor

ECU

E2, IDL, VTA, Vc

$E_{22}$, IDL, VTA, Vc, $E_1$

Vc, VTA, IDL, $E_2$

- VTA – $E_{22}$

There is no specified voltage at ECU terminals VTA and $E_{22}$. (IG S/W ON)

Check that there is voltage between ECU terminal +B and body ground. (IG S/W ON)

NO → Refer To No. 1 Test

OK → Check wiring between ECU terminal $E_{22}$ and body ground. BAD → Replace or repair

Refer To No. 1 Test — BAD → Repair or replace

OK → Check throttle position sensor. — BAD → Repair or replace

OK → Check wiring between ECU and throttle position sensor. — BAD → Repair or replace

OK → Try another ECU.

- IDL – $E_{22}$

There is no voltage between ECU terminals IDL and $E_{22}$. (IG S/W ON) (Throttle valve open)

Check that there is voltage between ECU terminal +B body and body ground. (IG S/W ON)

NO → Refer To No. 1 Test

OK → Check wiring between ECU terminal $E_{22}$ and body ground. BAD → Replace or repair

Refer To No. 1 Test — BAD → Replace or repair

OK → Check throttle position sensor.

BAD → Replace or repair throttle position sensor.

OK → Check wiring between ECU and throttle position sensor. BAD → Replace or repair

OK → Try another ECU.

- Vc – $E_{22}$

There is no voltage between ECU terminals Vc and $E_{22}$. (IG S/W ON)

Check that there is voltage between ECU terminal +B and body ground. (IG S/W ON)

NO → Refer To No. 1 Test

OK → Check throttle position sensor.

BAD → Repair or replace

OK → Check wiring between ECU and throttle position sensor.

OK → Try another ECU.

BAD → Repair or replace wiring.

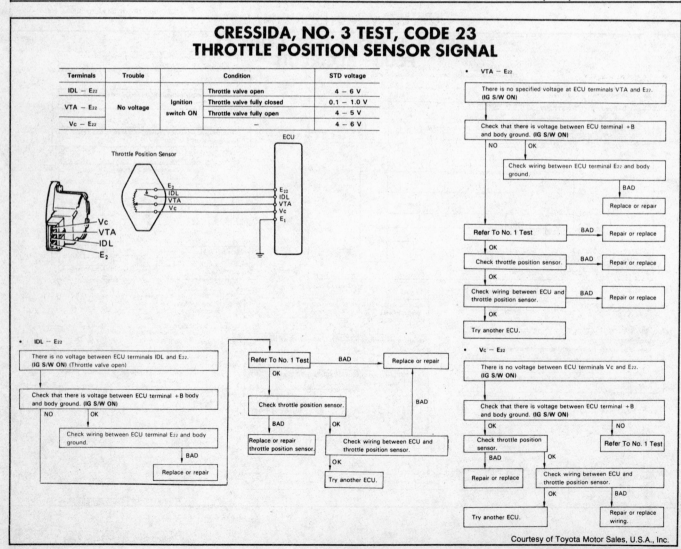

Courtesy of Toyota Motor Sales, U.S.A., Inc.

## CRESSIDA, NO. 4 TEST, CODE 43
## STARTER SIGNAL

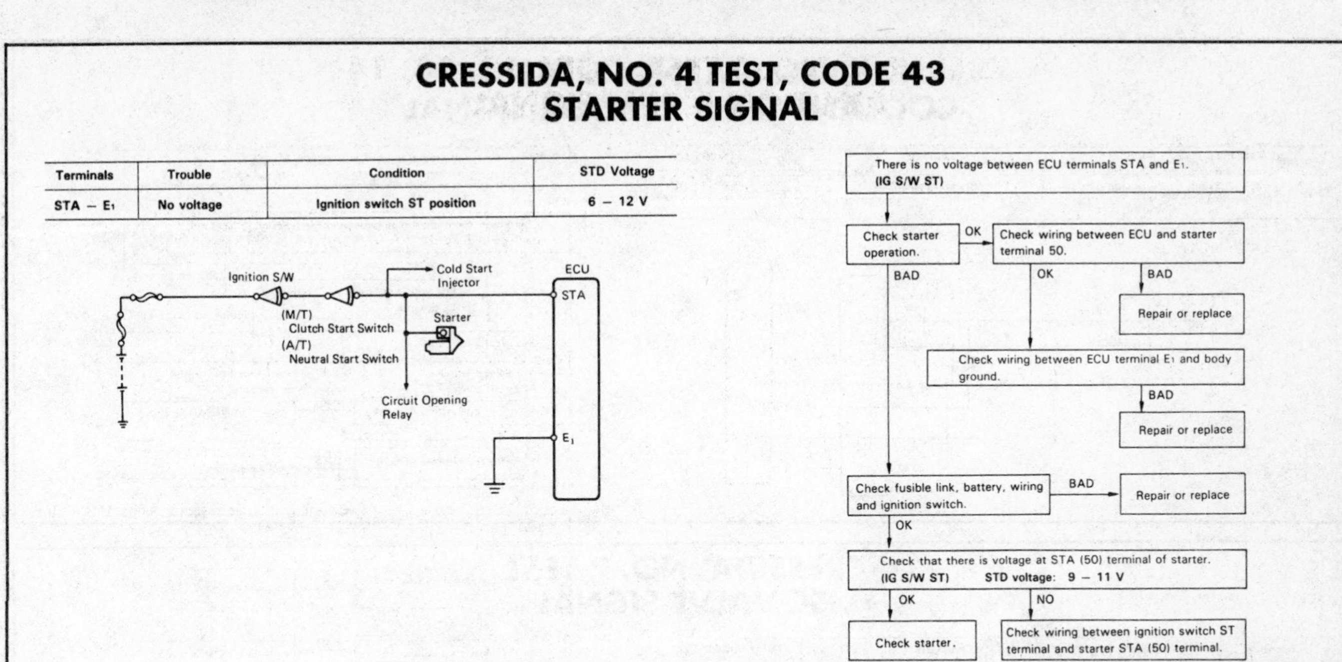

| Terminals | Trouble | Condition | STD Voltage |
|---|---|---|---|
| STA – $E_1$ | No voltage | Ignition switch ST position | 6 – 12 V |

Ignition S/W
Cold Start Injector
ECU
STA
(M/T) Clutch Start Switch
(A/T) Neutral Start Switch
Starter
Circuit Opening Relay
E1
There is no voltage between ECU terminals STA and E1. (IG S/W ST)
Check starter operation.
OK
Check wiring between ECU and starter terminal 50.
BAD
OK
BAD
Repair or replace
Check wiring between ECU terminal E1 and body ground.
BAD
Repair or replace
Check fusible link, battery, wiring and ignition switch.
BAD
Repair or replace
OK
Check that there is voltage at STA (50) terminal of starter. (IG S/W ST) STD voltage: 9 – 11 V
OK
NO
Check starter.
Check wiring between ignition switch ST terminal and starter STA (50) terminal.

Courtesy of Toyota Motor Sales, U.S.A., Inc.

## CRESSIDA, NO. 5 TEST
## AIRFLOW METER SIGNAL

| Terminal | Trouble | Condition | | STD Voltage |
|---|---|---|---|---|
| Vc – $E_2$ | No voltage | Ignition S/W ON | — | 4 – 6 V |
| Vs – $E_2$ | | | Measuring plate fully closed | 4 – 5 V |
| Vs – $E_2$ | | | Measuring plate fully open | 0.02 – 0.08 V |
| Vs – $E_2$ | | Idling | — | 2 – 4 V |
| Vs – $E_2$ | | 3,000 rpm | — | 0.3 – 1.0 V |
| THA – $E_2$ | | IG S/W ON | Intake air temperature 20°C (68°F) | 1 – 2 V |

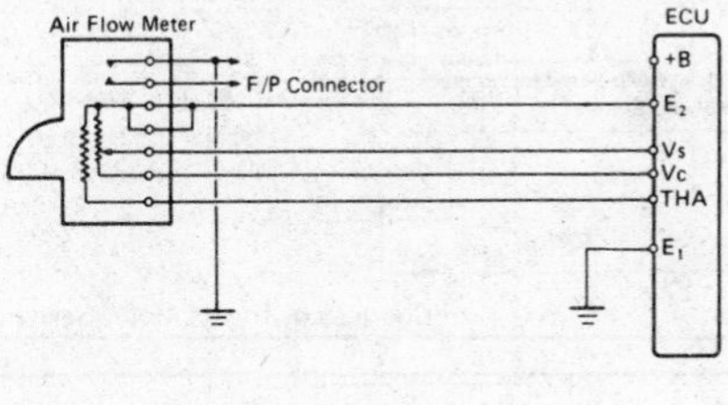

Air Flow Meter
F/P Connector
ECU
+B
$E_2$
Vs
Vc
THA
$E_1$

• Vc – $E_2$

- There is no voltage between ECU terminals Vc and $E_2$. (IG S/W ON)
- Check that there is voltage between ECU terminal +B and body ground. (IG S/W ON)
  - NO → Refer To No. 1 Test
  - OK → Check wiring between ECU terminal $E_2$ and body ground. BAD → Replace or repair
- Refer To No. 1 Test — BAD → Replace or repair
- OK → Check air flow meter. — BAD → Repair or replace
- OK → Check wiring between ECU and air flow meter. — BAD → Repair or replace
- OK → Try another ECU.

Ohmmeter
Air Flow Meter
$E_2$ Vs

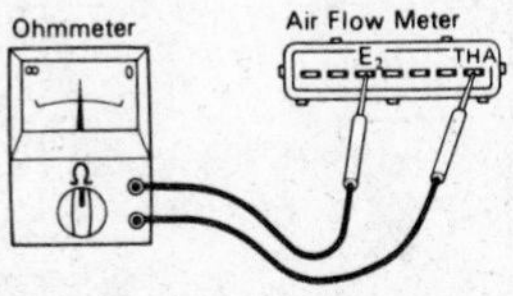

Ohmmeter
Air Flow Meter
$E_2$ THA

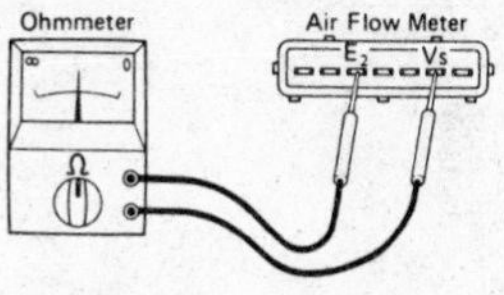

• Vs – $E_2$

- There is no specified voltage at ECU terminals Vs and $E_2$. (IG S/W ON)
- Check that there is voltage between ECU terminal +B and body ground. (IG S/W ON)
  - NO → Refer To No. 1 Test
  - OK → Check wiring between ECU terminal $E_2$ and body ground. BAD → Replace or repair
- Refer To No. 1 Test — BAD → Repair or replace
- OK → Check air flow meter. — BAD → Repair or replace
- OK → Check wiring between ECU and air flow meter. — BAD → Repair or replace
- OK → Try another ECU.

• THA – $E_2$

- There is no voltage between ECU terminals THA and $E_2$. (IG S/W ON)
- Check that there is voltage between ECU terminal +B and body ground. (IG S/W ON)
  - NO → Refer To No. 1 Test
  - OK → Check air temp. sensor.
    - BAD → Replace air temp. sensor.
    - OK → Check wiring between ECU and air temp. sensor.
      - BAD → Repair or replace wiring.
      - OK → Try another ECU.

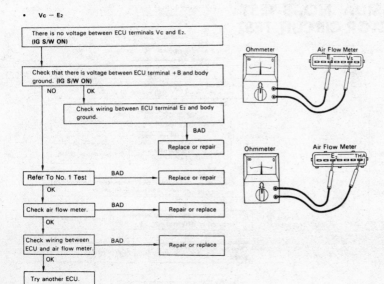

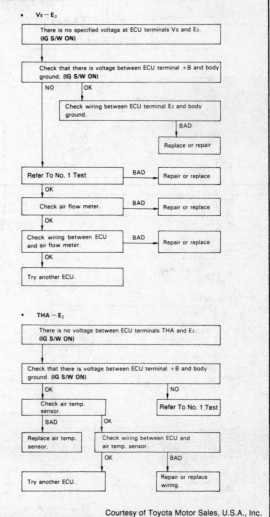

Courtesy of Toyota Motor Sales, U.S.A., Inc.

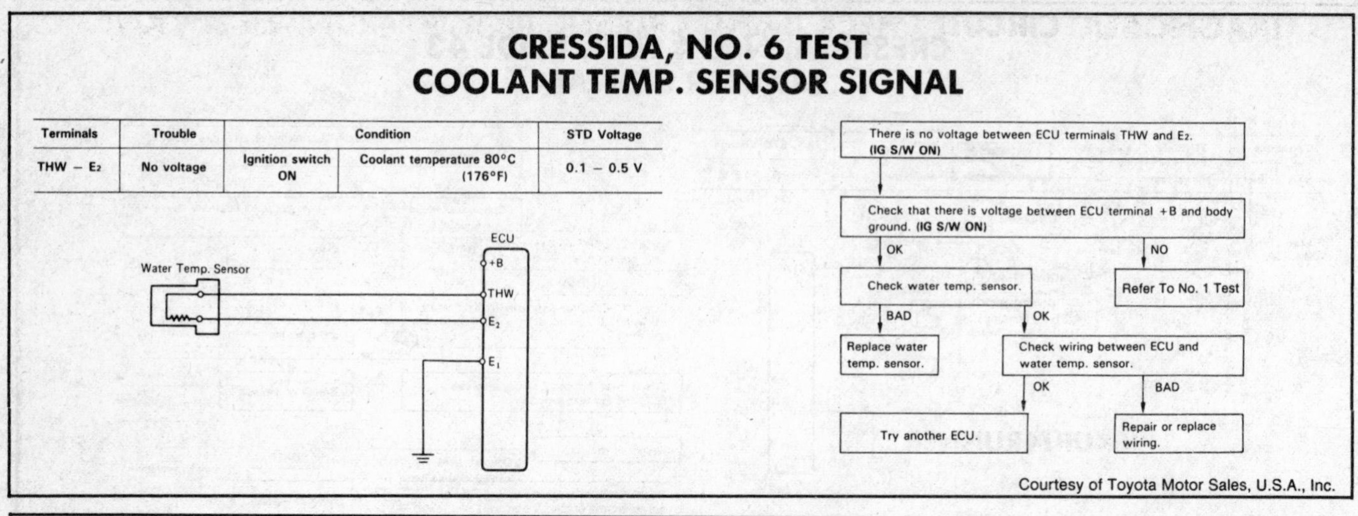

## CRESSIDA, NO. 6 TEST
## COOLANT TEMP. SENSOR SIGNAL

| Terminals | Trouble | Condition | | STD Voltage |
|---|---|---|---|---|
| THW – $E_2$ | No voltage | Ignition switch ON | Coolant temperature 80°C (176°F) | 0.1 – 0.5 V |


ECU
Water Temp. Sensor
+B
THW
E2
E1
There is no voltage between ECU terminals THW and E2. (IG S/W ON)
Check that there is voltage between ECU terminal +B and body ground. (IG S/W ON)
OK
NO
Check water temp. sensor.
Refer To No. 1 Test
BAD
OK
Replace water temp. sensor.
Check wiring between ECU and water temp. sensor.
OK
BAD
Try another ECU.
Repair or replace wiring.


Courtesy of Toyota Motor Sales, U.S.A., Inc.

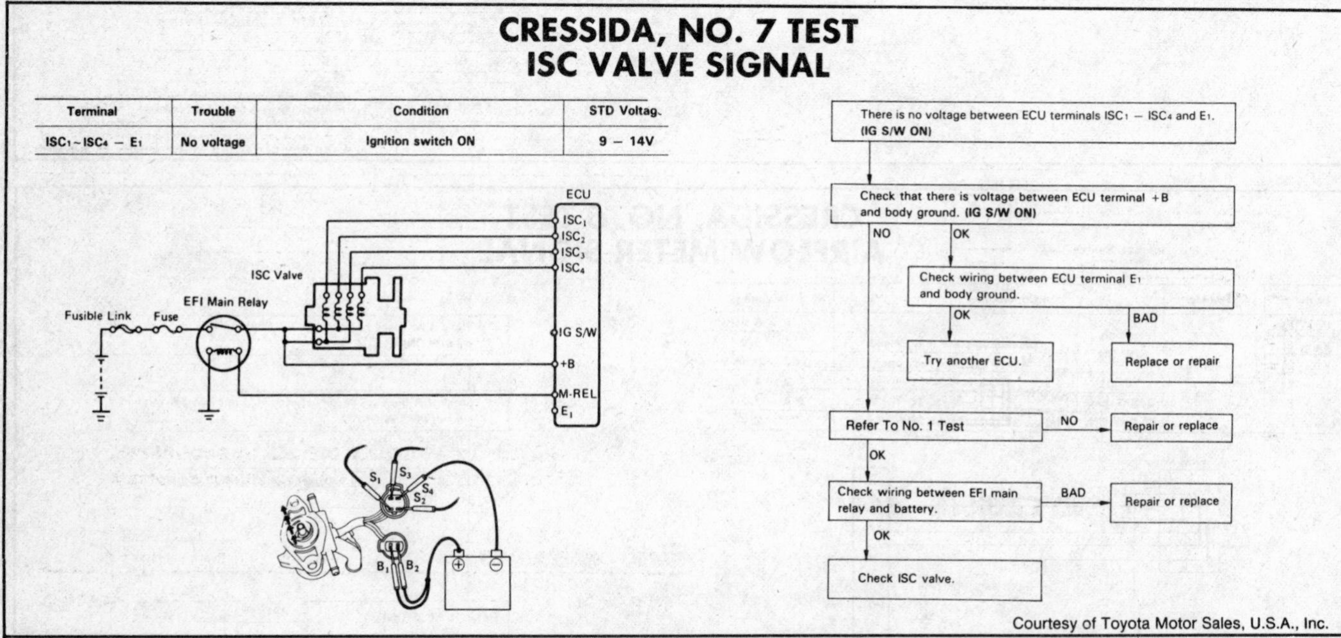

## CRESSIDA, NO. 7 TEST
## ISC VALVE SIGNAL

| Terminal | Trouble | Condition | STD Voltag. |
|---|---|---|---|
| $ISC_1$ ~ $ISC_4$ – $E_1$ | No voltage | Ignition switch ON | 9 – 14V |


ECU
ISC1
ISC2
ISC3
ISC4
ISC Valve
EFI Main Relay
Fusible Link
Fuse
IG S/W
+B
M-REL
E1
S1
S3
S4
S2
B1
B2
There is no voltage between ECU terminals ISC1 – ISC4 and E1. (IG S/W ON)
Check that there is voltage between ECU terminal +B and body ground. (IG S/W ON)
NO
OK
Check wiring between ECU terminal E1 and body ground.
OK
BAD
Try another ECU.
Replace or repair
Refer To No. 1 Test
NO
Repair or replace
OK
Check wiring between EFI main relay and battery.
BAD
Repair or replace
OK
Check ISC valve.


Courtesy of Toyota Motor Sales, U.S.A., Inc.

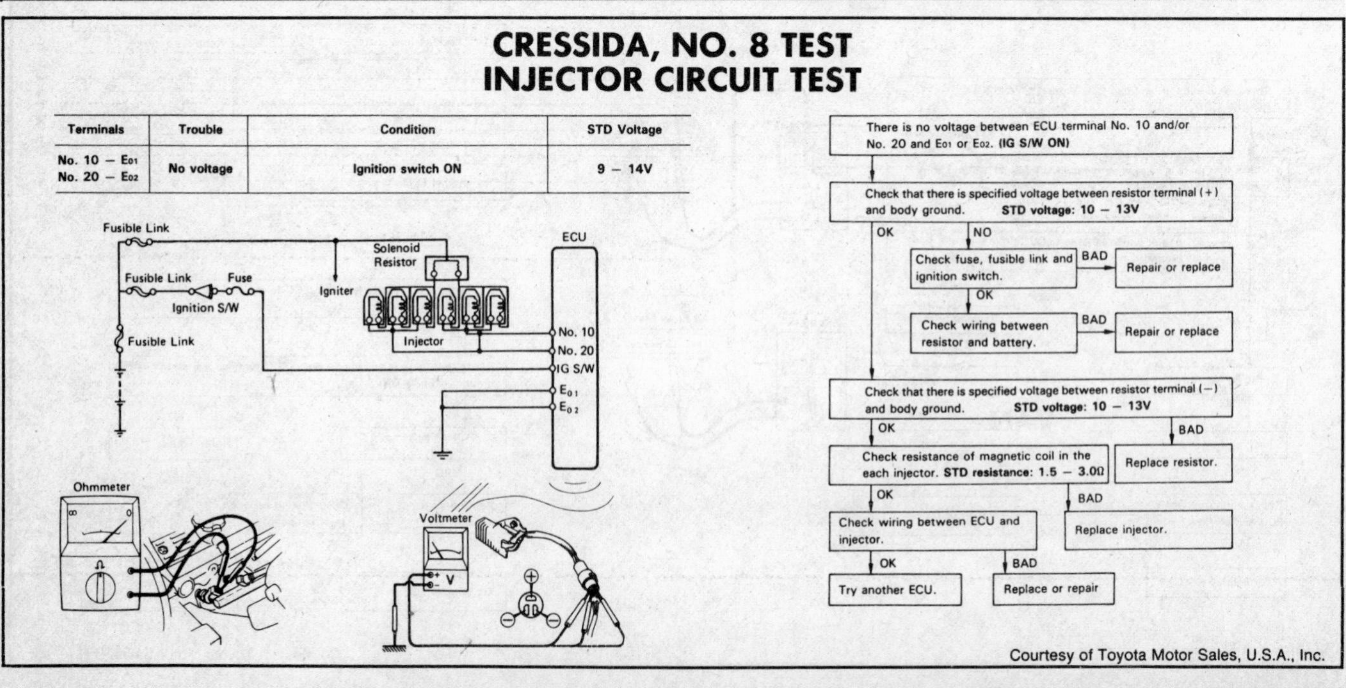

## CRESSIDA, NO. 8 TEST
## INJECTOR CIRCUIT TEST

| Terminals | Trouble | Condition | STD Voltage |
|---|---|---|---|
| No. 10 – $E_{01}$<br>No. 20 – $E_{02}$ | No voltage | Ignition switch ON | 9 – 14V |


Fusible Link
Fusible Link
Fuse
Ignition S/W
Fusible Link
Solenoid Resistor
Igniter
Injector
ECU
No. 10
No. 20
IG S/W
E01
E02
Ohmmeter
Voltmeter
There is no voltage between ECU terminal No. 10 and/or No. 20 and E01 or E02. (IG S/W ON)
Check that there is specified voltage between resistor terminal (+) and body ground. STD voltage: 10 – 13V
OK
NO
Check fuse, fusible link and ignition switch.
BAD
Repair or replace
OK
Check wiring between resistor and battery.
BAD
Repair or replace
Check that there is specified voltage between resistor terminal (–) and body ground. STD voltage: 10 – 13V
OK
BAD
Check resistance of magnetic coil in the each injector. STD resistance: 1.5 – 3.0Ω
Replace resistor.
OK
BAD
Check wiring between ECU and injector.
Replace injector.
OK
BAD
Try another ECU.
Replace or repair


Courtesy of Toyota Motor Sales, U.S.A., Inc.

## DIAGNOSTIC CIRCUIT CHECK (LAND CRUISER, PICKUP/4RUNNER & VAN)

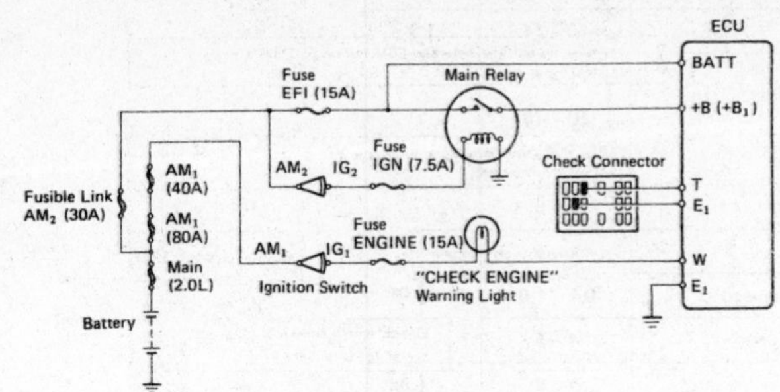
ECU
BATT
+B (+B1)
T
E1
W
E1
Fuse
EFI (15A)
Main Relay
Fuse
IGN (7.5A)
AM2
IG2
Check Connector
Fusible Link
AM2 (30A)
AM1
(40A)
AM1
(80A)
Main
(2.0L)
AM1
IG1
Fuse
ENGINE (15A)
Ignition Switch
"CHECK ENGINE"
Warning Light
Battery

### PICKUP/4RUNNER

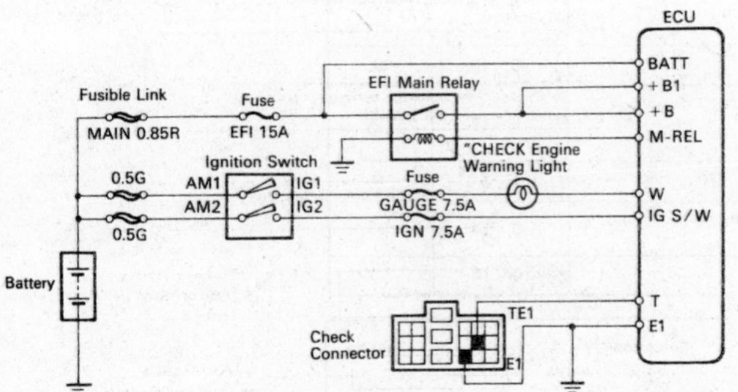
ECU
BATT
+B1
+B
M-REL
W
IG S/W
T
E1
Fusible Link
MAIN 0.85R
Fuse
EFI 15A
EFI Main Relay
"CHECK Engine
Warning Light
Ignition Switch
0.5G
AM1
AM2
IG1
IG2
0.5G
Fuse
GAUGE 7.5A
IGN 7.5A
Battery
TE1
Check
Connector
E1

### LAND CRUISER

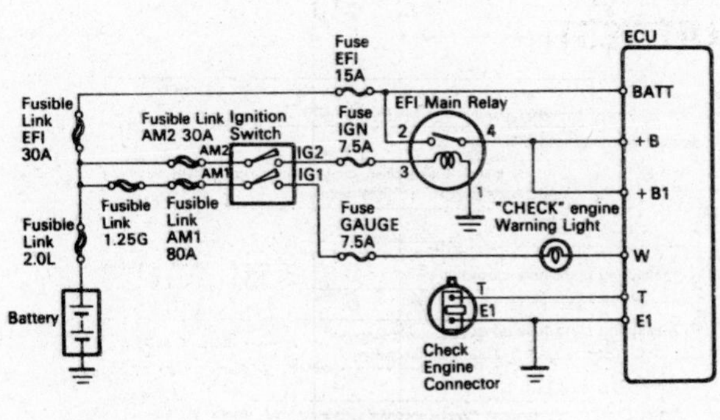
Fuse
EFI
15A
ECU
BATT
Fusible
Link
EFI
30A
Fusible Link
AM2 30A
Ignition
Switch
AM2
AM1
IG2
IG1
Fuse
IGN
7.5A
EFI Main Relay
+B
+B1
Fusible
Link
1.25G
Fusible
Link
AM1
80A
Fusible
Link
2.0L
Fuse
GAUGE
7.5A
"CHECK" engine
Warning Light
W
T
E1
Battery
Check
Engine
Connector

### VAN

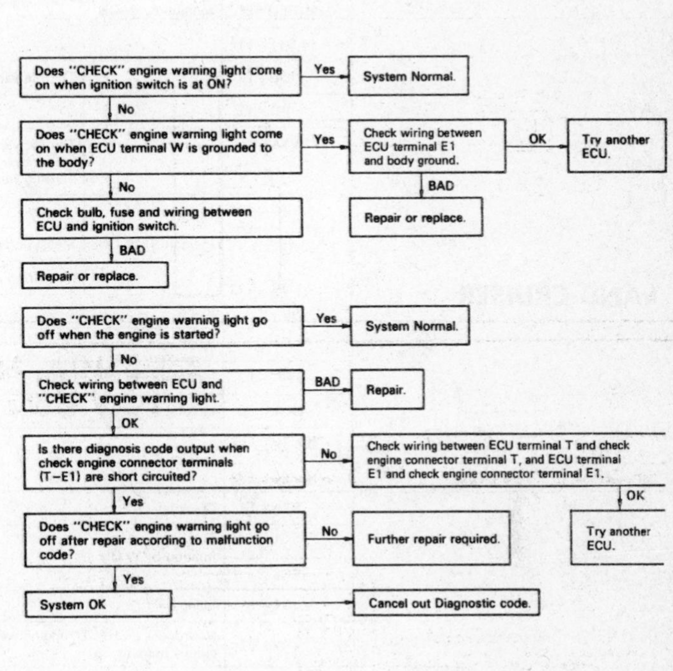
Does "CHECK" engine warning light come on when ignition switch is at ON?
Yes
System Normal.
No
Does "CHECK" engine warning light come on when ECU terminal W is grounded to the body?
Yes
Check wiring between ECU terminal E1 and body ground.
OK
Try another ECU.
BAD
Repair or replace.
No
Check bulb, fuse and wiring between ECU and ignition switch.
BAD
Repair or replace.
Does "CHECK" engine warning light go off when the engine is started?
Yes
System Normal.
No
Check wiring between ECU and "CHECK" engine warning light.
BAD
Repair.
OK
Is there diagnosis code output when check engine connector terminals (T−E1) are short circuited?
No
Check wiring between ECU terminal T and check engine connector terminal T, and ECU terminal E1 and check engine connector terminal E1.
OK
Try another ECU.
Yes
Does "CHECK" engine warning light go off after repair according to malfunction code?
No
Further repair required.
Yes
System OK
Cancel out Diagnostic code.

**NOTE: Turbo codes are not in sequence. See TURBO CODE LOCATION table below.**

***TURBO CODE LOCATION***

| Turbo Code | Test No. |
|---|---|
| 2 | 6 |
| 3 | 2 |
| 4 | 4 |
| 5 | 3 |
| 6 | 2 |
| 7 | 8 |
| 8 | 5 |
| 10 | 9 |
| 11, 12, 13 & 14 | [1] |

[1] – Information not available from manufacturer.

Courtesy of Toyota Motor Sales, U.S.A., Inc.

## ECU PIN VOLTAGE TEST (LAND CRUISER, VAN)

**LAND CRUISER**

| Terminals | Condition | | STD Voltage | Test No. |
|---|---|---|---|---|
| BATT – E1 | — | | 10 – 14 | 12 |
| IG S/W – E1 | Ignition S/W ON | | 10 – 14 | 1 |
| M-REL – E1 | | | | |
| +B (+B1) – E1 | | | | |
| IDL – E2 | Ignition S/W ON | Throttle valve open | 4 – 6 | 8 |
| VC – E2 | | — | 4 – 6 | |
| VTA – E2 | | Throttle valve fully closed | 0.1 – 1.0 | |
| | | Throttle valve fully open | 4 – 5 | |
| VC – E22 | Ignition S/W ON | — | 4 – 6 | 6 |
| VS – E22 | | Measuring plate fully closed | 4 – 5 | |
| | | Measuring plate fully open | 0.02 – 0.08 | |
| | Idling | | 2 – 4 | |
| | 3,000 rpm | | 0.3 – 1.0 | |
| THA – E2 | Ignition S/W ON | Intake air temperature 20°C (68°F) | 1 – 3 | 5 |
| THW – E2 | Ignition S/W ON | Coolant temperature 80°C (176°F) | 0.1 – 1.0 | 4 |
| No. 10 E01 – No. 20 E02 | Ignition S/W ON | | 9 – 14 | 15 |
| STA – E1 | Cranking | | 6 – 14 | 9 |
| ISC1 ~ ISC4 – E1 | Ignition S/W ON | | 9 – 14 | 16 |
| IGT – E1 | Idling | | 0.7 – 1.0 | 2 |
| W – E1 | No trouble ("CHECK" engine warning light off) and engine running | | 8 – 14 | 11 |
| A/C – E1 | Air conditioning ON | | 10 – 14 | 17 |

**VAN**

| Terminals | STD voltage | Condition | | Test No. |
|---|---|---|---|---|
| +B +B1 – E1 | 10 – 14 | Ignition switch ON | | 1 |
| BATT – E1 | 10 – 14 | — | | 12 |
| IDL – E1 | 8 – 14 | Ignition switch ON | Throttle valve open | 8 |
| PSW – E1 | 8 – 14 | | Throttle valve fully closed | |
| IGT – E1 | 0.7 – 1.0 | Idling | | 2 |
| STA – E1 | 6 – 12 | Cranking | | 9 |
| No. 10 – E01 No. 20 – E02 | 9 – 14 | Ignition switch ON | | 15 |
| W – E1 | 8 – 14 | No trouble ("CHECK" engine warning light off) and engine running | | 11 |
| VC – E2 | 6 – 10 | Ignition switch ON | — | 6 |
| VS – E2 | 0.5 – 2.5 | | Measuring plate fully closed | |
| | 5 – 10 | | Measuring plate fully open | |
| | 2 – 8 | — | | |
| THA – E2 | 1 – 3 | Ignition switch ON | Intake air temperature 20°C (68°F) | 5 |
| THW – E2 | 0.1 – 1.0 | Ignition switch ON | Coolant temperature 80°C (176°F) | 4 |
| A/C – E1 | 8 – 14 | Ignition switch ON | A/C ON | 17 |

Courtesy of Toyota Motor Sales, U.S.A., Inc.

## ECU PIN VOLTAGE TEST (PICKUP/4RUNNER)

### 4-CYLINDER

| Terminals | Condition | | STD Voltage | Test No. |
|---|---|---|---|---|
| +B − $E_1$ | Ignition switch ON | | 10 – 14 | 1 |
| BATT − $E_1$ | – | | 10 – 14 | 12 |
| IDL − $E_2$ | Ignition switch ON | Throttle valve open | 8 – 14 | 8 |
| Vcc − $E_2$ | | – | 4 – 6 | |
| VTA − $E_2$ | | Throttle valve fully closed | 0.1 – 1.0 | |
| | | Throttle valve fully open | 4 – 5 | |
| IGt − $E_1$ | Idling | | 0.7 – 1.0 | 2 |
| STA − $E_1$ | Ignition switch ST position | | 6 – 12 | 9 |
| No. 10 − $E_{01}$<br>No. 20 − $E_{02}$ | Ignition switch ON | | 9 – 14 | 15 |
| W − $E_1$ | No trouble (CHECK ENGINE light off) and engine running | | 8 – 14 | 11 |
| Vc − $E_2$ | Ignition switch ON | – | 6 – 10 | 6 |
| Vs − $E_2$ | | Measuring plate fully closed | 0.5 – 2.5 | |
| | | Measuring plate fully open | 5 – 10 | |
| | Idling | | 2 – 8 | |
| THA − $E_2$ | Ignition switch ON | Intake air temperature 20°C (68°F) | 1 – 3 | 5 |
| THW − $E_2$ | Ignition switch ON | Coolant temperature 80°C (176°F) | 0.1 – 1.0 | 4 |
| B/K − $E_1$ | Stop light switch ON | | 8 – 14 | 13 |
| *1 HAC − $E_2$ | Ignition switch ON | 760 mmHg (29.92 in.Hg, 101.3 kPa) | Approx. 3.6 | 7 |
| *2 STJ − $E_1$ | Ignition switch ST position | Coolant temperature 80°C (176°F) | 6 – 12 | 14 |

*1 C & C only
*2 22R-E only

### V-6

| Terminals | Condition | | STD voltage | Test No. |
|---|---|---|---|---|
| BATT − $E_1$ | – | | 10 – 14 | 12 |
| +B − $E_1$ | Ignition S/W ON | | | 1 |
| +$B_1$ − $E_1$ | | | | |
| IDL − $E_2$ | Ignition S/W ON | Throttle valve open | 8 – 14 | 8 |
| Vc − $E_2$ | | – | 4 – 6 | |
| VTA − $E_2$ | | Throttle valve fully closed | 0.1 – 1.0 | |
| | | Throttle valve fully opened | 4 – 5 | |
| Vc − $E_2$ | Ignition S/W ON | – | 4 – 6 | 6 |
| Vs − $E_2$ | | Measuring plate fully closed | 4 – 5 | |
| | | Measuring plate fully open | 0.02 – 0.08 | |
| | Idling | | 2 – 4 | |
| | 3,000 rpm | | 0.3 – 1.0 | |
| THA − $E_2$ | IG S/W ON | Intake air temperature 20°C (68°F) | 1 – 3 | 5 |
| THW − $E_2$ | IG S/W ON | Coolant temperature 80°C (176°F) | 0.1 – 1.0 | 4 |
| STA − $E_1$ | Ignition S/W ST position | | 6 – 12 | 9 |
| No. 10<br>No. 20 − $E_1$ | Ignition S/W ON | | 9 – 14 | 15 |
| IGt − $E_1$ | Cranking or idling | | 0.7 – 1.0 | 2 |
| W − $E_1$ | No trouble (CHECK ENGINE light off) and engine running | | 8 – 14 | 11 |
| STJ − $E_1$ | Ignition S/W ST position | Coolant temperature 80°C (176°F) | 6 – 12 | 14 |
| STP − $E_1$ | Stop light switch ON | | 8 – 14 | 13 |

Courtesy of Toyota Motor Sales, U.S.A., Inc.

# LAND CRUISER, PICKUP/4RUNNER, VAN
## NO. 1 TEST, CODE 11
## ECU (+B) CIRCUIT

| Terminals | Trouble | Condition | STD Voltage |
|---|---|---|---|
| +B – $E_1$ | No voltage | IG S/W ON | 10 – 14 V |

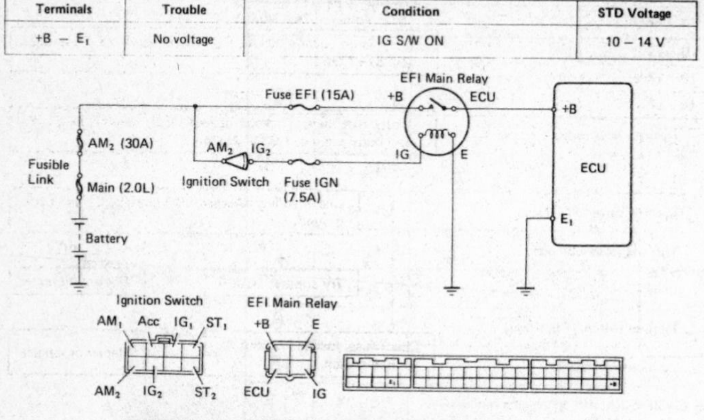
Fuse EFI (15A)
EFI Main Relay
+B
ECU
IG
E
+B
ECU
$E_1$
$AM_2$ (30A)
Fusible Link
Main (2.0L)
Battery
$AM_2$
$IG_2$
Ignition Switch
Fuse IGN (7.5A)
Ignition Switch
$AM_1$ Acc $IG_1$ $ST_1$
$AM_2$ $IG_2$ $ST_2$
EFI Main Relay
+B E
ECU IG

**PICKUP/4RUNNER (4-CYL.)**

| Terminals | Trouble | Condition | STD Voltage |
|---|---|---|---|
| +B<br>+B1 – E1 | No voltage | Ignition S/W ON | 10 – 14 V |

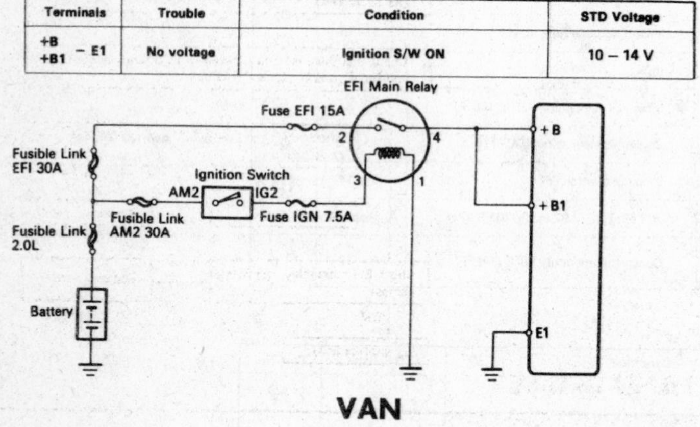
EFI Main Relay
Fuse EFI 15A
2
4
3
1
+B
+B1
E1
Fusible Link EFI 30A
Ignition Switch
AM2
IG2
Fusible Link AM2 30A
Fuse IGN 7.5A
Fusible Link 2.0L
Battery

**VAN**

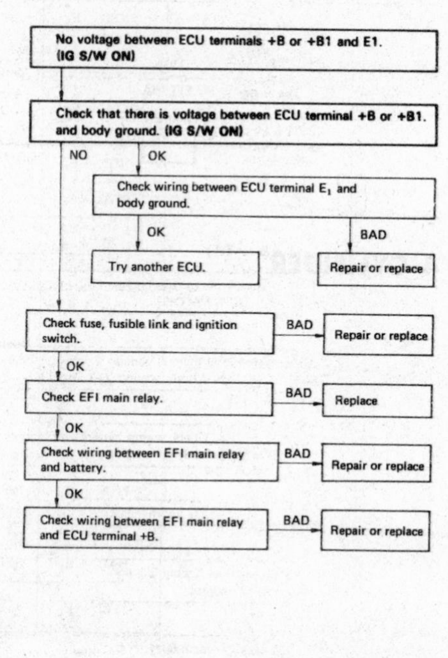
No voltage between ECU terminals +B or +B1 and E1. (IG S/W ON)
Check that there is voltage between ECU terminal +B or +B1. and body ground. (IG S/W ON)
NO
OK
Check wiring between ECU terminal $E_1$ and body ground.
OK
BAD
Try another ECU.
Repair or replace
Check fuse, fusible link and ignition switch.
BAD
Repair or replace
OK
Check EFI main relay.
BAD
Replace
OK
Check wiring between EFI main relay and battery.
BAD
Repair or replace
OK
Check wiring between EFI main relay and ECU terminal +B.
BAD
Repair or replace

| Terminals | Trouble | Condition | STD Voltage |
|---|---|---|---|
| BATT – $E_1$ | No voltage | Ignition switch ON | 10 – 14 V |
| +B – $E_1$ | | | |
| $+B_1$ – $E_1$ | | | |

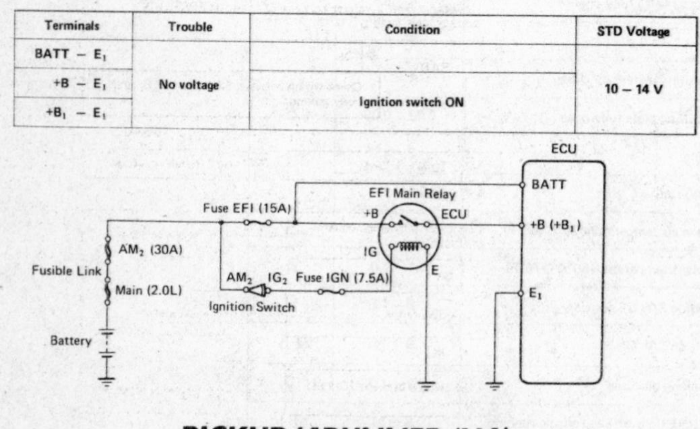
ECU
BATT
Fuse EFI (15A)
EFI Main Relay
+B
ECU
+B ($+B_1$)
IG
E
$E_1$
$AM_2$ (30A)
Fusible Link
Main (2.0L)
$AM_2$ $IG_2$ Fuse IGN (7.5A)
Ignition Switch
Battery

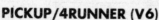

**PICKUP/4RUNNER (V6)**

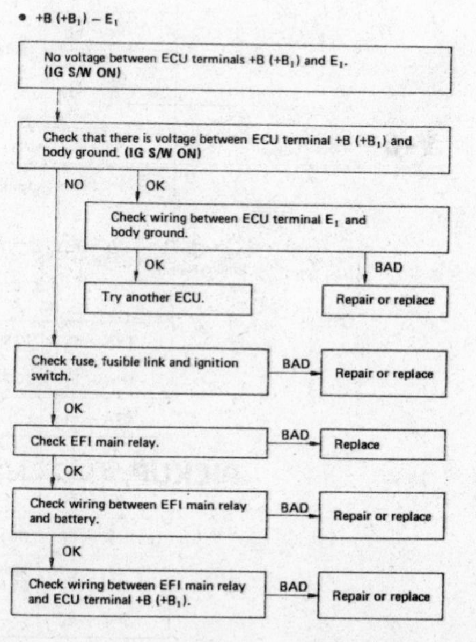
• +B ($+B_1$) – $E_1$
No voltage between ECU terminals +B ($+B_1$) and $E_1$. (IG S/W ON)
Check that there is voltage between ECU terminal +B ($+B_1$) and body ground. (IG S/W ON)
NO
OK
Check wiring between ECU terminal $E_1$ and body ground.
OK
BAD
Try another ECU.
Repair or replace
Check fuse, fusible link and ignition switch.
BAD
Repair or replace
OK
Check EFI main relay.
BAD
Replace
OK
Check wiring between EFI main relay and battery.
BAD
Repair or replace
OK
Check wiring between EFI main relay and ECU terminal +B ($+B_1$).
BAD
Repair or replace

Courtesy of Toyota Motor Sales, U.S.A., Inc.

## LAND CRUISER, PICKUP/4RUNNER, VAN
## NO. 1 TEST, CODE 11 (Cont.)
## ECU (+B) CIRCUIT

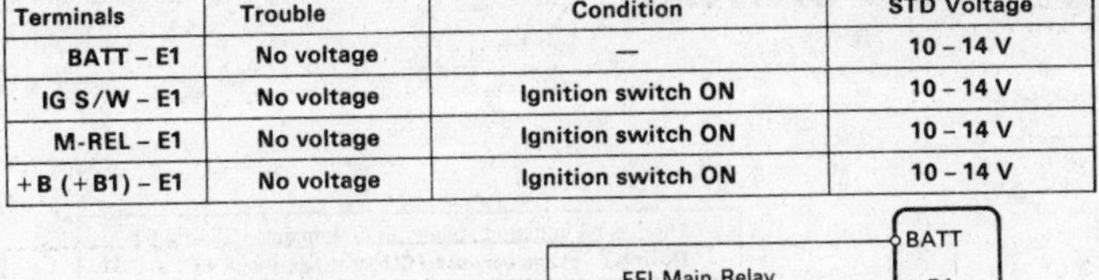

| Terminals | Trouble | Condition | STD Voltage |
|---|---|---|---|
| BATT – E1 | No voltage | — | 10 – 14 V |
| IG S/W – E1 | No voltage | Ignition switch ON | 10 – 14 V |
| M-REL – E1 | No voltage | Ignition switch ON | 10 – 14 V |
| +B (+B1) – E1 | No voltage | Ignition switch ON | 10 – 14 V |

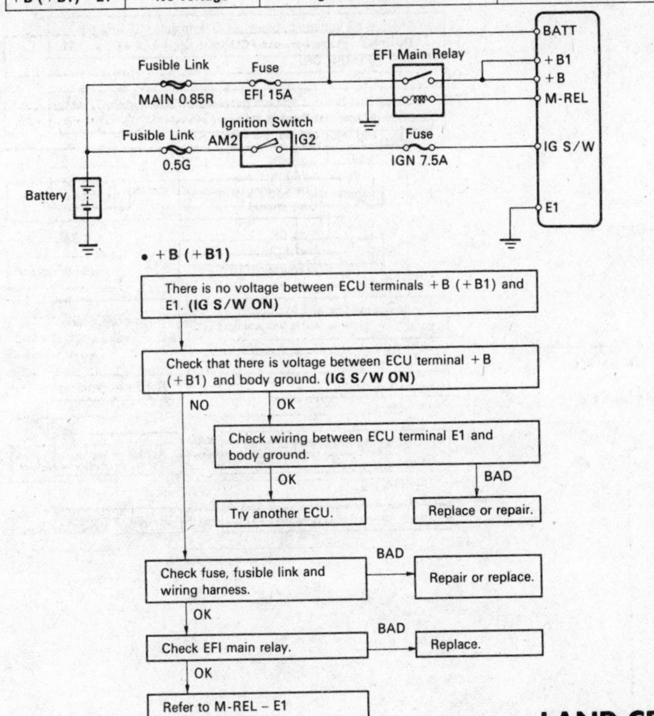
BATT
+B1
+B
M-REL
IG S/W
E1
Fusible Link
MAIN 0.85R
Fuse
EFI 15A
EFI Main Relay
Ignition Switch
AM2
IG2
Fusible Link
0.5G
Fuse
IGN 7.5A
Battery
• +B (+B1)
There is no voltage between ECU terminals +B (+B1) and E1. (IG S/W ON)
Check that there is voltage between ECU terminal +B (+B1) and body ground. (IG S/W ON)
NO
OK
Check wiring between ECU terminal E1 and body ground.
OK
BAD
Try another ECU.
Replace or repair.
Check fuse, fusible link and wiring harness.
BAD
Repair or replace.
OK
Check EFI main relay.
BAD
Replace.
OK
Refer to M-REL – E1

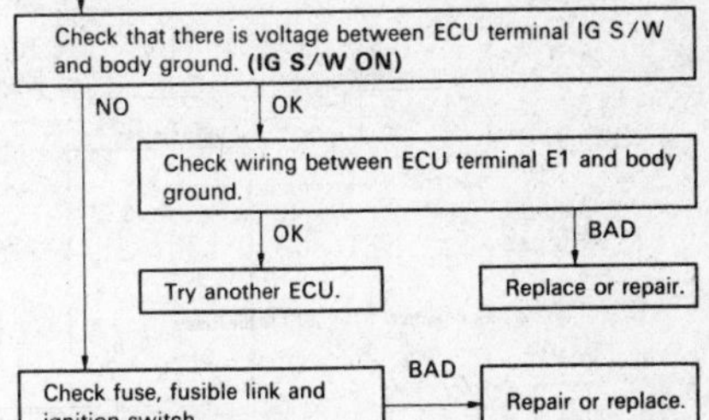
• IG S/W – E1
There is no voltage between ECU terminals IG S/W and E1. (IG S/W ON)
Check that there is voltage between ECU terminal IG S/W and body ground. (IG S/W ON)
NO
OK
Check wiring between ECU terminal E1 and body ground.
OK
BAD
Try another ECU.
Replace or repair.
Check fuse, fusible link and ignition switch.
BAD
Repair or replace.

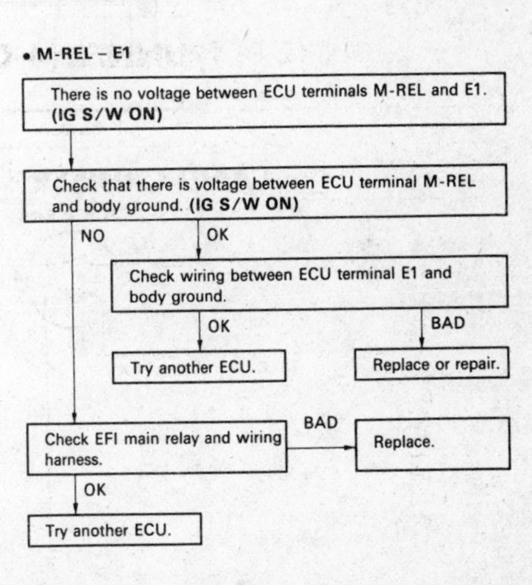
• M-REL – E1
There is no voltage between ECU terminals M-REL and E1. (IG S/W ON)
Check that there is voltage between ECU terminal M-REL and body ground. (IG S/W ON)
NO
OK
Check wiring between ECU terminal E1 and body ground.
OK
BAD
Try another ECU.
Replace or repair.
Check EFI main relay and wiring harness.
BAD
Replace.
OK
Try another ECU.

### LAND CRUISER

## NO. 2 TEST, CODE 12, 13, 14 (CODE 3, 6 ON TURBO)
## RPM & IGNITION SIGNAL

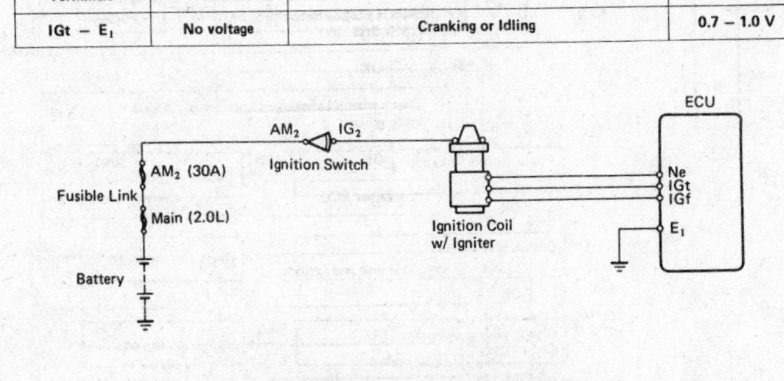

| Terminals | Trouble | Condition | STD Voltage |
|---|---|---|---|
| IGt – $E_1$ | No voltage | Cranking or Idling | 0.7 – 1.0 V |

ECU
$AM_2$
$IG_2$
Ignition Switch
$AM_2$ (30A)
Fusible Link
Main (2.0L)
Battery
Ignition Coil w/ Igniter
Ne
IGt
IGf
$E_1$

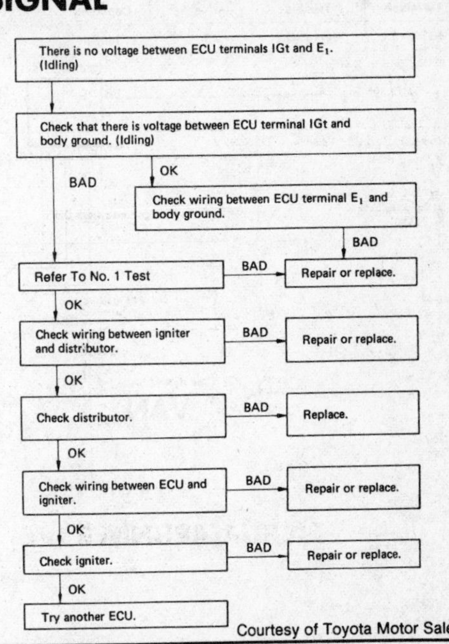
There is no voltage between ECU terminals IGt and $E_1$. (Idling)
Check that there is voltage between ECU terminal IGt and body ground. (Idling)
OK
BAD
Check wiring between ECU terminal $E_1$ and body ground.
BAD
Refer To No. 1 Test
BAD
Repair or replace.
OK
Check wiring between igniter and distributor.
BAD
Repair or replace.
OK
Check distributor.
BAD
Replace.
OK
Check wiring between ECU and igniter.
BAD
Repair or replace.
OK
Check igniter.
BAD
Repair or replace.
OK
Try another ECU.

### PICKUP/4RUNNER

Courtesy of Toyota Motor Sales, U.S.A., Inc.

## LAND CRUISER, PICKUP/4RUNNER, VAN
## NO. 2 TEST, CODE 12, 13, 14 (CODE 3, 6 ON TURBO) (Cont.)
## RPM & IGNITION SIGNAL

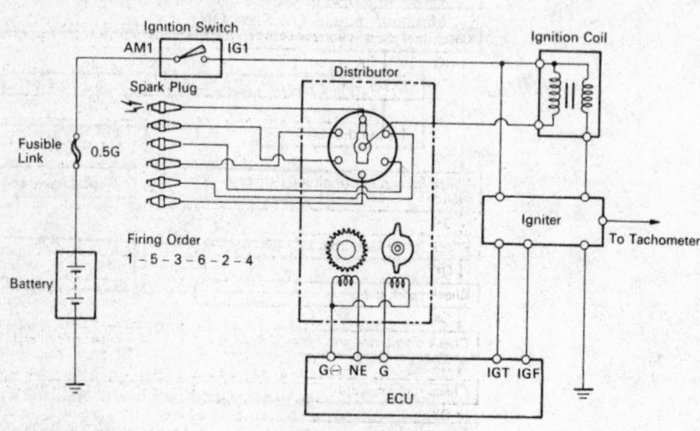
Ignition Switch
AM1
IG1
Ignition Coil
Distributor
Spark Plug
Fusible Link
0.5G
Igniter
To Tachometer
Firing Order
1 - 5 - 3 - 6 - 2 - 4
Battery
G⊖ NE G
IGT IGF
ECU

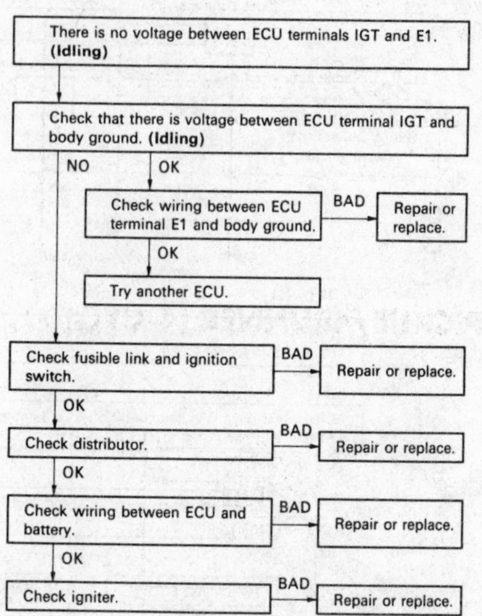
There is no voltage between ECU terminals IGT and E1. (Idling)
Check that there is voltage between ECU terminal IGT and body ground. (Idling)
NO
OK
Check wiring between ECU terminal E1 and body ground.
BAD
Repair or replace.
OK
Try another ECU.
Check fusible link and ignition switch.
BAD
Repair or replace.
OK
Check distributor.
BAD
Repair or replace.
OK
Check wiring between ECU and battery.
BAD
Repair or replace.
OK
Check igniter.
BAD
Repair or replace.

### LAND CRUISER

| No. | Terminals | Trouble | Condition | STD Voltage |
|---|---|---|---|---|
| 4 | IGT – E1 | No voltage | Idling | 0.7 – 1.0 V |

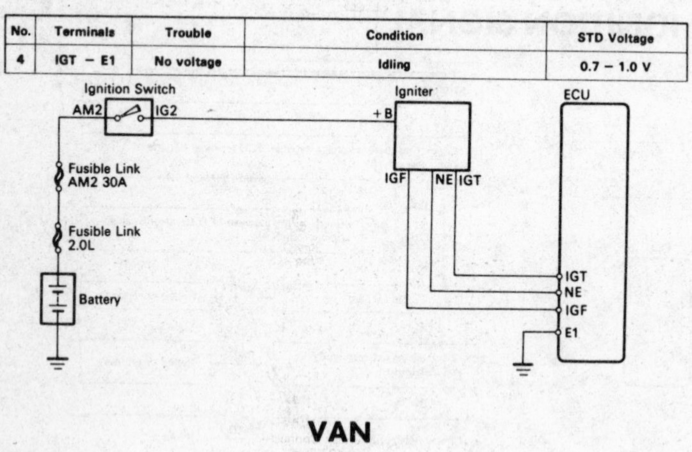
Ignition Switch
AM2
IG2
Fusible Link AM2 30A
Fusible Link 2.0L
Battery
Igniter
+B
IGF
NE
IGT
ECU
IGT
NE
IGF
E1

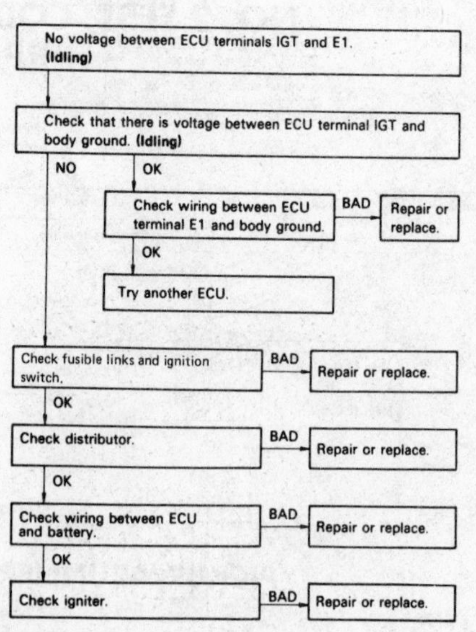
No voltage between ECU terminals IGT and E1. (Idling)
Check that there is voltage between ECU terminal IGT and body ground. (Idling)
NO
OK
Check wiring between ECU terminal E1 and body ground.
BAD
Repair or replace.
OK
Try another ECU.
Check fusible links and ignition switch.
BAD
Repair or replace.
OK
Check distributor.
BAD
Repair or replace.
OK
Check wiring between ECU and battery.
BAD
Repair or replace.
OK
Check igniter.
BAD
Repair or replace.

### VAN

Courtesy of Toyota Motor Sales, U.S.A., Inc.

### LAND CRUISER, PICKUP/4RUNNER, VAN
### NO. 3 TEST, CODE 21, 25, 26, 28 (CODE 5 ON TURBO)
### $O_2$ SYSTEM SIGNAL

**NOTE: Use terminals "VF1" or "VF2" on Land Cruiser models.**

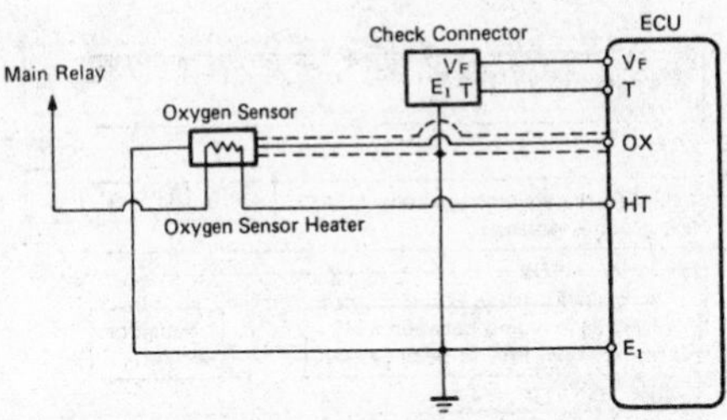

Check Connector
ECU
Main Relay
Oxygen Sensor
VF
E1 T
VF
T
OX
HT
Oxygen Sensor Heater
E1


**PICKUP/4RUNNER (4-CYL.)**

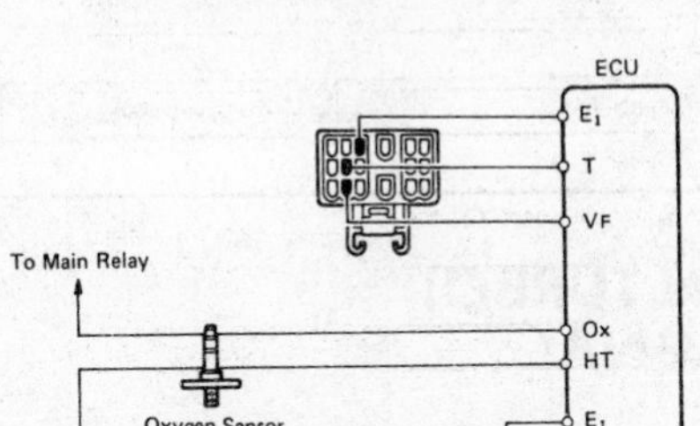

ECU
E1
T
VF
To Main Relay
Ox
HT
Oxygen Sensor
E1


**PICKUP/4RUNNER (V6)**

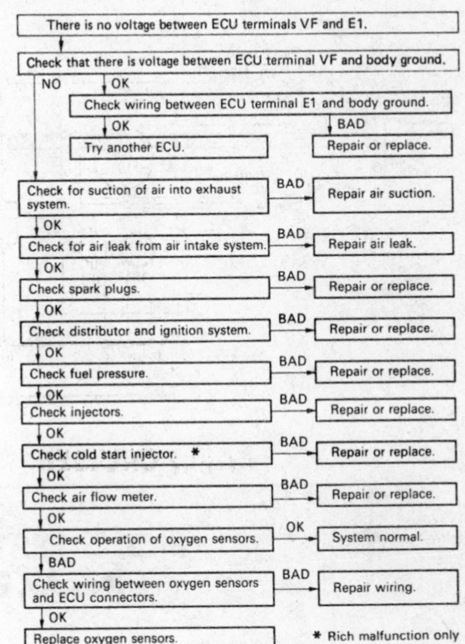

There is no voltage between ECU terminals VF and E1.
Check that there is voltage between ECU terminal VF and body ground.
NO
OK
Check wiring between ECU terminal E1 and body ground.
OK
BAD
Try another ECU.
Repair or replace.
Check for suction of air into exhaust system.
BAD
Repair air suction.
OK
Check for air leak from air intake system.
BAD
Repair air leak.
OK
Check spark plugs.
BAD
Repair or replace.
OK
Check distributor and ignition system.
BAD
Repair or replace.
OK
Check fuel pressure.
BAD
Repair or replace.
OK
Check injectors.
BAD
Repair or replace.
OK
Check cold start injector. *
BAD
Repair or replace.
OK
Check air flow meter.
BAD
Repair or replace.
OK
Check operation of oxygen sensors.
OK
System normal.
BAD
Check wiring between oxygen sensors and ECU connectors.
BAD
Repair wiring.
OK
Replace oxygen sensors.
* Rich malfunction only


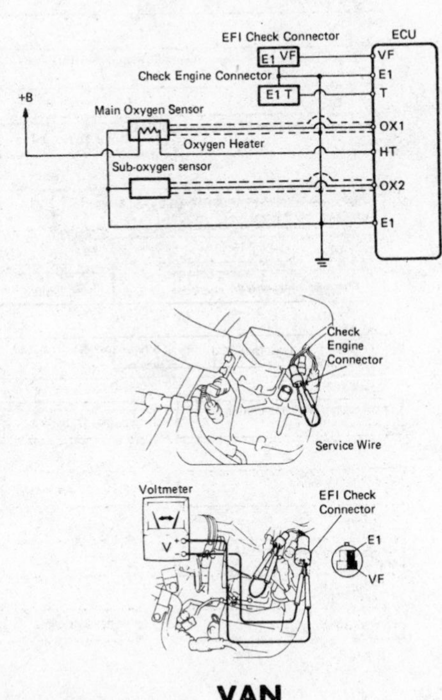

EFI Check Connector
ECU
E1 VF
VF
Check Engine Connector
E1
+B
E1 T
T
Main Oxygen Sensor
OX1
Oxygen Heater
HT
Sub-oxygen sensor
OX2
E1
Check Engine Connector
Service Wire
Voltmeter
EFI Check Connector
E1
VF
V


**VAN**

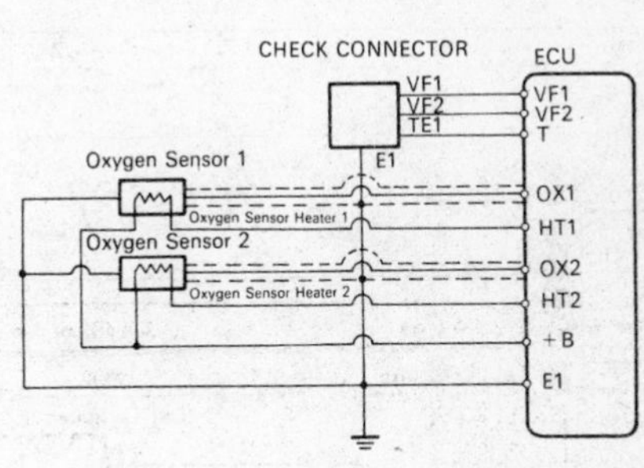

CHECK CONNECTOR
ECU
VF1
VF2
TE1
VF1
VF2
T
Oxygen Sensor 1
E1
OX1
Oxygen Sensor Heater 1
HT1
Oxygen Sensor 2
OX2
Oxygen Sensor Heater 2
HT2
+B
E1


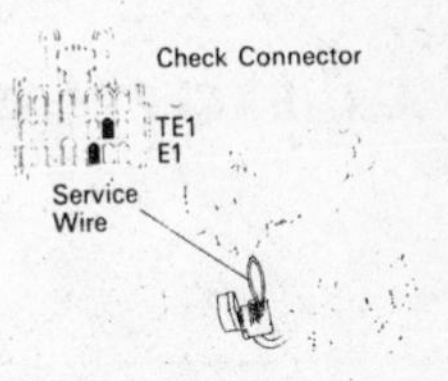

Check Connector
TE1
E1
Service Wire


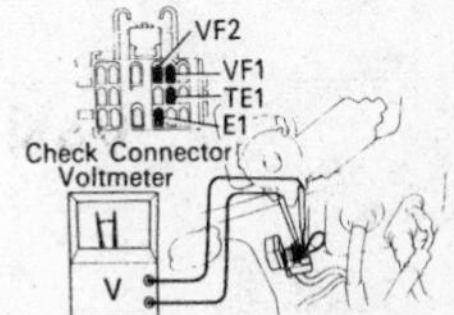

VF2
VF1
TE1
E1
Check Connector
Voltmeter
V


**LAND CRUISER**

Courtesy of Toyota Motor Sales, U.S.A., Inc.

## LAND CRUISER, PICKUP/4RUNNER, VAN
## NO. 4 TEST, CODE 22 (CODE 4 ON TURBO)
## COOLANT TEMP. SENSOR SIGNAL

| No. | Terminals | Trouble | Condition | | STD Voltage |
|---|---|---|---|---|---|
| 10 | THW – $E_2$ | No voltage | Ignition switch ON | Coolant temperature 80°C (176°F) | 0.1 – 1.0 V |

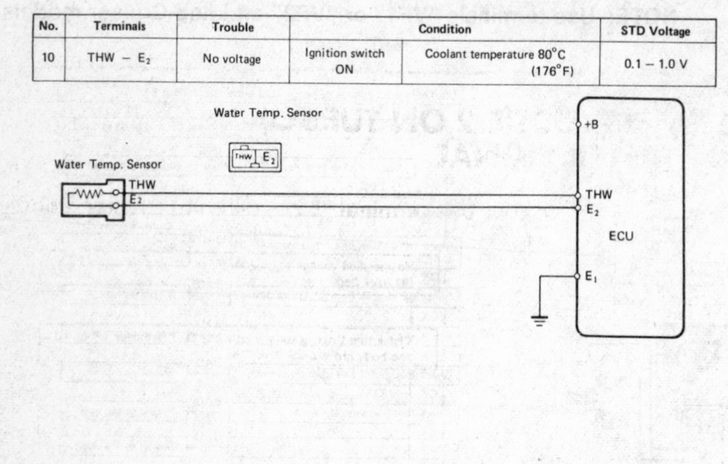
Water Temp. Sensor
THW
$E_2$
Water Temp. Sensor
+B
THW
$E_2$
ECU
$E_1$

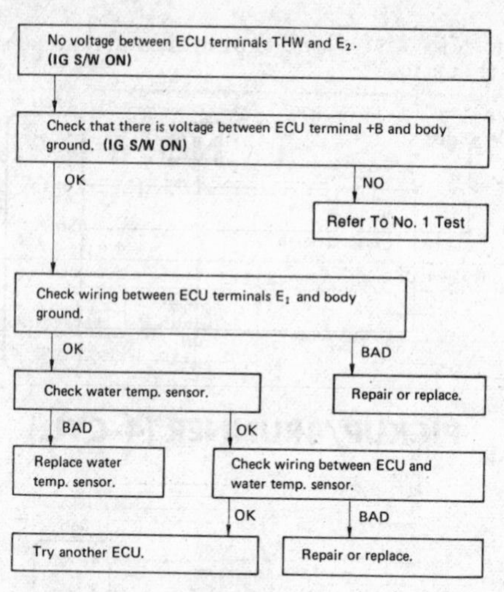
No voltage between ECU terminals THW and $E_2$. (IG S/W ON)
Check that there is voltage between ECU terminal +B and body ground. (IG S/W ON)
OK
NO
Refer To No. 1 Test
Check wiring between ECU terminals $E_1$ and body ground.
OK
BAD
Check water temp. sensor.
Repair or replace.
BAD
OK
Replace water temp. sensor.
Check wiring between ECU and water temp. sensor.
OK
BAD
Try another ECU.
Repair or replace.

## NO. 5 TEST, CODE 24 (CODE 8 ON TURBO)
## INTAKE AIR TEMP. SENSOR SIGNAL

**NOTE: Use terminals "THA" & "E22" on Land Cruiser.**

| Terminals | Trouble | Condition | | STD Voltage |
|---|---|---|---|---|
| THA – $E_2$ | No voltage | Ignition switch ON | Intake air temperature 20°C (68°F) | 1 – 3 V |

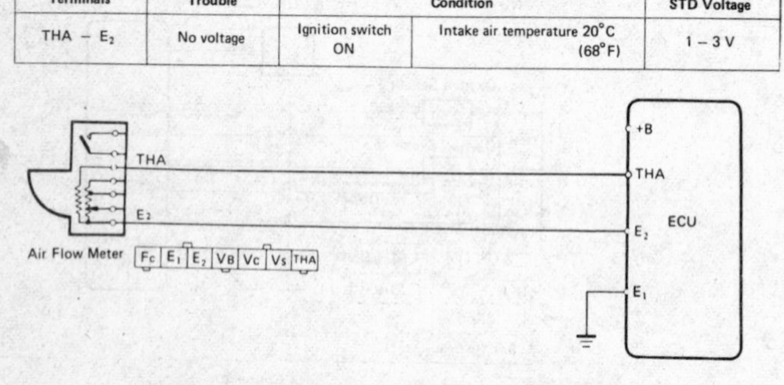
THA
$E_2$
Air Flow Meter
Fc
$E_1$
$E_2$
VB
Vc
Vs
THA
+B
THA
ECU
$E_2$
$E_1$

**ALL (EXCEPT LAND CRUISER)**

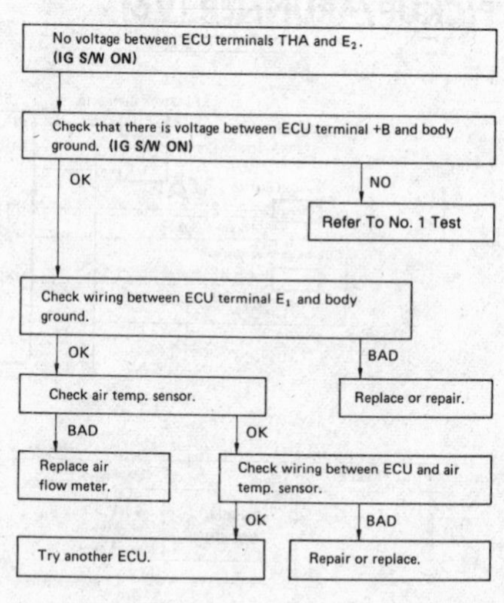
No voltage between ECU terminals THA and $E_2$. (IG S/W ON)
Check that there is voltage between ECU terminal +B and body ground. (IG S/W ON)
OK
NO
Refer To No. 1 Test
Check wiring between ECU terminal $E_1$ and body ground.
OK
BAD
Check air temp. sensor.
Replace or repair.
BAD
OK
Replace air flow meter.
Check wiring between ECU and air temp. sensor.
OK
BAD
Try another ECU.
Repair or replace.

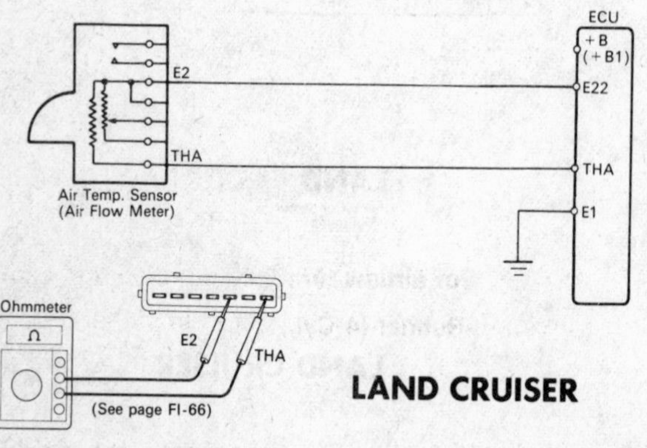
ECU
+B
(+B1)
E2
E22
THA
THA
E1
Air Temp. Sensor
(Air Flow Meter)
Ohmmeter
Ω
E2
THA
(See page FI-66)

**LAND CRUISER**

Courtesy of Toyota Motor Sales, U.S.A., Inc.

## LAND CRUISER, PICKUP/4RUNNER, VAN
## CODE 25, 26
## AIR/FUEL, LEAN OR RICH

**NOTE:** Use No. 3 test in this article.

## NO. 6 TEST, CODE 31, 32 (CODE 2 ON TURBO)
## AIRFLOW METER SIGNAL

**NOTE:** Use terminal "E22" on Land Cruiser models.

| Terminals | Trouble | Condition | | STD Voltage |
|---|---|---|---|---|
| $V_c - E_2$ | No voltage | Ignition switch ON | – | 6 – 10 V |
| $V_s - E_2$ | | | Measuring plate fully closed | 0.5 – 2.5 V |
| $V_s - E_2$ | | | Measuring plate fully open | 5 – 10 V |
| $V_s - E_2$ | | Idling | | 2 – 8 V |

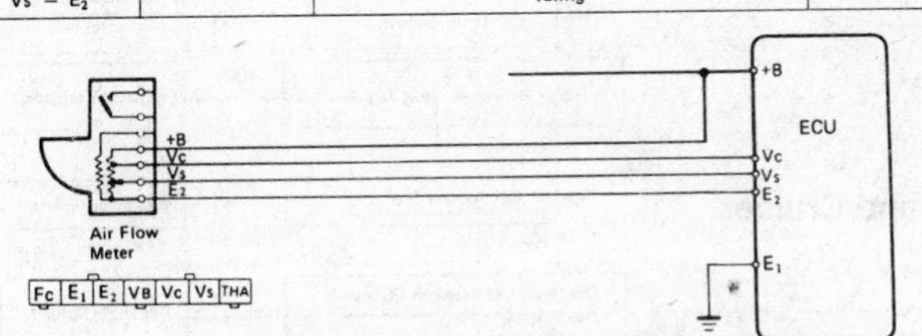
+B
ECU
+B
Vc
Vs
E2
Vc
Vs
E2
E1
Air Flow Meter
Fc E1 E2 VB Vc Vs THA

PICKUP/4RUNNER (4-CYL.)

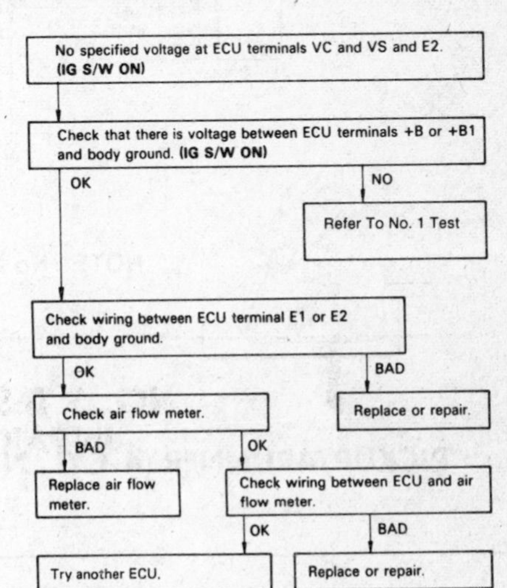
No specified voltage at ECU terminals VC and VS and E2. (IG S/W ON)
Check that there is voltage between ECU terminals +B or +B1 and body ground. (IG S/W ON)
OK
NO
Refer To No. 1 Test
Check wiring between ECU terminal E1 or E2 and body ground.
OK
BAD
Check air flow meter.
Replace or repair.
BAD
OK
Replace air flow meter.
Check wiring between ECU and air flow meter.
OK
BAD
Try another ECU.
Replace or repair.

ECU
+B
VB
VC
VS
E2
+B1
VC
VS
E2
E1
Air Flow Meter

VAN

| Terminals | Trouble | Condition | | STD Voltage |
|---|---|---|---|---|
| VC - E22 | No voltage | Ignition S/W ON | — | 4 - 6 V |
| VS - E22 | | | Measuring plate fully closed | 4 - 5 V |
| VS - E22 | | | Measuring plate fully open | 0.02 - 0.08 V |
| VS - E22 | | Idling | — | 2 - 4 V |
| VS - E22 | | 3,000 rpm | — | 0.3 - 1.0 V |

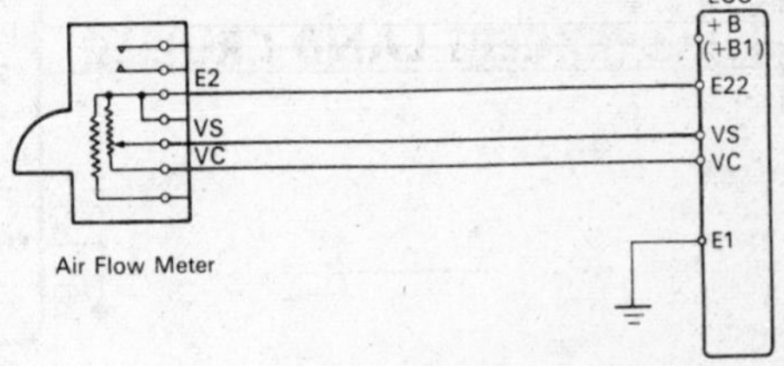
ECU
+B
(+B1)
E22
VS
VC
E1
E2
VS
VC
Air Flow Meter

LAND CRUISER

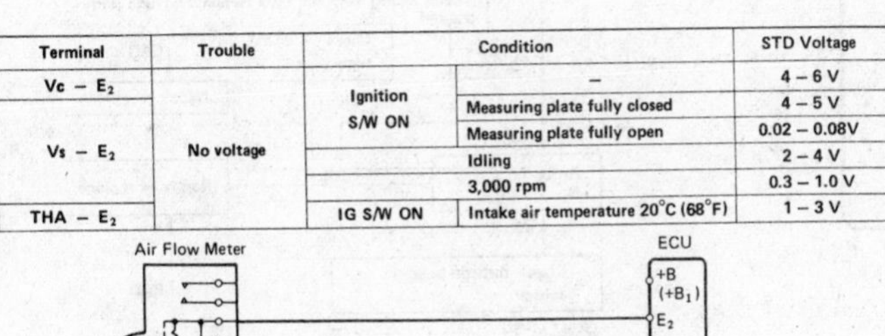

| Terminal | Trouble | Condition | | STD Voltage |
|---|---|---|---|---|
| $V_c - E_2$ | No voltage | Ignition S/W ON | – | 4 – 6 V |
| $V_s - E_2$ | | | Measuring plate fully closed | 4 – 5 V |
| | | | Measuring plate fully open | 0.02 – 0.08V |
| | | | Idling | 2 – 4 V |
| | | | 3,000 rpm | 0.3 – 1.0 V |
| THA – $E_2$ | | IG S/W ON | Intake air temperature 20°C (68°F) | 1 – 3 V |

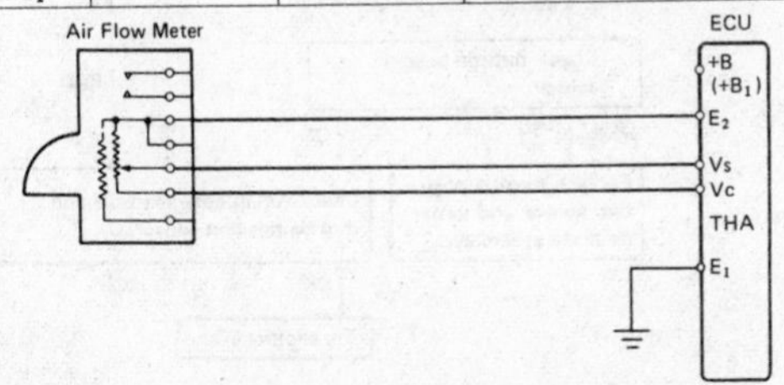
Air Flow Meter
ECU
+B
(+B1)
E2
Vs
Vc
THA
E1

PICKUP/4RUNNER (V6)

**NOTE:** For airflow terminal identification see Pickup/4Runner (4-Cyl.) diagram in this test.

Courtesy of Toyota Motor Sales, U.S.A., Inc.

# LAND CRUISER, PICKUP/4RUNNER, VAN
# NO. 7 TEST, CODE 35
# HAC SENSOR SIGNAL

| Terminals | Trouble | Condition | | STD Voltage |
|---|---|---|---|---|
| HAC – $E_2$ (C & C only) | No voltage | Ignition S/W ON | 760 mmHg (29.92 in.Hg, 101.3 kPa) | Approx. 3.6 V |

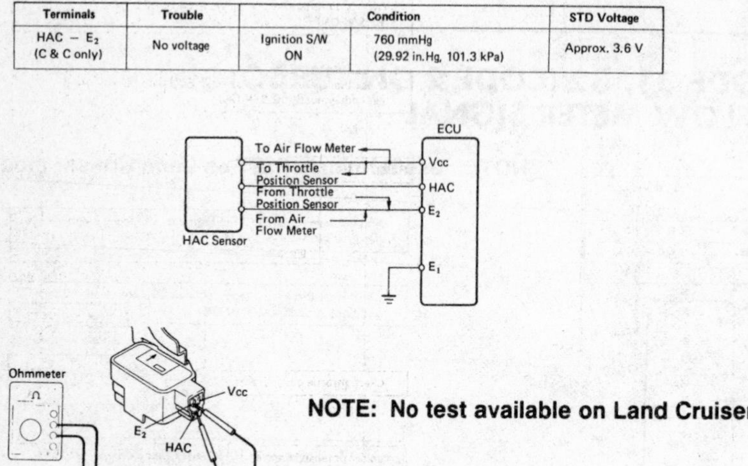
ECU
To Air Flow Meter
To Throttle Position Sensor
From Throttle Position Sensor
From Air Flow Meter
Vcc
HAC
$E_2$
$E_1$
HAC Sensor
Ohmmeter
Vcc
$E_2$
HAC

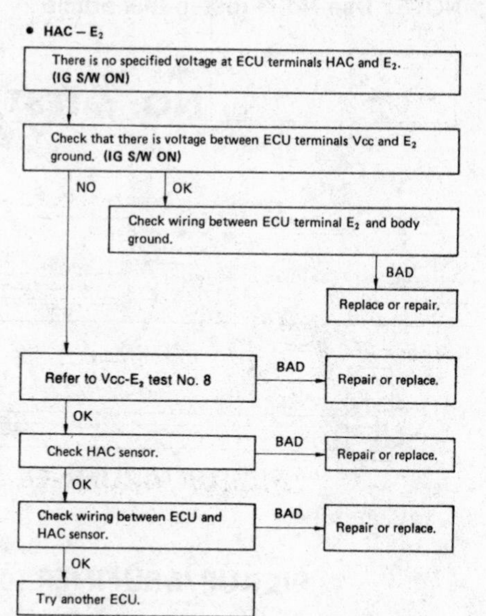
• HAC – $E_2$
There is no specified voltage at ECU terminals HAC and $E_2$. (IG S/W ON)
Check that there is voltage between ECU terminals Vcc and $E_2$ ground. (IG S/W ON)
NO
OK
Check wiring between ECU terminal $E_2$ and body ground.
BAD
Replace or repair.
Refer to Vcc-$E_2$ test No. 8
BAD
Repair or replace.
OK
Check HAC sensor.
BAD
Repair or replace.
OK
Check wiring between ECU and HAC sensor.
BAD
Repair or replace.
OK
Try another ECU.

**NOTE: No test available on Land Cruiser.**

## PICKUP/4RUNNER (4-CYL. NON TURBO ONLY)

# NO. 8 TEST, CODE 41 (CODE 7 ON TURBO)
# THROTTLE POSITION SENSOR SIGNAL

| Terminals | Trouble | Condition | | STD Voltage |
|---|---|---|---|---|
| IDL – E1 | No voltage | IG S/W ON | Throttle valve open | 8 – 14 V |
| PSW – E1 | | | Throttle valve fully closed | 8 – 14 V |

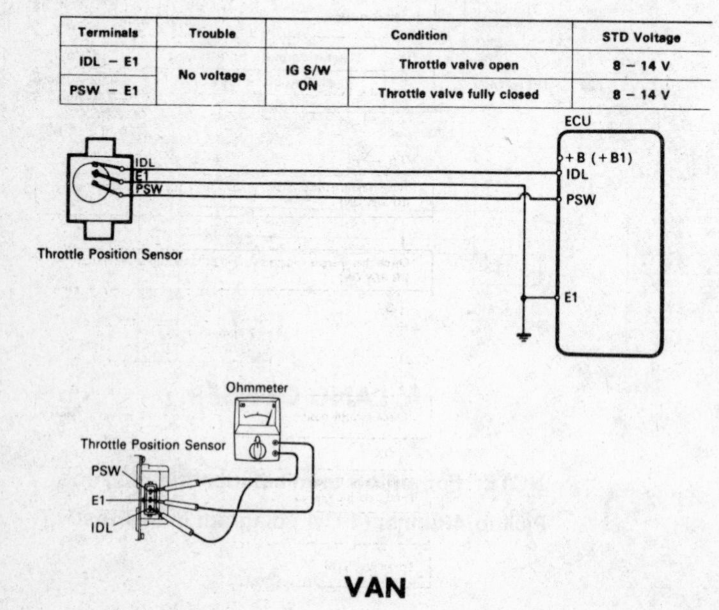
ECU
+B (+B1)
IDL
PSW
E1
IDL
E1
PSW
Throttle Position Sensor
Ohmmeter
Throttle Position Sensor
PSW
E1
IDL

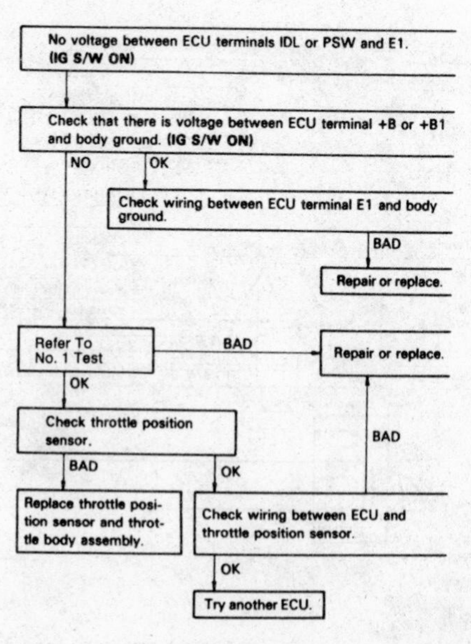
No voltage between ECU terminals IDL or PSW and E1. (IG S/W ON)
Check that there is voltage between ECU terminal +B or +B1 and body ground. (IG S/W ON)
NO
OK
Check wiring between ECU terminal E1 and body ground.
BAD
Repair or replace.
Refer To No. 1 Test
BAD
Repair or replace.
OK
Check throttle position sensor.
BAD
OK
BAD
Replace throttle position sensor and throttle body assembly.
Check wiring between ECU and throttle position sensor.
OK
Try another ECU.

## VAN

Courtesy of Toyota Motor Sales, U.S.A., Inc.

# LAND CRUISER, PICKUP/4RUNNER, VAN
# NO. 8 TEST, CODE 41 (CODE 7 ON TURBO) (Cont.)
# THROTTLE POSITION SENSOR SIGNAL

| Terminals | Trouble | | Condition | STD Voltage |
|---|---|---|---|---|
| IDL – $E_2$ | No voltage | Ignition switch ON | Throttle valve open | 8 – 14 V |
| Vcc – $E_2$ | | | – | 4 – 6 V |
| VTA – $E_2$ | | | Throttle valve fully closed | 0.1 – 1.0 V |
| | | | Throttle valve fully open | 4 – 5 V |

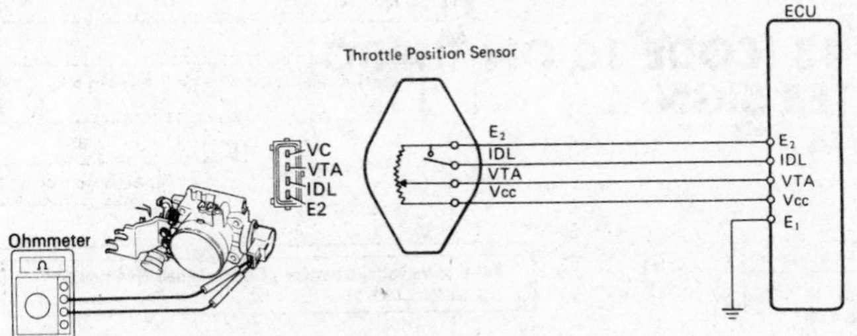
Throttle Position Sensor
ECU
$E_2$
IDL
VTA
Vcc
$E_1$
VC
VTA
IDL
E2
Ohmmeter

## PICKUP/4RUNNER (4-CYL.)

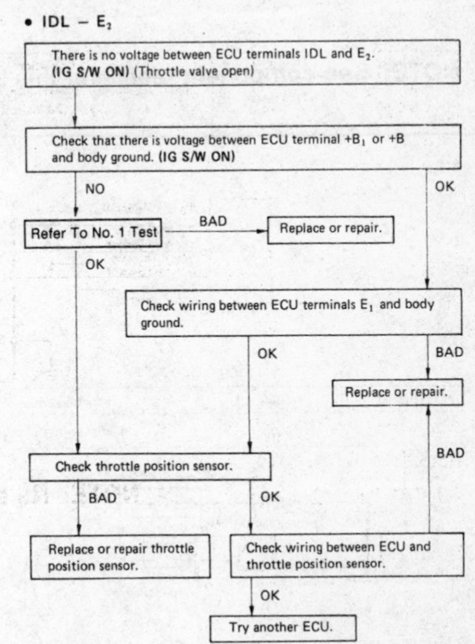
• IDL – $E_2$
There is no voltage between ECU terminals IDL and $E_2$. (IG S/W ON) (Throttle valve open)
Check that there is voltage between ECU terminal $+B_1$ or +B and body ground. (IG S/W ON)
NO
OK
Refer To No. 1 Test
BAD
Replace or repair.
OK
Check wiring between ECU terminals $E_1$ and body ground.
OK
BAD
Replace or repair.
BAD
Check throttle position sensor.
BAD
OK
Replace or repair throttle position sensor.
Check wiring between ECU and throttle position sensor.
OK
Try another ECU.

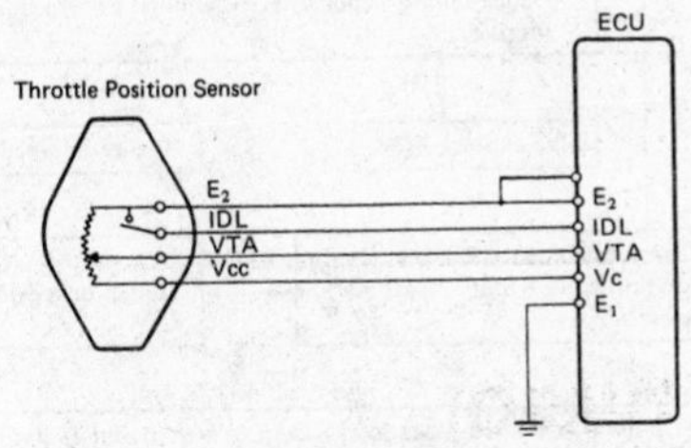
ECU
Throttle Position Sensor
$E_2$
IDL
VTA
Vcc
$E_2$
IDL
VTA
Vc
$E_1$

## PICKUP/4RUNNER (V6)

**NOTE: Terminals "VC" & or "VCC" will vary between models.**

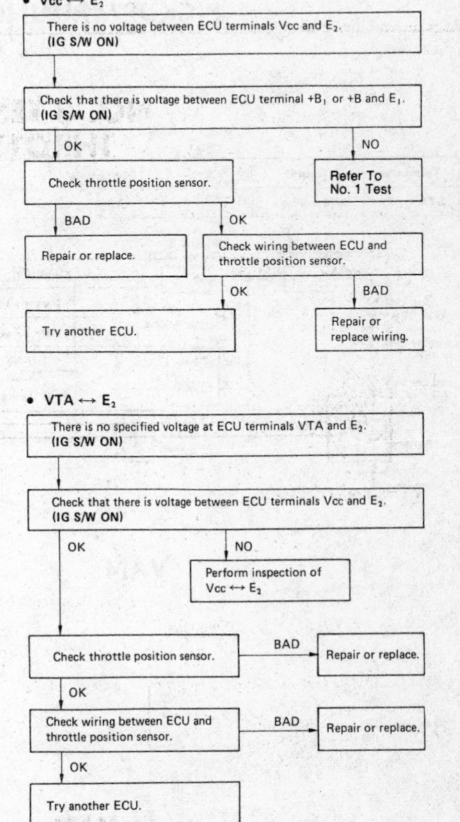
• Vcc ↔ $E_2$
There is no voltage between ECU terminals Vcc and $E_2$. (IG S/W ON)
Check that there is voltage between ECU terminal $+B_1$ or +B and $E_1$. (IG S/W ON)
OK
NO
Check throttle position sensor.
Refer To No. 1 Test
BAD
OK
Repair or replace.
Check wiring between ECU and throttle position sensor.
OK
BAD
Try another ECU.
Repair or replace wiring.
• VTA ↔ $E_2$
There is no specified voltage at ECU terminals VTA and $E_2$. (IG S/W ON)
Check that there is voltage between ECU terminals Vcc and $E_2$. (IG S/W ON)
OK
NO
Perform inspection of Vcc ↔ $E_2$
Check throttle position sensor.
BAD
Repair or replace.
OK
Check wiring between ECU and throttle position sensor.
BAD
Repair or replace.
OK
Try another ECU.

| Terminals | Trouble | | Condition | STD Voltage |
|---|---|---|---|---|
| IDL - E2 | No voltage | Ignition switch ON | Throttle valve open | 4 - 6 V |
| VC - E2 | | | — | 4 - 6 V |
| VTA - E2 | | | Throttle valve fully closed | 0.1 - 1.0 V |
| | | | Throttle valve fully open | 4 - 5 V |

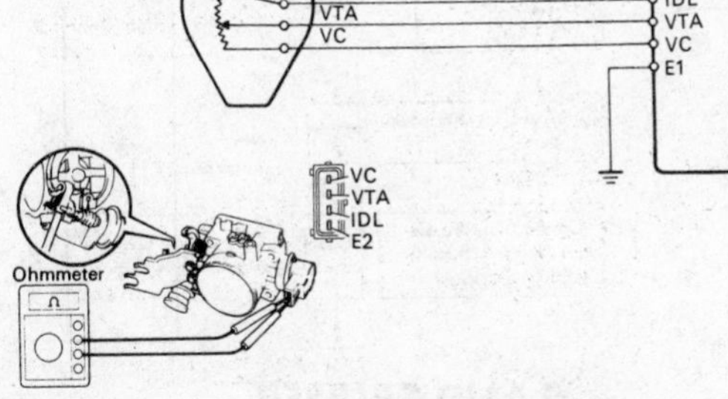
ECU
Throttle Position Sensor
+B
(+B1)
E2
IDL
VTA
VC
E2
IDL
VTA
VC
E1
VC
VTA
IDL
E2
Ohmmeter

## LAND CRUISER

Courtesy of Toyota Motor Sales, U.S.A., Inc.

## LAND CRUISER, PICKUP/4RUNNER, VAN
## CODE 42
## VEHICLE SPEED SENSOR

**NOTE: See component testing in this article.**

## NO. 9 TEST, CODE 43 (CODE 10 ON TURBO)
## STARTER SIGNAL

| Terminals | Trouble | Condition | STD Voltage |
|---|---|---|---|
| STA – $E_1$ | No voltage | Ignition switch ST position | 6 – 12 V |

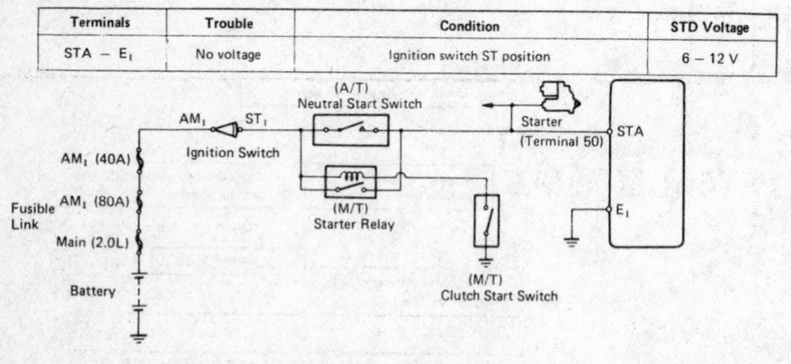
AM₁
ST₁
Ignition Switch
(A/T)
Neutral Start Switch
Starter
(Terminal 50)
STA
E₁
AM₁ (40A)
AM₁ (80A)
Fusible Link
Main (2.0L)
Battery
(M/T)
Starter Relay
(M/T)
Clutch Start Switch

PICKUP/4RUNNER

There is no voltage between ECU terminals STA and E1. (IG S/W START)

- Check starter operation.
  - OK → Check wiring between ECU terminal STA and ignition switch terminal ST1.
    - BAD → Repair or replace.
    - OK → Check wiring between ECU terminal E1 and body ground.
      - OK → Try another ECU.
      - BAD → Repair or replace.
  - BAD → Check fusible link, battery, wiring, ignition switch and neutral start switch.
    - BAD → Repair or replace.
    - OK → Check that there is voltage at STA (50) terminal of starter. (IG S/W START)
      - OK → Check starter.
      - NO → Check wiring between ignition switch terminal ST1 and starter terminal STA (50).

| Terminals | Trouble | Condition | STD Voltage |
|---|---|---|---|
| STA – E1 | No voltage | Cranking | 6 – 12 V |

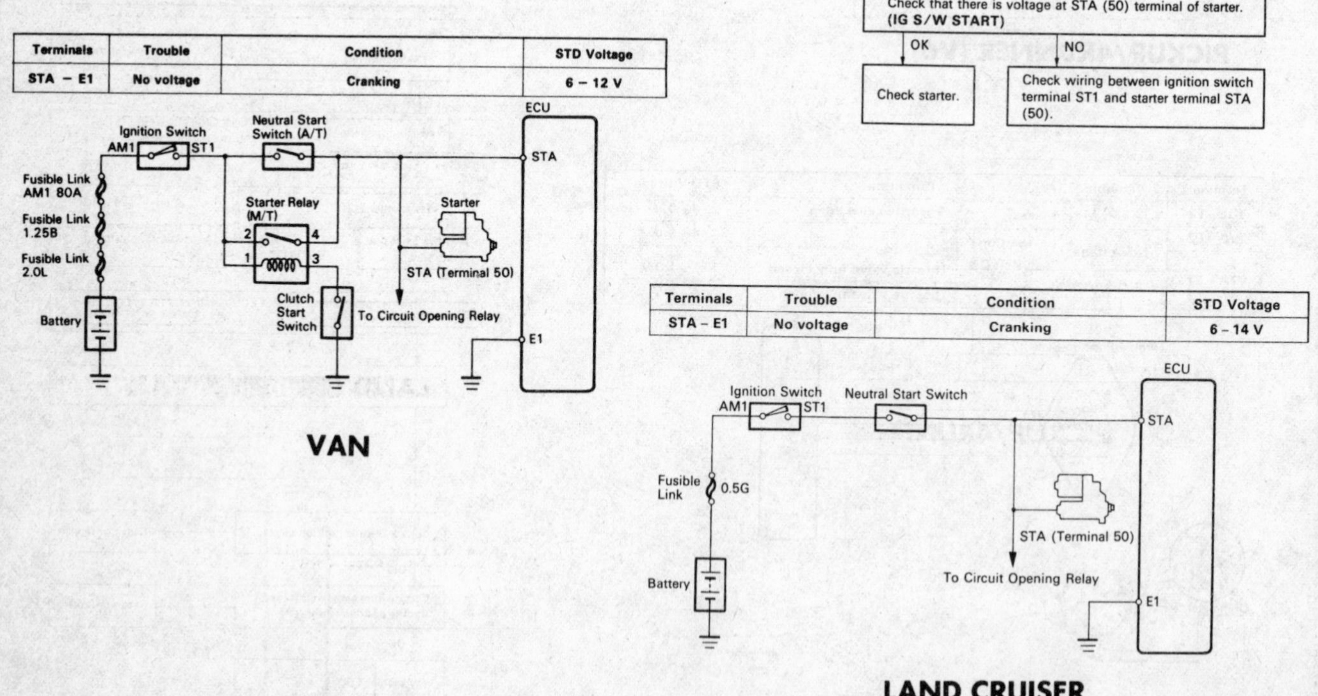
ECU
Ignition Switch
AM1
ST1
Neutral Start Switch (A/T)
STA
Fusible Link AM1 80A
Fusible Link 1.25B
Fusible Link 2.0L
Starter Relay (M/T)
Starter
STA (Terminal 50)
Battery
Clutch Start Switch
To Circuit Opening Relay
E1

VAN

| Terminals | Trouble | Condition | STD Voltage |
|---|---|---|---|
| STA – E1 | No voltage | Cranking | 6 – 14 V |

ECU
Ignition Switch
AM1
ST1
Neutral Start Switch
STA
Fusible Link
0.5G
STA (Terminal 50)
Battery
To Circuit Opening Relay
E1

LAND CRUISER

Courtesy of Toyota Motor Sales, U.S.A., Inc.

## LAND CRUISER, PICKUP/4RUNNER, VAN
## CODE 51 (CODE 11 ON TURBO)

### NO "IDL", "NSW" OR "A/C" SIGNAL TO ECU, WITH CHECK CONNECTOR TERMINALS "E1" & "T" SHORTED

**NOTE:** No further information available from manufacturer.

## CODE 52, 53 (CODE 12, 13 ON TURBO)

### OPEN OR SHORT IN KNOCK SENSOR (KNK) OR KNOCK CONTROL IN ECU FAULTY

**NOTE:** No further information available from manufacturer.

## NO. 10 TEST, CODE 71
## EGR SYSTEM SIGNAL

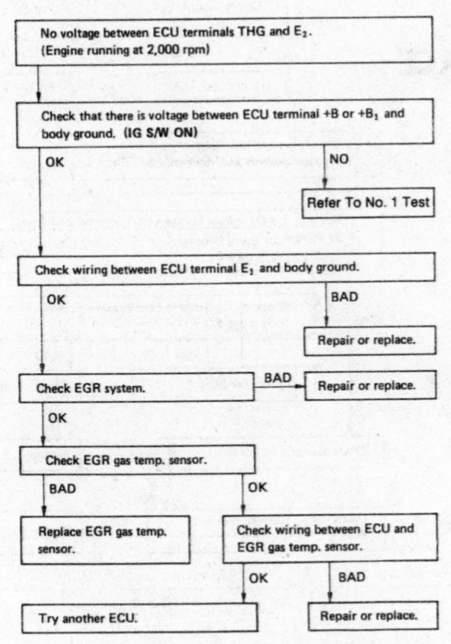
No voltage between ECU terminals THG and $E_2$. (Engine running at 2,000 rpm)
Check that there is voltage between ECU terminal +B or $+B_1$ and body ground. (IG S/W ON)
OK
NO
Refer To No. 1 Test
Check wiring between ECU terminal $E_1$ and body ground.
OK
BAD
Repair or replace.
Check EGR system.
BAD
Repair or replace.
OK
Check EGR gas temp. sensor.
BAD
OK
Replace EGR gas temp. sensor.
Check wiring between ECU and EGR gas temp. sensor.
OK
BAD
Try another ECU.
Repair or replace.

PICKUP/4RUNNER

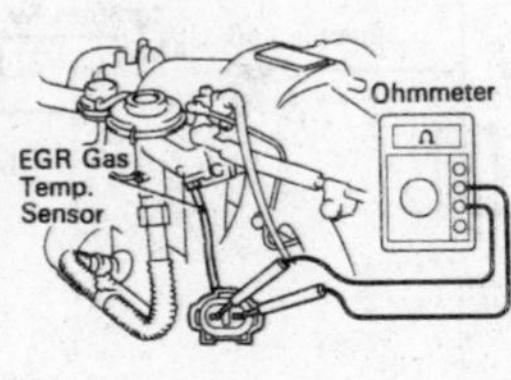
Ohmmeter
EGR Gas Temp. Sensor

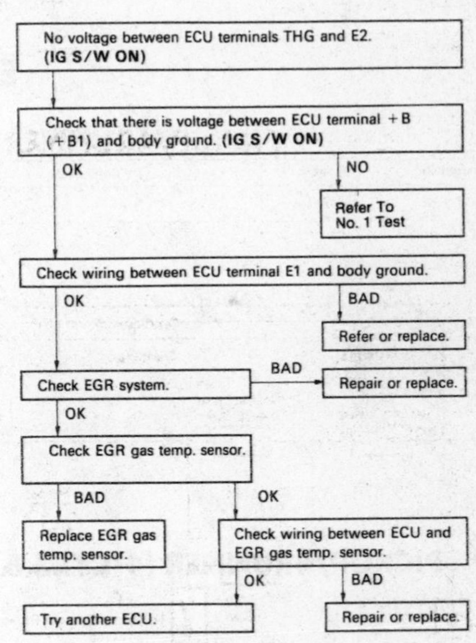
No voltage between ECU terminals THG and E2. (IG S/W ON)
Check that there is voltage between ECU terminal +B (+B1) and body ground. (IG S/W ON)
OK
NO
Refer To No. 1 Test
Check wiring between ECU terminal E1 and body ground.
OK
BAD
Refer or replace.
Check EGR system.
BAD
Repair or replace.
OK
Check EGR gas temp. sensor.
BAD
OK
Replace EGR gas temp. sensor.
Check wiring between ECU and EGR gas temp. sensor.
OK
BAD
Try another ECU.
Repair or replace.

LAND CRUISER & VAN

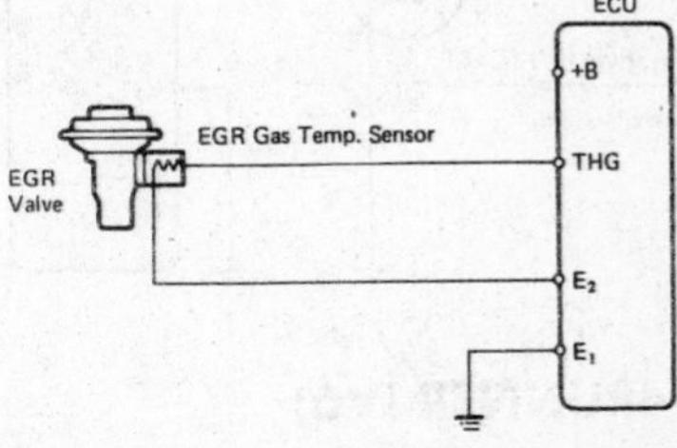
ECU
+B
EGR Gas Temp. Sensor
THG
EGR Valve
$E_2$
$E_1$

Courtesy of Toyota Motor Sales, U.S.A., Inc.

## LAND CRUISER, PICKUP/4RUNNER, VAN
## NO. 11 TEST
## "CHECK ENGINE" LIGHT TEST

| Terminals | Trouble | Condition | STD Voltage |
|---|---|---|---|
| W – $E_1$ | No voltage | No trouble (CHECK ENGINE light off) and engine running | 8 – 14 V |

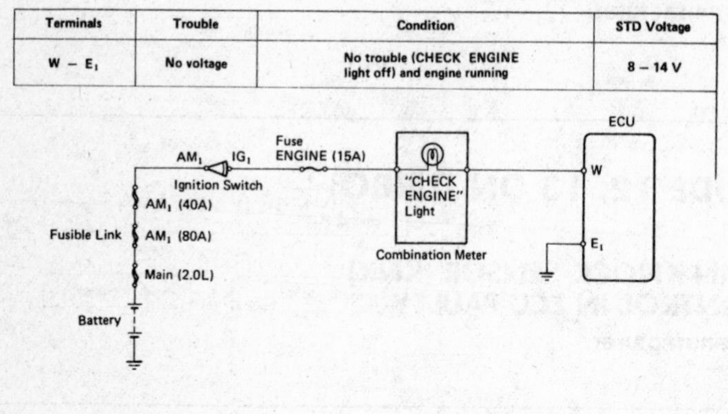
AM1
IG1
Ignition Switch
Fuse
ENGINE (15A)
"CHECK ENGINE" Light
Combination Meter
ECU
W
E1
AM1 (40A)
Fusible Link
AM1 (80A)
Main (2.0L)
Battery

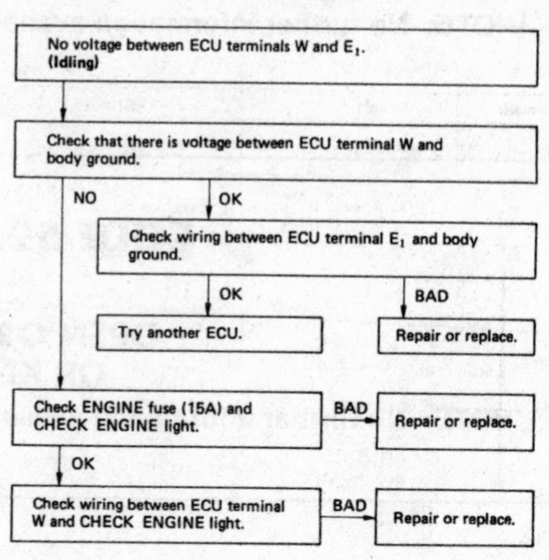
No voltage between ECU terminals W and E1. (Idling)
Check that there is voltage between ECU terminal W and body ground.
NO
OK
Check wiring between ECU terminal E1 and body ground.
OK
BAD
Try another ECU.
Repair or replace.
Check ENGINE fuse (15A) and CHECK ENGINE light.
BAD
Repair or replace.
OK
Check wiring between ECU terminal W and CHECK ENGINE light.
BAD
Repair or replace.

## NO. 12 TEST
## ECU POWER SOURCE

| Terminals | Trouble | Condition | STD Voltage |
|---|---|---|---|
| BATT – $E_1$ | No voltage | — | 10 – 14 V |

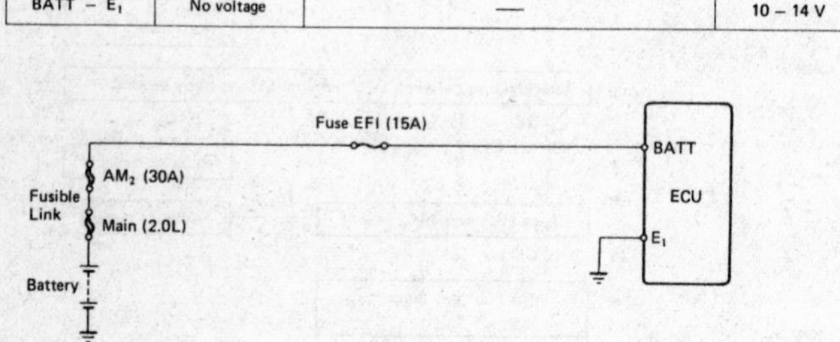
Fuse EFI (15A)
BATT
ECU
E1
AM2 (30A)
Fusible Link
Main (2.0L)
Battery

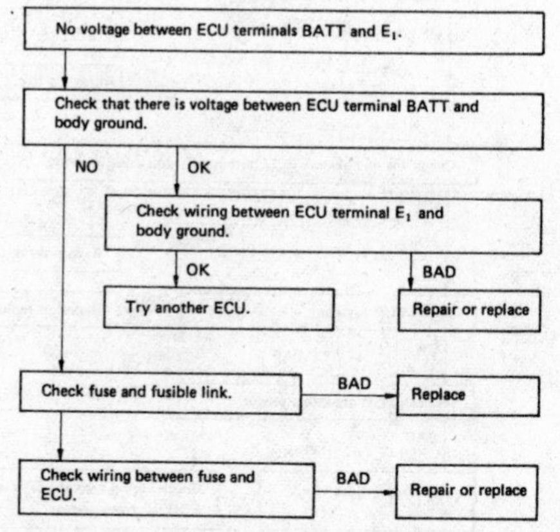
No voltage between ECU terminals BATT and E1.
Check that there is voltage between ECU terminal BATT and body ground.
NO
OK
Check wiring between ECU terminal E1 and body ground.
OK
BAD
Try another ECU.
Repair or replace
Check fuse and fusible link.
BAD
Replace
Check wiring between fuse and ECU.
BAD
Repair or replace

PICKUP/4RUNNER (4-CYL.) & VAN

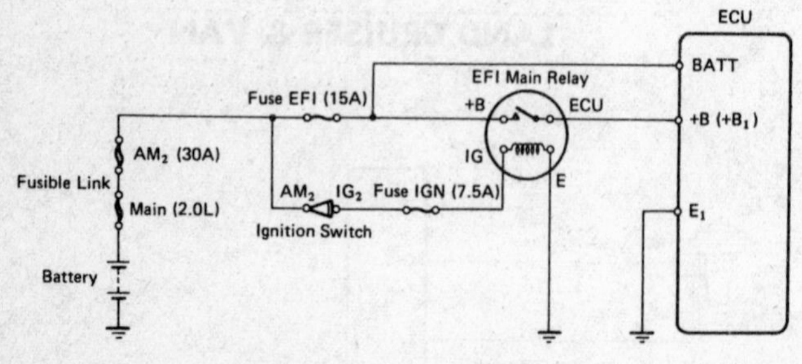
ECU
BATT
EFI Main Relay
+B
ECU
Fuse EFI (15A)
IG
E
+B (+B1)
E1
AM2 (30A)
Fusible Link
Main (2.0L)
AM2
IG2
Fuse IGN (7.5A)
Ignition Switch
Battery

PICKUP/4RUNNER (V6)

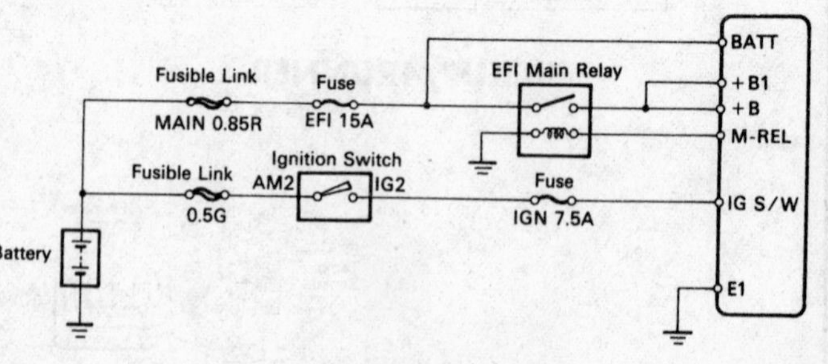
Fusible Link
MAIN 0.85R
Fuse
EFI 15A
EFI Main Relay
BATT
+B1
+B
M-REL
Fusible Link
0.5G
Ignition Switch
AM2
IG2
Fuse
IGN 7.5A
IG S/W
Battery
E1

LAND CRUISER

Courtesy of Toyota Motor Sales, U.S.A., Inc.

## Toyota Computer Control System (Cont.)

### LAND CRUISER, PICKUP/4RUNNER, VAN
### NO. 13 TEST
### STOP LIGHT CIRCUIT TEST

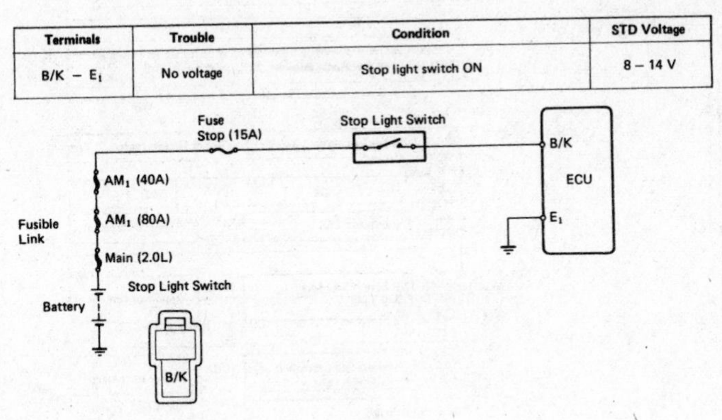

| Terminals | Trouble | Condition | STD Voltage |
|---|---|---|---|
| B/K − $E_1$ | No voltage | Stop light switch ON | 8 – 14 V |


Fuse
Stop (15A)
Stop Light Switch
B/K
ECU
$E_1$
AM₁ (40A)
AM₁ (80A)
Fusible Link
Main (2.0L)
Stop Light Switch
Battery
B/K


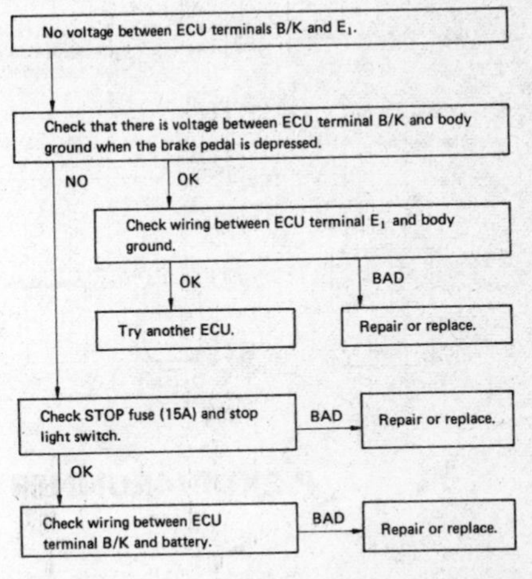

No voltage between ECU terminals B/K and $E_1$.
Check that there is voltage between ECU terminal B/K and body ground when the brake pedal is depressed.
NO
OK
Check wiring between ECU terminal $E_1$ and body ground.
OK
BAD
Try another ECU.
Repair or replace.
Check STOP fuse (15A) and stop light switch.
BAD
Repair or replace.
OK
Check wiring between ECU terminal B/K and battery.
BAD
Repair or replace.


PICKUP/4RUNNER (4-CYL.)

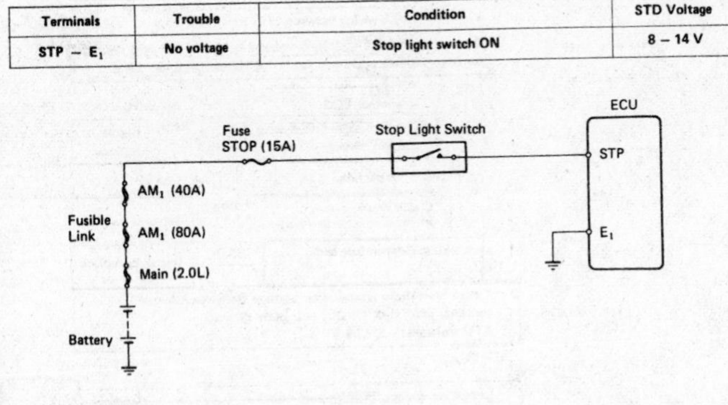

| Terminals | Trouble | Condition | STD Voltage |
|---|---|---|---|
| STP − $E_1$ | No voltage | Stop light switch ON | 8 – 14 V |


ECU
Fuse
STOP (15A)
Stop Light Switch
STP
AM₁ (40A)
Fusible Link
AM₁ (80A)
$E_1$
Main (2.0L)
Battery


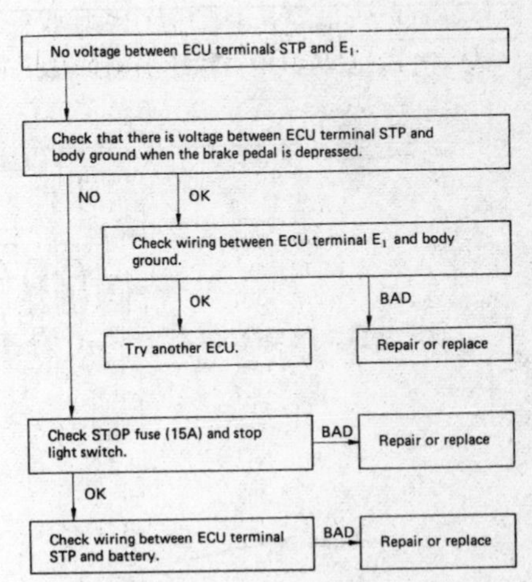

No voltage between ECU terminals STP and $E_1$.
Check that there is voltage between ECU terminal STP and body ground when the brake pedal is depressed.
NO
OK
Check wiring between ECU terminal $E_1$ and body ground.
OK
BAD
Try another ECU.
Repair or replace
Check STOP fuse (15A) and stop light switch.
BAD
Repair or replace
OK
Check wiring between ECU terminal STP and battery.
BAD
Repair or replace


PICKUP/4RUNNER (V6)

Courtesy of Toyota Motor Sales, U.S.A., Inc.

## LAND CRUISER, PICKUP/4RUNNER, VAN
## NO. 14 TEST
## COLD START INJECTOR CIRCUIT TEST

| Terminals | Trouble | Condition | | STD Voltage |
|---|---|---|---|---|
| STJ – $E_1$ | No voltage | Ignition switch ST position | Coolant temperature 80°C (176°F) | 6 – 12 V |

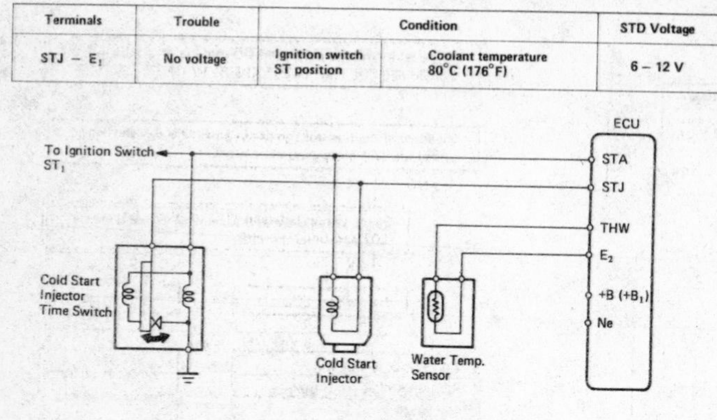
To Ignition Switch $ST_1$
ECU
STA
STJ
THW
$E_2$
+B (+$B_1$)
Ne
Cold Start Injector Time Switch
Cold Start Injector
Water Temp. Sensor

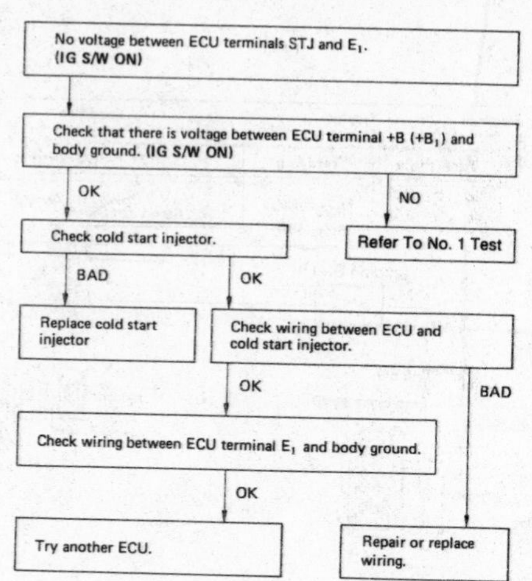
No voltage between ECU terminals STJ and $E_1$. (IG S/W ON)
Check that there is voltage between ECU terminal +B (+$B_1$) and body ground. (IG S/W ON)
OK
NO
Check cold start injector.
Refer To No. 1 Test
BAD
OK
Replace cold start injector
Check wiring between ECU and cold start injector.
OK
BAD
Check wiring between ECU terminal $E_1$ and body ground.
OK
Try another ECU.
Repair or replace wiring.

**PICKUP/4RUNNER**

## NO. 15 TEST
## INJECTOR CIRCUIT TEST

| Terminals | Trouble | Condition | STD Voltage |
|---|---|---|---|
| No.10 – E01<br>No.20 – E02 | No voltage | IG S/W ON | 9 – 14 V |

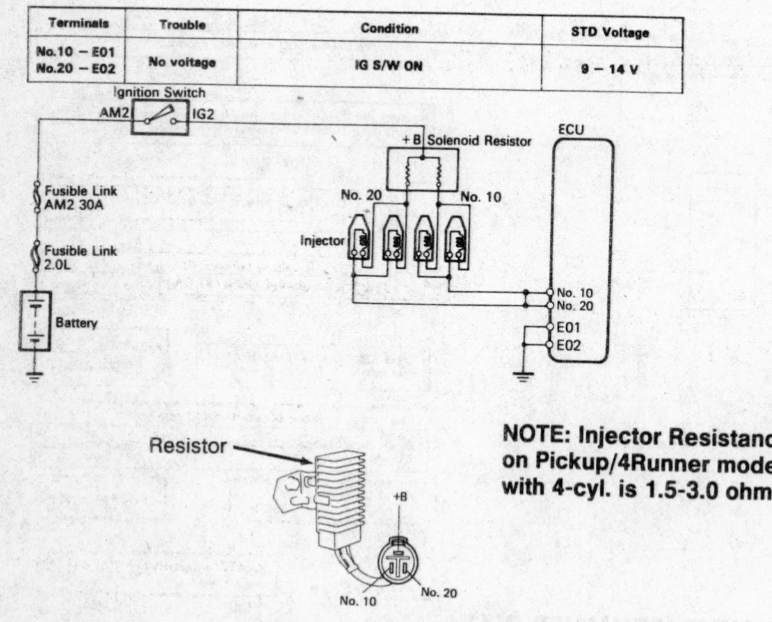
Ignition Switch
AM2
IG2
Fusible Link AM2 30A
Fusible Link 2.0L
Battery
+B Solenoid Resistor
No. 20
No. 10
Injector
ECU
No. 10
No. 20
E01
E02
Resistor
+B
No. 10
No. 20

**NOTE: Injector Resistance on Pickup/4Runner models with 4-cyl. is 1.5-3.0 ohms.**

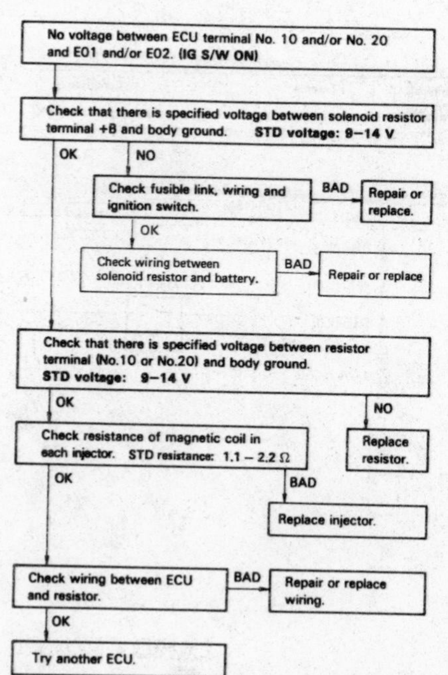
No voltage between ECU terminal No. 10 and/or No. 20 and E01 and/or E02. (IG S/W ON)
Check that there is specified voltage between solenoid resistor terminal +B and body ground. STD voltage: 9–14 V
OK
NO
Check fusible link, wiring and ignition switch.
BAD
Repair or replace.
OK
Check wiring between solenoid resistor and battery.
BAD
Repair or replace
Check that there is specified voltage between resistor terminal (No.10 or No.20) and body ground. STD voltage: 9–14 V
OK
NO
Check resistance of magnetic coil in each injector. STD resistance: 1.1 – 2.2 Ω
Replace resistor.
OK
BAD
Replace injector.
Check wiring between ECU and resistor.
BAD
Repair or replace wiring.
OK
Try another ECU.

**ALL (EXCEPT LAND CRUISER)**

Courtesy of Toyota Motor Sales, U.S.A., Inc.

## LAND CRUISER, PICKUP/4RUNNER, VAN
## NO. 15 TEST (Cont.)
## INJECTOR CIRCUIT TEST

| Terminals | Trouble | Condition | STD Voltage |
|---|---|---|---|
| No. 10 – E01<br>No. 20 – E02 | No voltage | Ignition switch ON | 9 – 14 V |

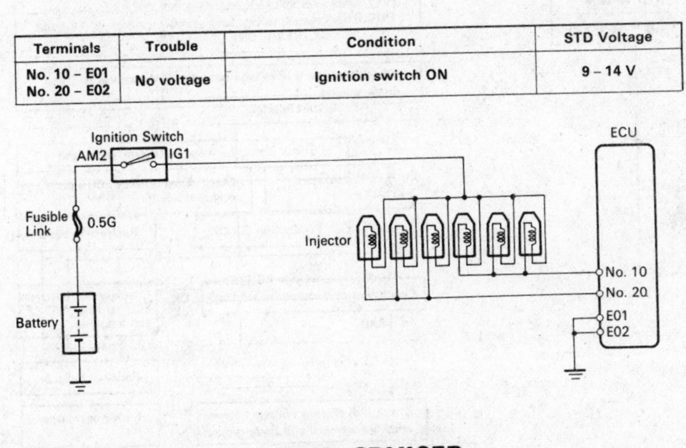
Ignition Switch
AM2
IG1
Fusible Link
0.5G
Injector
Battery
ECU
No. 10
No. 20
E01
E02

LAND CRUISER

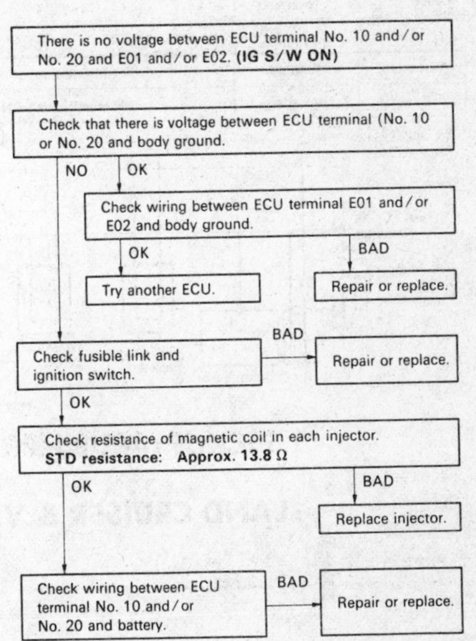
There is no voltage between ECU terminal No. 10 and/or No. 20 and E01 and/or E02. (IG S/W ON)
Check that there is voltage between ECU terminal (No. 10 or No. 20 and body ground.
NO
OK
Check wiring between ECU terminal E01 and/or E02 and body ground.
OK
BAD
Try another ECU.
Repair or replace.
Check fusible link and ignition switch.
BAD
Repair or replace.
OK
Check resistance of magnetic coil in each injector.
STD resistance: Approx. 13.8 Ω
OK
BAD
Replace injector.
Check wiring between ECU terminal No. 10 and/or No. 20 and battery.
BAD
Repair or replace.

## NO. 16 TEST
## ISC VALVE CIRCUIT TEST

| Terminals | Trouble | Condition | STD Voltage |
|---|---|---|---|
| ISC1 ~ ISC4 – E1 | No voltage | Ignition switch ON | 9 – 14 V |

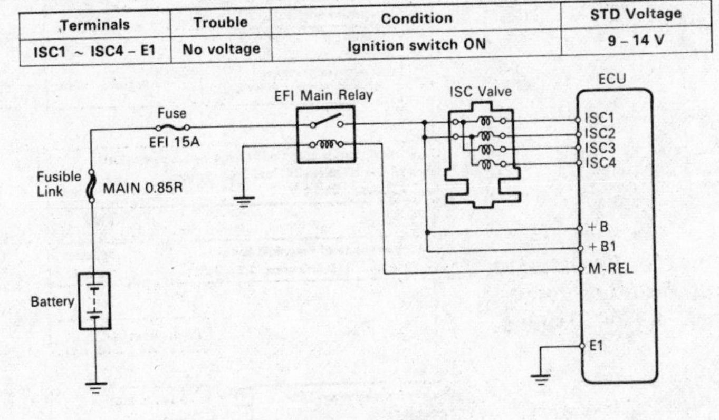
EFI Main Relay
ISC Valve
ECU
Fuse
EFI 15A
Fusible Link
MAIN 0.85R
Battery
ISC1
ISC2
ISC3
ISC4
+B
+B1
M-REL
E1

LAND CRUISER

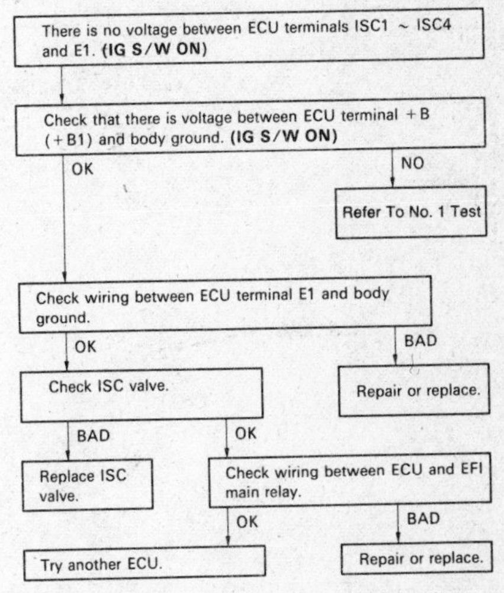
There is no voltage between ECU terminals ISC1 ~ ISC4 and E1. (IG S/W ON)
Check that there is voltage between ECU terminal +B (+B1) and body ground. (IG S/W ON)
OK
NO
Refer To No. 1 Test
Check wiring between ECU terminal E1 and body ground.
OK
BAD
Check ISC valve.
Repair or replace.
BAD
OK
Replace ISC valve.
Check wiring between ECU and EFI main relay.
OK
BAD
Try another ECU.
Repair or replace.

Courtesy of Toyota Motor Sales, U.S.A., Inc.

## LAND CRUISER, PICKUP/4RUNNER, VAN
## NO. 17 TEST
## A/C SYSTEM CIRCUIT TEST

| Terminals | Trouble | Condition | STD Voltage |
|---|---|---|---|
| A/C – E1 | No voltage | Air conditioning ON | 8 – 14 V |

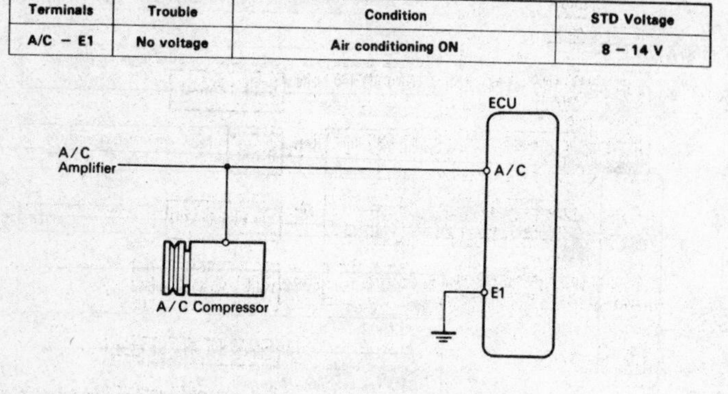
ECU
A/C Amplifier
A/C
E1
A/C Compressor

LAND CRUISER & VAN

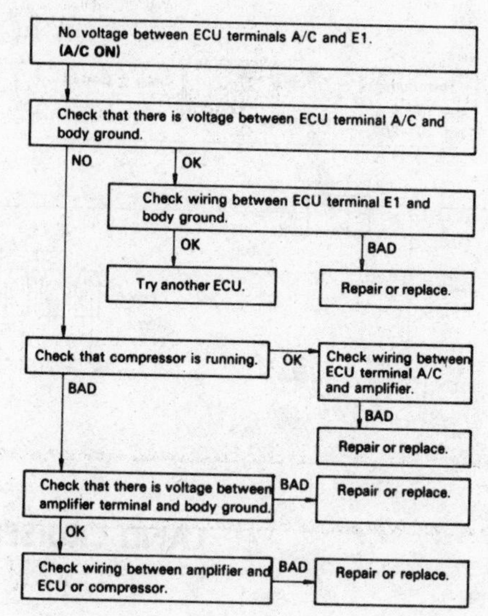
No voltage between ECU terminals A/C and E1. (A/C ON)
Check that there is voltage between ECU terminal A/C and body ground.
NO
OK
Check wiring between ECU terminal E1 and body ground.
OK
BAD
Try another ECU.
Repair or replace.
Check that compressor is running.
OK
Check wiring between ECU terminal A/C and amplifier.
BAD
Repair or replace.
BAD
Check that there is voltage between amplifier terminal and body ground.
BAD
Repair or replace.
OK
Check wiring between amplifier and ECU or compressor.
BAD
Repair or replace.

Courtesy of Toyota Motor Sales, U.S.A., Inc.

# 1988 COMPUTERIZED ENGINE CONTROLS
# Toyota Computer Control System (Cont.)

## DIAGNOSTIC CIRCUIT CHECK (MR2)

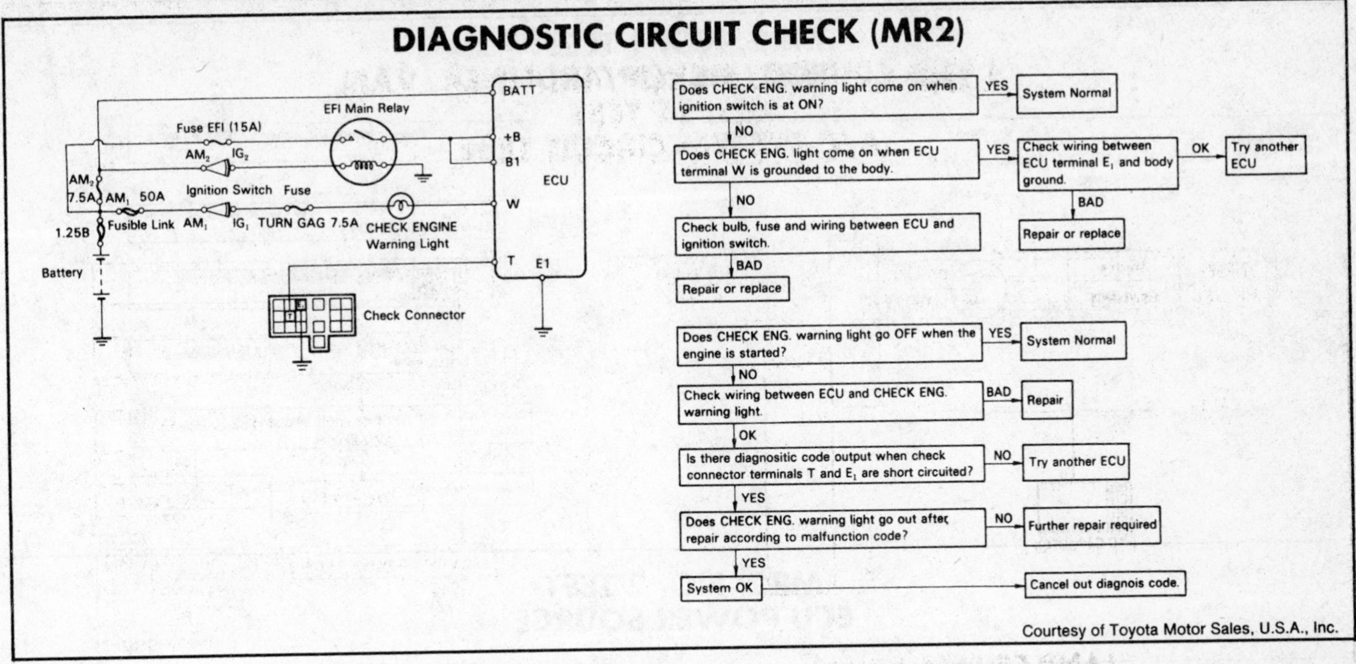

BATT
EFI Main Relay
Fuse EFI (15A)
$AM_2$
$IG_2$
+B
B1
ECU
$AM_2$
7.5A
$AM_1$ 50A
Ignition Switch
Fuse
W
1.25B
Fusible Link
$AM_1$
$IG_1$
TURN GAG 7.5A
CHECK ENGINE
Warning Light
Battery
T
E1
Check Connector
Does CHECK ENG. warning light come on when ignition switch is at ON?
YES
System Normal
NO
Does CHECK ENG. light come on when ECU terminal W is grounded to the body.
YES
Check wiring between ECU terminal $E_1$ and body ground.
OK
Try another ECU
NO
BAD
Check bulb, fuse and wiring between ECU and ignition switch.
Repair or replace
BAD
Repair or replace
Does CHECK ENG. warning light go OFF when the engine is started?
YES
System Normal
NO
Check wiring between ECU and CHECK ENG. warning light.
BAD
Repair
OK
Is there diagnositic code output when check connector terminals T and $E_1$ are short circuited?
NO
Try another ECU
YES
Does CHECK ENG. warning light go out after repair according to malfunction code?
NO
Further repair required
YES
System OK
Cancel out diagnois code.


Courtesy of Toyota Motor Sales, U.S.A., Inc.

## ECU PIN VOLTAGE TEST (MR2)

| Terminals | STD voltage | Condition | | Test No. |
|---|---|---|---|---|
| +B1 / +B – E1 | 10 – 14 | Ignition S/W ON | | 1 |
| BATT – E1 | 10 – 14 | – | | 2 |
| IDL – E2 | 10 – 14 | Ignition S/W ON | Throttle valve open | 8 |
| VTA – E2 | 0.1 – 1.0 | | Throttle valve fully closed | |
| | 4 – 5 | | Throttle valve fully open | |
| VCC – E2 | 4 – 6 | | – | |
| +B1 – E2 | 10 – 14 | Ignition S/W ON | – | 7 |
| VC – E2 | 6 – 10 | | – | |
| VS – E2 | 2 – 5.5 | | Measuring plate fully closed | |
| | 6 – 9 | | Measuring plate fully open | |
| | 2 – 8 | Idling | – | |
| No. 10 / No. 20 – E01 / E02 | 9 – 14 | Ignition S/W ON | | 12 |
| W – E1 | 9 – 14 | No trouble (Check engine warning light off) and engine running | | 13 |
| THA – E2 | 1 – 3 | Ignition S/W ON | Intake air temperature 20°C (68°F) | 5 |
| THW – E2 | 0.1 – 1.0 | Ignition S/W ON | Coolant temperature 80°C (176°F) | 4 |
| STA – E1 | 6 – 14 | Ignition S/W ST position and press on the clutch pedal (M/T) | | 9 |
| IGT – E1 | 0.7 – 1.0 | Idling | | 3 |
| A/C – E1 | 5 – 14 | Air conditioning ON | | 10 |

*1 : For A/T
*2 : For Calif.

Courtesy of Toyota Motor Sales, U.S.A., Inc.

# 1988 COMPUTERIZED ENGINE CONTROLS
# Toyota Computer Control System (Cont.)

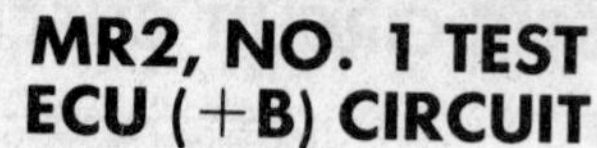

## MR2, NO. 1 TEST
## ECU (+B) CIRCUIT

| Terminals | Trouble | Condition | STD Voltage |
|---|---|---|---|
| +B1 – E1<br>+B | No voltage | Ignition switch ON | 10 – 14 V |

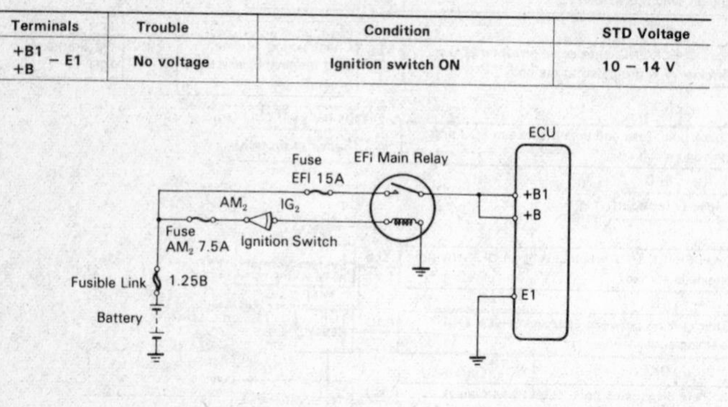

ECU
Fuse
EFI 15A
EFi Main Relay
$AM_2$
$IG_2$
+B1
+B
Fuse
$AM_2$ 7.5A
Ignition Switch
Fusible Link
1.25B
Battery
E1


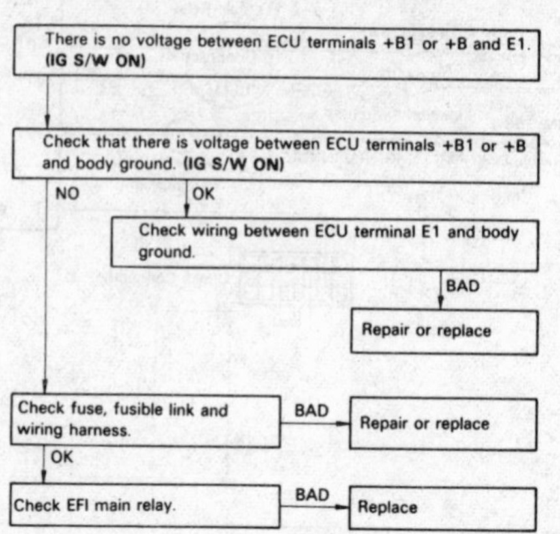

There is no voltage between ECU terminals +B1 or +B and E1. (IG S/W ON)
Check that there is voltage between ECU terminals +B1 or +B and body ground. (IG S/W ON)
NO
OK
Check wiring between ECU terminal E1 and body ground.
BAD
Repair or replace
Check fuse, fusible link and wiring harness.
BAD
Repair or replace
OK
Check EFI main relay.
BAD
Replace


## MR2, NO. 2 TEST
## ECU POWER SOURCE

| Terminals | Trouble | Condition | STD Voltage |
|---|---|---|---|
| BATT – E1 | No voltage | – | 10 – 14 V |

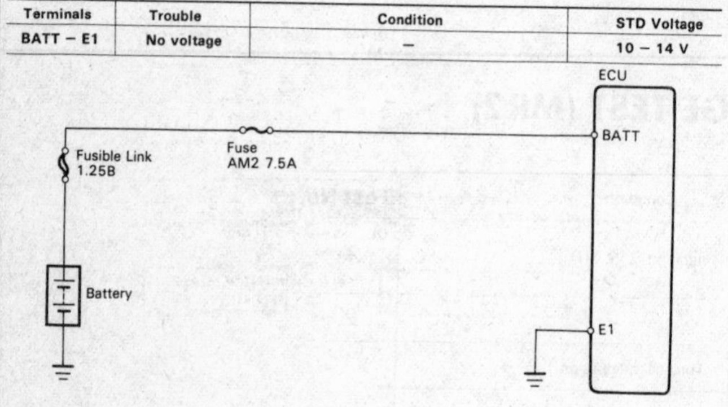

ECU
Fusible Link
1.25B
Fuse
AM2 7.5A
BATT
Battery
E1


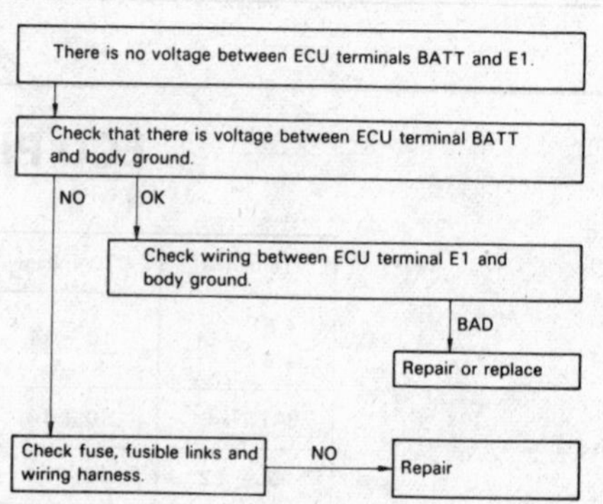

There is no voltage between ECU terminals BATT and E1.
Check that there is voltage between ECU terminal BATT and body ground.
NO
OK
Check wiring between ECU terminal E1 and body ground.
BAD
Repair or replace
Check fuse, fusible links and wiring harness.
NO
Repair


## MR2, NO. 3 TEST, CODE 12, 13, 14
## IGNITION & RPM SIGNAL

| Terminals | Trouble | Condition | STD Voltage |
|---|---|---|---|
| IGT – $E_1$ | No voltage | Idling | 0.7 – 1.0 V |

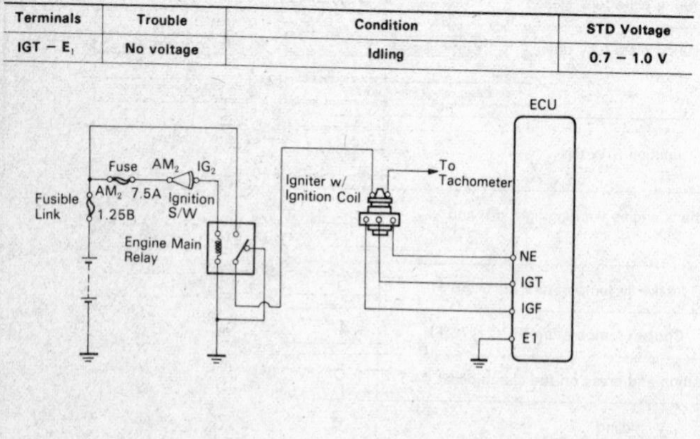

ECU
Fuse
$AM_2$
$IG_2$
Fusible Link
$AM_2$ 7.5A
1.25B
Ignition S/W
Engine Main Relay
Igniter w/ Ignition Coil
To Tachometer
NE
IGT
IGF
E1


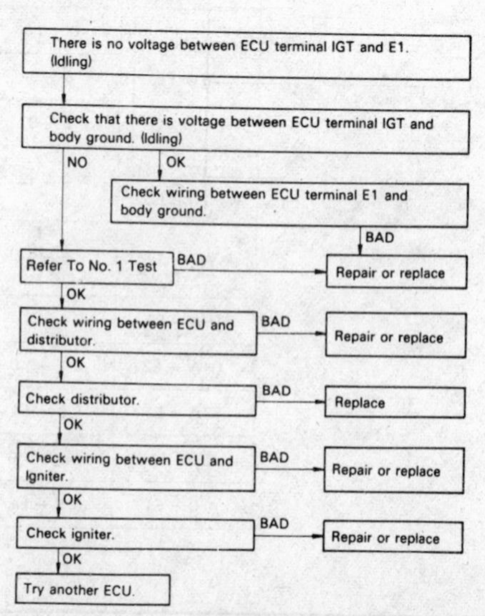

There is no voltage between ECU terminal IGT and E1. (Idling)
Check that there is voltage between ECU terminal IGT and body ground. (Idling)
NO
OK
Check wiring between ECU terminal E1 and body ground.
BAD
Refer To No. 1 Test
BAD
Repair or replace
OK
Check wiring between ECU and distributor.
BAD
Repair or replace
OK
Check distributor.
BAD
Replace
OK
Check wiring between ECU and Igniter.
BAD
Repair or replace
OK
Check igniter.
BAD
Repair or replace
OK
Try another ECU.


NOTE: To check ignitor, see TOYOTA ELECTRONIC IGNITION SYSTEM article in DISTRIBUTORS & IGNITION SYSTEMS section.

Courtesy of Toyota Motor Sales, U.S.A., Inc.

# 1988 COMPUTERIZED ENGINE CONTROLS
# Toyota Computer Control System (Cont.)

## MR2, NO. 4 TEST, CODE 22
## COOLANT TEMP. SENSOR CIRCUIT

| Terminals | Trouble | Condition | | STD Voltage |
|---|---|---|---|---|
| THW – E2 | No voltage | Ignition switch ON | Coolant temperature 80°C (176°F) | 0.1 – 1.0 V |

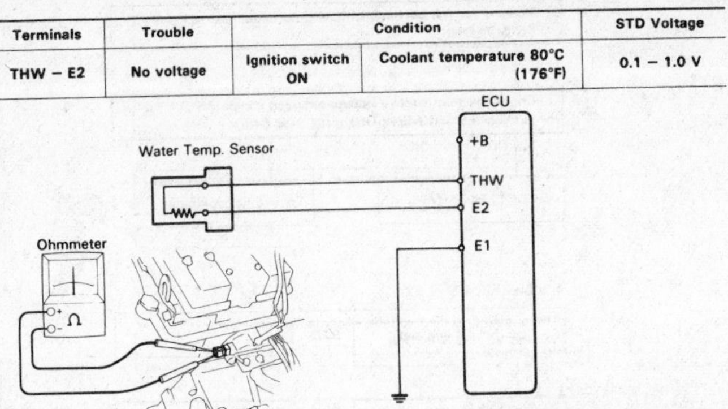

ECU
Water Temp. Sensor
+B
THW
E2
E1
Ohmmeter


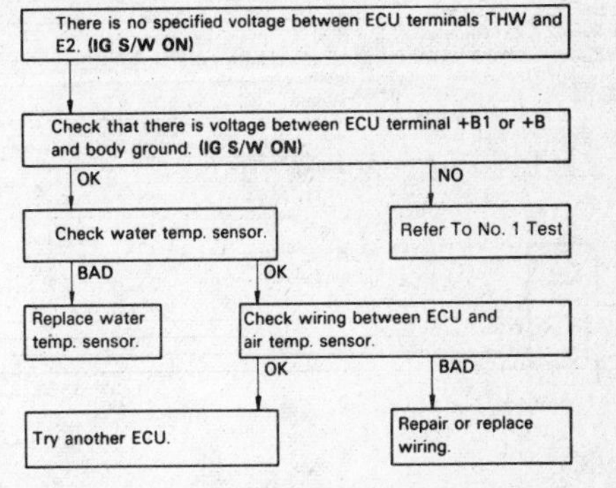

There is no specified voltage between ECU terminals THW and E2. (IG S/W ON)
Check that there is voltage between ECU terminal +B1 or +B and body ground. (IG S/W ON)
OK
NO
Check water temp. sensor.
Refer To No. 1 Test
BAD
OK
Replace water temp. sensor.
Check wiring between ECU and air temp. sensor.
OK
BAD
Try another ECU.
Repair or replace wiring.


## MR2, NO. 5 TEST, CODE 24
## AIR TEMP. SENSOR CIRCUIT (NON-TURBO)

| Terminals | Trouble | Condition | | STD voltage |
|---|---|---|---|---|
| THA – E2 | No voltage | Ignition switch ON | Intake air temperature 20°C (68°F) | 1 – 3 V |

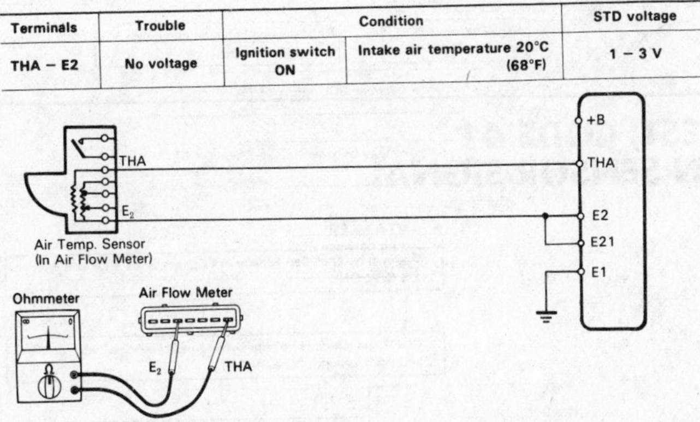

+B
THA
THA
E2
E2
E21
E1
Air Temp. Sensor (In Air Flow Meter)
Ohmmeter
Air Flow Meter
E2
THA


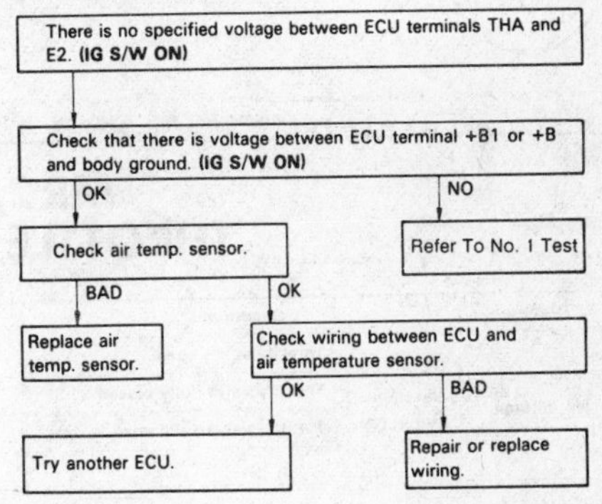

There is no specified voltage between ECU terminals THA and E2. (IG S/W ON)
Check that there is voltage between ECU terminal +B1 or +B and body ground. (IG S/W ON)
OK
NO
Check air temp. sensor.
Refer To No. 1 Test
BAD
OK
Replace air temp. sensor.
Check wiring between ECU and air temperature sensor.
OK
BAD
Try another ECU.
Repair or replace wiring.


## MR2, NO. 6 TEST, CODE 25, 26
## $O_2$ SENSOR CIRCUIT

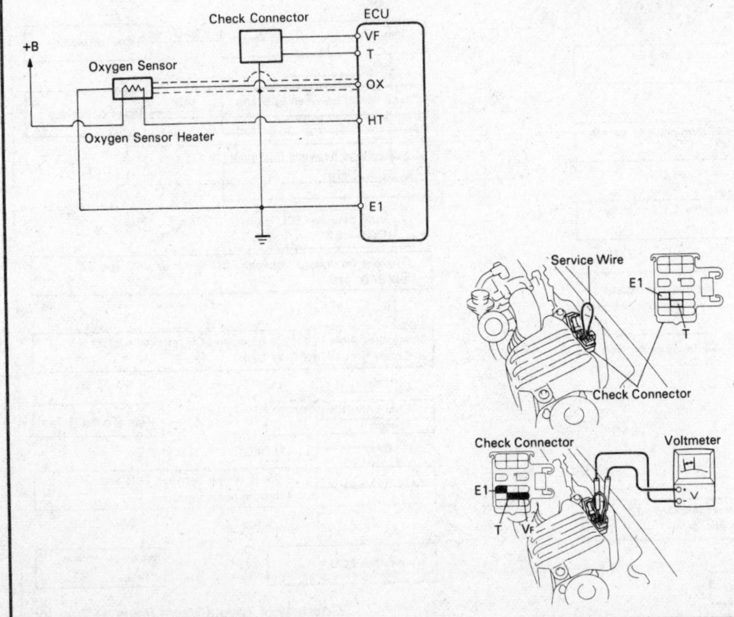

Check Connector
ECU
+B
VF
T
Oxygen Sensor
OX
HT
Oxygen Sensor Heater
E1
Service Wire
E1
T
Check Connector
Check Connector
Voltmeter
E1
T
VF


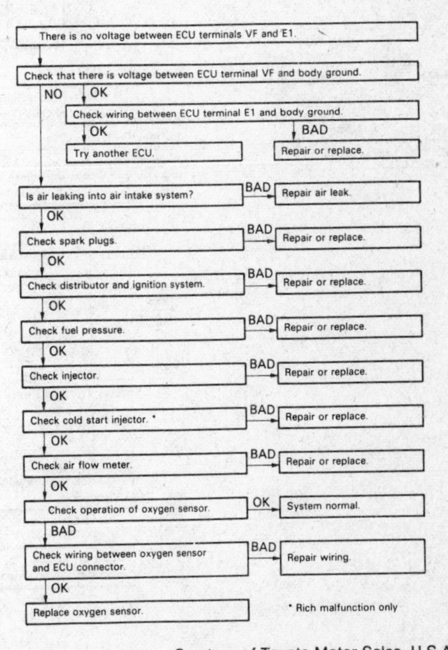

There is no voltage between ECU terminals VF and E1.
Check that there is voltage between ECU terminal VF and body ground.
NO
OK
Check wiring between ECU terminal E1 and body ground.
OK
BAD
Try another ECU.
Repair or replace.
Is air leaking into air intake system?
BAD
Repair air leak.
OK
Check spark plugs.
BAD
Repair or replace.
OK
Check distributor and ignition system.
BAD
Repair or replace.
OK
Check fuel pressure.
BAD
Repair or replace.
OK
Check injector.
BAD
Repair or replace.
OK
Check cold start injector. *
BAD
Repair or replace.
OK
Check air flow meter.
BAD
Repair or replace.
OK
Check operation of oxygen sensor.
OK
System normal.
BAD
Check wiring between oxygen sensor and ECU connector.
BAD
Repair wiring.
OK
Replace oxygen sensor.
* Rich malfunction only


Courtesy of Toyota Motor Sales, U.S.A., Inc.

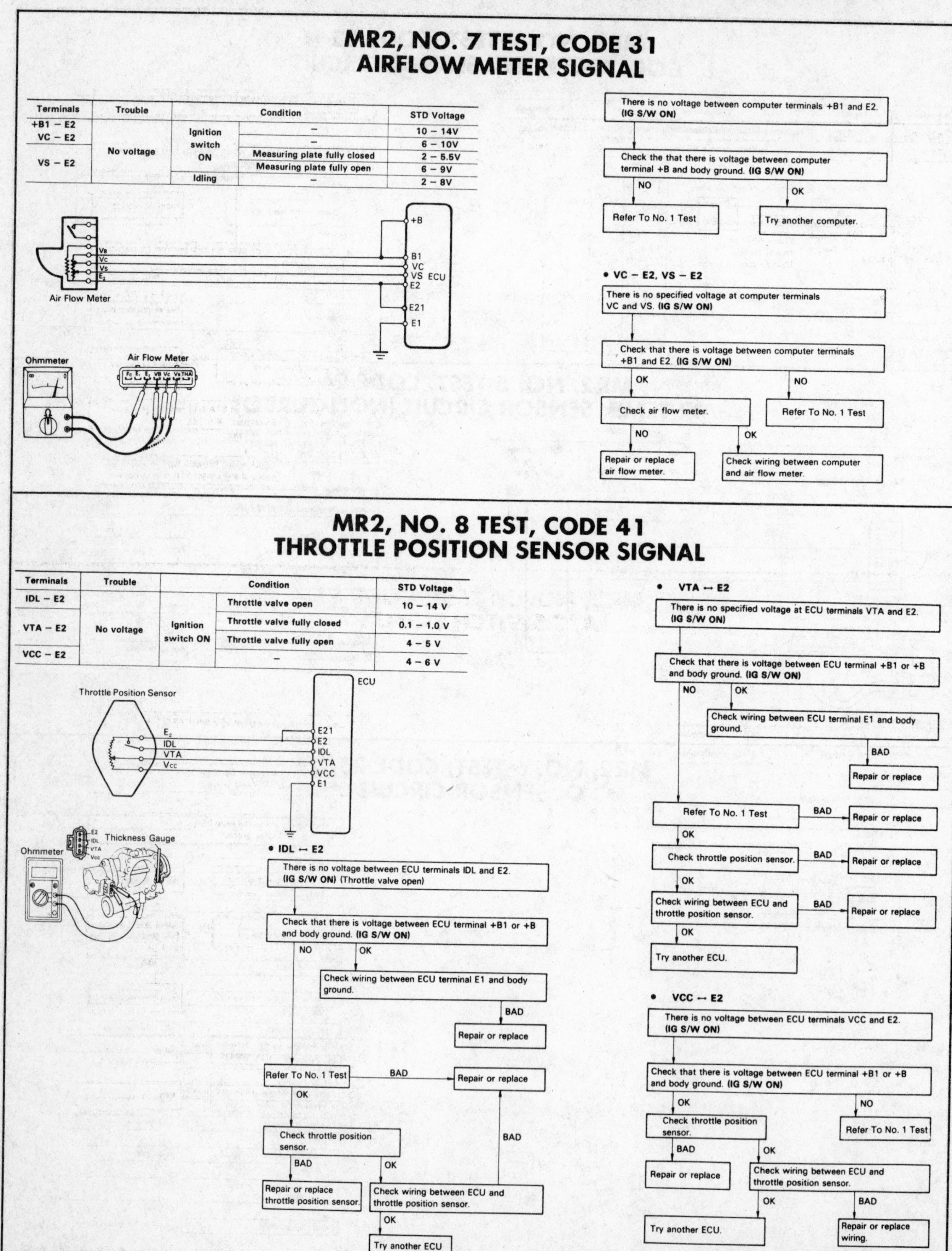

## MR2, NO. 7 TEST, CODE 31
## AIRFLOW METER SIGNAL

| Terminals | Trouble | Condition | | STD Voltage |
|---|---|---|---|---|
| +B1 – E2 | No voltage | Ignition switch ON | – | 10 – 14V |
| VC – E2 | | | – | 6 – 10V |
| VS – E2 | | | Measuring plate fully closed | 2 – 5.5V |
| | | | Measuring plate fully open | 6 – 9V |
| | | Idling | – | 2 – 8V |

Air Flow Meter
Vs
Vc
Vs
E2
+B
B1
VC
VS
ECU
E2
E21
E1
Ohmmeter
Air Flow Meter
Fc
E2
E1
VB
Vc
Vs
THA
There is no voltage between computer terminals +B1 and E2. (IG S/W ON)
Check the that there is voltage between computer terminal +B and body ground. (IG S/W ON)
NO
OK
Refer To No. 1 Test
Try another computer.
• VC – E2, VS – E2
There is no specified voltage at computer terminals VC and VS. (IG S/W ON)
Check that there is voltage between computer terminals +B1 and E2. (IG S/W ON)
OK
NO
Check air flow meter.
Refer To No. 1 Test
NO
OK
Repair or replace air flow meter.
Check wiring between computer and air flow meter.

## MR2, NO. 8 TEST, CODE 41
## THROTTLE POSITION SENSOR SIGNAL

| Terminals | Trouble | Condition | | STD Voltage |
|---|---|---|---|---|
| IDL – E2 | No voltage | Ignition switch ON | Throttle valve open | 10 – 14 V |
| VTA – E2 | | | Throttle valve fully closed | 0.1 – 1.0 V |
| | | | Throttle valve fully open | 4 – 5 V |
| VCC – E2 | | | – | 4 – 6 V |

Throttle Position Sensor
E2
IDL
VTA
Vcc
ECU
E21
E2
IDL
VTA
VCC
E1
Ohmmeter
Thickness Gauge
E2
IDL
VTA
Vcc
• IDL ↔ E2
There is no voltage between ECU terminals IDL and E2. (IG S/W ON) (Throttle valve open)
Check that there is voltage between ECU terminal +B1 or +B and body ground. (IG S/W ON)
NO
OK
Check wiring between ECU terminal E1 and body ground.
BAD
Repair or replace
Refer To No. 1 Test
BAD
Repair or replace
OK
Check throttle position sensor.
BAD
BAD
OK
Repair or replace throttle position sensor.
Check wiring between ECU and throttle position sensor.
OK
Try another ECU
• VTA ↔ E2
There is no specified voltage at ECU terminals VTA and E2. (IG S/W ON)
Check that there is voltage between ECU terminal +B1 or +B and body ground. (IG S/W ON)
NO
OK
Check wiring between ECU terminal E1 and body ground.
BAD
Repair or replace
Refer To No. 1 Test
BAD
Repair or replace
OK
Check throttle position sensor.
BAD
Repair or replace
OK
Check wiring between ECU and throttle position sensor.
BAD
Repair or replace
OK
Try another ECU.
• VCC ↔ E2
There is no voltage between ECU terminals VCC and E2. (IG S/W ON)
Check that there is voltage between ECU terminal +B1 or +B and body ground. (IG S/W ON)
OK
NO
Check throttle position sensor.
Refer To No. 1 Test
BAD
OK
Repair or replace
Check wiring between ECU and throttle position sensor.
OK
BAD
Try another ECU.
Repair or replace wiring.

Courtesy of Toyota Motor Sales, U.S.A., Inc.

# MR2, NO. 9 TEST, CODE 43
## STARTER SIGNAL

| Terminals | Trouble | Condition | STD Voltage |
|---|---|---|---|
| STA – E1 | No voltage | Ignition switch ST position | 6 – 14 V |

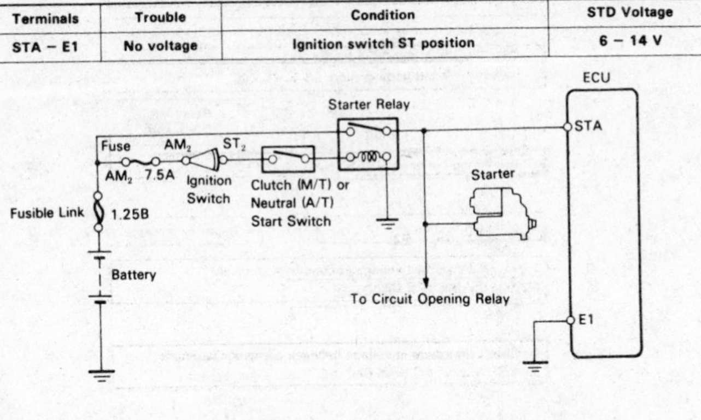
ECU
Starter Relay
STA
Fuse
$AM_2$
$ST_2$
$AM_2$
7.5A
Ignition Switch
Clutch (M/T) or Neutral (A/T) Start Switch
Starter
Fusible Link
1.25B
Battery
To Circuit Opening Relay
E1

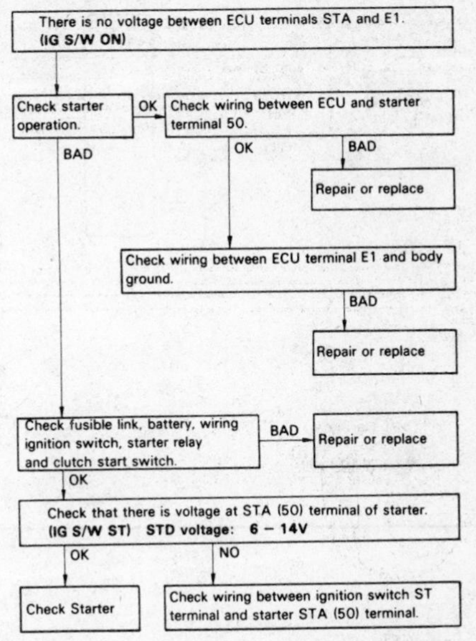
There is no voltage between ECU terminals STA and E1. (IG S/W ON)
Check starter operation.
OK
Check wiring between ECU and starter terminal 50.
BAD
OK
BAD
Repair or replace
Check wiring between ECU terminal E1 and body ground.
BAD
Repair or replace
Check fusible link, battery, wiring ignition switch, starter relay and clutch start switch.
BAD
Repair or replace
OK
Check that there is voltage at STA (50) terminal of starter. (IG S/W ST) STD voltage: 6 – 14V
OK
NO
Check Starter
Check wiring between ignition switch ST terminal and starter STA (50) terminal.

# MR2, NO. 10 TEST, CODE 51
## A/C SWITCH SIGNAL

| Terminals | Trouble | Condition | STD Voltage |
|---|---|---|---|
| A/C – E1 | No voltage | Air conditioning ON | 5 – 14 V |

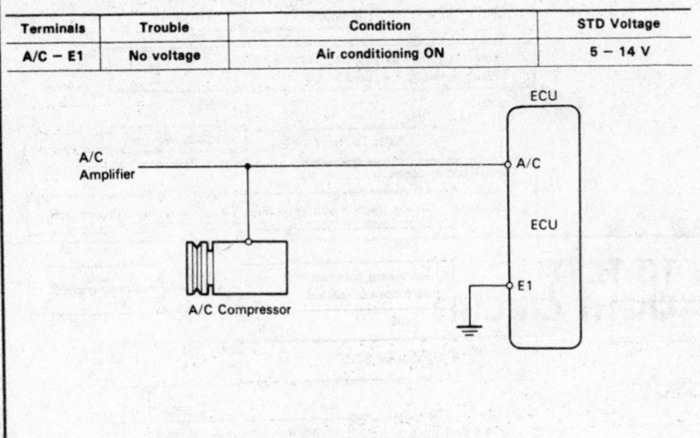
ECU
A/C Amplifier
A/C
ECU
E1
A/C Compressor

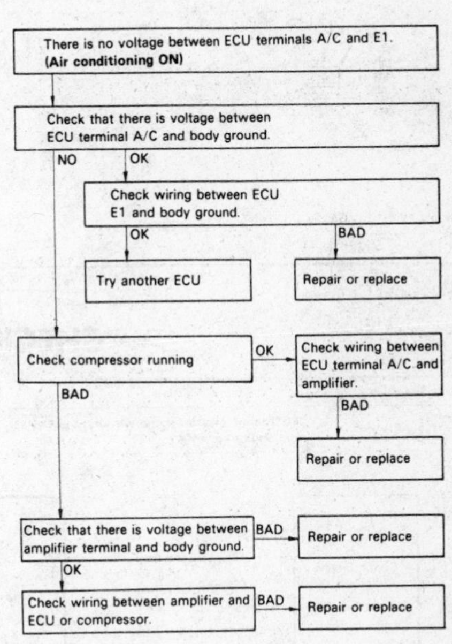
There is no voltage between ECU terminals A/C and E1. (Air conditioning ON)
Check that there is voltage between ECU terminal A/C and body ground.
NO
OK
Check wiring between ECU E1 and body ground.
OK
BAD
Try another ECU
Repair or replace
Check compressor running
OK
Check wiring between ECU terminal A/C and amplifier.
BAD
BAD
Repair or replace
Check that there is voltage between amplifier terminal and body ground.
BAD
Repair or replace
OK
Check wiring between amplifier and ECU or compressor.
BAD
Repair or replace

Courtesy of Toyota Motor Sales, U.S.A., Inc.

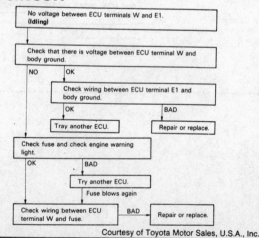

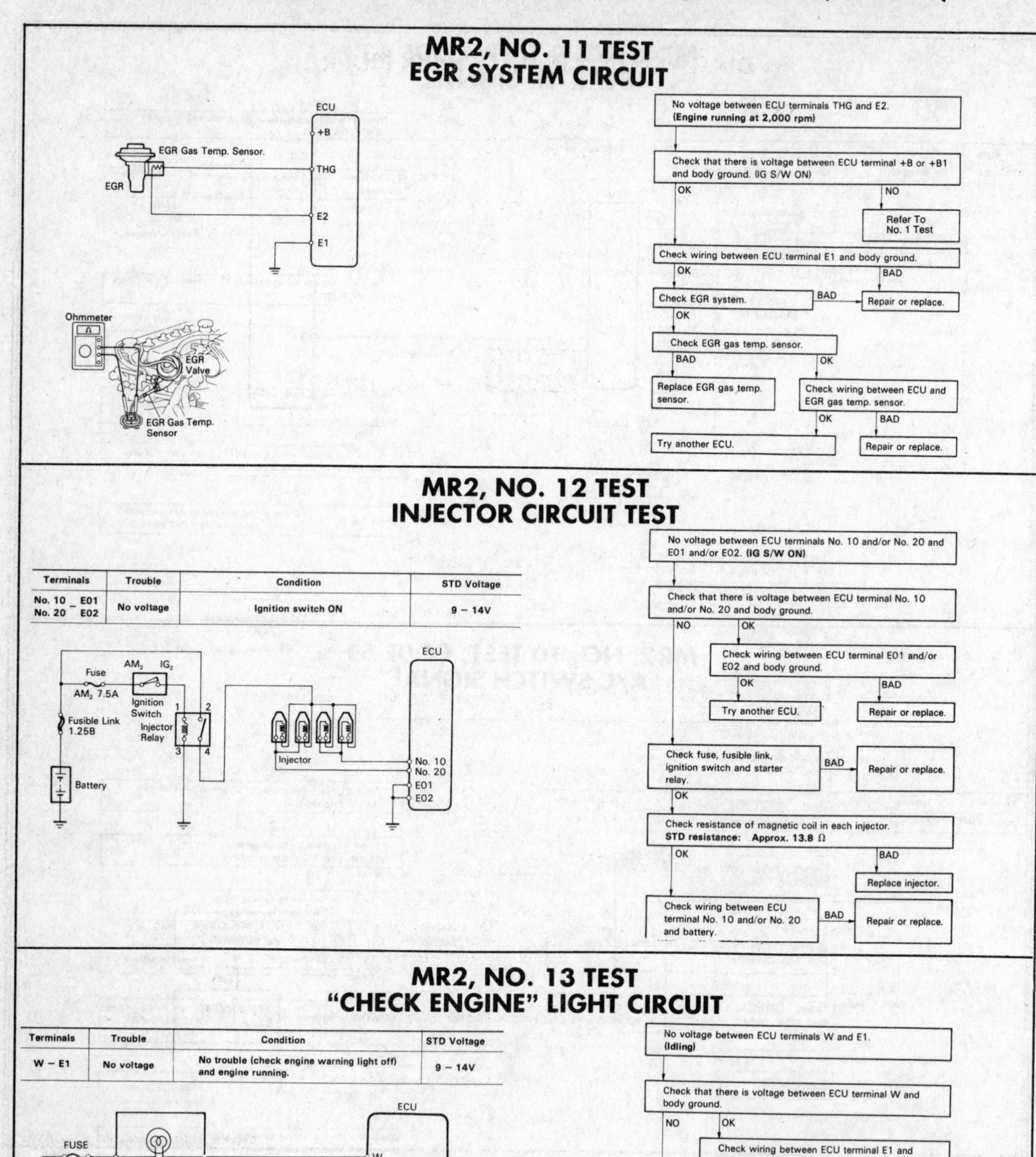

## MR2, NO. 11 TEST
## EGR SYSTEM CIRCUIT

ECU
+B
EGR Gas Temp. Sensor.
THG
EGR
E2
E1
Ohmmeter
EGR Valve
EGR Gas Temp. Sensor
No voltage between ECU terminals THG and E2. (Engine running at 2,000 rpm)
Check that there is voltage between ECU terminal +B or +B1 and body ground. (IG S/W ON)
OK
NO
Refer To No. 1 Test
Check wiring between ECU terminal E1 and body ground.
OK
BAD
Check EGR system.
BAD
Repair or replace.
OK
Check EGR gas temp. sensor.
BAD
OK
Replace EGR gas temp. sensor.
Check wiring between ECU and EGR gas temp. sensor.
OK
BAD
Try another ECU.
Repair or replace.

## MR2, NO. 12 TEST
## INJECTOR CIRCUIT TEST

| Terminals | Trouble | Condition | STD Voltage |
|---|---|---|---|
| No. 10 – E01<br>No. 20 – E02 | No voltage | Ignition switch ON | 9 – 14V |

Fuse
AM2 7.5A
AM2
IG2
Ignition Switch
Fusible Link 1.25B
Injector Relay
1
2
3
4
Battery
Injector
ECU
No. 10
No. 20
E01
E02
No voltage between ECU terminals No. 10 and/or No. 20 and E01 and/or E02. (IG S/W ON)
Check that there is voltage between ECU terminal No. 10 and/or No. 20 and body ground.
NO
OK
Check wiring between ECU terminal E01 and/or E02 and body ground.
OK
BAD
Try another ECU.
Repair or replace.
Check fuse, fusible link, ignition switch and starter relay.
BAD
Repair or replace.
OK
Check resistance of magnetic coil in each injector.
STD resistance: Approx. 13.8 Ω
OK
BAD
Replace injector.
Check wiring between ECU terminal No. 10 and/or No. 20 and battery.
BAD
Repair or replace.

## MR2, NO. 13 TEST
## "CHECK ENGINE" LIGHT CIRCUIT

| Terminals | Trouble | Condition | STD Voltage |
|---|---|---|---|
| W – E1 | No voltage | No trouble (check engine warning light off) and engine running. | 9 – 14V |

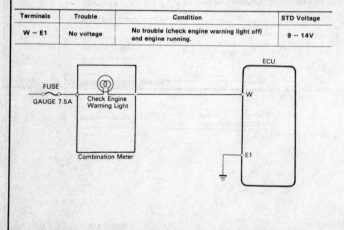

ECU
FUSE
GAUGE 7.5A
Check Engine Warning Light
W
Combination Meter
E1
No voltage between ECU terminals W and E1. (Idling)
Check that there is voltage between ECU terminal W and body ground.
NO
OK
Check wiring between ECU terminal E1 and body ground.
OK
BAD
Tray another ECU.
Repair or replace.
Check fuse and check engine warning light.
OK
BAD
Try another ECU.
Fuse blows again
Check wiring between ECU terminal W and fuse.
BAD
Repair or replace.

Courtesy of Toyota Motor Sales, U.S.A., Inc.

## DIAGNOSTIC CIRCUIT CHECK (SUPRA)

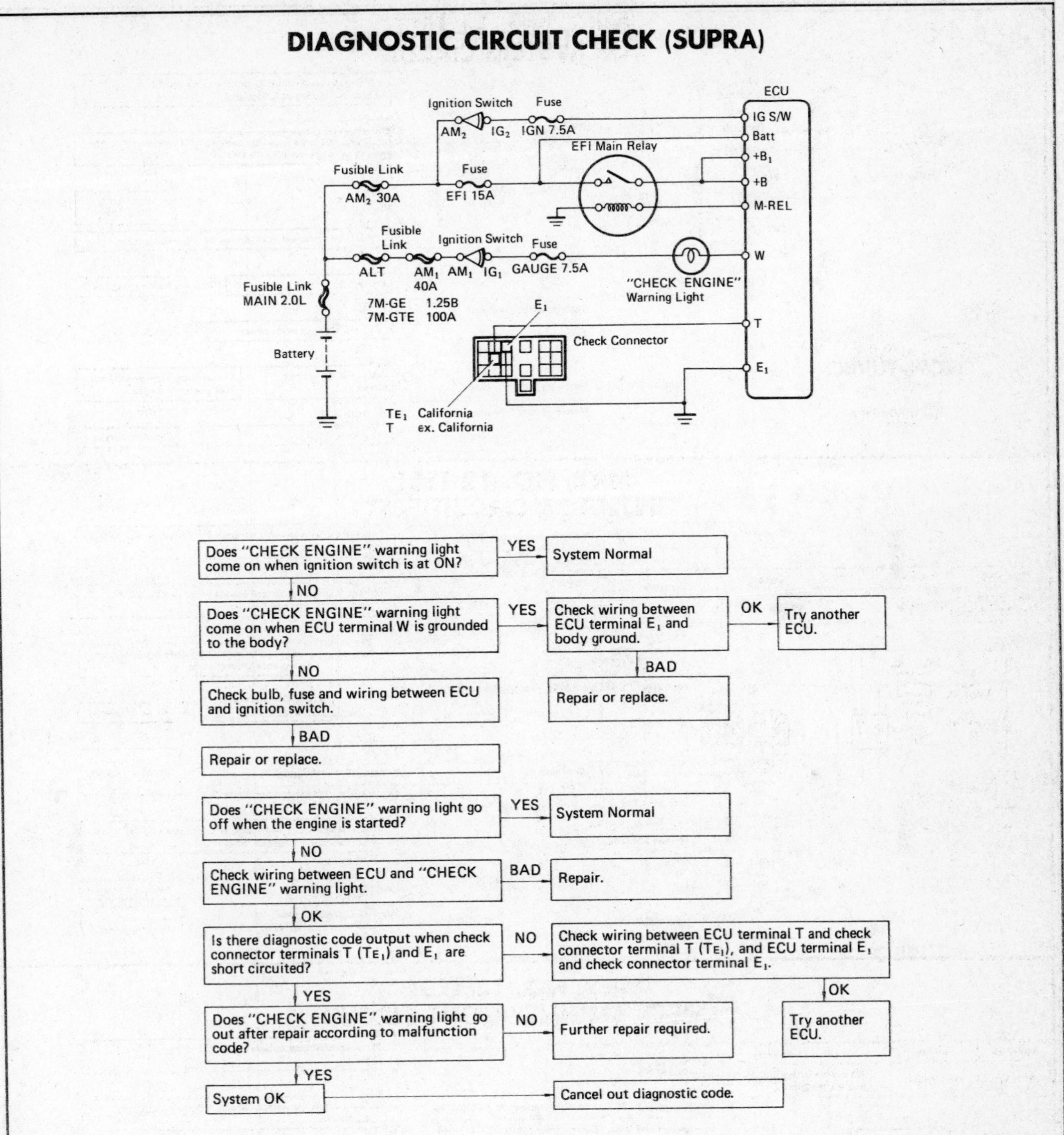
ECU
Ignition Switch
Fuse
AM2
IG2
IGN 7.5A
IG S/W
Batt
EFI Main Relay
+B1
+B
M-REL
Fusible Link
AM2 30A
EFI 15A
Fusible Link
Ignition Switch
ALT
AM1
AM1
IG1
GAUGE 7.5A
40A
W
"CHECK ENGINE" Warning Light
Fusible Link MAIN 2.0L
7M-GE 1.25B
7M-GTE 100A
E1
T
Check Connector
Battery
E1
TE1 California
T ex. California
Does "CHECK ENGINE" warning light come on when ignition switch is at ON?
YES
System Normal
NO
Does "CHECK ENGINE" warning light come on when ECU terminal W is grounded to the body?
YES
Check wiring between ECU terminal E1 and body ground.
OK
Try another ECU.
BAD
Repair or replace.
NO
Check bulb, fuse and wiring between ECU and ignition switch.
BAD
Repair or replace.
Does "CHECK ENGINE" warning light go off when the engine is started?
YES
System Normal
NO
Check wiring between ECU and "CHECK ENGINE" warning light.
BAD
Repair.
OK
Is there diagnostic code output when check connector terminals T (TE1) and E1 are short circuited?
NO
Check wiring between ECU terminal T and check connector terminal T (TE1), and ECU terminal E1 and check connector terminal E1.
OK
Try another ECU.
YES
Does "CHECK ENGINE" warning light go out after repair according to malfunction code?
NO
Further repair required.
YES
System OK
Cancel out diagnostic code.

Courtesy of Toyota Motor Sales, U.S.A., Inc.

## ECU PIN VOLTAGE TEST (SUPRA)

### NON-TURBO

| Terminals | Condition | | STD Voltage | Test No. |
|---|---|---|---|---|
| Batt – $E_1$ | – | | 10 – 14 | 1 |
| IG S/W – $E_1$ | Ignition S/W ON | | 10 – 14 | |
| M-REL – $E_1$ | | | | |
| +B (+$B_1$) – $E_1$ | | | | |
| IDL – $E_2$ | Ignition S/W ON | Throttle valve open | 10 – 14 | 6 |
| Vc – $E_2$ | | – | 4 – 6 | |
| VTA – $E_2$ | | Throttle valve fully closed | 0.1 – 1.0 | |
| | | Throttle valve fully open | 4 – 5 | |
| Vc – $E_2$ | Ignition S/W ON | – | 4 – 6 | 5 |
| Vs – $E_2$ | | Measuring plate fully closed | 4 – 5 | |
| | | Measuring plate fully open | 0.02 – 0.08 | |
| | Idling | | 2 – 4 | |
| | 3,000 rpm | | 0.3 – 1.0 | |
| No. 10, No. 20, No. 30 – $E_{01}$, $E_{02}$ | Ignition S/W ON | | 9 – 14 | 9 |
| THA – $E_2$ | Ignition S/W ON | Intake air temperature 20°C (68°F) | 1 – 3 | 4 |
| THW – $E_2$ | Ignition S/W ON | Coolant temperature 80°C (176°F) | 0.1 – 1.0 | 3 |
| STA – $E_1$ | Cranking | | 6 – 14 | 7 |
| IGf, IGt – $E_1$ | Idling | | 0.7 – 1.0 | 2 |
| $ISC_1$ ~ $ISC_4$ – $E_1$ | Ignition S/W ON | | 9 – 14 | 12 |
| W – $E_1$ | No trouble ("CHECK ENGINE" warning light off) and engine running | | 9 – 14 | 13 |
| A/C – $E_1$ | Air conditioning ON | | 10 – 14 | 14 |

### TURBO

| Terminals | Condition | | STD Voltage | Test No. |
|---|---|---|---|---|
| Batt – $E_1$ | – | | 10 – 14 | 1 |
| IG S/W – $E_1$ | Ignition S/W ON | | 10 – 14 | |
| M-REL – $E_1$ | | | | |
| +B (+$B_1$) – $E_1$ | | | | |
| IDL – $E_2$ | Ignition S/W ON | Throttle valve open | 10 – 14 | 6 |
| Vc – $E_2$ | | – | 4 – 6 | |
| VTA – $E_2$ | | Throttle valve fully closed | 0.1 – 1.0 | |
| | | Throttle valve fully open | 4 – 5 | |
| Ks – Body ground | Ignition S/W ON | | 4 – 6 | 10 |
| | Cranking or running | | 2 – 4 | |
| Vc – Body ground | Ignition S/W ON | | 4 – 6 | |
| No. 10, No. 20, No. 30 – $E_{01}$, $E_{02}$ | Ignition S/W ON | | 9 – 14 | 9 |
| THA – $E_2$ | Ignition S/W ON | Intake air temperature 20°C (68°F) | 1 – 3 | 4 |
| THW – $E_2$ | Ignition S/W ON | Coolant temperature 80°C (176°F) | 0.1 – 1.0 | 3 |
| STA – $E_1$ | Cranking | | 6 – 14 | 7 |
| IGf, IGt – $E_1$ | Idling | | 0.7 – 1.0 | 2 |
| IGdA, IGDB – $E_1$ | Idling | | 1 – 3 | 11 |
| $ISC_1$ ~ $ISC_4$ – $E_1$ | Ignition S/W ON | | 9 – 14 | 12 |
| W – $E_1$ | No trouble ("CHECK ENGINE" warning light off) and engine running | | 9 – 14 | 13 |
| A/C – $E_1$ | Air conditioning ON | | 10 – 14 | 14 |
| HAC – $E_2$ | Ignition S/W ON | 540 mmHg (21.26 in.Hg, 72.0 kPa) | Approx. 2.8 | 15 |
| | | 750 mmHg (29.53 in.Hg, 100.0 kPa) | Approx. 3.6 | |

Courtesy of Toyota Motor Sales, U.S.A., Inc.

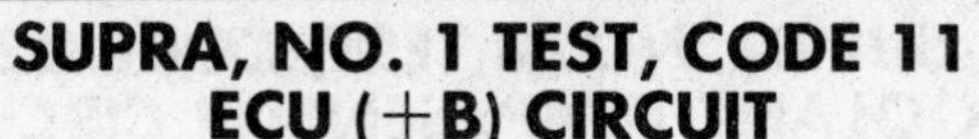

## SUPRA, NO. 1 TEST, CODE 11
## ECU (+B) CIRCUIT

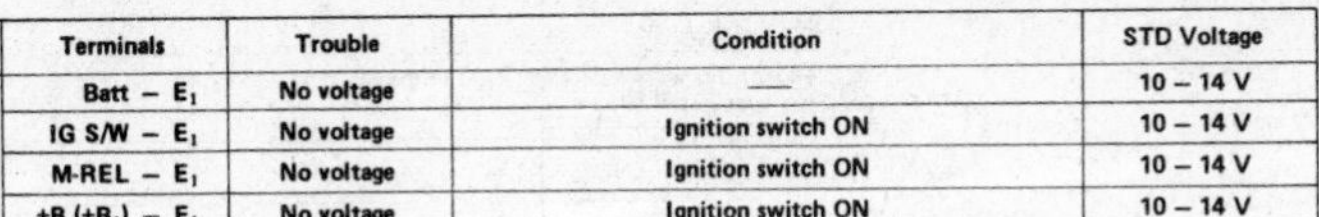

| Terminals | Trouble | Condition | STD Voltage |
|---|---|---|---|
| Batt – $E_1$ | No voltage | — | 10 – 14 V |
| IG S/W – $E_1$ | No voltage | Ignition switch ON | 10 – 14 V |
| M-REL – $E_1$ | No voltage | Ignition switch ON | 10 – 14 V |
| +B (+$B_1$) – $E_1$ | No voltage | Ignition switch ON | 10 – 14 V |

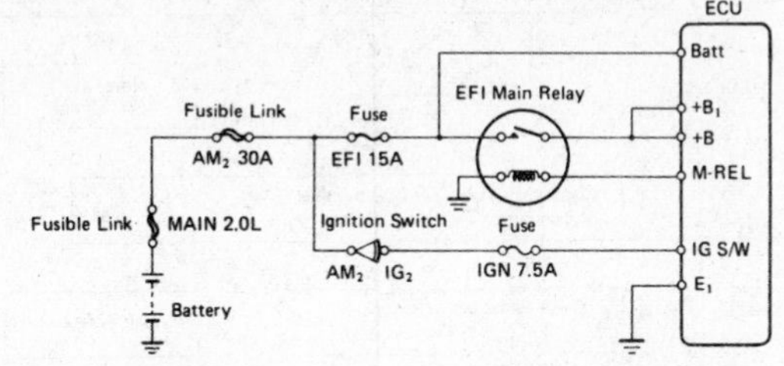
ECU
Batt
EFI Main Relay
Fusible Link
Fuse
+B1
+B
AM2 30A
EFI 15A
M-REL
Fusible Link
MAIN 2.0L
Ignition Switch
Fuse
IG S/W
AM2
IG2
IGN 7.5A
E1
Battery

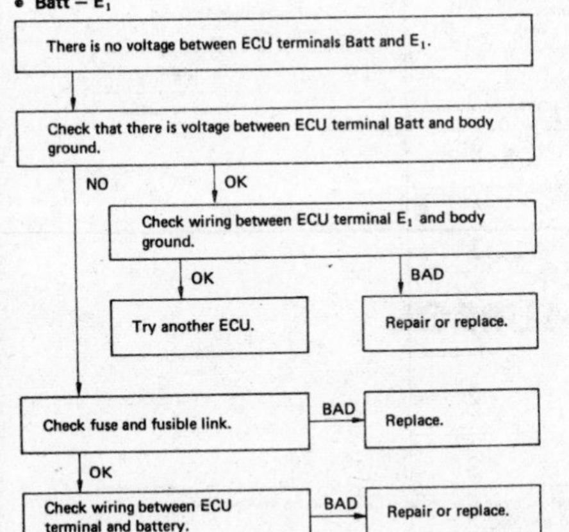
• Batt – E1
There is no voltage between ECU terminals Batt and E1.
Check that there is voltage between ECU terminal Batt and body ground.
NO
OK
Check wiring between ECU terminal E1 and body ground.
OK
BAD
Try another ECU.
Repair or replace.
Check fuse and fusible link.
BAD
Replace.
OK
Check wiring between ECU terminal and battery.
BAD
Repair or replace.

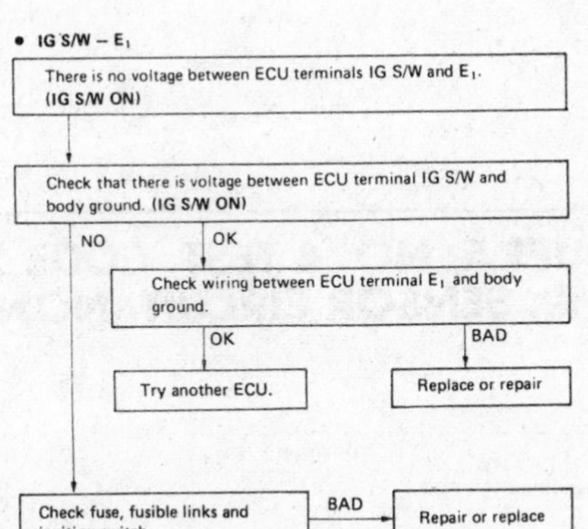
• IG S/W – E1
There is no voltage between ECU terminals IG S/W and E1. (IG S/W ON)
Check that there is voltage between ECU terminal IG S/W and body ground. (IG S/W ON)
NO
OK
Check wiring between ECU terminal E1 and body ground.
OK
BAD
Try another ECU.
Replace or repair
Check fuse, fusible links and ignition switch.
BAD
Repair or replace

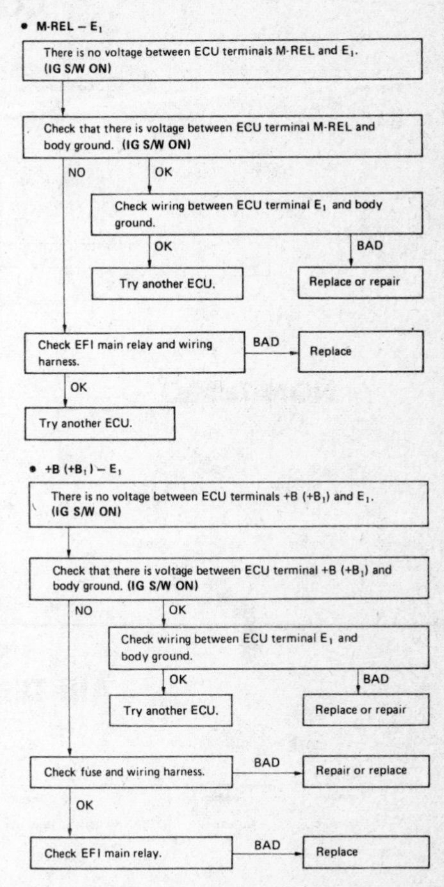
• M-REL – E1
There is no voltage between ECU terminals M-REL and E1. (IG S/W ON)
Check that there is voltage between ECU terminal M-REL and body ground. (IG S/W ON)
NO
OK
Check wiring between ECU terminal E1 and body ground.
OK
BAD
Try another ECU.
Replace or repair
Check EFI main relay and wiring harness.
BAD
Replace
OK
Try another ECU.
• +B (+B1) – E1
There is no voltage between ECU terminals +B (+B1) and E1. (IG S/W ON)
Check that there is voltage between ECU terminal +B (+B1) and body ground. (IG S/W ON)
NO
OK
Check wiring between ECU terminal E1 and body ground.
OK
BAD
Try another ECU.
Replace or repair
Check fuse and wiring harness.
BAD
Repair or replace
OK
Check EFI main relay.
BAD
Replace

## SUPRA, NO. 2 TEST, CODE 12, 13, 14
## IGNITION & RPM SIGNAL

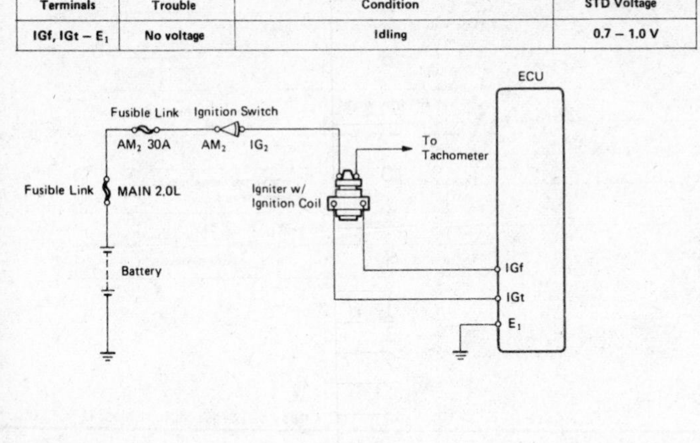

| Terminals | Trouble | Condition | STD Voltage |
|---|---|---|---|
| IGf, IGt – $E_1$ | No voltage | Idling | 0.7 – 1.0 V |

ECU
Fusible Link
Ignition Switch
AM2 30A
AM2
IG2
To Tachometer
Fusible Link
MAIN 2.0L
Igniter w/ Ignition Coil
Battery
IGf
IGt
E1

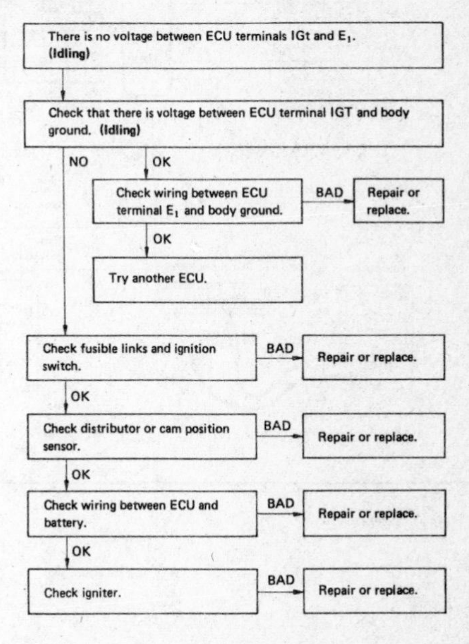
There is no voltage between ECU terminals IGt and E1. (Idling)
Check that there is voltage between ECU terminal IGT and body ground. (Idling)
NO
OK
Check wiring between ECU terminal E1 and body ground.
BAD
Repair or replace.
OK
Try another ECU.
Check fusible links and ignition switch.
BAD
Repair or replace.
OK
Check distributor or cam position sensor.
BAD
Repair or replace.
OK
Check wiring between ECU and battery.
BAD
Repair or replace.
OK
Check igniter.
BAD
Repair or replace.

NOTE: To check ignitor, see TOYOTA ELECTRONIC IGNITION SYSTEM article in DISTRIBUTORS & IGNITION SYSTEMS section.

## SUPRA, NO. 3 TEST, CODE 22
## COOLANT TEMP. SENSOR CIRCUIT

| Terminals | Trouble | Condition | | STD Voltage |
|---|---|---|---|---|
| THW – $E_2$ | No voltage | Ignition switch ON | Coolant temperature 80°C (176°F) | 0.1 – 1.0 V |

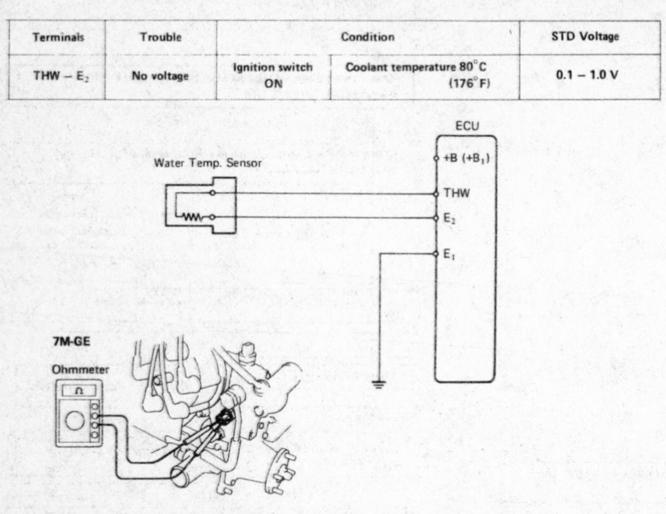
ECU
Water Temp. Sensor
+B (+$B_1$)
THW
$E_2$
$E_1$
7M-GE
Ohmmeter

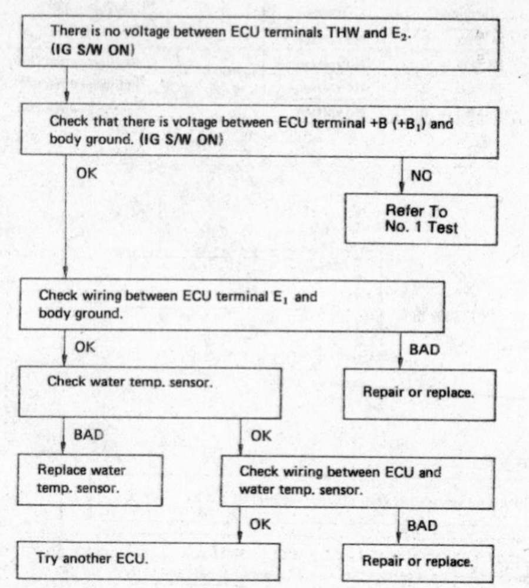
There is no voltage between ECU terminals THW and $E_2$. (IG S/W ON)
Check that there is voltage between ECU terminal +B (+$B_1$) and body ground. (IG S/W ON)
OK
NO
Refer To No. 1 Test
Check wiring between ECU terminal $E_1$ and body ground.
OK
BAD
Check water temp. sensor.
Repair or replace.
BAD
OK
Replace water temp. sensor.
Check wiring between ECU and water temp. sensor.
OK
BAD
Try another ECU.
Repair or replace.

## SUPRA, NO. 4 TEST, CODE 24
## AIR TEMP. SENSOR CIRCUIT (NON-TURBO)

| Terminals | Trouble | Condition | | STD Voltage |
|---|---|---|---|---|
| THA – $E_2$ | No voltage | IG S/W ON | Intake air temperature 20°C (68°F) | 1 – 3 V |

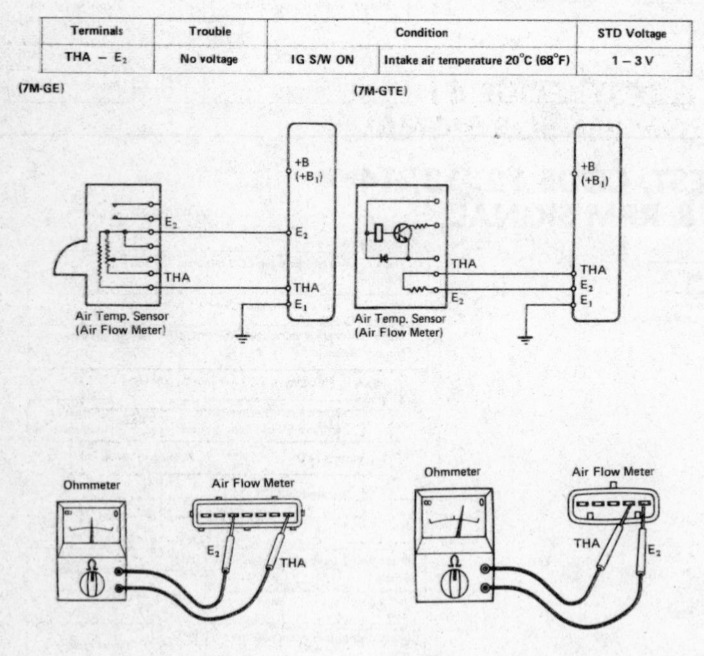
(7M-GE)
(7M-GTE)
+B (+$B_1$)
$E_2$
THA
$E_1$
Air Temp. Sensor (Air Flow Meter)
Ohmmeter
Air Flow Meter

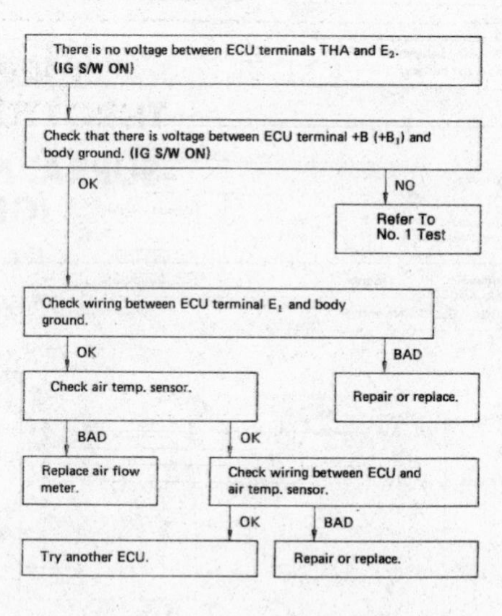
There is no voltage between ECU terminals THA and $E_2$. (IG S/W ON)
Check that there is voltage between ECU terminal +B (+$B_1$) and body ground. (IG S/W ON)
OK
NO
Refer To No. 1 Test
Check wiring between ECU terminal $E_1$ and body ground.
OK
BAD
Check air temp. sensor.
Repair or replace.
BAD
OK
Replace air flow meter.
Check wiring between ECU and air temp. sensor.
OK
BAD
Try another ECU.
Repair or replace.

Courtesy of Toyota Motor Sales, U.S.A., Inc.

# 1988 COMPUTERIZED ENGINE CONTROLS
## Toyota Computer Control System (Cont.)

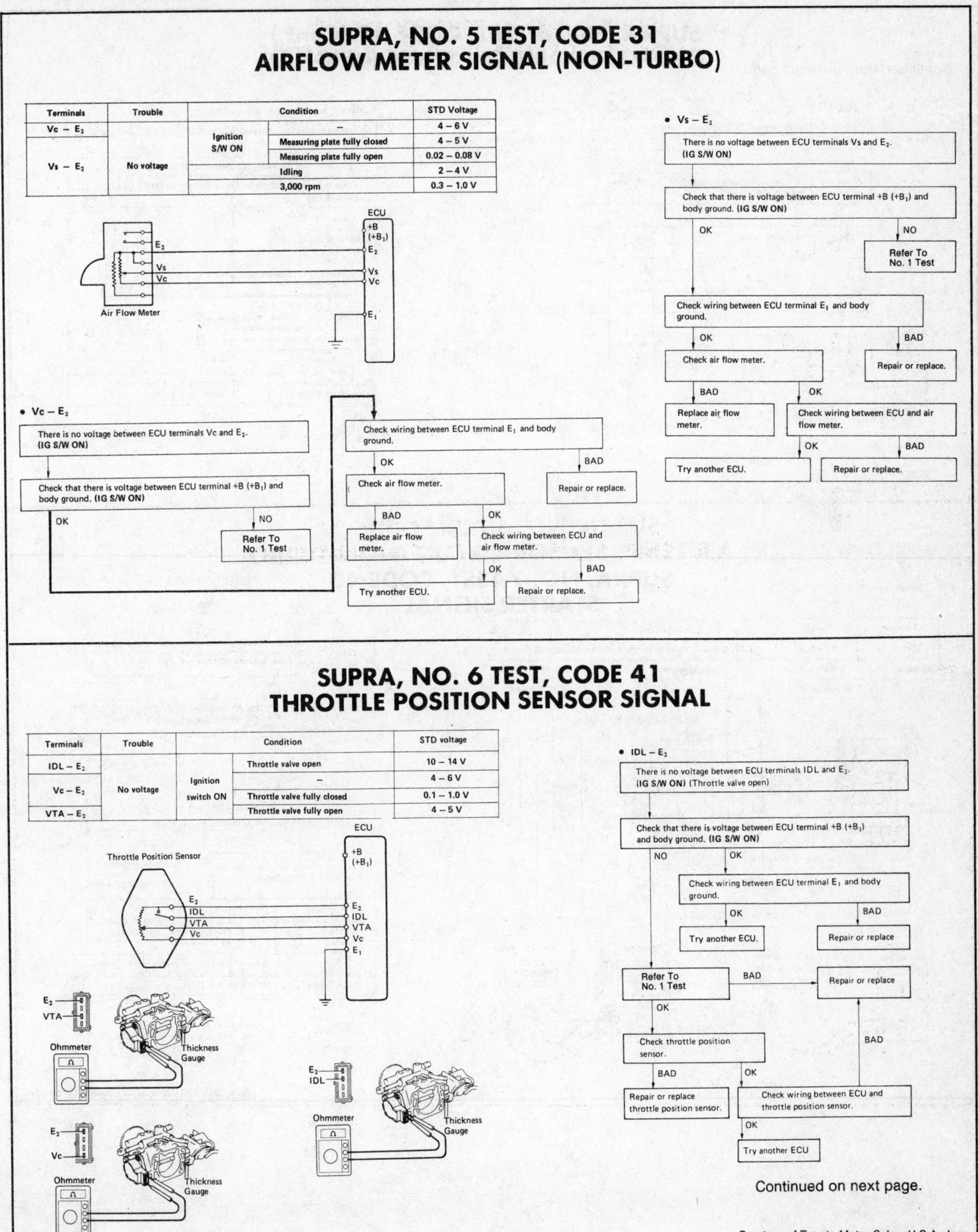

### SUPRA, NO. 5 TEST, CODE 31
### AIRFLOW METER SIGNAL (NON-TURBO)

| Terminals | Trouble | Condition | | STD Voltage |
|---|---|---|---|---|
| Vc – $E_2$ | No voltage | Ignition S/W ON | – | 4 – 6 V |
| Vs – $E_2$ | | | Measuring plate fully closed | 4 – 5 V |
| | | | Measuring plate fully open | 0.02 – 0.08 V |
| | | | Idling | 2 – 4 V |
| | | | 3,000 rpm | 0.3 – 1.0 V |


ECU
+B
(+B1)
E2
Vs
Vc
E1
Air Flow Meter
• Vs – E2
There is no voltage between ECU terminals Vs and E2. (IG S/W ON)
Check that there is voltage between ECU terminal +B (+B1) and body ground. (IG S/W ON)
OK
NO
Refer To No. 1 Test
Check wiring between ECU terminal E1 and body ground.
OK
BAD
Check air flow meter.
Repair or replace.
BAD
OK
Replace air flow meter.
Check wiring between ECU and air flow meter.
OK
BAD
Try another ECU.
Repair or replace.
• Vc – E2
There is no voltage between ECU terminals Vc and E2. (IG S/W ON)
Check that there is voltage between ECU terminal +B (+B1) and body ground. (IG S/W ON)
OK
NO
Refer To No. 1 Test
Check wiring between ECU terminal E1 and body ground.
OK
BAD
Check air flow meter.
Repair or replace.
BAD
OK
Replace air flow meter.
Check wiring between ECU and air flow meter.
OK
BAD
Try another ECU.
Repair or replace.


### SUPRA, NO. 6 TEST, CODE 41
### THROTTLE POSITION SENSOR SIGNAL

| Terminals | Trouble | Condition | | STD voltage |
|---|---|---|---|---|
| IDL – $E_2$ | No voltage | Ignition switch ON | Throttle valve open | 10 – 14 V |
| Vc – $E_2$ | | | – | 4 – 6 V |
| VTA – $E_2$ | | | Throttle valve fully closed | 0.1 – 1.0 V |
| | | | Throttle valve fully open | 4 – 5 V |


ECU
+B
(+B1)
E2
IDL
VTA
Vc
E1
Throttle Position Sensor
E2
VTA
Ohmmeter
Thickness Gauge
E2
Vc
Ohmmeter
Thickness Gauge
E2
IDL
Ohmmeter
Thickness Gauge
• IDL – E2
There is no voltage between ECU terminals IDL and E2. (IG S/W ON) (Throttle valve open)
Check that there is voltage between ECU terminal +B (+B1) and body ground. (IG S/W ON)
NO
OK
Check wiring between ECU terminal E1 and body ground.
OK
BAD
Try another ECU.
Repair or replace
Refer To No. 1 Test
BAD
Repair or replace
OK
Check throttle position sensor.
BAD
BAD
OK
Repair or replace throttle position sensor.
Check wiring between ECU and throttle position sensor.
OK
Try another ECU


Continued on next page.

Courtesy of Toyota Motor Sales, U.S.A., Inc.

## SUPRA, NO. 6 TEST, CODE 41 (Cont.)
## THROTTLE POSITION SENSOR SIGNAL

Continued from previous page.

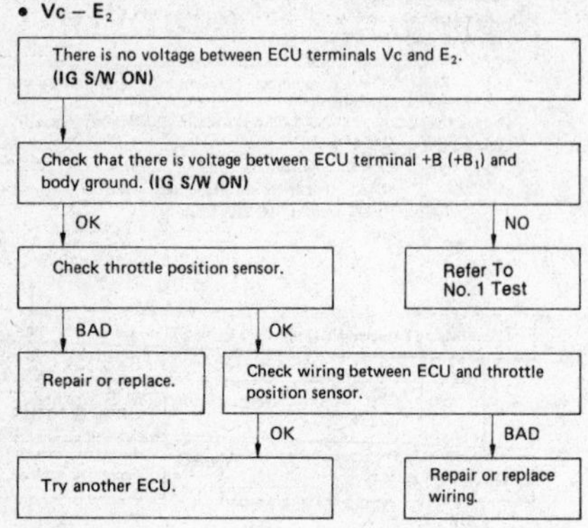
• Vc – E2
There is no voltage between ECU terminals Vc and E2. (IG S/W ON)
Check that there is voltage between ECU terminal +B (+B1) and body ground. (IG S/W ON)
OK
NO
Check throttle position sensor.
Refer To No. 1 Test
BAD
OK
Repair or replace.
Check wiring between ECU and throttle position sensor.
OK
BAD
Try another ECU.
Repair or replace wiring.

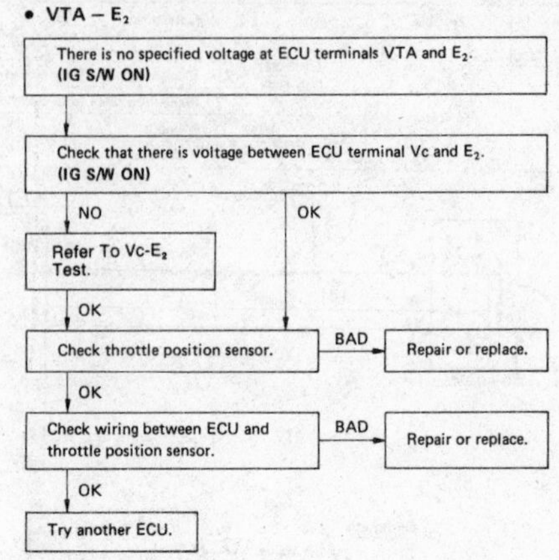
• VTA – E2
There is no specified voltage at ECU terminals VTA and E2. (IG S/W ON)
Check that there is voltage between ECU terminal Vc and E2. (IG S/W ON)
NO
OK
Refer To Vc-E2 Test.
OK
Check throttle position sensor.
BAD
Repair or replace.
OK
Check wiring between ECU and throttle position sensor.
BAD
Repair or replace.
OK
Try another ECU.

## SUPRA, NO. 7 TEST, CODE 43
## STARTER SIGNAL

| Terminals | Trouble | Condition | STD Voltage |
|---|---|---|---|
| STA – $E_1$ | No voltage | Cranking | 6 – 14 V |

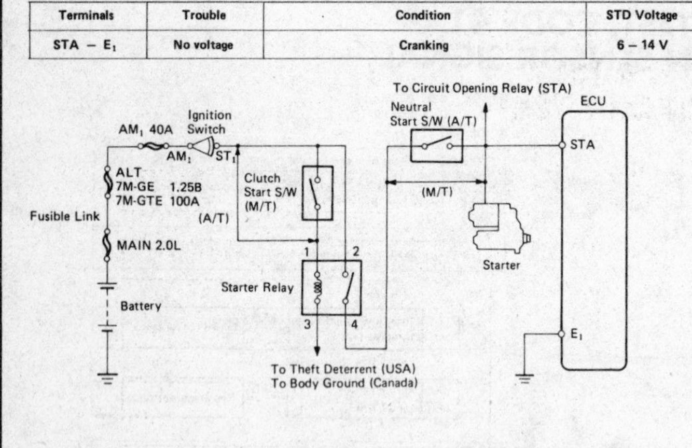
To Circuit Opening Relay (STA)
ECU
Neutral Start S/W (A/T)
AM1 40A
Ignition Switch
AM1
ST1
STA
ALT
7M-GE 1.25B
7M-GTE 100A
Clutch Start S/W (M/T)
(M/T)
(A/T)
Fusible Link
MAIN 2.0L
1
2
Starter
Starter Relay
Battery
3
4
E1
To Theft Deterrent (USA)
To Body Ground (Canada)

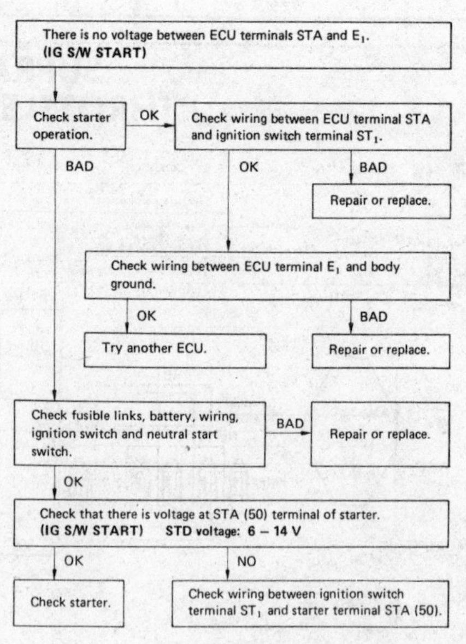
There is no voltage between ECU terminals STA and E1. (IG S/W START)
Check starter operation.
OK
Check wiring between ECU terminal STA and ignition switch terminal ST1.
BAD
OK
BAD
Repair or replace.
Check wiring between ECU terminal E1 and body ground.
OK
BAD
Try another ECU.
Repair or replace.
Check fusible links, battery, wiring, ignition switch and neutral start switch.
BAD
Repair or replace.
OK
Check that there is voltage at STA (50) terminal of starter. (IG S/W START) STD voltage: 6 – 14 V
OK
NO
Check starter.
Check wiring between ignition switch terminal ST1 and starter terminal STA (50).

## SUPRA, NO. 8 TEST, CODE 71
## EGR SYSTEM (NON-TURBO, CALIFORNIA)

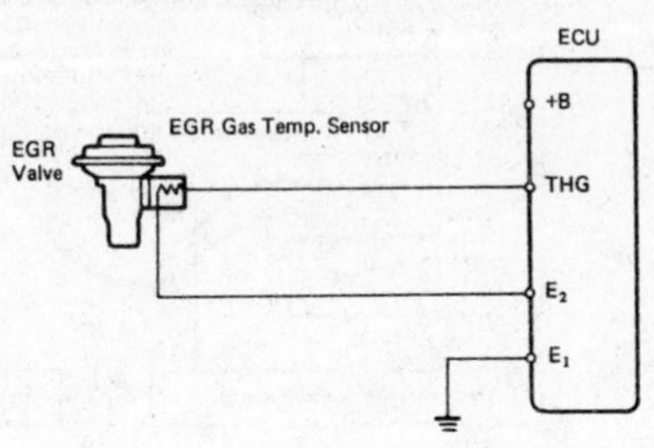

ECU
+B
EGR Gas Temp. Sensor
EGR Valve
THG
$E_2$
$E_1$


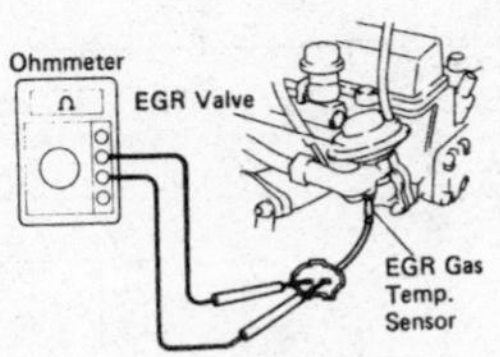

Ohmmeter
EGR Valve
EGR Gas Temp. Sensor


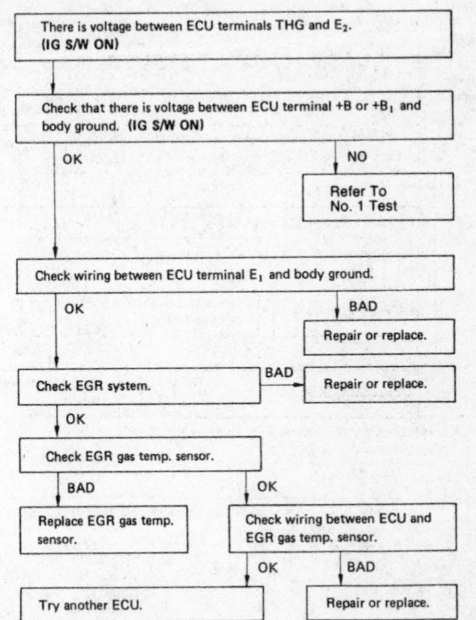

There is voltage between ECU terminals THG and $E_2$. (IG S/W ON)
Check that there is voltage between ECU terminal +B or $+B_1$ and body ground. (IG S/W ON)
OK
NO
Refer To No. 1 Test
Check wiring between ECU terminal $E_1$ and body ground.
OK
BAD
Repair or replace.
Check EGR system.
BAD
Repair or replace.
OK
Check EGR gas temp. sensor.
BAD
OK
Replace EGR gas temp. sensor.
Check wiring between ECU and EGR gas temp. sensor.
OK
BAD
Try another ECU.
Repair or replace.


## SUPRA, NO. 9 TEST
## INJECTOR CIRCUIT TEST

| Terminals | Trouble | Condition | STD Voltage |
|---|---|---|---|
| No. 10<br>No. 20 – $E_{01}$ $E_{02}$<br>No. 30 | No voltage | Ignition switch ON | 9 – 14 V |

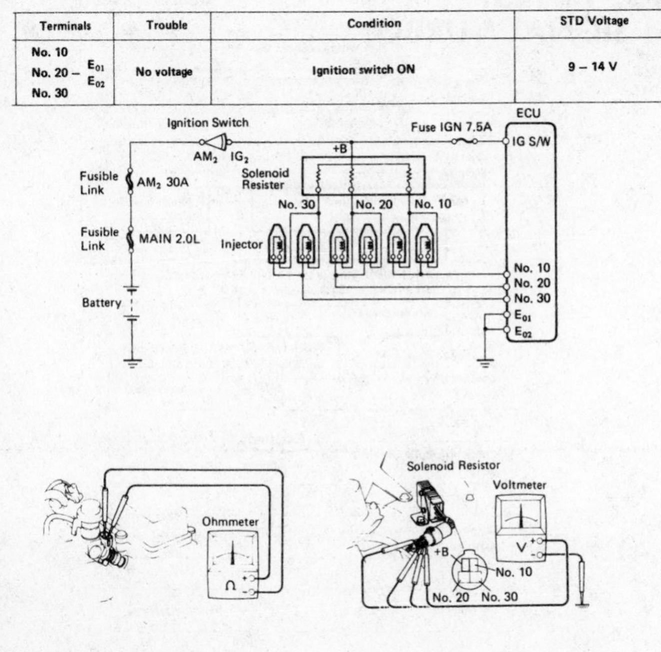

Ignition Switch
$AM_2$ $IG_2$
Fuse IGN 7.5A
ECU
IG S/W
+B
Fusible Link
$AM_2$ 30A
Solenoid Resister
No. 30
No. 20
No. 10
Fusible Link
MAIN 2.0L
Injector
No. 10
No. 20
No. 30
$E_{01}$
$E_{02}$
Battery
Ohmmeter
Solenoid Resistor
Voltmeter
+B
No. 10
No. 20
No. 30


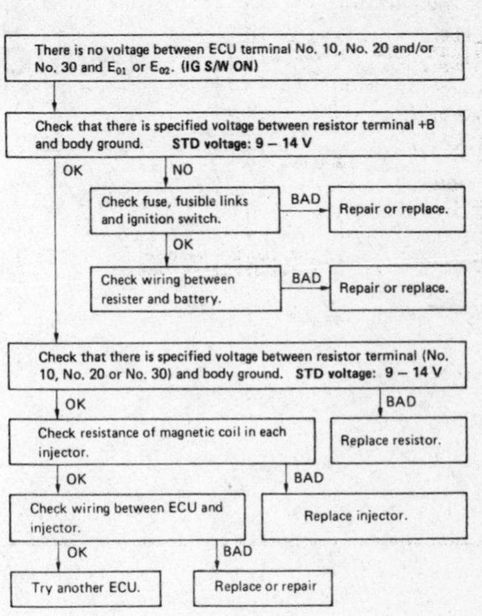

There is no voltage between ECU terminal No. 10, No. 20 and/or No. 30 and $E_{01}$ or $E_{02}$. (IG S/W ON)
Check that there is specified voltage between resistor terminal +B and body ground. STD voltage: 9 – 14 V
OK
NO
Check fuse, fusible links and ignition switch.
BAD
Repair or replace.
OK
Check wiring between resister and battery.
BAD
Repair or replace.
Check that there is specified voltage between resistor terminal (No. 10, No. 20 or No. 30) and body ground. STD voltage: 9 – 14 V
OK
BAD
Check resistance of magnetic coil in each injector.
Replace resistor.
OK
BAD
Check wiring between ECU and injector.
Replace injector.
OK
BAD
Try another ECU.
Replace or repair


Courtesy of Toyota Motor Sales, U.S.A., Inc.

## SUPRA, NO. 10 TEST
## AIRFLOW METER SIGNAL (TURBO)

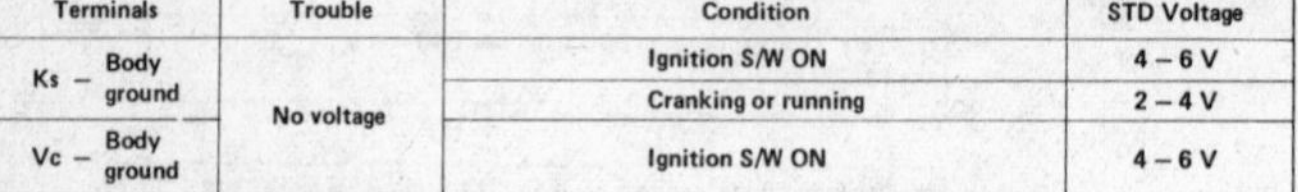

| Terminals | Trouble | Condition | STD Voltage |
|---|---|---|---|
| Ks – Body ground | No voltage | Ignition S/W ON | 4 – 6 V |
| | | Cranking or running | 2 – 4 V |
| Vc – Body ground | | Ignition S/W ON | 4 – 6 V |

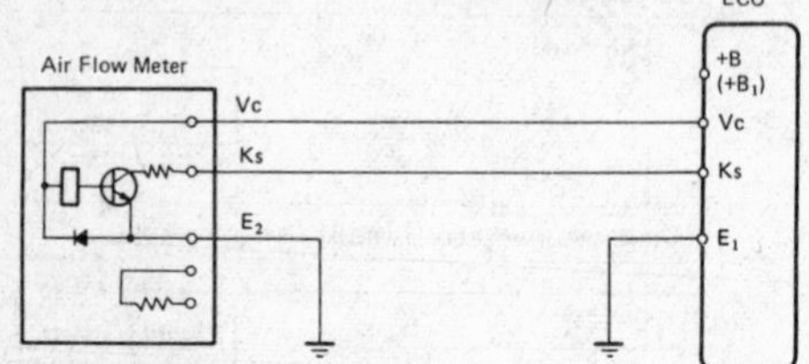
Air Flow Meter
Vc
Ks
$E_2$
ECU
+B
$(+B_1)$
Vc
Ks
$E_1$

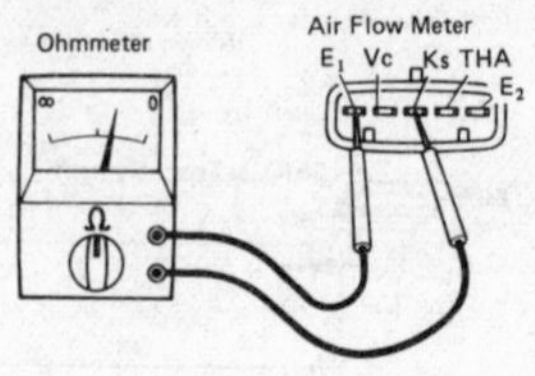
Ohmmeter
Air Flow Meter
$E_1$ Vc Ks THA
$E_2$

• Ks – Body ground

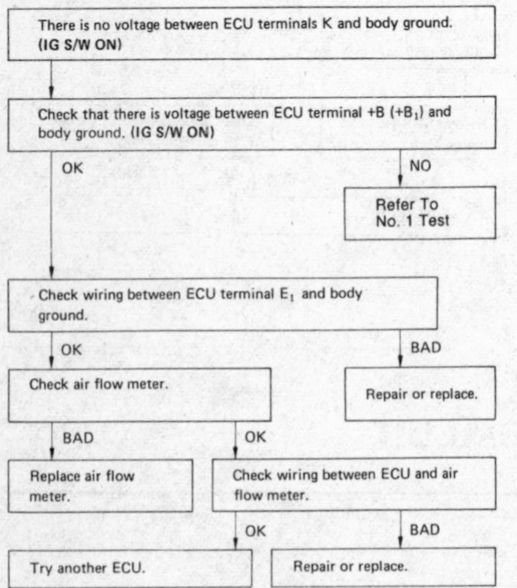
There is no voltage between ECU terminals K and body ground. (IG S/W ON)
Check that there is voltage between ECU terminal +B ($+B_1$) and body ground. (IG S/W ON)
OK
NO
Refer To No. 1 Test
Check wiring between ECU terminal $E_1$ and body ground.
OK
BAD
Check air flow meter.
Repair or replace.
BAD
OK
Replace air flow meter.
Check wiring between ECU and air flow meter.
OK
BAD
Try another ECU.
Repair or replace.

• Vc – Body ground

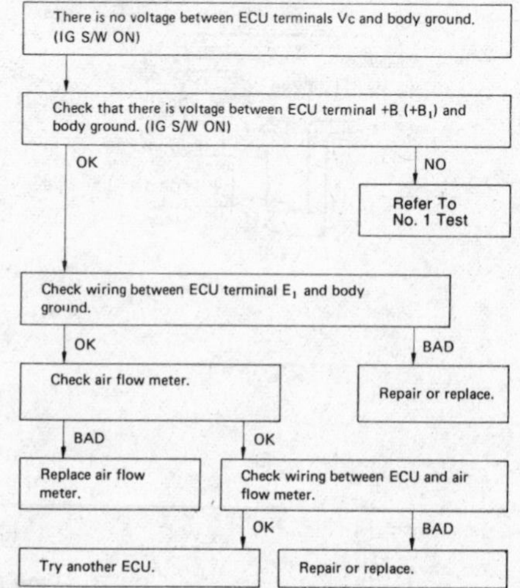
There is no voltage between ECU terminals Vc and body ground. (IG S/W ON)
Check that there is voltage between ECU terminal +B ($+B_1$) and body ground. (IG S/W ON)
OK
NO
Refer To No. 1 Test
Check wiring between ECU terminal $E_1$ and body ground.
OK
BAD
Check air flow meter.
Repair or replace.
BAD
OK
Replace air flow meter.
Check wiring between ECU and air flow meter.
OK
BAD
Try another ECU.
Repair or replace.

## SUPRA, NO. 11 TEST
## IGNITION & RPM SIGNAL (TURBO)

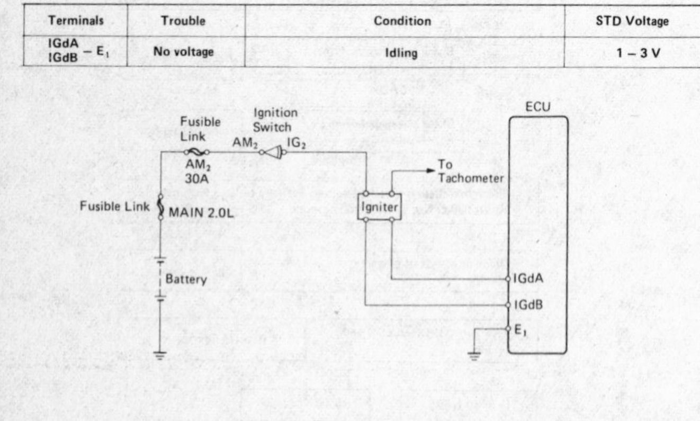

| Terminals | Trouble | Condition | STD Voltage |
|---|---|---|---|
| IGdA IGdB – $E_1$ | No voltage | Idling | 1 – 3 V |

Fusible Link
Ignition Switch
$AM_2$
$IG_2$
$AM_2$ 30A
To Tachometer
ECU
Fusible Link
MAIN 2.0L
Igniter
Battery
IGdA
IGdB
$E_1$

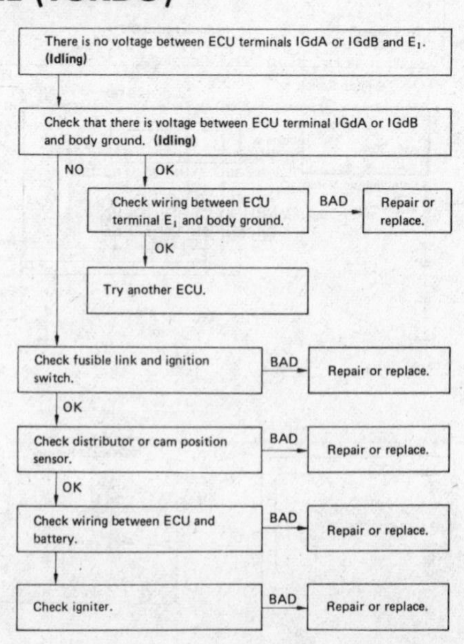
There is no voltage between ECU terminals IGdA or IGdB and $E_1$. (Idling)
Check that there is voltage between ECU terminal IGdA or IGdB and body ground. (Idling)
NO
OK
Check wiring between ECU terminal $E_1$ and body ground.
BAD
Repair or replace.
OK
Try another ECU.
Check fusible link and ignition switch.
BAD
Repair or replace.
OK
Check distributor or cam position sensor.
BAD
Repair or replace.
OK
Check wiring between ECU and battery.
BAD
Repair or replace.
Check igniter.
BAD
Repair or replace.

NOTE: To check ignitor, see TOYOTA ELECTRONIC IGNITION SYSTEM article in DISTRIBUTORS & IGNITION SYSTEMS section.

# SUPRA, NO. 12 TEST
# ISC VALVE CIRCUIT

| Terminals | Trouble | Condition | STD Voltage |
|---|---|---|---|
| $ISC_1 \sim ISC_4 - E_1$ | No voltage | Ignition switch ON | 9 – 14 V |

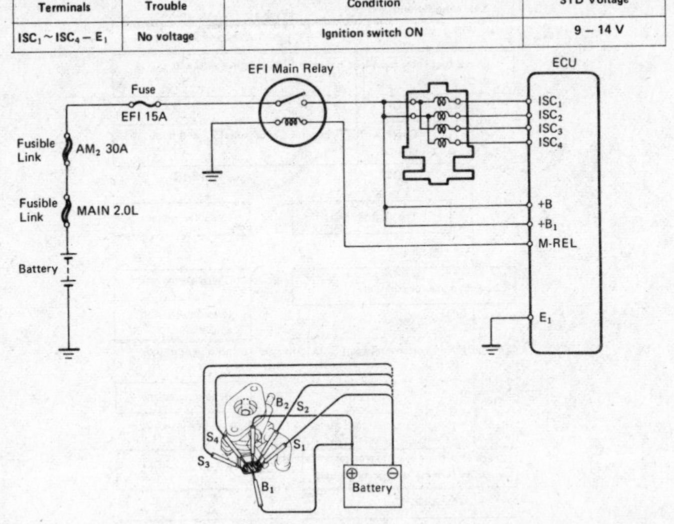
EFI Main Relay
ECU
Fuse
EFI 15A
Fusible Link
AM2 30A
Fusible Link
MAIN 2.0L
Battery
ISC1
ISC2
ISC3
ISC4
+B
+B1
M-REL
E1
B2
S2
S4
S1
S3
B1
Battery

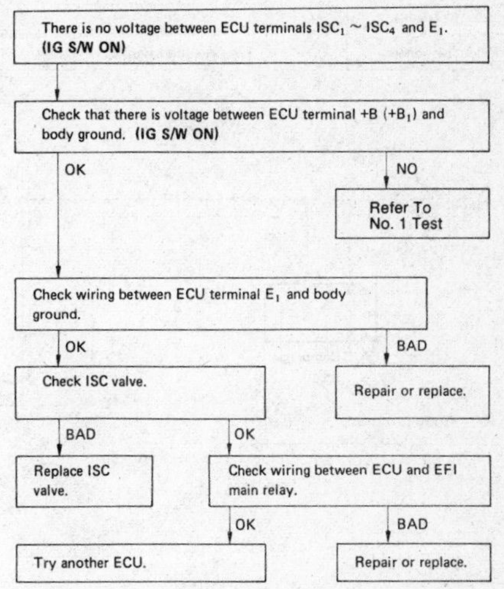
There is no voltage between ECU terminals ISC1 ~ ISC4 and E1. (IG S/W ON)
Check that there is voltage between ECU terminal +B (+B1) and body ground. (IG S/W ON)
OK
NO
Refer To No. 1 Test
Check wiring between ECU terminal E1 and body ground.
OK
BAD
Check ISC valve.
Repair or replace.
BAD
OK
Replace ISC valve.
Check wiring between ECU and EFI main relay.
OK
BAD
Try another ECU.
Repair or replace.

# SUPRA, NO. 13 TEST
# "CHECK ENGINE" LIGHT CIRCUIT

| Terminals | Trouble | Condition | STD Voltage |
|---|---|---|---|
| $W - E_1$ | No voltage | No. trouble ("CHECK ENGINE" warning light off) and engine running | 9 – 14 V |

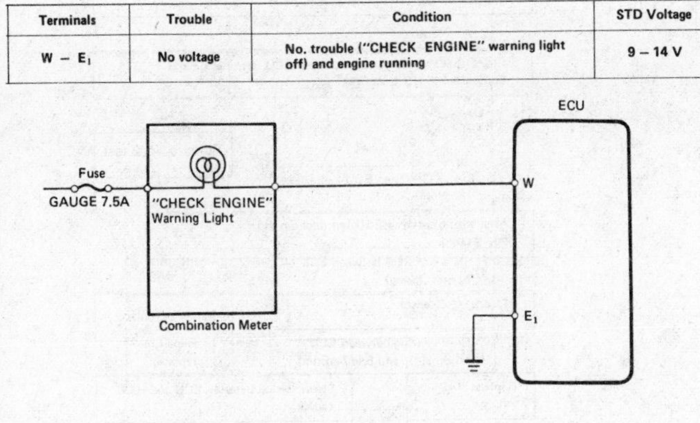
ECU
Fuse
GAUGE 7.5A
"CHECK ENGINE" Warning Light
W
E1
Combination Meter

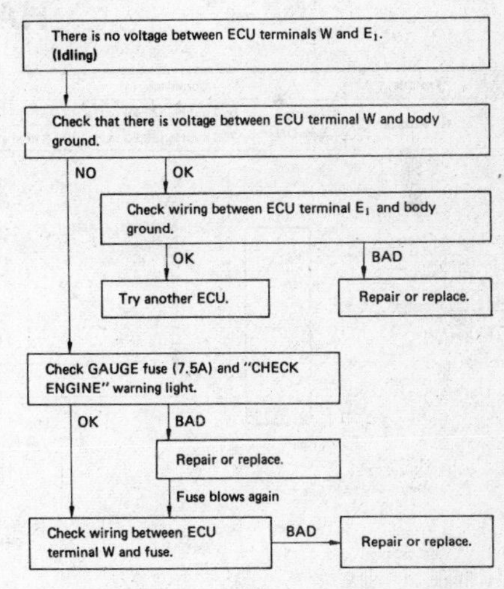
There is no voltage between ECU terminals W and E1. (Idling)
Check that there is voltage between ECU terminal W and body ground.
NO
OK
Check wiring between ECU terminal E1 and body ground.
OK
BAD
Try another ECU.
Repair or replace.
Check GAUGE fuse (7.5A) and "CHECK ENGINE" warning light.
OK
BAD
Repair or replace.
Fuse blows again
Check wiring between ECU terminal W and fuse.
BAD
Repair or replace.

Courtesy of Toyota Motor Sales, U.S.A., Inc.

## SUPRA, NO. 14 TEST
## A/C SWITCH SIGNAL

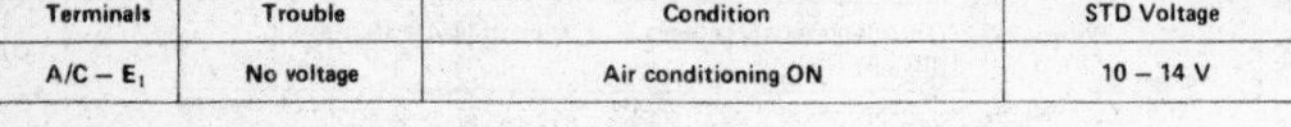

| Terminals | Trouble | Condition | STD Voltage |
|---|---|---|---|
| A/C – $E_1$ | No voltage | Air conditioning ON | 10 – 14 V |

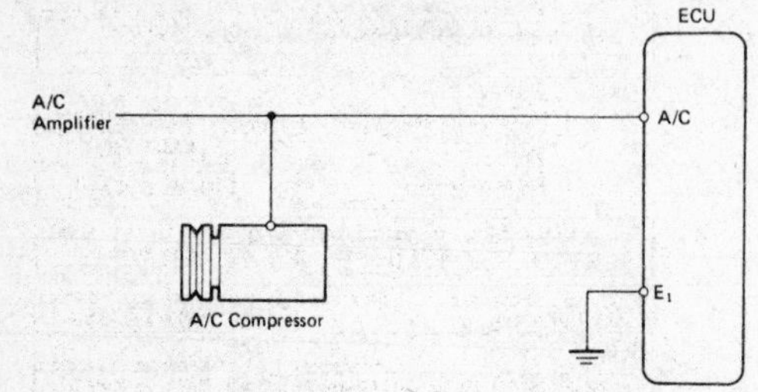
ECU
A/C
Amplifier
A/C
E1
A/C Compressor

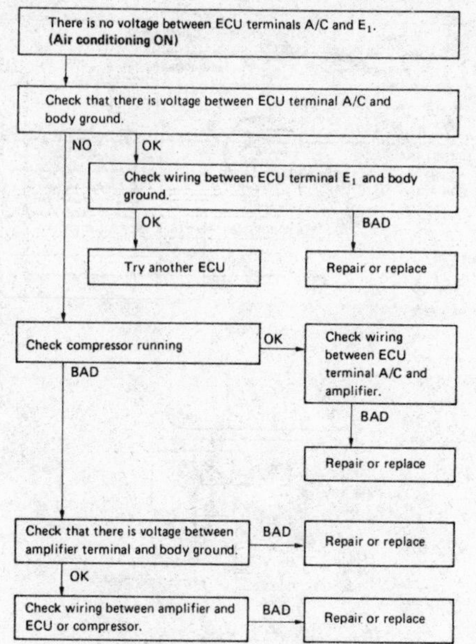
There is no voltage between ECU terminals A/C and E1. (Air conditioning ON)
Check that there is voltage between ECU terminal A/C and body ground.
NO
OK
Check wiring between ECU terminal E1 and body ground.
OK
BAD
Try another ECU
Repair or replace
Check compressor running
OK
Check wiring between ECU terminal A/C and amplifier.
BAD
BAD
Repair or replace
Check that there is voltage between amplifier terminal and body ground.
BAD
Repair or replace
OK
Check wiring between amplifier and ECU or compressor.
BAD
Repair or replace

## SUPRA, NO. 15 TEST
## HAC SENSOR (TURBO)

| Terminals | Trouble | Condition | | STD Voltage |
|---|---|---|---|---|
| HAC – $E_2$ | No voltage | Ignition S/W ON | 540 mmHg (21.26 in.Hg, 72.0 kPa) | Approx. 2.8 V |
| | | | 750 mmHg (29.53 in.Hg, 100.0 kPa) | Aoprox. 3.6 V |

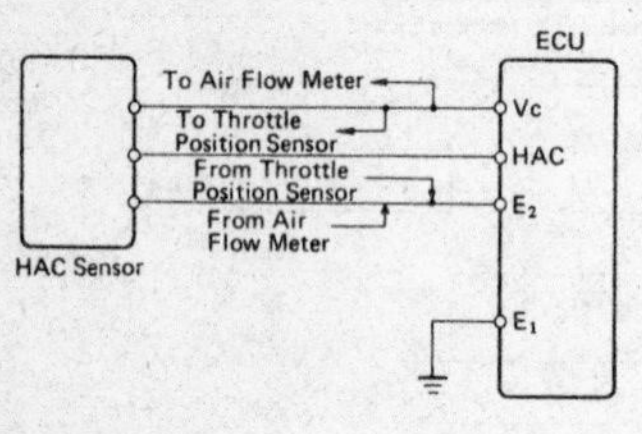
ECU
To Air Flow Meter
To Throttle Position Sensor
From Throttle Position Sensor
From Air Flow Meter
Vc
HAC
E2
E1
HAC Sensor

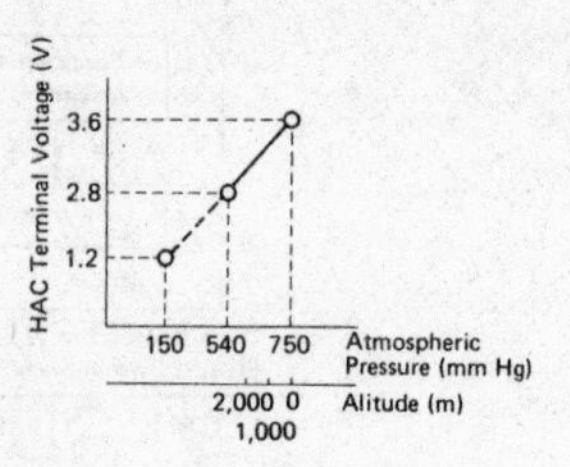
HAC Terminal Voltage (V)
3.6
2.8
1.2
150
540
750
Atmospheric Pressure (mm Hg)
2,000
0
1,000
Alitude (m)

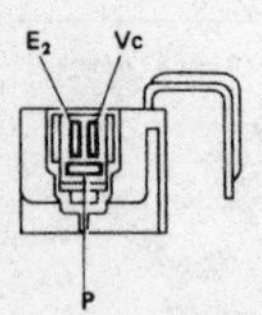
E2
Vc
P

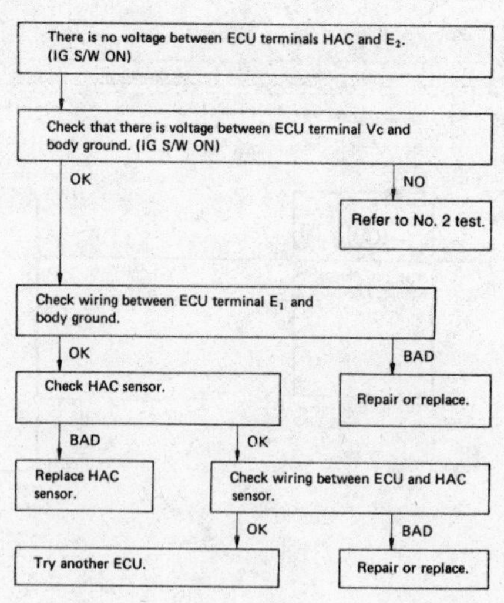
There is no voltage between ECU terminals HAC and E2. (IG S/W ON)
Check that there is voltage between ECU terminal Vc and body ground. (IG S/W ON)
OK
NO
Refer to No. 2 test.
Check wiring between ECU terminal E1 and body ground.
OK
BAD
Check HAC sensor.
Repair or replace.
BAD
OK
Replace HAC sensor.
Check wiring between ECU and HAC sensor.
OK
BAD
Try another ECU.
Repair or replace.

Courtesy of Toyota Motor Sales, U.S.A., Inc.

## SUPRA, NO. 16 TEST
## $O_2$ SENSOR CIRCUIT (NON-TURBO, CALIFORNIA)

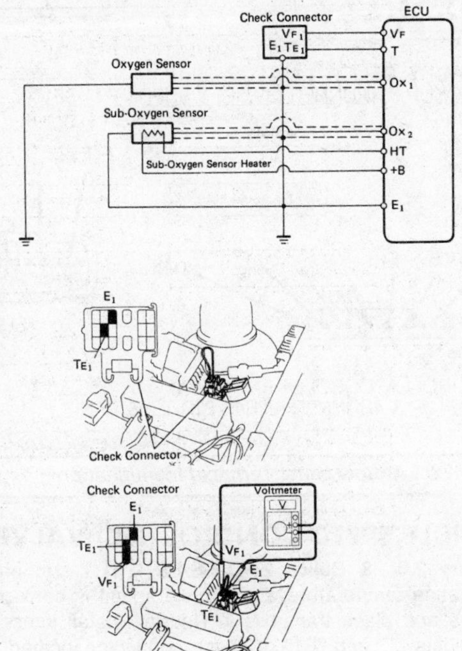
Check Connector
ECU
VF1
E1 TE1
VF
T
Oxygen Sensor
Ox1
Sub-Oxygen Sensor
Ox2
HT
Sub-Oxygen Sensor Heater
+B
E1
TE1
Check Connector
Voltmeter
VF1

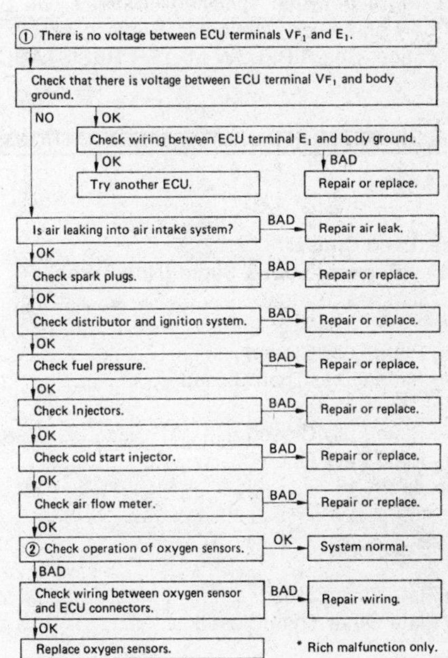
① There is no voltage between ECU terminals VF1 and E1.
Check that there is voltage between ECU terminal VF1 and body ground.
NO
OK
Check wiring between ECU terminal E1 and body ground.
OK
BAD
Try another ECU.
Repair or replace.
Is air leaking into air intake system?
BAD
Repair air leak.
OK
Check spark plugs.
BAD
Repair or replace.
OK
Check distributor and ignition system.
BAD
Repair or replace.
OK
Check fuel pressure.
BAD
Repair or replace.
OK
Check Injectors.
BAD
Repair or replace.
OK
Check cold start injector.
BAD
Repair or replace.
OK
Check air flow meter.
BAD
Repair or replace.
OK
② Check operation of oxygen sensors.
OK
System normal.
BAD
Check wiring between oxygen sensor and ECU connectors.
BAD
Repair wiring.
OK
Replace oxygen sensors.
* Rich malfunction only.

Courtesy of Toyota Motor Sales, U.S.A., Inc.

## COMPONENT TESTING

### AIRFLOW METER

Turn ignition off. Disconnect wiring connector from airflow meter. Note terminal identification. *See Fig. 22.* Using an ohmmeter, measure resistance between specified terminals. On Supra Turbo models, use only an analog ohmmeter. Replace airflow meter if not within specification. See AIRFLOW METER RESISTANCE SPECIFICATIONS table.

***TOYOTA AIRFLOW METER RESISTANCE SPECIFICATIONS***

| Application / Terminals | Ohms |
|---|---|
| **Camry, Celica, Land Cruiser, Pickup (3.0L), 4Runner (3.0L) & Supra (Non-Turbo)** | |
| $E_2$-Vc | 200-400 |
| $E_1$-Fc | |
| Measuring Plate Fully Closed | Infinity |
| Measuring Plate Other Than Closed | 0 |
| $E_2$-Vs | |
| Measuring Plate Fully Closed | 200-600 |
| Measuring Plate Fully Open | 20-1200 |
| **Corolla & Corolla FX-16** | |
| $E_2$-Vc | 100-300 |
| $E_2$-Vb | 200-400 |
| $E_1$-Fc | |
| Measuring Plate Fully Closed | Infinity |
| Measuring Plate Other Than Closed | 0 |
| $E_2$-Vs | |
| Measuring Plate Fully Closed | 20-400 |
| Measuring Plate Fully Open | 20-3000 |
| **Cressida, MR2 & Van** | |
| $E_2$-Vc | |
| Cressida | 200-400 |
| MR2 & Van | 100-300 |
| $E_2$-Vb | |
| MR2 & Van | 200-400 |
| $E_1$-Fc | |
| Measuring Plate Fully Closed | Infinity |
| Measuring Plate Other Than Closed | 0 |
| $E_2$-Vs | |
| Fully Closed | 20-400 |
| Fully Open | |
| Cressida | 20-1200 |
| MR2 | 20-3000 |
| Van | 20-1000 |
| **Pickup & 4Runner (22R-E & 22R-TE)** | |
| $E_2$-Vc | 100-300 |
| $E_1$-Fc | |
| Measuring Plate Fully Closed | Infinity |
| Measuring Plate Other Than Closed | 0 |
| $E_2$-Vs | |
| Measuring Plate Fully Closed | 20-400 |
| Measuring Plate Fully Open | 20-1200 |
| **Supra (Turbo)** | |
| Ks-$E_1$ | Infinity |
| $E_1$-Ks | 5000-10,000 |
| Vc-$E_1$ | 10,000-15,000 |
| $E_1$-Vc | 5000-10,000 |
| **All Models** | |
| $E_2$-THA | |
| -4°F (20°C) | 10,000-20,000 |
| 32°F (0°C) | 4000-7000 |
| 68°F (20°C) | 2000-3000 |
| 104°F (40°C) | 900-1300 |
| 140°F (60°C) | 400-700 |

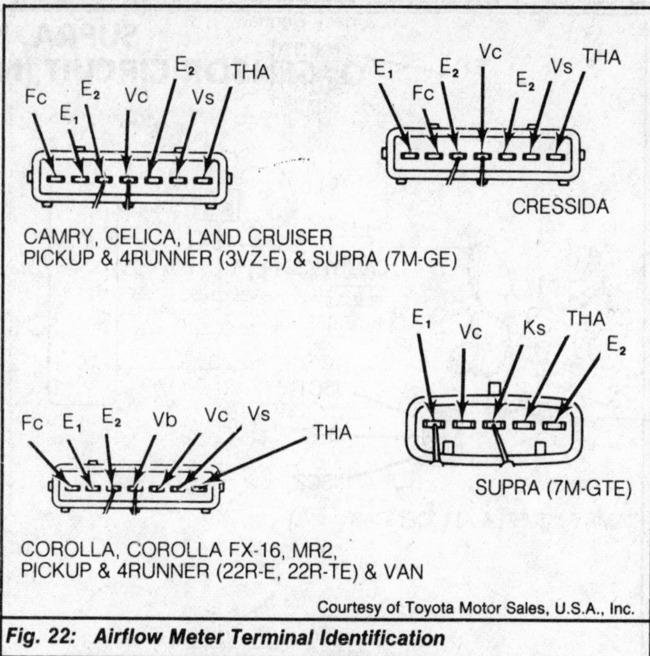
Fc $E_1$ $E_2$ Vc $E_2$ Vs THA
CAMRY, CELICA, LAND CRUISER
PICKUP & 4RUNNER (3VZ-E) & SUPRA (7M-GE)
$E_1$ Fc $E_2$ Vc $E_2$ Vs THA
CRESSIDA
Fc $E_1$ $E_2$ Vb Vc Vs THA
COROLLA, COROLLA FX-16, MR2,
PICKUP & 4RUNNER (22R-E, 22R-TE) & VAN
$E_1$ Vc Ks THA $E_2$
SUPRA (7M-GTE)
Courtesy of Toyota Motor Sales, U.S.A., Inc.

***Fig. 22: Airflow Meter Terminal Identification***

### IDLE SPEED CONTROL (ISC) VALVE

**Camry 2.0L & Celica 2WD 3S-FE – 1)** Warm engine to normal operating temperature. Ensure idle speed is correct. Apply parking brake and place transaxle in Neutral. Install jumper wire between terminals "T" and "E1" of check connector located near left shock tower. *See Fig 23.*

**2)** Note that engine RPM is maintained at 1000-1300 RPM for 5 seconds then returns to idle on Camry, or 600-800 RPM on Celica models.

**3)** If engine RPM was not within specification, disconnect ISC valve connector. Using ohmmeter, measure resistance between terminals "B +" and "ISC1" AND "ISC2". *See Fig. 23.* Replace valve if resistance is not within 16-17 ohms.

**Camry 2.5L, Cressida, Land Cruiser & Supra – 1)** Listen for "clicking" sound after engine is shut off. If no sound is heard, disconnect ISC valve connector.

**2)** Note terminal identification. *See Fig. 23.* Using an ohmmeter, check resistance between designated terminals. See ISC VALVE RESISTANCE SPECIFICATIONS table.

***ISC VALVE RESISTANCE SPECIFICATIONS***

| Terminals | Ohms |
|---|---|
| $B_1$ - $S_1$ or $S_3$ | 10-30 |
| $B_2$ - $S_2$ or $S_4$ | 10-30 |

**3)** To check valve operation, apply battery voltage to terminal "$B_1$" and terminal "$B_2$". *See Fig. 22.* Repeatedly ground terminals "$S_1$", "$S_2$", "$S_3$", "$S_4$" and "$S_1$" in sequence. Note that valve closes. *See Fig. 23.*

**4)** Apply battery voltage to terminals "$B_1$" and "$B_2$". Repeatedly ground terminals "$S_4$", "$S_3$", "$S_2$", "$S_1$" and "$S_4$" in sequence. Note that valve opens. Replace valve if it failed to operate properly.

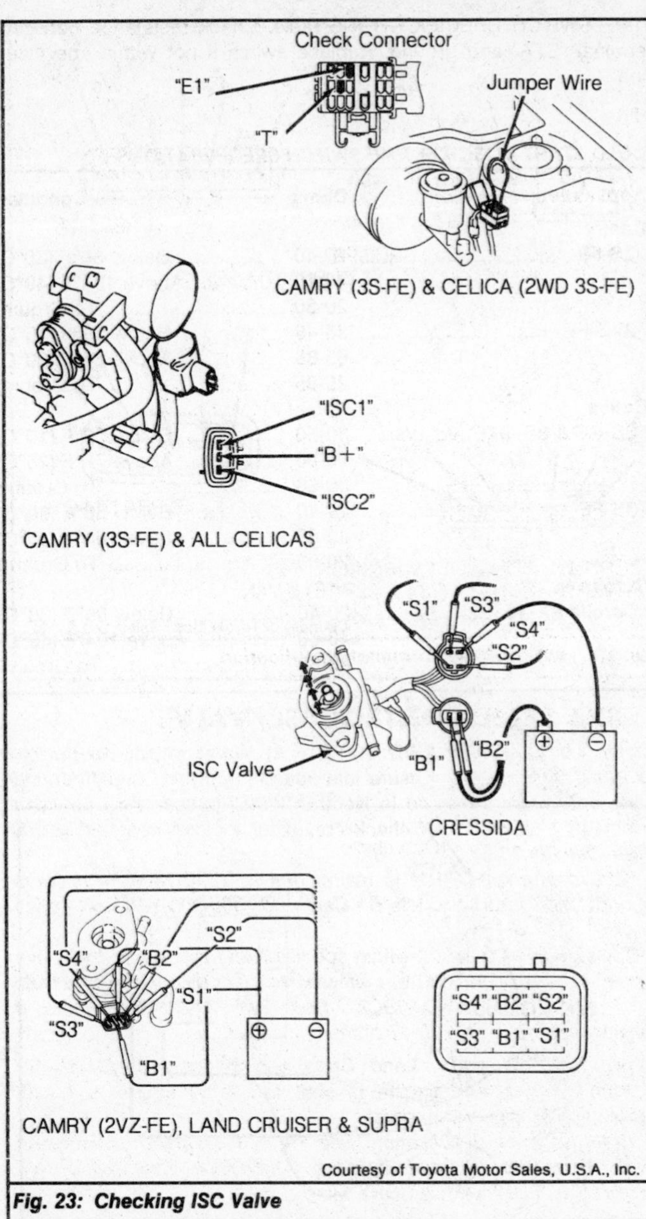
Check Connector
"E1"
"T"
Jumper Wire
CAMRY (3S-FE) & CELICA (2WD 3S-FE)
"ISC1"
"B+"
"ISC2"
CAMRY (3S-FE) & ALL CELICAS
"S1" "S3"
"S4"
"S2"
ISC Valve
"B1" "B2"
CRESSIDA
"S2"
"S4" "B2"
"S1"
"S3"
"B1"
"S4" "B2" "S2"
"S3" "B1" "S1"
CAMRY (2VZ-FE), LAND CRUISER & SUPRA
Courtesy of Toyota Motor Sales, U.S.A., Inc.

***Fig. 23: Checking ISC Valve***

**Celica 4WD – 1)** Warm engine to normal operating temperature. Ensure idle speed is correct. Disconnect ISC valve connector. Engine speed should be above 1000 RPM.

**2)** Reconnect ISC valve. Engine should return to idle speed of 700-800 RPM. If engine RPM was not within specification, disconnect ISC valve connector. Using ohmmeter, measure resistance between terminals "B +" and "ISC1" AND "ISC2". *See Fig. 23.* Replace valve if resistance is not within 16-17 ohms.

## THROTTLE POSITION SENSOR (TPS)

Turn ignition off and disconnect electrical connector at TPS. Note terminal identification. *See Fig. 24.* Insert specified thickness feeler gauge between throttle stop screw and throttle lever. See TPS RESISTANCE SPECIFICATIONS table. Using an ohmmeter, check for resistance or continuity. Replace or adjust TPS if not within specification. See TPS SPECIFICATIONS table.

***TPS RESISTANCE SPECIFICATIONS***

| Application | Clearance In. (mm) | Terminal | Ohmmeter Reading |
|---|---|---|---|
| **Camry** | | | |
| 3S-FE | | | |
| (W/ECT) | 0 (0) | VTA & $E_2$ | 200-800 |
| | .020 (.51) | IDL & $E_2$ | 2300 or Less |
| | .028 (.71) | IDL & $E_2$ | Infinity |
| | Fully Open | VTA & $E_2$ | 3300-10,000 |
| | | VC & $E_2$ | 3000-7000 |
| 3S-FE | | | |
| (W/O ECT) | .020 (.51) | IDL & $E_1$ | Continuity |
| | 020 (.51) | PSW & $E_1$ | No Continuity |
| | .035 (.89) | IDL & $E_1$ | No Continuity |
| | .035 (.89) | PSW & $E_1$ | No Continuity |
| | Fully Open | IDL & $E_1$ | No Continuity |
| | | PSW & $E_1$ | Continuity |
| 2VZ-FE | 0 (0) | VTA & $E_2$ | 300-6300 |
| | .012 (.30) | IDL & $E_2$ | 2300 or Less |
| | .028 (.71) | IDL & $E_2$ | Infinity |
| | Fully Open | VTA & $E_2$ | 3500-10,300 |
| | | VC & $E_2$ | 4250-8250 |
| **Celica** | | | |
| 3S-GE | 0 (0) | VTA & $E_2$ | 200-800 |
| | .020 (.51) | IDL & $E_2$ | 2300 or Less |
| | .028 (.71) | IDL & $E_2$ | Infinity |
| | Fully Open | VTA & $E_2$ | 3300-10,000 |
| | | VC & $E_2$ | 3000-7000 |
| 3S-GTE | 0 (0) | VTA & $E_2$ | 200-800 |
| | .020 (.51) | IDL & $E_2$ | 2300 or Less |
| | .028 (.71) | IDL & $E_2$ | Infinity |
| | Fully Open | VTA & $E_2$ | 3300-10,300 |
| | | VC & $E_2$ | 3000-8300 |
| 3S-FE | .020 (.51) | IDL & $E_1$ | Continuity |
| | .020 (.51) | PSW & $E_1$ | No Continuity |
| | .035 (.89) | IDL & $E_1$ | No Continuity |
| | .035 (.89) | PSW & $E_1$ | No Continuity |
| | Fully Open | IDL & $E_1$ | No Continuity |
| | | PSW & $E_1$ | Continuity |
| **Corolla &** | | | |
| **Corolla FX-16** | 0 (0) | VTA & $E_2$ | 200-800 |
| | .014 (.36) | IDL & $E_2$ | 2300 or Less |
| | .023 (.58) | IDL & $E_2$ | Infinity |
| | Fully Open | VTA & $E_2$ | 3300-10,000 |
| | | VCC & $E_2$ | 3000-7000 |
| **Cressida** | 0 (0) | VTA & $E_2$ | 200-800 |
| | .020 (.51) | IDL & $E_2$ | 0 |
| | .035 (.89) | IDL & $E_2$ | Infinity |
| | Fully Open | VTA & $E_2$ | 3300-10,000 |
| | | VC & $E_2$ | 3000-7000 |
| **Land Cruiser** | 0 (0) | VTA & $E_2$ | 300-6300 |
| | .030 (.76) | IDL & $E_2$ | 2300 or Less |
| | .043 (1.09) | IDL & $E_2$ | Infinity |
| | Fully Open | VTA & $E_2$ | 3500-10,300 |
| | | VC & $E_2$ | 4250-8250 |
| **Pickup & 4Runner** | | | |
| 22R-E, 22R-TE | 0 (0) | VTA & $E_2$ | 200-800 |
| | .022 (.56) | IDL & $E_2$ | 2300 or Less |
| | .034 (.86) | IDL & $E_2$ | Infinity |
| | Fully Open | VTA & $E_2$ | 3300-10,000 |
| | | VCC & $E_2$ | 3000-7000 |
| 3VZ-E | 0 (0) | VTA & $E_2$ | 200-800 |
| | .020 (.51) | IDL & $E_2$ | 2300 or Less |
| | .030 (.76) | IDL & $E_2$ | Infinity |
| | Fully Open | VTA & $E_2$ | 3300-10,000 |
| | | VCC & $E_2$ | 4000-9000 |

***TPS RESISTANCE SPECIFICATIONS (Cont.)***

| Application | Clearance In. (mm) | Terminal | Ohmmeter Reading |
|---|---|---|---|
| **Supra** | | | |
| Non-Turbo | 0 (0) | VTA & $E_2$ | 300-6300 |
| | .016 (.41) | IDL & $E_2$ | 2300 or Less |
| | .030 (.76) | IDL & $E_2$ | Infinity |
| | Fully Open | VTA & $E_2$ | 3500-10,300 |
| | | VC & $E_2$ | 4250-8250 |
| Turbo | 0 (0) | VTA & $E_2$ | 300-6300 |
| | .020 (.51) | IDL & $E_2$ | 2300 or Less |
| | .035 (.89) | IDL & $E_2$ | Infinity |
| | Fully Open | VTA & $E_2$ | 3500-10,300 |
| | | VC & $E_2$ | 4250-8250 |
| **Van** | .022 (.56) | IDL & $E_1$ | Continuity |
| | .022 (.56) | PSW & $E_1$ | No Continuity |
| | .022 (.56) | IDL & PSW | No Continuity |
| | .034 (.86) | IDL & $E_1$ | No Continuity |
| | .034 (.86) | PSW & $E_1$ | No Continuity |
| | .034 (.86) | IDL & PSW | No Continuity |
| | Fully Open | IDL & $E_1$ | No Continuity |
| | | PSW & $E_1$ | Continuity |
| | | IDL & PSW | No Continuity |

## COLD START INJECTOR TIME SWITCH

Disconnect switch connector. Note terminal identification. *See Fig. 25.* Using ohmmeter, check resistance between terminals "STA" & "STJ" at appropriate temperature. See COLD START INJECTOR TIME SWITCH SPECIFICATIONS table. Check resistance between terminal "STA" and ground. Replace switch if not within specification.

***COLD START INJECTOR TIME SWITCH SPECIFICATIONS***

| Application | Ohms | Condition |
|---|---|---|
| **Camry** | | |
| 3S-FE | 20-40 | Below 86°F (30°C) |
| | 40-60 | Above 104°F (40°C) |
| | 20-80 | To Ground |
| 2VZ-FE | 25-45 | Below 59°F (15°C) |
| | 65-85 | Above 86°F (30°C) |
| | 25-85 | To Ground |
| **Celica** | | |
| 3S-GE & 3S-GTE | 30-50 | Below 50°F (10°C) |
| | 70-90 | Above 77°F (25°C) |
| | 30-90 | To Ground |
| 3S-FE | 20-40 | Below 86°F (30°C) |
| | 40-60 | Above 104°F (40°C) |
| | 20-80 | To Ground |
| **Corolla & Corolla FX-16** | 20-40 | Below 86°F (30°C) |
| | 40-60 | Above 104°F (40°C) |
| | 20-80 | To Ground |

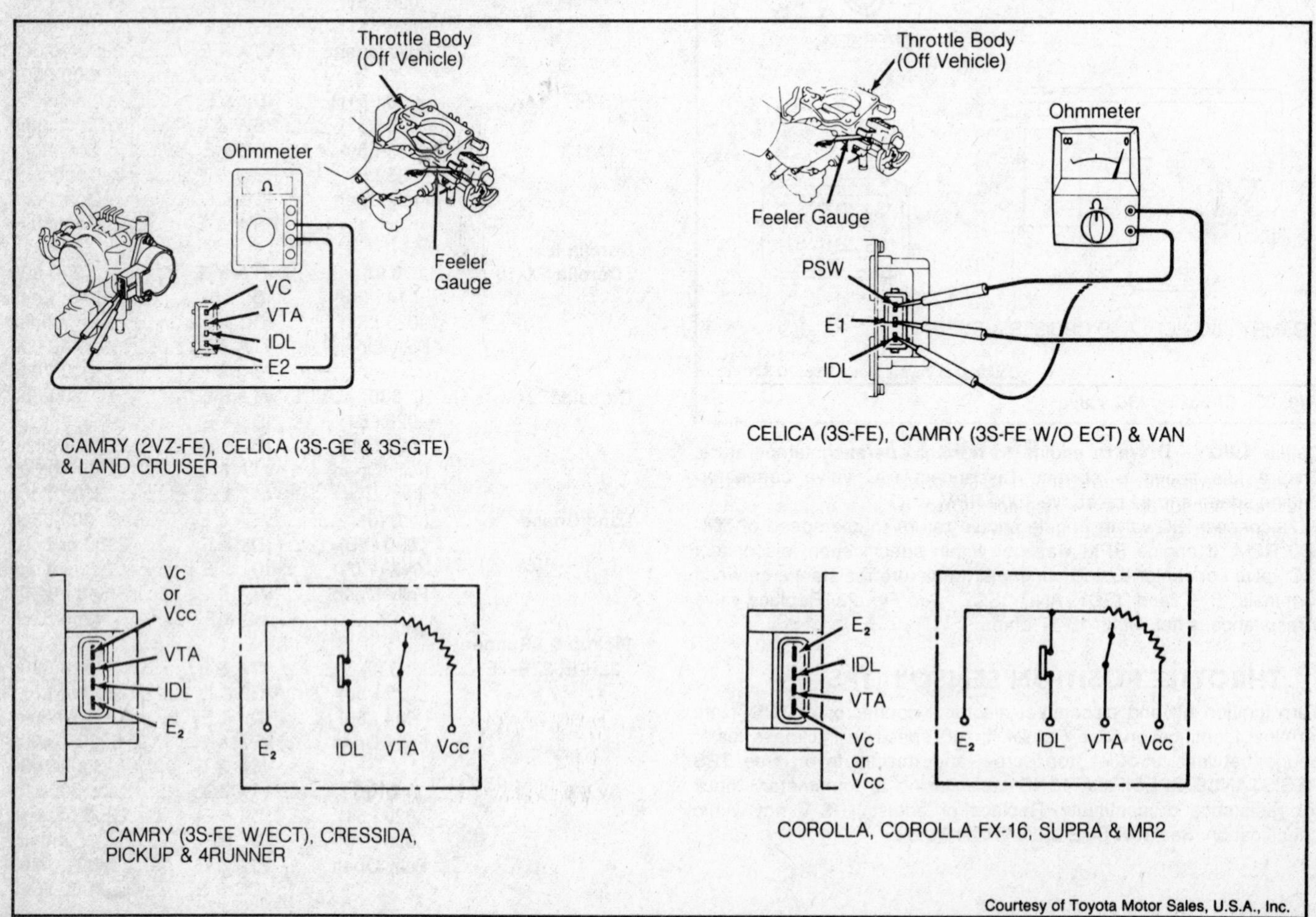
Throttle Body
(Off Vehicle)
Ohmmeter
Feeler Gauge
VC
VTA
IDL
E2
CAMRY (2VZ-FE), CELICA (3S-GE & 3S-GTE) & LAND CRUISER
Throttle Body
(Off Vehicle)
Ohmmeter
Feeler Gauge
PSW
E1
IDL
CELICA (3S-FE), CAMRY (3S-FE W/O ECT) & VAN
Vc or Vcc
VTA
IDL
E2
E2
IDL
VTA
Vcc
CAMRY (3S-FE W/ECT), CRESSIDA, PICKUP & 4RUNNER
E2
IDL
VTA
Vc or Vcc
E2
IDL
VTA
Vcc
COROLLA, COROLLA FX-16, SUPRA & MR2
Courtesy of Toyota Motor Sales, U.S.A., Inc.

***Fig. 24: Checking Throttle Position Sensor***

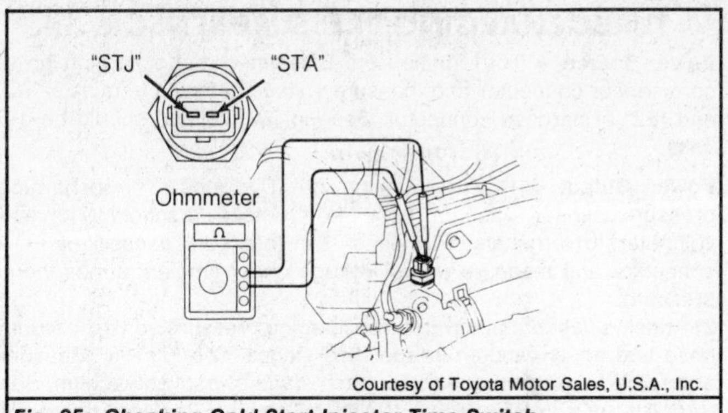

"STJ"
"STA"
Ohmmeter
Courtesy of Toyota Motor Sales, U.S.A., Inc.


*Fig. 25: Checking Cold Start Injector Time Switch*

**COLD START INJECTOR TIME SWITCH SPECIFICATIONS (Cont.)**

| Application | Ohms | Condition |
|---|---|---|
| Cressida | 24-40 | Below 86°F (30°C) |
| | 40-60 | Above 104°F (40°C) |
| | 20-80 | To Ground |
| Land Cruiser | 30-50 | Below 59°F (15°C) |
| | 70-90 | Above 86°F (30°C) |
| | 30-90 | To Ground |
| MR2 | 20-40 | Below 86°F (30°C) |
| | 40-60 | Above 104°F (40°C) |
| | 20-80 | To Ground |
| Pickup & 4Runner | | |
| 22R-E | 30-50 | Below 50°F (10°C) |
| | 70-90 | Above 77°F (25°C) |
| | 30-90 | To Ground |
| 22R-TE | 20-40 | Below 86°F (30°C) |
| | 40-60 | Above 104°F (40°C) |
| | 20-80 | To Ground |
| 3VZ-E | 30-50 | Below 50°F (10°C) |
| | 70-90 | Above 68°F (20°C) |
| | 30-90 | To Ground |
| Supra | 25-50 | Below 59°F (15°C) |
| | 60-85 | Above 86°F (30°C) |
| | 25-85 | To Ground |
| Van | 20-50 | Below 59°F (15°C) |
| | 60-85 | Above 86°F (30°C) |
| | 25-85 | To Ground |

### COOLANT TEMPERATURE SENSOR

Remove connector from sensor. Using ohmmeter, check resistance between sensor terminals. Replace sensor if resistance is not within specification at specified temperature. *See Fig. 26.*

### EGR TEMPERATURE SENSOR

Place threaded end of sensor and thermometer in container of oil. Attach ohmmeter to sensor terminals. Heat the oil and note the resistance at specified temperature. See EGR TEMPERATURE SENSOR SPECIFICATIONS table. Replace sensor if not within specification.

**EGR TEMPERATURE SENSOR SPECIFICATIONS**

| Temperature °F (°C) | Ohms |
|---|---|
| 122 (50) | 69-89 |
| 212 (100) | 12-14 |
| 302 (150) | 3-4 |

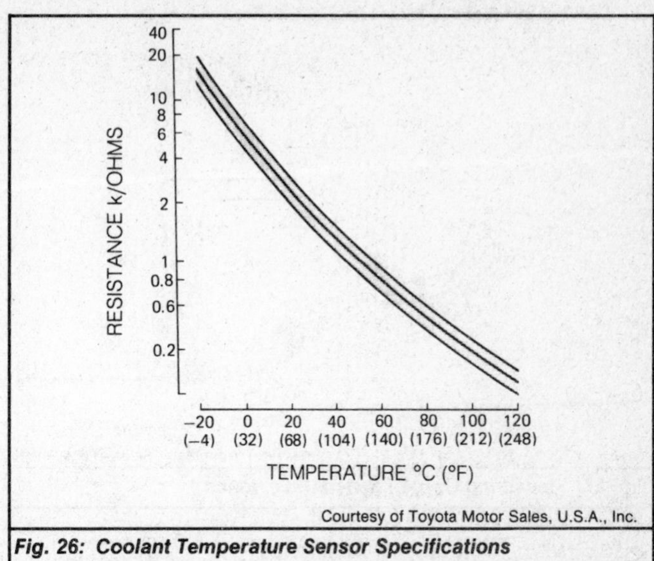

RESISTANCE k/OHMS
40
20
10
8
6
4
2
1
0.8
0.6
0.2
−20 (−4)
0 (32)
20 (68)
40 (104)
60 (140)
80 (176)
100 (212)
120 (248)
TEMPERATURE °C (°F)
Courtesy of Toyota Motor Sales, U.S.A., Inc.


*Fig. 26: Coolant Temperature Sensor Specifications*

### SUB-OXYGEN SENSOR

**Camry 2VZ-FE, Supra Non-Turbo & Van (Calif. Models) – 1)** Inspection is required when trouble code No. 27 exists. Clear trouble codes. See CLEARING TROUBLE CODES under DIAGNOSIS & TESTING in this article.

Warm engine to normal operating temperature.

**2)** On Camry models, drive vehicle between 50 and 62 MPH for at least 5 minutes in 4th or 5th gear (M/T) or "D" range (A/T). On Supra models, drive vehicle at 50 MPH or less for at least 5 minutes in 4th or 5th gear (M/T) or "D" range (A/T).

**3)** On Van models, drive vehicle between 40 and 62 MPH for at least 3 minutes in 4th or 5th gear (M/T) or "D" range (A/T). On all models, fully depress accelerator pedal for at least 2 seconds.

***CAUTION: On Camry and Van models, DO NOT exceed 62 MPH or trouble code will be canceled.***

**4)** Stop engine and turn ignition off. Repeat previous steps and note if trouble code No. 27 exists again. If trouble code exists again, check sub-oxygen sensor circuit for continuity, shorts or grounds. Replace sub-oxygen sensor if circuit is okay.

### OXYGEN ($O_2$) SENSOR HEATER

Disconnect sensor connector. Using ohmmeter, measure resistance between sensor terminals. Replace sensor if resistance is not within 5-6 ohms at 68°F (20°C).

### KNOCK SENSOR

Information not available from manufacturer.

### OXYGEN SENSOR

**Oxygen Sensor Resistance (Pickup & 4Runner With V6 Engine Only) –** Using an ohmmeter, measure resistance between terminals "+ B" and "HT" with oxygen sensor at 68°F (20°C). *See Fig. 27.* Resistance should be between 5.1-6.3 ohms at 68° F (20°C). If resistance is not as specified, replace oxygen sensor.

**Feedback Voltage Test – 1)** Warm engine to normal operating temperature. Connect an analog type voltmeter to appropriate EFI check connector terminal. *See Fig. 28.* Install jumper wire between appropriate check engine connector terminals. See CHECK ENGINE CONNECTOR TERMINALS table.

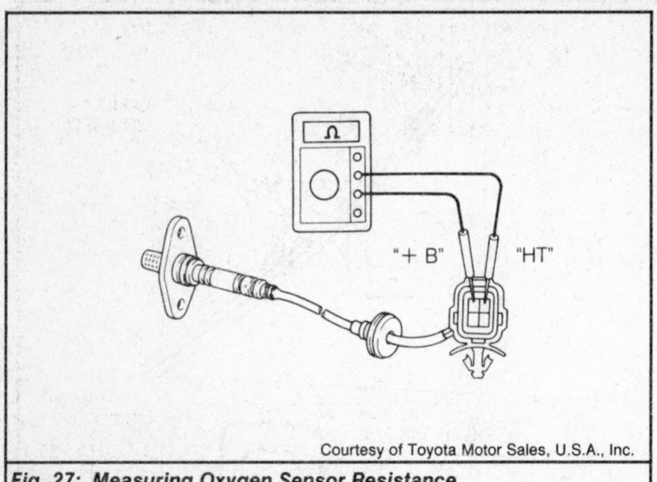
Ω
"+ B"
"HT"
Courtesy of Toyota Motor Sales, U.S.A., Inc.

*Fig. 27: Measuring Oxygen Sensor Resistance*

***CHECK ENGINE CONNECTOR TERMINALS***

| Application | Terminals |
|---|---|
| Camry, Land Cruiser, & Supra | T (TE1) & E1 |
| All Others | T & E1 |

**2)** Maintain engine speed at 2500 RPM and check the number of times voltmeter needle fluctuates in 10 seconds. See VOLTMETER NEEDLE FLUCTUATION table. If needle does not fluctuate at all, go to step **4)**. If needle fluctuations are less than amount specified, go to step **3)**. If needle fluctuations are as specified or more, oxygen sensor is okay.

***VOLTMETER NEEDLE FLUCTUATION***

| Application | Normal Fluctuations |
|---|---|
| Van | 6 Times |
| All Others | 8 Times |

**3)** If needle fluctuations are less than amount specified, remove jumper wire at check engine connector, but keep voltmeter connected to EFI check connector terminals. Maintain engine speed at 2500 RPM (ensuring oxygen sensor is thoroughly warmed), and measure voltage at EFI check connector terminals. If voltage reading is 0 (zero), go to step **4)**. If voltage is more than 0 (zero) volts, replace main oxygen sensor and repeat step **1)**.

**4)** Read and record diagnostic codes. See RETRIEVING TROUBLE CODES in DIAGNOSIS & TESTING in this article. Repair any codes that are nonrelated. If codes are relevant or are normal, remove jumper wire previously installed at check engine connector, but keep voltmeter connected to EFI check connector terminals.

**5)** Maintain engine speed at 2500 RPM and measure voltage again. If voltage is 5 volts or more, go to next step. If voltage does not exist, disconnect PCV hose and measure voltage again. If voltage reading remains at 0 (zero), replace oxygen sensor and repeat step **1)**. If voltage is more than 0 (zero) volts, repair for an over rich condition.

**6)** Unplug coolant temperature sensor connector. Connect a 4-8 ohm resistor across connector terminals. If resistor is not available, replace with new coolant temperature sensor. Repeat step **1)** and measure voltage at terminals. If voltage is not present, replace the main oxygen sensor and repeat step **1)**. If needle fluctuations are less than specified after replacing the oxygen sensor, replace ECU.

## TURBOCHARGING PRESSURE SENSOR

**Power Source** – Turn ignition on. Disconnect turbocharging pressure sensor connector and measure voltage between terminals "VC" and "E2" of harness connector. *See Fig. 29.* Voltage should be 4-6 volts.

**Power Output – 1)** Turn ignition on. Disconnect turbocharging pressure sensor vacuum hose from intake manifold. Connect voltmeter to terminals "PIM" and "E2" (pressure sensor) of ECU connector and measure output voltage under ambient atmospheric pressure.

**2)** Attach a vacuum pump to turbocharging pressure sensor vacuum hose and apply vacuum in specified stages. *See Fig. 30.* Measure and record voltage readings for each stage of applied vacuum. See VACUUM/VOLTAGE SPECIFICATIONS table. Replace sensor if readings are not within specifications.

***VACUUM/VOLTAGE SPECIFICATIONS***

| Applied Vacuum In. Hg | Volts |
|---|---|
| 3.94 | .15-.35 |
| 7.87 | .4-.35 |
| 11.81 | .65-.85 |
| 15.75 | .9-1.1 |
| 19.69 | 1.15-11.35 |

## TURBOCHARGING PRESSURE VACUUM SWITCHING VALVE (VSV)

**1)** Using an ohmmeter, check continuity between both terminals of turbocharging pressure VSV connector. *See Fig. 31.* Replace VSV if no continuity exists.

**2)** Check that no continuity exists between VSV case (body) and each terminal. If continuity exists, replace VSV.

**3)** Check that air does not flow from pipe "E" to pipe "F". If air flows through from pipe "E" to pipe "F", replace VSV.

## VEHICLE SPEED SENSOR

**Speed Sensor (Analog Type, Except Land Cruiser)** – Remove combination meter from instrument cluster. Connect ohmmeter between proper terminals. *See Fig. 32.* See NO. 1 SPEED SENSOR TEST TERMINALS (ANALOG TYPE). Rotate meter shaft and note reading. Ohmmeter should deflect from 0 (zero) to infinity ohms as shaft is rotated.

**Speed Sensor (Land Cruiser Analog Type) – 1)** Raise and support rear of vehicle. Unplug ECU (behind glove box). Place transmission or transaxle in Neutral.

**2)** Connect ohmmeter and 10-ohm resistor to instrument cluster connector cavity. *See Fig. 32.* Turn rear wheels and ensure ohmmeter deflects consistently.

**3)** If ohmmeter does not deflect, ensure speed sensor terminals at back of speedometer are tight. If connection is good, replace speedometer assembly.

***NO. 1 SPEED SENSOR TEST TERMINALS (ANALOG TYPE)***

| Application | Test Terminals |
|---|---|
| Camry, Corolla, Corolla FX-16 & Supra | A & B |
| Celica & Cressida | SPD (+) & SPD (-) |
| Land Cruiser, MR2, Pickup & 4Runner | [1] SPD & GND |
| Van | 2 & 3 |

[1] – No. 4 and No. 7 terminals on Land Cruiser.

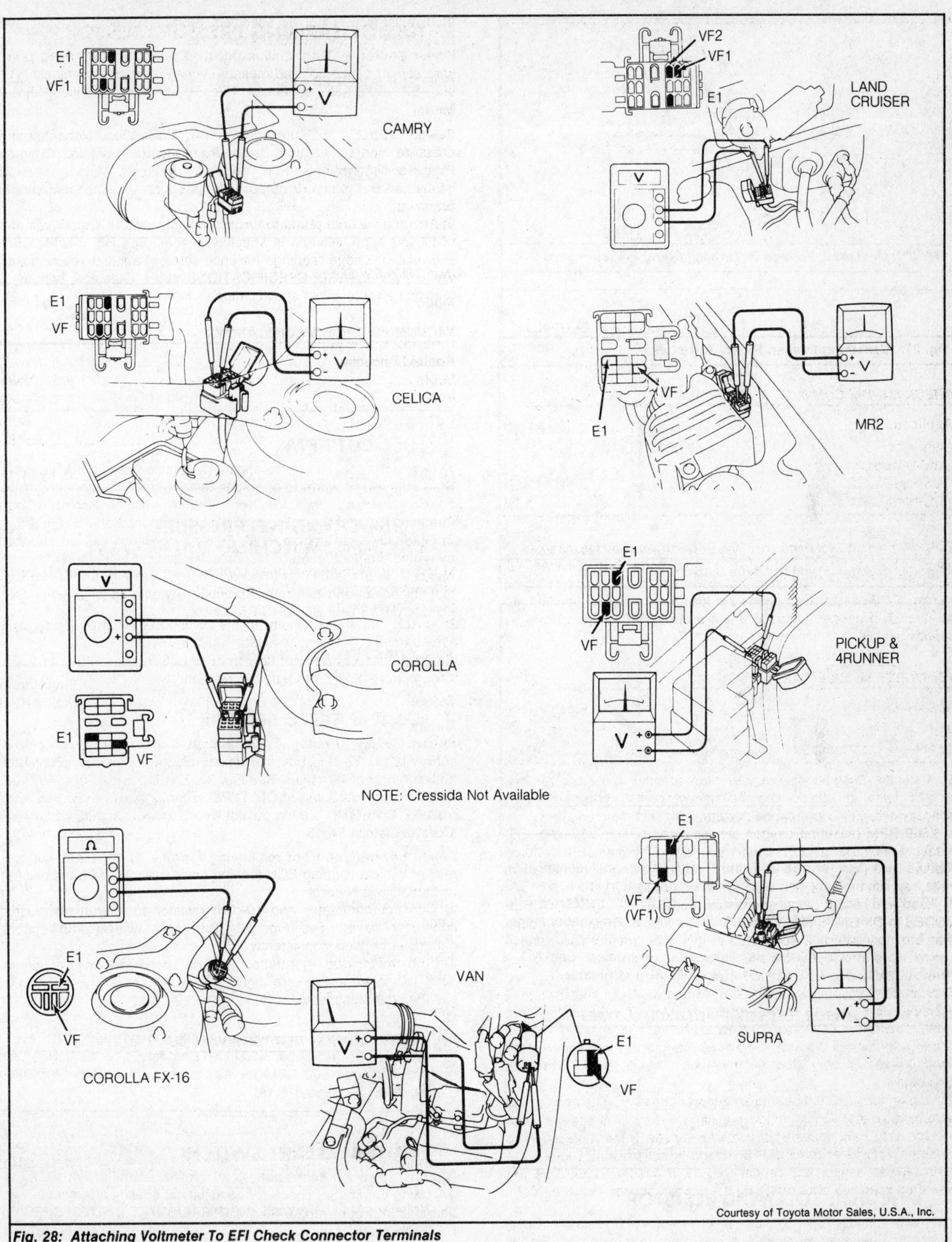
E1
VF1
CAMRY
VF2
VF1
E1
LAND
CRUISER
E1
VF
CELICA
VF
E1
MR2
COROLLA
E1
VF
E1
VF
PICKUP &
4RUNNER
NOTE: Cressida Not Available
E1
VF
COROLLA FX-16
VAN
E1
VF
E1
VF
(VF1)
SUPRA
Courtesy of Toyota Motor Sales, U.S.A., Inc.

*Fig. 28: Attaching Voltmeter To EFI Check Connector Terminals*

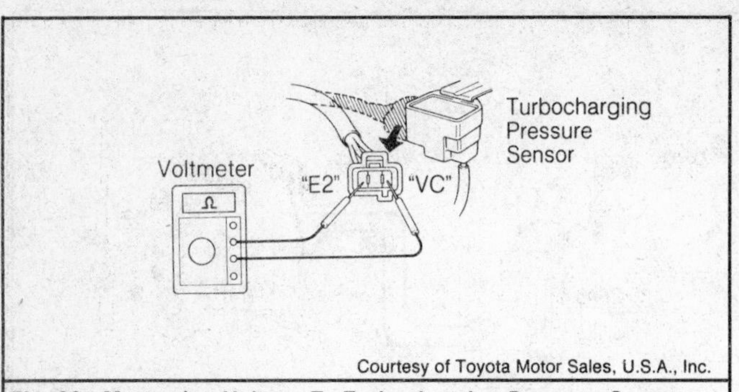
Turbocharging
Pressure
Sensor
Voltmeter
"E2"
"VC"
Courtesy of Toyota Motor Sales, U.S.A., Inc.

*Fig. 29: Measuring Voltage To Turbocharging Pressure Sensor*

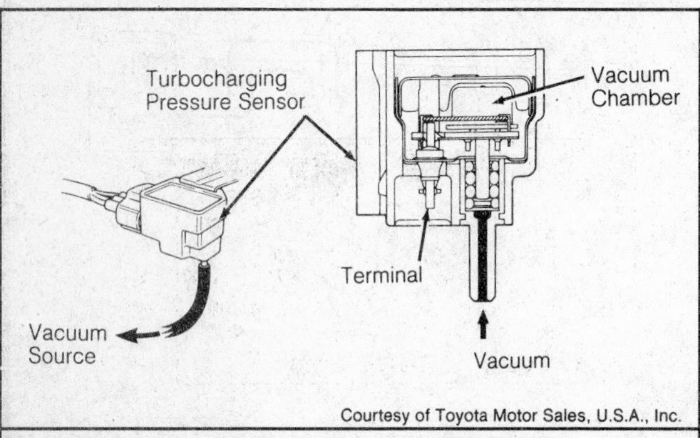
Turbocharging
Pressure Sensor
Vacuum
Chamber
Terminal
Vacuum
Source
Vacuum
Courtesy of Toyota Motor Sales, U.S.A., Inc.

*Fig. 30: Turbocharging Pressure Sensor Vacuum Hose*

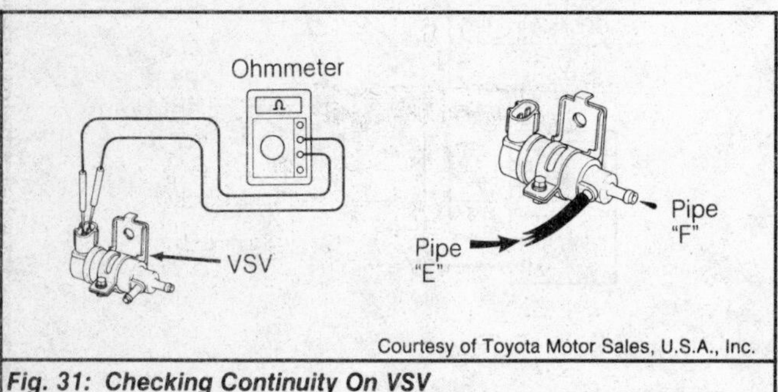
Ohmmeter
VSV
Pipe
"E"
Pipe
"F"
Courtesy of Toyota Motor Sales, U.S.A., Inc.

*Fig. 31: Checking Continuity On VSV*

**No. 1 Speed Sensor (Digital Type) – 1)** Note terminal identification. *See Fig. 33.* Connect voltmeter between proper terminals. See NO. 1 SPEED SENSOR TEST TERMINALS (DIGITAL TYPE) table for proper terminals. It may be necessary to remove combination meter.
**2)** Turn ignition on, with engine off. Voltmeter should deflect between specified voltage as meter shaft is rotated. See NO. 1 SPEED SENSOR TEST TERMINALS (DIGITAL TYPE) table.

***NO. 1 SPEED SENSOR TEST TERMINALS (DIGITAL TYPE)***

| Application | Test Terminals | Volt [1] Reading |
|---|---|---|
| Camry | 9 & 11 | 5 |
| Cressida | GND & SPD | 0-2 |
| Pickup & 4Runner | E2 & 4P | 0-1 |

[1] – Voltage should occur 4 times per meter shaft rotation.

## INJECTOR SOLENOID RESISTOR

**1)** Turn ignition off. Unplug injector solenoid resistor. Check resistance between terminal + B and other terminals. *See Fig. 34.* See INJECTOR SOLENOID RESISTANCE table.
**2)** If resistance is not as specified, replace solenoid resistor. See INJECTOR SOLENOID LOCATION table.

***INJECTOR SOLENOID RESISTANCE***

| Model | Ohms |
|---|---|
| Celica | 5-7 |
| Cressida | 2 |
| Pickup & 4Runner | |
| 4-Cyl. & V6 | 2-3 |
| Supra | 3 |
| Van | 2-3 |

***INJECTOR SOLENOID LOCATION***

| Model | Location |
|---|---|
| Celica | Left side of firewall |
| Cressida | Left Fenderwell |
| Pickup & 4Runner | Right Fenderwell |
| Supra | Left Shock Tower |
| Van | Left side of engine compartment |

## FUEL-CUT RPM

**1)** Connect a tachometer to engine (to monitor needle fluctuations). Start engine and warm to operating temperature. Disconnect throttle position sensor connector from throttle position sensor. Short terminals IDL and $E_1$ (or $E_2$) on wire side of connector. *See Fig. 35.*
**2)** Gradually raise engine RPM. Fuel-cut operation can be checked by noting the fluctuation of tachometer needle. Fluctuation indicates fuel-cut system is being turned on and off. *See Fig. 36.* Check that fuel-cut points and fuel return points are within specifications. See FUEL-CUT & FUEL RETURN RPM table.

***FUEL-CUT & FUEL RETURN RPM***

| Model | Fuel-Cut Engine RPM | Fuel Return Engine RPM |
|---|---|---|
| Camry | | |
| 4-Cyl. | 1700 | 1300 |
| V6 | 1800 | 1200 |
| Celica | | |
| 3S-FE | 1700 | 1300 |
| 3S-GE & 3S-GTE | 2000 | 1600 |
| Corolla, Corolla FX-16 & MR2 | | |
| A/C Off | 1600 | 1200 |
| A/C On | 1900 | 1500 |
| Cressida & Supra | 1800 | 1200 |
| Land Cruiser | 1300 | 1000 |
| Pickup (Turbo) | 1800 | 1600 |
| Pickup (Non-Turbo) & 4Runner | | |
| 4-Cyl. & V6 | [1] 1300 | [1] 1000 |
| Van | 2200 | 1800 |

[1] – Apply service brakes when testing 4-cylinder 2WD (M/T) models. On 4-cylinder 4WD (A/T) models, use 1900 RPM for fuel-cut and 1600 RPM for fuel return without service brakes applied.

## NEUTRAL/START SWITCH

Disconnect switch connector. Note terminal identification. *See Fig. 37.* Using ohmmeter, check for continuity at specified terminals with gearshift in proper range. See NEUTRAL/START SWITCH SPECIFICATIONS table.

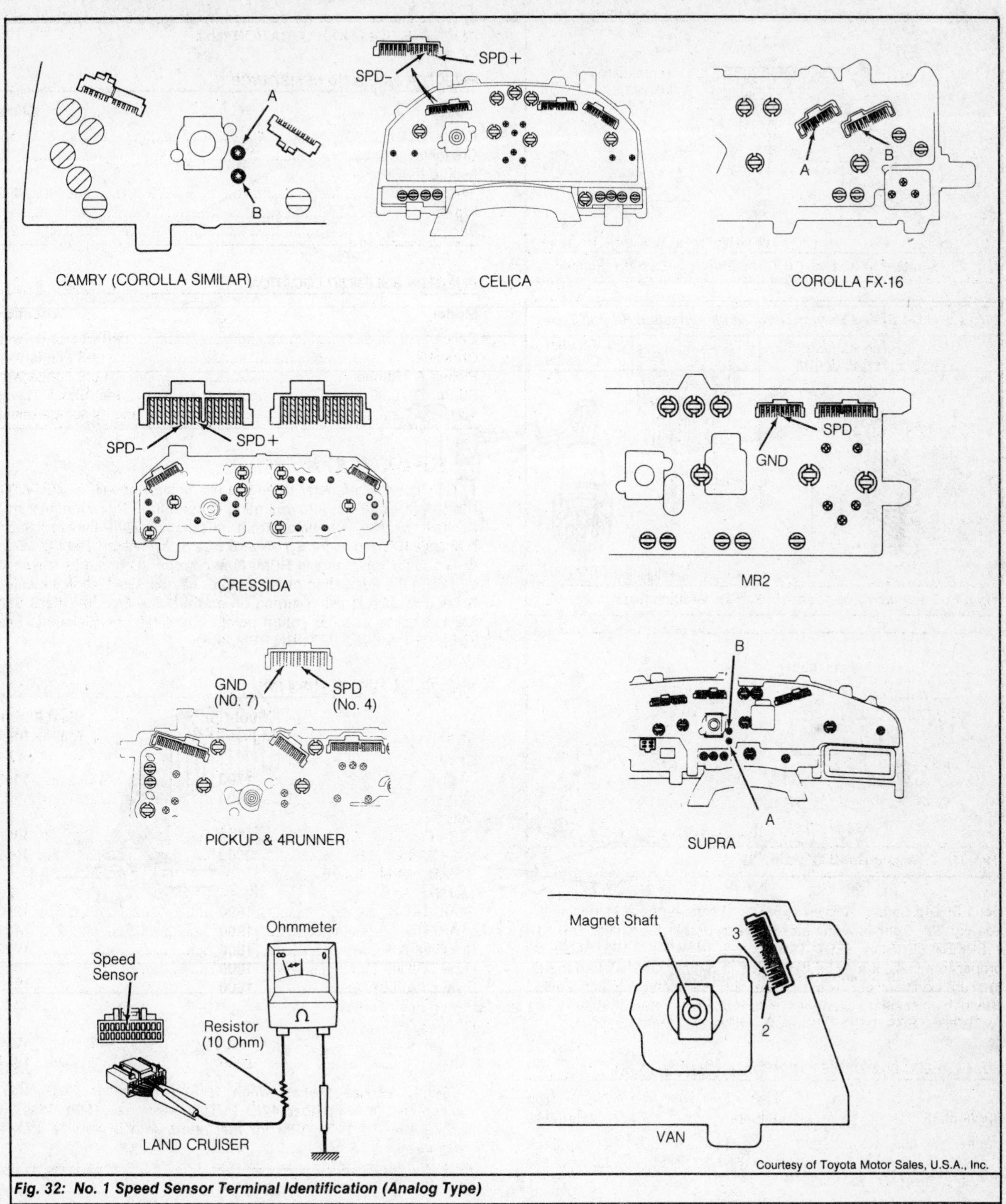
A
B
CAMRY (COROLLA SIMILAR)
SPD+
SPD-
CELICA
A
B
COROLLA FX-16
SPD-
SPD+
CRESSIDA
SPD
GND
MR2
GND
(N0. 7)
SPD
(No. 4)
PICKUP & 4RUNNER
B
A
SUPRA
Ohmmeter
Speed
Sensor
Resistor
(10 Ohm)
LAND CRUISER
Magnet Shaft
3
2
VAN

Courtesy of Toyota Motor Sales, U.S.A., Inc.

*Fig. 32: No. 1 Speed Sensor Terminal Identification (Analog Type)*

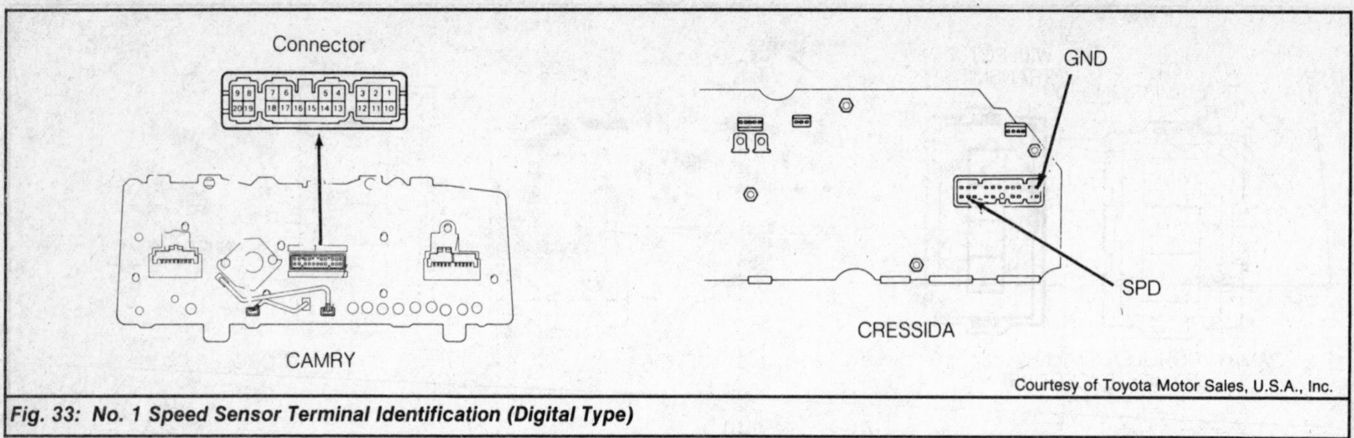
Connector
9 8 7 6 5 4 3 2 1
20 19 18 17 16 15 14 13 12 11 10
CAMRY
GND
SPD
CRESSIDA
Courtesy of Toyota Motor Sales, U.S.A., Inc.

*Fig. 33: No. 1 Speed Sensor Terminal Identification (Digital Type)*

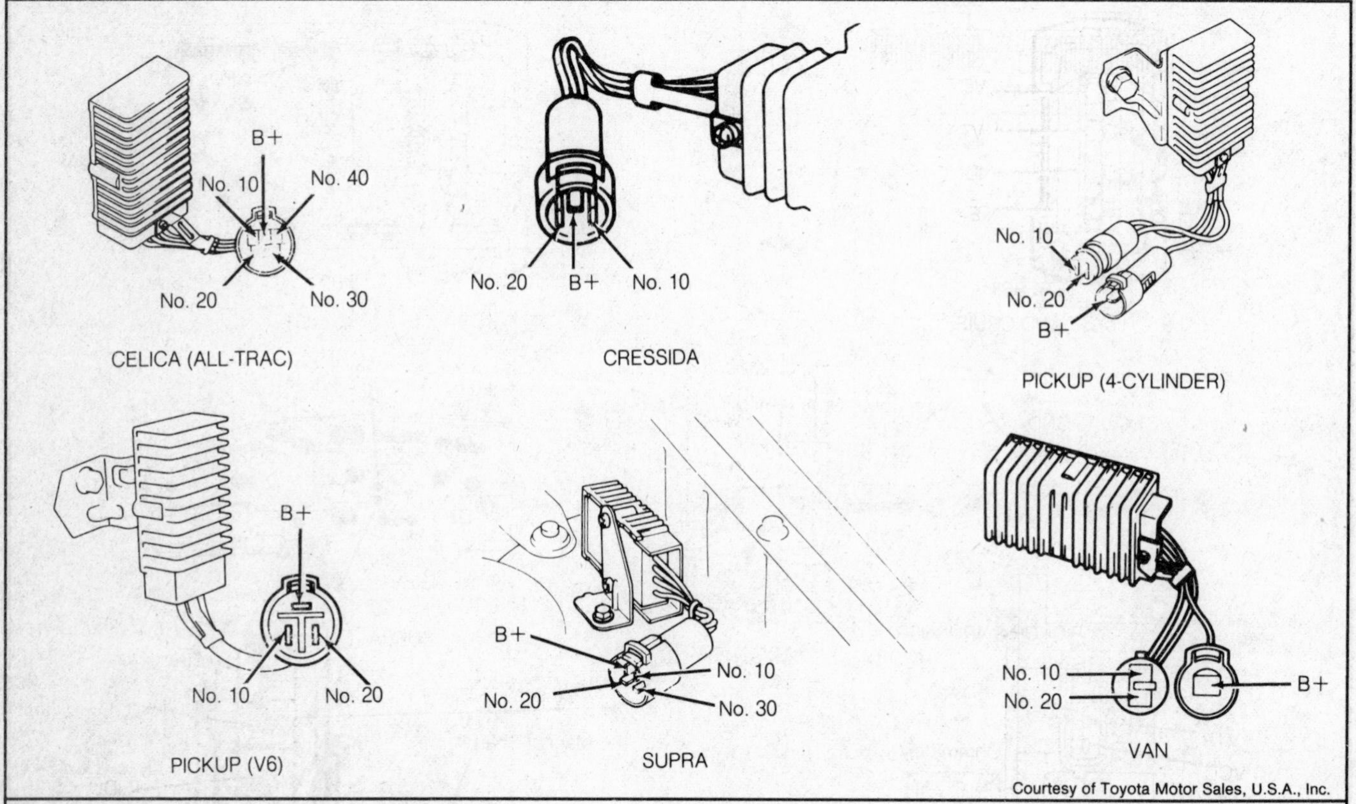

B+
No. 10
No. 40
No. 20
No. 30
CELICA (ALL-TRAC)

No. 20
B+
No. 10
CRESSIDA

No. 10
No. 20
B+
PICKUP (4-CYLINDER)

B+
No. 10
No. 20
PICKUP (V6)

B+
No. 10
No. 20
No. 30
SUPRA

No. 10
No. 20
B+
VAN

Courtesy of Toyota Motor Sales, U.S.A., Inc.

*Fig. 34: Injector Solenoid Resistor Identification*

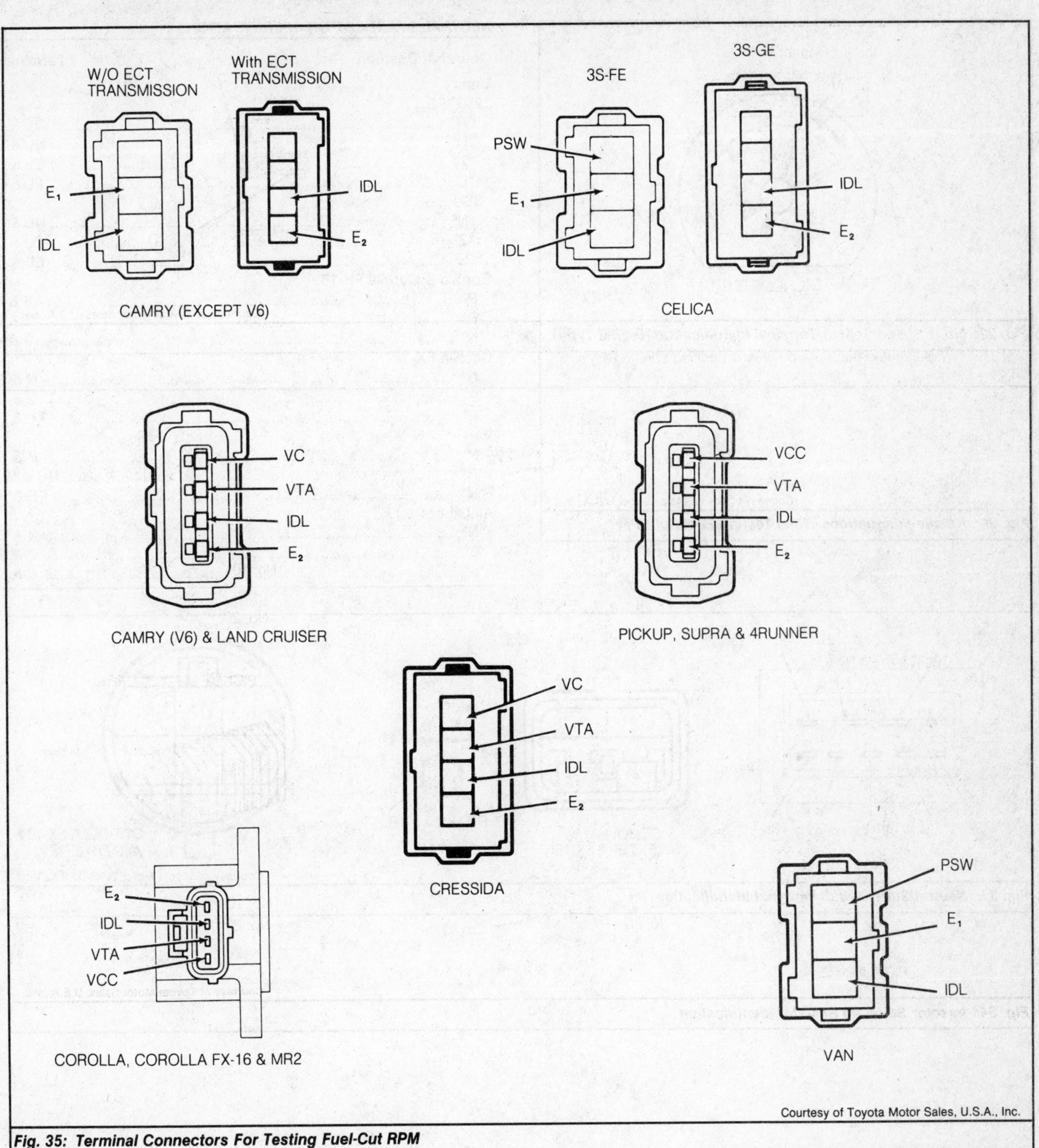
W/O ECT TRANSMISSION
With ECT TRANSMISSION
$E_1$
IDL
IDL
$E_2$
CAMRY (EXCEPT V6)
3S-FE
3S-GE
PSW
$E_1$
IDL
IDL
$E_2$
CELICA
VC
VTA
IDL
$E_2$
CAMRY (V6) & LAND CRUISER
VCC
VTA
IDL
$E_2$
PICKUP, SUPRA & 4RUNNER
VC
VTA
IDL
$E_2$
CRESSIDA
$E_2$
IDL
VTA
VCC
COROLLA, COROLLA FX-16 & MR2
PSW
$E_1$
IDL
VAN
Courtesy of Toyota Motor Sales, U.S.A., Inc.

*Fig. 35: Terminal Connectors For Testing Fuel-Cut RPM*

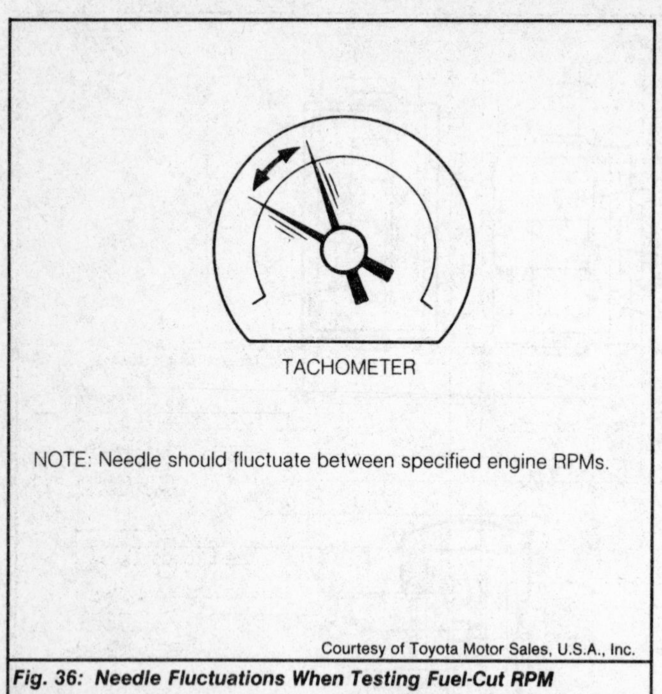
TACHOMETER
NOTE: Needle should fluctuate between specified engine RPMs.
Courtesy of Toyota Motor Sales, U.S.A., Inc.

***Fig. 36: Needle Fluctuations When Testing Fuel-Cut RPM***

***NEUTRAL/START SWITCH SPECIFICATIONS***

| Gearshift Position | Terminals |
|---|---|
| Camry | |
| 2VZ-FE | |
| "R" | RL & C |
| "N" | NL & C |
| "2" | 2L & C |
| "L" | LL & C |
| 3S-FE | |
| "N" | NL & C |
| "2" | 2L & C |
| "L" | LL & C |
| Corolla & Corolla FX-16 | |
| "P" | 3 & 4 |
| "R" | 1 & 2 |
| "N" | 3 & 4 |
| Corolla FX-16 | |
| "N" | N & C |
| "2" | 2 & C |
| "L" | L & C |
| Van | |
| "P" | B & N |
| "R" | RB & RL |
| "N" | B & N |
| All Others | |
| "N" | N & C |
| "2" | 2 & C |
| "L" | L & C |

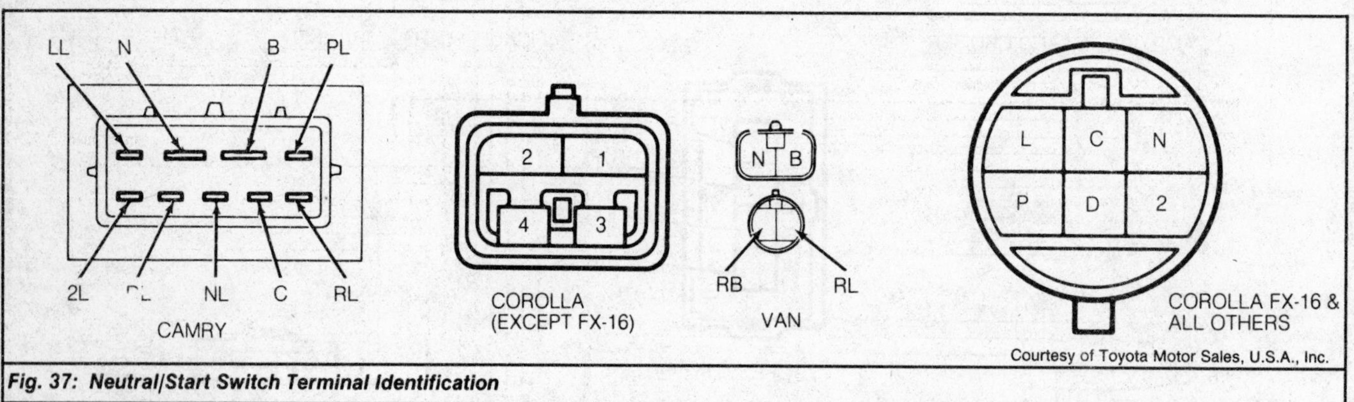
LL
N
B
PL
2L
NL
C
RL
CAMRY
2
1
4
3
COROLLA
(EXCEPT FX-16)
N
B
RB
RL
VAN
L
C
N
P
D
2
COROLLA FX-16 &
ALL OTHERS
Courtesy of Toyota Motor Sales, U.S.A., Inc.

***Fig. 37: Neutral/Start Switch Terminal Identification***

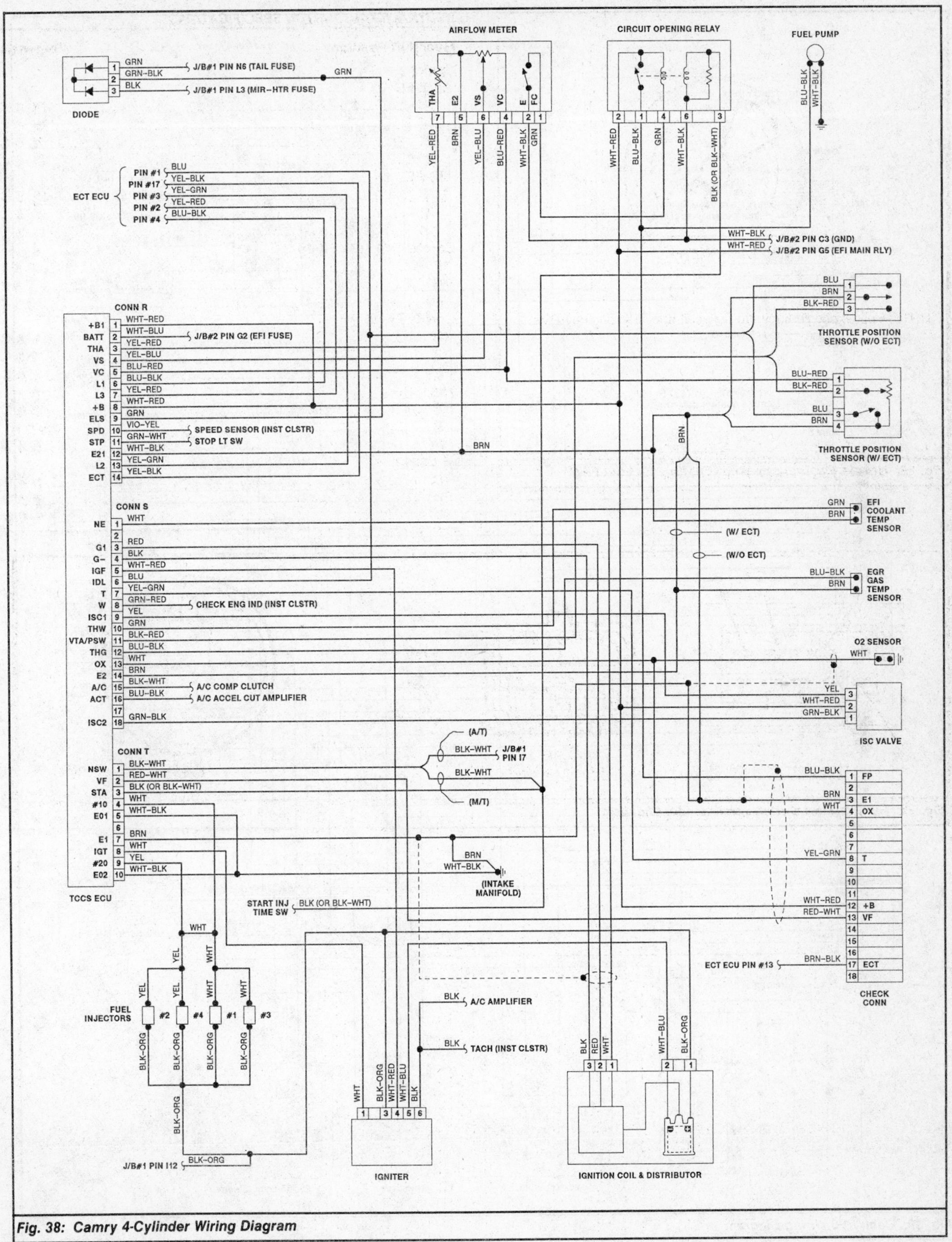
AIRFLOW METER
CIRCUIT OPENING RELAY
FUEL PUMP
DIODE
GRN
GRN-BLK
BLK
J/B#1 PIN N6 (TAIL FUSE)
J/B#1 PIN L3 (MIR-HTR FUSE)
THA E2 VS VC E FC
YEL-RED BRN YEL-BLU BLU-RED WHT-BLK GRN
WHT-RED BLU-BLK GRN WHT-BLK BLK (OR BLK-WHT)
BLU-BLK WHT-BLK
ECT ECU
PIN #1 BLU
PIN #17 YEL-BLK
PIN #3 YEL-GRN
PIN #2 YEL-RED
PIN #4 BLU-BLK
WHT-BLK J/B#2 PIN C3 (GND)
WHT-RED J/B#2 PIN G5 (EFI MAIN RLY)
THROTTLE POSITION SENSOR (W/O ECT)
THROTTLE POSITION SENSOR (W/ ECT)
CONN R
+B1 1 WHT-RED
BATT 2 WHT-BLU J/B#2 PIN G2 (EFI FUSE)
THA 3 YEL-RED
VS 4 YEL-BLU
VC 5 BLU-RED
L1 6 BLU-BLK
L3 7 YEL-RED
+B 8 WHT-RED
ELS 9 GRN
SPD 10 VIO-YEL
STP 11 GRN-WHT SPEED SENSOR (INST CLSTR)
E21 12 WHT-BLK STOP LT SW
L2 13 YEL-GRN
ECT 14 YEL-BLK
CONN S
NE 1 WHT
2
G1 3 RED
G- 4 BLK
IGF 5 WHT-RED
IDL 6 BLU
T 7 YEL-GRN
W 8 GRN-RED CHECK ENG IND (INST CLSTR)
ISC1 9 YEL
THW 10 GRN
VTA/PSW 11 BLK-RED
THG 12 BLU-BLK
OX 13 WHT
E2 14 BRN
A/C 15 BLK-WHT A/C COMP CLUTCH
ACT 16 BLU-BLK A/C ACCEL CUT AMPLIFIER
17
ISC2 18 GRN-BLK
EFI COOLANT TEMP SENSOR
(W/ ECT)
(W/O ECT)
EGR GAS TEMP SENSOR
O2 SENSOR
ISC VALVE
CONN T
NSW 1 BLK-WHT
VF 2 RED-WHT
STA 3 BLK (OR BLK-WHT)
#10 4 WHT
E01 5 WHT-BLK
6
E1 7 BRN
IGT 8 WHT
#20 9 YEL
E02 10 WHT-BLK
TCCS ECU
(A/T)
J/B#1 PIN I7
(M/T)
(INTAKE MANIFOLD)
START INJ TIME SW
CHECK CONN
1 FP
3 E1
4 OX
8 T
12 +B
13 VF
17 ECT
ECT ECU PIN #13
FUEL INJECTORS
#2 #4 #1 #3
A/C AMPLIFIER
TACH (INST CLSTR)
J/B#1 PIN I12
IGNITER
IGNITION COIL & DISTRIBUTOR

Fig. 38: Camry 4-Cylinder Wiring Diagram

# 1988 COMPUTERIZED ENGINE CONTROLS
## Toyota Computer Control System (Cont.)

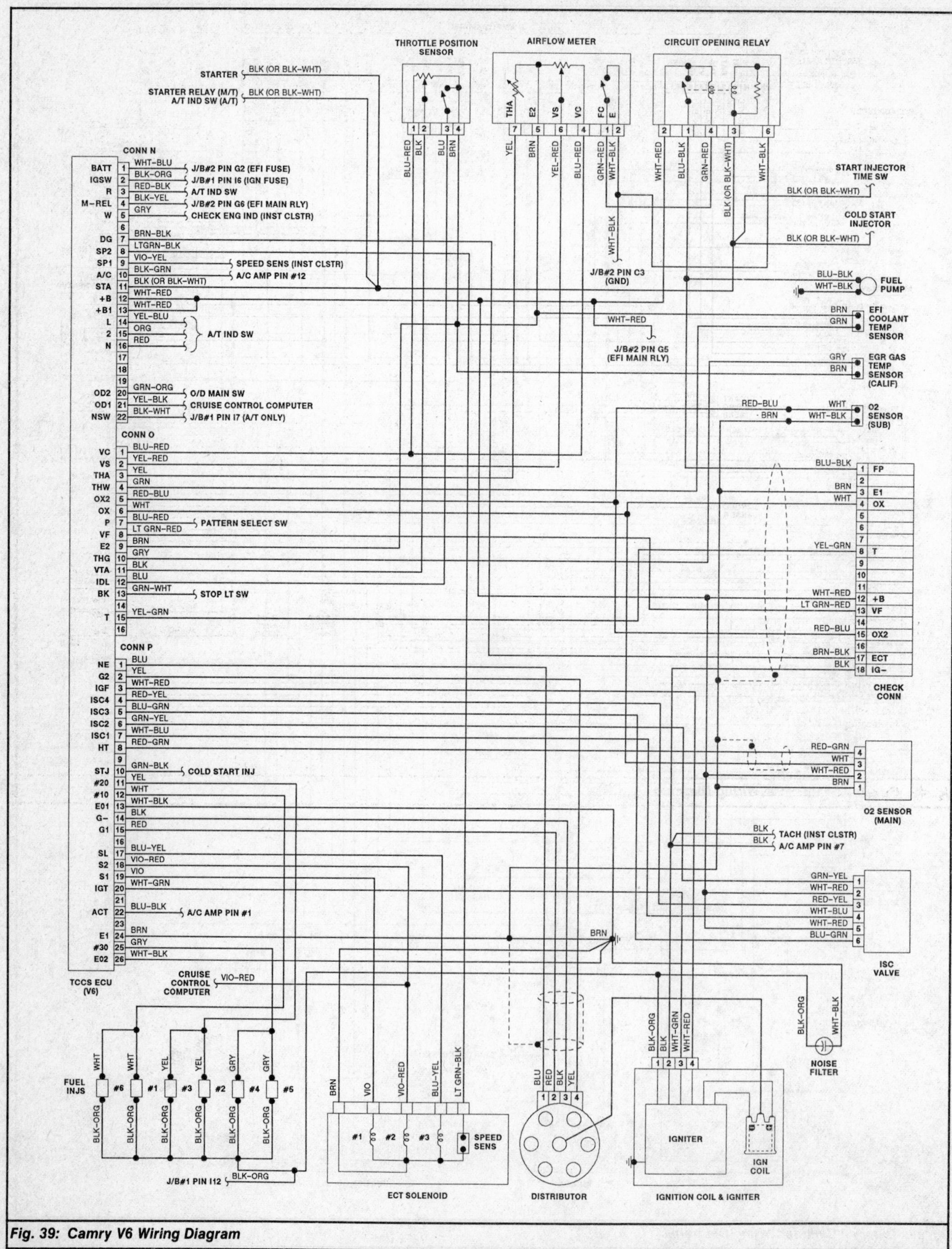
THROTTLE POSITION SENSOR
AIRFLOW METER
CIRCUIT OPENING RELAY
STARTER
STARTER RELAY (M/T) A/T IND SW (A/T)
BLK (OR BLK-WHT)
CONN N
J/B#2 PIN G2 (EFI FUSE)
J/B#1 PIN I6 (IGN FUSE)
A/T IND SW
J/B#2 PIN G6 (EFI MAIN RLY)
CHECK ENG IND (INST CLSTR)
SPEED SENS (INST CLSTR)
A/C AMP PIN #12
J/B#2 PIN C3 (GND)
J/B#2 PIN G5 (EFI MAIN RLY)
O/D MAIN SW
CRUISE CONTROL COMPUTER
J/B#1 PIN I7 (A/T ONLY)
CONN O
PATTERN SELECT SW
STOP LT SW
CONN P
COLD START INJ
A/C AMP PIN #1
TCCS ECU (V6)
CRUISE CONTROL COMPUTER
START INJECTOR TIME SW
COLD START INJECTOR
FUEL PUMP
EFI COOLANT TEMP SENSOR
EGR GAS TEMP SENSOR (CALIF)
O2 SENSOR (SUB)
CHECK CONN
O2 SENSOR (MAIN)
TACH (INST CLSTR)
A/C AMP PIN #7
ISC VALVE
NOISE FILTER
FUEL INJS
J/B#1 PIN I12
ECT SOLENOID
SPEED SENS
DISTRIBUTOR
IGNITER
IGN COIL
IGNITION COIL & IGNITER

*Fig. 39: Camry V6 Wiring Diagram*

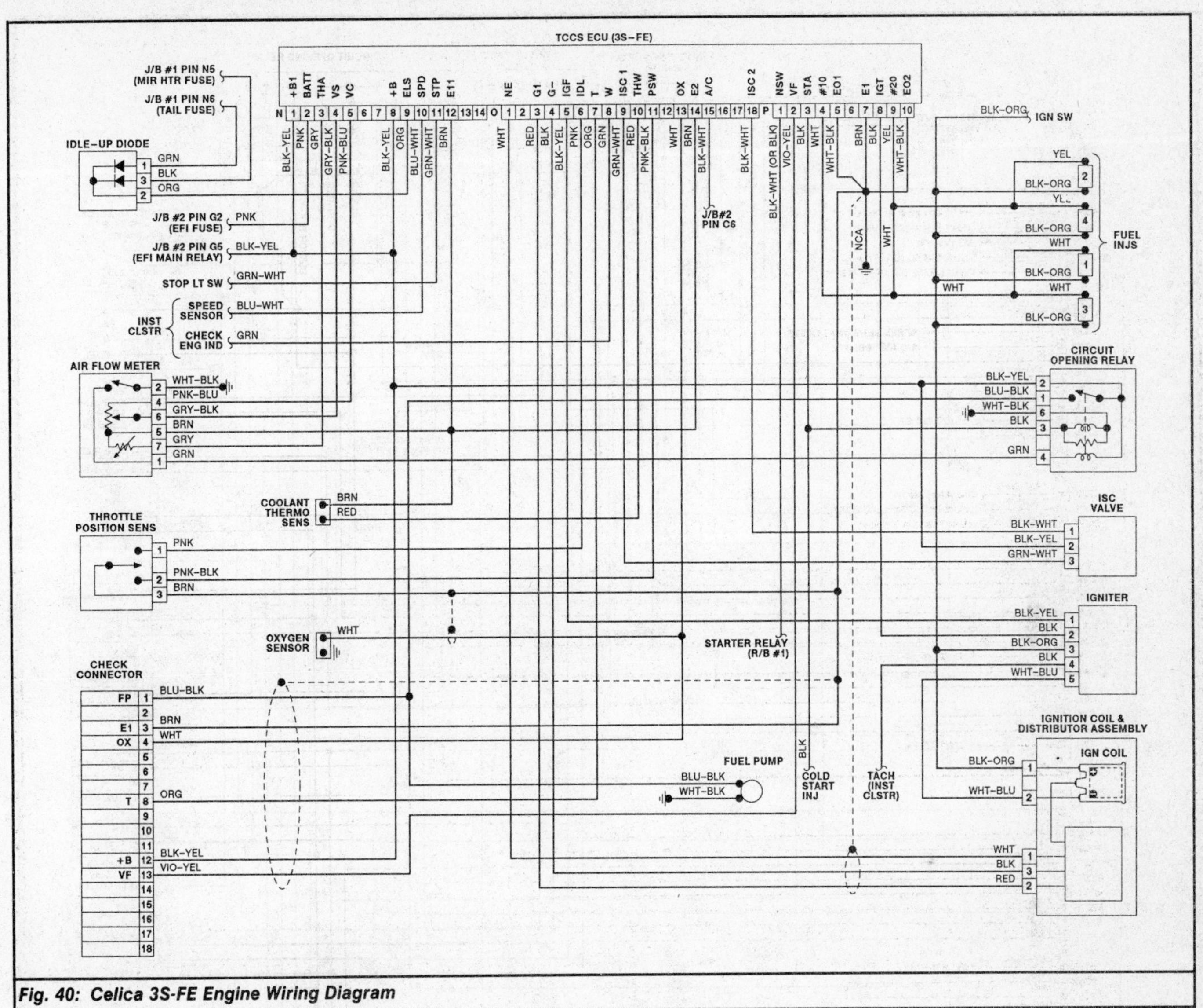
TCCS ECU (3S-FE)
J/B #1 PIN N5 (MIR HTR FUSE)
J/B #1 PIN N6 (TAIL FUSE)
IDLE-UP DIODE
J/B #2 PIN G2 (EFI FUSE)
J/B #2 PIN G5 (EFI MAIN RELAY)
STOP LT SW
INST CLSTR
SPEED SENSOR
CHECK ENG IND
AIR FLOW METER
COOLANT THERMO SENS
THROTTLE POSITION SENS
OXYGEN SENSOR
CHECK CONNECTOR
J/B#2 PIN C6
STARTER RELAY (R/B #1)
FUEL PUMP
COLD START INJ
TACH (INST CLSTR)
IGN SW
FUEL INJS
CIRCUIT OPENING RELAY
ISC VALVE
IGNITER
IGNITION COIL & DISTRIBUTOR ASSEMBLY
IGN COIL
NCA

*Fig. 40: Celica 3S-FE Engine Wiring Diagram*

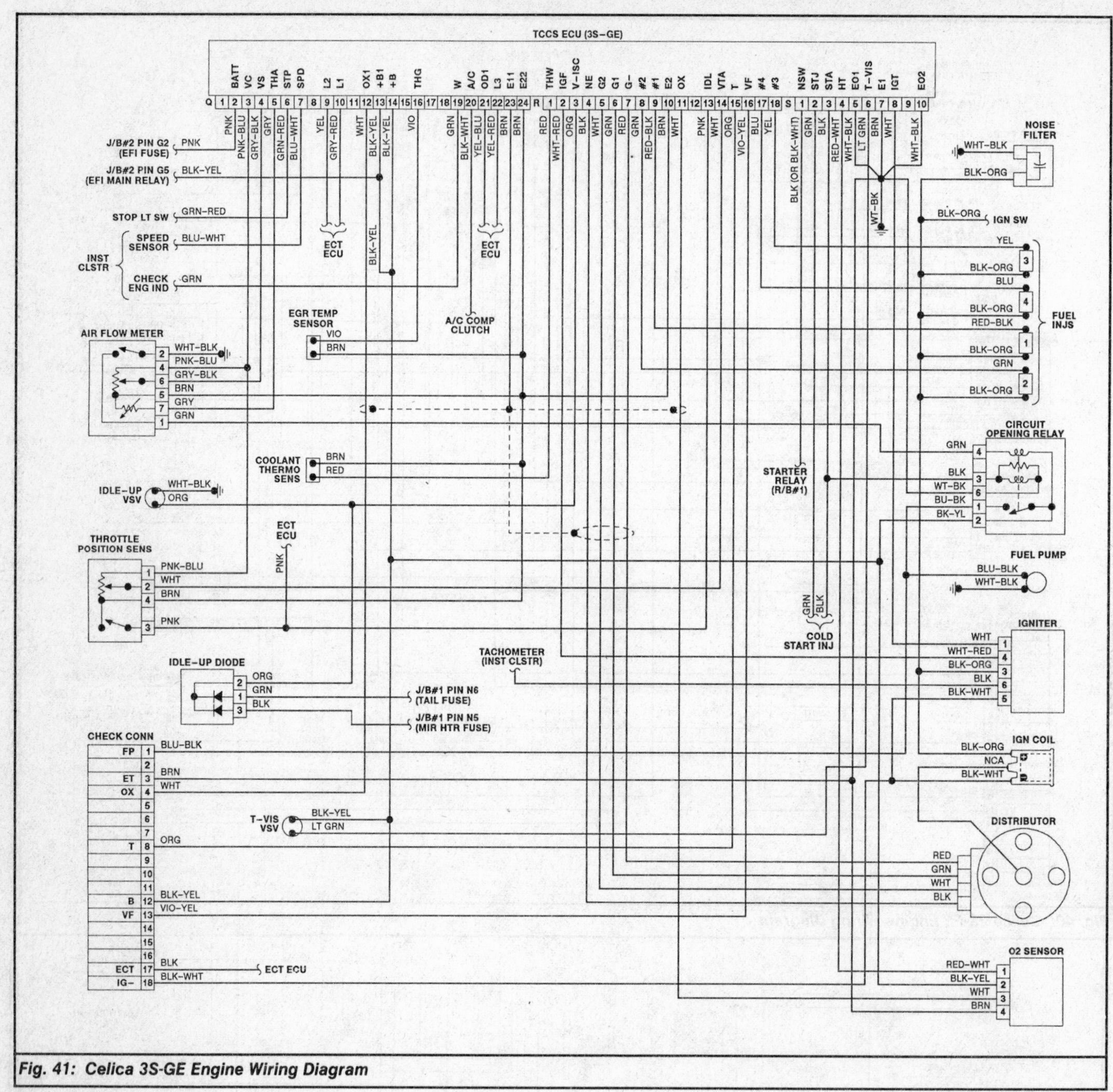
TCCS ECU (3S-GE)
J/B#2 PIN G2 (EFI FUSE)
J/B#2 PIN G5 (EFI MAIN RELAY)
STOP LT SW
SPEED SENSOR
INST CLSTR
CHECK ENG IND
AIR FLOW METER
EGR TEMP SENSOR
A/C COMP CLUTCH
ECT ECU
COOLANT THERMO SENS
IDLE-UP VSV
THROTTLE POSITION SENS
IDLE-UP DIODE
J/B#1 PIN N6 (TAIL FUSE)
J/B#1 PIN N5 (MIR HTR FUSE)
TACHOMETER (INST CLSTR)
CHECK CONN
T-VIS VSV
NOISE FILTER
IGN SW
FUEL INJS
CIRCUIT OPENING RELAY
STARTER RELAY (R/B#1)
FUEL PUMP
COLD START INJ
IGNITER
IGN COIL
DISTRIBUTOR
O2 SENSOR

*Fig. 41: Celica 3S-GE Engine Wiring Diagram*

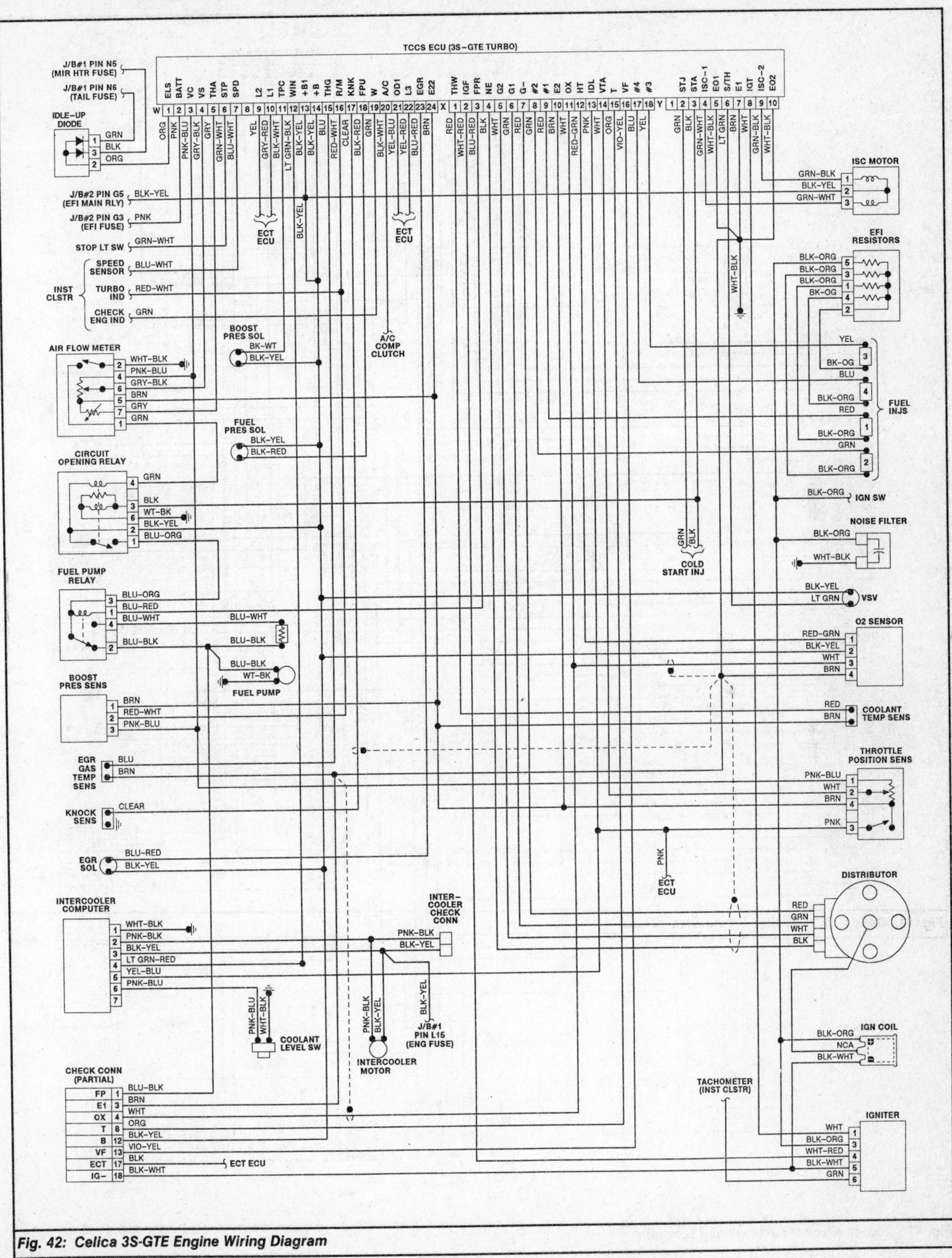
TCCS ECU (3S-GTE TURBO)
J/B#1 PIN N5 (MIR HTR FUSE)
J/B#1 PIN N6 (TAIL FUSE)
IDLE-UP DIODE
J/B#2 PIN G5 (EFI MAIN RLY)
J/B#2 PIN G3 (EFI FUSE)
STOP LT SW
SPEED SENSOR
INST CLSTR
TURBO IND
CHECK ENG IND
ECT ECU
BOOST PRES SOL
A/C COMP CLUTCH
AIR FLOW METER
FUEL PRES SOL
CIRCUIT OPENING RELAY
FUEL PUMP RELAY
FUEL PUMP
BOOST PRES SENS
EGR GAS TEMP SENS
KNOCK SENS
EGR SOL
INTERCOOLER COMPUTER
INTER-COOLER CHECK CONN
COOLANT LEVEL SW
J/B#1 PIN L15 (ENG FUSE)
INTERCOOLER MOTOR
CHECK CONN (PARTIAL)
ISC MOTOR
EFI RESISTORS
FUEL INJS
IGN SW
NOISE FILTER
COLD START INJ
VSV
O2 SENSOR
COOLANT TEMP SENS
THROTTLE POSITION SENS
DISTRIBUTOR
IGN COIL
TACHOMETER (INST CLSTR)
IGNITER

Fig. 42: Celica 3S-GTE Engine Wiring Diagram

# 1988 COMPUTERIZED ENGINE CONTROLS
## Toyota Computer Control System (Cont.)

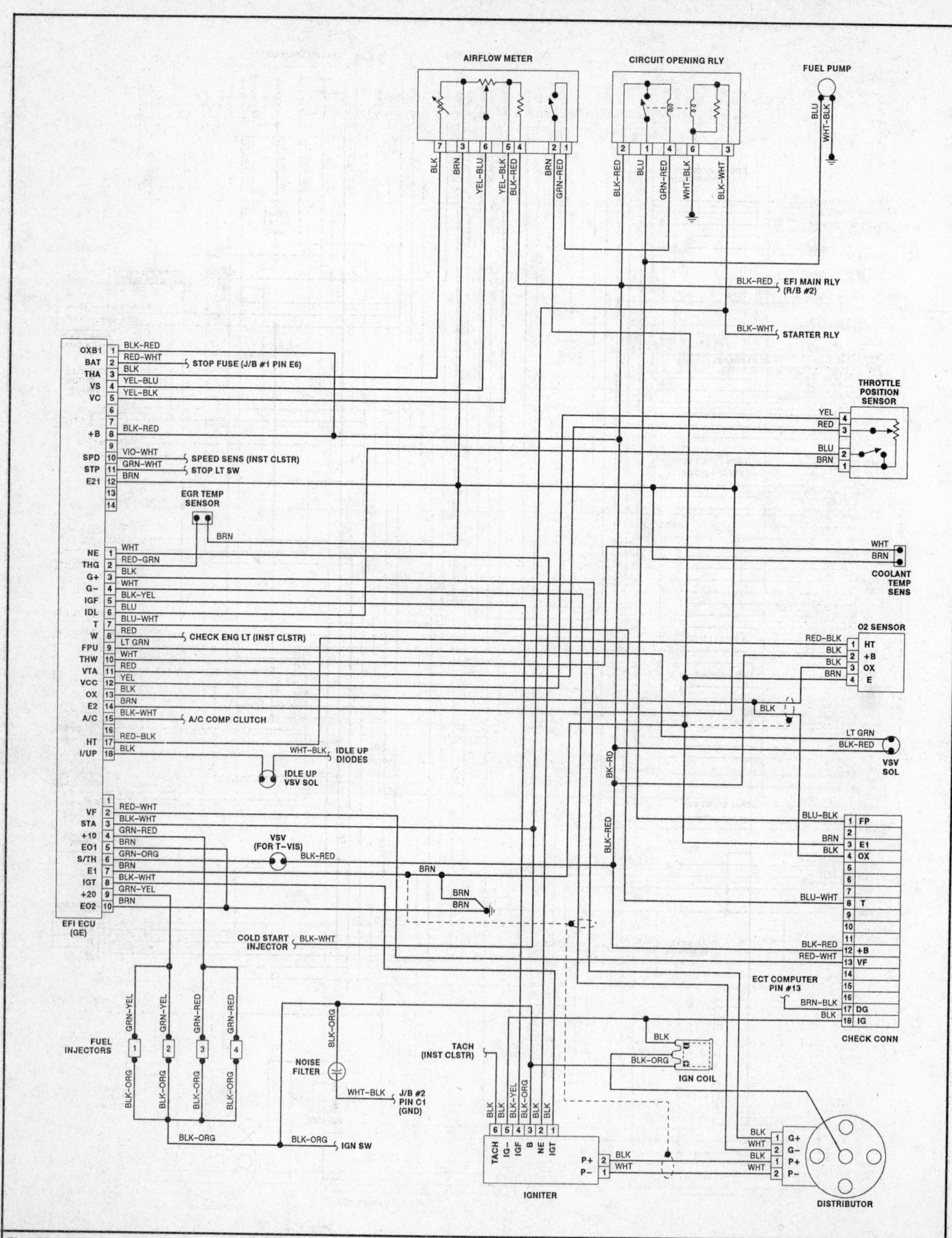

AIRFLOW METER
CIRCUIT OPENING RLY
FUEL PUMP
EFI MAIN RLY (R/B #2)
STARTER RLY
THROTTLE POSITION SENSOR
STOP FUSE (J/B #1 PIN E6)
SPEED SENS (INST CLSTR)
STOP LT SW
EGR TEMP SENSOR
COOLANT TEMP SENS
O2 SENSOR
CHECK ENG LT (INST CLSTR)
A/C COMP CLUTCH
IDLE UP DIODES
IDLE UP VSV SOL
VSV SOL
VSV (FOR T-VIS)
EFI ECU (GE)
COLD START INJECTOR
ECT COMPUTER PIN #13
CHECK CONN
FUEL INJECTORS
NOISE FILTER
J/B #2 PIN C1 (GND)
IGN SW
TACH (INST CLSTR)
IGN COIL
IGNITER
DISTRIBUTOR


Fig. 43: Corolla (Except FX-16) Wiring Diagram

# 1988 COMPUTERIZED ENGINE CONTROLS
## Toyota Computer Control System (Cont.)

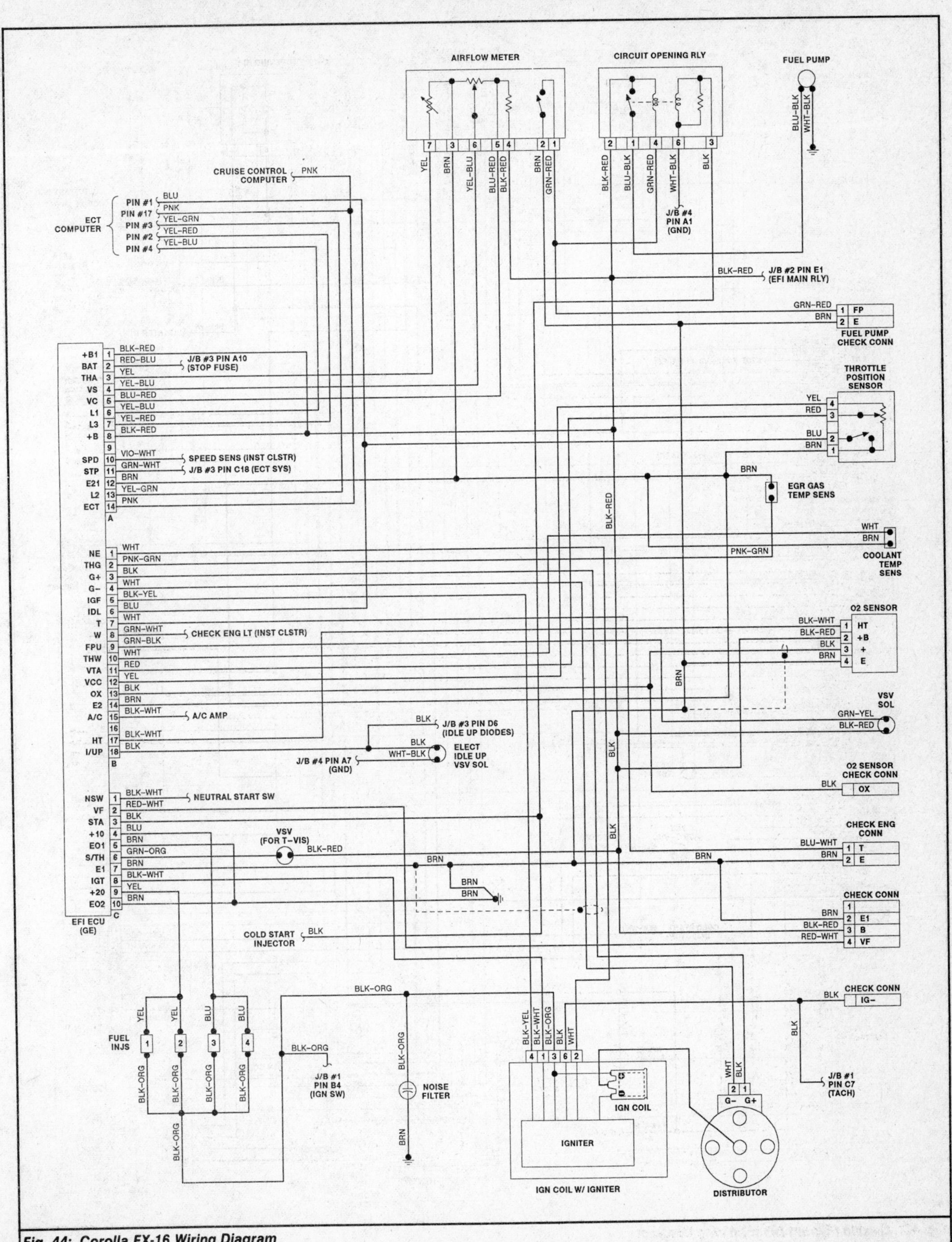

AIRFLOW METER
CIRCUIT OPENING RLY
FUEL PUMP
BLU-BLK
WHT-BLK
YEL
BRN
YEL-BLU
BLU-RED
BLK-RED
GRN-RED
BLU-BLK
GRN-RED
WHT-BLK
BLK
J/B #4 PIN A1 (GND)
CRUISE CONTROL COMPUTER
PNK
ECT COMPUTER
PIN #1
PIN #17
PIN #3
PIN #2
PIN #4
BLU
YEL-GRN
YEL-RED
J/B #2 PIN E1 (EFI MAIN RLY)
FP
E
FUEL PUMP CHECK CONN
THROTTLE POSITION SENSOR
RED
+B1
BAT
THA
VS
VC
L1
L3
+B
SPD
STP
E21
L2
ECT
RED-BLU
J/B #3 PIN A10 (STOP FUSE)
VIO-WHT
GRN-WHT
SPEED SENS (INST CLSTR)
J/B #3 PIN C18 (ECT SYS)
EGR GAS TEMP SENS
WHT
PNK-GRN
COOLANT TEMP SENS
NE
THG
G+
G-
IGF
IDL
T
W
FPU
THW
VTA
VCC
OX
E2
A/C
HT
I/UP
BLK-YEL
GRN-BLK
CHECK ENG LT (INST CLSTR)
BLK-WHT
A/C AMP
O2 SENSOR
HT
+B
+
E
VSV SOL
GRN-YEL
J/B #3 PIN D6 (IDLE UP DIODES)
WHT-BLK
ELECT IDLE UP VSV SOL
J/B #4 PIN A7 (GND)
O2 SENSOR CHECK CONN
OX
NSW
VF
STA
+10
EO1
S/TH
E1
IGT
+20
EO2
RED-WHT
NEUTRAL START SW
VSV (FOR T-VIS)
GRN-ORG
CHECK ENG CONN
BLU-WHT
EFI ECU (GE)
COLD START INJECTOR
CHECK CONN
E1
B
VF
BLK-ORG
IG-
FUEL INJS
J/B #1 PIN B4 (IGN SW)
NOISE FILTER
J/B #1 PIN C7 (TACH)
IGN COIL
IGNITER
IGN COIL W/ IGNITER
G-
G+
DISTRIBUTOR


***Fig. 44:** Corolla FX-16 Wiring Diagram*

# 1988 COMPUTERIZED ENGINE CONTROLS
## Toyota Computer Control System (Cont.)

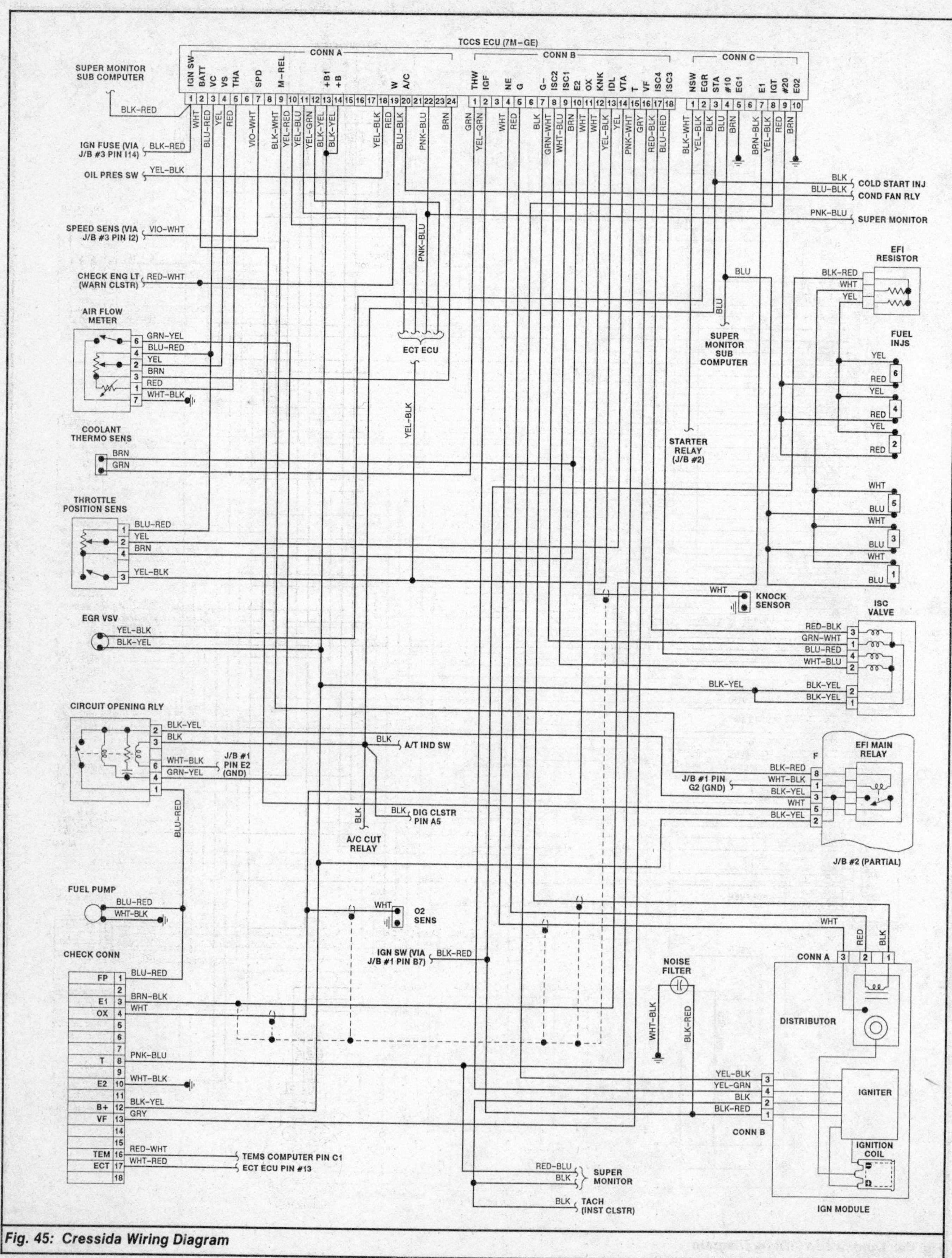

TCCS ECU (7M-GE)
CONN A
CONN B
CONN C
SUPER MONITOR SUB COMPUTER
IGN FUSE (VIA J/B #3 PIN I14)
OIL PRES SW
SPEED SENS (VIA J/B #3 PIN I2)
CHECK ENG LT (WARN CLSTR)
AIR FLOW METER
COOLANT THERMO SENS
THROTTLE POSITION SENS
EGR VSV
CIRCUIT OPENING RLY
J/B #1 PIN E2 (GND)
FUEL PUMP
CHECK CONN
ECT ECU
A/T IND SW
DIG CLSTR PIN A5
A/C CUT RELAY
O2 SENS
IGN SW (VIA J/B #1 PIN B7)
NOISE FILTER
COLD START INJ
COND FAN RLY
SUPER MONITOR
EFI RESISTOR
FUEL INJS
SUPER MONITOR SUB COMPUTER
STARTER RELAY (J/B #2)
KNOCK SENSOR
ISC VALVE
EFI MAIN RELAY
J/B #1 PIN G2 (GND)
J/B #2 (PARTIAL)
DISTRIBUTOR
IGNITER
IGNITION COIL
IGN MODULE
TEMS COMPUTER PIN C1
ECT ECU PIN #13
TACH (INST CLSTR)


Fig. 45: Cressida Wiring Diagram

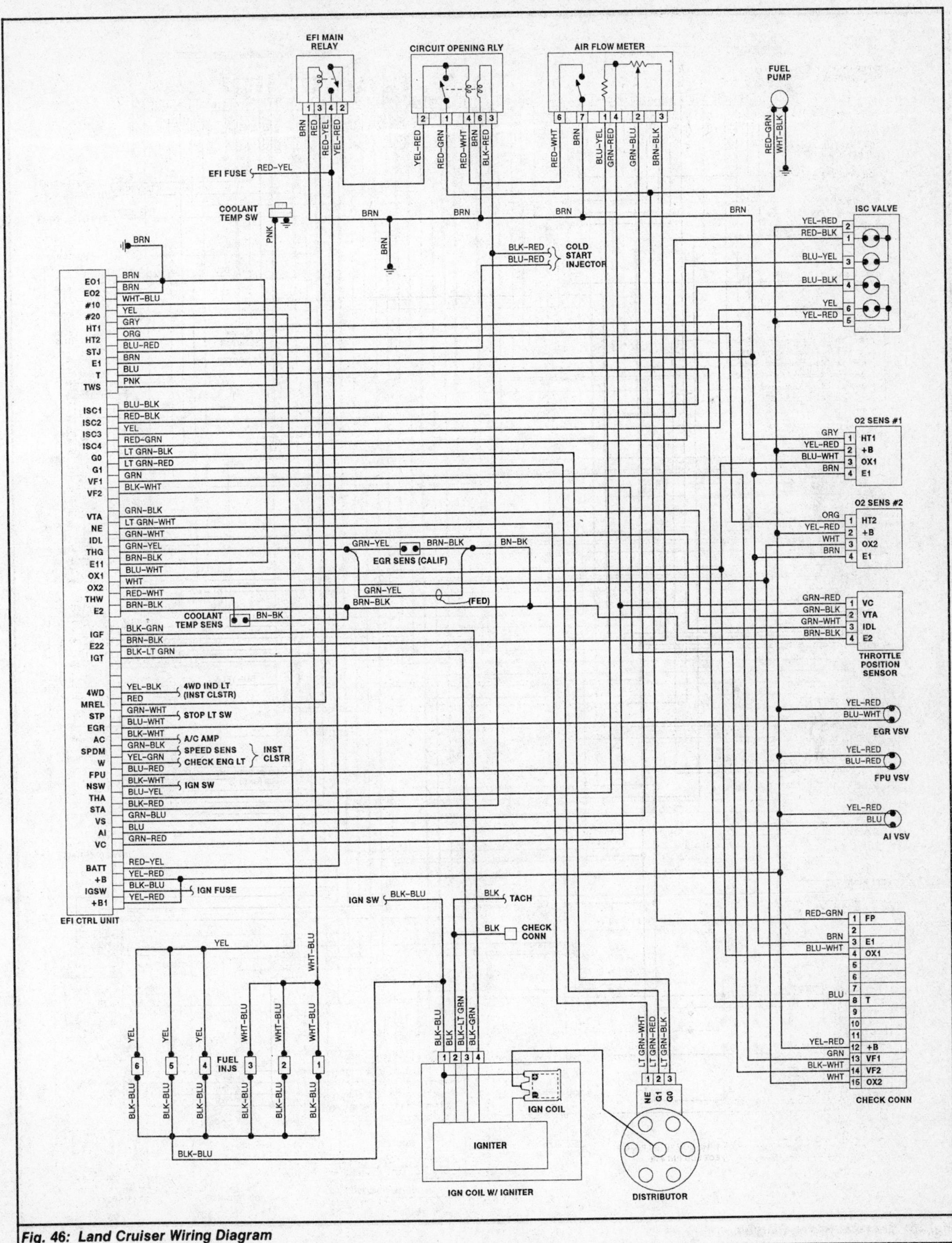

EFI MAIN RELAY
CIRCUIT OPENING RLY
AIR FLOW METER
FUEL PUMP
EFI FUSE
COOLANT TEMP SW
ISC VALVE
COLD START INJECTOR
EFI CTRL UNIT
O2 SENS #1
O2 SENS #2
EGR SENS (CALIF)
COOLANT TEMP SENS
THROTTLE POSITION SENSOR
4WD IND LT (INST CLSTR)
STOP LT SW
A/C AMP
SPEED SENS
CHECK ENG LT
INST CLSTR
IGN SW
EGR VSV
FPU VSV
AI VSV
IGN FUSE
TACH
CHECK CONN
FUEL INJS
IGN COIL
IGNITER
IGN COIL W/ IGNITER
DISTRIBUTOR


*Fig. 46: Land Cruiser Wiring Diagram*

# 1988 COMPUTERIZED ENGINE CONTROLS
## Toyota Computer Control System (Cont.)

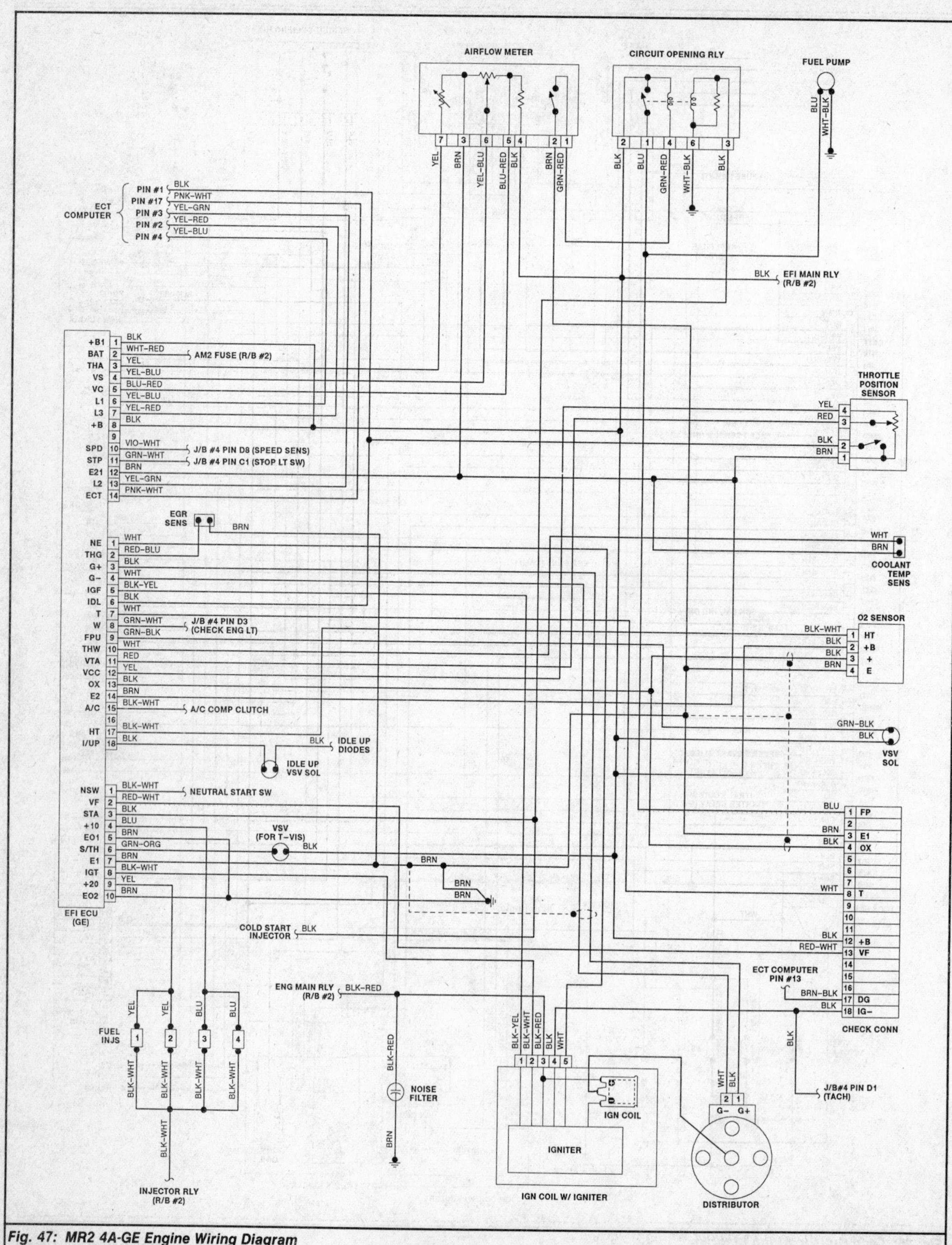
AIRFLOW METER
CIRCUIT OPENING RLY
FUEL PUMP
ECT COMPUTER
PIN #1 BLK
PIN #17 PNK-WHT
PIN #3 YEL-GRN
PIN #2 YEL-RED
PIN #4 YEL-BLU
BLK EFI MAIN RLY (R/B #2)
AM2 FUSE (R/B #2)
J/B #4 PIN D8 (SPEED SENS)
J/B #4 PIN C1 (STOP LT SW)
THROTTLE POSITION SENSOR
EGR SENS
COOLANT TEMP SENS
J/B #4 PIN D3 (CHECK ENG LT)
O2 SENSOR
A/C COMP CLUTCH
IDLE UP DIODES
IDLE UP VSV SOL
VSV SOL
NEUTRAL START SW
VSV (FOR T-VIS)
EFI ECU (GE)
COLD START INJECTOR
ECT COMPUTER PIN #13
ENG MAIN RLY (R/B #2)
FUEL INJS
NOISE FILTER
IGN COIL
IGNITER
CHECK CONN
J/B#4 PIN D1 (TACH)
INJECTOR RLY (R/B #2)
IGN COIL W/ IGNITER
DISTRIBUTOR

*Fig. 47: MR2 4A-GE Engine Wiring Diagram*

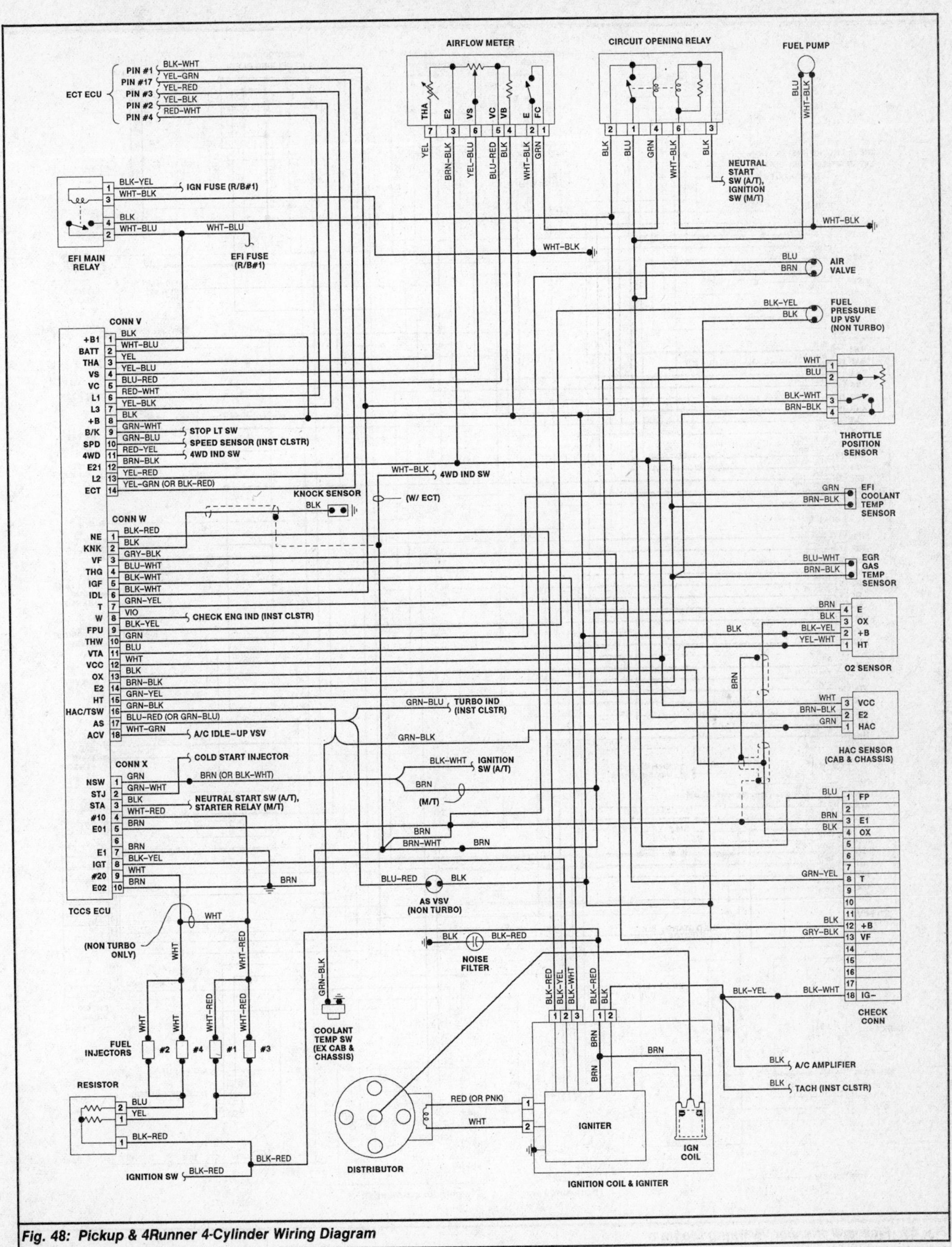

*Fig. 48: Pickup & 4Runner 4-Cylinder Wiring Diagram*

# 1988 COMPUTERIZED ENGINE CONTROLS
## Toyota Computer Control System (Cont.)

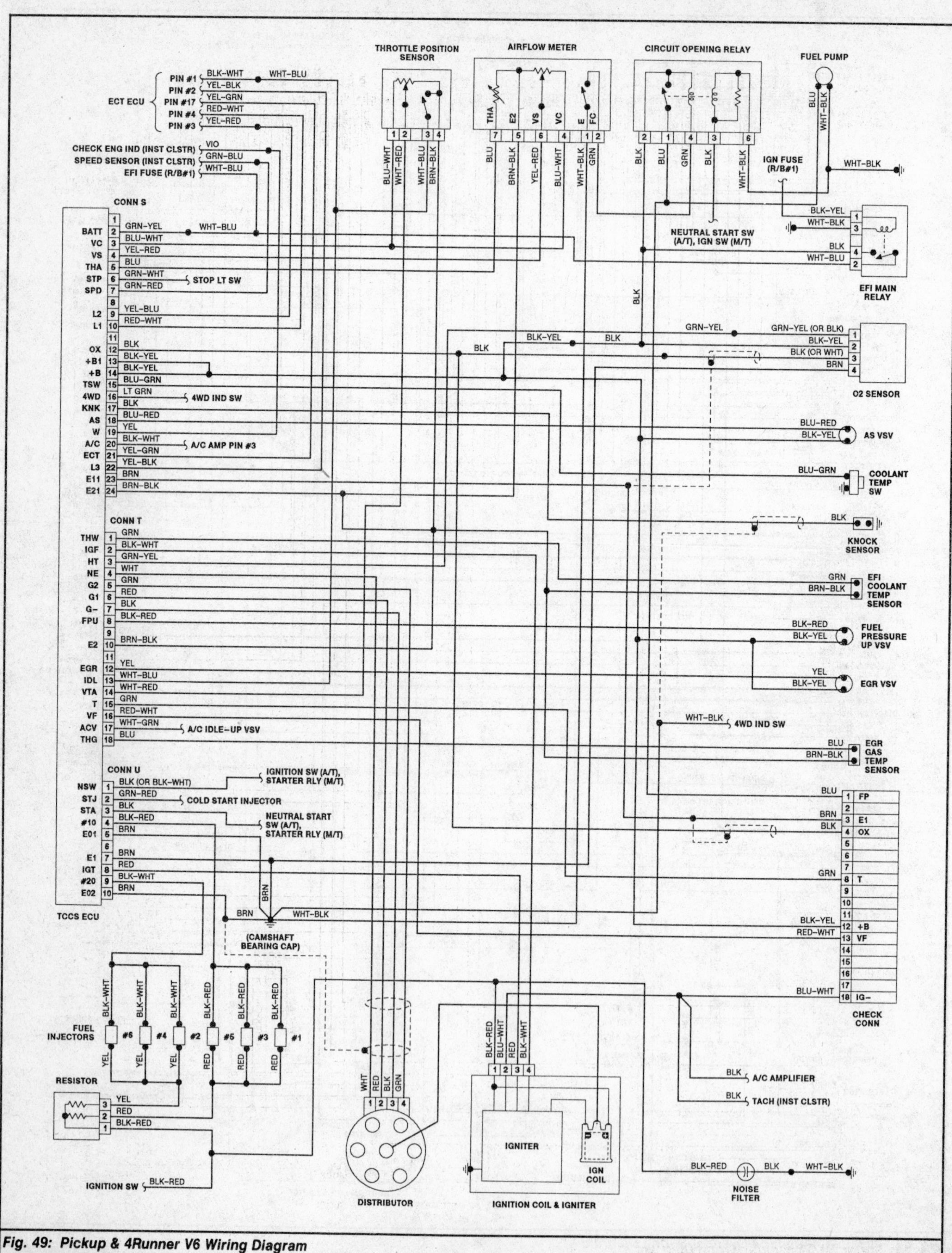
THROTTLE POSITION SENSOR
AIRFLOW METER
CIRCUIT OPENING RELAY
FUEL PUMP
ECT ECU
PIN #1 BLK–WHT WHT–BLU
PIN #2 YEL–BLK
PIN #17 YEL–GRN
PIN #4 RED–WHT
PIN #3 YEL–RED
CHECK ENG IND (INST CLSTR) VIO
SPEED SENSOR (INST CLSTR) GRN–BLU
EFI FUSE (R/B#1) WHT–BLU
THA E2 VS VC E FC
IGN FUSE (R/B#1)
WHT–BLK
NEUTRAL START SW (A/T), IGN SW (M/T)
EFI MAIN RELAY
CONN S
BATT 1 2 GRN–YEL WHT–BLU
VC 3 YEL–RED
VS 4 BLU
THA 5 GRN–WHT
STP 6 GRN–RED STOP LT SW
SPD 7
8
L2 9 YEL–BLU
L1 10 RED–WHT
11 BLK
OX 12 BLK–YEL
+B1 13 BLK–YEL
+B 14 BLU–GRN
TSW 15 LT GRN
4WD 16 BLK 4WD IND SW
KNK 17 BLU–RED
AS 18 YEL
W 19 BLK–WHT
A/C 20 YEL–GRN A/C AMP PIN #3
ECT 21 YEL–BLK
L3 22 BRN
E11 23 BRN–BLK
E21 24
O2 SENSOR
GRN–YEL (OR BLK)
BLK (OR WHT)
AS VSV
COOLANT TEMP SW
KNOCK SENSOR
EFI COOLANT TEMP SENSOR
FUEL PRESSURE UP VSV
EGR VSV
4WD IND SW
EGR GAS TEMP SENSOR
CONN T
THW 1 GRN
IGF 2 BLK–WHT
HT 3 GRN–YEL
NE 4 WHT
G2 5 GRN
G1 6 RED
G– 7 BLK
FPU 8 BLK–RED
9
E2 10 BRN–BLK
11
EGR 12 YEL
IDL 13 WHT–BLU
VTA 14 WHT–RED
T 15 GRN
VF 16 RED–WHT
ACV 17 WHT–GRN A/C IDLE–UP VSV
THG 18 BLU
CONN U
NSW 1 BLK (OR BLK–WHT) IGNITION SW (A/T), STARTER RLY (M/T)
STJ 2 GRN–RED COLD START INJECTOR
STA 3 BLK
#10 4 BLK–RED NEUTRAL START SW (A/T), STARTER RLY (M/T)
E01 5 BRN
6
E1 7 BRN
IGT 8 RED
#20 9 BLK–WHT
E02 10 BRN
TCCS ECU
(CAMSHAFT BEARING CAP)
CHECK CONN
FP E1 OX T +B VF IG–
FUEL INJECTORS
#6 #4 #2 #5 #3 #1
RESISTOR
IGNITION SW BLK–RED
DISTRIBUTOR
IGNITER
IGN COIL
IGNITION COIL & IGNITER
A/C AMPLIFIER
TACH (INST CLSTR)
NOISE FILTER

*Fig. 49: Pickup & 4Runner V6 Wiring Diagram*

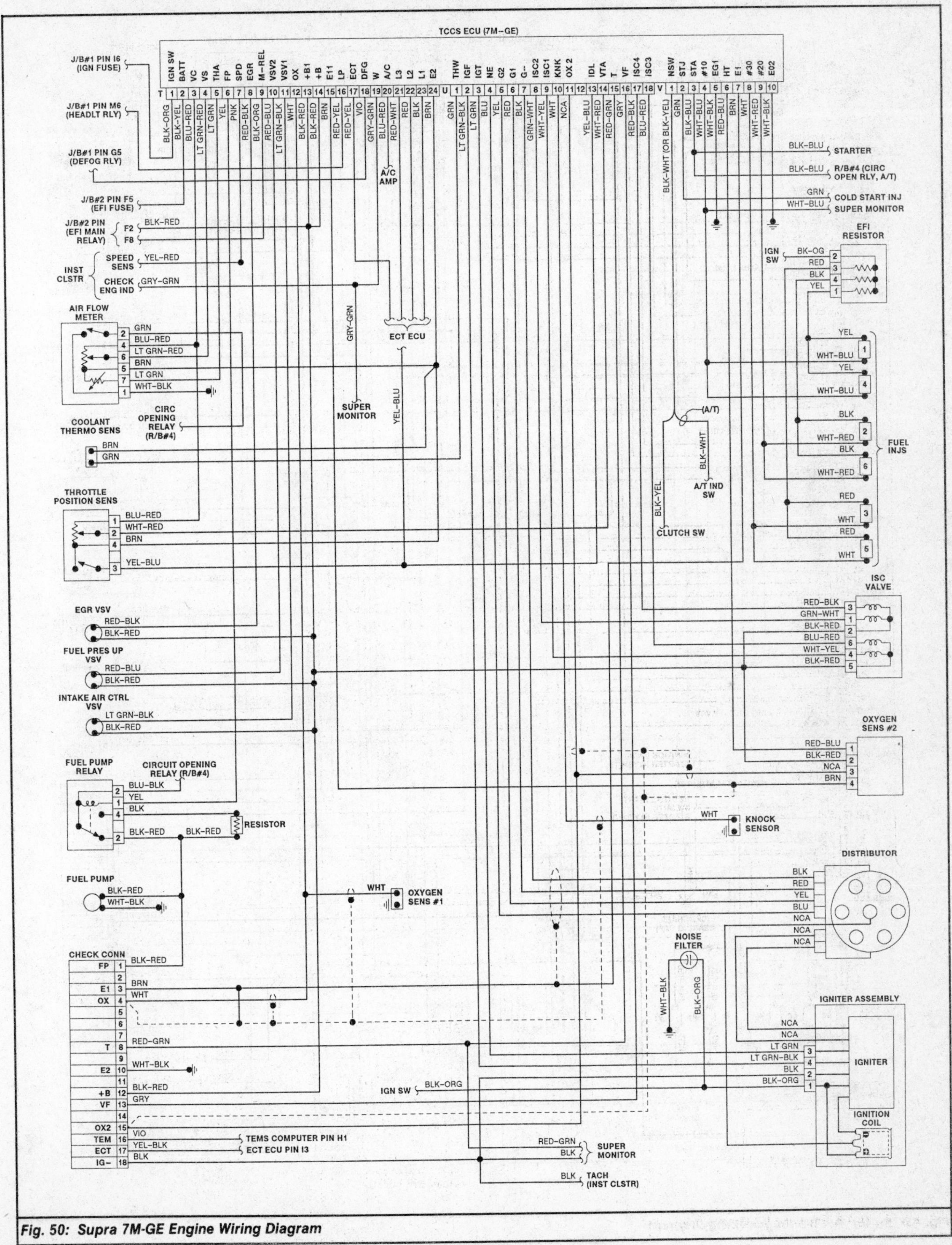

Fig. 50: Supra 7M-GE Engine Wiring Diagram

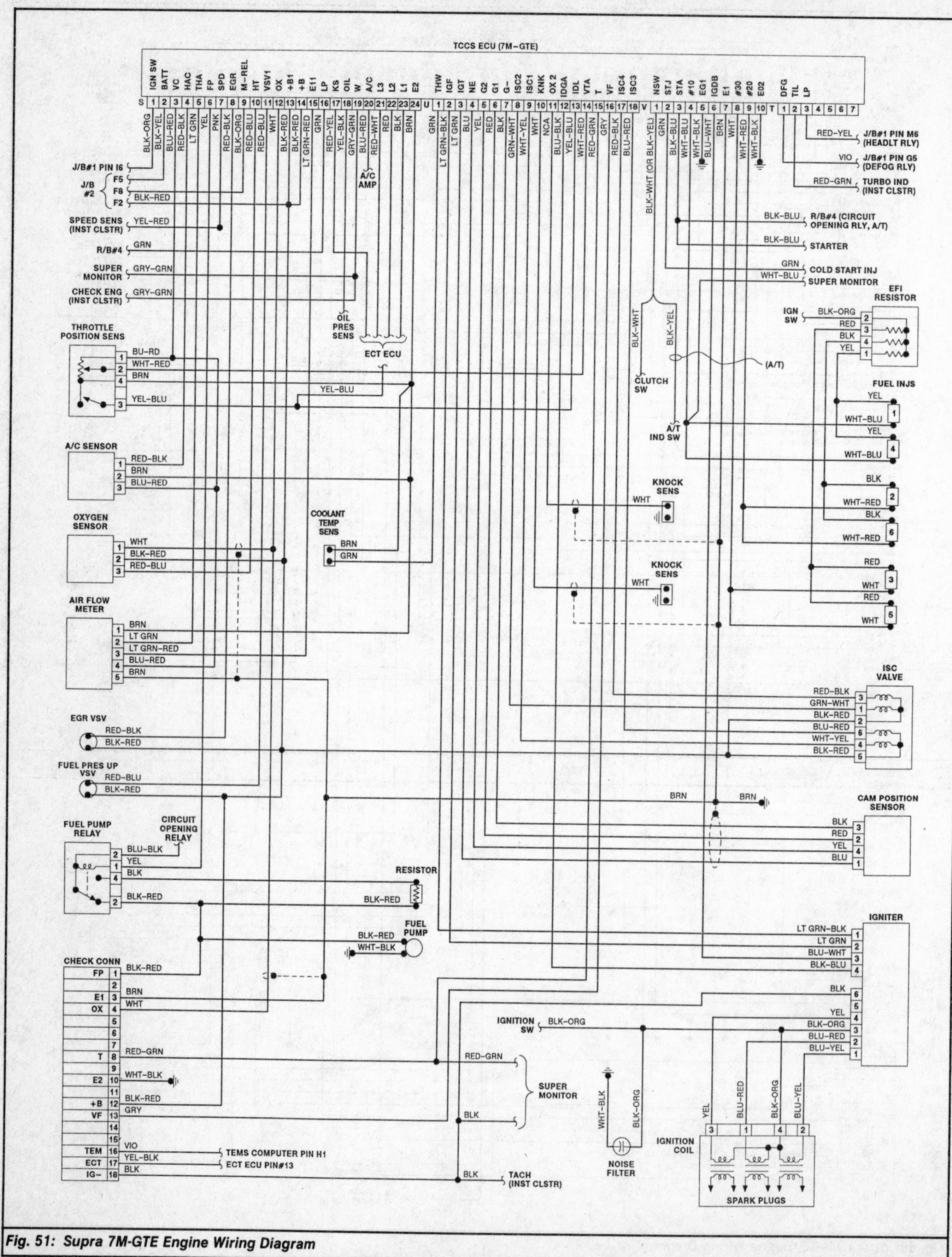

Fig. 51: Supra 7M-GTE Engine Wiring Diagram

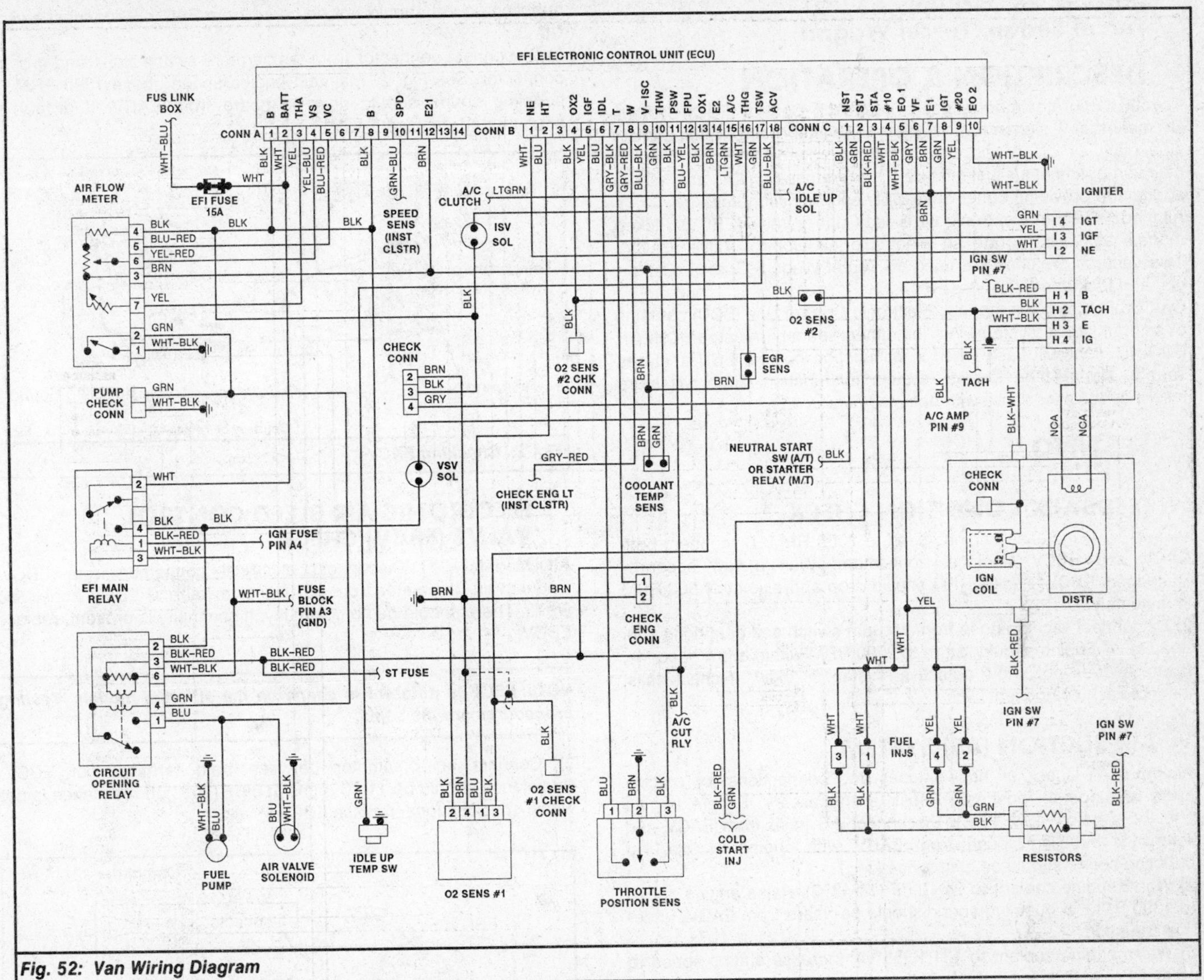
EFI ELECTRONIC CONTROL UNIT (ECU)
CONN A
CONN B
CONN C
FUS LINK BOX
EFI FUSE 15A
AIR FLOW METER
PUMP CHECK CONN
EFI MAIN RELAY
IGN FUSE PIN A4
FUSE BLOCK PIN A3 (GND)
ST FUSE
CIRCUIT OPENING RELAY
FUEL PUMP
AIR VALVE SOLENOID
IDLE UP TEMP SW
SPEED SENS (INST CLSTR)
A/C CLUTCH
ISV SOL
CHECK CONN
VSV SOL
CHECK ENG LT (INST CLSTR)
O2 SENS #2 CHK CONN
O2 SENS #1 CHECK CONN
O2 SENS #1
COOLANT TEMP SENS
CHECK ENG CONN
A/C CUT RLY
THROTTLE POSITION SENS
COLD START INJ
A/C IDLE UP SOL
O2 SENS #2
EGR SENS
NEUTRAL START SW (A/T) OR STARTER RELAY (M/T)
IGNITER
IGN SW PIN #7
TACH
A/C AMP PIN #9
CHECK CONN
IGN COIL
DISTR
FUEL INJS
RESISTORS

Fig. 52: Van Wiring Diagram

# 1988 COMPUTERIZED ENGINE CONTROLS
# Toyota Carburetor FBC System

**Corolla, FX, Pickup, Tercel Sedan, Tercel Wagon**

## DESCRIPTION & OPERATION

Toyota carburetor models use a Feedback Control (FBC) System. By means of a signal from Oxygen ($O_2$) sensor, carburetor primary side main air bleed and slow air bleed volume are controlled to maintain optimum air-fuel mixture. This reduces HC, CO, and NOx in addition to providing better driveability and fuel economy.

All models use an Electronic Air Bleed Control Valve (EBCV). Pickup models also incorporate an Electronic Air Control Valve (EACV). Two vacuum switches are used on Tercel Wagon, Corolla (California) and Pickup models. *See Fig. 4.*

On Corolla California models, Electronic Control Unit (ECU) contains a self-diagnosis system. An instrument panel mounted "CHECK ENGINE" light will flash when a malfunction occurs. ECU analyzes various signals and detects system malfunction. ECU will store failure codes associated with detected failure.

## TESTING

### FEEDBACK CONDITION CHECK

**Pickup – 1)** Increase engine speed to 2000 RPM. Disconnect both EACV and EBCV electrical connectors. Wait a few seconds. Reconnect EBCV. Engine RPM should drop approximately 300 RPM immediately.

**2)** Disconnect vacuum hose from vacuum switch and plug hose end. *See Fig. 1.* Engine should return to 2000 RPM within a few seconds. If check does not show defective, system is okay. If check fails, inspect each component.

### AIR SUCTION (AS) SYSTEM

**Pickup – 1)** Check all hoses, tubes and connections for cracks, kinks, damage or loosness. Repair as necessary. Ensure engine coolant is below 43°F (6°C). Disconnect AS hose from EACV and listen for bubbling sound from EACV with engine at idle. No bubbling sound should be heard. *See Fig. 1.*

**2)** Warm engine coolant to 64-109°F (18-43°C). Raise engine speed to 1390 RPM. A bubbling sound should be heard from EACV, under this condition.

**3)** Warm engine coolant to 131°F (55°C). Increase engine speed to 1390 RPM. An intermittent bubbling sound should be heard from EACV. Allow engine to idle and listen for a bubbling sound from EACV. A bubbling sound should be heard under hot conditions.

**4)** With engine coolant above 64°F (18°C), disconnect and plug vacuum hose from vacuum switch, located near EBCV. *See Fig. 1.* A bubbling sound should now be heard from the EACV. Replace components as necessary.

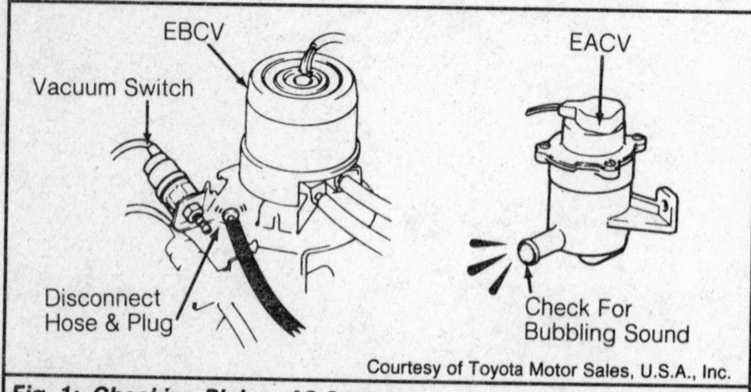
EBCV
Vacuum Switch
EACV
Disconnect Hose & Plug
Check For Bubbling Sound
Courtesy of Toyota Motor Sales, U.S.A., Inc.

*Fig. 1: Checking Pickup AS System*

### ELECTRONIC AIR CONTROL VALVE (EACV) CHECK

**Pickup – 1)** Disconnect AS hose from EACV. Disconnect connector from temperature switch No. 2 and ground connector. *See Fig. 2.* A bubbling sound should not be heard from EACV. Reconnect switch No. 2.

**2)** Disconnect connector from temperature switch No. 1 and ground connector. *See Fig. 2.* Maintain engine speed above 1390 PRM. A bubbling sound should now be heard from EACV. If a fault is encountered, replace EACV.

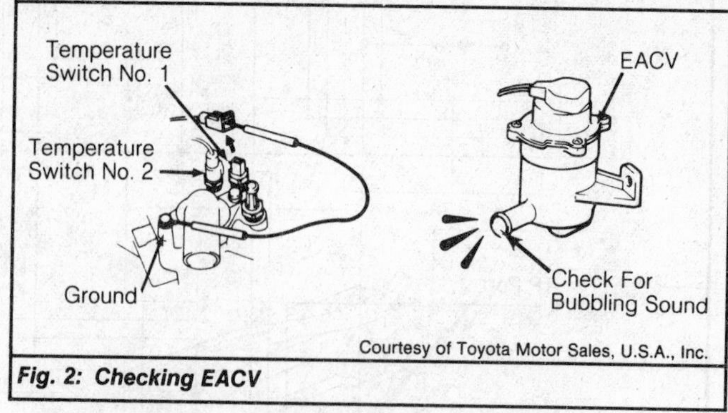
Temperature Switch No. 1
EACV
Temperature Switch No. 2
Ground
Check For Bubbling Sound
Courtesy of Toyota Motor Sales, U.S.A., Inc.

*Fig. 2: Checking EACV*

### ELECTRONIC AIR BLEED CONTROL VALVE (EBCV) CHECK

**All Models – 1)** Disconnect electrical connector from EBCV. Connect an ohmmeter from positive terminal and EBCV body. *See Fig. 3.* There should be no continuity. If continuity is present, replace EBCV.

***NOTE: EBCV is different in shape on the different models. Testing procedures are the same.***

**2)** Connect an ohmmeter between both terminals of EBCV. Resistance should be 11-13 ohms at 68°F (20°C). If resistance is not within specifications, replace EBCV.

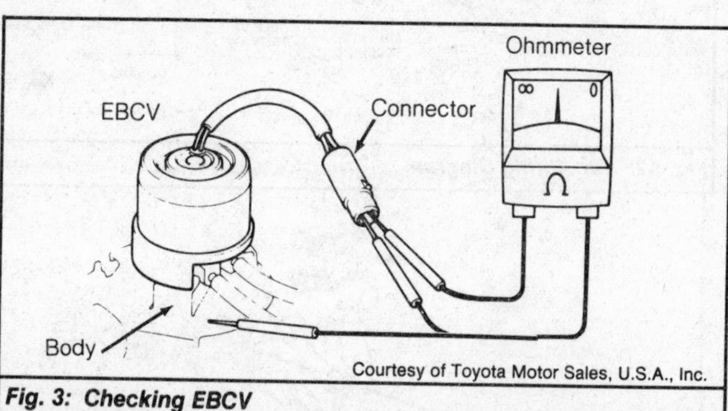
Ohmmeter
EBCV
Connector
Body
Courtesy of Toyota Motor Sales, U.S.A., Inc.

*Fig. 3: Checking EBCV*

**3)** On all models (except Pickup), also check EBCV with vehicle at normal operating temperature by disconnecting EBCV electrical connector. Increase engine speed to 2500 RPM. Reconnect connector and check for decrease of 300 RPM. Stop engine.

**4)** Restart and allow engine to idle with EBCV disconnected. Reconnect connector and check that engine RPM does not change. Disconnect vacuum hose from vacuum switch. Increase engine speed to 2500 RPM with EBCV disconnected. Reconnect EBCV and check that RPM does not change. If fault is noticed, check each component.

### BI-METALLIC VACUUM SWITCH VALVE (BVSV)

**Tercel Sedan –** Ensure oil temperature is below 41°F (5°C). Disconnect vacuum hose from vacuum switch. Start engine and check for vacuum at disconnected hose. Vacuum should be present. Warm vehicle above 66°F (19°C). Vacuum should be present. Replace BVSV as necessary.

# 1988 COMPUTERIZED ENGINE CONTROLS
## Toyota Carburetor FBC System (Cont.)

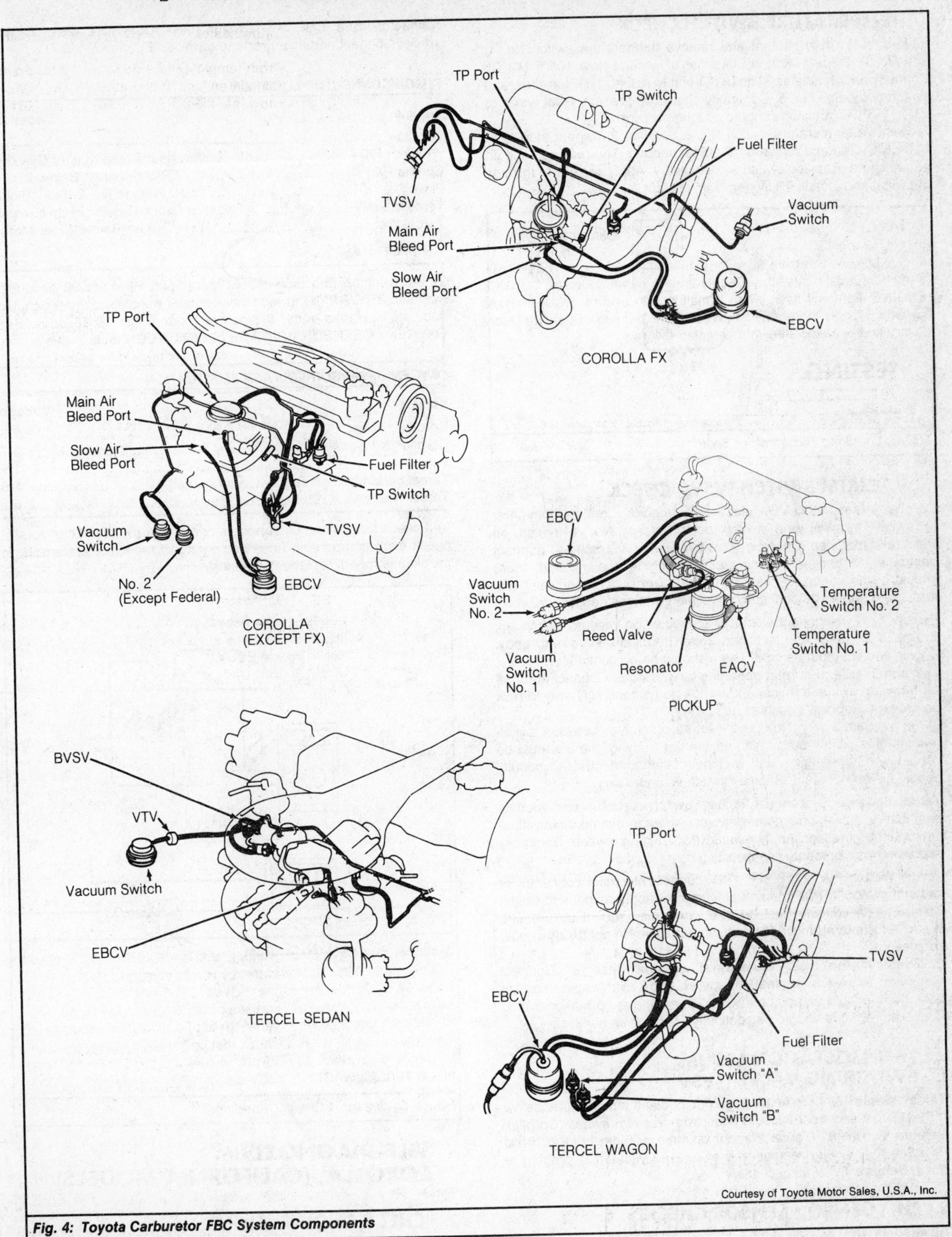
TP Port
TP Switch
Fuel Filter
TVSV
Vacuum Switch
Main Air Bleed Port
Slow Air Bleed Port
EBCV
COROLLA FX
TP Port
Main Air Bleed Port
Slow Air Bleed Port
Fuel Filter
TP Switch
TVSV
Vacuum Switch
No. 2 (Except Federal)
EBCV
COROLLA (EXCEPT FX)
EBCV
Vacuum Switch No. 2
Reed Valve
Vacuum Switch No. 1
Resonator
EACV
Temperature Switch No. 2
Temperature Switch No. 1
PICKUP
BVSV
VTV
Vacuum Switch
EBCV
TERCEL SEDAN
TP Port
TVSV
EBCV
Fuel Filter
Vacuum Switch "A"
Vacuum Switch "B"
TERCEL WAGON

Courtesy of Toyota Motor Sales, U.S.A., Inc.

*Fig. 4: Toyota Carburetor FBC System Components*

# 1988 COMPUTERIZED ENGINE CONTROLS
# Toyota Carburetor FBC System (Cont.)

## TEMPERATURE SWITCH CHECK

**Pickup - 1)** Drain coolant and remove temperature switch No. 1. *See Fig. 2.* Place switch in container of water below 109°F (43°C). Connect an ohmmeter (with a 10-ohms resistor) to terminal and switch body. *See Fig. 5.* Continuity should be present. Heat water to 131°F (55°C). Continuity should now be present.

**2)** Remove temperature switch No. 2. *See Fig. 2.* Repeat step **1)** at 43°F (6°C) first and above 64°F (18°C) second. The readings should be the same. Replace switch as necessary. Apply sealant to threads of switch and install. Fill system with coolant.

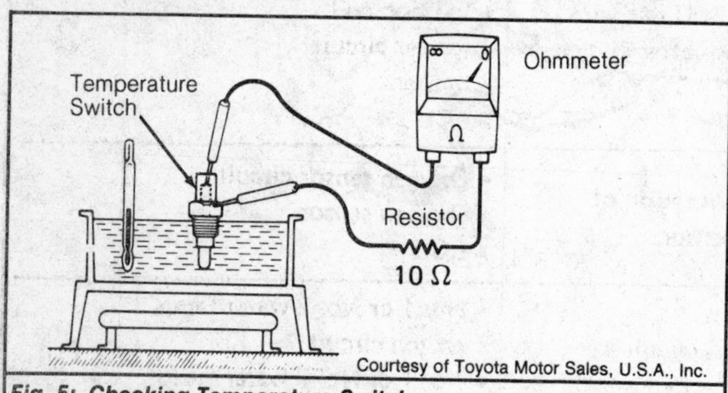
Temperature Switch
Ohmmeter
Ω
Resistor
10 Ω
Courtesy of Toyota Motor Sales, U.S.A., Inc.

*Fig. 5: Checking Temperature Switch*

## VACUUM SWITCH (VSW) CHECK

**Corolla -** Disconnect VSW electrical connector. Connect ohmmeter to switch terminal and switch body (except No. 1 switch on California models). On No. 1 switch California models, connect ohmmeter to between terminals. With engine coolant cold, there should be no continuity. With vehicle at normal operating temperature, there should be continuity. Replace switch as necessary.

**Pickup - 1)** Disconnect electrical connector on vacuum switch No. 2. Attach an ohmmeter between switch terminal and switch body. Engine coolant must be cold. There should be no continuity.

**2)** Warm vehicle to normal operating temperature. Connect ohmmeter between switch terminal and switch body, continuity should now be present. Replace switch as necessary.

**3)** For vacuum switch No. 1, connect an ohmmeter between switch terminal and switch body. With engine not running, there should be continuity. Start engine with ohmmeter still connected. Continuity should now be present. Replace switch as necessary.

**Tercel Sedan -** Disconnect vacuum switch electrical and vacuum connectors. Attach ohmmeter between switch terminals. No continuity should be present. Apply 4.3 in. Hg to vacuum switch. Continuity should now be present.

**Tercel Wagon ("A" & "B") - 1)** Disconnect electrical connector at vacuum switch "A". Connect ohmmeter to switch terminal and switch body. Engine coolant must be cold. Continuity should be present. Warm vehicle to normal operating temperature. No continuity should be present.

**2)** Disconnect electrical connector at vacuum switch "B". Connect ohmmeter to switch terminal and switch body. With engine coolant cold, there should be no continuity. With engine at normal operating temperature, there should be continuity. Replace as necessary.

## THERMOSTATIC VACUUM SWITCHING VALVE (TVSV)

**Tercel Wagon & Corolla (All) -** With coolant temperature below 45°F (7°C), disconnect vacuum hose from vacuum switch (Corolla), vacuum switch "B" (Tercel Wagon) or main vacuum hose (Corolla FX). *See Fig. 4.* Start engine and ensure no vacuum is present at hose. Replace TVSV as necessary.

## OXYGEN ($O_2$) SENSOR CHECK

**All Models - 1)** Warm vehicle to normal operating temperature. Connect positive voltmeter probe to $O_2$ sensor terminal of check connector. See CHECK CONNECTOR LOCATION table in this article. Connect negative probe to terminal "$E_1$". *See Fig. 6.*

***CHECK CONNECTOR LOCATION***

| Vehicle | Location |
|---|---|
| Corolla (Except FX) | [1] Left Fender, Near Brake Master Cylinder |
| Corolla FX | [1] Right Fender, Below EBCV |
| Pickup | [1] Next to No. 2 Relay Block |
| Tercel Sedan | [1] Next to Clutch Reservoir, on Firewall |
| Tercel Wagon | [1] Right Fender Below Wiper Motor |

[1] - *See Fig. 6.*

**2)** Start engine and increase RPM to 2500 RPM for 90 seconds. Maintain 2500 RPM and monitor voltmeter needle. Voltmeter should fluctuate specified volts, 8 times or more within 10 seconds. See OXYGEN $O_2$ SENSOR VOLTAGE FLUCTUATION table in this article.

***OXYGEN $O_2$ SENSOR VOLTAGE FLUCTUATION***

| Vehicle | Voltage |
|---|---|
| Corolla (Except FX) | 0-6 |
| Corolla FX | 0-7 |
| Pickup | 1-5 |
| Tercel Sedan | 1-5 |
| Tercel Wagon | 0-7 |

**3)** If check tests okay, $O_2$ sensor is operating properly. If check fails, check each component, hose and wiring of feedback system. If no problem is found, replace $O_2$ sensor.

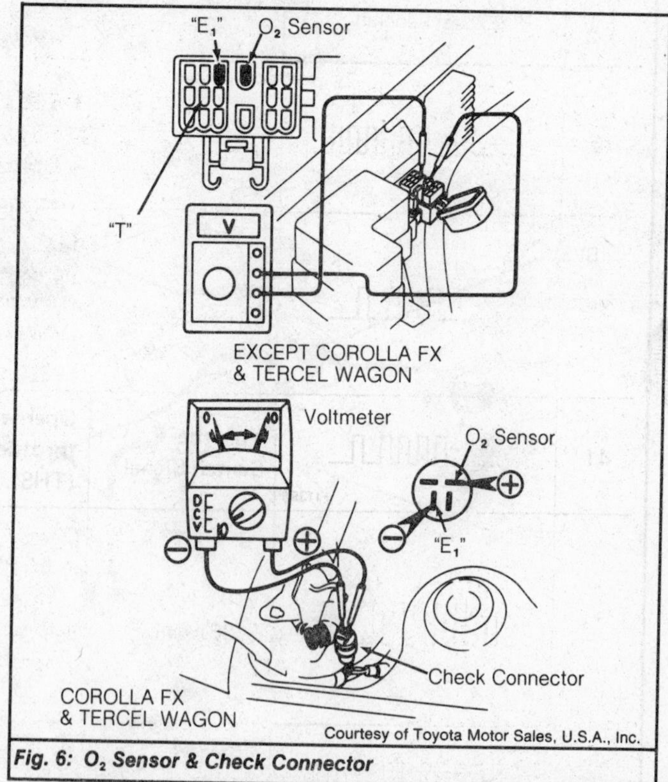
"E1"
O2 Sensor
"T"
V
EXCEPT COROLLA FX
& TERCEL WAGON
Voltmeter
O2 Sensor
"E1"
Check Connector
COROLLA FX
& TERCEL WAGON
Courtesy of Toyota Motor Sales, U.S.A., Inc.

*Fig. 6: $O_2$ Sensor & Check Connector*

## SELF-DIAGNOSIS
## COROLLA, (CALIFORNIA MODELS)

### "CHECK ENGINE" LIGHT

"CHECK ENGINE" light will come on and stay on when ignition is turned on and engine not started. Once engine is started, "CHECK

# 1988 COMPUTERIZED ENGINE CONTROLS
## Toyota Carburetor FBC System (Cont.)

| Code No. | Number of check engine blinks | System | Diagnosis | Trouble area | Test No. |
|---|---|---|---|---|---|
| – | 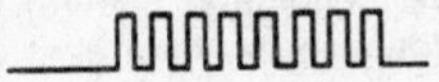 ON / OFF | Normal | This appears when none of the other codes are identified. | | |
| 12 | 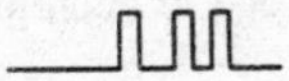 | RPM Signal | No signal to ECU within several seconds after engine is crankted (TAC). | • Ignition coil circuit<br>• Ignition coil<br>• Igniter circuit<br>• Igniter<br>• ECU | 3 |
| 21 |  | Oxygen Sensor Signal | Detects deterioration of the oxygen sensor. | • Oxygen sensor circuit<br>• Oxygen sensor<br>• ECU | – |
| 22 |  | Water Temp. Switch Signal | Open or short circuit in water temp. switch signal (TWS1, TWS2). | • No. 1 or No. 2 water temp. switch circuit<br>• No. 1 or No. 2 water temp. switches<br>• ECU | 5 |
| 25 |  | Lean Malfunction | • Open circuit in oxygen sensor signal (OX).<br>• EBCV always open.<br>• Short circuit in EBCV signal. | • Oxygen sensor circuit<br>• Oxygen sensor<br>• EBCV circuit<br>• EBCV<br>• ECU | 10 |
| 26 |  | Rich Malfunction | • EBCV always closed, or a clogged hose.<br>• Open circuit in EBCV signal. | • EBCV circuit<br>• EBCV hose<br>• EBCV<br>• ECU | 10 |
| 31 |  | Vacuum Switch Signal | Open or short circuit in vacuum switches signal (VSW1, VSW2). | • No. 1 or No. 2 vacuum switches signal<br>• No. 1 or No. 2 vacuum switches<br>• ECU | 6 |
| 41 |  FI1396 | Throttle Switch Signal | Open or short circuit in throttle switch signal (THS). | • Throttle switch circuit<br>• Throttle switch<br>• ECU | 7 |
| 71 |  | EGR Malfunction | • EGR valve normally closed, or a clogged hose.<br>• Open circuit in EGR gas temp. sensor signal (THG). | • EGR valve<br>• EGR hose<br>• EGR gas temp. sensor circuit<br>• EGR gas temp. sensor<br>• ECU | 11 |
| 72 |  | Fuel cut Solenoid Signal | Open circuit in fuel cut solenoid signal (FCS). | • Fuel cut solenoid circuit<br>• Fuel cut solenoid<br>• ECU | 9 |

Courtesy of Toyota Motor Sales, U.S.A., Inc.

*Fig. 7: Diagnostic Codes Identification*

ENGINE" light should go out. If light remains on, a failure or abnormality has been detected. Stored codes will be identified by number of "CHECK ENGINE" light flashes. If "CHECK ENGINE" light does not operate properly, proceed to DIAGNOSIS CIRCUIT TEST.

## RETRIEVING CODES

**1)** Ensure battery voltage is greater than 11 volts and throttle valve is fully closed. Place transaxle in Neutral and turn off all accessory switches. Turn ignition switch on but do not start engine. Place a jumper wire between terminals "$E_1$," and "T". *See Fig. 6.*

**2)** Count number of flashes from "CHECK ENGINE" light. If system is operating properly (with no codes), "CHECK ENGINE" light will blink continuously and evenly. A code will be identified by a .5 second flash on and off for the first number. A 1.5 second pause will occur followed by the second number. *See Fig. 7.*

**3)** If more than one code is stored, a 2.5 second pause will occur prior to the flashing of the second code. Once all codes have been displayed, a 4.5 second pause will occur and code(s) will repeat. Codes are given from smallest value in order to largest value. After code(s) are retrieved, remove jumper wire.

**4)** If codes are present, use chart for code identification and proceed to appropriate test number under NO VOLTAGE TESTING. *See Fig. 7.* If no codes are present and a problem exists, perform ECU terminal voltage test and proceed to appropriate test number under NO VOLTAGE TESTING. *See Fig. 9.*

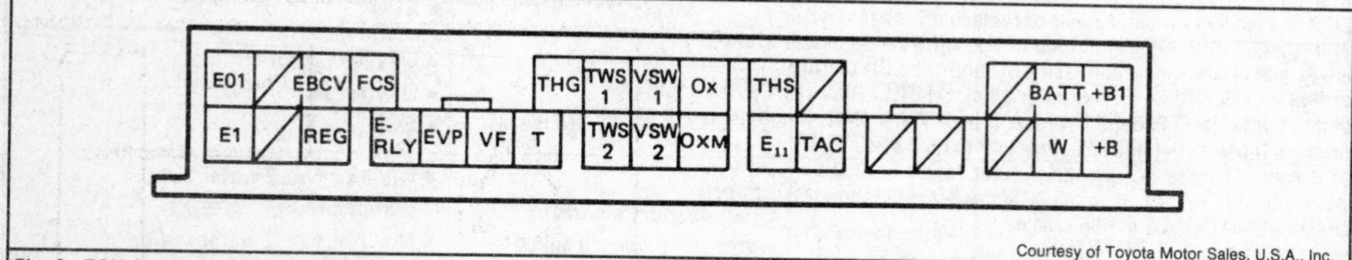
E01
EBCV
FCS
E1
REG
E-RLY
EVP
VF
THG
T
TWS 1
VSW 1
Ox
TWS 2
VSW 2
OXM
THS
E11
TAC
BATT
+B1
W
+B
Courtesy of Toyota Motor Sales, U.S.A., Inc.

*Fig. 8: ECU Connector Terminal Identification*

| Terminals | STD voltage | Condition | | Test No. |
|---|---|---|---|---|
| +B1 / +B – E1 | 10 – 14 | Ignition S/W ON | | 1 |
| BATT – E1 | 10 – 14 | — | | 2 |
| TAC – E01 | 9 – 14.5 | Ignition S/W ON | | 3 |
| | 12.5 – 14.5 | Idling | | |
| REG – E01 | 9 – 14.5 | Idling | | 4 |
| TWS1 – E01 | 9 – 14.5 | Ignition S/W ON | Above 61°C (142°F) | 5 |
| TWS2 – E01 | | | Below 83°C (181°F) | |
| VSW1 – E01 | 9 – 14.5 | Ignition S/W ON | 70 mmHg (2.76 in.Hg, 9.33 kPa) or less | 6 |
| VSW2 – E01 | | | 365 mmHg (14.37 in.Hg, 48.66 kPa) or more | |
| THS – E01 | 9 – 14.5 | Ignition S/W ON | Throttle valve fully closed and first idle cam disengaged | 7 |
| W – E1 | 9 – 14.5 | No trouble (Check engine warning light off) and engine running | | 8 |
| FCS – E01 | 9 – 14.5 | Idling | | 9 |
| EBCV – E01 | 9 – 14.5 | Idling | | 10 |

Courtesy of Toyota Motor Sales, U.S.A., Inc.

*Fig. 9: ECU Terminal Voltage Testing*

## CANCELING DIAGNOSTIC CODES

Repair code malfunction prior to canceling code. After repair is made, remove "STOP" fuse (15A) from fuse panel for more than 10 seconds, with ignition off. Fuse panel is located behind driver's side kick panel. Check and ensure code has been canceled. Test drive and ensure code does not return.

## DIAGNOSIS CIRCUIT TEST

**1)** If "CHECK ENGINE" light is not on with key on and engine off, jumper terminal W to ground. *See Fig. 8.* If "CHECK ENGINE" light is on, check and repair wiring between ECU terminal $E_1$ and ground. If wiring is okay, try a new ECU. If "CHECK ENGINE" light is not on with terminal W grounded, check bulb, fuse and wiring between ECU and ignition switch. Repair or replace as necessary.
**2)** If "CHECK ENGINE" light does not go off when engine is started, check and repair wiring between ECU and "CHECK ENGINE" light. If wiring is okay, check for stored code(s). See RETRIEVING CODES in this article. If no code(s) is present, try another ECU. If code(s) is present, repair code(s) failure. Proceed to next step.
**3)** If light still does not go out, further repair is necessary. If light does go out, system is okay. Cancel code(s). See CANCELING DIAGNOSTIC CODES in this article.

## TERMINAL VOLTAGE TEST

Perform all voltage measurements with connectors connected. Verify battery voltage is a minimum of 11 volts with ignition on engine off. Use a voltmeter with high impedance (10,000 ohm and volt minimum). Measure voltage at each terminal of wiring connector and proceed to appropriate test under NO VOLTAGE TESTING. *See Fig. 9.*

## NO VOLTAGE TESTING

**No. 1 Test – 1)** If no voltage is present between terminal +B1 or +B and E1, check for voltage between terminal +B1 or +B and ground with ignition on and engine off. If no voltage, check and repair fuse, fusible links and wiring harness. If no fault is found, check and repair wiring between terminal +B1 or +B and battery.
**2)** If voltage was present between +B1 or +B and ground, check and repair wiring between terminal E1 and ground. If no wiring fault is found, try another ECU.

**No. 2 Test – 1)** If no voltage is present between terminal +B1 or +B and E1, check for voltage between terminal BATT and ground. If voltage is not present, check and repair fuse and fusible link. If no fault is found, check wiring between terminal BATT and battery.
**2)** If voltage was present between terminal BATT and ground, check and repair wiring between terminal E1 and ground. If wiring is okay, try another ECU.

**No. 3 Test – 1)** If no voltage is present between terminal TAC and E01, check for voltage between terminal TAC and ground with ignition on. If no voltage, see NO. 1 TEST and check circuit terminal +B to E1. Repair as necessary.
**2)** If No. 1 test is okay, check and repair wiring between ECU and ignition coil negative terminal. *See Fig. 10.* If wiring checks okay, test and repair ignitor. See appropriate DISTRIBUTOR & IGNITION SYSTEMS article. If ignitor is okay, try another ECU.
**3)** If voltage was present between terminal TAC and ground, check and repair wiring between terminal E01 and ground.

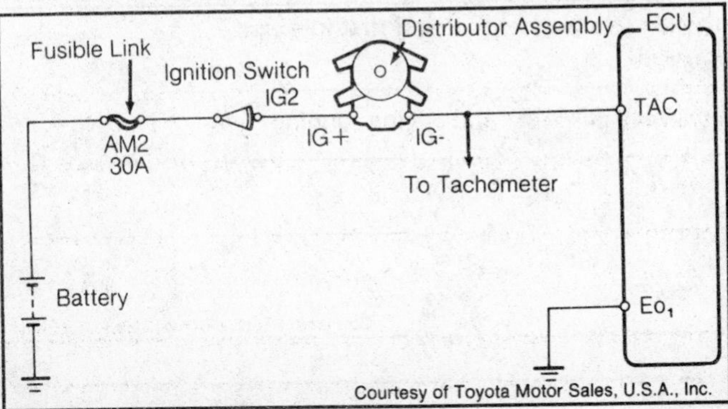
Fusible Link
Ignition Switch
IG2
Distributor Assembly
ECU
TAC
AM2
30A
IG+
IG-
To Tachometer
Battery
Eo1
Courtesy of Toyota Motor Sales, U.S.A., Inc.

*Fig. 10: Ignition Coil & ECU Wiring*

**No. 4 Test – 1)** If no voltage is present between terminal REG and E01 at idle, check for voltage between terminal REG and ground at idle. If no voltage, see NO. 1 TEST and test circuit terminal +B to E1. Repair as necessary.
**2)** If No. 1 test is okay, check and repair wiring between terminal REG and IC regulator. *See Fig. 11.* If wiring is okay, check and repair IC regulator. If IC regulator check okay, try another ECU.
**3)** If voltage was present between terminal REG and ground, check and repair wiring between terminal E01 and ground.

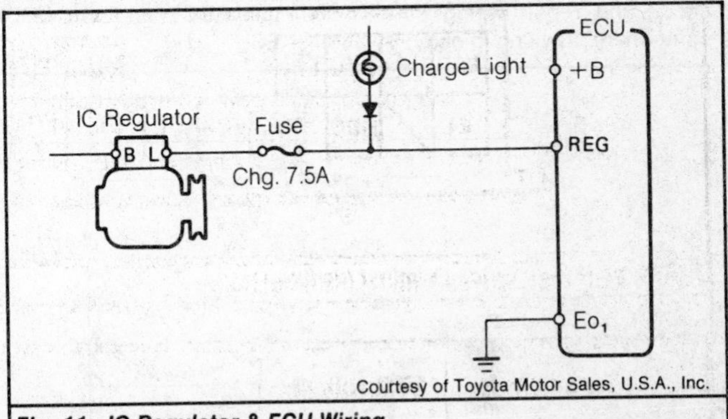
ECU
Charge Light
+B
IC Regulator
Fuse
B L
REG
Chg. 7.5A
Eo1
Courtesy of Toyota Motor Sales, U.S.A., Inc.

*Fig. 11: IC Regulator & ECU Wiring*

**No. 5 Test – 1)** If no voltage is present between terminal TWS1 or TWS2 and E01 with ignition on, check for voltage between terminal TWS1 or TWS2 and ground with ignition on. If no voltage, see NO. 1 TEST, and check circuit terminal +B to E1. Repair as necessary.
**2)** If No. 1 test is okay, check and repair wiring between terminal TWS1 or TWS2 and coolant temperature switches. If wiring is okay, replace switch(es). If problem still exists, try another ECU.
**3)** If voltage was present between TWS1 or TWS2 and ground, check and repair wiring between terminal E01 and ground.

**No. 6 Test – 1)** If no voltage is present between terminal VSW1 or VSW2 and E01 with ignition on, check for voltage between terminal VSW1 or VSW2 and ground. If no voltage, see NO. 1 TEST, and check circuit terminal +B to E1. Repair as necessary.
**2)** If No. 1 test is okay, check and repair vacuum switches (VSW). See VACUUM SWITCH CHECK under TESTING in this article. Replace as necessary. If VSW checks okay, check and repair wiring between terminal VSW1 or VSW2 and switch. If wiring checks okay, try another ECU.
**3)** If voltage was present between terminal VSW1 or VSW2 and ground, check and repair wiring between terminal E01 and ground.

**No. 7 Test – 1)** If no voltage is present between THS and E01 with ignition on, check for voltage between terminal THS and ground. If no voltage, see NO. 1 TEST and check circuit terminal +B to E1. Repair as necessary.
**2)** If No. 1 test is okay, check throttle position switch and replace as necessary. See TOYOTA THROTTLE POSITIONER SYSTEM article in 1988 EXHAUST EMISSION SYSTEMS section. If throttle position switch checks okay, check and repair wiring between terminal THS and throttle position switch. If wiring is okay, try another ECU.
**3)** If no voltage was present between terminal THS and ground, check and repair wiring between E01 and ground.

**No. 8 Test – 1)** If no voltage is present between terminal W and E1 at idle, check for voltage between terminal W and ground at idle. If no voltage, check and repair "GUAGE" fuse (7.5A) and check engine warning light. If okay, check and repair wiring between terminal W and fuse.
**2)** If voltage was present between terminal W and ground, check and repair wiring between terminal E1 and ground. If wiring checks okay, try another ECU.

# 1988 COMPUTERIZED ENGINE CONTROLS
## Toyota Carburetor FBC System (Cont.)

**No. 9 Test – 1)** If no voltage is present between terminal FCS and E01 at idle, check for voltage between terminal FCS and ground at idle. If no voltage, check fuel cut solenoid. See TOYOTA DECELERATION FUEL-CUT SYSTEM article in 1988 EXHAUST EMISSION SYSTEMS section. Replace as necessary. If okay, check and repair wiring between terminal FCS and fuel-cut solenoid. If okay, try another ECU.

**2)** If voltage was present between terminal FCS and ground, check and repair wiring between terminal E01 and ground. If wiring is okay, try another ECU.

**No. 10 Test – 1)** If no voltage is present between terminal EBCV and E01 at idle, check for voltage between terminal EBCV and ground at idle. If no voltage, check and repair EBCV. See ELECTRONIC AIR BLEED CONTROL VALVE (EBCV) under TESTING in this article. Replace as necessary. If EBCV checks okay, check and repair wiring between terminal EBCV and the EBCV component. If wiring is okay, try another ECU.

**2)** If voltage was present between terminal EBCV and ground, check and repair wiring between terminal E01 and ground. If wiring is okay, try another ECU.

**No. 11 Test – 1)** If no voltage is present terminal THG and E01 with ignition on, check for voltage between terminal +B or +B1 and ground with ignition on. If no voltage, see NO. 1 TEST and perform test. If voltage was present between terminal +B or +B1 and ground, check and repair wiring between terminal E01 and ground.

**2)** If wiring is okay, check and repair EGR. If EGR checks okay, check and repair EGR gas temperature sensor. See TOYOTA EGR article in 1988 EXHAUST EMISSION SYSTEMS section for EGR testing not covered in this article. If EGR gas temperature sensor checks okay, check and repair wiring between terminal THG and E01 to EGR gas temperature sensor. If wiring is okay, try another ECU.

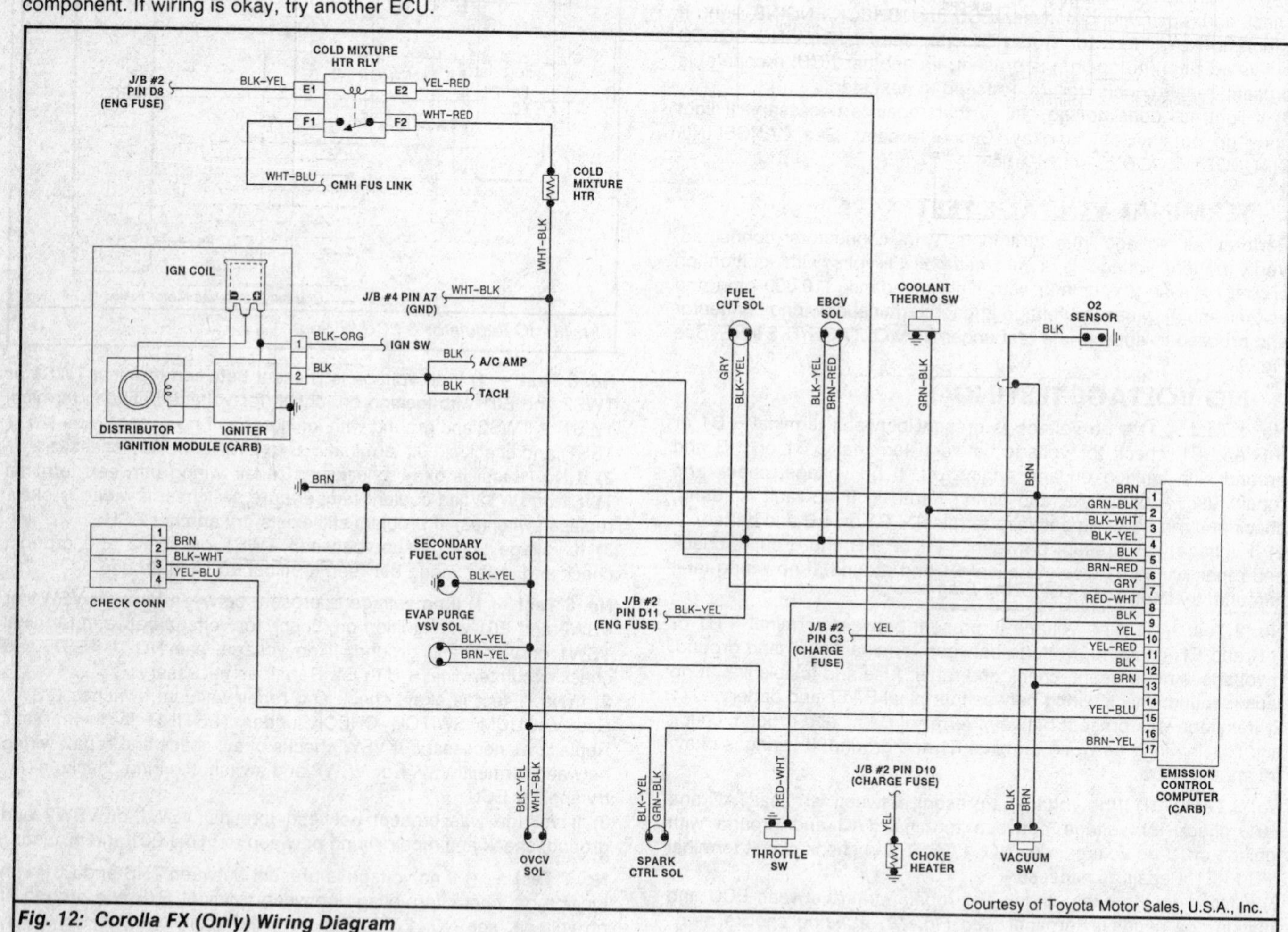

COLD MIXTURE HTR RLY
J/B #2 PIN D8 (ENG FUSE)
BLK-YEL
E1
E2
YEL-RED
F1
F2
WHT-RED
WHT-BLU
CMH FUS LINK
COLD MIXTURE HTR
WHT-BLK
IGN COIL
J/B #4 PIN A7 (GND)
BLK-ORG
IGN SW
BLK
A/C AMP
TACH
DISTRIBUTOR
IGNITER
IGNITION MODULE (CARB)
BRN
BLK-WHT
YEL-BLU
CHECK CONN
SECONDARY FUEL CUT SOL
EVAP PURGE VSV SOL
BRN-YEL
J/B #2 PIN D11 (ENG FUSE)
FUEL CUT SOL
GRY
EBCV SOL
BRN-RED
COOLANT THERMO SW
GRN-BLK
O2 SENSOR
J/B #2 PIN C3 (CHARGE FUSE)
YEL
RED-WHT
YEL-RED
EMISSION CONTROL COMPUTER (CARB)
OVCV SOL
SPARK CTRL SOL
THROTTLE SW
J/B #2 PIN D10 (CHARGE FUSE)
CHOKE HEATER
VACUUM SW
Courtesy of Toyota Motor Sales, U.S.A., Inc.


*Fig. 12: Corolla FX (Only) Wiring Diagram*

# 1988 COMPUTERIZED ENGINE CONTROLS
## Toyota Carburetor FBC System (Cont.)

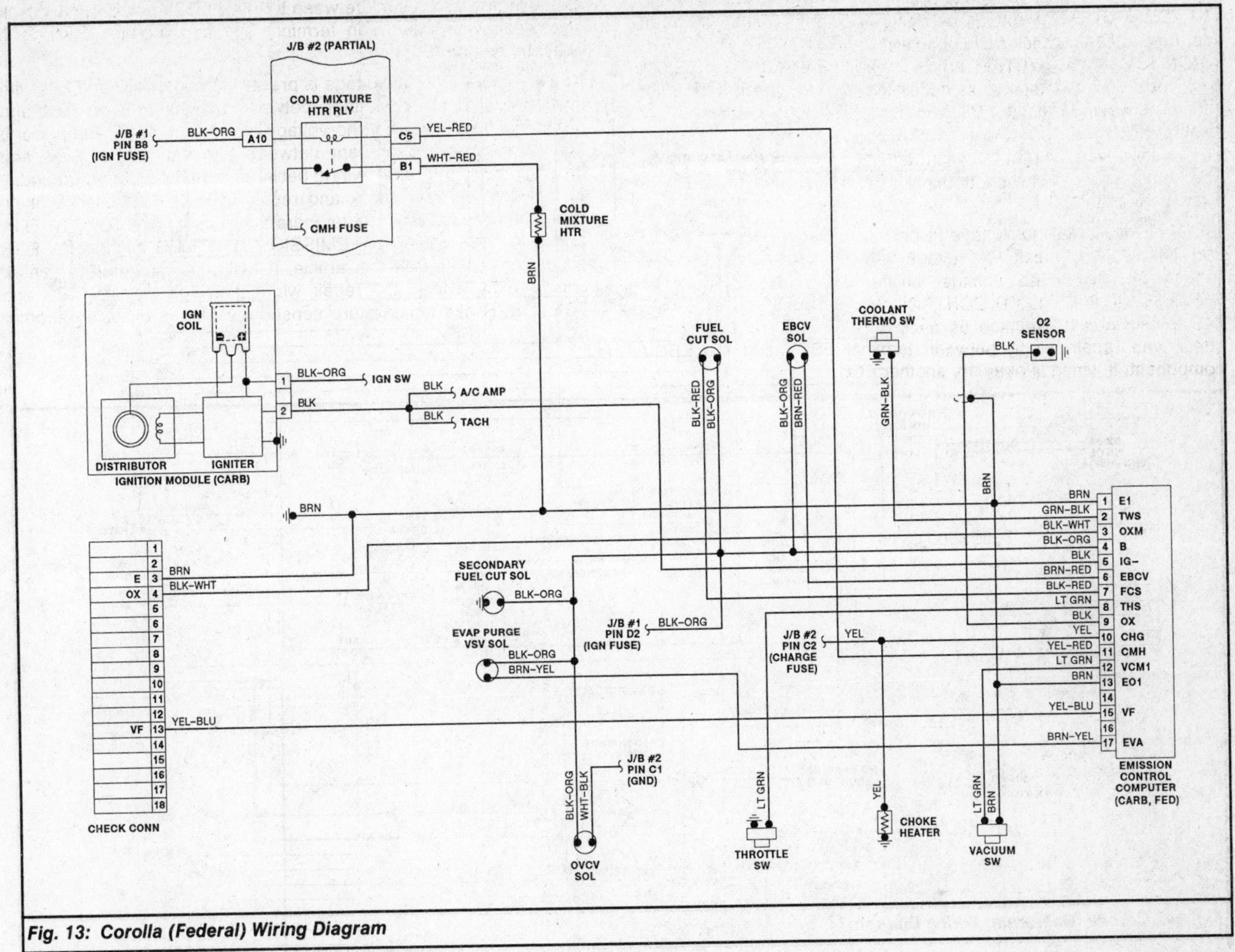

J/B #2 (PARTIAL)
COLD MIXTURE HTR RLY
J/B #1 PIN B8 (IGN FUSE)
BLK-ORG
A10
C5
YEL-RED
B1
WHT-RED
CMH FUSE
COLD MIXTURE HTR
BRN
IGN COIL
BLK-ORG
IGN SW
BLK
A/C AMP
TACH
DISTRIBUTOR
IGNITER
IGNITION MODULE (CARB)
FUEL CUT SOL
EBCV SOL
COOLANT THERMO SW
O2 SENSOR
BLK-RED
BLK-ORG
BRN-RED
GRN-BLK
E
OX
VF
YEL-BLU
BLK-WHT
SECONDARY FUEL CUT SOL
EVAP PURGE VSV SOL
BRN-YEL
J/B #1 PIN D2 (IGN FUSE)
J/B #2 PIN C2 (CHARGE FUSE)
YEL
J/B #2 PIN C1 (GND)
WHT-BLK
OVCV SOL
THROTTLE SW
LT GRN
CHOKE HEATER
VACUUM SW
CHECK CONN
E1
TWS
OXM
B
IG–
EBCV
FCS
THS
OX
CHG
CMH
VCM1
EO1
VF
EVA
EMISSION CONTROL COMPUTER (CARB, FED)


*Fig. 13: Corolla (Federal) Wiring Diagram*

# 1988 COMPUTERIZED ENGINE CONTROLS
## Toyota Carburetor FBC System (Cont.)

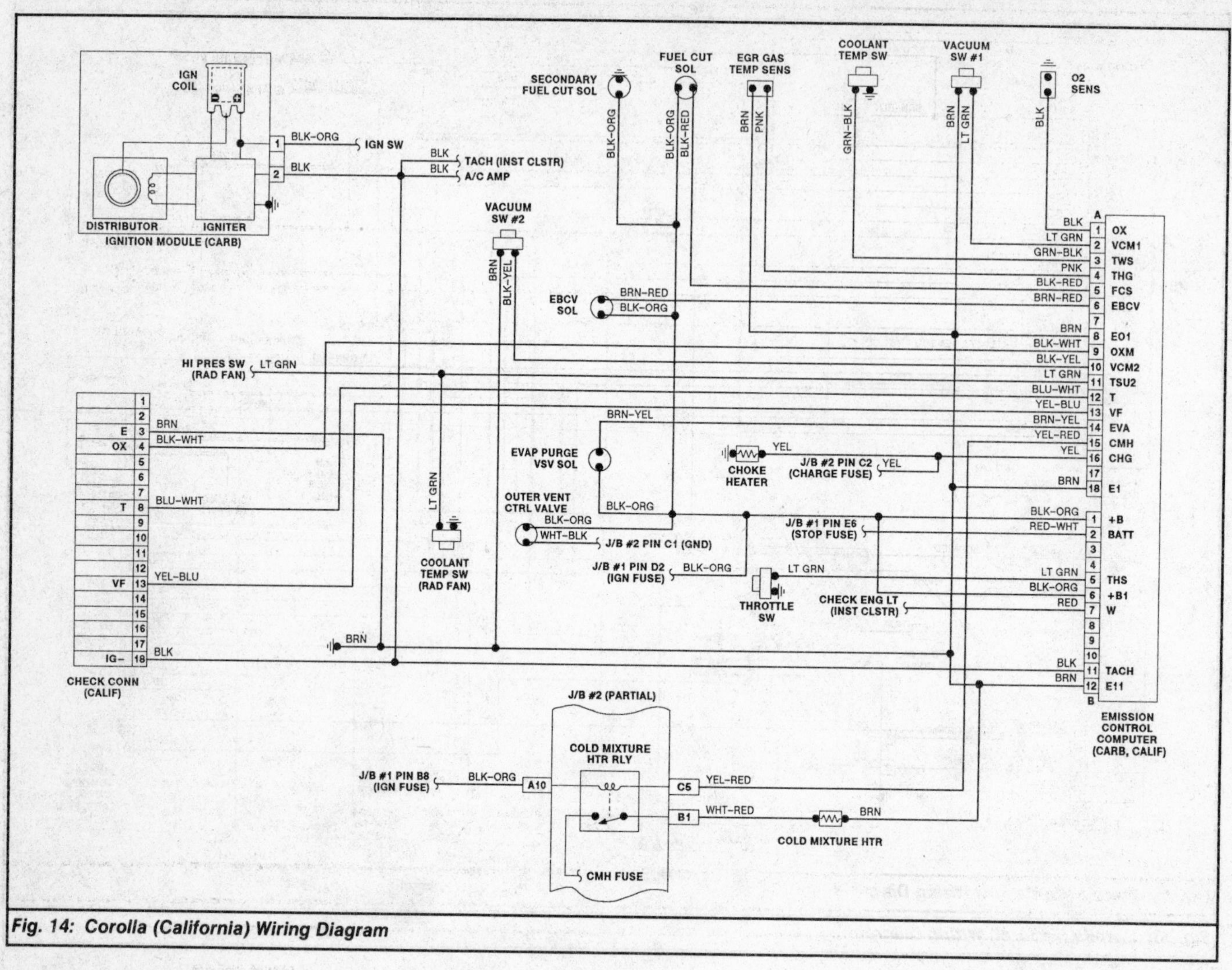
IGN COIL
DISTRIBUTOR
IGNITER
IGNITION MODULE (CARB)
BLK-ORG
IGN SW
BLK
TACH (INST CLSTR)
A/C AMP
SECONDARY FUEL CUT SOL
FUEL CUT SOL
EGR GAS TEMP SENS
COOLANT TEMP SW
VACUUM SW #1
O2 SENS
VACUUM SW #2
EBCV SOL
BRN-RED
HI PRES SW (RAD FAN)
LT GRN
CHECK CONN (CALIF)
EVAP PURGE VSV SOL
BRN-YEL
OUTER VENT CTRL VALVE
WHT-BLK
J/B #2 PIN C1 (GND)
COOLANT TEMP SW (RAD FAN)
J/B #1 PIN D2 (IGN FUSE)
CHOKE HEATER
J/B #2 PIN C2 (CHARGE FUSE)
J/B #1 PIN E6 (STOP FUSE)
THROTTLE SW
CHECK ENG LT (INST CLSTR)
EMISSION CONTROL COMPUTER (CARB, CALIF)
OX
VCM1
TWS
THG
FCS
EBCV
EO1
OXM
VCM2
TSU2
T
VF
EVA
CMH
CHG
E1
+B
BATT
THS
+B1
W
TACH
E11
J/B #2 (PARTIAL)
COLD MIXTURE HTR RLY
J/B #1 PIN B8 (IGN FUSE)
A10
C5
B1
YEL-RED
WHT-RED
COLD MIXTURE HTR
CMH FUSE

*Fig. 14: Corolla (California) Wiring Diagram*

# 1988 COMPUTERIZED ENGINE CONTROLS
## Toyota Carburetor FBC System (Cont.)

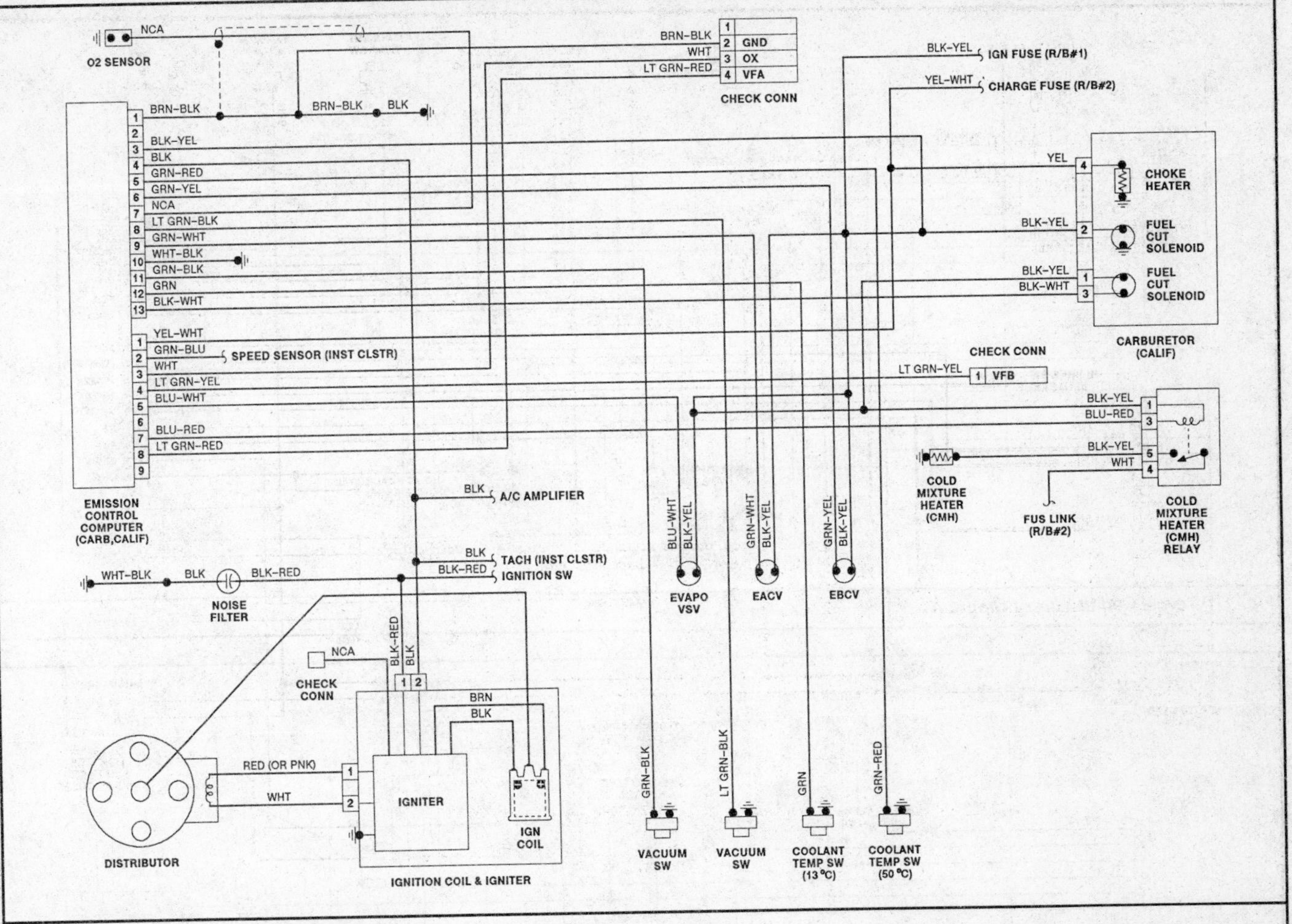

O2 SENSOR
NCA
BRN-BLK
WHT
LT GRN-RED
1
2 GND
3 OX
4 VFA
CHECK CONN
BLK-YEL IGN FUSE (R/B#1)
YEL-WHT CHARGE FUSE (R/B#2)
BRN-BLK
BRN-BLK
BLK
BLK-YEL
BLK
GRN-RED
GRN-YEL
NCA
LT GRN-BLK
GRN-WHT
WHT-BLK
GRN-BLK
GRN
BLK-WHT
YEL-WHT
GRN-BLU SPEED SENSOR (INST CLSTR)
WHT
LT GRN-YEL
BLU-WHT
BLU-RED
LT GRN-RED
EMISSION CONTROL COMPUTER (CARB,CALIF)
YEL
CHOKE HEATER
BLK-YEL
FUEL CUT SOLENOID
BLK-YEL
BLK-WHT
FUEL CUT SOLENOID
CARBURETOR (CALIF)
CHECK CONN
LT GRN-YEL
1 VFB
BLK-YEL
BLU-RED
BLK-YEL
WHT
COLD MIXTURE HEATER (CMH)
FUS LINK (R/B#2)
COLD MIXTURE HEATER (CMH) RELAY
BLK A/C AMPLIFIER
BLK TACH (INST CLSTR)
BLK-RED IGNITION SW
WHT-BLK
BLK
BLK-RED
NOISE FILTER
BLU-WHT
BLK-YEL
EVAPO VSV
GRN-WHT
BLK-YEL
EACV
GRN-YEL
BLK-YEL
EBCV
NCA
CHECK CONN
BLK-RED
BLK
BRN
BLK
RED (OR PNK)
WHT
IGNITER
IGN COIL
DISTRIBUTOR
IGNITION COIL & IGNITER
GRN-BLK
VACUUM SW
LT GRN-BLK
VACUUM SW
GRN
COOLANT TEMP SW (13 °C)
GRN-RED
COOLANT TEMP SW (50 °C)

*Fig. 15: Pickup (California) Wiring Diagram*

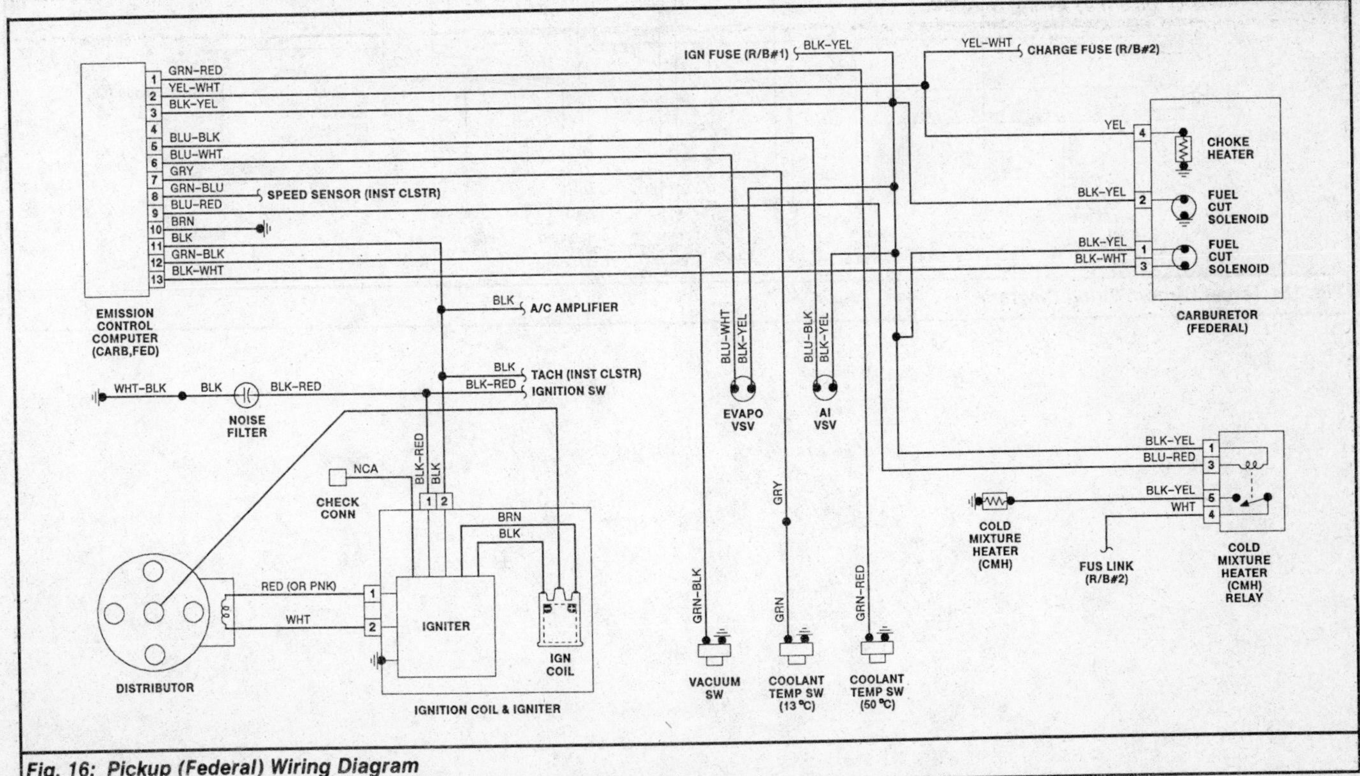
IGN FUSE (R/B#1)
BLK-YEL
YEL-WHT
CHARGE FUSE (R/B#2)
GRN-RED
YEL-WHT
BLK-YEL
BLU-BLK
BLU-WHT
GRY
GRN-BLU
SPEED SENSOR (INST CLSTR)
BLU-RED
BRN
BLK
GRN-BLK
BLK-WHT
EMISSION CONTROL COMPUTER (CARB,FED)
YEL
CHOKE HEATER
BLK-YEL
FUEL CUT SOLENOID
BLK-YEL
BLK-WHT
FUEL CUT SOLENOID
CARBURETOR (FEDERAL)
BLK
A/C AMPLIFIER
BLK
TACH (INST CLSTR)
BLK-RED
IGNITION SW
WHT-BLK
BLK
BLK-RED
NOISE FILTER
BLU-WHT
BLK-YEL
EVAPO VSV
BLU-BLK
BLK-YEL
AI VSV
BLK-YEL
BLU-RED
BLK-YEL
WHT
COLD MIXTURE HEATER (CMH)
FUS LINK (R/B#2)
COLD MIXTURE HEATER (CMH) RELAY
NCA
CHECK CONN
BLK-RED
BLK
BRN
BLK
RED (OR PNK)
WHT
IGNITER
IGN COIL
DISTRIBUTOR
IGNITION COIL & IGNITER
GRY
GRN-BLK
VACUUM SW
GRN
COOLANT TEMP SW (13 °C)
GRN-RED
COOLANT TEMP SW (50 °C)

*Fig. 16: Pickup (Federal) Wiring Diagram*

# 1988 COMPUTERIZED ENGINE CONTROLS
## Toyota Carburetor FBC System (Cont.)

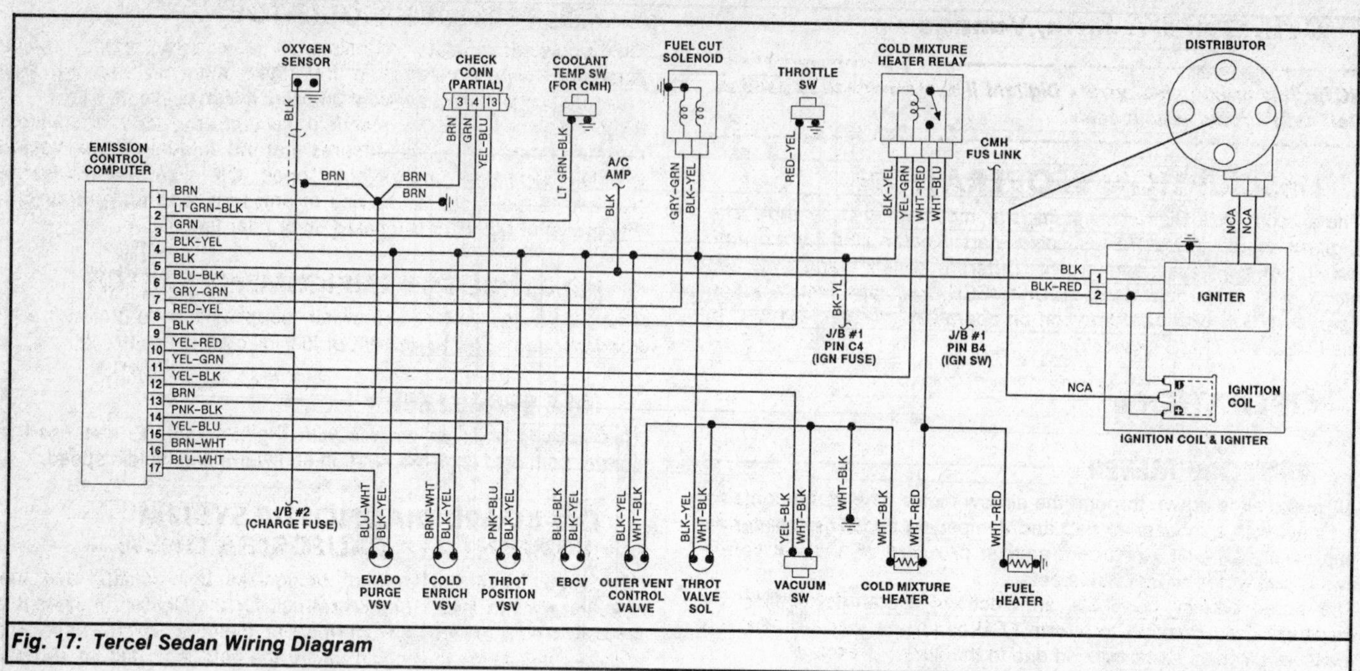

OXYGEN SENSOR
CHECK CONN (PARTIAL)
3 4 13
COOLANT TEMP SW (FOR CMH)
FUEL CUT SOLENOID
THROTTLE SW
COLD MIXTURE HEATER RELAY
DISTRIBUTOR
EMISSION CONTROL COMPUTER
1 BRN
2 LT GRN-BLK
3 GRN
4 BLK-YEL
5 BLK
6 BLU-BLK
7 GRY-GRN
8 RED-YEL
9 BLK
10 YEL-RED
11 YEL-GRN
12 YEL-BLK
13 BRN
14 PNK-BLK
15 YEL-BLU
16 BRN-WHT
17 BLU-WHT
BLK
BRN
GRN
YEL-BLU
LT GRN-BLK
A/C AMP
GRY-GRN
BLK-YEL
RED-YEL
BLK-YEL
YEL-RED
WHT-RED
WHT-BLU
CMH FUS LINK
NCA
BLK
BLK-RED
IGNITER
BK-YL
J/B #1 PIN C4 (IGN FUSE)
J/B #1 PIN B4 (IGN SW)
NCA
IGNITION COIL
IGNITION COIL & IGNITER
J/B #2 (CHARGE FUSE)
BLU-WHT
BLK-YEL
BRN-WHT
PNK-BLU
BLU-BLK
WHT-BLK
YEL-BLK
WHT-RED
EVAPO PURGE VSV
COLD ENRICH VSV
THROT POSITION VSV
EBCV
OUTER VENT CONTROL VALVE
THROT VALVE SOL
VACUUM SW
COLD MIXTURE HEATER
FUEL HEATER


Fig. 17: Tercel Sedan Wiring Diagram

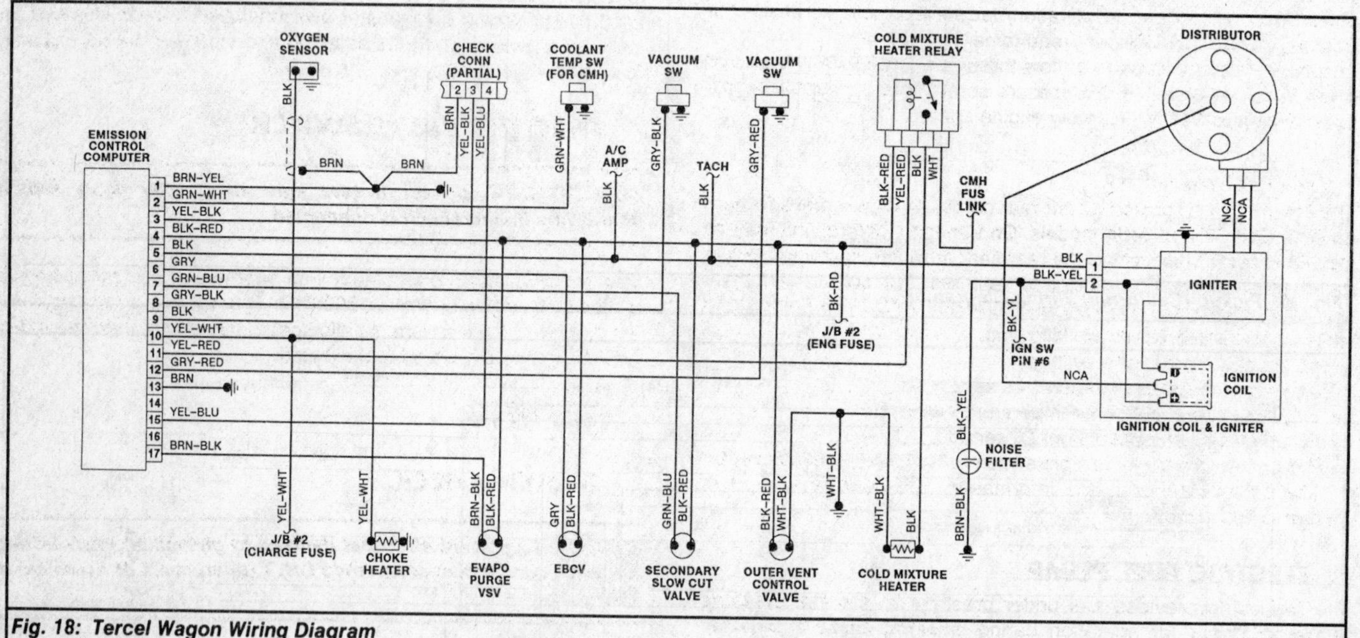

OXYGEN SENSOR
CHECK CONN (PARTIAL)
2 3 4
COOLANT TEMP SW (FOR CMH)
VACUUM SW
VACUUM SW
COLD MIXTURE HEATER RELAY
DISTRIBUTOR
EMISSION CONTROL COMPUTER
1 BRN-YEL
2 GRN-WHT
3 YEL-BLK
4 BLK-RED
5 BLK
6 GRY
7 GRN-BLU
8 GRY-BLK
9 BLK
10 YEL-WHT
11 YEL-RED
12 GRY-RED
13 BRN
14
15 YEL-BLU
16
17 BRN-BLK
BLK
BRN
YEL-BLK
YEL-BLU
GRN-WHT
A/C AMP
GRY-BLK
TACH
GRY-RED
BLK-RED
YEL-RED
WHT
CMH FUS LINK
NCA
BLK
BLK-YEL
IGNITER
BK-RD
J/B #2 (ENG FUSE)
BK-YL
IGN SW PIN #6
NCA
IGNITION COIL
IGNITION COIL & IGNITER
BLK-YEL
NOISE FILTER
BRN-BLK
YEL-WHT
J/B #2 (CHARGE FUSE)
CHOKE HEATER
BRN-BLK
BLK-RED
EVAPO PURGE VSV
GRY
EBCV
GRN-BLU
SECONDARY SLOW CUT VALVE
WHT-BLK
OUTER VENT CONTROL VALVE
WHT-BLK
COLD MIXTURE HEATER


Fig. 18: Tercel Wagon Wiring Diagram

# 1988 COMPUTERIZED ENGINE CONTROLS
# Volkswagen Digifant (Bosch AFC) System

## Golf, Golf GT, Jetta, Vanagon

***NOTE: This article also covers Digifant II system which is used on Golf, Golf GT and Jetta models.***

## DESCRIPTION & OPERATION

The Bosch AFC Digifant system is a modified AFC system. The Digifant system does not use cold start injector and thermo time switch for cold start enrichment. Different sensors and switches along with Electronic Control Unit (ECU) regulate fuel injection operation. For further information on operation, see BOSCH AFC in the FUEL SYSTEMS section.

## OPERATION

### AIRFLOW METER

All intake air is drawn through the airflow meter. The meter contains a tunnel with a measuring flap and dampening flap. The measuring flap swings in with air stream against pressure of a spiral spring and is connected to a potentiometer.

The potentiometer transmits an electrical signal determined by measuring flap position to inform ECU of engine load. At idle, the measuring flap is almost closed due to the spring pressure.

The potentiometer within the airflow meter prevents loss of engine power during sudden acceleration/deceleration by signaling the ECU of necessary enrichment requirements.

An idle air by-pass receives airflow through a small hole, the size of which is controlled by the idle mixture screw. This adjustable air by-pass influences CO levels at low engine speeds.

### CONTROL UNIT

The control unit is located on left rear corner of engine compartment on Golf, Golf GT and Jetta models. On Vanagon, control unit may be located in trunk floor behind the rear seat or in the equipment box in cargo area. These units cannot be repaired. The control unit limits maximum engine speed to about 5500-5800 RPM. The control unit receives information from the following:

- Air quantity from intake sensor.
- Air temperature from temperature sensor (I).
- Engine temperature from temperature sensor (II).
- Exhaust oxygen content from $O_2$ sensor.
- Position of throttle valve from switch for full throttle enrichment.

The control unit uses this information to determine amount of fuel to be injected.

### ELECTRIC FUEL PUMP

The fuel pump provides fuel under pressure to the fuel pressure regulator. Power for operation during cranking mode is provided from starter relay via the fuel pump relay. After the engine has started, control of the fuel pump is through the ignition signal (Digifant). The fuel pump is sealed unit.

### FUEL INJECTORS

A fuel rail links the fuel pressure regulator with the fuel injectors. Each cylinder is provided with a solenoid-operated injector which sprays fuel toward backside of each inlet valve. Each injector is energized through the ignition coil and grounded through the ECU to complete the circuit

Each injector is linked to a resistor (resistor may be external or integral with injector or ECU) to reduce operating voltage to 3 volts and to protect injectors from power surges. The ECU controls length of time each injector is open. The "ON" time of the injector governs the amount of fuel delivered. The injector delivers 1/2 the amount of fuel required for an operating cycle each time they open (twice per cycle).

### FUEL PRESSURE REGULATOR

The pressure regulator consists of a sealed, spring loaded diaphragm with a connection for intake manifold vacuum. Fuel pressure is maintained at about 36 psi (2.5 Bar) pressure.

A connection for intake manifold vacuum provides a constant pressure differential which ensures that the amount of fuel injected is solely dependent upon injector open "ON" time. Excess fuel is returned to fuel tank. No service of pressure regulator is required. The pressure regulator is located on or near fuel rail.

### FULL THROTTLE ENRICHMENT SWITCH

The full throttle enrichment switch supplies the control unit with information to increase amount of fuel injected at full throttle.

### IDLE STABILIZER

This valve is used on models with Digifant system. It is used to control both cold engine operation and warm engine idle speed.

### ON-BOARD DIAGNOSTIC SYSTEM (DIGIFANT II - CALIFORNIA ONLY)

"On-Board Diagnostic System" recognizes both ignition and fuel injection system fault. The control unit for the Digifant II system is equipped with an erasable permanent memory which stores and displays any faults that could cause the vehicle to fail an exhaust emission inspection.

Fault codes appear on indicator switch labeled "Check", located on instrument panel. If a fault is detected and stored in the control unit, fault light will illuminate after one minute.

### THROTTLE VALVE SWITCH

***NOTE: DO NOT connect a test light to throttle valve switch connectors if control unit is connected.***

This switch supplies control unit with information that throttle valve is closed. If engine is above 1500 RPM with throttle closed, fuel will be shut off to the injectors. At idle speed, this switch signals control unit to regulate amount of fuel injected.

## TESTING

### SYSTEM CHECK

***CAUTION: To prevent electrical damage to ohmmeter when testing system, connect ohmmeter leads ONLY to terminals as specified in charts.***

Electrical system functions may be checked at multi-pin connector of ECU. Turn ignition off. Disconnect connector from ECU. Using either ohmmeter or voltmeter, check system between terminals as noted. *See Fig. 1.* See AFC DIGIFANT SYSTEM VOLTAGE and RESISTANCE CHECKS charts.

On California models equipped with Digifant II system, an "On-Board Diagnostic System" is used. Trouble codes/fault memory can be read through the "Check" indicator switch which illuminates when a fault is detected and stored in memory or by activating fault memory. To activate fault memory/code(s), turn ignition switch to "ON" position, engine off. Depress "Check" indicator switch for at least 4 seconds. Indicator light on switch will start flashing codes. A flash code consists of 4 flash impulse groups, with a maximum of 4 flash impulse per group. Between each impulse group there is a 2.5 second pause between codes.

To erase fault codes from memory, turn ignition switch to "OFF" position, press and hold down indicator switch and turn ignition

# Volkswagen Digifant (Bosch AFC) System (Cont.)

switch to "ON" position. Continue depressing switch for about 5 seconds and turn ignition switch off. Test drive vehicle for a minimum of 10 minutes. Recheck codes and correct if necessary. Repeat fault erasing procedure until memory is cleared.

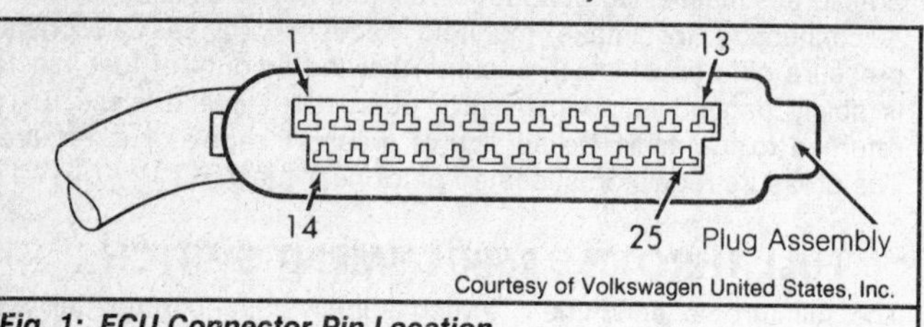
1
13
14
25
Plug Assembly

Courtesy of Volkswagen United States, Inc.

*Fig. 1: ECU Connector Pin Location*

***FAULT/TROUBLE CODES – DIGIFANT II***

| Flash Code | Circuit Affected |
|---|---|
| 2312 | Coolant Temperature Sensor |
| 2322 | Intake Air Temperature Sensor |
| 2232 | Airflow Sensor Potentiometer |
| 2142 | Knock Sensor |
| 2342 | Oxygen Sensor |
| 4444 | No Fault(s) in Memory |
| 0000 | End of Test Sequence |

***GOLF, GOLF GT & JETTA AFC DIGIFANT SYSTEM RESISTANCE CHECKS*** [1]

| Ohmmeter Between Terminals | Components Checked | Specifications |
|---|---|---|
| No. 12 & No. 14 | Injectors | 15-20 ohms with only 1 injector connected. |
| No. 6 [2] & No. 11 | Throttle Valve Switch (Idle & Full) | 0 ohms at idle & full throttle. |
| No. 2 & No. 13 | Oxygen Sensor | 0 ohms with $O_2$ sensor disconnected & grounded/infinity with sensor connected. |
| No. 6 [2] & 17 | Airflow Meter | Approximately 500-1000 ohms |
| No. 21 & No. 17 | Airflow Meter | Ohms varies when moving air sensor. |
| No. 6 [2] & No. 8/No. 6 [2] & No. 18 | Hall Sender Wiring | Continuity should exist w/ sensor removed & all 3 connectors jumped together. |
| No. 4 & No. 5/No. 4 & No. 7 | Knock Sensor | Continuity should exist w/ sensor removed & all 3 connectors jumped together. |
| No. 22 & No. 23 | Idle Stabilizer | Continuity |
| No. 16 & No. 13 | A/C Compressor | Continuity should exist w/ Green wire on brake booster grounded. |

[1] – Resistance checks are performed with ignition OFF. To prevent electrical damage, only check terminals listed.
[2] – NEVER connect test light to this terminal if multi-pin plug is connected to ECU.

***GOLF, GOLF GT & JETTA AFC DIGIFANT SYSTEM VOLTAGE CHECKS*** [1]

| Voltmeter Between Terminals | Components Checked | Specifications |
|---|---|---|
| No. 13 & No. 14/No. 14 & No. 19 | ECU Voltage Supply | About battery voltage. |
| No. 13 & No. 25 | To Ignition Coil Term. 1 | About battery voltage. |
| No. 1 & No. 13 | Voltage to Idle Stabilizer | Pull injector plugs off. Cranking voltage should be present when cranking engine. |
| No. 3 & No. 13 | Fuel Pump Relay | Place jumper wire across terminals. Turn ignition on and fuel pump must run. |

[1] – All system checks are performed with ignition ON.

***VANAGON AFC DIGIFANT SYSTEM RESISTANCE CHECKS*** [1]

| Ohmmeter Between Terminals | Components Checked | Specifications |
|---|---|---|
| No. 12 & No. 14 | Injectors | Connect only one injector at a time. 15-20 ohms |
| No. 6 [2] & No. 11 | Throttle Valve Switch | Continuity when closed or fully open. |
| No. 6 [2] & No. 17 | Intake Air Sensor | 500-1000 ohms |
| No. 17 & No. 21 | Intake Air Sensor | Resistance changes when moving air sensor plate. |
| No. 6 [2] & No. 8/No. 6 [2] & No. 18 | Hall Sender Wiring | Continuity should exist with Hall sender removed and all 3 connectors jumped together. |
| No. 2 & No. 13 | Oxygen Sensor Wiring | Continuity should exist with connector removed from oxygen sensor and Green wire grounded. No continuity with connector installed. |

[1] – All system checks performed with ignition OFF and ambient temperature of 32-104°F (0-40°C).
[2] – NEVER connect test light to this terminal if multi-pin plug is connected to ECU.

# 1988 COMPUTERIZED ENGINE CONTROLS
# Volkswagen Digifant (Bosch AFC) System (Cont.)

*VANAGON AFC DIGIFANT SYSTEM VOLTAGE CHECKS* [1]

| Voltmeter Between Terminals | Components Checked | Specifications |
|---|---|---|
| No. 13 & No. 14/No. 14 & No. 19 | Control Unit Voltage Supply | Approximate battery voltage. |
| No. 13 & No. 25 | Voltage To Ignition Coil Terminal No. 1 | Approximate battery voltage. |
| No. 1 & No. 13 | Voltage To Idle Stabilizer | Unplug all 4 injectors. Voltage at starter terminal No. 50 when cranking should be minimum 8 volts. |
| No. 3 & No. 13 | Voltage To Fuel Pump Relay | Connect jumper wire between terminals. Fuel pump should operate. |

[1] – All system checks performed with ignition on and ambient temperature of 32-104°F (0-40°C).

## AIRFLOW METER

***NOTE: Terminal numbers referred to in testing procedure are found on connector housing on side of airflow meter assembly.***

**Airflow Sensor Potentiometer – 1)** Turn ignition switch to "OFF" position. Remove high voltage wire from distributor ignition coil and connect to ground. Disconnect Digifant II control unit connector.

**2)** Connect ohmmeter leads between terminals No. 6 and 17 of control until connector. Resistance should be within 500-1000 ohms. If not okay, check sensor wiring harness.

**3)** Connect ohmmeter leads between terminals No. 17 and 21 of control unit connector. Move airflow sensor pressure flap or actuate starter. Resistance should change. If not okay, replace potentiometer.

**Air Temperature Sensor – 1)** Connect ohmmeter between terminals No. 1 and 4 of airflow sensor connector. Ohmmeter reading should be within specification depending on temperature. See TEMPERATURE SENSOR RESISTANCE SPECIFICATIONS table.

**2)** Replace airflow meter if sensor is defective. If replaced, idle speed and CO level must be adjusted.

## COOLANT TEMPERATURE SENSOR

**1)** Check coolant temperature. Using ohmmeter, check resistance of temperature sensor. Resistance will vary depending on coolant temperature.

**2)** Replace temperature sensor if resistance is not within specification. See TEMPERATURE SENSOR RESISTANCE SPECIFICATIONS table.

*TEMPERATURE SENSOR RESISTANCE SPECIFICATIONS*

| Sensor Temperature °F (°C) | Ohms |
|---|---|
| 50 (10) | 3100-4100 |
| 68 (20) | 2000-3000 |
| 86 (30) | 1500-2000 |
| 104 (40) | 1000-1500 |
| 122 (50) | 750-950 |
| 140 (60) | 540-650 |
| 158 (70) | 380-480 |
| 176 (80) | 290-360 |
| 194 (90) | 205-280 |
| 212 (100) | 160-220 |

## DECELERATION FUEL SHUTOFF

**1)** Warm engine to normal operating temperature of 176°F (80°C). Fuel shutoff will operate in these conditions; when engine RPM was above 2600, throttle is closed, coolant temperature is above 122°F (50°C) and engine RPM is between 1250 and 2600 RPM.

**2)** Locate double sided connector. Using Adapter (VW 1490), jump proper side of connector. *See Fig. 2.* Slightly accelerate engine. Note engine RPM.

**3)** Engine RPM should surge, then decelerate when shutoff operates. If engine RPM does not surge, check for damaged wiring, defective engine temperature sender or defective control unit.

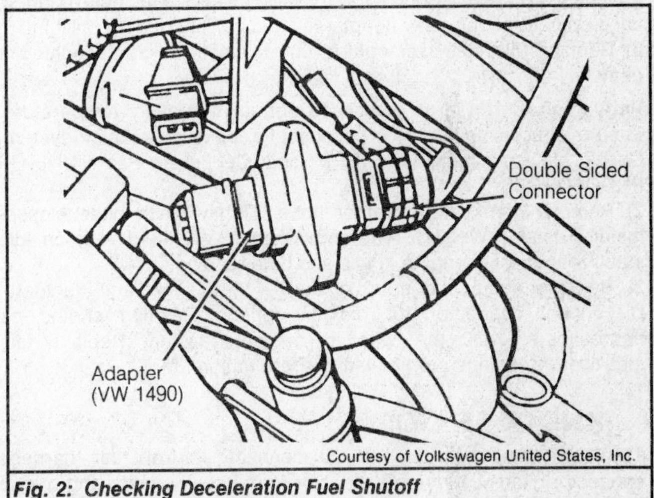
1
Double Sided
Connector
Adapter
(VW 1490)
Courtesy of Volkswagen United States, Inc.

*Fig. 2: Checking Deceleration Fuel Shutoff*

## FUEL INJECTORS

**Spray Pattern – 1)** Remove a pair of injectors, leaving electrical plugs and fuel lines connected. Disconnect electrical plugs from remaining installed fuel injectors.

**2)** Hold injectors over pan. Operate starter briefly. Spray pattern must be an even, cone-shaped spray. Repeat test for remaining injectors.

**Leak Test – 1)** Disconnect electrical connectors from injectors. Remove injectors in pairs, leaving fuel lines connected. Turn ignition on for approximately 5 seconds for fuel pump operation.

**2)** Note amount of fuel drops from injectors. Replace injectors if leakage exceeds more than 2 drops per minute.

**Voltage Supply – 1)** Disconnect electrical connectors from injectors. Connect Test Light (US 1115) across plug connector terminals.

***CAUTION: DO NOT ground connector contacts as ECU will be damaged.***

**2)** Test light should flicker while operating starter. If voltage is not present test wiring circuit. See TESTING in this section.

## FUEL PRESSURE REGULATOR

Using "T" fitting, connect fuel pressure gauge in fuel delivery line. Run engine at idle speed. Pressure should be 36 psi (2.6 kg/cm²) on

# Volkswagen Digifant (Bosch AFC) System (Cont.)

Golf, Golf GT and Jetta or 29 psi (2 kg/cm²) on Vanagon with pressure regulator vacuum line connected. With vacuum line disconnected from pressure regulator, pressure should be 44 psi (3.1 kg/cm²) on Golf, Golf GT and Jetta or 36 psi (2.6 kg/cm²) on Vanagon.

## FUEL PUMP

**Delivery Rate – 1)** Disconnect and plug fuel return line at pressure regulator. Attach hose to return line fitting and place other end in measuring container.
**2)** Disconnect fuel pump relay. Connect jumper wire between terminals No. 30 and 87 of relay harness connector for 30 seconds. Minimum delivery rate should be 16.9 ozs. (.5L) for 30 second period.

## IDLE STABILIZER

**Operation – 1)** Turn ignition switch on. Idle stabilizer should vibrate and hum. If stabilizer does not operate, disconnect connector from idle stabilizer. Using Tester (VW 1325 A-1), check for continuity. Continuity should exist.
**2)** Replace idle stabilizer if no continuity exists. If continuity is obtained, reconnect connector to valve. Check electrical connections on control unit relay adapter located in front of right taillight.
**3)** Replace idle stabilizer control unit if electrical connections are okay.

**Regulation – 1)** Warm engine to normal operating temperature. Ensure all accessories are off. Inspect for leaks in intake air system. Check ignition timing, idle RPM and CO level. See TUNE-UP PROCEDURES.
**2)** Remove crankcase breather hose. Tightly pinch hose closed. Install Tester (VW 1315 A-1) and Adapter (VW 1315 A-2) on idle stabilizer. Operate engine at idle and note reading.
**3)** Reading should be approximately 410-450 mA and fluctuate. Disconnect connector for oxygen sensor. Reading should be approximately 430 mA with a constant reading. Replace idle stabilizer if readings are not within specification.

## KNOCK SENSOR

**1)** Turn ignition switch off. Disconnect control unit harness connector. Remove wiring connector from knock sensor and bridge or jump wiring connector terminals No. 4 and 5 and terminals No. 4 and 7. Ohmmeter should read continuity.
**2)** If no continuity is present, repair knock sensor wiring. If knocking continues, replace knock sensor.

## OXYGEN SENSOR

**1)** Warm engine until engine oil temperature is at a minimum of 176°F (80°C). Check for leaks in exhaust system. Using Adapter (Sun 120 239), connect CO test equipment hose to the sampling point on left exhaust pipe.
**2)** Allow engine to idle for approximately 2 minutes and note CO reading. Remove hose from pressure regulator and pinch closed. This is done to check function of oxygen regulation. CO reading should increase briefly and then drop again.
**3)** If reading did not increase and then drop, disconnect connector at oxygen sensor. DO NOT allow oxygen sensor wire to touch ground. Hold $O_2$ sensor wiring harness connector wire to ground. CO reading should increase. Connect $O_2$ sensor wiring harness connector wire to alternator connector. CO reading should decrease.
**4)** If CO reading was incorrect, check wire connection on control unit. See TESTING in this section. If wiring connection is okay, replace control unit. Oxygen sensor is defective if test step **2)** was faulty, but test step **3)** was okay. Replace oxygen sensor.

## RELAY TEST (VANAGON ONLY)

The power supply and fuel pump relays are located in the engine compartment in a plastic box on the firewall. The fuel pump relay is mounted on the right side of the box and power supply relay on the left. To test relay, use the following procedures:
**1)** Unplug all electrical connectors to injectors. To check power to relays, turn ignition on. Use test light to check for voltage at terminals No. 30 and 85 of both relays. Power supply relay should also have voltage at terminal No. 85. If not, check wiring.
**2)** Terminal No. 87 of fuel pump relay should have voltage when starter is operated. If not, check wiring. If wiring is good, check relay. If relay is good, replace ECU.

## THROTTLE VALVE SWITCH

**Function – 1)** Closed throttle valve switch controls injection quantity for idle, switches off injection during deceleration fuel shutoff and ignition timing at idle. Open throttle valve switch controls fuel quantity at full throttle.
**2)** Disconnect wiring lead from throttle valve switch. Install ohmmeter between terminals on wiring lead. Reading should show continuity at idle and full throttle position of throttle valve switch.
**3)** To check switching point, open and close throttle valve slowly. When ohmmeter indicates continuity at idle stop position, measure gap between idle stop and idle adjusting screw with feeler gauge. *See Fig. 3.*

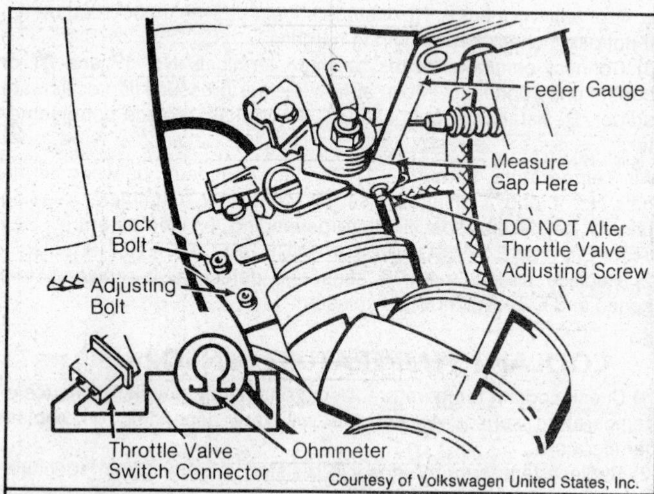
Feeler Gauge
Measure Gap Here
Lock Bolt
DO NOT Alter Throttle Valve Adjusting Screw
Adjusting Bolt
Throttle Valve Switch Connector
Ohmmeter
Courtesy of Volkswagen United States, Inc.

***Fig. 3: Checking & Adjusting Throttle Valve Switch***

**4)** Gap should be .002-.004" (.05-.10 mm). Proper adjustment of throttle valve switch is important. Excessive gap will cause engine surge when throttled slightly.
**5)** Insufficient gap causes cold engine to stall at full throttle acceleration and warm engine will have no deceleration fuel shutoff. If gap requires adjustment, see THROTTLE VALVE SWITCH under ADJUSTMENTS in this section.

---

***CAUTION: DO NOT perform following test unless plug is disconnected from ECU.***

---

**Switch Wiring** – Turn ignition on. Disconnect wiring lead from throttle valve switch. Using voltmeter, check voltage between both terminals of wiring lead. Reading should be approximately 5 volts. If voltage is incorrect, check for break in wiring or defective ECU.

**Full Throttle Enrichment Function – 1)** Warm engine until engine oil temperature is at a minimum of 176°F (80°C). Stop engine and connect CO tester and tachometer. Start engine and allow to idle for 2 minutes.

**2)** Remove connector from double sided connector at throttle valve switch. *See Fig. 3.* Slowly accelerate engine to approximately 4500 RPM. Note and record CO level reading.

**3)** Bridge connections of double sided connector using Adapter (VW 1490). Note CO reading. Reading should increase at least 1% over recorded CO reading.

**4)** If reading did not increase, check for defective wiring, engine temperature sending unit or control unit.

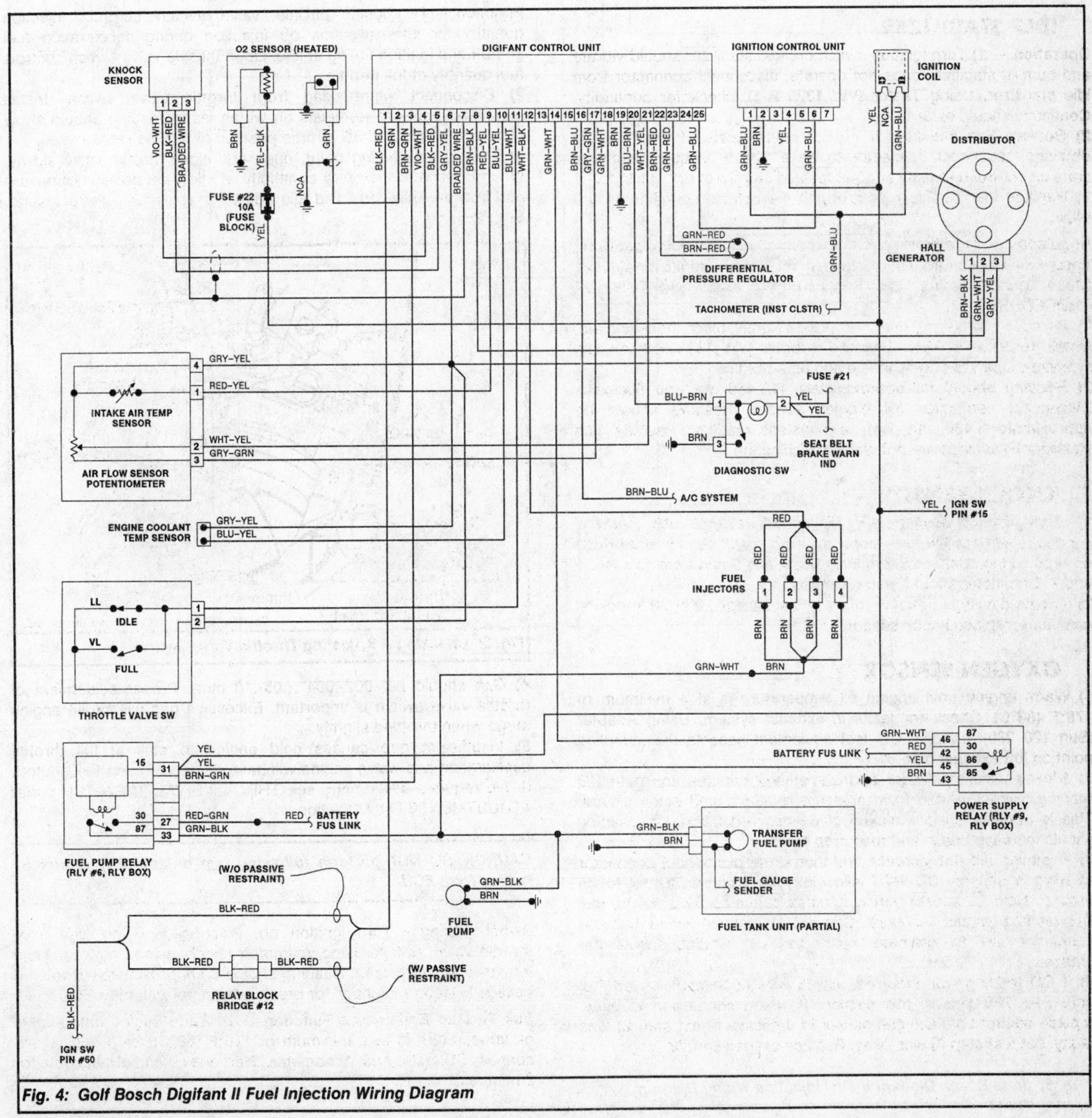

KNOCK SENSOR
O2 SENSOR (HEATED)
DIGIFANT CONTROL UNIT
IGNITION CONTROL UNIT
IGNITION COIL
DISTRIBUTOR
VIO-WHT
BLK-RED
BRAIDED WIRE
BRN
YEL-BLK
GRN
NCA
FUSE #22 10A (FUSE BLOCK)
YEL
BLK-RED
GRN
BRN-GRN
VIO-WHT
BLK-RED
GRY-YEL
BRAIDED WIRE
BRN-BLK
RED-YEL
BLU-YEL
BLU-WHT
WHT-BLK
GRN-WHT
BRN-BLU
GRY-GRN
BRN-WHT
BRN
BLU-BRN
WHT-YEL
BRN-RED
GRN-RED
GRN-BLU
GRN-BLU
GRN-RED
BRN-RED
DIFFERENTIAL PRESSURE REGULATOR
HALL GENERATOR
BRN-BLK
GRN-WHT
GRY-YEL
TACHOMETER (INST CLSTR)
GRY-YEL
RED-YEL
INTAKE AIR TEMP SENSOR
WHT-YEL
GRY-GRN
AIR FLOW SENSOR POTENTIOMETER
FUSE #21
BLU-BRN
YEL
DIAGNOSTIC SW
SEAT BELT BRAKE WARN IND
BRN-BLU
A/C SYSTEM
YEL
IGN SW PIN #15
ENGINE COOLANT TEMP SENSOR
GRY-YEL
BLU-YEL
RED
FUEL INJECTORS
LL
IDLE
VL
FULL
THROTTLE VALVE SW
GRN-WHT
BATTERY FUS LINK
POWER SUPPLY RELAY (RLY #9, RLY BOX)
YEL
YEL
BRN-GRN
RED-GRN
GRN-BLK
RED
BATTERY FUS LINK
FUEL PUMP RELAY (RLY #6, RLY BOX)
(W/O PASSIVE RESTRAINT)
GRN-BLK
BRN
TRANSFER FUEL PUMP
FUEL GAUGE SENDER
FUEL TANK UNIT (PARTIAL)
FUEL PUMP
BLK-RED
BLK-RED
BLK-RED
RELAY BLOCK BRIDGE #12
(W/ PASSIVE RESTRAINT)
BLK-RED
IGN SW PIN #50


*Fig. 4: Golf Bosch Digifant II Fuel Injection Wiring Diagram*

# 1988 COMPUTERIZED ENGINE CONTROLS
## Volkswagen Digifant (Bosch AFC) System (Cont.)

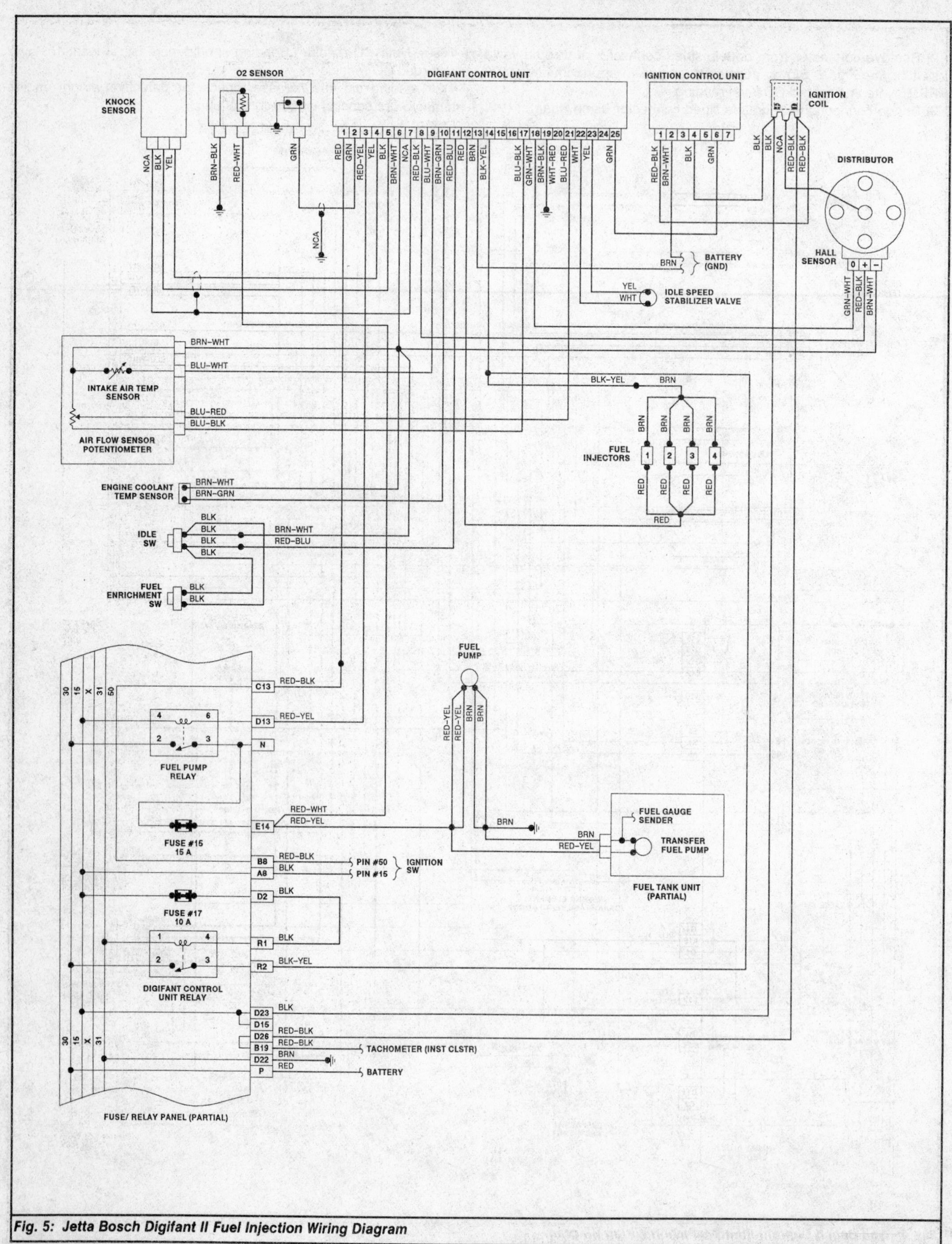

KNOCK SENSOR
O2 SENSOR
DIGIFANT CONTROL UNIT
IGNITION CONTROL UNIT
IGNITION COIL
DISTRIBUTOR
HALL SENSOR
BATTERY (GND)
IDLE SPEED STABILIZER VALVE
INTAKE AIR TEMP SENSOR
AIR FLOW SENSOR POTENTIOMETER
FUEL INJECTORS
ENGINE COOLANT TEMP SENSOR
IDLE SW
FUEL ENRICHMENT SW
FUEL PUMP
FUEL PUMP RELAY
FUSE #15 15 A
FUEL GAUGE SENDER
TRANSFER FUEL PUMP
FUEL TANK UNIT (PARTIAL)
PIN #50
PIN #15
IGNITION SW
FUSE #17 10 A
DIGIFANT CONTROL UNIT RELAY
TACHOMETER (INST CLSTR)
BATTERY
FUSE/ RELAY PANEL (PARTIAL)


*Fig. 5: Jetta Bosch Digifant II Fuel Injection Wiring Diagram*

# 1988 COMPUTERIZED ENGINE CONTROLS
## Volkswagen Digifant (Bosch AFC) System (Cont.)

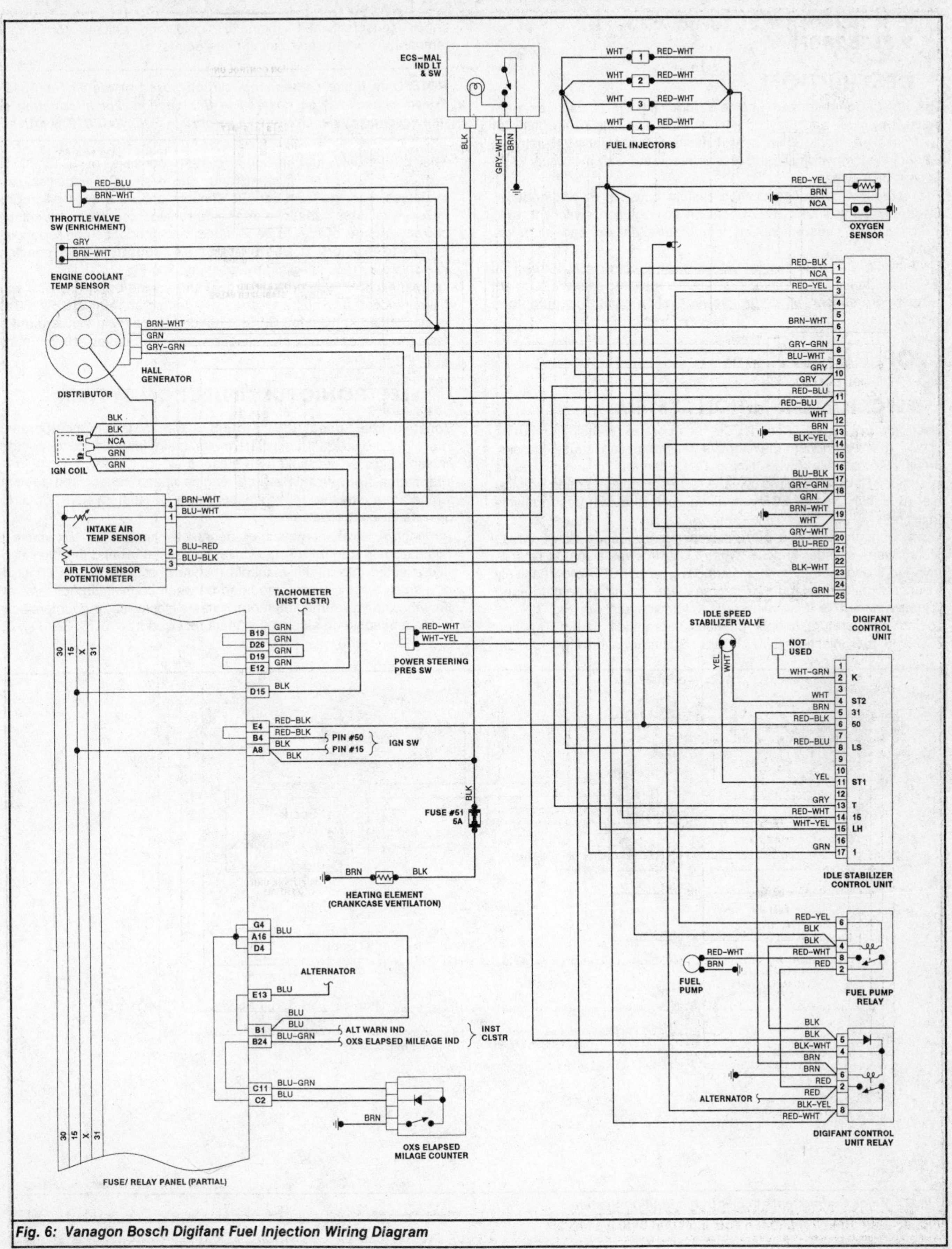
ECS-MAL IND LT & SW
FUEL INJECTORS
THROTTLE VALVE SW (ENRICHMENT)
ENGINE COOLANT TEMP SENSOR
OXYGEN SENSOR
HALL GENERATOR
DISTRIBUTOR
IGN COIL
INTAKE AIR TEMP SENSOR
AIR FLOW SENSOR POTENTIOMETER
TACHOMETER (INST CLSTR)
POWER STEERING PRES SW
DIGIFANT CONTROL UNIT
IDLE SPEED STABILIZER VALVE
NOT USED
IGN SW
FUSE #51 5A
HEATING ELEMENT (CRANKCASE VENTILATION)
IDLE STABILIZER CONTROL UNIT
ALTERNATOR
ALT WARN IND
OXS ELAPSED MILEAGE IND
INST CLSTR
FUEL PUMP
FUEL PUMP RELAY
OXS ELAPSED MILAGE COUNTER
DIGIFANT CONTROL UNIT RELAY
FUSE/ RELAY PANEL (PARTIAL)

*Fig. 6: Vanagon Bosch Digifant Fuel Injection Wiring Diagram*

## 2.3L (B230F), 2.3L Turbo (B230FT), 2.8L (B280F)

## DESCRIPTION

The Volvo Computerized Engine Control system is used on both Volvo 4-cylinder and 6-cylinder engines. It consists of a computer controlled electronic ignition with microprocessor and LH-Jetronic 2.2 fuel system with microprocessor integrated with a Constant Idle Speed (CIS) system.

The computer controlled ignition system consists of a distributor, Electronic Control Unit (ECU), ignition coil, ignition switch, throttle switch, knock sensor, coolant temperature sensor and air mass meter.

LH-Jetronic 2.2 fuel system consists of Electronic Control Unit (ECU), air mass meter, injectors, injector ballast resistors, coolant temperature sensor, air control valve, lambda sond, fuel pump and in-tank pump.

## OPERATION

### ELECTRONIC IGNITION SYSTEM

Electronic controlled ignition ECU incorporates a fault monitoring circuit. If a component develops a fault that can cause knocks, circuit automatically lowers timing 11-15 degrees to avoid damage to engine. Throttle switch signals ECU to set ignition timing point at idle. At higher speeds, ECU sets firing point to obtain best possible emissions.

Knock sensor produces current within a frequency range which occurs when cylinder knocks. When ECU receives signal, it retards timing in 3 degree intervals until knocking stops. ECU progressively advances ignition timing in .37 degree steps until programmed firing point is reached, or if cylinder starts to knock again. *See Fig. 1.*

Coolant temperature sensor provides information to both ignition ECU and fuel injection ECU. It cuts out information signals from knock sensors when engine is cold and adjusts for engine temperature when determining firing points.

***NOTE: Only those components directly used in the Constant Idle Speed system will be covered in this section. For information on fuel injection system, refer to appropriate FUEL INJECTION article.***

The LH-Jetronic fuel injection system consists of 3 functional sections: ECU, fuel system and sensors. ECU receives and evaluates readings from various sensors around engine. Microprocessor evaluates variations in engine running conditions, calculates correct amount of fuel to be injected, and produces corresponding signals to injectors. It also operates air control valve for constant idle speed by regulating airflow opening. *See Fig. 2.*

Air mass meter measures air drawn into engine by means of a wire filament located in intake air stream. A temperature of 212°F (100°C) is maintained at filament. Current needed to maintain temperature at filament is measured, providing precise information on air mass entering engine.

### ELECTRONIC FUEL INJECTION SYSTEM

**Constant Idle Speed (CIS) System** – CIS system is incorporated into LH-Jetronic 2.2 fuel system. Its main function is to control engine at idle or near idle by regulating air control valve. Combined information from throttle switch, engine speed sensor and coolant temperature sensor, is processed through fuel system ECU to operate air control valve.

Air control valve increases or decreases amount of air which is taken from in front of throttle valve, by-passed around throttle valve and injected into intake manifold (behind throttle valve). It consists of a small electric motor, mounted between connecting hoses at air flow throttle valve. Electric motor rotates clockwise or counterclockwise, depending on electrical signals received from ECU. *See Fig. 3.*

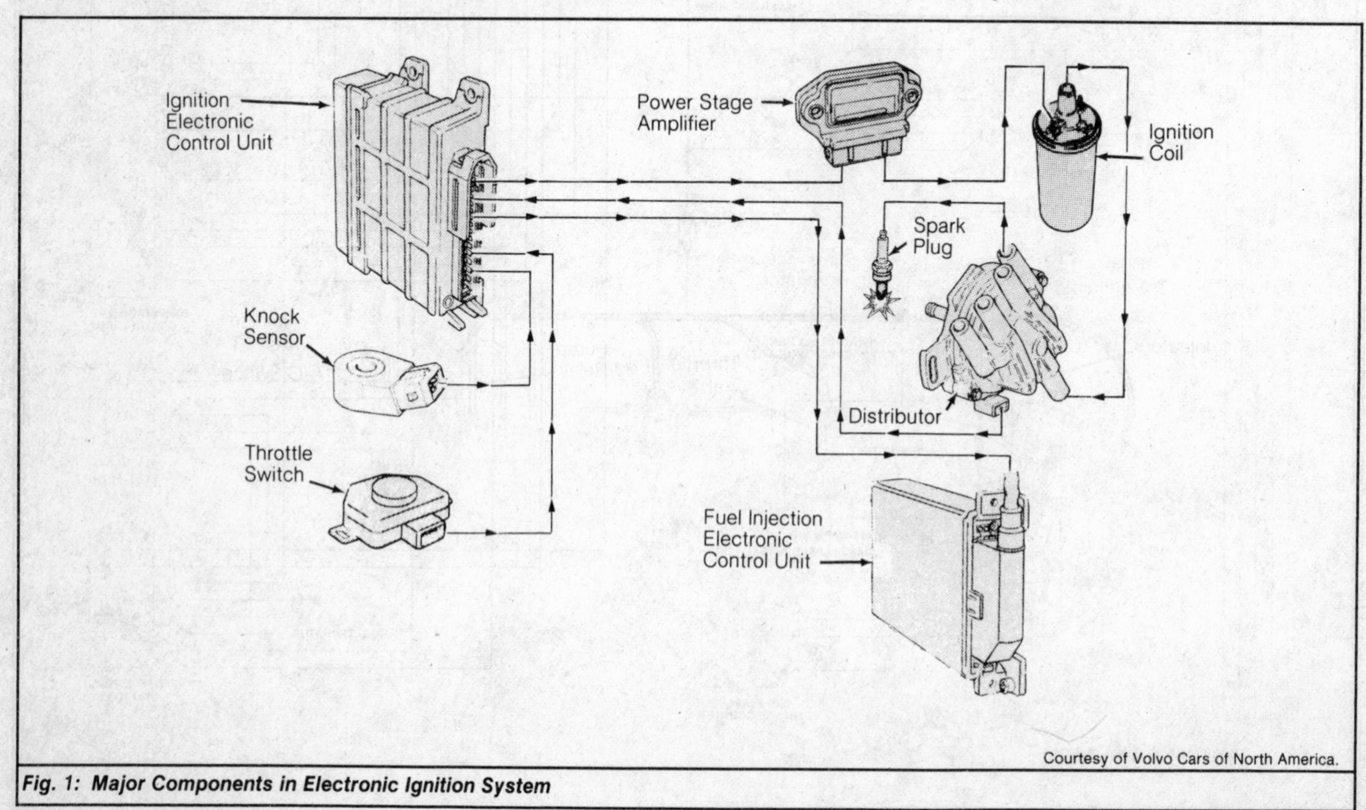
Ignition Electronic Control Unit
Power Stage Amplifier
Ignition Coil
Spark Plug
Knock Sensor
Distributor
Throttle Switch
Fuel Injection Electronic Control Unit
Courtesy of Volvo Cars of North America.

*Fig. 1: Major Components in Electronic Ignition System*

## TROUBLE SHOOTING

### ENGINE DOES NOT START

**B230F/FT – 1)** Check that ground connections are properly connected to intake manifold. Ignition ground may have one or 2 leads depending on model.

**2)** Disconnect lead from one of the spark plugs and connect a separate spark plug to it. Ground spark plug and crank starter motor. A strong, Blue/White spark indicates ignition is okay. Check for fuel system malfunction. If there is no spark, or if a weak spark occurs, turn off ignition.

**3)** Connect a lead with spark plug, to ignition coil High Tension (HT) terminal. Ground spark plug and crank starter motor. No spark or weak spark indicates ignition system malfunction. If spark plug fires, check distributor rotor and cap, and HT leads. Replace if necessary.

**B280F – 1)** Ensure that ground connections (BN) from control unit (ignition ECU), and power stage unit (next to left side front fender), are properly connected to intake manifold ground.

**2)** Disconnect lead from one of the spark plugs and connect a separate spark plug to it. Ground spark plug and crank starter motor. A strong, Blue/White spark indicates engine or fuel system malfunction. If there is no spark, or if a weak spark occurs, turn off ignition.

**3)** Connect a lead, plus spark plug, to ignition coil (HT) terminal. Ground spark plug and crank starter motor. No spark or weak spark indicates ignition system malfunction. If spark plug fires, check distributor rotor and cap, and HT leads. Replace if necessary.

### ENGINE STARTS, BUT RUNS ROUGH OR LACKS POWER

**B280F Only** – Operate engine at light load until normal operating temperature is reached. Engine temperature below 122°F (50°C) could effect timing check. Check timing at idle speed (750 RPM). Timing specification is 15 to 17 degrees BTDC.

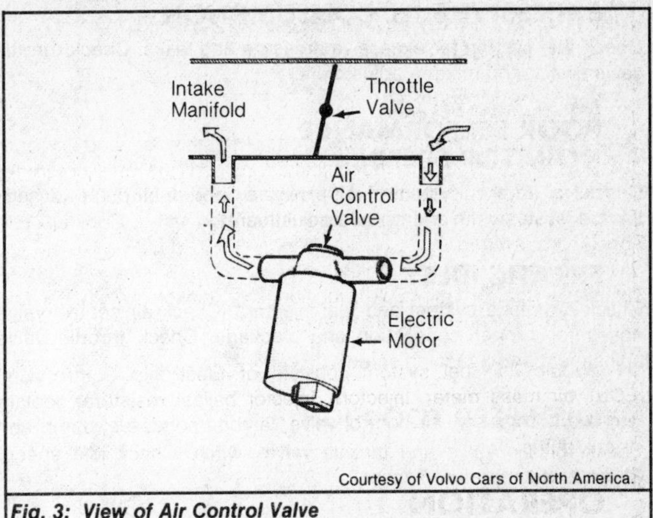
Intake
Manifold
Throttle
Valve
Air
Control
Valve
Electric
Motor
Courtesy of Volvo Cars of North America.

***Fig. 3: View of Air Control Valve***

***NOTE: There is no timing adjustment. If timing is incorrect, proceed to CIRCUIT CHECKS.***

### ENGINE HARD TO START (COLD & WARM)

Check starting and charging systems. Check electrical and fuel connectors for proper connections and routing. Check air intake system and fuel system. Check air temperature sensor.

### POOR OR NO IDLE

Check air intake system and fuel system. Check air mass meter.

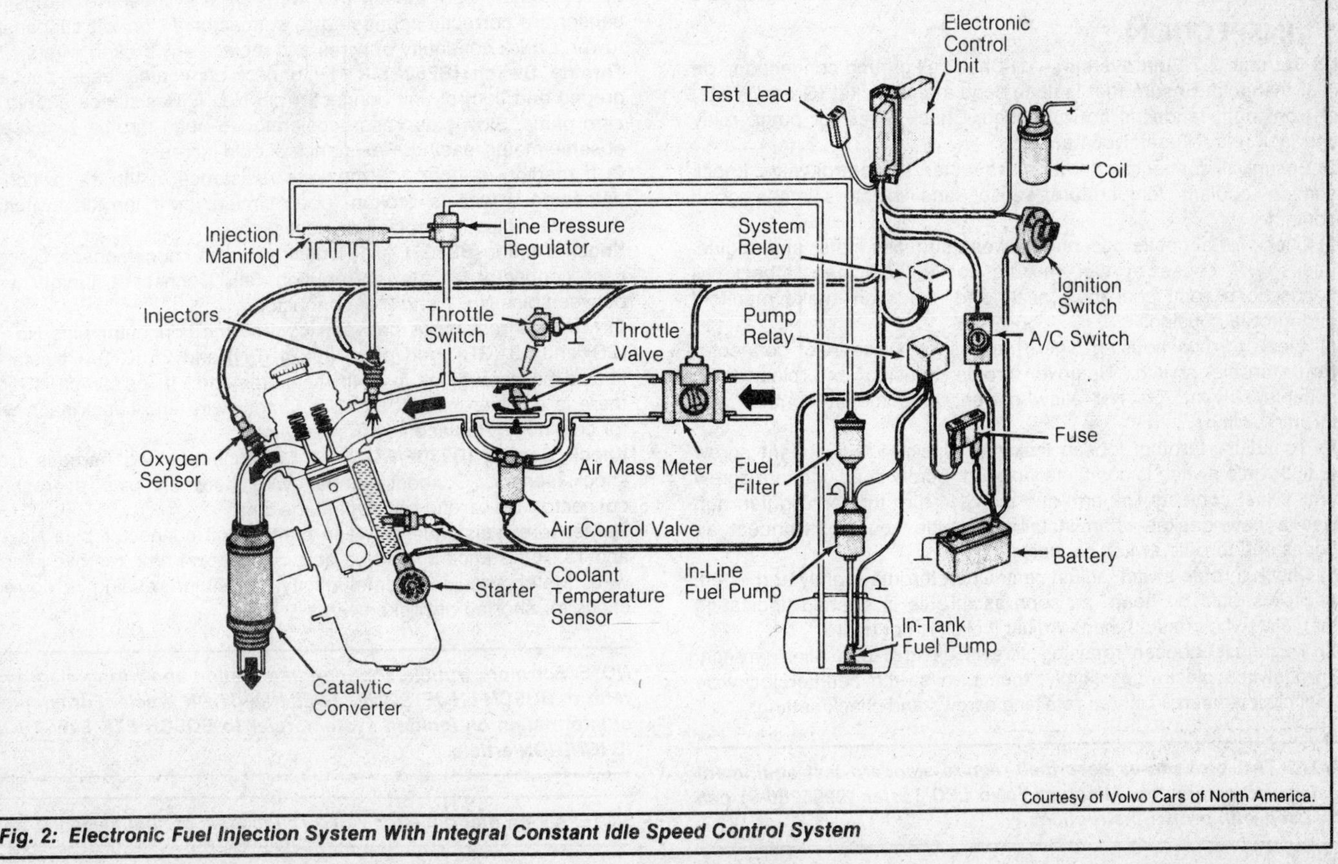

Courtesy of Volvo Cars of North America.

***Fig. 2: Electronic Fuel Injection System With Integral Constant Idle Speed Control System***

# 1988 COMPUTERIZED ENGINE CONTROLS
# Volvo (Cont.)

## EXCESSIVE FUEL CONSUMPTION

Check fuel system for excessive pressure and leaks. Check throttle valve switch and mixture adjustment.

## POOR PERFORMANCE (LOW TOP SPEED)

Check air intake system, fuel pressure, and fuel pump. Check throttle valve switch and mixture adjustment.

## ERRATIC IDLE

Check air intake system and fuel injectors. Check air control valve hoses for proper connection and blockage. Check throttle valve adjustment and attaching screws.

## IDLE SPEED TOO HIGH

Check throttle valve and throttle valve switch. Check idle speed. Check air temperature sensor.

## IDLE SPEED TOO LOW (ENGINE COLD)

Check air temperature sensor and air control valve. Check idle speed control system.

## JERKING, POOR ACCELERATION

Check acceleration enrichment.

# DIAGNOSIS & TESTING

***CAUTION:** Before testing components, ensure battery is properly charged, all wires are okay, and that connections are secure. Inspect distributor cap and rotor for cracks and carbon tracking. Turn ignition off when connecting test equipment, connecting or disconnecting ECU, or when replacing parts.*

## INSPECTION

**LH-Jetronic 2.2 Fuel System – 1)** Check all ground connections on inlet manifold. Ensure that lambda sond's test socket (Green/White) at front right fender is not grounded. Check fuses for pump relay and tank relay. Fuses No. 1 and 11.

**2)** Ensure all connectors for air mass meter, air control valve, knock sensor, coolant temperature sensor and injectors make good contact.

**3)** Check for air leaks occuring between air mass meter and engine. Leaks will cause air/fuel mixture to be too lean. Check all connections, joint couplings, seals and hoses on intake manifold and throttle housing.

**4)** Clean throttle housing where necessary. Disconnect connector from throttle switch. Remove throttle housing and clean with suitable solvent. Do not allow solvent to come in contact with throttle switch.

**5)** To adjust throttle, loosen lock nut. Unscrew adjustment screw until throttle switch is completely closed. Screw in adjustment screw until it just contacts link arm and then 1/4 turn further. Tighten nut. Use a new gasket when installing throttle housing. Connect air hoses and throttle switch connector.

**6)** Check throttle switch adjustment. Open throttle slightly and listen. A click should be heard as soon as throttle is opened (indicating that idle switch has opened). Adjust if click is not heard.

**7)** To adjust. Loosen retaining screws using 3 mm Allen wrench. Turn switch clockwise slightly, then turn switch counterclockwise until click is heard. Tighten retaining screws and check setting.

***NOTE:** Test procedures described require standard test equipment using volt/ohmmeter. Although Volvo LED Tester (9995280-6) can be used with proper instructions.*

## CIRCUIT CHECKS

***NOTE:** Unless otherwise mentioned, the connector referenced in following checks is the control unit (ignition ECU) connector. Terminal numbers are stamped on connector.*

**Coolant Temperature Sensor – 1)** Turn off ignition. Remove panel from lower left of dash board. Disconnect wiring harness from ignition control unit (located above accelerator pedal). Remove cover from connector. Check that all pin connection sleeves are the same height.

**2)** Using an ohmmeter, measure resistance between pin No. 2 of connector "F" (on left suspension tower), and ground. If reading is incorrect, repeat measurement directly at the sensor. See COOLANT TEMPERATURE SENSOR RESISTANCE table. Replace as applicable.

***COOLANT TEMPERATURE SENSOR RESISTANCE***

| Resistance (Ohms) | Temperature °F (°C) |
|---|---|
| 6000 | 32 (0) |
| 5000 | 68 (20) |
| 1300 | 104 (40) |
| 600 | 140 (60) |
| 325 | 176 (80) |
| 190 | 212 (100) |
| 120 | 248 (120) |

**Cylinder No. 1 Position Sensor (B280F) – 1)** Connect ohmmeter leads between connector pins No. 18 (Black/Yellow) and No. 19 (Yellow/Red). Resistance should read zero ohms. Ensure that shield wire is connected to connector pin No. 21. If problem still exists, continue to next step.

**2)** Check that wires from engine RPM/crankshaft sensor are correctly connected to connector "F" on left suspension tower. Replace any broken wire(s). If problem still exists, go on to next step.

**3)** Turn ignition off. Check that wires from cylinder No. 1 position sensor are correctly connected to connector "F" on left suspension tower. Check continuity of wires and replace any broken wire(s).

**Throttle Switch (B280F) – 1)** Connect ohmmeter leads between ground and control unit connector pin No. 7. Resistance should be zero ohms. Slowly depress accelerator to open throttle switch and observe meter reading. Resistance should increase.

**2)** If reading is incorrect, measure resistance at throttle switch to determine if wire is broken (open circuit), or if throttle switch is defective. Adjust or replace as necessary.

**Knock Sensor (B280F) – 1)** Check wires at knock sensor. Disconnect connector at fuel distribution rail. Connect a jumper wire between pins No. 1 and 2 of connector.

**2)** Measure resistance between control unit connector pins No. 12 (SB) and 13 (GR), and pins No. 24 (BN) and 25 (GN). Resistance should be zero ohms in both measurements. If resistance is high, there is an open circuit. Remove jumper wire and check each wire for continuity. Replace any broken wires.

**Knock Sensor (B230F/FT) – 1)** Disconnect wiring harness from knock sensor. Connect jumper wire between pins at rear of connector. Be careful not to damage pins.

**2)** Measure resistance between control unit connector pins No. 12 and 13. Resistance should be zero ohms. If correct, remove jumper wire. Meter should indicate infinity. If neither reading is correct, check for shorted or broken wires.

***NOTE:** For more trouble shooting information and wiring diagrams, refer to BOSCH LH-JETRONIC FUEL INJECTION article. For additional information on ignition system, refer to BOSCH EZK ELECTRONIC IGNITION article.*

***NOTE:** Wiring diagrams for Volvo 780 models are not available.*

# LATEST CHANGES & CORRECTIONS

CAUTION

## CONTENTS

### COMPUTERIZED ENGINE CONTROLS Page

# LATEST CHANGES & CORRECTIONS
# For 1988 & Earlier Models

***NOTE: Latest Changes and Corrections represents a collection of last minute information that arrived too late to be included in the regular data. This section is also comprised of relevant technical service bulletins, and prior year information received since the last edition.***

***It may be useful to read through this section, find any changes or helpful information, and then go to the appropriate manuals and make the changes. Then, when working on a vehicle, the correct information will already be in the manual and it won't be necessary to go through this section again.***

## COMPUTERIZED ENGINE CONTROLS
### HONDA

1 *1986 ACCORD & PRELUDE: HONDA ELECTRONIC CONTROL SYSTEM* – On pages 230 through 235 of the 1986 EMISSION CONTROL SERVICE & REPAIR IMPORTED CARS & TRUCKS SUPPLEMENT. Please add the following ECU SYSTEM TROUBLE SHOOTING information for Accord and Prelude fuel injected models.

## DESCRIPTION & OPERATION
### ELECTRONIC CONTROL UNIT

**Accord & Prelude** – The ECU is equipped with a self-diagnostic function. When an abnormality is detected, the Programmed Fuel Injection (PGM-FI) dash-mounted warning light will come on, and the Light Emitting Diode (LED) display on the ECU will blink. Troubles within the PGM-FI/electronic control system can be diagnosed according to the number of blinks from the LED display. On Accord, ECU is located under driver's seat. On Prelude, ECU is located behind left quarter trim panel, at base of driver's door pillar. See Prelude ECU Location & LED Display illustration.

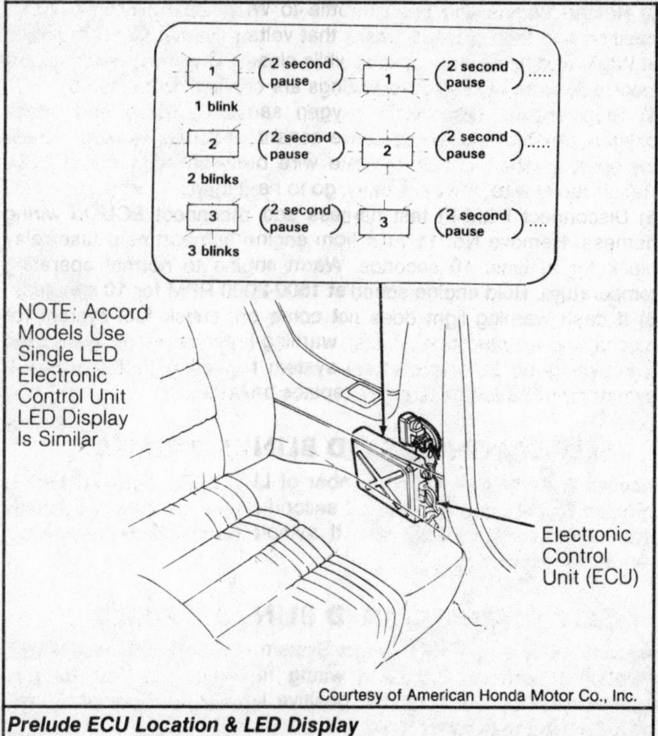
1
2 second pause
1
2 second pause
1 blink
2
2 second pause
2
2 second pause
2 blinks
3
2 second pause
3
2 second pause
3 blinks
NOTE: Accord Models Use Single LED Electronic Control Unit LED Display Is Similar
Electronic Control Unit (ECU)
Courtesy of American Honda Motor Co., Inc.

*Prelude ECU Location & LED Display*

## ECU SYSTEM TROUBLE SHOOTING
### ACCORD & PRELUDE

***ECU TROUBLE CODE IDENTIFICATION***

| Number Of LED Blinks [1] | Possible Cause |
|---|---|
| 0 (Dash Light Off) | Bad ECU ground wire. Faulty ECU. |
| 0 (Dash Light On) | Bad ECU power or ground wire. Short circuit in cluster or warning light wire. Faulty ECU. |
| 1 | Faulty oxygen sensor/circuit. Spark plug misfire. Faulty fuel system. |
| 2 | Faulty ECU |
| 3 | Faulty MAP sensor/circuit. |
| 4 | Faulty ECU. |
| 5 | Disconnected MAP sensor hoses. |
| 6 | Faulty coolant temperature sensor/circuit. |
| 7 | Faulty throttle angle sensor/circuit. |
| 8 | Faulty crank angle sensor/circuit. |
| 9 | Faulty crank angle sensor/circuit. |
| 10 | Faulty intake air temperature sensor/circuit. |
| 11 | Faulty ECU. |
| 12 | Faulty EGR sytem/circuit. |
| 13 | Faulty atmospheric pressure sensor/circuit. |

[1] – If the number of blinks between each 2 second pause exceeds 13, or if the LED stays on, the ECU is faulty.

***NOTE: Use Figure 8 of HONDA ELECTRONIC CONTROL SYSTEM article when trouble shooting ECU system on Accord and Prelude fuel injected models. Illustration shows system checker harness hook-up and ECU terminal identification.***

## SELF-DIAGNOSIS LED DOES NOT BLINK, DASH WARNING LIGHT IS OFF

**Accord & Prelude** – **1)** Connect System Checker Harness (07999-PD6000A) between ECU and wiring harness. *See Fig. 8*. Check for continuity between terminal "A2" and ground, and between terminal "A4" and ground.

**2)** If no continuity exists, repair faulty ground circuit. If continuity exists, substitute a known good ECU and retest system. If symptom/indication does not go away, check if dash-mounted warning light is on and the LED indicator is now blinking. If so, trouble shoot cause of problem.

## SELF-DIAGNOSIS LED DOES NOT BLINK, DASH WARNING LIGHT IS ON

**Accord & Prelude** – **1)** Connect System Checker Harness (07999-PD6000A) between ECU and wiring harness. *See Fig. 8*. Check for continuity between terminal "A16" and ground, and between terminal "A18" and ground.

**2)** If no continuity exists, repair faulty ground circuit. If continuity exists, turn ignition on. Measure voltage between terminal "A15" (positive) and terminal "A4" (ground), and between terminal "A13" (positive) and "A4". If reading at terminals is not 12 volts, go to step **5)**.

**3)** If reading at terminals is 12 volts, check for short circuit in Green/Red wire between instrument cluster and terminal "B6", as well as instrument cluster printed circuit board.

**4)** If circuit is okay, substitute a known good ECU and retest system. If symptom/indication goes away, replace original ECU. If circuit is damaged, repair faulty wire or instrument cluster circuit board.

**5)** If no voltage was detected in step **2)**, ensure that 10-amp fuse (PGM-FI/ECU fuse on Prelude) in engine compartment fuse/relay block is not blown. Check for open circuit in Yellow/Blue wire between fuse No. 1 and main relay. Check for defective main relay.

**6)** Also check for an open circuit in Yellow/Black wire between main relay and ECU. Check fuel pump fuse. Check for an open circuit in Black/Yellow wire between fuse No. 1 and main relay. Check for an open circuit in main relay Black wire. Check for faulty ECU.

# LATEST CHANGES & CORRECTIONS For 1988 & Earlier Models (Cont.)

## SELF-DIAGNOSIS LED BLINKS 1 TIME

**Accord & Prelude - 1)** Check spark plug condition for possible misfire. Warm engine to normal operating temperature. Quickly increase engine speed between idle and 4000 RPM. Stop engine.

**2)** Connect System Checker Harness (07999-PD6000A) between ECU and wiring harness. *See Fig. 8*. Connect digital voltmeter positive lead to terminal "C16" and negative lead to terminal "A18".

**3)** Restart engine and open throttle to Wide Open Throttle (WOT) position and then close it. Check that voltage varies to over .6 volts at WOT, and falls below .4 volts while closed. If voltage readings are incorrect, go to next step. If readings are correct, go to step **5)**.

**4)** Stop engine. Disconnect oxygen sensor harness and check oxygen sensor. Replace defective sensor. If sensor is okay, check for open or short circuit in White wire between sensor and ECU. Repair faulty wire. If wire is okay, go to next step.

**5)** Disconnect PGM-FI test harness and reconnect ECU to wiring harness. Remove No. 11 fuse from engine compartment fuse/relay block for at least 10 seconds. Warm engine to normal operating temperature. Hold engine speed at 1500-2000 RPM for 10 minutes.

**6)** If dash warning light does not come on, check fuel system for mechanical malfunctions. If dash warning light comes on, substitute a known good ECU and retest system repeating first 5 steps. If symptom/indication goes away, replace original ECU.

## SELF-DIAGNOSIS LED BLINKS 2 TIMES

**Accord & Prelude -** Count number of LED blinks again. If LED is blinking 2 times between each 2 second pause, substitute a known good ECU and retest system. If symptom/indication goes away, replace original ECU.

## SELF-DIAGNOSIS LED BLINKS 3 TIMES

**Accord & Prelude - 1)** Connect System Checker Harness (07999-PD6000A) between ECU and wiring harness. *See Fig. 8*. Turn ignition on. Connect voltmeter positive lead to terminal "C15" and negative lead to terminal "C14".

**2)** If voltage is between 4.75 and 5.25 volts, go to step **3)**. If not, substitute a known good ECU and retest system. If voltage reading is now correct, replace original ECU.

**3)** Connect voltmeter positive lead to terminal "C11" and negative lead to terminal "C14". If voltage is between 2.76 and 2.96 volts, substitute a known good ECU and retest system. If symptom/indication goes away, replace original ECU.

**4)** If reading is not between 2.76 and 2.96 volts, check for open or short circuit in White/Blue and Blue/White wires between manifold absolute pressure sensor and ECU. Manifold absolute pressure sensor may also be faulty.

***NOTE: If voltage is below specified range, there are open or poorly connected wires. If wires are okay, the manifold absolute pressure sensor is at fault.***

## SELF-DIAGNOSIS LED BLINKS 4 TIMES

**Accord & Prelude -** Count number of LED blinks again. If LED is blinking 4 times between each 2 second pause, substitute a known good ECU and retest system. If symptom/indication goes away, replace original ECU.

## SELF-DIAGNOSIS LED BLINKS 5 TIMES

**Accord & Prelude - 1)** Check that manifold absolute pressure sensor hose is securely connected, including inside emission control box. Ensure that hose routing is also correct. If necessary, correct hose routing.

**2)** Disconnect hose from manifold absolute pressure sensor and plug open end. Disconnect vacuum hose No. 21 from throttle body. Connect hand-held vacuum pump to hose No. 21 and check for leaks. Replace hose if leaks are found.

**3)** If no leaks are detected, connect System Checker Harness (07999-PD6000A) between ECU and wiring harness. *See Fig. 8*. Turn ignition on. Connect voltmeter positive lead to terminal "C15" and negative lead to terminal "C14".

**4)** If voltage is between 4.75 and 5.25 volts, go to step **5)**. If not, substitute a known good ECU and retest system. If voltage reading is now correct, replace original ECU.

**5)** Connect voltmeter positive lead to terminal "C11" and negative lead to terminal "C14". If reading is not between 2.76 and 2.96 volts, check for open or short circuit in White/Blue and Blue/White wires between manifold absolute pressure sensor and ECU. Manifold absolute pressure sensor may also be faulty.

**6)** If voltage is between 2.76 and 2.96 volts, connect a hand-held vacuum pump to manifold absolute pressure sensor. Check that voltage changes as vacuum is applied.

**7)** If voltage reading changes, substitute a known good ECU and retest system. If symptom/indication goes away, replace original ECU. If voltage reading does not change, replace faulty manifold absolute pressure sensor.

***NOTE: If there is no voltage or if voltage is low, check for a shorted wire. If voltage is high, wire may be open or may be poorly connected. If wire is okay, the manifold absolute pressure sensor is at fault.***

## SELF-DIAGNOSIS LED BLINKS 6 TIMES

**Accord & Prelude - 1)** Connect System Checker Harness (07999-PD6000A) between ECU and wiring harness. *See Fig. 8*. Warm engine until cooling fan comes on at least twice.

**2)** Connect voltmeter positive lead to terminal "C6" and negative lead to terminal "C12". If reading is between .50 and .90 volts, substitute a known good ECU and retest system. If symptom/indication goes away, replace original ECU.

**3)** If reading is not between .50 and .90 volts, stop engine. Check for open or short circuit in Yellow/Green and Green/White wires between ECU and coolant temperature sensor. Repair faulty wire. If wire is okay, go to next step.

**4)** Check coolant temperature sensor. Replace faulty sensor. If sensor is okay, substitute a known good ECU and retest system. If symptom/indication goes away, replace original ECU.

## SELF-DIAGNOSIS LED BLINKS 7 TIMES

**Accord & Prelude - 1)** Connect System Checker Harness (07999-PD6000A) between ECU and wiring harness. *See Fig. 8*. Turn ignition on. Connect voltmeter positive lead to terminal "C13" and negative lead to terminal "C12".

**2)** If voltage is between 4.75 and 5,25 volts, go to step **3)**. If not, substitute a known good ECU and retest system. If voltage reading is now correct, replace original ECU.

**3)** Connect voltmeter positive lead to terminal "C7" and negative lead to terminal "C12". Depress accelerator pedal to fully open throttle. Check that reading is .4-.6 volts with throttle closed, and 4.3-4.8 volts at full open position.

**4)** If readings are correct, substitute a known good ECU and retest system. If symptom/indication goes away, replace original ECU. If readings are incorrect, check for short or open circuit in Red/Yellow and Green/White wires between ECU and throttle position sensor. Repair faulty wires. If wires are okay, adjust or replace throttle position sensor.

## SELF-DIAGNOSIS LED BLINKS 8 TIMES

**Accord & Prelude - 1)** Check for open or short circuit in Orange/Blue and White/Blue wires between ECU and crank angle sensor. Repair faulty wires. If wires are okay, check crank angle sensor.

**2)** Replace faulty crank angle sensor. If crank angle sensor operates properly, substitute a known good ECU and retest system. If symptom/indication goes away, replace original ECU.

# LATEST CHANGES & CORRECTIONS For 1988 & Earlier Models (Cont.)

## SELF-DIAGNOSIS LED BLINKS 9 TIMES

**Accord & Prelude** – **1)** Check for open or short circuit in Orange and White wires between ECU and crank angle sensor. Repair faulty wires. If wires are okay, check crank angle sensor.
**2)** Replace faulty crank angle sensor. If crank angle sensor operates properly, substitute a known good ECU and retest system. If symptom/indication goes away, replace original ECU.

## SELF-DIAGNOSIS LED BLINKS 10 TIMES

**Accord & Prelude** – **1)** Connect System Checker Harness (07999-PD6000A) between ECU and wiring harness. *See Fig. 8.* Turn ignition on. Connect voltmeter positive lead to terminal "C5" and negative lead to terminal "C12".
**2)** Check that voltage is correct for intake air temperature sensor. See Air Temperature Sensor Voltage illustration. If reading is correct, substitute a known good ECU and retest system. If symptom/indication goes away, replace original ECU.
**3)** If reading is incorrect, turn ignition off. Check for open or short circuit in White/Red and Green/White wires between ECU and intake air temperature sensor. Repair faulty wires.
**4)** If wires are okay, check intake air temperature sensor. Replace faulty intake air temperature sensor. If sensor is okay, substitute a known good ECU and retest system. If symptom/indication goes away, replace original ECU.

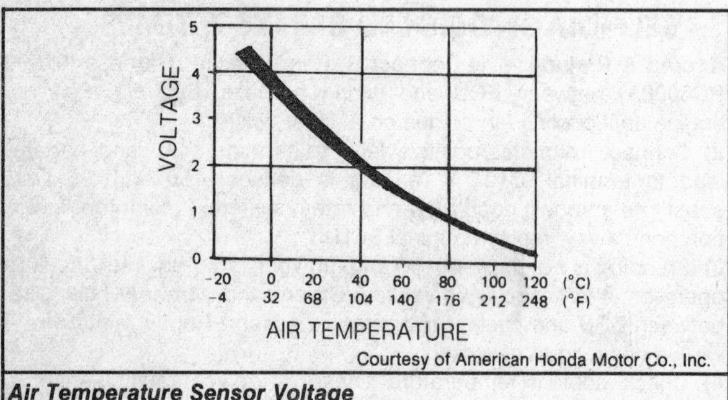
VOLTAGE
5
4
3
2
1
0
-20 0 20 40 60 80 100 120 (°C)
-4 32 68 104 140 176 212 248 (°F)
AIR TEMPERATURE
Courtesy of American Honda Motor Co., Inc.

*Air Temperature Sensor Voltage*

## SELF-DIAGNOSIS LED BLINKS 11 TIMES

**Accord & Prelude** – Count number of LED blinks again. If LED is blinking 11 times between each 2 second pause, substitute and known good ECU and retest system. If symptom/indication goes away, replace original ECU.

## SELF-DIAGNOSIS LED BLINKS 12 TIMES

**Accord & Prelude** – Test EGR control system. See HONDA EGR article.

## SELF-DIAGNOSIS LED BLINKS 13 TIMES

**Accord & Prelude** – **1)** Connect System Checker Harness (07999-PD6000A) between ECU and wiring harness. *See Fig. 8.* Turn ignition on. Connect voltmeter positive lead to terminal "C13" and negative lead to terminal "C12".
**2)** If voltage is between 4.75 and 5.25 volts, go to step **3)**. If not, substitute a known good ECU and retest system. If voltage reading is now correct, replace original ECU.
**3)** Connect voltmeter positive lead to terminal "C9" and negative lead to terminal "C12". If voltage is between 2.76 and 2.96 volts, substitute a known good ECU and retest system. If symptom/indication goes away, replace original ECU.
**4)** If reading is not between 2.76 and 2.96 volts, turn ignition off. Check for open or short circuit in Red and Green/White wires between ECU and atmospheric pressure sensor. Repair faulty wires.
**5)** If wires are okay, check atmospheric pressure sensor. Replace faulty sensor. If sensor operates correctly, substitute a known good ECU and retest system. If voltage reading is now correct, replace original ECU.

***NOTE: If there is no voltage, check for a short circuit. If voltage is high, there are open or poorly connected wires.***